THE OFFICIAL FOOTBALL ASSOCIATION

NON-LEAGUE CLUB DIRECTORY 1999

EDITOR TONY WILLIAMS

ISBN 1-869833-43-0

Published by Tony Williams Publications Ltd.
Printed by WBC Book Manufacturers Ltd. (Bridgend)
Typeset by Formatvisual, Typecast, Nina Whatmore, Keith Rye & T.W. Publications

Distributed by Tony Williams Publications Ltd.
Helland, North Curry, Taunton TA3 6DU.
Tel: 01823 490080 Fax: 01823 490281

Cover photograph: The front cover plate was sent to us by Emley supporter Jeremy Hodgson and we thought it was just perfect for our 21st anniversary celebration cover. The ballon epitomizes the party spirit and Emley taking the field at Premier League, West Ham United on a hazy winters afternoon, completes the excitement and atomsphere of one of footballs great moments.
Thank you Jeremy.

Introduction

Welcome to the Twenty-First Directory which we hope you will enjoy. The layout is similar to last season which proved to be one of the most popular since we launched our first little pocket book in 1978.

The Directory is, of course, an Official Football Association publication and, as usual, we have a full record of the F.A. Umbro Trophy, F.A. Carlsberg Vase and the F.A. Cup exploits of the 'pyramid' clubs.

We are a little frustrated that some senior clubs still do not have a team photo taken every season, but we are certainly including more squad photos and hopefully our aim to include a photo of all senior semi-professional players will be achieved.

We trust that all the regions and leagues will feel we have made an effort to present their achievements in the past season and hopefully the little nostalgic look at the past twenty-one years will bring back some happy memories.

Acknowledgements

Once more a huge 'team' of helpers have enabled us to present the Directory again, and this year it appears a couple of months earlier! Thanks to everyone:

The League Secretaries have kindly compiled the leagues' statistics and many have written a review of the season.

The Club Secretaries have up-dated their club details and searched for photos and programmes to help the book.

The Staff of The Football Association have, as ever, been helpful and co-operative with the competition department's superb input even under the stress of adverse weather causing replays, the World Cup and a nasty fire!

The Team Talk Photographers are an amazing bunch of cheerful, loyal and tireless enthusiasts dedicated to the game and thankfully, our publications. They are all appreciated very much indeed: Paul Barber, Peter Barnes, Clive Butchins, Andrew Chitty, Keith Clayton, Alan Coomes, Graham Cotterill, Paul Dennis, Tim Durrant, Tim Edwards, Keith Gillard, Ken Gregory, Garry Letts, Peter Lirettoc, Eric Marsh, Rob Monger, Ian Morsman, John Newton, Dennis Nicholson, Ray Pruden, Kevin Rolfe, Francis Short, Colin Stevens, Neil Thaler, Roger Turner, Alan Watson, Bill Wheatcroft, Gordon Whittington, Martin Wray.

There are so many contributors who help in different ways. It is very difficult to mention them all. So with apologies to those I have missed our thanks go to all contributors who so kindly sent in ideas, records, statistics for football at all levels: Albert Cole, Arthur Evans, Alan Wilson, Peter Dridge, Dave Phillips, Mike Ford - 'Bureau of Non-League Football' (League Tables & County Cup Results), Nick Robinson (ICIS League), Dennis Strudwick (Dr. Marten's League), Duncan Bayley (UniBond League), Wally Goss (A.F.A.), Mike Simmonds (Schools Football), Jeremy Biggs, Trevor Bailey (Sunday Football) Bob Morrison - 'First XI Sports Agency', Dudley Jackson, Stewart Davidson (Scottish Football), Bill Berry - 'Non-League Traveller' (League & Club Addresses), Robert Errington, Gareth Davies (North Wales Football), Rob Kelly, Peter Bentley, Mike Wilson, Leslie G. Moore, Richard Ralph, Andy Molden, Steve Layzell, Jon Weaver, John Bullen, Dave Edmunds, Steve Davies, Colin Timbrell, Paul Gardner, Mike Amos, Alan Turvey, Keith Masters, David Halford, Cathy Gibb (Womens' Football), Rob Grillo, Mark Jones, Peter Goringe, Jonathon Rouse, William Hughes, Andy Snowley, Dave Dorey, Keith Dixon, Rod Phillips, Tim Lancaster, John Anderson.

Contents

Only the major leagues are listed in this section. The full list will be found in the index of leagues on page 1016.

The county section starts at Page 905 and runs through the various county associations in alphabetical order.

Editorial

Who would have forecast, this time last year, that two 66-1 outsiders, Halifax Town and Cheltenham Town would dominate the semi-professional season?

The Halifax story is a happy one as a tough and battered ex-Football League club has been seen to bounce back refreshed, lively and hopefully ready to follow Wycombe Wanderers and Macclesfield Town through the Nationwide Third Division.

No silly money was spent and old fashioned football experience and common sense triumphed as George Mulhall and Keiran O'Regan guided their squad through to the title. Yes, they had a superb start inspired by Geoff Horsfield's goalscoring and the quite brilliant mid field play of Jamie Paterson, but they all kept their heads when the pressure was felt and on reflection, they were never really in any trouble at all.

Another surprise was the poor start suffered by Rushden and Diamonds but this may back fire on all their rivals this season as I am sure the favourites will be doubly determined to be up with the leaders from the very beginning.

If Halifax's championship was reasonably without pressure, so was Barrow's return to the top level. They saw off the UniBond pack, but in the Isthmian League, with new sponsors Ryman, Kingstonian with ex-Woking cult hero Geoff Chapple in charge, timed their run to perfection by overhauling Dagenham & Redbridge, Boreham Wood and Sutton United.

However the best battle for a Conference place was fought out in the Dr. Martens League as newly promoted Forest Green Rovers took on the gritty experience of Merthyr Tydfil and kept amazingly cool right to the end, to win a mommoth battle.

I suppose the warning had been available for all to see as Rovers had entertained and thrashed Woking in a pre-season game to open their smart new stand!

The F.A. Cup brought its usual moments of fame for little clubs enjoying the headlines after every round, but perhaps Solihull Borough and Emley were the clubs to grab most heart strings as they appeared to be less glamourous as their big brothers from Cheltenham Town and Stevenage Borough. And brave Basingstoke Town beat Wycombe Wanderers and only lost after a replay and penalties to Northampton Town after F.A. Cup ties. Other clubs who will remember the 1997-98 season with pride, are Stamford, Wrexham, Tow Law Town on the Eastern side, with Bloxwich Town, Kidsgrove Athletic and Leigh RMI thrilling their supporters a little further West. Aldershots spectacular promotion run will have all Ryman Premier League club treasurers rubbing their hands and there were also celebrations at Burgess Hill, AFC Lymington and, as usual Bury Town. Ambitious clubs to be watched are Bedlington Terriers, Hucknell Town, Brache Sparta, Ashford Town (Middlesex), Ely, Histon and Concord Rangers. While Ton Pentre and Bangor City enjoyed their season in Wales.

But Emley captured the hearts of all neutrals watching their tie at West Ham, when only fitness in the last ten minutes stopped them achieving a quite incredible result.

Much has been said about Stevenage Borough's squabble with Newcastle but let's just remember their very professional victories over Cambridge United and Swindon Town and, of course, their quite fantastic performances against the Premier League giant. Manager Paul Fairclough surely must have underlined the fact that you do not have to be a hardened old ex-pro to be a very good football manager at any level.

A glance through the annual awards will remind you of some exciting triumphs last season, but just imagine the celebrations at Grantham whose F.A. Trophy run was capped by promotion, and look at the number of goals scored by Ilkeston Town!

The F.A. Trophy produced some good attendances, as some of the less favoured Conference clubs moved in on Wembley. But I have a feeling that the new structure of the competition may well make it better balanced and spread the big game across the country over a longer period.

Cheltenham Town, following their excellent Conference form had hit the headlines again in the F.A. Cup and then capped the season by winning the Trophy at Wembley. You can hardly beat that for consistancy!

However, watch out for Southport this season their Wembley trip may just be the start of a concerted effort to regain their Football League place.

The F.A. Carlsberg Vase is possibly the game's most enjoyable and most evenly contested knock-out competition and it was good to see Tiverton Town gain their Wembley victory after working so consistantly over the last five years.

At the end of season the idea to set up 'Conference Two' was given a mixed reception. Many senior clubs welcomed the chance of national football, but the repercussions in the feeder league and their feeders worried those who considered the pyramid to have just about sorted itself out.

Tell that to Hastings United, however, who feel a little lonely down in their part of Sussex, as they travel around the midlands dominated Southern League. But their stay in the Dr. Martens League was enforced by Slough Town's recovery after what appeared to be a terminal problem. Full marks to Alan Turvey the Ryman chairman who was able to help sort out a nasty situation and hopefully they will be able to consolidate and recover their composure before trying to regain their Conference place.

This edition brings an emotional anniversary for all of us who have been associated with the non-League game for a very long time.

Twenty-one years ago our little publication attempted to give the level of the game outside the full time competitions a boost, with perhaps a bit more publicity, unity and general public awareness. The F.A.'s Adrian Titcombe and Steve Clark were also involved and we have benefitted from different publishers and sponsors over the years.

Before the recession, clubs happily ordered twenty books with some like Enfield, Wycombe Wanderers and Barnet hitting the eighty mark!

The Directory has regularly been a best seller in Sports Pages and W.H. Smith thus showing the sporting world the deep interest there is in the football world that represents 95 percent of our national winter game.

It is still very difficult to compile and we could certainly benefit from the club sales figures of ten years ago, but we have a huge loyal readership which we greatly appreciate.

Thank you all for your support and let's hope the Directory will continue with ever increasing support.

TONY WILLIAMS

Editorial Team
Tony Williams (Editor)
George Brown (House Editor)
Steve Whitney & Bill Mitchell

Editorial Address
Tony Williams Publications, Helland, North Curry, Taunton, Somerset TA3 6DU
Tel: 01823 490080 Fax: 01823 490281

DataSport Management Systems

Setting Future Sports Management Standards

Price Patrick & Associates Ltd

The Grange, Longmoor Grange, 24, Barkham Ride,
Wokingham Berkshire RG40 4EU

Telephone: 0118 973 4173 Fax: 01276452837 Email: martin@cable.co.uk

EuroFocus FC
School Of Excellence

A "Professional System" - That Sets Future Management Standards

Introduction

Price Patrick & Associates Ltd. have a significant financial investment in Sport. As part of our "Sports Development" programme we are pleased to announce that the "School Of Excellence Management System" is now available.

The system was developed over a period of seven months, and in close co-operation between experienced football professionals and I.T. analysts and consultants.
The School Of Excellence Management System provides a comprehensive Youth Development standard which will assist Clubs in protecting their 'youth investment', and provides indepth support for youth development programmes.

Player Registrations

The registration facility uses a highly developed "User friendly" interface, making data input a simple task. The Medical and Injury management facility provide a full history of incidents critical to the continued well being of the Players.

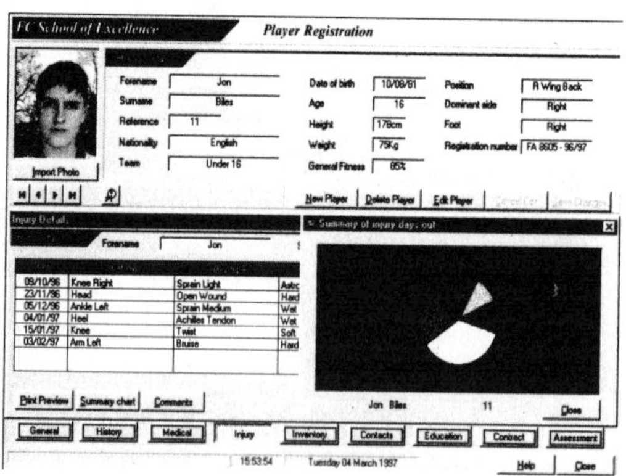

Careful attention to detail has been made to tailor the registration requirement for both the amateur and professional games, and includes registration details as currently required by the F.A.

Features Overview

Player information	**Player Playing History**
Medical Records	**Injury Management**
Player Contacts	**Player Education**
Player Contracts	**Full Player Reporting**

EuroFocus FC

Tomorrows Solutions - Available Today

The system provides excellent search facilities.The user can select a wide variety of criteria, including technical, physical and psychological attributes. Searches can be also be made against age, squad, position, dominant side etc.

Player Assessments

The assessment system which forms part of the School Of Excellence is fully user definable. Categories and Attributes can be based on the foundations developed by the F.A. and other knowledgeable bodies. These categories can be further extended to include the Club's coaching requirements.

Setting Up Categories & Attributes

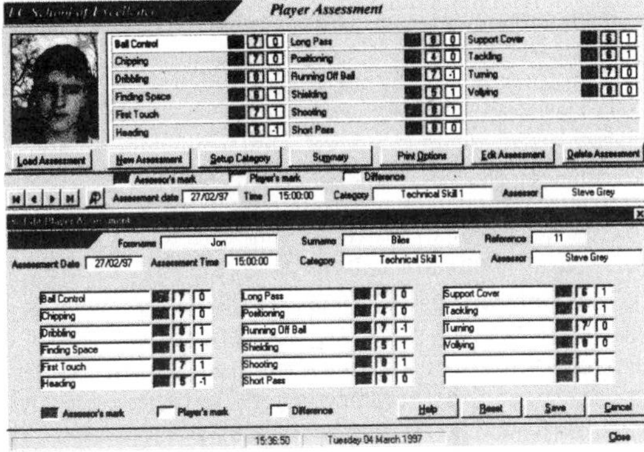

Graphic Output Of Assessment

The system provides a unique communication tool between the Coach and the Player. Assessments are made against a predefined set of attributes that are individually assessed both by Player and Coach.

The assessment system also provides a focus for the improvement of communications between the Club and Parents, utilising printed reports.

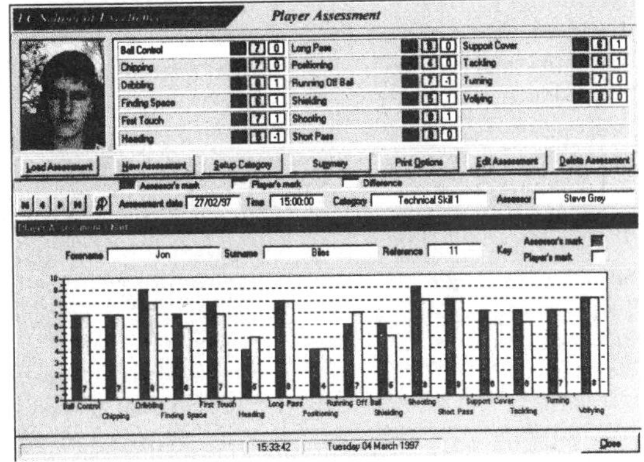

Operational Benefits

Reduced Administration	**Information on Demand**
Detailed Registration	**Detailed Reports**
Technical Assessments	**Psychological Assessments**
Injury Management	**Electronic Data Transfer**

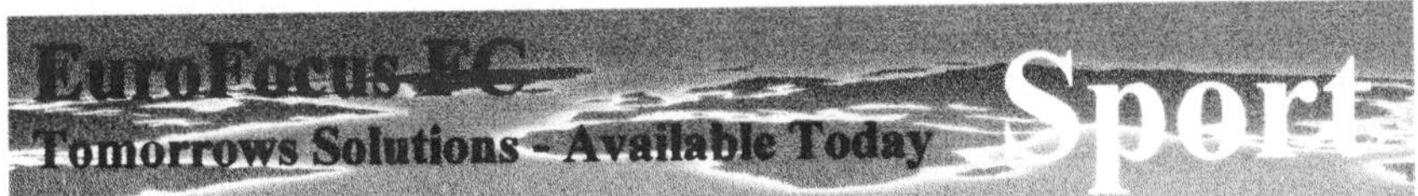

TOP ATTENDANCES 1997-98

	Club	Pld	Highest				Lowest				Average
1	Hereford United	27	7473	v	Tranmere Rvrs	(FAC)	1371	v	Telford Utd	(Lge)	2780
2	Stevenage Boro	28	8040	v	Newcastle Utd	(FAC)	842	v	Yeovil Town	(SC)	2568
3	Woking	28	5000	v	Southend Utd	(FAC)	559	v	Kettering Tn	(SC)	2560
4	Rushden & Dia	24	3866	v	Kettering Town	(Lge)	668	v	Raunds Tn	(NSC)	2447
5	Halifax Town	25	5357	v	Cheltenham T	(Lge)	788	v	Droylsden	(FAC)	2294
6	Yeovil Town	28	3857	v	Cheltenham T	(Lge)	302	v	Bristol M F	(SPC)	2205
7	Aldershot Town	26	4269	v	Berkhamsted T	(Lge)	972	v	Bournemouth	(HSC)	2023
8	Cheltenham Tn	31	6000	v	Reading	(FAC)	274	v	Bristol City	(GSC)	2019
9	Kidderminster H	26	4693	v	Hereford Utd	(Lge)	378	v	Stourbridge	(WSC)	1773
10	Barrow	28	4217	v	Dover Athletic	(FAT)	410	v	Marine	(PC)	1385
11	Kettering Town	28	4016	v	Rushden & Dia	(Lge)	604	v	Raunds Tn	(NSC)	1382
12	Morecambe	29	3914	v	Halifax Town	(Lge)	209	v	Burscough	(LATS)	1315
13	Hednesford Town	27	2396	v	Hereford Utd	(Lge)	30	v	Solihull Boro	(MC)	1274
14	Southport	29	4695	v	Slough Town	(FAT)	268	v	St Helens Tn	(LSC)	1249
15	Dover Athletic	25	3240	v	Cheltenham Tn	(FAT)	404	v	Kettering Town	(SC)	1208
16	Crawley Town	25	2163	v	Forest Gn Rvrs	(Lge)	278	v	St Leonards S	(LC)	1189
17	Nuneaton Boro	26	1960	v	Emley	(FAC)	528	v	Gloucester C	(Lge)	1187
18	King's Lynn	26	2847	v	Bromsgrove R	(FAC)	483	v	Gloucester C	(Lge)	1026
19	Northwich Vic	25	2105	v	Halifax Town	(Lge)	447	v	Hednesford T	(SC)	856
20	Kingstonian	24	2019	v	Sutton Utd	(Lge)	381	v	Chessington	(SSC)	833
21	Weymouth	23	2652	v	Bashley	(Lge)	253	v	Havant Town	(LC)	908
22	Boston United	25	1730	v	Gainsboro T	(Lge)	308	v	Bradford PA	(PC)	834
23	Slough Town	31	2262	v	Cardiff City	(FAC)	258	v	Baldock Town	(FAC)	832
24	Dagenham & R	23	1214	v	Sutton United	(Lge)	533	v	Boreham Wd	(Lge)	823
25	Basingstoke Tn	33	5025	v	Wycombe Wdrs	(FAC)	151	v	Newport IoW	(HSC)	776
26	Farnborough Tn	25	2125	v	Woking	(Lge)	102	v	AFC Totton	(HSC)	766
27	Ilkeston Town	25	2504	v	Boston United	(FAC)	357	v	Kings Lynn	(LC)	754
28	Worcester City	30	1819	v	Tamworth	(Lge)	56	v	Bolhall Swifts	(MI)	754
29	Telford United	25	1710	v	Hereford United	(Lge)	367	v	Northwich Vic	(SC)	751
30	Sutton United	24	1901	v	Kingstonian	(Lge)	188	v	Uxbridge	(LC)	748
31	Grantham Town	26	3695	v	Southport	(FAT)	169	v	Raunds Tn	(LC)	747
32	Burton Albion	26	2168	v	Gresley Rovers	(Lge)	203	v	Walsall	(BSC)	734
33	Stalybridge C	26	1656	v	Dover Athletic	(Lge)	224	v	Gateshead	(SC)	732
34	Merthyr Tydfil	29	1930	v	Forest Gn Rvrs	(Lge)	311	v	Forest Gn Rvrs	(LC)	730
35	Enfield	28	1143	v	Kingstonian	(Lge)	444	v	Yeading	(Lge)	725
36	Halesowen Town	33	1543	v	Worcester City	(Lge)	271	v	Aston Villa	(BSC)	702
37	Leek Town	25	1282	v	Halifax Town	(Lge)	165	v	Rocester	(SSC)	702
38	Welling United	25	1344	v	Halifax Town	(Lge)	160	v	Erith & Belv.	(KSC)	676
39	Tamworth	33	1410	v	Atherstone Utd	(Lge)	356	v	Halesowen T	(BSC)	663
40	Gloucester City	31	1540	v	Stevenage Boro	(FAT)	167	v	Cinderford T	(LC)	633
41	Bromsgrove Rvrs	27	1370	v	Halesowen Tn	(Lge)	356	v	Forest G Rvrs	(Lge)	632
42	Forest G Rovers	25	2891	v	Merthyr Tydfil	(Lge)	155	v	Yate Town	(GSC)	631
43	Wisbech Town	28	3593	v	Bristol Rovers	(FAC)	191	v	March Tn U	(CIC)	625
44	Hayes	33	1343	v	Boreham Wood	(FAC)	114	v	Staines Tn	(MCC)	621
45	Altrincham	34	1196	v	Southport	(FAT)	227	v	Colwyn Bay	(LC)	619
46	Bath City	27	1280	v	Merthyr Tydfil	(Lge)	179	v	Newport IoW	(LC)	613
47	Gresley Rovers	25	1752	v	Burton Albion	(Lge)	283	v	Belper Town	(DSC)	598
48	Gateshead	25	1238	v	Halifax Town	(Lge)	204	v	Morecambe	(SC)	588
49	Dorchester Town	29	1171	v	Tiverton Town	(FAC)	215	v	Fareham Town	(LC)	578
50	Newport AFC	25	943	v	Cinderford Town	(Lge)	134	v	Panteg	(GSC)	576

FOOTBALLER OF THE YEAR
Phil Everett

MANAGER OF THE YEAR
Steve Cotterill

INDIVIDUAL MERIT AWARDS
Bernard Fairbairn
Alan Turvey
Terry Owen
Frank Gregan
George Torrance

REGIONAL CLUB AWARDS

North East	Halifax Town
North West	Barrow
Midlands	Cheltenham Town
East of England	Billericay Town
Home Cos. North	Boreham Wood
Home Cos. South	Kingstonian
South West & Wales	Tiverton Town
F.A. Cup	Stevenage Borough

INDIVIDUAL MERIT AWARDS

BERNARD FAIRBAIRN (Tow Law Town Secretary)

Follows his father and grandfather as secretary to the family's beloved **Tow Law Town**. Bernard has served well over 30 years in office and his friendly efficiency was just as notable last year during the excitement of his club's Vase Final run as it was in my Rothmans sponsorship dealings with the Northern League in the seventies. He is a fine example of a truly dedicated football clubman.

ALAN TURVEY (Ryman League Chairman)

Has worked tirelessly to give his league the best in sponsorship, administration and all round image. His efforts on behalf of the F.A. Finance and Representative Committees have been immense but probably the most satisfying achievement has been the help he was able to give **Slough Town** who had appeared to be dead and buried. Another true football man who has dedicated his life to the game.

TERRY OWENS (Ex Chairman of Aldershot Town)

Took up the reigns when the little Hampshire club lost its Football League place and was battling to rebuild. The spirit in the town is now so much more obvious than in its Football League days and, as attendances build and the pyramid is scaled, Terry has stood back a little, but will still be there to help his club in its battle to achieve two more vital promotions.

FRANK GREGAN (Forest Green Rovers)

In a year when managers at Cheltenham, Halifax, Southport, Grantham, Ilkeston and Tiverton covered themselves in glory no one could feel more satisfaction than the management at the Dr. Martens champions in leafy Gloucestershire. Frank raised his club from the top of Dr Martens Southern Division to worthy Premier Division Champions with a squad to match. His team's football, spirit and consistency were a credit to a man who had spent much of his life in the army, but now seems a natural to pit his wits regularly against the best in the Conference.

GEORGE TORRANCE (Porthleven)

For those who watched George in his Army, Wokingham Town, Brentford and Maidstone United days, the news that he was the inspirational captain behind little Porthleven's exciting F.A. Carlsberg Vase run to the Quarter Finals will be a shock. George just lost his hair early! But anyone playing against him today will realise he is still an excellent player, and he did have a great season!

PHIL EVERETT
(Tiverton Town)

FOOTBALLER of the YEAR

Despite the efforts of Halifax Town and Cheltenham Town, no individual's season can really compare with the heroics of Phil Everett, Tiverton Town's leading goalscorer.

He spearheaded an attack which amassed 154 League goals and 83 in cup competitions to total 237, of which his share was 54 (33 League & 21 cup) in 52 + 1 appearances!

Phil is not razor sharp or particularly mobile but he is an honest worker with strength, determination and an eye for a goal, whether on the ground or in the air. He works selflessly for the team and is a real old fashioned `leader of the line' - no semi-professional manager could ask for more!

Doing what he does best - scoring the second and decisive goal against Spalding in the 6th Round of the FA Carlsberg Vase, and then celebrating.

All photographs by Peter Barnes.

MANAGER of the YEAR

STEVE COTTERILL
(Cheltenham Town)

To take your club into the Conference, having only finished as runners-up some eleven points behind the Dr Marten's champions, could be described as a daunting prospect!

So to then build a squad capable of an early twenty game unbeaten run, an F.A. Cup run to the Third Round from the qualifying stages, another Conference run to finish as runners-up and then an F.A. Umbro Trophy triumph at Wembley is quite remarkable and is certainly an achievement well worthy of this second official presentation of a Manager of the Year award.

REGIONAL AWARDS

NORTH EAST

From a last minute reprieve in the previous season to an outstanding Conference start just four months later, is something akin to football`magic'. **HALIFAX TOWN** attribute this trick to good management, solid administration and an old fashioned team spirit amongst a squad originally without obvious stars. The fact that Geoff Horsfield and Jamie Paterson had outstanding seasons was a bonus and now it is with pride that the Conference hands back a battling Halifax Town in much better condition than they received them in 1994.

NORTH WEST

On paper, the UniBond championship looked a very tough proposition last season, so all the more credit to **BARROW** for making it appear remarkably straight forward. A rock solid defence, with the giant Steve Farrelly supreme in goal, only conceded 28 goals, but lively attacking skills from Neil Morton and Marc Coates brought in sufficient fire power so that promotion and a Trophy semi-final place was just reward for Owen Brown's squad.

MIDLANDS

The manager's write up sums up **CHELTENHAM TOWN**'s season but credit must also go to a hard working board of directors who had ensured their Whaddon Road ground was well up to Conference standards and their local battle for honours with rivals Gloucester City was won. The satisfaction of seeing five `Robins' in the England squad must have been immense to all the club supporters and with the potential power of Dale Watkins, Jason Eaton and Neil Grayson the club will be hoping to carry on where they left off last season.

EAST OF ENGLAND

Since their initial burst onto the scene with three FA Vase Finals at Wembley in the first five years of the competition, **BILLERICAY TOWN** have flattered to deceive. However a fine FA Cup run last season saw them reach the First Round proper, they beat Aldershot to qqualify for a First Round proper Trophy tie at Dagenham & Redbridge and they gained promotion to the Ryman Premier Division - an excellent all-round season.

HOME COUNTIES NORTH

For three seasons now **BOREHAM WOOD** have had a Conference graded ground and a team on the fringe of promotion. Bob Makin has build an excellent squad and the club has progressed off the field under the guidence of one of the game's most talented young chairman, Phil Wallace. Unfortunately their excellent results in the F.A. Cup, F.A. Umbro Trophy plus League and County Cups took the edge off their promotion challenge last year, but continued consistency must bring its rewards.

HOME COUNTIES SOUTH

Having recruited Geoff Chappel, the games most successful manager in recent seasons, the `sleeping giant' tag for **KINGSTONIAN** was surely about to be lifted. Their exciting run-in to overtake Sutton United and Dagenham & Redbridge was timed to perfection and did, in fact, bring them that coveted Conference place. So a club with a fine pedigree has surely moved on to the level at which they belong.

SOUTH WEST

Last year's heroics by Porthleven in the F.A. Carlsberg Vase and Taunton Town's ever present challenge were once again overshadowed by the quite outstanding performance of **TIVERTON TOWN** who won the Screwfix Direct League and Cup double plus a superb Vase run culminating in a Wembley triumph. Individual and club goalscoring records were quite outstanding and manager Martyn Rogers has built a side which is the envy of all at their level of the game.

F.A. CUP

The romance of Basingstoke Town, Solihull Borough and Emley plus the satisfaction of Hereford United beating Brighton all brought glamour and excitement to the pyramid competitions, but despite the less endearing headlines written about their Fourth Round tie **STEVENAGE BOROUGH**'s victories over Cambridge United and Swindon Town, plus the way that Paul Fairclough master-minded their two quite incredible performances against Newcastle United must, in all fairness, earn them this year's award.

A lot has happened in 21 years and I'm sure those of you with a full set of the books will probably have enjoyed hours of browsing through past league tables, team pictures and playing squads.

The following review of the books progress was published in the 1995 Directory:

The idea to produce an annual for non-League football wasn't perhaps a suprise as I had managed to persuade an agent and publisher to launch the Rothmans Football Yearbook in 1970, and had enjoyed working with Greg Tesser on his 'Amateur Footballer' magazine in the late sixties.

Having played with a number of senior non-League clubs in the Isthmian, Athenian and Southern Leagues, and also having enjoyed managing and coaching at this level, the game was in my blood.

So, with the encouragement of Ted Croker at the Football Association and a little financial help, the first FA Non-League Football Annual was published as a Playfair Annual by Queen Anne Press for the 1978-79 season. It was a 252 page pocket book that cost 70p!

Blyth Spartans had thrilled the football world with their great FA Cup run when they featured in the Sixth Round draw, and our Editorial Committee was Ted Powell from Herefordshire, the chairman of the F.A. Publications Committee, and Adrian Titcombe of the F.A. who I am pleased to say has helped us ever since. On our first advisory committee were others who still give valuable support - Steve Clark and Glen Kirton (FA), Peter Grove, Bill Mitchell, Brian Lee, Barry Lenton (Marine FC) and Greg Tesser who has moved to Somerset to work with us.

'The Annual' increased to 304 and then 336 pages in the next two years being published by Macdonald & James (a part of Queen Anne) and then by myself, as confidence had eroded at the big publishing house. The F.A. now supported without a financial input, but a sponsor helped the 1980-81 edition in the form of Duripanel, an uncombustible building material suitable for the construction of stands. This issue also recorded the successful start of 'The Alliance' with the ex-amateurs of the Isthmian League resisting changes.

A significant boost to the publication's development came in 1981 when Rothmans sponsored the new 'Yearbook'. Geoff Peters co-ordinated this sponsorship and the book was published by Rothmans Publications. During my time with the company when we were the first sponsors of football leagues in the Seventies, I had helped run the Rothmans Football Yearbook and introduced the Rothmans Rugby Union and Rugby League Yearbooks, so this was a fitting and very welcome liaison.

The front cover showed action from Liverpool v Altrincham in the FA Cup and the Rothmans FA Non-League Football Yearbook really took off. I was 'in the depths' after a divorce which left me penniless, so the help of Geoff Peters and Rothmans will always be remembered with gratitude.

Rothmans sponsored for three years and during this time we published some hard backed editions which were a joy to see on the shelf. The size went from 336 (A5) pages to 512 pages, but Queen Anne Press, under the 'leadership' of Robert Maxwell, had persuaded Rothmans to hand over their sports publishing department to a 'proper publishers'. Geoff Peters, having been asked to go with his books, was promptly squeezed out by 'the chairman'. Prices of the books soared and there was no understanding of, or desire for, a non-League publication, so once again the title reverted to me.

It was at this stage that another friend, Barry Hugman, influenced the book's future. Barry introduced me to a director of Newnes Books, Tony Bagley, who commissioned two directories from me: 'The F.A. (they still encouraged their name to be associated with the book) Non-League Directory 1985' and The League Club Directory, which was later to be sponsored by Barclays and then Endsleigh.

Regular monthly payents for these books also enabled me to have my own rented flat for the first time in three years, so Tony Bagley's faith and Newnes Books will always have a special place in my memory.

The 1985 edition was 602 pages large but a real tragedy struck as Tony, who was diabetic, had a blackout and died in a road accident on holiday. His colleagues, with no feeling for - or faith in - Non-League football, relinquished the publishing rights so, after reducing the size of the 1986 edition (576 pages) despite having another sponsor in 'Safestand', the publishing rights again reverted to the editor!

The 1987 edition edged up to 640 pages with Composite Grandstands (the same parent company) sponsoring. Once again the book was shown as the 'Official Football Association Publication'. Although I remember we were instructed to ensure that 'views expressed in the book were not necessarily those of 'The Football Association'.

The 1988 book was the first with the now well know bright red cover, and much appreciated sponsorship was offered by Vauxhall-Opel whose parent company continued its involvement for five years during which time the size increased frm 736 pages to over the magic 1,000 mark, and the price from £8.98 to £11.95.

Kidderminster Harriers featured on the cover of the first and last editions sponsored by Vauxhall and the attitude, the football played, and the development of that club probably mirrors the spirit in which I feel the Annual/YearBook/Directory has also developed.

The 1993 edition was edited by James Wright, a lover of all that is good in our national winter sport throughout the Pyramid. I knew 'my baby' would be in good hands while I had to cope with the problems of keeping a small publishing house 'on the rails' during a recession.

During these recent difficult financial years 'The Non-League Club Directory' has continued to be a best seller with WH Smith, Sportspages, the book trade in general and, of course, our Mail Order customers. It is the flagship of our business and I know, from your letters, that it gives hours of enjoyment to our readers.

James has poured hours of love into its continued development and we are all very proud that this edition covers a wider span throughout the Pyramid and beyond than ever before.

Unfortunately, the recession did hit us badly. Mainly because the books ordered and paid for by WH Smith for the twenty titles we were publishing in the early nineties weren't sold and were eventually returned in large numbers for which we had to repay them.

We reduced the staff to four and ever since we have just published the Non League Club Directory, Steve McCormack's Official Rugby Union Club Directory and our monthly non-League magazine Team Talk.

For the last three years it has been touch and go whether we could survive and today we still need to be very careful.

James Wright is welcomed back with us this season and we will obviously continue to publish the book ourselves. We have greatly appreciated all our sponsors which have included national names such as Rothmans, Vauxhall Opel, and Lucozade and we are particuarly pleased to be an official F.A. publication once again.

The football 'family' we serve seem to appreciate our efforts and I must say that, despite all the changes and improved facilities, the friendliness and spirit seem to stay the same at this level of the game.

It's been a pleasure being involved and I hope the Directory will continue for many years to come.

TONY WILLIAMS

Southern Football League – Premier Division

	P	W	D	L	F	A	Pts.
Bath City	42	22	18	2	83	32	62
Weymouth	42	21	16	5	64	36	58
Maidstone United	42	20	11	11	59	41	51
Worcester City	42	20	11	11	67	50	51
Gravesend & Northfleet	42	19	11	12	57	42	49
Kettering Town	42	18	11	13	58	48	47
Barnet	42	18	11	13	63	58	47
Wealdstone	42	16	14	12	54	48	46
Telford United	42	17	11	14	52	45	45
Nuneaton Borough	42	15	13	14	38	36	44
Dartford	42	14	15	13	57	65	43
Yeovil Town	42	14	14	14	57	49	42
Hastings United	42	15	9	18	49	60	39
Cheltenham Town	42	12	14	16	43	52	38
Hillingdon Borough	42	13	9	20	45	54	35
Atherstone Town	42	10	15	17	41	56	35
Redditch United	42	15	5	22	40	55	35
A.P. Leamington	42	11	13	18	34	57	35
Minehead	42	11	12	19	43	48	34
Dover	42	9	13	20	41	63	31
Bedford Town	42	8	13	21	51	75	29
Grantham	42	11	6	25	40	66	28

Southern Football League – First Div. South

First Division South	P	W	D	L	F	A	Pts.
Margate	38	24	10	4	92	32	58
Dorchester Town	38	23	10	5	67	31	56
Salisbury	38	21	10	7	60	27	52
Waterlooville	38	19	13	6	66	36	51
Romford	38	17	15	5	58	37	49
Aylesbury United	38	20	7	11	56	42	47
Trowbridge Town	38	16	11	11	65	59	43
Chelmsford City	38	15	11	12	58	46	41
Folkestone & Shepway	38	16	9	13	64	56	41
Taunton Town	38	15	10	13	57	54	40
Addlestone	38	14	10	14	57	60	38
Crawley Town	38	14	9	15	61	60	37
Basingstoke Town	38	11	11	16	44	50	33
Tonbridge A.F.C.	38	13	5	20	64	77	31
Ashford Town	38	9	13	16	39	60	31
Hounslow	38	10	10	18	43	62	30
Bognor Regis Town	38	9	8	21	52	69	26
Poole Town	38	8	10	20	43	68	26
Andover	38	4	12	22	30	68	20
Canterbury City	38	2	6	30	31	113	10

Isthmian League – Premier Division

	P	W	D	L	F	A	Pts.
Enfield	42	35	5	2	96	27	110
Dagenham	42	24	7	11	78	55	79
Wycombe Wanderers	42	22	9	11	66	41	75
Tooting & Mitcham	42	22	8	12	64	49	74
Hitchin Town	42	20	9	13	69	53	69
Sutton United	42	18	12	12	66	57	66
Leatherhead	42	18	11	13	62	48	65
Croydon	42	18	10	14	61	52	64
Walthamstow Avenue	42	17	12	13	64	61	63
Barking	42	17	7	18	76	66	58
Carshalton Athletic	42	15	11	16	61	63	56
Hayes	42	15	11	16	46	53	56
Hendon	42	16	7	19	57	55	55
Woking	42	14	11	17	62	62	53
Boreham Wood	42	15	8	19	48	65	53
Slough Town	42	14	8	20	52	69	50
Staines Town	42	12	13	17	46	60	49
Tilbury	42	11	12	19	57	68	45
Kingstonian	42	8	13	21	43	65	37
Leytonstone	42	7	15	20	44	71	36
Southall & EB	42	6	15	21	43	74	33
Bishop's Stortford	42	7	8	27	36	83	29

Cheshire County Football League Final Table

	P	W	D	L	F	A	Pts.
Marine	42	26	10	6	101	48	62
Stalybridge Celtic	42	23	12	7	75	47	58
Witton Albion	42	21	14	7	98	54	56
Hyde United	42	21	13	8	68	37	55
Winsford United	42	24	7	11	80	51	55
Ashton United	42	20	13	9	88	56	53
Horwich RMI	42	19	14	9	62	50	52
Leek Town	42	20	10	12	62	45	50
Chorley	42	19	11	12	69	48	49
Formby	42	18	11	13	71	57	47
Middlewich Athletic	42	15	15	12	67	66	45
St Helens Town	42	15	15	12	53	55	45
Droylsden	42	15	10	17	54	56	40
Burscough	42	13	12	17	56	63	38
Darwen	42	14	6	22	50	68	34
Nantwich Town	42	9	13	20	56	69	31
Rhyl	42	10	10	22	44	67	30
New Brighton	42	10	10	22	35	69	30
New Mills	42	9	9	24	42	72	27
Rossendale United	42	11	4	27	51	110	26
Prestwich Heys	42	6	9	27	42	88	21
Radcliffe Borough	42	7	6	29	46	94	20

Southern Football League – First Div. North

	P	W	D	L	F	A	Pts.
Witney Town	38	20	15	3	54	27	55
Bridgend Town	38	20	9	9	59	45	49
Burton Albion	38	17	11	10	48	32	45
Enderby Town	38	17	10	11	59	44	44
Bromsgrove Rovers	38	16	12	10	56	41	44
Banbury United	38	17	10	11	52	47	44
Kidderminster Harriers	38	16	11	11	58	41	43
Merthyr Tydfil	38	18	6	14	85	62	42
Cambridge City	38	14	12	12	56	45	40
Barry Town	38	14	11	13	58	47	39
Wellingborough Town	38	11	15	12	47	43	37
King's Lynn	38	12	13	13	55	55	37
Gloucester City	38	14	8	16	68	75	36
Corby Town	38	9	17	12	46	48	35
Dunstable	38	11	13	14	49	59	35
Stourbridge	38	9	15	14	52	53	33
Tamworth	38	10	11	17	35	48	31
Bedworth United	38	8	14	16	36	58	30
Milton Keynes City	38	5	11	22	26	74	21
Oswestry Town	38	6	8	24	29	85	20

Northern Premier Footbal League

	P	W	D	L	F	A	Pts.
Boston United	46	31	9	6	85	35	71
Wigan Athletic	46	25	15	6	83	45	65
Bangor City	46	26	10	10	92	50	62
Scarborough	46	26	10	10	80	39	62
Altrincham	46	22	15	9	84	49	59
Northwich Victoria	46	22	14	10	83	55	58
Stafford Rangers	46	22	13	11	71	41	57
Runcorn	46	19	18	9	70	44	56
Mossley	46	22	11	13	85	73	55
Matlock Town	46	21	12	13	79	60	54
Lancaster City	46	15	14	17	66	82	44
Frickley Athletic	46	15	12	19	77	81	42
Barrow	46	14	12	20	58	61	40
Goole Town	46	15	9	22	60	68	39
Great Harwood	46	13	13	20	66	83	39
Gainsborough Trinity	46	14	10	22	61	74	38
Gateshead	46	16	5	25	65	74	37
Netherfield	46	11	13	22	50	80	35
Workington	46	13	8	25	48	80	34
Worksop Town	46	12	10	24	45	84	34
Morecambe	46	11	11	24	67	92	33
Macclesfield Town	46	12	9	25	60	92	33
Buxton	46	13	6	27	60	95	32
South Liverpool	46	9	7	30	53	111	25

Isthmian League – Division 1

	P	W	D	L	F	A	Pts.
Dulwich Hamlet	42	28	9	5	91	25	93
Oxford City	42	26	5	11	85	44	83
Bromley	42	23	13	6	74	41	82
Walton & Hersham	42	22	11	9	69	41	77
Ilford	42	21	14	7	57	47	77
St Albans City	42	22	10	10	83	46	76
Wokingham	42	19	12	11	68	48	69
Harlow Town	42	19	8	15	63	49	65
Harrow Borough	42	17	10	15	59	54	61
Maidenhead United	42	16	13	13	55	54	61
Hertford Town	42	15	14	13	57	51	59
Chesham United	42	14	13	15	69	70	55
Hampton	42	13	13	16	49	53	52
Harwich & Parkeston	42	12	13	17	68	79	49
Wembley	42	15	3	24	56	82	48
Horsham	42	12	10	20	41	57	46
Finchley	42	11	13	18	41	68	46
Aveley	42	13	7	22	47	75	46
Ware	42	8	13	21	61	95	37
Clapton	42	10	6	26	46	78	36
Hornchurch	42	8	10	24	47	81	34
Corinthian Casuals	42	3	10	29	40	88	19

Northern League

	P	W	D	L	For	Agst	Pts	C	D
Spennymoor United	38	30	5	3	103	36	95	3	4
Blyth Spartans	38	27	8	3	107	37	89	—	—
Whitby Town	38	22	7	9	84	61	73	7	4
Bishop Auckland	38	22	6	10	82	44	72	7	4
Consett	38	19	7	12	78	49	64	2	—
Horden Colliery Welfare	38	19	6	13	53	44	63	8	4
North Shields	38	16	10	12	55	39	55*	12	—
Durham City	38	15	9	14	55	51	54	4	4
Willington	38	16	6	16	53	62	54	5	—
Crook Town	38	12	17	9	56	47	53	17	—
West Auckland Town	38	12	15	11	49	51	51	5	8
Billingham Synthonia	38	14	8	16	65	64	50	7	12
South Bank	38	12	13	13	40	43	49	3	4
Whitley Bay	38	13	7	18	46	66	46	5	4
Ashington	38	15	7	16	56	54	43*	6	4
Shildon	38	11	8	19	55	64	41	9	—
Tow Law Town	38	9	5	24	59	103	32	6	4
Ferryhill Athletic	38	8	8	22	30	69	32	9	—
Evenwood Town	38	4	5	29	36	90	17	3	—
Penrith	38	3	5	30	25	113	14	6	4

*North Shields 3 points deducted *Ashington 9 points deducted

C—Caution (One Sportsmanship Point Lost)

D—Dismissal (Four Sportsmanship Points Lost)

Lancashire Combination

	P	W	D	L	F	A	Pts.
Accrington Stanley	34	25	7	2	99	32	57
Wren Rovers	34	22	8	4	64	27	52
Bootle	34	19	9	6	74	32	47
Kirkby Town	34	19	6	9	72	38	44
Colne Dynamoes	34	18	5	11	80	42	41
Maghull	34	15	11	8	57	41	41
Leyland Motors	34	15	10	9	63	47	40
Skelmersdale United	34	14	10	10	53	41	38
Atherton Collieries	34	14	8	12	63	52	36
Lytham	34	13	8	13	54	66	34
Ford Motors	34	11	8	15	57	64	30
Padiham	34	12	6	16	51	60	30
Bacup Borough	34	12	5	17	43	63	29
Blackpool Mechanics	34	10	6	18	38	65	26
Morecambe Res	34	6	9	19	36	69	21
Clitheroe	34	7	6	21	41	87	20
Ashton Town	34	4	5	25	32	89	13
Nelson	34	4	5	25	33	94	13

West Midlands League

	P	W	D	L	F	A	Pts.
Hednesford Town	36	20	11	5	82	28	51
Alvechurch	36	20	10	6	71	33	50
Bilston	36	19	10	7	68	37	48
Lye Town	36	20	8	8	64	46	48
Willenhall Town	36	20	7	9	76	37	47
Eastwood (Hanley)	36	17	10	9	75	51	44
Tividale	36	16	11	9	46	35	43
Hinckley Athletic	36	16	10	10	54	43	42
Halesowen Town	36	17	7	12	55	40	41
Dudley Town	36	14	13	9	53	42	41
Brereton Social	36	18	5	13	58	50	41
Armitage	36	13	12	11	63	53	38
V.S. Rugby	36	12	9	15	56	49	33
Brierley Hill Alliance	36	11	7	18	40	60	29
Gresley Rovers	36	9	7	20	44	66	25
Coventry Sporting	36	7	10	19	24	67	24
Darlaston	36	7	9	20	35	66	23
Gornal Athletic	36	2	5	29	26	116	9
Staffs Police	36	1	5	30	22	93	7

PREMIER CUP FINAL
Alvechurch 1 Eastwood (Hanley) 0

Kingsmead Athenian

	P	W	D	L	F	A	Pts.	Penalty points C	D
Billericay	34	23	7	4	80	21	53	2	
Leyton W.	34	21	8	5	73	42	50	15	8
Grays	34	20	8	6	72	31	48	2	
Burnham	34	20	8	6	69	33	48	5	4
Chalfont St. P.	34	20	5	9	59	31	45	5	
Edgware	34	14	14	6	54	29	42	14	
Alton	34	13	12	9	50	33	38	4	8
Marlow	34	14	7	13	61	59	35	8	4
Windsor & E	34	13	8	13	47	44	34	7	
Harefield	34	10	13	11	37	50	33	4	
Haringey	34	9	12	13	49	48	30	13	4
Uxbridge	34	10	9	15	30	37	29	4	
Hoddesdon	34	8	12	14	41	54	28	3	4
Ruislip M.	34	10	8	16	44	58	28	6	
Chertsey	34	8	8	18	47	77	24	5	
Kingsbury	34	6	9	19	33	60	21	13	12
Erith & Bel.	34	6	6	22	34	82	18	11	4
Redhill	34	2	4	28	19	110	8	7	

C Cautions (1 Sportsmanship Point Lost); D Dismissal (4 pts.)

Rothmans Western League – Premier Division

3 Points for a Win. 1 Point for a Draw. Placings on Goal-Difference.

PREMIER DIVISION

	P	W	D	L	F	A	Pts.
Falmouth Town	34	26	5	3	98	30	83
Bideford	34	25	8	1	86	25	83
Barnstaple Town	34	18	10	6	75	37	64
Saltash United	34	17	7	10	66	53	58
Bridport	34	14	13	7	44	21	55
Clevedon Town	34	16	9	9	62	41	*55
Frome Town	34	14	8	12	43	39	50
Paulton Rovers	34	15	5	14	55	52	50
Weston-super-Mare	34	14	8	12	44	48	50
Exeter City	34	11	13	10	48	41	46
Bridgwater Town	34	12	9	13	52	56	45
Tiverton Town	34	8	10	16	47	61	34
Shepton Mallet Town	34	9	6	19	52	93	33
Glastonbury	34	9	5	20	46	77	32
Mangotsfield United	34	7	10	17	50	75	31
Welton Rovers	34	8	6	20	34	68	30
Dawlish	34	6	10	18	39	67	28
St Luke's College	34	1	10	23	20	78	13

***Two points deducted for playing ineligible players.**

Yorkshire League

	P	W	D	L	F	A	Pts.
Emley	30	20	7	3	63	33	47
Winterton Rangers	30	15	12	3	62	35	42
Thackley	30	13	11	6	41	27	37
North Ferriby	30	12	11	7	50	40	35
Guiseley	30	13	8	9	59	41	34
Hallam	30	14	6	10	47	42	34
Sheffield	30	12	9	9	42	35	33
Frecheville C.A.	30	10	9	11	41	41	29
Tadcaster Albion	30	9	10	11	42	51	28
Bridlington Town	30	11	5	14	41	49	27
Lincoln United	30	8	9	13	42	61	25
Leeds Ashley Road	30	9	6	15	35	45	24
Ossett Albion	30	6	10	14	49	58	22
Leeds Carnegie Poly.	30	9	3	18	38	46	21
Farsley Celtic	30	5	11	14	41	63	21
Denaby United	30	8	5	17	39	65	21

Midland Football Combination

	P	W	D	L	F	A	Pts.
Sutton Town	38	20	12	6	77	34	52
Paget Rangers	38	21	9	8	74	36	51
Blakenhall	38	19	13	6	57	24	51
Walsall Sportsco	38	20	10	8	62	32	50
Cinderford Town	38	18	10	10	73	39	46
Bridgnorth Town	38	16	14	8	60	28	46
Moor Green	38	16	14	8	66	41	46
Malvern Town	38	16	13	9	59	41	45
Racing Club Warwick	38	16	10	12	51	44	42
Evesham Utd.	38	15	12	11	49	46	42
Solihull Borough	38	10	17	11	45	48	37
Highgate Utd.	38	14	7	17	56	62	35
Mile Oak Rovers	38	9	17	12	35	47	35
Northfield Town	38	11	12	15	55	60	34
Boldmere St Michaels	38	11	10	17	35	48	32
Oldbury Utd	38	10	12	16	51	65	32
Coleshill Town	38	8	10	20	38	79	26
West Midlands Police	38	4	17	17	32	61	25
Knowle	38	7	6	25	38	80	20
Stratford Town	38	4	5	29	29	127	13

Kent League

	P	W	D	L	F	A	Pts.
Faversham	34	23	8	3	83	24	54
Sheppey	34	24	5	5	87	32	53
Tun Wells	34	21	10	3	84	38	52
Hythe	34	19	6	9	73	57	44
Maidstone	34	18	6	10	46	39	42
Crockenhill	34	15	8	11	62	46	38
Dartford G.	34	15	8	11	59	45	38
Medway	34	15	8	11	53	49	38
Ramsgate	34	12	13	9	54	51	37
Deal	34	13	7	14	47	53	33
Whitstable	34	13	6	15	52	43	32
Herne Bay	34	10	9	15	43	72	29
S'bourne	34	8	9	17	37	60	25
Snowdown	34	8	6	20	44	76	22
Slade Green	34	4	12	18	40	60	20
Folkestone	34	6	7	21	37	61	19
Kent Police	34	6	6	22	34	81	18
Dover	34	9	0	25	35	87	18

United Counties League

Premier Division	P	W	D	L	F	A	Pts.
Stamford A.F.C.	38	30	2	6	93	31	62
Rushden Town	38	22	8	8	66	29	52
Wolverton Town	38	19	10	9	54	35	48
Spalding United	38	21	6	11	49	41	48
Rothwell Town	38	14	16	8	45	41	44
Irthlingborough Diamonds	38	19	5	14	73	50	43
Stewart & Lloyds (Corby)	38	16	10	12	46	40	42
Buckingham Town	38	14	13	11	44	39	41
St Neots Town	38	15	10	13	46	45	40
Olney Town	38	15	9	14	56	44	39
Desborough Town	38	13	12	13	62	55	38
Kempston Rovers	38	16	6	16	50	47	38
Wootton Blue Cross	38	11	13	14	43	50	35
Long Buckby A.F.C.	38	10	13	15	42	50	33
Potton United	38	12	9	17	46	55	33
Ampthill Town	38	9	13	16	44	66	31
Bourne Town	38	8	11	19	53	78	27
Northampton Spencer	38	7	13	18	41	66	27
Eynesbury Rovers	38	5	13	20	37	69	23
Holbeach United	38	3	10	25	24	83	16

FA CUP 1977-1998

The 21 years of the Directory has seen many heroic performances by Non-League clubs in the FA Cup. In fact the first edition recorded one of the most famous- by Blyth Spartans back in 1977-78 when only a last minute equaliser by Wrexham's Dixie McNeil prevented the North Easterners from reaching the quarter-finals. 21 years on, Alan Shoulder, one of the Blyth stars in those heady days, has returned to Croft Park as manager.

Below, we look at the FA Cup year-by-year during the life-span of the Directory. We show who got furthest, and how they got there. But, with exemptions, last survivors are not necessarily the those who survived the most ties - so we also show the club enduring the longest run and the non-league clubs to claim senior "scalps".

1977-78

BLYTH SPARTANS
(5th Rnd replay, 11 games)

1Q	SHILDON	A	3-0
2Q	CROOK TOWN	A	1-1
2Qr	CROOK TOWN	H	3-0
3Q	CONSETT	A	4-1
4Q	BISHOP AUCKLAND	A	1-0
1	BURSCOUGH	H	1-0
2	**CHESTERFIELD**	**H**	**1-0**
3	ENFIELD	H	1-0
4	**STOKE CITY**	**A**	**3-2**
5	WREXHAM	A	1-1
5r	WREXHAM	H	1-2
	@ Newcastle United		

ADDITIONAL GIANT KILLING PERFORMANCES

First Round

Wigan Athletic	1-0	York City
Scarborough	4-2	Rochdale
Runcorn	1-0	Southport
Nuneaton Borough	2-0	Oxford United
Wealdstone	3-2	Hereford United
Enfield	3-0	Wimbledon

Second Round

Wigan Athletic	1-0	Sheffield Wed.
Scarborough	2-0	Crewe Alexandra
Wealdstone	2-1	Reading
Northampton	0-2	**Enfield**

1978-79

MAIDSTONE UNITED
(3rd Round replay, 9 games)

1Q	HORSHAM Y M C A	H	2-0
2Q	DOVER	A	0-0
2Qr	DOVER	H	1-0
3Q	RAMSGATE	A	3-1
4Q	WATERLOOVILLE	A	2-1
1	WYCOMBE WANDERERS	H	1-0
2	**EXETER CITY**	**H**	**1-0**
3	CHARLTON ATHLETIC	A	1-1
3r	CHARLTON ATHLETIC	H	1-2

ALTRINCHAM
(3rd Round replay)

1	SOUTHPORT	H	4-3
2	DROYLSDEN	A	2-0
3	TOTTENHAM HOTSPUR	A	1-1
3r	TOTTENHAM HOTSPUR	H	0-3

WOKING
(9 games)

1Q	EPSOM & EWELL	H	3-1
2Q	TUNBRIDGE WELLS	A	2-0
3Q	HORSHAM	H	5-2
4Q	MARGATE	A	7-1

WOKING (cont)

1	BARNET	A	3-3
1r	BARNET	H	3-3
1r2	BARNET	N	3-0
	@ Brentford		
2	SWANSEA CITY	A	2-2
2r	SWANSEA CITY	H	3-5

WORCESTER CITY
(9 games)

1Q	BROMSGROVE ROVERS	H	1-0
2Q	HIGHGATE UNITED	A	0-0
2Qr	HIGHGATE UNITED	H	3-2
3Q	DARLASTON	H	7-1
4Q	BATH CITY	A	1-1
4Qr	BATH CITY	H	2-1
1	**PLYMOUTH ARGYLE**	**H**	**2-0**
2	NEWPORT COUNTY	A	0-0
2r	NEWPORT COUNTY	H	1-2

ADDITIONAL GIANT KILLING PERFORMANCES

First Round

Rochdale	0-1	**Droylsden**

1979-80

HARLOW TOWN
(4th Round, 11 games)

PRE	LOWESTOFT TOWN	A	2-1
1Q	HORNCHURCH	A	3-0
2Q	BURY TOWN	H	2-1
3Q	HARWICH & PARKESTON	H	1-0
4Q	MARGATE	H	1-0
1	LEYTONSTONE ILFORD	H	2-1
2	SOUTHEND UNITED	A	1-1
2r	**SOUTHEND UNITED**	**H**	**1-0**
3	LEICESTER CITY	A	1-1
3r	**LEICESTER CITY**	**H**	**1-0**
4	WATFORD	A	3-4

NORTHWICH VICTORIA
(11 games)

1Q	CAERNARFON TOWN	A	0-0
1Qr	CAERNARFON TOWN	H	3-1
2Q	FORMBY	A	1-1
2Qr	FORMBY	H	2-0
3Q	OSWESTRY TOWN	A	1-1
3Qr	OSWESTRY TOWN	H	4-1
4Q	ENDERBY TOWN	A	1-0
1	NUNEATON BOROUGH	A	3-3
1r	NUNEATON BOROUGH	H	3-0
2	WIGAN ATHLETIC	H	2-2
2r	WIGAN ATHLETIC	A	0-1

ADDITIONAL GIANT KILLING PERFORMANCES

First Round

Barking 1-0 Oxford United

1980-81

ENFIELD
(4th Round replay)

4Q	EPSOM & EWELL	H	5-0
1	WEMBLEY	H	3-0
2	**HEREFORD UNITED**	**H**	**2-0**
3	PORT VALE	A	1-1
3r	**PORT VALE**	**H**	**2-1**
4	BARNSLEY	A	1-1
4r	BARNSLEY	H	0-3
	@ Tottenham Hotspur		

MAIDSTONE UNITED
(11 games)

1Q	RAMSGATE	H	6-0
2Q	FOLKESTONE	A	2-0
3Q	BROMLEY	H	2-0

MAIDSTONE UNITED (cont)

4Q	BARKING	H	2-0
1	KETTERING TOWN	A	1-1
1r	KETTERING TOWN	H	0-0
1r2	KETTERING TOWN	H	3-1
2	GILLINGHAM	A	0-0
2r	GILLINGHAM	H	0-0
2r2	**GILLINGHAM**	**A**	**2-0**
3	EXETER CITY	H	2-4

ADDITIONAL GIANT KILLING PERFORMANCES

First Round

Mossley 1-0 Crewe Alexandra

Second Round

Altrincham 1-0 Scunthorpe Utd

1981-82

BARNET
(3rd Round replay)

4Q	CORINTHIAN CASUALS	H	2-0
1	HARLOW TOWN	A	0-0
1r	HARLOW TOWN	H	1-0
2	WYCOMBE WANDERERS	H	2-0
3	BRIGHTON & HOVE ALB.	H	0-0
3r	BRIGHTON & HOVE ALB.	A	1-3

DORCHESTER TOWN
(8 games)

1Q	HUNGERFORD TOWN	A	2-1
2Q	FROME TOWN	H	3-0
3Q	EASTLEIGH	A	4-2
4Q	CHELTENHAM TOWN	A	3-1
1	MINEHEAD	H	3-3
1r	MINEHEAD	A	4-0
2	A F C BOURNEMOUTH	H	1-1
2r	A F C BOURNEMOUTH	A	1-2

HENDON
(8 games)

PRE	ABINGDON TOWN	A	2-1
1Q	AMPTHILL TOWN	A	1-0
2Q	BANBURY UNITED	H	2-2
2Qr	BANBURY UNITED	A	4-3

HENDON (cont)

3Q	TRING TOWN	H	4-0
4Q	HARROW BOROUGH	H	2-1
1	WYCOMBE WANDERERS	H	1-1
1r	WYCOMBE WANDERERS	A	0-2

TAUNTON TOWN
(8 games)

1Q	SALTASH UNITED	H	1-0
2Q	BRIDGWATER TOWN	A	1-1
2Qr	BRIDGWATER TOWN	H	1-0
3Q	LISKEARD ATHLETIC	H	2-1
4Q	ADDLESTONE & WEY. T	A	2-2
4Qr	ADDLESTONE & WEY. T	H	0-0
4Qr2	ADDLESTONE & WEY. T	H	4-2
1	SWINDON TOWN	H	1-2
	@ Swindon Town		

ADDITIONAL GIANT KILLING PERFORMANCES

First Round

Penrith 1-0 Chester City
Altrincham 3-0 Sheffield United

Second Round

Enfield 4-1 Wimbledon
Altrincham 4-3 York City

1982-83

BISHOP'S STORTFORD
(3rd Round replay)

4Q	HARLOW TOWN	A	1-1
4Qr	HARLOW TOWN	H	4-0
1	**READING**	**A**	**2-1**
2	SLOUGH TOWN	A	4-1
3	MIDDLESBROUGH	A	2-2
3r	MIDDLESBROUGH	H	1-2

WOKINGHAM TOWN
(10 games)

PRE	ANDOVER	H	6-1
1Q	WHYTELEAFE	A	0-0
1Qr	WHYTELEAFE	H	1-0
2Q	STAINES TOWN @ Wokinhgam Town	A	2-0
3Q	KINGSTONIAN	H	2-2
3Qr	KINGSTONIAN	A	1-1

WOKINGHAM TOWN (cont)

3Qr2	KINGSTONIAN	H	2-0
4Q	LEATHERHEAD	H	1-0
1	CARDIFF CITY	H	1-1
1r	CARDIFF CITY	A	0-3

ADDITIONAL GIANT KILLING PERFORMANCES

First Round

Boston United	3-1	Crewe Alex
Altrincham	2-1	Rochdale
Halifax Town	0-1	**North Shields**
Slough Town	1-0	Millwall
Telford United	2-1	Wigan Athletic
Northwich Victoria	3-1	Chester

Second Round

Worcester City	2-0	Wrexham
Cardiff City	2-3	**Weymouth**

1983-84

TELFORD UNITED
(4th Round)

1	**STOCKPORT COUNTY**	**H**	**3-0**
2	NORTHAMPTON TOWN	A	1-1
2r	**NORTHAMPTON TOWN**	**H**	**3-2**
3	**ROCHDALE**	**A**	**4-1**
4	DERBY COUNTY	A	2-3

WATERLOOVILLE
(10 games)

1Q	R S SOUTHAMPTON	A	0-0
1Qr	R S SOUTHAMPTON	H	2-1
2Q	HUNGERFORD TOWN	A	3-3
2Qr	HUNGERFORD TOWN	H	3-0

WATERLOOVILLE (cont)

3Q	A F C TOTTON	A	1-1
3Qr	A F C TOTTON	H	3-0
4Q	WOKINGHAM TOWN	H	3-2
1	NORTHAMPTON TOWN	A	1-1
1r	NORTHAMPTON TOWN	H	1-1
1r2	NORTHAMPTON TOWN	A	0-2

ADDITIONAL GIANT KILLING PERFORMANCES

First Round

Halifax Town	2-3	**Whitby Town**
Maidstone United	2-1	Exeter City
Worcester City	2-1	Aldershot

1984-85

TELFORD UNITED
(5th Round)

1	LINCOLN CITY	A	1-1
1r	LINCOLN CITY	H	2-1
2	**PRESTON NORTH END**	**A**	**4-1**
3	**BRADFORD CITY**	**H**	**2-1**
4	DARLINGTON	A	1-1
4r	**DARLINGTON**	**H**	**3-0**
5	EVERTON	A	0-3

WHITBY TOWN
(9 games)

1Q	WILLINGTON	A	5-2
2Q	NORTH SHIELDS	H	1-1
2Qr	NORTH SHIELDS	A	2-2
2Qr2	NORTH SHIELDS	A	1-1
2Qr3	NORTH SHIELDS	H	2-0

WHITBY TOWN (cont)

3Q	RYHOPE COM. ASCN	A	1-1
3Qr	RYHOPE COMM. ASCN	H	5-1
4Q	MARINE	A	1-0
1	CHESTERFIELD	H	1-3

ADDITIONAL GIANT KILLING PERFORMANCES

First Round

Northwich Victoria	3-1	Crewe Alexandra
Blackpoool	0-1	**Altrincham**
Enfield	3-0	Exeter City
Swindon Town	1-2	**Dagenham**
Bognor Regis Town	3-1	Swansea City

Second Round

Dagenham	1-0	Peterborough U
Aldershot	0-3	**Burton Albion**

1985-86

ALTRINCHAM

(4th Round)

1	CHORLEY	A	2-0
2	**BLACKPOOL**	**A**	**2-1**
3	**BIRMINGHAM CITY (DIV 1)**	**A**	**2-1**
4	YORK CITY	A	0-2

SLOUGH TOWN

(11 games)

1Q	MERSTHAM	A	4-0
2Q	WOKING	A	5-1
3Q	WELLING UNITED	A	0-0
3Qr	WELLING UNITED	H	2-1
4Q	KINGSTONIAN	H	2-2
4Qr	KINGSTONIAN	A	1-1
4Qr2	KINGSTONIAN	H	2-1

SLOUGH TOWN (cont)

1	AYLESBURY UNITED	H	2-2
1r	AYLESBURY UNITED	A	5-2
	@ Tring Town		
2	ORIENT	A	2-2
2r	ORIENT	H	2-3

ADDITIONAL GIANT KILLING PERFORMANCES

First Round

Stockport County	0-1	**Telford United**
Wycombe Wndrs	2-0	Colchester Utd
Dagenham	2-1	Cambridge Utd

Second Round

Hartlepool Utd	0-1	**Frickley Athletic**

1986-87

CAERNARFON TOWN

(3rd Round replay)

1Q	MARINE	H	2-0
2Q	WINSFORD UNITED	A	3-1
3Q	EASTWOOD TOWN	A	4-1
4Q	CHESTER-LE-STREET T.	A	3-2
1	**STOCKPORT COUNTY**	**H**	**1-0**
2	YORK CITY	H	0-0
2r	**YORK CITY**	**A**	**2-1**
3	BARNSLEY	H	0-0
3r	BARNSLEY	A	0-1

SOUTHPORT

(10 games)

1Q	GARFORTH TOWN	H	1-1
1Qr	GARFORTH TOWN	A	1-1
1Qr2	GARFORTH TOWN	H	2-1

SOUTHPORT (cont)

2Q	LANCASTER CITY	A	1-1
2Qr	LANCASTER CITY	H	3-1
3Q	EMLEY	H	3-3
3Qr	EMLEY	A	4-4
3Qr2	EMLEY	H	2-0
4Q	MACCLESFIELD TOWN	A	1-0
1	SCUNTHORPE UNITED	A	0-2

ADDITIONAL GIANT KILLING PERFORMANCES

First Round

Telford United	3-0	Burnley
Chorley	3-0	Wolves

Second Round

Maidstone United	1-0	Cambridge United

1987-88

SUTTON UNITED

(3rd Round replay, 9 games)

1Q	WIVENHOE TOWN	A	3-0
2Q	REDHILL	H	3-1
3Q	BROMLEY	H	0-0
3Qr	BROMLEY	A	2-1
4Q	BASINGSTOKE TOWN	H	3-0
1	**ALDERSHOT**	**H**	**3-0**
2	**PETERBOROUGH UTD**	**A**	**3-1**
3	MIDDLESBROUGH	H	1-1
3r	MIDDLESBROUGH	A	0-1

ATHERSTONE UNITED

(9 games)

PRE	NORTHAMPTON SPNCR	A	5-2
1Q	MALVERN TOWN	H	1-1
1Qr	MALVERN TOWN	A	2-0
2Q	LYE TOWN	H	1-0
3Q	ALVECHURCH	H	4-3
4Q	LEYTON WINGATE	A	0-0
4Qr	LEYTON WINGATE	H	4-2
1	V S RUGBY	A	0-0
1r	V S RUGBY	H	0-2

MACCLESFIELD TOWN

(9 games)

1Q	STALYBRIDGE CELTIC	A	1-1
1Qr	STALYBRIDGE CELTIC	H	5-1
2Q	CHADDERTON	H	5-0
3Q	MARINE	H	0-0
3Qr	MARINE	A	2-1
4Q	WHITBY TOWN	H	3-1
1	**CARLISLE UNITED**	**H**	**4-2**
2	**ROTHERHAM UNITED**	**H**	**4-0**
3	PORT VALE	A	0-1

YEOVIL TOWN

(9 games)

1Q	GOSPORT BOROUGH	A	1-0
2Q	WATERLOOVILLE	A	1-1
2Qr	WATERLOOVILLE	H	3-2
3Q	WIMBORNE TOWN	A	4-0
4Q	WEYMOUTH	A	3-1
1	WORCESTER CITY	A	1-1
1r	WORCESTER CITY	H	1-0
2	**CAMBRIDGE UNITED**	**A**	**1-0**
3	NORWICH CITY	H	0-3

ADDITIONAL GIANT KILLING PERFORMANCES

First Round

Chester City	0-1	**Runcorn**

1988-89

SUTTON UNITED

(4th Round)

4Q	WALTON & HERSHAM	H	1-1
4Qr	WALTON & HERSHAM	A	3-0
1	DAGENHAM	A	4-0
2	AYLESBURY UNITED	A	1-0
3	**COVENTRY CITY**	**H**	**2-1**
4	NORWICH CITY	A	0-8

KETTERING TOWN

(4th Round, 9 games)

1Q	WARE	A	3-0
2Q	GREAT YARMOUTH TOWN	A	3-0
3Q	BOREHAM WOOD	H	4-0
4Q	WYCOMBE WANDERERS	A	2-1
1	DARTFORD	H	2-1
2	**BRISTOL ROVERS**	**H**	**2-1**
3	HALIFAX TOWN	H	1-1
3r	**HALIFAX TOWN**	**A**	**3-2**
4	CHARLTON ATHLETIC	A	1-2

GUISBOROUGH TOWN

(9 games)

1Q	ALNWICK TOWN	H	3-0
2Q	FARSLEY CELTIC	H	0-0
2Qr	FARSLEY CELTIC	A	1-0
3Q	BRIDLINGTON TOWN	H	1-1
3Qr	BRIDLINGTON TOWN	A	1-0
4Q	LEEK TOWN	A	0-0
4Qr	LEEK TOWN	H	0-0
4Qr2	LEEK TOWN	H	1-0
1	BURY	H	0-1

ADDITIONAL GIANT KILLING PERFORMANCES

First Round

Altrincham	3-2	Lincoln City
Runcorn	3-2	Wrexham
Bognor Regis Town	2-1	Exeter City
Leyton Orient	0-1	**Enfield**

1989-90

DARLINGTON
(4th Round replay)

4Q	RUNCORN	H	4-2
1	NORTHWICH VICTORIA	H	6-2
2	**HALIFAX TOWN**	**H**	**3-0**
3	CAMBRIDGE UNITED	A	0-0
3r	CAMBRIDGE UNITED	H	1-3

BISHOP AUCKLAND
(9 games)

1Q	CHESTER-LE-STREET T	H	3-2
2Q	LANGLEY PARK WELFARE	A	5-2
3Q	SOUTH BANK	H	1-1
3Qr	SOUTH BANK	A	3-1
4Q	MOSSLEY	A	1-1
4Qr	MOSSLEY	H	3-0
1	TOW LAW TOWN	H	2-0
2	CREWE ALEXANDRA	A	1-1
2r	CREWE ALEXANDRA	H	0-2

WHITLEY BAY
(9 games)

PRE	HORDEN C W	A	3-0
1Q	WILLINGTON	H	6-0
2Q	SPENNYMOOR UNITED	A	4-2
3Q	BARROW	A	2-2
3Qr	BARROW	H	3-1
4Q	SOUTHPORT	A	3-1
1	**SCARBOROUGH**	**A**	**1-0**
2	**PRESTON NORTH END**	**H**	**2-0**
3	ROCHDALE	A	0-1

ADDITIONAL GIANT KILLING PERFORMANCES
First Round

Aylesbury United	1-0	Southend U
Welling United	1-0	Gillingham

1990-91

WOKING
(4th Round)

4Q	BATH CITY	H	2-1
1	KIDDERMINSTER HARR.	H	1-1
1r	KIDDERMINSTER HARR.	A	2-1
2	MERTHYR TYDFIL	H	5-1
3	**WEST BROMWICH ALB.**	**A**	**4-2**
4	EVERTON @ Everton	H	0-1

WYCOMBE WANDERERS
(9 games)

1Q	MAIDENHEAD UNITED	H	3-0
2Q	TROWBRIDGE TOWN	A	0-0
2Qr	TROWBRIDGE TOWN	H	2-1
3Q	WOKINGHAM TOWN	H	4-1
4Q	BASINGSTOKE TOWN	H	6-0
1	BOSTON UNITED	A	1-1
1r	BOSTON UNITED	H	4-0
2	PETERBOROUGH UTD	H	1-1
2r	PETERBOROUGH UTD	A	0-2

BARNET
(9 games)

1Q	CLAPTON @ Dagenham	A	2-0
2Q	BRAINTREE TOWN	A	2-0
3Q	HARLOW TOWN	A	3-1
4Q	HEYBRIDGE SWIFTS	H	3-1
1	CHELMSFORD CITY	H	2-2
1r	CHELMSFORD CITY	A	2-0
2	NORTHAMPTON TOWN	H	0-0
2r	**NORTHAMPTON TOWN**	**A**	**1-0**
3	PORTSMOUTH	H	0-5

ADDITIONAL GIANT KILLING PERFORMANCES
First Round

Chorley	2-1	Bury
Scarborough	0-2	**Leek Town**
Hayes	1-0	Cardiff City

1991-92

WOKING
(3rd Round replay)

1	WINDSOR & ETON	A	4-2
2	YEOVIL TOWN	H	3-0
3	HEREFORD UNITED	H	0-0
3r	HEREFORD UNITED	A	1-2

FARNBOROUGH TOWN
(3rd Round replay)

4Q	SALISBURY	A	7-1
1	HALESOWEN TOWN	A	2-2
1r	HALESOWEN TOWN	H	4-0
2	TORQUAY UNITED	A	1-1
2r	**TORQUAY UNITED**	**H**	**4-3**
3	WEST HAM UNITED @ West Ham United	H	1-1
3r	WEST HAM UNITED	A	0-1

KETTERING TOWN
(9 games)

1Q	WISBECH TOWN	A	3-0
2Q	BRAINTREE TOWN	H	3-1
3Q	HEYBRIDGE SWIFTS	H	3-0
4Q	STAFFORD RANGERS	H	0-0
4Qr	STAFFORD RANGERS	A	2-0
1	WYCOMBE WANDERERS	H	1-1
1r	WYCOMBE WANDERERS	A	2-0
2	**MAIDSTONE UNITED**	**A**	**2-1**
3	BLACKBURN ROVERS	A	1-4

ADDITIONAL GIANT KILLING PERFORMANCES
First Round

Halifax Town	1-2	**Witton Albion**
Telford United	2-1	Stoke City
Crawley Town	4-2	Northampton Town
Fulham	0-2	**Hayes**
Aldershot	0-1	**Enfield**
Walsall	0-1	**Yeovil Town**

1992-93

WOKING

(3rd Round replay)

1	WINDSOR & ETON	A	4-2
2	YEOVIL TOWN	H	3-0
3	HEREFORD UNITED	H	0-0
3r	HEREFORD UNITED	A	1-2

FARNBOROUGH TOWN

(3rd Round replay)

4Q	SALISBURY	A	7-1
1	HALESOWEN TOWN	A	2-2
1r	HALESOWEN TOWN	H	4-0
2	TORQUAY UNITED	A	1-1
2r	**TORQUAY UNITED**	**H**	**4-3**
3	WEST HAM UNITED @ West Ham United	H	1-1
3r	WEST HAM UNITED	A	0-1

KETTERING TOWN

(9 games)

1Q	WISBECH TOWN	A	3-0
2Q	BRAINTREE TOWN	H	3-1
3Q	HEYBRIDGE SWIFTS	H	3-0
4Q	STAFFORD RANGERS	H	0-0
4Qr	STAFFORD RANGERS	A	2-0
1	WYCOMBE WANDERERS	H	1-1
1r	WYCOMBE WANDERERS	A	2-0
2	**MAIDSTONE UNITED**	**A**	**2-1**
3	BLACKBURN ROVERS	A	1-4

ADDITIONAL GIANT KILLING PERFORMANCES

First Round

Halifax Town	1-2	**Witton Albion**
Telford United	2-1	Stoke City
Crawley Town	4-2	Northampton Town
Fulham	0-2	**Hayes**
Aldershot	0-1	**Enfield**
Walsall	0-1	**Yeovil Town**

1993-94

MARLOW

(3rd Round)

4Q	SITTINGBOURNE	A	1-1
4Qr	SITTINGBOURNE	H	2-1
1	SALISBURY	H	3-3
1r	SALISBURY	A	2-2
2	V S RUGBY	A	0-0
2r	V S RUGBY	H	2-0
3	TOTTENHAM HOTSPUR @ Tottenham Hotspur	H	1-5

MARINE

(3rd Round)

1Q	EMLEY	H	5-0
2Q	HEANOR TOWN	H	2-0
3Q	NANTWICH TOWN	A	1-0
4Q	RUNCORN	A	4-1
1	**HALIFAX TOWN**	**H**	**4-1**
2	STAFFORD RANGERS	H	3-2
3	CREWE ALEXANDRA	A	1-3

YEOVIL TOWN

(3rd Round)

4Q	CRAWLEY TOWN	A	2-1
1	**TORQUAY UNITED**	**A**	**5-2**
2	HEREFORD UNITED	H	0-0
2r	**HEREFORD UNITED**	**A**	**2-1**
3	ARSENAL	H	1-3

ALTRINCHAM

(9 games)

1Q	CURZON ASHTON	H	3-0
2Q	SHEFFIELD	H	3-1
3Q	COLWYN BAY	A	3-3
3Qr	COLWYN BAY	H	1-1
3Qr2	COLWYN BAY	H	3-1
4Q	GAINSBOROUGH TRINITY	A	2-0
1	CHESTER CITY	A	1-1
1r	**CHESTER CITY**	**H**	**2-0**
2	PORT VALE	H	1-4

MACCLESFIELD TOWN

(9 games)

1Q	GLOSSOP NORTH END	A	1-0
2Q	HUCKNALL TOWN	A	1-1
2Qr	HUCKNALL TOWN	H	3-1
3Q	HORWICH R M I	H	1-0
4Q	NETHERFIELD	A	1-1
4Qr	NETHERFIELD	H	5-0
1	CHESTERFIELD	H	0-0
1r	**CHESTERFIELD** Macclesfield won 3-2 on penalties	**A**	**2-2**
2	STOCKPORT COUNTY	H	0-2

STAFFORD RANGERS

(9 games)

1Q	ALFRETON TOWN	A	0-0
1Qr	ALFRETON TOWN	H	3-0
2Q	BEDWORTH UNITED	A	1-1
2Qr	BEDWORTH UNITED	H	1-0
3Q	FRICKLEY ATHLETIC	H	3-0
4Q	BROMSGROVE ROVERS	H	3-0
1	LINCOLN CITY	A	0-0
1r	**LINCOLN CITY**	**H**	**2-1**
2	MARINE	A	2-3

SUTTON COLDFIELD TOWN

(9 games)

PRE	WEST BROMWICH TOWN	H	0-0
PREr	WEST BROMWICH TOWN	A	2-0
1Q	STEWARTS & LLOYDS	A	3-1
2Q	EASTWOOD HANLEY	H	2-1
3Q	RUSHALL OLYMPIC	H	0-0
3Qr	RUSHALL OLYMPIC	A	1-1
3Qr2	RUSHALL OLYMPIC	A	2-1
4Q	LEYTON	H	6-1
1	BOLTON WANDERERS	A	1-2

ADDITIONAL GIANT KILLING PERFORMANCES

First Round

Cardiff City	2-3	**Bath City**

1993-94

KIDDERMINSTER HARRIERS
(5th Round)

4Q	CHESHAM UNITED	A	4-1
1	KETTERING TOWN	H	3-0
2	WOKING	H	1-0
3	**BIRMINGHAM CITY**	**A**	**2-1**
4	**PRESTON NORTH END**	**H**	**1-0**
5	WEST HAM UNITED	H	0-1

NUNEATON BOROUGH
(9 games)

1Q	WINTERTON RANGERS	A	7-1
2Q	WEST MIDLANDS POLICE	H	3-3
2Qr	WEST MIDLANDS POLICE	A	3-0
3Q	WORKSOP TOWN	H	4-1
4Q	STEVENAGE BOROUGH	A	2-1
1	SWANSEA CITY	A	1-1
1r	**SWANSEA CITY**	**H**	**2-1**
2	A F C BOURNEMOUTH	A	1-1
2r	A F C BOURNEMOUTH	H	0-1

STALYBRIDGE CELTIC
(9 games)

1Q	FLEETWOOD TOWN	H	6-0
2Q	BOOTLE	H	2-2
2Qr	BOOTLE	A	3-1
3Q	WARRINGTON TOWN	A	1-0
4Q	WHITBY TOWN	H	1-1
4Qr	WHITBY TOWN	A	1-0
1	MARINE	H	1-1
1r	MARINE	A	4-4
2	CARLISLE UNITED	A	1-3

ADDITIONAL GIANT KILLING PERFORMANCES

First Round

Colchester United	3-4	**Sutton United**
Macclesfield Town	2-0	Hartlepool
Northampton Town	1-2	**Bromsgrove Rovers**

Second Round

Bath City	2-1	Hereford United
Torquay United	0-1	**Sutton United**

1994-95

ENFIELD
(3rd Round, 9 games)

1Q	HEMEL HEMPSTEAD	H	5-2
2Q	PURFLEET	H	3-1
3Q	RUISLIP MANOR	A	3-0
4Q	ST ALBANS CITY	A	0-0
4Qr	ST ALBANS CITY	H	4-2
1	**CARDIFF CITY**	**H**	**1-0**
2	TORQUAY UNITED	H	1-1
2r	**TORQUAY UNITED**	**A**	**1-0**
3	LEICESTER CITY	A	0-2

MARLOW
(3rd Round)

4Q	SUTTON UNITED	H	1-0
1	**OXFORD UNITED**	**H**	**2-0**
2	WOKING	H	2-1
3	SWINDON TOWN	A	0-2

AYLESBURY UNITED
(3rd Round)

1Q	BOREHAM WOOD	H	3-1
2Q	EDGWARE TOWN	H	2-0
3Q	BALDOCK TOWN	A	2-0
4Q	MOOR GREEN	A	1-1
4Qr	MOOR GREEN	H	3-1
1	NEWPORT I O W	A	3-2
2	KINGSTONIAN	A	4-1
3	QUEENS PARK RANGERS	H	0-4

@ Queens Park Rangers

ALTRINCHAM
(3rd Round)

4Q	MARINE	H	2-1
1	SOUTHPORT	H	3-2
2	**WIGAN ATHLETIC**	**H**	**1-0**
3	TOTTENHAM HOTSPUR	A	0-3

BASHLEY
(9 games)

1Q	HAVANT TOWN	A	1-1
1Qr	HAVANT TOWN	H	3-1
2Q	HUNGERFORD TOWN	H	3-0
3Q	DORCHESTER TOWN	H	1-1
3Qr	DORCHESTER TOWN	A	2-0
4Q	CHELTENHAM TOWN	A	1-1
4Qr	CHELTENHAM TOWN	H	2-1
1	CHESHAM UNITED	A	1-0
2	SWANSEA CITY	H	0-1

HITCHIN TOWN
(9 games)

1Q	NEWMARKET TOWN	A	2-1
2Q	TIPTREE UNITED	H	3-3
2Qr	TIPTREE UNITED	A	4-2
3Q	CAMBRIDGE CITY	H	3-3
3Qr	CAMBRIDGE CITY	A	3-2
4Q	BURTON ALBION	A	1-0
1	HEREFORD UNITED	A	2-2
1r	**HEREFORD UNITED**	**H**	**4-2**
2	WYCOMBE WANDERERS	H	0-5

ADDITIONAL GIANT KILLING PERFORMANCES

First Round

Kingstonian	2-1	Brighton

1995-96

WOKING

(3rd Round)

1	BARNET	A	2-2
1r	BARNET	H	2-1
2	ENFIELD	A	1-1
2r	ENFIELD	H	2-1
	@ Wycombe Wanderers		
3	SWINDON TOWN	A	0-2

GRAVESEND & NORTHFLEET

(3rd Round, 10 games)

1Q	GODALMING & GUILDFORD	H	7-0
2Q	MOLESEY	A	6-0
3Q	CARSHALTON ATHLETIC	H	2-1

GRAVESEND & NORTHFLEET (cont)

4Q	MARLOW	H	1-1
4Qr	MARLOW	A	3-3
4Qr2	MARLOW	H	4-0
1	**COLCHESTER UNITED**	**H**	**2-0**
2	CINDERFORD TOWN	A	1-1
2r	CINDERFORD TOWN	H	3-0
3	ASTON VILLA	H	0-3
	@ Aston Villa		

ADDITIONAL GIANT KILLING PERFORMANCES

First Round

Bury	0-2	**Blyth Spartans**
Hitchin Town	2-1	Bristol Rovers

1996-97

HEDNESFORD TOWN

(4th Round, 9 games)

1Q	WEDNESFIELD	A	0-0
1Qr	WEDNESFIELD	H	6-0
2Q	EVESHAM UNITED	H	6-1
3Q	TAMWORTH	H	4-2
4Q	TELFORD UNITED	H	2-0
1	SOUTHPORT	H	2-1
2	**BLACKPOOL**	**A**	**1-0**
3	**YORK CITY**	**H**	**1-0**
4	MIDDLESBROUGH	A	2-3

STEVENAGE BOROUGH

(9 games)

1Q	ARLESEY TOWN	A	3-0

STEVENAGE BOROUGH (cont)

2Q	BALDOCK TOWN	H	1-1
2Qr	BALDOCK TOWN	A	2-1
3Q	BRAINTREE TOWN	H	3-1
4Q	GRAVESEND & N'FLEET	A	5-1
1	HAYES	H	2-2
1r	HAYES	A	2-0
2	**LEYTON ORIENT**	**A**	**2-1**
3	BIRMINGHAM CITY	H	0-2
	@ Birmingham City		

ADDITIONAL GIANT KILLING PERFORMANCES

First Round

Millwall	0-1	**Woking**
Cambridge V	0-2	**Welling**

1997-98

STEVENAGE BOROUGH

(4th Round replay)

1	CARSHALTON ATHLETIC	A	0-0
1r	CARSHALTON ATHLETIC	H	5-0
2	CAMBRIDGE UNITED	A	1-1
2r	**CAMBRIDGE UNITED**	**H**	**2-1**
3	**SWINDON TOWN**	**A**	**2-1**
4	NEWCASTLE UNITED	H	1-1
4r	NEWCASTLE UNITED	A	1-2

BASINGSTOKE TOWN

(11 games)

1Q	HAVANT TOWN	A	1-1
1Qr	HAVANT TOWN	H	2-0

BASINGSTOKE TOWN (cont)

2Q	BATH CITY	H	1-1
2Qr	BATH CITY	A	3-1
3Q	CALNE TOWN	H	0-0
3Qr	CALNE TOWN	A	2-1
4Q	BRAINTREE TOWN	H	5-1
1	WYCOMBE WANDERERS	A	2-2
1r	**WYCOMBE WANDERERS**	**H**	**2-2**
	Basingstoke won after penalties		
2	NORTHAMPTON TOWN	A	1-1
2r	NORTHAMPTON TOWN	H	0-0
	Basingstoke lost after penalties		

F.A. CUP HEROES

TOP: Chris Kelly scores a famous winning goal for Leatherhead at Brighton in the Third Round in season 1974-75. Photo: Eric Marsh.

MIDDLE: Goalkeeper Seaman of First Division Birmingham City is stranded as the ball rolls towards the net following a tragic back-pass by Robert Hopkins (extreme right) to give Altrincham a 2-1 victory at St. Andrews in 1986. Paul Reid (left) and Gary Anderson are the Robins players in the picture. Photo: John Rooney..

BOTTOM: Steve Burr of Macclesfield, who scored a hat trick at home to Rotherham United in the 2nd Round, runs at the Port Vale defence during the 3rd Round tie at Vale Park. Photo: John Rooney.

SEASON 1977-78

Team of the year: Blyth Spartans

Special Merit Award: Enfield

F.A. Cup Award: Blyth Spartans

Players of the Season:
Dave Clark *(Blyth Spartans)*
Gerry Stewart *(Boston United)*
Paul Gover *(Bath City)*
John King *(Altrincham)*
Keith Searle *(Enfield)*

Merit Award for the F.A. Vase level Club:

F.A. Trophy Quarter Finalists:	F.A. Vase Quarter Finalists:
Spennymoor United	Barton Rovers†
Dagenham	Haringey Borough
Altrincham*	Hungerford Town
Winsford United	Irthlington Diamonds
Bedford Town	Almondsbury Greenway
Leatherhead†	Burnham
Merthyr Tydfil	Frethville Community
Runcorn	Blue Star*

** Winners   † Runners up*

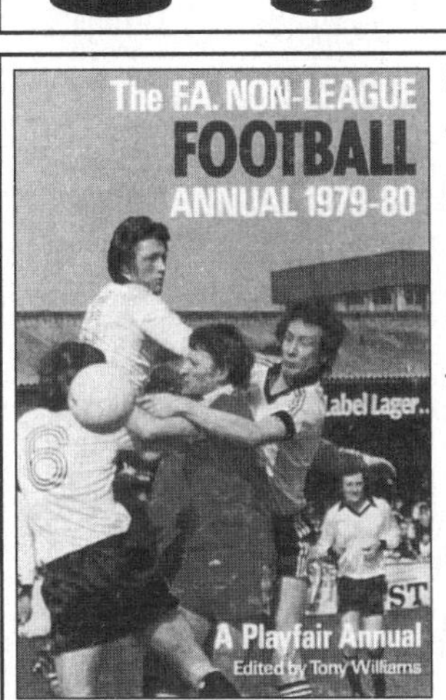

SEASON 1978-79

Team of the year: Barking

Special Merit Award: Worcester City

F.A. Cup Award: Altrincham

Players of the Season:
Jim Arnold *(Stafford Rangers)*
Tony Jennings *(Enfield)*
Billy Kellock *(Kettering Town)*
Chris Tudor *(Almondsbury Greenway)*
Howard Wilkinson *(England Semi-Pro Manager)*

Merit Award for the F.A. Vase level Club:
Billericay Town

F.A. Trophy Quarter Finalists:	F.A. Vase Quarter Finalists:
Runcorn	Eastbourne United
Hayes	Billericay Town*
Bishop Auckland	Barton Rovers
Stafford Rangers*	Shepshed Charterhouse
Dagenham	Almondsbury Greenway†
Yeovil Town	Farnborough Town
Kettering Town†	Whickham
Enfield	Willenhall Town

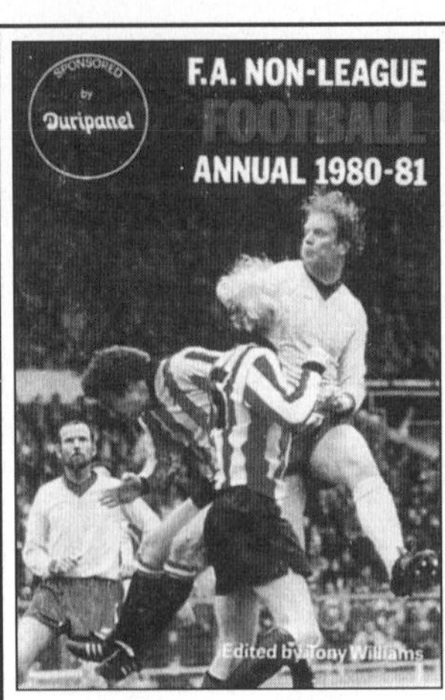

SEASON 1979-80

Team of the year: Dagenham

Special Merit Award: Altrincham

F.A. Cup Award: Harlow Town

Players of the Season:
Ted Hardy *(Manager – Enfield)*
Leo Skeete *(Mossley)*
Graham Smith *(Northwich Victoria)*
Adrian Titcombe *(F.A.)*
Mike Roberts *(Winsford United)*

Merit Award for the F.A. Vase level Club:
Guisborough Town

F.A. Trophy Quarter Finalists:
Dagenham
Nuneaton Borough
Woking
Barrow
Boston United
Dulwich Hamlet
Blyth Spartans
Mossley

F.A. Vase Quarter Finalists:
Guisborough Town
Windsor & Eton
Billericay Town
Hungerford Town
Irthlingborough Diamonds
Curzon Athletic
Cray Wanderers
Stamford

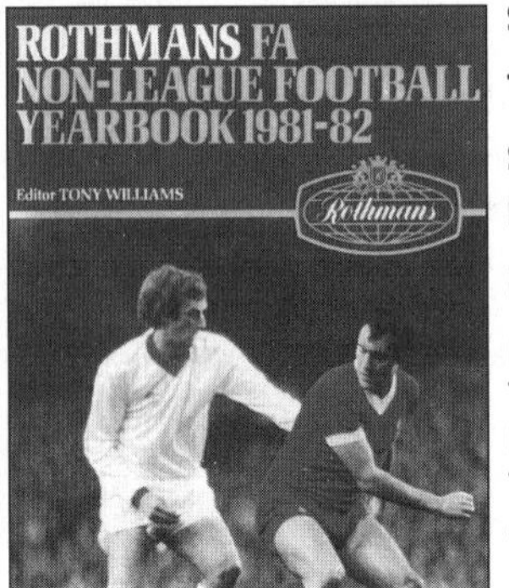

ROTHMANS FA
NON-LEAGUE FOOTBALL
YEARBOOK 1981-82
Editor TONY WILLIAMS
Rothmans

SEASON 1980-81

Team of the year: Altrincham

Special Merit Award:
Bishop's Stortford, Runcorn, Slough Town

F.A. Cup Award: Enfield

Players of the Season:
Tony Sanders *(Manager – Altrincham)*
Larry Pritchard *(Sutton United)*
Terry Moore *(Bishop's Stortford)*
Colin Williams *(Northwich Victoria)*
Keith Wright *(Manager – England Semi-Pro)*

Merit Award for the F.A. Vase level Club:
Willenhall

F.A. Trophy Quarter Finalists:
Whickham*
Devizes Town
Alma Swanley
Altrincham
Basildon United
Irthlingborough Diamonds
Guiseley
Willenhall Town†

F.A. Vase Quarter Finalists:
Bishop's Stortford*
Worcester City
Dartford
Windsor & Eton
Bangor City
Mossley
Aylesbury United
Sutton United†

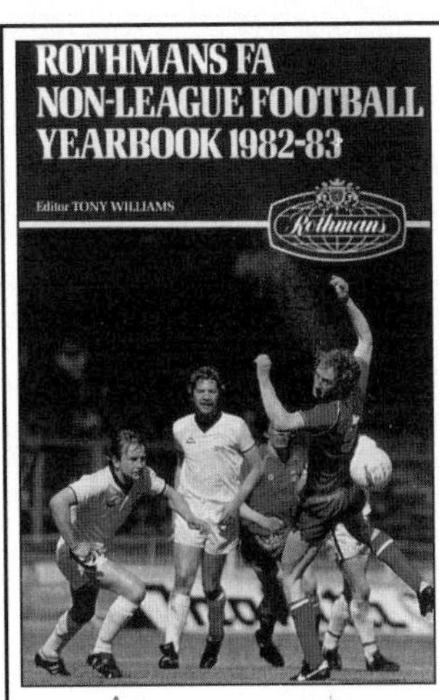

SEASON 1981-82

Team of the year: Leytonstone & Ilford

Special Merit Award:
Shepshed Charterhouse, Enfield, Runcorn, Wealdstone

F.A. Cup Award: Altrincham

Players of the Season:
Micky Burns *(Forest Green Rovers)*
Barry Howard *(Altrincham)*
John Williams *(Manager – Runcorn)*
Keith Barrett *(Enfield-England)*
Graham Bennett *(Bangor City)*

Merit Award for the F.A. Vase level Club:
Rainworth Miners Welfare

F.A. Trophy Quarter Finalists:	F.A. Vase Quarter Finalists:
Altrincham	Forest Green Rovers*
Bishop's Stortford	Willenhall Town
Wycombe Wanderers	Blue Star
Kidderminster Harrers	Cheshunt
Northwich Victoria	Barton Rovers
Worcester City	Irthlingborough Diamonds
Scarborough	Mossley
Enfield	Rainworth M.W.†

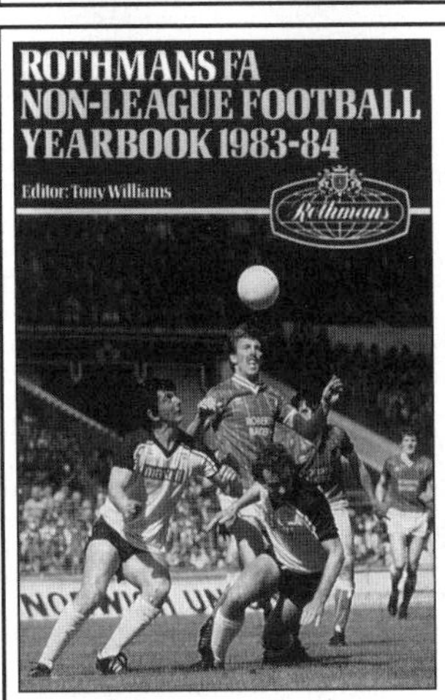

SEASON 1982-83

Team of the year: England Semi-Pro Squad

Special Merit Award:
Enfield, Sutton United, Gateshead, Harrow Borough

F.A. Cup Award: Bishop's Stratford

Players of the Season:
John Watson *(Scarborough)*
Bill Dellow *(Sec. to Southern League)*
John Davison *(Altrincham)*
John Bartley *(Maidstone United)*
Ken Jones *(Northwich Victoria)*
Tommy Dixon *(Blyth Spartans)*

Merit Award for the F.A. Vase level Club:
Harry Rudge (Halesowen Town)

F.A. Trophy Quarter Finalists:	F.A. Vase Quarter Finalists:
Northwich Victoria†	Halesowen Town†
Blyth Spartans	Shepshed Charterhouse
Dagenham	Burnham
Boston United	Forest Green Rovers
Harrow Borough	Great Yarmouth Town
Enfield	Brandon United
Dartford	Atherstone United
Telford United*	V. S. Rugby*

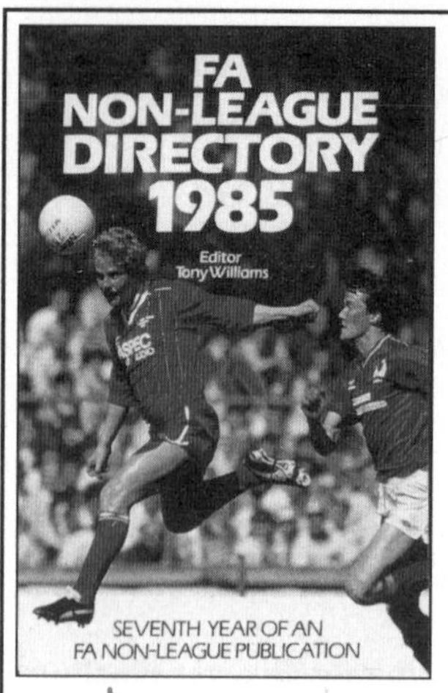

SEASON 1983-84

F.A. Cup Award: Telford United

Players of the Season:

Brian Thompson *(Maidstone United)* – ***Player of the year***
Paul Culpin *(Nuneaton Borough)*
Tommy Robson *(Stamford)*
Mark Newsome *(Maidstone United)*
Dave Ryan *(Northwich Victoria)*

F.A. Trophy Quarter Finalists:

Bangor City†
A. P. Leamington
Dagenham
Whitby Town
Telford United
Marine
Barnet
Northwich Victoria*

F.A. Vase Quarter Finalists:

Stamford†
Staveley Works
Irthlingborough Diamonds
Brandon United
Leyton-Wingate
Whickham
Old Georgians
Stansted*

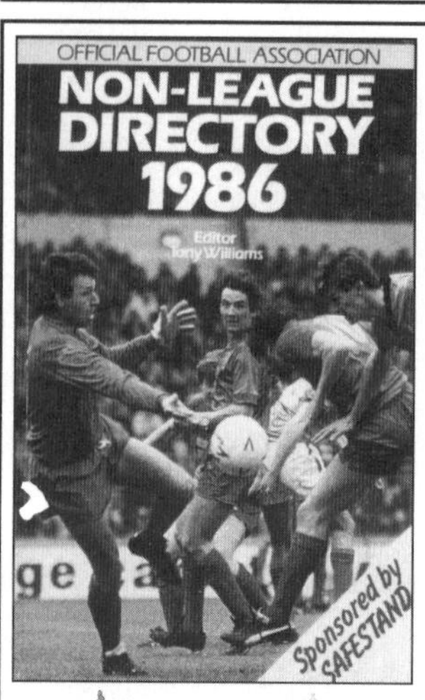

SEASON 1984-85

Team of the year: Wealdstone

Special Merit Award: Paul Culpin (Nuneaton Borough)

F.A. Cup Award: Telford United

Players of the Season:

Alan Cordice *(Wealdstone)* – ***Player of the year***
Paul Culpin *(Nuneaton Borough)*
David Howells *(Enfield)*
Paul Joinson *(Halesowen Town)*
Lee Joinson *(Halesowen Town)*

F.A. Trophy Quarter Finalists:

Boston United†
Runcorn
Maidstone United
Enfield
Altrincham
Stafford Rangers
Wealdstone*
Frickley Athletic

F.A. Vase Quarter Finalists:

Wisbech Town
Collier Row
Exmouth Town
Sudbury Town
Steyning Town
Halesowen Town*
Fleetwood Town†
Blue Star

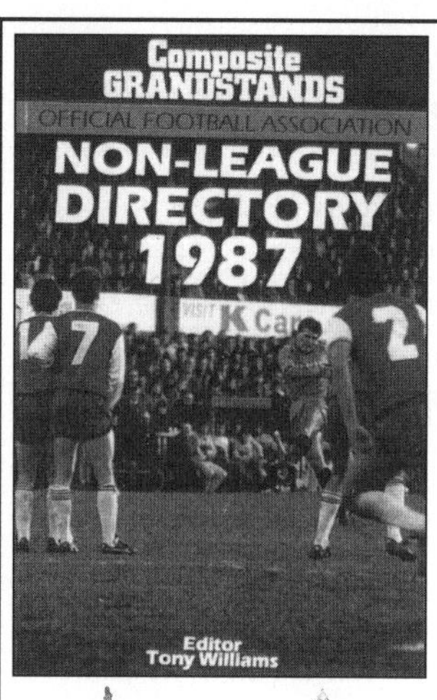

SEASON 1985-86

Special Merit Award:
Cyril Whiteside (Chariman – Clitheroe F.C.),
Barrie Williams (Football Manager – Sutton United)

F.A. Cup Award: Altrincham

Players of the Season:
Jeff Johnson *(Altrincham)* ***– Player of the year***
Kim Casey *(Kidderminster)*
Paul Shirtliff *(Frickley Athletic)*

F.A. Trophy Quarter Finalists:
Cheltenham Town
Altrincham*
Kettering Town
Wycombe Wanderers
Kidderminster Harriers
Runcorn†
South Bank
Enfield

F.A. Vase Quarter Finalists:
Halesowen Town*
Camberley Town
Havant Town
Wisbech Town
Southall†
Stevenage Borough
Warrington Town
Hucknall C.W.

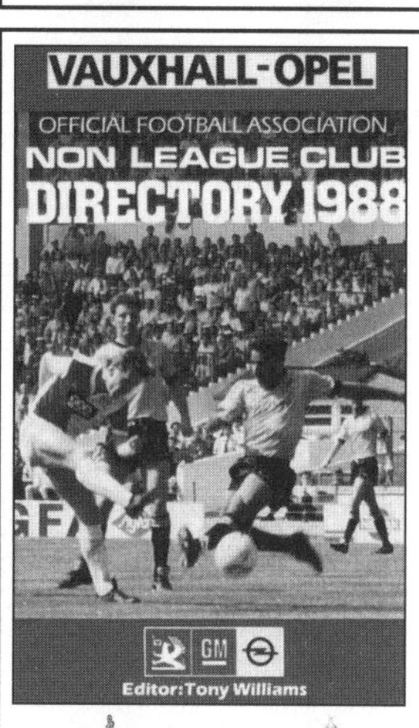

SEASON 1986-87

Special Merit Award:
Barry Fry (Manager – Barnet), Jim Thompson (Maidstone F.C.)
Peter Hunter (Secretary – Conference)
Mark Carter (Runcorn)
Paul Davies (Kidderminster Harriers)
Jim Thompson (Maidstone F.C.)

F.A. Cup Award: Caernarvon Town

F.A. Trophy Quarter Finalists:
Maidstone
Burton Albion†
Nuneaton Borough
Dartford
Dagenham
Kidderminster Harriers*
Barnet
Fareham Town

F.A. Vase Quarter Finalists:
St Helens Town*
Falmouth Town
Haverhill Rovers
Warrington Town†
Emley
Dawlish Town
Collier Row
Garforth Town

SEASON 1987-88

Player of the year: David Howell (Enfield)

Special Merit Award:
Kevin Verity (Manager – England Semi-Professional)
Bill McCullough (Chairman – Barrow)
Steve Burr (Macclesfield)

F.A. Cup Award: Sutton United

F.A. Trophy Quarter Finalists:
Enfield*
Lincoln City
Barrow
Altrincham
Wokingham Town
Macclesfield
Cheltenham Town
Telford United†

F.A. Vase Quarter Finalists:
Colne Dynamoes*
Farsley Celtic
Sudbury Town
Cleveland Town
Chertsey Town
Bashley
Durham City
Emley†

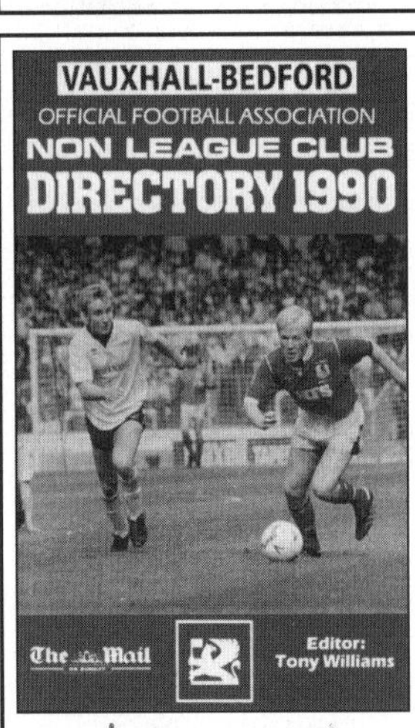

SEASON 1988-89

Player of the year: Steve Butler (Maidstone United)

Special Merit Award:
Barrie Williams (Manager – Sutton United)
Stan Storton (Manager – Telford United)
Micky Roberts (Macclesfield Town)
Nigel Ransom (Welling United)

F.A. Cup Award: Sutton United

F.A. Trophy Quarter Finalists:
Macclesfield†
Welling United
Dartford
Altrincham
Hyde United
Wycombe Wanderers
Newcastle Blue Star
Telford United*

F.A. Vase Quarter Finalists:
Bury Town
North Ferriby United
Sudbury Town†
Bashley
Tamworth*
Wisbech Town
Hungerford Town
Thatcham Town

SEASON 1989-90

Player of the year: Phil Gridelet

Special Merit Award:
Gary Wager (Merthyr Tydfil)
Gary Simpson (Altrincham)
Gordon Bartlett (Manager – Yeading)
Ray Wilkie (Manager – Barrow)

F.A. Cup Award: Whitley Bay

F.A. Trophy Quarter Finalists:
Barrow*
Kingstonian
Kidderminster Harriers
Colne Dynamoes
Bath City
Stafford Rangers
Darlington
Leek Town†

F.A. Vase Quarter Finalists:
Bridlington Town†
Billericay Town
Guiseley
Spalding United
Rushden Town
Hythe Town
Harefield Town
Yeading*

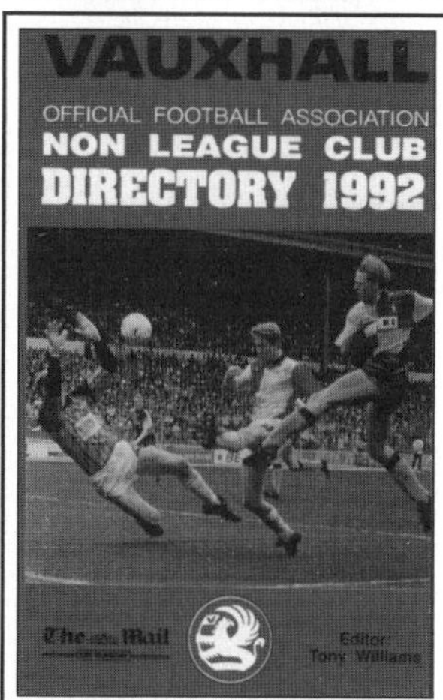

SEASON 1990-91

Player of the year: Mark West (Wycombe)

Special Merit Award:
Frank Northwood (Manager – Gresley Rovers),
Ted Pearce (Manager – Farnborough Town)
Mark West (Wycombe Wanderers) **– Player of the year**
Dereck Brown (Woking)

F.A. Cup Award: Woking

Merit Award for the F.A. Vase level Club:

F.A. Trophy Quarter Finalists:
Kidderminster Harriers†
Emley
Colchester United
Witton Albion
Altrincham
Horwich RMI
Northwich Victoria
Wycombe Wanderers*

F.A. Vase Quarter Finalists:
Gresley Rovers†
Harwich & Parkeston
Littlehampton Town
Great Harwood
Hythe Town
Trowbridge Town
Buckingham Town
Guiseley*

NON LEAGUE CLUB
DIRECTORY 1993
Publisher: Tony Williams
Editor: James Wright

SEASON 1991-92

Player of the year: Tommy Killick (Wimborne Town)

Special Merit Award:
Gordon Rayner (Manager – Guiseley)
James Bowdidge (Chairman – Colchester United)
Paul Cavell (Dagenham & Redbridge)
Tony Ricketts (Manager – Bath City)
Roly Howard (Manager – Marine)

F.A. Cup Award: Farnborough Town

Merit Award for the F.A. Vase level Club:

F.A. Trophy Quarter Finalists:	**F.A. Vase Quarter Finalists:**
Marine	Chertsey Town
Redbridge Forest	Bamber Bridge
Yeovil Town	Guiseley†
Macclesfield Town	Evesham United
Colchester United*	West Midlands Police
Telford United	Sudbury Town
Wycombe Wanderers	Diss Town
Witton Albion†	Wimborne Town*

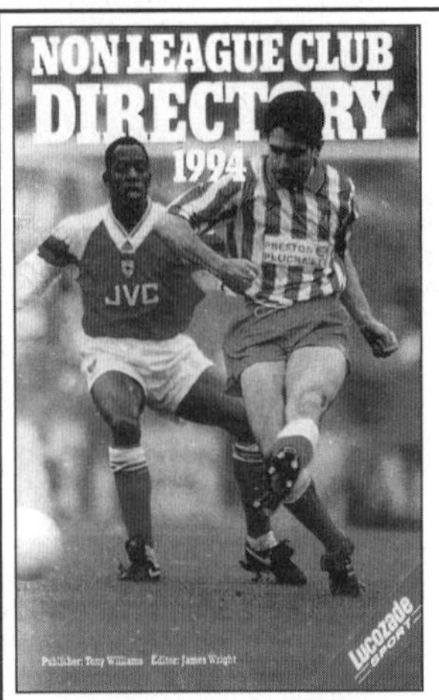

SEASON 1992-93

Player of the year: Steve Guppy (Wycombe Wanderers)

Special Merit Award:
Martin O'Neill (Manager – Wycombe Wanderers)
Steve Guppy (Wycombe Wanderers)
David Leworthy (Farnborough Town)
Brain Ross (Marine)
Hedley Steele (Tiverton Town)

F.A. Cup Award: Yeovil Town

Merit Award for the F.A. Vase level Club:

F.A. Trophy Quarter Finalists:	**F.A. Vase Quarter Finalists:**
Wycopmbe Wanderers*	Gresley Rovers
Gateshead	Dunston F.B.
Boston United	Buckingham Town
Runcorn	Tiverton Town†
Sutton United	Bridlington Town*
Warrington Town	Bansted Athletic
Witton Albion†	Canvey Island
Farnborough Town	Bilston Town

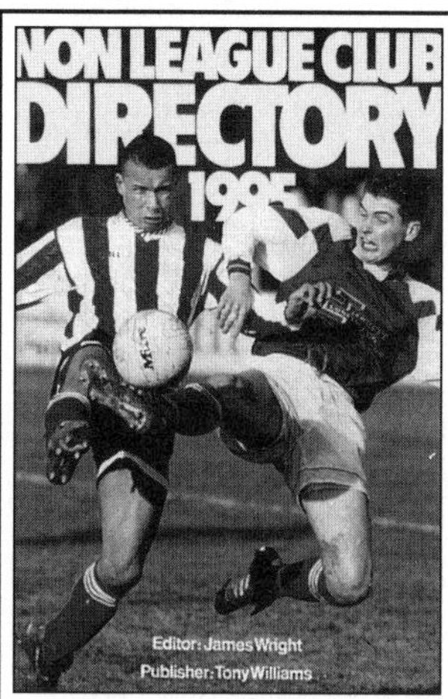

SEASON 1993-94

Player of the year: Chris Brindley (Kidderminster Harriers)

Special Merit Award:
Bill Punton (Manager – Diss Town),
T.W. Fox (Manager – Carr & Carr Sunday League)
Simon Smith (Gateshead)

F.A. Cup Award: Kidderminster Harriers

F.A. Trophy Quarter Finalists:	**F.A. Vase Quarter Finalists:**
Gateshead	Arlesey Town
Runcorn†	Boston
Sutton United	Diss Town*
Enfield	Tiverton Town
Woking*	Taunton Town†
Billingham Synthonia	Newbury Town
Guiseley	Aldershot Town
Morecambe	Atherton LR

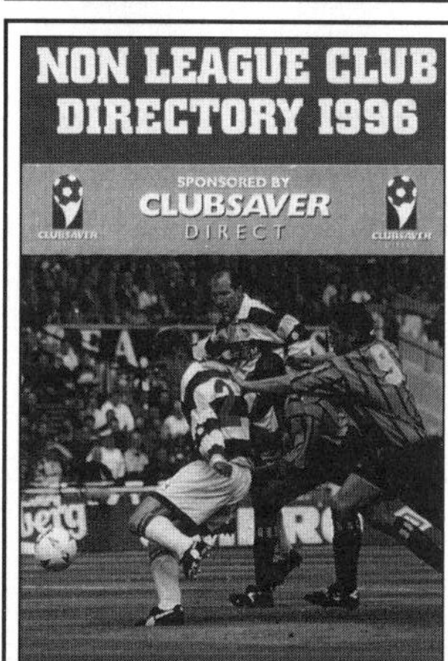

SEASON 1994-95

Player of the year: Kevan Brown (Woking)

Special Merit Award:
John Shepherd (Secretary – Oxford City),
Sammy McIroy (Manager – Macclesfield Town)
Paul Davies (Kidderminster Harriers)

F.A. Cup Award: Marlow

F.A. Trophy Quarter Finalists:	**F.A. Vase Quarter Finalists:**
Kidderminster Harriers†	Arlesey Town*
Altrincham	Cammell Laird
Marine	Metropolitan Police
Hyde United	Belper Town
Enfield	Oxford City†
Rushden & Diamonds	Canvey Island
Macclesfield Town	Basildon United
Woking*	Raunds Town

SEASON 1995-96

Player of the year: Barry Hayles (Stevenage Borough)

Special Merit Award:
Arthur Clarke (Northern League),
Paul Fairclough (Manager – Stevenage Borough)
Leon Shepherdson (Stamco)

F.A. Cup Award: Cinderford Town

F.A. Trophy Quarter Finalists:	F.A. Vase Quarter Finalists:
Hyde United	Brigg Town*
Stevenage Borough	Collier Row
Gresley Rovers	Mangotsfield United
Macclesfield Town*	Raunds Town
Bromsgrove Rovers	Clitheroe†
Northwich Victoria†	Peacehaven & Telscombe
Chorley	Flixton
Gateshead	Canvey Island

SEASON 1996-97

Player of the year: Howard Forinton (Oxford City & Yeovil Town)

Manager of the year: Paul Futcher (Manager – Gresley Rovers)

Special Merit Award:
Ted Hardy (Dagenham & Redbridge),
Bernard Manning Junior (Chairman – Radcliffe Borough)

F.A. Cup Award: Hednesford Town

Players of the Season:
Lee Hughes *(Kidderminster Harriers)*
Alan Odell *(Retired F.A. Councellor – Middlesex)*

F.A. Trophy Quarter Finalists:	F.A. Vase Quarter Finalists:
Bishop Auckland	Northwood
Gloucester City	Banstead Atheltic
Dagenham & Redbridge†	Guisborough Town
Ashton United	Taunton Town
Heybridge Swifts	Whitby Town*
Woking*	Mossley
Stevenage Borough	North Ferriby United†
Colwyn Bay	Bedlington Rovers

The Football Association

Challenge Cup

Sponsored by LITTLEWOODS Pools

Non-League Roll of Honour

FIRST ROUND (32)

Vauxhall Conference (11)
Cheltenham Town
Farnborough Town
Hayes
Hednesford Town
Hereford Town
Morecambe
Northwich Victoria
Slough Town
Southport
Stevenage Borough
Woking

Dr Martens (6)
Bromsgrove Rovers
King's Lynn
Ilkeston Town (Midland)
Solihull Borough (Midland)
Wisbech Town (Midland)
Margate (Southern)

Ryman (7)
Basingstoke Town
Boreham Wood
Carshalton Athletic
Dagenham & Redbridge
Hendon
Heybridge Swifts
Billericay Town (Div. One)

Unibond (7)
Blyth Spartans
Boston United
Colwyn Bay
Emley
Gainsborough Trinity
Winsford United
Lincoln United (Div. One)

Screwfix Direct Western
Tiverton Town

SECOND ROUND (12)

Basingstoke Town
Boreham Wood
Cheltenham Town
Dagenham & Redbridge
Emley
Hednesford Town
Hendon
Hereford United
Ilkeston Town
King's Lynn
Stevenage Borough
Wisbech Town

THIRD ROUND (4)

Cheltenham Town
Emley
Hereford Town
Stevenage Borough

FOURTH ROUND (1)

Stevenage Borough

Most of the editorial reports and comments regarding last seasons' F.A. Cup was first published in Team Talk, the monthly magazine that concentrates on all football outside the Amateur and Nationwide Leagues and highlights the F.A Cup, Trophy and Vase competitions.

1997-98 (non-league) Review

***Arnold Town** (Northern Counties East) **3 Shildon** (Arnott Insurance Northern League) **1** (Preliminary Round).*
Adrian Thrope (left) was enjoying an excellent game for Arnold until he was substituted because of injury – here he takes on Shildon's Neal Emmerson. Photo: Andrew Chitty.

***Hyde United** (UniBond Premier) **4 Lancaster City** (UniBond Premier) **1** (Second Qualifying Round). Gary Worthington of Lancaster City takes on the Hyde United defence.* Photo: Colin Stevens

SECTION 1

Preliminary Round - Sat. 30th August 1997 - 3.00

	Atherton Collieries	1 v 2	Maine Road
	Billingham Synthonia	1 v 1	Brandon United
r	*Brandon United*	*2 v 5*	*Billingham Synthonia*
	Skelmersdale United	3 v 2	Pickering Town
	Harrogate Railway	2 v 3	South Shields
	Matlock Town	3 v 1	Curzon Ashton

First Qualifying Round - Sat. 13th September 1997 - 3.00

	Gateshead	2 v 0	Matlock
	Billingham Synthonia	0 v 0	Maine Road
r	*Maine Road*	*2 v 2 aet*	*Billingham Synthonia*
	(Maine Road won 5-3 on pens)		
	South Shields	3 v 0	Skelmersdale United
	Witton Albion	0 v 5	Gainsborough Trinity

Second Qualifying Round - Sat. 27th Sept., 1997 - 3.00

	Gateshead	1 v 4	Gainsborough Trinity
	South Shields	2 v 0	Maine Road

Third Qualifying Round - Sat. 11th October, 1997 - 3.00

	Gainsborough Trinity	3 v 2	South Shields

SECTION 2

Preliminary Round - Sat. 30th August 1997 - 3.00

	Bedlington Terriers	6 v 1	Glapwell
	Blackpool (Wren) Rov.	1 v 4	Burscough
	Seaham Red Star	1 v 1	Ossett Town
r	*Ossett Town*	*1 v 0*	*Seaham Red Star*
	Denaby United	3 v 1	West Auckland Town
	Droylsden	4 v 1	Cheadle Town

First Qualifying Round - Sat. 13th September 1997 - 3.00

	Halifax	4 v 1	Droylsden
	Burscough	3 v 3	Bedlington Terriers
r	*Bedlington Terriers*	*1 v 2*	*Burscough*
	Denaby United	2 v 3	Ossett Town
	Leigh RMI	1 v 0	Accrington Stanley

Second Qualifying Round - Sat. 27th Sept., 1997 - 3.00

	Halifax	4 v 0	Leigh RMI
	Burscough	1 v 4	Ossett Town

Third Qualifying Round - Sat. 11th October, 1997 - 3.00

	Halifax	5 v 0	Ossett Town

SECTION 3

Preliminary Round - Sat. 30th August 1997 - 3.00

	Blidworth MW	3 v 5	Rossendale United
	Buxton	0 v 1	Ilkeston Town
	Tow Law Town	1 v 2	RTM Newcastle
	Peterlee Newtown	1 v 2	Warrington Town
	Pontefract Collieries	2 v 2	Ossett Albion
r	*Ossett Albion*	*0 v 3*	*Pontefract Colliries*

First Qualifying Round - Sat. 13th September 1997 - 3.00

	Chorley	3 v 1	Pontefract Collieries
	Ilkestone Town	3 v 0	Rossendale United
	Warrington Town	1 v 2	RTM Newcastle
	Radcliffe Borough	1 v 3	Bishop Auckland

Second Qualifying Round - Sat. 27th Sept., 1997 - 3.00

	Chorley	2 v 2	Bishop Auckland
r	*Bishop Auckland*	*2 v 3*	*Chorley*
	Ilkestone Town	7 v 1	RTM Newcastle

Third Qualifying Round - Sat. 11th October, 1997 - 3.00

	Chorley	1 v 3	Ilkestone Town

r = Replay

SECTION 4

Preliminary Round - Sat. 30th August 1997 - 3.00

	Arnold Town	3 v 1	Shildon
	Billingham Town	3 v 0	Brodsworth
	Maltby Main	0 v 1	Shotton Comrades
	Kidsgrove Athletic	1 v 1	Whitley Bay
r	*Whitley Bay*	*3 v 3 aet*	*Kidsgrove Athletic*
	(Whitley won 5-3 on pens)		
	Netherfield	1 v 1	Chadderton
r	*Chadderton*	*1 v 2*	*Netherfield*

First Qualifying Round - Sat. 13th September 1997 - 3.00

	Whitby Town	6 v 2	Netherfield
	Billingham Town	0 v 1	Arnold Town
	Whitley Bay	0 v 0	Shotton Comrades
r	*Shotton Comrades*	*1 v 0*	*Whitley Bay*
	Winsford United	1 v 0	Leek Town

Second Qualifying Round - Sat. 27th Sept., 1997 - 3.00

	Whitby Town	1 v 4	Winsford United
	Arnold Town	2 v 0	Shotton Comrades

Third Qualifying Round - Sat. 11th October, 1997 - 3.00

	Winsford United	1 v 1	Arnold Town
r	*Arnold Town*	*0 v 0 aet*	*Winsford United*
	(Winsford United won 6-5 penalties)		

SECTION 5

Preliminary Round - Sat. 30th August 1997 - 3.00

	Chester-Le-Street T.	0 v 2	Ryhope CA
	Congleton Town	1 v 1	Darwen
r	*Darwen*	*4 v 3*	*Congleton Town*
	St Helens Town	3 v 1	Sheffield
	Great Harwood Town	2 v 1	Stockton
	Louth United	1 v 0	Glasshoughton Welfare

First Qualifying Round - Sat. 13th September 1997 - 3.00

	Hyde United	3 v 0	Louth United
	Darwen	1 v 2	Ryhope CA
	Great Harwood Town	1 v 1	St Helens Town
r	*St Helens Town*	*3 v 1*	*Great Harwood Town*
	Lancaster City	2 v 2	Consett
r	*Consett*	*1 v 2*	*Lancaster City*

Second Qualifying Round - Sat. 27th Sept., 1997 - 3.00

	Hyde United	4 v 1	Lancaster City
	Ryhope CA	2 v 1	St Helens Town

Third Qualifying Round - Sat. 11th October, 1997 - 3.00

	Hyde United	8 v 0	Ryhope CA

SECTION 6

Preliminary Round - Sat. 30th August 1997 - 3.00

	Belper Town	2 v 2	Glossop North End
r	*Glossop North End*	*1 v 2*	*Belper Town*
	Bootle	3 v 1	Bradford (Park Avenue)
	Parkgate	2 v 0	Nantwich Town
	Eccleshill United	1 v 1	Thackley
r	*Thackley*	*0 v 2*	*Eccleshill United*
	Evenwood Town	0 v 3	Durham City

First Qualifying Round - Sat. 13th September 1997 - 3.00

	Knowsley United†	v	Durham City
	Bootle	2 v 3	Belper Town
	Eccleshill United	1 v 2	Parkgate
	Workington	0 v 3	Emley

† walkover for Durham City (Knowsley United withdrawn)

Second Qualifying Round - Sat. 27th Sept., 1997 - 3.00

	Durham City	0 v 5	Emley
	Belper Town	2 v 2	Parkgate
r	*Parkgate*	*0 v 2*	*Belper Town*

Third Qualifying Round - Sat. 11th October, 1997 - 3.00

	Emley	2 v 1	Belper Town

Gretna *(Unibond Div. 1)* **3 Liversedge** *(Northern Counties East Premier)* **1** *(Second Qualifying Round). Ian Fergusson rises to head home Gretna's second goal against Liversedge in the Second Qualifying Round.* Photo: Alan Watson

Brigg Town *(Northern Counties East)* **1 Worksop Town** *(Unibond Div.1)* **1** *(Second Qualifying Round). Midfield action at Brigg. Worksop won the replay 3-1.* Photo: M. Taylor

SECTION 7

Preliminary Round - Sat. 30th August 1997 - 3.00

	Home	Score	Away
	Crook Town	0 v 2	Mossley
	Gretna	4 v 2	Haslingden
	Tadcaster Albion	0 v 3	Stocksbridge Park Steels
	Liversedge	3 v 0	Willington
	Morpeth Town	5 v 0	Horden CW

First Qualifying Round - Sat. 13th September 1997 - 3.00

	Home	Score	Away
	Frickley Athletic	3 v 3	Morpeth Town
r	*Morpeth Town*	*4 v 1*	*Frickley Athletic*
	Gretna	3 v 0	Mossley
	Liversedge	3 v 3	Stocksbridge Park Steels
r	*Stocksbridge Park Steels*	*2 v 3*	*Liversedge*
	North Ferriby United	2 v 1	Barrow

Second Qualifying Round - Sat. 27th Sept., 1997 - 3.00

	Home	Score	Away
	Morpeth Town	0 v 0	North Ferriby United
r	*North Ferriby United*	*1 v 0*	*Morpeth Town*
	Gretna	3 v 1	Liversedge

Third Qualifying Round - Sat. 11th October, 1997 - 3.00

	Home	Score	Away
	North Ferriby United	2 v 0	Gretna

SECTION 8

Preliminary Round - Sat. 30th August 1997 - 3.00

	Home	Score	Away
	Atherton LR	0 v 1	Hucknall Town
	Brigg Town	1 v 0	Eastwood Town
	Oldham Town	4 v 2	Northallerton
	Guisborough Town	2 v 3	Worksop Town
	Hebburn	0 v 5	Garforth Town

First Qualifying Round - Sat. 13th September 1997 - 3.00

	Home	Score	Away
	Newcastle Town	3 v 5	Garforth Town
	Brigg Town	3 v 0	Hucknall Town
	Worksop Town	4 v 2	Oldham Town
	Spennymoor United	1 v 1	Blyth Spartans
r	*Blyth Spartans*	*1 v 0*	*Spennymoor United*

Second Qualifying Round - Sat. 27th Sept., 1997 - 3.00

	Home	Score	Away
	Garforth Town	0 v 1	Blyth Spartans
	Brigg Town	1 v 1	Worksop Town
r	*Worksop Town*	*3 v 1*	*Brigg Town*

Third Qualifying Round - Sat. 11th October, 1997 - 3.00

	Home	Score	Away
	Blyth Spartans	4 v 0	Worksop Town

SECTION 9

Preliminary Round - Sat. 30th August 1997 - 3.00

	Home	Score	Away
	Borrowash Victoria	1 v 2	Jarrow Roofing B. CA
	Castleton Gabriels	0 v 1	Clitheroe
	Selby Town	1 v 3	Lincoln United
	Flixton	2 v 3	Staveley MW
	Hatfield Main	2 v 3	Dunston Federation Brew.

First Qualifying Round - Sat. 13th September 1997 - 3.00

	Home	Score	Away
	Bamber Bridge	1 v 1	Dunston Federation Brew.
r	Dunston Federation B.	*2 v 3*	Bamber Bridge
	Clitheroe	4 v 3	Jarrow Roofing B. CA
	Staveley MW	1 v 5	Lincoln United
	Marine	1 v 0	Ashton United

Second Qualifying Round - Sat. 27th Sept., 1997 - 3.00

	Home	Score	Away
	Bamber Bridge	1 v 3	Marine
	Clitheroe	1 v 3	Lincoln United

Third Qualifying Round - Sat. 11th October, 1997 - 3.00

	Home	Score	Away
	Marine	1 v 1	Lincoln United
r	*Lincoln United*	*4 v 1 aet*	*Marine*

SECTION 10

Preliminary Round - Sat. 30th August 1997 - 3.00

	Home	Score	Away
	Penrith	3 v 0	Trafford
	Heanor Town	1 v 0	Salford City
	Yorkshire Amateur	1 v 4	Easington Colliery
	Harrogate Town	1 v 1	Armthorpe Welfare
r	*Armthorpe Welfare*	*1 v 3*	*Harrogate Town*

First Qualifying Round - Sat. 13th September 1997 - 3.00

	Home	Score	Away
	Guiseley	3 v 0	Alfreton Town
	Heanor Town	1 v 2	Penrith
	Harrogate Town	2 v 2	Easington Colliery
r	*Easington Colliery*	*4 v 1*	*Harrogate Town*
	Ashington	0 v 2	Farsley Celtic

Second Qualifying Round - Sat. 27th Sept., 1997 - 3.00

	Home	Score	Away
	Guiseley	0 v 0	Farsley Celtic
r	*Farsley Celtic*	*1 v 4*	*Guiseley*
	Penrith	6 v 3	Easington Colliery

Third Qualifying Round - Sat. 11th October, 1997 - 3.00

	Home	Score	Away
	Guiseley	1 v 2	Penrith

SECTION 11

Preliminary Round - Sat. 30th August 1997 - 3.00

	Home	Score	Away
	Fakenham Town	0 v 1	Stourbridge
	Eynesbury Rovers	1 v 2	Pershore Town
	Stratford Town	1 v 3	Desborough Town
	Dudley Town†	v	Bridgnorth Town

† walkover for Bridgnorth Town (Dudley withdrawn)

First Qualifying Round - Sat. 13th September 1997 - 3.00

	Home	Score	Away
	Telford United	1 v 2	Bedworth United
	Pershore Town	0 v 7	Stourbridge
	Bridgnorth Town	1 v 1	Desborough Town
r	*Desborough Town*	*1 v 3*	*Bridgnorth Town*
	Bury Town	1 v 2	Nuneaton Borough

Second Qualifying Round - Sat. 27th Sept., 1997 - 3.00

	Home	Score	Away
	Bedworth United	1 v 1	Nuneaton Borough
r	*Nuneaton Borough*	*6 v 0*	*Bedworth United*
	Stourbridge	2 v 1	Bridgnorth Town

Third Qualifying Round - Sat. 11th October, 1997 - 3.00

	Home	Score	Away
	Nuneaton Borough	4 v 1	Stourbridge

SECTION 12

Preliminary Round - Sat. 30th August 1997 - 3.00

	Home	Score	Away
	Banbury United	3 v 2	Rushall Olympic
	Blakenall	1 v 3	Great Yarmouth Town
	Stewarts & Lloyds	1 v 1	Soham Town Rangers
r	*Soham Town Rangers*	*1 v 3*	*Stewarts & Lloyds*
	Hinckley United	2 v 0	Wednesfield

First Qualifying Round - Sat. 13th September 1997 - 3.00

	Home	Score	Away
	Kettering Town	1 v 0	Mirrlees Blackstone
	Great Yarmouth Town	2 v 1	Banbury United
	Hinckley United	5 v 0	Stewarts & Lloyds
	Shepshed Dynamo	0 v 3	Cambridge City

Second Qualifying Round - Sat. 27th Sept., 1997 - 3.00

	Home	Score	Away
	Kettering Town	1 v 1	Cambridge City
r	*Cambridge City*	*2 v 4 aet*	*Kettering Town*
	Hinckley United	2 v 0	Great Yarmouth Town

Third Qualifying Round - Sat. 11th October, 1997 - 3.00

	Home	Score	Away
	Kettering Town	0 v 1	Hinckley United

r = Replay

***Spalding United** (United Counties East) **2 Loewstoft** (Jewson Eastern) **1** (Second Qualifying Round). Spalding 'keeper Ken Pearce denies Lowestoft forward Pete Chis.* Photo: Ray Pruden

***Wroxham** (Jewson Eastern) **3 Paget Rangers** (Dr Martens Midland) **1** (Preliminary Round). Visitors Stan Romaine causes problems for Wroxham defenders Steve Havers and Joe Appleyard.* Photo: Ray Pruden

SECTION 13

Preliminary Round - Sat. 30th August 1997 - 3.00

	Boston Town	0 v 2	Stapenhill
	Brackley Town	1 v 0	Cogenhoe United
	Sutton Coldfield Town	1 v 3	Stowmarket Town
	Rocester	1 v 1	West Midlands Police
r	*West Midlands Police*	*0 v 3*	*Rocester*
	Stafford Rangers	1 v 1	Ely City
r	*Ely City*	*1 v 3*	*Stafford Rangers*

First Qualifying Round - Sat. 13th September 1997 - 3.00

	Sudbury Wanderers	3 v 0	Stafford Rangers
	Brackley Town	4 v 0	Stapenhill
	Rocester	3 v 2	Stowmarket Town
	Tamworth	1 v 2	Bromsgrove Rovers

Second Qualifying Round - Sat. 27th Sept., 1997 - 3.00

	Sudbury Wanderers	1 v 1	Bromsgrove Rovers
r	*Bromsgrove Rovers*	*2 v 0*	*Sudbury Wanderers*
	Brackley Town	0 v 0	Rocester
r	*Rocester*	*2 v 1 aet*	*Brackley Town*

Third Qualifying Round - Sat. 11th October, 1997 - 3.00

	Bromsgrove Rovers	2 v 1	Rocester

SECTION 14

Preliminary Round - Sat. 30th August 1997 - 3.00

	Sandwell Borough	0 v 4	Spalding United
	Raunds Town	6 v 0	Shifnal Town
	Watton United†	v	Lowestoft Town
	Lye Town	2 v 1	Evesham United

† walkover for Lowestoft Town (Watton United withdrawn)

First Qualifying Round - Sat. 13th September 1997 - 3.00

	Knypersley Victoria	1 v 0	Atherstone United
	Raunds Town	2 v 4	Spalding United
	Lye Town	2 v 3	Lowestoft Town
	Holbeach United	3 v 6	Gresley Rovers

Second Qualifying Round - Sat. 27th Sept., 1997 - 3.00

	Knypersley Victoria	3 v 1	Gresley Rovers
	Spalding United	2 v 1	Lowestoft Town

Third Qualifying Round - Sat. 11th October, 1997 - 3.00

	Knypersley Victoria	3 v 1	Spalding United

SECTION 15

Preliminary Round - Sat. 30th August 1997 - 3.00

	Redditch United	4 v 0	Wellingborough Town
	Racing Club Warwick	3 v 1	St. Neots Town
	Willenhall Town	4 v 1	Gorleston
	Pelsall Villa	2 v 3	Barwell

First Qualifying Round - Sat. 13th September 1997 - 3.00

	Rothwell Town	2 v 1	Corby Town
	Racing Club Warwick	1 v 2	Redditch United
	Barwel	1 v 2	Willenhall Town
	Felixstowe Port & T.	2 v 5	Halesowen Town

Second Qualifying Round - Sat. 27th Sept., 1997 - 3.00

	Rothwell Town	1 v 1	Halesowen Town
r	*Halesowen Town*	*4 v 1 aet*	*Rothwell Town*
	Redditch United	3 v 1	Willenhall Town

Third Qualifying Round - Sat. 11th October, 1997 - 3.00

	Halesowen Town	2 v 2	Redditch United
r	*Redditch United*	*1 v 4 aet*	*Halesowen Town*

SECTION 16

Preliminary Round - Sat. 30th August 1997 - 3.00

	Newmarket Town	4 v 4	Stamford
r	*Stamford*	*1 v 4*	*Newmarket Town*
	Histon	2 v 0	Oldbury United
	VS Rugby	1 v 0	Chasetown
	Diss Town	1 v 0	Bloxwich Town

First Qualifying Round - Sat. 13th September 1997 - 3.00

	Moor Green	0 v 2	Bilston Town
	Histon	1 v 3	Newmarket Town
	Diss Town	0 v 1	VS Rugby
	Bourne Town	1 v 3	King's Lynn

Second Qualifying Round - Sat. 27th Sept., 1997 - 3.00

	Bilston Town	1 v 3	King's Lynn
	Newmarket Town	1 v 2	VS Rugby

Third Qualifying Round - Sat. 11th October, 1997 - 3.00

	King's Lynn	4 v 3	VS Rugby

SECTION 17

Preliminary Round - Sat. 30th August 1997 - 3.00

	Stourport Swifts	1 v 5	Woodbridge Town
	Northampton Spencer	0 v 0	Warboys Town
r	*Warboys Town*	*2 v 3*	*Northampton Spencer*
	Wroxham	3 v 1	Paget Rangers
	Long Buckby	2 v 4	Boldmere St Michaels

First Qualifying Round - Sat. 13th September 1997 - 3.00

	Solihull Borough	2 v 0	Burton Albion
	Northampton Spencer	1 v 1	Woodbridge Town
r	*Woodbridge Town*	*3 v 1*	*Northampton Spencer*
	Boldmere St Michaels	1 v 0	Wroxham
	Halesowen Harriers	0 v 1	Grantham Town

Second Qualifying Round - Sat. 27th Sept., 1997 - 3.00

	Solihull Borough	2 v 1	Grantham Town
	Woodbridge Town	4 v 1	Boldmere St Michaels

Third Qualifying Round - Sat. 11th October, 1997 - 3.00

	Solihull Borough	6 v 0	Woodbridge Town

SECTION 18

Preliminary Round - Sat. 30th August 1997 - 3.00

	Littlehampton Town	6 v 2	Southend Manor
	Folkestone Invicta	3 v 4	Marlow
	Welwyn Garden City	2 v 3	East Thurrock United
	Flackwell Heath	5 v 0	Barkingside

First Qualifying Round - Sat. 13th September 1997 - 3.00

	Whyteleafe	3 v 2	Crawley Town
	Marlow	2 v 2	Littlehampton Town
r	*Littlehampton Town*	*2 v 2 aet*	*Marlow*
	(Marlow won 11-10 on pens)		
	Flackwell Heath	1 v 0	East Thurrock United
	Chertsey Town	1 v 1	Heybridge Swifts
r	*Heybridge Swifts*	*2 v 1 aet*	*Chertsey Town*

Second Qualifying Round - Sat. 27th Sept., 1997 - 3.00

	Whyteleafe	0 v 2	Heybridge Swifts
	Marlow	2 v 3	Flackwell Heath

Third Qualifying Round - Sat. 11th October, 1997 - 3.00

	Heybridge Swifts	4 v 0	Flackwell Heath

r = Replay

Dover Athletic *(V. Conference)* ***0 Kingstonian*** *(Ryman Premier)* ***4*** *(Second Qualifying Round). Dean Hooper who later in the season won an England International cap, scored the first goal in 'Ks' brilliant away win which won them a Littlewoods regional result of the round award. Ron Fearon is the unlucky goalkeeper.* Photo: Roger Turner

Welling United *(V. Conference)* ***2 Sutton United*** *(Ryman Premier)* ***2*** *(Second Qualifying Round). Sutton United's No. 9 Joff Vansittard enjoyed a great season and a goal here against Welling. He has now signed for Conference club Dover Athletic.* Photo: Keith Gillard

SECTION 19

Preliminary Round - Sat. 30th August 1997 - 3.00

	Grays Athletic I	10 v 0	Langford
	Ford United	0 v 4	Great Wakering Rovers
	Pagham	1 v 3	Camberley Town
	Chatham Town	0 v 7	Banstead Athletic

First Qualifying Round - Sat. 13th September 1997 - 3.00

	St Leonards Stamcroft	1 v 0	Bishop's Stortford
	Great Wakering Rovers	1 v 2	Grays Athletic
	Banstead Athletic	2 v 2	Camberley Town
r	*Camberley Town*	*2 v 1*	*Banstead Athletic*
	Brimsdown Rovers	1 v 2	Canvey Island

Second Qualifying Round - Sat. 27th Sept., 1997 - 3.00

	St Leonards Stamcroft	2 v 0	Canvey Island
	Grays Athletic	1 v 2	Camberley Town

Third Qualifying Round - Sat. 11th October, 1997 - 3.00

	St Leonards Stamcroft	1 v 3	Camberley Town

SECTION 20

Preliminary Round - Sat. 30th August 1997 - 3.00

	Horsham	3 v 1	Northwood
	Croydon	2 v 1	Mile Oak
	Tunbridge Wells	4 v 4	Chichester City
r	*Chichester City*	*4 v 1*	*Tunbridge Wells*
	Corinthian-Casuals	0 v 2	Aveley

First Qualifying Round - Sat. 13th September 1997 - 3.00

	Hitchin Town	0 v 2	Bognor Regis Town
	Croydon	2 v 1	Horsham
	Aveley	2 v 1	Chichester City
	Burnham Ramblers	0 v 1	Hastings Town

Second Qualifying Round - Sat. 27th Sept., 1997 - 3.00

	Bognor Regis Town	2 v 1	Hastings Town
	Croydon	2 v 0	Aveley

Third Qualifying Round - Sat. 11th October, 1997 - 3.00

	Bognor Regis Town	1 v 1	Croydon
r	*Croydon*	*2 v 2*	*Bognor Regis Town*
	(Bognor Regis Town won 3-1 on pens)		

SECTION 21

Preliminary Round - Sat. 30th August 1997 - 3.00

	Leatherhead	2 v 0	Wealdstone
	Langney Sports	2 v 1	Southall
	Whitstable Town	1 v 1	Dorking
r	*Dorking*	*3 v 3 aet*	*Whitstable Town*
	(Dorking win 3-1 on pens)		
	Egham Town	1 v 1	Burnham
r	*Burnham*	*1 v 1 aet*	*Egham Town*
	(Burnham won 5-4 on pens)		

First Qualifying Round - Sat. 13th September 1997 - 3.00

	Sittingbourne	5 v 0	Molesey
	Langney Sports	2 v 1	Leatherhead
	Burnham	1 v 3	Dorking
	Concord Rangers	0 v 1	Purfleet

Second Qualifying Round - Sat. 27th Sept., 1997 - 3.00

	Sittingbourne	2 v 1	Purfleet
	Langney Sports	3 v 0	Dorking

Third Qualifying Round - Sat. 11th October, 1997 - 3.00

	Sittingbourne	2 v 1	Langney Sports

r = Replay

SECTION 22

Preliminary Round - Sat. 30th August 1997 - 3.00

	Redhill	1 v 1	Ware
r	*Ware*	*4 v 1*	*Redhill*
	Godalming & Guildford	0 v 6	Tonbridge
	Worthing	8 v 1	Eastbourne Town
	Epsom & Ewell	0 v 1	Canterbury City

First Qualifying Round - Sat. 13th September 1997 - 3.00

	Welling United	3 v 0	Leyton Pennant
	Tonbridge	1 v 0	Ware
	Canterbury City	1 v 1	Worthing
r	Worthing	*4 v 1*	Canterbury City
	Cheshunt	0 v 4	Sutton United

Second Qualifying Round - Sat. 27th Sept., 1997 - 3.00

	Welling United	2 v 2	Sutton United
r	*Sutton United*	*2 v 1*	*Welling United*
	Tonbridge	3 v 0	Worthing

Third Qualifying Round - Sat. 11th October, 1997 - 3.00

	Sutton United	5 v 1	Tonbridge

SECTION 23

Preliminary Round - Sat. 30th August 1997 - 3.00

	Ringmer	0 v 1	Wick
	Lewes	0 v 1	Tilbury
	Wingate & Finchley	1 v 1	Corinthian
r	*Corinthian*	*0 v 2*	*Wingate & Finchley*
	Leighton Town	2 v 1	Ashford Town

First Qualifying Round - Sat. 13th September 1997 - 3.00

	Walton & Hersham	2 v 0	Hampton
	Tilbury	3 v 1	Wick
	Leighton Town	1 v 2	Wingate & Finchley
	Baldock Town	0 v 0	Slough Town
r	*Slough Town*	*5 v 0*	*Baldock Town*

Second Qualifying Round - Sat. 27th Sept., 1997 - 3.00

	Walton & Hersham	0 v 0	Slough Town
r	*Slough Town*	*0 v 0*	*Walton & Hersham*
	(Slough won 3-2 on pens)		
	Tilbury	3 v 0	Wingate & Finchley

Third Qualifying Round - Sat. 11th October, 1997 - 3.00

	Slough Town	6 v 1	Tilbury

SECTION 24

Preliminary Round - Sat. 30th August 1997 - 3.00

	Hailsham Town	0 v 4	Metropolitan Police
	Erith Town	0 v 3	Harlow Town
	Wivenhoe Town	4 v 0	Chipstead
	Croydon Athletic	5 v 2	Beaconsfield SYCOB

First Qualifying Round - Sat. 13th September 1997 - 3.00

	Uxbridge	0 v 2	Dover Athletic
	Harlow Town	0 v 2	Metropolitan Police
	Croydon Athletic	0 v 4	Wivenhoe Town
	Bedford United	0 v 5	Kingstonian

Second Qualifying Round - Sat. 27th Sept., 1997 - 3.00

	Dover Athletic	0 v 4	Kingstonian
	Metropolitan Police	2 v 2	Wivenhoe Town
r	*Wivenhoe Town*	*2 v 1 aet*	*Metropolitan Police*

Third Qualifying Round - Sat. 11th October, 1997 - 3.00

	Kingstonian	1 v 0	Wivenhoe Town

Whyteleafe *(Ryman Div. 1)* ***0*** **Heybridge Swifts** *(Ryman Premier)* ***2*** *(Second Qualifying Round). Heybridge's excellent goalkeeper Kingsley Banks comes out to smother a dangerous attack spearheaded by Whyteleafe's experienced Nigel Golley.*
Photo: Garry Letts

Carshalton Athletic *(Ryman Premier)* ***1*** **Fisher Athletic** *(Dr. Martens Southern)* ***0*** *(Third Qualifying Round). Home skipper Eddie Sanders (white shirt) finished the season as one of Woking's stars, but here he is seen challenging Fishers' Matt Woolf, covered by Tim Alexander.*
Photo: Kevin Rolfe

SECTION 25

Preliminary Round - Sat. 30th August 1997 - 3.00

	Sheppey United	2 v 3	Windsor & Eton
	Hillingdon Borough	4 v 2	Stotfold
	Tiptree United	1 v 4	Clapton
	Hassocks	1 v 2	Barton Rovers

First Qualifying Round - Sat. 13th September 1997 - 3.00

	Gravesend & Northfleet	3 v 3	Braintree Town
r	*Braintree Town*	*3 v 1*	*Gravesend & Northfleet*
	Hillingdon Borough	0 v 2	Windsor & Eton
	Barton Rovers	1 v 0	Clapton
	Bedfont	2 v 4	Chesham United

Second Qualifying Round - Sat. 27th Sept., 1997 - 3.00

	Braintree Town	3 v 0	Chesham United
	Windsor & Eton	2 v 5	Barton Rovers

Third Qualifying Round - Sat. 11th October, 1997 - 3.00

	Braintree Town	4 v 1	Barton Rovers

SECTION 26

Preliminary Round - Sat. 30th August 1997 - 3.00

	Milton Keynes	1 v 1	Viking Sports
r	*Viking Sports*	*1 v 0*	*Milton Keynes*
	Kingsbury Town	1 v 2	Portfield
	Witham Town	1 v 1	Deal Town
r	*Deal Town*	*3 v 0 aet*	*Witham Town*
	Halstead Town	0 v 3	Berkhamsted Town

First Qualifying Round - Sat. 13th September 1997 - 3.00

	Margate	5 v 0	Bracknell Town
	Portfield	2 v 1	Viking Sports
	Berkhamsted Town	1 v 1	Deal Town
r	*Deal Town*	*2 v 1*	*Berkhamsted Town*
	Burgess Hill Town	1 v 3	Harrow Borough

Second Qualifying Round - Sat. 27th Sept., 1997 - 3.00

	Margate	4 v 0	Harrow Borough
	Portfield	1 v 1	Deal Town
r	*Deal Town*	*2 v 1*	*Portfield*

Third Qualifying Round - Sat. 11th October, 1997 - 3.00

	Margate	2 v 1	Deal Town

SECTION 27

Preliminary Round - Sat. 30th August 1997 - 3.00

	Peacehaven & Tels.	0 v 3	Potton United
	Oakwood	2 v 1	Potters Bar Town
	Romford	2 v 0	Hertford Town
	Hythe United	3 v 2	Chalfont St Peter

First Qualifying Round - Sat. 13th September 1997 - 3.00

	Yeading	4 v 2	Chelmsford City
	Oakwood	0 v 1	Potton United
	Hythe United	4 v 7	Romford
	Clacton Town	2 v 7	Stansted

Second Qualifying Round - Sat. 27th Sept., 1997 - 3.00

	Yeading	3 v 0	Stansted
	Potton United	1 v 6	Romford

Third Qualifying Round - Sat. 11th October, 1997 - 3.00

	Yeading	0 v 2	Romford

r = Replay

SECTION 28

Preliminary Round - Sat. 30th August 1997 - 3.00

	Three Bridges	1 v 2	Whitehawk
	Selsey	0 v 3	Wembley
	Wootton Blue Cross	3 v 2	Hemel Hempstead
	London Colney	0 v 2	Fisher Athletic

First Qualifying Round - Sat. 13th September 1997 - 3.00

	Edgware Town	2 v 5	Aylesbury United
	Wembley	3 v 1	Whitehawk
	Fisher Athletic	5 v 0*	Wootton Blue Cross
	Harwich & Parkeston	1 v 1	Carshalton Athletic
r	*Carshalton Athletic*	*4 v 0*	*Harwich & Parkeston*

Second Qualifying Round - Sat. 27th Sept., 1997 - 3.00

	Aylesbury United	0 v 3	Carshalton Athletic
	Wembley	1 v 3	Fisher Athletic

Third Qualifying Round - Sat. 11th October, 1997 - 3.00

	Carshalton Athletic	1 v 0	Fisher Athletic

SECTION 29

Preliminary Round - Sat. 30th August 1997 - 3.00

	Royston Town	0 v 0	Shoreham
r	*Shoreham*	*2 v 1*	*Royston Town*
	Maldon Town	0 v 3	Ruislip Manor
	Slade Green	1 v 1	Erith & Belvedere
r	*Erith & Belvedere*	*5 v 3*	*Slade Green*
	Hornchurch	2 v 2	Arundel
r	*Arundel*	*4 v 3*	*Hornchurch*

First Qualifying Round - Sat. 13th September 1997 - 3.00

	Tooting & Mitcham Utd	1 v 2	Billericay Town
	Ruislip Manor	4 v 1	Shoreham
	Arunde	1 v 4	Erith & Belvedere
	Bedford Town	1 v 1	Dulwich Hamlet
r	*Dulwich Hamlet*	*2 v 0*	*Bedford Town*

Second Qualifying Round - Sat. 27th Sept., 1997 - 3.00

	Billericay Town	2 v 1	Dulwich Hamlet
	Ruislip Manor	0 v 0	Erith & Belvedere
r	*Erith & Belvedere*	*3 v 0*	*Ruislip Manor*

Third Qualifying Round - Sat. 11th October, 1997 - 3.00

	Billericay Town	4 v 1	Erith & Belvedere

SECTION 30

Preliminary Round - Sat. 30th August 1997 - 3.00

	Arlesey Town	2 v 1	March Town United
	Barking	3 v 1	Basildon United
	Thamesmead Town	3 v 3	Saltdean United
r	*Saltdean United*	*4 v 0*	*Thamesmead Town*
	Hanwell Town	3 v 1	Tring Town
	Horsham YMCA	2 v 4	Dartford

First Qualifying Round - Sat. 13th September 1997 - 3.00

	Herne Bay	1 v 2	Dartford
	Barking	4 v 1	Arlesey Town
	Hanwell Town	3 v 2	Saltdean United
	Staines Town	3 v 1	Bromley

Second Qualifying Round - Sat. 27th Sept., 1997 - 3.00

	Dartford	1 v 2	Staines Town
	Barking	3 v 0	Hanwell Town

Third Qualifying Round - Sat. 11th October, 1997 - 3.00

	Staines Town	3 v 1	Barking

Clevedon Town *(Dr. Martens Southern)* **4** **Bemerton Heath Harlequins** *(Jewson Wessex)* **0** *(Preliminary Round). The home club recorded a convincing cup victory, but here Harlequins' Matt Coy threatens the Clevedon defence.* Photo: Ken Gregory

Portsmouth R. N. *(Jewson Wessex)* **1** **Waterlooville** *(Dr. Martens Southern)* **1** *(Second Qualifying Round). Navy 'keeper Mark Brown saves from experienced striker Jason Lovell at Burnaby Road.* Photo: Dennis Nicholson

SECTION 31

Preliminary Round - Sat. 30th August 1997 - 3.00

	Abingdon Town	1 v 1	Devizes Town
r	*Devizes Town*	*0 v 3*	*Abingdon Town*
	Bridgwater Town	1 v 0	Brislington
	Paulton Rovers	5 v 0	Fareham Town
	Cirencester Town	3 v 4	Tuffley Rovers
	Cove	1 v 3	Brockenhurst

First Qualifying Round - Sat. 13th September 1997 - 3.00

	Merthyr Tydfil	7 v 2	Brockenhurst
	Bridgwater Town	1 v 1	Abingdon Town
r	*Abingdon Town*	*1 v 2 aet*	*Bridgwater Town*
	Tuffley Rovers	1 v 3	Paulton Rovers
	Thatcham Town	0 v 1	Cheltenham Town

Second Qualifying Round - Sat. 27th Sept., 1997 - 3.00

	Merthyr Tydfil	0 v 2	Cheltenham Town
	Bridgwater Town	2 v 4	Paulton Rovers

Third Qualifying Round - Sat. 11th October, 1997 - 3.00

	Cheltenham Town	5 v 0	Paulton Rovers

SECTION 32

Preliminary Round - Sat. 30th August 1997 - 3.00

	Bashley	9 v 0	Torrington
	Chippenham Town	0 v 0	Eastleigh
r	*Eastleigh*	*0 v 1*	*Chippenham Town*
	Westfields	2 v 1	Westbury United
	Frome Town	0 v 5	Wokingham Town
	Lymington	6 v 0	Endsleigh

First Qualifying Round - Sat. 13th September 1997 - 3.00

	Worcester City	3 v 2	Lymington
	Chippenham Town	3 v 2	Bashley
	Wokingham Town	1 v 1	Westfields
r	*Westfields*	*1 v 3*	*Wokingham Town*
	Yeovil Town	1 v 1	Witney Town
r	*Witney Town*	*1 v 2*	*Yeovil Town*

Second Qualifying Round - Sat. 27th Sept., 1997 - 3.00

	Worcester City	1 v 2	Yeovil Town
	Chippenham Town	1 v 1	Wokingham Town
r	*Wokingham Town*	*0 v 1*	*Chippenham Town*

Third Qualifying Round - Sat. 11th October, 1997 - 3.00

	Yeovil Town	4 v 0	Chippenham Town

SECTION 33

Preliminary Round - Sat. 30th August 1997 - 3.00

	Tiverton Town	2 v 0	Weymouth
	St Blazey	1 v 0	Trowbridge Town
	Wimborne Town	3 v 2	Falmouth Town
	Odd Down	3 v 1	Backwell United

First Qualifying Round - Sat. 13th September 1997 - 3 .00

	Oxford City	1 v 1	Dorchester Town
r	*Dorchester Town*	*1 v 0*	*Oxford City*
	St Blazey	0 v 2	Tiverton Town
	Odd Down	1 v 4	Wimborne Town
	Downton	0 v 4	Forest Green Rovers

Second Qualifying Round - Sat. 27th Sept., 1997 - 3.00

	Dorchester Town	1 v 0	Forest Green Rovers
	Tiverton Town	11 v 1	Wimborne Town

Third Qualifying Round - Sat. 11th October, 1997 - 3.00

	Dorchester Town	0 v 1	Tiverton Town

r = Replay

SECTION 34

Preliminary Round - Sat. 30th August 1997 - 3.00

	Fleet Town	0 v 0	Thame United
r	*Thame United*	*1 v 3 aet*	*Fleet Town*
	Elmore	4 v 5	Hungerford Town
	Welton Rovers	1 v 5	Calne Town
	Clevedon Town	4 v 0	Bemerton Heath Harl.

First Qualifying Round - Sat. 13th September 1997 - 3 .00

	Havant Town	1 v 1	Basingstoke Town
r	*Basingstoke Town*	*2 v 0*	*Havant Town*
	Hungerford Town	1 v 4	Fleet Town
	Clevedon Town	1 v 1	Calne Town
r	Calne Town	*2 v 1*	Clevedon Town
	Bideford	0 v 2	Bath City

Second Qualifying Round - Sat. 27th Sept., 1997 - 3.00

	Basingstoke Town	1 v 1	Bath City
r	*Bath City*	*1 v 3*	*Basingstoke Town*
	Fleet Town	2 v 3	Calne Town

Third Qualifying Round - Sat. 11th October, 1997 - 3.00

	Basingstoke Town	0 v 0	Calne Town
r	*Calne Town*	*1 v 2*	*Basingstoke Town*

SECTION 35

Preliminary Round - Sat. 30th August 1997 - 3.00

	Bournemouth	2 v 4	Gosport Borough
	Bridport	1 v 2	Buckingham Town
	Newport AFC	2 v 1	Maidenhead United
	Didcot Town	1 v 5	Taunton Town
	Glastonbury	0 v 2	Chad Town

First Qualifying Round - Sat. 13th September 1997 - 3 .00

	Salisbury City	3 v 0	Chad Town
	Buckingham Town	1 v 1	Gosport Borough
r	*Gosport Borough*	*1 v 2*	*Buckingham Town*
	Taunton Town	3 v 2	Newport AFC
	Weston-Super-Mare	0 v 0	Cinderford Town
r	*Cinderford Town*	*0 v 1*	*Weston-Super-Mare*

Second Qualifying Round - Sat. 27th Sept., 1997 - 3.00

	Salisbury City	2 v 2	Weston-Super-Mare
r	*Weston-Super-Mare*	*2 v 2 aet*	*Salisbury City*
	(Salisbury City won 4-3 on pens)		
	Buckingham Town	0 v 2	Taunton Town

Third Qualifying Round - Sat. 11th October, 1997 - 3.00

	Salisbury City	3 v 0	Taunton Town

SECTION 36

Preliminary Round - Sat. 30th August 1997 - 3.00

	Andover	3 v 4	Portsmouth Royal Navy
	Barnstaple Town	1 v 4	Carterton Town
	Waterlooville	2 v 0	Reading Town
	Melksham Town	2 v 1	Yate Town
	Minehead	0 v 1	Mangotsfield United

First Qualifying Round - Sat. 13th September 1997 - 3 .00

	Gloucester City	3 v 0	Mangotsfield United
	Carterton Town	0 v 1	Portsmouth Royal Navy
	Melksham Town	1 v 2	Waterlooville
	Newport (IW)	2 v 1	Aldershot Town

Second Qualifying Round - Sat. 27th Sept., 1997 - 3.00

	Gloucester City	2 v 1	Newport (IW)
	Portsmouth Royal Navy	1 v 1	Waterlooville
r	*Waterlooville*	*7 v 0*	*Portsmouth Royal Navy*

Third Qualifying Round - Sat. 11th October, 1997 - 3.00

	Gloucester City	0 v 2	Waterlooville

4th ROUND QUALIFYING

Date 25th October 1997

Altrincham 0		**Morecambe** 2	Shirley 2, Grimshaw 15	*Att: 1,134*
Basingstoke T. 5	Coombs 18 (pen) 35, 71, Wilkinson 65, Tydeman 71	**Braintree T.** 1	Bennett 21	*Att: 867*
Billericay T. 1	Gutzmore 74	**Camberley T.** 1	Heath 19	*Att: 790*
Camberley T. *0*		***Billericay T.*** *1*	Gutzmore	*Att: 599*
Blyth Spartans 2	Henderson 27, Moat 32	**Kidderminster H.** 1	Casey 80	*Att: 656*
Bognor Regis T. 0		**Farnborough T.** 0		*Att: 1,124*
Farnborough T. *2*	Harlow 31, Mehe 90 (pen)	***Bognor Regis T.*** *1*	Thomas 84	*Att: 855*
Bromsgrove R. 2	Whitehouse 41, Grocutt 43	**Romford** 0		*Att: 880*
Cheltenham T. 1	Knight 74	**Sutton United** 0		*Att: 1505*
Enfield 1	St Hiliare 68	**Carshalton A.** 2	Thompson 55, 57	*Att: 727*
Gainsborough T. 2	Morrow 40, 75	**Halifax Town** 1	Horsfield	*Att: 1,730*
Gloucester City 1	Holloway 27	**Wisbech Town** 1	Irvine 72	*Att: 912*
Wisbech Town *3*	Munns 55, 71, Williams 83	***Gloucester City*** *2*	Fergusson 10 (pen), Mings 33	*Att: 1,094*
Halesowen Town 0		**Gloucester City** 2	Walters 59, Stallard 87	*Att: 1,206*
Heybridge Swifts 5	Green 5, 12, Caldon 30, 63, Raynor 76	**Ashford Town** 2	Bowyer 47, Scott 72	*Att: 535*
Hinckley United 1	Blake 77	**Colwyn Bay** 2	Lawton 45, Congreton 80	*Att: 939*
Ilkeston Town 3	Middleton 20, Fearon 60, 70	**Hyde United** 2	Nolan 43 (pen), Owen 47	*Att: 1,233*

Rushden & Diamonds *(Vauxhall Conference)* ***1 Boreham Wood*** *(Ryman Premier)* ***1*** *(Fourth Qualifying Round). Boreham Wood's goalkeeper Martin Taylor takes this corner cleanly despite the attention of Dr. Martens Chris Whyte (right) and Adrian Foster (armed raised).*

Photo: Peter Barnes

King's Lynn .... **5** McNamara 32, 68, Skelly 37, Hudson 70, Williams 75	**Salisbury City** .... **0** *Att: 1,946*
Knypersley Vic. .... **0** *Att: 575*	**Boston United** .... **1** Cavell 55
Nuneaton B. .... **2** King 18, Williams 29 *Att: 1,960*	**Emley** .... **3** Graham 4, Jones 65, Hurst 67
Rushden & Dia. ...... **1** Butterworth 18	**Boreham Wood** .... **1** Samuels 54 *Att: 2,107*
Boreham Wood .... ***1*** Shaw 119	***Rushden & Dia.*** ***0***
Sittingbourne .... **2** Mathewson (OG) 58 Miller 16	**Hereford United** .... **2** Fishlock 28, Cook 70 *Att: 1,011*
Hereford United ...... ***3*** Hargreaves 2, 44, Rodgerson 7	***Sittingbourne*** .... ***0*** *Att: 2,054*
Slough Town .... **2** Abbott 19 (pen) Luckett (OG) 31	**Kingstonian** .... **1** Dennis 34 *Att; 1,272*
Southport .... **2** Bolland 40, Thompson 78	**North Ferriby U.** ...... **0** *Att: 1,328*
St Albans City .... **1** Clark	**Hendon** .... **2** Simpson 22, 50
Stalybridge Celtic . **3** Trundle 11, 43 (pen) Sullivan 52 *Att: 570*	**Solihull Borough** .... **3** Powell (OG) 31 Dowling 62, Beagan 79
Solihull Borough ...... ***4*** Brogan 42, Beagan 92, 107, Dowling 104	***Stalybridge Celtic*** .... ***3*** Binne 80, 99, Jones 108 *Att: 402*
Tiverton Town .... **5** Daly 36, Everett 46, 55, 78 Nanekivell 84	**Sudbury Town** .... **0** *Att: 972*
Winsford United ... **2** Talbot 23, Dulson 75	**Penrith** .... **0** *Att: 651*
Yeovil Town .... **1** Pickard 64	**Hayes** .... **1** Goodliffe 12 (pen) *Att: 2,501*
Hayes .... ***1*** Goodliffe 40	***Yeovil Town*** .... ***0*** *Att: 1,123*

Slough Town *(Vauxhall Conference)* ***2 Kingstonian*** *(Ryman Premier)* ***1*** *(Fourth Qualifying Round). Slough Town goalkeeper Paul Wilkinson dives bravely at the feet of Eddie Akuamoah.* Photo: Peter Lirettoc

Nuneaton Borough *(Dr. Martens Premier)* ***2 Emley*** *(UniBond Premier)* ***3*** *(Fourth Qualifying Round). Emley's Michael Reynolds completes a superb goal-line clearance from a Gary Stalker header in this thrilling cup tie at Nuneaton.*
Photo: Keith Clayton

FIRST ROUND PROPER

Date 15th November 1997

Billericay Town 2 **Wisbech Town 3**
Battram 78, Moore 89 — Munns 19, Ward 56, McLaughlin 88 Att: 1,947
Billericay Town: *Root, Goldstone, Davidson, Moore, Walters, Hooker, Ridout (sub 66 mins Kelly), Barry, Gutzmore, Battram (sub 79 mins Barnett), Payne. Subs not used: Sinfield, Theoposiou, O'Brien.*
Wisbech Town: *Bray, Marshall, Lindsay, Irvine, Moore, Ward, McLaughlin, Rolph, Munns, Gallagher, Newell. Subs not used: Ablett, Topliss, Shelton, Blunden, Hardcastle.*

Blackpool 4 **Blyth Spartans 3**
Preece 4, Linighan 59, Atkinson 84, Clarkson 71 & 89 — Henderson 10, Di Lella 44, Att: 4,814
Blackpool: *Burridge, Farrey, Pike, Todd, Gamble, McGarrigle, Renforth, Hislop, Henderson (sub 76 mins Atkinson), Di Lella (sub 76 mins Ainsley). Subs not used: Cole, Tinkler.*

Bournemouth 3 **Heybridge Swifts 0**
Beadsmore 3, Robinson 58 & 66 Att: 3,385
Heybridge Swifts: *Cheesewright, Cranfield, Cutbush, Vickers, Keen, Pollard, Greene (sub 70 mins Adcock), Springett (sub 75 mins Rayner), Calden (sub 70 mins Harding), Jones, Kane. Subs not used: Gillespie, Barrett.*

Carshalton A. 0 **Stevenage Bor. 0**
Att: 1,405
Carshalton Athletic: *Blake, Robson, Smith, Saunders, Coney, Alexander, Jeffrey, Bassey, Bartley, Thompson, Kingsford. Subs not used: Ford, Allen, Beard, Read.*
Stevenage Borough: *Gallagher, Kirby, March, Holden, Trott, Beevor, Smith, Perkins, Crawshaw, Trebble, Love. Subs not used: Johansen, Marshall, Sampany, Soloman, Chang.*

Replay

Stevenage Bor. 5 ***Carshalton A. 0***
Love 7&47, Perkins 11, Smith 22, Trott 69 *Att: 2377*
Stevenage Borough: *Gallagher, Kirby, March (sub 71 mins Dillnut), Holden, Trott, Soloman, Smith, Perkins (sub 78 mins Johnson), Crawshaw, Beevor, Love. Subs not used: Marshall, Chang.*
Carshalton Athletic: *Blake, Robson, Smith (sub 12 mins Allen), Coney, Ford, Beard, Jeffrey, Bassey, Thompson (sub 76 mins Fowler), Kingsford, (sub 61 mins Adam), Bentley. Subs not used: Guy, Reid.*

Cheltenham T. 2 **Tiverton Town 1**
Eaton 2, Walker 88 — Saunders 42 Att: 2,781
Cheltenham Town: *Book, Duff (sub 48 mins Milton), Victory, Banks, Freeman, Smith (sub 46 mins Walker), Wright, Knight (sub 74 mins Crisp), Eaton, Watkins, Bloomer. Subs not used: Benton, Teague.*
Tiverton Town: *Edwards, Hynds, Saunders, Tatterton, Smith, Conning, Nancekivell, Varley, Everett, Daly, Leonard. Subs not used: Grimshaw, Waters, Rogers, Fallon.*

Chester City 2 **Winsford United 1**
Richardson 53, Priest 75 — Steele 11 Att: 3,885
Winsford Town: *Oakes, Clegg, German, Came (sub 82 mins Rusell), Talbot, Byme, Doherty, Bermincham, Shaugnessey (sub 85 mins Dulson), Steel, Wheeler (sub 66 mins Aspinal). Subs not used: Goodhall Burns*

Chesterfield 1 **Northwich Vic. 0**
Reeves 6 Att: 5,327
Northwich Victoria: *Greygoose, Crookes, Fairclough, Billing, Simpson, Bishop (sub 73 mins Sandeman), Stannard, Walters, Tait (sub 62 mins Williams), Cooke, Duffy. Subs not used: Carroll, Ward D, Hussin.*

***Margate** (Dr. Martens Southern) **1** **Fulham** (Nationwide Div. 2) **2** (First Round Proper). A Sunday match covered by Sky Television gave Margate great publicity and here we see an excellent crowd watching Ian O'Connell about to set up another attack against Fulham.* Photo: Francis Short

Darlington 1 Solihull Borough 1
Naylor 1 | Cross 60 | Att: 2,318
Solihull Borough: *Phillips, Abell, Wolsey, Bradley (sub 65 mins Rowe), Brown, Brogan, Mitchell, Myers, Cross, Dowling, Byrne. Subs not used: Beagan, Pippard, Randall, Adey.*

Replay

Solihull Bor. 3 Darlington 3
Dowling 42 & 90, Cross 55 | *Atkinson 44, Robinson 71, Dorner 89* | *Att: 2,000*
Solihull Borough: *Phillips, Abell, Wolsey, Bradley (sub 103 mins Woodley), Penny, Brogan, Mitchell, Beagan (sub 55 mins Rowe), Cross, Dowling, Byrne. Subs not used: Randall, Adey, Begley.*

Farnborough T. 0 Dagenham & Red. 1
Stimson 86 | Att: 1,236
Farnborough Town: *MacKenzie, Stemp (sub 57 mins Miller), Underwood, Rowlands M, Baker N, Robson, Baker S, Harlow, Laidlaw, Mehew, Winfield, Subs not used: Freeman, Harford, Harte, Rowlands K.*
Dagenham & Redbridge: *Gothard, Culverhouse, Pratt, Howard, Conner, Creaser, Parratt, Cobb, Broom, Stimson, Naylor (sub 65 mins Flanaghan), Subs not used: Hewes, Mas, Bird, Osborne.*

Hayes 0 Boreham Wood 1
Marshall 31 | Att: 1,343
Hayes: *Meara, Brady, Flynn, Bunce, Sparks, Goodliffe, Hall (sub 60 mins Boothe), Roddis (sub 68 mins Hayes), Randall, Hammatt (sub 68 mins Francis) Wilkinson. Subs not used: Beccles, Duncan.*
Boreham Wood: *Taylor, Daly, McCarthy, Robbins, Nesbit, Hollingdale, Shaw J, Marshall (sub 90 Shaw P), Heffer, Samuels T, Brown (sub 68 mins Hatchett). Subs not used: Dixon, Harrigan, Fitkin.*

Hendon 2 Leyton Orient 2
Simpson 23 & 57 | Griffiths 5, Smith 33 | Att: 2,421
Hendon: *McCann, White, Clarke, Kelly P, Nugent, Bateman, Heard, Hyatt, Simpson (sub 79 mins Lynch), Kelly T (sub 60 mins Howard), Lewis. Subs not used: Warmington, Lomas, Tello.*

Replay

Leyton Orient 0 Hendon 1
Lewis 75 | *Att: 3,355*
Hendon: *McCann, White, Clarke, Kelly P, Howard, Bateman, Heard, Hyatt, Simpson (sub 83 mins Banton), Kelly T (sub 64 mins Warmington), Lewis. Subs not used: Tello, Lynch, Lomas.*

Hereford Utd 2 Brighton 1
Grayson 57&74 | Storer 61 | Att: 5,787
Hereford United: *De Bont, Rodgerson (sub 46 mins McCue), Fishlock, Pitman, Warner, Walker, Cook, Grayson, Foster, Mahon, McGorry. Subs not used: Downing, Williams, Hill.*

Hull City 0 Hednesford Town 2
Norbury 37, O'Connor 90 | Att: 6,091
Hednesford Town: *Cooksey, Carty, Collins, Blades, Comyn, Beeston, Fitzpatrick, Ware, Norbury, Dennison (sub 79 mins Hemmings), O'Connor. Subs not used: Niblett, Ntamark, Francis, Simpson.*

Ilkeston T. 2 Boston United 1
Carmichael 25 & 80 | Cavell 62 | Att: 2,504
Ilkeston Town: *Rigsby, Feron, Ludlam, Middleton, Law, Knapper, Eshelby (sub 75 mins Huckerby), Robinson, Carmichael, Moore (sub 82 mins Shaw), Ball. Subs not used: Simpson, Thompson, Wilson.*
Boston United: *Bastock, Gowshall, Withe, Fee, (sub 82 mins Watts), Hardy, Charles, Stanhope, Appleby, Cavell, Chambers L, Mason. Subs not used: Cook, Marshall, Melson, Featherstone.*

Darlington *(Nationwide Div. 3)* ***1 Solihull Borough*** *(Dr. Martens Midlands)* ***1*** *(First Round Proper). Solihull Borough supplied one of the success stories of this year's F.A. Cup competition. Here Paul Brogan wins an aerial tussle with Darlington's Mario Dorner at Fleethams.* Photo: Dennis Nicholson

Kings Lynn 1 Bromsgrove Rov. 0
Hudson 26 Att: 2,847
Kings Lynn: *Hollman, Matthews, Skelly, Ellis, Wright, Spearing, Hopkins, Williams, Roberts, McNamara, Hudson. Subs not used: Delicata, Stock, Lewis, Read.*
Bromsgrove Rovers: *Anstiss, Davis, Dakes, Skelding, Grocutt, Payne (sub 61 mins Mainwaring), Fosley, (sub 80 mins Simpson), Elms, Whitehouse, Smith C, Gardner. Subs not used: Hickman, Peters, Moran.*

Lincoln City 1 Gainsborough Bor. 1
Walling 15 Morrow 54 Att: 6,014
Gainsboroough Trinity: *Sherwood, Price, Limber, Ogley, Timons, Ellender, Morrow, Circuit, Riley (sub 85 mins Maxwell), Brown, Dennis. Subs not used: Hanby, Taylor, Rhule, James.*

Replay

Gainsborough B. 2 Lincoln City 3
Maxwell 29, Price 39 *Walling 15&17, Whitney 18*
Att: 5,726
Gainsborough Trinity: *Sherwood, Hanby, Limber, Ogley, Timons, Ellender, Brown, Circuit, Maxwell, Riley, Price (sub 80 mins Taylor). Subs not used: Rhule, Lee, James, Morrow.*

Morecambe 1 Emley 1
Bignall 37 Banks 63 Att: 1,496
Morecambe: *Banks, Burns, Hughes D (sub 82 mins Takano), Hughes T, Mayers, Drummond, Monk (sub 78 mins Ceroala), Healy, Bignall (sub 78 mins Parkinson), Norman, Shirley. Subs not used: McIlhargey, Hodgson.*
Emley: *Marples, Nicholson, Jones, Thompson, Lacy, David, Banks, Hurst, Tonks (sub 62 mins Graham), Wilson (sub 88 mins Wood), Reynolds. Subs not used: Calcutt, Hutson*

Replay

Emley 3 Morecambe 3
Hurst 43 & 104, Marshall 120 — Mayers 24, Takano 118, Monk 119
Emley won 3-1 on penalties Att: 2,439
Emley: *Maples, Nicholson, Jones (sub 95 mins Wood), Thompson, Lacy, Tonks (sub 82 mins Calcutt), Banks, Hurst, Graham, Wilson, Reynolds (sub 116 mins Marshall). Subs not used: Hutson, Dennis*
Morecambe: *McIlhargey (sub 45 mins Banks), Lowe, Takano, McKearney, Hughes T, Drummond, Burns (sub 71 mins Monk), Healy, Ceroala (sub 54 mins Williams), Norman, Mayers. Subs not used: Parkinson, Grimhaw*

Slough Town 1 Cardiff City 1
Bold 68 O'Sullivan 16 Att: 2,262
Slough Town: *Wilkerson, Smart, Hardyman, McGinnis, Hercules, Angus, Bailey, Browne (sub 39 mins Owusu), Brazil, Abbott, Bolt. Subs not used: Fiore, Stowell, Randall, Miles.*

Replay

Cardiff City 3 Slough Town 2
Dale 22, Saville 55, White 114, Owusu 5, Angus 74Att: 2,343
Slough Town: *Wilkerson, Smart, Hardyman (sub 67 mins Simpson), McGinnis (sub 63 mins West), Hercules, Angus, Bailey, Owusu, Brazil, Abbott, Bolt. Subs not used: Miles, Stowell, Randall*

Southport 0 York City 4
Rowe 18 & 68, Bolland 69, Poulton 75 Att: 3,952
Southport: *Stewart, Farley, Ryan, Deary, Bolland, Futcher, Butler, Thompson (sub 79 mins Mitten), Whittaker (sub 56 mins Jones), Kielty, Formby (sub 72 mins Gamble). Subs not used: Moran, Bagnall.*

Henden** (Ryman Premier)* ***2 Leyton Orient** (Nationwide Div.3)* ***2 *(First Round Proper). Colin Simpson, Hendon (front), is just beaten to the ball by a Leyton Orient defender as goalkeeper Paul Hyde waits anxiously.* Photo: Roger Turner

Walsall 2 Lincoln United 0
Watson 35, Boli 90 Att: 3,279
Lincoln United: *Heath, Casey (sub 84 mins Baker), Carter, McDaid, Trotter, Heath, Gray, Wright, Ranshaw, Munton (sub 59 mins Simmons), Gibson. Subs not used: Farley, Reddington, Daniels.*

Woking 0 Southend 2
Jones N 88, Gridelet 90 Att: 4,059
Woking: *Batty, Betsy, Taylor, Howard (sub 45 mins Sutton), Brown, Danzey, Thompson, Jones (sub 78 mins Ellis), West, Hay (sub 62 mins Steele), Smith. Subs not used: Payne, Searle.*

Wycombe W. 2 Basingstoke Town 2
Cornforth 16&61 Coombes 68, Wilkinson 75
Att: 3,932
Basingstoke Town: *Beale, Barker, Richardson, Huxford, Harris, Morley, Wilkinson, Emsden, Mancy, Coombes, Tydeman. Subs not used: Carey, Drake, Ferrett, O'Neil.*

Replay

Basingstoke T. 2 Wycombe Wanderers 2
Coombes 40 & 85 McGavin 17 & 74 Att: 5,085
Basingstoke won 5-4 on penalties
Basingstoke Town: *Beale, Barker, Richardson, Line, Harris, Morley, Wilkinson, Emsden, Mancy, Coombes, Tydeman (sub 77 mins Carey). Subs not used: O'Neil, Drake, Ferrett, Galvin.*

Margate 1 Fulham 2
Munday 6 Carpenter 21, Scott 78
Att: 5,100
Margate: *Turner, O'Connell, Martin, Edwards, Blondrage, Dixon, Spiller, Munday, Sykes, Buglione (sub 46 mins Lamb), Pilkington (sub 90 mins Cory). Subs not used: Harrop, Emerick, Reddings.*

Notts County 2 Colwyn Bay 0
Hogg 59, Richardson 67 Att: 3,074
Colwyn Bay: *Roberts R, McCosh, Mann (sub 84 mins Drury), Graham, Caton, Price, Limbert (sub 24 mins Donnelly), Roberts G, Jones T (sub 68 mins Woods), Congleton, Lawton 7. Subs not used: Jones B, Nevitt.*

***King's Lynn** (Dr. Martens Premier) **1 Bromsgrove Rovers** (Dr. Martens Premier) **0** (First Round Proper). King's Lynn put the Bromsgrove Rovers defence under severe pressure.* Photo: Lynn News/Citizen Newspapers

SECOND ROUND RESULTS

Date 6th December 1997
(Reports first published in *Team Talk*)

Cambridge 1 Stevenage Borough 1
Butler 83 — Crawshaw 17 — Att: 4,847

Stevenage Borough: Gallagher, Kirby, Rogers (sub 45 mins March), Holden, Trott, Soloman, Smith, Love, Crawshaw (sub 88 mins Perkins), Wordsworth (sub 64 mins Beevor), Trebble. Subs not used: Cretton, Chang.

The Conference side took the lead from the penalty spot after 17 minutes, Gary Crawshaw slotting confidently low and hard to the goalkeepers left. Borough looked in control for much of the game but with just seven minutes to go Butler smashed in a loose ball after Gallagher had spilled a Taylor cross.

Stevenage Bor. 2 Cambridge 1
Campbell 41, Beevor 74 — Butler 17 — Att: 4,886

Stevenage Borough: Gallagher, Kirby, March, Smith, Trott, Beevor, Perkins, Trebble, Crawshaw, Wordsworth, Love. Subs not used: Johansen, Fenton, Chang, Stadhart, Meah.

Two sendings off virtually settled this tie although United nearly took the game into extra time. They had taken the lead through Butler after 17 minutes with a 25 yard drive. The goalscorer was sent off just three minutes later for a bad tackle and Smith followed him within fifteen to make matters worse. Campbell put through his own goal four minutes before half time. The second half was a battle but a through ball from Wordsworth gave Beevor the chance to win the game for Borough with a shot from the edge of the box with fifteen minutes to go.

Cardiff 3 Hendon 1
Dale 21 & 45, Saville 41 — Bashir 87 — Att: 2,578

Hendon: McCann, White, Clarke, Kelly P (sub 83 mins Banton), Nugent, Bateman, Heard, (sub 64 mins Bashir), Hyatt, Simpson, Howard, Sub 46 mins Tello), Lewis. Subs not used: Lynch, Lomas.

Hendon were never allowed to contest this cup tie with the welsh club scoring three goals through Dale (21 & 45 mins) and Saville (41 mins). The Nationwide League club hit top form and Hendon were pleased to grab a consolation goal from Bashir with just three minutes to go.

Cheltenham T. 1 Boreham Wood 1
Howells 75 — Marshall 13 — Att: 3,525

Cheltenham Town: Book, Duff, Victory, Banks, Freeman, Milton (sub 82 mins Crisp), Howells, Knight (sub 70 mins Teague), Eaton, Walker, Wright. Subs not used: Smith, Denton, Jackson.
Boreham Wood: Taylor, Daly, McCarthy, Robbins, Nisbet, Hollingdale, Shaw J, Marshall (sub 83 mins Dixon), Heffer, Samuels, Hatchett. Subs not used: Harrigan, Joyce, Shaw P, Fitkin

Boreham Wood 0 Cheltenham Town 2
Bloomer 42, Smith 70 — Att: 2,847

Boreham Wood: Taylor, Daly, McCarthy, Robbins, Nisbet, Hollingdale, Shaw J, Marshall, Heffer, Samuels, Brown (sub 59 mins Dixon). Subs not used: Hatchett, Shaw P, Harrigan, Fitkin.

Cheltenham Town: Book, Duff, Victory, Banks, Freeman, Milton (sub 53 mins Crisp), Howells, Walker (sub 74 mins Benton), Eaton sub 14 mins Smith), Watkins, Bloomer. Subs not used: Knight, Wright.

At last one 'pyramid' club was going to reach the Third Round but this game didn't decide which one. High scoring Shaun Marshall put the visitors ahead when Hollingdale crossed following a sliced Cheltenham clearance after just thirteen minutes. After a tough battle, the Robins managed an equaliser through Howells, who received from Milton and fired in a low deflected shot as the visitors failed to close him down.

It's not easy to come away from Meadow Park with a 'result' so Cheltenham were well pleased to score in each half and qualify for the tie with Reading. Bloomer took a pass from Walker to score just before half time and Smith sealed the game from an acute angle after good work by Walker and Watkins.

Colchester 1 Hereford United 1
Gregory 10 — Grayson 61 — Att: 3,558

Colchester: Emberson, Dunne, Betts, Gregory, Greene (sub 88 mins Haydon), Skelton, Duguid, Buckle, Sale, Adcock (sub 78 mins Lock), Hathaway (sub 87 mins Stamps). Subs not used: Forbes, Newell.
Hereford United: De Bont, Norton, Fishlock, Pitman, Brough, Walker, Hargreaves, McGorry, Grayson, Warner, Mahon. Subs not used: Cook, Withinton, McCue, Williams G.

Hereford United 1 Colchester 1
Grayson 48 — Forbes 47 — Att: 3,725
aet: Hereford win 5-4 on pens.

Hereford United: De Bont, Warner, Fishlock, Cook (sub 67 mins Pitman), Brough, Walker, Hargreaves, McGory, Grayson, McCue (sub 112 mins Williams G), Mahon. Subs not used: Withington, Mansell, Rodgerson.

A generally dull game could easily have gone Hereford's way after Grayson (61min) had equalised Gregory's (10 min) strike. The visitors leading scorer had three more good chances but at least a replay was forced and another money spinning evening set up for the club under severe financial pressure.

Another 1-1 draw after extra time had the fans holding their breath as the penalty competition had to find Tranmere Rovers next opponents. Once again a quiet first half led to an improved second period with Forbes equalizing Grayson's goal in a two min spell just after the break. The penalty shoot out went to the very last kick when de Bont saved and 'The Bulls' were through.

Hednesford T. 0 Darlington 1
Roberts 49 — Att: 1,900

Hednesford Town: Cooksey, Carty, Collins (sub 79 mins Hemmings), Blades, Comyn, Fitzpatrick, Ware, Beeston, Norbury (sub 87 mins Francis), Dennison, O'Connor. Subs not Simpson, Niblett, Ntamark

***Wisbech Town** (Dr. Martens League) **0 Bristol Rovers** (Nationwide Div. 2) **2** (Second Round Proper). Wisbech warming up before the match against Bristol Rovers.*
Photo: Garry Letts

Too much hype and too good an F.A. Cup record persuaded Hednesford supporters their side only had to turn up to win and Darlington certainly enjoyed being the underdog. The Nationwide League club won with a penalty by Roberts early in the second half but when trying to slam the ball into the net again in celebration the scorer connected with 'keeper Cooksey and was sent off! The Quakers hung on however and celebrated a surprise victory.

Lincoln	**2**	**Emley**	**2**
Fleming 12 & 90		Hurst 45, Graham 85	Att: 3,729

Emley: Marples, Nicholson, Jones, Thompson, Wood, David, Calcutt, Hurst (sub 89 mins Tonks), Graham, Wilson, Reynolds. Subs not used: Dennis, Marshall, Hutson, Johnson

One goal down, then 2-1 up with time running out. Emley enjoyed mixed emotions in a thrilling cup tie. Fleming scored both City goals but in between Hunt hit a 20 yard in off the post just before half time and Graham powered another drive in with just five minutes to go. City's final onslaught forced a reply however and more drama to come.

Emley	**3**	**Lincoln City**	**3**
Graham 75, Whitney 64, Nicholson 87 & 110		Alcide 69, Hone 115	Att: 4,891

aet: Emley win 4-3 on pens.

Emley: Marples, Nicholson, Jones, Thompson, Lacy, David, Calcutt, Hurst, Graham (sub 98 mins Viner), Wood (sub 72 mins Tonks), Reynolds. Subs not used: Johnson, Hutson, Dennis.

No goals for the first hour and then an avalanche as Lincoln took a two goal lead through Whitney and Aliade (69) both after long throws into the box. This brought a furious replay from the home team and Graham headed in a Jones cross (75) and skipper Nicholson smacked in an equaliser from 12 yards with three minutes of ordinary time remaining. The same player then converted a 110 minute penalty after Hunt had been up ended but this lead lasted just five minutes as Hone equalised after a scramble in the goalmouth. The penalty shoot-out produced a hero in goalkeeper Marples as he saved two Lincoln spot kicks and the Yorkshire village side was on their way to Upton Park.

Northampton	**1**	**Basingstoke Town**	**1**
Seal 39		Carey 75	Att: 5,881

Basingstoke Town: Beale, Barker, Richardson, Huxford (sub 70 mins Carey), Harris, Morley, Wilkinson, Emsden, Mancy, Coombes, Tydeman. Subs not used: Ferrett, Drake, O'Neil, Line

A tough battle seemed to be going the League club's way as they hung on to a 39th minute goal from Seal but substitute Carey made his mark with fifteen minutes to go and his 15 yard deflected shot forced a replay.

Basingstoke T.	**0**	**Northampton**	**0**
aet: Northampton win 4-3 on pens.			Att: 4,933

Basingstoke Town: Beale, Barker, Richardson, Carey (sub 103 mins Huxford), Harris, Morley (sub 46 mins Line), Wilkinson, Emsden, Mancy, Coombes, Tydeman (sub 119 mins Ferrett). Subs not used: Drake, O'Neil

Sky Television viewers could all see that the little Ryman League club had deserved better fortunes and had the best chances in a dour cup tie, 'The Cobblers' won 4-3 on penalties and their celebrations made you realise just how relieved they were to prevent 'Stoke' reaching their twelfth F.A. Cup Tie this season.

Peterborough	**3**	**Dagenham & Red.**	**2**
Carruthers 21, Quinn 74 & 82		Cobb 47, Shipp 71	Att: 5,572

Dagenham & Redbridge: Gothard, Culverhouse, Pratt, Bird (sub 83 mins Double), Conner, Creaser, Parratt, Cobb, Stimson (sub 69 mins Shipp), Cole (sub 83 mins Flanagan), Broom. Subs not used: Osborne, Mas.

The Daggers are not known for high scoring games but on the day they matched the attack conscious Peterborough side and after Carruthers had given the homeside a lead after 21 minutes, goals from Cobb just after half time following a Tyler mistake, and Shipp who smacked in a glorious

drive with half an hour to go, brought great pressure from Barry Fry's side. It was veteran star goalscorer Quin who won the game with two goals in a thrilling final to the match.

Rotherham 6 King's Lynn 0
Glover 48, Richardson 53, Garner 55, Druce 70, Berry 80, Hudson 89. Att: 5,883

Kings Lynn: Hollman, Matthews, Skelly, Hoyle, Ellis, Spearing (sub 75 mins Delicata), Hopkins, Wright, Roberts (sub 76 mins Stock), McNamara, Hudson. Subs not used: Lewis, Mead, Read.

Poor King's Lynn, having produced a battling goalless first half performance which brought a dressing room roasting for the Rotherham players. United lifted their game and 'turned it on' for their supporters with a brilliant second half performance that gave the 'Linnets' no chance.

Scunthorpe 1 Ilkeston Town 1
Forrester 76 — Robinson 52 Att: 4,187

Ilkeston Town: Rigby, Fearon, Ludlam, Wright, Law, Knapper, Shaw, Robinson, Carmichael, Moore (sub 89 mins Eshelby), Ball, Subs not used: Huckerby, Wilson, Simpson, Thompson.

This was a superb result from unfashionable Ilkeston Town who really rewarded manager Alexander for his hard work to lift the club to new levels. In fact 'Town' took the lead after 52 minutes when a long throw from skipper Nicky Low was touched on by Carmichael for Robinson to score with a header - a well practiced set piece! United put the visitors under great pressure from then on and it was Forrister who eventually equalised with a powerful drive.

Ilkeston Town 1 Scunthorpe 2
Moore 72 — Forrester 10, Wilcox 30 Att: 2,109

Ilkeston Town: Rigby, Fearon, Ludlam, Middleton, Law, Knapper (sub 65 mins Simpson), Shaw (sub 35 mins Eshelby), Robinson, Carmichael, Moore, Ball. Subs not used: Huckerby, Wilson, Wright

It was Forrister again who gave the Nationwide League club a lead after ten minutes and at half time another by Wilcox from close range following a freekick put the Dr. Martens side in severe trouble. Ilkeston continued to play far the better football and they did get a reward when Moore scored but it was not enough and a brave cup run came to an end.

Wisbech Town 0 Bristol Rovers 2
Beadle 52, Hayles 78 Att: 3,593

Wisbech Town: Bray, Marshall (sub 78 mins Newell), Lindsay, Irvine (sub 43 mins McLaughlin), Moore, Ward, Parrot (sub 83 mins Topliss), Childs, Munns, Gallagher, Williams. Subs not used: Hardcastle, Rolph.

What a thrill for the little club from the far east who had just gained promotion to the Dr. Martens League and had been rewarded with an attractive tie after a great cup run. The 'Fenmen' really battled but an excellent individual goal by Beadle and a second from Hayles gave the high riding Division Two club a convincing victory in the end.

***Basingstoke Town** (Ryman Premier) **0** **Northampton Town** (Nationwide Div.2) **0** (Second Round Proper). A Basingstoke attempt at goal is cleared off the line by the Northampton defenders.* Photo: Mark Sandom

Swindon **1** **Stevenage B.** **2**
Walters 5 Soloman 23, Grazioli 65
Att: 9,422

Stevenage B.: Gallagher, Kirby, Love, Smith, Trott, Soloman, Perkins, Grazioli, Crawshaw, Wordsworth (sub 77 mins Holden), Stapleton. Subs not used: Trebble, Inman, Beevor, Chang.

With a raging wind liable to worry the most experienced of players the chances of an upset were always on the cards at Swindon, where Stevenage Borough were to enjoy their second consecutive appearance in The Third Round.

However, it was nothing to do with the luck of the elements that Borough triumphed. A pre-match tactical plan from manger Paul Fairclough worked a treat despite an excellent early goal from Mark Walters after just five minutes.

An equaliser, with a goal just as dramatic, came from ex F.A. Lilleshall school student Jason Soloman and with the wind at their backs in the second half the Conference side could have won by more than the single goal, carefully slotted home by Guiliano Grazioli twenty five minutes from the end.

There was no doubt who was the better side both in style and attitude, so the door was open to the Fourth Round and a lot more publicity for the Hertfordshire club!

Cheltenham T. **1** **Reading** **1**
Watkins 23 Morley 71
Att: 6,000

Cheltenham Town: Book, Duff, Victory, Banks, Freeman, Knight, Howells, Walker (sub 75 mins Eaton), Smith (sub 70 mins Benton), Watkins, Bloomer. Subs not used: Crisp, Wright, Milton.

Having played a Conference game just two days before the scheduled visit of Reading, poor Cheltenham Town at least had a little bit of luck when their ground was declared unfit and they had a few days grace. But a draw with Boreham Wood at home in the Trophy meant that there would be four games in eight days before the well deserved mid winter holiday.

The home tie with Reading produced another piece of Walker magic as he lured Davies into a rash tackle inside the penalty area and Dale Watkins gleefully smacked in the spot kick. On a heavy pitch the 'Robins' defended solidly and supporters were just beginning to think of the perfect result when ex semi-professional international Trevor Morley played a one-two with Bowen and scored with a low drive that skidded under Book's dive to his right. Despite a great evening in front of a 6,000 attendance (the club's best since 1957) it wasn't quite a celebration although everyone looked forward to the replay.

Reading **2** **Cheltenham Town** **1**
Morley 38, Booty 72 Walker 51
Att: 9,686

Cheltenham Town: Book, Duff, Victory, Banks, Freeman, Benton (sub 78 mins Wright), Crisp, (sub86 mins Milton), Walker (sub 59 mins Knight), Eaton, Watkins, Bloomer. Subs not used: Smith, Teague.

Just under 10,000 gave Elm Park a typical F.A. Cup atmosphere and it was nearly half-time before Bowen provided Morley with another vital goal, again hit low and hard to the left hand corner of the net.

The 'Robins' hit back within six minutes of half-time and the lethal trio of strikers were all involved, Watkins and Eaton providing Walker with a chance to volley calmly in with his left foot from five yards. Again it looked as if this goal would lift Cheltenham to an historic victory and the football played by the Conference side impressed everyone.

It was not to be, however, as full back Booty chose that evening to score his first goal of the season with a terrific right foot drive with just nine minutes to go. Both right backs, Booty and Buck, were stars on the night but Cheltenham Town's best ever F.A. Cup run which had won them £5,000 from Littlewoods, as the club to go furthest after starting out in the First Qualifying Round, came to an end.

Perhaps they were just practising for the Trophy or were just toughening up for a Conference Championship run in?

Hereford Utd **0** **Tranmere Rovers** **3**
Att: 7,473 Jones, G 14 & 53, Hill 59

Hereford United: De Bont, Rodgerson, Fishlock, Pitman, Brough, Walker, Hargreaves, McGorry, Grayson, Agana, Mahon. Subs not used: Warner, Withinton, Cook, McCue, Mansell.

To reach the Third Round of the F.A. Cup in their first season back as 'outsiders' must have given Hereford United supporters a great deal of satisfaction, especially as their Conference form had been affected by administrative turmoil off the pitch.

They had put Brighton in their place, beaten Colchester United on penalties and here was a gate of over 7,000 to boost finances at a vital time.

Unfortunately that was all there was on the plus side as a solid performance by the Nationwide Division One club produced a single goal lead at half time and a comprehensive 3-0 victory by the end.

However, the Cup run played a vital part in Hereford's survival battle, so congratulations all round.

THIRD AND FOURTH ROUND RESULTS

3rd & 24th January 1998

THIRD ROUND

Report by Albert Cole

West Ham United (1) 2 Emley (0) 1

According to boss Ronnie Glavin, Emley were going to Upton Park to "give everything we've got and enjoy the day".This they most certainly did, and to top it all off they came within eight minutes of forcing an unlikely replay.

It all started so badly for the Unibond League 'minnows'. West Ham dominated the opening exchanges and as early as the third minute Paul Kitson found acres of space on the right hand edge of the area and unleashed a shot which rebounded off the bar. It was only a temporary reprieve – one minute later Frank Lampard Jnr tried his luck from a similar position and this time the ball went in off the underside of the bar. 1-0 to the Hammers and the dam looked set to burst. It got worse still; in the seventh minute centre back Neil Lacey limped off with a pulled hamstring, making way for Mark Wilson and forcing Glavin to shuffle his pack.

But the little village team – population 1800 – were not about to have their day spoilt by a couple of minor inconveniences. Just as prior to kick-off an almighty thunderstorm had eventually given way to a glorious rainbow, so Emley began to play a brand of delightful football of which few in the ground, save for their regular supporters, would have thought them capable. For much of the first half, it was only the final ball which was their undoing. At the other end, Hammers were also carving out chances aplenty, but their forwards, John Hartson in particular, appeared to be doing their best to miss them. When they did get the ball on target, they found visiting 'keeper Chris Marples in inspired form.

Just what the respective managers said to their players at half time is anyone's guess, but for much of the second half it was almost impossible to tell which team was playing in the Premiership. Emley didn't just battle for every ball, they actually unsettled Hammers by playing top quality, passing football. The 'long ball' was nowhere to be seen, except for the home defence's desperate clearances! In the 47th minute, Emley skipper Ian Banks tried a speculative shot from fully 30 yards which deceived home goalie Craig Forrest with a wicked dip at the last minute and deflected off the bar. Nine minutes later, a poor back pass by Lampard left Forrest with very little chance of preventing a corner, and from Banks' kick Paul David rose highest at the far post to head Emley level, with England International Rio Ferdinand only able to help the ball over the line. Two thousand plus Yorkshiremen went barmy in one small corner of the stadium, whilst all around a stunned hush descended for a few seconds, before the whole stadium rose to applaud the Emley heroes. Later, but for a slightly mis-timed pass from the particularly exciting Glynn Hurst when Emley had a four-on-two break, they may have silenced the Hammers faithful once and for all.

As time ticked away, and Hartson and substitute Samassi Abou missed further chances for the Hammer, I began to wonder how to get to the McAlpine Stadium, Huddersfield, for the replay in ten days time. Perhaps it was my fault, then, that, with just eight minutes to go, Aussie Stan Lazaridis for once escaped the attentions of Dean Calcutt down the left flank and delivered an inch-perfect cross that even Hartson couldn't miss. He didn't, and the dream was over. At the final whistle Emley took a deserved bow in front of their delirious fans, and then took off on a lap of honour, with even the Hammers fans, who gave them a standing ovation, cheering 'Emleee, Emleee'.

West Ham Utd: Craig Forrest, Tim Breacker (sub Samassi Abou 70th min), David Unsworth, Rio Ferdinand, Ian Pearce, Stan Lazaridis, Steve Potts, Frank Lampard, Eyal Berkovic, John Hartson, Paul Kitson. **Subs not used:** Bernard Lama, Keith Rowland, Iain Dowie, Paolo Alves.
Emley: Chris Marples, Steve Nicholson, Simon Jones, Michael Thompson, Neil Lacey sub Mark Wilson 5th min (sub Nicky Wood 90th min), Paul David, Ian Banks, Glynn Hurst, Deinoil Graham, Dean Calcutt (sub Robert Tonks 73rd min), Michael Reynolds. **Subs not used:** Paul Hutson, Ray Dennis. **Referee:** Mr J.T. Winter (Stockton on Tees)

FOURTH ROUND

Report by Arthur Evans

Stevenage Bor. (1) 1 Newcastle Utd (1) 1

"We're going on Monday morning to check the safety at Newcastle and we're not asking," joked Stevenage manager Paul Fairclough, in a reference to the well publicised Newcastle questioning of the safety procedures at Broadhall Way Stadium, after his team had forced a draw against Premier giants Newcastle United. As luck had it, Stevenage, having had their home tie, now also had a money spinning tie at St James Park to look forward to.

He was rather pessimistic about his side's chances in the replay, declaring, "We will have several key players suspended for the replay." His opposite number, Kenny Dalglish, would only say, when asked if he was happy with a draw," We're happy to be at home in the fourth round of the cup." Significantly no one dared to ask him what he thought of the safety at Stevenage now the tie was over, and Paul Fairclough would only point out he thought Dalglish had been genuine in his concerns. The seating erected by the home team certainly looked substantial, reminding me of the structures erected for Trooping the Colour or the Edinburgh Tattoo. Mind you the occupants, United fans, stood the whole way through so the seats were redundant. At one time they even performed a massed jig as if trying to test how robust it was.

Three sides of the ground were dominated br Borough's red and white while the temporary structure was a sea of black and white. There was a circus like feel to the pre-match entertainment, much of it centred on glamourous young females dressed sparingly, as befitted the main match sponsors, "The Sun". Crowd involvement in the proceedings was engendered by Stevenage's usual announcer with his roving microphone, which helps to induce a feeling of friendly togetherness.

When the two teams emerged it was therefore not surprising to see a clutch of mascots and another couple of pretty girls to witness the formal opening. The hype over we settled to the football.

Immediately the excitement was too much for one waving participant A flag belonging to one of the assistant referees gave up the ghost and had to be replaced. The reserve official had barely resumed his seat before we had a score and neutrals feared the worst for it was a goal for the Premier Leaguers. Michael Love was robbed on the halfway line by Keith Gillespie who raced away to the bye line and sent over a pin point cross to where Alan Shearer was hanging on the edge of the box having drawn away from his marker. The England striker flexed his neck muscles and, unchallenged, directed the ball firmly into the top corner, well beyond the reach of Des Gallagher. The Toon Army celebrated. Manager Fairclough admitted afterwards that when the early goal went in he feared the worst but that they had faced the same situation at Swindon, going behind to an early goal. He felt that it probably helped to settle his players.

A long range Jason Soloman effort was easily gathered by Shaka Hislop, and a Rob Lee shot, which went well wide at the other end, were poor fare before Stevenage showed more promise, Love's free kick forcing two corners in succession for the home side. Shearer's free kick was similarly diverted for a corner while Stuart Pearce stood ominously by. There was plenty of competitiveness in the tackling, John Beresford and David Batty certainly not looking too pussyfoot, and Gary Crawshaw and Alessandro Pistone were both booked after a jostling session when the Newcastle man tried to prevent a quick free kick. Eventually Love put in another testing free kick. The visitors' defence did not look at all steady in the middle when crosses were delivered. A Simon Stapleton free kick lead to Giuliano Grazioli forcing Hislop to trip over and then Grazioli did put the ball in the net from Neil Trebble's cross but the former was judged offside. Crawshaw saw Hislop get a hand to his attempt as Stevenage pressure built. Several times Beresford took the eye with passes the whole field width to Gillespie who provided Shearer with another heading opportunity but this time Gallagher clutched safely. After a frantic scramble in the Newcastle area Trebble saw Hislop flick his headed attempt over. From the resultant Crawshaw corner Grazioli beat Hislop with a close range header and the dream of victory was again alive. Three sides of the stadium rejoiced, one side was silenced. As the half closed it was the Conference side who were attacking.

The visitors started the second half goal mouth action when Pistone's centre was headed clear by Jamie March. Gillespie nutmegged Grazioli, beat March for speed and centred for Shearer whose volley was blocked at the expense of a corner. Gillespie was the Newcastle danger as Batty drove his side forward. Mark Smith and skipper Robin Trott were superb in the home rearguard and the splendid Dillnutt was not able to press forward as often as in the first half. Still Stevenage did make chances, Trebble's free kick and Crawshaw's corners causing problems for Hislop. A Philippe Albert header was tipped over by Gallagher when the substitute went up for a corner. Crawshaw's neat turn and flick put Grazioli away and Steve Watson was forced to give away a corner as Stevenage countered. As the corner was cleared Gillespie picked up the clearance and ran the whole length of the field before March's last ditch tackle blocked the danger. In the final minutes the fitness difference just began to show as Stevenage started to give the ball away but Newcastle could not mount anything dangerous and it was a toss up as to which set of supporters was urging referee Jones to blow the final whistle so that battle could be joined on another occasion.

When the three notes were heard there was an invasion of home fans wanting to congratulate the non-leaguers who had given such a good account of themselves and, in so doing, had acquitted non-league football as a whole in such a praiseworthy mannor. Northern Newcastle had come to Southern Stevenage and discovered what quality there is outside the football league. As Paul Fairclough said later, "Players here feel they have something to prove". Well they certainly did that. As he also remarked, To come back from such an early blow was great credit to my players". You can say that again, Paul.

Stevenage Borough : Des Gallagher, James Dillnutt, Michael Love (sub Jamie March 43rd min), Mark Smith, Robin Trott, Jason Soloman, Steve Perkins, Giuliano Grazioli (sub Dean Wordsworth 80th min), Gary Crawshaw, Neil Trebble, Simon Stapleton (sub Niall Inman 80th min). **Subs (not used):** Richard Wilmot and Darren Fenton.

Newcastle United: Shaka Hislop, Steve Watson, Steve Howey, Stuart Pearce, Alessandro Pistone, Keith Gillespie, David Batty, Robert Lee, John Beresford (sub Philippe Albert 69th min), Alan Shearer, John Barnes (sub Temuri Ketsbaia 69th min). **Subs (not used):** Shay Given, Ian Rush and John Dahl Tomasson.

Referee : Mr P. Jones (Loughborough)

Report by Arthur Evans

Newcastle Utd (1) 2 Stevenage Bor. (0) 1

Newcastle squeezed into the last sixteen courtesy of an Alan Shearer brace, the first of which, given only by a linesman's flag from an improbable position when Mark Smith looked to have acrobatically hooked the ball out from under the bar, was questionable to say the least. Television replays proved to be inconclusive, but to be fair, Smith himself did not contest the decision. (The special sky machine has proved the ball wasn't over the line)

Borough adopted a bold 4-3-3 attacking formation, with Dean Wordsworth coming in to the starting line-up in place of the injured Giuliano Grazioli, goal hero from the first clash at Broadhall Way. They competed toe to toe with their Premiership opponents from the very first whistle to the very last, soaking up long periods of Geordie pressure without much difficulty. The excellent Smith didn't put a foot wrong all night, Jamie March enjoyed a titanic battle with Keith Gillespie, and teenager James Dillnutt will no doubt have impressed many interested observers over the two games. The Premiership 'superstars' were clearly shaken by Borough's belief and terrified by the prospect of failure, and resorted to many long range efforts, none of which troubled Des Gallagher.

On 16 minutes, Allesandro Pistone's far post cross from the left, following a deft flick-on by Jon Dahl Tomasson, was headed downwards by Shearer and beyond the reach of Gallagher. Smith's magnificent overhead clearance looked to have kept it out, but the linesman thought otherwise and the goal stood. Newcastle's undoubted extra pace and experience meant that they continued to dominate possession and create openings, but Borough's excellent back four allowed them relatively few clear-out chances and provided the opportunities for their side to cause some anxious moments of their own for the home supporters. Leading scorer Gary Crawshaw just failed to connect with a fine cross from Neil Trebble, and Wordsworth fired a skidding shot just past the upright with Shaka Hislop beaten.

One-nil at half-time certainly looked promising, and when Gallagher made outstanding saves from free kicks by both Shearer and Pearce, and then caught and held a stinging volley from Robert Lee, you sensed that they were capable of almost anything. But on 65 minutes, the second goal arrived, and this time their was no doubting its validity. Lee took a pass from David Batty on the right side if the box, shook off his marker and delivered a quality cross beyond Gallagher to the far post. Shearer arrived like a train, getting ahead of Dillnut at the last moment and powering a header into the back of the net. But if Newcastle felt they could relax with a two-goal cushion, they were mistaken, and with 15 minutes left on the clock Stevenage produced the goal their football deserved. A neat exchange of passes in midfield between Stuart Beevor and Crawshaw allowed Beevor to send substitute Niall Inman free down the right. His low cross took a slight deflection off Pistone and fell invitingly for Crawshaw at the near post who volleyed superbly past Hislop. It set up a pulsating final quarter of a hour, and the Geordies will seldom be so relieved to hear the final whistle.

At the post match press conference, Newcastle boss Kenny Dalglish graciously paid tribute to Borough's football, saying they had done themselves and the Vauxhall Conference proud. Now that Newcastle have won the tie, perhaps he will forget all off the field grumblings (none of which had anything to do with football), smile, and get on with the FA Cup. Perhaps an 'easy' tie with Manchester United, if both sides can overcome their respective 5th round opponents, will ease some of the pressure on him!

When the dust settled

No amount of controversy in the media about what was or wasn't said, to or about each other before, between or after the two games which Stevenage Borough played against Newcastle United, should take anything away from the superb performances orchestrated by Paul Fairclough and achieved by Borough's excellent squad.

How a Conference mid table club could match full time International players on thousands of pounds each week is a mystery and it must make us all really doubt the real quality of the super stars and certainly realise that intelligent managers like Fairclough would run rings round many of his over-paid, often unqualified counterparts in the League.

Sadly what should have been a great celebration for non-League clubs and supporters as one of 'their' members proved their quality to the football world unfortunately turned into an embarrassing saga of daily bitchiness between club personnel who really should have known better.

We all know that the press will blow up situations out of all proportion and I dare say there were many 'misquotes' published, but sadly the 'underdogs' didn't finish up with the credit their play should have brought them. The image of the non-League semi-professionals as portrayed to the public have not necessarily left the rest of the football world with the correct view.

The final indignity was created when Graham Roberts (still smarting from the time three years ago when the Stevenage club didn't honour a gentleman's agreement that his contract as player/coach would be cancelled if he was offered a player/manager job elsewhere. Borough allowed him to go to Yeovil but asked for £25,000 from the debt ridden club so he couldn't play and Yeovil were relegated), sent a fax to an old friend Kenny Dalglish wishing him well, saying that not all non-League clubs were like Stevenage!

Kenny Dalglish in his wisdom left the fax for the Stevenage Borough party to see, (unkind). And they in turn ensured the media knew about it (unnecessary). So Graham Roberts' club suspended him for two weeks (unavoidable).

A complete public relations disaster for all involved and especially non-League football.

Very sad, very unnecessary and the end of an exciting period which could have been uplifting but in the end left many people feeling a little flat.

1997-98 REVIEW

*Guest of honour **Roger Hunt** presents the F. A. Umbro Trophy to Cheltenham Town's captain **Chris Banks.***

Photo: Peter Barnes

FIRST QUALIFYING ROUND

Saturday 18th October 1997

	Stafford Rangers	1 v 1	Hinckley United	Attn: 514
r	Hinckley United	1 v 0	Stafford Rangers	Attn: 240
	Moor Green	1 v 0	Atherstone United	Attn: 161
	Buxton	0 v 1	Alfreton Town	Attn: 234
	Bedworth United	3 v 1	Stocksbridge Park S.	Attn: 174
	Solihull Borough	3 v 0	Shepshed Dynamo	Attn: 162
	Lincoln United	5 v 2	Trafford	Attn: 141
	Tamworth	5 v 1	Congleton Town	Attn: 489
	Paget Rangers	0 v 0	Bilston Town	Attn: 62
	Bilston Town	2 v 2	Paget Rangers	Attn: 79 — *Bilston Town win 5-2 aet*
	Witton Albion	3 v 0	Farsley Celtic	Attn: 353
	Radcliffe Borough	v	Dudley Town	*(walkover for Radcliffe Borough – Dudley Town withdrawn)*
	Eastwood Town	1 v 1	Redditch United	Attn: 140
	Redditch United	3 v 0	Eastwood Town	Attn: 118
	Blakenall	2 v 3	Spennymoor United	Attn: 195
	Belper Town	2 v 2	Droylsden	Attn: 267
	Droylsden	2 v 3	Belper Town	Attn: 114
	Winsford United	2 v 0	Ilkeston Town	Attn: 287
	Flixton	0 v 3	Matlock Town	Attn: 147
	Netherfield	1 v 1	Whitby Town	Attn: 161
r	Whitby Town	3 v 3	Netherfield	Attn: 481 — *Whitby Town win 4-3 aet*
	Frickley Athletic	1 v 1	Leigh RMI	Attn: 171
r	Leigh RMI	2 v 1	Frickley Athletic	Attn: 86
	Knowsley United	v	Great Harwood T.	*(walkover for Great Harwood Town – Knowsley United withdrawn)*
	Sutton Coldfield T.	2 v 1	Gretna	Attn: 131
	Whitley Bay	0 v 1	Worksop Town	Attn: 173
	Wembley	**2 v 6**	**Gravesend & Northfleet**	Attn: 160 ‡†
	Whyteleafe	1 v 5	Margate	Attn: 125
	Corby Town	4 v 3	Newport A.F.C.	Attn: 163
	Yate Town	1 v 3	Moseley	Attn: 115

★ *BEST ATTENDANCE* † *LARGEST AWAY VICTORY* ‡ *LARGEST AGGREGATE* § *LARGEST HOME VICTORY*

Carshalton 2 Racing Club Warwick 0 *(First Qualifying Round). Richard Wade (8) and Mark Ford (10) of Carshalton watch the Warwick effort skim the crossbar.* Photo: Peter Lirettoc

Ashford Town 1 V.S. Rugby 0 *(First Qualifying Round). Matt Owen fires in a shot for V.S. Rugby.*
Photo: Francis Short

Crawley Town 2 Kingstonian 1 *(First Qualifying Round). Kingstonian's Eddie Akuamoah gets in a spectacular effort on goal as Crawley's Marc Pullen tries to close him down.*
Photo: Andrew Chitty

	Tonbridge	1 v 0	Newport (W)	Attn: 325
§	Oxford City	6 v 0	Cinderford Town	Attn: 162
	Havant Town	2 v 2	Hendon	Attn: 222
r	*Hendon*	*2 v 1*	*Havant Town*	Attn: 137
	Trowbridge Town	1 v 2	Raunds Town	Attn: 214
	Bognor Regis Town	4 v 0	Thames	Attn: 326
	Walton & Hersham	3 v 0	Staines Town	Attn: 270
	Aldershot Town	5 v 1	Croydon *	Attn: 1705
	Waterlooville	2 v 1	Fisher Athletic	Attn: 140
	Crawley Town	2 v 1	Kingstonian	Attn: 1587
	Brackley Town	2 v 2	Worcester City	Attn: 292
r	*Worcester City*	*5 v 0*	*Brackley Town*	Attn: 131
	Ashford Town	2 v 1	VS Rugby	Attn: 397
	Hampton	0 v 1	Wokingham Town	Attn: 212

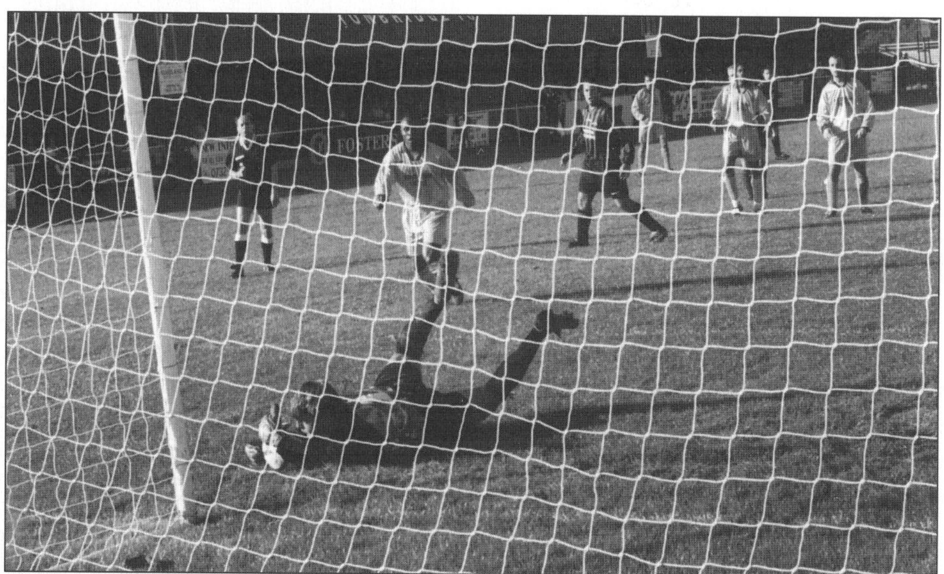

Tonbridge 1 Newport (I.O.W.) 0 *(First Qualifying Round). First half action from Longmead Stadium as Tonbridge 'keeper Joe Radford makes a desperate save to clear a Newport effort.*
Photo: Martin Wray

SECOND QUALIFYING ROUND

Saturday 8th November 1997

	Redditch United	1 v 3	Worksop Town *Att: 277*
	Winsford United	1 v 0	Speenymoor United *Att: 293*
	Hinckley United	3 v 1	Whitby Town *Att: 364*
	Radcliffe Borough	1 v 1	Leigh RMI *Att: 207*
r	Leigh RMI	1 v 0	Radcliffe Borough *Att: 201*
	Stourbridge Celtic	1 v 1	Great Harwood T. *Att: 195*
r	Great Harwood T.	3 v 1	Stourbridge *Att: 115*
	Witton Albion	0 v 0	Bliston Town *Att: 402*
r	Bliston Town *Att: 100*	2 v 2	Witton Albion *Witton Albion win 6-5 on pens*
§‡	Solihull Borough	9 v 1	Alfreton Town *Att: 188*
	Gainsborough Trin.	3 v 0	Bedworth United *Att: 387*
	Workington	1 v 1	Harrogate *Att: 166*
r	Harrogate Town *Att: 211*	0 v 0	Workington *Harrogate win 5-4 on pens*
	Matlock Town	4 v 1	Sutton Coldfield T. *Att: 238*
	Lincoln United	1 v 2	Belper Town *Att: 189*
	Tamworth	4 v 3	Moor Green *Att: 602*
	Abingdon Town	2 v 0	Wokingham Town *Att: 179*
	Margate	3 v 2	Waterlooville *Att: 244*
	Billericay Town	4 v 0	Forest Green Rovers *Att: 426*
	Carshalton Athletic	0 v 0	Aldershot Town *Att: 890*
★*r*	Aldershot Town	3 v 0	Carshalton Athletic *Att: 1602*
	Cambridge City	1 v 1	Dartford *Att: 328*
r	Dartford *Att: 260*	0 v 1	Cambridge City *(at Purfleet FC)*
	Crawley Town	1 v 2	Bishop's Stortford *Att: 1255*
	Berkhamsted Town	3 v 2	Worcester City *Att: 245*
	Baldock Town	1 v 2	Corby Town *Att: 156*
	Basingstoke Town	2 v 0	Witney Town *Att: 396*
	Tonbridge	0 v 3	Hastings Town † *Att: 577*
	Uxbridge	0 v 1	Worthing *Att: 137*
	Bognor Regis Town	2 v 3	Chesham United *Att: 328*
	Oxford City	0 v 2	Wisbech Town *Att: 313*
	Ashford Town	1 v 2	Raunds Town *Att: 434*
	Cirencester Town	1 v 0	Gravesend & Northfleet *Att: 186*
	Bromley	2 v 1	Hendon *Att: 303*
	Hitchin Town	3 v 0	Barton Rovers *Att: 349*
	Romford	5 v 1	Rothwell Town *Att: 257*
	Harrow Borough	5 v 0	Mossley *Att: 206*
	Walton & Hersham	0 v 0	Bashley *Att: 257*
r	Bashley	2 v 0	Walton & Hersham *Att: 225*

***Bognor Regis Town 2 Chesham Town 3** (Second Qualifying Round). Chesham's Chris McGuire (front), scorer of the third goal in the 3-2 victory over Bognor, is seen here in action with the Rocks defender Rob Ackroyd.*
Photo: Andrew Chitty

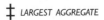

★ BEST ATTENDANCE † LARGEST AWAY VICTORY ‡ LARGEST AGGREGATE § LARGEST HOME VICTORY

THIRD QUALIFYING ROUND

Saturday 29th November 1997

	Marine	1 v 1	Grantham Town Attn: 255
r	Grantham Town	1 v 0	Marine Attn: 326
	Bradford Park Ave.	1 v 1	Leigh RMI Attn: 127
r	Leigh RMI	1 v 0	Bradford Park Ave. Attn: 120
	Tamworth	0 v 1	Lancaster City Attn: 618
	Belper Town	1 v 5	Boston United Attn: 502
	Bromsgrove Rovers	1 v 2	Worksop Town Attn: 517
†	Accrington Stanley	0 v 5	Runcorn Attn: 402
	Solihull Borough	2 v 1	Emley AFC Attn: 176
	Barrow	4 v 1	Hinkley United Attn: 1011
	Great Harwood T.	0 v 1	Witton Albion Attn: 95
	Matlock Town	1 v 1	Winsford United Attn: 231
r	Winsford United aet	0 v 0	Matlock Town Winsford won 5-3 on pens
	Gainsborough Trin.	1 v 0	Bamber Bridge Attn: 429
	Halesowen Town	1 v 2	Burton Albion Attn: 773
	Harrogate Town	0 v 3	Blyth Spartans Attn: 301
	Nuneaton Borough	0 v 2	Altrincham Attn: 903
	Bromley	1 v 4	Purfleet Attn: 270
	St Albans City	5 v 2	Bishop's Stortford Attn: 333
	Harrow Borough	1 v 3	Bath City Attn: 320

***Hitchin Town 0 Boreham Wood 2** (Third Qualifying Round). Steve Heffer pushing for a 'third' late in the match.*
Photo: Clive Butchins

***Bognor Regis Town 2 Chesham Town 3** (Third Qualifying Round). Stafford Brown, (Hasting Town), is beaten to the ball by Mark Keen, (Heybridge Swifts).* Photo: Roger Turner

	Hitchin Town	0 v 2	Boreham Wood Attn: 321	
	Berkhamsted Town	2 v 1	Salisbury City Attn: 112	
	Wisbech Town	2 v 2	Raunds Town Attn: 680	
r	Raunds Town	3 v 2	Wisbech Town	
	Dorchester Town	3 v 0	Worthing Attn: 626	
	Aylesbury United	0 v 3	Dulwich Hamlet Attn: 406	
	Bashley	4 v 1	Cirencester Town Attn: 203	
	Corby Town	2 v 2	Margate Attn: 168	
r	Margate	5 v 1	Corby Town Attn: 166	
	Kings Lynn	1 v 4	Chelmsford City Attn: 1016	*
	Basingstoke Town	4 v 0	Romford Attn: 592	
	Merthyr Tydfil	2 v 2	Cambridge City Attn: 469	
r	Cambridge City aet	6 v 3	Merthyr Tydfil Attn: 200	§‡
	Hastings Town	3 v 2	Heybridge Swifts Attn: 532	
	Chesham United	2 v 1	Sutton United Attn: 380	
	Yeading	2 v 0	St Leonards Stamcroft Attn: 120	
	Billericay Town	2 v 1	Aldershot Town Attn: 902	
	Sittingbourne	1 v 1	Abingdon Town Attn: 369	

FIRST ROUND PROPER

Saturday 10th January 1998

	Altrincham Harris 60, 67, Hardy 77	**3 v 2**	**Runcorn** Minaley 88, Ruffer 23 *Att: 555*
	Ashton United	**0 v 0**	**Chorley** *Att: 439*
r	***Chorley*** *Att: 430*	***0 v 2***	***Ashton United*** Clowes 23, Elliott 28
	Barrow Cooper 29	**1 v 1**	**Worksop Town** Walsh 42 *Att: 1,199*
r †	***Worksop Town*** Whitehead 36, 43 *Att: 1,044*	***2 v 4***	***Barrow*** Jones 23, Coates 34 Johnston 36, 43, Baurers (Pen) 90
	Bashley Taylor 17, Sales 73, Fox 88	**3 v 0**	**Raunds Town** *Att: 329*
	Basingstoke T. *Att: 715*	**0 v 1**	**Gloucester City** Mings 15
	Bath City	**0 v 0**	**Hastings Town** *Att: 662*
r	***Hastings Town*** *Att: 481*	***0 v 1***	***Bath City*** Colbourne 84
	Bishop Auckland Ellison 14, Taylor 28, Lee 29	**3 v 1**	**Colwyn Bay** Limbert (Pen) 53 *Att: 263*
	Boreham Wood Hollingdale 19, Samuels 24	**2 v 1**	**Chelmsford City** Reilly 59 *Att: 407*
	Burton Albion Stride 37, Holmes 83	**2 v 1**	**Witton Albion** Washington 63 *Att: 735*
	Dagenham & R. Sinfield 80 og	**1 v 0**	**Billericay Town** *Att: 1,056*
	Enfield Terry 90 pen	**1 v 1**	**Cheltenham Town** Watkins 18 *Att: 966*
r §	***Cheltenham T.*** Watkins 3, 27 (pen), 38, 63, Knight 54, Walker 76	***5 v 1***	***Enfield*** Endersby 90 (pen) *Att: 1,650*
	Grantham Town Thorpe 31	**1 v 1**	**Leigh RMI** Shaw 11 *Att: 560*
r	***Leigh RMI*** *(Grantham won aet after pens)*	***0 v 0***	***Grantham Town*** *Att: 171*
‡	**Gresley Rovers** Pit 19, Guyett 31, 87, Turner 88 *Att: 638*	**4 v 4**	**Leek Town** Callan 22, 60, Cunningham 65, Trott 78
r	***Leek Town*** Cunningham 4, Biggins 16,44	***3 v 1***	***Gresley Rovers*** Robinson 52 *Att: 324*
	Guiseley	**0 v 0**	**Telford United** *Att: 716*
r	***Telford United*** Palmer 40, 67, Turner 55	***3 v 2***	***Guiseley*** Matthews 44, Parke 46 *Att: 557*

Bashley 3 Raunds Town 0 *(First Round Proper). Bashley's James Taylor gets in his shot but it is destined to hit the post.*
Photo: Graham Cotterill

	Home	Score	Away
	Halifax Town Brook 11, Lyons 90	**2 v 1**	**Blyth Spartans** Moat 72 *Att: 1,712*
	Hayes Watts 56, Flynn 61, Boothe 81	**3 v 2**	**Cambridge City** Harris 27, Byatt 90 *Att: 533*
	Hednesford T. Eccleston 67, Lake 90	**2 v 1**	**Gainsborough T.** Price 20 (pen) *Att: 876*
	Hereford Utd Walker 24, 35, Agana 59	**3 v 0**	**Dulwich Hamlet** *Att: 2,101*
	Hyde United Lambert 6, Kimmins 29	**2 v 1**	**Boston United** Charles 55 *Att: 792*
	Kettering Town Mitchell 39	**1 v 0**	**Dorchester Town** *Att: 1,341*
	Kidderminster H. Yates 13, 83, Arnold 49, Robinson 74	**4 v 1**	**Berkhamsted T.** Yates 50 *Att: 1,206*
	Lancaster City *Att: 472*	**0 v 3**	**Northwich Vic.** Cooke 11, Wa;ters 48, Gardiner 51
	Morecambe McKearney 16 (pen), Shirley 47, Brogan 78 og	**3 v 2**	**Solihull Borough** Myers 27, Abell 41 *Att: 766*
	Purfleet *Att: 333*	**0 v 1**	**Dover Athletic** Adams 56
	Rushden & Dia. Cramman 28, Collins 83, 89	**3 v 2**	**Farnborough T.** Miller 27, Laidlaw 82 *Att: 2,164*
	Southport Butler 16, Ross 50, Gamble 86	**3 v 0**	**Winsford United** *Att: 996*
	St.Albans City	**0 v 0**	**Sittingbourne** *Att: 475*
r	***Sittingbourne*** *Att: 450*	***0 v 1***	***St.Albans City*** Gentle 73
	Stalybridge Burke 59, Goldborne 65 *Att: 524*	**2 v 4**	**Gateshead** † Ord 25, Rowe 32, Bowey 63, Kitchen 70
	Stevenage Bor. Inman 45, Perkins 82 *Att:2,685*	**2 v 2**	**Chesham United** * Fontaine 35, Lawford 80 (pen)
r	***Chesham Utd*** *Att: 986*	***0 v 3***	***Stevenage Bor.*** Crawshaw 42, Trebbie 87, Dillmott 89
	Welling United Farley 51	**1 v 1**	**Slough Town** Owusu 2 *Att: 633*
r	***Slough Town*** Owusu 47, Browne 55	***2 v 1***	***Welling United*** Vercesi 32 *Att: 560*
	Woking *Att:2,682*	**0 v 1**	**Margate** Martin 81
	Yeovil Town	**0 v 0**	**Yeading** *Att:2,016*
r	***Yeading*** Gell 87	***1 v 0***	***Yeovil Town*** *Att: 286*

* BEST ATTENDANCE † LARGEST AWAY VICTORY ‡ LARGEST AGGREGATE § LARGEST HOME VICTORY

***Burton Albion 2 Witton Albion 1** (First Round Proper). Mark Wright, (Witton), has his header saved by Nick Goodwin of Burton.*
Photo: Keith Clayton

SECOND ROUND PROPER

Saturday 31st January 1998

	Home	Score	Away	
	Altrincham	**2 v 0**	**Morecambe**	
	Terry 63, Taylor 88		*Att: 942*	
	Barrow	**2 v 1**	**St. Albans City**	
	Morton 5, Cooper 73		Haworth 53 *Att: 1,279*	
	Bath City	**2 v 3**	**Grantham Town**	
	Colbourne 25, Davis 46 pen		Taylor 48, 54, King 77	
	Bishop Auckland	**1 v 4**	**Boreham Wood**	
	Milroy 18 *Att: 369*		Marshall 31, 60 Hollingdale 66, Samuels 75	
	Cheltenham	**3 v 1**	**Rushden & Dia.**	
	Eaton 19, Watkins 21, 71		Collins 86 *Att: 2,058*	
	Dagenham & R	**0 v 5**	**Hyde United**	
	Att: 989		Nolan 13p, 32p, 79, Kimmins 45, James 52	
	Gateshead	**1 v 2**	**Stevenage**	
	Ord 45		Crawshaw 76p, 90 *Att: 902*	
	Gloucester	**1 v 1**	**Burton Albion**	
	Kemp 67		Smith 37 *Att: 963*	
r	***Burton Albion***	**2 v 2**	***Gloucester City***	
	(Gloucester City won 6-5 on pens)		*aet* *Att: 701*	
	Halifax Town	**1 v 1**	**Slough**	
	Paterson 52		West 85	
r	***Slough Town***	**2 v 0**	***Halifax Town***	
			Att: 876	
	Hayes	**5 v 0**	**Kidderminster H.**	§
	Hall 8, Randall 16 pen, 20, Hammat 80, Sparks 82		*Att: 698*	
	Hednesford	**5 v 0**	**Leek T**	§
	Lake 9, 70, Ware 32 Norbury 39, Fitzpatrick 73		*Att: 1,073*	
	Hereford Utd	**0 v 2**	**Dover Athletic**	*
	Att: 2,108		Dobbs 11, Godden 90	
	Margate	**1 v 2**	**Bashley**	
	Buglione 88		Fox 48, Sales 56	
	Northwich Vic.	**4 v 0**	**Kettering Town**	
	Cooke 47, Stannard 72 Williams 74, Vicary 88		*Att: 1,225*	
	Telford United	**0 v 1**	**Ashton United**	
	Att: 626		Twigg 40	
	Yeading	**0 v 6**	**Southport**	†‡
	Att: 342		Whitaker 26, 57, 71, 83, Ross 82, Kielty 90	

* *BEST ATTENDANCE* † *LARGEST AWAY VICTORY*

‡ *LARGEST AGGREGATE* § *LARGEST HOME VICTORY*

Hereford United 0 Dover Athletic 2 *(Second Round Proper). The nearest Hereford came to scoring as Trevor Matthewson's header shaves the upright.*

THIRD ROUND PROPER

Saturday 21st February 1998

	Home	Score	Away
	Altrincham *Att: 1,196*	**0 v 2**	**Southport** Ross 23/Bolland 39
	Ashton United *Att: 963*	**0 v 1**	**Cheltenham Town** Walker 21
	Barrow *Att: 2185*	**1 v 0**	**Northwich Vic.** Johnston 90
	Grantham Town King 45/Taylor 90	**2 v 1**	**Hednesford Town** Mills (O.G.) 19 *Att: 2214*
	Hayes Sparks 49/Boothe 83	**2 v 0**	**Bashley** *Att: 671*
	Hyde United *Att: 917*	**0 v 2**	**Dover Athletic** Budden 16/Le Bihan 69
	Slough Town Stowell 11	**1 v 1**	**Boreham Wood** Marshall 16 *Att: 1221*
r	**Boreham Wood** Robbins 35 (Pen) *aet*	**1 v 2**	**Slough Town** West 87/Abbott 102 *Att: 544*
*	**Stevenage B.** Soloman 19	**1 v 1**	**Gloucester City** Fergusson 62 (pen) *Att: 2835*
r	**Gloucester City** Webb 75	**1 v 2**	**Stevenage B.** Perkins 12/Trebble 32 *Att: 1540*

* *BEST ATTENDANCE*

Hayes 2 Bashley 0 *(Third Round Proper). Russell Meara, (Hayes), with a great save in the second half against Bashley.* Photo: Eric Marsh

Steve Mokler *at full stretch in the Gloucester City goal.* Photo: Peter Barnes

Slough Town 1 Boreham Wood 1 *(Third Round Proper). Slough's man of the match, Matt Stowell, keeps his feet in this attack against Boreham Wood.* Photo: Dennis Nicholson

Barrow A.F.C. 1 Northwich Victoria 0 *(Third Round Proper). Vic's 'keeper Dean Greygoose under pressure from Barrow's Marc Coates and Paul Jones.* Photo: Andrew Chitty

Ashton United 0 Cheltenham Town 1 *(Third Round Proper). Karl Bell (Ashton United) tangles with Jason Eaton (Cheltenham) in their F.A Umbro Trophy Third Round Proper tie.* Photo: Keith Clayton

Hyde United 0 Dover Athletic 2 *(Third Round Proper). Hyde United's George Switzer in action tackling Dover's Gerald Dobbs.* Photo: Colin Stevens

FOURTH ROUND PROPER

Saturday 14th March 1998

	Home	Score	Away
	Cheltenham T.	**1 v 0**	**Hayes**
	Victory 90		*Att: 2,383*
	Dover Athletic	**1 v 1**	**Barrow**
	Henry 60		Coates 24
			Att: 2,970
* r	**Barrow**	**0 v 0**	**Dover Athletic**
	Dover won 5-4 on pens		*Att: 4,217*
	Grantham Town	**1 v 1**	**Southport**
	Harbottle 80 (pen)		Ross 60
			Att: 3,695
r	**Southport**	**3 v 1**	**Grantham Town**
	Ross 9, 47, 75		King 72
			Att: 1,707
	Stevenage B.	**0 v 1**	**Slough Town**
	Att: 3,482		Bolt 32

* *BEST ATTENDANCE*

*Slough's **Paul Wilkerson** punches the ball clear.*
Photo: Steve Ayre

Cheltenham Town 1 Hayes 0 *(Fourth Round Proper). The ball rebounds off Russell Meara to the feet of Jamie Victory who makes no mistake to secure a 1-0 win for Cheltenham in the last minute.* Photo: Peter Barnes

SEMI FINAL TIES

1st Leg – Saturday 28th March 1998

SLOUGH TOWN **0 V 1** **SOUTHPORT**

Att: 2,106

Team: Wilkerson, Smart, Simpson (West 57), McGinnis,Hercules, Stowell, Bailey, Owush, Brazil, Abbot, Fiore.

Morris 68

Team: Stewart, Farley, Ryan, Kielty, Formby, Futcher, Thompson (Morgan 64), Butler, Ross, Gamble, Morris (Mitten 89).

CHELTENHAM TOWN **2 V 1** **DOVER ATHLETIC**

Easton 75, 82

Team: Book, Duff, Victory, Banks, Freeman, Milton, Howels, Walker, Smith (Easton 58), Watkins, Bloomer.

Dobbs 3

Att: 3,011

Team: Mitten, Munday, Palmer, Budden, Shearer, Stebbing, Dodds, Strouts, Ayorinde, Le Bihan, Henry (Weide 66).

2nd Leg – Saturday 4 April 1998

SOUTHPORT **1 v 1** **SLOUGH TOWN**

Formby 66

Team: Stewart, Farley, Ryan, Butler, Horner, Futcher, Thompson, Morris, Ross, Gamble, Formby.

Bailey 30

Att: 4,895

Team: Wilkerson, Smart, Stowell, McGinnis (West 75), Hercules, Angus, Bailey, Browne, Brazil,

DOVER ATHLETIC **2 V 2** **CHELTENHAM TOWN**

Le Bihan 70, Budden 78

Team: Mitten, Munday, Palmer, Budden, Shearer, Stebbing, Dobbs (Davies 68), Strout, Ayorinde,Le Bihan, Henry., Bloomer.

Watkins 6, Eaton 34

Att: 3,240

Team: Book, Duff, Victory, Banks, Freeman, Milton (Wright 74), Howells, Walker, Eaton, Watkins, Mitten 46, Jones for.

★ *BEST ATTENDANCE*

Four sound semi-professional clubs stayed the course in the F.A. Umbro Trophy this season, leaving the traditional glamour names behind.

Cheltenham Town, who only qualified for the Conference because Paul Futcher's Gresley Rovers' ground was not ready, were eleven points behind the champions but had enjoyed a superb season in all competitions and they joined Fulcher's new club Southport, Dover Athletic and Slough Town in the semi-finals.

It seemed strange that there was no place for Stevenage Borough, Woking, Rushden & Diamonds, Hereford United or Kidderminster Harriers – all much fancied Trophy clubs; but what a refreshing situation to have four semi-finalists with no Trophy experience at Wembley although Slough Town had once reached an F.A. Amateur Cup Final in 1973.

Slough Town faced Southport at home with three attacking players missing, but Andy Whittacker, 'The Sandgrounders' four goal hero in the Second Round, was also missing.

A very tentative first half produced little goalmouth action and the onus was on the home side to step up the pace after the interval. This they did with neat short passing, but the Rebels really didn't often threaten the Southport goal and, when they did, England's goalkeeper Billy Stewart looked in magnificent form.

At the other end Brian Ross, another International, was coming into the game more and with excellent close control was holding the ball up and encouraging David Thompson to surge forward on the right. However, it was Ross himself who chased a long ball down the right and reached it just before the on-rushing Slough goalkeeper Paul Wilkerson. A cool long clip to the far post was taking its time as Steve Munro bustled in to make sure it went over the line and Southport held on to a vital one goal lead.

The central defensive pairing of player/manager Fulcher and Tim Ryan, who had recently won his first cap for England against Holland, was the match winning combination and, on the day under a strangely hot sun, Brian McDermott's side really couldn't complain about the one goal deficit.

A super crowd of just under 5,000 gave Paul Fulcher's side a great welcome, but this time it was Slough's experienced mid-fielder Danny Bailey who really set the tie alight with an equaliser after 30 minutes.

Tension built and the half-time rally in the changing rooms brought two fully committed sides locked together and knowing the next goal was going to be vital.

The 41 year old player/manager was as cool as ever, however, and he started the move which was carried on from Morris to Ross. The experienced striker had scored in every round of the competition so far and, having set up the goal in the first leg, he now drilled a shot in, but lost the goal to a deflection by colleague Kevin Formby! But who cared? It was a lead and it turned out to be the vital goal.

The club which lost it's place in The Football League in 1977 and nearly packed up, had now reached a Wembley Trophy Final with a squad that could give them a great chance of returning to the senior ranks next season.

Slough Town fought all the way, they had their international Corey Browne and Danny Bolt back and certainly looked more dangerous, but were just edged out in a very well balanced contest.

An early goal for Dover Athletic was just the shock that favourites Cheltenham Town did not want at home in their first leg, especially with Jason Eaton one of their ace goalscorers only on the bench after injury, but Gerald Dobbs' crisp strike in the third minute thrilled the visitors.

A tight, even game was beginning to look encouraging for Bill Williams' side as half-time came and it wasn't until Eaton came on to renew his partnership with Dale Watkins that The Robins got back into the game.

The Dover supporters were not happy with the officials' handling of either goal but on both occasions the home side was given the benefit of the doubt and a header with fifteen minutes to go and then a winner seven minutes later gave Eaton the title of match winner, Cheltenham a vital lead and frustration for the Dover camp.

The home side had won without playing their best side. Dover probably didn't deserve to lose, but at least there was all to play for back on the Kent coast.

This time it was Cheltenham Town who stormed into a two goal lead by half-time. Dale Watkins after six minutes and that man Eaton again ten minutes before half-time had scored from close range and the sad Dover Supporters were fearing the worst. A possible hammering and no contest.

They needn't have worried as former Peterborough United mid fielder Neil Bihan crashed in an excellent drive with twenty minutes to go and then eight minutes later John Buddin scored an equally spectacular goal. The force was with the Kent club as the crowd desperately roared their heroes on and the Cheltenham party kept looking at their watches. The tie had come alive and Dover pushed their visitors to the very limit.

But it wasn't to be and Steve Cotterill's squad's excellent season was given what they really deserved, a visit to Wembley.

The sadness of losing in a semi-final, especially over two legs when there is a week to think about all the pressures, rewards, excitement and the possible outcome can create havoc in a normally well balanced football club.

When the hopes are smashed, there's no where to hide. You cannot blame the winners for celebrating, but it makes it all the worse to know it could have been you!

But Slough Town and Dover Athletic showed dignity and fortitude in defeat and the two proud, but sporting, winners were to present an excellent contest at Wembley on Sunday 17th May.

Dover Athletic 2 Cheltenham Town 2 *(Semi Finals 2nd Leg). Cheltenham's 'keeper Steve Book claims a corner in front of his side's travelling supporters.*
Photo: Francis Short

FINAL

Sunday 17 May 1998

CHELTENHAM TOWN 1 v 0 SOUTHPORT

Eaton 74

at Wembley Stadium
Att: 26,837

	Cheltenham Town		Southport
1	Book	1	Stewart
2	Duff	2	Horner
3	Freeman	3	Futcher
4	Banks	4	Ryan
5	Victory	5	Farley
6	Knight	6	Kielty
7	Howells	7	Butler
8	Bloomer	8	Gamble
9	Walker	9	Formby
10	Eaton	10	Thompson
11	Watkins	11	Ross

Substitutes
Milton *for Walker 78th minute*
Smith *for Jacques 75th minute*
Wright *Not used*

Referee:
G. S. Willard
(Worthing)

Substitutes
Whittaker *for Formby 80th minute*
Bollard *for Thompson 88th minute*
Mitten *not used*

Four Conference clubs contested the semi-finals of this year's F.A. Umbro Trophy with no previous experience of a Wembley Final in the competition between them.

Dover Athletic and Slough Town were the unlucky losers but it was certainly a strange season for the competition as the one club of the quartet to have enjoyed a good season in the Conference was Cheltenham Town who started the season (like Halifax Town) as 66-1 outsiders. None of the pre season favourites were in contention but that didn't affect the attendance.

Both clubs did extremely well with ticket sales with The Robins from Gloucestershire having the edge as they were very much nearer to Wembley. The crowd of 26,837 was the sixth best on record for a Trophy Final.

Much had been made of the meeting of the 'golden oldies', Southport's player/manager Peter Futcher and Cheltenham Town's Clive Walker, who had already won three Trophy winners medals with Woking.

Both men were a credit to the profession with Futcher hardly wasting a clearance and always in position to cover a defensive colleague, while Walker, obviously finding the responsibilities of the modern winger extremely taxing,worked as hard as anyone and still had the energy and speed to make one potentially match winning run to the bye line, only for his cross to be cut out by the other old fella!

To be fair to Southport, it was their neat passing that created most chances, but once they reached their opponents box they ran out of options through lack of numbers. Fullback Andy Farley was prominent in the first half and individual runs by Thompson and Brian Ross nearly opened the score.

Both 'keepers, and indeed the defences, looked well in control and it was a shame that two excellent teams managed to blot each other out, but neither side could string enough passes together to encourage their midfield forces to risk moving forward to support the lonely striker.Their skipper Brian Butler deservedly won the 'Man of the Match' award but more attackers were needed.

***Russell Milton** and **Mike Duff** celebrate in sytle.*
Photo: Peter Barnes

The only goal of the F. A. Umbro Trophy Final, scored by Cheltenham's ***Jason Eaton*** *after seventy-nine minutes.*
Photo: Gordon Whittington

Viewing Cheltenham's fire power and the superb season enjoyed by Dale Walkins and Jason Eaton one always felt the West County side would be more likely to break the deadlock and so it was in the 79th minute. The introduction of substitutes Jimmy Smith and Russell Milton had, in fact, given them an injection of new ideas and from a free kick by Milton, which hit the cross bar, it was flicked on by Jamie Victory and reached Eaton for him head down firmly just inside the post. A simple and well executed set piece, the sort of goal that coaches keep telling their players will make all the difference when games are deadlocked, did, in fact, make that vital difference.

It won the F.A. Umbro Trophy and Cheltenham Town did finish an excellent season with some silverware to show for their efforts. Steve Cotterill had 'managed' his club extremely well and the prize was well deserved but it you are putting money on potential Conference winners for next season ignore Southport at your peril. The Sandgrounders, at their best, are a very good side who will be strengthened and ready for the challenge. Paul Futcher, remember, had taken Gresley Rovers to the 1996-97 Dr. Martens Championship by eleven points from Cheltenham, The Robins getting promotion as Rover's ground was not ready. Mr. Futcher has a couple of scores to settle and this time he will have the ammunition to do it.

FA UMBRO TROPHY ATTENDANCES 1997/1998

	Total Attenance	*Average Attendance*	*Largest Attendance*	
1st Qualifying Round	15,881	370	1,705	Aldershot Town
2nd Qualifying Round	13,738	392	1602	Aldershot Town
3rd Qualifying Round	15,139	408	1016	Kings Lynn
1st Round Proper	36,347	1,101	2830	Woking
2nd Round Proper	19,166	1,008	2108	Hereford United
3rd Round Proper	16,284	1,628	2855	Stevenge Borough
4th Round Proper	18,456	3,076	4217	Barrow
Semi Finals	13,252	3,313	4895	Southport
Final	26,837	26,837	26,837	Wembley
Total	**174,270**			

PAST F.A. TROPHY FINALS

1970 MACCLESFIELD TOWN 2 (Lyond, B Fidler) TELFORD UNITED 0
Macclesfield: Cooke, Sievwright, Bennett, Beaumont, Collins, Roberts, Lyons, B Fidler, Young, Corfield, D Fidler.
Telford: Irvine, Harris, Croft, Flowers, Coton, Ray, Fudge, Hart, Bentley, Murray, Jagger. Att: 28,000. Ref: K Walker

1971 TELFORD UTD 3 (Owen, Bentley, Fudge) HILLINGDON BORO. 2 (Reeve, Bishop)
Telford: Irvine, Harris, Croft, Ray, Coton, Carr, Fudge, Owen, Bentley, Jagger, Murray.
Hillingdon B: Lowe, Batt, Langley, Higginson, Newcombe, Moore, Fairchild, Bishop, Reeve, Carter, Knox. Att: 29,500 Ref: D Smith

1972 STAFFORD RANGERS 3 (Williams 2, Cullerton) BARNET 0
Stafford: Aleksic, Chadwick, Clayton, Sargeant, Aston, Machin, Cullerton, Chapman, Williams, Bayley, Jones.
Barnet: McClelland, Lye, Jenkins, Ward, Embrey, King, Powell, Rerry, Flatt, Easton, Plume. Att: 24,000 Ref: P Partridge

1973 SCARBOROUGH 2 (Leask, Thompson) WIGAN ATHLETIC 1 (Rogers) aet
Scarboro: Garrow, Appleton, Shoulder, Dunn, Siddle, Fagan, Donoghue, Franks, Leask (Barmby), Thompson, Hewitt.
Wigan: Reeves, Morris, Sutherland, Taylor, Jackson, Gillibrand, Clements, Oats (McCunnell), Rogers, King, WorswickAtt: 23,000 Ref: H Hackney

1974 MORECAMBE 2 (Richmond, Sutton) DARTFORD 1 (Cunningham)
Morecambe: Coates, Pearson, Bennett, Sutton, Street, Baldwin, Done, Webber, Roberts (Galley), Kershaw, Richmond.
Dartford: Morton, Read, Payne, Carr, Burns, Binks, Light, Glozier, Robinson (Hearne), Cunningham, Halleday. Att: 19,000 Ref: B Homewood

1975 MATLOCK TOWN 4 (Oxley, Dawson, T Fenoughty, N Fenoughy) SCARBOROUGH 0
Matlock: Fell, McKay, Smith, Stuart, Dawson, Swan, Oxley, N Fenoughy, Scott, T Fenoughty, M Fenoughty.
Scarborough: Williams, Hewitt, Rettitt, Dunn, Marshall, Todd, Houghton, Woodall, Davidson, Barnby, Aveyard. Att: 21,000 Ref: K Styles

1976 SCARBOROUGH 3 (Woodall, Abbey, Marshall(p)) STAFFORD R. 2 (Jones 2) aet
Scarboro: Barnard, Jackson, Marshall, H Dunn, Ayre (Donoghue), HA Dunn, Dale, Barmby, Woodall, Abbey, Hilley.
Stafford: Arnold, Ritchie, Richards, Sargeant, Seddon, Morris, Chapman, Lowe, Jones, Hutchinson, Chadwick. Att: 21,000 Ref: R Challis

1977 SCARBOROUGH 2 (Dunn(p), Abbey) DAGENHAM 1 (Harris)
Scarboro: Chapman, Smith, Marshall (Barmby), Dunn, Ayre, Deere, Aveyard, Donoghue, Woodall, Abbey, Dunn.
Dagenham: Hutley, Wellman, P Currie, Dunwell, Moore, W Currie, Harkins, Saul, Fox, Harris, Holder. Att: 21,500 Ref: G Courtney

1978 ALTRINCHAM 3 (King, Johnson, Rogers) LEATHERHEAD 1 (Cook)
Altrincham: Eales, Allan, Crossley, Bailey, Owens, King, Morris, Heathcote, Johnson, Rogers, Davidson (Flaherty).
Leatherhead: Swannell, Cooper, Eaton, Davies, Reid, Malley, Cook, Salkeld, Baker, Boyle (Bailey). Att: 20,000 Ref: A Grey

1979 STAFFORD RANGERS 2 (A Wood 2) KETTERING TOWN 0
Stafford: Arnold, F Wood, Willis, Sargeant, Seddon, Ritchie, Secker, Chapman, A Wood, Cullerton, Chadwick (Jones).
Kettering: Lane, Ashby, Lee, Eastell, Dixey, Suddards, Flannagan, Kellock, Phipps, Clayton, Evans (Hughes). Att: 32,000 Ref: D Richardson

1980 DAGENHAM 2 (Duck, Maycock) MOSSLEY 1 (Smith)
Dagenham: Huttley, Wellman, Scales, Dunwell, Mooore, Durrell, Maycock, Horan, Duck, Kidd, Jones (Holder).
Mossley: Fitton, Brown, Vaughan, Gorman, Salter, Polliot, Smith, Moore, Skeete, O'Connor, Keelan (Wilson). Att: 26,000 Ref: K Baker

1981 BISHOP'S STORTFORD 1 (Sullivan) SUTTON UNITED 0
Stafford: Moore, Blackman, Brame, Smith (Worrell), Bradford, Abery, Sullivan, Knapman, Radford, Simmonds, Mitchell.
Sutton: Collyer, Rogers, Green, J Rains, T Rains, Stephens (Sunnucks), Waldon, Pritchard, Cornwell, Parsons. Att: 22,578 Ref: J Worrall

1982 ENFIELD 1 (Taylor) ALTRINCHAM 0
Enfield: Jacobs, Barrett, Tone, Jennings, Waite, Ironton, Ashford, Taylor, Holmes, Oliver (Flint), King. Ref: B Stevens
Altrincham: Connaughton, Crossley, Davison, Bailey, Cuddy, King (Whitbread), Allan, Heathcote, Johnson, Rogers, Howard. Att: 18,678

1983 TELFORD UTD 2 (Mather 2) NORTHWICH VICTORIA 1 (Bennett)
Telford: Charlton, Lewis, Turner, Mayman (Joseph), Walker, Easton, Barnett, Williams, Mather, Hogan, Alcock.
Northwich: Ryan, Fretwell, Murphy, Jones, Forshaw, Ward, Anderson, Abel (Bennett), Reid, Chesters, Wilson. Att: 22,071 Ref: B Hill

1984 NORTHWICH VICTORIA 1 (Chesters) BANGOR CITY 1 (Whelan) Att: 14,200 Ref: J Martin
Replay NORTHWICH 2 (Chesters(p), Anderson) BANGOR 1 (Lunn) Att: 5,805 (at Stoke)
Northwich: Ryan, Fretwell, Dean, Jones, Forshaw (Power 65), Bennett, Anderson, Abel, Reid, Chesters, Wilson.
Bangor: Letheren, Cavanagh, Gray, Whelan, Banks, Lunn, Urqhart, Morris, Carter, Howat, Sutcliffe (Westwood 105). Same teams in replay.

1985 WEALDSTONE 2 (Graham, Holmes) BOSTON UNITED 1 (Cook)
Wealdstone: Iles, Perkins, Bowgett, Byatt, Davies, Greenaway, Holmes, Wainwright, Donnellan, Graham (N Cordice 89), A Cordice.
Boston: Blackwell, Casey, Ladd, Creane, O'Brien, Thommson, Laverick (Mallender 78), Simpsom, Gilbert, Lee, Cook. Att: 20,775 Ref: J Bray

1986 ALTRINCHAM 1 (Farrelly) RUNCORN 0
A'cham: Wealands, Gardner, Densmore, Johnson, Farrelly, Conning, Cuddy, Davison, Reid, Ellis, Anderson. Sub: Newton.
Runcorn: McBride, Lee, Roberts, Jones, Fraser, Smith, S Crompton (A Crompton), Imrie, Carter, Mather, Carrodus. Att: 15,700 Ref: A Ward

1987 KIDDERMINSTER H. 0 BURTON ALBION 0 Att: 23,617 Ref: D Shaw
Replay KIDDERMINSTER H. 2 (Davies 2) BURTON ALBION 1 (Groves) Att: 15,685 (at West Brom)
K'minster: Arnold, Barton, Boxall, Brazier (sub Hazlewood in rep), Collins (sub Pearson 90 at Wembley), Woodall, McKenzie, O'Dowd, Tuohy, Casey, Davies. sub: Jones.
Burton: New, Essex, Kamara, Vaughan, Simms, Groves, Bancroft, Land, Dorsett, Redfern, (sub Wood in replay), Gauden. Sub: Patterson.

THE LAST TEN YEARS

1988 **ENFIELD 0** **TELFORD UNITED 0** Ref: L Dilkes
Att: 20,161

Replay **ENFIELD 3** **TELFORD 2** Att: 6,912
(Furlong 2, Howell) (Biggins, Norris(p)) (at West Brom)

Enfield: Pape, Cottington, Howell, Keen (sub Edmonds in rep), Sparrow (sub Hayzleden at Wembley), Lewis (sub Edmonds at Wembley), Harding, Cooper, King, Furlong, Francis.

Telford: Charlton, McGinty, Storton, Nelson, Wiggins, Mayman (sub Cunningham in rep (sub Hancock)), Sankey, Joseph, Stringer (sub Griffiths at Wembley, Griffiths in rep), Biggins, Norris.

1989 **TELFORD UNITED 1** **MACCLESFIELD TOWN 0** Ref: T Holbrook
(Crawley) Att: 18,102

Telford: Charlton, Lee, Brindley, Hancock, Wiggins, Mayman, Grainger, Joseph, Nelson, Lloyd, Stringer. Subs: Crawley, Griffiths.

Macclesfield: Zelem, Roberts, Tobin, Edwards, Hardman, Askey, Lake, Hanton, Imrie, Burr, Timmons. Subs: Devomshire, Kendall.

1990 **BARROW 3** **LEEK TOWN 0** Ref: T Simpson.
(Gordon 2, Cowperthwaite) Att: 19,011

Barrow: McDonnell, Higgins, Chilton, Skivington, Gordon, Proctor, Doherty (Burgess), Farrell (Gilmore), Cowperthwaite, Lowe, Ferris.

Leek: Simpson, Elsby (Smith), Pearce, McMullen, Clowes, Coleman (Russell), Mellor, Somerville, Sutton, Millington.

1991 **WYCOMBE W. 2** **KIDDERMINSTER H. 1** Ref: J Watson
(Scott, West) (Hadley) Att: 34,842

Wycombe: Granville, Crossley, Cash, Kerr, Creaser, Carroll, Ryan, Stapleton, West, Scott, Guppy (Hutchinson).

Kidderminster: Jones, Kurila, McGrath, Weir, Barnett, Forsyth, Joseph (Wilcox), Howell (Whitehouse), Hadley, Lilwall, Humphries.

1992 **COLCHESTER UTD 3** **WITTON ALBION 1** Ref: K P Barratt
(Masters, Smith, McGavin) (Lutkevitch) Att: 27,806

Colchester: Barrett, Donald, Roberts, Knsella, English, Martin, Cook, Masters, McDonough (Bennett 65), McGavin, Smith.

Witton: Mason, Halliday, Coathup, McNeilis, Jim Connor, Anderson, Thomas, Rose, Alford, Grimshaw (Joe Connor), Lutkevitch (McCluskie).

1993 **WYCOMBE W. 4** **RUNCORN 1** Ref: I J Borritt
(Cousins, Kerr, Thompson, Carroll) (Shaughnessy) Att: 32,968

Wycombe: Hyde, Cousins, Cooper, Kerr, Crossley, Thompson (Hayrettin 65), Carroll, Ryan, Hutchinson, Scott, Guppy. Sub: Casey.

Runcorn: Williams, Bates, Robertson, Hill, Harold (Connor 62), Anderson, Brady (Parker 72), Brown, Shaughnessy, McKenna, Brabin.

1994 **WOKING 2** **RUNCORN 1** Ref: Paul Durkin
(D Brown, Hay) (Shaw (pen)) Att: 15,818

Woking: L Batty, M Tucker, L Wye, G Berry, K Brown, A Clement, D Brown (K Rattray 32), C Fielder, S Steele, D Hay (D Puckett 46), C Walker.

Runcorn: A Williams, J Bates, P Robertson, N Shaw, A Lee, G Anderson, K Thomas, J Connor, I McInerney (G Hill 71), K McKenna, G Brabin. Sub: N Parker.

1995 **WOKING 2** **KIDDERMINSTER H. 1 aet** Ref: D J Gallagher
(Steele, Fielder) (Davies) Att: 17,815

Woking: L Batty, M Tucker, L Wye, C Fielder, K Brown, J Crumplin (K Rattray 42), S Wye, A Ellis, S Steele, D Hay (R Newberry 112), C Walker. Sub: T Read (gk).

Kidderminster: K Rose, S Hodson, P Bancroft, P Webb, C Brindley (N Cartwright 94), R Forsyth, J Deakin, M Yates, D Humphreys (L Hughes 105), P Davies, J Purdie. Sub: M Dearlove (gk).

1996 **MACCLESFIELD TOWN 3** **NORTHWICH VICTORIA 1** Ref: Mike D Reed
(Payne, OG, Hemmings) (Williams) Att: 8,672

Macclesfield: Ryan Price, Cec Edey, Mark Gardiner, Steve Payne, Neil Howarth (C), Neil Sorvel, Darren Lyons, Steve Wood (Kevin Hulme 83), Marc Coates, Phil Power, Tony Hemmings (Paul Cavell 88).

Northwich Victoria: Dean Greygoose, Derek ward, Chris Duffy, Dave Burgess (Wes Simpson 87), Graham Abel (Lee Steele), Steve Walters, Carwyn Williams, Brian Butler (C), Ian Cooke, Delwyn Humphries, Darren Vicary.

F.A. UMBRO TROPHY - THE "TOP 50"

The teams in the list are the teams with the best overall records in the FA Trophy since the competition commenced in 1970.

The points are awarded as follows:- 1 point for a win in the 1st round proper, 2 points for a win in the second round and so on until the winning team gets 7 points. The games played include qualifying round matches as well as the competition proper.

As you would expect, all the famous names are in there with Telford United leading the field by just one point from Altrincham.

A measure as to how the balance of power has changed over the years can be seen by the fact that just half of the current Conference teams feature in the Top 50. Three in the top 10 - Telford, Kidderminster and Northwich, followed by five in the top 20 - Kettering, Cheltenham, Yeovil, Morecambe and Barrow. That just leaves Woking at number 22, Dover at number 36 and Welling at number 42. Cheltenham's first Trophy success lifted them 7 places in the table from last year.

Other teams with worthy records who are not in the Conference at present include Runcorn, three times finalists but never winners at number 3, Enfield, twice winners at number 4, Macclesfield Town and Scarborough who are now gracing the Football League and the original Dagenham team who have an incredible record for the 18 seasons that they played in the competition. In that time they won 50 matches including a winning performance in 1980. They have the best percentage success rate for any team that have played in the competition for more than 10 seasons.

To see the names of Dartford and Bedford Town in the list is a reminder of the times when these teams were challenging the best the non-league game had to offer, Bedford making the semis in 1975 and Dartford finalists in 1974. Both teams are now back and have made great progress since reforming.

It is fascinating to look back at records and see how successful or not teams have been over the years, but next season's competition will be about the future, not the past. Will a team with a Trophy 'pedigree' win the competition or will it be someone from the lower reaches of this table. (The full list of teams having entered the Trophy goes down to number 467.) The choice is yours. As for me, I have not made up my mind yet. I'll let you know when I do!

John Anderson

FA TROPHY - OVERALL RECORDS

The following table comprises the complete records of every team that has played in the FA Trophy since its inception in 1970. The idea is to reward teams for their consistency over the years they have played in the competition and the points have been awarded as follows:-

1st round proper	1 point	2nd round proper	2 points
3rd round proper	3 points	4th round proper	4 points
semi-final	5 points	losing finalist	6 points
winners	7 points		

Other abbreviations are:-

- **S** Seasons played in the competition (maximum 29)
- **P** Total games played (including qualifying rounds)
- **W** Games won
- **L** Games lost
- **%** Percentage of games won compared with total games played
- **Best** The team's best performance in the competition

I have tried to keep to the following very general rules when compiling these records:-

If a team changes its name but everything else stays the same, then I have changed the name but kept the records ongoing

If two teams merge and a new name is chosen, then a new record is started with the new name

If two teams merge but the name of one of the teams is kept intact, then I have carried on with this name

F.A. TROPHY - TOP 50 OVERALL RECORDS

1997	1998		S	P	W	L	%	Pts	Best
1	1	Telford United	29	82	56	26	68.29	78	W x 9
2	2	Altrincham	29	86	59	27	68.60	77	W x 2
3	3	Runcorn	29	83	54	29	65.06	70	F x 3
4	4	Enfield	24	76	54	22	71.05	69	W x 2
6	5	Kidderminster Harriers	29	73	45	28	61.64	66	W 87
8	6	Northwich Victoria	29	76	48	28	63.16	65	W 84
5	7	Stafford Rangers	29	73	46	27	63.01	65	W x 2
7	8	Macclesfield Town	28	74	48	26	64.86	62	W x 2
9	9	Dagenham	18	67	50	17	74.63	55	W 80
10	10	Scarborough	18	54	39	15	72.22	55	W x 3
11	11	Boston United	29	66	37	29	56.06	54	F 85
12	12	Kettering Town	29	61	32	29	52.46	54	F 79
20	13	Cheltenham Town	28	79	52	27	65.82	52	W 98
15	14	Yeovil Town	29	59	30	29	50.85	52	SF x 2
13	15	Wycombe Wanderers	19	52	35	17	67.31	51	W x 2
14	16	Dartford	25	63	38	25	60.32	51	F 74
16	17	Morecambe	29	75	47	28	62.67	50	W 74
18	18	Burton Albion	29	71	42	29	59.15	48	F 87
17	19	Bangor City	22	53	31	22	58.49	47	F 84
24	20	Barrow	26	60	35	25	58.33	46	W 90
19	21	Bromsgrove Rovers	29	67	38	29	56.72	46	4 x 2
23	22	Woking	24	65	44	21	67.69	45	W x 3
21	23	Merthyr Tydfil	29	67	38	29	56.72	45	4 78
22	24	Weymouth	29	59	30	29	50.85	45	4 x 2
25	25	Bath City	29	66	37	29	56.06	42	4 90
28	26	Bishop Auckland	24	61	37	24	60.66	41	4 x 2
33	27	Slough Town	24	53	29	24	54.72	41	SF x 2
27	28	Witton Albion	29	78	49	29	62.82	40	F 92
26	29	Worcester City	28	58	30	28	51.72	40	4 x 4
29	30	Marine	24	54	30	24	55.56	39	SF x 2
30	31	Nuneaton Borough	29	60	31	29	51.67	38	4 x 3
31	32	Barnet	22	52	30	22	57.69	37	F 72
39	33	Hyde United	29	73	44	29	60.27	36	SF x 3
37	34	Gateshead	28	60	32	28	53.33	36	4 x 3
32	35	Sutton United	24	50	26	24	52.00	36	F 81
40	36	Dover Athletic	29	57	28	29	49.12	36	SF 98
36	37	Chorley	29	65	36	29	55.38	35	SF 96
38	38	Blyth Spartans	24	49	25	24	51.02	35	4 x 2
34	39	Bedford Town	13	38	25	13	65.79	34	SF 75
35	40	Matlock Town	29	71	42	28	60.56	34	W 75
44	41	Grantham	29	66	37	29	56.06	33	4 x 2
41	42	Welling United	16	36	20	16	55.56	31	4 89
45	43	Chelmsford City	29	61	32	29	52.46	30	SF 70
42	44	Maidstone United	17	43	26	17	60.47	29	4 x 2
43	45	Mossley	26	59	33	26	55.93	29	F 80
46	46	Wigan Athletic	9	27	18	9	66.67	27	F 73
47	47	Wealdstone	23	55	33	22	60.00	26	W 85
48	48	Hillingdon Borough	16	40	24	16	60.00	25	F 71
49	49	Bishops Stortford	24	52	29	23	55.77	25	W 81
52	50	Dagenham & Redbridge	9	25	16	9	64.00	24	F 97

FA UMBRO TROPHY AT A GLANCE

1st Round

Team	Score	Team	Score
Guiseley	0 2	Telford Utd	0 3
Ashton Utd	0 2	Chorley	0 0
Enfield	1 1	**Cheltenham T**	**1 5**
Rushden & Dia	3	Farnborough Tn	2
Hayes	3	Cambridge City	2
Kidderminster Har	4	Berkhamsted Tn	1
Woking	0	Margate	1
Bashley	3	Raunds Town	0
Dag & Redbridge	1	Billericay Town	0
Hyde United	2	Boston United	1
Hereford United	3	Dulwich Hamlet	0
Purfleet	0	Dover Athletic	1
Barrow	1 4	Worksop Tn	1 2
St Albans City	0 1	Sittingbourne	0 0
Lancaster City	0	Northwich Victoria	3
Kettering Town	1	Dorchester Town	0
Stalybridge Celtic	2	Gateshead	4
Stevenage Boro	2 3	Chesham Utd	2 0
Basingstoke Tn	0	Gloucester City	1
Burton Albion	2	Witton Albion	1
Halifax Town	2	Blyth Spartans	1
Welling United	1 1	Slough Town	1 2
Bishop Auckland	3	Colwyn Bay	1
Boreham Wood	2	Chelmsford City	1
Bath City	0 1	Hastings Town	0 0
Grantham T	1 *0 +4	Leigh RMI	1 *0 +3
Hednesford Town	2	Gainsborough Trin	1
Gresley Rovers	4 1	Leek Town	4 3
Altrincham	3	Runcorn	2
Morecambe	3	Solihull Borough	2
Yeovil Town	0 0	Yeading	0 1
Southport	**3**	Winsford United	0

2nd Round

Team	Score	Team	Score
Telford United	0	Ashton United	1
Cheltenham Town	**3**	Rushden & Dia	1
Hayes	5	Kidderminster Har	0
Margate	1	Bashley	2
Dag & Redbridge	0	Hyde United	5
Hereford United	0	Dover Athletic	2
Barrow	2	St Albans City	1
Northwich Vic	4	Kettering Town	0
Gateshead	1	Stevenage Boro	2
Gloucester C	1 *2 +6	Burton Alb	1 *2 +5
Halifax Town	1 0	Slough Town	1 2
Bishop Auckland	1	Boreham Wood	4
Bath City	2	Grantham Town	3
Hednesford Town	5	Leek Town	0
Altrincham	2	Morecambe	0
Yeading	0	**Southport**	**6**

3rd Round

Team	Score	Team	Score
Ashton United	0	**Cheltenham Town**	**1**
Hayes	2	Bashley	0
Hyde United	0	Dover Athletic	2
Barrow	1	Northwich Victoria	0
Stevenage Boro	1 2	Gloucester City	1 1
Slough Town	1 2	Boreham Wood	1 1
Grantham Town	2	Hednesford Town	1
Altrincham	0	**Southport**	**2**

4th Round

Team	Score	Team	Score
Cheltenham Town	**1**	Hayes	0
Dover Ath	1 *0 +5	Barrow	1 *0 +4
Stevenage Boro	0	Slough Town	1
Grantham Town	1 1	**Southport**	**1 3**

Semi-finals

Team	Score	Team	Score
Cheltenham Tn	**2 2**	Dover Athletic	1 2
Slough Town	0 1	**Southport**	**1 1**

Final

Team	Score	Team	Score
Cheltenham Tn	**1**	**Southport**	**0**

* After extra time
+ Penalties

F.A.

1997-98 REVIEW

Martyn Rogers, *manager of Tiverton Town (left), celebrates with his right hand man* ***Martyn Grimshaw****.* Photo: Roger Turner

FIRST QUALIFYING ROUND

Saturday 6th September 1997

	Home	Score	Away
	Easington Col.	1 v 0	Norton & Stockton Ancients
	Brandon United	0 v 2	Penrith
	Glapwell	1 v 3	Hall Road Rangers
	Oldham Town	3 v 4	Thackley
	Burscough *aet*	2 v 2	Blackpool (Wren) R.
r	*Blackpool M*	*v*	*Burscough*
	Long Eaton Utd	v	Harworth Cl
	(Long Eaton withdrawn – walkover to Harworth Cl)		
	Glossop N End *aet*	2 v 4	Vauxhall GM
	Maltby Main	1 v 2	Arnold Town
‡	Ramsbottom Utd	4 v 5	Chadderton
	St Helens Town	3 v 1	Ossett Town
	Pershore Town *aet*	3 v 4	Wellingborough T.
†	Shifnal Town	0 v 7	Wednesfield
	Barrow Town	1 v 5	Meir KA
	Stapenhill	3 v 2	Gornal Athletic
	Fakenham Town	2 v 0	Holbeach United
§	Braintree Town	6 v 1	Brightlingsea United
	Somersham Town	1 v 6	Warboys Town

	Home	Score	Away	
	Ipswich Wand.	3 v 0	Lowestoft Town	
	Stansted	1 v 2	East Thurrock Utd	
	Biggleswade Town	0 v 1	Beaconsfield SYCOB	
	Chalfont St Peter	4 v 2	Ilford	
	Hertford Town	0 v 3	Flackwell Heath	
	Hornchurch *aet*	4 v 5	Wealdstone	‡
	Hanwell Town *aet*	2 v 2	Harlow Town	
r	*Harlow Town*	*1 v 2*	*Hanwell Town*	
	Saltdean United	2 v 5	Three Bridges	
	Folkestone Invicta	3 v 1	East Preston	*
	Pagham *aet*	2 v 4	Redhill	
	Erith Town *aet*	3 v 5	Farnham Town	
	Mile Oak	1 v 2	Lancing	
	Slade Green	3 v 0	Dorking	
	Christchurch	0 v 2	Sandhurst Town	
	Brockenhurst	1 v 2	Cowes Sports	
	Bodmin Town	v	Bishop Sutton	
	(Bishop Sutton Withdrawn)			
	Odd Down	1 v 0	Torrington	
	Melksham Town	1 v 0	St Blazey	

* *BEST ATTENDANCE* † *LARGEST AWAY VICTORY* ‡ *LARGEST AGGREGATE* § *LARGEST HOME VICTORY*

Barrow Town 1 Meir KA 5 *(First Qualifying Round). Meir striker, Ant Steveaton, rifles in a fierce shot past the onlooking Chris Marsden during the first half at Riverside Park.* Photo: Martin Wray

SECOND QUALIFYING ROUND

Saturday 4th October 1997

	Home	Score	Away
	Easington Colliery	2 v 1	Penrith
	aet		
	Washington	2 v 3	RTM Newcastle
	Shildon	1 v 4	West Allotment Cel.
	Whickham	0 v 2	Stockton
	Northallerton	3 v 2	Morpeth Town
	Ryhope CA	1 v 3	Willington
	aet		
	Horden CW	1 v 2	Jarrow Roofing B. CA
	Billingham Town	3 v 1	Evenwood Town
	Tadcaster Albion	1 v 0	Pickering Town
	Marske United	1 v 1	Consett
	aet		
r	*Consett*	*0 v 3*	*Marske Utd*
	Shotton Com.	0 v 3	Peterlee Newtown
	Harrogate Railway	0 v 5	Ashington
	South Shields	3 v 0	Crook Town
	Eccleshill United	3 v 0	Leek CSOB
	Douglas High School OB	2 v 3	Glasshoughton Welfare
	Hatfield Main	3 v 2	Garforth Town
	Yorkshire Ama.	0 v 3	Borrowash Victoria
	Kidsgrove Athletic	4 v 2	Vauxhall GM
	Poulton Victoria	4 v 1	Selby Town
	Heanor Town	3 v 0	Atherton Collieries
	East Manchester	2 v 2	Cheadle Town
	aet		
r	*Cheadle Town*	*5 v 5*	*E. Manchester*
	E. Manchester won 3-2 after penalties		

	Home	Score	Away
	Armthorpe Wel.	2 v 1	Pontefract Collieries
	Hall Road Rangers	3 v 0	Bacup Borough
	Liversedge	0 v 2	Bootle
	Arnold Town	1 v 0	Maine Road
	Burscough	2 v 0	Salford City
	Louth United	0 v 1	Sheffield
	Parkgate	0 v 2	Castleton Gabriels
	Nettleham	0 v 1	St Helens Town
	Skelmersdale Utd	4 v 2	Hallam
	Brodsworth	4 v 1	Darwen
	Harworth CI	1 v 2	Blidworth MW
	Holker Old Boys	0 v 2	Prescot Cables
	Haslingden	0 v 0	Rossington Main
	aet		
r	*Rossington Main*	*6 v 0*	*Haslingden*
	Chadderton	2 v 0	Rainworth MW
	Grimethorpe MW	1 v 1	Thackley
	aet		
r	*Thackley*	*3 v 2*	*Grimethorpe MW*
	Worsbro B. MW	0 v 2	Rossendale United
	Ossett Albion	2 v 3	Staveley MW
	aet		
	Ford Sports Dav'ty	2 v 1	Oldbury United
	Wellingborough T.	2 v 3	Birstall United
	Oadby Town	3 v 2	Halesowen Harriers
	Worcester Ath.	2 v 1	Dunkirk
	St Andrews	0 v 2	Knypersley Victoria
	Desborough Town	0 v 2	Banbury United
	Stourport Swifts	5 v 0	Cradley Town

***Arundel 0 Windsor & Eton 6** (Second Qualifying Round). Windsor & Eton's Warren Bayliss hits the post with this effort but his side went on to thrash Arundel 6-0.* Photo: Graham Cotterill

	Home	Score	Away
	Sandwell Borough	3 v 3	Meir KA
	aet		
r	*Meir KA*	*2 v 5*	*Sandwell B*
	aet		
	Chasetown	2 v 1	Shirebrook Town
	Kings Heath	1 v 0	Gedling Town
	aet		
	Friar Lane OB	2 v 1	Willenahall Town
	Stewarts & Lloyds	2 v 0	Bolehall Swifts
	(at Corby Town FC)		
	Pelsall Villa	4 v 3	Northampton Spen.
	Tividale	0 v 0	Wednesfield
	aet		
r	*Wednesfield*	*1 v 0*	*Tividale*
	Coleshill Town	1 v 3	Newport Pagnell T.
	Kimberley Town	1 v 2	Rocester
	West Midlands P.	1 v 2	Sandiacre Town
	Walsall Wood	2 v 1	Highgate United
	Lye Town	3 v 2	Long Buckby
	Stratford Town	1 v 0	Ibstock Welfare
	Holwell Sports	0 v 4	Rushall Olympic
	Bloxwich Town	7 v 2	Anstey Nomads
	Westfields	1 v 4	Stapenhill
	Whitton Utd (Bye)		
	(Saffron Walden Town removed from Competition – walkover to Whitton United)		
	Boston Town	3 v 1	Eynesbury Rovers
	Mirrlees Black.	5 v 1	Clacton Town
	Sawbridgeworth T.	2 v 2	Hadleigh United
	aet		
r	*Hadleigh United*	*1 v 2*	*Sawbridgeworth T.*
	Fakenham Town	3 v 0	March Town United
	Stowmarket Town	3 v 3	Great Yarmouth T.
	aet		
	Soham T. Rangers	0 v 1	Warboys Town
	Burnham Ram.	2 v 4	Harwich & Park.
	Maldon Town	2 v 1	Felixstowe Port & T.
	Ely City	2 v 1	Thetford Town
	Basildon United	0 v 0	Newmarket Town
	aet		
r	*Newmarket Town*	*0 v 1*	*Basildon U.*
	Downham Town	1 v 3	St Neots Town

Stratford Town 1 Ibstock Welfare 2 *(Second Qualifying Round). Stratford Town on the attack during their 1-0 victory over Ibstock Welfare.* Photo: Keith Clayton

Hassocks 1 Littlehampton Town 2 *(Second Qualifying Round). Steve Guille, Littlehampton Town (right) attmepts to go around Hassocks' Mark Burnham near the corner flag.* Photo: Roger Turner

	Home	Score	Away
	Stanway Rovers	0 v 3	Sudbury Town
	Gorleston	1 v 2	Sudbury Wanderers
	Watton United	0 v 3	Norwich United
	Brightlingsea Utd	1 v 0	Swaffham Town
	Bourne Town	2 v 1	Haverhill Rovers
	Ipswich Wan.	1 v 2	Tiptree United
	Mildenhall Town	3 v 2	Cornard United
	Needham Market	1 v 3	Witham Town
	Yaxley	0 v 3	Great Wakering Rov.
	Brimsdown Rov.	2 v 2	Milton Keynes
	aet		
r	*Milton Keynes*	*5 v 1*	*Brimsdown Rov*
	East Thurrock Utd	1 v 4	Bowers United
	Hanwell Town	1 v 2	Tring Town
	Potters Bar Town	3 v 0	Potton United
	Ware	3 v 2	Harpenden Town
	Ford United	2 v 1	Bedford Town
	Wootton Blue C.	4 v 1	Tilbury
	Brache Sparta	3 v 0	Chalfont St Peter
	Edgware Town	6 v 0	Kingsbury Town
	Harefield United	1 v 4	Wealdstone
	London Colney	**9 v 0**	**Langford** §
	Aveley	3 v 1	Clapton
	Viking Sports	3 v 4	Welwyn Garden C.
	Hillingdon Bor.	3 v 0	Beaconsfield SYCOB
	Shillington	0 v 2	Waltham Abbey
	aet		
	Wingate & Fin.	2 v 3	Amersham Town
	Leighton Town	3 v 1	Southall
	Hoddesdon Town	4 v 3	Cheshunt
	Royston Town	2 v 2	Barkingside
	aet		
r	*Barkingside*	*3 v 0*	*Royston*
	Brook House	3 v 2	Haringey Borough
	Ruislip Manor	2 v 3	Hemel Hempstead
	Stotfold	2 v 0	Bedford United
	Letchworth	0 v 1	Flackwell Heath
	Godalming & G'd	3 v 2	Ringmer
	Ramsgate	3 v 1	Redhill
	Bracknell Town	0 v 2	East Grinstead
	Whitehawk	2 v 2	Slade Green
	aet		

	Home	Score	Away
	Portfield	2 v 3	Camberley Town
†	Arundel	0 v 6	Windsor & Eton
	Bedfont	2 v 1	Oakwood
	Hassocks	1 v 2	Littlehampton Town
	Southwick	2 v 4	Eastbourne Town
	Ashford T. (Middx)	2 v 2	Corinthian-Casuals
	aet		
r	*Corinthian-Casuals*	*1 v 3*	*Ashford T. (Middx)*
	Horsham (Bye)		
	(Beckenham Town removed from Competition – walkover to Horsham)		
	Langney Sports	1 v 0	Raynes Park Vale
	Lancing	0 v 2	Faversham Town
	Sheppey United	4 v 3	Ash United
	Chatham Town	2 v 1	Selsey
	(at Selsey FC)		
	Corinthian	2 v 1	Merstham
	Deal Town	2 v 1	Thamesmead Town
	Crowborough A.	0 v 4	Egham Town
	Hailsham Town	1 v 1	Croydon Athletic
	aet		
r	*Croydon Athletic*	*1 v 2*	*Hailsham Town*
	Lewes	0 v 5	Chipstead
	Three Bridges	0 v 3	Epsom & Ewell
	Farnham Town	5 v 0	Chichester City
	Canterbury City	3 v 5	Shoreham
	Folkestone Invicta	3 v 2	Cobham
	Tunbridge Wells	3 v 2	Hythe United
	Horsham YMCA	2 v 2	Sidley United
	aet		
r	*Sidley United*	*1 v 1*	*Horsham YMCA*
	aet – Sidley United win 4-3 after penalties		
	Sandhurst Town	1 v 4	Cowes Sports

Home	Score	Away
Didcot Town	1 v 3	North Leigh
aet		
Bicester Town	2 v 1	Stony Stratford T.
Calne Town	2 v 3	Andover
Downton	0 v 1	Gosport Borough
aet		
Totton	3 v 0	Cove
Romsey Town	0 v 1	Hungerford Town
Portsmouth R. N.	2 v 4	Newbury
Whitchurch Utd	0 v 5	Swindon Supermarine
Kintbury Rangers	0 v 2	BAT Sports
Bournemouth	4 v 1	Wantage Town
Eastleigh	4 v 0	Petersfield Town
First Tower Utd	3 v 1	Carterton Town
Backwell United	0 v 1	Bridgwater Town
Devizes Town	2 v 1	Shortwood United
Hallen	2 v 1	Barnstaple Town
Paulton Rovers	2 v 1	Odd Down
Elmore	4 v 1	Warminster Town
Newquay	1 v 2	Chard Town
Bideford	0 v 1	Bridport
Westbury United	2 v 1	Dawlish Town
aet		
Tuffley Rovers	1 v 2	Fairford Town
Almondsbury T.	0 v 2	Endsleigh
Melksham Town	4 v 0	Ilfracombe Town
Keynsham Town	2 v 0	Wellington Town
Welton Rovers	1 v 3	Bodmin Town
Credition United	2 v 6	Porthleven
Minehead	5 v 1	Frome Town
aet		
Brislington	3 v 0	Glastonbury

★ *BEST ATTENDANCE* † *LARGEST AWAY VICTORY* ‡ *LARGEST AGGREGATE* § *LARGEST HOME VICTORY*

Parkgate 0 Castleton Gabriels 2 *(Second Round Qualifying). No. 4, M. Clayton (out of picture), crosses the ball but accidentally scored to put Castleton Gabriels 1-0 ahead at Parkgate in the F.A. Vase Second Qualifying Round. Celebrating is No. 7 M. Heyes, but No. 8 T. Hopey was disappointed with the quality of the cross.* Photo:Bill Wheatcroft

FIRST ROUND PROPER

Saturday 1st November 1997

	Willington	1 v 4	Stockton	Att: 61
	Skelmersdale Utd	0 v 3	West Auckland T.	Att: 125
	South Shields *aet*	2 v 3	Chadderton	Att: 150
	East Manchester	2 v 3	Rossendale United	Att: 80
	Tow Law Town *aet*	2 v 1	St Helens Town	Att: 148
	Tadcaster Albion	1 v 4	Thackley	Att: 109
	Prudhoe Town	1 v 2	Brodsworth	Att: 49
	Poulton Victoria	4 v 2	Ashington	Att: 179
	Prescot Cables	0 v 2	Sheffield	Att: 50
	Murton	3 v 1	Rossington Main	
	Seaham Red Star	1 v 0	Hall Road Rangers	Att: 70
	Jarrow Roofing Bolden CA	2 v 0	Bootle	Att: 22
	Borrowash Victoria	1 v 0	Northallerton	Att: 75
	Easington Colliery *aet*	2 v 4	Burscough	Att: 54
	Glasshoughton Wel.	1 v 2	Billingham Town	Att: 81
	Kidsgrove Athletic *aet*	2 v 2	Rtm Newcastle	Att: 167
r	*Rtm Newcastle*	*0 v 1*	*Kidsgrove Athletic*	Att: 124
	Hebburn *aet*	2 v 2	Chester-Le-Street T.	Att: 157
r	*Chester-Le-Street T.*	*2 v 0*	*Hebburn*	

Banbury 1 Oadby Town 2 *(First Round Proper). Oadby's Richard Walker is closely watched by Banbury skipper Martin Singleton.* Photo: Dennis Nicholson

	Armthorpe Wel.	3 v 2	West Allotment Cel.	Att: 155	
	Billingham Synth.	5 v 1	Eccleshill United	Att: 151	
	Castleton Gabriels	1 v 2	Marske United	Att: 143	
	Hatfield Main	1 v 2	Nantwich Town	Att: 99	
	Peterlee Newtown	4 v 2	Heanor Town	Att: 80	
	Blidworth MW	0 v 8	Boston Town	Att: 37	†
	Kings Heath *aet*	2 v 2	Wednesfield	Att: 61	
r	*Wednesfield*	*4 v 0*	*Kings Heath*	Att: 35	
	Bridgnorth Town	0 v 5	Boldmere St Michaels	Att: 67	
	Stewarts & Lloyds	0 v 3	Rocester	Att: 84	
	Bloxwich Town	2 v 0	Rushall Olympic	Att: 112	
	Sandwell Borough *aet*	0 v 4	Staveley MW	Att: 63	
	Walsall Wood	1 v 2	Worcester Athletico	Att: 55	
	Stratford Town	0 v 2	Birstall United		
	Mirrlees Blackstone	4 v 2	Cogenhoe United	Att: 53	
	Banbury United	1 v 2	Oadby Town	Att: 196	
	Arnold Town	4 v 2	Stapenhill	Att: 123	
	Newcastle Town *aet*	1 v 0	Pelsall Villa	Att: 87	
	Knypersley Victoria	3 v 0	Sandiacre Town	Att: 85	
	Barwell	2 v 0	Ford Sports Daventry	Att: 128	
	Hucknall Town	2 v 0	Chasetown	Att: 162	
	Lye Town	2 v 4	Stourport Swifts	Att: 77	
	Newport Pagnell T.	0 v 4	Friar Lane OB	Att: 94	
	Flackwell Heath	2 v 1	Leighton Town	Att: 113	
	Harwich & Park.	3 v 1	Tring Town	Att: 140	
	London Colney	1 v 2	Brache Sparta	Att: 60	
	Braintree Town	3 v 0	Bury Town	Att: 293	
	Ely City	1 v 2	Wivenhoe Town	Att: 158	
	Concord Rangers	1 v 0	Great Yarmouth T.		
	Woodbridge Town	5 v 1	Southend Manor	Att: 140	
	Whitton United *aet*	1 v 3	Wealdstone	Att: 302	*

	Home	Score	Away	
	Wootton Blue C. *aet*	0 v 1	Edgware Town *Att: 155*	
	Ford United	2 v 3	Sudbury Wanderers *Att: 124*	
	Norwich United	3 v 1	Welwyn Garden C. *Att: 51*	
	Aveley *aet*	4 v 2	St Neots Town *Att: 75*	
	Stotfold *aet*	2 v 0	Maldon Town *Att: 101*	
	Histon	2 v 0	Witham Town *Att: 105*	
	Amersham Town	0 v 7	Halstead Town *Att: 60*	
	Hoddesdon Town *aet*	3 v 5	Bowers United	
	Fakenham Town	1 v 2	Potters Bar Town *Att: 201*	
	Sudbury Town	5 v 1	Bourne Town *Att: 230*	
	Milton Keynes	0 v 3	Great Wakering Rov. *Att: 80*	
	Warboys Town	0 v 1	Basildon United *Att: 120*	
	Hemel Hempstead	3 v 1	Barkingside *Att: 71*	
	Hillingdon Borough *aet*	1 v 1	Ware	
r	*Ware*	*2 v 4*	*Hillingdon Borough* *Att: 90*	
	Tiptree United	0 v 1	Sawbridgeworth T. *Att: 54*	
	Waltham Abbey	2 v 1	Mildenhall Town *Att: 93*	
	East Grinstead T.	0 v 2	Folkestone Invicta *Att: 341*	
	Thatcham Town	3 v 0	Reading Town *Att: 241*	
	Bedfont	1 v 2	Faversham Town *Att: 40*	
	Burnham	1 v 0	Egham Town *Att: 47*	
	Langney Sports	2 v 1	Farnham Town	
	Sidley United	0 v 2	Brook House *Att: 191*	

Ford United 2 Sudbury Wanderers 3 *(First Round Proper). Sudbury keeper, Jason Haygreen, safely holds the ball.*
Photo: Garry Letts

	Home	Score	Away	
	Chatham Town	3 v 1	Hailsham Town *Att: 112*	
	Ashford Town	2 v 1	Sheppey United *Att: 105*	
	Metropolitan Police	3 v 1	North Leigh *Att: 60*	
	Horsham *aet*	0 v 1	Ramsgate *Att: 210*	
	Cowes Sports	5 v 2	Epsom & Ewell *Att: 109*	
	Tunbridge Wells	2 v 4	Wick *Att: 134*	
	Windsor & Eton	0 v 1	Shoreham *Att: 108*	
	Corinthian *aet*	1 v 0	Slade Green *Att: 74*	
	Deal Town	3 v 1	Godalming & Guild. *Att: 190*	
	Bicester Town	2 v 5	Littlehampton Town *Att: 67*	
	Abingdon United	1 v 3	Camberley Town *Att: 85*	
	Eastbourne Town *aet*	1 v 4	Chipstead	
	Bodmin Town	2 v 0	Bournemouth *Att: 159*	
	Chard Town *aet*	1 v 0	First Tower United *Att: 89*	
	Chippenham Town *aet*	1 v 1	Devizes Town *Att: 181*	
r	*Devizes Town*	*0 v 4*	*Chippenham Town* *Att: 139*	
	Melksham Town	4 v 6	Wimborne Town *Att: 192*	‡
	Swindon Super. *aet*	1 v 1	Porthleven *Att: 86*	
r	*Porthleven* *aet*	*2 v 1*	*Swindon Supermarine* *Att: 122*	
	Paulton Rovers	4 v 0	Minehead *Att: 82*	
	Bat Sports *aet*	3 v 2	Hallen *Att: 77*	
	Hungerford Town	2 v 1	Westbury United *Att: 84*	
	Eastleigh	1 v 2	Bridport *Att: 127*	
	Falmouth Town	0 v 1	Bridgwater Town *Att: 290*	
	Brislington	2 v 3	Elmore	
	Bemerton Heath H.	2 v 0	Totton AFC *Att: 62*	
	Endsleigh *aet*	2 v 2	Newbury AFC	
r	*Newbury AFC*	*0 v 1*	*Endsleigh* *Att: 85*	
	Fairford Town	2 v 3	Gosport Borough *Att: 82*	
	Andover	5 v 0	Keynsham Town *Att: 163*	§

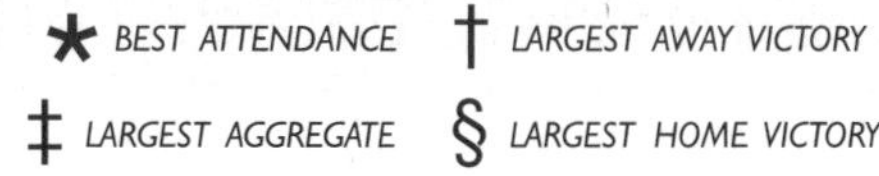

★ BEST ATTENDANCE
† LARGEST AWAY VICTORY
‡ LARGEST AGGREGATE
§ LARGEST HOME VICTORY

SECOND ROUND PROPER

Saturday 22nd November 1997

	Dunston Fed. Brew.	1 v 0	Atherton LR		Att: 112
	Seaham Red Star	2 v 1	Chadderton		Att: 83
	Rossendale United	1 v 2	Tow Law Town		Att: 179
	West Auckland T.	1 v 0	Curzon Ashton		Att: 80
	Armthorpe Welfare	0 v 0	Denaby United	aet	Att: 75
r	*Denaby United*	*1 v 0*	*Armthorpe Welfare*	aet	Att: 120
‡	**North Ferriby Utd**	**7 v 0**	**Murton**		Att: 250
	Peterlee Newtown	1 v 3	Brigg Town		Att: 73
	Warrington Town	0 v 1	Poulton Victoria		Att: 105
	Kidsgrove Athletic	2 v 2	Brodsworth	aet	
r	*Brodsworth*	*0 v 2*	*Kidsgrove Athletic*		Att: 140
	Nantwich Town	1 v 3	Burscough		Att: 56
	Stockton	3 v 1	Sheffield		Att: 78
	Mossley AFC	1 v 1	Jarrow Roofing Boldon CA	aet	
r	*Jarrow Roofing Bol.CA*	*1 v 5*	*Mossley AFC*		Att: 52
	Thackley	6 v 1	Borrowah Victoria		Att: 77
	Chester-Le-Street	4 v 4	Billingham Town	aet	Att: 85
‡ r	***Billingham Town***	***6 v 4***	***Chester-Le-Street***	aet	Att: 38
	Clitheroe	5 v 0	Guisborough Town		Att: 180
	Bedlington Terriers	5 v 0	Billingham Synthonia		Att: 222
	Durham City	0 v 1	Markse United		Att: 216
	Newcastle Town	0 v 1	Birstall United	aet	Att: 138
	Friar Lane OB	1 v 0	Wednesfield		Att: 97
	Boldmere St Mich.	0 v 0	Arnold Town	aet	Att: 112
	Arnold Town	2 v 1	Boldmere St Michaels	aet	Att: 125
	Spalding United	2 v 0	Mirrleess Blackstone		Att: 221
	Barwell	1 v 4	Boston Town		
	Knypersley Victoria	0 v 1	Stamford AFC		Att: 134
	Ely City	1 v 0	Worcester Athletico		Att: 161
	Oadby Town	5 v 1	Norwich United		Att: 153
	Staveley MW	1 v 3	Wroxham		Att: 175
	Bloxwich Town	2 v 1	Diss Town		Att: 114
	Rocester	2 v 2	Histon	aet	Att: 150
r	*Histon*	*1 v 0*	*Rochester*		Att: 204
	Hucknall Town	2 v 1	Stourport Swifts	aet	Att: 200
	Ashford T. (Middx)	5 v 3	Littlehampton T.		Att: 135
	Deal Town	2 v 2	Great Wakering Rov.	aet	Att: 217
r	Great Wakering R.	2 v 1	Deal Town		Att: 175
	Shoreham	2 v 4	Sudbury Town	aet	Att: 188
	Basildon United	3 v 2	Edgware Town		Att: 101

Taunton Town 5 Hungerford Town 1 *(Second Round Proper). Marcus Richardson climbs above Taunton's Paul Thorpe to win an aerial dual in the Second Round tie at Wordsworth Drive.* Photo: Ken Gregory

	Potters Bar Town	4 v 2	Whitstable Town	*Att: 206*
	Faversham Town	1 v 2	Banstead Athletic	
§	Braintree Town	8 v 1	Concord Rangers	*Att: 310*
	Peacehaven & Tel.	1 v 0	Chatham Town	
	Harwich & Park. *aet*	1 v 1	Fokestone Invicta	*Att: 187*
r	*Fokestone Invicta*	*5 v 1*	*Harwich & Parkeston*	*Att: 175*
	Chipstead *aet*	2 v 1	Barking	
	Metropolitan Police	0 v 1	Tooting & Mitcham United	*Att: 115*
†	Hillingdon Borough	1 v 6	Brook House	*Att: 100*
	Hemel Hempstead	3 v 2	Wick	*Att: 91*
	Camberley Town	3 v 0	Corinthian	*Att: 82*
	Brache Sparta	5 v 1	Halstead Town	*Att: 60*
	Sawbridgeworth T.	1 v 5	Stotfold	*Att: 100*
*	Burgess Hill Town	2 v 1	Canvey Island	*Att: 513*
	Sudbury Wanderers	4 v 0	Flackwell Heath	*Att: 162*
	Bowers United	3 v 0	Buckingham Town	*Att: 82*
	Northwood	0 v 2	Woodbridge Town	*Att: 177*
	Arlesey Town	3 v 2	Waltham Abbey	*Att: 135*
	Herne Bay	2 v 0	Langney Sports	*Att: 244*
	Aveley	2 v 2	Burnham	*Att: 47*
r	*Burnham*	*0 v 2*	*Aveley*	
	Ramsgate	0 v 1	Wealdstone	*Att: 217*
	Wimborne Town	3 v 1	Gosport Borough	*Att: 224*
	Elmore	2 v 4	Chard Town	*Att: 74*
	Paulton Rovers	2 v 4	Porthleven	*Att: 209*
	Chippenham Town	3 v 2	Andover	*Att: 190*
	Tiverton Town	5 v 1	Mangotsfield Utd	*Att: 552*
	Bridport	3 v 0	Bridgwater Town	*Att: 194*
	Taunton Town	5 v 1	Hungerford Town	*Att: 333*
	Thatcham Town	2 v 0	Marlow	*Att: 196*
	BAT Sports	1 v 3	Bodmin Town	*Att: 103*
	Lymington AFC *aet*	0 v 0	Bemerton Heath H.	*Att: 112*
r	Bemerton Heath H. *aet*	1 v 2	Lymington AFC	*Att: 47*
	Endsleigh	0 v 2	Cowes Sports	*Att: 91*

* *BEST ATTENDANCE* † *LARGEST AWAY VICTORY* ‡ *LARGEST AGGREGATE* § *LARGEST HOME VICTORY*

Staveley MW 1 Wroxham 3 *(Second Round Proper). Yachtsmen 'keeper Ryan Lemmon makes a fine punched clearance at a misty Staveley MX during the second half.* Photo: Martin Wray

THIRD ROUND PROPER

Saturday 13th December 1997

	Marske United	1 v 2	Bedlington Terriers	Attn: 305
	Stockton	1 v 2	Burscough	Attn: 73
	Mossley	0 v 2	West Auckland T.	Attn: 205
	Poulton Victoria	1 v 4	Kidsgrove Athletic	Attn: 161
	Tow Law Town	2 v 1	Dunston Fed. Brew.	Attn: 171
	Bilingham Town	1 v 0	Friar Lane OB	Attn: 98
	Arnold Town	1 v 3	North Ferriby Utd	Attn: 199
	Clitheroe	3 v 0	Boston Town	Attn: 250
	Oadby Town	4 v 1	Seaham Red Star	Attn: 179
	Brigg Town	1 v 2	Hucknall Town	Attn: 199
	Denaby United	0 v 1	Birstall United	Attn: 85
	Thackley *aet*	2 v 3	Stamford	Attn: 175
	Bloxwich Town	1 v 3	Spalding United	Attn: 119
	Braintree Town	4 v 2	Banstead Athletic	Attn: 302
	Hemel Hempstead	2 v 3	Taunton Town	Attn: 175
	Lymington	2 v 0	Woodbridge Town	Attn: 131
	Bodmin Town *aet*	5 v 3	Bowers United	Attn: 179
*†	**Wimborne Town**	**0 v 4**	**Tiverton Town**	**Attn: 622**
	Basildon United	1 v 3	Herne Bay	Attn: 146
	Cowes Sports *aet*	1 v 1	Chard Town	Attn: 188
r	Chard Town *aet*	0 v 0	Cowes Sports	Attn: 180 *Cowes won 4-1 on Pens*
	Porthleven	3 v 2	Arlesey Town	Attn: 275
†	**Bridport**	**0 v 4**	**Potters Bar T.**	**Attn: 261**
	Folkestone Invicta	2 v 1	Chipstead	Attn: 367
	Brook House *aet*	0 v 0	Histon	Attn: 110
r	Histon	3 v 0	Brook House	Attn: 111
	Peacehaven & Tels.	1 v 2	Sudbury Town	Attn: 261
	Aveley	1 v 2	Wroxham	Attn: 103
	Stotfold	2 v 1	Ashford T.(Midd.)	Attn: 167
	Thatcham Town	0 v 3	Burgess Hill T.	Attn: 252
	Great Wakering R.	2 v 1	Wealdstone	Attn: 304
§‡	**Brache Sparta**	**8 v 1**	**Ely City**	**Attn: 141**
	Chippenham Town	2 v 3	Tooting & M. Utd	Attn: 214
	Camberley Town *aet*	3 v 3	Sudbury Wan.	Attn: 80
r	Sudbury Wand'ers	3 v 1	Camberley Town	Attn: 123

***Peacehaven & Telscombe 1 Sudbury Town 2** (Third Round Proper). Chris Tracey, Sudbury Town's captain, climbs above the Peacehaven & Telescombe defender and heads towards goal.* Photo: Roger Turner

* BEST ATTENDANCE † LARGEST AWAY VICTORY ‡ LARGEST AGGREGATE § LARGEST HOME VICTORY

Hemel Hempsted 2 Taunton Town 3 *(Third Round Proper). Choreography from the lower reaches of the Pyramid.*

Bloxwich Town 1 Splading United 3 *(Third Round Proper). Kestrels 'keeper Gavin Brant makes an excellent block save to clear another Spalding United goal attempt.*

Photo: Martin Wray

FOURTH ROUND PROPER

Saturday 17th January 1998

	Home	Score	Away
	Taunton Town	5 v 2	Herne Bay *Attn: 632*
	Sudbury Wand'ers	3 v 0	Bedlington Terriers *Attn: 481*
	Oadby Town *aet*	2 v 2	Tooting & Mitcham. *Attn: 340*
r	Tooting & Mitcham	1 v 4	Oadby Town *Attn: 238*
	Hucknall Town	2 v 1	Wroxham *Attn: 502*
	Billingham Town	3 v 1	Bodmin Town *Attn: 290*
	Tow Law Town	3 v 0	Histon *Attn:*
	Kidsgrove Athletic *aet*	2 v 2	Brache Sparta *Attn:*
r	Brache Sparta	0v3	Kidsgrove Athletic *Attn: 282*
	Braintree Town *aet*	0 v 0	Lymington *Attn: 585*
r	Lymington	2 v 1	Braintree Town *Attn: 441*
	Stamford *aet*	0 v 1	Potters Bar Town *Attn: 359*
	Cowes Sports *aet*	1 v 1	North Ferriby Utd. *Attn: 592*
r	North Ferriby Utd	3 v 1	Cowes *Attn: 412*
	Sudbury Town *Match Postponed*	PP	Burscough
r	Burscough	1 v 0	Sudbury Town *Attn: 598*
	Tiverton Town	9 v 0	West Auckland T. *Attn: 936*
	Spalding United *aet*	2 v 1	Birstall United *Attn: 439*
	Stotfold	1 v 2	Porthleven *Attn: 626*
	Clitheroe *aet*	0 v 0	Burgess Hill Town *Attn: 430*
r	Burgess Hill Town	3 v 0	Clitheroe * *Attn: 857*
	Grt.Wakering Rvrs.	2 v 1	Folkestone Inv. *Attn: 454*

* *BEST ATTENDANCE*

Burgess Hill 3 Clitheroe 0 *(Fourth Round Proper). Clitheroe player/manager Gary Butcher launches a flying tackle to halt the progress of Hill's Paul Thomsett.* Photo: Andrew Chitty

***Tooting & Mitcham 1 Oadby Town 4** (Fourth Round Proper). Oadby Town's scorer Richard Walker (No. 3) is congratulated by a colleague after scoring Town's third.*
Photo: Peter Lirettoc

***Taunton Town 5 Herne Bay 2** (Fourth Round Proper). Home striker Ian Bastow, scorer of two of his sides goals, powers in a shot during the Fourth Round tie at Wordsworth Drive.*
Photo: Ken Gregory

FIFTH ROUND PROPER

Saturday 7th February 1998

★ Tiverton Town	2 v 1	Oadby Town	*Att: 1197*
Sudbury Wand'ers	1 v 0	Burgess Hill Town	*Att: 479*
Porthleven *aet*	1 v 0	Hucknall Town	*Att: 971*
Sudbury Town	1 v 2	Tow Law Town	*Att: 750*
Kidsgrove Ath.	3 v 2	Lymington	*Att: 540*
Spalding United	2 v 0	Billingham Town (N)	*Att: 743*
North Ferriby Utd	0 v 2	Taunton Town(W)	*Att: 466*
Great Wakering R. *aet*	0 v 1	Potters Bar T.	*Att: 659*

★ *BEST ATTENDANCE*

Sudbury Town 1 Tow Law Town 2 *(Fifth Round Proper). Sudbury Town's keeper, Paul Barber, is unable to stop Tow Law's winning goal by Trevor Laidler in the 89th minute.*

Kidsgrove Athletic 3 A.F.C Lymington 2 *(Fifth Round Proper). 'Larger than life' Linnets 'keeper Wayne Shaw safely gathers the ball following an Athletic corner during the first half at Hollinwood Road.* Photo: Martin Wray

SIXTH ROUND PROPER

Saturday 28th February 1998

	Taunton Town	2 v 0	Porthleven
	Cutler 22,83		*Attn: 1804*
	Spalding United	1 v 2	Tiverton Town
	Keeble 81		*Daly 7,*
	Attn: 2038		*Everett 35*
	Sudbury Wanderers	1 v 1	Tow Law Town
	Day 18		*Hague 90*
	aet		*Attn: 892*
r	Tow Law Town	2 v 0	Subury Wanderers
	Kidsgrove Athletic	2 v 0	Potters Bar Town
	Walklet 110		*aet*
	Dundas 116 (pen)		*Attn: 935*

Sudbury Wanderers' ***Richard Codling*** *just reaches the ball in front of Tow Law Town's Jarrod Suddick.*
Photo: Roger Turner

Kidsgrove Athletic 2 Potters Bar Town 0 *(Sixth Round Proper). Mark Mezan faces Kevin Williams in the sun.*

Referee Mr Baker in perfect position as Porthleven fail to get an equaliser in second half at Taunton. Photo: Eric Marsh

SEMI FINALS

1st Leg – Saturday 14th March 1998

TAUNTON TOWN 4 v 4 TOW LAW TOWN

TAUNTON TOWN

Cutler 5, 45, Thompson 84, West 90
Matthews, Edwards, Crook, Cann, Ewens, Thorpe, Bastow, Cutler, Loram, Joyce, Down.
Substitutes: Thompson for Edwards 61 mins, West for Joyce 63 mins, Fowler for Crook 63 mins

TOW LAW TOWN

Moan 17, Bailey 54, Darwent 63, Laidler 74
Dawson, Pickering, Derwent, Bailey, Hague, Moan, Moorhead, Nelson, Suddick, Laidler, Robinson.
Substitutes: Johnson for Moorhead 51
Att: 1569

TIVERTON TOWN 2 v 0 KIDSGROVE ATHLETIC

TIVERTON TOWN

Everett 26, Daly 74
Edwards, Fallon, Saunders, Tatterton, Smith J, Conning, Nancekivell, Smith K, Everett, Daly, Leonard. Substitutes: Varley for Smith K 79 mins

KIDSGROVE ATHLETIC

Att: 1885
Bentley, Chetwyn, Williams, Mountford, Davies, Kiely, Hobby, Key, Batho, Walklet, Dundas
Substitutes: Mottram for Walklet

2nd Leg – Saturday 21st March 1998

TOW LAW TOWN 1 v 0 TAUNTON TOWN

TOW LAW TOWN

Suddick 78
Aitken, Pickering, Darwent, Bailey, Hague, Moan, Johnson, Nelson, Suddick, Laidler, Robinson. *Substitutes:* Nil

TAUNTON TOWN

Att: 1819
Matthews, Edwards, Fowler, Cann, Ewens, Thorpe, West, Cutler, Loram, Bastow, Down. *Substitutes:* Parker for Bastow 20 mins, Thompson for Cann 47 mins, Lynch for Edwards 82mins

KIDSGROVE ATHLETIC 2 v 1 TIVERTON TOWN

KIDSGROVE ATHLETIC

Walklett 25, Dundas 88 (Pen)
Bentley, Chetwyn, Williams, Mountford, Conclough, Kiely, Hobby, Key, Batho, Walklet, Dundas.
Substitutes: Mottram for Hobby 72 mins
Att: 1903

TIVERTON TOWN

Varley 27
Edwards, Fallon, Saunders, Tatterton, Smith J, Conning, Nancekivell, Varley, Everett, Daly, Leonard.
Substitutes: Smith K. for Nancekivell 72 mins, Rogers for Varley 88 mins

***Tow Law Town 1 Taunton Town 0** (Semi Finals 2nd Leg). Tow Law Town's 'new' goalkeeper Aitken saves from Taunton's Dave Ewens (out of shot).* *Photo:Neil Thaler*

QUALITY QUARTET

With the two Screwfix Direct Western League clubs kept apart in the Semi Final draw there was a very real chance of both South West giants taking part in their own local derby at Wembley.

However, two quality clubs provided the opposition and we were treated to four excellent semi-finals contested bravely and skilfully until the very last seconds.

Suddick The Hero

At Taunton in the first leg, Tow Law Town's goalkeeper, Stuart Dawson, played with an injury and his lack of kicking power let in the competition's topscorer Mark Cutler to score a soft early opening goal.

A quite brilliant header by Glen Moan, to the bottom corner of the net after meeting an accurate free kick on the edge of the penalty area, brought the score level and Tow Law's more controlled football appeared to give them the edge.

However, the home side's raw aggression was rewarded by Mark Cutler, the competition's top scorer, who drove in an unstoppable shot to give them a half-time lead.

The silky skills of Jarrid Suddick inspired some neat passing movements from Tow Law but three goals in a devastating twenty minute spell could hardly have been expected by anyone.

Michael Bailey headed home from a Michael Robinson cross, then Darran Darwent scored after the Taunton 'keeper had parried a shot before Trevor Laidler smashed in what appeared to be a match winning fourth.

Two substitutions and good crowd support lifted Taunton, however, and finally the giant Richard Thompson headed home and then another superb Cutler shot was brilliantly tipped on to the post by Dawson, but second substitute Paul West was on hand jubilantly to knock in an equaliser that sent the home supporters wild.

So how much had been learned? What changes could Russell Musker or Peter Quigley make to break the deadlock between two very good Vase sides?

The two substitutes stayed in for Taunton and indeed the first chances went to the visitors when a Paul Edwards free kick scraped the post and Mark Cutler drove wide.

Tow Law replied with good efforts by Suddick and Laidler but with just three minutes to go before half time goalkeeper Ian Aitken brilliantly saved a Paul Thorpe header.

As at Taunton, Tow Law played down the slope in the second half but the clubs seemed locked together with extra time likely when the killer goal was slotted home by the lively Suddick, the result of a low pulled back cross from the left by Pickering.

With just eleven minutes to go the game became desperate for both sides, but Tow Law held on to emulate last year's Northern League champions Whitby Town by reaching Wembley.

'Tivvy' Return to Wembley

Mobile phones were being used regularly during both semi-finals, especially as the Western supporters were trying to find out how their neighbours were faring.

In the first game at Tiverton a very professional performance by the Western League champions produced a 2-0 victory.

A truly magnificent game of football was a real credit to the competition and both clubs played positively and attacked with both skill and method.

FA CARLSBERG VASE ATTENDANCES '97/'98

	Total Attenance	*Average Attendance*	*Largest Attendance*	
First Qualifying Round	3,471	99	273	Folkestone Invicta
Second Qualifying Round	13,619	80	329	Folkestone Invicta
First Round	11.400	114	341	East Grinstead Town
Second Round	8,730	125	552	Tiverton Town
Third Round	6,811	194	622	Wimborne Town
Fourth Round	9,779	445	936	Tiverton Town
Fifth Round	5,805	725	1,179	Tiverton Town
Sixth Round	6,303	1,240	2,038	Spalding United
Semi-Final	7,176	1,794	1,903	Kidsgrove Athletic
Final	13,139	13,139		Wembley
Total	**86,233**			

Phil Everett and Kevin Smith went close but Richard Batho should really have given the visitors the lead when he swivelled and shot wide at the far post.

Tivvy came back immediately through Everett who kept up his record of scoring in every round by tucking in a neat goal from Steve Daly's cross.

Paul Edwards saved another good Batho effort and half time came with just one goal separating the teams.

Tivvy certainly lifted their game after the interval and the important second goal came after 74 minutes when Mickey Fallon crossed accurately from Daly to power home a header.

The lead was certainly important to preserve as the Kidsgrove class was clearly seen. Indeed, they nearly scored themselves but at the final whistle both sides realised the tie was still very much in the balance.

An excellent cup-tie atmosphere welcomed both sides at Kidsgrove and right from the first whistle the well drilled and very experienced Tiverton rearguard looked in control in open play but were always at risk from set pieces, taken with much skill.

In fact it was from a left wing corner that Craig Walklet opened the tie right up by scoring with a smart header.

A little flurry from Tiverton brought much relief with a quick equaliser. Pete Varley, preferred to veteran goalscorer supreme Kevin Smith, craftily floated a lob in just under the crossbar.

*Tiverton Town's **Phil Everett** (left) wearing his lucky red boots with **Steve Daly.*** Photo: Peter Barnes

***Taunton Town 4 Tow Law Town 4** (Semi Final 1st Leg). Taunton Town's captain Dave Ewens heads the ball away from Darren Darwent with colleague Paul Edwards (2) on hand to clear the loose ball in the semi-final tie at Taunton.*

The game was played at a really hectic pace but, the experience of Pete Conning and Dave Leonard with the attacking bursts of Varley always threatened 'Rovers' if they threw too many players forward.

After half-time Kidsgrove attacked with even more determination and efforts by Kiely and Batho went close.

Giant centre back Jason Smith headed in for Tiverton but the excellent referee Mr. Baines had spotted an infringement, so the tension remained and Rovers fought back.

With two minutes left, a loose ball in the 'Tivvy' box appeared to be cleared but the whistle sounded and the referee had given a penalty to Kidsgrove. Scott Dundas scored his eighth goal of the competition (and fourth penalty) but the visitors held on and their excellent supporters were overjoyed by the realisation that their team had reached another Wembley Final.

So it was Tiverton Town v Tow Law Town, and judging by the semi-finals it promised a quality climax to an excellent competition.

What a pity the two excellent semi-final losers couldn't contest a third place play-off as a curtain raiser at Wembley!

FINAL

Saturday 9th May 1998

TIVERTON TOWN	**1 v 0**	**TOW LAW TOWN**
Peter Varley		*Att: 13,139* **at Wembley Stadium**

	Tiverton Town	Tow Law Town	
1	Edwards	Dawson	1
2	Felton	Pickering	2
3	Saunders	Darwent	3
4	Tatterton	Bailey	4
5	Smith J	Hague	5
6	Conning	Moan	6
7	Nancekivell	Johnson	7
8	Smith K	Nelson	8
9	Everett	Suddick	9
10	Daly	Laidler	10
11	Leonard	Robinson	11

Substitutes
Varley *for Smith K.*
Waters *for Leonard*
Rogers *for Nancekivell*

Substitutes
Bennett *for Laidler*

Referee:
M.A. Riley
(West Riding)

A classical North-South encounter was played in excellent spirit until the last ten minutes and the result was in the balance until the last seconds.

Tiverton Town's fantastic season obviously has bred great confidence but there is always the worry that too much superiority during the season can erode the battling spirit. In `Tivvys' case they produced quality performances in the F.A. Cup and the F.A. Vase thanks to the nice balance of experience and local youngsters.

When the ultimate challenge came at Wembley, Tow Law Town had the advantage of being underdogs but anyone who had seen them knew they were capable of gritty defence, quality football and the inspiration gained from the individual brilliance of Jarrod Suddick. With the game in deadlock, Tivvys' top goalscoring star of recent seasons, Phil Everett, continued to work hard but there was always the thought that he might have preferred the mid winter mud rather than the fine lush grass of Wembley, but he ran and ran.

Record club career goalscorer and captain Kevin Smith had been preferred to the popular Peter Varley as Everett's attacking partner and manager Martyn Rogers was obviously banking on the man who had done so much for him over his glorious years of success.

Kevin had suffered from a series of injuries but his potential was massive. However, the game dragged on and time was running out as the Tiverton supporters calls for Varley grew louder.

To hope for a flash of vintage Smith (which he was to provide twice, to score his 300th goal for the club with brilliant strikes against Taunton Town and Yeovil and win the Les Phillips Western League Cup the following Wednesday for his club), or to bring on younger legs – what was Martyn to do?

Meanwhile Peter Quigley, the Tow Law manager, could sense he had Tivvy worried and the longer the game went on the more successful set piece or flashing shot could keep the Vase in the North East. Young legs got the vote!

On came Peter Varley and within minutes his sharpness in front of goal had created the vital final score and had produced the winner for the West Countrymen.

The last minutes saw Tivvy bring on their two other substitutions and a very silly piece of unprofessional retaliation by Tow Law's Nelson having already been awarded a free kick, meant departure was sad but inevitable and the game came to an end after extra time added on for injuries.

So a fine run by `The Lawyers' had come to an end. On the day they were a credit to the North East and their Arnott Insurance Northern League. In Suddick they had most people's `Man of the Match' but possibly Tiverton's extra Wembley experience and their massive confidence from an unbeaten season in the Screwfix Direct Western League just saw them through.

Both clubs should be thanked for a wonderful day and a fitting climax to a super competition that benefited greatly from the enthusiastic sponsorship of Carlsberg.

"Joy and Despair". The feeling of joy showed by all of the Tiverton Town players and fans mixed here together with the feeling of despair shown by the Tow Law Town players after losing out in the F. A. Carlsberg Final. Photo: Eric Marsh

Sam Gordon, *Tow Law Town. The first mascot allowed at a Wembly Final.*
Photo: Eric Marsh

Jarrod Suddick, *Tow Law Town, and* **Micky Fallon,** *Tiverton Town.*
Photo: Andrew Chitty

***Peter Varley** (Tiverton Town) beats the desperate tackle by the Tow Law Town player to get in a winning strike, which won the Vase for Tiverton Town*
Photo: Colin Stevens

***Peter Varley**, 'Super Sub', comes on for club record goalscorer Kevin Smith to score Tiverton Town's only goal in the Final.*
Photo: Eric Marsh

F.A. VASE - THE "TOP 50"

The 50 Teams with the best overall records in the Vase certainly cover a wide cross-section of the Country. With locations ranging from Tiverton in the south-west to Whickham in the north-east, Newport IoW in the south to Warrington in the north-west there is not one geographical area that is not represented.

The following table is a complete record of every team's performances in the FA Vase since its inception in 1975, and comprises the following records:

S = Seasons played in the competition

P = Total games played in the competition

W = Games won

L = Games lost

% = Percentage of winning games in relation to total games played

Points:	Winner	=	9 points	Finalist	=	8 points
	Semi-final	=	7 points	6th round	=	6 points
	5th round	=	5 points	4th round	=	4 points
	3rd round	=	3 points	2nd round	=	2 points
	1st round	=	1 point			

BP is the team's best performance in the competition and the year it was achieved

x 2 means that the round was reached on two occasions, and so on.

As a general rule, where teams have amalgamated a new record has been started with the new team name or, if the name of one of the teams has been retained, the same name has been used.

The total games played include all games including qualifying and preliminary rounds.

Congratulations to Hungerford Town, who lead the table by a mere one point from Stamford. Other consistent teams in the Top 10 who are playing Vase football at present are Barton Rovers, Buckingham Town, North Ferriby United, Burnham and RTM Newcastle. I anticipate that all these teams will be competing in 1999 with the exception of Stamford who have finally achieved a position in the Doc Martens League. Good luck to them.

The Vase is, by its very nature, a transient competition with, on the one hand leading teams taking part, being successful, and moving on to the Trophy. On the other we have teams suffering relegation and competing in the Vase helps them to regroup and marshall their resources. It can also be the first 'National' competition for ambitious teams as they attempt to make their way up the 'Pyramid'. Taking these factors into account I believe a special mention should be given to the following twelve 'Top 50' teams who ave played in every Vase competition since its inception in 1974: Hungerford Town; Stamford; North Ferriby United; Brigg Town; Friar Lane OB; Harefield United; Banstead Athletic; Arlesey Town; Sheffield; Tunbridge Wells and Hoddesdon Town.

Some other points of interest flagged up by the table include the position of Irthingborough Diamonds at number 9 with 58 points. Before they became one half of Rushden & Diamonds they had a very successful Vase record with a success rate of over 70% and two semi-final appearances. RTM Newcastle's success came when they were named Blue Star. I hear a whisper that this name is to be used again. Will this be a sign of further Vase achievement? Special mention must be made of Billericay Town. In just nine seasons they have amassed 52 points, three wins and a success rate of 86%. Other percentage successes of over 70% are Guiseley 74%; Irthingborough Diamonds 71%; RTM Newcastle 72%; Tiverton Town 72%; Sudbury Town 76%; Collier Row at 74% and Halesowen Town at 77%.

And so to this season. Of last year's semi-finalists all will be eligible again. Will the Tiverton juggernaut roll relentlessly on? Will the Arnott Northern League produce another finalist? All this and more will be revealed come next May.

One thing's for certain. New teams will emerge to challenge the existing order and the fascination of this competition with its infinite variety of leagues, locations and friendships will increase in 1998-99.

F.A. VASE - TOP 50 OVERALL RECORDS

		S	P	W	L	%	Pts	Best
1	Hungerford Town	24	72	48	24	66.67	74	SF x 3
2	Stamford	24	69	46	23	66.67	73	W 80
3	Guiseley	17	63	47	16	74.60	64	W 91
4	Barton Rovers	20	63	43	20	68.25	64	F 78
5	Buckingham Town	20	54	34	20	62.96	64	6th x 2
6	North Ferriby United	24	71	47	24	66.20	61	F 97
7	Burnham	16	46	30	16	65.22	60	SF 83
8	Irthingborough Diamonds	15	53	38	15	71.70	58	SF x 2
9	Hinckley Athletlc	23	60	37	23	61.67	58	5th x 2
10	RTM Newcastle	14	48	35	13	72.92	57	W 78
11	Whickham	18	54	37	17	68.52	56	W 81
12	Wisbech Town	16	48	32	16	66.67	54	SF x 2
13	Brigg Town	24	61	38	23	62.30	53	W 69
14	Billericay Town	9	44	38	6	86.36	52	W x 3
15	Friar Lane Old Boys	24	62	38	24	61.29	52	SF x 2
16	Lincoln United	21	50	29	21	58.00	51	6th 75
17	Halesowen Town	12	45	35	10	77.78	50	W x 2
18	Tlverton Town	17	58	42	16	72.41	50	W 98
19	Harefield United	24	53	29	24	54.72	50	6th 90
20	Sudbury Town	10	43	33	10	76.74	49	F 89
21	Hucknall Town	17	53	36	17	67.92	49	6th 86
22	Bridgnorth Town	22	55	33	22	60.00	48	5th x 2
23	Warrington Town	18	50	32	18	64.00	47	F 87
24	Newport low	18	46	28	18	60.87	47	5th x 2
25	Gresley Rovers	19	53	34	19	64.15	46	F 91
26	Banstead Athletic	24	58	34	24	58.62	46	SF 97
27	Molesey	15	45	30	15	66.67	45	6th 82
28	Paulton Rovers	18	48	30	18	62.50	44	5th 90
29	Almondsbury Town	22	56	34	22	60.71	44	F 79
30	Arlesey Town	24	55	32	23	58.18	44	W 95
31	Newbury Town	20	45	25	20	55.56	44	6th 94
32	Thackley	20	57	37	20	64.91	42	5th 81
33	Guisborough Town	12	34	22	12	64.71	42	F 80
34	Sheffield	24	58	34	24	58.62	42	F 77
35	Rainworth MW	19	45	26	19	57.78	42	F 82
36	Tunbridge Wells	24	56	32	24	57.14	42	4th x 5
37	Wimborne Town	16	46	31	15	67.39	41	W 92
38	Eastwood Hanley	18	45	27	18	60.00	41	5th x 3
39	Diss Town	21	52	31	21	59.62	41	W 94
40	Abingdon Town	17	40	23	17	57.50	41	5th x 3
41	Clitheroe	22	50	28	22	56.00	41	F 96
42	Collier Row	11	43	32	11	74.42	40	SF 87
43	Windsor & Eton	13	42	29	13	69.05	40	SF 81
44	Yate Town	20	52	32	20	61.54	40	5th 92
45	Great Yarmouth Town	18	44	26	18	59.09	40	SF 83
46	Basildon United	19	45	26	19	57.78	40	6th x 2
47	Hallam	23	52	29	23	55.77	40	5th 81
48	Hoddesdon Town	24	50	27	23	54.00	40	W 75
49	Burgess Hill Town	21	55	34	21	61.82	39	5th 98
50	Bracknell Town	20	51	31	20	60.78	39	5th x 20

FA CARLSBERG VASE AT A GLANCE

3rd Round

Bloxwich Town	1
Spalding United	3
Denaby United	0
Birstall United	1
Billingham Town	1
Friar Lane OB	0
Bodmin Town	*5
Bowers United	3
Wimborne Town	0
Tiverton Town	**4**
Mossley	0
West Auckland Tn	2
Oadby Town	4
Seaham Red Star	1
Chippenham Town	2
Tooting & Mitcham	3
Poulton Victoria	1
Kidsgrove Athletic	4
Bracke Sparta	8
Ely City	1
Braintree Town	4
Banstead Athletic	2
AFC Lymington	2
Woodbridge	0
Gt Wakering Rvrs	2
Wealdstone	1
Folkestone Invicta	2
Chipstead	1
Thackley	*2
Stamford	3
Bridport	0
Potters Bar Tn	4
Cowes Sports	1, +0
Chard Town	1, 0
Arnold Town	1
North Ferriby Tn	3
Hemel Hempstead	2
Taunton Town	3
Basildon United	1
Herne Bay	3
Stotfold	2
Ashford T (M'sex)	1
Porthleven	3
Arlesey Town	2
Brigg Town	1
Hucknall Town	2
Aveley	1
Wroxham	2
Bamberley Town	1, 3
Sudbury Wndrs	3, 3*
Marske United	1
Bedlington Terr's	2
Clitheroe	3
Boston Town	0
Thatcham Town	0
Burgess Hill Town	3
Peacehaven & Tels	1
Sudbury Town	2
Stockton	1
Burscough	2
Tow Law Town	**1**
Dunston Fed. B.	1
Brook House	*0, 3
Histon	0, 0

+ Cowes won 4-1 after penalties

4th Round

Spalding United	2
Birstall United	1
Billingham Town	3
Bodmin Town	1
Tiverton Town	**9**
West Auckland Tn	0
Oadby Town	2 4
Tooting & Mitch.	2 1
Kidsgrove Ath.	2 3
Bracke Sparta	2 0
Braintree Town	0 1
AFC Lymington	0 2
Gt Wakering Rvrs	2
Folkestone Invicta	1
Stamford	0
Potters Bar Tn	*1
Cowes Sports	1 1
North Ferriby Tn	1 3
Taunton Town	5
Herne Bay	2
Stotfold	1
Porthleven	2
Hucknall Town	2
Wroxham	1
Sudbury Wndrs	1
Bedlington Terriers	0
Clitheroe	0 0
Burgess Hill Tn	0 3
Sudbury Town	1
Burscough	0
Tow Law Town	**3**
Histon	0

5th Round

Spalding United	2
Billingham Town	0
Tiverton Town	**2**
Oadby Town	1
Kidsgrove Athletic	3
AFC Lymington	2
Gt Wakering Rovers	0
Potters Bar Town	*1
North Ferriby Town	0
Taunton Town	2
Porthleven	*1
Hucknall Town	0
Sudbury Wndrs	1
Burgess Hill Tn	0
Sudbury Town	1
Tow Law Town	**2**

6th Round

Spalding Utd	1
Tiverton Town	**2**
Kidsgrove Ath	*2
Potters Bar Tn	0
Taunton Town	2
Porthleven	0
Sudbury Wndrs	1 0
Tow Law Town	**1 2**

Semi-finals

Tiverton Town	**2 1**
Kidsgrove Ath	0 2
Taunton Town	4 0
Tow Law Town	**4 1**

Final

Tiverton Town	**2 1**
Tow Law Town	**4 1**

THE TIMES FA YOUTH CUP 1997-98

PRELIMINARY ROUND

Home	Score	Away
Lancaster City	0 v 3	Yorkshire Amateur
Wigan Athletic	3 v 2	Billingham Town
Guisborough Town	0 v 0	Hartlepool United
(r) Hartelpool United	3 v 2	Guisborough Town
Farsley Celtic	w/o	Barrow
Carlisle United	w/o	Shotton Comrades
Stocksbridge Pk Steels	1 v 3	Preston North End
Chester City	10 v 1	Runcorn
Scunthorpe United	0 v 0	Lincoln City
(r) Lincoln City	1 v 2	Scunthorpe United
Notts County	0 v 9	Louth United
Hull City	7 v 3	Frickley Athletic
Nantwich Town	0 v 10	Stockport County
Southport	1 v 2	Mansfield Town
Warrington Town	2 v 2	Chadderton
(r) Chadderton	2 v 2*	Warrington Town
Warrington Town won 5-3 on kicks from the penalty mark		
Ilkeston Town	2 v 2	Morecambe
(r) Morecambe	1 v 3*	Ilkeston Town
Halifax Town	4 v 4	Denaby United
(r) Denaby United	3 v 0	Halifax Town
Atherton LR	5 v 0	Leigh RMI
Doncaster Rovers	4 v 0	Ashton United
Curzon Ashton	0 v 9	Rochdale
Kidderminster Harriers	4 v 0	Chasetown
Birstall United	3 v 2	Lye Town
Redditch United	1 v 3	Bromsgrove Rovers
Pershore Town	2 v 2	Racing Club Warwick
(r) Racing Club Warwick	1 v 2	Pershore Town
Ibstock Welfare	0 v 2	Halesowen Town
Bedworth United	4 v 2	Rothwell Town
Hinckley Town	4 v 1	Banbury United
Gresley Rovers	7 v 0	Willenhall Town
Somersham Town	3 v 0	VS Rugby
Westfields	2 v 5	Histon
Eynesbury Rovers	0 v 10	Wednesfield
Cambridge United	8 v 1	Solihull Borough
Harlow Town	2 v 1	Sudbury Town
Gorleston	4 v 7	Wivenhoe Town
Basildon United	3 v 2	Fakenham Town
Felixstowe Port & Town	0 v 2	Ipswich Wanderers
Walton & Hersham	10 v 0	Royston Town
Chesham United	4 v 2	Bedfont
Ruislip Manor	0 v 7	Wembley
Barnet	4 v 1	Hillingdon Borough
Chelmsford City	5 v 2	Boreham Wood
Kingsbury Town	0 v 4	Wingate & Finchley
Hayes	2 v 3	Bedford Town
Marlow	4 v 2	Hampton
Waltham Abbey	2 v 3	Cheshunt
Stevenage Borough	10 v 0	Arlesey Town
East Thurrock United	4 v 2	Purfleet
Leyton Sports	3 v 5	Concord Rangers
Hendon	4 v 3	Northwood
Tilbury	1 v 1	Stanway Rovers
(r) Stanway Rovers	2 v 1	Tilbury
Dartford	w/o	Harefield United
Thamesmead Town	w/o	Baldock Town
Welwyn Garden City	3 v 3	Yeading
(r) Yeading	5 v 0	Welwyn Garden City
Corinthian	1 v 3	Tonbridge
Herne Bay	5 v 1	Ashford Town (Middx)
Carshalton Athletic	0 v 3	Camberley Town
Farnborough Town	0 v 6	Sittingbourne
Croydon	5 v 1	Faversham Town
Whitstable Town	1 v 5	Chipstead
Kingstonian	1 v 0	Chatham Town
Bromley	3 v 2	Hastings Town
Chichester City	6 v 2	Hythe United
Redhill	0 v 3	Dover Athletic
Ringmer	0 v 9	Folkestone Invicta
Eastbourne Town	7 v 0	Raynes Park Vale
Crawley Town	1 v 0	Portfield
Aldershot Town	1 v 0	Reading Town
Merstham	2 v 1	Basingstoke Town
Fisher Athletic	3 v 0	Leatherhead
Wokingham Town	7 v 3	Dorking
Egham Town	0 v 4	Tooting & Mitcham Utd
Carterton Town	2 v 3	Newbury AFC
Bashley	2 v 3	Romsey Town
Abingdon Town	w/o	Havant Town
Thame United	3 v 1	Weymouth
Oxford City	3 v 1	Eastleigh
Warminster Town	1 v 1	Salisbury City
(r) Salisbury City	2 v 3	Warminster Town
Cinderford Town	2 v 3	Cheltenham Town
Mangotsfield United	1 v 2	Yeovil Town
Forest Green Rovers	0 v 0	Gloucester City
(r) Gloucester City	2 v 1*	Forest Green Rovers
Yate Town	1 v 3	Cirencester Town

* after extra time

FIRST ROUND QUALIFYING

Home	Score	Away
Wigan	2 v 1	Darlington
Scarborough	7 v 1	Farsley Celtic
Hartlepool United	4 v 1	Harrogate Town
Yorkshire Amateur	0 v 4	Carlisle United
Chester City	2 v 1	Barnsley
Northwich Victoria	0 v 5	Notts County
Scunthorpe United	5 v 1	Marine
Preston North End	1 v 0	Sheffield Wednesday
Stockport County	0 v 3	Chesterfield
Stalybridge Celtic	0 v 7	Warrington Town
Mansfield Town	7 v 2	Worksop Town
Hull City	11 v 1	Cheadle Town
Brigg Town	w/o	Denaby United
Emley	1 v 3	Doncaster Rovers
Atherton LR	0 v 2	Bamber Bridge
Ilkeston Town	2 v 1	Rochdale
Kidderminster Harriers	3 v 1	Gornal Athletic
Northampton Spencer	0 v 2	Bromsgrove Rovers
Birstall United	0 v 3	Bilston Town
Walsall Wood	0 v 5	Burton Albion
Halesowen Town	0 v 0	Atherstone United
(r) Atherstone United	0 v 2	Halesowen Town
Holwell Sports	0 v 4	Hinckley United
Bedworth United	4 v 0	Stourbridge
Pershore Town	0 v 4	Gresley Rovers
Histon	7 v 2	Tividale
Cambridge United	5 v 0	Cradley Town
Wednesfield	0 v 2	Cambridge City
Somersham Town	1 v 0	Tamworth
Wivenhoe Town	3 v 3	Maldon Town
(r) Maldon Town	0 v 4	Wivenhoe Town
Great Wakering Rovers	4 v 0	Ipswich Wanderers
Basildon United	2 v 4	Kings Lynn
Harlow Town	3 v 1	Braintree Town
Chesham United	0 v 2	Hornchurch
Staines Town	5 v 3	Barnet
Wembley	4 v 0	Beaconsfield SYCOB
Walton & Hersham	8 v 0	Leighton Town
Wingate & Finchley	2 v 3	Romford
Hitchin Town	5 v 1	Marlow
Bedford Town	2 v 0	Hemel Hempstead
Chelmsford City	5 v 1	Cheshunt
East Thurrock United	2 v 0	Uxbridge
(r) East Thurrock United	2 v 1	Uxbridge
Grays Athletic	1 v 0	Hendon
Concord Rangers	3 v 5	Hoddesdon Town
Stevenage Borough	6 v 1	Potters Bar Town
Dartford	1 v 0	Bishop's Stortford
St Albans City	1 v 1	Yeading
(r) Yeading	1 v 4	St Albans City
Thamesmead Town	1 v 3	Erith & Belvedere
Stanway Rovers	1 v 0	Southend Manor
Herne Bay	1 v 2	Sutton United
Southwick	0 v 3	Sittingbourne
Camberley Town	3 v 1	Bracknell Town
Tonbridge	0 v 5	Welling United
Chipstead	5 v 1	Margate
Banstead Athletic	1 v 2	Bromley
Kingstonian	0 v 0	Burgess Hill Town
(r) Burgess Hill Town	2 v 1	Kingstonian
Croydon	2 v 1	Horsham
Dover Athletic	5 v 0	Whitehawk
Horsham YMCA	0 v 7	Eastbourne Town
Folkestone Invicta	0 v 2	Three Bridges
Chichester City	1 v 3	Crawley Town
Merstham	4 v 2	Whyteleafe
Maidenhead United	3 v 0	Wokingham Town
Fisher Athletic	4 v 2	Saltdean United
Aldershot Town	1 v 3	Tooting & Mitcham Utd
Romsey Town	0 v 3	Fareham Town
Thatcham Town	4 v 2	Thame United
Abingdon Town	7 v 2	Witney Town
Newbury AFC	1 v 3	Oxford City
Cheltenham Town	4 v 0	Odd Down
Paulton Rovers	0 v 5	Gloucester City
Yeovil Town	2 v 1	Chippenham Town
Warminster	0 v 14	Cirencester Town

SECOND QUALIFYING ROUND

Hartlepool United 4 v 1 Wigan Athletic
Scarborough 3 v 2 Carlisle United
Scunthorpe United 1 v 2 Chester City
Notts County 2 v 1 Preston North End
Mansfield Town 2 v 1 Chesterfield
Warrington Town 0 v 8 Hull City
Bamber Bridge 4 v 0 Brigg Town
Doncaster Rovers 2 v 1 Ilkeston Town
Bilston Town 1 v 2 Kidderminster Harriers
Bromsgrove Rovers 1 v 1 Burton Albion
(r) Burton Albion 3 v 2 Bromsgrove Rovers
Bedworth United 2 v 1 Halesowen Town
Hinckley United 5 v 0 Gresley Rovers
Cambridge City 2 v 3 Histon
Cambridge United 2 v 3 Somersham Town
Kings Lynn 5 v 1 Wivenhoe Town
Great Wakering Rovers 2 v 2 Harlow Town
(r) Harlow Town 0 v 2 Great Wakering Rovers
Wembley 2 v 2 Hornchurch
Hornchurch 1 v 2* Wembley
Staines Town 0 v 0 Walton & Hersham
(r) Walton & Hersham 2 v 1 Staines Town
Bedford Town 3 v 1 Romford
Hitchin Town 2 v 4 Chelmsford City
Hoddesdon Town 5 v 1 East Thurrock United
Grays Athletic 1 v 3 Stevenage Borough
Erith & Belvedere 3 v 1 Dartford
St Albans City 2 v 1 Stanway Rovers
Camberley Town 1 v 1 Sutton United
(r) Sutton United 2 v Camberley Town
Sittingbourne 1 v 1 Welling United
(r) Welling United 2 v 1 Sittingbourne
Burgess Hill Town 0 v 1 Chipstead
Bromley 1 v 2 Croydon
Three Bridges 1 v 0 Dover Athletic
Eastbourne Town 0 v 2 Crawley Town
Fisher Athletic 2 v 2 Merstham
Merstham 2 v 2* Fisher Athletic
Merstham won 5-4 on kicks from the penalty mark
Maidenhead United 1 v 3 Tooting & Mitcham Utd
Abingdon Town 6 v 1 Fareham Town
Thatcham Town 1 v 3 Oxford City
Yeovil Town 1 v 1 Cheltenham Town
(r) Cheltenham Town 3 v 1 Yeovil Town
Gloucester City 2 v 0 Cirencester Town

FIRST ROUND PROPER

Shrewsbury Town 5 v 1 Boldmere St Michaels
Rotherham United 0 v 1 Bury
Bradford City 9 v 0 Nuneaton Borough
Bolton Wanderers 1 v 2 Scarborough
Stoke City 3 v 0 Wolverhampton Wndrs
Burton Albion 3 v 1 Bedworth United
Burnley 2 v 0 Wrexham
Peterborough United 2 v 1 Doncaster Rovers
Grimsby Town 0 v 1 Leicester City
Walsall 4 v 4 Port Vale
(r) Port Vale 1 v 2 Walsall
Derby County 0 v 2 Blackpool
Newcastle United 0 v 1 Hull City
Birmingham City 1 v 2 Crewe Alexandra
Hudderfield Town 1 v 2 York City
Aston Villa 2 v 4 Notts County
Enfield 5 v 1 Stevenage Borough
Torquay United 3 v 3 Leyton Orient
(r) Leyton Orient 0 v 4 Torquay United
Reading 3 v 2 Oxford United
Tooting & Mitcham Utd 0 v 2 Erith & Belvedere
Crawley Town 2 v 5 Great Wakering Rovers
Welling United 2 v 2 Dulwich Hamlet
(r) Dulwich Hamlet 0 v 1 Welling United
Bournemouth AFC 0 v 3 Gillingham
Exeter City 4 v 2 Colchester United
Gloucester City 0 v 6 Southampton
Histon 3 v 2 Gravesend & Northfleet
Chipstead 0 v 9 Chelsea
Plymouth Argyle 4 v 2 Hereford United
Croydon Athletic 2 v 5 Northampton Town
Woking 3 v 3 Brighton & Hove Albion
(r) Brighton & Hove Alb 1 v 3 Woking
Wycombe Wanderers 2 v 1 Cardiff City
Fulham 3 v 1 Abingdon Town
Swindon Town 1 v 1 Bristol Rovers
(r) Bristol Rovers 0 v 0* Swindon Town
Bristol Rovers won 10-9 on kicks from the penalty mark
Swansea City 3 v 2 Bedford Town
Walton & Hersham 0 v 3 Rushden & Diamonds

SECOND ROUND PROPER

Burton Albion 0 v 5 Nottingham Forest
Blackpool 0 v 1 Everton
Leicester City 2 v 3 Liverpool
Bury 0 v 2 Peterborough United
Notts County 2 v 1 Walsall
Bradford City 2 v 1 Scarborough
Shreswbury Town 1 v 2 Stoke City
Sheffield United 3 v 3 Tranmere Rovers
(r) Tranmere Rovers 5 v 3 Sheffield United
Sunderland 1 v 2 Crewe Alexandra
Leeds United 3 v 2 Oldham Athletic
York City 0 v 1 Middlesbrough
West Bromwich Albion 1 v 1 Manchester City
(r) Manchester City 3 v 2 West Bromwich Albion
Hull City 1 v 0 Burnley
Blackburn Rovers 1 v 1 Manchester United
(r) Manchester United 2 v 3* Blackburn Rovers
Rushden & Diamonds 1 v 6 Charlton Athletic
Southampton 6 v 0 Histon
West Ham United 2 v 0 Millwall
Torquay United 0 v 3 Bristol City
Watford 6 v 3 Northampton Town
Norwich City 0 v 0 Crystal Palace
(r) Crystal Palace 2 v 1 Norwich City
Enfield 0 v 1 Bristol Rovers
Chelsea 2 v 2 Wimbledon
(r) Wimbledon 1 v 3 Chelsea
Portsmouth 5 v 0 Erith & Belvedere
Ipswich Town 4 v 0 Great Wakering Rovers
Swansea 2 v 2 Brentford
(r) Brentford 0 v 1 Swansea City
Exeter City 1 v 1 Arsenal
(r) Arsenal 1 v 0 Exeter City
Queens Park Rangers 3 v 2 Southend United
Tottehnham Hotspur 1 v 0 Reading
Coventry City 0 v 4 Luton Town
Plymouth Argyle 0 v 3 Fulham
Wycombe Wanderers 2 v 0 Welling United
Woking 1 v 2 Gillingham

THIRD ROUND PROPER

Watford 2 v 0 Fulham
Middlesbrough 3 v 2 Charlton Athletic
Liverpool 1 v 2 Queens Park Rangers
West Ham United 1 v 4 Blackburn Rovers
Leeds United 3 v 1 Crystal Palace
Everton 1 v 0 Stoke City
Tranmere Rovers 2 v 5 Chelsea
Portsmouth 2 v 0 Gillingham
Southampton 3 v 0 Nottingham Forest
Ipswich Town 2 v 1 Bradford City
Peterborough United 2 v 0 Wycombe Wanderers
Hull City 3 v 1 Bristol Rovers
Bristol City 2 v 0 Swansea City
Luton Town 2 v 2 Tottehnham Hotspur
(r) Tottenham Hotspur 4 v 2 Luton Town
Notts County 1 v 6 Arsenal
Crewe Alexandra 2 v 0 Manchester City

FIFTH ROUND PROPER

Everton v Ipswich Town
Chelsea v Blackburn Rovers
Peterborough United v Crewe Alexandra
Arsenal v Leeds United

SEMI FINALS

Everton 2 v 1 Leeds United
Leeds United 0 v 1 Everton
(Everton won 3-1 on aggregate)

Blackburn Rovers 1 v 0 Peterborough United
Peterborough United 0 v 1 Blackburn Rovers
(Blackburn Rovers won 2-0 on aggregate)

FINAL

Blackburn Rovers 1 v 3 Everton
Everton 2 v 2 Blackburn Rovers
Everton won 5-3 on aggregate

FA SUNDAY CUP 1997-98

FIRST ROUND

Lion & Unicorn	1 v 4	Rob Roy
Albion Sports	0 v 4	Boulevard M. Force
Hartlepool Rovers	6 v 1	Seymour
BRNESC	2 v 1	Caldway
Bulford	1 v 3	Harltepool S'cliffe Htl
Allerton	3 v 0	Baildon Junction Ath
Britannia	0 v 2	Tanhouse Upholland L
Clubmoor Nalgo	1 v 0	Packaging DKS
Hudsons	5 v 3	Shankhouse Utd
Littlewoods Athletic	2 v 1	Nicosia
Humbledons Plain Fm	0 v 2	Salerno
Lobster	3 v 2	Mainstay
Newfield	2 v 2*	Queens Park
(r) Queens Park	3 v 0	Newfield
Bolton Woods	1 v 1*	Manfast
(r) Manfast	1 v 4	Bolton Woods
Grosvenor Park	0 v 2	Sandon
Birmingham Celtic	2 v 1	Cheadle United
Rovers Sports	w/0	Tuddenham Rovers
Sawston Keys	3 v 4*	Salde Celtic
Melton Youth Old Boys	0 v 2	Olympic Star
Hundred Acre	0 v 1	Mackadown Ln S&S
Lodge Cottrell	4 v 2	Sandwell
Heathfield	4 v 1	Leicester City Bus
Ford Basildon	1 v 3	Holderness United
Broad Plain House	2 v 3	Cobham
Fryerns	3 v 2	Winter Royals
BRSC Aidan	2 v 0	Duke of York
Mailcoach	1 v 1*	Pitsea
(r) Pitsea	6 v 1	Mailcoach
Continental	2 v 1	Golden Bottle
Northampton St Marg.	1 v 3	Ouzavich
Caversham Pk Village	3 v 5*	Hanham Sunday
Luton OB (Sunday)	0 v 0*	Theale (Sunday)
(r) Theale (Sunday)	3 v 2	Luton OB (Sunday)
Lebeq Tavern	w/o	Lomax Chestnuts
New Inn Keynsham	2 v 5	St Josephs (Luton)
Belstone	3 v 1	Courage
St Josephs (Bristol)	0 v 2	St Josephs (S Oxhey)
Northfield Rangers	2 v 0	Oxford Road Social
Kendall Albion	3 v 2	The Cutters Friday
Old Oak	2 v 1	Reading Borough
Active Signs	w/o	Shenley Hotel
Chequers	3 v 0	Gossoms End
Greenacres	4 v 1*	Watford Labour
Italia Wasteels	0 v 2	Morden Nomads

* after extra time

15 Exemptions:

Bournemouth Electric	Hartlepool Lion Hotel
Capel Plough	Marston Sports
Celtic SC (Luton)	Northwood
Clifton Albion	Oakwood Sports
Eden Vale	Park Inn
Forest Athletic	Stanley Road
Hammer	Warriors
	A3

7 byes:

Blyth Comrades Social	Arras
Brookvale Athletic	Bournemouth
Crown	Coach & Horses
	East Bowling Unity

SECOND ROUND

Hartlepool Rovers	1 v 3	Boulevard Mode Fce
Rob Roy	3 v 0	Hudsons
Eden Vale	5 v 1	Blyth Comrades Soc.
Tanhouse Upholland L	4 v 1	Allerton
Northwood	0 v 2	Queens Park
Bolton Woods	8 v 0	BRNESC
East Bowling Unity	4 v 2	Clubmoor Nalgo
Crown	3 v 1	H'pool Staincliffe H
Lobster	0 v 3*	H'pool Lion Hotel
A3	3 v 2	Stanley Road
Rovers Sports	3 v 0	Littlewoods Athletic
Birmingham-Celtic	2 v 3	Sandon
Mackadown Ln S&S	0 v 2	Salerno
Park Inn	2 v 0	Slade Celtic
Chequers	0 v 1	Olympic Star
Hanham Sunday	1 v 2	Marston Sports
Theale	0 v 4	Brookvale Athletic
Ouzavich	1 v 1*	BRSC Aidan
(r) BRSC Aidan	2 v 1	Ouzavich
Cobham	3 v 5	Lodge Cottrell
Holderness United	1 v 4*	Heathfield
Lebeq Tavern	1 v 0	Fryerns
Continental	2 v 4	Pitsea
Old Oak	0 v 5	St Josephs (Luton)
St Josephs (Oxhey)	3 v 0	Belstone
Greenacres	1 v 2	Northfield Rangers
Active Signs	6 v 0	Kendall Albion
Capel Plough	2 v 4	Arras
Coach & Horses	4 v 2*	Bournemouth
Forest Athletic	3 v 2	Bournemouth Electric
Clifton Albion	0 v 1+	Celtic SC (Luton)
Morden Nomads	3 v 0	Hammer
Warriors	5 v 0	Oakwood Sports

+ tie awarded to Clifton Albion. Celtic SC played ineligible player

THIRD ROUND

Salerno	1 v 0	Queens Park AFC
Bolton Woods	2 v 0	Rob Roy
Crown	2 v 1	Tanhouse Upholland L
Park Inn	0 v 3	Hartlepool Lion Hotel
A3	1 v 3	Sandon
Rovers Sports	3 v 1	East Bowling Unity
Eden Vale	1 v 0	Boulevard Mode Fce
Lebeq Tavern	1 v 3	Marston Sports
St Josephs (Luton)	4 v 0	Lodge Cottrell
Forest Athletic	4 v 1	Clifton Albion
BRSC Aidan	1 v 3	Olympic Star
St Josephs (S Oxhey)	2 v 6	Pitsea
Warriors	5 v 6*	Active Signs
Brookvale Athletic	4 v 0	Arras
Northfield Rangers	0 v 1	Morden Nomads
Heathfield	4 v 0	Coach & Horses

FOURTH ROUND

Hartlepool Lion Hotel	0 v 1	Olympic Star
Sandon	0 v 2	Bolton Woods
Crown	2 v 5*	Eden Vale
Rovers Sports	0 v 1	Salerno
Pitsea	2 v 0	Heathfield
Active Signs	2 v 4	Forest Athletic
Marston Sports	0 v 0*	Morden Nomads
(r) Morden Nomads	1 v 4	Marston Sports
Brookvale Athletic	1 v 3	St Josephs (Luton)

FIFTH ROUND

Eden Vale	2 v 1	Salerno
Bolton Woods	1 v 2	Olympic Star
Marston Sports	1 v 2	St Josephs (Luton)
Forest Athletic	1 v 6	Pitsea

SEMI FINALS

Eden Vale 1 v 2 St Josephs (Luton)
at Kidderminster Harriers FC, Att: 394

Olympic Star 3 v 1 Pitsea
at Rushden & Diamonds FC, Att: 300

FINAL

Olympic Star 1 v 1* St Josephs (Luton)
Olympic Star won 5-3 on kicks from the penalty mark

SEMI-PROFESSIONAL REPRESENTATIVE FOOTBALL

John Owens Takes Over

It was welcome John Owens, the ex-Altrincham centre half who had been looking after the England Under 15 schools side including Michael Owen, and farewell and good luck to Ron Reid who had left the England Semi-Professional manager's job to be the full time assistant manager to Neil Warnock at Oldham Athletic.

However, a squad was brought together after all senior clubs had been watched and the result was encouraging as you will read.

Most of the following reports and reviews were first published in Team Talk our monthly magazine that attempts to give the England team the publicity it deserves.

Sadly John could only look forward to one friendly international match with two FA XI's in two days just before Christmas and two of the less useful FA XI fixtures in mid winter. The usefulness of three games against the major feeder leagues lay in the fact that players on both sides were potential England players whereas the Combined Services (which was cancelled) and the British Universities were not full scale trials.

But once again may I ask in near desperation, when can our England Semi-Professional International Squad (who represent at least 95 percent of our nation's football) be treated with the respect that the full, Under 21, Youth at all levels, Schools at all levels and England's womens teams receive? One competitive tournament would be a start!

John Owens
Photo: Andrew Chitty

F.A. XI 5 Unibond League 0

On his first day in charge of an FA XI, new England Semi-Professional International squad manager John Owens had the pleasure of watching his selection of mostly Vauxhall Conference players from the Northern clubs emphatically defeat The Unibond League 5-0 at Leigh.

Both squads suffered last minute changes with Barrow pulling their two representatives out of the league line up and Stalybridge Celtic also withdrawing two from the FA XI.

Last season saw the league's first defeat for seven years but right from the kick off in this year's encounter the slick movement and sure passing of the Conference players always appeared to give the FA more time to develop their attacks. On form striker Geoff Horsfield struck up a good partnership with Paul Tait and the slick promptings of Brian Healey, Steve Walters and Paul Proudlock soon created chances and it was no surprise when Tait was sent clear to open the scoring after 25 minutes.

Another excellent passing movement saw Horsfield through to score, again down the middle and then the best move of the half sent the overlapping Andy Farley free to cut in and give the FA a 3-0 half time lead.

This pleased the noisy Southport supporters who also appreciated the fact that their goalkeeeper, Billy Stewart, was captain for the first half but he made way for Dean Greygoose at the interval.

The lively Mark Bradshaw, and goalscorers Tait and Farley were also substituted for Darren Vicary, Ian Monk and Mark Ceroalo.

The lovely Hilton Park surface was now livened up by heavy rain but the new formation for the FA looked no less impressive as Vicary and Ceroalo celebrated their inclusion with excellent second half goals and Ian Monk thoroughly enjoyed himself down the right flank.

Sadly, Steve Walters, another of the game's successes, left the field with an ankle injury near the end but many reputations were enhanced and John Owens was certainly pleased.

For Roly Howard's Unibond side, which suffered from seven late changes, Boston United's free scoring Leroy Chambers never gave up the battle with Tim Ryan, while Paul Ellender defended stoutly and Neil Hardy worked hard.

The 5-0 scoreline was the largest of the series so far but the sparse crowd enjoyed the entertainment and the excellent social facilities being developed by Leigh RMI in conjunction with their Rugby League partners made the stadium impressive to all in attendance.

Unibond League:
Dave Felgate (Leigh RMI), Sub: Simon Marsh (Chorley) 68 mins, Jason Gallagher (Hyde United), Chris Withe (Boston United), Paul Ellender (Gainsborough Trinity), Sub: Andy Draper (Marine) 68 mins, Greg Fee (Boston United), Dave Ridings (Leigh RMI), Paul McNally (Runcorn), Neil Hardy (Altrincham), Kevin Riley (Gainsborough Trinity) Sub: John Morgan (Marine) 80 mins, Leroy Chambers(Boston United), Tony Rodwell (Marine) Sub: Mark Schofield (Leigh RMI) 60 mins.

FA XI
Billy Stewart (Southport), Sub: Dean Greygoose (Northwich Victoria) 45 mins, Andy Farley (Southport), Sub: Ian Monk (Morecambe) 45 mins, Mark Bradshaw (Halifax Town), Sub: Darren Vicary (Northwich Victoria) 45 mins, Wes Simpson (Northwich Victoria), Dave Higgins (Barrow), Tim Ryan (Southport), Paul Proudlock (Gateshead), Brian Healey (Morecambe), Paul Tait (Northwich Victoria), Sub: Mark Ceroalo (Morecambe), Geoff Horsfield (Halifax Town), Steve Walters (Northwich Victoria).

FA XI 2 Dr. Martens League 1

(Greenman & Stott) (Shepherd)

at Gloucester

The FA XI beat the Dr. Martens League 2-1 after Martin Shepherd had given the League side the lead. A strong wind caused both sides difficulties but after initial pressure the quality of the Conference players in the FA XI gradually wore the opposition down. The experience of the England Internationals Paul Webb and Steve Stott in midfield took a stranglehold on the game and eventually an own goal by Greenman and a neat winner from Stott gave the FA a deserved victory.

Neil Grayson and Dale Watkins looked lively up front for the FA with both 'keepers looking confident despite the wind, while League players to shine were Ryan Cross, Lee Hornby, Gerald Murphy and Martin Shepherd.

FA XI

Tony Pennock (Yeovil Town) - Sub: Steve Book (Cheltenham Town), Chris Banks(Cheltenham Town), Jamie Victory (Cheltenham Town), Rob Cousins (Yeovil Town), Paul Webb (Kidderminster Harriers), Mark Yate (Kidderminster Harriers), Jamie Piman (Hereford United), Lee Howells (Cheltenham Town), Jason Eaton (Cheltenham Town) - Sub:Neil Grayson (Hereford United), Dale Watkins (Cheltenham Town), Steve Stott (Yeovil Town)

Dr. Martens XI:

Mark Blount (Burton Albion), Chris Burns (Gloucester City) - Sub: Danny Simmonds (Hastings Town), Simon Cooper (Gloucester City) - Sub: Martin Matthews (King'sLynn), Ryan Cross (Dorchester Town), Allan Davies (Burton Albion), Chris Greenman (Worcester City), James Hollman (King's Lynn), Les Hornby (Burton Albion), Paul Hunt (Forest Green Rovers), Lee Middleton (Atherstone United) - Sub: Mark Harrington (Bath City), Gerald Murphy (Gresley Rovers) - Sub: Michael Wyatt (Bath City), Martin Shepherd (Dorchester Town) - Sub: Matthew Coupe (Forest Green Rovers), Danny Simmonds (Hastings Town)

FA XI v Dr Martens
Back Row (L-R): Steve Stott, Tony Pennock, Lee Howells, Steve Book, Mark Yates, Neil Grayson, John Owens
Front Row (L-R): Chris Banks, Dale Watkins, Jason Eaton, Paul Webb (captain), Jamie Pitman, Rob Cousins, Jamie Victory

FA XI 1 British Universities 2

Morton House, Wilson

(At Durham)

F.A. XI:

Scott Cooksey (Hednesford Town) Sub: 13 Steve Farrelly (Barrow): Paul Jones (Barrow) Sub: 14 David Lobb (Bishop Auckland): Ritchie Watson (Spennymoor United): Andy Comyn (Hednesford Town): Paul Ellender (Gainsborough Trinity): David Bayles (Bishop Auckland): Michael Farrey (Blyth Spartans) Sub: 15 Steve Nicholson (Emley): Steven Bowey (Gateshead) Sub: 12 Michael Walker (Bishop Auckland): Neil Morton (Barrow): Andy Shaw (Bishop Auckland): Dean Calcutt (Emley) Sub: 16 Anthony Lee (Bishop Auckland).

British Universities:

David Edwards (Staffordshire): Boyd Young (Warwick): Richard Ward (Newcastle): Dave Leeming (Chester): Dean Tallentire (Nene): Bruce Sewell (North London): Rick Hume (Birmingham): Nick Roddis (St. Mary's College): John Leah (Chester): Paul Ainscough (Crewe & Alsager): David Cooke (Trinity & All Saints): G. Wilson (Wolverhampton): James Shutt (Crewe & Alsager): Darren Vine (Sheffield Hallam): Pete Moss (Cheltenham & Gloucester): Joe House (Birmingham).

FA XI 2 Ryman League 0

(Perkins) at Kingstonian

This fixture produced a very competitive battle last season so it was surprising that the meeting this year was a comparatively quiet affair!

The Ryman League looked sharper initially but once again the extra quality in keeping possession and passing shown by the Conference players made all the difference after the interval.

For Ryman's, Jimmy Dack worked hard, Paul Cobb looked dangerous in possession and Dean Hooper impressed in defence.

The F.A.'s goals were scored by Steve Perkins and impressive performances were also provided by Wayne Stemp, Kevin Betsey, David Harlow, Phil Wingfield and Mark Smith.

FA XI

Russell Meara (Hayes), Stuart Mackenzie (Farnborough Town), Wayne Stemp (Farnborough Town), Stuart Munday (Dover Athletic), Lewis Watts (Welling United), Cliff Hercules (Slough Town), Mark Smith (Stevenage Borough), Chris Sparks (Hayes), Michael Danzey (Woking), David Harlow (Farnborough Town),Steven Perkins (Stevenage Borough), Phil Wingfield (Farnborough Town), Steve West (Woking), Martin Randall (Hayes), Mike Danzey (Woking), Gary Crawshaw(Stevenage Borough).

Ryman XI

Paul Gothard (Dagenham & Redbridge) - Sub: Jerome John (Kingstonian), Dean Hooper (Kingstonian), Ashley Vickers (Heybridge Swifts), Gwynne Berry (Sutton United), Christian Metcalfe (Harrow Borough), Jimmy Dack (Sutton United), Andy Salako (Sutton United), Gary Paterson (Kingstonian), Paul Cobb (Dagenham &Redbridge), Josh Vansittart (Sutton United) - Sub: Junior Lewis (Hendon), Justin Gentle (St. Albans), Lee Endersby (Enfield).

ENGLAND'S 1998 SQUAD

GOALKEEPERS

Billy Stewart (Southport) - Caps 0 - Previous Clubs: Liverpool, Wigan Athletic, Chester, Chesterfield (Loan), Chester.

Scott Cooksey (Hednesford Town) - Caps 1 - Previous Clubs: Derby County, Shrewsbury Town, Bromsgrove Rovers, Peterborough United.

FULL BACKS

Mark Bradshaw (Halifax Town) - Caps 0 - Previous Clubs: Blackpool, Stafford Rangers, Macclesfield Town.

Chris Banks (Cheltenham Town) - Caps 0 - Previous Clubs: Port Vale, Exeter City, Bath City.

Dean Hooper (Kingstonian) - Caps 0 - Previous Clubs: Brentford, Marlow, Chalfont St. Peter, Hayes, Swindon Town, Peterborough United (Loan) Hayes, Stevenage Borough.

Jamie Victory (Cheltenham Town) - Caps 0 - Previous Clubs: AFC Bournemouth,West Ham United.

CENTRE BACKS

Andy Comyn (Hednesford Town) - Caps 0 - Previous Clubs: Manchester United, Alvechurch, Aston Villa, Derby County, Plymouth Argyle, West Bromwich Albion.

Michael Danzey (Woking) - Caps 0 - Previous Clubs: Nottingham Forest, Peterborough United, St. Albans City, Cambridge United, Aylesbury United.

Tim Ryan (Southport) - Caps 0 - Previous Clubs: Scunthorpe United, Buxton, Doncaster Rovers.

Mark Smith (Stevenage Borough) - Caps 2 - Previous Clubs: Hitchin Town, Letchworth GC, Hitchin Town, Woking, Hitchin Town.

MIDFIELD

Garry Butterworth (Rushden & Diamonds) - Caps 2 - Previous Clubs: Peterborough United, Dag & Redbridge.

Lee Howells (Cheltenham Town) - Caps 0 - Previous Clubs: Bristol Rovers, Melbourne City.

Steve Perkins (Stevenage Borough) - Caps 0 - Previous Clubs: Burscough, Plymouth Argyle.

Steve Walters (Northwich Victoria) - Caps 1 - Previous Clubs: Crewe Alexandra.

Kevin Betsey (Woking) - Caps 0 - Previous Clubs: Fleet Town (Loan), Bognor Regis Town (Loan).

Brian Healey (Morecambe) - Caps 0 - Previous Clubs: West Auckland, Billingham Town, Bishop Auckland, Gateshead, Spennymoor United.

FORWARDS

Neil Grayson (Hereford United) - Caps 0 - Previous Clubs: Rowntree Mackintosh, Doncaster Rovers, York City, Chesterfield, Gateshead, Boston United, Northampton Town.

Geoff Horsfield (Halifax Town) - Caps 0 - Previous Clubs: Worsbrough Bridge Miners Welfare, Scarborough, Halifax Town, Guiseley, Witton Albion.

Dale Watkins (Cheltenham Town) - Caps 0 - Previous Clubs: Sheffield United,Grimsby Town, Rotherham United, Peterborough United, Grantham, Rushden & Diamonds.

Owen Pickard (Yeovil Town) - Caps 0 - Previous Clubs: Plymouth Argyle, Hereford United, Dorchester Town.

The physiotherapist was Kidderminster Harriers' Jimmy Conway, who has been looking after the England team for four seasons and first helped the squad in1991.

Kevin Betsey (left) and Dean Hooper lead the squad in the warm up before training

Photo: Andrew Chitty

Once their Saturday league matches had been completed without mishap, the England squad members were requested to phone their manager John Owens with confirmation of their availability.

With John looking forward to his first match in charge he was to be disappointed that Steve Perkins, Stevenage Borough's promising young student, had collected a bad facial injury, Michael Danzey's injury, as feared, had not responded to treatment in time and Steve Walters had been injured in Saturday's game.

Woking's brilliant youngster Kevin Betsy, Morecambe's Brian Healey and Cheltenham Town's Jamie Victory were called up and then after a late kick off poor Geoff Horsfield was rewarded in scoring Halifax Town's winner and his 29th goal of the season by getting injured, and there was a late call up for Owen Pickard who had missed the chance of two FA XI games through injury and then postponement. The old cliché of luck evening itself out over a season had never been more accurate!

If anyone doubted the importance placed upon an England call up by modern players, then you only needed to see how proudly they wore the smart England casual wear supplied by the Football Association at the Holiday Inn in Crawley and certainly how the squad responded to all they were asked to do at the excellent training ground arranged for them by the town club.

Kidderminster physio Jim Conway is always an excellent right hand man for the manager in charge and for this game you could always tell where Doctor Feldmen was as he jogged around with bottles of pills in his pockets!

Goalscorer No 2: Mark Bradshaw (Halifax Town)
Photo: Andrew Chitty

Goalscorer No 1: Neil Grayson (Cheltenham Town)
Photo: Andrew Chitty

The squad looked smart and had an aura of genuine pride around them as they turned up on time, in the right kit, during the two days of preparation for this season's International.

John Owens was an unknown quantity as far as the lads were concerned. Most had met him briefly at the FA XI games but he was now in charge of them as they prepared for one of the most important games of their careers. The players seemed happy:

'He was an immediate 'hit' with the lads'

'The training was interesting'

'Our instructions were simple and sensible'

'He didn't try to cram in too much'

'We got to know each other as people and players'

'Everyone got on really well'

'We knew what was expected - and we expected to win'

'The whole stay was an enjoyable and an educational experience'

'What a pity we can't do it again or play in a competitive atmosphere'

John Owens let the squad know what the starting line-up was to be during training on Monday morning, and all credit to the disappointed few who made it clear they were thrilled to be there and in no way 'dropped their heads'.

Back Row (L-R): Jimmy Conway, Dale Watkins, Mark Smith, Chris Banks, Billy Stewart, Scott Cooksey, Brian Healy, Andy Comyn, Owen Pickard, Gary Butterworth, John Owens
Front Row (L-R): Dean Hooper, FA Doctor, Tim Ryan, Neil Grayson, Mark Bradshaw, Jamie Victory, Lee Howells, Kevin Betsey
Photo: Andrew Chitty

Cheltenham Town finished up with four in the starting line-up and one on the bench. This is quite an achievement and reflects well on the 'Robins' manager Steve Cotterill, who also encouraged the whole club to travel down to Crawley to support their representatives. The only black mark went to some of those supporters lacking in any charm or sportsmanship by rudely chanting at Owen Pickard when he came on the field to win his cap as a substitute (Owen had turned down the chance to join Cheltenham in the Summer!).

The torrential rain was a bitter disappointment to John Maggs and all the excellent admin 'team' at Crawley Town, who helped to present the match in superb fashion. The Broadfield Stadium is a real credit to the council, the club and all its members and supporters. The town deserves to see the club challenging at the top of the semi-professional pyramid.

Considering the rain, the playing surface was brilliant, although for the first ten minutes the England players, particularly in defence, found it difficult to settle into their planned 'shape'. However skipper and driving force Gary Butterworth was soon demanding the ball from the central back three and, as Chris Banks, Mark Smith and Tim Ryan settled down, we saw wing backs Dean Hooper (26!) and Mark Bradshaw come more and more into the game.

Some of the attacks built down the right flank were exact replicas of those planned in training and the only non-Conference player, Hooper, enjoyed an excellent half. Neil Grayson has recently moved from Hereford United to Cheltenham Town but was playing with Dale Watkins for England before teaming up with him for 'The Robins'. He had two good attempts, one drive and one far post header from which he might have hoped to score, but half-time came with the team looking a solid, well drilled unit with plenty of movement.

Half-time encouragement reassured the lads that they must now know the game was theirs for the taking, and out into the rain they went to see Grayson (33), their senior player, crash in an unstoppable drive which you only normally score for England in your dreams!

Confidence visably grew as the tackling became firmer, passing more accurate, support for each other more vocal and enthusiastic, so it was no surprise when Brian Healey, who had set up the first goal, slid a perfect pass through to the overlapping Mark Bradshaw, who moved forward with acceleration and a side step to steady himself and slide an equally perfect shot past the oncoming goalkeeper.

Mark's obvious pride and excitement at scoring in an England shirt was moving to see and the reaction of the Yorkshire photographer who had travelled all the way to Crawley in the rain was a revelation.

Proud Robins. Five Cheltenham Town players with their first England Caps against Holland: Lee Howells, Jamie Victory,and Chris Banks (standing), with Dale Watkins and Neil Grayson

Photo: Andrew Chitty

As the half wore on and the Dutch had used all their substitutes, John Owens was placed in the happy situation of being able to give his reserves the chance to win England caps. This he did with little detraction from the excellent style and shape adopted by the whole squad.

A hard low drive was spilled by Scott Cooksey and Gerald Kreuze did tap in a consolation goal near the end but it certainly would have been a travesty if this excellent England performance hadn't given John Owens and all involved a well deserved victory.

The Football Association Chairman Keith Wiseman was thoroughly impressed with the quality of the football and the facilities and hopefully it won't be long before our level of the game can stop being the poor relation of English football and can take part in their own competitive tournaments in future, just as our Schoolboys, Youth and Women already do.

Yes, it was a happy weekend, a good game and excellent occasion. Let's have some more please!

England: Stewart (Southport), Banks (Cheltenham), Smith (Stevenage), Ryan (Southport), Hooper (Kingstonian), Howells (Cheltenham), Butterworth (Rushden & Diamonds), Healy (Morecambe), Bradshaw (Halifax), Grayson (Cheltenham), Watkins (Cheltenham). Subs: Comyn (Hednesford) for Hooper 73, Victory (Cheltenham) for Bradshaw 73, Betsy (Woking) for Healy 76, Pickard (Yeovil) for Grayson 76,Cooksey (Hednesford) for Stewart 79. Booked: Butterworth.

Holland: Schoenmaker, Schoonhoven, Lageventerink, Knijn, Van Rijswijk, Eykemans, Kremers (Wissink 65), Van der Werf (Kreuze 46) Lindeboom, Drummen (van Beelen 70), Lineer (Peys 65) Sub: Boven. Booked: Kreymers.

Referee: G. Poll (Hertford)

The Football Conference

Founded: 1979

President: J C Thompson MBIM, Minst.M, FID

Chairman: W J King **Chief Executive:** P D Hunter

Secretary: J A Moules
The Football Conference Ltd., Collingwood House,
Schooner Court, Crossways, Dartford, Kent DA2 6QQ
Tel: 01322 303120 Fax: 01322 303121

So it was going to be between Rushden & Diamonds, Stevenage Borough, Woking and Kidderminster Harriers for last season's championship! What did we know about it? Not much, was the answer as the favourites never really seriously challenged for the championship and Halifax Town, who had only avoided relegation in the final moments of their last game at the end of the previous season, quickly built up their confidence after a good start and inspired by Geoff Horsfield's marksmanship, pulled away never to be seen again!

Another 66-1 outsider also made a considerable impact on the season as a long unbeaten Vauxhall Conference run was backed up by a run to the Third Round of the F.A. Cup and then a triumph tirp to Wembley in the F.A. Umbro Trophy. Cheltenham Town having only gained promotion because the Dr. Martens champions Gresley Rovers' new ground was not ready, showed no inferiority complex (they had been fourteen points behind Rovers) and completed a quite remarkable season.

If these two were the success stories there was disappointment at Kidderminster and Stevenage, although the Borough did hit the headlines with a spectacular F.A. Cup run, despite the squad being in a transitional stage.

By Woking's high standards, their supporters will have been a little disheartened, they too were going through a change of management but no doubt they will be more settled this season.

Morecambe won the Spalding Cup and only failed to score twice and Southport's visit to Wembley will also give good reason for optimism this season.

Telford United, Kettering Town and Northwich Victoria are the three ever present clubs in the Conference, but Kettering threatened to sink, and Telford United thought they had before the very sad problems at Slough gave them a second chance. No such luck for Gateshead and Stalybridge Celtic, but if southern clubs were relieved to lose the trip to Tyneside they will have a good substitute in the journey to old boys Barrow in Cumbria.

It is welcome for the first time to Kingstonian, a club with a good pedigree and Forest Green Rovers who sum up the romance of the pyramid by coming all the way from The Gloucestershire County League in twenty-five years.

A very big thank you goes out to Vauxhall Motors for the quite superb sponsorship and hopefully the Conference will soon be welcoming a new name to their now very well respected title.

TW

FOOTBALL CONFERENCE

Final League Table

		Home					Away							Leading Goalscorers (these include all goals as reported in the league bulletin)		
	P	W	D	L	F	A	W	D	L	F	A	PTS	GD			
Halifax Town	42	17	4	0	51	15	8	8	5	23	28	87	31	34 Horsfield	17 Patterson	9 Brook & Hulme
Cheltenham Town	42	15	4	2	39	15	8	5	8	24	28	78	20	29 Watkins	22 Eaton	7 Victory & Walker
Woking	42	14	3	4	47	22	8	5	8	25	24	74	26	21 Hay	18 Payne	14 West
Rushden & Diamonds	42	12	4	5	44	26	11	1	9	35	31	74	22	35 Collins	9 Foster	7 Mison
Morecambe	42	11	4	6	35	30	10	6	5	42	34	73	13	20 Norman	10 Milner	10 Shirley
Hereford United	42	11	7	3	30	19	7	6	8	26	30	67	7	16 Grayson	8 Agana	7 Leadbeater
Hednesford Town	42	14	4	3	28	12	4	8	9	31	38	66	9	10 Carty	9 Fitzpatrick	9 O'Connor
Slough Town	42	10	6	5	34	21	8	4	9	24	28	64	9	16 Abbott	13 Owusu	12 Bolt
Northwich Victoria	42	8	9	4	34	24	7	6	8	29	35	60	4	12 Cooke	11 Tait	10 Illman
Welling United	42	11	5	5	39	27	6	4	11	25	35	60	2	19 Cooper	15 Hanlon	7 Dolby
Yeovil Town	42	14	3	4	45	24	3	5	13	28	39	59	10	25 Pickard	19 Patmore	8 Archer
Hayes	42	10	4	7	36	25	6	6	9	26	27	58	10	21 Randall	8 Boothe	8 Hall
Dover Athletic	42	10	4	7	34	29	5	6	10	26	41	55	-10	13 Strouts	9 Adams	7 Alford
Kettering Town	42	8	6	7	29	29	5	7	9	24	31	52	-7	14 Pearson	11 Wilkes	10 Norman
Stevenage Borough	42	8	8	5	35	27	5	4	12	24	36	51	-4	15 Crawshaw	10 Trebble	8 Grazioli & Wordsworth
Southport	42	9	5	7	32	26	4	6	11	24	32	50	-2	14 Ross	12 Whittaker	6 by 4 players
Kidderminster Harriers	42	6	8	7	32	31	5	6	10	24	32	47	-7	11 Bignall	10 Arnold	7 Yates
Farnborough Town	42	10	3	8	37	27	2	5	14	19	43	44	-14	16 Mehew	9 Rowl;ands	8 Wingfield
Leek Town	42	8	8	5	34	26	2	6	13	18	41	44	-15	14 Soley	13 McAuley	12 Biggins
Telford United	42	6	7	8	25	31	4	5	12	28	45	42	-23	10 Gray	8 Murphy	6 Palmer
Gateshead	42	7	6	8	32	35	1	5	15	19	52	35	-36	14 Bowey	6 Harkus	6 Robinson
Stalybridge Celtic	42	6	5	10	33	38	1	3	17	15	55	29	-45	20 Burke	10 Sullivan	10 Trundle

Results 1997-98

		1	2	3	4	5	6	7	8	9	10	11	12	13	14	15	16	17	18	19	20	21	22	
1	Cheltenham Town	X	3-1 (1606)	1-0 (1436)	2-0 (1659)	4-0 (2508)	2-1 (1966)	1-0 (2,216)	1-2 (3039)	2-0 (1219)	0-1 (1902)	1-1 (1315)	2-1 (1717)	3-2 (1606)	2-0 (1614)	1-1 (1539)	2-0 (2171)	2-0 (1093)	1-1 (2580)	3-1 (1444)	1-1 (2326)	3-2 (1690)	2-0 (2700)	1
2	Dover Athletic	3-0 (982)	X	2-2 (809)	0-1 (1090)	0-1 (1316)	1-0 (889)	1-3 (1277)	1-1 (746)	0-0 (781)	0-4 (1182)	2-1 (1,092)	2-3 (1088)	4-0 (781)	0-3 (1,280)	2-1 (803)	3-1 (958)	3-1 (832)	1-1 (1787)	6-3 (953)	2-1 (1304)	0-2 (1384)	1-0 (1121)	2
3	Farnborough Town	1-2 (612)	1-0 (679)	X	4-0 (565)	1-2 (919)	0-2 (781)	1-3 (753)	0-2 (1097)	3-2 (771)	3-3 (678)	2-0 (618)	0-2 (589)	2-3 (744)	2-0 (905)	1-0 (642)	3-2 (532)	6-0 (621)	1-2 (897)	1-0 (543)	0-0 (603)	3-0 (2495)	2-2 (1093)	3
4	Gateshead	0-0 (672)	1-2 (596)	3-0 (803)	X	2-2 (1239)	1-1 (412)	2-5 (621)	1-1 (448)	2-0 (468)	2-0 (403)	0-2 (539)	1-4 (844)	2-2 (769)	2-1 (616)	5-1 (415)	0-2 (619)	3-3 (642)	2-1 (349)	0-2 (424)	2-1 (582)	1-2 (732)	0-3 (724)	4
5	Halifax Town	1-1 (6357)	1-1 (1949)	1-0 (2352)	2-0 (3194)	X	1-1 (2506)	1-1 (3338)	3-0 (2214)	3-0 (1836)	2-1 (1799)	2-1 (1329)	5-1 (2507)	4-2 (2165)	2-0 (3951)	1-0 (2,098)	4-3 (4701)	3-1 (2453)	4-0 (2138)	6-1 (1119)	1-0 (1011)	1-0 (2826)	3-1 (1500)	5
6	Hayes	1-1 (485)	0-0 (475)	3-1 (583)	1-0 (675)	1-2 (907)	X	4-0 (632)	2-0 (974)	0-1 (506)	1-1 (564)	3-1 (743)	0-3 (505)	1-1 (438)	1-2 (679)	0-1 (1224)	2-0 (460)	1-2 (691)	1-3 (921)	2-1 (525)	3-1 (650)	3-0 (667)	6-4 (715)	6
7	Hednesford Town	0-1 (1599)	1-0 (1051)	1-0 (1077)	3-0 (879)	0-0 (1865)	2-1 (1,265)	X	1-1 (2396)	1-1 (1911)	3-0 (1817)	1-0 (1302)	0-1 (1066)	2-0 (1013)	0-1 (1342)	2-1 (1685)	2-1 (1313)	1-0 (1054)	2-1 (1738)	1-0 (1479)	3-2 (1208)	1-1 (13540	1-0 (1366)	7
8	Hereford United	3-2 (3704)	0-1 (2147)	2-1 (1709)	1-0 (2007)	0-0 (3304)	3-0 (1663)	2-1 (2278)	X	3-2 (2,310)	1-0 (4671)	1-0 (1712)	1-0 (1720)	2-2 (2207)	1-1 (3055)	1-1 (2013)	1-1 (2663)	3-0 (2312)	0-2 (2937)	1-1 (1371)	1-2 (3138)	2-1 (2281)	1-1 (2768)	8
9	Kettering Town	0-1 (1274)	2-1 (1056)	2-1 1,433	3-0 (1201)	1-1 (2276)	1-1 (1006)	2-1 (2051)	1-2 (1404)	X	2-2 (1576)	1-0 (1287)	1-1 (1156)	1-3 (1156)	0-4 (4016)	3-3 (1349)	2-1 (1157)	3-1 (1547)	2-0 (1488)	1-3 (1405)	0-1 (1144)	0-1 (1215)	1-1 (1116)	9
10	Kidderminster Harriers	1-2 (2320)	3-3 (1636)	2-0 (1587)	1-1 (1592)	0-2 (3151)	1-0 (1076)	1-1 (1908)	1-4 (4693)	4-1 (1874)	X	1-1 (1802)	1-4 (1,717)	1-1 (2023)	1-2 (2210)	0-1 (1709)	1-1 (1612)	5-0 (1666)	1-3 (1941)	1-1 (2024)	2-1 (1525)	1-1 (1920)	3-1 (1868)	10
11	Leek Town	0-0 (708)	5-1 (562)	3-1 (664)	2-2 (535)	2-0 (1282)	1-2 (551)	3-3 (816)	2-2 (1138)	0-4 (662)	0-0 (1057)	X	1-1 (1015)	1-1 (636)	2-0 (809)	0-2 (565)	0-1 (1169)	2-2 (781)	2-1 (686)	3-1 (832)	1-2 (564)	2-0 (612)	2-0 (775)	11
12	Morecambe	1-0 (2075)	3-3 (1616)	1-1 (1270)	2-0 (1106)	1-1 (3914)	0-2 (1164)	1-3 (1460)	1-5 (1850)	1-3 (1241)	3-1 (1433)	1-1 (1237)	X	3-1 (1327)	3-1 (1449)	2-1 (1092)	2-0 (2160)	3-1 (1012)	0-2 (1156)	1-0 (1352)	4-2 (1370)	1-2 (1543)	1-0 (1,219)	12
13	Northwich Victoria	2-1 (1,118)	2-1 (897)	3-3 (862)	1-1 (873)	2-0 (2106)	1-1 (842)	1-1 (921)	0-2 (1002)	0-0 (1131)	1-1 (976)	3-1 (681)	5-0 (1015)	X	2-4 (932)	0-1 (878)	0-0 (974)	1-0 (1340)	1-1 (954)	2-2 (938)	5-1 (929)	0-2 (941)	2-1 (902)	13
14	Rushden & Diamonds	4-1 (3857)	4-1 (2284)	5-5 (2051)	3-2 (2211)	4-0 (3675)	1-3 (2158)	1-1 (2468)	1-0 (2728)	1-0 (3860)	4-1 (2234)	0-1 (2064)	3-3 (2758)	0-1 (2302)	X	0-1 (2193)	1-0 (2,477)	3-0 (2470)	2-0 (3527)	3-2 (2197)	0-1 (1459)	2-1 (2837)	2-2 (1784)	14
15	Slough Town	1-2 (1037)	2-4 (868)	1-0 (786)	1-0 (559)	1-1 (790)	0-0 (1219)	2-0 (770)	3-0 (1056)	1-1 (515)	2-0 (746)	1-1 (510)	3-3 (792)	3-0 (637)	1-2 (872)	X	1-0 (589)	4-0 (435)	3-1 (828)	1-0 (547)	1-2 (385)	1-3 (1288)	1-1 (912)	15
16	Southport	1-2 (1026)	0-1 (635)	3-1 (1187)	3-1 (800)	0-0 (1889)	0-2 (923)	4-1 (1326)	0-0 (662)	2-1 (973)	1-2 (1200)	2-2 (940)	1-1 (1640)	0-2 (964)	3-2 (1116)	1-2 (1460)	X	4-2 (909)	1-0 (1001)	1-2 (702)	3-1 912	0-0 (1050)	2-1 (849)	16
17	Stalybridge Celtic	1-4 (561)	1-0 (1666)	1-1 (505)	2-2 (605)	0-1 (1421)	1-1 (545)	1-1 (651)	2-3 (795)	3-4 (565)	2-1 (1013)	6-1 (974)	3-1 (756)	0-1 (1004)	2-4 (952)	0-1 (809)	1-3 (767)	X	1-1 (702)	1-2 (534)	2-1 (802)	0-3 710	3-2 (590)	17
18	Stevenage Borough	1-2 (1467)	2-2 (1951)	5-0 (2028)	6-1 (2102)	1-2 2,946	1-5 (2768)	1-1 (2143)	2-0 1,574	0-0 (3486)	3-1 (2012)	1-1 (1440)	0-3 (2248)	1-3 (2160)	2-1 (3107)	4-2 (1413)	1-0 (2128)	1-1 (2273)	X	1-1 (1941)	0-0 (1946)	0-0 (3254)	2-1 (2897)	18
19	Telford United	0-0 (740)	0-1 (808)	0-1 (587)	4-4 (568)	0-3 (805)	1-0 (630)	1-1 (922)	0-0 (1710)	1-1 (1041)	1-1 (1127)	3-0 (911)	1-3 (518)	2-1 (605)	4-2 (893)	0-1 (668)	2-2 (706)	1-0 (816)	3-0 (833)	X	0-3 (614)	0-3 (717)	1-4 (565)	19
20	Welling United	2-1 (550)	2-2 (1326)	1-0 (504)	2-0 (602)	6-2 (1344)	2-0 (665)	3-2 (533)	3-0 (949)	2-2 (637)	0-3 (613)	2-0 (575)	2-2 (519)	0-1 (611)	0-1 (833)	1-1 (604)	3-5 (643)	1-0 (503)	1-0 (565)	4-1 (577)	X	1-1 (1121)	1-3 (840)	20
21	Woking	2-0 (2651)	4-0 (1799)	3-0 (4124)	3-1 (2081)	2-2 (3319)	3-0 (2435)	4-2 (2292)	3-1 (3015)	0-1 (3101)	0-1 (2384)	5-2 (2806)	0-2 (3076)	1-0 (2687)	0-2 (3930)	2-1 (2829)	1-1 (2806)	3-1 (2829)	5-3 (2466)	1-1 (2626)	3-1 (2226)	X	2-0 (3429)	21
22	Yeovil Town	3-1 (3657)	4-1 (1817)	0-1 (3286)	6-3 (2567)	0-1 (2584)	4-3 (1705)	1-0 (2207)	2-0 (2601)	2-0 (2529)	1-0 (2129)	3-1 (2687)	2-3 (2140)	2-2 (2313)	1-2 (2317)	2-1 (2509)	0-0 (1927)	2-0 (1862)	2-1 (3602)	5-3 (2133)	1-1 (2,236)	2-0 (3005)	X	22

SPALDING CHALLENGE CUP

FIRST ROUND

DOVER ATHLETIC	1	v	3	KETTERING TOWN
HAYES	2	v	0	RUSHDEN & DIAMONDS
LEEK TOWN	3	v	1	SOUTHPORT
SLOUGH TOWN	1	v	0	WELLING UNITED
STALYBRIDGE CELTIC	3	v	1	HALIFAX TOWN
YEOVIL TOWN	3	v	1	CHELTENHAM TON

SECOND ROUND

KIDDERMINSTER HARRIERS	0	v	2	HEDNESFORD TOWN
HAYES	2	v	0	SLOUGH TOWN
MORECAMBE	3	v	2	LEEK TOWN
WOKING	4	v	0	KETTERING TOWN
STALYBRIDGE CELTIC	3	v	4	GATESHEAD
TELFORD UNITED	1	v	2	NORTHWICH VICTORIA
FARNBOROUGH TOWN	2	v	1	HEREFORD UNITED
STEVENAGE BOROUGH	0	v	3	YEOVIL TOWN

QUARTER FINAL

HAYES	3	v	0	YEOVIL TOWN
Roddis 73, Randall 89, Hammatt 90.		Att: 171		
NORTHWICH VICTORIA	3	v	2	HEDNESFORD TOWN
Williams 13, Stannard 103, Cooke 113.		Att: 447		Fitzpatrick 83, Norbury 116 (pen).
GATESHEAD	1	v	1	MORECAMBE
Harkus 115		Att: 204		Drummond 98
WOKING	3	v	1	FARNBOROUGH TOWN
Smith 14, Hay 15 (pen), Saunders 86.		Att: 998		Harford 33.
		Replay		
MORECAMBE	3	v	1	GATESHEAD
Monk 48, Milner 61, Drummond 87.		Att: 305		Marquis 85

SEMI-FINAL

1ST LEG	HAYES	0	v	2	WOKING
			Att: 647		Payne 31, Brown 66.
	MORECAMBE	3	v	0	NORTHWICH VICTORIA
	Milner 22, Mayers 52, Norman 58.		Att: 608		
2ND LEG	NORTHWICH VICTORIA	3	v	1	MORECAMBE
	Stannard 16, 75, Illman 51 (pen)		Att: 458		Norman 43
	WOKING	3	v	1	HAYES
	West 61, 83, Betsy 71.		Att: 826		Randall 54

FINAL

1ST LEG	MORECAMBE	1	v	1	WOKING
	Healy 63.		Att: 782		Hayward 5.
2ND LEG	WOKING	1	v	1	MORECAMBE
	Hay 53.		Att:2,045		Healy 84.

Morecambe won 4-3 after penalties

G.M. Vauxhall Conference TEN YEAR CLUB RECORD

	88/89	89/90	90/91	91/92	92/93	93/94	94/95	95/96	96/97	97/98
ALTRINCHAM	14	16	3	18	10	10	4	12	22	-
AYLESBURY UNITED	20	-	-	-	-	-	-	-	-	-
BARNET	8	2	1	-	-	-	-	-	-	-
BARROW	-	14	10	22	-	-	-	-	-	-
BATH CITY	-	-	20	9	7	12	12	18	20	-
BOSTON UNITED	3	18	18	8	22	-	-	-	-	-
BROMSGROVE ROVERS	-	-	-	-	2	18	13	11	21	-
CHELTENHAM TOWN	15	11	16	21	-	-	-	-	-	2
CHORLEY	17	20	-	-	-	-	-	-	-	-
COLCHESTER UNITED	-	-	2	1	-	-	-	-	-	-
DAGENHAM & REDBRIDGE	-	-	-	-	3	6	15	22	-	-
DARLINGTON	-	1	-	-	-	-	-	-	-	-
DOVER ATHLETIC	-	-	-	-	-	8	16	20	17	13
ENFIELD	13	22	-	-	-	-	-	-	-	-
FARNBOROUGH TOWN	-	21	-	5	21	-	14	10	7	18
FISHER ATHLETIC	18	19	22	-	-	-	-	-	-	-
GATESHEAD	-	-	17	14	14	11	7	5	10	21
HALIFAX TOWN	-	-	-	-	-	13	8	15	19	1
HAYES	-	-	-	-	-	-	-	-	15	12
HEDNESFORD TOWN	-	-	-	-	-	-	-	3	8	7
HEREFORD UNITED	-	-	-	-	-	-	-	-	-	6
KETTERING TOWN	2	5	4	3	13	2	6	16	14	14
KIDDERMINSTER HARRIERS	5	13	13	19	9	1	11	7	2	17
LEEK TOWN	-	-	-	-	-	-	-	-	-	19
MACCLESFIELD TOWN	7	4	7	13	18	7	1	4	1	-
MAIDSTONE UNITED	1	-	-	-	-	-	-	-	-	-
MERTHYR TYDFIL	-	9	9	4	16	20	20	-	-	-
MORECAMBE	-	-	-	-	-	-	-	9	4	5
NORTHWICH VICTORIA	10	15	12	11	11	15	10	8	6	9
REDBRIDGE FOREST	-	-	-	7	-	-	-	-	-	-
RUSHDEN & DIAMONDS	-	-	-	-	-	-	-	-	12	4
RUNCORN	6	3	8	16	19	5	9	21	-	-
SLOUGH TOWN	-	-	19	20	5	21	-	17	16	8
SOUTHPORT	-	-	-	-	-	4	3	6	11	16
STAFFORD RANGERS	19	17	15	17	6	9	21	-	-	-
STALYBRIDGE CELTIC	-	-	-	-	12	14	18	14	13	22
STEVENAGE BOROUGH	-	-	-	-	-	-	5	1	3	15
SUTTON UNITED	12	8	21	-	-	-	-	-	-	-
TELFORD UNITED	16	12	6	6	15	17	19	13	9	20
WELLING UNITED	11	6	11	12	20	16	17	19	18	10
WEYMOUTH	21	-	-	-	-	-	-	-	-	-
WITTON ALBION	-	-	-	10	17	22	-	-	-	-
WOKING	-	-	-	-	8	3	2	2	5	3
WYCOMBE WANDERERS	4	10	5	2	1	-	-	-	-	-
YEOVIL TOWN	9	7	14	15	4	19	22	-	-	11

WHAT A RECORD

The fourth FA Trophy winners medal for Clive Walker *Photo: Neil Thaler*

CONFERENCE DIARY

August 1997 — May 1998

1st – 25th August 1997

Relegated **Hereford United** start life as a Conference club by announcing they will remain full-time with Graham Turner as director of football. He makes a shrewd summer signing in bring in Northampton striker Neil Grayson to Edgar Street. **Gateshead** appoint midfielder Gary Robson as player-coach. Gary is the younger brother of Middlesbrough boss Bryan. The Tynesiders have also turned full-time with manager Jim Platt recruiting nine new players. It's the end of an era at **Woking,** with not only long-serving manager Geoff Chapple leaving, but also veteran winger Clive Walker, who joins Brentford as coach. **Southport** appoint Paul Futcher as their new boss. The 40-year old, who will continue to play, guided Gresley Rovers to the Dr Martens League title last season. Other managerial changes sees ex-Forest midfielder John McGovern taking on the unenviable task of replacing Geoff Chapple at **Woking** and **Steve Daley** taking over from Shrewsbury-bound John King at **Telford United,** while three clubs confirm appointments after caretaker status – **Cheltenham Town** had the reins to Steve Cotterill, **Dover Athletic** confirm the experienced Bill Williams as boss and **Leek Town** hand Peter Ward the post on a permanent basis.

***Neil Grayson** (Hereford United – Vaux Con.). Forward who has played for Doncaster, Chesterfield and Boston before joining Northampton Town and scoring 35 goals in over 100 league appearances.* Photo: Andrew Chitty

26th August – 7th September 1997

Kidderminster Harriers boost their title hopes by signing England striker Ian Arnold from **Stalybridge Celtic** for £15,000. Another England man and a former Harrier, Delwyn Humphreys, makes a move out of the Conference by joining Stafford Rangers from **Northwich Victoria** in a £10,000 deal. The crowds are out in force at the start of the season with gates representing a 30 per cent rise on the corresponding stage last season. **Kidderminster Harriers** sell England full back Marcus Bignot to First Division Crewe for an initial £100,000 fee. Appearances could take the fee to over £200,000 eventually. **Leek Town** lose their assistant-manager when Gary Bauress decides to join Unibond Leaguers Barrow as a player. **Morecambe** and **Halifax** are the early pacesetters in the league with **Kettering Town** still searching for their first win after losing at home to **Cheltenham Town** – their fifth game without a win.

8th – 21st September 1997

Hayes' exciting young striker Jason Roberts is in demand and is being tipped to follow in the footsteps of former Missioner Les Ferdinand who left Church Road some eleven years ago. Former champions **Stevenage Borough** sign New Zealand international Tim Stevens to succeed record sale Barry Hales. **Gateshead** showfighting spirit after coming from 4-1 down with just 16 minutes to go against **Telford United** to draw 4-4. **Dover Athletic** lose striker Ricky Reina, who joins Second Division Brentford for a £50,000 fee. The deal could eventually be worth double that to the Kent club. **Halifax Town** are the only unbeaten team after **Morecambe** lose at home to **Hednesford Town.** Jason Roberts finally leave **Hayes** to join First Division Wolves for a club record £250,000 fee. Additional clauses could take the fee close to the £600,000 they received when Les Ferdinand moved from QPR to Newcastle United. **Kettering Town** record their first win of the campaign, and first since March 31, when defeating United Counties League side Mirrlees Blackstone 1-0 in the F.A. Cup first qualifying round. There are a couple of shocks as **Telford United** are beaten at home by Dr Martens Midland Division side Bedworth United and **Leek Town** lose at UniBond Leaguers Winsford United. England midfielder Steve Stott moved from **Rushden & Diamonds** to **Yeovil Town** for a £9,000 fee.

22nd September – 5th October 1997

Rushden & Diamonds sign former Leeds and Arsenal defender Chris Whyte from Oxford United. **Halifax Town** make it eight games without defeat by beating **Farnborough Town. Hereford United** announce plans to move to a new 10,000-seater stadium. **Hednesford Town** lose assistant-manager John Allen, who takes over as manager of Midland Alliance side Rushall Olympic after six years with the Pitmen. **Telford United** follow Hereford by also announcing their intention to leave their ground and move to a new stadium. After nine games without a win **Kettering Town** boss Steve Berry puts his entire first-team squad up for sale, with England forward Dave Venables the first to go, signing for Ryman League side Enfield for £5,000. **Woking** sell striker Justin Jackson to Third Division Notts County for £30,000 – the same fee they paid to Morecambe last year. **Stalybridge Celtic** pay £7,000 for Chorley's highly-rated striker Lee Trundle, while **Farnborough Town** boss Alan Taylor makes his first ever loan signing, bringing in Gloucester City's former Yeovil Town goalkeeper David Coles to Cherrywood Road. **Hednesford Town** continue to add to their already strong squad by signing another player from the Football League – ex-Stoke and England under 21 international Carl Beeston from Southend.

Steve Berry watched by Lee Fowler. Photo: Peter Barnes

6th – 19th October 1997

Woking pay a new club record fee to sign Steve West from Enfield. Manager John McGovern shells out £35,000 for the replacement for Notts County bound Justin Jackson. **Northwich Victoria** winger Darren Vicary joins Newcastle United on trial. Stockport's John Jeffers becomes yet another experienced League man to join **Hednesford Town. Leek Town** appoint Kevin Lewis – a former manager of the club – as the new number number two to Peter Ward. **Kettering Town** extend their sequence of games without a win to ten – the worst start in the Conference since 1992. Their season of woe continues with a 1-0 home defeat by Dr Martens Midland Division club Hinckley United in the F.A. Cup 3rd qualifying round. Peter Jackson leaves **Halifax Town** to become the new manager at First Division Huddersfield Town. **Woking** lose to champions Macclesfield Town in the JC Thompson Championship Shield.

Chris Boothe – *(Hayes)*
Photo: Peter Barnes

Brian Kilcline – *(Halifax Town)*
Photo: Peter Barnes

20th October –2nd November 1997

Halifax Town sign veteran Brian Kilcline to replace Huddersfield-bound Peter Jackson. Meanwhile, Town's 4-0 win over **Stevenage Borough** extended their unbeaten their unbeaten start to eleven games – the best since 1990. **Kidderminster Harriers** sign Halesown Town defender Matt Clarke for £10,000. **Hayes'** search for a replacement for Jason Roberts ends when signing **Farnborough Town's** Chris Boothe, Boro's top scorer for the past four seasons. **Woking's** highly-rated midfielder Kevin Betsy joins **Farnborough Town.** However, Cards' fans need not worry as he has jointed the Cherrywood Road Club only as assistant community officer. Changes in the offing at **Kettering Town,** who sack assistant-manager John Gaunt and then shock fans with the announcement that they may merge with neighbours Corby Town. Jim Platt becomes the first managerial casualty of the season when he resigned as boss as **Gateshead** following a 2-0 home defeat by **Telford United.** Player coach Gary Robson and reserve team boss Alan Shoulder are put in temporary charge at the International Stadium. A proposal for Brighton to groundshare with **Woking** fall through. Shocks in the 4th qualifying round of the F.A. Cup when leaders **Halifax Town** bow out to Unibond Leaguers Gainsborough Trinity and **Kidderminster Harriers** lose at another UniBond side Blyth Spartans.

3rd - 16th November 1997

Halifax Town's unbeaten league run finally comes to an end when **Cheltenham Town** in 4-0 at Whaddon Road. Town's 12-game unbeaten run fell three short of the all-time record. **Hednesford Town,** many pundits' choice as champions at the start of the season, take top spot from Halifax Town after defeating **Yeovil Town** at Keys Park. Meanwhile **Kettering Town's** misery continues after a 2-1 defeat at **Southport** condemned the Poppies to their twelfth game without a win. The top of the table clash between **Halifax Town** and **Morecambe** attracts the biggest attendance of the season to date. The 1-1 draw was watched by 3,940 at Christie Park, Morecambe's highest gate since1962. There is great sadness at **Hayes** with the announcement of the death of reserve team boss Alan Christopher aged just 38. More shocks in the F.A. Cup as **Rushden & Diamonds** lose in a replay at Ryman League side Boreham Wood and **Stalybridge Celtic** bow out at Dr Martens League Solihull Borough. Clive Walker makes a return to the Conference by signing for **Cheltenham Town. Gateshead** appoint former Runcorn and Halifax Town boss John Carroll as their new manager. **Yeovil Town** appoint Colin Lippiatt as first-team coach. Lippiatt worked with Geoff Chapple at Woking throughout their successful years. **Farnborough Town** are awarded £103,357 from the National Lottery for ground improvements.

17th - 30th November

Kettering Town finally break their duck at the 14th attempt when **Dover Athletic** are beaten 2-1 at Rockingham Road. **Hereford United** gain some revenge on Brighton by sending the Third Division club out of the F.A. Cup. **Hednesford Town** also defeat League opposition, beating Hull 2-0, while **Slough Town** hold Cardiff City to a 1-1 draw. No giantkillings for **Woking** this season though, as they are beaten by Southend. One of the Conference's all-time record scorers. Mark Carter, makes a return by joining **Gateshead** on loan from Rochdale. **Kidderminster Harriers** strengthen their attack by signing Mike Bignall from **Morecombe** for a £10,000 fee. **Cheltenham Town** equal the seasonal best run of 12 games by beating **Gateshead** 2-0. The Conference welcomed its first ever Japanese player when Kelsuke Takano made his debut for **Morecombe** against **Rushden & Diamonds**. Yeovil Town charter a plane to take fans and officials to **Gateshead** for a league game. Vauxhall Confirm that their 12-year sponsorship of the Conference will end in June 1998. It draws to a close the world's longest sponsorship agreement.

1st - 14th December 1997

Stalybridge Celtic part company with manager Brian Kettle after a one-year spell at Bower Fold. England midfielder Mark Hine is put in temporary charge of team affairs. Meanwhile, former Stalybridge boss, Peter Wragg, returns to the Conference as number two to Paul Futcher at **Southport. Gateshead** equal a ten-year win-less run after a 3-0 home defeat by **Yeovil Town** condemned the Tynesiders to their seventeenth game without success. Three Conference clubs feature in a draw for the Third Round of the F.A. Cup after **Stevenage Borough, Cheltenham Town** and **Hereford United** all achieve 1-1 draws in the Second Round. The league's other representatives, **Hednesford Town,** bow out however, losing 1-0 to former Conference champions Darlington. **Kidderminster Harriers'** ex-Aston Villa striker Ian Olney announces his retirement from the game because of recurring knee problem and increased work commitments. Former Gateshead boss Colin Richardson joins **Stalybridge Celtic** as number two to caretaker boss Mark Hine. **Gateshead,** meanwhile, sign their fifth goalkeeper of the season to date, with Doncaster's Dean Williams being the latest to check in at the International Stadium, and then collect only their second win of the season against **Stevenage Borough**. Former Burnley boss Jimmy Mullen is appointed a the new manager of **Telford United** following the departure of Steve Daley.

22nd December 1997 – 11th January 1998

Stalybridge Celtic appoint former Sheffield Wednesday, Leeds and England defender Mel Sterland as their new manager with Imre Varadi brought in as number two. The last remaining 100 per cent home record goes when leaders **Halifax Town** are held to a 1-1 draw by **Hednesford Town.** Meanwhile, **Kettering Town's** 3-1 success at **Morecombe** was their first away win since March and enabled the Poppies to move out of the bottom two for the first time in the campaign. **Stevenage Borough** and **Hereford United** book their places in the F.A. Cup Third Round after replay victories over Cambridge United and Colchester United respectively. **Stevenage Borough** then record their best ever showing in the competition by defeating First Division Swindon Town at the County Ground. Hereford must wait a while for their chance against Tranmere due to a postponement. **Farnborough Town** sign former Manchester United and England defender Paul Parker. The biggest crowd of the season to date, 4,693, see **Kidderminster Harriers** lose at Aggborough to **Hereford United.**

Mel Sterland
(Team Manager – Stalybridge Celtic)
Photo: Peter Barnes

12th – 25th January 1998

Stevenage Borough win the right to play their F.A. Cup Fourth Round tie against Premiership giants Newcastle United at their Broadhall Way stadium following police and F.A. advice. The game will also be shown live on Sky Sports. **Woking's** disappointing cup season continued when Dr Martens Southern Division side Margate dumped the holders out of the F.A. Umbro Trophy first round at Kingfield. It was the Cards' first home defeat in the competition since 1986. There were no other real shocks, although five sides face tricky replays, including F.A. Cup giantkillers **Stevenage Borough**, who are held by Ryman Leaguers Chesham United. **Cheltenham Town** earn the right for a replay in the F.A. Cup Third Round by drawing 1-1 with First Division Reading in a much-delayed tie. **Stalybridge Celtic** continue to struggle and succumbed to their seventh straight defeat at home to **Woking. Hereford United** finally bow out of the F.A. Cup when First Division Tranmere Rovers win 3-0 at Edgar Street. **Telford United** sign England defender Simeon Hodson from **Rushden & Diamonds.**

26th January – 8th February

Stevenage Borough record one of the best F.A. Cup performances of recent years by holding Premiership Newcastle United to a 1-1 draw at Broadhall Way. Guiliano Grazioli becomes an instant household name with his goal to go alongside Alan Shearer's striker for the Magpies. Not such good news for **Cheltenham Town,** who are beaten by a late goal at Reading in a Third Round replay. **Stalybridge Celtic** finally end their run of seven straight defeats with a 2-2 draw at **Leek Town. Kettering Town** move out of the bottom three for the first time with a 2-1 win against **Farnborough Town.** Graham Roberts, linked earlier in the season with a move to an Australian club, is amongst the favourites to land the post at First Division Plymouth. **Telford United** are dumped out of the F.A. Umbro Trophy at the Buck's Head by Unibond First Division side Ashton United. It is however, the only real shock as Conference sides continue to dominate this season's competition.

Kevin Betsy
(Woking's Player of the Year).
Photo: Andrew Chitty

9th – 22nd February 1998

John Mc Govern signs a new two-year contract as manager of **Woking.** Conference officials call for an increase in the number of promotion places to the Nationwide League. They want a three up/three down system on the basis as the movement between the Nationwide and Premiership. **Stevenage Borough** put up a magnificent showing at St. James's Park before finally bowing out of the F.A. Cup to Newcastle United. The tie was soured though by some unecessary nastiness between the two camps. **Stalybridge Celtic** earn their first victory since October with a 1-0 win against **Dover Athletic.** An injury time winner sees **Hednesford Town** lose at Keys Park for the first time since April 1997. **Cheltenham Town's** victory brought an end to a 13-game unbeaten run at home by the Pitmen. **Gateshead** manager John Carroll goes into hospital after with an illness which will ultimately see him miss the rest of the season. **Rushden & Diamonds** add veteran striker Colin West to their squad on a permanent basis following a successful loan spell. **Woking's** exciting midfielder Kevin Betsy goes on trial with Fulham. **Yeovil Town** part company with manager Graham Roberts after three years in charge at Huish Park. Assistant boss Terry Cotton and coach Lippiatt are put in temporary charge. Graham Turner, director of football at **Hereford United,** is near to completing a take-over of the club. Non-League football's record signing, Carl Alford, joins **Dover Athletic** on loan from **Rushden & Diamonds.**

23rd February – 8th March 1998

Kettering Town fans are relieved when it is finally announced that the proposed merger with neighbouring Corby Town has come to an end. The Poppies have been offered an alternative site on the outskirts of town by the club's landlord. Local pride is dented again though when **Rushden & Diamonds** inflict a 4-0 home defeat on the Poppies, who have to contend themselves with the money generated from the 4,016 gate. Both **Southport** and **Dover Athletic** reach the quarter-finals of the F.A. Umbro Trophy for the first time. Meanwhile one of the other quarter-finalists, **Cheltenham Town,** add to their squad strength by signing **Hereford United** striker Neil Grayson, recently capped by England for the first time. **Telford United** set a new club transfer record by signing **Hednesford Town** striker Mike Norbury for £15.000. **Yeovil Town** appoint Colin Lippiatt as head coach in place of recently departed manager Graham Roberts. **Morecambe** reach their first ever national final when a semi-final win over **Northwich Victoria** earned the Shrimps a place in the Spalding Cup final. **Woking's** long-serving skipper Kevin Brown ends his 300-game spell with the club to join **Yeovil Town** for a £7,500 fee. Another Cards' stalwart, Steve Thompson, also makes the same move.

16th - 29th March 1998

Farnborough Town sign Eire International winger Mark Kelly and hope he will stay longer than previous international capture, Paul Parker, who joined Sunderland without actually playing for the Hampshire club. Boro's top scorer Dave Mehew leaves to join **Rushden & Diamonds.** There is a shock in the F.A. Umbro Trophy when favourites **Stevenage Borough** are beaten by **Slough Town.** Other quarter-final winners were **Cheltenham Town,** who beat **Hayes,** but the other two ties involving **Southport** and **Dover Athletic,** both held by lower league clubs. Struggling **Leek Town** part company with manager Peter Ward and put player-coach Ray Walker in temporary charge. **Halifax Town** open a 13-point lead at the top of the table after defeating second placed **Rushden & Diamonds** 2-0 at The Shay in front of a sell-out 3,951 crowd. **Woking** end their cup woe by reaching the final of the Spalding Cup. The Cards beat **Hayes** to earn the right to play **Morecambe** in the final. Both **Dover Athletic** and **Southport** come through their tricky F.A. Umbro Trophy replays. Dover beat Unibond Leaguers Barrow in a penalty shoot-out whilst Southport beat Dr Martens Midland Divisions side Grantham Town 3-1, courtesy of a Brian Ross hat-trick.

30th March - 13th April 1998

The transfer deadline passes with one of the fewest deals completed for thirteen years. However, **Southport** strengthen their squad by signing Port Vale striker Justin O'Reilly for £5,000. **Cheltenham Town's** 14 month unbeaten home run comes to an end with a 1-0 defeat by **Kidderminster Harriers.** The run stretched back to January 1997. **Gateshead** move off the bottom of the table for the first time for 19 weeks by beating **Welling United** at the International Stadium. **Morecambe** and **Woking** share a 1-1 draw in the first-leg of the Spalding Cup final, whilst in the F.A. Umbro Trophy, **Cheltenham Town** and **Southport** both open up single goal advantages in their semi-finals. Cheltenham beat **Dover Athletic** 2-1 and Southport earned a 1-0 win at **Slough Town. Leek Town** gain their first win under caretaker boss Ray Walker by beating fellow strugglers **Farnborough Town** 3-1 at Harrison Park. Three club, leaders **Halifax Town, Morecambe** and basement side **Stalybridge Celtic,** all gain 'A' grades for their stadiums following Football League inspection, The 1998 F.A. Umbro Trophy final at Wembley will be beaten **Southport** and **Cheltenham Town** after both came through the second legs with victories. Southport drew 1-1 at Haig Avenue with **Slough Town** whilst Cheltenham drew 2-2 at **Dover Athletic.**

Kevan Browne

(Ex- Woking Captain now playing for Yeovil Town).

Photo: V. Robertson

14th – 27th April 1998

Former Stroke and England full back Mike Pejic is appointed as the new manger of **Leek Town** but only until the end of the season. Player-manager Steve Berry announces he is to quit his post at **Kettering Town** at the end of the season. Conference attendances hit the 600,000-mark for only the second time in the league's history following the Easter fixtures. **Farnborough Town's** seven-game run without a win ends with a 4-0 success over **Gateshead.** It is confirmed already that Doncaster Rovers will be joining the conference next season after finishing well adrift of the second from bottom team in the Third Division. **Cheltenham Town** become the latest Conference club to be given an 'A' grading by the Football League. **Halifax Town** are crowned as champions following a 2-0 win at **Kidderminster Harriers.** The Shaymen's success is the earliest championship conclusion since 1992/93. **Yeovil Town's** new head coach Colin Lippiatt signs a two year contract. The Glovers then end **Hereford United's** 13-match unbeaten run. **Stevenage Borough** sign striker Carl Alford from **Rushden & Diamonds.** Non-League football's record signing will join the Broadhall Way outfit at the end of the season after seeing out the remainder of the 97/98 campaign with **Dover Athletic.** Congratulations to last season's Conference champions Macclesfield Town, who gained automatic promotion to the Second Division at the first attempt.

Carl Alford
Photo: Peter Barnes

28 April – End of Season

The Conference management committee announce plans to form a new second division for season 1999/2000. The proposal receives a mixed response, with, as expected, the three main feeder leagues announcing their opposition to the plans. **Gateshead** and **Stalybridge Celtic's** relegation from the Conference is confirmed following recent results. **Halifax Town** celebrate receiving the championship trophy with the biggest crowd of the season – 6,357 – at The Shay for the game against Trophy finalists **Cheltenham Town. Dover Athletic** reveal that striker Ricky Reina, sold to Brentford for £50,000 last September, is to re-sign for the Kent club after suffering a knee injury which has curtailed his full-time career. The Spalding Cup will have a new name on it after **Morecambe** and **Woking** meet in the second leg. The tie is all square at 1-1. The inclement weather sees **Leek Town's** match against Morecambe postponed, leaving the Staffordshire outfit with a hectic schedule of five games in six days in which to

BARROW

Conference football returns to Barrow after a splendid season in which the Unibond championship was never really in any doubt.

Owen Brown's squad of mainly 'scousers' showed great consistency and even had time to include an Umbro Trophy run to the quarter-final where they only lost after a replay and penalties in front of a massive 4,217 at Holker Street .

In the first half of the season Neil Morton had supplied the goals but it was Marc Coates who enjoyed a productive second half to the campaign.

However the real strength of the side was the defence in which giant goal-keeper Steve Farrelly returned to the kind of form which had won him an England place in 1995. To complement him Dave Higgins and Joe Johnston were both sound and reliable at all times.

Providing there is stability off the field, the present squad will make life very miserable for clubs journeying to Cumbria and if their away form is in any way reasonable there could be a good season ahead for The Bluebirds.

CLUB OFFICIALS 1998-99

Honorary President	**Frank Warren**
Chairman	**Stephen Vaughan**
Vice Chairman	**Graham Hodgson**
Secretary	**Pat Brewer** Address - c/o the club Tel: 01229 820346(B) 01229 828913 (H)
Press Officer	**Phil Yelland** 83 Camus Ave., Edinburgh EH10 6QY Tel: 0131 445 1010
Commercial Director	**David Murgatroyd**

Back Row (L-R): Franny Ventre (Asst), Dave Higgins, Paul Jones, Lee O'Keeffe, Gary Bauress, Steve Farrelly, Owen Brown (Mgr), Eddie Johnston, Stuart Humphreys, Neil Morton, Karl Marginson, Jeff Hughes (Physio). Front Row: Lee Cooper, Carl Macauley, Lee Prior, Mark Grugel, Anthony Wright, Paul Robertson, Jimmy Brown

BARROW - Match Facts 1997-98

Match No.	Date	Venue H / A	Comp.	Opponents	Result & Score		Att.	Goalscorers	League Position
1	23.08	A	UL	Altrincham	D	2-2	*928*	Wright 42, 70.	
2	25.08	H	UL	Marine	L	0-1	1,474		
3	30.08	H	UL	Bishop Auckland	W	3-1	1,100	Morton 26 (pen), 35, Prior.	11
4	02.09	A	UL	Chorley	W	2-0	*532*	Wright 35, 66.	6
5	07.09	A	UL	Guiseley	D	1-1	*472*	Robertson 34.	3
6	09.09	H	UL	Accrington Stanley	W	2-0	1,310	O'Keefe 16, Morton 51.	2
7	16.09	A	UL	Leigh RMI	W	1-0	*246*	Jones P 60.	1
8	20.09	H	UL	Colwyn Bay	D	1-1	1,220	Morton 45.	2
9	23.09	H	UL	Radcliffe Borough	**W**	**3-0**	1,143	Cooper 11, Robertson 25, Morton 45.	1
10	27.09	A	UL	Alfreton Town	**W**	**3-0**	*206*	Cooper 40, Morton 64 (pen), 67.	1
11	04.10	H	UL	Spennymoor United	L	1-2	1,174	Brown 65.	1
12	07.10	A	UL	Bamber Bridge	D	2-2	*529*	Morton 25, Brown 89.	1
13	11.10	H	UL	Frickley Athletic	W	2-1	938	O'Keefe 17, Morton 23.	1
14	14.10	H	UL	Chorley	W	1-0	973	Coates 73.	1
15	18.10	A	UL	Hyde United	**W**	**3-0**	*832*	Morton 27, Prior 45, O'Keefe 86.	1
16	21.10	A	UL	Accrington Stanley	W	1-0	*588*	Green 88.	1
17	01.11	H	UL	Alfreton Town	W	2-0	938	O'Keefe 53, Prior 79.	1
18	08.11	A	UL	Boston United	W	2-0	*1,239*	Morton 36, Coates 89.	1
19	11.11	A	UL	Runcorn	W	1-0	*373*	O'Keefe 25.	1
20	15.11	H	UL	Guiseley	L	0-1	1,277		1
21	22.11	A	UL	Frickley Athletic	W	1-0	*231*	Prior 24.	1
22	06.12	H	UL	Leigh RMI	L	0-1	1,012		1
23	13.12	H	UL	Winsford United	L	1-2	991	Bauress 83 (pen).	1
24	20.12	H	UL	Gainsborough Trinity	W	2-0	963	Coates 48, Cooper 55.	1
25	27.12	A	UL	Lancaster City	W	2-0	*1,119*	Prior 34, OG (Boyd) 44.	1
26	01.01	H	UL	Lancaster City	W	1-0	1,459	Bauress.	1
27	03.01	A	UL	Bishop Auckland	W	2-0	*759*	Johnston 24, Coates 89.	1
28	17.01	H	UL	Altrincham	D	0-0	1,429		1
29	24.01	A	UL	Gainsborough Trinity	**W**	**3-0**	*646*	O'Keefe 15, Farelly 35, Coates 52.	1
30	07.02	H	Ul	Bamber Bridge	W	2-0	1,246	Morton 68, Bauress 84.	1
31	14.02	A	UL	Colwyn Bay	D	1-1	*423*	Coates 48.	1
32	21.03	A	UL	Emley	**L**	**0-3**	*503*		1
33	24.03	A	UL	Winsford United	D	0-0	*213*		1
34	28.03	H	UL	Emley	W	1-0	1,271	Coates 31.	1
35	04.04	H	UL	Runcorn	W	1-0	1,743	Cooper 46.	1
36	11.04	H	UL	Blyth Spartans	W	3-1	1,406	Marginson 44, 51, Wright 80.	1
37	13.04	A	UL	Marine	L	0-1	*539*		1
38	15.04	A	UL	Radcliffe Borough	W	2-1	*254*	McCauley 3, Coates 58.	1
39	18.04	A	UL	Blyth Spartans	L	1-2	*591*	Marginson 85.	1
40	21.04	H	UL	Boston United	W	1-0	2,765	Marginson 60.	1
41	25.04	H	UL	Hyde United	D	2-2	1,995	Morton 80(pen), Coates 81.	1
42	02.05	A	UL	Spennymoor United	L	2-3	*370*	Wright 13, Johnson 89.	1

CUP COMPETITIONS ULCC - Unibond Lge. Chall. Cup ULPC - Unibond Lge. President's Cup ATS - Lancs. ATS Trophy

Date	Venue	Comp.	Opponents	Result	Score	Att.	Goalscorers
13.09	A	**FAC** 1Q	North Ferriby United	L	1-2	274	Wright 4.
29.11	H	**FAT** 3Q	Hinckley United	W	4-1	1,011	Robertson 9, Coates 35, 45, O'Keefe 40.
10.01	H	1	Worksop Town	D	1-1	1,199	Cooper 29.
13.01	A	1 R	Worksop Town	W	4-2	1,044	Jones 23, Coates 34, Johnson 76, Barnes 90 (pen).
31.01	H	2	St Albans City	W	2-1	1,279	Morton 5, Cooper 73.
21.02	H	3	Northwich Victoria	W	1-0	2,185	Johnston 90.
14.03	A	4	Dover Athletic	D	1-1	2,970	Coates 24.
17.03	H	4 R	Dover Athletic	D	*0-0	4,217	AET Lost 4-5 after penalties.
21.01	A	**ATS** 2	Radcliffe Borough	W	1-0	113	Cooper 80.
03.02	A	3	Southport	L	0-1	428	
28.10	H	**ULCC** 2	Lancaster City	L	0-3	658	
25.11	H	**ULPC** 1	Marine	L	2-5	410	Higgins 41, Morton 77.

League Attendances	HIGHEST: 2,765 v Boston United	LOWEST: 938 v Frickley A. & Alfreton T.
NORTHERN PREMIER: Champions	**FA CUP:** 1st Qual. Round	**FA TROPHY:** Fourth Round

1	2	3	4	5	6	7	8	9	10	11	12 14 15	
Farrelly	McCauley	Robertson	Higgins	Johnston	Humphreys	Brown	O'Keefe	Wright	Morton	Prior	Grugel, Moore, Leeming.	1
Farrelly	McCauley	Robertson	Grugel	Johnston	Humphreys	Moore	O'Keefe	Wright	Morton	Prior	McAlinden(4), Watt(5), Leeming(7).	2
Farrelly	McCauley	Robertson	Higgins	Jones	Humphreys	Bauress	O'Keefe	Wright	Morton	Prior	Grugel(3), Leeming, Marginson(9).	3
Farrelly	McCauley	Robertson	Higgins	Jones	Humphreys	Bauress	Marginson	Wright	Morton	Prior	Grugel(7), Moore, Brown(10).	4
Farrelly	McCauley	Robertson	Higgins	Jones	Humphreys	Brown	Marginson	Wright	Morton	Prior	Cooper, Grugel, Hennigan.	5
Farrelly	McCauley	Robertson	Higgins	Jones	Humphreys	Brown	Marginson	Wright	Morton	O'Keefe	Cooper(7), Grugel(9l, Hennigan(10).	6
Farrelly	McCauley	Robertson	Higgins	Jones	Humphreys	Bauress	Prior	Wright	Morton	O'Keefe	Brown(9), Marginson(10), Cooper(11).	7
Farrelly	McCauley	Robertson	Higgins	Jones	Humphreys	Bauress	Prior	Cooper	Morton	O'Keefe	Wright(6), Marginson(8), Brown(11).	8
Farrelly	McCauley	Robertson	Higgins	Jones	Humphreys	Bauress	Prior	Cooper	Morton	O'Keefe	Wright(2), Marginson(3), Brown(10).	9
Farrelly	McCauley	Marginson	Higgins	Jones	Humphreys	Bauress	Prior	Cooper	Morton	O'Keefe	Wright(8), Hennigan(10), Brown(11).	10
Farrelly	Prior	Robertson	Higgins	Jones	Humphreys	Bauress	Brown	O'Keefe	Morton	Marginson	Hennigan((6), Grugel(11), Leeming.	11
Farrelly	Prior	Robertson	Higgins	Jones	Humphreys	Bauress	Brown	Coates	Morton	O'Keefe	Marginson(2),Hennigan,Johnston(11).	12
Farrelly	Prior	Robertson	Higgins	Jones	Humphreys	Bauress	Brown	Coates	Morton	O'Keefe	Marginson(6),Hennigan,Johnston(10).	13
Farrelly	Prior	Robertson	Higgins	Jones	Johnston	Bauress	Brown	Coates	Morton	O'Keefe	Marginson(3),Hennigan(12),Johnston.	14
Farrelly	Prior	Robertson	Higgins	Jones	Johnston	Bauress	Brown	Coates	Morton	O'Keefe	Hennigan(8),McCauley,Grugel(10).	15
Farrelly	Prior	Robertson	Higgins	Jones	Johnston	Bauress	Brown	Coates	Morton	O'Keefe	Hennigan,McCauley,Grugel(11).	16
Farrelly	McCauley	Robertson	Higgins	Jones	Johnston	Bauress	Prior	O'Keefe	Morton	Humphreys	Hennigan(2),Grugel(9),Wright(10).	17
Farrelly	McCauley	Robertson	Higgins	Jones	Johnston	Bauress	Prior	Coates	Morton	O'Keefe	Humphreys(2),Grugel(10),Hennigan(11)	18
Farrelly	McCauley	Robertson	Higgins	Jones	Johnston	Bauress	Prior	Coates	Humphreys	O'Keefe	Brown, Grugel, Hennigan.	19
Farrelly	McCauley	Robertson	Higgins	Jones	Johnston	Bauress	Prior	Coates	Morton	O'Keefe	Brown(3), Grugel(8), Hennigan(9).	20
Farrelly	McCauley	Robertson	Higgins	Jones	Humphreys	Bauress	Prior	Coates	Morton	O'Keefe	Brown(3),Hennigan(6),Marginson(7).	21
Farrelly	McCauley	Robertson	Higgins	Jones	Johnston	Bauress	Brown	Coates	Morton	O'Keefe	Cooper(7), Grugel, Marginson(8).	22
Farrelly	McCauley	Robertson	Higgins	Jones	Johnston	Bauress	Marginson	Coates	Cooper	O'Keefe	Wright(15),Grugel(2),Hennigan(8).	23
Farrelly	McCauley	Robertson	Higgins	Jones	Johnston	Bauress	Moran	Coates	Cooper	Hennigan	Marginson(2),Grugel(9),Wright(11).	24
Farrelly	McCauley	Robertson	Higgins	Jones	Johnston	Bauress	Moran	Coates	Cooper	Prior	Marginson(3),Grugel(9),Wright(10).	25
Farrelly	McCauley	Robertson	Higgins	Jones	Johnston	Bauress	Moran	Coates	Cooper	Prior	Marginson(3),Morton(8),O'Keefe(10).	26
Farrelly	McCauley	Robertson	Higgins	Jones	Johnston	Bauress	O'Keefe	Coates	Cooper	Prior	Marginson, Morton(10), Brown(11).	27
Farrelly	McCauley	Robertson	Higgins	Jones	Johnston	Bauress	Prior	Coates	Morton	O'Keefe	Cooper(8),Brown(10),Marginson(11).	28
Farrelly	McCauley	Robertson	Higgins	Jones	Johnston	Bauress	Brown	Coates	Morton	O'Keefe	Marginson93),Cooper(6),Williams(10).	29
Farrelly	McCauley	Robertson	Higgins	Jones	Johnston	Bauress	Marsh	Coates	Morton	O'Keefe	Cooper(9),Brown(10),Marginson(11).	30
Farrelly	McCauley	Robertson	Higgins	Jones	Johnston	Bauress	Marsh	Coates	Morton	O'Keefe	Cooper(7),Brown(11),Marginson.	31
Farrelly	McCauley	Robertson	Higgins	Jones	Johnston	Bauress	Prior	Coates	Cooper	O'Keefe	Brown(6),Marginson(8),Morton(10).	32
Pearce	McCauley	Robertson	Higgins	Jones	Johnston	Bauress	Prior	Coates	Morton	Brown	Cooper(8),Marginson(9),Hennigan(11).	33
Clarke	McCauley	Marginson	Higgins	Jones	Johnston	Bauress	Hennigan	Coates	Morton	O'Keefe	Brown(8),Cooper(10),Wright(11).	34
Farrelly	McCauley	Robertson	Higgins	Jones	Johnston	Bauress	Williams	Coates	Cooper	Marginson	Wright(1), Tippett, Kennedyy.	35
Farrely	McCauley	Robertson	Higgins	Jones	Johnston	Bauress	Williams	Wright	Cooper	Marginson	Morton(15),Tippett(10),Hennigan97).	36
Farrelly	McCauley	Robertson	Higgins	Jones	Johnston	Brown	Coates	Wright	Cooper	Marginson	Williams, Morton(7), Prior(10).	37
Farrelly	McCauley	Robertson	Higgins	Jones	Johnston	Bauress	Prior	Coates	Morton	Marginson	Wright(9), Cooper(10), Brown.	38
Clarke	McCauley	Robertson	Brown	Jones	Williams	Bauress	Prior	Coates	Morton	Marginson	Wright(4), Cooper(10), Tippett.	39
Farrelly	McCauley	Robertson	Higgins	Jones	Johnston	Bauress	Prior	Coates	Morton	Marginson	Brown(9), Cooper(10), Wright.	40
Farrelly	McCauley	Robertson	Higgins	Jones	Johnston	Bauress	Prior	Coates	Morton	Marginson	Brown J(11),Cooper(8),Wright(15).	41
Clarke	McCauley	Brown J	Higgins	Jones	Johnston	Bauress	Prior	Coates	Wright	Marginson	Williams(3),Cooper(10),Brown O.	42

Farrelly	McCauley	Robertson	Higgins	Jones	Humphreys	Brown	Marginson	Wright	Morton	O'Keefe	Johnston, Cooper(8), Prior(9).	
Farrelly	McCauley	Robertson	Higgins	Jones	Johnston	Bauress	Prior	Coates	Morton	O'Keefe	Brown(2), Cooper(10), Marginson.	
Farrelly	McCauley	Robertson	Higgins	Jones	Johnston	Bauress	O'Keefe	Coates	Cooper	Prior	Marginson, Morton(8), Brown(10).	
Farrelly	McCauley	Robertson	Higgins	Jones	Johnston	Bauress	Prior	Coates	Morton	O'Keefe	Marginson(9),Brown(10),Cooper(8).	
Farrelly	McCauley	Robertson	Higgins	Jones	Williams	Bauress	Brown	Coates	Morton	O'Keefe	Marginson(10),Moran(9),Cooper(8).	
Farrelly	McCauley	Robertson	Higgins	Jones	Johnston	Bauress	Marsh	Coates	Morton	O'Keefe	Brown(2),Cooper(10),Prior.	
Farrelly	Prior	Robertson	Higgins	Jones	Johnston	Bauress	Marsh	Coates	Cooper	O'Keefe	Brown(11).Marginson, Williams.	
Farrelly	Prior	Robertson	Higgins	Jones	Johnston	Bauress	Marsh	Coates	Cooper	O'Keefe	Brown(11). Marginson(8), Williams.	
Farrelly	Prior	Marginson	Higgins	Jones	Johnston	Bauress	Brown	Cooper	Morton	O'Keefe	McCauley(2), Moran, Wright(10).	
Rodden	McCauley	Marginson	Higgins	Marsh	Williams	Bauress	Moran	O'Keefe	Cooper	Brown	Wright(8), Robertson(9), Gill(11).	
Farrelly	Prior	Robertson	Higgins	Jones	Johnston	Hennigan	Humphreys	Coates	Grugel	O'Keefe	Wright((7), McCauley(9), Moore(11).	
Rodden	McCauley	Marginson	Higgins	Jones	Brown	Bauress	Prior	Coates	Morton	O'Keefe	Hennigan(5), Grugel(7), Cooper(12)	

OWEN BROWN (MANAGER)

Born in Liverpool, Owen began his playing career with Liverpool and featured in their Central League team before being released. He made his Football League debut with Carlisle United, playing in four games in which he scored twice. Following his release he joined Tranmere Rovers and made 37 appearances for them, scoring eight times before being released at the end of the 1981-82 season.
He began the following season with Crewe Alexandra but after just one appearance, he re-joined Tranmere and finished the season as their top scorer. At the end of the 1983-84 season he was released again, having made 56 appearances in his second spell at Prenton Park, scoring 12 times.
He then had a spell with Chester City but he left after scoring three times in ten games. His non-league career began with Hyde United, before spells at Oswestry Town and Bootle. In 1991 he had a short spell in charge of Prescot in the North West Counties League.
Since then Owen has scouted for both Luton Town and Crystal Palace as well as coaching at the Liverpool School of Excellence.
He was appointed manager at Barrow to replace the departed Mike Walsh in early October 1996.

Owen's assistant is 34 year old Franny Ventre, Liverpool based with considerable experience as a player round the north-west circuit. He was joint caretaker-manager at Barrow for a spell in March 1996 with Neil McDonald.

Neil Morton challenging Wayne Fairclough of Northwich during the 3rd Round FA Trophy match last season.

Photo: Andrew Chitty.

MATCHDAY PROGRAMME

Number of pages	32
Price	£1.20
Programme Editor	
Other club publications:	
Local Newspapers:	North West Evening Mail
	Barrow & West Cumberland Advertiser
Local Radio Stations:	BBC Radio Furness
	BBC Radio Cumbria
	Red Rose Radio
	Bay Radio

1997-98 PLAYING SQUAD

PLAYER	Birthplace Honours	Birthdate	CLUBS
GOALKEEPERS			
Steve Farrelly	Liverpool ESP, GMVC, UL	27.3.65	Chester C, Knowsley U, Macclesfield T, Rotherham U
DEFENDERS			
Paul Robertson	Stockport UL	5.2.72	York C, Stockport Co, Bury, Runcorn, Doncaster R, Witton Alb, £5k to Accrington Stanley
Dave Higgins	Liverpool UL	19.8.61	Eagle, Tranmere R, South Liverpool, Caernarfon T, Tranmere R
Mark Maddox *	Liverpool		Tranmere R, Altrincham
Paul Jones	Liverpool UL	3.6.78	Tranmere R
Mark Williams	Liverpool UL		Tranmere R, Northwich V
Gary Bauress	Liverpool UL	19.1.71	Everton, Tranmere R, Stalybridge C, Ashton U, Stalybridge C, Leek T
Lee Coathup *	Singapore	2.5.67	Everton, Newtown, Vauxhall GM, Stalybridge C, Witton Alb, Stalybridge C
Carl MacAuley	Liverpool UL		Bromborough Pool, Prescot Cables, Vauxhall GM, Witton Alb, Lancaster C
Eddie Johnston	Liverpool UL	8.1.60	South Liverpool, Bangor C, Accrington Stanley, Knowsley U
Mark Seagrave	Bootle E: Y(4), S; Div.2 '96.	22.10.66	Liverpool, Norwich C., Man. City, Bolton W., Swindon T.
MIDFIELDERS			
Jimmy Brown	Liverpool UL		Bootle, Vauxhall GM, Morecambe, Skelmersdale U, Runcorn, Stalybridge C, Witton Alb, Barrow, Lancaster C, Halifax T
Mike Marsh	Liverpool UL	21.7.69	Kirkby T, Liverpool, West Ham U, Coventry C, Galatasaray (Turkey), Southend U
Stuart Humphreys	Whiston UL	27.6.66	St.Helens T, Ellesmere Port T, Atherton LR, Knowsley U, Atherton LR
Ged Kielty *	Manchester	1.9.76	Manchester C, Cobh Ramblers, Southport
Lee Prior	Liverpool FAYC, UL	30.10.77	Liverpool
Ged Hennigan	Liverpool UL	2.8.77	Everton, Barrow, Lancaster C
FORWARDS			
Karl Marginson	Manchester UL	11.11.70	Stockport Co, Blackpool, Curzon Ashton, Droylsden, Ashton U, Rotherham U, Macclesfield T, Chorley, £5k to Barrow
Neil Morton	Congleton UL	21.12.68	Crewe Alexandra, Northwich V, Chester C, Wigan Ath, Altrincham, £11k to Barrow
Lee O'Keefe	Barrow UL		Dalton U, Vickers SC, Morecambe, Holker OB, Workington, Holker OB
Lee Cooper	Liverpool UL		Maghull, St.Helens T, Worcester C, Southport, St.Helens T, Northwich V, Knowsley U, Ashton U, Stockbridge, Burscough
Anthony Wright	Liverpool UL	6.3.78	Wrexham, Barrow, Droylsden
Marc Coates	Swansea GMVC, UL, British Univ		Swansea C, Merthyr Tydfil, Yeovil T, Macclesfield T, Rhyl
Rod McDonald			South Liverpool, Colne Dyn., Walsall, Partick Th., Chester.

Departures - David Moore (Netherfield), Steve Eyre (Bamber Bridge), Ian Leeming (Holker OB), Steve Moran (Droylsden), Steve Watt (Netherfield)

Holker Street, Barrow.

GROUND ADDRESS: Holker Street Stadium, Wilkie Road, Barrow-in-Furness, Cumbria LA14 5UW

TELEPHONE NUMBERS: 01229 820346. **Barrow Soccer Hotline:** 0930 555 820

Commercial Office (on ground) 01229 823061 - Manager Mrs Linda Barker.

SIMPLE DIRECTIONS: M6 to junction 36, A590 to Barrow, enter Barrow on Park Road and after about 2 miles turn left into Wilkie Rd - ground on right.B.R.1/4 mile .

CAPACITY: 3,500 **SEATED:** 1000 **COVERED TERRACING:** 1,200

SOCIAL FACILITIES: Barrow Sports & Leisure centre next to ground. Open matchdays and Functions only. Snack bars on ground.

CLUB SHOP: Situated on the ground the shop is open 9.30-5.00 Monday - Friday and on matchdays.

Barrow Fact File

Nickname: Bluebirds **Sponsors:** TBA at time of going to press.

Club Colours: White shirts with blue trim, white shorts with blue trim, white socks.

Change Colours: Yellow shirts with blue trim, blue shorts with yellow trim, blue socks.

Midweek matchday: Tuesday

Reserves' League: Bolton Combination

PREVIOUS - **Leagues:** Lancs Comb 01-21; Football Lge 21-72; Northern Premier 72-79, 83-84, 86-89, 92-98; GM Vauxhall Conference 79-83, 84-86, 89-92.
Grounds: The Strawberry & Little Park, Roose. **Names:** None

CLUB RECORDS - **Attendance:** 6,002 v Enfield, FA Trophy Semi-Final, Apr 88.
Career Goalscorer: Colin Cowperthwaite 282 (Dec '77-Dec '92).
Career Appearances: Colin Cowperthwaite 704.
Defeat: 1-10 v Hartlepool Utd, Football Lge Div 4, 1959.
Win: 12-0 v Cleator, FA Cup 1920.
Transfer Fee Paid: £9,000 for Andy Whittaker (Ashton Utd, July 94).
Transfer Fee Received: £40,000 for Kenny Lowe (Barnet, Jan 91).

BEST SEASON - **FA Cup:** Third Round Proper on nine occasions including once as a non-League club (90-91, lost 0-1 at Bolton Wanderers).
FA Trophy: Winners 1989-90 (Semi-Final 87-88).

HONOURS - F.A. Trophy Winners 89-90, Northern Premier League 97-98, 88-89, 83-84 (Lge Cup R-up 87-88, Lge Shield 84-85), Bob Lord Trophy R-up 90-91, Cumbrian Cup 82-83 83-84 (R-up 84-85), Lancs Floodlit Cup R-up 86-87, Lancs Sen Cup 54-55 (R-up 51-52 65-66 66-67 69-70), Lancs Challenge Trophy 80-81 (R-up 81-82 84-85), Lancs Comb 20-21 (R-up 13-14, Div 2 R-up 04-05 10-11).

Players progressing to Football League: I McDonald, N McDonald, J Laisby, B Diamond, F Gamble, B Knowles, G Skivington, P Byron, L Edwards, K Lowe, M Dobie, T Rigby, N Doherty.

97-98 Captain: Gary Bauress
97-98 P.o.Y.: Official Supporters Club - Eddie Johnston. National Supporters Club - Dave Higgins.
97-98 Top scorer: Neil Morton (15).

CHELTENHAM TOWN

Season 1997-98 was easily the most successful in the club's 106 year history. Having grasped promotion to the Conference on the final day of the previous campaign, the first priority for Steve Cotterill and his squad was to establish themselves in the higher tier and, hopefully improve upon the Robins previous best Conference finish of 11th.

The season went on to surpass the wildest dreams of even the most optimistic supporter.

CLUB OFFICIALS 1998-99

Chairman	**Paul Baker**
Vice Chairman	**Arthur Hayward**
Company Secretary	**Brian Sandland**
Football Secretary	**Reg Woodward**
3 Harveys Lane, Winchcombe, Glos. GL54 5QS. Tel: 01242 602261	
Commercial Manager	**Gordon Cook**
Press Officer	**Arthur Hayward** **Paul Godfrey**

Quality new signings including Dale Watkins, Russell Milton, Mark Crisp, Steve Book, Neil Grayson and the living legend Clive Walker, all arrived at Whaddon Road. Mr Cotterill also helped the existing players realise a belief in their own ability and, coupled with a wonderful team spirit, the squad achieved one milestone after another -

- a 17-match unbeaten run in the Conference
- a best-ever performance in the FA Cup
- 5 players (Howells, Victory, Banks, Grayson & Watkins) represented England.
- Conference Runners-up.
- FA Trophy Winners

The team's return hame from Wembley was greeted by a civic reception with 12,000 people lining the streets of the Cotswold town to salute their team.

Paul Godfrey

L-R, Back Row: Kevin Keating (Kit Manager), Clive Walker, Russell Milton, Jimmy Smith, Keith Knight, Dale Watkins, Simon Teague, John Atkinson(Physio). Middle Row: Mike Davis (1st Team Coach), Jamie Victory, Mark Freeman, Steve Book, Michael Duff, Stephen Murphy, Ryan Gannaway, Darren Wright, Neil Grayson, Bob Bloomer (PLayer Coach). Front Row: Michael Jackson, Lee Howells, Chris Banks, Steve Citterill (Manager), Jason Eaton, Steve Benton, Ross Casey.

CHELTENHAM TOWN- Match Facts 1997-98

Match No.	Date	Venue H / A	Comp.	Opponents	Result & Score		Att.	Goalscorers	League Position
1	16.08	A	VC	Dover Athletic	L	0-3	*982*		21
2	19.08	H	VC	Hayes	W	2-1	1,196	Eaton 50, Victory 75	-
3	23.08	H	VC	Woking	W	3-2	1,690	Victory 4, Watkins 69 (pen), Eaton 75.	5
4	25.08	A	VC	Hereford United	L	2-3	*3,704*	Watkins 13, Eaton 82.	9
5	30.08	A	VC	Kettering Town	W	1-0	*1,274*	Smith 12.	5
6	07.09	H	VC	Rushden & Diamonds	W	2-0	1,614	Eaton 5, Watkins 59 (pen).	4
7	09.09	H	VC	Leek Town	D	1-1	1.315	Eaton 63.	5
8	16.09	A	VC	Hayes	D	1-1	*485*	Eaton 88.	4
9	20.09	A	VC	Stalybridge Celtic	W	4-1	*561*	Howells 14, Watkins 48, Victory 70, Eaton 87.	3
10	23.09	H	VC	Slough Town	D	1-1	1,539	Victory 75.	3
11	29.09	A	VC	Kidderminster Harriers	W	2-1	*2,320*	Watkins 44, 60.	2
12	04.10	H	VC	Northwich Victoria	W	3-2	1,606	Eaton 9, 14, Knight 51.	2
13	18.10	A	VC	Gateshead	D	0-0	*672*		4
14	01.11	H	VC	Halifax Town	**W**	**4-0**	2,508	**Eaton 3** (61,63,72), Bloomer 67.	4
15	08.11	A	VC	Slough Town	W	2-1	*1,037*	Howells 33, Watkins 45.	3
16	22.11	H	VC	Gateshead	W	2-0	1,659	Eaton 8, Victory 65.	3
17	29.11	A	VC	Leek Town	D	0-0	*708*		4
18	13.12	H	VC	Morecambe	W	2-1	1,717	Walker 15, Watkins 76.	4
19	19.12	A	VC	Stevenage Borough	W	2-1	*1,467*	Smiith 55,Watkins 74.	2
20	26.12	H	VC	Yeovil Town	W	2-0	2,700	Walker 66,81.	2
21	29.12	H	VC	Welling United	D	1-1	2,326	Watkins(pen) 90.	2
22	01.01	A	VC	Yeovil Town	L	1-3	*3,657*	Watkins 77.	2
23	17.01	H	VC	Hednesford Town	W	1-0	2,216	Smith 72.	2
24	24.01	A	VC	Northwich Victoria	L	1-2	*1,118*	Eaton 24.	3
25	07.02	A	VC	Hednesford Town	W	1-0	*1,599*	Eaton 90.	2
26	14.02	H	VC	Stevenage Borough	D	1-1	2,580	Watkins 45.	2
27	07.03	A	VC	Rushden & Diamonds	**L**	**1-4**	*3,857*	Victory 81.	5
28	10.03	H	VC	Farnborough Town	W	1-0	1,436	Howells 20.	4
29	21.03	A	VC	Morecambe	L	0-1	*2,075*		5
30	24.03	H	VC	Kidderminster Harriers	L	0-1	1,902		5
31	31.03	A	VC	Telford United	D	0-0	740		7
32	07.04	H	VC	Dover Athletic	W	3-1	1,606	Grayson 12, 52, Smith 68 (pen).	7
33	11.04	A	VC	Woking	L	0-2	*2,651*		7
34	13.04	H	VC	Hereford United	L	1-2	3,039	Eaton 79.	7
35	15.04	A	VC	Southport	W	2-1	*1,026*	Watkins 17, 89.	6
36	18.04	H	VC	Telford United	W	3-1	1,444	OG (Hodson) 23, Freeman 76, Watkins 85 (pen).	4
37	21.04	A	VC	Welling United	L	1-2	*550*	Knight 45.	4
38	23.04	H	VC	Stalybridge Celtic	W	2-0	1,093	Watkins 45, Grayson 79.	4
39	25.04	A	VC	Halifax Town	D	1-1	*6,357*	Watkins 25.	4
40	27.04	H	VC	Kettering Town	W	2-0	1,219	Walker 25, OG (Ridgway) 50.	2
41	29.04	A	VC	Farnborough Town	W	2-1	*612*	Grayson 13, 56.	2
42	02.05	H	VC	Southport	W	2-0	2,171	Grayson 31, Smith 50.	2

CUP COMPETITIONS

Date	Venue	Comp.	Opponents	Result	Score	Att.	Goalscorers
13.09	A	**FAC** 1Q	Thatcham Town	W	1-0	313	Watkins 9.
27.09	A	2Q	Merthyr Tydfil	W	2-0	790	Eaton 22, Watkins 87.
11.10	H	3Q	Paulton Rovers	W	5-0	827	OG (Goodwin) 47, Watkins 65, Bloomer 85, Smith 89, Crisp 90.
25.10	H	4Q	Sutton United	W	1-0	1,505	Knight 74.
15.11	H	1	Tiverton Town	W	2-1	2,781	Eaton 2, Walker 88.
06.12	H	2	Boreham Wood	D	1-1	3,528	Howells 75.
16.12	A	2 R	Boreham Wood	W	2-0	1,615	Bloomer 41, Smith 68.
13.01	H	3	Reading	D	1-1	6,000	Watkins 23 (pen).
20.01	A	3 R	Reading	L	1-2	9,686	Walker 51.
10.01	A	**FAT** 1	Enfield	D	1-1	966	Watkins 18.
22.01	H	1 R	Enfield	W	5-1	1,650	**Watkins 3** (27 (pen), 38, 63), Knight 54, Walker 76.
31.01	H	2	Rushden & Diamonds	W	3-1	2,058	Eaton 20, Watkins 21, 70.
21.02	A	3	Ashton United	W	1-0	963	Walker 21.
14.03	H	4	Hayes	W	1-0	2,383	Victory 90.
28.03	H	SF - 1	Dover Athletic	W	2-1	3,011	Eaton 75, 82.
04.04	A	SF - 2	Dover Athletic	D	2-2	3,240	Watkins 6, Eaton 34.
17.05	N	FINAL	Southport	W	1-0	26,837	Eaton 79.
07.10	A	**SCC** 1	Yeovil Town	L	1-3	1,007	Watkins 43.
14.10	H	**GSC** 2	Bristol City	D	1-1	274	Smith. Lost 2-4 on penalties.

SCC - Spalding Challenge Cup
GSC Gloucestershire senior Cup

League Attendances: **HIGHEST:** 3,039 v Hereford Utd. **LOWEST:** 1,093 v Stalybridge C.
CONFERENCE: Runners-up **FA CUP:** 3rd Round replay **FA TROPHY:** Winners

1	2	3	4	5	6	7	8	9	10	11	12 14 15	
Book	Duff	Benton	Banks	Knight	Victory	Howells	Milton	Crisp	Watkins	Bloomer	Freeman, Wright (11), Eaton (9).	1
Book	Duff	Knight	Banks	Freeman	Victory	Howells	Milton	Crisp	Watkins	Bloomer	Wright, Eaton (9), Smith (3).	2
Book	Duff	Victory	Banks	Freeman	Smith	Howells	Milton	Eaton	Watkins	Bloomer	Parker, Wright, Crisp.	3
Book	Duff	Victory	Banks	Freeman	Smith	Howells	Milton	Eaton	Watkins	Bloomer	Parker, Wright (2), Crisp (8).	4
Book	Duff	Victory	Banks	Freeman	Smith	Howells	Milton	Eaton	Watkins	Bloomer	Benton, Wright, Crisp.	5
Book	Duff	Victory	Banks	Freeman	Smith	Howells	Milton	Eaton	Watkins	Bloomer	Wright, Crisp (11), Knight.	6
Book	Duff	Victory	Banks	Benton	Smith	Howells	Milton	Eaton	Watkins	Bloomer	Wright, Crisp, Knight.	7
Book	Duff	Victory	Banks	Clark	Smith	Howells	Wright	Eaton	Watkins	Bloomer	Knight (6), Benton, Crisp (8).	8
Book	Duff	Victory	Banks	Clark	Smith	Howells	Milton	Eaton	Watkins	Bloomer	Knight (6), Wright, Crisp (8).	9
Book	Duff	Victory	Banks	Clark	Smith	Howells	Crisp	Eaton	Watkins	Bloomer	Knight (8), Benton, Wright.	10
Book	Duff	Victory	Benton	Clark	Smith	Howells	Knight	Eaton	Watkins	Bloomer	Wright (6), Parker, Crisp.	11
Book	Duff	Victory	Banks	Clark	Smith	Howells	Knight	Eaton	Watkins	Bloomer	Wright (8), Crisp (9), Benton (6).	12
Book	Duff	Victory	Banks	Clark	Smith	Howells	Milton	Eaton	Watkins	Bloomer	Knight (8), Wright, Crisp.	13
Book	Duff	Victory	Banks	Freeman	Smith	Howells	Knight	Eaton	Watkins	Bloomer	Wright (9), Crisp (10), Benton (6).	14
Book	Duff	Victory	Banks	Freeman	Smith	Howells	Knight	Eaton	Watkins	Bloomer	Wright (8), Crisp (9), Walker (6).	15
Book	Duff	Victory	Banks	Freeman	Milton	Wright	Knight	Eaton	Walker	Bloomer	Smith (10), Crisp (9), Benton (6).	16
Book	Duff	Victory	Banks	Freeman	Milton	Wright	Knight	Eaton	Walker	Crisp	Smith, Benton (6), Teague.	17
Book	Duff	Victory	Banks	Freeman	Milton	Howells	Walker	Eaton	Watkins	Wright	Knight (8), Crisp (2), Smith (10).	18
Book	Duff	Victory	Banks	Freeman	Benton	Howells	Walker	Smith	Watkins	Bloomer	Knight, Crisp (8), Wright.	19
Book	Duff	Victory	Banks	Freeman	Knight	Howells	Walker	Smith	Watkins	Bloomer	Crisp (6), Benton (9), Wright.	20
Book	Duff	Victory	Banks	Freeman	Knight	Howells	Walker	Smith	Watkins	Bloomer	Crisp (14), Milton (6), Benton.	21
Book	Duff	Victory	Banks	Freeman	Benton	Howells	Walker	Smith	Watkins	Bloomer	Crisp (6), Milton, Knight (8).	22
Book	Duff	Victory	Banks	Freeman	Knight	Crisp	Walker	Smith	Watkins	Bloomer	Eaton, Wright, Milton.	23
Book	Duff	Victory	Banks	Freeman	Knight	Howells	Walker	Eaton	Watkins	Bloomer	Smith, Crisp (8), Benton (2).	24
Book	Crisp	Victory	Banks	Wright	Knight	Howells	Walker	Eaton	Watkins	Bloomer	Smith, Milton (2), Casey.	25
Book	Duff	Victory	Banks	Thorp	Knight	Howells	Walker	Eaton	Watkins	Wright	Smith(14), Crisp(5), Teague.	26
Book	Duff	Victory	Thorp	Freeman	Knight	Howells	Walker	Grayson	Watkins	Bloomer	Eaton (10), Milton (8), Smith.	27
Book	Duff	Victory	Banks	Freeman	Knight	Howells	Walker	Grayson	Watkins	Bloomer	Eaton, Milton (8), Smith.	28
Book	Duff	Victory	Banks	Milton	Walker	Howells	Grayson	Eaton	Watkins	Bloomer	Smith(9), Jackson, Casey.	29
Book	Duff	Victory	Banks	Freeman	Smith	Howells	Milton	Grayson	Watkins	Bloomer	Eaton, Walker (10), Knight.	30
Book	Duff	Victory	Banks	Freeman	Knight	Howells	Milton	Eaton	Grayson	Bloomer	Watkins (9), Walker, Wright (7).	31
Book	Duff	Victory	Banks	Freeman	Milton	Howells	Walker	Smith	Grayson	Wright	Knight (9), Watkins (7), Eaton (8).	32
Book	Duff	Victory	Banks	Freeman	Milton	Howells	Walker	Knight	Grayson	Wright	Watkins (6), Casey (11), Eaton (8).	33
Book	Duff	Victory	Banks	freeman	Milton	Howells	Knight	Eaton	Grayson	Wright	Walker (11), Watkins (8), Casey.	34
Book	Duff	Victory	Banks	Freeman	Milton	Wright	Walker	Knight	Watkins	Bloomer	Eaton, Jackson, Howells.	35
Book	Duff	Victory	Banks	Freeman	Milton	Wright	Knight	Eaton	Watkins	Bloomer	Grayson (11), Walker, Howells.	36
Book	Duff	Victory	Banks	Freeman	Milton	Wright	Walker	Knight	Grayson	Bloomer	Eaton (10), Watkins (8), Jackson.	37
Book	Victory	Duff	Knight	Bloomer	Freeman	Casey	Watkins	Walker	Wright	Eaton	Banks (7), Jackson (4),m Grayson (8).	38
Book	Knight	Duff	Eaton	Jackson	Walker	Grayson	Banks	Wright	Watkins	Victory	Howells, Bloomer, Casey.	39
Book	Freeman	Duff	Eaton	Victory	Walker	Jackson	Watkins	Wright	Grayson	Banks	Knight (7), Howells, Bloomer.	40
Book	Knight	Duff	Eaton	Jackson	Walker	Grayson	Banks	Wright	Watkins	Victory	Freeman, Casey, Smith (10).	41
Book	Victory	Banks	Duff	Jackson	Knight	Watkins	Wright	Walker	Grayson	Eaton	Smith (11), Casey (9), Teague (7).	42

1	2	3	4	5	6	7	8	9	10	11	12 14 15
Book	Duff	Victory	Banks	Benton	Smith	Howells	Wright	Eaton	Watkins	Bloomer	Crisp (3), Knight, Jackson.
Book	Duff	Victory	Banks	Benton	Smith	Howells	Knight	Eaton	Watkins	Bloomer	Wright (7), Parker (9), Crisp (6).
Book	Duff	Victory	Banks	Benton	Smith	Howells	Knight	Eaton	Watkins	Bloomer	Wright (10), Parker (9), Crisp (11).
Book	Duff	Victory	Banks	Freeman	Smith	Howells	Knight	Eaton	Watkins	Bloomer	Wright, Crisp, Teague.
Book	Duff	Victory	Banks	Freeman	Smith	Wright	Knight	Eaton	Watkins	Bloomer	Crisp (8), Walker (6), Milton (2).
Book	Duff	Victory	Banks	Freeman	Milton	Howells	Knight	Eaton	Walker	Wrtight	Smith, Crisp (6), Teague (8).
Book	Duff	Victory	Banks	Freeman	Milton	Howells	Walker	Eaton	Watkins	Bloomer	Smith (9), Crisp (6), Benton (8).
Book	Duff	Victory	Banks	Freeman	Knight	Howells	Walker	Smith	Watkins	Bloomer	Crisp, Eaton (8), Benton (9).
Book	Duff	Victory	Banks	Freeman	Benton	Crisp	Walker	Eaton	Watkins	Bloomer	Knight (8), Smith (6), Wright (7).
Book	Duff	Victory	Banks	Freeman	Knight	Howells	Walker	Smith	Watkins	Bloomer	Crisp, Benton (9), Eaton (10).
Book	Duff	Victory	Banks	Freeman	Knight	Howells	Smith	Eaton	Watkins	Bloomer	Walker (10), Wright (11), Crisp (6).
Book	Crisp	Victory	Banks	Freeman	Knight	Howells	Walker	Eaton	Watkins	Bloomer	Smith (9), Benton, Milton.
Book	Duff	Victory	Smith	Freeman	Knight	Howells	Walker	Eaton	Watkins	Parker	Casey, Bloomfield, Teague
Book	Duff	Victory	Banks	Freeman	Knight	Howells	Walker	Eaton	Watkins	Bloomer	Casey, Milton (8), Smith (6).
Book	Duff	Victory	Banks	Freeman	Milton	Howells	Walker	Smith	Watkins	Bloomer	Wright, Eaton(9), Knight.
Book	Duff	Victory	Banks	Freeman	Milton	Howells	Walker	Eaton	Watkins	Bloomer	Knight, Smith, Wright (6).
Book	Duff	Victory	Banks	Freeman	Knight	Howells	Walker	Eaton	Watkins	Bloomer	Smith (6), Wright, Milton (8)
Book	Duff	Victory	Banks	Clark	Smith	Crisp	Knight	Eaton	Watkins	Wright,	Parker (6), Benton, Howells (7).
Taylor	Duff	Victory	Banks	Freeman	Smith	Howells	Knight	Crisp	Watkins	Milton	Wright (6), Parker (8), Bloomer (11).

STEVE COTTERILL (MANAGER)

Date of Appointment	21.01.97
Date of Birth:	20.07.64
Place of Birth:	Cheltenham

PREVIOUS CLUBS

As manager	Sligo Rovers (L.o.Ireland)
As player	Cheltenham T., Alvechurch, Burton Albion, Wimbledon, Brighton & H.A., AFC Bournemouth.

HONOURS

As manager	European Qualification with Sligo Rovers. Promotion to Conference 96-97. FA Trophy 97-98, Conference R-up 97-98.
As player	3 x "Player of the Year" awards.

1st Team Coach: Mike Davis **Player/Coach:** Bob Bloomer **Physio:** John Atkinson

DALE WATKINS
Leading Goalscorer 1997-98

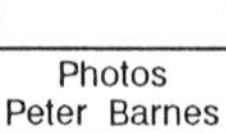

Photos
Peter Barnes

LEE HOWELLS
Players 'Player of the Year' 1997-98

MATCHDAY PROGRAMME

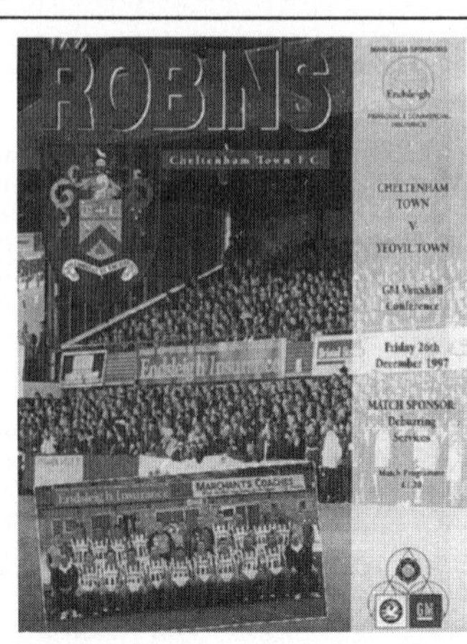

Number of pages	48
Price	£1.20
Programme Editor	Paul Godfrey 01242 262980
Other club publications:	Review of season 1997-98
Local Newspapers:	Western Daily Press (d) Gloucestershire Echo (d) Citizen 'Pink un' (w/e)
Local Radio Stations:	BBC Radio Gloucestershire Cheltenham Radio Severn Sound

PLAYING SQUAD

Player	*Birthplace* / *Honours*	*D.O.B.*	*Previous Clubs*
GOALKEEPERS			
Steve Book	Bournemouth FA XI, FAT.	07.07.69	Welton Rov., Weston-s-Mare, Brighton & H.A., Lincoln C., Forest Green Rov.
Ryan Gannaway	Gloucester	28.08.73	Forest Green Rov., Shortwood Utd.
DEFENDERS			
Michael Duff	Oxford FAT	11.01.78	None
Jamie Victory	London FA XI, Eng. S-P, FAT.	14.11.75	West Ham Utd. (YTS), AFC Bournemouth.
Chris Banks	Stone, Staffs. FA XI, Eng. S-P, FAT.	22.11.65	Port Vale, Exeter C., Bath City.
Mark Freeman	Walsall SLP	27.01.70	Bilston T., Wolves, Willenhall T., Hednesford T., Gloucester City.
Steve Benton	Bristol	20.12.73	Bristol City (YTS), Clevedon Town.
MIDFIELDERS			
Lee Howells	Freemantle (Aus). FA XI, Eng S-P, FAT.	14.10.68	Bristol Rovers (YTS), Brisbane Utd. (Aus)
Bob Bloomer	Sheffield FAT	21.06.66	Chesterfield, Bristol Rovers.
Russell Milton	Folkestone SLP, FA XI, Eng. S-P, FAT.	12.01.69	Arsenal, South China (H.K.), Dover Athletic.
Darren Wright	West Bromwich FAT.	14.03.68	Wolves, Wrexham, Worcester C., Willenhall T., Atherstone Utd.
Keith Knight	Cheltenham Eng: Schoolboys, FAT	16.02.69	Cheltenham T., Reading, Veendam(Holland), Gloucester C., Trowbridge T.,Yeovil T., Gloucester C., Halesowen T.
Mark Crisp	Bromsgrove SLP, BLT.	15.09.64	Redditch Utd., Bromsgrove Rov., Alvechurch, Bromsgrove Rov., Macclesfield T., Bromsgrove R.
Michael Jackson	Cheltenham	26.06.80	None
Ross Casey	Stroud	07.08.79	None
FORWARDS			
Jason Eaton	Bristol FA XI, FAT	29.01.69	Bristol Rov., Clevedon T., Trowbridge T., Bristol City, Gloucester City.
Neil Grayson	York FA XI, Eng. S-P, Div 3 P/O.	01.01.64	Doncaster Rovers, York City, Chesterfield, Gateshead, Boston Utd., Northampton T., Hereford Utd.
Dale Watkins	Peterborough SLM, SLP, FA XI, Eng: S-P, FAT	04.11.71	Sheffield Utd.(YTS), Peterborough Utd., Rotherham Utd., Bakers Perkins, Grantham T., Rushden & Diamonds, Gloucester City.
Jimmy Smith	Johnstone, Renfrews. FAT	22.11.69	Torquay Utd., Salisbury City.
Clive Walker	Oxford Eng: Schoolboy, FAT (x4)	25.06.57	Chelsea, Sunderland, Q.P.R., Fulham, Brighton & H.A., Woking, Brentford (Asst. Man.)

DEPARTURES (during season): Chris Taylor (Kettering Town)
PLAYERS ON LOAN: Billy Clark (Bristol Rovers), Michael Thorp (Reading).

Whaddon Road, Cheltenham

ADDRESS: Whaddon Road, Cheltenham, Gloucestershire GL52 5NA
TELEPHONE NUMBER: 01242 573558

SIMPLE DIRECTIONS: From North: M5 J 10, then A4019, over one island, over next lights, left at next junct. into Poole Way, then bear right, over next lights, left at next lights into Portland St., right at next lights then bear left onto B4632 Prestbury Road, over next island then right into Whaddon Rd. **From South:** M5 J 11 then A40, over one island, 2nd exit from next island, left at next junct. onto B4633 Gloucester Road, over next island (next to railway station) then right at 3rd set of lights, left at next junction into Poole Way then as above. **From East:** M4 J 15 then A417 to Cheltenham. Down the hill then 3rd exit from next island into Bath Road, right at 2nd set of lights, then left into College Road, over next lights into Hewlett Road, 2nd exit at next island into All Saints Road, over large island, right at next island into B4632 Prestbury Road, then right into Whaddon Road.

CAPACITY: 6,114 **COVERED TERRACING:** 2,605 **COVERED SEATING:** 1,088

SOCIAL FACILITIES: Clubhouse open every evening, three bars, two function rooms for private hire, bar open before and after matches.

CLUB SHOP: Access from outside & inside ground, sells souvenirs of all descriptions.

Cheltenham Fact File

Nickname: Robins **Sponsors:** Endsleigh Insurance
Club Colours: Red & white striped shirts, white shorts, white socks.
Change Colours: Yellow & blue halved shirts, blue shorts, blue socks.
Midweek matchday: Tuesday
Reserves' League: Optimum Interiors Central Conference

PREVIOUS - **Leagues:** Local leagues to 1932, Birmingham Combination 32-35, Southern 35-85, GMV Conf 85-92, Southern League 92-97.
Names: None.
Grounds: Whaddon Lane, Carter's Field (pre-war).

CLUB RECORDS - **Win:** 12 - 0 v Chippenham Rovers, FA Cup 3rd Qual., 2.11.35.
Defeat: 1 - 10 v Merthyr Tydfil, Southern League, 8.3.52.
Attendance: 8,326 v Reading, FA Cup 1st Rd 56-57.
Career Goalscorer: Dave Lewis 290 (1970-83).
Career Appearances: Roger Thorndale 701 (58-76).
Transfer fee paid: £20,000 to Kidderminster Harriers for Kim Casey, 1990.
Transfer fee received: £60,000 (initial) from Southampton for Christer Warren, 1995.

BEST SEASON - **FA Cup:** Third Round - 97-98, 1-2 v Reading (A) after 1-1;
33-34, 1-3 v Blackpool (H).
League clubs defeated: Carlisle United 33-34.
FA Trophy: Winners 1997-98, Q-F 85-86, 88-89. **FA Amateur Cup:** N/A.

HONOURS - F.A. Trophy Winners 97-98; Vauxhall Conference Runners-up 97-98; Southern Lge 84-85, R-up 92-93 94-95 96-97, Midland Div 82-83, Lg Cup 57-58 (R-up 68-69 84-85), Championship Shield 58-59, Merit Cup 84-85); Nth Glos. Snr Professional Cup (30 times), Midland Floodlit Cup 85-86 86-87 87-88.

Players progressing to Football League: Peter Goring (Arsenal), Roy Shiner (Huddersfield), Peter Rushworth (Leicester), Paul Tester (Shrewsbury), Keith Knight (Reading), Peter Shearer (Bournemouth), Brett Angell (Derby), Simon Brain (Hereford), Chris Burns (Portsmouth), Christer Warren (Southampton), Steve Jones (Swansea).

1997-98 Captain: Chris Banks **1997-98 Top Goalscorer:** Dale Watkins (29)
1997-98 Player of the Year: Chris Banks (Supporters). Lee Howells (Players).

DONCASTER ROVERS

There isn't really a lot you can say in positive fashion about a season when you win only four of your 50 competitive games, score only 33 goals and concede 127.

And, as if that was not bad enough, there seemed to be constant conflict between club and supporters throughout the season.

CLUB OFFICIALS 1998-99

Chairman **K Haran**

Club Secretary **Mrs K J Odale**
c/o the club
Tel: 01302 539441 Fax: 01302 539679

Commercial Executive **Terry Burdass**
c/o the club (see above)

As the club were in the process of being taken over as we were going to press the details here are unfortunately rather scarce.

It is not our place to take sides or to be political, but fans and club alike must learn that no club has an inalienable right to sucess or even to existance, and they must all learn to work together.

Although Rovers' fans were devastated to lose their League status they should take heart from some of their predecessors - Halifax Town who will replace them in the League being a fine example, not to mention Lincoln City, Darlington and Colchester.

During the season no less than 45 players turned out for Rovers, only three of whom - Lee Warren, Harvey Cunningham and Adie Mike - started both the first and last League games. The club also went through the season without a shirt sponsor.

All in all a grim season for Rovers but let us hope that they can at least enjoy their first season in the Conference.

Pictured before their final game in the Football League - L-R, Back Row: Danny Bergera (Director of Football), danny George, Lee Warren, Craig Davies, Darren Brookes, Harvey Cunningham, Robert Pell, Mark Hawthorne, Maurice Hilton. Front Row: Robert Debenham, Prince Moncrieffe, Robert Betts, Mark Donnelly, Padi Wilson, Adie Mike. The mascot is 4-year-old Natalie Greenwood. Photo: Courtesy of Frank Gilligan.

DONCASTER ROVERS - Match Facts 1997-98

Match No.	Date	Venue H / A	Comp.	Opponents	Result & Score		Att.	Goalscorers	League Position
1	09.08	A	NL	Shrewsbury Town	L	1-2	*3,049*	Conlon.	16
2	16.08	H	NL	Peterborough United	L	0-5	1,920		22
3	23.08	A	NL	Macclesfield Town	L	0-3	*2,635*		23
4	30.08	H	NL	Exeter City	L	0-1	1,186		24
5	02.09	H	NL	Leyton Orient	L	1-4	1,098	Moncrieffe.	24
6	05.09	A	NL	Mansfield Town	D	1-1	*2,874*	Moncrieffe.	24
7	13.09	A	NL	Scunthorpe United	D	1-1	*3,378*	McDonald.	24
8	20.09	H	NL	Cambridge United	D	0-0	1,258		24
9	27.09	A	NL	Torquay United	L	0-2	*1,650*		24
10	04.10	H	NL	Brighton & Hove Albion	L	1-3	2,351	Cunningham.	24
11	11.10	H	NL	Hartlepool United	D	2-2	1,526	Moncrieffe 2.	24
12	18.10	A	NL	Darlington	L	1-5	*2,451*	Moncrieffe	24
13	21.10	A	NL	Colchester United	L	1-2	*2,588*	McDonald.	24
14	24.10	H	NL	Swansea City	L	0-3	1,170		24
15	01.11	A	NL	Scarborough	L	0-4	*2,345*		24
16	04.11	H	NL	Cardiff City	D	1-1	1,004	Moncrieffe	24
17	08.11	A	NL	Barnet	D	1-1	*2,015*	Warren.	24
18	18.11	A	NL	Lincoln City	L	1-2	*2,957*	Moncrieffe.	24
19	22.11	H	NL	Rochdale	L	0-3	1,503		24
20	29.11	A	NL	Hull City	L	0-3	*4,721*		24
21	02.12	H	NL	Chester City	**W**	**2-1**	864	M Smith, Helliwell.	24
22	13.12	A	NL	Notts County	L	2-5	*4,024*	M Smith (pen), Pell.	24
23	19.12	H	NL	Rotherham United	L	0-3	3,533		24
24	28.12	A	NL	Leyton Orient	**L**	**0-8**	*4,437*		24
25	10.01	H	NL	Shrewsbury Town	W	1-0	1,116	Moncrieffe.	24
26	17.01	A	NL	Exeter City	L	1-5	*4,145*	Pemberton.	24
27	24.01	H	NL	Macclesfield Town	L	0-3	1,707		24
28	30.01	H	NL	Scunthorpe United	L	1-2	2,036	Mike.	24
29	03.02	H	NL	Mansfield Town	L	0-3	1,538		24
30	07.02	A	NL	Cambridge City	L	1-2	*2,478*	Wilson.	24
31	10.02	A	NL	Peterborough United	W	1-0	*4,577*	M Smith.	24
32	14.02	A	NL	Brighton & Hove Albion	D	0-0	*6,339*		24
33	21.02	H	NL	Torwuay United	L	0-1	1,424		24
34	24.02	H	NL	Darlington	L	0-2	1,324		24
35	28.02	A	NL	Hartlepool United	L	1-3	*1,920*	Rowe.	24
36	03.03	H	NL	Barnet	L	0-2	739		24
37	10.03	H	NL	Scarborough	L	1-2	1,129	Rowe.	24
38	14.03	A	NL	Cardiff City	L	1-7	*2,931*	Mike.	24
39	21.03	H	NL	Lincoln City	L	2-4	2,357	Donnelly, George.	24
40	28.03	A	NL	Rochdale	L	1-4	*1,858*	Tedaldi.	24
41	04.04	H	NL	Hull City	W	1-0	2,597	Mike.	24
42	11.04	A	NL	Chester City	L	1-2	*1,593*	Mike.	24
43	13.04	H	NL	Notts County	L	1-2	2,485	Messer.	24
44	18.04	A	NL	Rotherham United	L	0-3	*4,328*		24
45	25.04	A	NL	Swansea City	D	0-0	*3,661*		24
46	02.05	H	NL	Colchester United	L	0-1	3,572		24

CUP COMPETITIONS

Date	Venue	Round	Opponents	Result	Score	Att.	Goalscorers
F.A. CUP							
15.11	A	1	Preston North End	L	2-3	7,953	Mike, Hammond..
AUTO WINDSCREEN TROPHY							
09.12	H	1	Rochdale	L	0-1	580	
COCA COLA CUP							
11.08	H	1-1	Nottingham Forest	L	0-8	4,547	
27.08	A	1-2	Nottingham Forest	L	1-2	9.908	OG

League Attendances	HIGHEST: 3,572 v Colchester Utd.	LOWEST: 864 v Chester City
NATIONWIDE DIV. 3: 24th	**FA CUP:** 1st Round	**COCA-COLA CUP:** 1st Round

1	2	3	4	5	6	7	8	9	10	11	12 14 15	
Ingham	DrEsdaille	Dowell	Warren	Gore	Brookes	Cunningham	McDonald	Mike	Pemberton	Ireland	DvEsdaille(10), Sanders(3), Conlon(7)	1
Ingham	DrEsdaille	Sanders	Warren	Gore	Brookes	Cunningham	McDonald	Mike	Pemberton	Ireland	Moncrieffe(14),Donnelly(6),Conlon(10)	2
Ingham	Utley	Sanders	Warren	Gore	Brookes	Dobbin	McDonald	Mike	Conlon	Ireland	Cunningham(4),Clarke(2),Pemberton(10)	3
Ingham	Finley	Sanders	DvEsdaille	Gore	Dobbin	Cunningham	McDonald	Mike	Pemberton	Ireland	Ramsay(8), Moncrieffe, Conlon(4)	4
Ingham	Ramsay	Sanders	Warren	Ireland	Finley	Cunningham	McDonald	Moncrieffe	Pemberton	Clark	Dobbin(11), Utley(2), Conlon(10)	5
Ingham	Ireland	DrEsdaille	Warren	Ramsay	Brookes	Cunningham	McDonald	Moncrieffe	Pemberton	Finley	Dobbin(5), Sanders(6), Conlon(11).	6
Ingham	Ireland	DrEsdaille	Warren	Gore	Sanders	Cunningham	McDonald	Moncrieffe	Pemberton	Mike	Dobbin, Ramsay(6), Conlon.	7
Ingham	Ireland	DrEsdaille	Warren	Gore	Thorpe	Cunningham	Hawes	Moncrieffe	Pemberton	Mike	Sanders, Ramsay(5),Conlon (8).	8
Ingham	Ireland	DrEsdaille	Warren	Finley	Thorpe	Cunningham	Sanders	Moncrieffe	Pemberton	Mike	Dobbin(6), Ramsay(3), Conlon(10)	9
D Smith	Ireland	Sanders	Warren	Finley	Brookes	Cunningham	Hawes	Thornley	Conlon	Pemberton	Thorpe, Ramsay, Moncrieffe (9).	10
Ingham	Sanders	Pemberton	Warren	Gore	Conlon	Cunningham	McDonald	Mike	Moncrieffe	Hawes	Ramsay(6), Dr Esdaille, Finley(8).	11
Williams	Dr Esdaille	Pemberton	Warren	Gore	Finley	Cunningham	Conlon	Mike	Moncrieffe	Hawes	Sanders(8), Ramsay, M Smith.	12
Williams	Sanders	Pemberton	Warren	Gore	Dobbin	Cunningham	McDonald	Mike	Ireland	Hawes	Moncrieffe(11), Brookes, Ramsay.	13
Williams	Hawes	Pemberton	Warren	Gore	Dobbin	Cunningham	McDonald	Mike	Ireland	Moncrieffe	Sanders(2), Ramsay(7), Messer(11).	14
Williams	Dr Esdaille	Sanders	Dobbin	Gore	Warren	Ireland	McDonald	Mike	Moncrieffe	Pemberton	Ramsay(2), M Smith(11), Conlon(7).	15
Williams	Warren	Sanders	Dobbin	Gore	Mike	Ireland	McDonald	Helliwell	Moncrieffe	Pemberton	M Smith(10), Hawes(3), Brookes.	16
Williams	Warren	M Smith	Dobbin	Gore	Mike	Ireland	McDonald	Helliwell	Moncrieffe	Hawes	Brookes, Sanders(14), Messer(9).	17
Hoggeth	Brookes	Hilton	Dobbin	Gore	Mike	Ireland	Warren	Hammond	Moncrieffe	Hawes	Sanders, M Smith(9), Ramsay.	18
Hoggeth	Brookes	Hilton	Dobbin	Gore	Pell	Ireland	Warren	Mike	Moncrieffe	McDonald	Sanders(13), M Smith(2), Hammond.	19
Davis	Sanders	Smith	Cunningham	Gore	Mike	Ireland	Dobbin	Helliwell	Moncrieffe	McDonald	Pell, Hilton, Brookes(4).	20
Davis	Sanders	M Smith	Warren	Gore	Mike	Ireland	Dobbin	Helliwell	Moncrieffe	Cunningham	Brookes, Ramsay, Conlon.	21
Hoggeth	Cunningham	M Smith	Warren	Utley	Pell	Ireland	Dobbin	Helliwell	Moncrieffe	Mike	Brookes(1), Hilton, Conlon(6).	22
Davis	Sanders	M Smith	Warren	Gore	Mike	Ireland	Cunningham	Helliwell	Moncrieffe	Dobbin	Hilton, Utley(10), Conlon(8).	23
Hoggeth	Sanders	M Smith	Hawthorne	Gore	Mike	Dr Esdaille	Warren	Helliwell	Moncrieffe	Dobbin	Pemberton(10),Ramsay(2),Messer(9)	24
Davis	Ireland	Hilton	Warren	Gore	Brookes	Moncrieffe	Dr Esdaille	Mike	Pemberton	Dobbin	Sanders, Dv Esdaille(10), Pell.	25
Davis	Ireland	Hilton	Warren	Gore	Brookes	Moncrieffe	Dr Esdaille	Mike	Pemberton	Dobbin	Sanders, George(6), DvEsdaille.	26
Davis	Ireland	Hilton	Warren	Gore	Mike	Moncrieffe	Dobbin	Helliwell	Pemberton	Wilson	George(11), Dr Esdaille, Pell(9).	27
Davis	Ireland	Pemberton	Warren	Gore	George	Moncrieffe	Dobbin	Mike	Dr Esdaille	Dv Esdaille	Sanders, M Smith, Messer(11).	28
Davis	Ireland	Pemberton	Warren	George	Dobbin	Dv Esdaille	Edwards	Mike	Moncrieffe	Wilson	Messer(10), Sanders, Ramsay(8).	29
Davis	Ireland	Pemberton	Warren	Gore	George	Cunningham	Dobbin	Mike	Dv Esdaille	Wilson	Moncrieffe(2), Sanders, M Smith(10).	30
Davis	Ireland	Pemberton	Warren	Cunningham	George	Dr Esdaille	Dobbin	Mike	Moncrieffe	Wilson	M Smith(5), Sanders, Edwards.	31
Parks	Ireland	Pemberton	Warren	Mike	George	Cunningham	Dobbin	Dr Esdaille	Moncrieffe	Wilson	M Smith(10), Sanders, Dv Esdaille.	32
Parks	Ireland	Pemberton	Warren	Mike	Sanders	Cunningham	Dobbin	Dr Esdaille	Rowe	Wilson	Hawes, M Smith(9), Dv Esdaille.	33
Parks	Ireland	Sanders	Warren	Mike	George	Cunningham	Dobbin	Rowe	Dv Esdaille	Dr Esdaille	M Smith(6), Hawes(7), Messer(10).	34
Parks	Ireland	M Smith	Warren	Mike	Sanders	Cunningham	Dobbin	Rowe	Dv Esdaille	Dr Esdaille	Edwards(10), Messer(3), Hawes(11).	35
Parks	Dr Esdaille	Ireland	Warren	Mike	Sanders	Cunningham	Dobbin	Rowe	Dv Esdaille	Wilson	Edwards, M Smith(10), Messer.	36
Parks	Ireland	M Smith	Warren	Gore	George	Cunningham	Dobbin	Rowe	Moncrieffe	Messer	Dv Esdaille, Dr Esdaille, Edwards(10).	37
Davis	Dr Esdaille	M Smith	Warren	Mike	George	Cunningham	Dobbin	Rowe	Moncrieffe	Dv Esdaille	Edwards(2), Pell(11), Messer(10).	38
Hoggeth	Debenham	Edwards	Warren	Mike	George	Dr Esdaille	Donnelly	Pell	Messer	Dv Esdaille	Hawthorne, Borg, Moncrieffe(3).	39
Hoggeth	Debenham	Edwards	Warren	George	Mike	Borg	Donnelly	Pell	Messer	Dv Esdaille	Hawthorne(2), Russell(11), Tedaldi(10)	40
Hoggeth	Debenham	Hilton	Warren	Hawthorne	George	Cunningham	Donnelly	Pell	Mike	Russell	Tedaldi(3), Borg, Messer(9).	41
Hoggeth	Debenham	Hilton	Warren	Hawthorne	George	Cunningham	Donnelly	Pell	Mike	Russell	Dr Esdaille(9),Edwards(3),Moncrieffe(2)	42
Davis	Dr Esdaille	Edwards	Warren	Hawthorne	George	Cunningham	Donnelly	Messer	Mike	Russell	Debenham(3), Pell(5), Moncrieffe(2).	43
Davis	Moncrieffe	Edwards	Warren	Hawthorne	George	Cunningham	Donnelly	Mike	Wilson	Russell	Hilton(3), Betts(8), Messer.	44
Davis	Moncrieffe	Hilton	Warren	George	Hawthorne	Cunningham	Donnelly	Betts	Mike	Wilson	Debenham(8), Dv Esdaille(2), Pell.	45
Davis	Donnelly	Hilton	Warren	George	Hawthorne	Cunningham	Moncrieffe	Betts	Mike	Wilson	Debenham, Brookes, Pell(2).	46

1	2	3	4	5	6	7	8	9	10	11	12 14 15
Williams	Ireland	Hilton	Warren	Gore	Brookes	McDonald	Dobbin	Mike	Moncrieffe	M Smith	Sanders, Hawthorne, Hammond(6), Ramsay(11).
Davis	Sanders	M Smith	Warren	Gore	Mike	Ireland	Dobbin	Helliwell	Moncrieffe	Cunningham	Brookes(10), Ramsay, Conlon.
Ingham	DrEsdaille	Sanders	Warren	Gore	Brookes	DvEsdaille	McDonald	Mike	Moncrieffe	Ireland	Cunningham(7), Middlemass, Conlon.
Ingham	Finley	Sanders	Dv Esdaille	Gore	Brookes	Cunningham	McDonald	Mike	Moncrieffe	Smith	Ireland(11),Pemberton(10),Ramsay(4).

IAN SNODIN (MANAGER)

Date of Appointment	1st August 1998
Date of Birth:	15th August 1963
Place of Birth:	Rotherham

PREVIOUS CLUBS

As manager	None
As asst. manager/coach	None
As player	Doncaster Rovers, Leeds Utd., Everton, Sunderland (loan), Oldham Ath., Scarborough.

HONOURS

As manager	N/A
As asst. manager/coach	N/A
As player	England: u21 x4.

Physio: Phil Mcloughlin

MATCHDAY PROGRAMME

Number of pages	36
Price	£1.50
Programme Editor	Bernard Jordan (0161 456 2542)
Other club publications:	Supporters' Club Handbook Two fanzines
Local Newspapers:	Doncaster Star Yorkshire Post
Local Radio Stations:	Radio Hallam Radio Sheffield

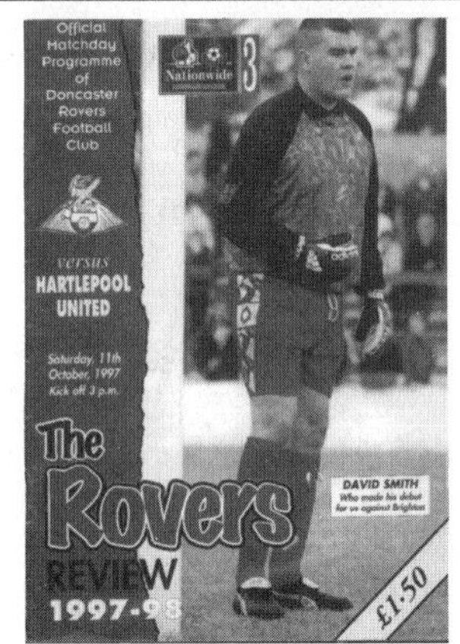

As Westferry Limited only completed their take-over of Doncaster Rovers officially on 1st August, Chief Executive Ian McMahon and player-manager Ian Snodin could not start to recruit their squad until after this date.

Unfortunately this did not not leave us a lot of time prior to publication, to collect details of their players, so please accept our apologies if the following squad details are rather sparse.

PLAYING SQUAD

DONCASTER ROVERS

Player	*Birthplace* *Honours*	*D.O.B.*	*Previous Clubs*
GOALKEEPERS			
Neville Southall	Llandudno W: 74, Div 185, 87, FAC 84, 95, ECWC 85.	16.09.58	Bangor C., Winsford Utd., Bury, Everton, Port Vale (L),
DEFENDERS			
Darren Brooks	Sheffield	07.07.73	Worksop Town
Danny George	Lincoln	22.10.78	Nottingham Forest
Mark Hume	Barnsley	21.05.78	Barnsley
Simon Shaw	Middlesbrough	21.09.73	Darlington
Colin Sutherland	Glasgow	15.03.75	Clydebank, Scarborough
Lee Warren	Manchester	28.02.69	Leeds Utd., Rochdale, Hull C., Lincoln C., Doncaster R.
MIDFIELDERS			
Mark Bradley	Glasgow	10.08.76	Ashfield Jun., Hearts
Harvey Cunningham	Manchester	11.09.68	Doncaster Rovers.
David Esdaile	Manchester	22.07.63	Droylsden, Doncaster Rovers.
Scott Maxfield	Doncaster	13.07.76	Doncaster Rovers (T), Hull City
Ian Snodin	Rotherham E: B 2, u21 4, Y 4; Div.1 '87	15.08.63	Doncaster Rovers (A), Leeds Utd., Everton, Sunderland (loan), Oldham Ath., Scarborough.
FORWARDS			
Shaun Goodwin	Rotherham	14.06.69	Rotherham Utd (T),
Tommy Wright	Dunfermline S: u21.	10.01.66	Leeds Utd.,Oldham Ath., Leicester C., Middlesbrough, Bradford C., Oldham Ath., St. Johnstone

OTHER PLAYERS:
Kevin McIntyre (D) (Tranmere R.) (Loan) , Andy Woods (G) (Trial), Jason Minnett (M) (Exeter City) (Trial)

Belle Vue Ground, Doncaster.

GROUND ADDRESS: Belle Vue Ground, Doncaster, S. Yorks. DN4 5HT.

TELEPHONE NUMBERS: 01302 539441. Fax 01302 539679

SIMPLE DIRECTIONS: From north & west into doncaster town centre and follow signs to Bawtry (A368) and after 1.2 miles take 3rd exit at r'about into Bawtry Road. From east - M18, then A630, A18 and A638 (Bawtry Road). From south - M18 junct 3, A6182, then A18 and A638 (Bawtry Road).

CAPACITY: 8,608 **SEATED:** 1,259 **COVERED TERRACING:** 2,125

SOCIAL FACILITIES:

No Clubhouse. Food outlets on ground on matchdays.

CLUB SHOP: Open only on matchdays.

Doncaster Fact File

Nickname: The Rovers **Sponsors:** TBA

Club Colours: Red shirts, red shorts, red socks.

Change Colours: Yellow shirts, light blue shorts, white socks.

Midweek matchday: Tuesday

Reserve League: No reserve team.

PREVIOUS - **Leagues:** Midland Alliance Lge 1890-91; Midland League 1891-1901, 03-04 & 05-15, 20-23; Football League 1901-3, 04-05, 23-Sept 39, 42-44, 45-98; Midland Comb. Lge 1915-16; E Midlands War Lge Oct 1939-40; War Lge North 1940-42, 44-45.
Names: None **Ground:** 1880-1916 Intake Ground; 1920-22 Benetthorpe Ground; 1922 onwards Belle Vue (formerly known as Low Pasture).

CLUB RECORDS - **Attendance:** 37,149 v Hull City, Div. 3N, 2.10.1948.
Career Goalscorer: Tom Keetley, 180, 1923-29.
Career Appearances: Fred Emery, 417, 1925-36.
Win: 10-0 v Darlington, Div. 4, 25.01.64 - Home or Away
Defeat: 0-12 v Small Heath, Division 2, 11.04.03 - Home or Away ??
Transfer Fee Paid: £62,500 to Torquay United for Darren Moore, July 1995.
Transfer Fee Received: £350,000 from Bradford City for Darren Moore, 1997.

BEST SEASON - **FA Trophy:** Not applicable
FA Cup: 5th Rd 1951-52, 53-54, 54-55 & 55-56.
League Cup: 5th Round 1975-76.

HONOURS - Division 3 N 1934-35, 46-47, 49-50. Division 4 1965-66, 68-69; Sheffield County Cup 1890-91, 1911-12, 35-36, 37-38, 55-56, 67-68, 75-76, 85-86; Yorkshire Electricity Cup 1995-96; Midland Counties League 1896-97, 98-99; Northern Intermediate Lge Cup 1984-95, 86-87.

Players Progressing to Football Lge: Not applicable.

97-98 Captain: Lee Warren
97-98 Supporters' Player of the Year: Lee Warren
97-98 Top scorer: Prince Moncrieffe

DOVER ATHLETIC

Three straight wins at the beginning of the season put Dover at the top of the table and gave Bill Williams, their experienced manager, a wonderful return to Conference management.

Their home crowd swelled from 982 on the opening day to 1,787 for their second home game but football is a strange game and only two victories in the next ten Conference games proved to be the norm in a very inconsistent season.

The highlight of the season was certainly the F.A.Umbro Trophy run to the semi-finals - where two very questionable refereeing decisions gave Cheltenham a 2-1 first leg lead and an exciting 2-2 draw at the Crabble only brought great disappointment.

Some sound team building has bolstered the squad during the summer and it will be important that they find form quickly next season.

CLUB OFFICIALS 1998-99

Chairman **John Husk**

Directors **J T Husk, A G Husk, J F Durrant, K F Stamp, G A Goodacre, D Hammond, C J Harman, T J Parmenter.**

Secretary **John Durrant**
c/o the club Tel: 01304 822373

Commercial Manager/ Press Officer **Jean Haves**

L-R, Back Row: Gary Stebbing, Stuart Munday, Lee Palmer, Scott Daniels, Ricky Reina, Phil Barber. Middle Row: Frank Brooks (Physio), John Budden, Charlie Mitten, Liburd Henry, Jimmy Srtouts, Ron Fearon, Neil Le Bihan, Clive Walker (Assistant Manager). Front Row: Steve Jones, Ryan McCabe, Jake Leberl, Bill Williams (Manager), Darren Adams, Paul Wilson, Gerald Dobbs. Players no longer at the club - Ricky Reina (Brentford) & Phil Barber (Crawley Town).

DOVER ATHLETIC - Match Facts 1997-98

Match No.	Date	Venue H / A	Comp.	Opponents	Result & Score		Att.	Goalscorers	League Position
1	16.08	H	VC	Cheltenham Town	W	3-0	982	Strouts 14, Barber 40, Le Bihan 65.	2
2	19.08	A	VC	Slough Town	W	4-2	*868*	OG (Randell) 33), Reina 37, 47, Wilson 65.	1
3	23.08	A	VC	Telford United	W	1-0	*808*	Strouts 75.	1
4	25.08	H	VC	Stevenage Borough	D	1-1	1,787	Wilson 13.	2
5	30.08	H	VC	Hednesford Town	L	1-3	1,277	Budden 7.	3
6	03.09	A	VC	Farnborough Town	L	0-1	*679*		4
7	07.09	A	VC	Northwich Victoria	L	1-2	*897*	Adams 10.	6
8	09.09	H	VC	Yeovil Town	W	1-0	1,121	Adams 73.	5
9	20.09	H	VC	Kidderminster Harriers	L	0-4	1,182		10
10	30.09	A	VC	Woking	L	0-4	*1,712*		11
11	04.10	A	VC	Morecambe	D	3-3	*1,616*	OG (Hughes) 14, Hanson 68, Budden 82.	13
12	18.10	H	VC	Stalybridge Celtic	W	3-1	832	Strouts 65, McRobert 71(pen), 74.	10
13	25.10	H	VC	Woking	L	0-2	1,384		11
14	01.11	A	VC	Leek Town	**L**	**1-5**	*562*	Strouts 73.	
15	08.11	H	VC	Hayes	W	1-0	889	Adams 35.	10
16	15.11	A	VC	Kettering Town	L	1-2	*1,056*	Barber 63.	10
17	29.11	A	VC	Hereford United	W	1-0	*2,147*	McRobert 62.	11
18	06.12	A	VC	Kidderminster Harriers	W	3-3	*1,636*	Avorinde 26, Henry 43, Barber 73.	11
19	13.12	A	VC	Rushden & Diamonds	L	1-4	*2.284*	Ayorinde 75	12
20	20.12	H	VC	Northwich Victoria	**W**	**4-0**	781	**Strouts 4** (32, 57, 83, 89)	11
21	26.12	H	VC	Welling United	W	2-1	1,304	Ayornde 66, Budden 89(pen)	11
22	01.01	A	VC	Welling United	D	2-2	*1,326*	Adams 17, Budden 68(pen)	12
23	17.01	H	VC	Leek Town	W	2-1	1,092	Strouts 3, Henry 89.	11
24	24.01	H	VC	Rushden & Diamonds	L	0-3	1,280		12
25	07.02	A	VC	Stalybridge Celtic	L	0-1	*1,666*		13
26	10.02	H	VC	Farnbroough Town	D	2-2	809	Munday 31, Le Bihan 82.	13
27	14.02	H	VC	Halifax Town	L	0-1	1,316		13
28	28.02	H	VC	Telford United	W	6-3	953	**Alford 3** (3, 51, 55), Dobbs 66, Adams 69, 83.	11
29	07.03	A	VC	Halifax Town	D	1-1	*1,949*	Strouts 13.	11
30	21.03	H	VC	Gateshead	L	0-1	1,090		15
31	31.03	H	VC	Hereford United	D	1-1	746	Alford 5.	16
32	07.04	A	VC	Cheltenham Town	L	1-3	*1,606*	Alford 57.	17
33	11.04	A	VC	Gateshead	W	2-1	*596*	Henry 33, Ayorinde 68.	17
34	13.04	A	VC	Stevenage Borough	D	2-2	*1,951*	Alford 52, Godden 85.	17
35	15.04	H	VC	Kettering Town	D	0-0	781		17
36	18.04	H	VC	Southport	W	3-1	958	Ayorinde 53, Strouts 61, 77.	14
37	21.04	H	VC	Slough Town	W	2-1	803	Shearer 66, Le Bihan 69.	13
38	23.04	A	VC	Hayes	D	0-0	*475*		13
39	25.04	H	VC	Morecambe	L	2-3	1,088	Henry 48, Alford 58.	13
40	28.04	A	VC	Yeovil Town	L	1-4	*1,817*	Strouts 39.	13
41	30.04	A	VC	Southport	W	1-0	*635*	Adams 89.	13
42	02.05	A	VC	Hednesford Town	L	0-1	*1,051*		13

CUP COMPETITIONS SCC - Spalding Challenge Cup KSC - Kent Senior Cup

Date	Venue	Comp.	Opponents	Result	Score	Att.	Goalscorers
13.08	A	**FAC** 1Q	Uxbridge	W	2-0	290	Le Bihan 16, Adams 36 (pen).
27.09	H	2Q	Kingstonian	L	0-4	938	
10.01	A	**FAT** 1	Purfleet	W	1-0	333	Adams 55.
31.01	A	2	Hereford United	W	2-0	2,108	Dobbs 11, Godden 90.
21.02	A	3	Hyde United	W	2-0	917	Budden 16, Le Bihan 69.
14.03	H	4	Barrow	D	1-1	2,970	Henry 60.
17.03	A	4 R	Barrow	D	0-0	4,217	AET Won 5-4 on penalties.
28.03	A	SF - 1	Cheltenham Town	L	1-2	3,011	Dobbs 2.
04.04	H	SF - 2	Cheltenham Town	D	2-2	3,240	Le Bihan 70, Budden 78.
07.10	H	**SCC** 1	Kettering Town	L	1-3	404	McRobert 18.
20.01	A	**KSC**	Bromley	W	1-0	200	Dobbs.
24.03	A	SF	Gravesend & Northfleet	L	1-3	584	Godden.

League Attendances **HIGHEST:** 1,787 v Stevenage Borough	**LOWEST:** 781 v Northwich Victoria & Kettering T.
CONFERENCE: 13th **FA CUP:** 2nd Qual. Round	**FA TROPHY:** Semi-Finalists

1	2	3	4	5	6	7	8	9	10	11	12 14 15	
Fearon	Munday	Palmer	Leberl	Daniels	Stebbing	Dobbs	Strouts	Wilson	Le Bihan	Barber	Jones (7), Henry (4), McCabe.	1
Fearon	Munday	Palmer	Budden	Daniels	Stebbing	Wilson	Strouts	Reina	Le Bihan	Barber	Henry, Jones, McCabe.	2
Fearon	Munday	Palmer	Budden	Daniels	Stebbing	Wilson	Strouts	Reina	Le Bihan	Barber	Henry (7), Jones, McCabe.	3
Fearon	Munday	Palmer	Budden	Daniels	Stebbing	Wilson	Strouts	Adams	Le Bihan	Barber	McCabe, Henry (9), Jones.	4
Fearon	Munday	Palmer	Budden	Daniels	Stebbing	Wilson	Strouts	Reina	Le Bihan	Barber	Adams (7), Henry (11), McCabe.	5
Fearon	Munday	Palmer	Budden	Daniels	Stebbing	Wilson	Strouts	Reina	Le Bihan	Henry	Adams (11), Dobbs (6), McCabe.	6
Fearon	Leberl	Palmer	Budden	Daniels	Le Bihan	Wilson	Strouts	Reina	Adams	Henry	Barber, McCabe(11), Mitten.	7
Fearon	Leberl	Palmer	Budden	Daniels	Le Bihan	Wilson	Strouts	Henry	Adams	Barber	McCabe, Mitten.	8
Fearon	Munday	Palmer	Budden	Leberl	Le Bihan	Wilson	Strouts	Henry	Adams	Barber	McRobert (2), McCabe, Godden.	9
Fearon	Munday	Palmer	Budden	Daniels	Le Bihan	Stebbing	Strouts	Hanson	Adams	Barber	McRobert (11), Dobbs, Wilson (10).	10
Fearon	Munday	Palmer	Budden	Daniels	Stebbing	Hanson	Strouts	McRobert	Le Bihan	Henry	Adams (11), Wilson, Barber.	11
Davies	Leberl	Henry	Budden	Daniels	Stebbing	Wilson	Strouts	Hanson	Le Bihan	McRobert	Adams (7), Jones, Barber (10).	12
Davies	Leberl	Henry	Budden	Daniels	Stebbing	McRobert	Strouts	Hanson	Le Bihan	Adams	Dobbs (11), Palmer (3), Barber.	13
Fearon	Leberl	Palmer	Budden	Daniels	Stebbing	McRobert	Strouts	Ayorinde	Le Bihan	Adams	Dobbs (7), Henry (5), Barber.	14
Davies	Munday	Barber	Budden	Leberl	Stebbing	Dobbs	Strouts	Ayorinde	Le Bihan	Adams	French, McRobert (11), Henry.	15
Davies	Munday	Palmer	Budden	Daniels	Stebbing	Dobbs	Barber	Ayorinde	Le Bihan	Adams	Leberl (5), French (11), McRobert.	16
Davies	Leberl	Palmer	Budden	Shearer	Stebbing	McRobert	Dobbs	Ayorinde	Le Bihan	Barber	Henry, Wilson (7), French.	17
Davies	Leberl	Palmer	Budden	Shearer	Stebbing	McRobert	Barber	Ayorinde	Le Bihan	Henry	Jones (11), Godden, Wilson.	18
Davies	Munday	Palmer	Budden	Shearer	Stebbing	Jones	Strouts	Ayorinde	Dempsey	Henry	Wilson (7), Godden, Mitten.	19
Davies	Munday	Palmer	Budden	Shearer	Stebbing	Jones	Strouts	Ayorinde	Henry	Adams	Wilson (11), McCabe, Godden.	20
Davies	Munday	Palmer	Budden	Shearer	Stebbing	Adams	Strouts	Ayorinde	Henry	Dempsey	Wilson, Jones, Daniels.	21
Davies	Munday	Palmer	Budden	Shearer	Stebbing	Dempsey	Strouts	Ayorinde	Henry	Adams	Dobbs (9), Le Bihan (11), Daniels.	22
Davies	Munday	Palmer	Budden	Shearer	Stebbing	Adams	Strouts	Ayorinde	Henry	Dempsey	Leberl (4), Dobbs, Le Bihan.	23
Davies	Leberl	Palmer	Budden	Shearer	Stebbing	Adams	Strouts	Ayorinde	Henry	Dempsey	Le Bihan, Dobbs (3), Jones.	24
Davies	Munday	Palmer	Budden	Shearer	Stebbing	Clarke	Dobbs	Henry	Le Bihan	Adams	Daniels, Leberl, Godden (10)	25
Davies	Munday	Palmer	Budden	Shearer	Stebbing	Adams	Strouts	Dobbs	Le Bihan	Henry	Daniels, Leberl, Clarke (11).	26
Davies	Munday	Palmer	Budden	Shearer	Stebbing	Clarke	Strouts	Alford	Le Bihan	Adams	Daniels, Leberl (2), Dobbs (11).	27
Davies	Leberl	Palmer	Budden	Shearer	Stebbing	Dobbs	Strouts	Alford	Le Bihan	Henry	Adams (11), Daniels, Wilson.	28
Mitten	Leberl	Palmer	Budden	Shearer	Stebbing	Dobbs	Strouts	Alford	Adams	Henry	Jones (7), Daniels, Wilson.	29
Mitten	Munday	Palmer	Budden	Shearer	Stebbing	Le Bihan	Strouts	Ayorinde	Alford	Clarke	Dobbs (3), Daniels, Leberl.	30
Davies	Munday	Palmer	Daniels	Shearer	Clarke	Le Bihan	Dobbs	Ayorinde	Alford	Henry	Stebbing (4), Strouts (9), Wilson.	31
Davies	Munday	Palmer	Budden	Leberl	Stebbing	Henry	Strouts	Ayorinde	Alford	Adams	Le Bihan (8), Dobbs, Wilson.	32
Davies	Leberl	Palmer	Clarke	Shearer	Stebbing	Dobbs	Alford	Ayorinde	Le Bihan	Henry	Adams (4), Hogg (10), Godden.	33
Davies	Leberl	Palmer	Budden	Shearer	Stebbing	Henry	Strouts	Ayorinde	Alford	Dobbs	Jones (9), Adams (10), Godden (11).	34
Davies	Leberl	Munday	Budden	Shearer	Stebbing	Clarke	Alford	Ayorinde	Dobbs	Henry	Adams (7), Godden (9), Wilson.	35
Davies	Munday	Palmer	Budden	Shearer	Stebbing	Adams	Wilson	Ayorinde	Strouts	Henry	Clarke (8), Dobbs (9), Leberl.	36
Davies	Munday	Palmer	Budden	Shearer	Adams	Clarke	Strouts	Alford	Le Bihan	Henry	Stebbing (11), Leberl, Dobbs.	37
Davies	Munday	Palmer	Budden	Shearer	Stebbing	Clarke	Strouts	Le Bihan	Alford	Adams	Henry (9), Leberl (11), Ayorinde.	38
Davies	Clarke	Palmer	Budden	Shearer	Stebbing	Adams	Strouts	Alford	Le Bihan	Henry	Dobbs (7), Godden (11), Leberl.	39
Davies	Munday	Palmer	Leberl	Shearer	Stebbing	Henry	Strouts	Clarke	Alford	Le Bihan	Godden (10), Adams, Hogg.	40
Davies	Munday	Palmer	Clarke	Shearer	Godden	Henry	Hogg	Wilson	Alford	Adams	Durrant	41
Davies	Leberl	Palmer	Budden	Shearer	Clarke	Henry	Strouts	Le Bihan	Alford	Adams	Godden (2), Munday, Hogg.	42

1	2	3	4	5	6	7	8	9	10	11	12 14 15
Fearon	Munday	Palmer	Budden	Leberl	Le Bihan	Wilson	Strouts	Henry	Adams	Barber	McCabe, Godden (10), Hogg.
Fearon	Munday	Palmer	Budden	Leberl	Le Bihan	Wilson	Strouts	Stebbing	Adams	Barber	Henry (7), Godden, Mitten (11).

1	2	3	4	5	6	7	8	9	10	11	12 14 15
Fearon	Munday	Palmer	Budden	Leberl	Stebbing	Henry	Strouts	Dobbs	Le Bihan	Adams	Mitten, Jones, Wilson.
Davies	Leberl	Palmer	Budden	Shearer	Stebbing	Henry	Dobbs	Ayorinde	Le Bihan	Adams	Daniels, Godden (9), Wilson (11).
Davies	Leberl	Palmer	Budden	Shearer	Stebbing	Wilson	Strouts	Dobbs	Le Bihan	Henry	Daniels (2), Adams (7), Godden (14).
Mitten	Munday	Palmer	Budden	Shearer	Stebbing	Dobbs	Strouts	Ayorinde	Adams	Henry	Leberl(7), Jones(9), Daniels.
Mitten	Munday	Palmer	Budden	Shearer	Stebbing	Leberl	Strouts	Ayorinde	Le Bihan	Henry	Adams(7), Daniels, Dobbs.
Mitten	Munday	Palmer	Budden	Shearer	Stebbing	Dobbs	Strouts	Ayorinde	Le Bihan	Henry	Leberl(11), Daniels, Wilson.
Mitten	Munday	Palmer	Budden	Shearer	Stebbing	Dobbs	Strouts	Ayorinde	Adams	Henry	jones(7), Davies(11), Wilson.

1	2	3	4	5	6	7	8	9	10	11	12 14 15
Fearon	Munday	Palmer	Budden	Daniels	Stebbing	McRobert	Strouts	Adams	Le Bihan	Henry	Wilson (11), Jones (9), Barber.

1	2	3	4	5	6	7	8	9	10	11	12 14 15
Mitten	Munday	Palmer	Leberl	Shearer	Dobbs	Henry	Strouts	Ayorinde	Le Bihan	Adams	Wilson, Budden (3), Godden.
davies	Leberl	Henry	Daniels	Shearer	Clarke	Dobbs	Osbourne	Alford	Wilson	Godden	Golden(3), A Hogg(8), Johnson.

BILL WILLIAMS (MANAGER)

Date of Appointment	24.01.97
Date of Birth:	23rd August 1942
Place of Birth:	Esher, Surrey.

PREVIOUS CLUBS

As manager	Durban City (SA), Sacramento Gold (ASL), Atlanta Chiefs (NASL), Maidstone Utd.
As coach	None
As player	Portsmouth, West Brom. A., Q.P.R., Gillingham, Maidstone Utd.

HONOURS

As manager	Championships with Durban City (x2), Sacramento (x2), Atlanta. GMVC & F.Lge 4 with Maidstone U.
As player	England: Youth (8).

FOOTBALL MANAGEMENT TEAM

Assistant Manager
Clive Walker

Reserve Team Managers
Les Hall &
Julian Holmes

Youth Team Managers
Steve Nolan, Jim Gleeson,
Dennis Mitchell & Steve Williams

Physiotherapist
Frank Brooks

LEFT
John Budden
Player of the Year
1997-98

Photo
Andrew Chitty

RIGHT
Jimmy Strouts
Leading Goalscorer
1997-98

Photo
Peter Barnes

MATCHDAY PROGRAMME

Number of pages	40
Price	£1.50
Programme Editor	Chris Collings 01304 822074

Other club publications:

"Tales from the River End" (fanzine)

Local Newspapers:	Dover Express Dover Mercury
Local Radio Stations:	Radio Kent Invicta FM

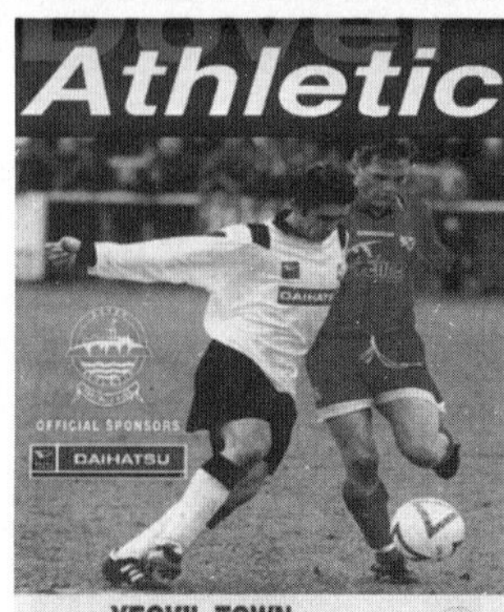

Athletic
OFFICIAL SPONSORS
DAIHATSU
YEOVIL TOWN
The Vauxhall Conference
Tuesday 9th September 1997 - Kick Off 7.45pm

1997-98 PLAYING SQUAD

PLAYER	Birthplace Honours	Birthdate	CLUBS
GOALKEEPERS			
Ashley Harrison *	Southend		Southend Manor, Canvey Island
Charlie Mitten	Kent		Thamesmead T
DEFENDERS			
Lee Shearer *	Rochford	23.10.77	Leyton Orient
Stuart Munday	Newham	28.9.72	Brighton
Jake Leberl	Manchester		Crewe Alexandra
Scott Daniels	Benfleet	22.11.69	Colchester U, Exeter C
David Clarke	Nottingham		Notts Co, Eastwood T, Harrow Borough, £5k to Dover Ath
Lee Palmer	Croydon	19.9.70	Gillingham, Cambridge U
MIDFIELDERS			
James Strouts	York		Harrogate RA, Frickley Ath, Harrogate T, Sittingbourne Army, Combined Services
Anthony Hogg	Kent		From Youth team
Andy Ogiesby	Hereford		Hereford U
Neil Le Bihan	Croydon	14.3.76	Tottenham Hotspur, Peterborough U
FORWARDS			
Liburd Henry	London	29.8.67	Millwall, Colchester U, Leytonstone & Ilf, Rainham T, Watford, Maidstone U, Gillingham, Woking, Welling U, Dag & Red, Bromley, C.Row & Romford, B Stortford, Boreham Wood, Erith & Belvedere
Simon Elliott *	Kent		Gillingham, Tunbridge Wells
Ricky Reina *	Kent		Gillingham, Folkestone Invicta, Sing Tao (HK), Dover Ath, £50k to Brentford
Roy Godden	Kent		From Youth team
Darren Adams	Newham	12.1.74	Danson Furnace, Bashley, Cardiff C, Aldershot T, £8k to Dover Ath
Joff Vansittart *	Sussex	12.9.74	Brighton, Crawley T, Sutton U, £10k to Dover Ath

DEPARTURES during the season
Iain O'Connell (Margate - £3K), Ricky Reina (Brentford - £50k), Shane Samways (Released), Jay French (Ashford T), Phil Barber (Crawley T)

PLAYERS ON LOAN: Lee Shearer (Leyton Orient), Lee McRobert (Millwall), Dave Hanson (Leyton Orient), Mark Dempsey (Shrewsbury), Carl Alford (Rushden & D)

Crabble Athletic Ground, Dover

GROUND ADDRESS: Crabble Athletic Ground, Lewisham Road, River, Dover, Kent. CT17 0JB.
Telephone: 01304 822373

SIMPLE DIRECTIONS: Follow the A2 from Canterbury until you pass the Forte Posthouse Hotel on your left and approach a roundabout with MacDonald's drive-in restuarant and a petrol station at the roundabout on your left. Turn right signposted to Town Centre and go down the hill. At the mini-roundabout at the bottom turn left. At the next traffic lights turn right and follow the road under the railway bridge. The ground is up the hill on your left.

CAPACITY: 6,500 **SEATED:** 1,000 **COVERED TERRACING:** 4,900

CLUB SHOP: At the ground, open matchdays for general souvenirs, programmes, replica shirts (home & away) etc. Also at Worthington Street in the town, open daily. Contact Jean Haves 01304 240041.

SOCIAL FACILITIES:
Social Club open 7 days a week. Meals available. Steward - Gavin Hughes 01304 822306.

Dover Fact File

Nickname: Lilywhites **Club Sponsors:** Daihatsu (UK) Ltd.
Club colours: White shirts, black shorts and black & white socks.
Change colours: Red shirts, red shorts and black & red socks.
Reserve team league: Winstonlead Kent League Div.2.
Midweek home matchday: Tuesday

PREVIOUS - **Leagues:** Kent League, Southern League.
Grounds None **Names:** Dover United, Dover FC.

CLUB RECORDS: **Attendance:** 4,035 v Bromsgrove Rovers, Beazer Homes League April 1992
Win: 7-0 v Weymouth 3rd April 1990.
Defeat: 1-7 v Poole Town.
Career Goalscorer: Lennie Lee - 160.
Career Appearances: Jason Bartlett - 539.
Transfer Fee paid: £50,000 for David Leworthy from Farnborough Town - Aug. 1993.
Transfer Fee received: £50,000 for Ricky Reina from Chelmsford City 1997.

BEST SEASON - **FA Cup:** Fourth Qual. Round 86-87, 88-89, 90-91, 91-92, 94-95.
(as Dover FC - Second Round, 1-4 v Southend Utd. (A) 75-76.)
FA Trophy: Semi-Finals 1997-98, 3-4 (agg.) v Cheltenham Town.

HONOURS - Southern League Premier Division Champions 89/90, 92/93; Southern League Southern Division Champions 87/88; Beazer Homes League Championship Match Winners 90 & 93; Premier Inter League Cup Winners 90/91; Southern League Cup Winners 91/92; Kent Senior Cup Winners 90/91, Runners-up 93/94, 96/97.

1997-98 **Captain:** Scott Daniels
1997-98 **Top Goalscorer:** Jimmy Strouts - 13 (all Conference)
1997-98 **Player of the Year:** John Budden

FARNBOROUGH TOWN

Another club who showed good form in the first half of the season only to fall away drastically near the end.

Indeed it looked as if relegation was to be 'snatched' in dramatic fashion and only two fine individual performances by Martin and Keith Rowlands, who both produced hat tricks to provide the clubs only two victories in their last dozen games, saved an embarrassing end to the campaign.

There was always enough quality in the squad to give the impression of better results to come but poor support and the loss of form and injuries gave Alan Taylor problems, and even the various Cup competitions failed to bring any light relief.

There is no doubt that there will be some hard work to be done during the Summer to ensure that the talented players on their books will be producing their best for Farnborough Town more consistently in the coming season.

CLUB OFFICIALS 1998-99

President **Charles Mortimer**

Chairman **Tony Alper**

Vice Chairman **Hal Carter**

Directors **Gerry Darcey, Michael McCarthy, Terry Parr, Alan Spaven**

Football Secretary **Terry Parr**
c/o Club. Tel: 01252 541469

Commercial Manager **Graham Willis**
Tel: 01924 266393

Asst. Sec./Press Officer **Vince Williams**
Tel: 01252 522161

L-R, Back Row: Ken Ballard (now left the club), Mike savage (Coach), Phil Wingfield, Jon Underwood, Paul Harford, Stuart MacKenzie, Barry Miller, Brian Horne, Darren Robson, Neil Baker, Chris White, David Mehew (now left the club), Mike Critchell (Caoch), Cliff Cobb (Physio). Front Row: dave Beard (Reserve Team Manager), Jamie Laidlaw, Richard Dobson, Wayne Stemp (Team Captain), Alan Taylor (Manager), David Harlow (Club Captain), Keith Rowlands, Steve Baker, Martin Rowlands, Ron Manville (Kit & Groundsman).

FARNBOROUGH TOWN - Match Facts 1997-98

Match No.	Date	Venue H / A	Comp.	Opponents	Result & Score		Att.	Goalscorers	League Position
1	16.08	A	VC	Gateshead	L	0-3	*803*		22
2	20.08	H	VC	Rushden & Diamonds	W	2-0	905	Wingfield 49, Mehew 86.	
3	23.08	H	VC	Hereford United	L	0-2	1,097		17
4	25.08	A	VC	Yeovil Town	W	1-0	*3,286*	Mehew 47.	10
5	30.08	A	VC	Southport	L	1-3	*1,187*	Mehew 90.	14
6	03.09	H	VC	Dover Athletic	W	1-0	679	Wingfield 38.	7
7	07.09	H	VC	Kettering Town	W	3-2	771	Harlow 7, Mehew 18, Robson 60.	5
8	09.09	A	VC	Hereford United	L	1-2	*1,709*	Mehew 66.	7
9	13.09	A	VC	Rushden & Diamonds	D	5-5	*2,051*	Boothe 22, Wingfield 44, Robson 48, 79, Mehew 80.	7
10	20.09	H	VC	Halifax Town	L	1-2	919	Boothe 35.	11
11	27.09	A	VC	Kidderminster Harriers	L	0-2	*1,587*		12
12	04.10	H	VC	Hayes	L	0-2	781		14
13	11.10	H	VC	Morecambe	L	0-2	589		17
14	18.10	A	VC	Telford United	W	1-0	*587*	Wingfield 14.	13
15	01.11	H	VC	Welling United	D	0-0	603		
16	08.11	A	VC	Northwich Victoria	D	3-3	*802*	Laidlaw 4, 23, Wingfield 15.	13
17	22.11	A	VC	Stevenage Borough	**L**	**0-5**	*2,028*		16
18	29.11	H	VC	Kidderminster Harriers	D	3-3	678	M Rowlands 57, Mehew 61,76.	16
19	13.12	H	VC	Yeovil Town	D	2-2	1,093	Mehew 11, Wingfield63	18
20	20,12	H	VC	Stalybridge Celtic	**W**	**6-0**	621	Harford 29, **Mehew 3** (50,73,78),Harlow 58,Baker 59	15
21	26.12	A	VC	Woking	L	0-3	*4,124*		16
22	29.12	A	VC	Slough Town	L	0-1	*786*		
23	01.01	H	VC	Woking	W	3-0	2,125	Underwood 47,Miller 60,Wingfield 83.	16
24	17.01	H	VC	Northwich Victoria	L	2-3	744	Robson 65, Laidlaw 79.	16
25	24.01	A	VC	Kettering Town	L	1-2	*1,433*	M Rowlands 39.	17
26	07.02	H	VC	Leek Town	W	2-0	618	Mehew 3, 89.	16
27	10.02	A	VC	Dover Athletic	D	2-2	*809*	Mehew 50, K Rowlands 90.	16
28	18.02	H	VC	Slough Town	W	1-0	642	K Rowlands 56.	15
29	21.02	H	VC	Telford United	W	1-0	543	Laidlaw 84.	13
30	23.02	A	VC	Hednesford Town	L	0-1	*1,707*		15
31	28.02	A	VC	Halifax Town	L	0-1	*2,352*		15
32	10.03	A	VC	Cheltenham Town	L	0-1	*1,436*		16
33	21.03	H	VC	Stevenage Borough	L	1-2	897	Wingfield 72.	17
34	24.03	A	VC	Welling United	L	0-1	*504*		17
35	28.03	A	VC	Leek Town	L	1-3	*664*	K Rowlands 58.	18
36	11.04	A	VC	Hayes	L	1-3	*583*	K Rowlands 28.	18
37	13.04	H	VC	Gateshead	W	4-0	565	Laidlaw 27, **M Rowlands 3** (45, 61, 87).	18
38	18.04	A	VC	Stalybridge Celtic	D	1-1	*505*	Baker 36.	18
39	23.04	H	VC	Southport	W	3-2	532	**K Rowlands 3** (49, 67, 72).	18
40	25.04	H	VC	Hednesford Town	L	1-3	753	M Rowlands 55.	18
41	29.04	H	VC	Cheltenham Town	L	1-2	612	Wingfield 48.	18
42	02.05	A	VC	Morecambe	D	1-1	*1,270*	K Rowlands 48.	18

CUP COMPETITIONS

	Date	Venue	Round	Opponents	Result		Att.	Goalscorers	
F.A. CUP									
	25.10	A	4Q	Bognor Regis Town	D	0-0	1,124		
	29.10	H	4Q R	Bognor Regis Town	W	2-1	855	Harlow 31, Mehew 90 (pen).	
	15.11	H	1	Dagenham & Redbridge	L	0-1	1,236		
F.A. TROPHY									
	10.01	A	1	Rushden & Diamonds	L	2-3	2,164	Miller 27, Laidlaw 82.	
SPALDING CHALLENGE CUP									
	26.11	H	2	Hereford United	W	2-1	256	Robson 65, Underwood 82.	-
	20.01	A	3	Woking	L	1-3	998	Hartford 33.	-
HAMPSHIRE SENIOR CUP									
	20.10	H	2	AFC Totton	W	3-2	102	M Rowlands (2), Laidlaw.	
	11.11	A	3	Waterlooville	L	0-3	120		

League Attendances	HIGHEST: 2,125 v Woking	LOWEST: 532 v Southport
CONFERENCE: 18th	**FA CUP:** 1st Round	**FA TROPHY:** 1st Round

1	2	3	4	5	6	7	8	9	10	11	12 14 15	
MacKenzie	Stemp	Mintram	N Baker	Miller	Harford	S Baker	Harlow	Boothe	Mehew	Wingfield	Underwood,M Rowlands(11),K Rowlands(3)	1
MacKenzie	Stemp	Mintram	Underwood	Miller	Harford	S Baker	M Rowlands	Boothe	Mewhew	Wingfield	N Baker(8), Laidlaw, K Rowlands.	2
MacKenzie	Stemp	Mintram	Underwood	Miller	Harford	S Baker	M Rowlands	Boothe	Mehew	Wingfield	N Baker, Harlow(6), Laidlaw (9).	3
MacKenzie	Stemp	Mintram	N Baker	Miller	Harford	S Baker	Harlow	M Rowlands	Mehew	Wingfield	Boothe, Robson(9), Laidlaw.	4
MacKenzie	Stemp	Mintram	Underwood	Miller	Harford	S Baker	Harlow	M Rowlands	Mehew	Wingfield	N Baker, Robson(6), Laidlaw.	5
MacKenzie	Stemp	Mintram	Underwood	Miller	Robson	S Baker	Harlow	M Rowlands	Mehew	Wingfield	N Baker(9), Boothe(10), Laidlaw(11).	6
MacKenzie	Stemp	Mintram	Underwood	Miller	Harford	S Baker	Harlow	Robson	Mehew	Wingfield	N Baker(3),Boothe(12),M Rowlands.	7
MacKenzie	Stemp	Boothe	Underwood	Miller	Harford	S Baker	Harlow	Robson	Mehew	Wingfield	N Baker,M Rowlands,Laidlaw.	8
MacKenzie	Stemp	Underwood	Robson	Miller	Harford	S Baker	Harlow	Boothe	Mehew	Wingfield	N Baker(3),M Rowlands(8),K Rowlands.	9
Rowe	Stemp	M Rowlands	Robson	Miller	Harford	S Baker	Harlow	Boothe	Mehew	Underwood	N Baker,Wingfield, Laidlaw (8).	10
Coles	Stemp	N Baker	Robson	Miller	Harford	S Baker	M Rowlands	Boothe	Mehew	Wingfield	Underwood(5),Harlow(6),K Rowlands(11).	11
Coles	Stemp	Underwood	Robson	N Baker	Harford	S Baker	M Rowlands	Boothe	Mehew	Wingfield	Miller (5), Harlow(6), Laidlaw.	12
Coles	Stemp	Underwood	Robson	N Baker	Miller	S Baker	Harlow	M Rowlands	Mehew	Wingfield	Harford, K Rowlands(4), Laidlaw.	13
MacKenzie	Stemp	Miller	Robson	N Baker	Harford	S Baker	Harlow	M Rowlands	Mehew	Wingfield	Underwood(8),Harte,K Rowlands(10).	14
MacKenzie	Stemp	Underwood	Harte	N Baker	Robson	K Rowlands	Harlow	Laidlaw	Mehew	Wingfield	Dobson(7), Kemp, Davis.	15
MacKenzie	Stemp	Underwood	Harte	N Baker	M Rowlands	Robson	Harlow	Laidlaw	Mehew	Wingfield	K Rowlannds, Kemp, Davis.	16
MacKenzie	Stemp	Miller	M Rowlands	N Baker	Robson	S Baker	Harlow	Laidlaw	Mehew	Wingfield	Harte (7), Kemp (5), K Rowlands(10).	17
MacKenzie	Stemp	Underwood	Miller	N Baker	Robson	S Baker	Harlow	M Rowlands	Mehew	Wingfield	Harte, Dobson, K Rowlands.	18
Horne	Stemp	Underwood	M Rowlands	N Baker	Harford	S baker	Harlow	Laidlaw	Mehew	Wingfield	Harte(4), Dobson, K Rowlands(12).	19
Horne	Stemp	Underwood	White	N Baker	Harford	S Baker	Harlow	M Rowlands	Mehew	Wingfield	Laidlaw(3),Dobson, K Rowlands.	20
Horne	Stemp	Miller	White	N Baker	Harford	S Baker	Harlow	M Rowlands	Mehew	Wingfield	Harte, Laidlaw(5), K Rowlands.	21
Horne	Stemp	Underwood	M Rowlands	N Baker	Robson	S Baker	Harlow	Laidlaw	Mehew	White	Harte, Miller (6), K Rowlands (9).	22
Horne	Stemp	Underwood	White	N Baker	Robson	S Baker	Harlow	M Rowlands	Mehew	Wingfield	Miller(4),Laidlaw, K Rowlands(9).	23
Horne	Stemp	Mintram	Miller	N Baker	Robson	K Rowlands	Harlow	Laidlaw	Mehew	Wingfield	Dobson(7), Harte, Laidlaw.	24
Horne	Stemp	Mintram	White	Underwood	Harford	S Baker	Harlow	M Rowlands	Mehew	Wingfield	N Baker(3),Laidlaw(10),Robson(11).	25
Horne	Stemp	Mintram	White	Underwood	Harford	S Baker	Harlow	M Rowlands	Mehew	Wingfield	K Rowlands(11),Miller(8),Robson(9).	26
Horne	Stemp	Mintram	White	Underwood	M Rowlands	S Baker	Harlow	Harford	Mehew	Wingfield	K Rowlands(3), Miller, Robson(6).	27
MacKenzie	Stemp	Mintram	Miller	Underwood	Harford	S Baker	Harlow	Robson	Mehew	Wingfield	N Baker(3),M Rowlands,K Rowlands(11).	28
MacKenzie	Stemp	N Baker	Miller	Underwood	Harford	S Baker	Harlow	Robson	Mehew	K Rowlands	Wingfield(11), Freeman, Laidlaw(10).	29
MacKenzie	Stemp	N Baker	Miller	Underwood	Harford	S Baker	Harlow	Robson	Mehew	Wingfield	K Rowlands(9),Laidlaw(11),Harte.	30
MacKenzie	Stemp	N Baker	Miller	Underwood	Harford	S Baker	Harlow	Robson	Mehew	K Rowlands	Kemp, Harte, M Rowlands(5).	31
MacKenzie	Stemp	Mintram	Miller	N Baker	Harford	S Baker	Harlow	Robson	Mehew	K Rowlands	Underwood(3),M Rowlands(9),Hooper(11).	32
MacKenzie	Stemp	Mintram	Underwood	N Baker	Harford	Kelly	M Rowlands	Robson	Laidlaw	Wingfield	Kemp, K Rowlands, Hooper(7).	33
MacKenzie	Stemp	Mintram	Kemp	Underwood	Robson	Hooper	Harlow	Laidlaw	M Rowlands	Wingfield	Harte(11), Kelly, K Rowlands(7).	34
MacKenzie	Stemp	Mintram	Underwood	N Baker	Robson	S Baker	Harlow	Laidlaw	M Rowlands	Hooper	Harte, Kemp, K Rowlands(11).	35
MacKenzie	Stemp	Mintram	Miller	N Baker	Harford	S Baker	Harlow	K Rowlands	Underwood	Wingfield	Robson(3), Kemp, Laidlaw(10).	36
MacKenzie	Stemp	Mintram	M Rowlands	N Baker	Harford	S Baker	Harlow	Laidlaw	K Rowlands	Wingfield	Miller, Robson(11), Underwood.	37
MacKenzie	Stemp	Mintram	M Rowlands	N Baker	Harford	S Baker	Harlow	Laidlaw	K Rowlands	Wingfield	Underwood(3),Robson(10),Miller(8).	38
MacKenzie	Stemp	Mintram	M Rowlands	N Baker	Harford	S Baker	Harlow	Laidlaw	K Rowlands	Wingfield	Miller(4),Underwood(6),Robson(3).	39
MacKenzie	Stemp	Underwood	M Rowlands	N Baker	Harford	S Baker	Harlow	Laidlaw	K Rowlands	Wingfield	Miller(9),White(6),Robson(10).	40
MacKenzie	Stemp	Underwood	White	Miller	Harford	S Baker	Harlow	Robson	K Rowlands	Wingfield	N Baker(14),Mintram(6),M Rowlands(4).	41
MacKenzie	Stemp	Underwood	M Rowlands	Miller	White	S Baker	Harlow	Robson	K Rowlands	Wingfield	N Baker(10),Harford(11),Harte(6).	42

1	2	3	4	5	6	7	8	9	10	11	12 14 15
MacKenzie	Stemp	Underwood	Miller	N Baker	Harford	S Baker	Harlow	Robson	Mehew	Wingfield	Dobson, K Rowlands(6), Laidlaw.
MacKenzie	Stemp	Underwood	Miller	N Baker	Robson	S Baker	Harlow	K Rowlands	Mehew	Wingfield	Dobson, Harford, Laidlaw (9).
MacKenzie	Stemp	Underwood	M Rowlands	N Baker	Robson	S Baker	Harlow	Laidlaw	Mehew	Wingfield	Miller,Harford,Harte,Freeman,K Rowlands

1	2	3	4	5	6	7	8	9	10	11	12 14 15
Horne	Stemp	Underwood	Miller	N Baker	Robson	K Rowlands	Harlow	Dobson	Mehew	Wingfield	Laidlaw(4), Harte (7), Freeman.

1	2	3	4	5	6	7	8	9	10	11	12 14 15
MacKenzie	Stemp	Miller	Underwood	N Baker	Robson	Harte	Harlow	M Rowlands	Mehew	Wingfield	Dobson, Freeman, K Rowlands.
Horne	Stemp	Mintram	White	Miller	Harford	S Baker	Harlow	M Rowlands	Mehew	Wingfield	N Baker(3),Laidlaw(11),Robson.

1	2	3	4	5	6	7	8	9	10	11	12 14 15
Collar	Harte	Shaw	Raby	Kemp	M Rowlands	A Sullivan	Dobson	K Rowlands	Laidlaw	Fowler	Glover, T Sullivan, Hooper.
Freeman	Harte	Shaw	Raby	Kemp	Davis	Dobson	A Sullivan	Harford	K Rowlands	Fowler	Glover, Thompson(8), Hooper.

ALAN TAYLOR (MANAGER)

Date of Appointment	August 1993
Date of Birth:	05.12.53
Place of Birth:	Barking

PREVIOUS CLUBS

As manager	Chesham United
As coach	Fulham (Youth team)
As player	West Ham United, AFC Bournemouth

HONOURS

As manager	Southern League 93-94
As player	-

FOOTBALL MANAGEMENT TEAM

Assistant Mananagers:	Simon Read & Mark Turkington
Coaches:	Mike Savage, Mike Critchell,
Reserve Team Man.	Dave Beard
Physio:	Cliff Cobb *BTAA*
Chief Scout:	Ted Shepherd

Phil Wingfield. Photo: Peter Barnes

Left
Paul Hartford.
Photo: Andrew Chitty

MATCHDAY PROGRAMME

Number of pages	40
Price	£1.30
Programme Editor	Michael O'Connor
Other club publications:	"Simon Read's Haircut" (fanzine)
Local Newspapers:	Farnborough News
Local Radio Stations:	BBC Southern Counties County Sound

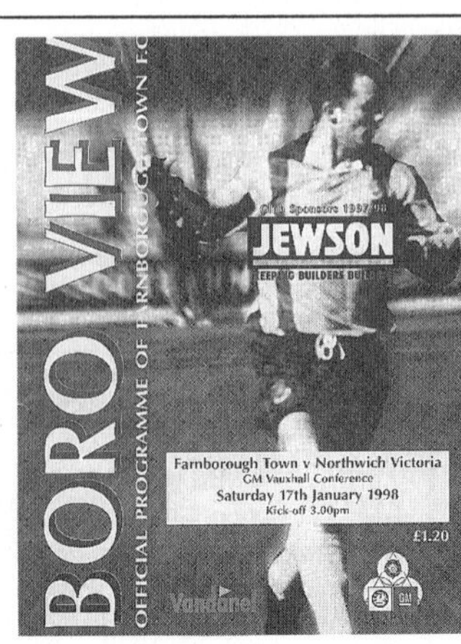

1997-98 PLAYING SQUAD

PLAYER	Birthplace Honours	Birthdate	CLUBS
GOALKEEPERS			
Stuart Mackenzie	Tooting FAV	21.3.65	Hounslow, Southall, Hounslow, Harrow Borough, Yeading, £3,250 to Farnborough
DEFENDERS			
Wayne Stemp	Epsom BHL	9.9.70	Brighton, Woking, Staines T, Bognor Regis T
Neil Baker	Southampton		Southampton, Wycombe Wanderers
Spencer Mintram	Brighton		Brighton, Lewes, Worthing, £5k to Farnborough
Chris White	Chatham ILP	11.12.70	Portsmouth, Peterborough U, Exeter C, Yeovil T
Barry Miller	Surrey		Brentford, Wokingham T, Epsom & Ewell, Wokingham T
MIDFIELDERS			
Phil Wingfield	London		Walton & Hersham, Kingstonian, Walton & Hersham, Hayes, Kingstonian, £7,500 to Farnborough
Steve Baker	Newcastle BHL	2.12.61	Southampton, Leyton Orient, Aldershot
David Harlow	Epsom ESP	2.11.67	Fulham, Farnborough T, Kingstonian, £10k to Farnborough
Darren Robson	Woolwich	18.11.69	Petersfield U, Andover, Waterlooville, Basingstoke T, Gosport B, Southwick, Worthing
Martin Rowlands	Berkshire		Wycombe Wanderers
Andy Sullivan	Southampton		Southampton
Paul Harford	Chelmsford	21.10.74	Arsenal, Blackburn R
FORWARDS			
Mark Kelly	Sutton EY, RIu-21 & Full Int.	27.11.69	Portsmouth, Sligo Rovers, Carolina Dynamoes (USA)
Justin Day *	Berkshire	2.2.72	Bracknell T, Egham T, Bracknell T, Miramar Rangers (NZ)
Mark West *	Wycombe ESP, FAT	16.2.66	West Ham U, Reading, Wycombe Wanderers, Slough T
Nick Hooper	Southampton Div 3		Southampton
Keith Rowlands	London		Hanwell T
Jamie Laidlaw	Doncaster	27.7.77	Swindon T, Yeovil T, Bashley

DEPARTURES (During the season)
Chris Boothe (Hayes - £10k), Richard Williams (Retired), Paul Parker (Sunderland), Dave Mehew (Rushden & D)

PLAYERS ON LOAN - David Coles (Gloucester C)

Cherrywood Road, Farnborough

ADDRESS:
John Roberts Ground, Cherrywood Road, Farnborough, Hampshire GU14 8UD.
TELEPHONE NUMBER: 01252 541469 **Fax:** 01252 375613 **Club Newsline:** 0898 88 44 07.

SIMPLE DIRECTIONS:
M3 exit 4, A325 towards Farnborough, right into Prospect Avenue (club signposted), 2nd right into Cherrywood Rd, ground on right. 20-30 min walk from Farnborough Main, Farnborough North and Frimley BR stations. Whippet mini-bus route 19 passes ground.

CAPACITY: 4,900 **SEATED:** 630 **COVERED TERRACING:** 1,350

SOCIAL FACILITIES: Clubhouse open during normal pub hours and matchdays. Hot pies, bar meals, crisps etc. Darts, pool, fruit machines, jukebox & big screen.

CLUB SHOP: Boro' Leisurewear shop - all types of club leisurewear and matchballs (contact Graham Willis - 01924 266393). Supporters Club shop - old progs, scarves, badges etc (contact Paul Doe).

Farnborough Fact File

Nickname: The "Boro" **Club Sponsor:** McDonalds
Club Colours: Yellow & blue
Change colours: Red & black
Midweek matchday: Tuesday
Reserves' League: Suburban League (Premier Division)

PREVIOUS - **Leagues:** Surrey Senior 68-72/ Spartan 72-76/ Athenian 76-77/ Isthmian 77-89/ Alliance Premier (GMV Conference) 89-90 91-93/ Southern 90-91 93-94.
Grounds: Queens Road, Farnborough (1969-1976)

CLUB RECORDS - **Attendance:** 3,581 v Brentford 22/11/95 (FA Cup).
Win: 11-0 v Chertsey Town (H), Spartan League 72-73.
Defeat: 2-10 v Worplesdon (H), Surrey Senior League Division One 68-69.
Career Goalscorer: Simon Read 209, 1986-1994.
Season Goalscorer: Simon Read 53, 1988-89.
Career Appearances: Brian Broome 529, 1980-1994.
Transfer Fee Paid: £10,000 to Kingstonian for David Harlow December 1994.
Transfer Fee Received: £50,000 from Dover Athletic for David Leworthy, August 1993.

BEST SEASON - **FA Cup:** 3rd Rd Proper replay 91-92 (lost 0-1 at West Ham United after 1-1 draw).
League clubs defeated: Torquay United 91-92.
FA Trophy: Quarter Final 92-93.

HONOURS - Southern Lg 90-91 93-94, Isthmian Lg R-up 88-89 (Div 1 84-85, Div 2 78-79), Athenian Lg Div 2 78-79, Spartan Lg 72-73 73-74 74-75 (Lg Cup 74-75), London Spartan Lg 75-76 (Lg Cup 75-76), Hants Snr Cup 74-75 81-82 83-84 85-86 90-91 (R-up 93-94), FA Trophy QF 92-93, FA Vase SF 75-76 76-77.

Past Players progressing to Football League: Dennis Bailey (Crystal Palace & Birmingham City), Paul Mortimer (Charlton Athletic), Tommy Jones (Aberdeen & Swindon Town), Allan Cockram (Brentford), Paul Holsgrove (Millwall & Reading), Maik Taylor (Barnet, Southampton, Fulham).

1997-98 Captain: Dave Harlow (Club); Wayne Stemp (Team).
1997-98 Top Goalscorer: David Mehew (16)
1997-98 Player of the Year: Paul Harford

FOREST GREEN ROVERS

A Forest Fairytale which will be told many times in the years ahead, brought great satisfaction and excitement to rural Gloucestershire last season. Ex Army regular Frank Gregan has proved himself to be an excellent manager and the squad he built just stormed through the Dr.Martens season without a really bad patch at any time.

Indeed the worst spell was one league win in four games at the end of November. Eight victories and two draws in the first ten was considered by some to be a flash in the pan as Paul Hunt was 'on fire' scoring over 20 goals before Christmas. But Rovers were never to drop out of the top three and a run in of seven victories in the last ten games showed their fantastic consisiency. They were under pressure from Merthyr Tydfil all the way so their success is even more impressive as every match was important.

Conference football at 'The Lawn' will be a treat for the locals. The ground is smart and compact with an excellent playing surface. It is only 25 years since the club moved up from The Gloucestershire County League to The Hellenic League and just sixteen years since they graced Wembley with one of the best F.A. Vase performances seen in a final.

It is a great story and hopefully there are many more happy chapters.

CLUB OFFICIALS 1998-99

President **E G Smith**

Chairman **Trevor Horsley**

Secretary/ Managing Director **Colin Peake**

Club Admin. Office, Unit 14, Springfield Bus. Centre, Stonehouse, Glos. GL10 3SX.
Tel: 01453 791232 Fax: 791305

Press Officer **Heather Cook**
Tel: 01453 823281 Mobile 07775 603287

Commercial Manager **Colin Peake**

L-R, Back Row: Dave Tyrell (Physio), Alan McDougal (Chief Scout), Mark Hallam, Christian Honor, Rob Cook, Justin Shuttlewood, Martin Woodhouse, Don Forbes, Martin Boyle, Tim Banks, Tommy Callinan (Player/Asst. Manager), Mike Kilgour (Player/Coach). Front Row: Tom Jones, Paul Hunt, Grantley Dicks, Paul McLoughlin, Frank Gregan (Manager), Gary Smart (Captain), Alex Sykes, Matthew Coupe, Toby Jackson, Steve Winter.

FOREST GREEN ROVERS - Match Facts 1997-98

Match No.	Date	Venue H / A	Comp.	Opponents	Result & Score		Att.	Goalscorers	League Position
1	16.08	H	DM	Cambridge City	W	2-0	342	Callinan 53, Mitchell 82.	
2	19.08	A	DM	Dorchester Town	D	1-1	*560*	McLoughlin 39.	
3	23.08	A	DM	Rothwell Town	W	5-2	*224*	Smart 24, Mitchell 53, Hunt 72, Bayliss 87, Ford 90.	1
4	25.08	H	DM	Bromsgrove Rovers	W	2-1	693	Hunt 42, 86 (pen).	1
5	30.08	H	DM	King's Lynn	W	4-2	418	Hunt 12, 42 (pen), McLoughlin 25, Smart 53.	1
6	01.09	A	DM	Worcester City	W	3-2	*816*	Hunt 42, 43, Ford 75.	1
7	05.09	H	DM	Ashford Town	W	3-0	449	OG (Munden) 47, Kilgour 49, Smart 74.	1
8	20.09	A	DM	Gresley Rovers	**W**	**5-1**	*557*	**Hunt 3** (22 (pen), 62, 63), Mitchell 72, Bayliss 90.	1
9	24.09	H	DM	Dorchester Town	W	1-0	530	Hunt 87.	1
10	04.10	A	DM	Crawley Town	D	2-2	*2,163*	Hunt 21, 30.	1
11	11.10	H	DM	Burton Albion	L	1-3	461	Boyle 8.	1
12	18.10	A	DM	Nuneaton Borough	L	1-2	*1,560*	Dicks 25.	2
13	21.10	A	DM	Bromsgrove Rovers	L	1-2	*356*	Hunt t 9.	2
14	25.10	H	DM	St Leonards Stamcroft	D	2-2	485	Kilgour 58, Mitchell 70.	2
15	01.11	H	DM	Hastings Town	W	5-2	371	Smart 6, 66, Cook 35, Callinan 51, OG (Playford) 64.	2
16	15.11	A	DM	Halesowen Town	L	0-3	*749*		3
17	19.11	H	DM	Worcester City	D	0-0	402		3
18	22.11	H	DM	Atherstone United	W	3-1	364	Birkby 2, Cook 57, Smart 75.	2
19	06.12	A	DM	Burton Albion	**L**	**1-4**	*609*	Sykes 86.	2
20	13.12	H	DM	Nuneaton Borough	W	4-2	402	Birkby 5, Smart 29, Kilgour 51, Hunt 84.	2
21	20.12	A	DM	King's Lynn	D	2-2	*814*	Winter 44, McLoughlin 58.	3
22	26.12	H	DM	Gloucester City	D	1-1	1,333	Hunt 53 (pen).	3
23	27.12	A	DM	Cambridge City	W	2-1	*282*	Hunt 45 (pen), Smart 70.	2
24	01.01	A	DM	Salisbury City	W	2-0	*506*	Cook 11, Hunt 32.	2
25	10.01	A	DM	Ashford Town	W	1-0	*389*	Hunt 45.	2
26	17.01	H	DM	Rothwell Town	W	2-0	365	Cook 1, Smart 74.	2
27	24.01	A	DM	Sittingbourne	W	5-4	*436*	Winter 14, 17, OG (Seager) 39, Hunt 57, 82.	2
28	31.01	H	DM	Crawley Town	W	3-2	428	Callinan 12, McLoughlin 64, 67.	1
29	07.02	A	DM	Gloucester City	W	4-1	*1,095*	Winter 43, Sykes 51, Smart 76, Hallam 84.	1
30	14.02	A	DM	St Leonards Stamcroft	W	2-1	*418*	Smart 18, Sykes 32.	1
31	21.02	H	DM	Tamworth	W	5-0	548	McLoughlin 10, 73, Hunt 27, 75 (2 pens), Hallam 42.	1
32	07.03	H	DM	Gresley Rovers	L	0-1	569		1
33	14.03	A	DM	Bath City	D	1-1	*1,019*	Hallam 76.	2
34	21.03	A	DM	Hastings Town	W	1-0	*469*	Smart 39.	2
35	28.03	H	DM	Sittingbourne	W	3-0	534	Sykes 65, Hallam 72, Callinan 82.	2
36	04.04	A	DM	Tamworth	W	2-1	*467*	Hunt 16, Callinan 66.	2
37	10.04	H	DM	Salisbury City	W	3-2	865	Smart 68, Hunt 72, Sykes 79.	1
38	13.04	A	DM	Merthyr Tydfil	L	0-4	*1,930*		2
39	18.04	H	DM	Halesowen Town	W	2-0	701	Sykes 28, Hallam 65.	1
40	25.04	A	DM	Atherstone United	D	1-1	*364*	Smart 63.	2
41	29.04	H	DM	Merthyr Tydfil	W	3-1	2,891	McLoughlin 72, Sykes 74, Winter 82.	1
42	02.05	H	DM	Bath City	W	2-0	1,678	Smart 34, Sykes 78.	1

CUP COMPETITIONS DMC - Dr. Martens Cup GSC - Gloucestershire Senior Cup

Date	Venue	Comp.	Opponents	Result	Score	Att.	Goalscorers
13.09	A	**FAC** 1Q	Downton	W	4-0	123	Callinan 37, Sykes 51, 75, Smart 70.
27.09	A	2Q	Dorchester Town	L	0-1	652	
08.11	A	**FAT** 2Q	Billericay Town	L	0-4	426	
07.10	A	**DMC** 1-1	Merthyr Tydfil	D	0-0	311	
29.10	H	1-2	Merthyr Tydfil	W	3-1	309	Mitchell 36, Sykes 47, Callinan 59.
13.01	A	2	Clevedon Town	L	1-4	255	Sykes 84.
09.09	H	**GSC** 1	Cirencester Town	W	*2-1	248	Hunt 67 (pen), 116.
14.10	H	2	Yate Town	W	5-0	155	Hunt 8, 87, O.G. 18, Callinan 25, Boyle 60..
25.11	H	S-F	Gloucester City	W	2-1	439	Smart 60, Cook 73.
24.03	A	Final	Bristol City	L	1-2	590	Hunt 77.

League Attendances	**HIGHEST:** 2,891 v Merthyr Tydfil	**LOWEST:** 342 v Cambridge City
DR. MARTENS: Champions	**FA CUP:** Second Qual. Round	**FA TROPHY:** Second Qual. Round

1	2	3	4	5	6	7	8	9	10	11	12 14 15	
Mogg	Jackson	Dicks	Hendy	Kilgour	Cook	McLoughlin	Callinan	Mitchell	Hunt	Forbes	Bayliss(9), Ford(7), Smart(10).	1
Mogg	Jackson	Dicks	Hendy	Kilgour	Cook	McLoughlin	Callinan	Mitchell	Smart	Forbes	Bayliss(9), Ford(7), Coupe(2).	2
Mogg	Jackson	Dicks	Smart	Kilgour	Cook	McLoughlin	Callinan	Mitchell	Hunt	Forbes	Bayliss(9), Ford(7), Coupe(2).	3
Mogg	Coupe	Dicks	Smart	Kilgour	Cook	McLoughlin	Callinan	Mitchell	Hunt	Forbes	Bayliss(9), Ford(4), Jackson(6).	4
Mogg	Coupe	Dicks	Smart	Kilgour	Cook	McLoughlin	Callinan	Mitchell	Hunt	Forbes	Bayliss(6), Ford(7), Jackson(9).	5
Mogg	Jackson	Dicks	Smart	Kilgour	Cook	Bayliss	Callinan	Mitchell	Hunt	Forbes	Ford(9),Fitzpatrick(7),Shuttlewood.	6
Shuttlewood	Jackson	Dicks	Smart	Kilgour	Coupe	Ford	Callinan	Bayliss	Hunt	Forbes	Cook(8),Sykes(9),Fitzpatrick(7).	7
Shuttlewood	Coupe	Dicks	Smart	Kilgour	Cook	Sykes	Callinan	Mitchell	Hunt	Forbes	Jackson(7),Ford(9),Bayliss(4).	8
Shuttlewood	Coupe	Dicks	Smart	Kilgour	Jackson	McLoughlin	Callinan	Mitchell	Hunt	Forbes	Cook(6),Sykes(3),Hendy(10).	9
Mogg	Coupe	Dicks	Smart	Hendy	Jackson	McLoughlin	Cook	Mitchell	Hunt	Forbes	Sykes(3),Boyle(9),Kilgour(5).	10
Shuttlewood	Coupe	Dicks	Smart	Kilgour	Cook	McLoughlin	Callinan	Boyle	Hunt	Sykes	Forbes,Jackson(6),Ward.	11
Mogg	Mitchell	Dicks	Smart	Kilgour	Cook	McLoughlin	Callinan	Boyle	Hunt	Forbes	Jackson(5),Sykes(9),Ward.	12
Mogg	Winter	Dicks	Smart	Jackson	Cook	McLoughlin	Callinan	Boyle	Hunt	Sykes	Mitchell, Forbes, Shuttlewood.	13
Mogg	Winter	Dicks	Cook	Kilgour	Jackson	McLoughlin	Callinan	Boyle	Hunt	Sykes	Mitchell(4),Forbes,Fretigne(9).	14
Mogg	Coupe	Dicks	Smart	Kilgour	Cook	Winter	Callinan	Mitchell	McLoughlin	Sykes	Boyle(8),Jackson(7),Fretigne(10).	15
Shuttlewood	Coupe	Dicks	Smart	Kilgour	Honor	Winter	Callinan	Birkby	Hunt	Forbes	Cook(7),Sykes(10),Jackson(6).	16
Shuttlewood	Coupe	Dicks	Smart	Kilgour	Honor	Winter	Callinan	Birkby	Hunt	Forbes	Cook(6), Jackson, Sykes.	17
Shuttlewood	Honor	Dicks	Smart	Kilgour	Cook	Winter	Callinan	Birkby	Hunt	Forbes	Sykes, Jackson(7), Boyle.	18
Shuttlewood	Honor	Dicks	Smart	Kilgour	Cook	Winter	Callinan	Birkby	Hunt	Forbes	Jackson(8), Sykes(9), McLoughlin(4).	19
Shuttlewood	Honor	Dicks	Smart	Kilgour	Cook	Winter	Sykes	Birkby	McLoughlin	Forbes	Coupe, Huny(8), Jackson(9).	20
Shuttlewood	Honor	Dicks	Smart	Kilgour	Cook	Winter	Sykes	McLoughlin	Hunt	Forbes	Jackson(4), Boyle, Coupe(8).	21
Shuttlewood	Honor	Dicks	Smart	Kilgour	Cook	Winter	Jones	McLoughlin	Hunt	Forbes	Sykes(8), Jackson, Coupe(2).	22
Shuttlewood	Honor	Dicks	Smart	Kilgour	Cook	Winter	jones	McLoughlin	Hunt	Forbes	Sykes, Jackson, Callinan.	23
Shuttlewood	Honor	Dicks	Smart	Kilgour	Cook	Winter	jones	Callinan	Hunt	Forbes	Jackson(20, Sykes(8), Boyle(6).	24
Shuttlewood	Honor	Sykes	Smart	Coupe	Cook	Jackson	jones	Callinan	Hunt	Forbes	Boyle(10),Evans, Woodhouse(1).	25
Shuttlewood	Honor	Sykes	Smart	Kilgour	Cook	Coupe	jones	Callinan	Hunt	Forbes	Jackson(6),Boyle, Dicks(3).	26
Woodhouse	Honor	Dicks	Sykes	Kilgour	Cook	Winter	jones	Callinan	Hunt	Forbes	Jackson(4), Coupe(9), Smart(6).	27
Shuttlewood	Honor	Dicks	Smart	Kilgour	Sykes	Winter	jones	Callinan	Hunt	Forbes	Jackson(7),Coupe, McLoughlin(3).	28
Shuttlewood	Honor	Dicks	Smart	Kilgour	Sykes	Winter	jones	Callinan	Hunt	Forbes	Jackson, Hallam(10), McLoughlin(3).	29
Shuttlewood	Coupe	Dicks	Smart	Kilgour	Sykes	Winter	jones	Callinan	Hunt	Forbes	Jackson(10), Hallam(6), McLoughlin.	30
Shuttlewood	Coupe	Dicks	McLoughlin	Kilgour	Sykes	Winter	jones	Callinan	Hunt	Forbes	Jackson, Hallam(8), Banks.	31
Shuttlewood	Coupe	Dicks	McLoughlin	Kilgour	Sykes	Winter	jones	Callinan	Hunt	Forbes	Jackson93), Hallam(9), Honor.	32
Shuttlewood	Honor	Dicks	Smart	Kilgour	Sykes	Winter	jones	Callinan	McLoughlin	Forbes	Hunt93), Coupe, Hallam(10).	33
Shuttlewood	Honor	Dicks	Smart	Kilgour	McLoughlin	Winter	jones	Hallam	Hunt	Forbes	Callinan(10),Sykes(4),Coupe(5)	34
Shuttlewood	Coupe	Dicks	McLoughlin	Honor	Callinan	Winter	jones	Hallam	Hunt	Forbes	Sykes(3), Smart(8), Jackson(7).	35
Shuttlewood	Honor	Sykes	Smart	Kilgour	Callinan	Winter	jones	Hallam	Hunt	Forbes	mcLoughlin(7),Dicks(2),Coupe(8).	36
Shuttlewood	McLoughlin	Sykes	Smart	Kilgour	Callinan	Winter	jones	Hallam	Hunt	Forbes	Dicks(11),Jackson(7),Banks.	37
Shuttlewood	Honor	Dicks	Smart	Kilgour	Callinan	Winter	jones	McLoughlin	Hunt	Sykes	Hallam(6), Coupe, Jackson.	38
Shuttlewood	Honor	Dicks	Smart	Coupe	Callinan	McLoughlin	jones	Hallam	Hunt	Sykes	Kilgour(2),Winter(7),Jackson.	39
Woodhouse	Coupe	Dicks	Smart	Kilgour	Callinan	McLoughlin	jones	Hallam	Hunt	Sykes	Winter(8), Jackson(4), Banks.	40
Shuttlewood	Coupe	Dicks	McLoughlin	Honor	Callinan	Winter	jones	Hallam	Hunt	Sykes	Smart(8),Jackson(7),Boyle.	41
Shuttlewood	Honor	Dicks	Smart	Coupe	Callinan	Winter	McLoughlin	Hallam	Hunt	Sykes	Jones(4), Kilgour(8), Jackson(11).	42

1	2	3	4	5	6	7	8	9	10	11	12 14 15
Shuttlewood	Jackson	Dicks	Coupe	Kilgour	Cook	Smart	Callinan	Sykes	Hunt	Forbes	Ford(6), Mitchell(10), Hendy(8).
Mogg	Coupe	Dicks	Smart	Hendy	Jackson	McLoughlin	Callinan	Mitchell	Hunt	Forbes	Cook(8), Sykes99), Ford(4).
Shuttlewood	Coupe	Dicks	Smart	Kilgour	Cook	Winter	Callinan	Mitchell	Jackson	Sykes	Boyle(6), Fretigne(8),Forbes.
Shuttlewood	Ward	Dicks	Smart	Hendy	Jackson	McLoughlin	Cook	Sykes	Hunt	Forbes	Kilgour(10), Boyle(6), Coupe(2).
Mogg	Coupe	Dicks	Smart	Kilgour	Fretigne	Winter	Callinan	Mitchell	Hunt	Sykes	McLoughlin(7),Boyle(10),Jackson(6).
Woodhouse	Callinan	Sykes	Hendy	Coupe	Cook	Jackson	Jones	Evans	Hunt	Forbes	Embling(7),Gardiner(9),Shuttlewood.
Shuttlewood	Coupe	Dicks	Smart	Hendy	Cook	Ford	Fitzpatrick	Bayliss	Hunt	Forbes	Mitchell(9),Sykes(2),Jackson(3).
Mogg	Winter	Dicks	Ward	Kilgour	Fretigne	Cook	Callinan	Boyle	Hunt	Sykes	Jackson(5),Tarrant(2),Smart(6).
Shuttlewood	Honor	Sykes	Smart	Kilgour	Cook	Jackson	Callinan	Boyle	Hunt	Forbes	Dicks, Winter(7),McLoughlin(9).
Shuttlewood	Coupe	Dicks	Smart	Honor	McLoughlin	Winter	Jones	Callinan	Hunt	Forbes	Jackson(7), Sykes(3), Banks(8).

FRANK GREGAN (MANAGER)

Date of Appointment 01.01.94

Date of Birth: 09.08.57

Place of Birth: Newcastle-upon-Tyne

PREVIOUS CLUBS

As manager - None As player - None

HONOURS

As manager Southern League -
Southern Div. Championship 96-97
Premier Div. Championship 97-98

Assistant Manager: Tommy Callinan

Coach: Mike Kilgour **Physio:** Bob Baird

Paul Hunt - Leading Goalscorer and Player of the Year

Photo: Roger Turner

Frank Gregan and Gary Smart hold aloft the Dr Marten's League Champions Trophy. Photo: Ian Gregory.

MATCHDAY PROGRAMME

Number of pages 48

Price £1.00

Programme Editor Julie Davis

Tel: 01453 791232

Other club publications: None

Local Newspapers: Stroud News & Journal
Gloucester Citizen

Local Radio Stations: Severn Sound
BBC Radio Gloucestershire

1997-98 PLAYING SQUAD

PLAYER	Birthplace Honours	Birthdate	CLUBS
GOALKEEPERS			
Justin Shuttlewood	Trowbridge DMP	8.2.71	Westbury U
Martin Woodhouse	Calne	2.5.69	Calne Town
DEFENDERS			
Grantley Dicks	Bristol DMP	17.10.66	Clandown, Paulton R, Bath C, Trowbridge T
Mike Kilgour	Dartford	25.5.65	Bath C, Larkhall Ath, Melksham T, Trowbridge T, Salisbury C, Stroud, Trowbridge T, Gloucester C, Dorchester T, Salisbury C
Ian Hedges *	Bristol	5.2.69	Bristol Manor F, Gloucester C, AFC Bournemouth, Bath C
Don Forbes	Bristol DMP	17.9.68	Avon St.Phillips, Bath C
Chris Honor	Bristol DMP	5.6.68	Bristol C, Bath C, Slough T, Bath C, Newport AFC, Airdrie
Matthew Coupe	North Wales ES, DMP	7.10.78	Bristol City
Toby Jackson	Bath DMP	24.2.71	Larkhall Ath, Bath C, Trowbridge T, Gloucester C, Clevedon T, Witney T
Jim Rollo	Wisbech	22.5.76	Walsall, Cardiff City.
MIDFIELDERS			
Tommy Callinan	Cheltenham DMP	6.6.66	Cheltenham T, Cheltenham Saracens, Cinderford T, Gloucester C
Gary Smart	Bristol DMP	8.12.63	Mangotsfield U, Bristol R, Cheltenham T, Bath C, Mangotsfield U
Tom Jones	Aldershot ESP, FAT, Div 2, DMP	7.10.64	Chelsea, Farnborough T, Weymouth, Aberdeen, Swindon T, Reading, Woking
Rob Cook	Forest Green DMP	28.3.70	Shortwood U, Forest Green R, Cinderford T
Alex Sykes	Newcastle-u-Lyme British Univ, DMP	2.4.74	Westfields, Mansfield T, Cheltenham T, Endsleigh
FORWARDS			
Paul Hunt	Swindon DMP	8.10.70	Swindon T, Charlton Ath, Cardiff C, Bristol R, Brann (Nor), Cirencester T
Martin Boyle	Bristol DMP		Bristol R, Trowbridge T, Mangotsfield U, Bath C, Cheltenham T, Newport AFC
Steve Winter	Bristol DMP	26.10.73	Yate T, Walsall, Yate T, Taunton T, Torquay U, Yeovil T, Salisbury C, Forest Green R, Dorchester T
Mark Hallam	Leicester DMP		Leicester U, Boston U, Hednesford T, £5k to Gloucester C, £5k to Ilkeston T, £5 to Hinckley T, £2k to Worcester C, £2k to Forest Green R

DEPARTURES - David Mogg (Salisbury C), Paul Fitzpatrick (Gresley R), Richard Ford (Salisbury C), Dave Mitchell (Cirencester T), Shaun Rouse (Trowbridge T), Karl Bayliss (Newport AFC), Nick Hendy (Retired - injury), Paul McLoughlin (released).

The Lawn, Nympsfield Rd., Forest Green.

ADDRESS: 'The Lawn', Nympsfield Road, Forest Green, Nailsworth, Glos. GL6 0ET.
TELEPHONE NUMBER: 01453 834860 (Matchdays). 01453 791232 (Club Administration Office).

SIMPLE DIRECTIONS: About 4 miles south of Stroud on the A46 towards Bath. In Nailsworth turn into Spring Hill from the mini roundabout and the ground is approx. half a mile up the hill on the left. The nearest BR station is Stroud.

CAPACITY: 3,030 **COVERED TERRACING:** 1050 **SEATED** 526

SOCIAL FACILITIES: Clubhouse open every evening. Bar and lounge. Open before and after Saturday matches.

CLUB SHOP: Open only on matchdays selling souvenirs and programmes. Contact Andy Whiting.

Forest Green Fact File

Nickname: Rovers **Sponsors:** Sheffield Insulations

Club Colours: Black & white striped shirts, black shorts, red socks.

Change Colours: All Yellow.

Midweek matchday: Wednesday

Reserves' League: Complete Music Hellenic League. Youth League: Glos. County Youth Lge.

PREVIOUS - **Leagues:** Stroud & Dist. 1890-1921, Glos Northern Snr 22-67, Glos Co. 67-73, Hellenic 73-82, Southern League 82-98, Conference 98-.
Name: Stroud FC, 1989-92. **Ground:** None.

CLUB RECORDS - **Attendance:** 2,891 v Merthyr Tydfil, DM Prem Div. 29.4.98
Win: 8-0 v Fareham Town Southern Lge. Southern Div. 96-97
Defeat: 0-7 v Moor Green, Southern Lge. Midland Div. 85-86.
Career Goalscorer: Karl Bayliss
Career Appearances: Tommy Callinan
Transfer Fee paid: Karl Bayliss from Gloucester City.
Transfer Fee Received: Steve Book to Cheltenham Town

BEST SEASON - **FA Cup:** Third Qual Round 87-88.
FA Trophy: Third Round Proper 90-91.
FA Vase: Winners 81-82.

HONOURS - FA Vase 81-82, Southern League - *Premier Div.* 97-98, *Southern Div.* 96-97; Hellenic Lg 81-82, Gloucs Nthn Sen Lg 37-38 49-50 50-51, Gloucs Sen Cup 84-85 85-86 86-87, Gloucs Sen Amat Cup (N) 26-27 45-46 71-72 75-76 77-78, Gloucs Sen Prof Cup 84-85 85-86.

Players progressing to Football League: G Rogers/K Gill (Newport Cnty 85), M England (Bristol Rov 85).

97-98 Captain: Gary Smart

97-98 Player of the Year: Paul Hunt

97-98 Top Goalscorer: Paul Hunt

HAYES

Playing in West London with the choice of rival Nationwide and Premier clubs all around you, doesn't really give a Conference club the best of chances to succeed. However, there are plenty of players in the area and a good manager with good contacts should never have a bad side. Add to this a little skill in finding rare talent and selling it on (Cyrille Regis, Les Ferdinand and Jason Roberst) and you should also be able to spend a pound or two keeping the squad up to standard !

Terry Brown is definitely 'streetwise' when it comes to football life in the home counties and he has built a solid, if unspectacular squad at Church Road. In Martin Randall he unearthed one of the sharpest strikers in local football but he has lost Jon Brady (albeit for a very handy £40,000) to Rushden & Diamonds.

His uncompromising defence is looked after by the excellent Russell Meara in goal and it will be interesting to see if the experienced goalscorer Martin Buglione can shine in Conference football. Understandably, support is not easy to attract but Hayes form in recent seasons has demanded recognition. It may be difficult to keep it going, but it should still be difficult for visitors to take a point away from The Missioners.

CLUB OFFICIALS 1998-99

President	**Les Lovering**
Chairman	**Derek Goodall**
Vice Chairman	**Trevor Griffith**
Financial Director	**Roger Harrison**
Directors	**C Porter, E Stevens, C Mackintosh, A Bond, D Goodall.**
Football Secretary	**John Bond** Jnr.
Press Officer	**Trevor Griffith** c/o the club Tel: 0181 573 2075

A Hayes corner against Dover during their goal-less draw in April this year.

HAYES - Match Facts 1997-98

Match No.	Date	Venue H / A	Comp.	Opponents	Result & Score		Att.	Goalscorers	League Position
1	16.08	H	VC	Halifax Town	L	1-2	907	Flynn 75.	15
2	19.08	A	VC	Cheltenham Town	L	1-2	*1,196*	OG (Banks) 6.	
3	23.09	H	VC	Morecambe	**L**	**0-3**	505		21
4	25.09	H	VC	Welling United	W	3-1	650	Cox 28, Hall 61, Roberts 81.	19
5	30.09	A	VC	Kidderminster Harriers	L	0-1	*1,706*		22
6	01.09	A	VC	Stevenage Borough	**W**	**5-1**	*2,768*	Goodliffe 13, Roberts 14, 84, Randall 62, Bunce 69.	13
7	06.09	H	VC	Hereford United	W	2-0	974	Roberts 11,32.	5
8	13.09	A	VC	Stalybridge Celtic	D	1-1	*545*	Bunce	12
9	16.09	H	VC	Cheltenham Town	D	1-1	485	Randall 56 (pen).	11
10	20.09	A	VC	Leek Town	W	2-1	*551*	Randall 45, 69.	8
11	27.09	H	VC	Hednesford Town	W	4-0	632	Randall 13, Haynes 43, 85, Roddis 90.	
12	04.10	A	VC	Farnborough Town	W	2-0	*781*	Randall 64, Flynn 81.	5
13	11.10	H	VC	Stalybridge Celtic	L	1-2	691	Duncan 80.	5
14	18.10	A	VC	Kettering Town	D	1-1	*1,006*	OG (Vowden) 89.	6
15	01.11	H	VC	Gateshead	W	1-0	675	Haynes 77.	6
16	08.11	A	VC	Dover Athletic	L	0-1	*889*		7
17	22.11	H	VC	Northwich Victoria	D	1-1	438	Sparks 87.	8
18	29.11	A	VC	Rushden & Diamonds	W	3-1	*2,158*	Bunce 5, Randall 37, 78.	7
19	06.12	H	VC	Telford United	W	2-1	525	Hall 63, Randall 90.	6
20	13.12	A	VC	Woking	**L**	**0-3**	*2,435*		
21	20.12	H	VC	Rushden & Diamonds	L	1-2	679	Hall 29	8
22	26.12	A	VC	Slough Town	D	0-0	*1,219*		8
23	01.01	H	VC	Slough Town	L	0-1	1,224		11
24	03.01	A	VC	Morecambe	W	2-0	*1,164*	Wikinson 57, Hammatt 73.	8
25	17.01	H	VC	Kidderminster Harriers	D	1-1	564	Randall 21 (pen).	8
26	20.01	A	VC	Yeovil Town	L	3-4	*1,705*	Boothe 35, Francis 62, Randall 68.	
27	24.01	A	VC	Hednesford Town	L	1-2	*1,265*	Brady 15.	9
28	07.02	A	VC	Southport	W	2-0	*923*	Bunce 3, Randall 77.	8
29	14.02	H	VC	Yeovil Town	W	6-4	715	Flynn 1, 57, Hall 13, 89, Randall 60, Roddis 90.	7
30	24.02	A	VC	Hereford United	L	0-3	*1,663*		
31	28.02	H	VC	Stevenage Borough	L	1-3	921	Cox 66.	10
32	07.03	A	VC	Telford United	L	0-1	*631*		10
33	21.03	H	VC	Southport	W	2-0	460	Hall 53, Metcalfe 68.	10
34	28.03	A	VC	Halifax Town	D	1-1	*2,506*	Domingos 27.	9
35	04.04	A	VC	Northwich Victoria	D	1-1	*842*	Boothe 72.	9
36	07.04	H	VC	Kettering Town	L	0-1	506		9
37	11.04	H	VC	Farnborough Town	W	3-1	583	Boothe 32, 60 (pen), OG (Baker) 85.	9
38	13.04	A	VC	Welling United	L	0-2	*665*		10
39	23.04	H	VC	Dover Athletic	D	0-0	475		
40	25.04	A	VC	Gateshead	D	1-1	*412*	Randall 8.	12
41	28.04	H	VC	Woking	W	3-0	667	Hall 9, Wilkinson 64, Metcalfe 83.	12
42	02.05	H	VC	Leek Town	W	3-1	743	Flynn 19, Randall 67, Roddis 88.	12

CUP COMPETITIONS

Date	Venue H / A	Comp.	Opponents	Result & Score		Att.	Goalscorers
25.10	A	**FAC** 4Q	Yeovil Town	D	1-1	2,501	Goodliffe 22 (pen)
28.10	H	4QR	Yeovil Town	W	1-0	1,132	Goodliffe
15.11	H	1	Boreham Wood	L	0-1	1,343	
10.01	H	**FAT** 1	Cambridge City	W	3-2	533	Watts 56, Flynn 61, Boothe 81.
31.01	H	2	Kidderminster Harriers	W	5-0	698	Hall 8, Randall 16 (pen), 20, Hammatt 80, Sparks 83.
21.02	H	3	Bashley	W	2-0	671	Sparks 49, Boothe 83 (pen).
14.03	A	4	Cheltenham Town	L	0-1	2,383	
07.10	H	**SCC** 1	Rushden & Diamonds	W	2-0	438	Roddis 17, Hammatt 26.
18.11	H	2	Slough Town	W	2-0	374	Hammatt 15, Haynes 70.
16.12	H	3	Yeovil Town	W	3-0	171	Roddis73, Randall 89, Hammatt 90.
17.02	H	SF 1	Woking	L	0-2	647	
17.03	A	SF 2	Woking	L	1-3	826	Randall 54.
06.01	H	**MSC** 2	Edgware Town	W	5-3	123	Warrington, Boothe, Domingos (2), Randall
04.02	A	3	Enfield	D	1-1	166	Randall
10.02	H	3 R	Enfield	L	0-1	186	
30.09	H	**MCC** 1	Feltham	W	3-1	124	Duncan, Cox (2).
09.12	H	2	Staines Town	W	4-3	111	Brady, Flynn, Boothe, OG.
03.03	A	3	Ashford Town (Middx)	W	7-2	120	Francis2 , Roddis, Domingos, Randall2 , Hammatt..
02.04	H	S-F	Waltham Abbey	L	1-3	117	Brady.

SCC - Spalding Challenge Cup
MSC - Middx Senior Cup MCC - Middx. Charity Cup

League Attendances:	HIGHEST: 1,224 v Slough Town	LOWEST: 438 v Northwich Victoria
CONFERENCE: 12th	**FA CUP:** 1st Round	**FA TROPHY:** 4th Round

1	2	3	4	5	6	7	8	9	10	11	12 14 15	
Meara	Brady	Flynn	Sparks	Cox	Goodliffe	Francis	Pye	Randall	Roberts	Wilkinson	Duncan (5), Haynes (8), Bunce (4)	1
Meara	Brady	Flynn	Sparks	Cox	Goodliff	Francis	Pye	Randall	Roberts	Wilkinson	Bunce (4), Hall (8), Haynes (9).	2
Meara	Brady	Flynn	Bunce	Cox	Goodliffe	Francis	Hall	Craft	Roberts	Wilkinson	Pye (7), Haynes (8), Sparks(9).	3
Meara	Brady	Flynn	Sparks	Cox	Goodliffe	Francis	Hall	Haynes	Roberts	Pye	Duncan (8), Randall (9), Bunce (10).	4
Meara	Brady	Flynn	Sparks	Cox	Goodliffe	Wilkinson	Hall	Haynes	Roberts	Pye	Bunce (2), Randall (8), Francis (4).	5
Meara	Brady	Flynn	Sparks	Cox	Goodliffe	Pye	Hall	Randall	Roberts	Wilkinson	Bunce (6), Francis (8), Haynes (9).	6
Meara	Brady	Flynn	Sparks	Cox	Goodliffe	Pye	Hall	Randall	Roberts	Wilkinson	Francis (7), Haynes (9), Bunce (8).	7
Meara	Duncan	Flynn	Bunce	Roddis	Goodliffe	Francis	Hall	Randall	Haynes	Wilkinson	Hammatt (7), Craft (9), Dell.	8
Meara	Duncan	Flynn	Bunce	Roddis	Goodliffe	Francis	Hall	Hammatt	Haynes	Wilkinson	Randall (2), Brady (5), Passmore (8).	9
Meara	Brady	Flynn	Bunce	Duncan	Goodliffe	Pye	Hall	Randall	Hammatt	Wilkinson	Haynes (10), O'Connor, Craft.	10
Meara	Brady	Flynn	Bunce	Sparks	Goodliffe	Pye	Hall	Randall	Haynes	Wilkinson	Roddis (10), Hammatt (9), Duncan (7).	11
Meara	Brady	Flynn	Bunce	Sparks	Goodliffe	Pye	Hall	Randall	Haynes	Wilkinson	Francis (7), Duncan (8), Hammatt (9).	12
Meara	Brady	Flynn	Bunce	Sparks	Goodliffe	Pye	Roddis	Randall	Haynes	Wilkinson	Duncan (9), Hammatt (8), Francis (7).	13
Meara	Brady	Flynn	Bunce	Sparks	Goodliffe	Pye	Roddis	Boothe	Haynes	Wilkinson	Duncan (7), Cox (5), Hammatt (8).	14
Meara	Brady	Flynn	Sparks	Cox	Goodliffe	Pye	Hall	Roddis	Hammatt	Duncan	Sparks (5), Randall (10), Haynes (11).	15
Meara	Brady	Flynn	Bunce	Sparks	Goodliffe	Hall	Roddis	Randall	Hammatt	Wilkinson	Haynes (10), Francis (8), Djemai (11).	16
Beccles	Brady	Flynn	Bunce	Sparks	Goodliffe	Francis	Haynes	Boothe	Hammatt	Wilkinson	Beer (6), Randall (8), Hall (10).	17
Meara	Brady	Flynn	Bunce	Sparks	Beer	Pye	Hall	Boothe	Randall	Wilkinson	Hammatt (8), Haynes (10), Francis.	18
Meara	Brady	Flynn	Bunce	Sparks	Beer	Pye	Hall	Boothe	Randall	Wilkinson	Haynes (6), Roddis (7), Hammatt (9).	19
Meara	Brady	Flynn	Bunce	Sparks	Goodliffe	pye	Hall	Randall	Boothe	Wilkinson	Roddis (7), Haynes (8), Francis (6).	20
Meara	Brady	Flynn	Bunce	Sparks	Watts	Roddis	Hall	Hammatt	Randall	Wilkinson	Boothe (6), Haynes (9), Beer.	21
Meara	Brady	Flynn	Bunce	Sparks	Watts	Roddis	Hall	Hammatt	Randall	Wilkinson	Pye (8), Haynes (9), Francis.	22
Meara	Brady	Flynn	Bunce	Sparks	Watts	Roddis	Hall	Pye	Hammatt	Wilkinson	Boothe (10), Haynes (8), Francis (9)	23
Meara	Brady	Flynn	Bunce	Sparks	Watts	Pye	Roddis	Boothe	Hammatt	Wilkinson	Francis (7), Goodliffe, Craft.	24
Meara	Brady	Flynn	Bunce	Cox	Wattss	Francis	Hall	Boothe	Randall	Wilkinson	Beer, Hammatt (8), Goodliffe.	25
Meara	Brady	Flynn	Bunce	Cox	Watts	Francis	Hall	Boothe	Randall	Wilkinson	Hammatt (8), Goodliffe, Beer.	26
Meara	Brady	Duncan	Bunce	Cox	Watts	Francis	Roddis	Boothe	Randall	Wilkinson	Hall (10), Metcalfe (7), Flynn (3).	27
Meara	Brady	Flynn	Bunce	Duncan	Sparks	Metcalfe	Hall	Boothe	Randall	Wilkinson	Hammatt (9), Beer, Francis.	28
Meara	Brady	Flynn	Bunce	Sparks	Watts	Metcalfe	Hall	Hammatt	Randall	Wilkinson	Pye(5), Roddis(9), Dell.	29
Meara	Brady	Beer	Sparks	Cox	Watts	Metcalfe	Hall	Boothe	Rodddis	Wilkinson	Hammatt(3), Pye(9), Francis.	30
Meara	Brady	Beer	Bunce	Cox	Sparks	Pye	Roddis	Boothe	Randall	Hammatt	Francis(3), Wilkinson, Watts.	31
Meara	Beer	Taylor	Bunce	Sparks	Watts	Domingos	Rodis	Boothe	Randall	Wilkinson	Hammatt(10), Cox, Dell.	32
Meara	Brady	Taylor	Bunce	Cox	Sparks	Metcalfe	Hall	Boothe	Randall	Wilkinson	Roddis(7), Domingos, Watts.	33
Meara	Watts	Beer	Bunce	Cox	Sparks	Metcalfe	Hall	Domingos	Randall	Taylor	Brady(8), Hammatt(9), Boothe(10)	34
Meara	Brady	Taylor	Bunce	Cox	Beer	Metcalf	Hall	Boothe	Randall	Gallagher	Dell(4), Craft, Domingos.	35
Meara	Brady	Taylor	Watts	Cox	Beer	Metcalfe	Hall	Boothe	Randall	Wilkinson	Gallagher(6),Domingos(8),Dell.	36
Meara	Brady	Taylor	Watts	Cox	Beer	Metcalfe	Hall	Domingos	Boothe	Wilkinson	Randall(9),Roddis(11),Gallagher.	37
Meara	Brady	Gallagher	Taylor	Cox	Watts	Metcalfe	Hall	Boothe	Randall	Roddis	Beer(8), Domingos(9), Dell(11).	38
Meara	Brady	Taylor	Watts	Flynn	Rodis	Metcalfe	Randall	Boothe	Domingos	Wilkinson	Hall(8), Craft910), Gallagher.	39
Meara	Brady	Flynn	Taylor	Cox	Watts	Gallagher	Hall	Domingos	Randall	Wilkinson	Beer(2), Dell(8),Boothe.	40
Meara	Brady	Flynn	Watts	Cox	Taylor	Metcalfe	Hall	Roddis	Randall	Wilkinson	Domingos(8), Gallagher(10), Beer.	41
Meara	Brady	Flynn	Watts	Cox	Taylor	Metcalfe	Hall	Domingos	Randall	Wilkinson	Bunce(5), Roddis(7), Beer(9).	42

Meara	Brady	Flynn	Bunce	Cox	Goodliffe	Pye	Hall	Boothe	Hammatt	Wilkinson	Sparks (8), Haynes (9), Roddis (11).
Meara	Brady	Flynn	Bunce	Cox	Goodliffe	Pye	Hall	Sparks	Hammatt	Francis	Haynes, (8), Roddis (7), Duncan.
Meara	Brady	Flynn	Bunce	Sparks	Goodliffe	Hall	Roddis	Randall	Hammatt	Wilkinson	Boothe (7), Francis (8), Haynes (10).
Meara	Brady	Flynn	Bunce	Watts	Goodliffe	Hall	Randall	Boothe	Hammatt	Wilkinson	Cox, Francis (10), Roddis (7).
Meara	Brady	Flynn	Bunce	Cox	Sparks	Pye	Roddis	Boothe	Randall	Hall	Hammatt (10), Duncan (11), Beer (7).
FAT 3											
FAT 4											
Meara	Brady	Flynn	Bunce	Sparks	Goodliffe	Francis	Roddis	Hammatt	Haynes	Wilkinson	Watts (4), Craft (10), Bell.
Beccles	Beer	Duncan	Bunce	Sparks	Flynn	Brown	Francis	Boothe	Haynes	Wilkinson	Brady (2), Hammatt (7), Watts (3).
Meara	Brady	Flynn	Bunce	Sparks	Beer	Domingos	Roddis	Hammatt	Randall	Wilkinson	Boothe (7), Hall (12), Pye.
Meara	Brady	Flynn	Sparks	cox	Watts	Pye	Hall	Boothe	Randall	Wilkinson	Roddis93),Francis(7),Hammatt(10).
Meara	Beer	Roddis	Bunce	Taylor	Watts	Pye	Hall	Boothe	Randall	Wilkinson	Domingos(9), Walsh, Hammatt.
Davey	Warrington	T Hall	Watts	Cox	Goodliffe	Francis	Beer	Craft	Boothe	Domingos	Randall (9), Dell, Roddis (2).
Meara	Brady	Flynn	Bunce	Roddis	Sparks	Francis	Duncan	Hammatt	Randall	Beer	Hall (5), Boothe (11).
Meara	Beer	Flynn	Watts	Duncan	Goodliffe	Francis	Pye	Hammatt	Randall	Roddis	Brady (2), Bunce (5), Hall (8).
Beccles	Duncan	Dell	Sparks	Cox	Roddis	Passmore	Francis	Hammatt	Warrington	Craft	Watts (3), Brady (10), O'Connor (5).
Lynham	Brady	Flynn	Roddis	Watts	Dell	Beer	Hall	Boothe	Haynes	Wilkinson	Passmore (9), O'Connor (8), Tilbury.
Lynham	Goodliffe	Beer	Watts	Bunce	Walsh	Francis	Roddis	Domingos	Randall	Wilkinson	Hammatt(2), Sparks(7), Cox.
Meara	Brady	Beer	Dav Tilbury	Watts	Taylor	Walsh	Hall	Randall	Gallagher	Metcalfe	Domingos(6),Croft(9),Dan Tilbury(10).

TERRY BROWN (MANAGER)

Date of Appointment	November 1993
Date of Birth:	5th August 1952
Place of Birth:	Hillingdon

PREVIOUS CLUBS

As manager	
As coach	Wokingham Town
As player	Hayes, Slough Town, Hayes, Wokingham Town

HONOURS

As manager	ICIS League Championship 95-96
As player	None

Assistant Manager: Willy Wordsworth

Coach: Dave Killick **Physio:** Karl Ballard

Terry Brown talking to the fans.

Photos: Peter Barnes

Martin Randall
Hayes' Leading Goalscorer 97-98.

MATCHDAY PROGRAMME

Number of pages	32
Price	£1.50
Programme Editor	Robert Frape
	0181 848 8848
Other club publications:	None
Local Newspapers:	Hayes Gazette
Local Radio Stations:	Capital Radio Star FM

1997-98 PLAYING SQUAD

PLAYER	Birthplace Honours	Birthdate	CLUBS
GOALKEEPERS			
Russell Meara	Hammersmith ILP	12.7.74	Southampton, Brighton, Barnet, Aylesbury U, Wokingham T
DEFENDERS			
Jamie Beer	London		Brentford, Chertsey T, Chesham U, Chertsey T, Walton & Hersham
Chris Sparks	London ILC		Brentford, Chertsey T £5k to Hayes
Andy Cox	Hemel H ILP, FA XI	1.5.69	Chipperfield, Tring T, Berkhamsted T, St.Albans C, £6k to Hayes
Jason Goodliffe	Hillingdon ILP	7.3.74	Brentford
Nathan Bunce	Hillingdon	2.5.75	Brentford, Yeading, £2k to Hayes
Iain Duncan	Oxford	31.7.72	Leicester C, Thatcham T, Basingstoke T, Wealdstone, Windsor & Eton, Wokingham T
MIDFIELDERS			
Steve Baker	Hillingdon ILP	31.5.74	Brentford, Brook House, Hayes, Southall, Yeading
Nick Roddis	Rotherham	18.2.73	Nottingham F, Boston FC, Boston U, Yeading
Darron Wilkinson	Reading ILP	24.11.69	Wokingham T, Brighton, Kuitan (HK)
Christian Metcalfe	London		Chelsea, Harrow Borough £4k to Hayes
FORWARDS			
Martin Randall	Pinner ILP	3.3.73	Northwood, £1,500 to Hayes
Mark Hall	Islington Barbados Int.	13.1.73	Tottenham Hotspur, Southend U, Torquay U, Dover Ath, Grays Ath
Bryan Hammatt	London	25.1.73	Enfield, Hertford T, Boreham Wood, Northwood, Hertford T, Cheshunt, Northwood, Wembley, Wealdstone
Chris Boothe	London BHL		Hanwell T, Farnborough T, £10k to Hayes
Darryl Craft	London		Colchester U

DEPARTURES - Mark Hawthorne (Crawley T), Jason Roberts (Wolves - £250K), Craig Ravenscroft (Yeading), Justin Brown (Released), Kevin Beckles (Wembley), Junior Haynes (Sutton U), Lee Passmore (Yeading), John Brady (Rushden & Diamonds).

PLAYERS ON LOAN - Kieran Gallagher (Aylesbury U)

Church Road, Hayes

GROUND ADDRESS: Townfield House, Church Road, Hayes, Middx UB3 2LE.

TELEPHONE NUMBER: 0181 573 2075. Fax: 0181 573 2075. **Club News:** 0891 884484. **Buzzline:** 0891 101922.

SIMPLE DIRECTIONS: M25, M4, A312 (Hayes By-Pass), A4020 (Uxbridge Road), Church Road on left.

CAPACITY: 6,500 **SEATED:** 450 **COVERED TERRACING:** 2,000

CLUB SHOP:
Wide range of programmes, replica kits, souvenirs and books. Contact Lee Hermitage c/o Hayes FC.

SOCIAL FACILITIES: Clubhouse open Sat. 12 - 3pm, 4.45 - 11pm. Sun. 12 - 3pm, 7 - 11pm. Midweek 7 - 11pm. Match nights 6.30 - 11pm. Some cold snacks available.

Hayes Fact File

Nickname: The Missioners **Club Sponsors:**

Club colours: Red and white shirts, black shorts, and black socks.

Change colours: Blue shirts, blue shorts, blue socks.

Reserve team league: Suburban Premier.

Midweek home matchday: Tuesday.

PREVIOUS - **Leagues:** Local leagues 09-14; Gt Western Suburban 19-22; London 22-24; Spartan 24-30; Athenian 30-71; Isthmian 71-96. **Ground:** Botwell Common.

CLUB RECORDS - **Attendance:** 15,370 v Bromley - FA Amateur Cup - 10.2.51.

Win: 12-1 v Newbury Town, FA Cup, 01.10.1927

Defeat: 1-8 v Sutton United, Isthmian League, 11.09.1993.

Transfer fee paid: £6,000 to Hendon for Gary Keen, 1990
to Enfield for Joe FRancis, 1996

Transfer fee received: £30,000 from QPR for Les Ferdinand - 1987.

Career goalscorer: Unknown.

Career appearances: Reg Leather - 701.

BEST SEASON - **FA Amateur Cup:** Runners-up 30-31

FA Cup: 2nd Round (replay) 72-73, 0-1 v Reading (H) after 0-0.
Also 2nd Rd. 90-91, 92-93.

League clubs defeated: Fulham, Bristol Rovers, Cardiff City.

FA Trophy: Quarter Final - 78-79, 1-2 v Runcorn (A); 97-98, 0-1 v Cheltenham (A).

HONOURS - ICIS League Premier Div. 95-96, FA Amateur Cup R-up 30-31, Isthmian Lg R-up 78-79, 87-88, Athenian Lg 56-57, Spartan Lg 27-28, Gt Western Suburban Lg 20-24, London Snr Cup 31-32, 80-81, Middx Snr Cup 19-21, 25-26, 30-31, 35-36, 39-40, 49-50, 81-82, 95-96, London Charity Cup 60-61, Middx Charity Cup (15 times), Middx Premier Cup 87-88, 88-89, Suburban Lg (North) 88-89, 91-92, 96-97.

Past players who progressed to the Football League: Cyril Bacon (Orient 1946), Phil Nolan (Watford 1947), Dave Grommbridge (Orient 1951), Jimmy Bloomfield (Brentford 1952), Derek Neale & Les Champleover (Brighton 1956 & 57), Gordon Phillips (Brentford 1963), Robin Friday (Reading 1974), Les Smith (A Villa), Cyrille Regis (WBA 1977), Les Ferdinand (QPR 1987), Derek Payne (Barnet 1988), Paul Hyde (Wycombe 1991), Dean Hooper (Swindon 1995), Jason Roberts (Wolverhampton W. 1997).

1997-98 Captain: Andy Cox

1997-98 Top scorer: Martin Randall - 22

1997-98 Player of the Year: Russell Meara

HEDNESFORD TOWN

John Badwin's side suffered last season from their spectacular successes of the previous season. They were many peoples' favourite for honours and when it didin't happen, heads dropped a little around Keys Park. This was particularly unfortunate as the Pitmen are still comparatively new boys to The Football Conference and they were still settling in while their stadium was being developed around them. Indeed everything and everybody concerned with the club should have been given a little breathing space before expecting honours.

As it turned out it was a solid season in which the club were never out of the top eight after September and indeed top spot was achieved in Novemeber.

A victory over Hull City was followed by a disappointing home Cup defeat against Darlington but there was no doubt that the club had set such high standards for itself so quickly that their supporters were in danger of underestimating the fantastic achievements of all at the club.

There is no doubt that having 'taken breath' and re-grouped for the coming season the club will be back on course and the introduction of Ged Kimmins, the Hyde United International striker, may well prove to be the signing of the summer.

CLUB OFFICIALS 1998-99

Joint Owners	**John Baldwin & Steve Price**
President	**Nigel Tinsley**
Chairman	**Mike Smith**
General Manager	**David Degg**
Football Secretary	**Richard Munning**
Club Secretary	**Sue Thomas**
Commercial Manager	**Terry Brumpton**
Press Officer	**Neil Holden**

L-R, Back Row: D Drakley (Physio), D Francis, P Ward, C Ntamark *, P Blades, R Dennison, T Hemmings *, P Carty, P Windson (Kit Manager). Middle Row: N Broadhurst, C McKenzie (now Redditch), M Norbury (now Telford), A Comyn, S Cooksey, M Keys, N Niblett (now Kidderminster), S Lake, L Knight (now Blakenall), T Eccleston. Front Row: W Simpson, K Collins, D Chatterton (Reserve Team Manager), J Allen (now Rushall), J Baldwin (Manager/Jt owner), S T Price (Jt owner), S Griffiths (Chief Scout), J O'Connor, G Fitzpatrick. * - no longer at the club.

HEDNESFORD TOWN - Match Facts 1997-98

Match No.	Date	Venue H / A	Comp.	Opponents	Result & Score		Att.	Goalscorers	League Position
1	16.08	A	VC	Southport	L	1-4	*1,326*	Carty 70.	
2	18.08	H	VC	Hereford United	D	1-1	2,396	Lake 63.	
3	23.08	H	VC	Stalybridge Celtic	W	1-0	1,054	Fitzpatrick 76.	14
4	25.08	A	VC	Rushden & Diamonds	D	1-1	*2,468*	O'Connor 10.	15
5	30.08	A	VC	Dover Athletic	W	3-1	*1,277*	O'Connor 56, 90, Carty 63.	9
6	07.09	H	VC	Woking	D	1-1	1,354	Comyn 15.	11
7	13.09	A	VC	Morecambe	W	3-1	*1,460*	Ware 18, 62, Carty 65.	8
8	20.09	H	VC	Southport	W	2-1	1,313	Carty 16(pen), Fitzpatrick 81.	5
9	22.09	H	VC	Leek Town	W	1-0	1,302	Carty 87.	3
10	27.09	A	VC	Hayes	**L**	**0-4**	*632*		5
11	04.10	H	VC	Kidderminster Harriers	W	3-0	1,817	Norbury 28, 60, O'Connor 80.	4
12	06.10	H	VC	Telford United	W	1-0	1,479	OG (Turner) 29.	3
13	13.10	A	VC	Northwich Victoria	D	1-1	*921*	Dennison 26.	3
14	18.10	H	VC	Welling United	W	3-2	1,208	Carty 66, Dennison 67, Comyn 87.	2
15	25.10	A	VC	Stevenage Borough	D	1-1	*2,143*	Dennison 88 (pen).	2
16	01.11	H	VC	Yeovil Town	W	1-0	1,366	Norbury 75	1
17	08.11	A	VC	Gateshead	**W**	**5-2**	*621*	Beeston 14, Fitzpatrick 36, 73, O'Connor 62, 63.	1
18	22.11	H	VC	Slough Town	W	2-1	1,685	Carty 56, Ware 90.	2
19	29.11	A	VC	Stalybridge Celtic	D	1-1	*651*	Dennison 54.	2
20	13,12	A	VC	Hereford United	L	1-2	*2,278*	Hemmings 31.	2
21	20.12	A	VC	Halifax Town	D	1-1	*3,338*	O'Connor 80.	3
22	26.12	H	VC	Kettering Town	D	1-1	1,191	Ware 16	4
23	29.12	H	VC	Stevenage Borough	W	2-1	1,738	Eccleston 19, Norbury 35	
24	01.01	A	VC	Kettering Town	L	1-2	*2,051*	Sedgemore 32	3
25	17.01	A	VC	Cheltenham Town	L	0-1	*2,216*		5
26	24.01	H	VC	Hayes	W	2-1	1,265	Norbury 64, Eccleston 77.	5
27	07.02	H	VC	Cheltenham Town	L	0-1	1,599		6
28	14.02	A	VC	Leek Town	D	3-3	*816*	Eccleston 74, 79, Carty 88.	6
29	23.02	H	VC	Farnborough Town	W	1-0	1,707	Ware 48.	6
30	28.02	A	VC	Welling United	L	2-3	*533*	O'Connor 47, Fitzpatrick 90.	6
31	07.03	A	VC	Slough Town	L	0-2	*770*		6
32	09.03	A	VC	Kidderminster Harriers	D	1-1	*1,908*	Comyn 26.	6
33	14.03	H	VC	Halifax Town	D	0-0	1,856		7
34	21.03	A	VC	Telford United	D	1-1	*922*	Ware 71.	7
35	23.03	H	VC	Rushden & Diamonds	L	0-1	1,342		7
36	28.03	H	VC	Northwich Victoria	W	2-0	1,103	Anderson 63, 74.	6
37	04.04	H	VC	Gateshead	W	3-0	879	Francis 31, 38, Anderson 85.	5
38	11.04	A	VC	Yeovil Town	L	0-1	*2,207*		6
39	13.04	H	VC	Morecambe	L	0-1	1,066		6
40	18.04	A	VC	Woking	L	2-4	*2,292*	Fitzpatrick 14, Francis 82.	7
41	25.04	A	VC	Farnborough Town	W	3-1	*753*	Carty 42, 52, Fitzpatrick 90.	7
42	02.05	H	VC	Dover Athletic	W	1-0	1,051	Carty 52.	7

CUP COMPETITIONS SCC - Spalding Challenge Cup SSC - Staffordshire Senior Cup

Date	Venue	Comp.	Opponents	Result	Score	Att.	Goalscorers
15.11	A	**FAC** 1	Hull City	W	2--0	6,091	Norbury 38 (pen), O'Connor 90.
06.12	H	2	Darlington	L	0-1	1,900	
10.01	H	**FAT** 1	Gainsborough Trinity	W	2-1	876	Eccleston 69, Lake 90.
31.01	H	2	Leek Town	W	5-0	1,073	Lake 10, 71, Ware 32, Norbury 39, Fitzpatrick 74.
21.02	A	3	Grantham Town	L	1-2	2,214	OG (Mills) 19.
17.11	A	**SCC** 2	Kidderminster Harriers	W	2-0	734	Francis 50, Hemmings 61 (pen).
16.12	A	3	Northwich Victoria	L	2-3	447	Fitzpatrick 83, Norbury 116(pen)
14.10	A	**SSC** 1	Shifnal Town	W	4-1		Dandy (pen), Eccleston, Francis, Niblett.
13.11	H	2	Stoke City	L	1-3		McKenzie

League Attendances	HIGHEST: 2,396 v Hereford United	LOWEST: 1,051 v Dover Athletic
CONFERENCE: 7th	**FA CUP:** 2nd Round	**FA TROPHY:** 3rd Round

1	2	3	4	5	6	7	8	9	10	11	12 14 15	
Cooksey	Ntamark	Collins	Simpson	Blades	Fitzpatrick	Ware	Lake	Norbury	Dennison	O'Connor	Ecclestone, Hemmings, Carty.	1
Cooksey	Ntamark	Collins	Simpson	Blades	Fitzpatrick	Ware	Lake	Norbury	Dennison	Hemmings	Ecclestone, Knight, McKenzie.	2
Cooksey	Ntamark	Collins	Blades	Comyn	Fitzpatrick	Carty	Ware	Norbury	Dennison	O'Connor	Lake, Simpson, Ecclestone.	3
Cooksey	Ntamark	Collins	Blades	Comyn	Fitzpatrick	Carty	Ware	Norbury	Dennison	O'Connor	Lake, Simpson, Ecclestone.	4
Cooksey	Ntamark	Collins	Blades	Comyn	Fitzpatrick	Carty	Ware	Norbury	Dennison	O'Connor	Lake, Simpson, Ecclestone.	5
Cooksey	Ntamark	Collins	Blades	Comyn	Fitzpatrick	Carty	Ware	Norbury	Dennison	Ecclestone	Lake, Francis, Simpson.	6
Cooksey	Ntamark	Collins	Blades	Comyn	Fitzpatrick	Carty	Lake	Dennison	Ware	O'Connor	Francis, Hemmings, Simpson.	7
Cooksey	Ntamark	Collins	Blades	Comyn	Fitzpatrick	Carty	Lake	Dennison	Ware	O'Connor	Francis, McKenzie, Niblett.	8
Cooksey	Comyn	Collins	Blades	Niblett	Fitzpatrick	Carty	Lake	Beeston	Francis	O'Connor	Smith, McKenzie, Knight.	9
Cooksey	Carty	Ntamark	Niblett	Comyn	Fitzpatrick	Beeston	Lake	Norbury	Francis	O'Connor	Smith, McKenzie, Knight.	10
Cooksey	Ntamark	Collins	Blades	Comyn	Beeston	Dennison	Lake	Norbury	Hemmings	O'Connor	McKenzie, Francis, Knight.	11
Cooksey	Ntamark	Collins	Blades	Comyn	Beeston	Dennison	Lake	Norbury	Francis	O'Connor	Niblett, Francis, Carty.	12
Cooksey	Ntamark	Collins	Blades	Comyn	Beeston	Dennison	Lake	Norbury	Hemmings	O'Connor	Niblett, Francis, Carty.	13
Cooksey	Ntamark	Collins	Blades	Comyn	Beeston	Hemmings	Lake	Norbury	Dennison	O'Connor	Niblett, Carty, Francis.	14
Cooksey	Carty	Collins	Blades	Comyn	Fitzpatrick	Ware	Beeston	Norbury	Dennison	Hemmings	O'Connor, Ntamark, Niblett.	15
Cooksey	Carty	Collins	Blades	Comyn	Fitzpatrick	Ware	Beeston	Norbury	Dennison	O'Connor	Hemmings, Ntamark, Niblett.	16
Cooksey	Ntamark	Collins	Blades	Comyn	Fitzpatrick	Carty	Beeston	Ware	Hemmings	O'Connor	Niblett(5), Francis(7), Lake(9).	17
Cooksey	Carty	Collins	Simpson	Comyn	Fitzpatrick	Ware	Beeston	Norbury	Dennison	O'Connor	Niblett, Ntamark, Hemmings.	18
Cooksey	Carty	Collins	Simpson	Comyn	Fitzpatrick	Ware	Beeston	Norbury	Dennison	O'Connor	Ntamark(2), Francis(9), Hemmings.	19
Cooksey	carty	Francis	Blades	Comyn	Collins	Ware	Beeston	Dennison	Fitzpatrick	O'Connor	Hemmings(3), Norbury(6), Ntamark.	20
Cooksey	Carty	Hemmings	Blades	Comyn	Niblett	Ware	Simpson	Fitzpatrick	Dennison	O'Connor	Norbury(10), Sedgemore, Ntamark.	21
Cooksey	Carty	Hemmings	Blades	Comyn	Niblett	Dennison	Beeston	Norbury	Ware	O'Connor	Simpson, Ntamark, Sedgemore.	22
Cooksey	Ntamark	Comyn	Blades	Niblett	Carty	Ware	Beeston	Norbury	Hemmings	Ecclestone	Simpson(7),O'Connor(11),Dennison.	23
Cooksey	Carty	Hemmings	Blades	Comyn	Niblett	Simpson	Beeston	Fitzpatrick	Sedgemore	O'Connor	Norbury(6),Dennison(10),Ntamark.	24
Cooksey	Simpson	Collins	Blades	Brindley	Fitzpatrick	Ware	lake	Ecclestone	Hemmings	O'Connor	Norbury, Ntamark, Comyn.	25
Cooksey	Ntamark	Collins	Blades	Brindley	Fitzpatrick	Carty	Lake	Norbury	Ware	Francis	Ecclestone(11), Simpson, Comyn.	26
Cooksey	Ntamark	Collins	Blades	Brindley	Fitzpatrick	Carty	Beeston	Ecclestone	Ware	O'Connor	Dennison(11), Comyn, Simpson.	27
Cooksey	Ntamark	Carty	Blades	Brindley	Fitzpatrick	Ware	Beeston	Norbury	Dennison	Ecclestone	Collins(2), Lake(10), Comyn.	28
Cooksey	Carty	Collins	Broadhurst	Comyn	Beeston	Fitzpatrick	Ware	landon	Dennison	O'Connor	Ntamark, Norbury, Lake.	29
Cooksey	Carty	Collins	Broadhurst	Comyn	Fitzpatrick	Ware	Beeston	Landon	Lake	O'Connor	Blades94), Lake(8), Norbury(10).	30
Cooksey	Sedgemore	Dennison	Blades	Comyn	Collins	Carty	Beeston	Landon	Lake	O'Connor	Dandy, Ntamark, Broadhurst.	31
Cooksey	Sedgemore	Collins	Blades	Comyn	Dandy	Carty	Beeston	Ecclestone	Lake	Francis	Braodhurst (6), Dennison(7),Landon.	32
Cooksey	Sedgemore	lake	Blades	Brindley	Collins	Ware	Beeston	Ecclestone	Fitzpatrick	Francis	O'Connor (11), Dennison, Dandy..	33
Cooksey	Sedgemore	Lake	Blades	Brindley	Collins	Ware	Beeston	Ecclestone	Fitzpatrick	Francis	Anderson (9), Dandy, Dennison.	34
Cooksey	Sedgemore	Lake	Blades	Brindley	Collins	Ware	Fitzpatrick	Dennison	Carty	Francis	Anderson (10), Dandy, Broadhurst.	35
Cooksey	Sedgemore	Colkin	Blades	Brindley	Lake	Ware	Fitzpatrick	Dennison	Carty	Francis	Collins (6), Anderson(10), O'Connor.	36
Cooksey	Sedgemore	Colkin	Blades	Brindley	Lake	Ware	Carty	Anderson	Fitzpatrick	Francis	Beeston, Collins, Dennison.	37
Cooksey	Sedgemore	Colkin	Blades	Brindley	Comyn	Ware	Fitzpatrick	Anderson	Dandy	Francis	Dennison (7), Broadhurst, Collins.	38
Cooksey	Sedgemore	Colkin	Blades	Brindley	Comyn	Ware	Fitzpatrick	Anderson	Dennison	Francis	Broadhurst (4), Dandy, Collins.	39
Cooksey	Sedgemore	Colkin	Blades	Brindley	Comyn	Carty	Ware	Anderson	Fitzpatrick	Francis	Dennison (9), Dandy, Broadhurst.	40
Cooksey	Sedgemore	Colkin	Blades	Brindley	Comyn	Carty	Beeston	Francis	Ware	Fitzpatrick	Dennison, Dandy, Broadhurst.	41
Cooksey	Sedgemore	Colkin	Blades	Brindley	Comyn	Carty	Beeston	Francis	Ware	Fitzpatrick	Dennison(9), Broadhurst(10), Collins.	42

Cooksey	Carty	Collins	Blades	Comyn	Beeston	Fitzpatrick	Ware	Norbury	Dennison	O'Connor	Noblett, Simpson, Francis.
Cooksey	Carty	Collins	Blades	Comyn	Fittzpatrick	Ware	Beeston	Norbury	Dennison	O'Connor	Simpson, Ntamark, Niblett.

Cooksey	Carty	Collins	Simpson	Comyn	Fitzpatrick	Lake	Beeston	Norbury	Eccleston	Francis	Hemmings, Ntamark, Sedgemore.
Cooksey	Ntamark	Collins	Blades	Brindley	Fitzpatrick	Carty	Lake	Norbury	Ware	Eccleston	Comyn, Francis, O'Connor.
Cooksey	Fitzpatrick	Collins	Comyn	Brindley	Beeston	Carty	Lake	Norbury	Ware	Eccleston	O'Connor, Ntamark, Francis.

Cooksey	Broadhurst	Collins	Simpson	Niblett	Fitzpatrick	Carty	Dandyy	Ntamark	Hemmings	Francis	Burden, Devine, Comyn.
Cooksey	Ntamark	Devine	Simpson	Niblett	Dandy	Sedgemore	Beeston	Norbury	Lake	Burden	Braodhurst, Fitzpatrick, Comyn.

Keys	Burden	Knight	Broadhurst	Niblett	Dandy	Carty	Lake	Eccleston	Francis	McKenzie	Rowlands, Beeston, Dennison.
Keys	Burden	Homer	Rowlands	Hatton	Bunny	Broadghurst	Dandy	McKenzie	Francis	Shan	O'Connor, James, Kearns.

JOHN BALDWIN (MANAGER)

Date of Appointment	January 1990
Date of Birth:	05.05.54
Place of Birth:	London

PREVIOUS CLUBS

As manager	Electricity, Harrisons.
As coach	
As player	Hednesford Town

HONOURS

As manager	Southern League Prem Div. 94-95
As player	England: Youth. British Universities

FOOTBALL MANAGEMENT TEAM

First Team Coach
Steve Devine

Physio
Don Drakeley

2nd Team Manager
TBA

2nd Team Physio
Terry Rowland

Chief Scout
Steve Griffiths

Youth Team Co-ordinator
James Thomas

Crowded goalmouth action at Keys Park, with Scott Cooksey claiming the ball from this corner from Halifax Town. Forming the background is the new terracing opened last season. Photo: Keith Clayton.

MATCHDAY PROGRAMME

Number of pages	48
Price	£1.50
Programme Editor	Terry Brumpton
Other club publications:	None
Local Newspapers:	Express & Star Chase Post; Cannock Mercury Lichfield Trader; The Chronicle
Local Radio Stations:	Radio WM; BRMB: WABC; Beacon: Signal; BBC Radio Stoke.

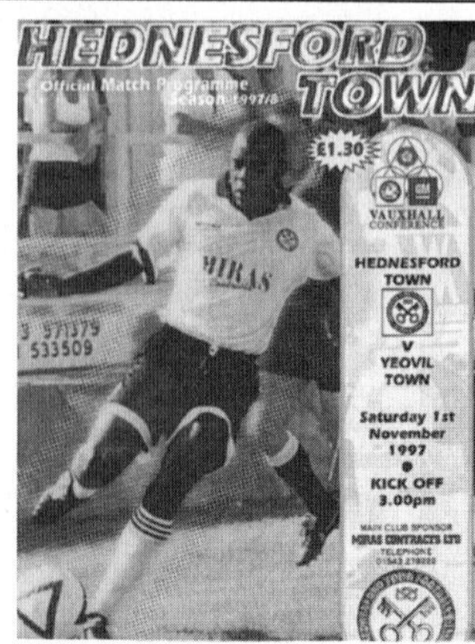

1997-98 PLAYING SQUAD

PLAYER	Birthplace Honours	Birthdate	CLUBS
GOALKEEPERS			
Scott Cooksey	Birmingham ESP, SLP	24.6.72	Derby Co, Shrewsbury T, Bromsgrove R, Peterborough U
DEFENDERS			
Wayne Simpson	Newcastle ESP, SLP, FA XI	19.9.68	Port Vale, Stafford Rangers
Andy Comyn	Wakefield ESP	2.8.68	Manchester U, Alvechurch, Aston Villa, Derby Co, Plymouth A, W.B.A.
Paul Blades	Peterborough EY, Div 2	5.1.65	Derby Co, £700k to Norwich C, £325k to Wolverhampton W, £110k to Rotherham U
Chris Brindley	Stoke GMVC, FAT, FA XI	5.7.69	Hednesford T, Wolves, Telford U, £20k to Kidderminster H
Russell Bradley *	Birmingham	28.3.66	Dudley T, Nottingham Forest, Hereford U, Halifax T, Scunthorpe U, Hartlepool U
Kevin Collins	Birmingham FAT, SLP	21.7.64	Boldmere St.Michaels, Shrewsbury T, Stourbridge, Pelsall Villa, Burton A, Kidderminster H, Rushall Olympic
Paul Edwards	Birkenhead	25.12.63	Altrincham, Crewe A, Coventry C, Wolverhampton W, W.B.A.
MIDFIELDERS			
Gary Fitzpatrick	Birmingham Ei u-20, SLP	5.8.71	Leicester C, VS Rugby, Moor Green, Rannberg (Swe)
Lee Colkin *	Nuneaton	15.7.74	Northampton T
Carl Beeston	Stoke England U-21	30.6.67	Stoke C, Southend U
Paul Ware	Congleton Div 2	7.11.70	Stoke C, Stockport Co
Paul Carty	Birmingham SLP	22.10.66	Everton, Nuneaton B, Bromsgrove R, Tamworth
John Jeffers	Liverpool ES	5.10.68	Liverpool, Port Vale, Stockport Co
Stuart Lake	Stone SLP	15.10.75	Walsall
Robbie Dennison	Banbridge NI, Div 3, Div 4	30.4.63	Glenavon, £40k to W.B.A., £20k to Wolverhampton W
FORWARDS			
Joe O'Connor	Wolverhampton ESP, SLP	20.10.67	Lye T, Stafford Rangers
Jake Sedgemore	Birmingham		W.B.A.
Ged Kimmins *	Manchester ESP		Salford C, Hyde U
Tony Eccleston	Birmingham		Wolverhampton U, Tamworth, Bloxwich T

DEPARTURES - (During the season)
Bernard McNally (Telford U), Richard Mason (Boston U), John Cotterill (Gresley R), Nigel Niblett (Kidderminster H), Tony Hemmings (Released), Mike Norbury (Telford U - £15k), Lee Knight (Blakenall), Neil Smith (Released)

PLAYERS ON LOAN - Richard Landon (Macclesfield T), Lee Colkin (Northampton T)

Keys Park, Hednesford

GROUND ADDRESS: Keys Park, Hednesford, Cannock, Staffordshire.
TEL. NO. 01543 422870 **FAX:** 01543 428180 **HOTLINE:** 0930 555880

SIMPLE DIRECTIONS: M6 J11 to Cannock, through traffic lights to island , 3rd exit, next island, 2nd exit onto Lichfield Rd. Next island 1st exit, next island straight on, next island 3rd exit, continue to mini-island. Keys Park is straight on (signposted from 2nd island.)

CAPACITY: 6,000 **SEATED:** 1,000 **COVERED TERRACING:** 1,000

CLUB SHOP: Yes. Open throughout the week.

SOCIAL FACILITIES: Strikers Bar open matchdays and every evening except Sunday 7-11. No food available. Chase Suite hold functions.

Hednesford Fact File

Nickname: The Pitmen **Club Sponsors:** Miras Contracts

Club colours: White shirts & black & red trim, black shorts, white trim.

Change colours: Gold shirts, navy sleeves, navy shorts, gold trim.

Reserve team league: Central Conference League, and Endsleigh Midland Combination (Reserve Div.).

Midweek home matchday: Monday.

PREVIOUS - **Grounds:** The Tins (behind Anglesey Hotel) until 1904, Cross Keys until 1995.
Leagues: Walsall & District; Birmingham Combination 08-15, 45-53; West Mids 19-39, 53-72, 74-84; Midland Counties 72-74; Southern League 84-95; Conference 95-.

CLUB RECORDS - **Attendance:** 10,000 v Walsall, FA Cup 1919-20

Win: 12-1 v Birmingham City- Birmingham Wartime League Cup 40-41
v Redditch United, Birmingham Combination 52-53.

Defeat: 0-15 v Burton , Birmingham Combination 24-25.

Career goalscorer: Tosh Griffiths

Career appearances: Kevin Foster

Transfer fee paid: £12,000 for Steve Burr (Macclesfield Town 1991)

Transfer fee received: £50,000 for Dave Hanson (Leyton Orient)

BEST SEASON - **FA Cup:** 1996-97, 4th Round v Middlesbrough (2-3 at Middlesbrough).
League clubs defeated: Blackpool, York City.
FA Trophy: 1997-98, 3rd Round, 1-2 v Grantham Town (A).

HONOURS - Welsh Cup R-up 91-92: Southern League Prem. Div. 94-95; Midland Div. R-up 91-92; Lge. Cup R-up 86-87: West Midlands. Lge 77-78; R-up 83-84; Lge. Cup 83-84: Birmingham Combination 09-10, 50-51; R-up 12-13, 52-53: Staffs Senior Cup 69-70, 73-74; R-up 92-93: Birmingham Senior Cup 35-36; R-up 93-94.

Past players who progressed to the Football League:
Brian Horton (Port Vale 1970), Vernon Allatt (Halifax Town 1979), Chris Brindley (Wolverhampton W. 1986), Dave Hanson (Leyton Orient), Keith Russell (Blackpool 1997).

1997-98 **Club Captain:** Kevin Collins **Team Captain:** Paul Ware

1997-98 Top scorer: Joe O'Connor

1997-98 Player of the Year: Gary Fitzpatrick. Won all three -
Players' P.o.Y.; Supporters' P.o.Y. and Travel Club P.o.Y.

HEREFORD UNITED

After the heartbreak of losing their battle with Brighton for a Football League place, on the last day of the previous season, it could have been understood if morale was a little shaky at Edgar Street when the Conference season opened.

But the supporters were taking a positive stand and Graham Turner had dedicated himself to the club's cause and so off they went with experienced striker Neil Grayson in spectacular form. The opportunity to quickly claim a little compensation from Brighton was accepted in The F.A. Cup with a victory. This was followed by a place in the Third Round after a further success against Colchester United. This distraction was particularly welcome as financial matters were proving troublesome off the field and a visit from Tranmere Rovers was just what everyone needed to concentrate the mind on footballing matters.

Sadly, United never quite joined the promotion race but with the example of Darlington, Colchester United and Halifax Town before them Hereford will see that recouperation isn't instant.

But a couple of seasons rebuilding and enjoying the atmosphere of the Football Conference will probably see the club bouncing back stronger and happier than ever.

CLUB OFFICIALS 1998-99

Directors	**Graham Turner**
	Joan Fennessy
	Tristram Richmond-Sterry
	Sam Lodh
	George Hyde
	Ron Jukes
Club Secretary	**Joan Fennesy**
	c/o the club
	Tel: 01432 276666
	Fax: 01432 341359

L-R, Back Row: Gavin Mahon, Andy de Bont, Trevor Matthewson, Chris Mackenzie, Gary Cook. Middle Row: Simon Shakeshaft, Jamie Pitman, Brian McGorry, Neil Grayson, John Brough, Riuchard Walker, Chris Hargreaves, Rob Warner, Keith Downing. Front Row: Tony Agana, Ian Foster, David Norton, Graham Turner, Murray Fishlock, Roy Jordan, Ian Rodgerson.

HEREFORD UNITED - Match Facts 1997-98

Match No.	Date	Venue H / A	Comp.	Opponents	Result & Score		Att.	Goalscorers	League Position
1	16.08	H	VC	Welling United	L	1-2	3,138	Agana 57.	16
2	18.08	A	VC	Hednesford Town	D	1-1	*2,396*	Grayson 40.	15
3	23.08	A	VC	Farnborough Town	W	2-0	*1,097*	Fishlock 67, Grayson 79.	7
4	25.08	H	VC	Cheltenham Town	W	3-2	3,704	Grayson 42, 65, Foster 62.	4
5	30.08	H	VC	Stevenage Borough	L	0-2	2,937		11
6	02.09	A	VC	Leek Town	D	2-2	*1,138*	Grayson 46, Brough 90.	8
7	05.09	A	VC	Hayes	L	0-2	*974*		13
8	09.09	H	VC	Farnborough Town	W	2-1	1,709	Brough 84, Pitman 88.	7
9	13.09	H	VC	Northwich Victoria	D	2-2	2,207	Grayson 2, OG (Simpson) 82.	9
10	20.09	A	VC	Kettering Town	W	2-1	*1,404*	Grayson 20, 68.	6
11	27.09	H	VC	Stalybridge Celtic	W	3-0	2,312	Milner 32, Foster 45, Pitman 85.	4
12	04.10	A	VC	Telford United	D	0-0	*1,710*		8
13	11.10	A	VC	Rushden & Diamonds	L	0-1	*2,728*		8
14	18.10	H	VC	Southport	D	1-1	2,663	Pitman 25.	8
15	01.11	A	VC	Morecambe	**W**	**5-1**	*1,850*	Foster 22, **Milner 3** (43, 46, 58), Cook 90.	8
16	08.11	H	VC	Yeovil Town	D	1-1	2,768	Milner 30.	8
17	22.11	A	VC	Halifax Town	**L**	**0-3**	*2,214*		9
18	29.11	H	VC	Dover Athletic	L	0-1	2,147		9
19	13.12	H	VC	Hednesford Town	W	2-1	2,278	Fishlock 59, Grayson 61	10
20	20.12	A	VC	Welling United	**L**	**0-3**	*749*		10
21	26.12	H	VC	Kidderminster Harriers	W	1-0	4,671	Grayson 56 (pen)	10
22	01.01	A	VC	Kidderminster Harriers	W	4-1	*4,693*	**Leadbeater 3** (9,34,37) Agana 89	10
23	17.01	H	VC	Kettering Town	W	3-2	2,310	OG (Vowden) 50, Brough 73, Leadbeater 84.	10
24	19.01	A	VC	Stevenage Borough	L	0-2	*1,574*		11
25	07.02	A	VC	Slough Town	**L**	**0-3**	*1,056*		11
26	10.02	H	VC	Telford United	D	1-1	1,371	Grayson 89.	
27	14.02	H	VC	Morecambe	W	1-0	1,720	Pitman 41.	10
28	21.02	H	VC	Leek Town	W	1-0	1,712	Agana 52.	7
29	24.02	H	VC	Hayes	W	3-0	1,663	Leadbeater 18, Pitman 58, Hargreaves 90.	7
30	03.03	A	VC	Southport	D	0-0	*662*		7
31	07.03	A	VC	Northwich Victoria	W	2-0	*1,002*	Leadbeater 44, McGorry 82.	7
32	14.03	H	VC	Gateshead	W	1-0	2,007	Agana 68.	6
33	21.03	H	VC	Slough Town	D	1-1	2,013	Cook 30.	6
34	28.03	H	VC	Woking	W	2-1	2,281	Hargreaves 30 (pen), Leadbeater 36.	5
35	31.03	A	VC	Dover Athletic	D	1-1	*746*	Williams 43.	5
36	04.04	A	VC	Stalybridge Celtic	W	3-2	*795*	Hargreaves 29, Matthewson 78, 89.	4
37	11.04	H	VC	Halifax Town	D	0-0	3,304		5
38	13.04	A	VC	Cheltenham Town	W	2-1	*3,039*	Brough 13, Hargreaves 85.	5
39	18.04	A	VC	Yeovil Town	L	0-2	*2,601*		6
40	22.04	A	VC	Gateshead	D	1-1	*448*	Agana 43.	6
41	25.04	H	VC	Rushden & Diamonds	D	1-1	3,055	Agana 3.	6
42	02.05	A	VC	Woking	L	1-3	*3,015*	Agana 44.	6

CUP COMPETITIONS

F.A. CUP

Date	Venue	Round	Opponents	Result	Score	Att.	Goalscorers	
25.10	A	4Q	Sittingbourne	D	2-2	1,011	Fishlock 28, Cook 70.	
28.10	H	4Q R	Sittingbourne	W	3-0	2,054	Hargreaves 2, 44, Rogerson 7.	
15.11	H	1	Brighton & Hove A.	W	2-1	5,787	Grayson 62, 73 (pen).	
06.12	A	2	Colchester United	D	1-1	3,558	Grayson 61.	
16.12	H	2 R	Colchester United	W	1-1	3,725	Grayson 48	Won 5-4 after penalties.
13.01	H	3	Tranmere Rovers	L	0-3	7,473		

F.A. TROPHY

Date	Venue	Round	Opponents	Result	Score	Att.	Goalscorers
10.01	H	1	Dulwich Hamlet	W	3-0	2,101	Walker 24, 35, Agana 59.
31.01	H	2	Dover Athletic	L	0-2	2,108	

SPALDING CHALLENGE CUP

Date	Venue	Round	Opponents	Result	Score	Att.	Goalscorers
26.11	A	2	Farnborough Town	L	1-2	256	Grayson 63.

League Attendances	HIGHEST: 4,671 v Kidderminster H.	LOWEST: 1,371 v Telford United
CONFERENCE: 6th	**FA CUP:** 3rd Round	**FA TROPHY:** 2nd Round

1	2	3	4	5	6	7	8	9	10	11	12 14 15	
de Bont	Rodgerson	Fishlock	Matthewson	Norton	Walker	Hargreaves	Agana	Grayson	Foster	Mahon	Pitman, Warner, McGorry (10).	1
MacKenzie	Rodgerson	Fishlock	Matthewson	Norton	Walker	Hargreaves	Agana	Grayson	McGorry	Mahon	Pitman, Warner, Foster.	2
MacKenzie	Rodgerson	Fishlock	Matthewson	Norton	Walker	Hargreaves	Agana	Grayson	McGorry	Mahon	Brough, Pitman, Foster (11).	3
MacKenzie	Rodgerson	Fishlock	Matthewson	Norton	Walker	Hargreaves	Agana	Grayson	McGorry	Mahon	Brough (8), Foster (10), Pitman.	4
MacKenzie	Rodgerson	Fishlock	Matthewson	Brough	Walker	Hargreaves	McGorry	Grayson	Foster	Mahon	Pitman (5), Warner (7), Jordan (8).	5
MacKenzzie	Rodgerson	Fishlock	Matthewson	Brough	Walker	Hargreaves	Warner	Grayson	Foster	Mahon	Pitman, Jordan, Downing.	6
MacKenzie	Rodgerson	Fishlock	Matthewson	Brough	Walker	Hargreaves	Warner	Grayson	Foster	Mahon	Pitman, Downing, Agana.	7
de Bont	Rodgerson	Fishlock	Pitman	Brough	Walker	Hargreaves	Warner	Grayson	Foster	Mahon	Matthewson, Cook (7), Williams.	8
MacKenzie	Rodgerson	Fishlock	Pitman	Brough	Walker	Hargreaves	Milner	Grayson	Foster	Mahon	Matthewson, Warner(11), McGorry (3).	9
Gayle	Warner	McGorry	Pitman	Brough	Walker	Hargreaves	Milner	Grayson	Foster	Mahon	Matthewson, Cook, Jordan.	10
Gayle	Warner	Rodgerson	Pitman	Brough	Walker	Hargreaves	Milner	Grayson	Foster	Mahon	Matthewson, Fishlock, Cook (10).	11
Gayle	Warner	Rodgerson	Pitman	Brough	Walker	Hargreaves	Milner	Grayson	Foster	Mahon	Matthewson, Fishlock (9), Cook (10).	12
Gayle	Warner	Rodgerson	Pitman	Brough	Walker	Hargreaves	Milner	Cook	Fishlock	Mahon	Matthewson, Jordan, Foster (9).	13
Gayle	Rodgerson	Fishlock	Pitman	Brough	Matthewson	Hargreaves	Milner	McGorry	Foster	Mahon	Warner, Cook, Williams.	14
Quy	Rodgerson	Fishlock	Pitman	Brough	Matthewson	Walker	McGorry	Milner	Foster	Mahon	Warner (2), Cook (10), Williams (3).	15
Quy	Rodgerson	Fishlock	Pitman	Brough	Matthewson	Walker	McGorry	Milner	Foster	Mahon	Warner (5), Cook (10), Grayson (9).	16
Quy	Warner	Fishlock	Pitman	Brough	Walker	Hargreaves	McGorry	Grayson	McCue	Mahon	Cook (2), Downing, Foster (5).	17
Quy	Warner	Fishlock	Pitman	Rodgerson	Walker	Hargreaves	McGorry	Grayson	McCue	Mahon	Brough (4), Norton, Cook (10).	18
Quy	Norton	Fishlock	Pitman	Brough	Walker	Hargreaves	McGorry	Grayson	Warner	Mahon	McCue (4), Cook (2), Williams.	19
Quy	Warner	Fishlock	Pitman	Brough	Walker	Hargreaves	McGorry	Grayson	McCue	Mahon	Rodgerson(2), Cook(8), G Williams(10)	20
Quy	Rodgerson	Fishlock	Pitman	Brough	Walker	Hargreaves	McGorry	Grayson	Leadbeater	Mahon	Warner, Cook (10), McCue.	21
Quy	Rodgerson	Fishlock	Pitman	Brough	Walker	Hargreaves	McGorry	Grayson	Leadbeater	Mahon	Warner, McCue (7), Agana (2).	22
Quy	Warner	Fishlock	Pitman	Brough	Walker	Hargreaves	McGorry	Grayson	Leadbeater	Mahon	Rodgerson(2), Agana (7), McCue.	23
Quy	Rodgerson	Fishlock	Pitman	Brough	Walker	Hargreaves	McGorry	Agana	Leadbeater	Mahon	Grayson (6), Warner (4), McCue.	24
Quy	Rodgerson	Fishlock	Agana	Warner	Matthewson	Hargreaves	McGorry	Grayson	Leadbeater	Mahon	McCue (10), Pitman, Foster.	25
Quy	Warner	Fishlock	Pitman	Agana	Matthewson	Hargreaves	McGorry	Grayson	Foster	Mahon	McCue (10), Downing, G Williams.	26
Quy	Rodgerson	Fishlock	Pitman	Walker	Matthewson	Hargreaves	McGorry	Leadbeater	McCue	Mahon	Warner, Downing, G Williams.	27
Quy	Rodgerson	Fishlock	Pitman	Walker	Matthewson	Hargreaves	McGorry	Leadbeater	McCue	Mahon	Cook (9), Agana (10), Warner.	28
Quy	Rodgerson	Fishlock	Pitman	Walker	Matthewson	Hargreaves	Warner	Grayson	Leadbeater	Mahon	Agana (10), Brough, Cook.	29
Quy	Brough	Warner	Pitman	Walker	Matthewson	Hargreaves	Cook	Agana	Leadbeater	Mahon	Mansell(4),G Williams(8),Durham.	30
Quy	Rodgerson	Fishlock	Pitman	Brough	Matthewson	Hargreaves	McGorry	Cook	Leadbeater	Mahon	Agana(10), Warner, G Williams.	31
Quy	Rodgerson	Fishlock	Pitman	Brough	Matthewson	Warner	McGorry	Cook	Agana	Mahon	Mansell, G Williams, Hill.	32
Quy	Rodgerson	Fishlock	Walker	Brough	Matthewson	Warner	McGorry	Cook	Agana	Mahon	Mansell(4), G Williams(11), Durham.	33
Quy	Rodgerson	Fishlock	Pitman	Brough	Matthewson	Hargreaves	McGorry	Cook	Leadbeater	Mahon	Walker, G Williams, Warner.	34
Quy	Rodgerson	Fishlock	Pitman	Brough	Matthewson	Hargreaves	Warner	Cook	Leadbeater	Mahon	Durham(7), G Williams(9), Parry.	35
Quy	Rodgerson	Walker	Pitman	Brough	Matthewson	Hargreaves	McGorry	Agana	G Williams	Mahon	Warner, Durham, Parry.	36
Quy	Rodgerson	Fishlock	Pitman	Brough	Matthewson	Hargreaves	McGorry	Agana	G Williams	Mahon	Warner(4), Walker, Parry.	37
Quy	Rodgerson	Fishlock	Warner	Brough	Matthewson	Hargreaves	McGorry	Agana	Walker	Mahon	G Williams, Mansell, Parry.	38
Quy	Rodgerson	Fishlock	Warner	Brough	Walker	Hargreaves	McGorry	Agana	G Williams	Mahon	Mansell(10), Pitman, Parry.	39
Quy	Rodgerson	Fishlock	Warner	Brough	Matthewson	Hargreaves	McGorry	agana	Walker	Mahon	G Williams, Pitman, Parry.	40
Quy	Rodgerson	Fishlock	Warner	Walker	Matthewson	Hargreaves	McGorry	Agana	Pitman	Mahon	Mansell(4), G Williams, Parry.	41
Quy	Rodgerson	Fishlock	Warner	Walker	Matthewson	Hargreaves	McGorry	Agana	Brough	Mahon	G Williams(4), Durham, Parry.	42

1	2	3	4	5	6	7	8	9	10	11	12 14 15
de Bont	Rodgerson	Fishlock	Pitman	Brough	Matthewson	Walker	McGorry	Hargreaves	Foster	Mahon	Warner, Cook (6), Williams.
de Bont	Rodgerson	Fishlock	Pitman	Brough	Matthewson	Walker	McGorry	Hargreaves	Foster	Mahon	Warner (3), Cook (4), Williams (10).
de Bont	Rodgerson	Fishlock	Pitman	Warner	Walker	Cook	McGorry	Grayson	Foster	Mahon	McCue (2),Downing, G Williams.
de Bont	Norton	Fishlock	Pitman	Brough	Walker	Hargreaves	McGorry	Grayson	Warner	Mahon	Cook, Withington, McCue.
de bont	Warner	Fishlock	Cook	Brough	Walker	Hargreaves	McGorry	Grayson	McCue	Mahon	Pitman (4), Withington, Mansell.
de Bont	Rodgerson	Fishlock	Pitman	Brough	Walker	Hargreaves	McGorry	Grayson	Agana	Mahon	Warner, Withington, Cook.

1	2	3	4	5	6	7	8	9	10	11	12 14 15
de Bont	Warner	Fishlock	Pitman	Brough	Walker	Hargreaves	McGorry	Grayson	Agana	Mahon	Cook (8), Quy (1), McCue (10).
Quy	Rodgerson	Fishlock	Pitman	Brough	Matthewson	Hargreaves	Warner	Grayson	McCue	Mahon	Mansell(4), G Williams(12), Foster(5).

1	2	3	4	5	6	7	8	9	10	11	12 14 15
de Bont	Warner	Fishlock	Pitman	Brough	Walker	Hargreaves	McGorry	Grayson	McCue	Mahon	Cook(4), Mansell (9), Norton (2).

GRAHAM TURNER (MANAGER)

Date of Appointment	August 1995
Date of Birth:	5th October 1947
Place of Birth:	Ellesmere Port
PREVIOUS CLUBS	
As manager	Shrewsbury T., Aston Villa, Wolverhampton W.
As coach	None
As player	Wrexham, Chester City, Shrewsbury T.
HONOURS	
As manager	League: Div.3 78-79 (Shrewsbury), Div.4 87-88, Div.3 88-89; S.V.T. 87-88 (Wolves)
As player	England - Youth cap.

Chief Scout: Ron Jukes

GAVIN MAHON
Player of the Year 1997-98
Photo: Andrew Chitty

Left
Neil Grayson, who was the club's leading goalscorer last season, seen here getting in a tackle aginst Jon Underwood of Farnborough Town.
Photo: Andrew Chitty

MATCHDAY PROGRAMME

Number of pages	32
Price	£1.50
Programme Editor	Gary Watts
Other club publications:	None
Local Newspapers:	Hereford Journal Hereford Times Evening News
Local Radio Stations:	BBC Hereford & Worcester

1997-98 PLAYING SQUAD

PLAYER	Birthplace Honours	Birthdate	CLUBS
GOALKEEPERS			
Andy Quy	Harlow	4.7.76	Tottenham Hotspur, Derby Co, Grimsby T, Kettering T
Andy Debont	Wolverhampton	7.2.74	Wolverhampton W
DEFENDERS			
Robert Warner	Stratford	20.4.77	From YTS
Matthew Cross *	Sheffield		Barnsley
Trevor Matthewson	Sheffield GMVC, ANMC	12.2.63	Sheffield Wed, Newport Co, Stockport Co, £13k to Lincoln C, £45k to Birmingham C, Preston, Bury, Witton A
Stuart Evans *	Birmingham		Wolves, Gresley R, £7,250k to Halesowen T
MIDFIELDERS			
Jamie Pitman	Trowbridge	6.1.76	Swindon T
Gavin Mahon	Birmingham	2.1.77	Wolverhampton W
John Snape *	Birmingham		West Bromwich Albion, Bromsgrove R, Northfield T, Stourbridge, Halesowen T
Craig Mansell	Birmingham		Bristol City, Ettingshall Holy Trinity, Paget R, Pelsall Villa
FORWARDS			
Tony Agana	London ESP	2.10.63	Welling U, Weymouth, £35k to Watford, £45k to Sheffield U, £750k to Notts Co
Chris Hargreaves	Cleethorpes	12.5.72	Grimsby T, Hull C, W.B.A.
Brian Gray	Birmingham	25.11.72	Birmingham C, Bromsgrove R, Telford Utd.

DEPARTURES - Chris Mackenzie (Leyton Orient), Roy Jordan (Merthyr Tydfil), Andy Ogiesby (Dover Ath), Neil Grayson (Cheltenham T - £20k), Dave Norton (Retired), Murray Fishlock (Yeovil T.).

PLAYERS ON LOAN - Mark Gayle (Crewe Alexandra), Andy Milner (Chester C), Richard Leadbetter (Wolves)

RECENT SIGNINGS - Tony James (West Brom. Alb.)

Edgar Street, Hereford

GROUND ADDRESS: Edgar Street, Hereford. HR4 9JU.

TELEPHONE NUMBER: 01432 276666 **Fax** 01432 341359
Club Call 0891 121645 **E-mail** HUFC@msn.com

SIMPLE DIRECTIONS: From Hereford city centre follow signs to Leominster (A49) into Edgar Street. Car parking for 1000 (approx.) available near the ground. Nearest railway station Hereford.

CAPACITY: 8,843 **SEATED:** 2,761 **COVERED TERRACING:** 6,082

SOCIAL FACILITIES: Clubhouse open on matchdays.

CLUB SHOP: Yes.

Hereford Fact File

Nickname: The Bulls **Sponsors:** Sun Valley

Club Colours: White shirts, black trim; black shorts, white trim; black socks, white tops

Change Colours: Red & black quarters; black shorts; black socks.

Midweek matchday: Tuesday

Reserve League: Central Conference

Local Press: Herefordshire Times, Evening News.

Local Radio: BBC Hereford & Worcester

PREVIOUS -
Leagues: Birmingham League; Birmingham Combination; Southern League 39-72; Football League 72-97.
Names: None
Ground: None

CLUB RECORDS -
Attendance: 18,114 v Sheffield Wed., FA Cup 3rd Rd, 4.1.58
Career Goalscorer: Unknown
Career Appearances: unknown
Win: 6-0 v Burnley (A), Div. 4 24.1.87.
Defeat: 0-6 v Rotherham Utd (A), Div. 4 29.4.89
Transfer Fee Paid: £75,000 to Walsall for Dean Smith, 7.94.
Transfer Fee Received: £250,000 for Darren Peacock from Q.P.R., 3.91
+ a further £240,000 when he moved to Newcastle Utd. 3.91.

BEST SEASON -
FA Trophy: 2nd Round 97-98, 0-2 v Dover Athletic (H).
FA Cup: 4th Rd 71-72 (as Southern League side), 76-77, 81-82, 89-90, 91-92.

HONOURS - Welsh Cup 89-90, R-up 3 times; League Div. 3 75-76; Southern League R-up 71-72.

Players Progressing to Football Lge: Not applicable yet.

97-98 Player of the Year: Gavin Mahon

97-98 Top scorer: Neil Grayson

KETTERING TOWN

The Poppies are one of the competition's most famous members but for a long time last season it loOked as if their run in the Conference was going to come to a nasty end.

The whole of the playing staff were put up for sale before Christmas and Steve Berry produced a minor miracle by rebuilding a side capable of survival after such a terrible start.

Defeat by Hinckley United in the F.C.Cup didn't help but the form in the second half of the season will have given hope to their supporters and the return of Peter Morris will have lifted spirits for the season ahead.

No doubt the experienced campaigner will build a brand new squad so a good start will be imperative for the new boys to settle down conidently.

Speedy striker Chris Pearson did as much as anyone last ternm to ensure Kettering kept their uninterrupted run in the Conference. He will be missed but supporters will be able to rely on their manager to produce new stars to enjoy - just look at his track record in his previous seasons at Rockingham Road.

CLUB OFFICIALS 1998-99

President	**Sid Chapman**
Chairman	**Peter Mallinger**
Vice Chairman	**Peter Oliver**
Directors	**Richard Davis**
Club Secretary/ Press Officer	**Gerry Knowles** c/o the club
Tel: 01536 483028/410815	Fax: 01536 412273
Commercial Manager	**Brian Baker**

L-R, Back Row: Peter Costello, Bradley Sandeman, Tim Wilkes, David Moore, Dean Holliday, Rob Mutchell, Ian Ridgway, Chris Pearson. Middle Row: Julie Frost (physio), Neil Lyne, Mickey Nuttell, Kevin Shoemake, Chris Taylor, Ray Van Dulleman, Mark Tucker, Paul Miles. Front Row: Paul Cox, Carl Adams, Steve Berry (ex-manager), Craig Norman, Colin Vowden.

KETTERING TOWN - Match Facts 1997-98

Match No.	Date	Venue H / A	Comp.	Opponents	Result & Score		Att.	Goalscorers	League Position
1	16.08	H	VC	Slough Town	D	3-3	1,349	Costello 10, Norman 54 (pen), 72.	9
2	18.08	A	VC	Stevenage Borough	D	0-0	*3,486*		
3	23.08	A	VC	Northwich Victoria	D	0-0	*1,131*		15
4	25.08	H	VC	Telford United	L	1-3	1,405	Vowden 77.	18
5	30.08	H	VC	Cheltenham Town	L	0-1	1,274		21
6	02.09	A	VC	Welling United	D	2-2	*637*	Vowden 54, Norman 62.	22
7	07.09	A	VC	Farnborough Town	L	2-3	*771*	Nuttall 48, Norman 76 (pen).	22
8	09.09	H	VC	Woking	L	0-1	1,215		22
9	20.09	H	VC	Hereford United	L	1-2	1,404	Costello 74.	22
10	04.10	A	VC	Halifax Town	L	0-3	*1,836*		22
11	18.10	H	VC	Hayes	D	1-1	1,006	Vowden 69.	22
12	01.11	A	VC	Southport	L	1-2	*973*	Pearson 27.	22
13	08.11	H	VC	Morecambe	D	1-1	1,156	Pearson 27.	22
14	15.11	H	VC	Dover Athletic	W	2-1	1,056	Tucker 46, Norman 90 (pen).	21
15	22.11	A	VC	Kidderminster Harriers	L	1-4	*1,874*	Wilkes 27.	21
16	25.11	A	VC	Rushden & Diamonds	L	0-1	*3,866*		21
17	29.11	H	VC	Stevenage Borough	W	2-0	1,488	Wilkes 44, Pearson 83.	21
18	06.12	A	VC	Yeovil Town	L	0-2	*2,529*		21
19	13.12	H	VC	Welling United	L	0-1	1,144		
20	20.12	A	VC	Morecambe	W	3-1	*1,241*	Pearson 30, Adams 40(pen), 55	20
21	26.12	A	VC	Hednesford Town	D	1-1	*1,911*	Berry 71	20
22	29.12	H	VC	Halifax Town	D	1-1	2,246	Van Dullerman 43	20
23	01.01	H	VC	Hednesford Town	W	2-1	2,051	Sandeman 2,Vowden 50	20
24	17.01	A	VC	Hereford United	L	2-3	*2,310*	Norman 14, Pearson 52.	20
25	24.01	H	VC	Farnborough Town	W	2-1	1,433	Mutchell 47, Norman 79 (pen).	18
26	07.02	H	VC	Gateshead	W	3-0	1,201	Pearson 30, 89, Adams 61.	18
27	14.02	A	VC	Woking	W	1-0	*3,101*	Pearson 14.	17
28	21.02	H	VC	Rushden & Diamonds	**L**	**0-4**	4,016		17
29	28.02	A	VC	Gateshead	L	0-2	*468*		19
30	07.03	H	VC	Southport	W	2-1	1,157	Pearson 5, Wilkes 53.	18
31	10.03	H	VC	Yeovil Town	D	1-1	1,116	Pearson 54.	
32	21.03	H	VC	Leek Town	W	1-0	1,287	Adams 50.	18
33	31.03	A	VC	Leek Town	**W**	**4-0**	*662*	Sandeman 34, Costello 36, Wilkes 71, 87.	17
34	07.04	A	VC	Hayes	W	1-0	*506*	Pearson 10.	16
35	11.04	H	VC	Stalybridge Celtic	W	3-1	1,547	Vowden 51, Adams 74 (pen), Costello 80.	15
36	13.04	A	VC	Telford United	D	1-1	*1,041*	Pearson 64.	16
37	15.04	A	VC	Dover Athletic	D	0-0	*781*		15
38	18.04	H	VC	Northwich Victoria	L	1-3	1,156	Sandeman 29.	16
39	23.04	A	VC	Slough Town	D	1-1	*515*	Mutchell 71.	16
40	25.04	H	VC	Kidderminster Harriers	D	2-2	1,576	Pearson 6, Wilkes 19.	16
41	27.04	A	VC	Cheltenham Town	L	0-2	*1,219*		16
42	02.05	A	VC	Stalybridge Celtic	W	4-3	*565*	Pearson 15, Wilkes 26, Norman 50 (pen), Costello 89.	14

CUP COMPETITIONS SCC - Spalding Challenge Cup HC - Northants `Hillier' Sen. Cup

Date	Venue	Comp.	Opponents	Result	Score	Att.	Goalscorers
13.09	H	**FAC** 1Q	Mirlees Blackstone	W	1-0	768	Nuttall 13.
27.09	H	2Q	Cambridge City	D	1-1	921	Berry 43.
30.09	A	2QR	Cambridge City	W	*4-2	498	Berry 74, Adams 86, Ridgway 91, Wilkes 106.
11.10	H	3Q	Hinckley United	L	0-1	1,002	
10.01	H	**FAT** 1	Dorchester Town	W	1-0	1,341	Mutchell 39.
31.01	A	2	Northwich Victoria	L	0-4	1,225	
07.10	A	**SCC** 1	Dover Athletic	W	3-1	404	Wilkes 2, Costello 32, Norman 84.
18.11	A	2	Woking	L	0-4	559	
11.11	H	**HC** 2	Wellingborough	W	1-0	329	Sinden.
17.02	H	SF	Long Buckby	W	7-1	442	Norman, Sandeman, Wilkes 2, Van Dullemen, Adams, Vowden, OG.
24.03	H	Final	Raunds Town	W	2-1	604	Wilkes 60, 89.

League Attendances	HIGHEST: 4,016 v Rushden & Diamonds	LOWEST: 1,056 v Dover Athletic
CONFERENCE: 14th	**FA CUP:** 3rd Qual. Round	**FA TROPHY:** 2nd Round

1	2	3	4	5	6	7	8	9	10	11	12 14 15	
Sheppard	Ridgway	Mutchell	Gaunt	Tucker	Vowden	Pick	Norman	Nuttell	Costello	Hercock	Pearson, Wilkes (9), Berry (5).	1
SHeppard	Ridgway	Mutchell	Gaunt	Tucker	Vowden	Pick	Norman	Nuttell	Costello	Hercock	Pearson(10), Wilkes, Berry (2).	2
Sheppard	Berry	Mutchell	Gaunt	Tucker	Vowden	Pick	Norman	Nuttell	Costello	Hercock	Pearson(10), Wilkes, Venables (2).	3
Sheppard	Berry	Mutchell	Gaunt	Tucker	Vowden	Pick	Norman	Nuttell	Pearson	Hercock	Costello(11), Wilkes(10), Venables(7).	4
Sheppard	Berry	Mutchell	Gaunt	Tucker	Vowden	Pick	Norman	Nuttell	Costello	Ridgway	Hercock(11), Venables(10), Wilkes(3).	5
Sheppard	Berry	Mutchell	Gaunt	Tucker	Vowden	Venables	Norman	Wilkes	Costello	Hercock	Miles, Ridgway (7), Adams.	6
Sheppard	Berry	Mutchell	Gaunt	Tucker	Vowden	Venables	Norman	Nuttell	Rowe	Hercock	Wilkes (7), Costello, Miles (11).	7
Sheppard	Berry	Mutchell	Gaunt	Tucker	Vowden	Venables	Norman	Nuttell	Rowe	Adams	Wilkes (7), Hercock (11), Miles.	8
Quy	Berry	Mutchell	Gaunt	Tucker	Vowden	Ridgway	Hercock	Nuttell	Costello	Adams	Miles (4), Wilkes (9), Shoemake.	9
Quy	Berry	Mutchell	DeVito	Tucker	Vowden	Ridgway	Norman	Wilkes	Costello	Adams	Miles, Holliday, Sheppard.	10
Shoemake	Berry	Mutchell	Gaunt	Tucker	Vowden	DeVito	Norman	Wilkes	Costello	Ridgway	Adams, Miles, Pack	11
Sheppard	DeVito	Mutchell	Norman	Tucker	Vowden	Pearson	Adams	Nuttell	Costello	Ridgway	Wilkes (9), Miles (2), Shoemake.	12
Sheppard	DeVito	Mutchell	Norman	Tucker	Vowden	Ridgway	Adams	Pearson	Costello	Wilkes	Miles (9), Leczynski (11), Shoemake.	13
Sheppard	DeVito	Mutchell	Norman	Tucker	Vowden	Ridgway	Berry	Pearson	Costello	Wilkes	Sinden (11), Adams, Miles.	14
Sheppard	DeVito	Mutchell	Norman	Tucker	Vowden	Ridgway	Berry	Pearson	Costello	Wilkes	Cox (2), Sinden, Adams.	15
Taylor	DeVito	Mutchell	Norman	Tucker	Vowden	Adams	Berry	Pearson	Costello	Wilkes	Ridgway, Cox, Sinden.	16
Taylor	DeVito	Mutchell	Norman	Tucker	Vowden	Adams	Berry	Pearson	Costello	Wilkes	Ridgway, Cox, Sinden.	17
Taylor	DeVito	Mutchell	Norman	Tucker	Vowden	Adams	Berry	Pearson	Costello	Wilkes	Ridgway, Cox, Sinden.	18
Taylor	Sandeman	Mutchell	Adams	Cox	Vowden	Ridgway	Sinden	Pearson	Costello	Wilkes	Miles, Holliday, Brown.	19
Taylor	Ridgway	Mutchell	Moore	Cox	Vowden	Sandeman	Adams	Pearson	VanDullemen	Wilkes	Miles (10), Sinden, Holliday.	20
Taylor	Ridgway	Mutchell	Moore	Cox	Vowden	Sandeman	Adams	Pearson	VanDullemen	Wilkes	Berry (7), Miles, Holliday.	21
Taylor	Ridgway	Mutchell	Moore	Cox	Vowden	Sandeman	Adams	Pearson	VanDullemen	Berry	Wilkes, Noramn (11), Miles.	22
Taylor	Ridgway	Mutchell	Moore	Cox	Vowden	Sandeman	Norman	Pearson	VanDullemen	Adams	Wilkes (9), Miles, Tucker.	23
Taylor	Ridgway	Mutchell	Moore	Cox	Vowden	Sandeman	Norman	Pearson	VanDullemen	Adams	Costello (4), Wilkes (10), Tucker.	24
Taylor	Ridgway	Mutchell	Moore	Cox	Vowden	Sandeman	Norman	Costello	VanDullemen	Adams	Berry (2), Wilkes (10), Tucker.	25
Taylor	Ridgway	Mutchell	Moore	Cox	Tucker	Sandeman	Berry	Pearson	VanDullemen	Adams	Norman, Wilkes, Costello.	26
Taylor	Ridgway	Mutchell	Moore	Norman	Tucker	Sandeman	Costello	Pearson	VanDullemen	Adams	Wilkes (7), Nuttell, Miles.	27
Taylor	Ridgway	Mutchell	Moore	Norman	Tucker	Sandeman	Costello	Pearson	VanDullemen	Adams	Vowden (8), Wilkes (9), Cox.	28
Taylor	Berry	Mutchell	Vowden	Cox	Tucker	Sandeman	Norman	Pearson	VanDullemen	Adams	Costello (3), Wilkes (4), Ridgway.	29
Taylor	Berry	Mutchell	Moore	Cox	Vowden	Costello	Norman	Pearson	Nuttell	Adams	Wilkes(9), Tucker(4), VanDullemen(10)	30
Taylor	Berry	Mutchell	Moore	Cox	Vowden	Sandeman	Norman	Pearson	Nuttell	Adams	Wilkes99), Costello, Tucker.	31
Taylor	Berry	Mutchell	Moore	Tucker	Vowden	Sandeman	Costello	Pearson	Nuttell	Adams	Ridgeway(10), Wilkes, Norman.	32
Taylor	Berry	Mutchell	Moore	Tucker	Vowden	Sandeman	Costello	Pearson	Wilkes	Adams	Norman(3), Cox, Ridgeway.	33
Taylor	Berry	Mutchell	Moore	Tucker	Vowden	Sandeman	Costello	Pearson	Wilkes	Adams	Ridgeway(9), Norman, Cox..	34
Taylor	Berry	Mutchell	Cox	Tucker	Vowden	Sandeman	Costello	Pearson	Wilkes	Adams	Ridgeway(2), Norman, Nuttell.	35
Taylor	Ridgeway	Mutchell	Cox	Tucker	Vowden	Sandeman	Costello	Pearson	Wilkes	Adams	Norman, Nuttell, Shoemake.	36
Taylor	Ridgeway	Mutchell	Cox	Tucker	Vowden	Sandeman	Costello	Pearson	Wilkes	Adams	Nuttell(10), Miles, Berry.	37
Taylor	Ridgeway	Mutchell	Cox	Tucker	Vowden	Sandeman	Costello	Pearson	Wilkes	Berry	Nuttell(8), Miles, Norman.	38
Taylor	Berry	Mutchell	Cox	Tucker	Vowden	Sandeman	Costello	Pearson	Wilkes	Adams	Ridgeway(2), Norman, Nuttell.	39
Taylor	Berry	Ridgeway	Cox	Tucker	Vowden	Sandeman	Costello	Pearson	Wilkes	Adams	Miles(2), Norman, Shoemake.	40
Taylor	Ridgeway	Mutchell	Norman	Tucker	Vowden	Sandeman	Costello	Pearson	Wilkes	Adams	Nuttell(10, Miles, Berry.	41
Taylor	Berry	Mutchell	Norman	Tucker	Vowden	Sandeman	Costello	Pearson	Wilkes	Adams	Miles(2), Ridgeway(5), Nuttell(9).	42
Shoemake	Berry	Mutchell	Gaunt	Tucker	Vowden	Venables	Norman	Nuttell	Wilkes	Miles	Hercock (10), Costello (11), Ridgway.	
Shoemake	Berry	Mutchell	DeVito	Tucker	Vowden	Miles	Adams	Wilkes	Costello	Ridgway	Gaunt, Nuttell (7), Holliday.	
Shoemake	Berry	Mutchell	DeVito	Tucker	Vowden	Miles	Adams	Nuttell	Costello	Ridgway	Wilkes (9), Gaunt, Holliday.	
Shoemake	DeVito	Mutchell	Norman	Tucker	Vowden	Ridgway	Adams	Wilkes	Costello	Benjamin	Gaunt (8), Miles, Pack.	
Taylor	Ridgway	Mutchell	Moore	Cox	Vowden	Sandeman	Norman	Pearson	Berry	Adams	Wilkes (8), Tucker, Costello.	
Taylor	Berry	Mutchell	Moore	Cox	Vowden	Sandeman	Norman	Costello	Wilkes	Adams	Ridgway (4), Nuttell (9), Tucker.	
Sheppard	DeVito	Mutchell	Gaunt	Berry	Vowden	Brace	Pack	Wilkes	Costello	Ridgway	Holliday (11), Miles (7), Noramn (5).	
Sheppard	DeVito	Mutchell	Norman	Tucker	Cox	Miles	Adams	Pearson	Costello	Sinden	Wilkes, Ridgway, Vowden.	
Shappard	DeVito	Mutchell	Norman	Tucker	Vowden	Wilkes	Miles	Sinden	Leczynski	Ridgway	Pearson (10), Adams, Holliday.	
Taylor	Ridgway	Mutchell	Moore	Norman	Tucker	Sandeman	Costello	Wilkes	VanDullemen	Adams	Cox, Vowden (6), Pearson (9).	
Taylor	Ridgway	Mutchell	Moore	Tucker	Vowden	Sandeman	Costello	Pearson	Nuttell	Adams	Wilkes(8),Norman(5),Berry.	

PETER MORRIS (MANAGER)

Date of Appointment	May 1998
Date of Birth:	8th November 1943
Place of Birth:	New Houghton, Mansfield.

PREVIOUS CLUBS

As manager	Mansfield T., Peterborough U., Crewe A., Southend U., Nuneaton B., Kettering T., King's Lynn.
As asst. man./coach	Newcastle U., Leicester C.
As player	Mansfield T., Ipswich T., Norwich C., Mansfield T., Peterborough U.,

Assistant Manager: Robbie Cooke **Physio:** Peter Barnett

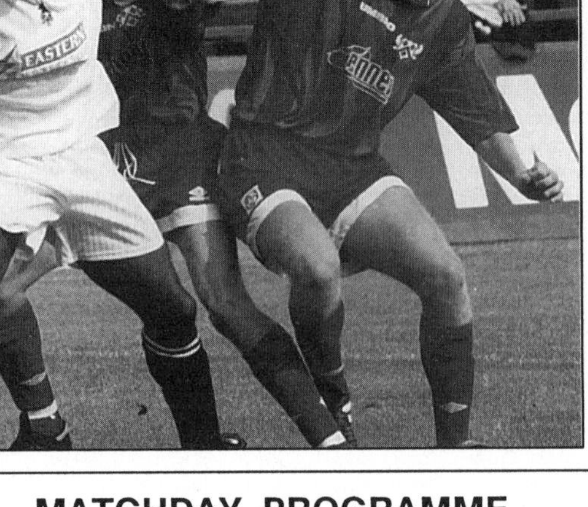

Above: Raymond Van Dulleman who had a 10 match loan spell from Northampton Town.

Photos: Peter Barnes

Left: Working in tanden - Colin Vowden & Mark Tucker (partly hidden) challenge Brian Gray of Telford.

MATCHDAY PROGRAMME

Number of pages	32
Price	£1.50
Programme Editor	Fox Design to Print 0116 222 8500

Other club publications:

"Poppies at the Gates of Dawn" (Fanzine)

Local Newspapers:	Evening Telegraph Chronicle & Echo Herald & Post; Citizen
Local Radio Stations:	Radio Northampton Northants 96; KCBC

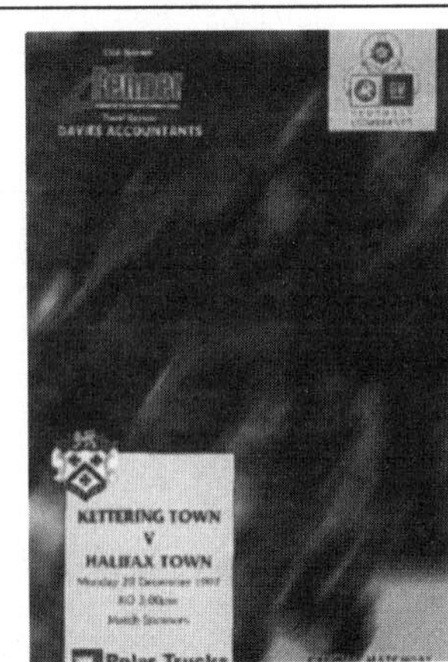

1997-98 PLAYING SQUAD

PLAYER	Birthplace Honours	Birthdate	CLUBS
GOALKEEPERS			
Adam Sollitt *	Sheffield	22.6.77	Barnsley, Gainsborough Trinity
DEFENDERS			
Colin Vowden	Newmarket	13.9.71	Newmarket T, Cambridge C, Cambridge U
Craig Norman	Perivale	21.3.75	Chelsea
Eddie King	Haverhill	2.12.78	From Youth Team
Mark Tucker	Woking ESP, FAT	27.4.72	Fulham, Woking, £45k to Rushden & Diamonds
Paul Cox	Nottingham	6.1.72	Notts Co, Kettering T, Gresley R, Ilkeston T, Halifax T
Paul Miles	Haverhill	18.9.78	From Youth Team
Rob Mutchell	Solihull GMVC	3.1.74	Oxford U, Barnet, Telford U, Stevenage B
MIDFIELDERS			
Martin Matthews *	Peterborough	22.12.75	Derby Co, Northampton T, King's Lynn
Adie Hayes *	Norwich	22.5.78	Cambridge U
Ian Ridgway	Nottingham	28.12.75	Notts Co
Matt Fisher *	Mansfield Army		Army, Ashfield U, Gedling T
Craig Hopkins *	Nottingham		Shirebrook Coll, King's Lynn, Spalding U
Ian Stringfellow *	Nottingham	8.5.69	Mansfield T, £5k to Kettering T, Dag & Red, King's Lynn
FORWARDS			
Brett McNamara *	Peterborough		Stamford, Northampton T, King's Lynn
Tim Wilkes	Nottingham	7.11.77	Notts Co
Phil Brown *	Sheffield GMVC, Div 4	16.1.66	Chesterfield, Stockport Co, Lincoln C, Kettering T, Boston U, Gainsborough Trin
Lee Hudson *	Peterborough		Moulton Harrox, Spalding U, Boston T, King's Lynn
Mickey Nuttell	Boston SLM	22.11.68	Peterborough U, £8k to Cheltenham T, £6k to Wycombe W, £10k to Boston U, Kettering T, Dag & Red, £10k to Rushden & D, Burton Alb

DEPARTURES
Dave Venables (Enfield - £5k), Dave Hercock (Ilkeston T), Gary Pick (Brackley T), Andy Quy (Hereford U), Craig Gaunt (Ilkeston T), Simon Sheppard (Hemel Hempstead), Steve Berry (Stevenage B.), Chris Taylor (Stevenage B.).

PLAYERS ON LOAN
Zeke Rowe (Peterborough U), Alex Leczynski, Ray Van Dullerman & Claudio De Vito (Northampton T)

Rockingham Road, Kettering

GROUND ADDRESS: Rockingham Road, Kettering, Northants, NN16 9AW.
TELEPHONE NUMBERS: 01536 83028/410815 (Office). 01536 410962 (Social Club). **Fax:** 01536 412273.

SIMPLE DIRECTIONS: From south - M1 junction 15, A43 to Kettering use A14 and Kettering Northern by pass, turn right A6003, ground half a mile. From north - M1 or M6 use junction 19 then A14 to Kettering. Exit junction 7 A1 use A14 at Huntingdon then as above. British Rail - Inter-City Midland - 50mins from London (St.Pancras), 20mins from Leicester.

CAPACITY: 6,100 **COVERED SEATING:** 1,800 **COVERED TERRACING:** 2,200

CLUB SHOP: Open before and after matches, and office staff will open on request on non-match days. Situated in front of main stand. Also Ken Burton's Sports in town centre.

SOCIAL FACILITIES: Social Club (Poppies), Vice-Presidents Bar & Sponsor's Lounge.

Kettering Fact File

Nickname: Poppies **Club Sponsors:** Polar Trucks Ltd.
Club colours: Red & black shirts, red shorts, black socks.
Change colours: Green & yellow shirts, green shorts, green & yellow socks.
Midweek home matchday: Tuesday

PREVIOUS - **Leagues:** Southern League, Northants League, Midland League, Birmingham League, Central Alliance, United Counties League.
Grounds: North Park / Green Lane.

CLUB RECORDS - **Attendance:** 11,536 Kettering v Peterborough (pre-Taylor report).
Win: 16-0 v Higham YMCI (FA Cup 1909)
Defeat: 0-13 v Mardy (Southern League Div. 2, 1911/12)
Transfer fee paid: £25,000 to Macclesfield for Carl Alford, 1994.
Transfer fee received: £150,000 from Newcastle United for Andy Hunt.
Career goalscorer: Roy Clayton 171 (1972 - 1981)
Career appearances: Roger Ashby.

BEST SEASON - **FA Trophy:** Runners-up 78-79.
FA Cup: 4th Round - 1988-89, 1-2 v Charlton Ath.; 91-92, 1-4 v Blackburn R.
League clubs defeated: Swindon T., Millwall, Swansea C., Halifax T., Maidstone & Bristol Rovers.

HONOURS - Premier Inter League Cup winners; FA Trophy Runners-up 78-79; Alliance Premier League R-up (x3); Southern League Winners, County Cup Winners, Daventry Charity Cup Winners (x2); Northants Senior Cup (x27); Maunsell Cup Winners (x12).

Past players who progressed to the Football League: Billy Kellock (Peterborough), Gary Wood (Notts Co.), Dave Longhurst (Nott'm Forest), Scott Endersby (Ipswich), Steve Fallon (Cambridge U.), Andy Rogers (Plymouth), Martyn Foster (Northampton), Cohen Griffith (Cardiff C.), Andy Hunt (Newcastle), Richard Brown (Blackburn R.).

1997-98 Captain: Craig Norman
1997-98 Top scorer: Chris Pearson - 14
1997-98 Player of the Year: Colin Vowden

KIDDERMINSTER HARRIERS

As usual Harriers started last season as many people's favourites to win promotion to the Nationwide League.

But it just didn't go right.

By the half-way stage of the campaign the club were fighting to keep their spirits up, and indeed even managing to retain their place in the Conference did not look very likely at all at one stage.

However, the most important characteristic of the club in recent years has been stability and once again Chairman Dave Reynolds kept cool.

Graham Allner, the longest serving manager in the Conference, called upon all his experience and in the second half of the season some sparkling performances by Ian Arnold lifted morale and the club eventually survived a season of serious injuries, poor form and even self doubt.

Everyone will have learnt from this experience and with the ground now one of the best and supporters still loyal who would bet against a fully fit `Kiddy' just bouncing right back into contention?

CLUB OFFICIALS 1998-99

Vice Chairman	**Lionel Newton**
Chairman	**David L Reynolds**
Company Secretary	**J Richard Painter**
Directors	**Graham R Lane** **Colin C Youngjohns**
Chief Executive	**Alan Biggs**
Football Secretary	**Roger Barlow**
Commercial Manager	**Mark Searl**

L-R, BackArchie Richards, Kevin Willetts, Ian Arnold, Wayne Thomas, Neil Doherty, Paul Moore, Dean Tilly, Kim Casey, Matthew Beard, John Deakin, Ginger Jordan. Middle Row: Adie Smith, Matt Clarke, Chris Brindley, Darren Steadman, Stuart Brock, Steve Prindiville, Jim Skelding, Steve Lilwall. Front Row: Jim Conway, Mike Bignall, Mark Yates, Graham Allner, Paul Webb, Tony Robinson, Paul Davies.

KIDDERMINSTER HARRIERS - Match Facts 1997-98

Match No.	Date	Venue H / A	Comp.	Opponents	Result & Score		Att.	Goalscorers	League Position
1	16.08	A	VC	Stalybridge Celtic	L	1-2	*1,013*	Yates 38.	17
2	18.08	H	VC	Northwich Victoria	D	1-1	2,023	OG (Fairclough) 72.	
3	23.08	H	VC	Gateshead	D	1-1	1,592	Smith 80.	19
4	25.08	A	VC	Morecambe	L	1-3	*1,433*	Smith 47.	21
5	30.08	H	VC	Hayes	W	1-0	1,706	Cartwright	17
6	08.09	A	VC	Leek Town	D	0-0	*1,057*		19
7	13.09	H	VC	Stevenage Borough	L	1-3	1,941	Doherty 76.	21
8	20.09	A	VC	Dover Athletic	W	4-0	*1,182*	Arnold 21, Doherty 33, Deakin 61, Yates 77.	16
9	23.09	A	VC	Yeovil Town	L	0-1	*2,129*		17
10	27.09	H	VC	Farnborough Town	W	2-0	1,587	Brindley 11, Smith 45.	13
11	29.09	H	VC	Cheltenham Town	L	1-2	2,320	Arnold 7.	15
12	04.10	A	VC	Hednesford Town	L	0-3	*1,817*		16
13	11.10	A	VC	Southport	W	2-1	*1,200*	Doherty 47 (pen), Deakin 82.	12
14	16.10	H	VC	Rushden & Diamonds	L	1-2	2,210	Yates 29.	14
15	01.11	H	VC	Woking	D	1-1	1,920	Doherty 36(pen).	14
16	08.11	A	VC	Halifax Town	L	1-2	*1,799*	Willetts 48.	15
17	15.11	A	VC	Rushden & Diamonds	**L**	**1-4**	*2,234*	Doherty 56.	17
18	22.11	H	VC	Kettering Town	W	4-1	1,874	Doherty 30(pen), 84, Bignall 39, Willetts 67.	14
19	29.11	A	VC	Farnborough Town	D	3-3	*678*	Yates 13, Arnold 60, Doherty 90.	15
20	06.12	H	VC	Dover Athletic	D	3-3	1,636	**Bignall 3** (12, 49, 78).	14
21	13.12	A	VC	Slough Town	L	0-2	*746*		17
22	20.12	H	VC	Leek Town	D	1-1	1,802	Arnold 47	17
23	26.12	A	VC	Hereford United	L	0-1	*4,671*		18
24	01.01	H	VC	Hereford United	**L**	**1-4**	4,693	Thomas 90	18
25	17.01	A	VC	Hayes	D	1-1	*564*	Arnold 78 (pen).	18
26	24.01	H	VC	Morecambe	**L**	**1-4**	1,717	Robinson 1.	19
27	07.02	A	VC	Telford United	D	1-1	*1,127*	Doherty 79.	19
28	14.02	H	VC	Southport	D	1-1	1,612	Arnold 53.	19
29	21.02	A	VC	Welling United	W	3-0	*613*	Arnold 5 (pen), Bignall 66, 72.	18
30	23.02	H	VC	Stalybridge Celtic	**W**	**5-0**	1,666	OG (Powell) 12, Bignall 50, 90, Davies 67, 89.	17
31	28.02	H	VC	Yeovil Town	W	3-1	1,868	Davies 72, Yates 85, Bignall 89.	17
32	09.03	H	VC	Hednesford Town	D	1-1	1,908	Beard 87.	17
33	18.03	A	VC	Gateshead	L	0-2	*403*		17
34	21.03	A	VC	Woking	W	1-0	*2,384*	Arnold 22.	16
35	24.03	A	VC	Cheltenham Town	W	1-0	*1,902*	Davies 42.	15
36	28.03	H	VC	Telford United	D	1-1	2,024	Robinson 18.	15
37	04.04	A	VC	Stevenage Borough	L	1-3	*2,012*	OG (Soloman) 4.	15
38	11.04	H	VC	Welling United	W	2-1	1,525	Bignall 55, 62.	15
39	13.04	A	VC	Northwich Victoria	D	1-1	*976*	Arnold 4 (pen).	15
40	18.04	H	VC	Halifax Town	L	0-2	3,151		17
41	25.04	A	VC	Kettering Town	D	2-2	*1,576*	Robinson 75, Davies 79.	17
42	02.05	H	VC	Slough Town	L	0-1	1,709		17

CUP COMPETITIONS

Date	Venue	Round	Opponents	Result	Score	Att.	Goalscorers	
F.A. CUP								
25.10	A	4Q	Blyth Spartans	L	1-2	656	Casey 88.	
F.A. TROPHY								
10.01	H	1	Berkhamsted Town	W	4-1	1,206	Yates 13, 83, Arnold 49, Robinson 74.	
31.01	A	2	Hayes	L	0-5	698		
SPALDING CHALLENGE CUP								
17.11	H	2	Hednesford Town	L	0-2	734		
WORCS. SENIOR CUP								
27.01	A	2	Stourbridge	D	0-0	296		
18.02	H	2 R	Stourbridge	D	1-1	379	Yates 107.	A.E.T. Won 3-0 on penalties
12.03	H	SF	Halesowen Town	W	1-0	558	Bignall 57.	
27.04	N	Final	Solihull Borough	W	2-1	739	Casey 89, Weir 90.	

League Attendances	**HIGHEST:** 4,693 v Hereford United	**LOWEST:** 1,525 v Welling United
CONFERENCE: 17th	**FA CUP:** 4th Qual. Round	**FA TROPHY:** 2nd Round

1	2	3	4	5	6	7	8	9	10	11	12 14 15	
Barber	Bignot	Prindiville	Weir	Brindley	Yates	Webb	Willetts	Casey	Cartwright	Doherty	Lilwall, Shpeherd, McCue (9).	1
Barber	Bignot	Prindiville	Weir	Brindley	Yates	Webb	Willetts	Olney	Casey	Doherty	Lilwall(8), McCue (10), Cartwright.	2
Steadman	Bignot	Prindiville	Smith	Brindley	Yates	Webb	Lilwall	Olney	Arnold	Dohertry	Weir (8), Deakin ((7), McCue (9).	3
Steadman	Bignot	Prindiville	Weir	Brindley	Yates	Smith	Deakin	Olney	Arnold	Doherty	Willetts, Lilwall (7), McCue (10).	4
Steadman	Willetts	Prindiville	Smith	Brindley	Yates	Deakin	Cartwright	Olney	Arnold	Doherty	Moore, Lilwall, McCue (9).	5
Steadman	Smith	Prindiville	Weir	Brindley	Yates	Deakin	Cartwright	Olney	Arnold	Doherty	Willetts, Shepherd, McCue (9).	6
Steadman	Smith	Prindiville	Weir	Brindley	Yates	Deakin	Willetts	Shepherd	Arnold	Doherty	Cartwright, Fraser, McCue (10).	7
Steadman	Smith	Prindiville	Weir	Brindley	Yates	Deakin	Willetts	Olney	Arnold	Doherty	Fraser, Shepherd, Casey .	8
Steadman	Smith	Prindiville	Weir	Brindley	Yates	Deakin	Willetts	Olney	Arnold	Doherty	Fraser, Shepherd, Casey.	9
Steadman	Smith	Prindiville	Weir	Brindley	Fraser	Deakin	Willetts	Shepherd	Arnold	Doherty	Brighton (6), Moore, Casey (10).	10
Steadman	Smith	Prindiville	Weir	Brindley	Yates	Deakin	Willetts	Shepherd	Arnold	Doherty	Brighton(11), Fraser(8), Casey(9).	11
Steadman	Smith	Prindiville	Weir	Brindley	Yates	Deakin	Willetts	Shepherd	Arnold	Robinson	Brighton (9), Lilwall, Moore (5).	12
Steadman	Smith	Brighton	Weir	Webb	yates	Deakin	Willetts	Olney	Arnold	Doherty	Lilwall (4), Casey, Robinson.	13
Steadman	Smith	Brighton	Webb	Brindley	Yates	Deakin	Willetts	Olney	Arnold	Doherty	Clarke (2), Casey, Robinson (9).	14
Steadman	Clarke	Prindiville	Smith	Brindley	Yates	Deakin	Willetts	Olney	Arnold	Doherty	Lilwall, Casey, Robinson (11).	15
Steadman	Clarke	Prindiville	Smith	Brindley	Yates	Deakin	Willetts	Olney	Arnold	Doherty	Lilwall, Casey (7), Robinson (9).	16
Steadman	Clarke	Prindiville	Weir	Smith	Yates	Deakin	Thomas	Robinson	Arnold	Doherty	Lilwall, Casey, Davies.	17
Brock	Clarke	Skelding	Smith	Brindley	Yates	Willetts	Thomas	Bignall	Arnold	Doherty	Weir, Robinson, Webb.	18
Brock	Clarke	Skelding	Smith	Brindley	Yates	Willetts	Thomas	Bignall	Arnold	Doherty	Prindiville, Robinson, Webb (8).	19
Brock	Clarke	Skelding	Smith	Brindley	Yates	Willetts	Thomas	Bignall	Arnold	Doherty	Prindiville, Robinson, Webb (7).	20
Brock	Clarke	Skelding	Smith	Brindley	Yates	Willetts	Thomas	Bignall	Arnold	Doherty	Prindiville, Robinson (8), Webb (1).	21
Barber	Skelding	Prindiville	Smith	Brindley	Yates	Webb	Thomas	Bignall	Arnold	Doherty	Deakin, Robinson, Willetts.	22
Steadman	Skelding	Prindiville	Smith	Brindley	Yates	Webb	Thomas	Bignall	Arnold	Doherty	Weir (4(, Robinson (9), Deakin (7).	23
Steadman	Clarke	Skelding	Smith	Brindley	Yates	Webb	Thomas	Bignall	Arnold	Doherty	Weir, Robinson(4), Deakin (7).	24
Westhead	Clarke	Skelding	Weir	Niblett	Yates	Webb	Deakin	Bignall	Arnold	Robinson	Doherty, Casey (11), Lilwall.	25
Westhead	Clarke	Lilwall	Weir	Niblett	Yates	Webb	Smith	Bignall	Arnold	Robinson	Casey, Doherty (11), Deakin (8).	26
Steadman	Skelding	Prindiville	Weir	Pope	Yates	Webb	Deakin	Casey	Arnold	Doherty	Beard, Robinson, Davies (9).	27
Steadman	Skelding	Prindiville	Weir	Pope	Yates	Webb	Deakin	Bignall	Arnold	Doherty	Niblett, Robinson, Davies.	28
Steadman	Skelding	Prindiville	Weir	Biblett	Yates	Deakin	Davies	Bignall	Arnold	Willetts	Doherty (4), Robinson, Beard.	29
Steadman	Skelding	Prindiville	Pope	Niblett	Yates	Deakin	Davies	Bignall	Arnold	Willetts	Doherty, Robinson, Beard.	30
Steadman	Skelding	Prindiville	Pope	Niblett	Yates	Deakin	Davies	Bignall	Arnold	Willetts	Doherty, Robinson, Webb (5).	31
Steadman	Skelding	prindiville	Weir	Webb	Yates	Doherty	Davies	Robinson	Lilwall	Willetts	Moore(8), Beard(10), Tilley.	32
Steadman	Skelding	Prindiville	Weir	Pope	Yates	Webb	Davvies	Bignall	Arnold	Deakin	Willetts(9), Doherty, Robinson.	33
Steadman	Willetts	Prindiville	Weir	Pope	Yates	Webb	Davies	Bignall	Arnold	Deakin	Beard, Doherty, Robinson.	34
Steadman	Willetts	Prindiville	Weir	Pope	Yates	Webb	Davies	Bignall	Arnold	Deakin	Beard, Doherty, Robinson.	35
Steadman	Willetts	Prindiville	Weir	Pope	Yates	Webb	Davies	Bignall	Arnold	Deakin	Robinson(9), Beard, Doherty,.	36
Steadman	Webb	Willetts	Weir	Niblett	yates	Beard	davies	Bignall	Arnold	Deakin	Robinson(7), Lilwall, Doherty.	37
Steadman	Webb	Willetts	Weir	Pope	Yates	Beard	Davies	Bignall	Arnold	Deakin	Robinson, Niblett, Doherty.	38
Steadman	Willetts	Prindiville	Weir	Pope	Yates	Webb	Davies	Bignall	Arnold	Deakin	Robinson, Niblett, Beard.	39
Steadman	Willetts	Prindiville	Weir	Pope	Yates	Webb	Davies	Bignall	Arnold	Deakin	Robinson, Niblett, Beard.	40
Steadman	Webb	Willetts	Weir	Pope	Yates	Beard	Davies	Bignall	Arnold	Deakin	Casey(9), Robinson(11), Niblett.	41
Steadman	Webb	Lilwall	Weir	Pope	Yates	Beard	Davies	Robinson	Arnold	Deakin	Bignall(2), Doherty(3), Casey(8).	42
Steadman	Smith	Prindiville	Weir	Brindley	Yates	Webb	Willetts	Olney	Arnold	Doherty	Deakin (3), Casey (11), Robinson (9).	
Westhead	Clarke	Skelding	Weir	Tilley	Yates	Webb	Deakin	Bignall	Arnold	Robinson	Casey, Doherty, Lilwall (5).	
Westhead	Clarke	Prindiville	Weir	Niblett	Yates	Webb	Skelding	Bignall	Arnold	Doherty	Lilwall, Casey (5), Robinson (11).	
Steadman	Clarke	Prindiville	Weir	Smith	Yates	Deakin	Thomas	Robinson	Arnold	Doherty	Lilwall (7), Casey, Davies.	
Steadman	Clarke	Webb	Weir	Niblett	Yates	Deakin	Lilwall	Bignall	Casey	Doherty	Robinson, Davies, Tilley.	
Steadman	Webb	Skelding	Weir	Niblett	Yates	Pope	Deakin	Bignall	Arnold	Doherty	Willetts (5), Robinson (11), Beard (4).	
Steadman	Skelding	Prindiville	Weir	Webb	Yates	Deakin	Doherty	Bignall	Robinson	Willetts	Beard(4), Tilley, Moore.	
Steadman	Webb	Willetts	Weir	Pope	Yates	Beard	Davies	Bignall	Arnold	Deakin	Niblett(5), Casey(7), Robinson(9).	

GRAHAM ALLNER (MANAGER)

Date of Appointment	October 1983
Date of Birth:	7th September 1949
Place of Birth:	Birmingham

PREVIOUS CLUBS

As manager	AP Leamington
As Asst. Man.	Cheltenham Town
As player	Walsall, Worcester City, Stafford Rangers, Alvechurch.

HONOURS

As manager	GMV Conference 93-94; FA Trophy 86-87 Southern League (with Leamington)
As player	England: Youth, Middlesex Wanderers.

FOOTBALL MANAGEMENT TEAM

Physio / Assistant Manager
Jimmy Conway

Player / Coach
Paul Davies

Chief Scout
Ralph Puncheon

Youth Development Manager
Brian Forsbrook

Youth Team Manager
Geoff Allard

Steve Prindiville (3) nearly 'loses his head' while clearing from Ritchie Hanlon of Welling, with captain Mark Yates on hand to 'pick up the pieces' and Ian Arnold (10) looking on.

Photo: Keith Gillard

MATCHDAY PROGRAMME

Number of pages	40
Price	£1.50
Programme Editor	Steve Thomas
Other club publications:	None
Local Newspapers:	Kidderminster Shuttle / Times Kidderminster Chronicle Evening Mail; Express & Star Worcester Evening News
Local Radio Stations:	BBC Hereford & Worcester Radio Wyvern Beacon Radio; BRMB.

1997-98 PLAYING SQUAD

PLAYER	Birthplace Honours	Birthdate	CLUBS
GOALKEEPERS			
Stuart Brock	Sandwell	26.9.76	Aston Villa, Northampton T, Solihull B
Darren Steadman	Kidderminster ES	26.1.70	From YTS
DEFENDERS			
Steve Prindiville	Harlow ESP	26.12.68	Leicester C, Chesterfield, Mansfield T, Doncaster R, Wycombe W, Halifax T, Dagenham & Redbridge
Steve Pope *	Mow Cop	8.9.76	Crewe Alexandra
Martin Weir	Birmingham GMVC, FA XI, Middx Wanderers	4.7.68	Birmingham C
Matthew Clarke	Birmingham British Univ.		West Bromwich Albion, Cradley T, Halesowen Harriers, Halesowen T, £10k to Kidderminster H
Nigel Niblett	Stratford SLC, FA XI	12.8.67	Snitterfield Sports, Stratford T, VS Rugby, £5k to Telford U, £10k to Hednesford T, P/E to Kidderminster H
Kevin Willetts	Gloucester FA XI, Middx Wanderers	15.8.62	Sharpness, Cheltenham T, Forest Green R, Gloucester C, Weston-Super-Mare
Adie Smith	Birmingham BLT		Willenhall T, Birmingham C, Bromsgrove R, £10k to Kidderminster H
Jimmy Skelding	Birmingham SLP, FA XI	30.5.64	Bilston T, Wolves, Bromsgrove R, Burton Alb, Worcester C, Bromsgrove R
MIDFIELDERS			
Mark Yates	Birmingham	24.1.70	Birmingham C, Burnley, Doncaster R
Dean Tilley	Birmingham		Birmingham C
John Deakin	Sheffield GMVC	29.9.66	Barnsley, Doncaster R, Grimsby T, Frickley A, Shepshed Alb, Birmingham C, Carlisle U, Wycombe W
Matthew Beard	Birmingham		Youth team
Paul Webb	Wolverhampton ESP, GMVC, SLP, FA XI	30.11.67	Bilston T, Shrewsbury T, Bromsgrove R, £17,500 to Kidderminster H
FORWARDS			
Paul Davies	Kidderminster ESP, GMVC, FAT, FA XI	9.10.60	Cardiff C, Trowbridge T, SC Hercules (Holl)
Mike Bignall	Liverpool		Wrexham, Runcorn, Stevenage B, £6k to Morecambe, £10k to Kidderminster H
Tony Robinson	Birmingham		Coventry C, Birmingham C
Ian Arnold	Durham ESP	4.7.72	Middlesbrough, Carlisle U, £10k to Kettering T, £15k to Stalybridge C, £15k to Kidderminster H

DEPARTURES -
(During the season)
Marcus Bignot (Crewe Alexandra - £100k), Fred Barber (Retired), Neil Cartwright (Telford U - £4.5k), Jimmy Fraser (Worcester C), James McCue (Hereford U), Mark Shepherd & James Wills (Moor Green), Stewart Brighton (Redditch U), Ian Olney (Retired), Chris Brindley (Hednesford T), Mark Westhead (Telford U)

PLAYERS ON LOAN - Wayne Thomas (Walsall), Steve Pope (Crewe Alexandra)

Aggborough, Kidderminster

GROUND ADDRESS: Aggborough Stadium, Hoo Road, Kidderminster, Worcs. DY10 1NB.

COMMUNICATION:
Tel: 01562 823931 **Fax:** 01562 827329 **E-mail** info@khfc.co.uk **Web** www.khfc.co.uk

SIMPLE DIRECTIONS:
On all the main approach roads into Kidderminster - follow the yellow & blacks signs to the ground.

CAPACITY: 6,237 **COVERED SEATING:** 1,100 **COVERED TERRACING:** 4,690

CLUB SHOP: Open Monday to Friday 9am-5pm, plus 1st XI match days.

SOCIAL FACILITIES: Lounge bar for members, officials & players. Social & supporters club (3 bars) open to visiting supporters before & after the match, temporary admission 50p. Hot & cold food available.

Kidderminster Fact File

Nickname: Harriers **Sponsors:** OGL Computer

Club colours: Red & white halved shirts, red shorts, red socks.

Change colours: Yellow & black

Reserve team league: Central Conference

Midweek home matchday: Mondays 7.45pm.

PREVIOUS - **Leagues:** Birmingham League 1889-1890, 1891-1939, 1947-1948, 1960-1962, Midland League 1890-1891, Southern League 1939-1945 (Abandoned - World War II), 1948-1960, 1972-1983, Birmingham Combination 1945-1947, West Midlands League 1962-1972.
Grounds: None **Names:** None

CLUB RECORDS - **Attendance:** 9,155 - Hereford United - FA Cup 1st Round Proper 27.11.48.

Win: 25-0 v Hereford (H) - 12.10.1889 - Birmingham Senior Cup 1st Rnd.

Defeat: 0-13 v Darwen (A) - 24.01.1891 - FA Cup 1st Rnd Proper.

Transfer fee paid: £20,000 for Chris Brindley from Telford - 1992

Transfer fee received: £180,000 + apps for Lee Hughes to West Bromwich Albion.

Career goalscorer: Peter Wassall 432 - 1963-1974

Career appearances: Brendan Wassall 686 - 1962-1974

BEST SEASON - **FA Cup:** 5th Round 1993-94. 0-1 v West Ham United.
League clubs defeated: Birmingham City, Preston North End.
FA Trophy: Winners 86-87, R-up 90-91, 94-95.

HONOURS - GMV Conference Champions 1994, R-up 1997; FA Trophy Winners 1987, Runners-up 1991, 1995; Spalding Cup 1997, Welsh FA Cup Runners-up 1986, 1989; Southern League Cup 1980; Worcester Senior Cup (20); Birmingham Senior Cup (7); Staffordshire Senior Cup (4); West Midland League Champions (6), Runners-up (3); Southern Premier Runners-up (1); West Midland League Cup winners (7); Keys Cup winners (7); Border Counties Floodlit League Champions (3), Camkin Floodlit Cup Winners (3); Bass County Vase Winners (1); Conference Fair Play Trophy (5).

Recent past players who progressed to the Football League: Lee Hughes (West Brom. A.), Richard Forsyth (Birmingham C., now Stoke C.), Paul Jones (Wolverhampton W., now Stockport Co.), Dave Barnett (Barnet, now Birmingham C.), Steve Lilwall (West Brom. A.), Marcus Bignot (Crewe Alex.).

1997-98 Captain: Mark Yates

1997-98 Top scorer: Mike Bignall

1997-98 Player of the Year: Ian Arnold

KINGSTONIAN

The fact that Geoff Chapple had joined the club from neighbours Woking lifted everyone's morale at Kingsmeadow.

Anything was now possible for the K's and a few exciting signings gave the impression that Conference football was the club's very real ambition.

A solid but unspectacular start kept the club in touch, although always a few points behind, as first Dagenham then Sutton United and finally Boreham Woodall all-looked powerful with spells of excellent form.

However, the team developed steadily, David Leworthy kept scoring and the managers' experience was vital as Kingstonian maintained their form while the others stuttered and a last push saw K's move smooothly away from the pack.

A good tradition, excellent potential support and a fine stadium will give the back up to a proven manager and a more than useful squad who should all enjoy themselves this season.

CLUB OFFICIALS 1998-99

President **C J Webster**

Chairman **P Gellard**

Vice Chairman **Chris Kelly**

Directors **L Cooley, T Dixon, T Weir, R M Woolfson, G Chapple, B Gold, A Kingston**.

Football Secretary **Bill McNully**
71 Largewood Ave., Tolworth, Surbiton. KT6 7NX
Tel: 0181 391 4552

Commercial & Admin. Manager **Chris Kelly**

Press Officer **Brendan Fawley**
Tel: 0181 398 6705

Kingstonian pictured before their final home game last season. L-R, Back Row: Jim Pearce (Physio), Steve Talboys, Gary Patterson, Matt Crossley,, Jerome John, Terry Evans, Eddie Akuamoah, Scott Corbett, Clive Howes (Asst. Manager), Lenny Dennis. Front Row: Joe Francis, Danny Smith, Geoff Pitcher, Colin Luckett, Dave Leworthy, Dean Hooper. Photo: Andrew Chitty.

KINGSTONIAN - Match Facts 1997-98

Match No.	Date	Venue H / A	Comp.	Opponents	Result & Score		Att.	Goalscorers	League Position
1	16.08	H	IL	Bishop's Stortford	W	1-0	1,034	Leworthy.	8
2	19.08	A	IL	Hitchin Town	D	0-0	*514*		
3	23.08	A	IL	Basingstoke Town	D	0-0	*765*		8
4	26.08	H	IL	Enfield	D	0-0	1,002		
5	30.08	H	IL	Bromley	W	4-1	958	Pitcher, Darlington, Leworthy, Cooper.	6
6	02.09	A	IL	St Albans City	W	3-0	*612*	Leworthy 2, Darlington.	
7	05.09	A	IL	Walton & Hersham	W	4-1	*687*	**Leworthy 3,** Smith.	2
8	20.09	A	IL	Carshalton Athletic	D	1-1	*642*	Cooper.	3
9	23.09	H	IL	Harrow Borough	W	5-2	805	Akuamoah 2, Evans, Patterson, Dennis (pen).	3
10	04.10	A	IL	Hendon	D	1-1	*458*	Hooper.	3
11	07.10	H	IL	Boreham Wood	**L**	**2-5**	640	Leworthy, Darlington.	3
12	14.10	A	IL	Aylesbury United	L	0-2	*374*		3
13	01.11	H	IL	Chesham United	W	3-1	701	Dennis (pen), Leworthy, Pitcher.	4
14	08.11	A	IL	Yeading	W	3-1	*331*	Akuamoah, Freeman, Leworthy.	4
15	15.11	H	IL	Sutton United	D	0-0	2,019		4
16	18.11	H	IL	Gravesend & Northfleet	W	3-1	783	Patterson, Ndah, Leworthy.	3
17	22.11	A	RL	Heybridge Swifts	W	3-1	*428*	Luckett, Ndah 2.	3
18	25.11	H	RL	Purfleet	D	2-2	581	Evans, Dennis.	
19	29.11	H	RL	Dagenham & Redbridge	L	0-2	1,411		3
20	06.12	A	RL	Enfield	W	1-0	*1,143*	Ndah.	3
21	13.12	A	RL	Chesham United	D	1-1	*434*	Luckett (pen).	3
22	20.12	H	RL	Oxford City	D	0-0	669		3
23	27.12	A	RL	Dulwich Hamlet	L	1-2	*603*	Ndah.	3
24	03.01	H	RL	St Albans City	W	5-0	894	Crossley, Luckett, Leworthy , Roach 2..	3
25	10.01	H	RL	Hitchin Town	L	0-2	754	Roach, Luckett (pen).	3
26	17.01	A	RL	Bishop's Stortford	W	1-0	*319*	Corbett.	3
27	24.01	H	RL	Basingstoke Town	W	2-0	704	Corbett, Leworthy .	3
28	31.01	A	RL	Bromley	W	2-0	*460*	Pitcher, Corbett.	2
29	07.02	H	RL	Carshalton Athletic	W	5-1	675	Patterson, Luckett (pen), Crossley, Akuamoah, Leworthy.	2
30	14.02	A	RL	Harrow Borough	W	2-0	*430*	Hooper, Leworthy.	2
31	21.02	A	RL	Dagenham & Redbridge	D	2-2	*1,076*	Smith, Crossley .	2
32	28.02	H	RL	Hendon	W	2-1	911	Pitcher, Leworthy (pen).	2
33	07.03	A	RL	Gravesend & Northfleet	W	2-1	*753*	Pitcher 2.	1
34	14.03	H	RL	Walton & Hersham	**W**	**7-0**	1,011	Luckett (pen), Francis, Corbett, Ackuamoah, **Leworthy 3.**	1
35	21.03	A	RL	Boreham Wood	W	1-0	*1,029*	Leworthy.	1
36	28.03	H	RL	Aylesbury United	W	3-0	1,247	Akuamoah, Pitcher, Leworthy.	1
37	04.04	H	RL	Yeading	L	0-1	1,297		1
38	13.04	H	RL	Dulwich Hamlet	W	2-1	1,203	Akuamoah, Luckett (pen).	1
39	18.04	A	RL	Sutton United	D	3-3	*1,901*	Leworthy, Akuamoah, Evans.	1
40	25.04	H	RL	Heybridge Swifts	W	3-0	1,595	Pitcher, Patterson, France.	1
41	30.04	A	RL	Oxford City	W	1-0	*361*	Pitcher.	1
42	02.05	A	RL	Purfleet	D	1-1	*603*	Dennis.	1

CUP COMPETITIONS

F.A. CUP

Date	Venue	Round	Opponents	Result	Score	Att.	Goalscorers
14.09	A	1Q	Bedford United	W	5-0	200	Pitcher, Luckett 2, Cooper, Crossley.
27.09	A	2Q	Dover Athletic	W	4-0	938	Hooper 48, 89, Cooper 57, Ndah 73.
11.10	H	3Q	Wivenhoe Town	W	1-0	529	Hooper.
25.10	A	4Q	Slough Town	L	1-2	1,372	Dennis.

F.A. TROPHY

Date	Venue	Round	Opponents	Result	Score	Att.	Goalscorers
18.10	A	1Q	Crawley Town	L	1-2	1,587	Akuamoah 48.

GUARDIAN INSURANCE CUP

Date	Venue	Round	Opponents	Result	Score	Att.	Goalscorers
09.09	A	1	Camberley Town	L	1-2	-	Leworthy.

FULL MEMBERS CUP

Date	Venue	Round	Opponents	Result	Score	Att.	Goalscorers
04.11	A	1	Dulwich Hamlet	W	3-0	152	Dennis, Akuamoah, Leworthy.
23.12	A	2	Basingstoke Town	L	2-3	-	Leworthy, Freeman.

League Attendances	**HIGHEST:** 2,019 v Sutton United	**LOWEST:** 640 v Boreham Wood
ISTHMIAN PREMIER: Champions	**FA CUP:** 4th Qual. Round	**FA TROPHY:** 1st Qual. Round

1	2	3	4	5	6	7	8	9	10	11	12 14 15	
John	Deadman	Luckett	Crossley	Evans	Brown	Patterson	Pitcher	Jones	Leworthy	Akuamoah	Harper, Dennis(10), Darlington(11).	1
John	Smith	McCann	Crossley	Evans	Brown	Patterson	Jones	Dennis	Leworthy	Luckett	Pitcher(11), Elverson, Darlington(8).	2
John	Smith	Cooper	Crossley	Evans	Harper	Patterson	Pitcher	Hooper	Leworthy	Darlington	Deadman, Dennis, Akuamoah(11).	3
John	Smith	Cooper	Crossley	Evans	Harper	Patterson	Pitcher	Hooper	Leworthy	Akuamoah	Deadman(8),Dennis,Darlington(11).	4
John	Smith	Cooper	Crossley	Evans	Brown	Patterson	Pitcher	Darlington	Leworthy	Hooper	Dennis(10),Akuamoah(9),Deadman(11).	5
John	Smith	Cooper	Crossley	Evans	Harper	Patterson	Pitcher	Hooper	Leworthy	Darlington	Deadman(9),Luckett(2),Akuamoah(11)	6
Gregory	Smith	Cooper	Crossley	Evans	Harper	Patterson	Pitcher	Hooper	Leworthy	Darlington	Deadman(9),Luckett(7),Akuamoah(11)	7
Gregory	Luckett	Cooper	Crossley	Evans	Harper	Patterson	Picher	Hooper	Leworthy	Akuamoah	Dennis(10),Deadman(4),Darlington(11)	8
Gregory	Hooper	Luckett	Crossley	Evans	Harper	Patterson	Pitcher	Dennis	Leworthy	Akuamoah	Brown, Smith, Darlington(10).	9
John	Hooper	Cooper	Crossley	Evans	Harper	Patterson	Pitcher	Luckett	Ndah	Akuamoah	Deadman(8), Smith, Darlington.	10
John	Hooper	Cooper	Crossley	Evans	Harper	Patterson	Pitcher	Luckett	Leworthy	Akuamoah	Smith(3),Deadman(8),Darlington(11).	11
John	Hooper	Cooper	Crossley	Evans	Wye	Patterson	Rattray	Dennis	Ndah	Luckett	Akuamoah(10), Harper, Pitcher.	12
John	Smith	Luckett	Crossley	Evans	Wye	Rattray	Pitcher	Akuamoah	Dennis	Freeman	Brown, Leworthy(10), Corbett..	13
John	Smith	Luckett	Crossley	Brown	Wye	Rattray	Pitcher	Akuamoah	Leworrthy	Freeman	Evans, Ndah(10), Harvey.	14
John	Hooper	Luckett	Crossley	Evans	Wye	Patterson	Pitcher	Akuamoah	Leworthy	Freeman	Dennis99),Rattray(11),Ndah(10).	15
John	Hooper	Luckett	Crossley	Evans	Wye	Patterson	Pitcher	Ndah	Leworthy	Freeman	Dennis(10),Rattray(11),Akuamoah.	16
John	Hooper	Luckett	Crossley	Evans	Wye	Patterson	Pitcher	Ndah	Leworthy	Freeman	Dennis, Rattray(11),Akuamoah(10).	17
John	Hooper	Luckett	Crossley	Evans	Wye	Patterson	Pitcher	Ndah	Leworthy	Freeman	Dennis(10),Rattray, Akuamoah(11).	18
John	Hooper	Luckett	Crossley	Evans	Wye	Patterson	Pitcher	Ndah	Dennis	Akuamoah	Rattray, Freeman, Smith.	19
John	Hooper	Luckett	Crossley	Evans	Brown	Patterson	Pitcher	Akuamoah	Dennis	Freeman	Rattray, Smith, Ndah(9).	20
John	Hooper	Luckett	Crossley	Evans	Brown	Patterson	Pitcher	Akuamoah	Ndah	Freeman	Dennis99), Smith(8), Harvey..	21
John	Hooper	Luckett	Crossley	Evans	Wye	Patterson	Pitcher	Akuamoah	Leworthy	Freeman	Smith(8),Rattray(7),Ndah(9).	22
Wells	Hooper	Luckett	Crossley	Evans	Brown	Patterson	Pitcher	Ndah	Leworthy	Rattray	Smith(6),Corbett, Akuamoah(7).	23
MacKenzie	Hooper	Luckett	Crossley	Evans	Rattray	Patterson	Smith	Roach	Leworthy	Akuamoah	Dennis, Ndah(10), Corbett(6).	24
MacKenzie	Smith	Luckett	Crossley	Wrightson	Rattray	Patterson	Corbett	Roach	Leworthy	Akuamoah	Dennis, Ndah(60, Harvey.	25
MacKenzie	Smith	Luckett	Crossley	Wrightson	Corbett	Hooper	Pitcher	Roach	Leworthy	Akuamoah	Dennis(10),Ndah(2), Harvey.	26
MacKenzie	Smith	Luckett	Crossley	Evans	Corbett	Hooper	Pitcher	Roach	Leworthy	Akuamoah	Dennis(9),Wrightson(7),Ndah(10).	27
MacKenzie	Hooper	Luckett	Crossley	Evans	Wrightson	Patterson	Pitcher	Roach	Leworthy	Akuamoah	Corbett(3),Dennis(9),Ndah(10).	28
MacKenzie	Hooper	Luckett	Crossley	Evans	Corbett	Patterson	Pitcher	Roach	Leworthy	Akuamoah	Brown, Smith (6), John.	29
MacKenzie	Hooper	Luckett	Crossley	Evans	Corbett	Patterson	Pitcher	Roach	Leworthy	Akuamoah	Smith(6), Dennis((9), Brown(10).	30
John	Hooper	Luckett	Crossley	Evans	Smith	Patterson	Pitcher	Roach	Leworthy	Akuamoah	Ajikawa, Dennis(9), Brown.	31
John	Hooper	Smith	Crossley	Evans	Brown	Patterson	Pitcher	Roach	Leworthy	Akuamoah	Dennis(2), rattray(9), Ajikawa.	32
John	Hooper	Francis	Crossley	Evans	Brown	Patterson	Pitcher	Dennis	Leworthy	Akuamoah	Smith(6), Rattray(9), Dowling.	33
John	Hooper	Luckett	Crossley	Evans	Francis	Williamson	Pitcher	Corbett	Leworthy	Akuamoah	Pitwood(6), Smith(3), Rattray(9).	34
John	Hooper	Luckett	Crossley	Omogbebia	Francis	Patterson	Pitcher	Williamson	Leworthy	Akuamoah	Dennis, Smith(9), Rattray (6).	35
John	Hooper	Luckett	Crossley	Evans	Francis	Patterson	Pitcher	Williamson	Leworthy	Akuamoah	Dennis(11), Smith(3), Talboys(6).	36
John	Hooper	Smith	Crossley	Evans	Francis	Patterson	Pitcher	Williamson	Leworthy	Dennis	Talboys(9),Rattray(11),Corbett(8).	37
John	Hooper	Luckett	Crossley	Evans	Francis	Patterson	Pitcher	Talboys	Leworthy	Akuamoah	Corbett((9), Smith, Williamson(6).	38
John	Hooper	Luckett	Crossley	Evans	Francis	Patterson	Pitcher	Corbett	Leworthy	Akuamoah	Dennis, Smith, Rattray99).	39
John	Hooper	Luckett	Crossley	Evans	Francis	Patterson	Pitcher	Smith	Leworthy	Akuamoah	Dennis(10), Talboys(2), Corbett(6).	40
John	Hooper	Luckett	Crossley	Evans	Francis	Patterson	Pitcher	Smith	Leworthy	Akuamoah	Dennis, Corbett(9), Talboys.	41
John	Hooper	Luckett	Crossley	Evans	Francis	Patterson	Pitcher	Smith	Leworthy	Akuamoah	Dennis(9),Corbett(8), Talboys(6).	42
Gregory	Hooper	Cooper	Crossley	Evans	Harper	Patterson	Pitcher	Akuamoah	Leworthy	Luckett	Dennis(7),Deadman(8),Darlington(9).	
John	Hooper	Cooper	Crossley	Evans	Harper	Patterson	Pitcher	Dennis	Luckett	Akuamoah	Deadman, Ndah(9), Darlington.	
John	Hooper	Cooper	Crossley	Evans	Luckett	Patterson	Deadman	Darlington	Dennis	Akuamoah	Pitcher, Harper(11), Smuith.	
John	Dan Smith	Luckett	Crossley	Evans	Harper	Hooper	Pitcher	Rattray	Dennis	Akuamoah	Corbett, Brown, Dar. Smith.	
John	Hooper	Luckett	Crossley	Evans	Wye	Patterson	Pitcher	Hemming	Akuamoah	Rattray	Harper, Smith(9), Corbett.	
Gregory	Smith	Luckett	Crossley	Deadman	Harper	Patterson	Pitcher	Hooper	Leworthy	Darlington	Akuamoah(8), Elverson, Evans.	
John	Corbett	Luckett	Crossley	Brown	Wye	Freeman	Pitcher	Rattray	Dennis	Akuamoah	Leworthy(10), Smith(2), Harvey.	
John	Hooper	Crossley	Evans	Wye	Patterson	Pitcher	Ndah	Leworthy	Freeman	Rattray(8), Smith(6), Harvey.		

GEOFF CHAPPLE (MANAGER)

Date of Appointment	May 1997
Date of Birth:	7th November 1945
Place of Birth:	Farnham, Surrey.

PREVIOUS CLUBS

As manager — Windsor & Eton, Woking.

As player — Woking, Guildford City, Windsor & Eton.

HONOURS

As manager — FA Trophy 93-94, 94-95, 96-97; Isthmian League - Premier Div. 91-92, 97-98, Div. 1 R-up 89-90, Div. 2 S 86-87, League Cup 90-91, Charity Shield 91-92; Conference - R-up 94-95, 95-96, Championship Shield 94-95, R-up 95-96.

FOOTBALL MANAGEMENT TEAM

Assistant Manager
Clive Howse

Coach
Ian McDonald

Physio
Jim Pearce

Youth Team Manager
S McIntyre

Youth Development Officer
S Chamberlain

LEFT

MATT CROSSLEY

Player of the Year 97-98

Photo:
Andrew Chitty

RIGHT

Celebrations with the Ryman League Championship Shield.

Photo:
Mark Sandom

MATCHDAY PROGRAMME

Number of pages	28
Price	£1.50
Programme Editor	Brian Giffard Tel: 0181 940 6448
Other club publications:	None
Local Newspapers:	Surrey Comet 0181 546 2261
Local Radio Stations:	County Sound

1997-98 PLAYING SQUAD

PLAYER	Birthplace Honours	Birthdate	CLUBS
GOALKEEPERS			
Jerome John	London RLP		West Ham U, Dulwich Hamlet, Altrincham
DEFENDERS			
Matt Crossley	Basingstoke GMVC, FAT, RLP	18.3.68	Overton U, Wycombe W
Wayne Brown	Waterloo RLP, FA XI	19.1.70	Welling U, £3,500 to Kingstonian
Terry Evans	Hammersmith RLP	12.4.65	Hillingdon B, Brentford, Wycombe W
Dean Hooper	Harefield ESP, RLP	13.4.71	Brentford, Chalfont St.Peter, Yeading, Marlow, Hayes, Swindon T, Hayes, Swindon T, Hayes, Stevenage B
MIDFIELDERS			
Gary Patterson	Newcastle RLP	27.11.72	Notts County, Shrewsbury T, Wycombe W
Colin Luckett	London RLP		Millwall
Kevin Rattray	London FAT, RLP	6.10.68	Woking, Gillingham, Barnet
Jeff Wrightson	Newcastle FAYC, NPL, RLP	18.5.68	Newcastle U, Preston NE, Gateshead, B Auckland, Stalybridge C, Yeovil T
Danny Smith	London RLP	7.9.75	Tottenham Hotspur, Welling U
Geoff Pitcher	Carshalton RLP	15.8.75	Millwall, Watford, Carshalton Ath, Kingstonian, Colchester U
Jimmy Dack			Brentford, Epsom & Ewell, Sutton U., Crawley T., Carshalton Ath., Sutton U.
FORWARDS			
David Leworthy	Portsmouth ESP, RLP	22.10.62	Portsmouth, Fareham T, Tottenham Hotspur, £175k to Oxford U, Reading, Farnborough T, £50k to Farnborough T, £15k to Rushden & D, £18k to Kingstonian
Eddie Akuamoah	London RLP		Bedfont, Carshalton Ath
Steve Talboys	Bristol RLP	18.9.66	Mangotsfield U, Bath C, Trowbridge T, Gloucester C, Wimbledon, Watford, Boreham Wood

DEPARTURES - John Gregory (Northwood), Lloyd Wye (Staines T), Matt Elverson (Walton & H), Mark Harper (Aldershot T), David Flemming (Felixstowe T), Steve Darlington (Enfield), Jamie Ndah (Dulwich Hamlet), John Deadman (Enfield), Gary Cooper (Enfield), Tony Wells (Carshalton Ath)

Kingsmeadow Stadium, Kingston-upon-Thames

ADDRESS: Kingsmeadow Stadium, Kingston Road, Kingston-upon-Thames, Surrey. KT1 3PB.
TELEPHONE NUMBER: 0181 547 3335

SIMPLE DIRECTIONS: From town centre - Cambridge Rd on to Kingston Rd (A2043) to Malden Rd. From A3, turn off at New Malden, turn left on to A2043 - grd 1 mile on left. Half mile from Norbiton (BR)

CAPACITY: 9,000 **COVERED TERRACING:** 3,500 **SEATED** 690

SOCIAL FACILITIES: Banqueting centre, open 7 days. 3 bars capacity 400. Contact Chris Kelly (0181 547 3335). Banquets & Conference manager Cathrine Cole (0181 974 5712).

CLUB SHOP: Sells programmes, shirts, badges etc. Contact Mrs ann Dickinson (0181 747 3336)

Kingstonian Fact File

Nickname: The Ks

Sponsors: The Emporium Club

Club Colours: Red & white hooped shirts, black shorts, black socks.

Change Colours: Yellow shirts, royal blue shorts, white socks

Midweek matchday: Tuesday

Newsline: 0660 666 300

Reserves' League: Suburban

Geoff Chapple's Buzz Line: 0660 666 333

PREVIOUS -

Leagues: Kingston & Dist.; West Surrey; Southern Suburban; Athenian 1919-29; Isthmian League 29-98.
Names: Kingston & Surbiton YMCA 1885-87, Saxons 87-90, Kingston Wanderers 1893-1904, Old Kingstonians 08-19.
Grounds: Several to 1921; Richmond Rd 21-89.

CLUB RECORDS -

Attendance: 4,582 v Chelsea (Friendly) 22.7.95.
Goalscorer: Johnny Whig 295
Appearances: Micky Preston 555.
Win: 15-1 v Delft, friendly 5/9/51 (competitive: 10-0 v Hitchin (H), Isthmian Lge 19/3/66).
Defeat: 0-11 v Ilford (A), Isthmian Lge 13/2/37.
Transfer Fee Paid: £10,000 for R Cherry (Redbridge Forest 91)
Transfer Fee Received: £20,000 for Jamie Ndah (Torquay Utd. '95)

BEST SEASON -

FA Amateur Cup: Winners 32-33 R-up 59-60.
FA Trophy:
FA Cup: 2nd Rd Proper 94-95 (v Aylesbury U) 95-96 (v Plymouth A.).
League clubs defeated: Brighton & H.A. 94-95 1-0.

HONOURS -

Isthmian Lg 33-34, 36-37, 97-98 (R-up 47-48 62-63, Div 1 R-up 84-85), Isthmian Lge. Cup 95-96; Athenian Lge 23-24 25-26 (R-up 26-27); London Snr Cup 62-63 64-65 86-87 (R-up 5); Surrey Snr Cup(9),(R-up 90-91).

Players progressing to Football League: C Nastri (C Palace), H Lindsay (Southampton 65), G Still (Brighton 79), D Byrne (Gillingham 1985), J Power (Brentford 87), Jamie Ndah (Torquay).

1997-98 **Captain.** Terry Evans
1997-98 **Player of the Year:** Matt Crossley
1997-98 **Top scorer:** David Leworthy

LEEK TOWN

No club in any competition should have to play six important fixtures in eight days - which is exactly what happened to Leek.

So I am sure that everyone involved within The Conference breathed a mighty sigh of relief when Leek Town's brave squad managed to avoid relegation and in the process won much admiration from their fellow members.

CLUB OFFICIALS 1998-99

President	**Godfrey Heath**
Chairman	**Linden Davies**
Vice Chairman	**Mike Cope**
Directors	**Robin Halton, Carl France, Warren France, Tony Pickford.**
Football Secretary	**Mike Rowley**
62 London Rd., Chesterton, Newcastle, Staffs. ST5 7DY	Tel: 01782 562890
Commercial Manager	**Ken Warburton**
Press Officer	**Mike Cope**

A mixture of bad weather, a below standard playing surface and just pure bad luck had created the situation they found themselves in at the end of last season, but now, under new management and with a few new faces in the squad, their luck could change. It does need to as the Blues may find it hard to consolidate in the ever improving Conference.

Apart from the traumas of the run in to the end of the season, their introduction to the top flight had been a little shaky, as only one victory in twelve games showed.

However, there was no doubt that the townsfolk of Leek were proud of their team's battling qualities as improving crowds of 564, 775 and 1,015 in the last week of the season proved.

They all deserve some luck in the coming campaign.

L-R, Back Row: Kenny Birch-Martin (Physio), J Hassall, D Baker, Aiden Callan, Jeff Parker, Dale Hawtin, Gary Germaine, Ray Newland, Neil Ellis, Ray Walker, Dean Trott, Wayne Biggins, Martin Parr (Asst. Physio). Front Row: Godfrey Heath (President), Steve Tobin, Stuart Leicester, Matt Beeby, John Diskin (Captain), Iain Brunskill, Hugh McAuley, Dean Cunningham, Steve Soley..

LEEK TOWN - Match Facts 1997-98

Match No.	Date	Venue H / A	Comp.	Opponents	Result & Score		Att.	Goalscorers	League Position
1	16.08	A	VC	Morecambe	D	1-1	*1,237*	Trott 83.	11
2	19.08	H	VC	Southport	L	0-1	1,169		
3	23.08	H	VC	Rushden & Diamonds	W	2-0	809	Trott 15, Soley 90.	9
4	25.08	A	VC	Stalybridge Celtic	**L**	**1-6**	*974*	Soley 24.	17
5	30.08	A	VC	Yeovil Town	L	1-3	*2,687*	Trott 64.	20
6	02.09	H	VC	Hereford United	D	2-2	1,138	Biggins 34, McAuley 83.	21
7	07.09	H	VC	Kidderminster Harriers	D	0-0	1,057		21
8	09.09	A	VC	Cheltenham Town	D	1-1	*1,315*	Beeby 66.	18
9	20.09	H	VC	Hayes	L	1-2	551	Trott 22.	20
10	22.09	A	VC	Hednesford Town	L	0-1	*1,302*		20
11	30.09	A	VC	Halifax Town	L	1-2	*1,329*	Biggins 12.	20
12	04.10	H	VC	Slough Town	L	0-2	565		21
13	11.10	A	VC	Gateshead	W	2-0	*539*	McAuley 59, Cunningham 67.	20
14	18.10	A	VC	Woking	L	2-5	*2,806*	Lester 43, McAuley 77.	20
15	01.11	H	VC	Dover Athletic	**W**	**5-1**	562	Ellis 22, Biggins 33, Diskin 44, Soley 69, McAuley 80.	20
16	08.11	H	VC	Stevenage Borough	W	2-1	686	McAuley 45, Biggins 76.	16
17	15.11	H	VC	Gateshead	D	2-2	535	Soley 21, 85.	15
18	29.11	H	VC	Cheltenham Town	D	0-0	708		17
19	06.12	A	VC	Southport	D	2-2	*940*	Tobin 42, Biggins 90(pen).	16
20	13.12	H	VC	Halifax Town	W	2-0	1,282	Soley 7,Ellis 22.	14
21	20.12	A	VC	Kidderminster Harriers	D	1-1	*1,802*	Cunningham 89	14
22	26.12	H	VC	Telford United	W	3-1	832	Biggins 29, Trott 58, Tobin 83	13
23	01.01	A	VC	Telford United	L	0-3	*911*		15
24	17.01	A	VC	Dover Athletic	L	1-2	*1,092*	Tobin 90.	15
25	24.01	H	VC	Stalybridge Celtic	D	2-2	781	Tobin 10, Soley 40.	16
26	07.02	A	VC	Farnborough Town	L	0-2	*618*		17
27	14.02	H	VC	Hednesford Town	D	3-3	816	Hawtin 36, Soley 58, 89.	18
28	21.02	A	VC	Hereford United	L	0-1	*1,712*		19
29	28.02	H	VC	Northwich Victoria	D	1-1	636	McAuley 77.	18
30	14.03	A	VC	Welling United	L	0-2	*575*		19
31	17.03	A	VC	Northwich Victoria	L	1-3	*681*	McAuley 89.	19
32	21.03	A	VC	Kettering Town	L	0-1	*1,287*		20
33	28.03	H	VC	Farnborough Town	W	3-1	664	OG (Baker) 81, Soley 82, Tobin 90.	19
34	31.03	H	VC	Kettering Town	L	0-4	662		19
35	13.04	H	VC	Woking	W	2-0	612	McAuley 54, 59.	19
36	18.04	A	VC	Rushden & Diamonds	W	1-0	*2,064*	McAuley 28.	19
37	25.04	H	VC	Welling United	L	1-2	564	Biggins 29.	20
38	27.04	A	VC	Stevenage Borough	D	1-1	*1,440*	Soley 44.	19
39	28.04	A	VC	Slough Town	D	1-1	*510*	Biggins 45.	20
40	30.04	H	VC	Yeovil Town	W	2-0	775	Walker 30, McAuley 39 (pen).	18
41	01.05	H	VC	Morecambe	D	1-1	1,015	Beeby 70.	18
42	02.05	A	VC	Hayes	L	1-3	*743*	Soley 34.	19

CUP COMPETITIONS SCC Spalding Challenge Cup SSC - Staffs. Senior Cup

Date	Venue	Comp.	Opponents	Result	Score	Att.	Goalscorers
13.09	A	**FAC** 1Q	Winsford United	L	0-1	287	
10.01	A	**FAT** 1	Gresley Rovers	D	4-4	638	Callan 21, 60, Cunningham 65, Trott 76.
14.01	H	1 R	Gresley Rovers	W	3-1	324	Cunningham 4, Biggins 16, 44.
31.01	A	2	Hednesford Town	L	0-5	1,073	
07.10	H	**SCC** 1	Southport	W	3-1	349	Filson 23, McAuley 45, 66.
18.11	A	2	Morecambe	L	2-3	356	OG (Lowe) 10, Ellis 75.
21.10	H	**SSC** 2	Rocester	W	2-0	150	Biggins (2).
22.12	H	3	Kidsgrove Athletic	W	3-0	238	Soley (2), McAuley.
24.03	A	SF	Tamworth	D	*3-3	410	Soley 15,56, McAuley 88.
07.04	H	SF R	Tamworth	L	1-3	201	Cunningham 8

League Attendances	HIGHEST: 1,169 v Southport	LOWEST: 535 v Gateshead
CONFERENCE: 19th	**FA CUP:** 1st Qual. Round	**FA TROPHY:** 2nd Round

1	2	3	4	5	6	7	8	9	10	11	12 14 15	
Newland	Brunskill	Hawtin	Walker	Bauress	Soley	Ellis	Tobin	Diskin	Biggins	Trott	Callan, McAuley, Cunningham.	1
Newland	Brunskill	Hawtin	Walker	Bauress	Soley	Ellis	Tobin	Diskin	Biggins	Trott	Callan, McAuley, Cunningham.	2
Newland	Brunskill	Hawtin	Walker	Filson	Soley	Ellis	Tobin	Diskin	Biggins	Trott	Callan, Beeby, Cunningham.	3
Newland	Brunskill	Hawtin	Walker	Filson	Soley	Ellis	Tobin	Diskin	Biggins	Trott	Bauress, Beeby,Cunningham.	4
Newland	Brunskill	Hawtin	Walker	Filson	Soley	Ellis	Tobin	Diskin	Biggins	Trott	Callan, McAuley, Beeby.	5
Newland	Brunskill	Hawtin	Beeby	Filson	Soley	Ellis	Tobin	Diskin	Biggins	McAuley	Callan, Cunningham, Leicester.	6
Newland	Brunskill	Beeby	Walker	Filson	Soley	Ellis	Tobin	Diskin	Biggins	McAuley	Cunningham, Callan, Leicester.	7
Newland	Brunskill	Hawtin	Walker	Beeby	Soley	Ellis	Tobin	Diskin	Biggins	McAuley	Cunningham, Callan, Leicester.	8
Newland	Brunskill	Callan	Walker	Filson	Soley	Ellis	Cunningham	Diskin	Biggins	Trott	McAuley, Leicester, Hawtin.	9
Newland	Brunskill	Hawtin	Walker	Beeby	Soley	Ellis	Tobin	Callan	Leicester	Trott	Cunningham, McAuley, Biggins	10
Newland	Brunskill	Hawtin	Walker	Filson	Cunningham	Ellis	Tobin	Diskin	Biggins	Trott	McAuley, Leicester, Beeby.	11
Knowles	Beeby	Hawtin	Walker	Cunningham	Callan	McAuley	Tobin	Diskin	Filson	Leicester	Giblin, Hawkes, Wooley.	12
Cutler	Beeby	Hawtin	Walker	Cunningham	Callan	McAuley	Tobin	Diskin	Filson	Leicester	Biggins, Newland, Hawkes.	13
Cutler	Beeby	hawtin	Walker	Cunningham	Callan	McAuley	Tobin	Diskin	Filson	Leicester	Biggins, Brunskill, Ellis.	14
Cutler	Beeby	Diskin	Walker	Filson	Soley	Ellis	Brunskill	McAuley	Biggins	Leicester	Hawtin, Cunningham, Tobin.	15
Cutler	Beeby	Diskin	Walker	Filson	Soley	Ellis	Brunskill	McAuley	Biggins	Leicester	Hawtin, Cunningham, Tobin.	16
Cutler	Beeby	Diskin	Walker	Hawtin	Soley	Ellis	Brunskill	McAuley	Biggins	Leicester	Calln, Cunningham, Tobin.	17
Cutler	Beeby	Diskin	Tobin	Hawtin	Soley	Ellis	Brunskill	McAuley	Biggins	Leicester	Callan, Cunningham, Trott.	18
Cutler	Beeby	Diskin	Tobin	Hawtin	Soley	Ellis	Brunskill	McAuley	Biggins	Leicester	Callan, Cunningham, Trott.	19
Cutler	Beeby	Diskin	Tobin	Hawtin	Soley	Ellis	Brunskill	McAuley	Biggins	Leicester	Callan, Cunningham, Trott.	20
Cutler	Leicester	Callan	Walker	Diskin	Soley	Ellis	Parker	McAuley	Biggins	Trott,	Cunningham, Robinson, Newland.	21
Cutler	Beeby	Brunskill	Walker	Diskin	Soley	Ellis	Parker	McAuley	Biggins	Leicester	Trott, Tobin, Hawtin.	22
Cutler	Hawtin	Parker	Walker	Diskin	Soley	Tobin	Brunskill	Cunningham	Biggins	Trott	Callan, Newland, Robinson.	23
Newland	Parker	Hawtin	Walker	Diskin	Soley	Ellis	Brunskill	Cunningham	Biggins	Trott	Tobin, McAuley, Callan.	24
Newland	Parker	Hawtin	Walker	Diskin	Soley	Ellis	Tobin	Leicester	Biggins	Trott	Callan, McAuley, Cunningham.	25
Newland	Parker	Hawtin	Walker	Diskin	Soley	Leicester	Brunskill	Callan	Biggins	Trott	McAuley, Cunningham, Tobin.	26
Newland	Hawtin	Callan	Walker	Parker	Soley	Leicester	Brunskill	McAuley	Birch	Trott	Ellis, Cunningham, Tobin.	27
Newland	hawtin	Callan	Walker	Parker	Soley	Leicester	Brunskill	McAuley	Birch	Trott	Ellis, Cunningham, Tobin.	28
Newland	Hawtin	Birch	Tobin	Diskin	Soley	Ellis	Brunskill	McAuley	Leicester	Trott	Biggins, Cunningham, Parker.	29
Germaine	Birch	Hawtin	Walker	Diskin	Soley	Ellis	Brunskill	McAuley	Biggins	Hassall	Trott Cunningham, Tobin.	30
Newland	Birch	Hawtin	Tobin	Beeby	Soley	Ellis	Brunskill	McAuley	Leicester	Trott	Hassall, Biggins, Walker.	31
Newland	Birch	Hawtin	Walker	Beeby	Soley	Ellis	Brunskill	McAuley	Biggins	Trott	Cunningham, Callan, Tobin.	32
Newland	Birch	Hawtin	Walker	Diskin	Soley	Ellis	Brunskill	McAuley	Biggins	Hawtin	Trott, Cunningham, Tobin.	33
Germaine	Beeby	Hawtin	Walker	Diskin	Soley	Ellis	Brunskill	McAuley	Biggins	Tobin	Trott, Cunningham, Callan.	34
Germaine	Beeby	Parker	Walker	Diskin	Soley	Ellis	Cunningham	McAuley	Biggins	Callan	Leicester(8), Trott, Hassall.	35
Germaine	Beeby	Parker	Walker	Diskin	Hawtin	Ellis	Cunningham	McAuley	Trott	Callan	Leicester, Astell, Baker.	36
Germaine	Beeby	Parker	Walker	Diskin	Soley	Ellis	Hawtin	McAuley	Biggins	Callan	Trott(5),Brunskill(8),Cunningham (11).	37
Germaine	Beeby	Parker	Walker	Brunskill	Soley	Tobin	Cunningham	McAuley	Biggins	Callan	Leicester, Hassall, Newlands.	38
Germaine	Beeby	Leicester	Walker	Brunskill	Soley	Tobin	Cunningham	McAuley	Biggins	Callan	Hassall, Jones, Niceley.	39
Germaine	Beeby	Leicester	Walker	Brunskill	Soley	Ellis	Cunningham	McAuley	Biggins	Callan	Tobin(4), Trott, Jones.	40
Germaine	Beeby	Leicester	Tobin	Brunskill	Soley	Ellis	Cunningham	McAuley	Biggins	Callan	Jones(9), Trott(10), Walker.	41
Germaine	Beeby	Leicester	Walker	Brunskill	Soley	Ellis	Cunningham	McAuley	Trott	Callan	Tobin (4), Jones (9), Biggins (10).	42

Newland	Brunskill	Callan	Walker	Filson	Soley	Ellis	McAuley	Diskin	Biggins	Trott	Cunningham, Leicester, Tobin.

Newland	Leicester	Hawtin	Walker	Tobin	Callan	Ellis	Brunskill	McAuley	Biggins	Trott	Cunningham, Baker, Robinson.
Newland	Leicester	Hawtin	Walker	Tobin	Callan	Ellis	Brunskill	Cunningham	Biggins	Trott	Baker, Robinson, Giblin.
Newland	Parker	Hawtin	Walker	Diskin	Soley	Ellis	Tobin	McAuley	Biggins	Callan	Trott, Leicester, Cunningham.

Newland	Beeby	Hawtin	Walker	Cunningham	Callan	McAuley	Tobin	Diskin	Filson	Leicester	Giblin, Hawkes, Knowles.
Cutler	Beeby	Diskin	Walker	Hawtin	Soley	Ellis	Tobin	McAuley	Biggins	Leicester	Callan, Cunningham, Brunskill.

Cutler	Beeby	Diskin	Walker	Filson	Callan	Ellis	Brunskill	McAuley	Biggins	Leicester	Cunningham, Hawtin, Tobin.
Newland	Leicester	Beeby	Walker	Diskin	Soley	Ellis	Parker	McAuley	Cunningham	Callan	Cutler, Robinson, Biggins.
Newland	Beeby	Hassall	Hawtin	Diskin	Soley	Callan	Brunskill	McAuley	Tobin	Trott	Biggins, Cunningham, Leicester.
Newland	Beeby	Hassal	Walker	Diskin	Soley	Leicester	Callan	Cunningham	Biggins	Trott	Parker, Robinson, Baker.

ERNIE MOSS (MANAGER)

Date of Appointment	26th May 1998
Date of Birth:	19th October 1949
Place of Birth:	Chesterfield

PREVIOUS CLUBS

As manager	Gainsborough Trinity
As coach	Kettering Town, Boston United
As player	Chesterfield, Peterborough, Mansfield T., Chesterfield, Port Vale, Lincoln C., Doncaster R., Chesterfield, Stockport C., Scarborough, Rochdale, Kettering T.

HONOURS

As manager	Unibond Lge: Chall. Cup, Charity Shield.
As player	Championship medal - Div. 3 76-77, Div. 4 69-70, 84-85; Anglo-Scottish Cup 80-81.

All-time leading goalscorer for Chesterfield with 165 league goals.

Assistant Manager: Phil Tingay **Physio:** K Birch-Martin

Steve Soley, last season's joint top scorer, seen here getting in a tackle on Welling's Mark Hynes. Photo: Keith Gillard

MATCHDAY PROGRAMME

Number of pages	40
Price	£1.50
Programme Editor	Dave Stringer
Other club publications:	None
Local Newspapers:	Leek Post & Times Evening Sentinel
Local Radio Stations:	Radio Stoke Signal Radio

1997-98 PLAYING SQUAD

PLAYER	Birthplace Honours	Birthdate	CLUBS
GOALKEEPERS			
Gary Germaine	Birmingham Scottish u-21	2.8.76	West Bromwich Albion, Moor Green
DEFENDERS			
Jeff Parker	Liverpool	23.1.69	Everton, Crewe Alexandra, Northwich V, Brunei Darrosalem, Northwich V, Barrow, £3k to Runcorn, £3k to Leek T
Aiden Callan	Stoke	8.10.76	Stoke C
John Diskin	Manchester ULP		Nantwich T
Iain Brunskill	Ormskirk ES, EY	5.11.76	Liverpool, Bury
Chris James *	Sheffield FAV	16.1.69	Sheffield, Worksop T, Scarborough, Bridlington T, Worksop T, Boston U, Gainsborough Trin
Dale Hawtin	Crewe	28.12.75	Crewe A
MIDFIELDERS			
Steve Circuit *	Sheffield	11.4.72	Sheffield U, Stafford R, Halifax T, Boston U, Macclesfield T, Gainsborough Trin
Steve Tobin	Manchester GMVC, BLT, ULP	24.3.75	Leeds U, Macclesfield T, Flixton
John Giblin	Stoke		Stoke C, Port Vale, Newcastle T, Milton U, Nantwich T, Congleton T, Nantwich T
Steve Soley	Liverpool ULP		Avon A, Warrington T
Hugh McAuley	Liverpool		Skelmersdale U, Bangor C, Conwy U
FORWARDS			
Neil Ellis	Chester	30.4.69	Tranmere R, Oswestry T, Bangor C, Chester C, Maidstone U, Kettering T, Corby T, Worcester C, Chorley, Ashton U, Stalybridge C
Wayne Biggins	Sheffield Div 3	20.11.61	Lincoln C, Matlock T, King's Lynn, £7,500 to Burnley, £40k to Norwich C, £150k to Manchester C, £250k to Stoke C, £200k to Barnsley, Celtic, Stoke C, Oxford U, Wigan A
Dean Trott	Barnsley	13.5.67	Ossett A, Frickley A, Boston U, Northampton T, Gateshead, Stalybridge C, £5k to Leek
Marc Hawkes	Stoke ULP	22.9.76	Stoke C, Leek T, Shrewsbury T

DEPARTURES - Michael Bates (Newcastle T), Gary Bauress (Barrow), Martin Filson (Boston U), Dean Cunningham (Telstar(Hol)).

PLAYERS ON LOAN - Justin O'Reilly (Port Vale), Neil Cutler (Crewe Alexandra), Mark Birch (Stoke C)

RECENT SIGNINGS - Leon Jackson (Port Vale), Adam Stanier (Scunthorpe).

Harrison Park, Leek

GROUND ADDRESS: Harrison Park, Macclesfield Road, Leek ST13 8LD
TEL. NO. 01538 399278 Fax: 01538 399826

SIMPLE DIRECTIONS: Opposite Courtaults chemical works on A523 Macclesfield to Buxton road half a mile out of Leek heading towards Macclesfield.

CAPACITY: 3,600 **SEATED:** 625 **COVERED TERRACING:** 2,675

RECORD ATTENDANCE: 5,312 v Macclesfield Town, F.A. Cup Second Qualifying Round 73-74.

CLUB SHOP: Contact club on 01538 399278.

SOCIAL FACILITIES: 'Blues' Bar open nightly & weekend lunchtimes. 01538 383734

Leek Town - Fact File

Nickname: The Blues **Club Sponsors:** Kerrygold
Club colours: All blue
Change colours: All yellow
Reserve team league: Manchester League
Midweek home matchday: Tuesday
Newsline: 0930 55 54 53

PREVIOUS - **Leagues:** Staffs County, Manchester 51-54 57-73, West Mids (B'ham) 54-56, Cheshire County 73-82, North West Counties 82-87, Northern Premier 87-94, Southern League 94-95, Northern Premier 95-97.

Names: Abbey Green Rovers/ Leek Lowe Hamil. **Grounds:** None

CLUB RECORDS - **Win:** Unknown
Defeat: Unknown
Transfer fee paid: £2,000 for Simon Snow (Sutton Town)
Transfer fee received: £30,000 for Tony Bullock (Barnsley)
Career goalscorer: Dave Suttons 144.
Career appearances: Gary Pearce 447.

BEST SEASON - **FA Cup:** 2nd Rd 90-91 (0-4 v Chester (A) after 1-1).
League clubs defeated: Scarborough 90-91.
FA Trophy: Runners-up 89-90, Q-F 85-86.
FA Vase:

HONOURS - FA Trophy R-up 89-90; Northern Premier Lg 96-97, R-up 93-94 (Div 1 89-90, Div 1 Cup R-up 88-89, Presidents Cup R-up 93-94, Lg Shield 90-91); North West Co's Lg Cup 84-85 (Charity Shield 84-85); Cheshire County Lg 74-75 (Challenge Shield 74-75); Manchester Lg 51-52 71-72 72-73 (Lg Cup 72-73); Staffs Snr Cup 95-96, R-up 54-55 81-82 95-96, Jnr Cup 51-52 70-71 (R-up 47-48 48-49 49-50)); Staffs Co. Lg 50-51 69-70 70-71 73-74 (R-up 47-48 49-50, Lg Cup 70-71 73-74); Leek Post Charity Shield 46-47; Leek Cup 47-48 52-53 70-71 71-72 (R-up 46-47); May Bank Cup 47-48 50-51 71-72; Hanley Cup 48-49 70-71 (R-up 49-5); Mid Cheshire Lg Div 2 87-88 (Div 2 Cup 87-88); Evans Halshaw Floodlit Cup Winners 93-94 94-95; Doc Martens(Southern Lg) Cup Finalists 94-95; Unibond Lge Chall Cup R-up 95-96

Past players who progressed to the Football League: Geoff Crosby (Stockport 1952), Bill Summerscales (1970), Mark Bright (1981) & Martyn Smith (1984) all to Port Vale, Paul Edwards (Crewe 1989), Tony Bullock (Barnsley 1997).

1997-98 **Captain:** John Diskin
1997-98 **Joint Top scorers:** Steve Soley & Hugh McAuley

MORECAMBE

After a quiet opening to the season, when a home draw with Leek didn't auger too well for the The Shrimps, eight victories in the next ten games took Jim Harvey's attractive side to the top spot and it wasn't until the middle of February that they failed to score in a Conference match.

Inded in the whole season (58 games) they only failed to find the net on four occasions.

The quality of the football was a pleaure to watch and in Brian Healy the club possessed a much travelled player who had at last found the stage on which he felt most comfortable.

His passing and midfield quality won him an England cap and supporters will be looking forward to next season with relish, as their smart new stand gives the ground more presence and their clubs' passing game produces plenty of goals

The highlight of the season was probably a spectacular run in the Spalding Cup which was won on penalties after two 1-1 draws with Woking. The Final of the ATS Trophy was also reached but Southport ran out winners by 2-0 at Deepdale.

All in all it was a happy season with spirits high.

CLUB OFFICIALS 1998-99

Honorary President	**Jim Bowen**
Chairman	**Rod Taylor**
Vice Chairman	**Graham Hodgson**
Directors	**Dickie Danson**
	David Derham
	Peter McMcGuigan
Company & Club Secretary	**Neil Marsdin**
Commercial Manager	**Peter Howard**

L-R, Back Row: Robert Howarth, David Miller, Stuart Drummond, Brian Healy, Kenny Mayers, Steve McIlhargey, Andy Banks, Steve Hodgson, Tony Hughes, Mark Ceroalo, Mike Bignall, Ian Monk. Front Row: Paul Rushton, John Norman, Dave McKearney, Tony Hesketh (Assistant Manager), Jim Harvey (Manager), Andrew Grimshaw, Paul Burns, Gary Williams.

MORECAMBE - Match Facts 1997-98

Match No.	Date	Venue H / A	Comp.	Opponents	Result & Score		Att.	Goalscorers	League Position
1	16.08	H	VC	Leek Town	D	1-1	1,237	Bignall 34.	12
2	20.08	A	VC	Gateshead	**W**	**4-1**	*844*	Shirley 4, Bignall 21, Rushton 44, Hughes 78.	
3	23.08	A	VC	Hayes	W	3-0	*505*	McKearney 69(pen), Norman 71, Parkinson 87.	2
4	25.08	H	VC	Kidderminster Harriers	W	3-1	1,433	Bignall 46, Norman 51, 67.	1
5	30.08	H	VC	Telford United	W	1-0	1,352	Bignall 43.	1
6	07.09	A	VC	Stevenage Borough	W	3-0	*2,248*	Bignall 27, Shirley 51,61.	1
7	13.09	H	VC	Hednesford Town	L	1-3	1,460	Ceraolo 90.	1
8	20.10	H	VC	Welling United	W	4-2	1,370	Ceraolo 24, 51, Grimshaw 55, Shirley 65.	2
9	27.09	A	VC	Woking	W	2-0	*3,076*	Monk 61, Mayers 89.	1
10	04.10	H	VC	Dover Athletic	D	3-3	1,616	Ceroalo 5, Healy 64, 69.	3
11	11.10	A	VC	Farnborough Town	W	2-0	*589*	Norman 1, 85.	2
12	17.10	A	VC	Slough Town	D	3-3	*792*	Healy 6, Norman 32, Ceroalo 54.	3
13	28.10	H	VC	Halifax Town	D	1-1	3,914	OG (O'Rogan) 60.	3
14	01.11	H	VC	Hereford United	L	1-5	1,850	Healy 2.	3
15	08.11	A	VC	Kettering Town	D	1-1	*1,156*	Norman 49.	5
16	22.11	H	VC	Rushden & Diamonds	W	3-1	1,449	Norman 10, Shirley 44, OG (Whyte) 88.	4
17	29.11	A	VC	Telford United	W	3-1	*518*	Grimshaw 20, Norman 23, Milner 25.	3
18	06.12	H	VC	Gateshead	W	2-0	1,106	Norman 42, Milner 45.	3
19	13.12	A	VC	Cheltenham Town	L	1-2	*1,717*	Healy 41	4
20	20.12	H	VC	Kettering Town	L	1-3	1,241	Norman 65	4
21	26.12	H	VC	Southport	W	2-0	2,150	Milner8, Norman 36	3
22	01.01	A	VC	Southport	D	1-1	*1,640*	McKearney 81(pen)	5
23	03.01	H	VC	Hayes	L	0-2	1,164		5
24	17.01	H	VC	Yeovil Town	W	1-0	1,219	Norman 89.	4
25	24.01	A	VC	Kidderminster Harriers	**W**	**4-1**	*1,717*	Monk 15, Milner 22, 26, Ceroalo 82.	2
26	07.02	H	VC	Woking	L	1-2	1,534	OG (Betsy) 43.	5
27	14.02	A	VC	Hereford United	L	0-1	*1,720*		5
28	21.02	A	VC	Stalybridge Celtic	L	1-3	*756*	McKearney 89 (pen).	5
29	28.02	H	VC	Slough Town	W	2-1	1,092	Norman 13, Drummond 87.	5
30	07.03	A	VC	Yeovil Town	W	3-2	*2,140*	Milner 39, Shirley 57, Ceroalo 84.	4
31	14.03	A	VC	Northwich Victoria	**L**	**0-5**	*1,015*		5
32	17.03	A	VC	Halifax Town	L	1-5	*2,507*	Norman 13.	5
33	21.03	H	VC	Cheltenham Town	W	1-0	2,075	Milner 55.	4
34	28.03	A	VC	Rushden & Diamonds	D	3-3	*2,758*	Milner 36, Burns 38, Shirley 70.	4
35	04.04	A	VC	Welling United	D	2-2	*519*	Healy 8, Shirley 60.	6
36	11.04	H	VC	Northwich Victoria	W	3-1	1,327	Norman 18, 57 (pen), Mayers 74.	4
37	13.04	A	VC	Hednesford Town	W	1-0	*1,066*	Mayers 12.	4
38	18.04	H	VC	Stevenage Borough	L	0-2	1,156		5
39	25.04	A	VC	Dover Athletic	W	3-2	*1,088*	Curtis 39, Burns 68, Shirley 72.	5
40	28.04	H	VC	Stalybridge Celtic	W	3-1	1,102	McKearney 8, Curtis 14, Healy 64.	5
41	01.05	A	VC	Leek Town	D	1-1	*1.015*	Norman 71.	3
42	02.05	H	VC	Farnborough Town	D	1-1	1,270	Shirley 41.	5

CUP COMPETITIONS

Date	Venue	Comp.	Opponents	Result	Score	Att.	Goalscorers
25.10	A	**FAC** 4Q	Altrincham	W	2-0	1,134	Ceraolo7, Grimshaw 15.
15.11	H	1	Emley	D	1-1	1,496	Bignall 37.
25.11	A	1 R	Emley	D	3-3	2,439	Mayers 27, Takano 116, Monk 119. **Lost** 1-3 on penalties
10.01	H	**FAT** 1	Solihull Borough	W	3-2	766	McKearney 18 (pen), Shirley 46, OG (Brogan) 80.
31.01	A	2	Altrincham	L	0-2	942	
18.11	H	**SCC** 2	Leek Town	W	3-2	356	Norman 44, OG (Hawtin) 76, McKearney 85(pen).
17.12	A	3	Gateshead	D	1-1	204	Drummond 98
20.01	H	3 R	Gateshead	W	3-1	305	Monk 48, Milner 61, Drummond 87.
17.02	H	SF 1	Northwich Victoria	W	3-0	608	Milner 22, Mayers 52, Norman 58.
02.03	A	SF 2	Northwich Victoria	L	1-3	458	Norman 43.
25.03	H	F 1	Woking	D	1-1	782	Healy 63.
04.05	A	F 2	Woking	D	1-1	2,045	Curtis 84. Won 4-3 after penalties.
06.01	H	**ATS** 2	Burscough	W	2-1	209	Milner 37, Grimshaw 77.
03.02	H	3	Bamber Bridge	W	3-1	300	Milner 18, Grimshaw 80, Healy 90.
24.02	H	SF	Lancaster City	W	2-0	1,442	Norman 12, Milner 64.
04.05	A	F	Southport	L	0-2	1,540	Played at Deepdale.

SCC - Spalding Challenge Cup
ATS - Lancs. FA ATS Trophy

League Attendances:	**HIGHEST:** 3,940 v Halifax Town	**LOWEST:** 1,102 v Stalybridge Celtic
CONFERENCE: 5th	**FA CUP:** 1st Round	**FA TROPHY:** 2nd Round

1	2	3	4	5	6	7	8	9	10	11	12 14 15	
McIlhargey	Rushton	McKearney	Miller	Hughes T	Grimshaw	Monk	Healy	Bignall	Norman	Shirley	Drummonsd(8), Mayers(10), Parkinson(9)	1
McIlhargey	Rushton	McKearney	Miller	Hughes T	Grimshaw	Monk	Healy	Bignall	Norman	Shirley	Parkinson(9), Mayers (10), Burns (11).	2
McIlhargey	Rushton	McKearney	Miller	Hughes T	Grimshaw	Monk	Healy	Bignall	Norman	Shirley	Parkinson(11), Mayers(9), Burns (7).	3
McIlhargey	Rushton	McKearney	Miller	Hughes T	Grimshaw	Monk	Healy	Bignall	Norman	Shirley	Parkinson(10), Mayers(9), Burns(7).	4
McIlhargey	Rushton	Burns	Miller	McKearney	Grimshaw	Monk	Healy	Bignall	Norman	Shirley	Parkinson, Mayers (9), Knowles.	5
McIlhargey	Rushton	Burns	Miller	McKearney	Grimshaw	Monk	Healy	Bignall	Norman	Shirley	Ceraolo(9), Mayers (3), Hughes T(10)	6
McIlhargey	Rushton	Burns	Miller	McKearney	Grimshaw	Monk	Healy	Bignall	Norman	Shirley	Ceraolo(10), Mayers(9), Hughes D(3).	7
McIlhargey	Knowles	Hughes D	Miller	McKearney	Grimshaw	Monk	Healy	Ceraolo	Mayers	Shirley	Norman(3), Burns(7), Bignall(9).	8
McIlhargey	Rushton	Hughes D	Miller	McKearney	Grimshaw	Monk	Healy	Ceraolo	Norman	Shirley	Parkinson(9), Mayers(10), Knowles(2).	9
McIlhargey	Knowles	Hughes D	Miller	McKearney	Grimshaw	Monk	Healy	Ceraolo	Norman	Shirley	Burns(2), Mayers(9), Parkinson(7).	10
McIlhargey	Burns	Hughes D	Miller	McKearney	Grimshaw	Monk	Healy	Ceraolo	Norman	Shirley	Drummond(2), Mayers(9), Parkinson(11)	11
McIlhargey	Burns	Hughes D	Miller	McKearney	Grimshaw	Monk	Healy	Ceraolo	Norman	Parkinson	Drummond(6), Mayers(11), Bignall(9).	12
Banks	Burns	Hughes D	Miller	McKearney	Grimshaw	Monk	Healy	Ceraolo	Norman	Shirley	Parkinson, Mayers(4), Bignall.	13
Banks	Burns	Hughes D	Hodgson	McKearney	Grimshaw	Monk	Healy	Ceraolo	Norman	Shirley	Parkinson(7), Mayers(4), Drummond(10)	14
Banks	Burns	Hughes D	Mayers	McKearney	Grimshaw	Monk	Healy	Ceraolo	Norman	Shirley	Bignall(9), Takano(11), Drummond(6).	15
Banks	Lowe	Takano	McKearney	Hughes T	Drummond	Parkinson	Healy	Milner	Norman	Shirley	Williams(11), Mayers(10),Monk(7).	16
Banks	Rushton	Takano	McKearney	Mayers	Grimshaw	Monk	Healy	Milner	Norman	Shirley	Williams, Drummond(5), Parkinson(7).	17
Banks	Rushton	Takano	McKearney	Mayers	Grimshaw	Monk	Healy	Milner	Norman	Shirley	Williams(11), Drummond(6), Parkinson	18
Banks	Rushton	Takano	McKearney	Mayers	Grimshaw	Monk	Healy	Milner	Norman	Shirley	Burns(11), Drummond(6), Parkinson(7).	19
McIlhargey	Rushton	Takano	McKearney	Mayers	Drummond	Parkinson	Healy	Milner	Norman	Shirley	Lowe(7), Knowles(8), Williams(11).	20
McIlhargey	Rushton	Hughes T	McKearney	Mayers	Drummond	Knowles	Healy	Milner	Norman	Takano	Lowe(4), Monk(10), Williams.	21
McIlhargey	Rushton	Burns	McKearney	Hughes T	Drummond	Monk	Lowe	Milner	Knowles	Shirley	Norman(8), Mayers(3), Williams(11).	22
McIlhargey	Rushton	Burns	McKearney	Hughes T	Drummond	Knowles	Grimshaw	Milner	Norman	Mayers	Hunt(8), Monk, Shirley(7).	23
McIlhargey	Lowe	Burns	McKearney	Mayers	Grimshaw	Monk	Healy	Milner	Norman	shirley	Rushton(2),Parkinson(11),Drummond.	24
McIlhargey	Rushton	Hodgson	McKearney	Mayers	Grimshaw	Monk	Healy	Milner	Norman	Parkinson	Ceraolo (11),Drummond, Hayton.	25
McIlhargey	Rushton	Burns	McKearney	Mayers	Grimshaw	Monk	Healy	Milner	Norman	Shirley	Drummond(2),Mitchell(10),Ceraolo(1).	26
McIlhargey	Rushton	McKearney	Miller	Mayers	Grimshaw	Monk	Healy	Milner	Norman	Shirley	Mitchell(11),Burns(2),Hodgson.	27
McIlhargey	McKearney	Burns	Miller	Mayers	Grimshaw	Monk	Healy	Milner	Norman	Shirley	Mitchell(10),Drummond,Hodgson.	28
McIlhargey	Burns	Hodgson	Miller	Mayers	Drummond	Mitchell	Healy	Milner	Norman	Shirley	Ceraolo(8),Grimshaw,Hayton.	29
Banks	Burns	Kennedy	Hodgson	Mayers	Drummond	Mitchell	Healy	Milner	Norman	Shirley	Rushton(7),Ceraolo(9),Knowles(10)	30
Banks	Burns	Kennedy	Rushton	Mayers	Drummond	Knowles	Healy	Milner	Norman	Shirley	Ceraolo(8),Hodgson(10),Mitchell(11).	31
Banks	Lowe	Kennedy	Rushton	Mayers	Drummond	Knowles	Healy	Milner	Norman	Shirley	Hodgson(3),Ceraolo(7),Hunt(9).	32
McIlhargey	Knowles	Kennedy	Rushton	Mayers	Drummond	Hunt	Healy	Milner	Norman	Shirley	Williams(7),Ceraolo(9),Monk.	33
McIlhargey	Burns	Kennedy	Rushton	Hodgson	Drummond	Knowles	Healy	Milner	Norman	Shirley	Williams(7),Ceraolo(9),Hunt(10).	34
McIlhargey	Burns	Kennedy	Hodgson	Mayers	Drummond	Knowles	Healy	Milner	Norman	Shirley	Monk(7),Ceraolo,Swanick.	35
McIlhargey	Burns	Kennedy	Rushton	Mayers	Drummond	Monk	Healy	Milner	Norman	Shirley	Knowles(7),Williams(9),Hodgson.	36
McIlhargey	Burns	Kennedy	Rushton	Mayers	Drummond	Monk	Healy	Williams	Norman	Shirley	Knowles(3),Parkinson(9),Hodgson.	37
McIlhargey	Burns	Kennedy	Rushton	Mayers	Drummond	Monk	McKearney	Williams	Norman	Shirley	Knowles(4),Hodgson,Parkinson.	38
Banks	Burns	Kennedy	McKearney	Mayers	Drummond	Monk	Healy	Curtis	Norman	Shirley	Parkinson(9),Hodgson, Knowles.	39
Banks	Burns	Kennedy	McKearney	Mayers	Drummond	Monk	Healy	Curtis	Norman	Shirley	Knowles(8),Parkinson(9),Hodgson.	40
Banks	Burns	Kennedy	McKearney	Mayers	Drummond	Monk	Healy	Curtis	Norman	Shirley	Hodgson(2),Knowles(6),Rushton(9).	41
Banks	Burns	Kennedy	McKearney	Mayers	Drummond	Monk	Healy	Curtis	Norman	Shirley	Knowles9(0,Parkinson(11),Hodgson.	42

1	2	3	4	5	6	7	8	9	10	11	12 14 15
McIlhargey	Burns	Hughes D	Miller	McKearney	Grimshaw	Monk	Healy	Ceraolo	Norman	Shirley	Drummond(6), Mayers(7), Bignall(9).
Banks	Burns	Hughes D	Hughes T	Mayers	Drummond	Monk	Healy	Bignall	Norman	Shirley	Ceraolo(9), Takano(3), Parkinson(7).
McIlhargey	Lowe	Takano	McKearney	Hughes T	Drummond	Burns	Healy	Ceraolo	Norman	Mayers	Williams(9), Banks(1), Monk(7).

1	2	3	4	5	6	7	8	9	10	11	12 14 15
McIlhargey	McKearney	Burns	Mayers	Hughes T	Grimshaw	Monk	Healy	Milner	Norman	Shirley	Drummond(6), Hodgson(11), Parkinson(10)
McIlhargey	Rushton	Hodgson	McKearney	Mayers	Grimshaw	Monk	Healy	Milner	Norman	Parkinson	Drummond((7)K Hayton(10),Ceraolo(11)

1	2	3	4	5	6	7	8	9	10	11	12 14 15
Banks	Lowe	Takano	McKearney	Hughes T	Drummond	Parkinson	Healy	Milner	Norman	Shirley	Mayers(5), Ceraolo(3), Williams(11).
Banks	Rushton	Takano	McKearney	Mayers	Drummond	Parkinson	Healy	Milner	Norman	Shirley	Lowe(7), Knowles(10), Burns(11).
McIlhargey	Rushton	Burns	McKearney	Mayers	Grimshaw	Monk	Healy	Milner	Norman	Parkinson	Hodgson(2),Drummond(6),Ceraolo(10).
McIlhargey	McKearney	Burns	Miller	Mayers	Grimshaw	Monk	Healy	Milner	Norman	Shirley	Mitchell(11), Drummond, Hodgson.
McIlhargey	Burns	Hodgson	Miller	Mayers	Drummond	Mitchell	Grimshaw	Milner	Norman	Shirley	Knowles(4),Ceraolo(7),Kennedy(11)
McIlhargey	Knowles	Burns	Rushton	Mayers	Drummond	Parkinson	Healy	Milner	Norman	Kennedy	Williams(7),Ceraolo(10), Hodgson.
McIlhargey	Burns	Kennedy	McKearney	Mayers	Drummond	Knowles	Healy	Ceraolo	Norman	Hodgson	Curtis(66),Monk(7),Parkinson(9).

1	2	3	4	5	6	7	8	9	10	11	12 14 15
McIlhargey	Knowles	Burns	McKearney	Hughes T	Grimshaw	Monk	Healy	Milner	Mayers	Shirley	Drummond(8), Norman, Parkinson.
Banks	Rushton	Burns	MCKearney	Mayers	Grimshaw	Monk	Healy	Milner	Norman	Shirley	Hodgson(11), Ceraolo, Drummond.
McIlhargey	McKearney	Burns	Miller	Mayers	Grimshaw	Monk	Healy	Milner	Norman	Shirley	Hodgson(2),Drummond(6)Mitchell(7).
McIlhargey	Burns	Kennedy	Rushton	Mayers	Drummond	Monk	Healy	Williams	Norman	Knowles	Parkinson(9),Lowe,Hodgson,Banks.

JIM HARVEY (MANAGER)	
Date of Appointment	June 1994
Date of Birth:	2nd May 1958
Place of Birth:	Lurgan, Northern Ireland
PREVIOUS CLUBS	
As manager	
As assistant manager	Morecambe (Jan - June 1994)
As player	Glenavon, Arsenal, Hereford Utd., Bristol City, Tranmere Rovers, Crewe Alexandra.
HONOURS	
As manager	Spalding Cup 97-98; NPL R-up 94-95
As player	N. Ireland - u23., Leyland Daf winner, Mercantile Trophy Winner, promotion from Division 4 & Division 3.

FOOTBALL MANAGEMENT TEAM

Assistant Manager
Tony Hesketh

Second Team Manager
Jeff Udall

2nd Team Assistant Manager
Mick Lingwood

Football in the Community
Derek Quinn

Sports Therapist
David Edge

Brian Healy missed only two Conference matches last season.

Photo
Peter Barnes

MATCHDAY PROGRAMME

Number of pages	48
Price	£1.30
Programme Editor	Martin Shaw
Other club publications:	"Corpus Christie" (fanzine) "Going Up?" (part fanzine) "Gazetta de la Shrimpa"
Local Newspapers:	Morecambe Visitor Morecambe Guardian Lancashire Evening Post The Citizen
Local Radio Stations:	Radio Lancashire Red Rose Radio; Bay Radio

1997-98 PLAYING SQUAD

PLAYER	Birthplace Honours	Birthdate	CLUBS
GOALKEEPERS			
Steve McIlhargey	Glasgow SC	10.12.62	Blantyre Celtic, Walsall, Blackpool
Andy Banks	Preston	21.4.76	Preston, Bury
DEFENDERS			
David Miller	Burnley SC	8.1.64	Burnley, Tranmere R, Colne Dynamoes, Preston, £30k to Carlisle U, £25k to Stockport Co, Wigan A
Paul Burns	Liverpool SC	1.10.67	Grimsby T, Burscough, Prescot, Caernarfon T, Altrincham, Accrington Stanley
Paul Rushton	Chester SC	25.1.74	Crewe A
Dave McKearney	Crosby SC	20.6.68	Prescot, Bolton W, Northwich Victoria, Crewe A, Wigan A, Chorley
Kyle Hayton	Preston		Preston NE
Tony Hughes	Liverpool EY, SC	3.10.73	Crewe A
Steve Hodgson	Kendal SC	28.8.76	From Youth Team
MIDFIELDERS			
Michael Knowles	Morecambe SC	3.3.74	From Youth Team
Andy Grimshaw	Bacup NPL, SC	30.3.64	Rossendale U, Manchester U, Bury, Colne Dynamoes, Witton A
David Lowe	Manchester		Altrincham, Trafford, Buxton
Kenny Mayers	Manchester NPL, FA XI, SC		Bamber Bridge, £12k to Chorley
John Norman	Birkenhead SC	26.6.71	Tranmere R, Bury, Heswall, Mold A
Stuart Drummond	Preston SC	11.12.75	From Youth Team
Brian Healy	Durham FA XI, SC		West Auckland T, Billingham T, Bishop Auckland, Gateshead, Spennymoor U
FORWARDS			
Andy Milner	Kendal SC	10.2.67	Netherfield, Manchester C, Rochdale, Chester C, £8k to Morecambe
Mark Ceraolo	Birkenhead SC	10.11.75	Crewe A
Stuart Parkinson	Blackpool SC	18.2.76	Blackpool
Mark Shirley	Liverpool SC		Nottingham F, Netherley RBL, Caernarfon T, Ashton U, Lancaster C

DEPARTURES - David Leaver (Acc.Stanley), Mike Bignall (Kidderminster H - £10k), Darren Hughes (Released), Neil Mitchell (Blackpool R)

RECENT ARRIVALS - Dave Swanwick (Wrexham), Paul Tomlinson (Caerarfon).

Christie Park, Morecambe

GROUND ADDRESS: Christie Park, Lancaster Road, Morecambe, Lancashire LA4 5TJ

TELEPHONE NUMBERS: 01524 411797 Fax: 01524 411797

SIMPLE DIRECTIONS: From south leave M6 motorway at junction 34. Follow signs for Morecambe through Lancaster, on A589, go straight across the first 2 roundabouts, and at the third (with the Shrimp pub on your left), follow the signs for Town Centre - Christie Park is approx. 600 metres on your left.

CAPACITY: 6,000 **SEATED:** 1,200 **COVERED TERRACING:** 4,000

CLUB SHOP: On ground and open on matchdays, also commercial office open Monday to Friday 9.00 - 5.00 selling the same goods.

SOCIAL FACILITIES: J B's open normal licensing hours.

Morecambe Fact File

Nickname: The Shrimps **Club sponsor:** Oasis Leisure

Club colours: Red shirts, black shorts, red & white socks.

Change colours: All yellow.

Midweek home matchday: Tuesdays, 7.45pm kick-off.

Reserve Team's League: Lancashire League, Div. A&B

PREVIOUS - **Leagues:** Lancs Combination 1920-68, Northern Premier 1968-1995.
Grounds: Woodhill Lane 1920-25, shared with cricket club who still play there.

CLUB RECORDS - **Attendance:** 9,324 v Weymouth FA Cup 4.1.62

Win: 16-0 v Rossendale Utd, Lancs Combination Sept 1967 (Arnold Timmins scored 8)

Defeat: 0-7 v Darwen, November 7th 1953

Transfer fee paid: £8,000 to Chester City for Andy Milner, November 1997.

Transfer fee received: £30,000 from Woking for Justin Jackson, January 1997
Career Goalscorer:
Keith Borrowdale 289 goals 1956-68, 78-79 Lancashire Combination.
John Coleman 130 goals 1990-1995 (Northern Premier League)

Career Appearances: Steve Done 523 + 7 sub. (1968-78)

BEST SEASON - **FA Trophy:** Winners 73-74, Q-final 72-73, 77-78, 93-94.
FA Cup: 3rd Round 1961-62, 0-1 v Weymouth.
League clubs defeated: Chester City.

HONOURS - FA Trophy 73-74, Spalding Cup 97-98, Northern Premier Lge Presidents Cup 91-92, NPL Runners-up 94-95, Lancs Combination(5) 24-25 61-63 66-68 (R-up 25-26, Lg Cup 26-27 45-46 64-65 66-68), Lancs Jnr Cup (now ATS Tphy)(8) 25-27 61-63 68-69 85-87 92-93, 95-96; Lancs Snr Cup 67-68, Lancs Lg Div 2 83-84.

Past players who progressed to the Football League: Fred Blondel & Malcolm Darling (Bury 1946 & 78), Herbert Harrison (Accrington 1947), Gordon Milne (Preston 1956), Ray Charnley (Blackpool 1957), Geoff Slack (Stockport 1958), Ron Mitchell (Leeds 1958), Derek Armstrong (Carlisle 1961), Alan Taylor (Rochdale 1973), John Coates (Southport via Burscough & Skelmersdale 1975), Keith Galley (Southport 1975), Brian Thompson (West Ham 1977), David Eyres (Blackpool), Kenny Lowe (Barnet via Barrow), Steve Gardner (Bradford City), Dave Lancaster (Chesterfield).

97-98 **Captain:** Dave McKearney

97-98 **Player of the Year:** Kenny Mayers

97-98 **Top Goalscorer:** John Norman - 21.

NORTHWICH VICTORIA

With their famous Drill Field given a very smart face lift and the presence in their squad of such experienced mid fielders as Mark Ward and Eddie Bishop it was felt that their lively strikers Paul Tait, Ian Cooke, John Stannard and Darren Vicary could get the service to set up a great season with plenty of goals.

CLUB OFFICIALS 1998-99

Chairman **Rod J Stitch**

Vice Chairman **Dave Stone**

Company Secretary **Graham Cookson**

Chief Executive **John Stitch**

Directors **Dave Price, Jim Rafferty**

Associate Directors
Graham Cookson, Dave Edgeley, Dave Bush, Roger Stubbs.

President & Football Secretary **Derek Nuttall**
c/o the club
Tel: 01606 41450 Fax: 01606 330577

However, only two of their first seventeen games were won although in fairness eleven of them were drawn!

Carwyn Williams rejoined the club to give them even more attacking options but apart from a purple patch over the festive season when five consecutive victories lifted morale the Vics never quite took off.

Mid field ace Steve Walters had his season ruined by injury but there is no doubt that the famous Cheshire club are quite capable of emulating neighbours Macclesfield and will once again be a very difficult side to beat.

Just imagine what their season could have been if those draws had been turned into victories, as it was they finished ninth.

So watch out for some spectacular parades on the Drill Field in the season ahead.

NORTHWICH VICTORIA - Match Facts 1997-98

Match No.	Date	Venue H / A	Comp.	Opponents	Result	& Score	Att.	Goalscorers	League Position
1	16.08	A	VC	Rushden & Diamonds	W	1-0	*2,302*	Bishop 68.	8
2	18.08	A	VC	Kidderminster Harriers	D	1-1	*2,023*	Tait 13.	
3	23.08	H	VC	Kettering Town	D	0-0	1,131		6
4	25.08	A	VC	Gateshead	D	2-2	*769*	Bishop 25, Tait 90.	8
5	30.08	A	VC	Woking	L	0-1	*2,687*		13
6	07.09	H	VC	Dover Athletic	W	2-1	897	Tait 73, 89.	12
7	13.09	A	VC	Hereford United	D	2-2	*2,207*	Walters 35 (pen), Bishop 65.	13
8	20.09	A	VC	Slough Town	L	0-3	*637*		15
9	27.09	H	VC	Stevenage Borough	D	1-1	954	Carroll 78.	16
10	29.09	H	VC	Gateshead	D	1-1	873	OG (Kitchen) 12.	16
11	04.10	A	VC	Cheltenham Town	L	2-3	*1,606*	Vicary 56, Dowell 84.	17
12	11.10	H	VC	Hednesford Town	D	1-1	921	Tait 40.	16
13	18.10	A	VC	Yeovil Town	D	2-2	*2,313*	Williams 35, OG (Hannigan) 82.	15
14	01.11	H	VC	Telford United	D	2-2	938	Cooke 23, Walters 58 (pen).	
15	08.11	H	VC	Farnborough Town	D	3-3	862	Cooke 12, 37, Stannard 35.	15
16	22.11	A	VC	Hayes	D	1-1	*438*	Crookes 33.	17
17	29.11	H	VC	Welling United	W	5-1	929	**Williams 3** (15, 40, 43), Tait 55, Collins 63.	14
18	06.12	H	VC	Rushden & Diamonds	L	2-4	932	Collins 58, Tait 89.	15
19	09.12	A	VC	Halifax Town	L	2-4	*2,165*	Walters 20, Cooke 82.	
20	13.12	H	VC	Southport	D	0-0	974		16
21	20.12	A	VC	Dover Athletic	**L**	**0-4**	*781*		18
22	26.12	H	VC	Stalybridge Celtic	W	1-0	1,340	Gardiner 84	15
23	01.01	A	VC	Stalybridge Celtic	W	1-0	*1,004*	OG (Browning) 48.	13
24	17.01	A	VC	Farnborough Town	W	3-2	*744*	Duffy 8, Stannard 48, Collins 87.	14
25	24.01	H	VC	Cheltenham Town	W	2-1	1,118	Walters 16, Tait 86.	13
26	07.02	A	VC	Welling United	W	1-0	*611*	Crookes 21.	12
27	14.02	H	VC	Slough Town	L	0-1	878		12
28	24.02	A	VC	Telford United	L	1-2	*605*	Cooke 18.	
29	28.02	A	VC	Leek Town	D	1-1	*636*	Cooke 76.	18
30	07.03	H	VC	Hereford United	L	0-2	1,002		13
31	14.03	H	VC	Morecambe	**W**	**5-0**	1,015	Ward 6, Tait 7, Illman 23, Walters 69, Crookes 71.	13
32	17.03	H	VC	Leek Town	W	3-1	681	Illman 6, 84, Tait 52.	
33	21.03	H	VC	Yeovil Town	W	2-1	90-2	Vicary 52, Cooke 86.	9
34	28.03	A	VC	Hednesford Town	L	0-2	*1,013*		10
35	04.04	H	VC	Hayes	D	1-1	842	Tait 65.	10
36	08.04	A	VC	Southport	W	2-0	*964*	Illman 62, 72.	
37	11.04	A	VC	Morecambe	L	1-3	*1,327*	Cooke 62.	10
38	13.04	H	VC	Kidderminster Harriers	D	1-1	976	Walters 46(pen).	9
39	18.04	A	VC	Kettering Town	W	3-1	*1,156*	Milligan 33, Walters 45, Illman 79.	9
40	20.04	H	VC	Halifax Town	W	2-0	2,106	Illman 22, 90 (pen).	9
41	25.04	H	VC	Woking	L	0-2	941		9
42	02.05	A	VC	Stevenage Borough	W	3-1	*2,160*	Illman 7, Tait 50, Bishop 77.	9

CUP COMPETITIONS SCC - Spalding Challenge Cup UCSC - Unibond Cheshire Senior Cup

Date	Venue	Comp.	Opponents	Result	Score	Att.	Goalscorers
25.10	A	**FAC** 4Q	Halesowen Town	W	2-0	1,206	Walters 58, Stannard 87.
15.11	A	1	Chesterfield	L	0-1	5,327	
10.01	A	**FAT** 1	Lancaster City	W	3-0	600	Cooke 11, Walters 48, Gardiner 51.
31.01	H	2	Kettering Town	W	4-0	1,225	Cooke 47, Stannard 72, Williams 75, Vicary 88.
21.02	A	3	Barrow	L	0-1	2,185	
25.11	A	**SCC** 2	Telford United	W	2-1	307	Ward 75, Cooke 89.
16.12	H	3	Hednesford Town	W	3-2	447	Williams 13, Stannard 89, Cooke 113
17.02	A	SF 1	Morecambe	L	0-3	608	
02.03	H	SF 2	Morecambe	W	3-1	458	Stannard 16, 75, Illman 51 (pen).
17.11	A	**UCSC** 2	Hyde United	W	2-1	454	Carroll 29, Cooke 83.
02.02	H	S-F 1	Macclesfield Town	D	2-2	869	Vicary, OG.
10.02	A	S-F 2	Macclesfield Town	D	1-1	832	Cooke Lost on the away goals rule.

League Attendances	HIGHEST: 2,106 v Halifax Town	LOWEST: 681 v Leek Town
CONFERENCE: 9th	**FA CUP:** 1st Round	**FA TROPHY:** 3rd Round

1	2	3	4	5	6	7	8	9	10	11	12 14 15	
Greygoose	Crookes	Billing	Fairclough	Simpson	Bishop	M Ward	Walters	Tait	Stannard	Vicary	D Ward(7),Carroll910),Hussin(11).	1
Greygoose	Crookes	Billing	Fairclough	Simpson	Bishop	M Ward	Walters	Tait	Stannard	Vicary	D Ward(6),Carroll(10),Hussin.	2
Greygoose	Crookes	Billing	Fairclough	Simpson	Bishop	M Ward	Walters	Tait	Stannard	Vicary	D Ward(2),Cooke(6),Carroll(10)	3
Greygoose	Crookes	Billing	Fairclough	D Ward	Bishop	M Ward	Walters	Tait	Carroll	Vicary	Cooke(7),Hussin(10),Stannard(11)	4
Greygoose	Crookes	Billing	Fairclough	Simpson	Bishop	Duffy	Walters	Tait	Cooke	Vicary	Stannard(2),Carroll(10),Hussin(11).	5
Greygoose	Crookes	Billing	Fairclough	Simpson	Bishop	M Ward	Walters	Tait	Cooke	Vicary	Duffy(3),Carroll(11),Hussin.	6
Greygoose	Crookes	Billing	Fairclough	Simpson	Bishop	M Ward	Walters	Tait	Cooke	Carroll	Duffy(3),Vicary(11),Hussin(7).	7
Greygoose	Crookes	Duffy	Fairclough	Simpson	Hussin	M Ward	Walters	Tait	Cooke	Vicary	Carroll(5),Stannard(6),Bishop(11).	8
Greygoose	Crookes	Hemming	Fairclough	Simpson	Bishop	Stannard	Walters	Tait	Cooke	Vicary	D Ward(3),M Ward(7),Carroll(10).	9
Greygoose	Crookes	Hussin	Fairclough	Simpson	Bishop	Duffy	Walters	Tait	Carroll	Vicary	D Ward(6),Stannard(7),Cooke(10).	10
Greygoose	Crookes	Hussin	Fairclough	Simpson	M Ward	Sandeman	Walters	Tait	Carroll	Vicary	Dowell(2),Stannard(3),Cooke(10).	11
Greygoose	Sandeman	Billing	Fairclough	Simpson	M Ward	Stannard	Walters	Tait	Williams	Vicary	Crookes(7),Duffy(6),Carroll.	12
Greygoose	Sandeman	Billing	Fairclough	Simpson	Cooke	Stannard	Walters	Tait	Williams	Vicary	Crookes(11),Duffy(7),Carroll.	13
Greygoose	Sandeman	Duffy	Billing	Simpson	Bishop	Stannard	Walters	Tait	Cooke	Williams	Carroll(7),Vicary(11),Crookes.	14
Greygoose	Sandeman	Duffy	Billing	Simpson	Crookes	Stannard	Walters	Tait	Cooke	Williams	Vicary(3),Carroll(11),Bishop.	15
Greygoose	D Ward	Fairclough	Crookes	Simpson	Duffy	Stannard	Walters	Tait	Cooke	Williams	Carroll,Vicary(8), Sandeman.	16
Greygoose	D Ward	Billing	Crookes	Simpson	Duffy	Collins	Walters	Tait	Cooke	Williams	Carroll(11),Vicary(6), Bishop.	17
Greygoose	D Ward	Billing	Fairclough	Simpson	Duffy	Collins	Walters	Tait	Cooke	Williams	Carroll(10),Vicary(6), Bishop.	18
Greygoose	D Ward	Fairclough	Crookes	Simpson	Duffy	Collins	Walters	Tait	Cooke	Williams	Stannard(7),Billing(9),Bishop.	19
Greygoose	D Ward	Fairclough	Crookes	Simpson	Collins	Williams	Walters	Tait	Cooke	Vicary	Stannard, Bishop, Duffy.	20
Greygoose	D Ward	Fairclough	Crookes	Billing	Collins	Williams	Walters	Tait	Cooke	Vicary	Duffy(6), Bishop (8), Stannard(11).	21
Greygoose	D Ward	Gardiner	Fairclough	Crookes	Bishop	Williams	Walters	Tait	Cooke	Duffy	Collins(6),Stannard(7),Billing.	22
Greygoose	D Ward	Gardiner	Fairclough	Crookes	Bishop	Stannard	Walters	Williams	Cooke	Duffy	Collins(7), Billing, Vicary.	23
Greygoose	D Ward	Gardiner	Fairclough	Simpson	Crookes	Stannard	Walters	Williams	Cooke	Duffy	Collins(3), Billing, Vicary.(9).	24
Greygoose	D Ward	Gardiner	Fairclough	Simpson	Crookes	Stannard	Walters	Williams	Cooke	Duffy	Vicary(3), Bishop (7), Tait (9).	25
Greygoose	D Ward	Gardiner	Fairclough	Simpson	Crookes	Stannard	Walters	Williams	Cooke	Duffy	Tait(7), Bishop, Vicary.	26
Greygoose	D Ward	Gardiner	Fairclough	Simpson	Crookes	Stannard	Walters	Williams	Cooke	Duffy	Tait(3), Vicary (9), Billing.	27
Greygoose	D Ward	Gardiner	Fairclough	Simpson	Crookes	Vicary	Walters	Tait	Cooke	Duffy	Bishop(2), Stannard(3), Williams.	28
Greygoose	Duffy	Gardiner	Crookes	Simpson	Bishop	Illman	Walters	Tait	Cooke	Vicary	D Ward(6), Williams, Billing.	29
Greygoose	Duffy	Gardiner	Crookes	Simpson	Bishop	Stannard	Walters	Illman	Cooke	Vicary	Fairclough(4), Ward(11), Tait(10).	30
Greygoose	D Ward	Gardiner	Fairclough	Simpson	Crookes	Duffy	Walters	Illman	Tait	Vicary	Mulligan(6),Williams(7),Lampkin(9).	31
Greygoose	D Ward	Gardiner	Fairclough	Simpson	Mulligan	Duffy	Walters	Illman	Tait	Vicary	Williams(8),Stannard, Lampkin.	32
Greygoose	D Ward	Gardiner	Fairclough	Mulligan	Crookes	Duffy	Walters	Illman	Tait	Vicary	Cooke(9), Stannard(10), Williams.	33
Greygoose	D Ward	Gardiner	Fairclough	Mulligan	Crookes	Duffy	Walters	Illman	Tait	Vicary	Williams(3), Cooke(10), Stannard.	34
Greygoose	Crookes	Gardiner	Fairclough	Simpson	Mulligan	Duffy	Tait	Illman	Cooke	Vicary	Bishop(7), Stannard(9), Williams(10).	35
Greygoose	D Ward	Gardiner	Fairclough	Simpson	Mulligan	Stannard	Walters	Illman	Tait	Crookes	Cooke(7), Williams(9), Bishop.	36
Greygoose	D Ward	Gardiner	Fairclough	Simpson	Mulligan	Duffy	Walters	Illman	Tait	Crookes	Bishop(7), Williams(10), Cooke(11).	37
Greygoose	D Ward	Gardiner	Fairclough	Simpson	Crookes	Cooke	Walters	Illman	Tait	Duffy	Milligan(4), Williams(7), Bishop.	38
Greygoose	D Ward	Gardiner	Crookes	Simpson	Milligan	Duffy	Walters	Cooke	Tait	Illman	Williams, Bishop, Vicary.	39
Greygoose	D Ward	Gardiner	Crookes	Simpson	Milligan	Duffy	Walters	Cooke	Tait	Illman	Bishop(8), Vicary(9), Williams.	40
Greygoose	D Ward	Gardiner	Crookes	Simpson	Milligan	Duffy	Bishop	Vicary	Tait	Illman	Stannard(2), Cooke(9), Williams.	41
Greygoose	D Ward	Gardiner	Crookes	Simpson	Milligan	Duffy	Walters	Cooke	Tait	Illman	Bishop(6), Williams(11), Vicary.	42

1	2	3	4	5	6	7	8	9	10	11	12 14 15
Greygoose	Sandeman	Duffy	Billing	Simpson	Bishop	Stannard	Walters	Tait	Cooke	Vicary	Carroll, Ward(5), Crookes(11).
Greygoose	Crookes	Fairclough	Billing	Simpson	Bishop	Stannard	Walters	Tait	Cooke	Duffy	Williams((6),Sandeman(9), Carroll.
Greygoose	D Ward	Gardiner	Fairclough	Simpson	Crookes	Stannard	Walters	Williams	Cooke	Duffy	Billing, Hussin(8), Vicary(9).
Greygoose	D Ward	Gardiner	Fairclough	Simpson	Crookes	Stannard	Walters	Williams	Cooke	Duffy	Bishop93), Vicary(8), Tait.
Greygoose	D Ward	Gardiner	Fairclough	Simpson	Crookes	Stannard	Walters	Williams	Cooke	Duffy	Tait(7), Vicary, Bishop.
Greygoose	D Ward	Fairclough	Crookes	Simpson	Duffy	Stannard	Collins	Tait	Cooke	Williams	Vicary(7), Carroll(11), Bishop.
Greygoose	D Ward	Billing	Crookes	Simpson	Duffy	Williams	Walters	Tait	Cooke	Vicary	Bishop(3),Stannard(6),Carroll(11).
Greygoose	D Ward	Gardiner	Fairclough	Simpson	Crookes	Stannard	Walters	Williams	Cooke	Duffy	Tait(3), Vicary(5), Billing(8).
Greygoose	Duffy	Gardiner	Crookes	Simpson	Bishop	Stannard	Illman	Tait	Cooke	Vicary	D Ward(6), Willaims, Billing.
Greygoose	D Ward	Fairclough	Crookes	Simpson	Sandeman	Stannard	Walters	Tait	Cooke	Carroll	Bishop(8), Hussin, Vicary.
Greygoose	D Ward	Tait	Fairclough	Simpson	Crookes	Stannard	Walters	Vicary	Cooke	Duffy	Billing(3), Hussin, Lampkin(7).
Greygoose	D Ward	Tait	Fairclough	Simpson	Crookes	Bishop	Walters	Vicary	Cooke	Duffy	Stannard(70, Hussin(9), Lampkin(10).

PHIL WILSON (MANAGER)

Date of Appointment	December 1996
Date of Birth:	6th December 1950
Place of Birth:	Wallasey

PREVIOUS CLUBS

As manager	Caernarfon T., Stalybridge C., Leek T.
As coach	
As player	New Brighton, Runcorn, Mossley, Altrincham, Northwich Vics.

HONOURS

As manager	NPL 91-92
As player	FA Trophy 84, R-up 80, 83. NPL (x2), APL

Director of Football: John Williams **Coach:** Paul Bennett **Physio:** Phil Lea

LEFT
Mark Gardiner

Photos
John L Newton
0161 720 7957

RIGHT
Wayne Fairclough

MATCHDAY PROGRAMME

Number of pages	36
Price	£1.30
Programme Editor	William Hughes & James Wood
Other club publications:	None
Local Newspapers:	Northwich Guardian (Wed.)
	Northwich Chronicle (Wed.)
	Daily Post
	Manchester Evening News Pink (Sat.)
Local Radio Stations:	GMR (BBC Manchester)
	Piccadilly Radio; Signal Radio

1997-98 PLAYING SQUAD

PLAYER	Birthplace Honours	Birthdate	CLUBS
GOALKEEPERS			
Dean Greygoose	Thetford EY	8.12.64	Cambridge U, Leyton Orient, Crystal Palace, Crewe Alexandra, Holywell T
DEFENDERS			
Derek Ward	Birkenhead	17.5.72	Bury, Southport
Wayne Fairclough	Nottingham	27.4.68	Notts County, Mansfield T, Chesterfield
Wes Simpson	Winsford	29.3.77	Crewe Alexandra
Dominic Crookes	Nottingham	7.12.74	Mansfield T, Telford U, Dag & Red
David Clegg	Liverpool	23.10.76	Liverpool, Hartlepool U, Winsford U
Mark Gardiner	Cirencester GMVC, FAT	25.12.66	Swindon T, Torquay U, Crewe Alexandra, Macclesfield T
Wayne Dowell	Co Durham	28.12.73	Burnley, Rochdale
Jamie Bates	Manchester		Maine Road, Runcorn, Stalybridge C.
MIDFIELDERS			
Steve Walters	Plymouth EY, ESP	9.1.72	Crewe Alexandra
Chris Duffy	Manchester	31.10.73	Crewe Alexandra, Wigan Ath
John Stannard	Liverpool		Liverpool, Witton Alb, Knowsley U
Paul Tait	Newcastle	24.10.74	Everton, Wigan Ath, Runcorn
Eddie Hussin	Liverpool	13.12.77	Everton
Stuart Terry			Bangor City, Altrincham
FORWARDS			
Darren Vicary	Liverpool		Vauxhall GM, Cammell Lairds
Ian Cooke	Bebington	1.11.73	Cammell Laird
Carwyn Williams	Pwllheli	21.10.74	Crewe Alexandra, Northwich V, Macclesfield T, £3k to Stalybridge C, £3k to Northwich V
Neil Illman	Doncaster	29.4.75	Middlesbrough, Eastwood T, £10k to Plymouth A, Eastwood T, Exeter C, Eastwood T

DEPARTURES - Delwyn Humphreys (Stafford R), Shane Reddish (Dundalk), Bradley Sandeman (Kettering T), Tony Carroll (Radcliffe B), Mark Williams (Barrow), Mark Ward (Southend U)

PLAYERS ON LOAN - James Collins (Crewe Alexandra)

Drill Field, Northwich

GROUND ADDRESS: The Drill Field, Drill Field Road, Northwich, Cheshire. CW9 5HN.

TELEPHONE NUMBERS: 01606 41450. Fax: 01606 330577. **Club Newsline:** 0930 30 122 713
Internet address: http://www.u-net.com/~sandiway/home.htm.

SIMPLE DIRECTIONS: Leave M6 at Junc.19 and follow A556 towards Chester. At second roundabout (approx. 6 miles), turn right onto A533. Ground on right behind Volunteer Public House.

CAPACITY: 6,000 **SEATED:** 660 **COVERED TERRACING:** 3,500

CLUB SHOP: Located inside ground. Open match days. Manager: Andy Dakin.

SOCIAL FACILITIES: Large social club with members lounge and separate function room - both available for hire Tel: 0606 43120. Food available on matchdays with prior notice. Bass beers, Pool, Darts, TV. New suite now available offering matchday & midweek catering.

Northwich Fact File

Nickname: The Vics, Greens, Trickies. **Club Sponsors:** Harvey's Tyres.

Club colours: Green shirts, white shorts and black socks.

Change colours: All Yellow

Midweek home matchday: Monday.

Reserve Team's league: None.

PREVIOUS - **Leagues:** The Combination 1890-1892, Football League Div.2 1892-94, The Combination 1894-1898, The Cheshire League 1898-1900, Manchester League 1900-12, Lancashire 1912-19, Cheshire County League 1919-68, Northern Premier League 1968-79.
Grounds: None

CLUB RECORDS - **Attendance:** 11,290 v Witton Albion, Cheshire League, Good Friday 1949.

Win: 17-0 v Marple Ass. 15.12.1883 **Defeat:** 3-10 v Port Vale 7.2.1931

Career Goalscorer: Peter Burns 160 - 1955-65.

Career Appearances: 970 by Ken Jones 1969-85.

Transfer Fee paid: £10,000 to Hyde United for Malcolm O'Connor - August 1988 and to Kidderminster Harriers for Delwyn Humphreys - September 1995.

Transfer Fee received: £50,000 from Chester City for Neil Morton - October 1990.

BEST SEASON - **FA Cup:** Quarter Finals 1883-84
League clubs defeated: Rochdale, Peterborough, Watford, Chester C., Crewe Alex.

FA Trophy: Winners 83-84, R-up 82-83 95-96.

HONOURS - Welsh Cup R-up 1881/82,1888-89; FA Trophy 1983/84, R-up 1982/83 & 1995/96; Bob Lord Trophy 1979/80, 92/93; Northern Premier Lge R-up 1976/77; Northern Premier Lge Cup 1972/73, R-up 1978/79; Cheshire County Lge Champions 1956/57, R-up 1924/25, 47/48; Cheshire County Lge Cup 1925/35; Manchester Lge Champions 1902/03, R-up 1900/01, 03/04, 07/08, 08/09, 11/12; The Combination R-up 1890/91; Cheshire Senior Cup 1880-81, 81/82, 82/83, 83/84, 84/85, 85/86, 1928/29, 36/37, 49/50, 54/55, 71/72, 76/77, 78/79, 83/84, 93/94. R-up 1891/92, 96/97, 1905/06, 08/09, 47/48, 50/51, 63/64, 65/66, 69/70, 70/71, 77/78, 85/86; Staffordshire Senior Cup 1978/79, 79/80, 89/90, R-up 1986/87, 90/91; Cheshire Amateur Cup 1901/02, R-up 1898/99, 02/93, Northwich Senior Cup 1948/49, 58/59, 59/60, 63/64, 64/65, 65/66, 67/68, 68/69, 69/70, 71/72, 74/75, R-up x7; Mid Cheshire Senior Cup 1984/85, 85/86, 87/88, 89/90, 91/92, 93/94, 94/95, 96/97, R-up 1982/83, 83/84, 90/91, 92/93; North-West Floodlit Lge 1966/67, 75/76; Cheshire Lge Lancs. Comb. Inter-Lge Cup 1961/62; Guardian Charity Shield 1985/86, 86/87, 87/88.

Past players who progressed to the Football Lge in the last five years:
Tony Hemmings (Wycombe W.), Tony Bullock (Barnsley), Darren Tinson (Macclesfield), Lee Steele (Shrewsbury T.)

1997-98 Captain: Steve Walters

1997-98 Top Goalscorer: Paul Tait (Lge), Ian Cooke (Overall).

1997-98 Player of the Year: Dean Greygoose.

RUSHDEN & DIAMONDS

Just about everybody's favourites for a good season started the 1997-98 campaign in quite incredible style - three straight defeats and a draw left them at the foot of the table before we had reached the end of August.

Despite eventually finishing in the top four, Diamonds never really gave the impression that they could overhaul Halifax Town, but then they had given them too good a start. They didn't finish the season very well either - only 2 wins from their last 8 games to match the 2 wins in their first 8.

Now this season should be very different.

Full time training, an even stronger squad and the experience of the last two seasons should bring the superb Nene Park the Nationwide football it deserves.

Brian Talbot has strengthened the squad carefully and with Max Griggs' enthusiastic support, the club should really be a happy place.

The only problem they face is the expectation of all around them and it is the burden of this expectatation that could turn every game into a cup final for them.

However, it is a problem most clubs would willingly accept, to have such a realistic chance to gain promotion.

CLUB OFFICIALS 1998-99

President	**D Attley**
Chairman	**W M Griggs CBE**
Managing Director	**M G Darnell**
Directors	**A N Gant, S W Griggs, A C Jones, R W Langley, C M Smith**
Football Secretary	**David Joyce** c/o the club Tel: 01933 392821 (H) 01933 6520000 (B)
Press Offiicer	**David Joyce**
Commercial Manager	**Bernard Lake**

L-R, Back Row: Brian Talbot (Head Coach), Darren Collins, Chris Whyte, Jim Rodwell, Mark Smith, Darren Watts, Tim Wooding, Michael Mison, Danny O'Shea (now left the club), Simon Parsell (Physiotherapist). Front Row: Paul Underwood, Julian Capone, Adrian Foster, Kenny Cramman, Gary Butterworth, Darren Bradshaw, Mark Cooper, Warren Kelly, John Hamsher. Missing from photograph - Colin West.

RUSHDEN & DIAMONDS - Match Facts 1997-98

Match No.	Date	Venue H / A	Comp.	Opponents	Result	& Score	Att.	Goalscorers	League Position
1	16.08	H	VC	Northwich Victoria	L	0-1	2,302		19
2	20.08	A	VC	Farnborough Town	L	0-2	*905*		
3	23.08	A	VC	Leek Town	L	0-2	*809*		22
4	25.08	H	VC	Hednesford Town	D	1-1	2,468	Collins 68	22
5	30.08	H	VC	Gateshead	W	3-2	2,211	Mison 5, Ndah 19, Collins 37.	19
6	02.09	A	VC	Slough Town	W	2-1	*872*	Collins 52, Mison 75.	12
7	07.09	A	VC	Cheltenham Town	L	0-2	*1,614*		17
8	13.09	H	VC	Farnborough Town	D	5-5	2,051	**Foster 4** (12, 39, 53, 76), Underwood 37.	17
9	20.09	A	VC	Yeovil Town	W	2-1	*2,317*	Collins 61, Hackett 65.	14
10	27.09	A	VC	Southport	L	2-3	*1,116*	Foster 23, Rawle 72.	7
11	04.10	H	VC	Woking	W	2-1	2,837	Mison 17, Foster 89.	11
12	11.10	H	VC	Hereford United	W	1-0	2,728	Collins 43.	10
13	18.10	A	VC	Kidderminster Harriers	W	2-1	*2,210*	Mison 7, Cramman 63.	9
14	01.11	H	VC	Slough Town	L	0-1	2,193		9
15	08.11	A	VC	Welling United	W	1-0	*833*	Underwood 19.	9
16	15.11	H	VC	Kidderminster Harriers	W	4-1	2,234	**Barnwell 3** (11, 68, 71), Collins 74.	6
17	22.11	A	VC	Morecambe	L	1-3	*1,449*	Capone 82.	7
18	25.11	H	VC	Kettering Town	W	1-0	3,860	Collins 43.	
19	29.11	H	VC	Hayes	**L**	**1-3**	2,158	OG (Flynn) 87.	6
20	06.12	A	VC	Northwich Victoria	W	4-2	*932*	OG (Tait) 16), Capone 54, Collins 70, 88.	5
21	13.12	H	VC	Dover Athletic	**W**	**4-0**	2,284	Collins 29, 83 West 31, 65	5
22	20.12	A	VC	Hayes	W	2-1	*679*	Collins 43, Hackett 55	5
23	26.12	H	VC	Stevenage Borough	W	2-0	3,527	West 67, Capone 90	5
24	01.01	A	VC	Stevenage Borough	L	1-2	*3,107*	Collins 7	6
25	17.01	H	VC	Southport	W	1-0	2,477	Collins 43.	6
26	24.01	A	VC	Dover Athletic	W	3-0	*1,280*	Underwood 23, Alford 37, 85.	4
27	07.02	H	VC	Halifax Town	**W**	**4-0**	3,675	Collins 1, 59, Butterworth 32, Underwood 66.	3
28	14.02	A	VC	Gateshead	L	1-2	*616*	Collins 12.	3
29	21.02	A	VC	Kettering Town	**W**	**4-0**	*4,016*	Mison 19, Underwood 42, West 57, 87.	2
30	28.02	H	VC	Stalybridge Celtic	W	3-0	2,470	Mison 27, Collins 44, Foster 82.	2
31	07.03	H	VC	Cheltenham Town	W	4-1	3,857	Cramman 37 (pen), Collins 65, Foster 83, Cooper 87.	2
32	14.03	A	VC	Woking	W	2-0	*3,930*	Mison 5, Foster 90.	2
33	21.03	A	VC	Halifax Town	L	0-2	*3,951*		2
34	23.03	A	VC	Hednesford Town	W	1-0	*1,342*	Hamsher 13.	2
35	28.03	H	VC	Morecambe	D	3-3	2,758	Collins 10, 15, Underwood 35.	2
36	04.04	A	VC	Telford United	L	2-4	*893*	Collins 72, Cooper 85.	2
37	13.04	A	VC	Stalybridge Celtic	W	4-2	*952*	**Collins 3** (36, 69, 80), Cooper 47.	2
38	18.04	H	VC	Leek Town	L	0-1	2,064		2
39	21.04	H	VC	Yeovil Town	D	2-2	1,784	Collins 11, Mehew 41.	2
40	25.04	A	VC	Hereford United	D	1-1	*3,055*	Collins 86.	3
41	28.04	H	VC	Welling United	L	0-1	1,459		4
42	02.05	H	VC	Telford United	W	3-2	2,197	Collins 37, 72 (pen), West 71.	4

CUP COMPETITIONS SCC - Spalding Challenge Cup NSC - Northants. Senior Cup

Date	Venue	Comp.	Opponents	Result	Score	Att.	Goalscorers
25.10	H	**FAC** 4Q	Boreham Wood	D	1-1	2,107	Butterworth 18.
28.10	A	4QR	Boreham Wood	L	*0-1	*704*	
10.01	H	**FAT** 1	Farnborough Town	W	3-2	2,164	Cramman 28, Collins 83, 89.
31.01	A	2	Cheltenham Town	L	1-3	*2,058*	Collins 86.
07.10	A	**SCC** 1	Hayes	L	0-2		
18.11	A	**NSC** 2	Brackley Town	W	3-1	*245*	**Collins 3** (18, 45, 90).
27.01	H	SF	Raunds Town	L	0-1	868	

League Attendances	**HIGHEST:** 3,860 v Kettering Town	**LOWEST:** 1,459 v Welling United
CONFERENCE: 4th	**FA CUP:** 4th Qual. Round	**FA TROPHY:** 2nd Round

1	2	3	4	5	6	7	8	9	10	11	12 14 15	
Cherry	Hodson	Underwood	Mison	Rodwell	Peaks	Collins	Stapleton	Capone	Alford	Cramman	Stott, Chapman, Sterling.	1
Cherry	Hodson	Underwood	Mison	Rodwell	Peaks	Collins	Stapleton*	Capone	Alford*	Cramman	Stott*, Ndah*, Chapman.	2
Cherry	Hodson*	Underwood*	Mison	Rodwell	Peaks	Capone	Stott	Ndah	Collins	Cramman	Cann*, Chapman, Hamsher*	3
Cherry	Hamsher	Cramman	Mison	Rodwell	Peaks	Crosby	Butterworth	Ndah	Collins	Hackett	Cann, Green, Underwood.	4
Cherry	Hamsher	Cramman	Mison	Rodwell	Peaks	Crosby	Butterworth	Ndah*	Collins	Hackett*	Underwood*, Cann, Alford*.	5
Cherry	Hamsher	Cramman	Mison	Rodwell	Fuff	Crosby*	Butterworth	Ndah*	Collins	Hackett	Underwood*, Alford*, Green.	6
Cherry	Hamsher	Cramman	Stott	Rodwell	Fuff	Crosby*	Butterworth	Alford*	Collins	Hackett*	Foster*, Underwood*, Chapman*.	7
Cherry	Hamsher	Cramman	Mison	Rodwell	Fuff	Hackett	Butterworth	Foster	Collins	Underwood	Rawle, Peaks, Wooding.	8
Watts	Wooding	Cramman*	Mison	Rodwell	Whyte	Hackett*	Butterworth	Foster*	Collins	Underwood	Rawle*, Hamsher*, Kelly*.	9
Watts	Wooding*	Kelly	Mison	Rodwell*	Whyte	Hackett*	Butterworth	Foster	Collins	Underwood	Cramman*, Hamsher*, Rawle*.	10
Watts	Hackett*	Cramman	Mison	Fuff	Whyte	Kelly	Butterworth	Foster	Collins	Underwood	Wooding, Hamsher, Rawle*.	11
Watts	Hackett	Kelly	Mison	Branston	Whyte	Cramman	Butterworth	Foster	Collins	Underwood	Wooding, Fuff, Rawle.	12
Smith	Wooding	Cramman	Mison	Branston	Whyte	Kelly	Butterworth	Foster*	Collins	Underwood	Hackett, Fuff, Ndekwe*.	13
Smith	Wooding*	Cramman*	Mison	Branston	Whyte	Kelly	Bradshaw	Foster	Collins*	Underwood	Capone*, Hackett*, Barnwell*.	14
Smith	Hackett	Cramman	Mison	Branston	Whyte*	Kelly	Bradshaw	Barnwell	Collins	Underwood	Wooding, Capone*, Ndekwe.	15
Smith	Wooding	Cramman	Mison	Branston	Whyte	Bradshaw	Butterworth	Barnwell	Collins	Underwood*	Hackett*, Capone*, Ndekwe.	16
Smith	Hodson	Cramman	O'Shea*	Branston	Whyte	Bradshaw	Butterworth	Barnwell	Collins	Underwood*	Hackett*, Capone*, Ndekwe.	17
Smith	Hackett	Cramman	Bradshaw	Branston	Whyte	Kelly*	Butterworth	Barnwell	Collins	Underwood*	Capone*, Rodwell*, Rawle.	18
Smith	Cotterell*	Cramman	Bradshaw	Branston*	Whyte	Kelly	Butterworth	Collins	West	Hackett*	Rawle*, Capone*, Chapman*.	19
Smith	Wooding	Bradshaw	Mison	Branston	Whyte	Capone	Butterworth	West	Collins	Hackett	Hamsher, Kelly, Rawle.	20
Smith	Wooding	Bradshaw	Mison*	Branston	Whyte	Capone	Butterworth	West	Collins*	Hackett*	Hamsher*, Kelly*, Ndekwe*.	21
Smith	Wooding	Bradshaw	Mison	Hamsher	Whyte	Capone	Butterworth	West	Collins	Hackett	Kelly, Rodwell, Rawle.	22
Smith	Wooding	Bradshaw	Mison	Hamsher	Whyte	Capone	Butterworth	West	Collins	Hackett	Kelly, Ndekwe, Underwood.	23
Smith	Wooding	Bradshaw	Mison	Hamsher	Whyte	Capone*	Butterworth	West	Collins	Hackett*	Branston*, Rawle*, Watts.	24
Smith	Wooding	Bradshaw	Cramman	Hamsher	Whyte	Hackett*	Butterworth	West	Collins	Underwood	Alford, Capone*, Kelly.	25
Smith	Wooding	Bradshaw	Mison	Cramman	Whyte*	Hamsher	Butterworth	West	Alford	Underwood*	Cooper*, Capone*, Ndekwe.	26
Smith	Wooding	Bradshaw	Mison*	Cramman	Whyte	Hamsher	Butterworth	West*	Collins*	Underwood	Cooper*, Smith*, Capone*.	27
Smith	Wooding	Bradshaw	Mison*	Cramman	Whyte	Hamsher*	Butterworth	Smith*	Collins	Underwood	Cooper*, Foster*, Capone*.	28
Smith	Wooding	Bradshaw	Mison	Cramman	Whyte	Capone	Cooper	West	Collins	Underwood	Hamsher, Hackett*, Foster*.	29
Smith	Wooding	Bradshaw	Mison	Cramman	Whyte	Capone	Butterworth	West	Collins	Underwood	Hamsher*, Foster*, Cooper*.	30
Smith	Wooding	Bradshaw	Cooper	Cramman	Whyte	Capone	Butterworth	Foster	Collins	Underwood	Hamsher*, Rodwell*, Rawle.	31
Smith	Wooding	Bradshaw	Mison	Cramman	Whyte	Capone	Butterworth	Foster	Mehew	Underwood	Hamsher*, Cooper, Rawle*.	32
Smith	Wooding	Bradshaw	Mison	Cramman	Whyte	Hamsher	Butterworth	West	Foster	Underwood	Capone*, Mehew*, Rawle*.	33
Smith	Wooding	Bradshaw	Mison	Cramman	Whyte	Hamsher	Cooper	Foster	Collins	Underwood	Capone, Mehew*, Rawle.	34
Smith	Wooding	Bradshaw	Mison	Cramman	Whyte	Capone	Cooper	Foster	Collins	Underwood	Mehew*, Hackett*, Hamsher*.	35
Smith	Wooding	Bradshaw	Cooper	Cramman	Whyte	Cappone	Butterworth	Mehew	Collins	Hamsher	Foster, Hackett, Rodwell*.	36
Smith	Wooding	Bradshaw	Hamsher	Cramman	Whyte	Capone	Cooper	Foster	Collins	Hackett	Mehew, Rodwell, Underwood.	37
Smith	Wooding	Bradshaw	Hamsher	Cramman	Whyte	Capone	Rodwell	Foster	Collins	Hackett	Kelly(8), Mehew(9), Rawle(11).	38
Smith	Wooding	Bradshaw	Hamsher	Cramman	Whyte	Capone	Cooper	Mehew	Collins	Hackett	Kelly(7), Foster, Rodwell.	39
Smith	Wooding	Rodwell	Hamsher	Cramman	Whyte	Kelly	Cooper	Mehew	Collins	Hackett	Capone(8), West(9), Foster(11).	40
smith	Wooding	Bradshaw	Hamsher	Cramman	Whyte	Mehew	Cooper	West	Collins	Kelly	Capone(7), Rodwell, Foster.	41
Smith	Wooding	Bradshaw	Hamsher	Cramman	Whyte	Capone	Kelly	West	Collins	Hackett	Cooper(8), Mehew(11), Rodwell.	42

1	2	3	4	5	6	7	8	9	10	11	12 14 15
Smith	Wooding	Cramman*	Mison	Rodwell	Whyte	Kelly	Butterworth	Foster*	Collins	Underwood	Capone*, Fuff, Rawle*.
Smith	Wooding*	Cramman	Mison	Rodwell	Whyte	Kelly	Butterworth*	Foster*	Collins	Underwood	Capone*, Hackett*, Rawle*.
Smith	Wooding	Bradshaw	Cramman	Hamsher	Whyte	Capone*	Butterworth	Alford	Collins	Hackett	Kelly, Underwood*, Ndekwe.
Smith	Wooding	Bradshaw	Mison*	Cramman	Whyte	Hamsher*	Butterworth	Alford*	Collins	Underwood	Cooper*, Ndekwe*, Capone*.
Watts	Peaks	Cramman	Mison	Fuff*	Whyte	Hackett	Butterworth	Foster	Collins*	Underwood	Rawle*, Hamsher * *, Wooding*
Watts	Wooding	Capone	Mison	Branston	Fuff	Rodwell	Talbot*	Furnell*	Collins	Underwood	Hamsher*, Barnwell, Ndekwe*.
Watts	Wooding	Bradshaw*	Mison*	Cramman	Rodwell	Hamsher	Butterworth*	Alford	Cooper	Hackett	Capone*, Ndekwe*, O'Shea*.

BRIAN TALBOT (HEAD COACH)

Date of Appointment	April 1997
Date of Birth:	21st July 1953
Place of Birth:	Ipswich

PREVIOUS CLUBS

As manager	West Bromwich Albion, Kettering T., Hibernians (Malta)
As coach	
As player	Ipswich T., Arsenal, Watford, Stoke C., Fulham, Aldershot.

HONOURS

As manager	Maltese Championship.
As player	England - 6 full, 1 'B' & u23 caps FA Cup winner x 2, Texaco Cup winner.

FOOTBALL MANAGEMENT TEAM

Assistant Head Coach
Billy Jeffrey

Chief Scout
Cyril Lea

Reserve & Youth Team Coach
Jeff Vetere

Physiotherapist
Simon Parsell

Asst. Physiotherapist
Nigel Gore

LEFT

Darren Collins
Leading Goalscorer & Player of the Year for 1997-98 season.

Photos
Peter Barnes

RIGHT

Captain
Gary Butterworth
'on the charge'.

MATCHDAY PROGRAMME

Number of pages	48
Price	£1.50
Programme Editor	Ted Carrol
Other club publications:	
Local Newspapers:	Northants Evening Telegraph Chronicle & Echo Citizen Herald & Post
Local Radio Stations:	Radio Northampton KCBC Northants 96 Radio Diamonds

1997-98 PLAYING SQUAD

PLAYER	Birthplace Honours	Birthdate	CLUBS
GOALKEEPERS			
Mark Smith	Birmingham	2.1.73	Nottingham Forest, Crewe Alexandra, Walsall
DEFENDERS			
Jim Rodwell	Lincoln SLP	20.11.70	Darlington, Sabam (Malaysia), Bury, Boston FC, Boston U, Bedworth U, Hednesford T, Nuneaton B, Halesowen T, £40K to Rushden & Diamonds
Paul Wilson *	Bradford	2.8.68	Huddersfield T, Norwich C, Northampton T, Halifax T, Burnley, York C, Scunthorpe U, Cambridge U
Michael McElhatton *	Co.Kerry	16.4.75	AFC Bournemouth, Scarborough
Tim Wooding	Wellingborough SLP	5.7.73	Norwich C, AFC Bournemouth
Darren Bradshaw	Sheffield	19.3.67	Matlock T, Chesterfield, York C, Newcastle U, Peterborough U, Blackpool
Glen Fuff	Northampton		Northampton T
Chris Whyte	London	2.9.61	Arsenal, Los Angeles R(USA), WBA, Leeds U, Birmingham C, Charlton Ath, Detroit Neon(USA), Leyton Orient, Oxford U
John Brady *	Newcastle(Aust) ILP	14.1.75	Adamstown Rosebuds (Aust), Swansea C, Brentford, Hayes, Mjolner (Nor), Hayes
John Hamsher	Lambeth	14.1.78	Fulham
Paul Underwood	London		Sutton U, Kingstonian, Carshalton A, Enfield, £50k to Rushden & Diamonds
MIDFIELDERS			
Gary Butterworth	Peterborough ESP, SLP	8.9.69	Peterborough U, Dagenham & Redbridge, £20k to Rushden & Diamonds
Kenny Cramman	Gateshead ESP	17.8.69	Hartlepool U, Bishop Auckland, Gateshead, £40k to Rushden & Diamonds
Mike Mison	London	8.11.75	Fulham
Mark Cooper	Wakefield	18.12.68	Bristol C, Exeter C, Birmingham C, Fulham, Wycombe W, Exeter C, Hartlepool U, Leyton Orient
Carel Van der Velden *	Arnheim	3.8.72	Den Bosch (Holl), Barnsley, Scarborough, Stevenage B
FORWARDS			
David Mehew	Camberley Div 3	29.10.67	Leeds U, Bristol Rovers, Walsall, Yate T, Weston-S-M, Bath C, Farnborough T
Darren Collins	Winchester ESP, SLP	24.5.67	Petersfield U, Northampton T, Aylesbury U, Enfield, £20k to Rushden & Diamonds
Colin West	Wallsend	13.11.62	Sunderland, Watford, Glasgow Rangers, Sheffield Wednesday, WBA, Swansea C, Leyton Orient
Julian Capone	Northampton SLP	3.6.72	Northampton T, Raunds T, Bedford T
Lee Archer *	Bristol	6.11.72	Bristol R, Yeovil T
Ritchie Hanlon *	Kenton	26.5.78	Chelsea, Southend U, Welling U
Adrian Foster	Kidderminster	19.3.71	W.B.A., Torquay U, £60k to Gillingham, Hereford U

DEPARTURES - Jamie Ndah (Kingstonian), Steve Stott (Yeovil T - £9k), Gary Crosby (Released), Martin Davies (Dover Ath), Darren Beckford (Released), Andy Furnell (Nuneaton B), Simeon Hodson (Telford U), Andy Chapman (Released), Mark Jones (Aylesbury U), Danny O'Shea (Released), Carl Alford (Stevenage B.), Brendan Hackett (Burton Alb.). **PLAYERS ON LOAN -** Guy Branston (Leicester C), Jamie Barnwell-Edinboro (Cambridge U), Craig Smith (Derby Co), Ben Lewis (Southend U)

Nene Park, Irthlingborough

GROUND ADDRESS: Nene Park, Diamond Way, Irthlingborough, Northants (01933 652000).

TELEPHONE NUMBER: 01933 652000. Fax: 01933 650418. **Newsline:** 0891 44 00 33.

SIMPLE DIRECTIONS:
South from M1 exit 15, A45 bypassing Northampton until A6 - 1st exit North - ground approx 400 yards right. North & West from A14 exit A6 South (Bedford), follow A6 for approx 6 miles, ground on left. East from A14 exit A45 (Northampton) follow A45 for approx 4 miles to A6 - 3rd exit North - ground approx 400 yards on right.

CAPACITY: 6,635. **SEATED:** 4,654. **COVERED:** 4,182 (all covered by Nov. 1998)

SOCIAL FACILITIES:
Lounge facilities. Open all day, every day. Full restaurant facilities.

CLUB SHOP / DOC SHOP:
Sells programmes, replica shirts, scarves, hats, footwear etc. Contact Bernard Lake (01933 652000, extn.2263).

Rushden & Diamonds Fact File

Nickname: Diamonds **Team Sponsors:** Dr. Martens
Club colours: White, red & blue trim, shirts, blue shorts, white socks.
Change colours: Yellow and black.
Reserve Team's league: Capital League.
Midweek home matchday: Tuesday.

PREVIOUS - **Grounds:** *Rushden Town*: Hayden Road, Rushden (pre-1992). *Irthlingborough Diamonds:* Manton Road, Irthlingborough.
Leagues: Southern League 92-96.
(*Rushden Town*: Midland 1894-1901; Utd Co's 01-04, 19-56, 61-83; Central Alliance 61-83. *Irthlingborough Diamonds*: Rushden Yth; Rushden & Dist; Kettering Amat.; United Counties.)
Names: Rushden Town (1894-1992) merged with Irthlingborough Diamonds (1946-92) in 1992 to form Rushden & Diamonds.

CLUB RECORDS - **Attendance:** 5,170 v Kettering Town - GM Vauxhall Conference March 1997
Win: 7-0 v Redditch Utd (H), Southern League Midland Div. 7/5/94.
Defeat: 0-5 v Slough Town (A), GM Vauxhall Conference 96/97.
Career goalscorer: Darren Collins 119. **Career appearances:** Andy Peaks - 211.
Transfer fee paid: £85,000 to Kettering Town for Carl Alford - 1996.
Transfer fee received: £18,000 from Kingstonian for David Leworthy - June 1997.

BEST SEASON - **FA Cup:** First Round replay 96-97, 2-3 v Boreham Wood (H) after 1-1.
FA Trophy: Semi-Final 94-95.

HONOURS - Southern Lg Premier Div 95-96, Southern Lg Midland Div 94-95, Northants Snr Cup 94-95, Daventry Charity Cup 92-93, Campri Leisurewear Cup 92-93, FA Trophy S/F 94-95. (Rushden Town*: Southern Lg Midland Div R-up 88-89, Utd Co's Lg 02-03, 26-27, 29-30, 31-32, 34-38, 63-64, 72-73, R-up 12 times, Lg Cup 33-35, 36-38, 46-47, Northants Snr Cup 25-28, 29-31, 34-35, 36-37, 57-58, 77-78, FA Vase QF 89-90.* Irthlingborough Diamonds: *Utd Co's Lg 70-71, 76-77, 78-79, 82-83, KO Cup 78-79, 80-81, Northants Snr Cup 80-81.*)

Past players who progressed to the Football League: From Rushden Town: Gordon Inwood (WBA 1949), Robert Peacock (Northampton 1957). From Irthlingborough Diamonds: Scott Endersby (Ipswich), Steve Brown & Dave Johnson (Northampton),

1997-98 Captain: Gary Butterworth
1997-98 Top scorer: Darren Collins
1997-98 Player of the Year: Darren Collins

SOUTHPORT

There is no doubt that Paul Futcher has what it takes to be an excellent football club manager.

After taking Gresley Rovers to an overwhelming Dr.Martens Championship, only to miss promotion because of ground criteria failures, he then built a Southport side that reached Wembley.

There is no doubt that next seaon that very well balanced squad will be challenging for all honours.

A crowd of 4,895 roared the Sandgrounders to a Trophy Semi-Final success and those supporters will be back again to push them towards the Football League if at all possible.

Alongside the player manager last season in defence was one of their most promising young defenders in Tim Ryan and the best Conference goalkeeper in Billy Stewart who both won caps for England.

Perhaps Brian Butler, Dave Thompson and Stewart could be described as 'mature' players but judging by their spirit they will be about for a few more seasons.

In Brian Ross, Justin O'Reilly and Andy Whittaker, Futcher had a good choice of strikers last season and who knows, they could become stronger in the months ahead.

CLUB OFFICIALS 1998-99

President	**Jack Carr**
Chairman	**Charles Clapham**
Directors	C Clapham, D McIlwaine, B J Hedley, A Pope, T Medcroft, J Carr, S Porter, S Shrouder.
Football Secretary	**Ken Hilton** 34 Mill Lane, Burscough, Ormskirk, Lancs. L40 5TS Tel: 01704 894504 (H) 01704 840775 (B)
Commercial Manager	**Kevin Warburton**
Press Officer	**Ken Hilton**

L-R, Back Row: Andy Whittaker, Kevin Formby, Dave Thompson, John Deary. Middle Row: Mel Singleton (Physio), Brian Ross, Dave Gamble, Billy Stewart, Leroy Dove (now Stalybridge), John Bagnall, Phil Horner, Phil Bolland, Max Thompson (Physio). Front Row: Tim Ryan, Ged Kielty, Paul Mitten, Paul Futcher (Manager), Brian Butler (Captain), Andy Farley, Paul Jones   Photograph courtesy of Southport FC.

SOUTHPORT - Match Facts 1997-98

Match No.	Date	Venue H / A	Comp.	Opponents	Result	& Score	Att.	Goalscorers	League Position
1	16.08	H	VC	Hednesford Town	**W**	**4-1**	1,326	Kielty 15, 61, Whittaker 55, Butler 81.	1
2	19.08	A	VC	Leek Town	W	1-0	*1,169*	Formby 90.	
3	23.08	A	VC	Stevenage Borough	L	0-1	*2,128*		3
4	25.08	H	VC	Halifax Town	D	0-0	1,889		3
5	30.05	H	VC	Farnborough Town	W	3-1	1,187	Formby 41, Ross 51,Mitten 67.	2
6	03.09	A	VC	Gateshead	W	2-0	*619*	Ross 65, Mitten 69.	2
7	07.09	H	VC	Slough Town	L	1-2	1,460	Deary 9.	3
8	13.09	A	VC	Woking	D	1-1	*2,806*	Ross 55.	3
9	20.09	A	VC	Hednesford Town	L	1-2	*1,313*	Butler 20.	7
10	27.09	H	VC	Rushden & Diamonds	W	3-2	1,116	Whittaker 24, 56, Deary 59.	7
11	04.10	A	VC	Welling United	W	5-3	*643*	Deary 2, OGs 3 (Knight 14, Perkins 19, 38), Kielty 73.	6
12	11.10	H	VC	Kidderminster Harriers	L	1-2	1,200	Deary 49.	6
13	18.10	A	VC	Hereford United	D	1-1	*2,663*	Mitten 90.	7
14	01.11	H	VC	Kettering Town	W	2-1	973	Thompson 8, Bolland 45.	7
15	08.11	A	VC	Telford United	D	2-2	*706*	Ryan 32, Mitten 69.	6
16	22.11	H	VC	Stalybridge Celtic	W	4-2	909	Gamble 42, 69, Kielty 52, Butler 73.	6
17	29.11	A	VC	Slough Town	L	0-1	*589*		8
18	06.12	H	VC	Leek Town	D	2-2	940	Horner 64, Gamble 81.	8
19	13.12	A	VC	Northwich Victoria	D	0-0	*974*		8
20	20.12	H	VC	Gateshead	W	3-1	800	Thompson 10, 50 Ross 13	7
21	26.12	A	VC	Morecambe	L	0-2	*2,150*		7
22	29.12	A	VC	Stalybridge Celtic	W	3-1	*767*	Formby 3, OG (Hall) 49, Butler 83.	7
23	01.01	H	VC	Morecambe	D	1-1	1,640	Whittaker 7	7
24	17.01	A	VC	Rushden & Diamonds	L	0-1	*2,477*		7
25	24.01	H	VC	Welling United	W	3-1	912	Kielty 2, Whittaker 19, 42.	7
26	07.02	H	VC	Hayes	L	0-2	923		7
27	14.02	A	VC	Kidderminster Harriers	D	1-1	*1,612*	Whittaker 55.	9
28	28.02	H	VC	Woking	D	0-0	1,050		8
29	03.03	H	VC	Hereford United	D	0-0	662		9
30	07.03	A	VC	Kettering Town	L	1-2	*1,157*	Ross 24.	9
31	21.03	A	VC	Hayes	L	0-2	*460*		12
32	31.03	A	VC	Yeovil Town	D	0-0	*1,927*		12
33	08.04	H	VC	Northwich Victoria	L	0-2	964		14
34	11.04	H	VC	Stevenage Borough	W	1-0	1,001	Formby 27.	12
35	13.04	A	VC	Halifax Town	L	3-4	*4,701*	Ross 49, O'Reilly 67, 69.	13
36	15.04	H	VC	Cheltenham Town	L	1-2	1,026	O'Reilly 8.	14
37	18.04	A	VC	Dover Athletic	**L**	**1-3**	*958*	O'Reilly 58.	15
38	23.04	A	VC	Farnborough Town	L	2-3	*532*	Gamble 30 (pen), O'Reilly 63.	15
39	25.04	H	VC	Yeovil Town	W	2-1	849	Morris 45, O'Reilly 72.	14
40	28.04	H	VC	Telford United	L	1-2	702	Whittaker 81.	15
41	30.04	H	VC	Dover Athletic	L	0-1	635		15
42	02.05	A	VC	Cheltenham Town	L	0-2	*2,171*		16

CUP COMPETITIONS SCC - Spalding Challenge Cup **ATS** - Lancashire FA `ATS' Trophy

Date	Venue	Comp.	Opponents	Result	Score	Att.	Goalscorers
25.10	H	**FAC** 4Q	North Ferriby United	W	2-0	1,328	Bolland 40, Thompson **78.**
15.11	H	1	York City	L	0-4	3,952	
10.01	H	**FAT** 1	Winsford United	W	3-0	996	Butler 15, Ross 50, Gamble 86.
31.01	A	2	Yeading	W	6-0	342	**Whittaker 4** (26, 57, 71, 83), Ross 82, Kielty 90.
14.02	A	3	Altrincham	W	2-0	1,196	Ross 23, Bolland 39.
14.03	A	4	Grantham Town	D	1-1	3,695	Ross 60.
17.03	H	4 R	Grantham Town	W	3-1	1,707	**Ross 3** (9, 47, 75).
28.03	A	SF - 1	Slough Town	W	1-0	2,106	Morris 68
04.04	H	SF - 2	Slough Town	D	1-1	4,895	Formby 1.
17.05	N	Final	Cheltenham Town	L	0-1	26,837	
07.10	A	**SCC** 1	Leek Town	L	1-3	349	Beckford 84.
13.01	H	**ATS** 2	Marine	W	4-0	487	Ryan 22, Gamble 50, Thompson 68, 79.
03.02	H	3	Barrow	W	1-0	428	Horner.
24.02	A	SF	Accrington Stanley	W	1-0	348	Ross 23.
21.04	N	Final	Morecambe	W	2-0	1,540	Morris (2). Played at Deepdale.

League Attendances	HIGHEST: 1,889 v Halifax Town	LOWEST: 635 v Dover Athletic
ONFERENCE: 16th	**FA CUP:** 1st Round	**FA TROPHY:** Runners-up

1	2	3	4	5	6	7	8	9	10	11	12 14 15	
Stewart	Farley	Ryan	Deary	Horner	Futcher	Kielty	Butler	Whittaker	Mitten	Formby	Thompson(10), Ross, Dove	1
Stewart	Farley	Ryan	Deary	Horner	Futcher	Butler	Kielty	Thompson	Mitten	Formby	Gamble(9), Dove, Jones	2
Stewart	Farley	Ryan	Deary	Dove	Futcher	Butler	Kielty	Whittaker	Mitten	Formby	Thompson (10, Ross (8), Jones.	3
Stewart	Farley	Ryan	Deary	Dove	Futcher	Butler	Kielty	Ross	Thompson	Formby	Mitten (4), Gamble, Jones.	4
Stewart	Farley	Ryan	Deary	Dove	Futcher	Butler	Mitten	Ross	Gamble	Formby	Kielty (7), Thompson (8), Bolland.	5
Stewart	Farley	Ryan	Deary	Dove	Futcher	Butler	Mitten	Ross	Gamble	Formby	Kielty (10), Thompson (11), Bolland.	6
Stewart	Farley	Ryan	Deary	Dove	Futcher	Butler	Mitten	Ross	Kielty	Formby	Bolland(5), Thompson 2), Whittaker(8).	7
Stewart	Farley	Ryan	Deary	Bolland	Futcher	Butler	Whittaker	Ross	Kielty	Formby	Thompson, Mitten, Gamble.	8
Stewart	Farley	Ryan	Deary	Bolland	Futcher	Butler	Whittaker	Ross	Kielty	Formby	Thompson (2), Pepper (8), Gamble.	9
Stewart	Farley	Ryan	Deary	Bolland	Futcher	Butler	Whittaker	Ross	Kielty	Formby	Pepper (9), Gamble (10), Thompson.	10
Stewart	Farley	Ryan	Deary	Bolland	Futcher	Butler	Whittaker	Mitten	Kielty	Formby	Jones (11), Thompson (9), Gamble.	11
Stewart	Farley	Ryan	Deary	Bolland	Futcher	Butler	Whittaker	Mitten	Kielty	Formby	Thompson (10), Pepper (9), Gamble (8).	12
Stewart	Farley	Ryan	Deary	Bolland	Futcher	Butler	Thomspon	Mitten	Kielty	Formby	Jones (7), Gamble (10).	13
Stewart	Farley	Ryan	Kielty	Bolland	Futcher	Butler	Thompson	Whittaker	Gamble	Formby	Mitten (9), Jones (4), Pepper (8).	14
Stewart	Farley	Ryan	Kielty	Bolland	Futcher	Butler	Thomspon	Whittaker	Gamble	Formby	Mitten (9), Moran, Jones.	15
Stewart	Farley	Jones	Kielty	Horner	Futcher	Butler	Thomspon	Mitten	Gamble	Formby	Whittaker (8), Moore (9), Moran.	16
Stewart	Farley	Dove	Kielty	Horner	Futcher	Thompson	Jones	Mitten	Gamble	Formby	Ross (9), Moran (8), Moore.	17
Stewart	Farley	Dove	Kielty	Horner	Futcher	Thompson	Jones	Whittaker	Gamble	Formby	Moore (3), Ross (11), Mitten (9).	18
Stewart	Farley	Ryan	Kielty	Horner	Futcher	Thompson	Moore	Whittaker	Gamble	Formby	Jones (8), Ross (9), Bolland.	19
Stewart	Farley	Ryan	Kielty	Horner	Futcher	Thompson	Butler	Ross	Gamble	Formby	Bolland (7), Moore, Jones.	20
Stewart	Farley	Ryan	Kielty	Horner	Futcher	Thompson	Butler	Ross	Gamble	Formby	Mitten (6), Bolland (2), Moore (11).	21
Stewart	Bolland	Ryan	Kielty	Horner	Futcher	Thompson	Butler	Whittaker	Gamble	Formby	Ross (10), Moore (9), Mitten.	22
Stewart	Bolland	Ryan	Kielty	Horner	Futcher	Thompson	Butler	Whittaker	Moore	Formby	Gamble (10), Ross, Farley.	23
Stewart	Farley	Ryan	Kielty	Horner	Bolland	Thompson	Butler	Ross	Gamble	Whittaker	Futcher (10), Mitten (11), Jones.	24
Stewart	Farley	Ryan	Kielty	Horner	Futcher	Thompson	Butler	Ross	Whittaker	Jones	Bolland, Gamble, Mitten.	25
Stewart	Farley	Ryan	Kielty	Horner	Futcher	Formby	Butler	Ross	Gamble	Whittaker	Mitten(10), Jones, Bolland.	26
Stewart	Farley	Ryan	Kielty	Bolland	Futcher	Thompson	Butler	Whittaker	Gamble	Formby	Ross(10), Jones(4), Gallagher.	27
Stewart	Farley	Ryan	Jones	Horner	Futcher	Thompson	Ross	Whittaker	Gamble	Formby	Morris, Bolland, Butler.	28
Bagnall	Farley	Horner	Butler	Bolland	Futcher	Thompson	Ross	Whittaker	Gamble	Formby	Morris(9), Mitten(8), Jones.	29
Stewart	Farley	Ryan	Butler	Horner	Bolland	Thompson	Ross	Morris	Gamble	Formby	Jones(7), Mitten(9), Kielty(4).	30
Stewart	Farley	Morgan	Kielty	Horner	Futcher	Thomspon	Mitten	Ross	Gamble	Formby	Powell(11), Ryan, Morris.	31
Stewart	Farley	Ryan	Clarke	Horner	Futcher	O'Reilly	Butler	Morris	Gamble	Formby	Ross(9), Mitten, Thompson.	32
Steawrt	Farley	Ryan	Kielty	Horner	Futcher	Thompson	Butler	O'Reilly	Morris	Formby	Gamble(8), Bolland(11), Jones.	33
Stewart	Farley	Ryan	Horner	Bolland	Futcher	O'Reilly	Butler	Ross	Gamble	Formby	Jones(4), Thompson(10), Morris(7).	34
Stewart	Farley	Ryan	Horner	Bolland	Futcher	Thompson	Butler	Ross	Morris	Formby	O'Reilly(6), Jones(7), Gamble(9).	35
Stewart	Thompson	Morgan	Horner	Bolland	Jones	Mitten	Kielty	Ross	Gamble	O'Reilly	Ryan(7), Clarke(3), Morris(9).	36
Stewart	Farley	Ryan	Kielty	Horner	Futcher	Thompson	O'Reilly	Ross	Gamble	Formby	Morris(9), Morgan (5), Jones(10).	37
Stewart	Farley	Ryan	Butler	Bolland	Jones	Thompson	O'Reilly	Whittaker	Gamble	Formby	Kielty(9), Mitten(2), Morgan(11).	38
Bagnall	Farley	Ryan	Jones	Bolland	Kielty	Thompson	Butler	Morris	Gamble	O'Reilly	Whittaker, Mitten, Clarke.	39
Bagnall	Jones	Ryan	Kielty	Bolland	Futcher	Thompson	Butler	Whittaker	Gamble	O'Reilly	Morris(2), Mitten, Farley..	40
Bagnall	Thompson	Ryan	Kielty	Bolland	Futcher	Jones	Butler	Whittaker	Gamble	O'Reilly	Blythe(2), Mitten(9), Taylor.	41
Bagnall	Jones	Ryan	Kielty	Bolland	Futcher	Mitten	Butler	O'Reilly	Gamble	Blythe	Clarke(8), Taylor(10), Blakeman.	42

Stewart	Farley	Ryan	Deary	Bolland	Futcher	Butler	Thompson	Mitten	Gamble	Formby	Pepper (9), Kielty, Jones.
Stewart	Farlwey	Ryan	Deary	Bolland	Futcher	Butler	Thompson	Whittaker	Kielty	Formby	Jones (9), Mitten (8), Gamble (11)

Stewart	Farley	Ryan	Kielty	Horner	Bolland	Thompson	Butler	Whittaker	Ross	Formby	Gamble (11), Jones (3), Mitten (9).
Stewart	Farley	Ryan	Kielty	Horner	Futcher	Thompson	Butler	Ross	Gamble	Whittaker	Bolland (7), Jones (3), Mittenm.
Stewart	Farley	Horner	Kielty	Bolland	Futcher	Thompson	Butler	Whittaker	Ross	Formby	Gamble, Mitten, Jones.
Stewart	Farley	Ryan	Horner	Bolland	Futcher	Thompson	Butler	Ross	Gamble	Morris	Kielty(7), Formby(11), Mitten.
Stewart	Farley	Ryan	Kielty	Horner	Futcher	Thompson	Butler	Ross	Gamble	Morris	Jones(4), Mitten(11), Formby(3).
Stewart	Farley	Ryan	Kielty	Formby	Futcher	Thompson	Butler	Ross	Gamble	Morris	Morgan(7), Mitten(11), Clarke.
Stewart	Farley	Ryan	Butler	Horner	Futcher	Thompson	Morris	Ross	Gamble	Formby	Bolland, Kielty, Bagnall.
Stewart	Farley	Ryan	Kielty	Horner	Futcher	Thompson	Butler	Ross	Gamble	Formby	Whittaker(11),Bollard(7), Mitten.

Stewart	Dove	Ryan	Deary	Blakeman	Horner	Pepper	Mitten	Gamble	Kielty	Thompson	Beckford (7), Jones (3), Moran (4)

Stewart	Farley	Ryan	Kielty	Horner	Bolland	Thompson	Butler	Whittaker	Gamble	Formby	Mitten (11), Jones (3), Futcher.
Stewart	Farley	Ryan	Kielty	Horner	Bolland	Thomspon	Butler	Whittaker	Gamble	Formby	Mitten(11)Jones(3), Futcher.
Stewart	Farley	Jones	Kielty	Horner	Bolland	Thompson	Ross	Whittaker	Gamble	Formby	Blythe(9), Mitten(8), Butler (11).
Stewart	Farley	Ryan	Butler	Bolland	Futcher	Thompson	Morris	O'Reilly	Gamble	Formby	Kielty, Whittaker, Jones.

PAUL FUTCHER (MANAGER)

Date of Appointment	June 1997
Date of Birth:	25th September 1956
Place of Birth:	Chester

PREVIOUS CLUBS

As manager	Darlington, Gresley Rovers.
As player	Chester C., Luton T., Manchester C., Oldham A., Derby Co., Barnsley, Halifax T., Grimsby.

HONOURS

As manager	Southern Lge Prem. 1996-97, Derbys. Sen. Cup (x2) (Gresley R.) FA Trophy R-up 97-98
As player	England: u21 (11).

Assistant Manager: Peter Wragg **Physio:** Max Thompson

Left

BRIAN BUTLER
Club Captain

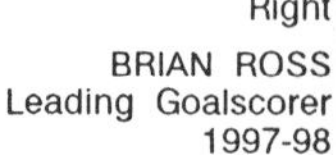

Photos
Andrew Chitty

Right

BRIAN ROSS
Leading Goalscorer
1997-98

MATCHDAY PROGRAMME

Number of pages	36
Price	£1.30
Programme Editor	Derek Hitchcock (01704 579458)
Other club publications:	None
Local Newspapers:	Southport Visitor The Champion
Local Radio Stations:	Dune F.M. Radio Merseyside Red Rose Radio City Radio Lancashire

1997-98 PLAYING SQUAD

PLAYER	Birthplace Honours	Birthdate	CLUBS
GOALKEEPERS			
Billy Stewart	Liverpool	1.1.68	Liverpool, Wigan A, Chester C, Northampton T, Chester C
John Bagnall	Southport	23.11.73	Preston NE, Chester C, Wigan Ath, Bury, Chester C
DEFENDERS			
Kevin Formby	Ormskirk	22.7.71	Burscough, Rochdale
Chris Blakeman	Southport	3.6.78	Southport, Accrington Stanley
Phil Horner	Leeds EY	10.11.68	Leicester C, Halifax T, Blackpool
Scott Guyett *	Australia SLP		Brisbane C, Gresley R
Tim Ryan	Stockport ESP	10.12.74	Scunthorpe U, Buxton, Doncaster R
Paul Jones	Douglas	22.5.78	Stockport Co
Phil Bolland	Manchester		Altrincham, Salford C, Trafford, Knowsley U, Altrincham
Paul Futcher	Chester E u-21, FL XI	25.9.56	Chester C, £100k to Luton T, £350k to Manchester C, £150k to Oldham A, £44k to Derby Co, £30k to Barnsley, Halifax T, £10k to Grimsby T, Droylsden, Gresley R
MIDFIELDERS			
Brian Butler	Salford ESP, BLT	4.7.66	Blackpool, Stockport Co, Halifax T, Northwich Victoria
Dave Gamble	Liverpool NPL	23.3.71	Grimsby T, Altrincham
John Deary	Ormskirk	18.10.62	Blackpool, Burnley, Rochdale
Andy Farley	Preston	18.12.74	From Youth Team
FORWARDS			
Brian Ross	Rochdale ESP	2.7.66	Manchester U, Rochdale, Winsford U, Chorley, Marine, £16k to Chorley
Justin O'Reilly	Derby	29.6.73	Gresley R, £30k to Port Vale, £5k to Southport
Francis Powell	Burnley	17.6.77	Burnley, Rochdale
Mark Quayle	Liverpool	2.10.78	Everton
Andy Whittaker	Preston	29.1.68	Bamber Bridge, Netherfield, Barrow

DEPARTURES (During the season)
Steve Haw (Acc.Stanley), Chris Sharratt (Altrincham), Kevin Ellison (Chorley), Darren Beckford (Released), Leroy Dove (Stalybridge Celtic), Steve Moran (Barrow), Mick Gallagher (TNS Llansantffraid)

Haig Avenue, Southport

GROUND ADDRESS:
Haig Avenue, Southport, Merseyside. PR9 7DR.

TELEPHONE NUMBER:
Ground: 01704 533422 Ticket Office: 01704 533422 Fax: 01704 533422.

SIMPLE DIRECTIONS:
From M6 - M58 through Ormskirk (A570) to Southport. Straight on at Tesco/McDonalds roundabout. Right at the mini roundabout and the ground is on the right.

CAPACITY: 6,012 **SEATED:** 1,880 **COVERED TERRACING:** 1,100

SOCIAL FACILITIES:
Open 7.30-11.00 every night and match days. (Tel: 01704 530182).

CLUB SHOP:
Scarves, replica kits, programmes and various other souvenirs for sale. Contact D Hitchcock, c/o Southport F.C.

Southport Fact File

Nickname: The Sandgrounders **Club Sponsors:** Apollo Leisure
Club colours: Old Gold & black
Change colours: All sky blue.
Midweek home matchday: Tuesday
Reserves' League: Lancashire League (+ youth team).

PREVIOUS - **Leagues:** Northern Premier League, Football League, Lancashire Combination
Grounds: Ash Lane **Names:** None

CLUB RECORDS - **Attendance:** 20,000 v Newcastle United - FA Cup - 1932
Record win: 8-1 v Nelson - 01.01.31.
Record defeat: 0-11 v Oldham - 26.12.62
Career goalscorer: Alan Spence 98
Career appearances: Arthur Peat 401 - 1962-72
Transfer fee paid: £20,000 for Martin McDonald from Macclesfield Town - 1995.
Transfer fee received: £25,000 from Rochdale for Steve Whitehall - 1991

BEST SEASON - **FA Cup:** Quarter Final, 1931-32. Lost to Newcastle Utd.
(The first Division 3 North team to reach the Quarter Finals)
FA Trophy: Runners-up 97-98, 0-1 v Cheltenham Town.

HONOURS - FA Trophy R-up 97-98; Football League Division Four Champions 1972/73 (Runners-up 1966/67); Northern Premier League Champions 1992/93 (League Cup Winners 1990/91, League Shield 1993/94); Third Division North Section Cup Winners 1937/38; Liverpool Senior Cup Winners 1930/31, 1931/32, 1943/44, 1957/58 (shared), 1963/64 (shared), 1974/75, 1990/91, 1992/93 (Runners-up 1993/94); Lancashire Senior Cup Winners 1904/05; Lancashire Junior Cup (now ATS Challenge Trophy) Winners 1919/20, 1992/93, 1996-97, 1997-98 (Runners-up 1993/94).

Past players who have progressed to the Football League:
Shaun Teale, Andy Mutch, Steve Whitehall, Tony Rodwell.

1997-98 Captain: Brian Butler
1997-98 Top scorer: Brian Ross 14
1997-98 Player of the Year: Tim Ryan

STEVENAGE BOROUGH

A quiet start to the Conference season was shaken into a memorable orgy of headlines, excitement and controversy as Paul Fairclough's squad took on the full timers and proved themselves evry bit as well prepared and professional as anyone they met in a famous F.A. Cup run.

CLUB OFFICIALS 1998-99

President	**Rod Resker**
Chairman	**Victor Green**
Vice Chairman	**Michael Palmer**
Club Administrator	**Frank Radcliffe**
	c/o the club. Tel: 01438 223223 (B)
	Fax: 01438 743666
Commercial Manager	**Clive Abrey**
Press Officer	**Michael Palmer**

Cambridge United and Swindon Town were soundly beaten and despite some unsavoury publicity when the clubs aired their differences in public, the actual games with Newcastle United brought immense credit to the the manager and his players.

At no time were they out of their depth and indeed the giants of European football were eventually very relieved to scrape through to the 5th Round.

Paul Fairclough is an outstanding manager who has built two excellent Stevenage sides already and appears to have remodelled his squad again for the coming season.

Some very shrewd signings will I am sure put Borough back into contention for all the honours once again.

L-R, Back Row: John Harding (1st Team Coach), Rob Marshall, Dean Wordsworth, Neil Trebble, Scott Cretton, Thomas Johansen, Mark Smith, Matthew Vier, Noal Blackwell (Asst. Manager). Middle Row: Michael Shortland (Director), Clive Abrey (Cammercial Manager), Michael Palmer (Director), Darren Fenton, Jason Soloman, Steve Pekins, Des Gallagher, Simon Chang, Ryan Kirby, Stuart Beevor, Simon Stapleton, Frank Radcliffe (Club Administrator), Dave Jude (Physio), John Jackson (Asst. Secretary). Front Row: Gary Dixon (seated), Steve Holden, Gary Crawshaw, Paul Thompson, Paul Fairclough (Manager), Robin Trott, Victor Green (Chairman), Michael Love, Giuliano Grazioli, Jamie March, Niall Inman (seated - now Peterborough Utd.)

STEVENAGE BOROUGH - Match Facts 1997-98

Match No.	Date	Venue H / A	Comp.	Opponents	Result & Score		Att.	Goalscorers	League Position
1	16.08	A	VC	Yeovil Town	L	1-2	*3,602*	Trebble 48.	18
2	18.08	H	VC	Kettering Town	D	0-0	3,486		
3	23.08	H	VC	Southport	W	1-0	2,128	Crawshaw 27.	11
4	25.08	A	VC	Dover Athletic	D	1-1	*1,787*	Trebble 39.	14
5	30.08	A	VC	Hereford United	W	2-0	*2,937*	Kirby 5, Trebble 8.	6
6	01.09	H	VC	Hayes	**L**	**1-5**	2,768	Catlin 16.	9
7	07.09	H	VC	Morecambe	L	0-3	2,248		16
8	13.09	A	VC	Kidderminster Harriers	W	3-1	*1,941*	Stevens 28, 67, Catlin 41.	11
9	16.09	A	VC	Welling United	L	0-1	*565*		12
10	20.09	H	VC	Telford United	D	1-1	1,941	Trott 7.	12
11	27.09	A	VC	Northwich Victoria	D	1-1	*954*	Perkins 46.	11
12	04.10	H	VC	Gateshead	**W**	**6-1**	2,102	OG (Wildgrass) 26, Stevens 28, Crawshaw 45, Love 50, Trebble 66, 72.	9
13	11.10	H	VC	Woking	D	0-0	3,254		9
14	18.10	A	VC	Halifax Town	L	0-4	*2,138*		11
15	25.10	H	VC	Hednesford Town	D	1-1	2,143	Crawshaw 16.	10
16	01.11	A	VC	Stalybridge Celtic	D	1-1	*702*	Crawshaw 9.	11
17	08.11	A	VC	Leek Town	L	1-2	*686*	Smith 74.	12
18	22.11	H	VC	Farnborough Town	W	5-0	2,028	Wordsworth 10, 80, Soloman 32, Trott 60, Crawshaw 70(pen).	10
19	29.11	A	VC	Kettering Town	L	0-2	*1,488*		13
20	13.12	A	VC	Gateshead	L	1-2	*349*	Perkins 23	13
21	19.12	H	VC	Cheltenham Town	L	1-2	1,467	Beevor 42	16
22	26.12	A	VC	Rushden & Diamonds	L	0-2	*3,527*		17
23	29.12	A	VC	Hednesford Town	L	1-2	*1,738*	Wordsworth (pen) 78	17
24	01.01	H	VC	Rushden & Diamonds	W	2-1	3,107	Wordsworth 59, Grazioli 60	17
25	17.01	H	VC	Halifax Town	L	1-2	2,946	Trott 26.	17
26	19.01	H	VC	Hereford United	W	2-0	1,574	Crawshaw 23, 59.	15
27	07.02	H	VC	Yeovil Town	W	2-1	2,897	Soloman 40, Crawshaw 41.	14
28	14.02	A	VC	Cheltenham Town	D	1-1	*2,580*	Wordsworth 90 (pen).	15
29	28.02	A	VC	Hayes	W	3-1	*921*	Wordsworth 32, Beevor 76, Crawshaw 90.	16
30	07.03	H	VC	Stalybridge Celtic	D	1--1	2,273	Grazioli 90.	15
31	09.03	H	VC	Welling United	D	0-0	1,946		14
32	16.03	H	VC	Slough Town	W	4-2	1,413	Perkins 3, Wordsworth 35(pen), Beevor 52, Grazioli 88.	14
33	21.03	A	VC	Farnborough Town	W	2-1	*897*	Grazioli 58, Crawshaw 59.	13
34	31.03	A	VC	Woking	L	3-5	*2,466*	Grazioli 28, 47, Wordsworth 89 (pen).	14
35	04.04	H	VC	Kidderminster Harriers	W	3-1	2,012	Beevor 16, Crawshaw 22, Grazioli 60.	11
36	07.04	A	VC	Slough Town	L	1-3	*828*	Soloman 54.	
37	11.04	A	VC	Southport	L	0-1	*1,001*		13
38	13.04	H	VC	Dover Athletic	D	2-2	1,951	Trebble 36, Perkins 79.	14
39	18.04	A	VC	Morecambe	W	2-0	*1,156*	Trebble 8, 19.	12
40	25.04	A	VC	Telford United	L	0-3	*833*		15
41	27.04	H	VC	Leek Town	D	1-1	1,440	Smith 45.	15
42	02.05	H	VC	Northwich Victoria	L	1-3	2,160	Thompson 12 (pen).	15

CUP COMPETITIONS

Date	Venue	Comp.	Opponents	Result	Score	Att.	Goalscorers
15.11	A	**FAC 1**	Carshalton Athletic	D	0-0	1,405	
24.11	H	1 R	Carshalton Athletic	W	5-0	2,377	Love 10, 51, Perkins 14, Smith 24, Trott 73.
06.12	A	2	Cambridge United	D	1-1	4,847	Crawshaw 17 (pen).
15.12	H	2 R	Cambridge United	W	2-1	4,886	OG (Campbell) 41, Beevor 74
03.01	A	3	Swindon Town	W	2-1	9,422	Soloman 23, Grazioli 65.
25.01	H	4	Newcastle United	D	1-1	8,040	Grazioli 43.
04.02	A	4 R	Newcastle United	L	1-2	36,705	Crawshaw 74.
10.01	H	**FAT 1**	Chesham United	D	2-2	2,685	Inman 45, Perkins 85.
13.01	A	1 R	Chesham United	W	3-0	918	Crawshaw 44, Trebble 87, Dillnut 90.
31.01	A	2	Gateshead	W	2-1	902	Crawshaw 77, 89.
21.02	H	3	Gloucester City	D	1-1	2,835	Soloman 19.
24.02	A	3 R	Gloucester City	W	2-1	1,540	Perkins 12, Trebble 32.
14.03	H	4	Slough Town	L	0-1	3,482	
01.12	H	**SCC 2**	Yeovil Town	L	0-3	816	

SCC - Spalding Challenge Cup

League Attendances **HIGHEST:** 3,486 v Kettering Town **LOWEST:** 1,413 v Slough Town
CONFERENCE: 15th **FA CUP:** 4th Round replay **FA TROPHY:** 4th round

1	2	3	4	5	6	7	8	9	10	11	12 14 15	
Gallagher	Marshall	Kirby	Kelly	Trott	March	Beevor	Smith	Soloman	Trebble	Simpson	Holden, Elad (11), Quy.	1
Gallagher	Sandeman	Kirby	Kelly	Trott	March	Beevor	Smith	Soloman	Trebble	Crawshaw	Holden, Archer (10), Sampanay (11).	2
Gallagher	Sandeman	Kirby	Kelly	Trott	March	Codner	Fenton	Catlin	Trebble	Crawshaw	Holden, Beevor (9), Elad (11).	3
Gallagher	Sandeman	Kirby	Kelly	Trott	March	Smith	Fenton	Catlin	Trebble	Crawshaw	Holden, Beevor (8), Grime.	4
Gallagher	Sandeman	Kirby	Kelly	Trott	March	Soloman	Codner	Catlin	Trebble	Crawshaw	Holden, Beevor, Simpson (11).	5
Gallagher	Sandeman	Kirby	Kelly	Trott	March	Soloman	Codner	Catlin	Trebble	Fenton	Holden, Beevor, Simpson (6).	6
Gallagher	Sandeman	Kirby	Trott	Smith	March	Soloman	Codner	Catlin	Crawshaw	Trebble	Kelly(6), Allen (9), Stevens (10)	7
Wilmot	Sandeman	Kirby	Beevor	Trott	Love	Smith	Soloman	Catlin	Trebble	Stevena T	Holden, Crawshaw (11),Fenton (9).	8
Wilmot	Sandeman	Kirby	Beevor	Trott	March	Smith	Soloman	Cattlin	Trebble	Fenton	Holden, Crawshaw (4)Stevens T.	9
Wilmot	Kirby	Perkins	Beevor	Trott	March	Smith	Soloman	Crawshaw	Love	Stevens T	Trebble (3), Sandeman (8) Gallen (9).	10
Wilmot	Kirby	Perkins	Elad	Trott	March	Smith	Catlin	Crawshaw	Love	Stevens T	Holden (4), Fenton (9) Gallen (11).	11
Wilmot	Kirby	Rogers	Smith	Trott	Perkins	Love	Crawshaw	Stevens T	Trebble	Beevor	Holden, Johansen (3) Gallen (9).	12
Wilmot	Kirby	Love	Smith	Trott	Barrowcliff	Johansen	Crawshaw	Stevens T	Trebble	Beevor	Holden, Soloman (1), March.	13
Gallagher	Kirby	Love	Smith	Trott	Barrowcliff	Stevens T	Perkins	Crawshaw	Trebble	Beevor	Holden (7), March (8) Gallen (9).	14
Wilmot	Kirby	March	Holden	Trott	Barrowcliff	Perkins	Dixon	Crawshaw	Trebble	Love	Beevor (8), Stevens T, Soloman.	15
Wilmot	Kirby	March	Holden	Trott	Barrowcliff	Beevor	van der Velden	Crawshaw	Trebble	Love	Soloman (1), Stevens S. (9), Perkins.	16
Gallagher	Kirby	March	Holden	Trott	Barrowcliff	Perkins	Smith	Crawshaw	Trebble	Love	Soloman, Stevens T (9), Stevens S.	17
Gallagher	Kirby	March	Holden	Trott	Soloman	Smith	Perkins	Crawshaw	Wordsworth	Love	Beevor, Dixon (10), Kaldjob(9).	18
Gallagher	Kirby	March	Holden	Trott	Soloman	Smith	Perkins	Crawshaw	Wordsworth	Love	Beevor, Dixon (6), Kaldjob.	19
Gallagher	Kirby	Love	Holden	Trott	Stapleton	Smith	Beevor	Crawshaw	Wordsworth	Perkins		20
Gallagher	Kirby	March	Smith	Trott	Beevor	Perkins	Trebble	Crawshaw	Wordsworth	Love		21
Gallagher	Stapleton	March	Smith	Trott	Beevor	Perkins	Grazioli	Crawshaw	Trebble	Love	Fenton(10), Inman (6), Wordsworth (2)	22
Gallagher	Kirby	March	Smith	Trott	Soloman	Perkins	Grazioli	Crawshaw	Trebble	Love	Wordsworth (3), Inman (10)	23
Gallagher	Kirby	Love	Smith	Trott	Soloman	Perkins	Grazioli	Crawshaw	Wordsworth	Stapleton	Trebble (10)	24
Gallagher	Dillnut	Love	Smith	Trott	Soloman	Perkins	Trebble	Crawshaw	Wordsorth	Fenton	Dixon ((8), Inman (10)	25
Gallagher	Dillnut	Love	Smith	Trott	Soloman	Perkins	Trebble	Crawshaw	Wordsworth	Fenton		26
Gallagher	Kirby	March	Smith	Trott	Beevor	Perkins	Wordsworth	Crawshaw	Trebble	Soloman	Thnompson ((8), Inman (7)	27
Gallagher	Kirby	March	Smith	Trott	Beevor	Inman	Thompson	Crawshaw	Trebble	Soloman	Wordsworth (8)	28
Gallagher	Kirby	March	Dillnut	Trott	Beevor	Perkins	Wordsworth	Crawshaw	Trebble	Soloman	Meah (7), Harvey (11).	29
Gallagher	Kirby	March	Harvey	Trott	Beevor	Meah	Wordsworth	Crawshaw	Trebble	Soloman	Dillnutt (7), Grazioli (8).	30
Gallagher	Kirby	March	Smith	Trott	Beevor	Meah	Grazioli	Crawshaw	Trebble	Soloman	Wordsworth(3), Harvey(11), Dillnutt.	31
Gallagher	Kirby	March	Smith	Trott	Beevor	Perkins	Grazioli	Crawshaw	Wordsworth	Johanson	Molden(5), Soloman(10), Wilmot.	32
Gallagher	Kirby	March	Smith	Trott	Beevor	Soloman	Grazioli	Crawshaw	Wordsworth	Johanson	Harvey(10), Meah(11), Holden.	33
Gallagher	Kirby	March	Smith	Dillnutt	Beevor	Perkins	Grazioli	Crawshaw	Wordsworth	Soloman	Love(3), Trebble (9), Thompson.	34
Gallagher	Dillnutt	March	Harvey	Love	Beevor	Meah	Grazioli	Crawshaw	Wordsworth	Soloman	Perkins (6), Trebble (7), Thompson.	35
Gallagher	Dillnutt	Love	Smith	Trott	Beevor	Perkins	Grazioli	Crawshaw	Wordsworth	Soloman	Trebble (6),Harvey (8),Thompson(10).	36
Gallagher	Dillnutt	Love	Harvey	Trott	Beevor	Perkins	Grazioli	Crawshaw	Trebble	Soloman	Thompson(10), Fenton(11), March.	37
Gallagher	Dillnutt	Love	Harvey	Trott	Beevor	Perkins	Grazioli	Crawshaw	Trebble	Soloman	March(5),Wordsworth(8),Thompson(9)	38
Gallagher	Harvey	March	Smith	Trott	Love	Perkins	Dean	Trebble	Thompson	Soloman	Fenton(8), Dillnutt(10), Cretton.	39
Wilmot	Harvey	March	Holden	Trott	Love	Perkins	Dean	Trebble	Thompson	Soloman	Beevor(7),Crawshaw(8),Dillnutt.	40
Gallagher	Harvey	March	Holden	Trott	Love	Trebble	Beevor	Crawshaw	Thompson	Smith	Dean(2), Dillnutt(4), Wilmot.	41
Wilmot	Dillnutt	March	Smith	Trott	Beevor	Perkins	Love	Crawshaw	Trebble	Thompson	Soloman(6), Dean(9), Cretton.	42
Gallagher	Kirby	March	Holden	Trott	Beevor	Smith	Perkins	Crawshaw	Trebble	Love	Soloman, Johansen,	
Gallagher	Kirby	March	Holden	Trott	Soloman	Smith	Perkins	Crawshaw	Beevor	Love	Dillnut (3), Johansen (8).	
Gallagher	Kirby	Rogers	Holden	Trott	Soloman	Smith	Love	Crawshaw	Wordsworth	Trebble	March (3), Beevor (10), Perkins (9).	
Gallagher	Kirby	March	Smith	Trott	Beevor	Perkins	Trebble	Crawshaw	Wordsworth	Love		
Gallagher	Kirby	Love	Smith	Trott	Soloman	Perkins	Grazioli	Crawshaw	Wordsworth	Stapleton		
Gallagher	Dillnut	Love	Smith	Trott	Soloman	Perkins	Stapleton	Trebble	Crawshaw	Grazioli	March(3), Inman(8), Wordsworth(11).	
Gallagher	Dillnut	March	Smith	Trott	Beevor	Perkins	Wordsworth	Crawshaw	Trebble	Stapleton	Inman (11), Fenton (7), Thompson (8).	
Gallagher	Kirby	Love	Holden	Trott	Soloman	Perkins	Grazioli	Crawshaw	Inman	Fenton	Trebble (8)	
Gallagher	Dillnut	Love	Smith	Trott	Soloman	Perkins	Trebble	Crawshaw	Inman	Fenton		
Gallagher	Dillnut	March	Smith	Trott	Beevor	Perkins	Fenton	Trebble	Crawshaw	Grazioli	Dixon (11), Inman (7)	
Gallagher	Kirby	March	Smith	Meah	Dillnut	Inman	Thompson	Crawshaw	Trebble	Soloman	Harvey (5), Cretton (10)	
Gallagher	Kirby	March	Smith	Meah	Dillnut	Perkins	Thomspon	Crawshaw	Trebble	Soloman		
Gallagher	Kirby	March	Smith	Trott	Beevor	Meah	Grazioli	Crawshaw	Trebble	Harvey	Perkins (7).	
McKenzie	Dillnut	Rogers	Marshall	White	Beevor	Smith	Johansen	Dixon	Trebble	Kaldjob	Soloman(3), Meah(5), Sampany 10).	

PAUL FAIRCLOUGH (MANAGER)

Date of Appointment	August 1990
Date of Birth:	31st January 1950
Place of Birth:	Liverpool

PREVIOUS CLUBS

As manager	Hertford Town
As coach	Hemel Hempstead, Finchley.
As player	Harlow Town, St Albans City, Hertford Town

HONOURS

As manager	GMVC 95-96, Isthmian Lge. Prem. 93-94, Div.1 91-92
As player	None

Assistant Manager
Noel Blackwell

Coach
John Harding

Reserve Team Manager
Dave Bullock

Physiotherapist
Keith Allinson

Chief Scout
Robbie Morgan

Scouts
Alan Dawson, Steve Williams
Mick Davie, Keith Blackham

LEFT

Paul Fairclough seems to be prepared for all eventualities.

Photo: Alan Coomes

RIGHT

Mark Smith warming up before the FA Cup match away to Carshalton last season.

Photo: Garry Letts.

MATCHDAY PROGRAMME

Number of pages	36
Price	£1.50
Programme Editor	Paul Fry (01438 748684)
Other club publications:	The Borough Yearbook "Gitts is Up" (fanzine)
Local Newspapers:	Stevenage Gazette; Comet Stevenage Mercury; Herald
Local Radio Stations:	Chiltern Radio BBC Three Counties Radio

1997-98 PLAYING SQUAD

PLAYER	Birthplace Honours	Birthdate	CLUBS
GOALKEEPERS			
Des Gallagher	Luton GMVC, ILP	23.1.62	Watford, Eaton Bray U, Stevenage B, Dunstable
Chris Taylor *	Bromsgrove SC		Everton, Bromsgrove R, Halesowen T, Evesham U, Moor Green, Solihull B, Bromsgrove R, Cheltenham T, Kettering T
DEFENDERS			
Mark Smith	Luton ESP, GMVC, ILP		Hitchin T, Letchworth GC, Hitchin T, Woking, Hitchin T
Ryan Kirby	Chingford	6.9.74	Arsenal, Doncaster R, Northampton T
Darren Rogers	Birmingham	9.4.70	WBA, Birmingham C, Walsall
James Dilnutt	London		From YTS
Dominic Naylor *	Watford	12.8.70	Watford, Halifax T, Barnet, Plymouth Argyle, Gillingham, Leyton Orient
Robin Trott	Orpington	17.8.74	Gillingham, Welling U, £8k to Stevenage B
MIDFIELDERS			
Steve Perkins	Southport	5.11.75	Burscough, Plymouth Argyle
Stuart Beevor	Welwyn G. C. GMVC	23.4.75	Stevenage B, Hatfield T
Paul Barrowcliff *	London GMVC		Hendon, Ruislip Manor, Hayes, Harrow B, Kingstonian, Wycombe W, Sutton U, Aylesbury U, Stevenage B, £50k to Brentford
Lee Harvey *	Harlow EY	21.12.66	Harrow Borough, Leyton Orient, Nottingham Forest, Brentford
Steve Berry *	Gosport GMVC	4.4.63	Portsmouth, Sunderland, Swindon T, Northampton T, Instant Dict (HK), Stevenage B, Kettering T
FORWARDS			
Carl Alford *	Denton ESP, SLP	11.2.72	Rochdale, Stockport Co, Burnley, Witton Alb, £1,700 to Macclesfield T, £25k to Kettering T, £85k to Rushden & D
Jamie Barnwell *	Hull	26.12.75	Coventry C, Cambridge U
Paul Thompson	Newcastle	17.4.73	Hartlepool U, Gateshead, £19k to Stevenage B
Micky Love	Stockport	27.11.73	Bedworth U, Hinckley T, Hinckley Ath, Wigan Ath, Wycombe W, Hinckley Ath, Northampton T, Tamworth
Chris Pearson *	Leicester	5.1.76	Hinckley T, Notts Co, Hinckley T, £5k to Kettering T, £14k to Stevenage B

DEPARTURES - Corey Browne (Slough T - £10k), Warren Kelly (Rushden & D - £8k), Joe Gallen (Released), Efan Elad (Hitchin T), Worrell Sterling (Spalding U), Simon Kaldjob (Released), Rob Marshall (Basingstoke T), Guilliano Grazioli (Peterborough U.).
PLAYERS ON LOAN - Paul Barrowcliff (Brentford)

Broadhall Way, Stevenage

GROUND ADDRESS:
Stevenage Stadium, Broadhall Way, Stevenage, Herts SG2 8RH (01438 743322).

TELEPHONE NUMBER: 01438 223223 Fax: 01438 743666.

SIMPLE DIRECTIONS:
Stevenage South exit off A1(M) - ground on right at second roundabout. Spectators are however advised to go straight on at this roundabout and park in the Showground opposite the stadium. The stadium is one mile from Stevenage BR station. Buses SB4 and SB5.

CAPACITY: 6,546 **SEATED:** 2,002 **COVERED TERRACING:** 2,000

CLUB SHOP: Mon - Sat 9-5.30. 27 Market Place, Stevenage. 01438 218061. Sells a complete range of club merchandise including a customising service. Mail Order, credit cards accepted, contact Brian Ellis.

SOCIAL FACILITIES:
Tel.: 01438 218079. Clubhouse at ground open Monday to Friday 7 - 11pm, Saturday noon - 2.00 & 4.30 - 11pm, Sunday: All day from noon. Contact: Pam Terry.

Stevenage Borough Fact File

Nickname: Boro' **Club Sponsors:** Sun Banking Corporation

Reserve Team's League: Essex & Herts Border Combination & Capital League.

Club colours: Red with black & white trim shirts, black shorts and white socks.

Change colours: Light blue shirts, dark blue shorts, light & dark blue socks.

Midweek home matchday: Monday

PREVIOUS -
Leagues: Chiltern Youth 76-79; Wallspan South Combination 79-80; United Counties 80-84; Isthmian 84-94.
Grounds: King George V Playing Field 1976-80.

CLUB RECORDS -
Attendance: 6,489 v Kidderminster H., GM Vauxhall Conference 25.1.97
Win: 11-1 v British Timken Athletic (H), United Counties League Div.1, 1980-81.
Defeat: 0-7 v Southwick (H), Isthmian League Div. 1, 1987-88.
Career goalscorer: Barry Hayles
Career appearances: Martin Gittings
Transfer fee paid: £17,000 for Paul Thompson to Gateshead, 1997.
Transfer fee received: £300,000 for Barry Hayles (Bristol R.) July 97.

BEST SEASON -
FA Cup: Fourth Round replay 97-98. 1-2 v Newcastle Utd. (A) after 1-1.
also 3rd Round 1996-97. 0-2 v Birmingham City (A).
League clubs defeated: Leyton Orient 96-97; Cambridge Utd., Swindon Town 97-98.
FA Trophy: Semi Final 1996-97. 1-2 v Woking in Replay at Watford.

HONOURS -
GM Vauxhall Conference 95-96, Isthmian Lge Prem 93-94, Div 1 91-92, Div 2 (North) 85-86 90-91; Utd Counties Lg Div 1 80-81 (Div 1 Cup 80-81), Herts Snr Cup R-up 85-86, 93/94; Herts Charity Cup R-up 93-94, Herts Charity Shield R-up 83-84, Herts Charity Cup R-up 93/94; Televised Sports Snr Floodlit Cup 89-90, Eastern Professional F'lit Cup Group winners 81-82 85-86 86-87 88-89 90-91 91-92, South Co's Comb. Cup 91-92; Essex & Herts Border Comb.(Reserves) 94/95, Essex & Herts (Western Div) 95-96.

Past players who progressed to the Football League: Richard Wilmot & Neil Trebble (Scunthorpe Utd) 1993, Simon Clark (Peterborough United) 1994, Leo Fortune West (Gillingham) 1995, Phil Simpson (Barnet) 1995. Barry Hayles (Bristol C.) 1997).

1997-98 Captain: Robin Trott

1997-98 Top scorer: Gary Crawshaw

1997-98 Player of the Year: Robin Trott

TELFORD UNITED

CLUB OFFICIALS 1998-99

President	**Gerald Smith**
Chairman	**Tony Esp**
Chief Executive	**Andy Shaw**
Football Secretary	**Mike Ferriday**

199 Trench Road, Telford, Shropshire TF2 7DX
Tel: 01952 - 605193(H) 292929(B)

Commercial Manager	**Terry Brumpton** Tel: 01543 468880
Press Officer	**Robert Cave** Tel: 01952 270767

1997/98 is a season most Telford supporters would probably like to forget, but are unlikely to do so for some time.

It all started quite brightly as the team went to fancied Woking and were only denied a 3 point start by a very late equaliser at Kingfield. When this was followed by wins against Stalybridge and Kettering, separated only by an unlucky 1-0 defeat against then leaders Dover, the team had made a sound start and held 5th place in the league.

What really started the slide appears in retrospect to have been the 2-1 home FA Cup defeat by Bedworth United in September. Confidence was shattered and one solitary league success (2-0 at Gateshead) was obtained between mid-September and mid-December, as a result of which manager Steve Daley was replaced by present manager Jimmy Mullen.

The new manager's reign got off to a bright start with a win at Stalybridge, but apart from this results continued to be poor. New players were brought in to try and rescue what was beginning to appear desperate situation, the manager securing the services on loan from his old club Burnley of Phil Eastwood and Ian Duerden. Their arrival prompted an immediate improvement and stemmed the tide as the manager worked against the clock to bring in long-term new players. A club record fee was paid for Mickey Norbury from Hednesford, but his services were missed for some time as he started a suspension. Probably more significant were the signings of Craig Shakespeare, who added much-needed craft to the midfield and young striker Gez Murphy, who was an immediate success with 8 goals in as many games.

Results began to improve in the last month. All now depended on the final day visit to Rushden where Telford supporters noisily occupied a complete end of their magnificent stadium. It didn't take long to send them into ecstasy, either, as Gez Murphy opened the scoring after just 3 minutes, a lead which was held until just before the interval when a defensive error gifted Darren Collins an equaliser. All was not done, however, and when Murphy again finished a fine move involving Norbury some 25 minutes from the end hopes were high until Rushden equalised from a well-worked corner. As if this wasn't bad enough, this was followed by a penalty award which surprised even Rushden's players and effectively ruled out a finish out of the bottom 3. The supporters continued to roar out their support for the players long after the final whistle, even though many were singing through their tears.

It was in many ways a day to be proud of. Whatever the result, the team had given their all and the supporters had responded as true supporters do.

When it turned out that the club in fact retained their Conference status, albeit through a very sad event elsewhere, it did seem that some broader justice had been done to those wonderful players and supporters. Rollo Sheridan

L-R, Back Row: S Palmer, S Eccleston, B Wilcox, M Turner, A Joseph, M Jones, P Parkes, D Dudley, R Darby, B Gray, N Colley, P Challinor.
Front Row: A Chearlton, J Purdie, L Fowler, S Colcombe, S Daley, E Wright, T Langford, K Ashby, T Collins.

TELFORD UNITED - Match Facts 1997-98

Match No.	Date	Venue H / A	Comp.	Opponents	Result & Score		Att.	Goalscorers	League Position
1	16.08	A	VC	Woking	D	1-1	*2,626*	Fowler 7 (pen).	13
2	19.08	H	VC	Stalybridge Celtic	W	1-0	816	Wright 60.	
3	23.08	H	VC	Dover Athletic	L	0-1	808		12
4	25.08	A	VC	Kettering Town	W	3-1	*1,405*	Gray 37, Wright 42, Langford 78.	5
5	30.08	A	VC	Morecambe	L	0-1	*1,352*		10
6	02.09	H	VC	Halifax Town	L	0-3	805		11
7	07.09	H	VC	Gateshead	D	4-4	568	**Langford 3** (49, 55, 74), Gray 59.	14
8	16.08	A	VC	Halifax Town	**L**	**1-6**	*1,119*	Daley 24.	17
9	20.09	A	VC	Stevenage Borough	D	1-1	*1,941*	Gray 35.	18
10	04.10	H	VC	Hereford United	D	0-0	1,710		19
11	06.10	A	VC	Hednesford Town	L	0-1	*1,479*		
12	18.10	H	VC	Farnborough Town	L	0-1	587		
13	25.10	A	VC	Gateshead	W	2-0	*424*	Gray 13, 41.	19
14	01.11	A	VC	Northwich Victoria	D	2-2	*938*	Bentley 20, 35.	18
15	08.11	H	VC	Southport	D	2-2	706	Ashley 10, Gray 24.	18
16	15.11	A	VC	Yeovil Town	L	3-5	*2,133*	Taylor 48, Gray 49, Palmer 56.	19
17	22.11	A	VC	Welling United	L	1-4	*577*	Taylor 9.	**19**
18	29.11	H	VC	Morecambe	L	1-3	518	Langford 46.	20
19	26.12	A	VC	Hayes	L	1-2	*525*	Bentley 67.	20
20	13.12	A	VC	Stalybridge Celtic	W	2-1	*534*	Turner 11, Colley 13	19
21	20.12	H	VC	Woking	L	0-3	717		19
22	26.12	A	VC	Leek Town	L	*1-3*	832	Turner 20	19
23	01.01	H	VC	Leek Town	**W**	**3-0**	911	Bentley 44, OG (Diskin) 48, Fowler 70	19
24	17.01	H	VC	Slough Town	L	0-1	668		19
25	07.02	H	VC	Kidderminster Harriers	D	1-1	1,127	Eastwood 17.	20
26	10.02	A	VC	Hereford United	D	1-1	*1,371*	Turner 40.	20
27	14.02	H	VC	Welling United	L	0-3	614		20
28	21.02	A	VC	Farnborough Town	L	0-1	*543*		20
29	24.02	H	VC	Northwich Victoria	W	2-1	605	Eastwood 31, Palmer 63.	20
30	28.02	A	VC	Dover Athletic	L	3-6	*953*	Palmer 6, Turner 33, Bentley 42.	20
31	03.03	A	VC	Slough Town	L	0-1	*547*		20
32	07.03	H	VC	Hayes	W	1-0	631	Norbury 67.	20
33	17.03	H	VC	Yeovil Town	L	1-4	565	Gray 64.	20
34	21.03	H	VC	Hednesford Town	D	1-1	922	Fowler 87.	19
35	28.03	A	VC	Kidderminster Harriers	D	1-1	*2,024*	Murphy 59.	20
36	31.03	H	VC	Cheltenham Town	D	0-0	740		20
37	04.04	H	VC	Rushden & Diamonds	W	4-2	893	Shakespeare 16, Murphy 18, 84, Moore 60.	19
38	13.04	H	VC	Kettering Town	D	1-1	1,041	Palmer 86.	19
39	18.04	A	VC	Cheltenham Town	L	1-3	*1,444*	Murphy 85.	20
40	25.04	H	VC	Stevenage Borough	W	3-0	833	Moore 19, Gray 30, Murphy 62.	19
41	28.04	A	VC	Southport	W	2-1	*702*	Murphy 34, Gray 42.	19
42	02.05	A	VC	Rushden & Diamonds	L	2-3	*2,197*	Murphy 4, 64.	20

CUP COMPETITIONS

F.A. CUP

Date	Venue	Round	Opponents	Result	Score	Att.	Goalscorers
13.09	H	1Q	Bedworth United	L	1-2	520	Colley 28.

F.A.. TROPHY

Date	Venue	Round	Opponents	Result	Score	Att.	Goalscorers
10.01	A	1	Guiseley	D	0-0	716	
13.01	H	1 R	Guiseley	W	3-2	557	Palmer 40, 67, Turner 55.
31.01	H	2	Ashton United	L	0-1	626	

SPALDING CHALLENGE CUP

Date	Venue	Round	Opponents	Result	Score	Att.	Goalscorers
25.11	H	2	Northwich Victoria	L	1-2	307	Cartwright 60.

League Attendances	HIGHEST: 1,710 v Hereford United	LOWEST: 518 v Morecambe
CONFERENCE: 20th	**FA CUP:** 1st Qual. Round	**FA TROPHY:** 2nd Round

1	2	3	4	5	6	7	8	9	10	11	12 14 15	
Jones	Ashley	Colcombe	Wilcox	Turner	Eccleston	Palmer	Wright	Gray	Langford	Fowler	Colley (10), Daley, Joseph (7).	1
Jones	Ashley	Colcombe	Ecclestone	Bentley	Turner	Wilcox	Fowler	Gray	Langford	Wright	Colley, Daley (8), Joseph.	2
Jones	Ashley	Colcombe	Ecclestone	Turner	Bentley	Wilcox	Fowler	Gray	Langford	Wright	Palmer (3), Daley (9), Bryan.	3
Jones	Ashley	Fowler	Bentley	Ecclestone	Turner	Colcombe	Wilcox	Palmer	Gray	Wright	Colley, Daley (9), Langford (4).	4
Jones	Ashley	Fowler	Ecclestone	Turner	Colcombe	Wilcox	Palmer	Langford	Gray	Wright	Colley (9), Daley (11), Collins (8).	5
Jones	Ashley	Fowler	Turner	Bentley	Wilcox	Ecclestone	Colcombe	Langford	Gray	Bennett	Daley (8), Colley (10), Palmer (11).	6
Jones	Ashley	Fowler	Bentley	Turner	Wilcox	Palmer	Colcombe	Gray	Langford	Wright	Daley (6), Colley, Dudley.	7
Dudley	Ashley	Colcombe	Bentley	Turner	Cartwright	Daley	Palmer	Colley	Wright	Bennett	Charlton (3), Collins (6), Jones.	8
Dudley	Ecclestone	Ashley	Palmer	Bentley	Challinor	Colcombe	Daley	Colley	Gray	Turner	Charlton (5), Bennett, Corns.	9
Dudley	Ashley	Fowler	Wilcox	Challinor	Ecclestone	Turner	Cartwright	Ward	Gray	Palmer	Colcombe (5), Colley , Daley.	10
Jones	Ashley	Fowler	Wilcox	Challinor	Ecclestone	Turner	Cartwright	Ward	Gray	Palmer	Daley (5), Colley, Colcombe.	11
Jones	Ecclestone	Fowler	Wilcox	Bentley	Challinor	Turner	Cartwright	Taylor	Daley	Gray	Langford (2), ashley, Dudley.	12
Jones	Ashley	Fowler	Wilcox	Bentley	Challinor	Turner	Cartwright	Taylor	Gray	Palmer	Charlton (3), Colley (11), Ecclestone.	13
Jones	Ashley	Fowler	Wilcox	Bentley	Challinor	Turner	Cartwright	Taylor	Gray	Palmer	Langford (11), Purdie, Charlton.	14
Jones	Ashley	Charlton	Cartwright	Challinor	Ecclestone	Turner	Palmer	Taylor	Gray	Fowler	Purdie (8), Langford (9), Bytheway.	15
Jones	Ashley	Charlton	Cartwright	Challinor	Ecclestone	Turner	Palmer	Taylor	Gray	Fowler	Purdie (8), Langford (3), Daley.	16
Dudley	Ashley	Fowler	Cartwright	Challinor	Ecclestone	Turner	Palmer	Taylor	Gray	Fowler	Langford (8), Charlton, Daley.	17
Dudley	Bytheway	Fowler	Wilcox	Bentley	Challinor	Turner	Cartwright	Taylor	Langford	Purdie	Palmer (7), Ecclestone (3), Daley.	18
Dudley	Bytheway	Fowler	Cartwright	Bentley	Palmer	Turner	Ecclestone	Taylor	Hodson	Purdie	Daley (6), Colley, Charlton.	19
Jones	Bytheway	Charlton	Ecclestone	Bentley	Collins	Cartwright	Colley	Daley	Taylor	Turner	Challinor (9), Parkes, Dudley.	20
Jones	Bytheway	Charlton	Challinor	Bentley	Hodson	Cartwright	Turner	Colley	Daley	Taylor	Gray, Ecclestone (6), Collins (3).	21
Jones	Bytheway	Ashley	Challinor	Bentlry	Ecclestone	Turner	Cartwright	Taylor	Gray	Purdie	Collins (6), Colley (11), Langford.	22
Jones	Bytheway	Ashley	Bywater	Bentley	Hodson	Turner	Ecclestone	Taylor	Fowler	Gray	Challinor(2), Daley(10), Colley(11)	23
Jones	Ashley	Fowler	Bywater	Bentley	Hodson	Palmer	Turner	Gray	Purdie	Taylor	Colley(2), McNally(7), Challinor.	24
Jones	Hodson	Fowler	Eccleston	Bywater	Challinor	Duerden	Turner	Bentley	Purdie	Eastwood	Cartwright (6), Palmer(10), Taylor.	25
Jones	Bytheway	Colcombe	Bywater	Bentley	Hodson	Joseph	Turner	Duerden	Eastwood	Fowler	Palmer(7), Colley(9), Purdie.	26
Jones	Bytheway	Colcombe	Bywater	Bentley	Joseph	Duerden	Turner	Taylor	Eastwood	Colcombe	Palmer(6), Purdie(9), Dudley.	27
Jones	Bytheway	Colcombe	Eccleston	Bywater	Hodson	Joseph	Turner	Bentley	Eastwood	Palmer	Cartwright(7), Gray(10), Duerden.	28
Jones	Bytheway	Colcombe	Eccleston	Bywater	Hodson	Gray	Turner	Bentley	Eastwood	Palmer	Colley(7), Cartwright, Duerden.	29
Jones	Bytheway	Colcombe	Eccleston	Bywater	Hodson	Turner	M Jones	Bentley	Eastwood	Palmer	Gray(9), Cartwright, Duerden(6).	30
Westhead	Duerden	Colcombe	Eccleston	Bywater	Hodson	M Jones	Turner	Atkinson	Eastwood	Palmer	Gray(9), Cartwright(11), Colley (10).	31
Westhead	Duerden	Fowler	Bywater	Bentley	Hodson	M Jones	Turner	Norbury	Eastwood	Palmer	Eccleston(2), Gray(10, Colley(7).	32
Westhead	Hodson	Fowler	Eccleston	Bywater	M Jones	Gray	Turner	Bentley	Moore	Palmer	Cartwright(8), Wilcox(11), Colley(10).	33
Westhead	Simpson	Fowler	Bentley	Bywater	Hodson	M Jones	Turner	Murphy	Moore	Gray	Colley911), Bytheway(2), Wilcox(8).	34
Westhead	Simpson	Fowler	Bywater	Bentley	Hodson	M Jones	Turner	Norbury	Shakespeare	Murphy	Gray(6), Moore, Wilcox.	35
Westhead	Simpson	Fowler	Bywater	Bentley	Shakespeare	M Jones	Turner	Norbury	Murphy	Moore	Gray(11), Palmer, Wilcox.	36
Westhead	Simpson	Fowler	Bywater	Bentley	Hodson	M Jones	Moore	Norbury	Murphy	Shakespeare	Palmer(8), Grays(9), Challinor.	37
Westhead	Simpson	Colcombe	Challinor	Bentley	Hodson	M Jones	Moore	Norbury	Murphy	Shakespeare	Gray(7), Turner(8), Palmer(2).	38
Jones	Simpson	Colcombe	Challinor	Bentley	Hodson	M Jones	Turner	Norbury	Murphy	Shakespeare	Anderson(3), Palmer(4), Gray(8).	39
Jones	Simpson	Fowler	Bywater	Bentley	Hodson	M Jones	Moore	Gray	Murphy	Shakespeare	Palmer(6), Turner(8), Norbury.	40
Jones	Turner	Fowler	Bywater	Bentley	Hodson	M Jones	Moore	Gray	Murphy	Shakespeare	Challinor(8), Norbury(9), Palmer(11).	41
Jones	Turner	Fowler	Bywater	Bentley	Hodson	M Jones	Moore	Gray	Murphy	Shakespeare	Norbury(3), Palmer(8), Challinor.	42
Jones	Ashley	Fowler	Turner	Bentley	Wilcox	Palmer	Colcombe	Colley	Langford	Wright	Daley (3), Collins, Joseph.	
Jones	Collins	Ashley	Challinor	Bentley	Ecclestone	Joseph	Turner	Gray	Fowler	Taylor	Palmer (5), Daley, Colley.	
Jones	Asleyy	Fowler	Turner	Challinor	Palmer	Joseph	Colley	Gray	Purdie	Taylor	Daley, Collins, Charlton.	
Jones	Turner	Fowler	Challinor	Eccleston	Hodson	Cartwright	McNally	Bentley	Purdie	Colley	Palmer(7), Taylor(10), Colcombe.	
Dudley	Bytheway	Fowler	Wilcox	Bentley	Challinor	Turner	Cartwright	Taylor	Langford	Purdie	Palmer (11), Ecclestone, Daley..	

JIMMY MULLEN (MANAGER)

Date of Appointment	December 1997
Date of Birth:	8th November 1952
Place of Birth:	Jarrow

PREVIOUS CLUBS

As manager	Newport County, Cardiff City (Jt), Blackpool, Burnley.
As assistant manager	Aberdeen, Blackpool.
As player	Sheffield Wednesday, Rotherham Utd., Preston North End (loan), Cardiff City, Newport County.

HONOURS

As manager	4th Div. Championship, Promotion to Div. 1 via play-offs.

Assistant Manager: Alan Lewer **Reserve Team Man.:** Antone Joseph **Physio:** Paul Heath

Left

Brian Gray
Leading Goalscorer
1997-98

Photos
Peter Barnes

Right

Craig Shakespeare
Came on loan from Scunthorpe United towards the end of the season.

MATCHDAY PROGRAMME

Number of pages	48
Price	£1.30
Programme Editor	Rollo Sheridan 106 Boulton Grange, Telford TF3 2LF. 01952 406570
Other club publications:	None
Local Newspapers:	Shropshire Star Telford Journal
Local Radio Stations:	BBC Radio Shropshire Beacon Radio

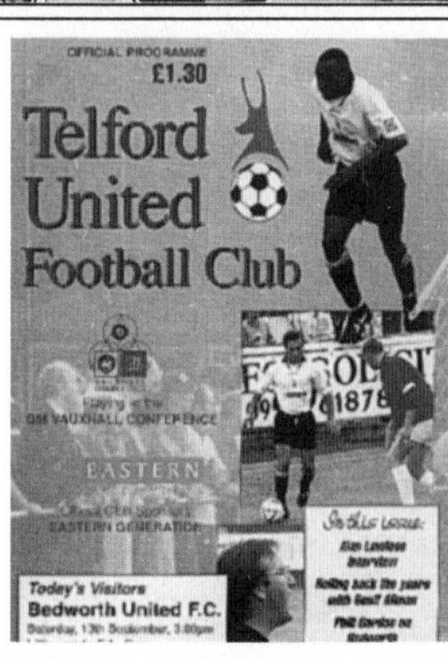

1997-98 PLAYING SQUAD

PLAYER	Birthplace Honours	Birthdate	CLUBS
GOALKEEPERS			
Mark Westhead	Blackpool	19.7.75	Bolton Wanderers, Sligo Rovers, Kidderminster Harriers
DEFENDERS			
Simeon Hodson	Lincoln ESP, GMVC	5.3.66	Notts Co, Charlton Ath, Lincoln C, Newport Co, WBA, Doncaster R, Kidderminster H, £10k to Rushden & D
Paul Challinor	Newcastle(Staffs)	6.4.76	Birmingham C, Baldock T
Matt Bytheway	Birmingham	11.3.77	Wolves, Willenhall T, Aero Lucas
Paul Bywater	Bridgnorth	10.8.71	Shrewsbury T, Worcester C, Gloucester C, Bridgnorth T, Stafford R, RC Warwick
Lee Fowler	Nottingham	26.1.69	Stoke C, Preston, Doncaster R, Halifax T
MIDFIELDERS			
Neil Cartwright	Stourbridge GMVC	20.2.71	WBA, Kidderminster H, £4,500 to Telford U
Mark Turner	Bebbington	4.10.72	Wolverhampton W, Northampton T, Telford U, Hereford U
Marcus Jones	Birmingham		Stoke C, Chasetown, Bolehall Swifts, Willenhall T, Hinckley Ath, VS Rugby, Kingstonian, VS Rugby, Stafford R
Lee Martin	Birmingham	3.10.76	Shrewsbury T
Steve Palmer	Birmingham		Wednesfield
FORWARDS			
Mike Norbury	Hemsworth	22.1.69	Ossett T, Scarborough, Bridlington T, Cambridge U, Preston NE, Doncaster R, Guiseley, Stafford R, Halifax T, £10k to Hednesford T, £15k to Telford U
Lee Farrell	Leicester	12.10.79	Lincoln C, Leicester C, Hinckley U
Gez Murphy	Leicester		Leicester C, VS Rugby, Solihull B, Atherstone U, Gresley R
Ryan Daley	Birmingham		Wednesfield

DEPARTURES - Evran Wright (Halesowen T - £3k), Bernard McNally (Released), Derek Dudley, Kevin Ashley & Steve Taylor (Bromsgrove R), Dave Bennett (Released), Damon Russell (Welshpool)

PLAYERS ON LOAN - Nicky Ward (Shrewsbury T), Ian Overden & Phil Eastwood (Burnley), Craig Shakespeare (Scunthorpe U), Michael Anderson (Notts Co)

RECENT ARRIVALS - Michael Anderson (Notts Co.)

Bucks Head, Telford

ADDRESS: Bucks Head Ground, Watling Street, Wellington, Telford, Shropshire TF1 2NJ.

TELEPHONE NUMBER: 01952 270767. Fax: 01952 246431.

SIMPLE DIRECTIONS:
M54 Junction 6, A518 to B5061 (Watling Street). Ground is on several bus routes. Nearest railway station - Wellington.

CAPACITY: 7,000 **SEATED:** 1,200 **COVERED TERRACING:** 1,500

SOCIAL FACILITIES:
Social club adjacent to ground - open matchdays and selected other hours.

CLUB SHOP:
Telephone 01952 270767 for details.

Telford United Fact File

Nickname: Lilywhites **Club Sponsors:** Eastern Generation.

Club colours: White shirts, black shorts, white socks.

Change colours: Orange shirts, orange shorts and orange socks.

Midweek home matchday: Tuesday

Reserves' League: Central Conference

PREVIOUS - **Leagues:** Southern League, Cheshire League, Birmingham League.
Name: Wellington Town (prior to 1969). **Grounds:** None

CLUB RECORDS - **Attendance:** 13,000 v Shrewsbury Town - Birmingham League - 1936.
Win: Unknown. **Defeat:** Unknown. **Career appearances:** Unknown
Career goalscorer: Jack Bentley
Transfer fee paid: £15,000 to Hednesford T. for Mickey Norbury.
Transfer fee received: £50,000 from Scarborough for Stephen Norris.

BEST SEASON - **FA Cup:** 5th Round 84-85, 0-3 v Everton (A), 47,402. Also 4th Rd. 83-84, 3rd Rd. 86-87, 2nd Rd. 82-83, 85-86, 91-92.
League clubs defeated: Wigan, Rochdale, Stockport C., Darlington, Stoke C., Lincoln U., Bradford C.
FA Trophy: Winners 71-72, 82-83, 88-89. R-up 69-70, 87-88.

HONOURS - FA Trophy Winners 71-72, 82-83, 88-89. R-up 69-70, 87-88; Birmingham League 1920-21, 1934-35, 1935-36; Cheshire League 1945-46, 1946-47, 1951-52; Edward Case Cup 1952-53, 1954-55; Welsh Cup 1901-02, 1905-06, 1939-40; Birmingham Senior Cup 1946-47; Walsall Senior Cup 1946-47; Birmingham League Challenge Cup 1946-47; Shropshire Senior Cup (30); Southern League Cup 1970-71; Midland Floodlit Cup 1970-71; Midland Floodlit Cup 1970-71, 1982-83, 1988-89, Runners-up 1969-70, 1987-88.

Past Players who progressed to the Football League: A.Walker (Lincoln City), G.French (Luton Town), K.McKenna (Tranmere Rovers), S.Norris (Scarborough), David Pritchard (Bristol Rovers) 1994, Sean Parrish (Doncaster Rovers) 1994, Steve Foster (Bristol R.); Peter Wilding, Roger Preece, Mark Williams & Martyn Naylor - all to Shrewsbury 1997.

1997-98 Captain: jim Bentley
1997-98 Top scorer: Brian Gray (10)
1997-98 Player of the Year: Lee Fowler

WELLING UNITED

The Kent club who have battled all the way from park football, through the pyramid of leagues and into the Football Conference are quite happy to be called the Wimbledon of senior semi-professional football.

Every season sees the ' experts ' forcasting a difficult time for The Wings.

CLUB OFFICIALS 1998-99

President	**E Brackstone**
Chairman	**Paul Websdale**
Vice Chairman	**Steven Pain**
General Manager	**Graham Hobbins**
Club Secretary	**Barrie Hobbins**
	c/o the club
Tel: 0181 301 1196	Fax: 0181 301 5676
Marketing Manager	**Steve Wells**
Press Officer	**Paul Carter**
	c/o the club
Tel: 0181 301 1196	Fax: 0181 301 5676

But you won't hear anyone complaining at Welling, as Kevin Hales and his men will take a delight in turning over the big names.

They did this last season.

Although they ended the campaign in a respectable 10th position they finished the season as one of the top form clubs - in their last five matches they recorded five straight wins including Cheltenham Town, Rushden & Diamonds and of course their final day 6-2 defeat of champions Halifax Town.

Mark Cooper enjoyed an excellent season in front of goal and Dereck Brown was his usual classy act in mid field and you can bet that the teamwork and spirit of the so called unfashionable will make it difficult for any visitors to take anything away from Park View Road again this season.

WELLING UNITED - Match Facts 1997-98

Match No.	Date	Venue H / A	Comp.	Opponents	Result	& Score	Att.	Goalscorers	League Position
1	16.08	A	VC	Hereford United	W	2-1	3,138	Copley 4, Cooper 27.	6
2	19.08	H	VC	Woking	D	1-1	1,121	Dolby 16 (pen).	
3	23.08	H	VC	Yeovil Town	L	1-3	840	Dolby 5.	13
4	25.08	A	VC	Hayes	L	1-3	650	Rutherford 68.	16
5	30.08	A	VC	Halifax Town	L	0-1	1,011		18
6	02.09	H	VC	Kettering Town	D	2-2	637	Appiah 58, Rutherford 90.	20
7	07.09	H	VC	Stalybridge Celtic	W	1-0	503	Cooper 72.	15
8	10.09	A	VC	Slough Town	W	2-1	385	Copley 43, Hanlon 79.	8
9	16.09	H	VC	Stevenage Borough	W	1-0	565	Cooper 26.	5
10	20.09	A	VC	Morecambe	L	2-4	1,370	Hanlon 49, Rutherford 69.	9
11	04.10	H	VC	Southport	L	3-5	643	Dolby 7, Cooper 46, 54.	13
12	18.10	A	VC	Hednesford Town	L	2-3	1,208	Cooper 13, Appiah 14.	16
13	01.11	A	VC	Farnborough Town	D	0-0	603		16
14	08.11	H	VC	Rushden & Diamonds	L	0-1	833		
15	22.11	H	VC	Telford United	W	4-1	577	Copley 42, Cooper 71, 73, Watson 90.	15
16	29.11	A	VC	Northwich Victoria	**L**	**1-5**	929	Skiverton 70.	18
17	06.12	H	VC	Slough Town	D	1-1	604	Copley 87.	17
18	13.12	A	VC	Kettering Town	W	1-0	1,144	Cooper 57	15
19	20.12	H	VC	Hereford United	W	3-0	749	Cooper 22, Braithwaite 39, Watson76	13
20	26.12	A	VC	Dover Athletic	L	1-2	1,304	Hanlon 70	14
21	29.12	A	VC	Cheltenham Town	D	1-1	2,326	Hanlon 83	-
22	01.01	H	VC	Dover Athletic	D	2-2	1,326	Dolbý 82, 90 (pen)	14
23	17.01	H	VC	Gateshead	W	2-0	602	Cooper 43, 55.	13
24	24.01	A	VC	Southport	L	1-3	912	Vercesi 80.	14
25	31.01	A	VC	Yeovil Town	D	1-1	2,236	Vercesi 57.	14
26	07.02	H	VC	Northwich Victoria	L	0-1	611		15
27	14.02	A	VC	Telford United	W	3-0	614	Skiverton 44, Hanlon 78, 89.	14
28	21.02	H	VC	Kidderminster Harriers	L	0-3	613		15
29	28.02	H	VC	Hednesford Town	W	3-2	533	Cooper 8, Hanlon 54, Dolby 68 (pen).	14
30	07.03	A	Vc	Woking	L	1-3	2,226	Hanlon 14.	14
31	09.03	A	VC	Stevenage Borough	D	0-0	1,946		13
32	14.03	H	VC	Leek Town	W	2-0	575	Hanlon 66, Cooper 87.	12
33	21.03	A	VC	Stalybridge Celtic	L	1-2	802	Hynes 75.	14
34	24.03	H	VC	Farnborough Town	W	1-0	504	Hanlon 82.	12
35	28.03	A	VC	Gateshead	L	1-2	582	Watts 89.	12
36	04.04	H	VC	Morecambe	D	2-2	519	Hanlon 9, Hynes 23.	13
37	11.04	A	VC	Kidderminster Harriers	L	1-2	1,525	Hynes 17.	16
38	13.04	H	VC	Hayes	W	2-0	665	Dolby 45 (pen), Hanlon 64.	12
39	21.04	H	VC	Cheltenham Town	W	2-1	550	Cooper 55, 75.	
40	25.04	A	VC	Leek Town	W	2-1	564	Hanlon 77, 85.	10
41	28.04	A	VC	Rushden & Diamonds	W	1-0	1,459	Hanlon 89.	10
42	02.05	H	VC	Halifax Town	**W**	**6-2**	1,344	Hynes 3 (4, 21, 44), Farley 52, Vercesi 55, Cooper 63.	10

CUP COMPETITIONS

Date	Venue	Comp.	Opponents	Result	Score	Att.	Goalscorers
F.A. CUP							
13.09	H	1Q	Leyton Pennant	W	3-0	444	Appiah 29, 56,OG (Sach) 71.
27.09	H	2Q	Sutton United	D	2-2	704	Rutherford 51, Appiah 65.
30.09	A	2Q R	Sutton United	L	1-2	502	Cooper
F.A. TROPHY							
10.01	H	1	Slough Town	D	1-1	663	Farley 51.
13.01	A	1 R	Slough Town	L	1-2	560	Vercesi 32.
SPALDING CHALLENGE CUP							
07.10	A	1	Slough Town	L	0-1	293	
KENT SENIOR CUP							
25.11	H	KSC	Erith & Belvedere	L	1-2	180	Rutherford 83.

League Attendances	HIGHEST: 1,344 v Halifax Town	LOWEST: 503 v Stalybridge Celtic
CONFERENCE: 10th	**FA CUP:** 2nd Qual. Round	**FA TROPHY:** 1st Round

1	2	3	4	5	6	7	8	9	10	11	12 14 15	
Knight	L Watts	Farley	Skiverton	Copley	Horton	King	Chapman	Watson	Cooper	Lakin	Simpson(7), Dimmock(9), Turner.	1
Knight	L Watts	Dolby	Skiverton	Copley	Horton	Chapman	Rutherford	Watson	Cooper	Lakin	farley(3), Dimmock(9), King.	2
Knight	L Watts	Dolby	Perkins	Copley	Horton	Chapman	Rutherford	Watson	Cooper	Lakin	Dimmock(5), Farley(11), King.	3
Knight	L Watts	Dolby	Perkins	Copley	Horton	Chapman	Rutherford	Watson	Cooper	Lakin	Farley(11), Dimmock, King.	4
Knight	L Watts	Dolby	Martin	Copley	Horton	Chapman	Rutherford	Watson	Cooper	Lakin	Farley(3), Dimmock(5), King.	5
												6
Knight	L Watts	Farley	Martin	Copley	Horton	Hanlon	Rutherford	Appiah	Cooper	Dolby	Vercesi(3), Watson(9), Dimmock.	7
Knight	L Watts	Farley	Martin	Copley	Horton	Hanlon	Rutherford	Appiah	Watson	Dolby	Vercesi(9), Perkins, Dimmock.	8
Knight	L Watts	Farley	Martin	Copley	Chapman	Hanlon	Rutherford	Appiah	Cooper	Dolby	Watson(9), Vercesi(10), Perkins.	9
Knight	L Watts	Farley	Martin	Copley	Chapman	Hanlon	Rutherford	Appiah	Cooper	Dolby	Vercesi(5), Perkins(6), Watson.	10
Knight	L Watts	Farley	Lakin	Copley	Perkins	Hanlon	Rutherford	Appiah	Cooper	Dolby	Watson(6), Vercesi(7), King.	11
Knight	Lakin	Farley	Chapman	Copley	Dolby	Hanlon	Vercesi	Appiah	Cooper	Watson	Dimmock(11), Abbot, McCann.	12
Ilic	L Watts	Farley	Skiverton	Copley	Lakin	Hanlon	Brown	Appiah	Cooper	Watson	Chapman(7), Vercesi(11), Abbot.	13
Ilic	Perkins	Farley	Skiverton	Copley	Lakin	Brown	Rutherford	Appiah	Cooper	Watson	Hanlon(7), Vercesi(9), Abbot(11).	14
Knight	L Watts	Farley	Skiverton	Copley	Horton	Brown	Rutherford	Watson	Cooper	Chapman	Hanlon, Vercesi, Lakin.	15
Knight	L Watts	Dolby	Skiverton	Copley	Horton	Brown	Rutherford	Farley	Cooper	Chapman	Watson(6), Hanlon(10), Lakin.	16
Knight	L Watts	Farley	Skiverton	Copley	Horton	Brown	Rutherford	Watson	Hanlon	Chapman	Dolby(3), Abbot(8), Lakin.	17
Knight	L Watts	Dolby	Skiverton	Copley	Horton	Brown	Rutherford	Watson	Cooper	Chapman	Hanlon910), Lakin, Farley..	18
Knight	L Watts	Dolby	Skiverton	Copley	Horton	Brown	Rutherford	Braithwaite	Cooper	Chapman	Farley(5), Hanlon(8), Watson(10).	19
Knight	L Watts	Dolby	Skiverton	Hanlon	Horton	Brown	Rutherford	Braithwaite	Watson	Chapman	Abbot(6), Farley(7), Cooper.	20
Knight	L Watts	Dolby	Skiverton	Farley	Horton	Hanlon	Rutherford	Braithwaite	Vercesi	Chapman	Brown(1), Cooper, Abbot.	21
Knight	L Watts	Dolby	Skiverton	Farley	Horton	Hanlon	Rutherford	Braithwaite	Cooper	Chapman	Brown(6), Watson(7), Vercesi(11).	22
Knight	L Watts	Farley	Skiverton	Copley	Horton	Brown	Hanlon	Braithwaite	Cooper	Chapman	king(5), Watson, Vercesi.	23
Knight	L Watts	Farley	Skiverton	King	Horton	Hanlon	Rutherford	Vercesi	Cooper	Chapman	Abbot(7), Watson(10), Copley..	24
Knight	L Watts	Farley	Skiverton	Copley	Horton	Hanlon	Rutherford	Watson	Vercesi	Dolby	King(7), Abbot, Side.	25
Knight	L Watts	Farley	Skiverton	Copley	Horton	Hanlon	Rutherford	Hynes	Cooper	Dolby	Vercesi(7), Watson(9), King.	26
Knight	L Watts	Farley	Skiverton	Copley	Horton	Hanlon	Rutherford	Vercesi	Cooper	Chapman	Watson, Hynes, Dolby.	27
Knight	L Watts	Farley	Skiverton	Copley	Horton	Hanlon	Rutherford	Vercesi	Cooper	Chapman	Dolby(5), Hynes(6), Watson(9).	28
Knight	L Watts	Dolby	Skiverton	Copley	Horton	Hanlon	Rutherford	Vercesi	Cooper	Chapman	Hynes(9), Farley, Abbot.	29
Knight	L Watts	Dolby	Skiverton	Copley	Horton	Hanlon	Rutherford	Hynes	Cooper	Chapman	Farley(5), Abbot(9), King.	30
Knight	L Watts	Dolby	Skiverton	Farley	Horton	Hanlon	Rutherford	Hynes	Cooper	Chapman	Omigie(9), King, Abbot.	31
Knight	L Watts	Dolby	Skiverton	Farley	Horton	Hanlon	Rutherford	Hynes	Cooper	Chapman	Brown(2), King(9), Copley..	32
Knight	L Watts	Dolby	Farley	Copley	Horton	Hanlon	Rutherford	Hynes	Cooper	Lindsey	Abbot(2), Brown, Gibson.	33
Knight	L Watts	Dolby	Farley	Copley	Horton	Hanlon	Rutherford	Hynes	Cooper	Vercesi	King, Abbot, Gibson.	34
Knight	L Watts	Dolby	Farley	Copley	Horton	Hanlon	Rutherford	Hynes	Vercesi	Chapman	Watts(3), King, Gibson.	35
Knight	L Watts	Dolby	Farley	Skiverton	Horton	Hanlon	Rutherford	Hynes	Cooper	Chapman	Brown(6), Vercesi(10), King.	36
Knight	L Watts	Dolby	Farley	Skiverton	Brown	Hanlon	Rutherford	Hynes	Cooper	Chapman	Abbot(6), Vercesi(9), King.	37
Knight	L Watts	Dolby	Farley	Skiverton	Brown	Hanlon	Rutherford	Hynes	Cooper	Chapman	King, Vercesi, Abbot.	38
Knight	L Watts	Dolby	Farley	Skiverton	Brown	Hanlon	Rutherford	Hynes	Cooper	Chapman	King, Vercesi, Abbot.	39
Knight	L Watts	Dolby	Farley	Skiverton	Brown	Hanlon	Rutherford	Hynes	Cooper	Chapman	King, Verces (9), Abbot.	40
Knight	L Watts	King	Farley	Skiverton	Vercesi	Hanlon	Rutherford	Hynes	Cooper	Chapman	Abbot(7), Watts, Side.	41
Knight	L Watts	Dolby	Farley	Skiverton	Vercesi	Hanlon	Rutherford	Hynes	Cooper	Chapman	Side(6), Abbot(7), King.	42

1	2	3	4	5	6	7	8	9	10	11	12 14 15
Knight	Watts	Farley	Perkins	Copley	Horton	Hanlon	Rutherford	Appiah	Cooper	Dolby	Watson(9), Vercesi(6), Dimmock(10)
Knight	Watts	Farley	Lakkin	Copley	Perkins	Hanlon	Rutherford	Appiah	Cooper	Dolby	Watson, King, Vercesi.
Knight	Watts	Farley	Lakin	Copley	Perkins	Hanlon	Rutherford	Appiah	Cooper	Dolby	Watson(9), King, Vercesi(10).

1	2	3	4	5	6	7	8	9	10	11	12 14 15
Knight	Watts	Farley	Skiverton	Chapman	Horton	Brown	Rutherford	Vercesi	Hanlon	Watson	Copley, Perkins, Abbott(10).
Knight	Watts	Farley	Perkins	Chapman	Horton	Brown	King	Vercesi	Hanlon	Watson	Copley, Abbott(11), Watts S(8).

1	2	3	4	5	6	7	8	9	10	11	12 14 15
Knight	Lakin	Farley	Wye	Copley	Watts	Vercesi	Rutherford	Watson	Appiah	King	Cooper(5), Hanlon, McCann(11)

1	2	3	4	5	6	7	8	9	10	11	12 14 15
Knight	Watts	Farley	Skiverton	Copley	Horton	Brown	Rutherford	Watson	Cooper	Chapman	Lakin(7), Hanlon(9), Dolby(10).

KEVIN HALES (MANAGER)

Date of Appointment	August 1995
Date of Birth:	13th January 1961
Place of Birth:	Dartford

PREVIOUS CLUBS

As manager	None
As coach	None
As player	Chelsea, Leyton Orient

HONOURS

As manager	None
As player	None

FOOTBALL MANAGEMENT TEAM

Assistant Manager
Ray Burgess

Coach
Kevin Hales

Reserve Team Manager
Ken Geiste

Youth Team Manager
Ken Geiste

Youth Development Manager
Kevin Hales

Physio
Peter Green

Mark Cooper scoring against Hednesford - just one of his 18 Conference goals last season. Photo: Keith Gillard.

MATCHDAY PROGRAMME

Number of pages	32
Price	£1.20
Programme Editor	Barrie Hobbins
Other club publications:	"Winning isn't Everything" (Fanzine)
Local Newspapers:	Kentish Times Bexleyheath & Welling Mercury
Local Radio Stations:	Radio Kent Radio Invicta R.T.M.

1997-98 PLAYING SQUAD

PLAYER	Birthplace Honours	Birthdate	CLUBS
GOALKEEPERS			
Glen Knight	London		Millwall
DEFENDERS			
Tony Dolby	Greenwich	16.4.74	Millwall
Paul Copley	Dartford	13.8.70	Slade Green, Crockenhill
Terry Skiverton	Mile End	26.6.75	Chelsea, Wycombe W
MIDFIELDERS			
Lewis Watts	Maidstone	14.9.74	Gravesend & Northfleet, Fisher A
Mike Rutherford	Woolwich	6.6.72	Q.P.R.
Dereck Brown	London ESP, FAT, FA XI	8.8.63	Wembley, Hendon, Wembley, Hendon, Woking, Walton & Hersham
Danny Chapman	Greenwich	21.11.74	Millwall, Leyton Orient
John Farley	Greenwich	18.2.73	Lewisham Elms
Paul Linger			Charlton Athletic, Brighton & H.A.
FORWARDS			
Mark Cooper	Watford	5.4.67	Cambridge U, Tottenham H, £105k to Gillingham, Leyton Orient, Barnet, Northampton T
Richard Vercesi	Cornwall		Penzance, Banstead Ath
Joe Omigie	Hammersmith	13.6.72	Donna, Brentford
Tyrone King	Kent		Sittingbourne
Mark Hynes	London		Brentford, Croydon, Merstham, Croydon Ath, Fisher Ath, Whyteleafe, Sutton U

DEPARTURES -
(During the season)
Richard Dimmock (Gravesend), Barry Lakin (Chelmsford C), Mark Watson (Sutton U), Lloyd Wye (Staines T)

PLAYERS ON LOAN - Dave Martin (Northampton T), Sasha Illic (Charlton Ath), Leon Braithwaite (Exeter C)

Park View Road, Welling

GROUND ADDRESS:
Park View Road Ground, Welling, Kent DA16 1SY.

TELEPHONE NUMBER: 0181 301 1196. Fax: 0811 301 5676. **Welling Wingsline:** 0891 80 06 54.

SIMPLE DIRECTIONS: M25, then A2 towards London. Take Welling turn-off, ground 1 mile. By rail to Welling station (BR) - ground 3/4 mile.

CAPACITY: 5,500 **SEATED:** 500 **COVERED TERRACING:** 1,500

SOCIAL FACILITIES:
Clubhouse open on match days

CLUB SHOP:
On sale programmes (League & non-League), scarves, mugs, caps, hats, badges, replica kits and Conference merchandise - matchday manager Peter Mason.

Welling United Fact File

Nickname: The Wings

Club Sponsors:

Club colours: Red shirts, red shorts, white socks.

Change colours: All jade.

Midweek home matchday: Tuesday

Reserves' League: Capital League

PREVIOUS -
Leagues: Eltham & District League 1963/71, London Spartan League 1971/77, Athenian League 1977/79, Southern League 1979/86.
Grounds: Butterfly Lane, Eltham - 1963/78

CLUB RECORDS -
Attendance: 4,100 v Gillingham, FA Cup
Record win: 7-1
Record defeat: 0-7
Goalscorer (career): John Bartley - 533
Appearances (career): Nigel Ransom - 1,066 & Ray Burgess - 1,044.
Record transfer fee paid: £30,000 for Gary Abbott from Enfield
Record transfer fee received: £95,000 from Birmingham City for Steve Finnan. 1995.

BEST SEASON -
FA Cup: Third Round 1988-89, 0-1 v Blackburn R.
League clubs defeated: Gillingham
FA Trophy: Quarter Final 1988-89, 0-1 v Macclesfield.

HONOURS -
London Spartan League 1978; Southern League Premier Division 1985/86;
Kent Senior Cup 1985/86; London Senior Cup 1989/90;
London Challenge Cup 1991/92, Runners-up 1993/94.

Past players who progressed to the Football League: Paul Barron (Plymouth, Arsenal, Stoke, WBA, C. Palace, QPR), Andy Townsend (Southampton, Norwich, Chelsea), Ian Thompson (AFC Bournemouth), John Bartley (Millwall), Dave Smith (Gillingham, Bristol City), Murray Jones (C. Palace, Bristol City, Exeter City), Kevin Shoemaker (Peterborough), Tony Agana (Watford, Sheffield Utd), Duncan Horton (Barnet), Mark Hone (Southend), Steve Finnan & Steve Barnes (Birmingham City).

1997-98 Captain: Mike Rutherford

1997-98 Top scorer: Mark Cooper

WOKING

It was all change at Kingfield Stadium, a new board had seen popular manager Geoff Chapple move over to local rivals Kingstonian and high profile manager John McGovern was changing the image of the side and the club.

Personnel changed quickly with old favourites such as Kevan Brown and Steve Thompson going out, but Eddie Saunders and Michael Danzey were playing well with youngster Kevin Betsy earning a place in the England squad.

CLUB OFFICIALS 1998-99

President	**Leslie A Gosden MBE**
Chairman	**Jon Davies**
Vice Chairman	**John Taylor**
Football Secretary	**Phil J Ledger**
19 Ainsdale Way, Woking, Surrey. GU21 3PP. Tel: 01483 725295 (H), 0831 271369 (M).	
Commercial Director & Press Officer	**Michael Church**
Club Administrator	**Sue Day**
Commercial Manager	**Rosemary Hurl**

Perhaps there were disappointments as the F.A.Cup didn't bring it's usual excitement and of couse The Cardinals never really challenged at the top of the Conference and failed to go to Wembley. To be fair, a finishing place of third and a Spalding Cup Final appearance would be acceptable to most Conference clubs but perhaps Woking have set very high standards in recent years.

There is no doubt that the coming season will provide the answers to the club's immediate future.

This will be McGovern's own side and his discipline and determination will, I am sure, keep Woking involved in the battle for all the honours.

L-R, Back Row: Scott Steele, Grant Payne, Robin Taylor, Darran Hay, Kevin Betsy, Ben Kamara, Dave Timothy, Scott Smith. Middle Row: Malcolm Hague (Kit Manager), Steve Wood (now left), Stuart Girdler, Laurence Batty, Stuart Searle, Terry Howard (now Yeovil), Andy Ellis, Barry Kimber (Physio). Front Row: Steve Thompson (now Yeovil), Tom Jones (now left), Kevan Brown (now Yeovil), John McGovern (Manager), Brian Finn (Assistant Manager), Junior Hunter (now left), Justin Jackson (now left), Aiden Kilner.

WOKING - Match Facts 1997-98

Match No.	Date	Venue H / A	Comp.	Opponents	Result & Score		Att.	Goalscorers	League Position
1	16.08	H	VC	Telford United	D	1-1	2,626	Payne 88.	14
2	19.08	A	VC	Welling United	D	1-1	*1,121*	Payne 30.	
3	23.08	A	VC	Cheltenham Town	L	2-3	*1,690*	Payne 57, Steele 65.	18
4	25.08	H	VC	Slough Town	W	2-1	2,829	Jackson 1, OG (Angus) 38.	13
5	30.08	H	VC	Northwich Victoria	W	1-0	2,687	Betsy 33.	8
6	07.09	A	VC	Hednesford Town	D	1-1	*1,354*	Hay 29.	11
7	09.09	A	VC	Kettering Town	W	1-0	*1,215*	Hay 65.	4
8	13.09	H	VC	Southport	D	1-1	2,806	Hay 88 (pen).	5
9	20.09	A	VC	Gateshead	W	2-1	*732*	Payne 18, Thompson 60.	4
10	27.09	H	VC	Morecambe	L	0-2	3,076		8
11	30.09	H	VC	Dover Athletic	**W**	**4-0**	1,799	Betsy 22, Howard 34, West 65(pen), Taylor 90.	4
12	04.10	A	VC	Rushden & Diamonds	L	1-2	*2,837*	Payne 23.	7
13	11.10	A	VC	Stevenage Borough	D	0-0	*3,254*		7
14	18.10	H	VC	Leek Town	W	5-2	2,806	Hay 4, 37, West 27, OG (Diskin) 33, Thompson 59.	5
15	25.10	A	VC	Dover Athletic	W	2-0	*1,384*	Betsy 54, Hay 88.	4
16	01.11	A	VC	Kidderminster harriers	D	1-1	*1,920*	West 18.	5
17	08.11	H	VC	Stalybridge Celtic	W	3-1	2,829	Hay 45, 70, Betsy 79.	4
18	22.11	A	VC	Yeovil Town	L	0-2	*3,005*		5
19	29.11	H	VC	Halifax Town	D	2-2	3,319	Betsy 4, Taylor 42.	5
20	13.12	H	VC	Hayes	W	3-0	2,435	Payne 28, Danzey 40, Steele 47	6
21	20.12	A	VC	Telford United	W	3-0	*717*	Danzey 10, Hay59, Payne 84	6
22	26.12	H	VC	Farnborough Town	W	3-0	4,124	Danzey 66, Payne 87, 88(pen)	6
23	29.12	H	VC	Yeovil Town	W	2-0	3,429	Steele 13, Hay 36	-
24	01.01	A	VC	Farnborough Town	**L**	**0-3**	*2,125*		4
25	17.01	A	VC	Stalybridge Celtic	W	3-0	*710*	**Hay 3** (16, 70, 74).	3
26	07.02	A	VC	Morecambe	W	2-1	*1,534*	Taylor 65, Payne 79.	4
27	14.02	H	VC	Kettering Town	L	0-1	3,101		4
28	21.02	H	VC	Gateshead	W	3-1	2,081	Hay 1, 28, Payne 68.	3
29	28.02	A	VC	Southport	D	0-0	*1,050*		3
30	07.03	H	VC	Welling United	W	3-1	2,226	OG (Horton) 5, Hay 55, Betsy 83.	3
31	10.03	A	VC	Slough Town	W	3-1	*1,288*	Steele 20, Saunders 75, Payne 78.	2
32	14.03	H	VC	Rushden & Diamonds	L	0-2	3,930		3
33	21.03	H	VC	Kidderminster Harriers	L	0-1	2,384		3
34	28.03	A	VC	Hereford United	L	1-2	*2,281*	West 17.	3
35	31.03	H	VC	Stevenage Borough	W	5-3	2,466	Hayward 22, 85, McAree 74, Payne 82, West 90.	3
36	04.04	A	VC	Halifax Town	L	0-1	*2,826*		3
37	11.04	H	VC	Cheltenham Town	W	2-0	2,651	Hayward 36, 58.	3
38	13.04	A	VC	Leek Town	L	0-2	*612*		3
39	18.04	H	VC	Hednesford Town	W	4-2	2,292	McAree 45, Hay 48 (pen), 59, Payne 71.	3
40	25.04	A	VC	Northwich Victoria	W	2-0	*941*	West 4, Payne 74.	3
41	28.04	A	VC	Hayes	**L**	**0-3**	*667*		3
42	02.05	H	VC	Hereford United	W	3-1	3,015	Hay 5, West 45, 49.	3

CUP COMPETITIONS SCC Spalding Challenge Cup SSC - Surrey Senior Cup

Date	Venue	Comp.	Opponents	Result	Score	Att.	Goalscorers	
15.11	H	**FAC** 1	Southend United	L	0-2	5,000		
10.01	H	**FAT** 1	Margate	L	0-1	2,682		
07.10	A	Ch. Shield	Macclesfield Town	L	1-3	732	West.	
18.11	H	**SCC** 2	Kettering Town	W	4-0	559	Steele 18, 66, Timothy 36, West 44.	
20.01	H	3	Farnborough Town	W	3-1	998	Smith 14, Hay 15 (pen), Saunders 86.	
17.02	A	SF- 1	Hayes	W	2-0	647	Payne 31, Brown 66.	
17.03	H	SF- 2	Hayes	W	3-1	826	West 61, 83, Betsy 71.	
25.03	A	Final - 1	Morecambe	D	1-1	782	Hayward 5.	
04.05	H	Final - 2	Morecambe	D	1-1	2,045	Hay 53.	Lost 3-4 after penalties
09.12	H	**SSC** 1	Croydon Athletic	W	7-0	426	Payne 2, Sutton, Thompson, Hay, Steele, O.G.	
13.01	H	2	Godalming & Guildford	W	1-0	1,025	Sutton.	
03.02	H	3	Leatherhead	W	4-0	725	Steele 2, West 2.	
03.03	H	SF	Chertsey Town	W	2-1	832	Payne, West.	
22.04	N	Final	Kingstonian	D	*1-1	1,584	West AET	at Sutton United FC
07.05	N	Final R	Kingstonian	L	1-2		Betsy	at Sutton United FC

League Attendances	**HIGHEST:** 4,124 v Farnborough Town	**LOWEST:** 1,712 v Dover Athletic
CONFERENCE: 3rd	**FA CUP:** 1st Round	**FA TROPHY:** 1st Round

1	2	3	4	5	6	7	8	9	10	11	12 14 15	
Batty	Smith	Taylor	Howard	Brown	Wood	Thompson	Jones	Payne	Jackson	Steele	Betsy (8), Ellis (6), Hay (10).	1
Batty	Taylor	Timothy	Howard	Brown	Smith	Thompson	Jones	Payne	Jackson	Betsy	Steele (7), Hay, Ellis.	2
Batty	Smith	Timothy	Howard	Brown	Stewart	Betsy	Jones	Payne	Jackson	Steele	Hay (10), Hunter, Ellis.	3
Batty	Betsy	Smith	Howard	Stewart	Brown	Ellis	Thompson	Payne	Jackson	Steele	Hay, Hunter, Kamara (7).	4
Batty	Betsy	Smith	Howard	Brown	Stewart	Thompson	Ellis	Payne	Jackson	Steele	Hay (10), Taylor, Jones (8).	5
Batty	Betsy	Taylor	Howard	Stewart	Danzey	Thompson	Ellis	Hay	Jackson	Steele	Jones, Brown, Payne.	6
Batty	Betsy	Taylor	Howard	Stewart	Danzey	Thompson	Ellis	Hay	Jackson	Steele	Jones, Brown, Payne (10).	7
Batty	Smith	Taylor	Howard	Stewart	Danzey	Thompson	Betsy	Hay	Jackson	Steele	Brown, Timothy (2), Payne (10).	8
Batty	Betsy	Taylor	Howard	Stewart	Danzey	Thompson	Ellis	Payne	Jackson	Jones	Brown, Smith, Steele.	9
Batty	Betsy	Taylor	Howard	Brown	Danzey	Thompson	Ellis	Payne	Hunter	Jones	Smith (10), Timothy, Steele (11).	10
Batty	Betsy	Taylor	Howard	Brown	Danzey	Thompson	Jones	Payne	West	Steele	Smith, Ellis, Hay..	11
Batty	Betsy	Taylor	Howard	Brown	Danzey	Thompson	Jones	Payne	West	Steele	Smith, Hay, Ellis (11).	12
Batty	Betsy	Taylor	Howard	Brown	Danzey	Thompson	Jones	West	Payne	Hay	Smith, Timothy, Ellis.	13
Batty	Betsy	Taylor	Goddard	Brown	Danzey	Thompson	Jones	West	Hay	Steele	Payne (10), Howard (11), Smith (8).	14
Batty	Betsy	Taylor	Goddard	Brown	Danzey	Thompson	Sutton	Payne	Hay	Steele	Jones (11), Howard, Smith.	15
Batty	Betsy	Taylor	Howard	Brown	Danzey	Thompson	Sutton	West	Hay	Smith	Jones, Ellis, Payne.	16
Batty	Betsy	Taylor	Howard	Brown	Danzey	Thompson	Sutton	Payne	Hay	Smith	Jones (2), Ellis, Timothy.	17
Batty	Betsy	Taylor	Saunders	Brown	Danzey	Thompson	Ellis	West	Hay	Steele	Smith, Sutton, Payne.	18
Batty	Betsy	Taylor	Saunders	Brown	Danzey	Thompson	Ellis	West	Payne	Steele	Hay, Timothy, Sutton.	19
Batty	Betsy	Timothy	Saunders	Brown	Danzey	Thompson	Ellis	Payne	Hay	Steele	Kilner (11), Smith, Sutton.	20
Batty	Betsy	Timothy	Saunders	Brown	Danzey	Thompson	Ellis	Payne	Hay	Steele	Kilner (2), Smith (11), Sutton (8).	21
Batty	Betsy	Timothy	Saunders	Brown	Danzey	Thompson	Ellis	Payne	Hay	Steele	Kilner, Smith (8), Sutton.	22
Batty	Betsy	Timothy	Saunders	Brown	Sutton	Thompson	Ellis	Payne	Hay	Steele	Kilner, Smith, Taylor.	23
Batty	Betsy	Timothy	Saunders	Brown	Sutton	Thompson	Ellis	Payne	Hay	Steele	Kilner (11), Smith (7), Taylor.	24
Batty	Smith	Taylor	Saunders	Brown	Sutton	Thompson	Ellis	Hay	Payne	Steele	Timothy (6), Girdler (7), West.	25
Batty	Betsy	Taylor	Saunders	Brown	Sutton	Girdler	Ellis	Hay	Payne	Steele	West (10), Kilner, Kamara.	26
Batty	Betsy	Taylor	Saunders	Brown	Sutton	Thompson	Ellis	Hay	Payne	Steele	Girdler, West (7), Smith (11).	27
Abbey	Betsy	Smith	Saunders	Brown	Sutton	Thompson	Ellis	Hay	Payne	Taylor	West (10), Kilner, Steele (7).	28
Abbey	Betsy	Smith	Saunders	Brown	Sutton	Taylor	Ellis	Hay	West	Steele	Payne, Thompson, Kilner.	29
Abbey	Betsy	Smith	Taylor	Brown	Sutton	McAree	Ellis	Hay	Payne	Steele	West (11), Kamara, Alighieri.	30
Abbey	Betsy	Taylor	Saunders	Goddard	Sutton	McAree	Ellis	Hay	Payne	Steele	Smith (11), West, Kamara.	31
Batty	Betsy	Taylor	Saunders	Goddard	Sutton	McAree	Ellis	Hay	West	Steele	Smith (6), Kilner, Kamara.	32
Batty	Betsy	Smith	Saunders	Goddard	Taylor	McAree	Ellis	Payne	West	Hayward	Danzey(10), Steele(7), Kamara	33
Batty	Betsy	Smith	Saunders	Goddard	Danzey	Taylor	Ellis	Payne	West	Hayward	Steele(9), McAree, Kamara.	34
Batty	Betsy	Taylor	Saunders	Goddard	Danzey	McAree	Ellis	Hayward	West	Steele	Smith(5), Payne(8), Kamara.	35
Batty	Smith	Taylor	Saunders	Sutton	Danzey	McAree	Ellis	Payne	West	Hayward	Betsey (6), Hay (9), Steele (11).	36
Batty	Betsy	Smith	Saunders	Sutton	Taylor	McAree	Ellis	Hay	Payne	Hayward	West, Girdler, Kamara.	37
Batty	Betsy	Sm,ith	Saunders	Sutton	Taylor	McAree	Ellis	Hay	Payne	Hayward	West(10), Girdler, Timothy.	38
Batty	Betsy	Smith	Taylor	Sutton	Danzey	McAree	Ellis	Hay	Payne	Steele	West, Kamara, Kilner.	39
Batty	Betsy	Kamara	Saunders	Smith	Danzey	Payne	Ellis	Hay	West	Steele	Kilner, Timothy, Girdler.	40
Batty	Betsy	Kamara	Saunders	Smith	Danzey	Payne	Ellis	Hay	West	Steele	McAree(8), Kilner, Timothy..	41
Batty	Batsy	Kamara	Saunders	Smith	Danzey	Payne	Ellis	Hay	West	Steele	McAree, Sutton, Kilner.	42

1	2	3	4	5	6	7	8	9	10	11	12 14 15
Batty	Betsy	Taylor	Howard	Brown	Danzey	Thompson	Jones	West	Hay	Smith	Sutton (4), Ellis (8), Steele (10).
Batty	Betsy	Timothy	Sutton	Brown	Danzey	Thompson	Ellis	Hay	Payne	Steele	West (9), Smith (7), Taylor.
Searle	Kamara	Timothy	Sutton	Brown	Smith	Thompson	Jones	West	Payne	Hay	Kilner (7), Betsy (11), Batty.
Batty	Smith	Timothy	Sutton	Brown	Danzey	Ellis	Kamara	West	Payne	Steele	Jones, Hay, Taylor (4).
Batty	Smith	Timothy	Saunders	Brown	Taylor	Betsy	Ellis	Hay	West	Steele	Payne, Girdler (2), Searle.
Searle	Betsy	Smith	Saunders	Brown	Sutton	Thompson	Taylor	Payne	West	Kilner	Elklis (6), Steele (11), Hay (7).
Batty	Betsy	Smith	Saunders	Goddard	Taylor	McAree	Ellis	Hayward	West	Steele	Danzey (11), Kamara (8), Hay.
Abbey	Betsy	Smith	Saunders	Goddard	Danzey	Kamara	Hayward	Payne	West	Steele	Kilner, French, Girdler.
Batty	Betsy	Kamara	Saunders	Smith	Danzey	McAree	Ellis	Payne	Hayward	Steele	West, Kilner, Timothy.

1	2	3	4	5	6	7	8	9	10	11	12 14 15
Batty	Smith	Timothy	Saunders	Brown	Sutton	Thompson	Ellis	Payne	Hay	Steele	Betsy (8), Taylor (4), West (10).
Searle	Smith	Taylor	Saunders	Sutton	Danzey	Girdler	Kamara	West	Hay	French	Steele (8), Brown (6), Payne (10)
Batty	Betsy	Taylor	Saunders	Brown	Sutton	Thompson	Ellis	Hay	Payne	Steele	Girdler (7), West (9), Kamara (8).
Searle	Kamara	Smith	Taylor	Brown	Sutton	Thompson	Ellis	Payne	West	Steele	Kilner (7), Hay (9), Alighieri (2).
Batty	Betsy	Taylor	Saunders	Sutton	Danzey	Smith	Ellis	Hay	Payne	Steele	Kilner, Timothy, Girdler.
Batty	Betsy	Taylor	Saunders	Sutton	Danzey	McAree	Ellis	Hay	Payne	Steele	West, Smith, Kamara.

JOHN McGOVERN (MANAGER)

Date of Appointment July 1997

Date of Birth: 28th October 1949
Place of Birth: Montrose

PREVIOUS CLUBS
As manager
As player/manager Bolton Wanderers
As player Hartlepool U., Derby C., Leeds U., Nottingham Forest

HONOURS
As manager
As player S: u23 (2); European Cup 78-79,79-80, Div. 1 71-72, 78-79; Div. 2 68-69; League Cup 77-78, 78-79, R-up 79-80.

Assistant Manager / Coach: Brian Finn
Physio: Barry Kimber

KEVIN BETSY
Woking Player of the Year 1997-98
Kevin also won his first England Semi-Pro cap last season when he came on as sub against Holland.

Photo: Mark Sandom

MATCHDAY PROGRAMME

Number of pages 40
Price £1.30
Programme Editor Paul Beard
Other club publications:
"Winning isn't Everything" (fanzine)

Local Newspapers: Woking News & Mail
Woking Herald
Surrey Advertiser

Local Radio Stations: BBC Surrey Sussex
County Sound
BBC Southern Counties

1997-98 PLAYING SQUAD

PLAYER	Birthplace Honours	Birthdate	CLUBS
GOALKEEPERS			
Laurence Batty	Westminster ESP, FAT, ILP	15.2.64	Maidenhead U, Fulham, Brentford, Farense (Belg)
DEFENDERS			
Wayne Sutton	Derby	1.10.75	Derby Co
Michael Danzey	Widnes	8.2.71	Nottingham Forest, Peterborough U, St.Albans C, Cambridge U, Aylesbury U, £10k to Woking
Eddie Saunders	London		Civil Service, Sutton U, Yeading, Carshalton Ath
Richard Goddard	Burnt Oak	31.3.78	Arsenal, Brentford, £7,500 to Woking
Scott Smith	Christchurch New Zealand Int.	6.3.75	Rotherham U, Kettering T
Robin Taylor	Leicester FAT, British Students		Cambridge C, Hinckley T, Kettering T, Peterborough U, Kettering T, Port Vale, Dagenham & Redbridge
MIDFIELDERS			
Andy Ellis	Cardiff FAT, WSP		Barry T, Inter Cardiff, Barry T
Scott Steele	Motherwell FAT, SS	19.9.71	Airdrie
Grant Payne	Woking	25.12.75	Wimbledon
Kevin Betsy	London		From Youth team
FORWARDS			
Steve West	Essex	15.11.72	Arsenal, Purfleet, Tilbury, Aveley, East Thurrock U, Concord R, Enfield, £25k to Woking
Darron Hay	Hitchin FAT	17.12.69	Biggleswade T, Cambridge U

DEPARTURES (During the season)
Justin Jackson (Notts Co - £30k), Junior Hunter (Woking), Terry Howard, Kevan Brown & Steve Thompson (Yeovil T), Tom Jones (Forest Green R)

PLAYERS ON LOAN
Simon Stewart (Fulham), Richard Goddard (Brentford), Nathan Abbey (Luton T), Rod McAree (Fulham)

Kingfield Stadium, Woking

GROUND ADDRESS:
Kingfield Stadium, Kingfield, Woking, Surrey. GU22 9AA.
TELEPHONE NUMBER: 01483 772470

SIMPLE DIRECTIONS:
M25 J10 or 11, signposted from outskirts of Town. Ground 1 mile. Woking B.R.Station & buses from Woking.

CAPACITY: 6,000 **SEATED:** 2,500 **TERRACING - Covered:** 1,400 **Uncovered:** 2,100

SOCIAL FACILITIES:
Clubhouse open on matchdays. Food available.

CLUB SHOP:
Phone 01483 772470 for details.

Woking Fact File

Nickname: The Cards

Club Sponsors:

Club colours: Red/white halves & black shorts
Change colours: Blue & jade, white shorts.
Reserve team's league: Capital League
Midweek home matchday: Tuesday 7.45pm.

PREVIOUS - **Leagues:** West Surrey League 1895-1907, Isthmian League 1911-92
Grounds: Wheatsheaf, Ivy Lane (pre 1922)

CLUB RECORDS - **Attendance:** 6,000 v Swansea, FA Cup - 1978/79
v Coventry C., FA Cup - 1996-97
Win: 17-4 v Farnham, 1912-13.
Defeat: 0-16 v New Crusaders, 1905-06.
Career goalscorer: C Mortimore 331, 1953-65
Career appearances: B Finn 564, 1962-74
Transfer fee paid: £35,000 for Steve West to Enfield, Sept 1997.
Transfer fee received: £150,000 from Bristol Rovers for Steve Foster, May 1997.

BEST SEASON - **FA Cup:** 3rd Round replay 96-97, 1-2 (H) v Coventry after 1-1 (A)
League clubs defeated: Cambridge U., Millwall (96-97)
FA Trophy: Winners 93-94, 94-95, 96-97.
FA Amateur Cup: Winners 57-58.

HONOURS - FA Trophy 93-94, 94-95, 96-97; FA Amateur Cup 57-58; GM Vauxhall Conference R-up 94-95, 95-96; Isthmian League R-up 56-57, Lge AC Delco Cup 90-91, Div.1 R-up 89-90, Div.2 South 86-87, Reserve Section (2); West Surrey Lge (4), London Senior Cup R-up 82-83; Surrey Senior Cup 12-13, 26-27, 55-56, 56-57, 71-72, 90-91, 93-94, 95-96; Surrey Senior Shield (9); Surrey Premier Cup (2); Surrey Invitation Cup 66-67; Surrey Intermediate Cup (2); Channel Islands Victory Cup (2); Suburban Lge (2), Lge Cup (2); Diadora Premier Division 91-92; Isthmian League Charity Shield 91-92, 92-93; Vauxhall Championship Shield 94-95, R-up 95-96.

Past players who progressed to the Football League: Ray Elliott (M'wall 1946), Charlie Mortimore (A'shot 1949), Robert Edwards (Chelsea 1951), Ron Newman (Portsmouth 1955), Mervyn Gill (Southampton 1956), John Mortimore (Chelsea 1951), Reg Stratton (Fulham 1959), George Harris (Newport 1961), Norman Cashmore (A'shot 1963), Alan Morton (C.Palce 1967), William Holmes (Millwall 1970), Richard Forbes (Exeter 1979), Kevin Rattray (Gillingham 1995), Steve Foster (Bristol Rovers 1997), Justin Jackson (Notts Co. 1998).

1997-98 Captain: Kevan Brown / Andy Ellis.
1997-98 Top scorer: Darren Hay (22)
1997-98 Player of the Year: Kevin Betsy

YEOVIL TOWN

Yeovil's return to the top flight was welcomed by everyone, as the support and facilities at Huish Park are awelcome asset to any competition.

However the playing quality has to match those facets.

Initially the season got off to a solid start, and although never seriously in contention Yeovil were always there or thereabouts. Then came the unfortunate circumstances that produced a change of management and half the squad, and a slide in form.

It was going to be interesting to see whether the much needed consolidation could take place.

CLUB OFFICIALS 1998-99

Chairman	**John Fry**
President	**S N Burfield**
Company Secretary	**G R Smith**
Club Secretary	**Jean Cotton**
c/o the club. 01935 423662 (Tel) 473956 (Fax)	
Commercial Manager	**Alan Skirton**
Press Officer	**Jean Cotton**

The fact that it did, and with some style is a credit to Colin Lippiatt the new coach and his blend of exciting younsters, Ben Smith and David Piper and well respected senior players including internationals, Steve Stott, Kevan Brown, Steve Thompson and Owen Pickard and F.A. representatives Rob Cousins and Tony Pennock.

Add to them the goalscoring of Warren Patmore, the battlinhg qualities of Al James Hannigan and a carefully selected quartet of newcomers and you have another club, who with the confidence of a good start, are quite capable of testing the best.

L-R, Back Row: Terry Hardwell (Physio), Terry Cotton (Assistant Manager), Lee Archer, Al-James Hannigan, Tony Pennock, Dean Birkby, Warren Patmore, Rob Cousins, Kevan Brown, Colin Fielder (Player Coach), Colin Lippiatt (Team Manager & Head Coach). Front Row: David Piper, Ben Smith, Owen Pickard, Steve Stott (Captain), Steve Parmenter, Steve Thompson, Sam Winston.

YEOVIL TOWN - Match Facts 1997-98

Match No.	Date	Venue H / A	Comp.	Opponents	Result & Score		Att.	Goalscorers	League Position
1	16.08	H	VC	Stevenage Borough	W	2-1	3,602	Pickard 24, Patmore 76.	7
2	23.08	A	VC	Welling United	W	3-1	*840*	Patmore 9 (pen), 22, Pickard 53.	4
3	25.08	H	VC	Farnborough Town	L	0-1	3,286		7
4	30.08	H	VC	Leek Town	W	3-1	2470	Patmore 42, Pickard 68, 69.	4
5	06.09	A	VC	Halifax Town	L	1-3	*1,500*	Patmore	6
6	09.09	A	VC	Dover Athletic	L	0-1	*1,121*		10
7	20.09	H	VC	Rushden & Diamonds	L	1-2	2,317	Pickard 29.	17
8	23.09	H	VC	Kidderminster Harriers	W	1-0	2,129	Pickard 81.	12
9	04.10	A	VC	Stalybridge Celtic	L	2-3	*590*	Pickard 76, Patmore 85.	15
10	18.10	H	VC	Northwich Victoria	D	2-2	2,313	Hayfield 69, Archer 67.	17
11	01.11	A	VC	Hednesford Town	L	0-1	*1,366*		19
12	08.11	A	VC	Hereford United	D	1-1	*2,768*	Parmenter 45 (pen).	19
13	15.11	H	VC	Telford United	W	5-3	2,133	Pickard 11, Stott 24, Patmore 36, 79, Fielder 85 (pen)	14
14	22.11	H	VC	Woking	W	2-0	3,005	Stott 7, Roberts 76.	11
15	29.11	A	VC	Gateshead	W	3-0	*724*	Patmore 18, 38, Archer 56.	10
16	06.12	H	VC	Kettering Town	W	2-0	2,529	Archer 8, Pounder 80.	9
17	13.12	A	VC	Farnborough Town	D	2-2	*1,093*	Archer 18, Hannigan 25	9
18	20.12	H	VC	Slough Town	W	2-1	2,509	Pickard 45,69	9
19	26.12	A	VC	Cheltenham Town	L	0-2	*2,700*		
20	29.12	A	VC	Woking	L	0-2	*3,429*		
21	01.01	H	VC	Cheltenham Town	W	3-1	3,657	Chandler 45, Pickard 67, Stott 79	9
22	17.01	A	VC	Morecambe	L	0-1	*1,219*		12
23	20.01	H	VC	Hayes	W	4-3	1,705	Engwell 13, Pickard 21, Stott 72, Patmore 81.	8
24	31.01	H	VC	Welling United	D	1-1	2,236	Denys 20.	8
25	07.02	A	VC	Stevenage Borough	L	1-2	*2,897*	Stott 8.	10
26	14.02	A	VC	Hayes	**L**	**4-6**	*715*	Fielder 12 (pen), Patmore 22, 90, Thompson 72.	11
27	21.02	H	VC	Halifax Town	L	0-1	2,584		11
28	28.02	A	VC	Kidderminster Harriers	L	1-3	1,868	Pickard 31.	12
29	07.03	H	VC	Morecambe	L	2-3	2,140	Pickard 59, Winston 61.	12
30	10.03	A	VC	Kettering Town	D	1-1	1,116	Winston 75.	12
31	14.03	H	VC	Stalybridge Celtic	W	2-0	1,862	Parmenter 59, Winston 86.	11
32	17.03	A	VC	Telford United	**W**	**4-1**	*565*	Archer 66, Smith 68, 74, Winston 88.	9
33	21.03	A	VC	Northwich Victoria	L	1-2	*902*	Winston 90.	11
34	31.03	H	VC	Southport	D	0-0	1,927		11
35	11.04	H	VC	Hednesford Town	W	1-0	2,207	Thompson 52.	11
36	13.04	A	VC	Slough Town	D	1-1	*912*	Stott 63.	11
37	18..04	H	VC	Hereford United	W	2-0	2,601	Smith 12, 44.	10
38	21.04	A	VC	Rushden & Diamonds	D	2-2	*1,784*	Smith 53, Winston 62.	10
39	25.04	A	VC	Southport	L	1-2	*849*	Patmore 33.	11
40	28.04	H	VC	Dover Athletic	**W**	**4-1**	1,817	Pickard 3, 62, Archer 45(pen), 65.	11
41	30.04	A	VC	Leek Town	L	0-2	*775*		11
42	02.05	H	VC	Gateshead	W	6-3	2,567	**Patmore 3** (9, 25, 45), Pickard 10, Archer 15, Stott 31.	11

CUP COMPETITIONS SCC - Spalding Chall. Cup SPC - Somerset Prem. Cup ICS - Isthmian Championship Shield

Date	Venue	Comp.	Opponents	Result	Score	Att.	Goalscorers
13.09	H	**FAC 1Q**	Witney Town	D	1-1	1,704	Pickard 8.
17.09	A	1Q R	Witney Town	W	2-1	322	Pickard 6, 41.
27.09	A	2Q	Worcester City	W	2-1	1,201	Pickard 65, Kemp 76.
11.10	H	3Q	ChippenhamTown	W	4-0	1,762	Pickard 15, Kemp 45, Birkby 65 (pen), Hannion 71.
25.10	H	4Q	Hayes	D	1-1	2,501	Pickard 64.
28.10	A	4Q R	Hayes	L	0-1	1,132	
10.01	H	**FAT 1**	Yeading	D	0-0	2,016	
13.01	A	1 R	Yeading	L	0-1	286	
19.08	H	**ICS**	Boreham Wood	W	1-0	864	Patmore (pen)
07.10	H	**SCC 1**	Cheltenham Town	W	3-1	1007	**Birkby 3** (21, 22, 76).
01.12	A	2	Stevenage Borough	W	3-0	816	Pickard 43 , Patmore 51, Calderhead 65
16.12	A	3	Hayes	L	0-3	171	
14.10	H	**SPC** 1	Bristol Manor Ffarm	W	6-0	320	**Birkby 3**, Pickard, O.G., Archer.
25.11	A	2	Paulton Rovers	W	4-1	189	Miller, **Gale 3** (1 pen).
10.02	A	3	Brislington	W	2-0	300	Gale 2.
03.03	A	SF	Weston-super-Mare	W	2-1	275	Patmore 7, Gale 63.
07.04	N	**Final**	Clevedon Town	W	1-0	478	Stott 35. Played at Twerton Park (Bath City F.C.)

League Attendances	HIGHEST: 3,657 v Cheltenham Town	LOWEST: 1,705 v Welling United
CONFERENCE: 11th	**FA CUP:** 4th Qual. Round	**FA TROPHY:** 1st Round

1	2	3	4	5	6	7	8	9	10	11	12 14 15	
Pennock	Harvey	Engwell	White	Hannigan	Cousins	Fielder	Browne	Patmore	Pickard	Winter	Kemp(11), Roberts, Wimble (8).	1
Pennock	Harvey	Engwell	White	Hannigan	Cousins	Fielder	Browne	Patmore	Pickard	Birkby	Kemp(2), Wimble(3), Winter(11).	2
Pennock	Harvey	Engwell	White	Hannigan	Cousins	Fielder	Browne	Patmore	Pickard	Birkby	Kemp(8), Braybrook(3), Winter(2).	3
Pennock	Harvey	White	Roberts	Hannigan	Cousins	Fielder	Browne	Patmore	Pickard	Wimble	Winter(11), Braybrook(8), Birkby(2).	4
Pennock	White	Harvey	Roberts	Hannigan	Cousins	Fielder	Kemp	Patmore	Pickard	Winter	Braybrook Pounder Miller	5
Pennock	Kemp	White	Roberts	Hannigan	Cousins	Fielder	Braybrook	Patmore	Pickard	Harvey	Pounder(4), Winter(3), Birkby(8).	6
Pennock	Hayfield	White	Stott	Hannigan	Cousins	Fielder	Parmenter	Patmore	Pickard	Kemp	Birkby(11), Winter(2), Engwell(10).	7
Pennock	Hayfield	Engwell	White	Hannigan	Cousins	Kemp	Parmenter	Birkby	Pickard	Stott	Fielder(2), Patmore(4), Browne(9).	8
Pennock	Kemp	White	Stott	Hayfield	Cousins	Fielder	Browne	Patmore	Pickard	Parmenter	Harvey(8), Birkby(?), Calderhead(5).	9
Pennock	Kemp	Engwell	Hayfield	Hannigan	Cousins	Fielder	Parmenter	Archer	Birkby	Stott	Pickard(10), Harvey(3), Browne(7).	10
Pennock	White	Engwell	Hayfield	Hannigan	Cousins	Fielder	Browne	Parmenter	Pickard	Stott	Kemp(3), Archer(8), Harvey(5).	11
Pennock	Browne	Engwell	White	Harvey	Cousins	Fielder	Stott	Patmore	Pickard	Parmenter	Kemp(9), Calderhead(7), Archer(?).	12
Pennock	White	Engwell	Browen	Harvey	Cousins	Fielder	Archer	Patmore	Pickkard	Stott	Roberts, Kemp, Hannigan(5).	13
Pennock	Browne	Engwell	Roberts	Hannigan	Cousins	Fielder	Stott	Patmore	Pickard	Archer	Pounder(2), Kemp(3), Calderhead	14
Pennock	Browne	Kemp	Chandler	Hannigan	Cousins	Fielder	Sott	Patmore	Pickard	Archer	Pounder(2), Roberts, Calderhead(8).	15
Pennock	Browne	Kemp	Chandler	Hannigan	Cousins	Fielder	Stott	Patmore	Pickard	Archer	Pounder(10), Roberts, Calderhead(2).	16
Penncok	Browne	Kemp	Chandler	Hannigan	Cousins	Fielder	Stott	Patmore	Pickard	Archer	Pounder, Engwell(3), Calderhead(2).	17
Pennock	Browne	Engwell	Chandler	Hannigan	Cousins	Fielder	Stott	Patmore	Pickard	Archer	Kemp, Roberts(?), Calderhead(?).	18
Pennock	Pounder	Engwell	Chandler	Hannigan	Cousins	Fielder	Stott	Patmore	Pickard	Archer	Kemp, Browne(11), Birkby(5).	19
Pennock	Archer	Engwell	Chandler	Hannigan	Cousins	Fielder	Browne	Patmore	Pickard	Stott	Calderhead(7), Kemp(8), Birkby(10).	20
Penncok	Chandler	Engwell	Roberts	Hannigan	Cousims	Kemp	Stott	Patmore	Pickard	Freeman	Calderhead, Browne(11), Archer(9).	21
Pennock	Freeman	Engwell	Chandler	Hannigan	Cousins	Fielder	Stott	Patmore	Pickard	Browne	Kemp(2), Howard, Archer(9).	22
Pennock	Archer	Engwell	Chandler	Hannigan	Cousins	Fielder	Stiott	Patmore	Pickard	Browne	Kemp (11), Howard (7), Freeman	23
Pennock	D Thompson	Archer	Howard	Hannigan	Cousins	Fielder	Stott	Denys	Pickard	Browne	Kemp (7), Roberts, Pounder (8)	24
Pennock	Browne	Kemp	Howard	Hannigan	D Thompson	Fielder	Stott	Denys	Pickard	Archer	Pounder (5), Collier, Miller.	25
Pennock	Engwell	Archer	Howard	D Thompson	Cousins	Fielder	Stott	Patmore	Pickard	Browne	Pounder(3), Denys(2), Calderhead(11).	26
Pennock	D Thompson	Pounder	Howard	Hannigan	Cousins	Fielder	Stott	Patmore	Pickard	Calderhead	Spencer (8), Denys (12), Birkby (10).	27
•Pennock	Engwell	Archer	Howard	Hannigan	Cousins	Fielder	Calderhead	Patmore	Pickard	Piper	Denys 98), Birkby (3), Thompson.	28
Pennock	Piper	Smith	Howard	Onogbehin	Cousins	Fielder	Stott	Patmore	Pickard	Parmenter	Pounder (7), Archer (4), Winston (9).	29
Pennock	Piper	Smith	Birkby	Brown	Cousins	Fielder	Stott	Patmore	Pickard	Parmenter	Archer, Howard, Winston (9).	30
Pennock	Piper	Smith	Birkby	Hannigan	Cousins	Thompson	Stott	Patmore	Pickard	Parmenter	Fielder (4), Archer (11), Winston (10).	31
Pennock	Piper	Smith	K Brown	Hannigan	Cousins	Thompson	Stott	Patmore	Pickard	Parmenter	Archer (11), Winston (10), Pounder.	32
Pennock	Piper	Smith	Winston	Hannigan	Cousins	Thompson	Stott	Patmore	Pickard	Parmenter	Pounder (?), Archer (11), Birkby.	33
Pennock	Piper	Smith	K Brown	Hannigan	Cousins	Thompson	Stott	Winston	Birkby	Parmenter	Pounder, Archer (11), Fielder.	34
Penncok	Piper	Smith	K Brown	Hannigan	Cousins	Thompson	Stott	Patmore	Winston	Parmenter	Pickard(10), Fielder(3), Archer.	35
Pennock	Pounder	Smith	K Brown	Hannigan	Cousins	Thompson	Stott	Patmore	Pickard	Parmenter	Winston(10), Archer(11), Fielder.	36
Pennock	Piper	Smith	K Brown	Hannigan	Cousins	Thompson	Stott	Patmore	Pickard	Archer	Winston((10), Fielder(3), Pounder(11).	37
Penncok	Piper	Smith	K Brown	Hannigan	Cousins	Thompson	Stott	Patmore	Winston	Archer	Parmenter(10), Fielder, Pounder.	38
Penncok	Piper	Smith	K Brown	Hannigan	Cousins	Thompson	Stott	Patmore	Pickard	Archer	Fielder, Winston(2), Parmenter(3)	39
Penncok	Piper	Smith	K Brown	Hannigan	Cousins	Thompson	Stott	Patmore	Pickard	Archer	Fielder(8), Winston(10),Parmenter(11)	40
Penncok	Piper	Smith	K Brown	Hannigan	Cousins	Thompson	Stott	Patmore	Winston	Archer	Fielder(2), Pounder(3), Parmenter(10).	41
Pennock	Piper	Smith	K Brown	Hannigan	Cousins	Thompson	Stott	Patmore	Pickard	Archer	Winston(3), Fielder(7),Parmenter(10).	42

1	2	3	4	5	6	7	8	9	10	11	12 14 15
Pennock	Harvey	White	Braybrook	Hannigan	Browne	Fielder	Kemp	Patmore	Pickard	Winter	Roberts, Birkby(10), Wimble(6).
Pennock	Pounder	White	Roberts	Hannigan	Cousins	Fielder	Kemp	Patmore	Pickard	Birkby	Harvey, Winter(11), Calderhead(10).
Pennock	White	Engwell	Browne	Hannigan	Cousins	Fielder	Kemp	Patmore	Pickard	Stott	Birkby(4), Harvey,, Winter(9).
Pennock	Kemp	Harvey	Roberts	Hannigan	Cousins	Fielder	Browne	Birkby	Pickard	Stott	Pounder(2), White(4), Calderhead(7).
Pennock	White	Engwell	Roberts	Hannigan	Cousins	Browne	Kemp	Archer	Pickard	Stott	Harvey(2), Fielder(8), Birkby(7).
Pennock	White	Engwell	Birkby	Hannigan	Cousins	Kemp	Browne	Archer	Pickard	Stott	Harvey(7), Fielder, Calderhead(5).
Pennock1	Howard	Engwell	Archer	Hannigan	Cousins	Kemp	Stott	Birkby	Pickard	Browne	Calderhead(11), Pounder(2), Roberts(4).
Pennock	Kemp	Engwell	Howard	Hannigan	Cousins	Fielder	Stott	Calderhead	Pickard	Pounder	Browne(7), Roberts(3), Archer(2).
Pennock	Harvey	Engwell	White	Hannigan	Cousins	Fielder	Browne	Patmore	Picjkard	Kemp	Wimble(10), Braybrook(11), Stone.
Pennock	Hayfield	Kemp	Roberts	Hannigan	Cousins	Fielder	Parmenter	Archer	Birkby	Stott	Harvey(4), Browne(11), Calderhead(10).
Pennock	Kemp	Pounder	Chandler	Hannigan	Cousins	Fielder	Stott	Patmore	Pickard	Brown	Collier(7), Claderhead(11), Miller(5).
Pennock	Archer	Engwell	Chandler	Hannigan	Cousins	Calderhead	Kemp	Patmore	Pounder	Stott	Pickard(11), Fielder(8), Birkby(9).
Pennock	White	Engwell	Harvey	Hannigan	Cousins	Calderhead	Browne	Pickard	Birkby	Archer	Pounder(2), Miller(6), Gale(9).
Pennock	Miller	Collier	Cousins	Kemp	Stott	Fielder	Archer	Gale	Pounder	Smith	Patmore, Engwell, Hannigan.
Pennock	Pounder	Engwell	Howard	Collier	Miller	Calderhead	Browne	Patmore	Kemp	Gale	Smith (11), Birkby (10), Fricker (8).
Pennock	Engwell	Archer	Howard	Calderhead	Cousins	Gale	Fielder	Patmore	Birkby	Miller	Collier (3), Pounder (11), Fricker.
Penncok	Piper	Archer	Fielder	Hannigan	Cousins	Miller	Stott	Pounder	Birkby	Calderhead	Fricker(10), Smith (2), Collier.

COLIN LIPPIAT (HEAD COACH)

Date of Appointment — February 1998

Date of Birth: — 1st January 1942
Place of Birth: — Hayes

PREVIOUS CLUBS

As asst. manager/coach
Windsor & Eton, Farnbrough Town, Woking, Kingstonian.

As player — Hayes, Wokingham & Maidenhead

HONOURS

As asst. manager/coach
(Woking) FA Trophy 94, 95, 97, Conf R-up 95, 96;
(Windsor & Eton) Athenian Lge (2); FA Vase S-F & Q-F.

As player — None

Assistant Manager: Terry Cotton **Player/Coach:** Steve Thompson **Physio:** Terry Hardwell

Owen Pickard
Leading Goalscorer 1997-98
Photo: Andrew Chitty

Tony Pennock
Ever-present last season playing 59 matches.
Photo: Ken Gregory

MATCHDAY PROGRAMME

Number of pages — 48

Price — £1.50

Programme Editor — Bryan Moore

Other club publications: — "100 Huish Heroes" £3.
Centenary Book £14.95.
(Both available from the club)

Local Newspapers: — Western Gazette
Western Daily Press
Bristol Evening Post; Sunday Independent.

Local Radio Stations: — Radio Bristol
Somerset Sound
Orchard FM.

1997-98 PLAYING SQUAD

PLAYER	Birthplace Honours	Birthdate	CLUBS
GOALKEEPERS			
Tony Pennock	Swansea ILP	10.4.71	Stockport Co, Wigan A, Hereford U
DEFENDERS			
Kevan Brown	Andover ESP, FAT, Div 3	25.6.68	Southampton, Brighton & H.A., Aldershot, Woking, £7,500 to Yeovil T
Rob Cousins	Bristol ILP	9.1.71	Bristol C, Bath C, £15k to Yeovil T Grays A
Murray Fishlock	Marlborough	23.9.73	Swindon T, Gloucester C, Trowbridge T, Hereford U.
Al-James Hannigan	London ILP, SLP	26.1.71	Arsenal, Barnet, Harwich & Parkeston, Harlow T, Marlow, Enfield, £5k to Rushden & Diamonds, £6k to Enfield
David Piper	Bournemouth	31.10.77	Southampton
MIDFIELDERS			
Rob Calderhead	Liverpool	8.12.76	Watford, Bideford
Ben Smith	Chelmsford	23.11.78	Arsenal, Reading
Steve Stott	Leeds ESP, SLP	3.2.65	Alvechurch, Bromsgrove R, £18k to Kettering T, £30k to Rushden & D, £9k to Yeovil T
Steve Stott	Leeds ESP, SLP	3.2.65	Alvechurch, Bromsgrove R, £18k to Kettering T, £30k to Rushden & D, £9k to Yeovil T
Steve Thompson	Plymouth ESP, GMVC, FAT, ILP	12.1.63	Bristol C, Torquay U, Saltash U, Slough T, Wycombe W, Woking, £5k to Yeovil T
FORWARDS			
Dean Birkby	Castleford ILP	3.3.71	Mangotsfield U, Clevedon T, Mangotsfield U, Gloucester C, Yate T, Bath C, £10k to Yeovil T
Sufyan Ghazghazi	Honiton	24.08.77	Exeter City (T)
Steve Parmenter	Chelmsford	22.1.77	QPR, Bristol R
Warren Patmore	Kingsbury ILP	14.8.71	Northwood, Cambridge U, Millwall, Northampton T, Ards
Owen Pickard	Barnstaple	18.11.69	Plymouth A, Hereford U, Dorchester T

Departures: Kevin Braybrook (Salisbury C), Shaun Wimble (Witney T), Steve Winter (Taunton T), Chris White (Foranborough T), Andy Clement (Staines T), Lee Harvey (Aylesbury U - £2k), Jeff Wrightson (Kingstonian), Graham Roberts (Wealdstone), Micky Engwell, Graham Kemp, David Thompson & Steve Browne (Chesham U), Simon Spencer (Released), Terry Howard (Aldershot), Lee Archer (Rushden & Ds.), Chris Seymour (Released), Colin Fielder (Released), Sammy Winston (N.C.

PLAYERS ON LOAN - Steve Parmenter & Matt Hayfield (Bristol R), Dean Chandler (Lincoln C), Andy Freeman (Reading), Ryan Denys (Brentford), Colin Omogbehin (Luton T)

Huish Park, Yeovil

GROUND ADDRESS: Huish Park, Lufton Way, Yeovil Somerset, BA22 8YF.

TELEPHONE NUMBERS: 01935 423662. Fax 01935 73956.

SIMPLE DIRECTIONS: Leave A303 at Cartgate r'about, take A3088 signposted Yeovil. 1st exit at next r'about, 1st exit at next r'about into Lufton Way. Railway station - Yeovil Pen Mill (Bristol/Westbury to Weymouth) 2.5 miles from ground. Bus service from stations on Saturday.

CAPACITY: 8,720 **SEATED:** 5,212 **COVERED TERRACING:** 3,508

SOCIAL FACILITIES: Matchdays hot + cold food available. Meals can be ordered provided advance notice is given. All weather astro turf pitch available for bookings 9am-10pm.

CLUB SHOP: Open on matchdays selling full range of souvenirs, match programmes, scarves, hats, replica kits and badges.

Yeovil Fact File

Nickname: Glovers **Sponsors:** Precision Publishing Papers.

Club Colours: Green & white/white/green & white

Change Colours: French navy & red quarters/red/navy.

Midweek matchday: Tuesday

Reserve League: Screwfix Direct, Western Lge Prem. Div.

Local Press: Western Gazette, Western Daily Press, Bristol Evening Post, Sunday Independent.

Local Radio: Radio Bristol, Somerset Sound, Orchard FM.

PREVIOUS -
Leagues: Western League, London Combination, Southern League, Alliance Premier, Isthmian, GMV Conference, Isthmian.
Names: Yeovil & Petters Utd
Ground: The Huish until 1993

CLUB RECORDS -
Attendance: 8,612 v Arsenal 3rd Rd FA Cup 02/1/93.
Career Goalscorer: Dave Taylor 285 1960-69
Career Appearances: Len Harris, 691, 1958-72
Win: 10-0 v Kidderminster Harriers (H), Southern Lge. 27.12.1955
v Bedford Town (H), Southern Lge. 4.3.61
Defeat: 0-8 v Manchester Utd., FA Cup 5th Rd. 12.2.49 at Maine Rd. (81,565).
Transfer Fee Paid: £17,500 to Oxford City for Howard Forinton 1.97.
Transfer Fee Received: £75,000 for Mark Shail from Bristol City.
for Howard Forinton from Birmingham City 1997

BEST SEASON -
FA Trophy: Semi-Final 70-71 71-72.
FA Cup: 5th Rd 1948-49 3rd Rd 92-93.
League clubs beaten: (14)

HONOURS - Southern Lge 54-55, 63-64, 70-71, R-up 23-24, 31-32, 34-35, 69-70, 72-73. Southern Lge Cup 48-49, 54-55, 60-61, 65-66. Vauxhall-Opel Lge (Isthmian) 87-88, R-up 85-86, 86-87. ICIS Prem. (Isthmian) 96-97; AC Delco Cup 87-88. Bob Lord Trophy 89-90, R-up 93-94.

Players Progressing to Football Lge: Over 40 players & 18 managers including, since 1985, Nigel Jarvis (Torquay), Ian Davies (Bristol Rovers), Alan Pardew (Crystal Palace), Paul Miller (Wimbledon) John McGinlay (Bolton), Guy Whittingham (Portsmouth), Mark Shail (Bristol City), Malcom McPherson (West Ham), Howard Forinton & Jerry Gill (Birmingham City).

97-98 **Captain:** Steve Stott
97-98 **Player of the Year:** Steve Stott
97-98 **Supporters P.o.Y.:** Rob Cousins
97-98 **Top scorer:** Owen Pickard

NORTHERN PREMIER LEAGUE

PYRAMID SECTION

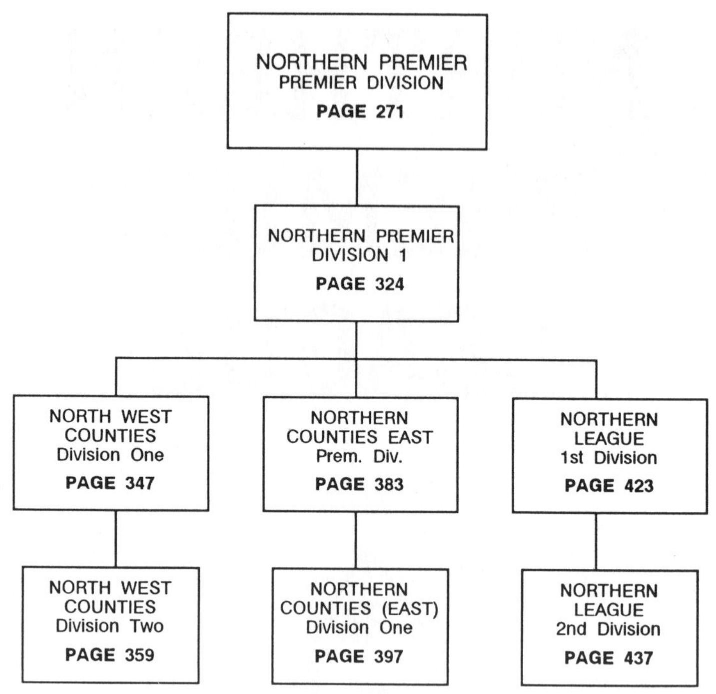
NORTHERN PREMIER
PREMIER DIVISION
PAGE 271
NORTHERN PREMIER
DIVISION 1
PAGE 324
NORTH WEST
COUNTIES
Division One
PAGE 347
NORTHERN
COUNTIES EAST
Prem. Div.
PAGE 383
NORTHERN
LEAGUE
1st Division
PAGE 423
NORTH WEST
COUNTIES
Division Two
PAGE 359
NORTHERN
COUNTIES (EAST)
Division One
PAGE 397
NORTHERN
LEAGUE
2nd Division
PAGE 437

FEEDER & OTHER FEATURED LEAGUES

UniBond League

President: N White F.S.C.A.

Chairman: Ken Marsden

Vice Chairman: K F Brown

Secretary & Treasurer: R D Bayley,
22 Woburn Drive, Hale, Altrincham, Cheshire WA15 8LZ
Tel: 0161 980 7007 Fax: 0161 904 8850

There was little doubt as to who the teams of the season were in either of the two Divisions of the UniBond League with eventual respective Champions Barrow and Whitby Town being everybody's favourites for a long time.

In the top flight Barrow hit the top in September and were never headed thereafter and despite a few nervous moments in March when their lead, which had been as much as thirteen points in January, was whittled down to four points the "Bluebirds" still had enough fuel left in the tank to pull away again in the finishing straight.The final day saw Boston United clinch runners-up spot whilst the surprise package of the campaign, newly promoted Leigh, finished in third - their highest ever UniBond placing. In fourth came Runcorn on the back of Liam Watson's 39 goals but they had the consolation of lifting the President's Cup to capture their first silverware in nine years despite having appeared in ten various finals during that period. Gainsborough Trinity had a very solid season to finish fifth and again made the Challenge Cup Final only to lose out to Altrincham and fail to retain the Cup. Altrincham's success was, surprisingly, their first trophy for twelve years and came courtesy of two strikes from record signing Keith Russell who notched 20 goals in just 19 appearances.

The big disappointments were the previous season's runners-up and third place clubs Bishop Auckland and Hyde United who finished 10th and 12th this time round whilst First Division Champions last time round, Radcliffe Borough, found life at the top tough and were relegated straight back along with Alfreton Town who only managed two seasons in the top tier.

Whitby Town's UniBond debut was spoiled by Workington who were surprising opening day victors over the newcomers. Thereafter, though, the two clubs' seasons went on diverging courses with Whitby finishing as Champions and the former Football League outfit suffering the demise of relegation yet again. Ashton United, Worksop Town, Witton Albion and Droylsden all harboured ambitions of joining Whitby but a poor spell around Christmas hampered the last named for the rest of the season whilst Albion faded badly towards the end and didn't even manage a top six finish. That left Ashton and Worksop fighting for the one spot with Worksop lasting home the stronger. One cannot help feel sympathy, however, for Ashton who finished with the highest number of points for a club not promoted since the formation of the First Division in 1987. They also lost out in two semi-finals and have now finished third in three of their six UniBond campaigns.

Newcomers Trafford lifted the Unifilla First Division Cup at the expense of Lincoln United who themselves did well to finish fifth in the league after a disappointing start. Lincoln, like Ashton have been a model of consistency and achieved two third places and a fifth in their three seasons in the League. Sadly, the season saw the second relegation in successive seasons of Buxton and the Derbyshire club who have contributed much to the NPL over the years are now bound for the feeder leagues.

The lasting memory of the campaign, however, will be that of Emley who were almost national celebrities, let alone UniBond heroes, with their fantastic FA Cup run that saw them give West Ham United a severe fright before bowing out by the odd goal in three.

Tony Carrol, Radcliffe Borough
Photo: John L Newton

Paul Heavey, Runcorn FC
Photo: Andrew Chitty

Gary Robson, Gateshead
Photo: Peter Barnes

Paul Pitman, Whitby Town
Photo: Neil Thaler

CHALLENGE CUP 1997-98

FIRST ROUND

Alfreton Town	1 v 3	Matlock Town
	After 1-1	
Bamber Bridge	2 v 1	Gretna
Belper Town	3 v 0	Buxton
Bradford Park Ave.	1 v 0	Lincoln United
Droylsden	2 v 1	Witton Albion
Flixton	0 v 1	Ashton United
	After 2-2	
Leigh RMI	3 v 1	Workington
	After 1-1	
Radcliffe Borough	3 v 0	Gt. Harwood Town
Stocksbridge P. S.	3 v 0	Farsley Celtic
Trafford	1 v 2	Congleton Town
Whitby Town	6 v 1	Harrogate Town
Whitley bay	8 v 3	Netherfield
Worksop Town	1 v 4	Eastwood Town

SECOND ROUND

Altrincham	3 v 0	Droylsden
Bamber Bridge	0 v 1	Chorley
Barrow	0 v 3	Lancaster City
Belper Town	1 v 0	Stocksbridge Park S.
Blyth Spartans	1 v 0	Whitley Bay
Boston United	1 v 0	Emley
Bardford Park Ave.	0 v 2	Frickley Athletic
Colwyn Bay	1 v 0	Hyde United
* Congleton Town	3 v 2	Winsford United
	After 3-3	
Gainsborough Trinity	2 v 0	Matlock Town
Guiseley	0 v 3	Bishop Auckland
Leigh RMI	2 v 0	Radcliffe Borough
	After 0-0	
Marine	2 v 0	Accrington Stanley
	After 4-4	
Whitby Town	0 v 1	Spennymoor United
	After 1-1	

** Congleton Town were expelled from the competition for playing an ineligible player*

THIRD ROUND

Altincham	4 v 2	Colwyn Bay
* Belper Town	3 v 2	Bishop Auckland
	After 1-1	
Blyth Spartans	4 v 1	Frickley Athletic
Chorley	5 v 2	Leigh RMI
Gainsborough Trinity	4 v 2	Eastwood Town
Marine	1 v 0	Runcorn
Spennymoor United	1 v 3	Boston United
Winsford United	1 v 0	Lancaster City

** Belper Town were expelled from the competition for playing an ineligible player*

FOURTH ROUND

Altrincham	2 v 1	Boston United
	After 1-1	
Blyth Spartans	2 v 0	Marine
Gainsborough Trinity	2 v 1	Bishop Auckland
	After 0-0	
Winsford United	0 v 1	Chorley
	After 0-0	

SEMI FINAL (Two Legs)

Altrincham	2 v 0	Chorley
Chorley	3 v 2	Altrincham
Blyth Spartans	1 v 2	Gainsborough Trinity
Gainsborough Trinity	2 v 1	Blyth Spartans

FINAL (at Chesterfield F.C.)

Altrincham	**2** v 1	Gainsborough Trinity
	A.E.T.	

PRESIDENT'S CUP 1997-98

FIRST ROUND

Altrincham	0 v 1	Leigh RMI
Ashton United	2 v 1	Worksop Town
Barrow	2 v 5	Marine
Blyth Spartans	3 v 2	Bishop Auckland
Boston United	1 v 0	Bradford Park Ave.
Emley	2 v 0	Stocksbridge P.S.
Farsley Celtic	0 v 1	Guiseley
Runcorn	3 v 1	Radcliffe Borough
	After 0-0	

SECOND ROUND

Ashton United	2 v 1	Emley
Blyth Sparttans	4 v 2	Boston United
	After Extra Time & after 3-3	
Guiseley	0 v 0	Leigh RMI
	After 0-0	
Runcorn	2 v 1	Marine

SEMI-FINALS (Two Legs)

Ashton United	1 v 1	Guiseley
Guiseley	2 v 1	Ashton United
Blyth Spartans	2 v 1	Runcorn

No 2nd leg - Blyth were expelled for playing an ineligbile player in the 1st leg.

FINAL

Guiseley	1 v **2**	**Runcorn**
Runcorn	**3** v 2	Guiseley

UNIBOND PREMIER DIVISION

Final League Table

		HOME					AWAY							Leading Goalscorers (these include all goals as reported in the league bulletin)		
	P	W	D	L	F	A	W	D	L	F	A	PTS	GD			
Barrow	42	13	3	5	29	13	12	5	4	32	16	83	32	15 Morton	13 Coates	7 by 3 players
Boston United	42	11	6	4	29	23	11	6	4	26	17	78	15	16 Charles	12 Chambers	7 Cavell & Cook
Leigh RMI	42	12	6	3	32	15	9	7	5	31	26	76	22	17 Evans	12 Shaw	9 Ridings
Runcorn	42	13	5	3	43	19	9	4	8	37	31	75	30	39 Watson	20 McNally	10 Salt
Gainsborough Trinity	42	14	2	5	32	16	8	7	6	28	23	75	21	16 Brown	15 Morrow	13 Riley
Emley	42	14	5	2	45	21	8	3	10	36	40	74	20	19 Banks	18 Graham	18 Hurst
Winsford United	42	9	8	4	26	15	10	4	7	28	28	69	11	13 Steele	8 Shaughnessy	8 Wheeler
Altrincham	42	14	4	3	51	15	4	7	10	25	29	65	32	21 Hardy	17 Russell,	9 C-Excell & Taylor
Guiseley	42	7	9	5	35	31	9	7	5	26	22	64	8	23 Matthews	20 Davison	6 Foreman
Bishop Auckland	42	9	6	6	46	34	8	6	7	32	26	63	18	23 Ellison	22 Shaw	13 Peverill
Marine	42	8	5	8	27	28	7	6	8	29	31	56	-3	15 Morgan	9 Bainbridge	9 Gautrey
Hyde United	42	8	6	7	32	29	5	10	6	28	26	55	5	18 Nolan	14 James	13 Kimmins
Colwyn Bay	42	10	5	6	37	28	5	4	12	16	29	54	-4	12 Limbert	9 Lawton	8 Roberts
Spennymoor United	42	6	8	7	26	31	8	3	10	32	41	*52	-14	13 Alderson	13 Preen	9 Innes
Chorley	42	9	4	8	27	28	5	3	13	24	42	49	-19	20 Swailes	9 Thompson	7 Potts
Frickley Athletic	42	11	4	6	28	22	1	8	12	17	40	48	-17	9 Armstrong	9 Hancock	5 by 4 players
Lancaster City	42	10	5	6	35	26	3	3	15	20	48	47	-19	13 Dobie	8 Lancaster	7 Cheal
Blyth Spartans	42	6	6	9	26	33	6	7	8	26	30	!39	-11	19 Fletcher	17 Atkinson	11 Moat
Bamber Bridge	42	6	5	10	32	36	3	7	11	19	38	39	-23	11 Diggle	11 Vickers	5 Eaves
Accrington Stanley	42	5	9	7	28	30	3	5	13	21	38	38	-19	13 Welch	11 Haw	6 Smith
Radcliffe Borough	42	2	6	13	20	32	4	6	11	19	38	30	-31	9 Lunt	6 McCrory,	5 Carroll & Connor
Alfreton Town	42	2	7	12	19	40	1	6	14	13	46	22	-54	4 Brady	4 Dempsey	3 Stacey

* 1 point, ! 10 points - deducted, for breach of rule.

Results 1997-98

		1	2	3	4	5	6	7	8	9	10	11	12	13	14	15	16	17	18	19	20	21	22	
1	Accrington Stanley	X	1-1 (470)	1-1 (576)	1-1 (515)	0-1 (588)	1-1 (428)	2-0 (507)	1-1 (527)	0-3 (492)	1-2 (313)	4-2 (549)	3-0 (480)	0-2 (417)	2-3 (525)	1-1 (362)	1-1 (421)	1-3 (1461)	1-1 (460)	2-2 (662)	0-3 (604)	3-0 (409)	2-1 (549)	1
2	Alfreton Town	0-1 (262)	X	0-3 (324)	1-2 (165)	0-3 (206)	2-6 (279)	0-3 (195)	1-2 (285)	1-1 (165)	1-1 (149)	1-1 (384)	2-1 (162)	2-3 (273)	1-1 (149)	0-0 (154)	1-1 (153)	3-2 (130)	0-0 (178)	0-2 (175)	1-3 (141)	2-3 (208)	0-1 (160)	2
3	Altrincham	1-0 (612)	5-0 (612)	X	5-0 (602)	2-2 (928)	1-1 (573)	3-0 (654)	1-2 (630)	3-0 (575)	3-0 (732)	7-1 (599)	2-1 (490)	0-0 (507)	2-0 (729)	1-3 (761)	1-0 (670)	2-2 (348)	3-1 (687)	3-0 (706)	2-1 (704)	4-0 (444)	0-1 (621)	3
4	Bamber Bridge	2-1 (741)	4-1 (260)	0-3 (538)	X	2-2 (529)	2-1 (245)	1-4 (303)	2-2 (281)	4-0 (838)	0-2 (288)	2-3 (296)	3-0 (246)	0-2 (301)	1-2 (279)	1-1 (234)	0-1 (408)	1-1 (341)	1-2 (318)	1-0 (374)	1-3 (297)	2-2 (254)	2-3 (292)	4
5	Barrow	2-0 (1310)	2-0 (938)	0-0 (1,429)	2-0 (1246)	X	3-1 (1100)	3-1 (1406)	1-0 (2765)	1-0 (973)	1-1 (1220)	1-0 (1271)	2-1 (938)	2-0 (963)	0-1 (1277)	2-2 (1995)	1-0 (1459)	0-1 (1012)	0-1 (1474)	3-0 (1143)	1-0 (1743)	1-2 (1174)	1-2 (991)	5
6	Bishop Auckland	2-2 (512)	1-1 (88)	5-2 (211)	1-1 (191)	0-2 (759)	X	1-1 (204)	0-2 (202)	5-2 (193)	0-2 (92)	4-3 (175)	4-1 (122)	1-3 (197)	1-1 (159)	2-1 (213)	3-1 (219)	3-2 (174)	2-4 (233)	3-0 (161)	1-2 (206)	1-1 (216)	6-0 (120)	6
7	Blyth Spartans	2-2 (512)	4-2 (467)	3-3 (419)	1-1 (390)	2-1 (591)	1-4 (419)	X	0-1 (375)	2-1 (603)	3-1 (492)	0-2 (339)	2-3 (491)	0-0 (575)	1-1 (652)	1-1 (425)	0-1 (515)	0-1 (490)	1-0 (446)	1-0 (467)	0-4 (630)	2-3 (542)	0-1 (462)	7
8	Boston United	1-3 (752)	2-0 (863)	1-0 (1077)	1-1 (806)	0-2 (1239)	1-0 (905)	2-2 (956)	X	1-1 (1080)	1-0 (1010)	3-2 (769)	3-0 (485)	1-0 (1730)	2-1 (652)	1-1 (751)	2-0 (869)	1-0 (1145)	1-1 (884)	2-2 (980)	0-3 (938)	1-3 (602)	2-1 (938)	8
9	Chorley	1-1 (488)	2-0 (288)	1-0 (534)	2-1 (801)	0-2 (532)	1-0 (296)	1-3 (369)	0-2 (431)	X	2-0 (253)	1-2 (383)	0-0 (275)	1-1 (316)	1-0 (293)	1-5 (347)	2-1 (288)	0-1 (342)	0-3 (295)	1-1 (239)	4-2 (235)	4-0 (276)	2-0 (216)	9
10	Colwyn Bay	2-1 (284)	3-0 (261)	0-0 (309)	3-1 (302)	1-1 (423)	0-1 (259)	2-0 (306)	0-3 (283)	3-3 (321)	X	1-3 (399)	1-1 (279)	1-1 (273)	0-1 (385)	3-1 (410)	5-2 (269)	2-3 (323)	4-1 (307)	2-1 (263)	2-1 (373)	2-0 (316)	0-3 (323)	10
11	Emley	5-3 (275)	2-0 (243)	2-1 (403)	0-0 (289)	3-0 (502)	1-2 (321)	1-1 (263)	0-0 (289)	3-1 (276)	1-0 (266)	X	1-0 (347)	1-0 (287)	3-3 (345)	2-1 (294)	5-3 (237)	2-2 (299)	2-0 (245)	2-0 (185)	6-2 (238)	3-0 (171)	0-2 (298)	11
12	Frickley Athletic	2-1 (134)	2-1 (162)	2-1 (274)	1-0 (135)	0-1 (231)	2-3 (125)	0-0 (204)	1-0 (268)	2-0 (166)	1-3 (181)	2-1 (476)	X	1-1 (230)	0-1 (179)	2-1 (146)	2-1 (139)	0-0 (138)	1-1 (1750	1-0 (142)	1-3 (148)	2-3 (179)	3-0 (119)	12
13	Gainsborough Trinity	0-0 (460)	4-0 (474)	2-1 (563)	3-2 (417)	0-3 (646)	1-0 (439)	0-0 (628)	0-1 (1295)	2-1 (474)	1-0 (479)	2-1 (401)	3-1 (638)	X	0-1 (534)	3-1 (647)	2-1 (440)	3-0 (588)	2-0 (582)	3-0 (506)	1-0 (581)	0-1 (481)	0-2 (544)	13
14	Guiseley	1-0 (380)	1-2 (263)	2-2 (443)	1-1 (373)	1-1 (472)	3-3 (355)	1-3 (634)	1-1 (403)	2-1 (358)	3-1 (272)	0-2 (491)	4-0 (380)	1-3 (356)	X	1-1 (431)	2-1 (453)	2-1 (227)	2-2 (458)	4-1 (429)	2-2 (324)	1-1 (296)	0-2 (300)	14
15	Hyde United	1-1 (572)	4-1 (364)	0-1 (989)	1-1 (583)	0-3 (832)	1-2 (395)	1-0 (348)	0-2 (526)	0-2 (442)	2-0 (346)	1-0 (624)	1-1 (332)	4-1 (539)	1-1 (432)	X	4-1 (590)	3-3 (522)	1-1 (558)	0-1 (410)	0-2 (747)	3-2 (232)	4-3 (687)	15
16	Lancaster City	3-2 (342)	1-1 (275)	2-2 (322)	1-0 (229)	0-2 (1119)	1-0 (219)	3-1 (192)	3-1 (214)	4-1 (245)	0-1 (150)	2-2 (239)	2-2 (163)	0-1 (233)	3-2 (339)	0-1 (222)	X	0-1 (176)	3-2 (232)	0-1 (189)	3-0 (251)	3-2 (163)	1-1 (153)	16
17	Leigh	1-0 (243)	1-0 (159)	2-2 (449)	4-0 (236)	0-1 (246)	1-3 (181)	1-1 (208)	0-1 (237)	2-0 (367)	3-0 (228)	2-1 (267)	1-1 (201)	1-0 (133)	0-0 (201)	2-1 (251)	2-0 (246)	X	1-0 (201)	0-0 (281)	2-2 (319)	4-2 (140)	2-0 (171)	17
18	Marine	3-1 (238))	2-0 (297)	1-0 (474)	3-1 (302)	1-0 (539)	0-0 (320)	1-2 (301)	1-2 (211)	1-2 (297)	1-0 (351)	3-5 (332)	1-1 (252)	2-2 (254)	0-1 (3088)	0-2 (267)	2-0 (269)	1-1 (322)	X	1-2 (235)	3-2 (386)	0-4 (277)	0-0 (405)	18
19	Radcliffe Borough	1-2 (485)	1-1 (186)	0-1 (334)	3-0 (143)	1-2 (254)	1-2 (182)	1-2 (201)	1-1 (244)	1-2 (218)	1-1 (255)	1-2 (228)	1-1 (151)	1-3 (163)	0-2 (113)	0-0 (375)	6-2 (174)	0-1 (144)	0-3 (204)	X	0-0 (178)	0-2 (147)	0-2 (152)	19
20	Runcorn	3-0 (345)	3-1 (295)	1-0 (670)	4-2 (327)	0-1 (373)	2-1 (349)	1-1 (326)	3-0 (475)	2-3 (377)	0-0 (285)	1-0 (362)	2-1 (278)	2-0 (300)	1-1 (302)	0-1 (400)	3-0 (220)	2-2 (385)	3-0 (330)	6-3 (233)	X	2-0 (334)	2-2 (246)	20
21	Spennymoor United	2-0 (246)	1-1 (165)	2-1 (159)	0-3 (192)	3-2 (370)	1-1 (454)	2-1 (314)	1-2 (201)	2-0 (190)	2-1 (151)	2-2 (208)	0-0 (157)	1-4 (152)	1-2 (248)	2-2 (179)	1-1 (166)	0-3 (198)	1-2 (127)	1-1 (167)	0-1 (161)	X	1-1 (169)	21
22	Winsford United	3-0 (200)	0-0 (75)	2-1 (444)	0-1 (215)	0-0 (213)	0-0 (168)	3-0 (158)	0-0 (222)	1-0 (193)	2-0 (360)	0-1 (278)	2-1 (232)	1-1 (147)	2-1 (260)	1-1 (252)	3-0 (120)	0-1 (153)	2-4 (148)	2-2 (184)	1-1 (362)	1-0 (134)	X	22

PROGRAMME DETAILS
Pages: 32 **Price:** £1
Editor: P Terry/D Ellis.
(01282 866768)

ACCRINGTON STANLEY

Colours: Red/white/red **Formed:** 1968
Change colours: White/black/white **Nickname:** Reds
Midweek home matchday: Tuesday **Sponsors:** Asda.
Reserve's Lge: Lancashire League. **Newsline:** 0891 227 343.
Youth Lge: Lancs Youth Floodlit League.
Local Press: Accrington Observer, Lancashire Evening Telegraph.
Local Radio Stations: Radio Lancashire, Red Rose Radio.

Chairman: Eric Whalley **President:** J C Prescott/J Hudson
Secretary: Philip Terry, 8 Princess Street, Colne, Lancs BB8 9AN (01286 866768 H, 01282 864000 B)
Manager: Bill Rodaway **Asst Manager:** TBA
Osteopath: Martin Dixon D.O. **Commercial Director:** John de Maine

GROUND - Address: Crown Ground, off Livingstone Road, Accrington (01254 383235). **Directions:** Arriving on A680 from Clayton-le-Moors Livingstone Road is on left 50 yds past Crown Hotel. From M62/M66, through town centre on A680 - Livingstone Road 500 yds on right after Victoria Hospital. One and a half miles from Accrington (BR).
Capacity: 4,000 **Cover:** 1,650 **Seats:** 700 **Floodlights:** Yes
Clubhouse: Open two nights and matchdays. Private functions. Well stocked tea bar in ground.
Club Shop: Sells replica kits, sweaters, t-shirts, videos, photos etc. Contact John De Maine.

PREVIOUS - **Leagues:** Lancs Combination 70-78; Cheshire County 78-82; North West Counties 82-87. **Names:** None. **Grounds:** None.

CLUB RECORDS - **Attendance:** 2,270 v Gateshead 14/11/92 FA Cup 1st Rd *(10,081 v Crewe Alexandra, F.A. Cup Second Round Proper 5/12/92 - played at Ewood Park, Blackburn).* **Career Goalscorer:** David Hargreaves 318. **Career Appearances:** Chris Grimshaw 352. **Win:** 9-0 v Ashton Town, Lancashire Combination 75-76. **Defeat:** 1-9 v Runcorn (A), FA Cup 2nd Qual Rd replay 85-86. **Transfer Fee Paid:** £2,250 for Bernie Hughes (Droylsen 90-91). **Transfer Fee Received:** £50,000 for Brett Ormerod (Blackpool March 97)

BEST SEASON - **FA Trophy:** 1st Rd 72-73 78-79 92-93. **FA Cup:** Second Rd Proper 92-93, 1-6 v Crewe Alexandra (H). **League clubs defeated:** None.

HONOURS - N West Counties Lg R-up 86-87; Cheshire County Lg Div 2 80-81 (R-up 79-80); Lancs Comb 73-74 77-78 (R-up 71-72 75-76), Lg Cup 71-72 72-73 73-74 76-77; George Watson Trophy 71-72 73-74 74-75; John Duckworth Trophy 85-86; Lancs Junior Cup (now ATS Trophy) R-up 85-86 96-97; Lancs under-18 Yth Cup 89-90; N.W.All Div Cup 94-95; Anglo-Barbados Cup 95.

Players progressing to Football League: David Hargreaves (Blackburn R. 77), Ian Blackstone (York C.), Gus Wilson (Crewe), Glen Johnstone (Preston), Darren Lyons (Bury), Martin Clark (Crewe 92-93), Mark Wright (Wigan 93-94), Paul Collings (Bury 93-94), Brett Ormerod (Blackpool 96-97), Harvey Cunningham (Doncaster Rovers).

Back Row (L-R); Steve Haw, Tony Black, Chris Sutton, Paul Horridge, Russ Procter, Darren Quick, Jel Baldwin, Greg Challenger, Ian Fay. Front Row; Ashley Hoskins, Brian Welch, Andy Cavanagh, Greg Abbott, John Borland, Gary Bickerton, Adrian Cheetham
Photo; Roy Gabryszak

ACCRINGTON STANLEY - Match Facts 97-98

ATS - Lancs 'ATS' Trophy

Match No	Date	Venue H / A	Comp	Opponents	Result & Score		Att	Goalscorers	League Position
1	23.08	H	UL	Winsford United	W	2-1	549	Hutchinson 70, 79.	
2	25.08	A	UL	Radcliffe Borough	W	2-1	*485*	McCluskie 25, Davies 49.	
3	30.08	A	UL	Alfreton Town	W	1-0	*262*	McCluskie 52.	1
4	02.09	H	UL	Runcorn	L	0-3	604		2
5	08.09	A	UL	Barrow	L	0-2	*1,310*		7
6	13.09	A	**FAC 1Q**	Leigh	L	0-1	*343*		-
7	16.09	H	UL	Colwyn Bay	L	1-2	313	Rogerson 86.	7
8	20.09	H	UL	Guiseley	L	2-3	525	Rogerson 2, McCluskie 43.	13
9	23.09	A	UL	Leigh	L	0-1	*243*		16
10	27.09	A	UL	Frickley Athletic	L	1-2	*134*	McCluskie 26.	17
11	30.09	H	UL	Lancaster City	D	1-1	421	Haw 40.	15
12	04.10	H	UL	Boston United	D	1-1	527	Haw 23.	17
13	07.10	A	UL	Chorley	D	1-1	*488*	Rogerson 66.	17
14	11.10	A	UL	Bishop Auckland	D	2-2	*195*	Cliff 17, Welch 67.	16
15	18.10	A	UL	Blyth Spartans	D	2-2	*512*	McCluskie 15, Welch 57.	19
16	21.10	H	UL	Barrow	L	0-1	588		
17	25.10	A	UL	Spennymoor United	L	0-2	*246*		17
18	28.10	H	**ULCC 2**	Marine	D	4-4	266	Haw 40 (pen), 63, Leaver 57, Proctor 77.	-
19	01.11	H	UL	Emley	W	4-2	549	Haw 26, 30 (pen), Baldwin 51, Welch 79.	15
20	08.11	A	UL	Hyde United	D	1-1	*572*	Leaver 16.	15
21	11.11	A	**ULCC 2 R**	Marine	L	0-2	*190*		-
22	15.11	H	UL	Frickley Athletic	**W**	**3-0**	480	Welch 20, 85, Smith 68.	14
23	19.11	A	UL	Gainsborough Trinity	D	0-0	*460*		
24	22.11	H	UL	Bishop Auckland	D	1-1	428	Proctor 17.	14
25	25.11	H	UL	Hyde United	D	1-1	362	Smith 68.	14
26	29.11	H	**FAT 3Q**	Runcorn	L	0-5	402		-
27	07.12	A	UL	Guiseley	L	0-1	*380*		14
28	09.12	A	UL	Marine	L	1-3	*238*	Smith 17.	
29	13.12	H	UL	Altrincham	D	1-1	576	Haw 40.	18
30	20.12	H	UL	Spennymoor United	**W**	**3-0**	409	Leaver 46, Smith 61, Haw 77.	14
31	27.12	A	UL	Bamber Bridge	L	1-2	*741*	Welch 12.	15
32	01.01	H	UL	Radcliffe Borough	D	2-2	662	Smith 49, Welch 88.	13
33	06.01	H	**ATS 2**	Great Harwood Town	W	1-0	353	Moss 90.	-
34	17.01	H	UL	Blyth Spartans	W	2-0	507	Haw 33, Welch 89.	14
35	24.01	A	UL	Lancaster City	L	2-3	*342*	Haw 45, Welch 73.	15
36	31.01	H	UL	Chorley	**L**	**0-3**	492		17
37	03.02	H	**ATS 3**	Ramsbottom United	W	1-0	274	Haw 48.	-
38	07.02	A	UL	Runcorn	**L**	**0-3**	*345*		19
39	21.02	H	UL	Marine	D	1-1	460	Welch 40.	19
40	24.02	H	**ATS SF**	Southport	L	0-1	348		-
41	28.02	A	UL	Boston United	W	3-1	*752*	Bickerton 2, 27, Welch 11.	19
42	07.03	A	UL	Altrincham	L	0-1	*612*		19
43	14.03	H	UL	Lerigh RMI	L	1-3	1,461	Borland 86.	19
44	28.03	H	UL	Gainsborough Trinity	L	0-2	417		19
45	30.03	A	UL	Emley	L	3-5	*275*	Cavanagh 62, Hoskin 70, Black 83.	19
46	11.04	A	UL	Colwyn Bay	L	1-2	*284*	Welch 75.	19
47	13.04	H	UL	Bamber Bridge	D	1-1	515	Welch 84.	19
48	25.04	H	UL	Alfreton Town	D	1-1	470	Haw 36.	19
49	02.05	A	UL	Winsford United	**L**	**0-3**	*200*		20

PLAYING SQUAD 1998

Goalkeepers: Rob Mulloy (Nelson, Crosshills, Colne Dynamoes, Crosshills). **Defenders:** Greg Challender (Stalybridge C, Altrincham, Bath C, Southport,Preston NE, Mossley, Horwich RMI, Oldham Ath), Jez Baldwin (Bamber Bridge,Fleetwood T, Bamber Bridge, Leyland Celtic), Darren Davies (Leyland Motors,Preston NE, Leyland Motors), Richard Fogarty (Bury, Burnley), Chris Sutton (Congleton T, Acc.Stanley, Clitheroe, Chorley), Russell Proctor (Gt.Harwood T,Acc.Stanley, Clitheroe, Chorley), Ben Lavelle (Bamber Bridge, Morecambe,Ashton U, Morecambe, Fleetwood T, Blackpool R, Fleetwood T, Morecambe, PrestonNE, Bury), Andy Cavanagh (Marine, Burscough, Southport).
Midfielders: Tony Black (Wigan Ath, Bamber Bridge, Burnley U), John Borland (Scunthorpe U, Burnley), Greg Abbott (Guiseley, Hull C, Guiseley, Halifax T,Bradford C, Coventry C), Darren Quick (Salford C, Blackpool), Matthew Shields (Nelson, Burnley, Colne Dynamoes).
Forwards: Steve Haw (Southport, Chorley, Southport, Marine, Altrincham,Marine, Kirkby T, Runcorn, Wigan Ath), Peter Smith (Barrow, Gt.Harwood T, BACPreston, Barrow), Brian Welch (Netherfield, Droylsden, Acc.Stanley, Barrow,Burnley, Hebburn), Gary Bickerton (Malung IF (Swe), Manchester U), Ashley Hoskin (Gt.Harwood T, Bamber Bridge, Barrow, Acc.Stanley, Burnley Bank Hall,Wrexham, Burnley)

PROGRAMME DETAILS
Pages: 36, **Price:** £1.20
Editors: Graham Rowley
Tel: 0161 928 1045

ALTRINCHAM

Colours: Red & white striped/black/white **Formed:** 1903
Change colours: Yellow/green/green **Nickname:** The Robins
Midweek matchday: Tuesday **Sponsor:** TBA
Reserve's League: Bolton & Dist **Youth League:** Altrincham Youth
Local Press: Sale & Altrincham Messenger, Sale & Altrincham Express, Manchester Evening News
Local Radio Stations: GMR (BBC), Signal Radio, Piccadilly Radio.

Chairman: Gerry Berman **President:** Noel White
Deputy Chairman: Mark Harris **Vice President:** Bill King
Secretary: Graham Heathcote
Manager: Bernard Taylor **Asst Manager:** Noel Gleghorn
Physio: Mandy Johnson **Press Officer:** Mark Harris
GROUND - Address: Moss Lane, Altrincham, Cheshire WA15 8AP. Tel: 0161 928 1045. Fax: 0161 926 9934. **Directions:** M6 junction 19; A556/M56 (Manchester Airport) to junction 7; signs Hale and Altrincham; through 1st traffic lights and 3rd right into Westminster Road and continue into Moss Lane. Ground on right.
Capacity: 6,085 **Cover:** Yes **Seats:** 1,154 **Floodlights:** Yes
Clubhouse: Two snack bars on ground for pies, crisps, soft drinks and chocolate etc; bar under the stand open on match days only. **Club Shop:** Yes

PREVIOUS - Leagues: Manchester League 03-11, Lancashire Combination 11-19, Cheshire County Lge 19-68, Northern Premier Lge 68-79, GMVC 79-97; **Grounds:** Pollitts Field - 1903-1910
RECORDS - Attendance: 10,275 - Altrincham Boys v Sunderland Boys - English Schools Shield 3rd Round 28.02.25: **Scorer:** Jack Swindells 252 - 1965-71: **Appearances:** John Davison 677 - 1971-86: **Win:** 9-2 v Merthyr Tydfil,Vauxhall Conference, Feb 1991: **Defeat:** Unknown: **Fees - Paid:** £15,000 to Blackpool for Keith Russell: **Received:** From Crewe Alexandra for Paul Edwards - 1988.
BEST SEASON - FA Trophy: Winners 77-78, 85-86. **FA Cup:** 85-86 4th Round, 0-2 v York City (A). - **League clubs defeated:** 10.
HONOURS - Alliance Premier League 80, 81; FA Trophy 78, 86; Bob Lord Trophy 81; N.P.L. Cup 70 98; N.P.L. Shield Winners 80; Cheshire County League 66, 67; Cheshire County League Cup 51, 53, 64; Cheshire Senior Cup Winners 05, 34, 67, 82; Manchester League 05; Cheshire Amateur Cup 04.
Players progressing to Football League: G Barrow (Wigan Ath. 81), E Bishop (Tranmere R. 88), F Carrodus (Manchester C. 69), T Carke (Shrewsbury T. 93), P Conning (Rochdale, 86), R Dale/ N Daws/ S Johnson/ A Reid (Bury, 51 77 92 92), P Edwards (Crewe, 88), B Green (Exeter C., 62), J Hughes/ A Kilner (Stockport Co., 76 90), J Kennedy/ E Robinson (West Brom, 48 57), S March (Port Vale, 59), Charlie Mitten (Halifax T., 65), B Phillips (Middlesbrough, 54), J Rogers (Wigan Ath., 82), P Showler (Barnet, 91), N Stiffle (Chesterfield, 54), J Street (Barrow, 69), C Freeman (Doncaster R. 93).
97-98 - Captain: **P.o.Y.:** **Top Scorer:**

Altrincham celebrate after beating Gainsborough 2-1 in the Unibond Challenge Cup Final.

ALTRINCHAM - Match Facts 97-98

UCSC - Cheshire Senior Cup

Match No.	Date	Venue H / A	Comp.	Opponents	Result & Score	Att.	Goalscorers	League Position
1	23.08	H	UL	Barrow	D 2-2	928	Toner 6, Carmody 71.	
2	25.08	A	UL	Emley	L 1-2	*403*	Terry 26.	
3	30.09	A	UL	Bamber Bridge	W 3-0	*538*	Hardy 50, 69, Terry 64 (pen).	7
4	02.09	H	UL	Blyth Spartans	W 3-0	654	Harris 17, France 33, Hardy 57.	5
5	09.09	A	UL	Alfreton Town	W 3-0	*324*	McGoona 18, Hardy 38, Harris 75.	
6	13.09	A	UL	Runcorn	L 0-1	*670*		3
7	16.09	H	UL	Winsford United	L 0-1	621		5
8	20.09	A	UL	Gainsborough Trinity	L 1-2	*563*	Toner 41.	6
9	23.09	A	**UCSC 1**	Stalybridge Celtic	L 0-2	*311*		-
10	27.09	H	UL	Boston United	L 1-2	630	Terry 27 (pen).	12
11	04.10	A	UL	Lancaster Citty	D 2-2	*322*	Hardy 6, Russell 88.	16
12	06.10	A	UL	Hyde United	W 1-0	*989*	Sharrett 47.	11
13	11.10	H	UL	Colwyn Bay	W 3-0	732	Russell 74, Moore 75, Hardy 64.	6
14	14.10	H	UL	Bamber Bridge	W 5-0	602	**Russell 4** (22, 50 (pen), 87, 90), Hardy 75.	5
15	18.10	A	UL	Chorley	L 0-1	*534*		6
16	21.10	H	UL	Runcorn	W 2-1	704	France 41, Moore 45.	4
17	25.10	H	**FAC 4Q**	Morecambe	L 0-2	1,134		-
18	28.10	H	**ULCC 2**	Droylsden	W 3-0	347	Sharratt 20, Hardy 62, 88.	-
19	01.11	H	UL	Hyde United	L 1-3	761	Maddox 77.	8
20	08.11	A	UL	Guiseley	D 2-2	*443*	Hardy 19, Kelly 77 (pen).	4
21	11.11	H	UL	Lancaster City	W 1-0	670	Hardy 40.	3
22	15.11	H	UL	Radcliffe Borough	W 3-0	706	Ferrt 7, Russell 33, Hardy 42.	2
23	22.11	A	UL	Marine	L 0-1	*474*		4
24	25.11	H	**ULPC 1**	Leigh RMI	L 0-1	269		-
25	29.11	A	**FAT 3Q**	Nuneaton Borough	W 2-0	*903*	Hardy 34, Taylor 43.	-
26	06.12	H	UL	Frickley Athletic	W 2-1	490	Kelly 70, Shepherd 86.	4
27	10.12	A	UL	Bishop Auckland	**L 2-5**	*211*	Adams 37, France 71.	
28	13.12	A	UL	Accrington Stanley	D 1-1	*576*	Taylor 31.	5
29	16.12	H	**ULCC 3**	Colwyn Bay	W 4-2	227	Conley-Excell 13, 50, Hardy 23, 36.	-
30	20.12	H	UL	Marine	W 3-0	687	Hardy 5, 55, Conley-Excell 64.	3
31	01.01	A	UL	Winsford United	L 1-2	*444*	OG (Hibbert) 80.	4
32	06.01	H	UL	Leigh RMI	D 2-2	348	Taylor 27, McGoona 51.	
33	17.01	A	UL	Barrow	D 0-0	*1,429*		5
34	19.01	H	**FAT 1**	Runcorn	W 3-2	555	Harris 60, 67, Hardy 77.	-
35	24.01	H	UL	Guiseley	W 2-0	729	McGoona 64, Kelly 70 (pen).	
36	31.01	H	**FAT 2**	Morecambe	W 2-0	942	Terry 63, Taylor 88.	-
37	07.02	A	UL	Frickley Athletic	L 1-2	*274*	France 85.	5
38	11.02	A	**ULCC 4**	Boston United	D 1-1	*378*	France 37.	-
39	14.02	H	UL	Alfreton Town	W 5-0	612	France 16, McGoona 39, Hardy 44, Sharratt 68, Conley-Excell 84.	5
40	17.02	A	UL	Radcliffe Borough	W 1-0	*334*	Taylor 5.	5
41	21.02	H	**FAT 3**	Southport	L 0-2	1,196		-
42	24.02	H	**ULCC 4 R**	Boston United	W 2-1	283	Taylor 6, Conley-Excell 16.	-
43	28.02	H	UL	Gainsborough Trinity	D 0-0	507		5
44	07.03	H	UL	Accrington Stanley	W 1-0	612	Taylor 25.	5
45	10.03	A	UL	Colwyn Bay	D 0-0	*309*		4
46	16.03	H	**ULCC SF-1**	Chorley	W 2-0	452	France 17, Russell 39.	-
47	21.03	A	UL	Leigh RMI	D 2-2	*449*	Maddox 84, Russell 90.	7
48	24.03	A	**ULCC SF-2**	Chorley	L 2-3	*469*	Taylor 42, Russell 88 (pen).	-
49	28.03	H	UL	Chorley	W 3-0	575	Russell 1 (pen), Hardy 38, 73.	4
50	31.03	A	UL	Spennymoor United	L 1-2	*159*	Adams 17.	
51	11.04	H	UL	Bishop Auckland	D 1-1	573	Russell 77.	7
52	13.04	A	UL	Blyth Spartans	D 3-3	*419*	Conley-Excell 3, Harris 32, Taylor 63.	8
53	25.04	H	UL	Emley	**W 7-1**	599	**Russell 3** (17,62,80), **Conley-Excell 3** (26,48,84), France 52.	9
54	27.04	H	UL	Spennymoor United	W 4-0	444	**Russell 3** (6(pen),11,61), McNeil 89.	
55	29.04	N	**ULCC Final**	Gainsborough Trinity	W *2-1	671	Russell 65, 100. Played at Chesterfield F.C.	
56	02.05	A	UL	Boston United	L 0-1	*1,077*		8

PLAYING SQUAD 1998 - **Goalkeepers:** Matt Dickens (Stockport Co, Blackburn R, Lincoln C, Sheffield U). **Defenders:** Paul France (Burnley, Bristol C, Huddersfield T), George Shepherd (Macclesfield T, Hyde U, Bolton W, Manchester C), Neil Marsh (Stalybridge C,York C, Bolton W), Chris Waring (Conwy U, Caernarfon T, Rotura (NZ), Knowsley U, Rhyl, Southport, Witton Alb, Wigan Ath, Danny Adams (Congleton T, NorthwichV, Bury), Andy Brown (Local football), Barry Butler (Barrow, Chester C,Atherton T), Paul Ellender* (Gainsborough Trin, Scunthorpe U), Chris Timons* (Gainsborough Trin, Leyton O, Gainsborough Trin, Mansfield T, Clipstone MW), Brian Kilcline* (Halifax T, Mansfield T, Swindon T, Newcastle U, Oldham Ath,Coventry C, Notts Co). **Midfielders:** Nigel Gleghorn * (Burnley, Stoke C, Birmingham C, Manchester C,Ipswich T, Seaham Red Star), Neil Hardy (Northwich V, Crewe Alex, Bolton W), Jamie Taylor (Rochdale), Mike Carmody (Emley, Tranmere R, Emley, HuddersfieldT), Martin Faulkner (Witton Alb, Congleton T, Witton Alb, Caernarfon T,Congleton T, Northwich V, Stockport Co), Jason Donnelly * (Trafford, Hyde U,Winsford U, Maine Road, Trafford). **Forwards:** Sam Harris (Witton Alb, Stafford R, Manchester C), Keith Russell (Blackpool, Hednesford T, Atherstone U, Tamworth, Walsall), Nathan Comley-Excell (Local football), Paul Cain (Liverpool), Ricky Harris (Hyde U,Runcorn, Hyde U, Altrincham, Ashton U), Darren Lyons* (Halifax T, Winsford U,Macclesfield T, Southport, Bury, Ashton U, Mossley, Leek T, Macclesfield T,Droylsden, Rhyl, Oldham Ath).

BAMBER BRIDGE

Colours: White/black/white.
Change Colours: All yellow
Midweek Matches: Tuesday
Reserve Teams League: North West Alliance.

Founded: 1952
Nickname: Brig
Sponsors: Baxi Partnership

President: Harold Hargreaves **Chairman:** D Allan
Vice Chairman: Brian Ginty **Secretary & Press Officer:** D G Spencer, 11 Tennyson Place, Walton-le-Dale, Preston, Lancs PR5 4TT (011772 34355).
Manager: Martin Eatough **Commercial Manager:** Nigel Webster.
Asst Manager: Dave Sargent **Physio:** A Jones
GROUND Address: Irongate, Brownedge Road, Bamber Bridge, Preston, Lancs. Tel Nos: Club Office 01772-909690; Social Club 01772-909695; Fax No. 01772-909691. 627387).
Directions: M6 Junct 29, A6 (Bamber Bridge Bypass) towards Walton-le-Dale, to r'bout, A6 London Road to next r'bout, 3rd exit signed Bamber Bridge (Brownedge Road) and first right. Ground 100 yds at end of road on left. Just over a mile from Bamber Bridge (BR).
Seats: 250 **Cover:** 800 **Capacity:** 2,500 **Floodlights:** Yes
Clubhouse: On ground. Open all day Saturday matchdays, every evening and Sunday lunch. Refreshment cabin on ground serves hot & cold drinks & snacks etc during matches.
Club Shop: Sells various club souvenirs etc plus large selection of programmes. Contact Russ Rigby (01772 909690)

PROGRAMME DETAILS:
Pages: 36 **Price:** £1.
Editor: Dave Rowland.
(01772 465659)

PREVIOUS - **Leagues:** Preston & District 52-90; North West Counties 90-93.
Ground: King George V Ground, Higher Walton 1952-86. **Names:** None

CLUB RECORDS - **Attendance:** 2,300 v Czech Republic, Pre-Euro 96 Friendly.
Win: 8-0 v Curzon Ashton N.W.Co. 94-95.
Transfer Fee Paid: £10,000 to Horwich R.M.I.for Mark Edwards.
Transfer Fee Received: £15,000 from Wigan Athletic for Tony Back, 1995.

BEST SEASON - **FA Vase:** Semi Final 91-92 (lost 0-2 on agg to Wimborne Tn).
FA Cup: Second Qualifying Round 92-93 (0-4 v Spennymoor United {H}).

HONOURS - Nth West Co's Lge R-up 92-93 (Div 2 91-92, F'lit Cup R-up 91-92); Preston & Dist Lge(4) (R-up (3); Guildhall Cup 78-79 80-81 84-85 89-90, R-up 77-78 79-80 87-88; Lancs Amtr Shield 81-82, R-up 80-81 89-90; Lancastrian Brigade Cup 76-77 89-90 90-91; A.T.S.Lancs Trophy 94-95, R-Up 95-96, NPL Chall Cup 94-95; NPL 1st Div R-Up 94-95; NPL Prem Div Champ 95-96.

Bamber Bridge's Mark Milligan attempts to clear the ball under pressure from Hyde United's Lutel James.
Photo: Colin Stevens

BAMBER BRIDGE - Match Facts 97-98

ATS - Lancashire 'ATS' Trophy

Match No.	Date	Venue H / A	Comp	Opponents	Result & Score		Att.	Goalscorers	League Position
1	23.08	H	UL	Emley	L	2-3	296	Spencer 60, Trainor 79.	
2	25.08	H	UL	Chorley	**W**	**4-0**	838	**Eaves 3** (43, 81, 86), Vickers 71.	
3	30.08	H	UL	Altrincham	L	0-3	538		16
4	02.09	A	UL	Marine	L	1-3	*302*	Vickers.	
5	09.09	H	UL	Leigh RMI	D	1-1	341	Burswell 71.	19
6	13.09	H	**FAC 1Q**	Dunston F.B.	D	1-1	182	Burswell 43.	-
7	16.09	A	**FAC 1Q R**	Dunston F.B.	W	3-2	*94*	Ainscough 53, Walsh 85, Spencer 90.	-
8	20.09	A	UL	Alfreton Town	W	2-1	*165*	Hoskin 74 (pen), Milligan 74.	19
9	23.09	A	UL	Colwyn Bay	L	1-3	*302*	Burswell 77.	19
10	27.09	H	**FAC 2Q**	Marine	L	1-3	318	Maddock 24.	-
11	01.10	H	**ULCC 1**	Gretna	W	2-1	116	Vickers 23, Milligan 77.	-
12	04.10	H	UL	Runcorn	L	2-4	322	Vickers 38, Eaves 80.	19
13	07.10	H	UL	Barrow	D	2-2	529	Trainer 46, Milligan 59.	20
14	11.10	A	UL	Spennymoor United	W	3-0	*192*	Vickers 32, Ainscough 49, Hoskin 89.	19
15	14.10	A	UL	Altrincham	**L**	**0-5**	*602*		19
16	18.10	H	UL	Gainsborough Trinity	L	0-2	301		20
17	21.10	H	UL	Hyde United	D	1-1	234	Vickers 35.	
18	25.10	A	UL	Lancaster City	L	0-1	*229*		19
19	28.10	H	**ULCC 2**	Chorley	L	0-1	335		-
20	01.11	A	UL	Bishop Auckland	D	1-1	*191*	OG (Driscoll) 35.	16
21	08.11	H	UL	Frickley Athletic	W	3-0	246	Vickers 33, Eaves 66, Milligan 86.	18
22	15.11	A	UL	Leigh RMI	L	0-4	*236*		18
23	19.11	A	UL	Winsford United	W	1-0	*215*	Walsh 54.	
24	22.11	H	UL	Colwyn Bay	L	0-2	288		18
25	29.11	A	**FAT 3Q**	Gainsborough Trinity	L	0-1	*429*		-
26	13.12	A	UL	Boston United	D	1-1	*806*	Hoskin73.	19
27	20.12	H	UL	Blyth Spartans	L	1-4	303	Trainer 68.	20
28	27.12	H	UL	Accrington Stanley	W	2-1	741	Borrowdale 5, Lavelle 79.	20
29	01.01	A	UL	Chorley	L	1-2	*801*	Lavelle 64.	20
30	10.01	H	UL	Marine	L	1-2	318	Diggle 67.	20
31	17.01	A	UL	Guiseley	D	1-1	*373*	Diggle 67.	19
32	20.01	H	**ATS 2**	Blackpool Wren Rovers	W	5-1	95	**Diggle 3** (26, 34, 46), OG (Carter) 71, Spencer 88.	-
33	24.01	A	UL	Hyde United	D	1-1	*583*	Diggle 30.	20
34	31.01	H	UL	Lancaster City	L	0-1	408		20
35	03.02	A	**ATS 3**	Morecambe	L	1-3	*300*	Diggle 20.	-
36	07.02	A	UL	Barrow	L	0-2	*1,246*		20
37	14.02	H	UL	Winsford United	L	2-3	292	Leaver 27, Diggle 76 (pen).	20
38	21.02	A	UL	Gainsborough Trinity	D	2-2	*417*	Reynolds 61, Emerson 72.	20
39	28.02	H	UL	Spennymoor United	D	2-2	254	Diggle 12, Borrowdale 53.	20
40	14.03	H	UL	Runcorn	L	1-3	297	Vickers 72.	20
41	16.03	A	UL	Emley	D	0-0	*289*		20
42	21.03	H	UL	Boston United	D	2-2	281	Vickers 111, Maddock 82.	20
43	28.03	A	UL	Frickley Athletic	L	0-1	*135*		20
44	04.04	H	UL	Radcliffe Borough	W	1-0	374	Vickers 69.	20
45	11.04	H	UL	Alfreton Town	W	4-1	260	Vickers 15, Diggle 36, Eyre 78(pen), Borrowdale 83.	20
46	13.04	A	UL	Accrington Stanley	D	1-1	*515*	Vickers 47.	20
47	18.04	H	UL	Guiseley	L	1-2	279	Wilson 63.	20
48	21.04	A	UL	Radcliffe Borough	L	0-3	*143*		20
49	25.04	H	UL	Bishop Auckland	W	2-1	245	Maddock 38, Reynolds 83.	20
50	02.05	A	UL	Blyth Spartans	D	1-1	*390*	Diggle 32.	19

PLAYING SQUAD 1998

Goalkeepers: Mike Finch (Burscough).

Defenders: Steve Walmsley (Congleton T, Leigh RMI, Stantondale), Brian Duffy (Burnley), W ayne Maddock (Morecambe, Barrow, Netherfield, Marine, BAC Preston,Leyland Motors), Lee Sculpher (Clitheroe, Atherton LR, Clitheroe, Gt. HarwoodT, Acc.Stanley), Neil Kennedy (Gt.Harwood T, Bamber Bridge), Darren Brown (Gt.Harwood T, Preston NE).

Midfielders: Ged Walsh (Acc.Stanley, Gt.Harwood T, Bacup B, Rossendale U,Bacup B), David Leaver (Acc.Stanley, Morecambe, Bamber Bridge, Leyland Daf), Steve Eyre (Barrow, Southport, Runcorn, Chorley, Stockport Co, Wigan Ath,Burnley), Paul Ainscough (Gt.Harwood T, Blackburn R), David Eaves (Morecambe,Preston NE), Neil Spencer (Atherton LR, Bamber Bridge).

Forwards: Peter Borrowdale (Lancaster C, Morecambe, Blackpool Mechs,Netherfield), Ian Vickers (Southport, Blackpool), Stuart Diggle (Lancaster C,Fleetwood T, Blackpool R, Southport, Blackpool Mechs, Halifax T), Paul Heavey (Runcorn, Curzon Ashton, Warrington T, Preston NE, Netherfield).

BISHOP AUCKLAND

Colours: Sky & Navy blue | **Formed:** 1886
Change colours: Red & white. | **Nickname:** Bishops
Midweek home matchday: Wednesday. | **Sponsors:**
Reserve Team: None.
Local Press: Northern Echo, Evening Gazette, N'castle Journal.
Local Radio: Radio Cleveland, Radio Tees, Radio Metro, Radio Newcastle.

Chairman: B T Newton | **President:**
Vice-Chairman: C Backhouse | **Secretary:** Tony Duffy, 8 Ennerdale Grove, West Auckland, Co.Durham. DL14 9LN. (01388 833410)
Manager: Tony Lee | **Asst Mgr:**
Press Officer: Secretary | **Physio:** Dave Nesbitt
Commercial Manager: Brian Collinson
GROUND Address: Kingsway, Bishop Auckland, County Durham (01388 603686). **Directions:** A1 to Scotch Corner (Turn off A68 from A1) or M6 Junc A38 (A685 to Brough), then follow signs to Bishop Auckland. Ground in town centre (rear of Newgate Str). Half mile from station.
Capacity: 3,500 **Cover:** 2,000 **Seats:** 600 **Floodlights:** Yes
Clubhouse: Open every lunchtime and evening noon-4 & 7-11pm, and Saturday matchdays noon-4 & 5-6 & 7-11pm. Large bar, pool, juke box. Also snack bar within grounds sells hot & cold pies & drinks.
Club Shop: Yes **Metal Badges:** £3.00.

PROGRAMME DETAILS:
Pages: 28 **Price:** £1.
Editor: Bobby Wake
(01388 609428)

PREVIOUS - **Leagues:** N East Counties 1889-90/ Northern Alliance 1890-91/ Northern 1893-1988.

CLUB RECORDS - **Attendance:** 17,000 v Coventry, FA Cup 2nd Rd 6/12/52. **Appearances:** Bob Hardisty. **Win:** 12-3 v Kingstonian, Amateur Cup 55. **Defeat:** 0-7 v Halifax Tn FA Cup 2nd Rd 66-67. **Fees - Paid:** £2,000. **Received:** £9,000 for David Laws from Weymouth.

BEST SEASON - **FA Cup:** 4th Rd 54-55 (lost 1-3 at home to York City). **League clubs beaten in FA Cup:** Crystal Palace, Ipswich 54-55, Tranmere 56-57.

HONOURS - FA Amateur Cup 1895-96, 1899-1900 13-14 20-22 34-35 38-39 54-56 57-58 (R-up(8) 01-02 05-06 10-11 14-15 45-46 49-51 53-54); FA Trophy QF 78-79 88-89 96-97; Northern Lg(19) 1898-99 1900-02 08-10 11-12 20-21 30-31 38-39 46-47 49-52 53-56 66-67 84-86, R-up (17) 78-79 86-87 96-97, Lg Cup(7) 49-51 53-55 59-60 66-67 75-76); D'ham Chall Cup 1891-92 98-99 1930-31 38-39 51-52 55-56 61-62 66-67 84-85 85-86 87-88 96-97; HFS Loans Lg Div 1 R-up 88-89. Plus tournaments in Isle of Man, Spain, Portugal etc.

Players progressing to Football League: B Paisley (Liverpool), F Richardson & S O'Connell (Chelsea 46 & 54), R Hardisty & K Williamson (Darlimgton 46 & 52), W Shergold (Newport 47), N Smith (Fulham 48), R Steel & K Murray (Darlington 50), A Adey (Doncaster 50), F Palmer & A Stalker (Gateshead 51 & 58), A Sewell (Bradford City 54), G Barker (Southend 54), J Major (Hull 55), H Sharratt (Oldham 56), F McKenna (Leeds 56), J Barnwell (Arsenal 56), D Lewis (Accrington Stanley 57), C Cresswell (Carlisle 58), W Bradley (Man Utd), L Brown (Northampton), P Baker (Southampton), M Gooding (Rotherham), K Nobbs & A Toman (Hartlepool), P Hinds (Dundee Utd).

97-98 Capain: D Lobb | **P.o.Y.:** | **Top scorer:** Lee Ellison (32)

Back Row (L-R); C Backhouse (Asst Coach), Tony Lee (Mgr), Dave Nesbitt (Physio), Chris Heron, David Bayles, Andrew Shaw, Michael Waller, Simon Bishop, Jonothan Milroy, Ian Lowes, Stephen Jones. Front Row; Lee Ellison, Darren Roulston, Dave Lobb, Andy Banks, David Gallagher, Anthony Lee, Stephen Moore.

BISHOP AUCKLAND - Match Facts 97-98

DCC - Durham Challenge Cup

Match No.	Date	Venue H / A	Comp.	Opponents	Result & Score		Att.	Goalscorers	League Position
1	23.08	A	UL	Marine	D	0-0	*320*		
2	25.08	A	UL	Spennymoor United	D	1-1	*454*	Gallagher.	
3	30.08	A	UL	Barrow	**L**	**1-3**	*1,100*	Watson 39.	20
4	01.09	A	UL	Emley	W	2-1	*321*	Adams 69, OG (Thompson) 74.	7
5	10.09	H	UL	Guiseley	D	1-1	159	Shaw 86.	15
6	13.09	A	**FAC 1Q**	Radcliffe Borough	W	3-1	*257*	Osbourne 20, Shaw 46, Ellison 78.	-
7	20.09	A	UL	Radcliffe Borough	W	2-1	*182*	Peverell 1, Bayles 13.	11
8	24.09	H	UL	Boston United	L	0-2	202		16
9	27.09	A	**FAC 2Q**	Chorley	D	2-2	*337*	Peverell 24, 37.	-
10	01.10	H	**FAC 2Q R**	Chorley	L	2-3	135	Adams 52, Peverell 88.	-
11	04.10	H	UL	Hyde United	W	2-1	213	Peverell 28, Ellison 82.	15
12	07.10	A	UL	Guiseley	D	3-3	*355*	Peverell 40, Ellison 75, Adams 87.	14
13	11.10	H	UL	Accrington Stanley	D	2-2	195	Adams 2, McKenna 45.	13
14	15.10	H	UL	Frickley Athletic	W	4-1	122	**Shaw 3** (29, 57, 61), Gallagher 82.	8
15	18.10	A	UL	Runcorn	L	1-2	*349*	Gallagher 46.	11
16	21.10	A	UL	Blyth Spartans	W	4-1	*419*	Shaw 35, 36, Bates 62, Peverell 87.	
17	25.10	H	UL	Leigh RMI	W	3-2	174	Shaw 10, 48, Ellison 84.	7
18	27.10	A	**DCC 1**	West Auckland	W	1-0	*263*	Ellison 59.	-
19	01.11	H	UL	Bamber Bridge	D	1-1	191	Peverell 53.	7
20	04.11	A	**ULCC 2**	Guiseley	W	3-0	*277*	Ellison 25, Shaw 64, Banks 72.	-
21	08.11	A	UL	Chorley	L	0-1	*296*		6
22	11.11	A	UL	Frickley Athletic	W	3-2	*125*	Peverell 36, 81, Shaw 50.	
23	15.11	H	UL	Chorley	W	5-2	193	Peverell 44, 73, Bayles 55, Shaw 65, Ellison 87.	3
24	19.11	H	**DCC 2**	Cockfield	W	3-1	279	Peverell 12, Shaw 30, Ellison 74.	-
25	22.11	A	UL	Accrington Stanley	D	1-1	*428*	Lee 17.	3
26	25.11		**ULPC 1**	Blyth Spartans	L	2-3	313	Watson 12, Ellison 54.	-
27	29.11	H	UL	Radcliffe Borough	W	3-0	161	Lobb 15, Shaw 27, Ellison 58.	2
28	06.12	A	UL	Hyde United	W	2-1	*395*	Banks 65, Milroy 87.	2
29	10.12	H	UL	Altrincham	W	5-2	211	Banks 26, 51, Ellison 43, 83, Shaw 90.	2
30	13.12	A	UL	Gainsborough Trinity	L	0-1	*439*		2
31	17.12	H	**ULCC 3**	Belper Town	D	1-1	72	Banks 85.	-
32	20.12	H	UL	Lancaster City	W	3-1	219	Milroy 49, Bayles 54, Ellison 73.	2
33	27.12	A	UL	Alfreton Town	W	6-2	*279*	Heron 19, Milroy 30, Ellison 35, Osbourne 44, 69, Taylor 51.	2
34	03.01	H	UL	Barrow	L	0-2	759		2
35	10.01	H	**FAT 1**	Colwyn Bay	W	3-0	263	Ellison 14, Taylor 28, Lee 29.	-
36	12.01	H	**DCC 3**	Peterlee Newtown	W	9-1	75	**Ellison 3** (3, 31, 53), Shaw 8, 37, Banks **3** (36, 67, 89), Lee 58.	-
37	17.01	A	UL	Boston United	L	0-1	*905*		2
38	20.01	A	**ULCC 3 R**	Belper Town	L	2-3	*135*	Shaw 15 (pen), 52.	-
39	24.01	H	UL	Marine	L	2-4	233	Ellison 19, OG (Richardson) 56.	3
40	31.01	H	**FAT 2**	Boreham Wood	L	1-4	369	Milroy 18.	-
41	07.02	A	UL	Leigh RMI	W	3-1	*181*	Shaw A 60, Heron 63, 85.	4
42	10.02	A	**DCC SF**	Spennymoor United	D	2-2*	*317*	Bayles 66, Ellison 92.	-
43	14.02	H	UL	Runcorn	L	1-2	206	Bayles 25.	4
44	18.02	H	**DCC SF R**	Spennymoor United	L	1-3	267	Osborne 79.	-
45	21.02	A	UL	Winsford United	D	0-0	*168*		4
46	25.02	H	**ULCC 4**	Gainsborough Trinity	D	0-0	96		-
47	28.02	H	UL	Winsford United	**W**	**6-0**	120	Ellison 10, 82, Heron 37, Shaw 56, Bayles 66, Milroy 72.	4
48	04.03	A	**ULCC 4 R**	Gainsborough Trinity	L	1-2	*371*	Shaw 68 (pen).	-
49	07.03	H	UL	Gainsborough Trinity	**L**	**1-3**	197	Ellison 38.	4
50	25.03	H	UL	Spennymoor United	D	1-1	216	Lobb 52.	9
51	28.03	A	UL	Lancaster City	L	0-1	*219*		9
52	01.04	H	UL	Alfreton Town	D	1-1	88	Shaw 16.	9
53	04.04	A	UL	Colwayn Bay	L	0-2	*92*		9
54	10.04	H	UL	Blyth Spartans	D	1-1	204	Osbourne 39.	
55	11.04	A	UL	Altrincham	D	1-1	*573*	Waller 57 (pen).	10
56	18.04	H	UL	Emley	W	4-3	175	Milroy 8, Robinson 38, Banks 60, Waller 70 (pen).	10
57	25.04	A	UL	Bamber Bridge	D	1-1	*245*	Osbourne 10.	10
58	02.05	A	UL	Colwyn Bay	W	1-0	*259*	Milroy 88.	10

PLAYING SQUAD 1998

Goalkeepers: Simon Bishop (Northallerton T, Whitby T, Guisborough T, NewcastleU)

Defenders: David Lobb (Hartlepool T, Peterlee Newtown), Paul Harnett (Gateshead, Dunston Fed, Whitley Bay, Spennymoor U, B Auckland, Ferryhill Ath,Black & Decker), Steve West (Youth team), Chris Lynch (Hartlepool U), Michael Driscoll (Norton, Easington CW, Guisborough T, Doncaster R, Middlesbrough)

Midfielders: Andy Banks (Billingham Synthonia, Ipswich T), George Adams (Shildon), David Bayles (Shildon, Consett, West Auckland T, B Auckland), David Gallagher (Guisborough T, Marske U, Mannion Park, Dormans Ath), Wayne Osbourne (York C), Tony Lee (Guisborough T, Whitby T, B Auckland, Ferryhill Ath,Northallerton T, Newcastle U), Chris Heron (Brandon U, Ferryhill Ath)

Forwards: Nick Peverell (York C, Hartlepool U, Middlesbrough), Andy Shaw (Spennymoor U, Whitley Bay, B Auckland, Crook T), Steve Jones (Gateshead), Jon Milroy (West Auckland T, Blyth S, Cockfield, Dunston Fed, Ferryhill Ath), Michael Parkinson (Seaham Red Star, Newcastle U).

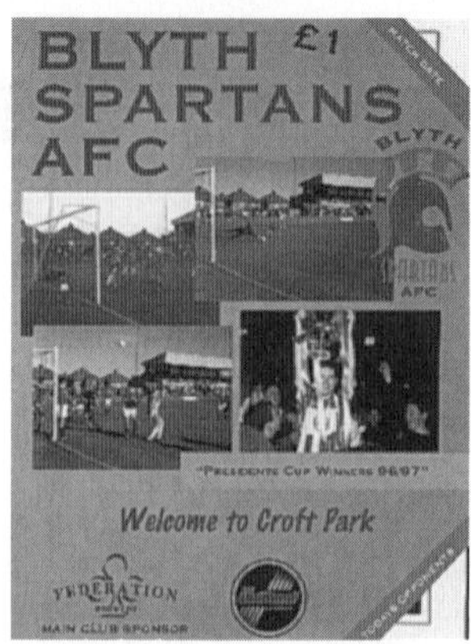

PROGRAMME DETAILS:
Pages: 64 **Price:** £1
Editor: Brian Grey.
(0191 2650119)

BLYTH SPARTANS

Colours: Green & white stripes **Formed:** 1899
Change colours: Claret **Nickname:** Spartans
Midweek Matches: Tuesday **Sponsors:** Federation Brewery.
Reserve Team's League:
Local Press: Newcastle Journal & Evening Chronicle.

Chairman: Mike Mitchell
Secretary: Scott Sawyer, 53 Ninth Avenue, Blyth, Northumberland NE24 2TE (01670 355669).
Press Officer: Ken Teasdale
Manager: Alan Shoulder **Assistant Manager:**

GROUND Address: Croft Park, Blyth, Northumberland. (01670) 354818
Directions: Through Tyne tunnel heading north on A19, take Cramlington turn A1061, follow signs for Newsham/Blyth. Right fork at railway gates in Newsham, down Plessey Rd, ground can be seen on left. Buses X24, X25, X26, X1 from Newcastle.
Seats: 300 **Cover:** 1,000 **Capacity:** 6,000 **Floodlights:** Yes
Clubhouse: Open every night plus Saturday & Sunday lunch & matchdays. Available for wedding functions. Pies & sandwiches available.
Souvenir Shop: Large selection. Contact: Malcom Allen (01670 369209)

PREVIOUS - **Leagues:** Northumberland 01-07; Northern Alliance 07-13, 46-47; North Eastern 13-14 19-39 47-58 62-64; Northern Combination 45-46; Midland 58-60; Northern Counties 60-62; Northern 62-94. **Names:** None **Grounds:** None

CLUB RECORDS - **Transfer Fee - Received:** £30,000 for Les Mutrie (Hull City) 1979. **Paid:**

BEST SEASON - **FA Trophy:** Quarter-Final replay 79-80 82-83. **FA Amateur Cup:** Semi-Final 71-72. **FA Cup:** 5th Rd replay 77-78 (lost to Wrexham). 1st Round on 47 occasions. **League Clubs defeated in FA Cup:** Ashington, Gillingham 22-23, Crewe Alexandra, Stockport County 71-72, Chesterfield, Stoke City 77-78, Bury 95-96.

HONOURS - Nth Lg(10) 72-73 74-76 79-84 86-88 94-95, (R-up 71-72 73-74 77-78 84-85 94-95), Lg Cup(5) 72-73 77-79 81-82 91-92 94-95, Presidents Cup 96-97; Nth Eastern Lg 35-36 (R-up 22-23, Lg Cup 49-50 54-55); Northumberland Lg 03-04; Northern All. 08-09 12-13 (R-up 46-47); Northumberland Snr Cup (19); Shields Gazette Cup 95-96.

Players progressing to Football League: William McGlen (Manchester Utd 46), Joe Roddom (Chesterfield 48), Henry Mills (Huddersfield 48), John Allison (Reading 49), James Kelly (Watford 49), Robert Millard (Reading 49), Jim Kerr (Lincoln 52), James Milner (Burnley 52), John Hogg (Portsmouth 54), John Allison (Chesterfield 55), John Inglis (Gateshead 57), John Longland (Hartlepool 58), Alan Shoulder (Newcastle 79), Les Mutrie (Hull City 79), Steve Carney (Newcastle 80), Craig Liddle (Middlesbrough 94), Paul O'Connor (Hartlepool 95).

97-98 Captain: John Gamble **Top Scorer:** Keith Fletcher/John Atkinson **P.o.Y.:** Kevin McGarrigle/John Gamble

Back Row (L-R); Gamble (Capt), Kennedy (Kit Mgr), Dann, Jones, Wilson, Pike, McGarrigle, Atkinson, Glen Martin (Physio). Front Row; Mascot, Walker, Woat, Renforth, Cole, Skedd

BLYTH SPARTANS - Match Facts 97-98

Match No.	Date	Venue H / A	Comp.	Opponents	Result & Score		Att.	Goalscorers	League Position
1	23.08	A	UL	Chorley	W	3-1	*369*	Fletcher 76, 83, Thompson 86.	
2	25.08	H	UL	Guiseley	D	1-1	652	Tinckler 10.	
3	30.08	H	UL	Gainsborough Trinity	D	0-0	575		5
4	02.09	A	UL	Altrincham	L	0-3	*654*		14
5	07.09	A	UL	Marine	W	2-1	*301*	Atkinson 14, Todd 56.	7
6	09.09	H	UL	Lancaster City	L	0-1	515		
7	913.09	A	**FAC 1Q**	Spennymoor United	D	1-1	*340*	Fletcher 47.	-
8	16.09	H	**FAC 1Q R**	Spennymoor United	W	1-0	360	Fletcher 11.	-
9	20.09	H	UL	Leigh RMI	L	0-1	490		17
10	23.09	H	UL	Spennymoor United	L	2-3	542	Fletcher 72, 74.	18
11	27.09	A	**FAC 2Q**	Garforth	W	1-0	*365*	Pike 84.	-
12	29.09	A	UL	Emley	D	1-1	*263*	Pike 80.	17
13	04.10	H	UL	Winsford United	L	0-1	462		18
14	07.10	A	UL	Frickley Athletic	D	0-0	*204*		17
15	11.10	H	**FAC 3Q**	Worksop Town	W	4-0	596	Atkinson 7, Fletcher 8, 51, Moat 13.	-
16	14.10	A	UL	Spennymoor United	L	1-2	*314*	Fletcher 16.	20
17	18.10	H	UL	Accrington Stanley	D	2-2	512	McGargle 11, Atkinson 14.	19
18	21.10	H	UL	Bishop Auckland	L	1-4	419	Fletcher 2.	20
19	25.10	H	**FAC 4Q**	Kidderminster Harriers	W	2-1	656	Henderson 27, Moat 32.	-
20	28.10	H	**ULCC 2**	Whitley Bay	W	1-0	506	McGiven 79.	-
21	01.11	A	UL	Runcorn	D	1-1	*326*	Moat 88.	20
22	08.11	H	UL	Colwyn Bay	W	3-1	492	Gamble27, Fletcher 46, 49.	20
23	15.11	A	**FAC 1**	Blackpool	L	3-4	*4,814*	Henderson 10, Di Lellia 44, Atkinson 84.	-
24	18.11	H	UL	Emley	L	0-2	339		
25	22.11	A	UL	Radcliffe Borough	W	2-1	*201*	Gamble 40, Moat 82.	19
26	25.11	H	**ULPC 1**	Bishop Auckland	W	3-2	313	McGargle 43, 47, Tinkler 78.	-
27	29.11	A	**FAT 3Q**	Harrogate Town	W	3-0	*301*	Atkinson 60, 83, Ainsley 85.	-
28	06.12	H	UL	Boston United	L	0-1	375		20
29	13.12	H	UL	Hyde United	D	1-1	425	Ainsley 36.	20
30	16.12	H	**ULCC 3**	Frickley Athletic	W	4-1	231	Fletcher 18, 58, Atkinson 31, Ainsley 36.	
31	20.12	A	UL	Bamber Bridge	**W**	**4-1**	*303*	Pike 4, Henderson 55, Hislop 71, Fletcher 72.	19
32	27.12	A	UL	Guiseley	W	3-1	*634*	Fletcher 10, Atkinson 23, Hislop 51.	19
33	03.01	H	UL	Chorley	W	2-1	603	Fletcher 75, 81.	16
34	10.01	A	**FAT 1**	Halifax Town	L	1-2	*1,712*	Moat 72.	-
35	17.01	A	UL	Accrington Stanley	L	0-2	*507*		18
36	21.01	A	**ULPC 2**	Boston United	D	3-3	*348*	Atkinson 3, 78, Moat 39.	-
37	24.01	H	UL	Runcorn	**L**	**0-4**	630		19
38	31.01	H	UL	Alfreton Town	W	4-2	467	Atkinson 11, 82, Fletcher 27, Gamble 56.	19
39	03.02	H	**ULPC 2 R**	Boston United	W	4-2*	303	Pike 25 (pen), 111, Atkinson 82, Moat 107.	-
40	07.02	A	UL	Boston United	D	2-2	*956*	Di Lella 2, OG (Fee) 12.	18
41	14.02	H	UL	Frickley Athletic	L	2-3	491	Pike 41, Atkinson 90.	18
42	17.02	H	**ULCC 4**	Marine	W	2-0	386	Di Lella 5, Wilson 90.	-
43	21.02	A	UL	Leigh RMI	D	1-1	*208*	Moat 90.	18
44	28.02	H	UL	Marine	W	1-0	446	Hislop 10.	18
45	07.03	A	UL	Alfreton Town	W	3-0	*195*	Gamble 4, McGargle 7, Hislop 44.	17
46	10.03	H	**ULPC SF-1**	Runcorn	W	2-1	294	Gamble 12, 40.	-
47	14.03	A	UL	Winsford United	L	0-3	*158*		17
48	21.03	H	UL	Radcliffe Borough	W	1-0	467	Hislop 23.	16
49	24.03	H	**ULCC SF-1**	Gainsborough Trinity	L	1-2	331	McGarrigle 87.	-
50	28.03	A	UL	Hyde United	L	0-1	*348*		17
51	01.04	A	**ULCC SF-2**	Gainsborough Trinity	L	1-2	*602*	Atkinson 85 (pen).	-
52	04.04	A	UL	Gainsborough Trinity	D	0-0	*628*		17
53	10.04	A	UL	Bishop Auckland	D	1-1	*204*	Pike 58.	
54	11.04	A	UL	Barrow	L	1-3	*1,406*	Pike 34.	17
55	13.04	H	UL	Altrincham	D	3-3	419	Atkinson 8, 90, McGargle 52.	17
56	15.04	H	ULPC SF-2	Runcorn	-	No second leg played - Blyth expelled for playing an ineligible player in first leg.			
57	18.04	H	UL	Barrow	W	2-1	591	McGargle 10, Moat 78.	18
58	21.04	A	UL	Lancaster City	L	1-3	*192*	Moat 72.	
59	25.04	A	UL	Colwyn Bay	L	0-2	*306*		18
60	02.05	H	UL	Bamber Bridge	D	1-1	390	Moat 82.	18

PLAYING SQUAD 1998 - **Goalkeepers:** Steve Jones (B Auckland, Billingham T, Hartelpool U). **Defenders:** John Ramsey (Doncaster R), John Gamble (Fleetwood T, B Auckland,Seaham Red Star, Newcastle Blue Star, Queen of the South), Michael Farrey (Gateshead, Chester-le-Street, Whickham), John Tinkler (Morpeth T, Durham C,Spennymoor U, Fleetwood T, Gateshead, Walsall, Hartlepool U), Steve Dann (Darlington), Kevin McGarrigle (Spennymoor U, Brighton), Wes Byrne (Gateshead, Darlington, Middlesbrough), Anthony Cole (Berwick R, Gateshead,St.Johnstone, Middlesbrough, Newcastle U), Martin Pike (Durham C, Rotherham U,Fulham, Sheffield U, Peterborough U, WBA). **Midfielders:** Kona Hislop (Carlisle U, Hartlepool U, Livingston), Tony Skedd (Hartlepool U, Gateshead, Spennymoor U, Hartlepool U), Jon Atkinson (MorpethT, Alnwick T, Sunderland), Steve McGargle (Gateshead, Middlesbrough), Steve Walker (Doncaster R, Blyth S, Morpeth T, Whitley Bay, Morpeth T), Tony Simpson (Ferryhill Ath), Glen Renforth (Whitley Bay, Prudhoe T, Blyth S, Everton), Willie Wilson (Chester-le-Street, Bedlington Terr, Blyth S, Bedlington Terr,Gretna, Dunston Fed), Jason Ainsley (Spennymoor U, Hartlepool U, Spennymoor U,B Auckland, Spennymoor U, Guisborough T). **Forwards:** Willie Moat (Whitley Bay, Hebburn, Gretna, Brandon U, Swalwell), Steve Adams (Ashington).

PROGRAMME DETAILS:
Pages: 32 **Price:**£1.
Editor: Alan Robinson

CHORLEY

Colours: White & black stripes/black/black & white **Formed:** 1883
Change colours: All yellow **Founded:** The Magpies
Midweek matchday: Tuesday **Sponsors:** Coloroll.
Reserve League: Alliance League.
Local Press: Lancs Evening Post, Chorley Guardian.
Local Radio: Radio Lancs, Red Rose.

Chairman: Jack Kirkland **President:** Dr P J Wren.
Vice Chairman: **Commercial Manager:** Ernie Howe.
Secretary / Press Officer: Mick Wearmouth, 6 Avondale Road, Chorley, Lancs. PR7 2ED (01257 271395).
Manager: Brian Griffiths **Asst Manager:** Ken Wright

GROUND Address: Victory Park, Duke Street, Chorley, Lancs (01257 263406). **Directions:** M61 jct 6, A6 to Chorley, going past Yarrow Bridge Hotel on Bolton Rd turn left at 1st lights into Pilling Lane, 1st right into Ashley Str., ground 2nd left. From M6; jct 27, follow signs to Chorley, left at lights, continue for two and a half miles on A49, right onto B5251, on entering Chorley turn right into Duke Street 200yds after Plough Hotel. Quarter mile from Chorley (BR).
Capacity: 9,000 **Cover:** 4,000 **Seats:** 900 **Floodlights:** Yes
Clubhouse: (01257 275662). Open every evening. Entertainment at weekends. Snacks available. **Club Shop:** Yes.

PREVIOUS - **Leagues:** Lancs Alliance 1890-94; Lancs 94-1903; Lancs Comb. 03-68, 69-70; Northern Premier 68-69, 70-72, 82-88; Cheshire County 72-82; GMV Conference 88-90. **Grounds:** Dole Lane 1883-1901; Rangletts Park 01-05; St George's Park 05-20. **Name:** None

CLUB RECORDS - **Attendance:** 9,679 v Darwen, 1931-32. **Goalscorer:** Peter Watson. **Transfer Fee Paid:** Undisclosed fee to Marine for Brian Ross 1995. **Received:** £22,500 for Paul Mariner (Plymouth, 1973).

BEST SEASON - **FA Cup:** 2nd Rd 86-87 (lost in replay at Preston), 90-91 (lost at Shrewsbury). **FA Trophy:** Semi-Final 1995-96.

HONOURS - Northern Premier Lg 87-88, Cheshire Co. Lg 75-76 76-77 81-82, Lancs Comb. 19-20 22-23 27-28 28-29 32-33 33-34 45-46 59-60 60-61 63-64 (R-up 21-22 26-27 48-49 62-63 64-65 65-66, Lg Cup 24-25 58-59 62-63), Lancs Lg 1896-97 98-99, Lancs Alliance 1892-93 (R-up 94-95), Lancs Jnr Cup 1894-95 1908-09 23-24 39-40 45-46 57-58 58-59 60-61 63-64 64-65 75-76 79-80 81-82 82-83.

Players progressing to Football League: Charles Ashcroft (Liverpool 1946), William Healey (Arsenal 49), Stan Howard (Huddersfield 52), Derek Hogg (Leicester 52), William Norcross (Southport 59), Micky Walsh (Blackpool 71), Paul Mariner (Plymouth 73), Graham Barrow (Wigan 76), Steve Galliers (Wimbledon 77), Kevin Tully (Bury 80), Geoff Twentyman (Preston 83), Gary Buckley (Bury 84), Chris Hunter (Preston 84).

Back Row (L-R); Mark Jones, Danny Worthington, Neil Wright, Peter Thomson, Derek Goulding, Lee Owler, Adam Critchley, Matty Swailes. Middle Row; Deuis Haslam, Mick Jones, Andy Westwell, Chris Clarke, Simm Marsh, Paul Higginbotham, John Hyde, G Ashton (Physio). Front Row; Terry Stubbs, Ian Harold, Andy Gayle, Ian Cain, Ken Wright (Asst Mgr), Brian Griffiths (Mgr), Colin Potts, James Price, Andy McIntosh, Richard Lodge.

CHORLEY - Match Facts 97-98

ATS - Lancashire `ATS' Trophy

Match No.	Date	Venue H / A	Comp	Opponents	Result & Score	Att	Goalscorers	League Position
1	23.08	H	UL	Blyth Spartans	L 1-3	369	OG (Dunn) 82.	
2	25.08	A	UL	Bamber Bridge	L 0-4	*838*		
3	30.08	A	UL	Boston United	D 1-1	*1,080*	OG (Mason) 40.	22
4	02.09	H	UL	Barrow	L 0-2	532		22
5	09.09	A	UL	Colwyn Bay	D 3-3	*321*	Higginbotham 8, 84, Cain 25.	22
6	13.09	H	**FAC 1Q**	Pontefract Collieries	W 3-1	272	Thomspon 8, Potts 15, Gayle 54.	-
7	16.09	H	UL	Runcorn	W 4-2	235	Stubbs 53, Mark Jones 63, Mick Jones 74, Swailes 77.	18
8	20.09	A	UL	Spennymoor United	L 0-2	*198*		
9	23.09	A	UL	Lancaster City	L 1-4	*245*	Mick Jones 37.	21
10	27.09	H	**FAC 2Q**	Bishop Auckland	D 2-2	337	Jones 25, Cain 20.	-
11	01.10	A	**FAC 2Q R**	Bishop Auckland	W 3-2	*135*	Swailes 62, Stubbs 80, Goulding 82.	-
12	04.10	A	UL	Emley	L 1-3	*276*	Stubbs 67.	21
13	07.10	H	UL	Accrington Stanley	D 1-1	488	Swales 22.	21
14	11.10	H	**FAC 3Q**	Ilkeston Town	L 1-3	477	Stubbs 22.	-
15	14.10	A	UL	Barrow	L 0-1	*973*		21
16	18.10	H	UL	Altrincham	W 1-0	534	Stubbs 83.	21
17	21.10	H	UL	Lancaster City	L 2-3	288	Potts 9, Swales 53.	
18	25.10	H	UL	Guiseley	W 1-0	293	Thompson 75.	20
19	28.10	A	**ULCC 2**	Bamber Bridge	W 1-0	*335*	Swales 35.	-
20	01.11	A	UL	Frickley Athletic	L 0-2	*166*		21
21	08.11	H	UL	Bishop Auckland	W 1-0	296	Ellison 82.	20
22	11.11	H	UL	Hyde United	**L 1-5**	347	Potts 43.	21
23	15.11	A	UL	Bishop Auckland	L 2-5	*193*	Cain 17, 42.	21
24	18.11	H	**ATS 1**	Holker O.B.	W 3-0	136	Swales 11, Jones 16, Grimshaw 57.	-
25	22.11	A	UL	Guiseley	L 1-2	*358*	Swailes 17.	21
26	25.11	H	UL	Winsford United	W 2-0	216	Swailes 27, Higginbotham 85.	
27	29.11	H	UL	Alfreton Town	W 2-0	288	Higginbotham 29, Swailes 89 (pen).	16
28	06.12	A	UL	Radcliffe Borough	W 2-1	*218*	Higginbotham 19, Critchley 60.	15
29	13.12	H	UL	Spennymoor United	**W 4-1**	276	Higginbotham 44, **Swailes 3** (62, 73, 79).	13
30	20.12	A	UL	Runcorn	W 3-2	*377*	Swailes 30, 87, Daley 84.	11
31	01.01	H	UL	Bamber Bridge	W 2-1	801	Allardyce 72, Swailes 77.	
32	03.01	A	UL	Blyth Spartans	L 1-2	*603*	Critchley 20.	9
33	05.01	A	**ATS 2**	Clitheroe	W 2-0*	*100*	Thompson 111, Swailes 115.	-
34	10.01	A	**FAT 1**	Ashton United	D 0-0	*439*		-
35	13.01	H	**FAT 1 R**	Ashton United	L 0-2	430		-
36	17.01	A	UL	Leigh RMI	L 0-2	*327*		11
37	21.01	H	**ULCC 3**	Leigh RMI	W 5-2	210	Thorpe 16, Cain 33, 86, Potts 40, 62.	-
38	24.01	H	UL	Boston United	L 0-2	431		12
39	31.01	A	UL	Accrington Stanley	W 3-0	*492*	Critchley 25, Allardyce 34, Swailes 48.	11
40	03.02	A	**ATS 3**	Lancaster City	D 1-1*	*217*	Thompson 90.	-
41	07.02	A	UL	Gainsborough Trinity	L 1-2	*474*	Swailes 75.	14
42	10.02	H	**ATS 3 R**	Lancaster City	L 1-2	281	Thompson 71.	-
43	14.02	H	UL	Gainsborough Trinity	D 1-1	316	Harold 56.	15
44	17.02	H	**ULCC 4**	Winsford United	D 0-0	280		-
45	21.02	H	UL	Emley	L 1-2	383	Potts 90.	17
46	24.02	A	**ULCC 4 R**	Winsford United	W 1-0	*132*	Harold 64.	-
47	28.02	A	UL	Alfreton Town	D 1-1	*165*	Swailes 68.	16
48	03.03	A	UL	Marine	W 2-1	*297*	Swailes 1, Allardyce 7.	
49	07.03	A	UL	Hyde United	W 2-0	*442*	Thompson 11, 86.	11
50	14.03	H	UL	Frickley Athletic	D 0-0	275		11
51	16.03	A	**ULCC SF-1**	Altrincham	L 0-2	452		-
52	21.03	A	UL	Winsford United	L 0-1	*193*		12
53	24.03	H	**ULCC SF-2**	Altrincham	W 3-2	467	Ashcroft 66, Swailes 81, Simms 90.	-
54	28.03	A	UL	Altrincham	L 0-3	*575*		16
55	31.03	H	UL	Radcliffe Borough	D 1-1	239	Thompson 27.	15
56	07.04	H	UL	Leigh RMI	L 0-1	342		16
57	13.04	H	UL	Colwyn Bay	W 2-0	253	Thompson 50, Potts 56.	14
58	21.03	H	UL	Marine	L 0-3	295		15

PLAYING SQUAD 1998 - **Goalkeepers:** Simon Marsh (Hyde U, Blackpool). **Defenders:** Mark Jones (Witton Alb, Winsford U, Hyde U, Northwich V, Southport,Preston NE, Runcorn), Adam Critchley (Witton Alb, Mossley, Chorley, PrestonNE), Andy Thorpe (Doncaster R, Chorley, Buxton, Witton Alb, Melbourne C(Aust), Stockport Co, Tranmere R, Stockport Co), Mark Simms (Bangor C, LeighRMI, Ashton U, Chorley, Southport, Northwich V, Fleetwood T, Bury, Preston NE,Blackburn R), Craig Allardyce (Rushden & D, Bury, Blackpool, Preston NE), Derek Goulding (Halifax T, Southport, Chorley, Stafford R, Oswestry T, BangorC, Altrincham), James Price (Rochdale), Ian Harold (Barrow, Halifax T,Barrow, Altrincham, Stalybridge C, Runcorn, Newton), Keith Ellison (Southport), John Hyde (Youth team), Paul Ashcroft (Blackpool). **Midfielders:** Peter Daley (Cemaes Bay, Vauxhall GM, Runcorn, Knowsley U,Southport, Redbridge F, Chelmsford C, Southend U, Tranmere R, Liverpool), Barry Norris (Cemaes Bay, Fleetwood T, Droylsden, Chester C, Everton), Colin Potts (Rochdale), Lee Owler (Blackburn R), Ian Cain (Morecambe, Fleetwood T, WrenR), Matty Swailes (Hulton, Bury), Andy Westwell (Witton Alb, Chorley, HorwichRMI, Leyland M), Peter Thomson (Bury), Stuart Carrington (Chester C, KnowsleyU, Royal Racing Club (Belg), Andy Grimshaw * (Morecambe, Witton Alb, Colne D,Bury, Manchester U, Rossendale U). **Forwards:** Mick Jones (Knowsley U, Skelmersdale U), Kevin Hagan (Cemaes Bay,Ashton U, Knowsley U, Fleetwood T, Liverpool), Terry Stubbs (Frickley Ath,BCCI), Paul Higginbotham (Conwy U, Leek T, Bangor C, Stalybridge C,Altrincham, Stalybridge C, Barrow, Witton Alb, Manchester C), Colin Taylor (Caernarfon T, Worcester C, Bangor C, Runcorn, Telford U, Wolves), Jim McCluskie * (Acc.Stanley, Morecambe, Acc.Stanley, Witton Alb, Hyde U, Mossley,Rochdale).

PROGRAMME DETAILS:
Pages: 28 **Price:** £1
Editor: M Richardson
(011492 878953)

COLWYN BAY

Colours: Maroon with wide blue stripes/maroon/maroon. **Formed:** 1885
Change colours: White/navy/navy **Nickname:** 'Bay' or 'Seagulls'
Reserve Team: None. **Sponsors:** Colwyn Shopping Centre
Midweek home matchday: Tuesday
Local Press: North Wales Weekly News, North Wales Pioneer.

Chairman: Glynne Owens
Vice Chairman: J A Humphreys
Secretary / Press Officer: Alan J Banks, 15 Smith Avenue, Old Colwyn, N Wales LL29 8BE. 01492 516941 (H), 01492 515133 (B).
Manager: Bryn Jones 01244 531974 (H), 01244 812154 (B)
Assistant Manager: Dave Brett **Physio:** John Carmichael
GROUND Address: Llanelian Road, Old Colwyn, N.Wales. (01492 516554)
Directions: M55 North Wales Coast - approaching Colwyn Bay take 1st exit signposted Old Colwyn, left at bottom slip road, straight over r'bout into Llanelian Rd - ground half mile on right. 2 miles from Colwyn Bar BR station.
Capacity: 2,500 **Seats:** 250 **Cover:** 700 **Floodlights:** Yes
Clubhouse: Open matchdays only.
Club Shop: Yes - contact: A Holden 01492 534287 **Metal Badges:** Yes

PREVIOUS - **Leagues:** Nth Wales Coast 01-21 33-35; Welsh National 21-30; Nth Wales Comb. 30-31; Welsh Lg (Nth) 45-84; North West Counties 84-91. **Grounds:** Eiras Park 1930-82; Llanelian Road 82-92; Northwich Victoria FC 92-93; Ellesmere Port Stadium 94-95 *(2 years in exile thro' dispute with FAW re League of Wales).*

CLUB RECORDS - **Attendance:** 5,000 (at Eiras Park) v Borough United, 1964. **Win:** **Defeat:** **Scorer:** Peter Donnelly **Appearances:** Bryn A Jones

BEST SEASON - **FA Cup:** Second Round Proper 95-96. **FA Trophy:** Qtr Finals 96-97. **League clubs defeated in FA Cup:** None.

HONOURS - Northern Premier Lg Div 1 91-92 (Div 1 Cup 91-92); North West Counties Lg R-up 90-91 (Div 3 R-up 83-84, Lg Cup 88-89, Floodlit Cup 90-91; Welsh Cup SF 91-92; Welsh National Lg R-up 27-28 29-30; Nth Wales Comb. 30-31; Welsh Lg Nth 64-65 82-83 83-84 (R-up 35-36 45-46 63-64), Lg Cup 27-28; Alves Cup 63-64; Cookson Cup 73-74 79-80 80-81 81-82 83-84; Barritt Cup 79-80 81-82 83-84; Nth Wales Coast Chal. Cup 30-31 31-32 81-82 82-83 83-84 95-96 97-98; Nth Wales Coast Jnr Cup 1898-99.

Players progressing to Football League: Peter Suddaby (Blackpool), Gareth Davies (Wrexham).
97-98 Captain: Peter Donnelly **P.o.Y.:** Craig Lawton **Top scorer:** Marc Lambert (15)

Back Row (L-R); Colin Caton, Graham Roberts, Richie Roberts, Glen Graham, Mark Price, Gary McCosh, Tommy Jones, Dave Fuller. Front Row; Steve Mann, Marc Limbert, Craig Lawton, Lee Congerton, Mark Woods, Neil Rigby.

COLWYN BAY - Match Facts 97-98

Match No.	Date	Venue H / A	Comp.	Opponents	Result & Score		Att.	Goalscorers	League Position
1	23.08	H	UL	Hyde United	W	3-1	410	Congerton 36, Graham 74, Limbert 88.	
2	25.08	A	UL	Winsford United	L	0-2	*360*		
3	30.08	A	UL	Radcliffe Borough	D	1-1	*255*	Mottram 6.	12
4	02.09	H	UL	Winsford United	**L**	**0-3**	323		17
5	09.09	H	UL	Chorley	D	3-3	321	Limbert 42, Roberts 66, 72.	17
6	13.09	H	UL	Boston United	L	0-3	283		18
7	16.09	A	UL	Accrington Stanley	W	2-1	*313*	Mottram 3, 53.	10
8	20.09	A	UL	Barrow	D	1-1	*1,220*	Lawton 59.	14
9	23.09	H	UL	Bamber Bridge	W	3-1	302	Mottram 29, 50, Woods 56.	6
10	27.09	H	UL	Runcorn	W	2-1	373	Limbert 46, Roberts 72.	4
11	04.10	H	UL	Guiseley	L	0-1	385		9
12	07.10	H	UL	Marine	W	4-1	307	Limbert 7, 44, Donnelly 51, Lawton 89.	5
13	11.10	A	UL	Accrington Stanley	**L**	**0-3**	*732*		5
14	14.10	A	UL	Lancaster City	W	1-0	*150*	Hughes 41.	4
15	18.10	H	UL	Emley	L	1-3	399	Hughes 46.	5
16	25.10	A	**FAC 4Q**	Hinckley United	W	2-1	*939*	Lawton 45, Congerton 80.	-
17	28.10	H	**ULCC 2**	Hyde United	W	1-0	256	Caton 33.	-
18	01.11	H	UL	Spennymoor United	W	2-0	316	Limbert 45, Roberts 66.	7
19	08.11	A	UL	Blyth Spartans	L	1-3	*492*	Limbert 60.	8
20	16.11	A	**FAC 1**	Notts County	L	0-2	*3,074*		-
21	22.11	A	UL	Bamber Bridge	W	2-0	*288*	Mann 15, Congerton 25.	8
22	06.12	H	UL	Gainsborough Trinity	D	1-1	273	Donnelly 4.	8
23	13.12	A	UL	Alfreton Town	D	1-1	*149*	Donnelly 22.	9
24	16.12	A	**ULCC 3**	Altrincham	L	2-4	*227*	Lawton 49, Roberts 64.	
25	20.12	H	UL	Radcliffe Borough	W	2-1	263	Donnelly 13, 31.	8
26	10.01	A	**FAT 1**	Bishop Auckland	L	1-3	*263*	Limbert 53 (pen).	-
27	17.01	A	UL	Marine	L	0-1	*351*		13
28	24.01	H	UL	Leigh RMI	L	2-3	323	Fuller 55, Hughes 64.	14
29	31.01	H	UL	Frickley Athletic	D	1-1	279	Limbert 75.	15
30	07.02	A	UL	Guiseley	L	1-3	*272*	Twynham 82.	16
31	14.02	H	UL	Barrow	D	1-1	423	Caton 12.	17
32	17.02	A	UL	Leigh RMI	**L**	**0-3**	*228*		
33	21.02	A	UL	Frickley Athletic	W	3-1	*181*	Roberts 21, 86, Woods 25.	15
34	28.02	H	UL	Lancaster City	**W**	**5-2**	269	Drury 22, 50, Limbert 44, Lawton 71, 75.	13
35	07.03	A	UL	Emley	L	0-1	*266*		15
36	10.03	H	UL	Altrincham	D	0-0	309		15
37	14.03	A	UL	Gainsborough Trinity	L	0-1	*479*		15
38	17.03	A	UL	Runcorn	D	0-0	*285*		
39	21.03	H	UL	Alfreton Town	W	3-0	261	Limbert 11, Drury 35, Lawton 53.	11
40	28.03	A	UL	Spennymoor United	L	1-2	*151*	Lawton 41.	14
41	04.04	A	UL	Bishop Auckland	W	2-0	*92*	McCobb 28, Limbert 89.	13
42	11.04	H	UL	Accrington Stanley	W	2-1	284	Roberts 68, Congleton 83.	
43	13.04	A	UL	Chorley	L	0-2	*253*		11
44	18.04	A	UL	Boston United	L	0-1	*1010*		12
45	20.04	A	UL	Hyde United	L	0-2	*346*		13
46	25.04	H	UL	Blyth Spartans	W	2-0	306	Lawton 32, Roberts 80.	13
47	02.05	H	UL	Bishop Auckland	L	0-1	259		13

PLAYING SQUAD 1998

Goalkeepers: Richie Roberts (Christleton), Gerard McGuigan (Conwy U)

Defenders: Dave Fuller (Southport, Witton Alb, Bangor C, Gainsborough Trin,Bangor C), Colin Caton (Witton Alb, Colwyn Bay, Rhyl), Mark Woods (Pieksamaki (Fin), Colwyn Bay, Flint Town U, United Services), Mark Price (Connah's Quay Nomads, Holywell T, Upton AA), Steve Mann (Caernarfon T, MoldAlex, Newtown, Upton T, Connah's Quay Nomads), Glen Graham (Flint Town U,Mostyn, Holywell T), Neil Davies (Ruthin T), Gary McGosh (Local football), Craig Crawford (Conwy (U)

Midfielders: Craig Lawton (Port Vale, Manchester U), Frank Mottram (Llansantffraid, Macclesfield T, Bangor C, Welshpool), Gareth Drury (VauxhallGM, Knowsley U, Marine), Marc Limbert (Altrincham, Colwyn Bay, Connah's QuayNomads, Chester C, Everton), Lee Congerton (Knowsley U, Weymouth, Knowsley U,Rhyl, Newtown, Crewe Alex)

Forwards: Graham Roberts (Macclesfield T, Colwyn Bay, Caernarfon T, Flint TownU, Mold Alex, British Steel), Tommy Jones (Holywell T, Conwy U, Llandudno,Colwyn Bay), Peter Donnelly (Northwich V, Colwyn Bay, Rhyl, Oswestry T,Chester C), Marc Williams (Altrincham, Stockport Co, Bangor C, Porthmadog,Llanberis), Alun Evans (Ebbw Vale, Flint Town U, Bangor C).

PROGRAMME DETAILS:
Pages: 34 **Price:** £ 1
Editor: Alan Blackman
(01924 403959)

EMLEY

Colours: Maroon and blue/blue/maroon. **Formed:** 1903
Change Colours: White/maroon/white **Nickname:** 'The Pewits'
Midweek matchday: Monday. **Sponsors:** Arrow Self Drive
Reserve League: Nth Co's (E) Res Div.
Local Press: Huddersfield Examiner, Huddersfield & District Chronicle.
Local Radio: Radio Leeds, Radio Sheffield, Pulse FM, Huddersfield FM.

Chairman: Peter Matthews. **President:** Peter Maude
Secretary: Richard Poulain, 17, Smithy Lane, Skelmanthorpe, Huddersfield HD8 9DF. (01484 860323 H, Web HTTP://WWW.EMLEYAFC.Force9.Co.UK, 0411 620726 Mob & B.
Manager: Ronnie Glavin. **Asst Manager:** Peter Price
Physio: Daryl Brook. **Press Officer:** Secretary
GROUND Address: Emley Welfare Sports Ground, Emley, Huddersfield (01924 848398. Office: 840087). **Directions:** Follow Huddersfield signs from M1 junct 38, left onto A636 at r'bout, then right after about 3/4 mile for Emley. 7 miles from Huddersfield (BR) station - buses to Emley Cross.
Capacity: 3,000 **Cover:** 1,000 **Seats:** 300 **Floodlights:** Yes
Clubhouse: (01924 848398). Members' social club open five nights a week and Saturday & Sunday. Bingo, discos, occasional caberet.
Club Shop: Yes Contact Mrs Linda Sykes (01484 325077)

PREVIOUS - **Leagues:** Huddersfield; Yorkshire 69-82; Northern Counties East 82-89. **Names:** None **Grounds:** None.

CLUB RECORDS - **Attendance:** 5,134 v Barking, Amateur Cup Third Round Proper 1/2/69. *18629 v West Ham Utd, Upton Pk, 3rd Rd Proper 3/1/99.* **Win:** 12-0 v Ecclesfield Red Rose 9-6-97. **Defeat:** 7-1 v Altringham 25-4-98. **Goalscorer:** Mick Pamment 305. **Appearances:** Ray Dennis 762. **Transfer Fee Received:** £30,000 for Glynn Hurst (Ayr Utd 96).

BEST SEASON - **FA Amateur Cup:** Third Round replay 69-70. **FA Vase:** Runners-up 87-88 (Semi-Final 86-87). **FA Trophy:** Fourth Round 90-91. **FA Cup:** Third Round Proper 97-98 (1-2 v West Ham Utd)

HONOURS - FA Vase Runners-up 87-88; Northern Premier Lge Div 1 R-up 90-91; Northern Counties E Lge 87-88, 88-89 (R-up 85-86); Yorkshire Lg 75-76 77-78 79-80 81-82 (R-up(5) 72-74 76-77 78-79 80-81, Lg Cup 69-70 78-79 81-82, Div 2 R-up 69-70; Sheffield & Hallamshire Senior Cup 75-76 79-80 80-81 83-84 88-89 90-91 91-92 97-98; Huddersfield Challenge Cup 82-83 83-84 85-86; Huddersfield Lg(4) 65-69.

Players progressing to Football League: A Sweeney (Hartlepool Utd 79), G Cooper (Huddersfield Tn 84), J Francis (Sheffield Utd 88), S Smith (Crewe Alexandra 1992), C Alcide (Lincoln City 95), C Hurst (Huddersfield Tn 97), G Hurst (Ayr Utd 98)

97-98 Captain: I Banks **P.o.Y.:** M Thompson **Top scorer:** I Banks

Back Row (L-R); Richard Poulain (Sec), Neil Lacey, Michael Thompson, Dean Calcutt, Chris Marples, Darron Clyde, Paul David, Rob Tonks, Peter Matthews (Chairman), Simon Jones. Front Row ; Paul Hutson, Steve Nicholson, Deiniol Graham, Ian Banks, Michael Reynolds, Mark Wilson, Glynn Hurst,

EMLEY - Match Facts 97-98

S&HSC - Sheffield & Hallamshire Sen. Cup

Match No.	Date	Venue H / A	Comp.	Opponents	Result & Score	Att.	Goalscorers	League Position
1	23.08	A	UL	Bamber Bridge	W 3-2	*296*	Banks 19, 27 (pen), Graham 86.	
2	25.08	H	UL	Altrincham	W 2-1	403	Churst 36, David 54.	
3	30.08	A	UL	Runcorn	L 0-1	*362*		4
4	01.09	H	UL	Bishop Auckland	L 1-2	321	Reynolds 41.	4
5	09.09	A	UL	Spennymoor United	D 2-2	*208*	Jones 46, David 69.	13
6	20.09	H	UL	Lancaster City	W 5-3	237	Hurst 5, 61, Graham 18, Banks 28, Reyynolds 86.	7
7	22.09	A	UL	Hyde United	L 0-1	*624*		
8	29.09	H	UL	Blyth Spartans	D 1-1	263	Banks 63 (pen).	12
9	04.10	H	UL	Chorley	W 3-1	276	David 14, 87, Graham 61.	9
10	08.10	A	UL	Boston United	L 2-3	*769*	David 24, Thompson 83.	
11	13.10	H	UL	Boston United	D 0-0	289		11
12	18.10	A	UL	Colwyn Bay	W 3-1	*399*	Reynolds 35, Calcutt 47, Hurst 55.	10
13	22.10	A	UL	Gainsborough Trinity	L 1-2	*401*	Hurst 50.	
14	29.10	A	**ULCC 2**	Boston United	L 0-1	*398*		-
15	01.11	A	UL	Accrington Stanley	L 2-4	*549*	Thompson 21, David 43.	14
16	08.11	A	UL	Lancaster City	D 2-2	*239*	David 23, Hurst 42.	
17	10.11	H	UL	Gainsborough Trinity	W 1-0	287	Banks 66 (pen).	13
18	18.11	A	UL	Blyth Spartans	W 2-0	*339*	David 32, Wilson 63.	9
19	22.11	A	UL	Winsford United	W 1-0	*278*	David 70.	7
20	03.12	A	**FAT 3Q**	Solihull Borough	L 1-2	*116*	Hurst 74.	-
21	08.12	H	**S&HSC 2**	Grimethorpe M.W.	W 1-0	112	Thompson 24.	-
22	13.12	H	UL	Marine	W 2-0	245	Graham 33, Tonks 52.	7
23	20.12	A	UL	Leigh RMI	L 1-2	*267*	Reynolds 60.	9
24	27.12	A	UL	Frickley Athletic	L 1-2	*476*	Lacey 87.	10
25	12.01	H	**S&HSC 3**	Frickley Athletic	W 2-1	338	Graham 30, 42.	-
26	17.01	A	UL	Alfreton Town	D 1-1	*354*	Wilson 5.	12
27	21.01	H	**ULPC 1**	Stocksbridge Park Steels	W 2-1	238	Calcutt 65, Hurst 90.	-
28	24.01	H	UL	Winsford United	L 0-2	298		-
29	26.01	A	**ULPC 2**	Ashton United	L 1-2	*216*	Reynolds 33.	-
30	31.01	H	UL	Guiseley	D 3-3	345	Banks 16 (pen), 33, Graham 40.	14
31	07.02	H	UL	Hyde United	W 2-1	294	Hurst 25, David 78.	12
32	14.02	H	UL	Leigh RMI	D 2-2	299	David 61, Banks 83.	14
33	21.02	A	UL	Chorley	W 2-1	*383*	Banks 40, Thompson 58.	12
34	23.02	H	UL	Radcliffe Borough	W 2-0	185	Graham 23, Wood 30.	9
35	28.02	H	UL	Runcorn	**W 6-2**	238	**Hurst 3** (13, 17, 48), Graham 45, 78, Dysart 86.	7
36	07.03	H	UL	Colwyn Bay	W 1-0	266	Thompson 56.	7
37	09.03	H	**S&H SC SF**	Worksop Town	W 3-1	305	Hurst 20, 83, Reynolds 71.	-
38	14.03	A	Ul	Marine	W 5-3	*332*	**Banks 3** (23, 66, 76 - all pens), Graham 53, Reynolds 68.	7
39	16.03	H	UL	Bamber Bridge	D 0-0	289		
40	21.03	H	UL	Barrow	W 3-0	502	Thompson 23, Graham 33, Midwood 63.	5
41	28.03	A	UL	Barrow	L 0-1	*1,271*		6
42	30.03	H	UL	Accrington Stanley	W 5-3	275	Banks 17(pen), **Bidwood 3** (43, 64, 66), Graham 44.	4
43	04.04	H	UL	Alfreton Town	W 2-0	247	David 15, Lacey 56.	5
44	11.04	A	UL	Radcliffe Borough	W 2-1	*228*	Reynolds 6, Banks 24 (pen).	5
45	13.04	H	UL	Frickley Athletic	W 1-0	347	Banks 44 (pen).	5
46	18.04	A	UL	Bishop Auckland	L 3-4	*175*	David 28, Reynolds 50, Thompson 89.	5
47	23.04	H	UL	Spennymoor United	W 3-0	171	Banks 10, Graham 40, David 49.	6
48	25.04	A	UL	Altrincham	**L 1-7**	599	Banks 49 (pen).	6
49	28.04	N	**S&HSC Final**	Parkgate	W 3-0	671	David 24, Reynolds 55, Tonks 60.	-
50	02.05	A	UL	Guiseley	W 2-0	*491*	Wilson 9, Banks 42 (pen).	6

F.A. CUP

Date	Venue	Round	Opponents	Result & Score	Att.	Goalscorers	
13.09	A	1Q	Workington	W 3-0	186	Thompson 24, 70, Wood 90.	
27.09	A	2Q	Durham City	W 5-0	292	Reynolds 48, 84, Lacey 62, Hurst 83, Tonks 89.	
11.10	H	3Q	Belper Town	W 2-1	396	Calcutt 30, Graham 84.	
25.10	A	4Q	Nuneaton Borough	W 3-2	1,960	Graham 4, Jones 66, Hurst 68.	
15.11	A	1	Morecambe	D 1-1	1,496	Banks 63 (pen).	
25.11	H	1 R	Morecambe	D *3-3	2,439	Hurst 42, 104, Marshall 120.	(Won 3-1 on penalties)
06.12	A	2	Lincoln City	D 2-2	3,729	Hurst 45, Graham 85.	
17.12	H	2R	Lincoln City	D *3-3	4,891	Grahm 75, Nicholson 87, 111 (pen).	(Won 4-3 on penalties)
03.01	A	3	West Ham United	L 1-2	18,629	David 56.	

F.A. CUP

PLAYING SQUAD 1998

Goalkeepers: Chris Marples (Chesterfield, York C, Stockport Co, Chesterfield,Goole T, Sutton T)

Defenders: Neil Lacey (Frickley Ath, Gateshead, Frickley Ath, Goole T, DenabyU), Steve Nicholson (Farsley Celtic, Leeds U), Mike Thompson (Frickley Ath,Ashfield U, Frickley Ath, Goole T, Scunthorpe U), Nicky Wood (Huddersfield T), Phil McDonald (Halifax T), Chris Higgins (Grimethorpe MW)

Midfielders: Ian Banks (Darlington, Rotherham U, Barnsley, WBA, Bradford C,Huddersfield T, Leicester C, Barnsley), Paul David (Bradley R), Mark Wilson (Bradford PA, Farsley Celtic, Shepshed Alb, Frickley Ath, Huddersfield T,Rotherham U), Paul Cummings (Port Glasgow, St.Mirren), Robert Tonks (Localfootball), Michael Midwood (Halifax T, Huddersfield T)

Forwards: Deniol Graham (Dag & Red, Halifax T, Barnsley, Manchester U), GaryMarshall (Berwick R), Michael Reynolds (Local football), Dean Calcutt (Brackenhall), Linton Brown (Swansea C, Hull C, Halifax T, Guiseley).

PROGRAMME DETAILS:
Pages: 40 **Price:** £1
Editor: S Pennock
Tel: 01302 835956

FRICKLEY ATHLETIC

Colours: All blue
Change colours: Yellow & black.
Midweek home matchday: Tuesday
Reserves' League: None
Local Press: South Yorks Times, Hemsworth & South Elmsall Express.
Local Radio: Radio Sheffield, Radio Hallam, Radio Leeds.

Formed: 1910
Nickname: The Blues
Sponsors: TBA

Chairman: Mike Twiby (01977 648070)
Financial Secretary: D Fisher (01977 609940 B)
Secretary / Treasurer: D Fisher, 31 Vickers Ave., South Elmsall WF9 3LW. (01977 643316)
Manager: Ian Thompson (01977 609748)

GROUND: Address: Westfield Lane, South Elmsall, Pontefract (01977 642460 + Fax).
Directions: Follow signs for South Elmsall from A1 and A638. Left at Superdrug warehouse, right at T junction and immediately left up Westfield Lane. Left into Oxford Road (opposite Westfield Hotel) - ground at bottom on right. Two miles from South Elmsall (BR).
Capacity: 6,000 **Cover:** 2,500 **Seats:** 800 **Floodlights:** Yes
Clubhouse: On ground open matchdays, food available. **Club Shop:** Yes

PREVIOUS - **Leagues:** Sheffield; Yorkshire 22-24; Midland Counties 24-33 34-60 70-76; Cheshire County 60-70; Northern Premier 76-80; GMV Conference (Alliance Premier) 80-87. **Name:** Frickley Colliery

CLUB RECORDS - **Attendance:** 6,500 v Rotherham United, FA Cup First Round 1971. **Scorer:** K Whiteley. **Defeat:** 0-4 **Fee Paid:** £1,800. **Fee Received:** £12,500 for Paul Shirtliff (Boston Utd) & £12,500 for Russ Wilcox (Northampton)

BEST SEASON - **FA Trophy:** Quarter-Finals 84-85. **FA Cup:** 3rd Rd 1985-86 (1-3 v Rotherham H). 2nd Rd 84-85 (0-1 at Darlington). 1st Rd 36-37 57-58 63-64 71-72 73-74 83-84 86-87 88-89. **League clubs defeated:** Hartlepool United 85-86.

HONOURS: Alliance Premier Lg R-up 85-86, Midland Counties Lg R-up 72-73 (Lg Cup 75-76), Yorkshire Lg R-up 23-24, Sheffield & Hallamshire Senior Cup 27-28 56-57 60-61 62-63 66-67 78-79 85-86 87-88 89-90, Sheffield Association Lg 20-21 (R-up 11-12).

Players progressing to Football League: Dennis Smith & Jack Brownsword (Hull 1946), Stan Scrimshaw (Halifax 1947), William Callaghan (Aldershot 1949), Leo Dickens 1950), John Ashley & Graham Caulfield (York 1950 & 67), Ron Barritt (Leeds 1951), John Pickup (Bradford PA 1955), Tom Hymers & Arthur Ashmore & Stewart Gray (Doncaster 1958 & 66 & 78), Colin Roberts (Bradford City 1959), Derek Downing (Middlesbrough 1965), Graham Reed & Russell Wilcox (Northampton 1985 & 86), Will Foley (Swansea 1986), Gary Brook (Newport 1987), Wayne Scargill (Bradford City 94-95), Andy Hayward (Rotherham Utd.).

97-98 Captain: Mark Hancock **Top Scorer:** Scott Armstrong (7) **P.o.Y.:** Chris Hilton

Back Row (L-R); G Duffty, M Thorpe, G Yates, R Coyles, S Fuller, C Williams, C Hilton. Front Row; G Hatto, D Field, M Hancock, I Frank, S Armstrong, D Dickinson

FRICKLEY ATHLETIC - Match Facts 97-98

S&HSC - Sheffield & Hallamshire Sen. Cup

Match No.	Date	Venue H / A	Comp.	Opponents	Result & Score		Att.	Goalscorers	League Position
1	23.08	A	UL	Alfreton Town	L	1-2	*162*	Green 18.	
2	25.08	H	UL	Gainsborough Trinity	D	1-1	230	Frank 24.	
3	30.08	H	UL	Lancaster City	W	2-1	139	Thorpe 52, Fuller 87.	13
4	09.09	H	UL	Boston United	W	1-0	268	Armstrong 2.	12
5	13.09	H	**FAC 1Q**	Morpeth Town	D	3-3	109	Williams 74, Armstrong 83, Thorpe 90.	-
6	16.09	A	**FAC 1Q R**	Morpeth Town	L	1-4	*74*	Thorpe 2.	-
7	20.09	A	UL	Winsford United	L	1-2	*232*	Hancock 26 (pen).	18
8	23.09	H	UL	Alfreton Town	W	2-1	162	O'Donnell 15, Hancock 74 (pen).	14
9	27.09	H	UL	Accrington Stanley	W	2-1	134	OG (Davies) 58, Hancock 82 (pen).	7
10	30.09	A	UL	Spennymoor united	D	0-0	*157*		7
11	04.10	A	UL	Leigh RMI	D	1-1	*201*	Fuller 73.	5
12	07.10	H	UL	Blyth Spartans	D	0-0	204		7
13	11.10	A	UL	Barrow	L	1-2	*938*	Armstrong 55.	9
14	15.10	A	UL	Bishop Auckland	L	1-4	*127*	Fuller 39.	10
15	18.10	H	**FAT 1Q**	Leigh RMI	D	1-1	171	Thorpe 21.	-
16	21.10	A	**FAT 1Q R**	Leigh RMI	L	*1-2	*86*	Armstrong 46.	-
17	25.10	A	UL	Marine	D	1-1	*252*	Hancock 55.	13
18	01.11	H	UL	Chorley	W	2-0	166	Green 75, OG (Harold) 85.	11
19	08.11	A	UL	Bamber Bridge	L	0-3	*246*		12
20	11.11	H	UL	Bishop Auckland	L	2-3	125	Field 79, Green79.	
21	15.11	A	UL	Altrincham	L	0-3	*480*		15
22	19.11	A	**ULCC 2**	Bradford Park Avenue	W	2-0	*135*	Green 21, Armstrong 85.	-
23	22.11	H	UL	Barrow	L	0-1	231		17
24	29.11	H	UL	Hyde United	W	2-1	146	Hancock 36 (pen), Thorpe 41.	15
25	06.12	A	UL	Altrincham	L	1-2	*490*	Fuller 90.	18
26	09.12	H	UL	Winsford United	**W**	**3-0**	119	Fuller 5, Hancock 18, Armstrong 90.	17
27	13.12	H	**S&HSC 2**	High Green Villa	W	3-0	90	Hancock 66, Armstrong 68, Duffy 87.	-
28	16.12	A	**ULCC 3**	Blyth Spartans	L	1-4	*231*	O'Donnell 71.	-
29	20.12	A	UL	Guiseley	**L**	**0-4**	*380*		17
30	27.12	H	UL	Emley	W	2-1	476	O'Donnell 13, Haran 30.	13
31	10.01	H	UL	Spennymoor United	L	2-3	179	OG (Lowes) 39, Hancock 66 (pen).	16
32	12.01	A	**S&HSC 3**	Emley	L	1-2	*338*	Armstrong 56.	-
33	17.01	A	UL	Runcorn	L	1-2	*278*	Annon 34.	17
34	24.01	H	UL	Radcliffe Borough	W	1-0	142	O'Donnell 30.	16
35	31.01	A	UL	Colwyn Bay	D	1-1	*279*	Kelly 88.	16
36	07.02	H	UL	Altrincham	W	2-1	274	Annan 19, Kelly 57.	11
37	14.02	A	UL	Blyth Spartans	W	3-2	*491*	Annan 3, Armstrong 47, O'Donnell 81.	11
38	21.02	H	UL	Colwyn Bay	L	1-2	181	Annan 87.	13
39	07.03	H	UL	Marine	D	1-1	175	OG (Baines) 38.	16
40	14.03	A	UL	Chorley	D	0-0	*275*		16
41	21.03	A	UL	Hyde United	D	1-1	*332*	Haran 60.	17
42	28.03	H	UL	Bamber Bridge	W	1-0	135	Stratford 73.	15
43	01.04	A	UL	Boston United	L	0-3	*485*		16
44	07.04	A	UL	Lancaster City	D	2-2	*163*	Fothersgill 44, Green 74.	15
45	11.04	H	UL	Guiseley	L	0-1	179		14
46	13.04	A	UL	Emley	L	0-1	*347*		16
47	18.04	H	UL	Runcorn	L	1-3	148	Hancock 34.	16
48	22.04	A	UL	Gainsborough Trinity	L	1-3	*638*	Fothersgill 65.	16
49	25.04	H	UL	Leigh RMI	D	0-0	138		16
50	02.05	A	UL	Radcliffe Borough	D	1-1	*151*	Fothersgill 70.	16

PLAYING SQUAD 1998

Goalkeepers: Paul Setterfield (Brodworth Welfare), David Goldsborough (Glasshoughton Welf)

Defenders: Ian Thompson (Altrincham, Frickley Ath, Goole T, Worksop T, GooleT, Worksop T, Gainsborough Trin), Mark Hancock (Wharncliffe Arms, GrimethorpeMW), Chris Hilton (Rotherham U), Russell Green (Farsley Celtic, Emley,Altrincham, Emley, Barnsley), Gary Hatto (Ossett T, Frickley Ath, Doncaster R,Huddersfield T), Mark Haran (Eastwood T, Rotherham U), Ian Reidford (Pontefract Coll, Hemsworth T), Lee Stratford (Nottingham F)

Midfielders: Simon Fuller (Ossett T, Bradford C), Paul Hayward (Emley), Craig Elkin (Hemsworth T, Frickley Ath), Darren Fields (Pontefract Coll,Grimethorpe Welf, Barnsley), Dave Dickinson (Local football), Mick Priestley (Guiseley)

Forwards: Gary Duffty (Alfreton T, Frickley Ath, Rotherham U), Scot Armstrong (Huddersfield T), Ian Frank (Denaby U, Maltby MW, Sheffield Wed), Miles Thorpe (Parkgate, Worsbrough Br. MW), James O'Donnell (Matlock T, Emley, HatfieldMain, Armthorpe Welfare, Brodsworth MW, Harworth Cl, Doncaster R), Carey Williams (Emley, Denaby U, Rotherham U, Denaby U, Brunsmere Ath), CarlFothergill (Pontefract Coll, Worsbrough Bridge MW).

PROGRAMME DETAILS:
Pages: 32 **Price:** £1
Editor: Basil Godley
(01427 611612)

GAINSBOROUGH TRINITY

Colours: All Blue **Formed:** 1873
Change colours: Green/black/green **Nickname:** The Blues
Midweek home matchday: Wednesday **Sponsors:** Eastern Generation.
Reserve Team's League:
Local Press: Gainsborough News, Lincolnshire Echo.
Local Radio: BBC Radio Lincs, Lincs FM

Chairman: John Davis. **President:** Ken Marsden.
Secretary: Frank Nicholson, 9 North Street, Morton, Gainsborough, Lincs DN21 3AS. Tel. 01427 615239, Fax 01427 615239.
Manager: Steve Richards **Asst Manager:** Paul Olsson.
Physio: Mick Gilbert
Commercial Director: Tim Hanson. **Press Officer:** Frank Nicholson
GROUND Address: The Northolme, Gainsborough, Lincs DN21 2QW (01427 613295 - office or 01427 615625 - club) (Fax 01427 613295)
Directions: The Northolme is situated near the town centre 250 yards from the Magistrates Court and the Post Office. Two miles from Lea Road (BR).
Capacity: 3,500 **Cover:** 2,500 **Seats:** 303 **Floodlights:** Yes
Clubhouse: Executive 'Club on the Park' (01427 615625) open Saturday matchday lunchtimes. Restaurant facilities.
Club Shop: Yes, contact Nigel Tasker on 01522 542014.

PREVIOUS - **Leagues:** Midland Counties 1889-96, 12-60, 61-68, Football Lge 1896-1912, Central Alliance 60-61. **Names:** None **Grounds:** None

CLUB RECORDS - **Attendance:** 9,760 v Scunthorpe Utd. Midland Lge. 1948. **Fee Paid:** £3,000 for Stuart Lowe (Buxton 89-90). **Received:** £30,000 for Tony James (Lincoln 1988). **Win:** 7-0 v Fleetwood Town and Great Harwood Town. **Defeat:** 2-7 v Hyde Utd.

BEST SEASON - **FA Cup:** 3rd Rd 1886-87, 1st Rd on 33 occasions. **FA Trophy:** 2nd Rd, 2nd replay 86-87.

HONOURS - Northern Premier Lge Cup 81-82 96-97 (R-up 71-72); Midland Co's Lge 1890-91, 1927-28, 48-49, 66-67 (R-up 1891-92, 1895-96, 13-14, 28-29); Lincs Senior Cup (15) 1889-90, 92-93, 94-95, 97-98, 1903-05, 06-07, 10-11, 46-49, 50-51, 57-59, 63-64

Players progressing to Football League: Since 1980 - Stewart Evans (Sheffield Utd 80), Tony James, Ian Bowling & John Schofield (Lincoln 88), Dave Redfern (Stockport 91), Richard Logan (Huddersfield 93), Glenn Humphries (Hull City).

97-98 Captain: Mark Ogley **P.o.Y.:** Mark Ogley **Top scorer:** Phil Brown

Back Row (L-R); Mick Gilbert (Physio), Ernie Moss (Mgr), Steve Circuit, Steve Price, Chris Timons, Paul Ellender, Adam Sollitt, Jason Maxwell, Rob Hanby, Kev Riley, Phil Tinsay (Asst Mgr), Pete Brown (Scout). Front Row; Nick Kimber, Rich Taylor, Grant Morron, Mark Osley, Chris James, Phil Brown, Luke Todd.

GAINSBOROUGH TRINITY - Match Facts 97-98

Match No.	Date	Venue H / A	Comp.	Opponents	Result & Score		Att.	Goalscorers	League Position
1	23.08	H	UL	Spennymoor United	L	0-1	481		
2	25.08	A	UL	Frickley Athletic	D	1-1	*230*	Timmons	
3	30.08	A	UL	Blyth Spartans	D	0-0	*575*		19
4	02.09	H	UL	Alfreton Town	**W**	**4-0**	474	Riley 15, 69, Limber 63, Brown 86.	10
5	08.09	A	UL	Hyde United	**L**	**1-4**	*539*	Morrow 69.	16
6	13.09	A	**FAC 1Q**	Witton Albion	W	5-1	*388*	Morrow 1, Price 2, Limber 39, Brown 42, Riley 65.	-
7	20.09	H	UL	Altrincham	W	2-1	563	Circuit 72, Riley 82.	15
8	23.09	A	UL	Guiseley	W	3-1	*356*	James 25, Riley 59, 78.	6
9	27.09	A	**FAC 2Q**	Gateshead	W	4-1	*369*	Brown 7, Price 41, Circuit 50, Riley 56.	-
10	04.10	H	UL	Radcliffe Borough	W	3-0	506	Maxwell 1, Riley 9, Timmons 48.	7
11	07.10	A	UL	Alfreton Town	W	3-2	*273*	Brown 15, Riley 32, Ellender 81.	6
12	11.10	H	**FAC 3Q**	South Shields	W	3-2	608	Ellender 45, Dennis 51, Hanby 89.	-
13	15.10	H	UL	Guiseley	L	0-1	534		7
14	18.10	A	UL	Bamber Bridge	W	2-0	*301*	Hanby 9, Riley 71.	
15	22.10	H	UL	Emley	W	2-1	401	Price 9 (pen), Brown 90.	5
16	25.10	H	**FAC 4Q**	Halifax Town	W	2-1	1,730	Morrow 40, 75.	-
17	29.10	H	**ULCC 2**	Matlock Town	W	2-0	443	Sykes 32, Maxwell 85.	-
18	01.11	H	UL	Winsford United	L	0-2	544		9
19	08.11	H	**FAT 2Q**	Bedworth Town	W	3-0	387	Maxwell 25, Price 37, Brown 79.	-
20	10.11	A	UL	Emley	L	0-1	*287*		12
21	15.11	A	**FAC 1**	Lincoln City	D	1-1	*6,014*	Morrow 54.	-
22	19.11	H	UL	Accrington Stanley	D	0-0	460		
23	22.11	A	UL	Runcorn	L	0-2	*300*		13
24	25.11	*H	**FAC 1 R**	Lincoln City	L	2-3	5,726	Ellender 29, Price 39. (Played at Lincoln City FC.)	
25	29.11	H	**FAT 3Q**	Bamber Bridge	W	1-0	429	Circuit 79.	-
26	03.12	H	**ULCC 3**	Eastwood Town	W	4-2	296	Taylor 37, 62, Price 43 (pen), Riley 85.	-
27	06.12	A	UL	Colwyn Bay	D	1-1	*273*	Riley 60.	13
28	13.12	H	UL	Bishop Auckland	W	1-0	439	Riley 37.	10
29	20.12	A	UL	Barrow	L	0-2	*963*		13
30	26.12	H	UL	Boston United	L	0-1	1,295		14
31	01.01	A	UL	Boston United	L	0-1	*1,730*		15
32	10.01	A	**FAT 1**	Hednesford Town	L	1-2	*876*	Price 20 (pen).	-
33	17.01	A	UL	Lancaster City	W	1-0	*233*	Circuit 32.	15
34	24.01	H	UL	Barrow	L	0-3	646		17
35	31.01	A	UL	Radcliffe Borough	W	3-1	*163*	Brown 14, Price 42, Maxwell 49.	12
36	07.02	H	UL	Chorley	W	2-1	474	Ellender 57, Brown 86.	11
37	14.02	A	UL	Chorley	D	1-1	*316*	Brown 76.	12
38	21.02	H	UL	Bamber Bridge	W	3-2	417	Morrow 56, Ellender 74, Price 78 (pen).	10
39	25.02	A	**ULCC 4**	Bishop Auckland	D	0-0	*96*		-
40	28.02	A	UL	Altrincham	D	0-0	*507*		10
41	04.03	H	**ULCC 4 R**	Bishop Auckland	W	2-1	371	Price 43, Morrow 77.	-
42	07.03	A	UL	Bishop Auckland	W	3-1	*197*	James 47, Brown 64, 80.	9
43	14.03	H	UL	Colwyn Bay	W	1-0	479	Brown 48.	9
44	17.03	A	UL	Leigh RMI	L	0-1	*133*		9
45	21.03	H	UL	Lancaster City	W	2-1	440	Price 38 (pen), Brown 44.	9
46	24.03	A	**ULCC SF-1**	Blyth Spartans	W	2-1	*331*	Ellender 4, Timons 21.	-
47	28.03	A	UL	Accrington Stanley	W	2-0	*417*	Ellender 50, Brown 80.	10
48	01.04	H	**ULCC SF-2**	Blyth Spartans	W	2-1	602	Timmins 60, Price 90 (pen).	-
49	04.04	H	UL	Blyth Spartans	D	0-0	628		10
50	11.04	A	UL	Spennymoor United	W	4-1	*152*	**Brown 3** (27, 38, 58), Morrow 77.	8
51	13.04	H	UL	Hyde United	W	3-1	647	Morrow 13, 41, Timmons 82.	6
52	15.04	H	UL	Leigh RMI	W	3-0	588	Price 4 (pen), Morrow 49, Brown 90.	6
53	18.04	H	UL	Marine	W	2-0	582	Circuit 36, Riley 81.	6
54	22.04	H	UL	Frickley Athletic	W	3-1	638	**Morrow 3** (4, 8, 85).	5
55	25.04	A	UL	Winsford United	D	1-1	*147*	Morrow 1.	5
56	27.04	H	UL	Runcorn	W	1-0	581	Circuit 90.	5
57	29.04	N	**ULCC Final**	Altrincham	L	1-2	1,540	Ellender 75.	-
58	02.05	A	UL	Marine	D	2-2	*254*	Ellender 58, Limber 87.	5

PLAYING SQUAD 1998

Goalkeepers:

Defenders: Richard Hanby (Scarborough, Barnsley), Nicky Limber (Weymouth,Doncaster R, Manchester C, Doncaster R), Mark Ogley (Leek T, Stalybridge C,Altrincham, York C, Aldershot, Carlisle U, Burnley), Steve Price (Oldham Ath), Neil Brown (Hallam, Ashfield U, Sheffield FC, Alfreton T, Glossop NE,Chesterfield)

Midfielders: Richard Taylor (Matlock T, Frecheville Comm, Scarborough), Kevin Riley (Armthorpe Welfare, Harworth CI), Neil Sykes (Rossington), Luke Todd (Chesterfield, Sheffield Wed, Liverpool)

Forwards: Grant Morrow (Boston U, Colchester U, Doncaster R, Rowntree Mackintosh), Jason Maxwell (Buxton, Grantham T, Appleby Frodingham, ScunthorpeU).

GATESHEAD

Club colours: Black & white/black/white **Sponsors:** ?????
Change colours: All yellow Cameron Hall Developments Ltd
Midweek home matchday: Wednesday **Founded:** 1930
Reserves League: Vaux Wearside League **Nickname:** The Tynesiders
Local Press: Gateshead Post, Newcastle Chronicle & Echo, Sunderland Echo, Sunday Sun.
Local Radio: BBC Radio Newcastle, Metro FM, Century Radio.

PROGRAMME DETAILS:
Pages: 36 **Price:** £1.20
Editor: Andy Wilson
(0191 478 3883)

Chairman: John Gibson **President:** J C Thomas
Vice Chairman: Peter Robinson **Director:** Norman Lakey
General Manager: Mark Donnelly **Fixture Secretary:** Arthur Waggott
Press Officer: Andy Wilson **Commercial Manager:** Cheryl Smith
Manager: Jim Platt **Asst. Man.:** Jack Wilson
Player Coach: Gary Robson **Physio:** Bev Dougherty
GROUND Address: International Stadium, Neilson Road, Gateshead, NE10 0EF. Tel: 0191 4783883, Fax: 0191 4771315.
Simple Directions: From the South follow A1(M) to Granada services (Birtley), take right hand fork marked A194(M) (Tyne Tunnel, South Shields) follow A194 to first roundabout, turn left onto A184 - then 3 miles to stadium. Turn right at traffic lights into Neilson Road. BY RAIL to Newcastle Central Station, transfer to the Metro System and then to Gateshead Stadium.
Capacity: 11,795 **Seats:** 11,795 **Cover:** 3,300
Clubhouse: Bar inside Tyne & Wear stand open before, during and after matches. The Stadium P.H. adjacent to ground.
Club Shop: Sells full range of souvenirs, badges, programmes & fanzines. Contact: Mark Donnelly (0191 4783883).

PREVIOUS - **Leagues:** Football League - Div. 3 N. 30-58, Div.4 58-60, Northern Counties League 60-62, North Regional League 1962-1968, Northern Premier 68-70, 73-83, 85-86, 87-90; Wearside 70-71; Midland Lge 71-72; Alliance Premier (Conference) 83-85, 86-87, 90-98.
Grounds: Redheugh Park - 1930-1971

CLUB RECORDS - **Attendance:** 11,750 v Newcastle United (Pre-Season Friendly. 7th August 95) **Win:** 8-0 v Netherfield, Northern Premier League. **Defeat:** 0-9 v Sutton United - 22/09/90 - GMVC. **Career goalscorer:** Bob Topping **Career appearances:** Simon Smith - 450 - 85-94 **Transfer fee paid:** £9,000 for Paul Cavell (Dagenham & Redbridge). **Transfer fee received:** For Kenny Cramman from Rushden & Diamonds

BEST SEASON - **FA Cup:** Quarter Final, 1952-53.
FA Trophy: Quarter Final, 0-1 v Wycombe W. (A) 13.3.93

HONOURS: Football League Div. 3 North R-up 31-32, 49-50; Northern Premier - Champions 82-83, 85-86; Runners-up 89-90; Northern Premier League Cup R-up 89-90; Multipart Shield 85-86.

Past players who progressed to the Football League: Osher Williams (Southampton, Stockport, Port Vale, Preston), John McGinley (Sunderland, Lincoln), Billy Askew (Hull City, Newcastle United), Lawrie Pearson (Hull City, Port Vale), Ian Johnson (Northampton Town), Ken Davies (Stockport), Kenny Lowe (Birmingham C., Barnet, Darlington, Stoke C.)

Gateshead FC Photo: Tim Lancaster

GATESHEAD - Match Facts 97-98

Match No.	Date	Venue H / A	Comp.	Opponents	Result	& Score	Att.	Goalscorers	League Position
1	16.08	H	VC	Farnborough Town	W	3-0	803	Connor 11, 29, Innes 90.	3
2	20.08	H	VC	Morecambe	L	1-4	844	Connor 27.	
3	23.08	A	VC	Kidderminster Harriers	D	1-1	*1,592*	Bowey 46.	10
4	25.08	H	VC	Northwich Victoria	D	2-2	769	Proudlock 36, Robson 68.	12
5	30.08	A	VC	Rushden & Diamonds	L	2-3	*2,211*	Bowey 70, Robinson 76.	15
6	03.09	H	VC	Southport	L	0-2	619		17
7	07.09	A	VC	Telford United	D	4-4	*568*	Kitchen 47, Robinson 77, Proudlock 82, Innes 88.	20
8	20.09	H	VC	Woking	L	1-2	732	Innes 45.	21
9	29.09	A	VC	Northwich Victoria	D	1-1	*873*	Bowey 67	19
10	04.10	A	VC	Stevenage Borough	**L**	**1-6**	*2,102*	Innes 29.	20
11	11.10	H	VC	Leek Town	L	0-2	539		21
12	18.10	H	VC	Cheltenham Town	D	0-0	672		21
13	25.10	H	VC	Telford United	L	0-2	424		21
14	01.11	A	VC	Hayes	L	0-1	*675*		21
15	08.11	H	VC	Hednesford Town	L	2-5	621	Harkus 5, Robinson 25.	21
16	15.11	A	VC	Leek Town	D	2-2	*535*	Robinson 17, Marquis 53.	22
17	22.11	A	VC	Cheltenham Town	L	0-2	*1,659*		22
18	29.11	H	VC	Yeovil Town	L	0-3	724		22
19	06.12	A	VC	Morecambe	L	0-2	*1,106*		22
20	13.12	H	VC	Stevenage Borough	L	1-2	349	Perkins 23	22
21	20.12	A	VC	Southport	L	1-3	*800*	Carter 51	22
22	26.12	H	VC	Halifax Town	D	2-2	1,239	Harkus 22,35	22
23	01.01	A	VC	Halifax Town	L	0-2	*3,194*		22
24	17.01	A	VC	Welling United	L	0-2	*602*		22
25	07.02	A	VC	Kettering Town	L	0-3	*1,201*		22
26	14.02	H	VC	Rushden & Diamonds	W	2-1	616	Proudlock 48, Peverell 90.	22
27	17.02	A	VC	Stalybridge Celtic	D	2-2	*605*	Bowey 16, Hutchinson 87.	22
28	21.02	A	VC	Woking	L	1-3	*2,081*	Bowey 34.	22
29	28.02	H	VC	Kettering Town	W	2-0	468	Bowey 24, 45.	22
30	14.03	A	VC	Hereford United	L	0-1	*2,007*		22
31	18.03	H	VC	Kidderminster harriers	W	2-0	403	Bowey 24, 86.	22
32	21.03	A	VC	Dover Athletic	W	1-0	*1,090*	Harkus 79.	22
33	25.03	H	VC	Stalybridge Celtic	D	3-3	642	Bowey 3 (pen), Proudlock 43, Harkus 64.	22
34	28.03	H	VC	Welling United	W	2-1	582	Peverill 5, Marquis 61.	21
35	31.03	A	VC	Slough Town	L	0-1	*559*		21
36	04.04	A	VC	Hednesford Town	L	0-3	*879*		21
37	11.04	H	VC	Dover Athletic	L	1-2	596	Bowey 75 (pen).	21
38	13.04	A	VC	Farnborough Town	L	0-4	*565*		21
39	18.04	H	VC	Slough Town	**W**	**5-1**	415	Peverell 28, 80, Marquis 40, Proudlock 53, Pearson 72.	21
40	22.04	H	VC	Hereford United	D	1-1	448	Hall 83.	21
41	25.04	H	VC	Hayes	D	1-1	412	Proudlock 86.	21
42	02.05	A	VC	Yeovil Town	L	3-6	*2,567*	Robinson 20, 71, Bowey 81.	21

CUP COMPETITIONS

Date	Venue	Comp.	Opponents	Result	Score	Att.	Goalscorers
13.09	H	**FAC** 1Q	Matlock Town	W	2-0	282	Innes 52, Willgrass 75.
27.09	H	2Q	Gainsborough Trinity	L	1-4	369	Bowey.
10.01	A	**FAT** 1	Stalybridge Celtic	W	4-2	524	Ord 25, Rowe 32, Bowey 63, Kitchen 70.
31.01	H	2	Stevenage Borough	L	1-2	902	Ord 45.
25.11	A	**SCC** 2	Stalybridge Celtic	W	*4-3	224	Carter 53, Twynham 85, 119, OG (Thomas) 96.
17.12	H	3	Morecambe	D	1-1	204	Harkus 115
20.01	A	3 R	Morecambe	L	1-3	305	Marquis 85.

SCC Spalding Challenge Cup

PLAYING SQUAD 1998

Goalkeepers: Dean Williams (Doncaster R, Brentford, Tamworth)

Defenders: Justin Robson (Gretna, Durham C, Bridlington T, North Shields,Newcastle Blue Star, Gateshead, Newcastle U), Derek Ord (Gretna, Durham C, B Auckland, Spennymoor U, Chester-le-Street, Gateshead, Blyth S, North Shields), Sam Kitchen (Doncaster R, Leyton Orient, Frickley Ath, Goole T, Stafford R,Goole T, Yorkshire Main), Anthony Hall (Kilkenny C, East Fife, Queen of theSouth), Alex Wilgrass (Bromsgrove R, Scarborough), Paul Marquis (St.Albans C,Doncaster R, West Ham U)

Midfielders: Kenny Lowe (Darlington, Gateshead, Birmingham C, Stoke C, Barnet,Barrow, Scarborough, Barrow, Morecambe, Gateshead, Spearwood Dalmatic (Aust),Gateshead, Billigham T, Hartlepool U), Jon Sunderland (Hartlepool U,Scarborough, Blackpool), Steve Hutchinson (Youth team), Gary Robson (BradfordC, WBA), Brian Rowe (Doncaster R), Steve Bowey (Forest Green R, Bristol R)

Forwards: Graham Robinson (Whitby T, Kaiser Chiefs (SA), Paul Proudlock (Carlisle U, Middlesbrough, Hartlepool U), Steve Harkus (Blyth S, SouthShields, Hebburn), Gary Innes (Darlington, Sheffield U).

GUISELEY

Colours: White/blue/white. **Formed:** 1909
Change colours: Yellow/Navy **Nickname:**
Midweek home matchday: Tuesday. **Sponsors:** OHS Ltd.
Reserves' League: Bolton & Dist Comb, Alliance Div
Local Press: Yorkshire Evening Post, Bradford Telegraph & Argus, Airedale & Wharfedale Observer, Wharfe Valley Times.

PROGRAMME DETAILS:
Pages: 40 **Price:** £1
Editor: Les Wood
(01532 509181)

Chairman: Philip Rogerson **President:**
Secretary: Alan Walker, Riva Bungalow, Goose Lane, Hawksworth LS20 8PL (01943 875955)
Match Secretary: Bruce Speller, (01943 874534)
Manager: Steve Richards. **Asst Manager:** Greg Abbott.
Physio: John Rhodes
Commercial Manager: Les Wood (01132 509181)
Press Officer: John Martin (01943 879473)
GROUND Address: Nethermoor, Otley Road, Guiseley, Leeds LS20 8BT (0943 873223).
Directions: Via M1 to M62 junction 28, follow Leeds road to Leeds ring-road to junction of A65 at Horsforth. At r-about turn left onto A65 through Rawdon to Guiseley centre. Ground quarter of a mile past traffic lights, on the right, entrance on A65 opposite Silver Cross factory. Additional car parking available off Ings Crescent. Five mins walk from Guiseley (BR/Metro) station.
Capacity: 3,000 **Cover:** 1,040 **Seats:** 427 **Floodlights:** Yes
Clubhouse: (01943 872872) Open before and after all games (closes 11pm). Snack bar within ground open before and during matches.
Club Shop: Sells programmes, various items of clothing, key rings, badges, mugs etc. Phone Jennifer Roseron 01943 879236
Metal Badges: Yes

PREVIOUS - **Leagues:** West Riding Co. Amtr; West Yorks; Yorkshire 68-82; Northern Co's East 82-91.

CLUB RECORDS - **Attendance:** 2,486 v Bridlington Town, FA Vase Semi Final 1st Leg 89-90.

BEST SEASON - **FA Cup:** First Round Proper 1994-95 (lost 1-4 at Valley Parade). **FA Vase:** Winners 1990-91 (R-up 91-92, S.F.94-95). **FA Trophy:** Semi-Final 1994-95.

HONOURS - FA Vase 90-91 (R-up 91-92), Northern Premier Lg Div 1 94-95 (Presidents Cup 94-95, Div 1 Cup 92-93), Northern Counties (East) Lg 90-91 (Lg Cup 90-91), West Riding County Cup(5 inc 94-95), Yorkshire Lg R-up 79-80 81-82 (Lg Cup 79-80).

Players progressing to Football League: Keith Walwyn (York City), Frank Harrison (Halifax Town), Dean Walling (Carlisle United), Richard Annan (Crewe Alexandra).

Action from Guiseley's match with Emley

GUISELEY - Match Facts 97-98

WRSC - West Riding Senior Cup

Match No.	Date	Venue H / A	Comp.	Opponents	Result & Score		Att.	Goalscorers	League Position
1	23.08	H	UL	Radcliffe Borough	W	4-1	429	Foreman 37, 45, Matthews 47, 53.	
2	25.08	A	UL	Blyth Spartans	D	1-1	*652*	OG (McGarrigle) 82.	
3	30.08	A	UL	Winsford United	L	1-2	*260*	Matthews 71.	8
4	02.09	H	UL	Boston United	D	1-1	403	Allison 86.	11
5	07.09	H	UL	Barrow	D	1-1	472	Foreman 57.	8
6	10.09	A	UL	Bishop Auckland	D	1-1	*159*	Foreman 90.	
7	13.09	H	**FAC 1Q**	Alfreton Town	W	3-0	379	Book 10, Wood 57, Foreman 70.	-
8	16.09	A	UL	Alfreton Town	D	1-1	*149*	Atkinson 62.	8
9	20.09	A	UL	Accrington Stanley	W	3-2	*525*	**Davison 3 (**15, 62, 67).	5
10	23.09	H	UL	Gainsborough Trinity	**L**	**1-3**	356	Hunter 63.	7
11	27.09	H	**FAC 2Q**	Farsley Celtic	D	0-0	574		-
12	01.10	A	**FAC 2Q R**	Farsley Celtic	W	4-1	*324*	Foreman 30, Parsley 44, Davison 46, 73.	-
13	04.10	A	UL	Colwyn Bay	W	1-0	*385*	Atkinson 90 (pen).	11
14	07.10	H	UL	Bishop Auckland	D	3-3	355	Davison 3, 16, Jordan 90.	8
15	11.10	H	**FAC 3Q**	Penrith	L	1-2	557	Davison 53.	-
16	15.10	A	UL	Gainsborough Trinity	W	1-0	*534*	Davison 75.	
17	18.10	H	UL	Marine	D	2-2	458	Matthews 26, Davison 60.	9
18	21.10	H	UL	Alfreton Town	L	1-2	263	Matthews 1.	
19	25.10	A	UL	Chorley	L	0-1	*293*		11
20	01.11	H	UL	Lancaster City	W	2-1	453	Matthews 54, 74 (pen).	
21	04.11	H	**ULCC 2**	Bishop Auckland	L	0-3	277		-
22	08.11	H	UL	Altrincham	D	2-2	443	Davison 55, 79.	10
23	11.11	H	**WRSC 1**	Halifax Town	W	1-0	459	Matthews 50.	-
24	15.11	A	UL	Barrow	W	1-0	*1,277*	Hazell 48.	7
25	22.11	H	UL	Chorley	W	2-1	358	Matthews 55, 87 (pen).	6
26	26.11	A	**ULPC 1**	Farsley Celtic	W	1-0	*240*	Proctor 12.	-
27	29.11	H	UL	Spennymoor United	D	1-1	296	Matthews 55.	
28	06.12	H	UL	Accrington Stanley	W	1-0	380	Proctor 22.	5
29	20.12	H	UL	Frickley Athletic	**W**	**4-0**	380	Matthews 8, 39, Davison 51, 72.	6
30	27.12	H	UL	Blyth Spartans	**L**	**1-3**	634	Matthews 61 (pen).	6
31	10.01	H	**FAT 1**	Telford United	D	0-0	716		-
32	13.01	A	**FAT 1 R**	Telford United	L	2-3	*557*	Matthews 44, Parks 46.	-
33	17.01	H	UL	Bamber Bridge	D	1-1	373	Ryan 26.	7
34	21.01	A	**WRSC 2**	Bradford Park Avenue	D	2-2*	*217*	Davison 54, Watts 116.	-
35	24.01	A	UL	Altrincham	L	0-2	*729*		8
36	31.01	A	UL	Emley	D	3-3	*345*	Hook 48, 85, Davison 73.	9
37	03.02	H	**ULPC 2**	Leigh RMI	D	0-0	137		-
38	07.02	H	UL	Colwyn Bay	W	3-1	272	Matthews 6, 14, Hazel 26.	6
39	10.02	H	**WRSC 3**	Ossett Albion	L	0-2	127		-
40	14.02	A	UL	Lancaster City	L	2-3	*339*	Bottomley 45, Davison 45.	8
41	16.02	A	UL	Hyde United	D	1-1	*432*	Jordan 23.	7
42	21.02	A	UL	Spennymoor United	W	2-1	*248*	Hazel 7, Bottomley 27.	7
43	24.02	A	**ULPC 2R**	Leigh RMI	W	3-0	*146*	Davison 33, Matthews 43, 75.	-
44	28.02	H	UL	Leigh RMI	W	2-1	227	Parsley 42, Elam 50.	6
45	07.03	A	UL	Leigh RMI	D	0-0	*201*		8
46	09.03	A	**ULPC SF-1**	Ashton United	W	2-1	*204*	Matthews 25 (pen), Hook 43.	-
47	14.03	H	UL	Hyde United	D	1-1	431	Davison 55.	8
48	18.03	A	UL	Radcliffe Borough	W	2-0	*113*	Elam 43, Williams 88.	
49	21.03	A	UL	Marine	W	1-0	*308*	Parke 53.	6
50	24.03	H	**ULPC SF-2**	Ashton United	D	1-1	329	Davison 73.	-
51	28.03	A	UL	Boston United	L	1-2	*652*	Matthews 59 (pen).	7
52	31.03	A	UL	Runcorn	D	1-1	*302*	Williams 66.	
53	04.04	H	UL	Winsford United	L	0-2	300		8
54	11.04	A	UL	Frickley Athletic	W	1-0	*179*	Parke 76.	6
55	13.04	H	UL	Runcorn	D	2-2	324	Morrell 41, 55.	7
56	18.04	A	UL	Bamber Bridge	W	2-1	*279*	Phillips 27, Matthews 47.	7
57	25.04	H	**ULPC Final-1**	Runcorn	L	1-2	312	Matthews 29.	-
58	30.04	A	**ULPC Final-2**	Runcorn	L	2-3	*454*	Matthews 56, Hunter 78.	-
59	02.05	H	UL	Emley	L	0-2	491		9

PLAYING SQUAD 1998

Goalkeepers: Steve Dickinson (Bradford C)

Defenders: Paul Ryan (Ossett T, Liversedge), Paul Bottomley (Bridlington T,Guiseley, Garforth T), Neil Allison (Chesterfield, Swindon T, Hull C), PeterAtkinson (Otley T), Neil Parsley (Witton Alb, Exeter C, WBA, Huddersfield T,Leeds U, Witton Alb), Colin Hogarth (Lancaster C, Guiseley, Harrogate T,Guiseley, Otley T, Thackley), Steve Hook (Chorley, Goole T, Halifax T)

Midfielders: Colin Hunter (Harrogate Railway), Simon Wood (Mansfield T,Coventry C), Gavin Haigh (Hull C), Lee Elam (Youth team), Matt Flanagan (Lancaster C, Garforth T, Guiseley)

Forwards: Bobby Davison (Halifax T, Rotherham U, Sheffield U, Leicester C,Leeds U, Derby Co, Halifax T, Huddersfield T, Seaham CW), Andy Williams (Matlock T, Gainsborough Trin, Scarborough), Michael Jordan (Otley T), Des Hazel (Joodalup (Aust), Guiseley, Chesterfield, Rotherham U, Sheffield Wed), Jimmy Proctor (Chorley, Rochdale, Bradford C), Simon Parke (Bradford PA).

HYDE UNITED

Colours: Red & black/black/black **Formed:** 1919
Change colours: Yellow/black/yellow & black **Nickname:** The Tigers
Midweek home matchday: Monday **Club Sponsors:** TMI Metals.
Local Press: North Cheshire Herald & Hyde Reporter.
Local Radio: GMR, Picadilly.

Chairman: S C Hartley **Vice Chairman:**
Secretary / Press Officer: Ray Stanley, 15 Balmain Avenue, Gorton, Manchester M18 7PF (0161 223 2445)
Manager: Mike McKenzie **Coach:** Billy Garton
Commercial Manager: Roy Ollerenshaw **Physio:** G Clowes

GROUND Address: Tameside Stadium, Ewen Fields, Walker Lane, Hyde SK14 5PL (0161 368 1031).
Directions: On entering Hyde follow signs for Tameside Leisure Park - in Walker Lane take 2nd car park entrance nr Leisure Pool, follow road around to the stadium. Quarter of a mile from Newton (BR).
Capacity: 4,000 **Cover:** 2,000 **Seats:** 400 **Floodlights:** Yes
Clubhouse: (0161 368 1621). Open most nights, full facilities, 150 seats. Stewards: Lil & Doug.
Club Shop: Replica shirts, scarves, sports shirts, baseball caps, bronx hats, badges. Contact either Roy Ollerenshaw (0161 612 1781) or Secretary

PROGRAMME DETAILS
Pages: 32 **Price:** £1.
Editor: M Dring

PREVIOUS - **Leagues:** Lancs & Cheshire 19-21; Manchester 21-30; Cheshire County 30-68, 70-82; Northern Prem. 68-70

CLUB RECORDS - **Attendance:** 9,500 v Nelson, FA Cup 1952. **Scorer:** P O'Brien 247. **Appearances:** S Johnson 623. **Defeat:** (as Hyde F.C.) 0-26 v Preston North End, F.A. Cup. **Fee Paid:** £8,000 for Jim McCluskie (Mossley, 1989). **Fee Received:** £50.000 for Colin Little (Crewe Alexandra) 1995.

BEST SEASON - **FA Cup:** 1st Rd 54-55 (v Workington), 83-84 (v Burnley),94-95 v Darlington.

HONOURS - FA Trophy SF 88-89 94-95 95-96; Prem Inter-Lge Cup R-up(2) 88-90; NPL R-up(2) 87-89 (Lg Cup 85-86 88-89 95-96 (R-up 83-84 94-95), Chal. Shield 96-97, (R-up 86-87 90-91); Cheshire Co. Lg(3) 54-56 81-82 (Lg Cup 33-34 52-53 54-55 72-73 81-82, Lg Chal. Shield(2) 80-82; Manchester Lg(5) 20-23 28-29 29-30 (Lg (Gilgryst) Cup(4) 27-29 49-50 70-71); Cheshire Snr Cup 45-46 62-63 69-70 80-81 89-90 96-97; Manchester Prem. Cup 93-94, 94-95, 95-96, Snr Cup 74-75, Int Cup 55-56 56-57(jt), Jnr Cup 21-22 68-69; Lancs & Cheshire F'lit Cup(2) 54-56; Ashton Chal. Cup(6) 30-34 39-40 47-48; Hyde Chal Cup(2) 27-29; Reporter Cup(3) 72-74 75-76; Gavin Nicholson Mem Trophy 79-80; Lancs F'lit Trophy(2) 86-88; Edward Case Cup(4) 56-8 59-60 80-81.

Players progressing to Football League: C McClelland & J Webber & P Barry (B'burn 1946 & 47 & 48), L Battrick (Manc. City 1968), J Hilton (Wrexham 1950), D Teece (Hull 1952), R Calderbank & William Bell & Neil Colbourne (R'dale 1953 & 74 & 80), Jeff Johnson (Stockport 1976), David Constantine & Donald Graham (Bury 1979), George Oghani (Bolton 1983), Kevin Glendon (Burnley 1983), Peter Coyne (Swindon 1984), Colin Little (Crewe Alex. 1995)

Hyde United's Ged Kimmins attempts to beat Louth United's Lee Pratt Photo: Colin Stevens

HYDE UNITED - Match Facts 97-98

Match No.	Date	Venue H / A	Comp.	Opponents	Result & Score		Att.	Goalscorers	League Position
1	23.08	A	UL	Colwyn Bay	L	1-3	*410*	Lambert.	
2	25.08	H	UL	Lancaster City	W	4-1	590	Nolan 18 seconds, James 26, 82, Owen 70.	
3	30.08	H	UL	Marine	D	1-1	558	Murray 25.	10
4	08.09	H	UL	Gainsborough Trinity	W	4-1	539	Kimmins 33, James 47, Nolan 53 (pen), Snape 88.	10
5	13.09	H	**FAC 1Q**	Louth United	W	3-0	478	Lambert 68, Snape 71, Kimmins 80.	-
6	17.09	A	UL	Boston United	D	1-1	*751*	Nolan 78.	
7	20.09	A	UL	Runcorn	W	1-0	*400*	Annan 44.	4
8	22.09	H	UL	Emley	W	1-0	624	Nolan 36.	3
9	27.09	H	**FAC 2Q**	Lancaster City	W	4-1	598	Nolan 40, Annan 46, Kimmins 62, Snape 75.	-
10	04.10	A	UL	Bishop Auckland	L	1-2	*213*	Lambert 36.	8
11	06.10	H	UL	Altrincham	L	0-1	989		8
12	11.10	H	**FAC 3Q**	Ryhope C.W.	W	8-0	573	Annan 32, OG 45, Varden 48, Kimmins 49, Snape 50, 84, Nolan 71, Lambert 75.	
13	18.11	H	UL	Barrow	**L**	**0-3**	832		13
14	21.10	A	UL	Bamber Bridge	D	1-1	*234*	Murray 82.	
15	25.10	A	**FAC 4Q**	Ilkeston Town	L	2-3	*1,233*	Nolan 43 (pen), Owen 47.	-
16	28.10	A	**ULCC 2**	Colwyn Bay	L	0-1	*255*		-
17	01.11	A	UL	Altrincham	W	3-1	*761*	Kimmins 24, 69, Nolan 68.	13
18	08.11	H	UL	Accrington Stanley	D	1-1	522	James 76.	
19	11.11	A	UL	Chorley	**W**	**5-1**	*347*	**James 3** (45, 56, 69), Nolan 52.	
20	15.11	A	UL	Spennymoor United	D	2-2	*179*	James 69, Lambert 84.	11
21	17.10	H	**UCSC 2**	Northwich Victoria	L	1-2	454	Garton 61.	-
22	22.10	H	UL	Leigh RMI	D	3-3	522	Snape 46, Owen 48, James 59.	12
23	25.11	A	UL	Accrington Stanley	D	1-1	*362*	Nolan 73.	
24	29.11	A	UL	Frickley Athletic	L	1-2	*146*	Lambert 2.	12
25	06.12	H	UL	Bishop Auckland	L	1-2	395	Nolan 69 (pen).	12
26	09.12	A	UL	Alfreton Town	D	0-0	*154*		
27	13.12	A	UL	Blyth Spartans	D	1-1	*425*	Kimmins 81.	11
28	15.12	H	UL	Spennymoor United	W	3-1	232	Owen 20, Gallagher 69, Lambert 90.	
29	20.12	H	UL	Alfreton Town	W	4-1	364	**Kimmins 3** (7, 38, 79), Nolan.	7
30	26.12	A	UL	Radcliffe Borough	D	0-0	*375*		
31	03.01	H	UL	Winsford United	W	4-3	687	Varden 41, 78, Lambert 62, Switzer 86.	6
32	10.01	H	**FAT 1**	Boston United	W	2-1	792	Lambert 6, Kimmins 29.	-
33	17.01	A	UL	Winsford United	D	1-1	*252*	Lockett 76.	6
34	24.01	H	UL	Bamber Bridge	D	1-1	583	Varden 54.	6
35	31.01	A	**FAT 2**	Dagenham & Redbridge	W	5-0	*989*	**Nolan 3** (13 (pen), 32 (pen), 79), Kimmins 45, James 52.	-
36	07.02	A	UL	Emley	L	1-2	*294*	Johnson 63.	9
37	14.02	H	UL	Boston United	L	0-2	526		10
38	16.02	H	UL	Guiseley	D	1-1	432	James 45.	11
39	21.02	H	**FAT 3**	Dover Athletic	L	0-2	917		-
40	28.02	H	UL	Radcliffe Borough	L	0-1	410		12
41	07.03	H	UL	Chorley	L	0-2	442		14
42	14.03	A	UL	Guiseley	D	1-1	*431*	Nolan 84.	14
43	21.03	H	UL	Frickley Athletic	D	1-1	332	James 39.	15
44	28.03	H	Ul	Blyth Spartans	W	1-0	348	Lambert 35.	13
45	31.03	A	UL	Marine	W	2-0	*267*	James 40, Varden 74.	
46	04.04	A	UL	Leigh RMI	L	1-2	*251*	Nolan 19.	12
47	13.04	A	UL	Gainsborough Trinity	L	1-3	*647*	James 90.	15
48	18.04	A	UL	Lancaster City	W	1-0	*222*	Nolan 61.	
49	20.04	H	UL	Colwyn Bay	W	2-0	346	Kimmins 61, James 89.	11
50	25.04	A	UL	Barrow	D	2-2	*1,995*	Lambert 20, James 66.	11
51	02.05	H	UL	Runcorn	L	0-2	747		12

PLAYING SQUAD 1998

Goalkeepers: Jon Scargill (Chesterfield, Sheffield Wed).

Defenders: Gus Wilson (Crewe Alex, Runcorn, Acc.Stanley, Droylsden, Flixton,Northwich V), Richard Annan (Morecambe, Halifax T, Guiseley, Farsley Celtic,Crewe Alex, Guiseley), Jason Gallagher (Caernarfon T, Witton Alb, Marine,Ternia (Belg), Newton), George Switzer (Darlington, Manchester U), BillyGarton (Witton Alb, Salford C, Manchester U), Phil Lockett (Oldham Ath), GaryFinley (Netherfield, Doncaster R, Netherfield, Curzon Ashton, Warrington T,Vauxhall GM, Warrington T, Marine), Paul Cox (Altrincham, Bramhall, Sale U), Gordon Tucker (Brigg T, Scunthorpe U, Huddersfield T, Derby Co), Cec Edey * (Macclesfield T, Witton Alb, Lancaster C, Chorley, Lancaster C, Morecambe,Winsford U)

Midfielders: Vince Brockie (Guiseley, Goole T, Doncaster R, Leeds U), ColinLambert (Hednesford T, Halifax T, Macclesfield T, Winsford U, Flixton), Val Owen (Local football), Jimmy Shaw (Bury), Darren Thornton (Thackley,Hatfield Main, Thackley, Acc.Stanley, Droylsden, Hyde U, Baildon Ath, Salt GSOB), Phil Iannou (Blackpool Mechs, Crewe Alex, Blackpool), Ged Manning (Flixton, Maine Road, Flixton, Droylsden, Winsford U, North Trafford), Neil Hall * (Droylsden, Flixton, Witton Alb, Winsford U)

Forwards: Paul Varden (Winsford U, Maine Rd, Atherton Coll, Maine Rd), Lutel James (Guiseley, Selby T, Guiseley, Yorkshire Am), Paul Snape (CheadleT, Radcliffe B, Bury), Colin Heywood (Curzon Ashton, Droylsden, Ashton U,Droylsden, Stalybridge C, Mossley, Buxton, Leek T, Acc.Stanley, Mossley, HydeU, Sheffield U), Darren Washington * (Witton Alb, Congleton T, Leek T,Congleton T, Eastwood Hanley, Knypersley V), Peter Bland * (Bollington).

PROGRAMME DETAILS:
Pages: 32 **Price:** £1
Editor: Paul Wilkinson
(c/o the club)

LANCASTER CITY

Colours: Blue/white/blue
Change colours: All yellow
Midweek matchday: Tuesday.
Sponsors: Reebok
Nickname: Dolly Blues
Formed: 1902
Reserve League: North Western Alliance.
Club Fanzines: The Mad Axeman, Bambula Azzurri.
Local Press: Lancaster Guardian, Morcambe Visitor, Lancashire Evening Post, Lancaster Citizen
Local Radio: Red Rose, Radio Lancashire and Bay Radio.

Chairman: Terry McWilliams **President:** M Woodhouse.
Vice-Chairman: K Lancaster. **Secretary:** Mike Sparks, 30 Salisbury Road, Lancaster LA1 5PJ (01524 33483).
Manager: Alan Tinsley **Coach:** Tony Chilton
Physio: D McKevitt/F Charlton
Commercial Manager / Press Officer: Mike Hoyle (c/o the club).

GROUND Address: Giant Axe, West Road, Lancaster LA1 5PE (01524 382238 Office). **Directions:** M6 junc 33, follow into city, left at lights immediately after Waterstones bookshop, 2nd right, pass railway station on right, follow road down hill, ground 1st right. 5 mins walk from both bus & rail stations.
Capacity: 2,500 **Cover:** 800. **Seats:** 300 **Floodlights:** Yes
Clubhouse: "The Dolly Blue Tavern" just outside the ground. Two bars,hot and cold food available. Also a new tea bar inside ground serving food and drinks.
Club Shop: Inside ground, selling metal badges, pennants, programmes and other souvenirs etc. Contact Dave Crawford at club.

PREVIOUS - **Leagues:** Lancs Combination 05-70; Northern Premier 70-82; North West Counties 82-87. **Name:** Lancaster Town. **Ground:** Quay Meadow 05-06 (club's 1st 2 games only!)

CLUB RECORDS - **Attendance:** 7,500 v Carlisle, FA Cup 1936. **Goalscorer:** David Barnes 130 League & cup. **Appearances:** Edgar J Parkinson, 591 league & cup. **Win:** 8-0 v Leyland Motors (A), 83-84. **Defeat:** 0-10 v Matlock T, NPL Division One, 73-74.

BEST SEASON - **FA Vase:** Second Rd 86-87 90-91. **FA Trophy:** Third Rd 74-75 75-76. **FA Cup:** 2nd Rd 46-47 (1-4 v Gateshead) 72-73 (1-2 v Notts County).
League Clubs defeated: Barrow, Stockport County 21-22.

HONOURS - Northern Prem. Lg Cup R-up 79-80 (Div 1 Cup R-up 90-91), Lancs Combination 21-22 29-30 34-35 35-36 (R-up 19-20 22-23 27-28 51-52, Lg Cup 21-22, Div 2 R-up 14-15), Lancs Jun. Cup (ATS Challenge Trophy) 27-28 28-29 30-31 33-34 51-52 74-75 (R-up 06-07 08-09 19-20 26-27), FA Vase 2nd Rd 86-87 90-91, FA Trophy 3rd Rd 74-75 75-76, Lancs Yth (u18) Cup 87-88 88-89 (R-up 86-87 89-90), President's Cup 1994-95. Unibond Div 1 95-96, Lge Cup 95-96.

Players progressing to Football League: J McNamee (Workington 75), B O'Callaghan (Stoke C.), I Stevens (Stockport Co. 86), G Johnstone (P.N.E. 93), M Clark & W Collins (Crewe Alex.), G Wilson (Crewe Alex.).
97-98 Captain: J Flannery **Top Scorer:** M Dobie **P.o.Y:** J Flannery/S Hartley

Lancaster City *Photo: David Hirksman*

LANCASTER CITY - Match Facts 97-98

ATS - Lancashire `ATS' Trophy

Match No.	Date	Venue H / A	Comp.	Opponents	Result & Score		Att.	Goalscorers	League Position
1	23.08	H	UL	Runcorn	W	3-0	251	Lancaster 9, 23, Dobie 89.	
2	25.08	A	UL	Hyde United	L	1-4	*590*	Craven 83.	
3	30.08	A	UL	Frickley Athletic	L	1-2	*139*	Jones 32.	17
4	02.09	H	UL	Spennymoor United	W	3-2	163	Dring 50, Lancaster 63, Bairstow 78.	8
5	09.09	A	UL	Blyth Spartans	W	1-0	*515*	Lancaster 80.	6
6	13.09	H	**FAC 1Q**	Consett	D	2-2	148	Jones 15, Dring 31.	-
7	16.09	A	**FAC 1Q R**	Consett	W	*2-1	*110*	Lancaster 10, Jones 120.	-
8	20.09	A	UL	Emley	L	3-5	*237*	Dobie 42, Craven 58 (pen), OG (David) 80.	12
9	23.09	H	UL	Chorley	**W**	**4-1**	245	Boyd 22, Wallington 49, 50, Dobie 87.	6
10	27.09	A	**FAC 2Q**	Hyde United	L	1-4	*598*	Lancaster 70.	-
11	30.09	A	UL	Accrington Stanley	D	1-1	*424*	Jones 87.	8
12	04.10	H	UL	Altrincham	D	2-2	322	Lancaster 18, Dobie 43.	10
13	07.10	A	UL	Radcliffe Borough	**L**	**2-6**	*174*	Dobie 35, Boyd 78.	11
14	11.10	H	UL	Radcliffe Borough	L	0-1	189		
15	14.10	H	UL	Colwyn Bay	L	0-1	150		14
16	18.10	A	UL	Boston United	L	0-2	*869*		15
17	21.10	A	UL	Chorley	W	3-2	*288*	Martin 41, 58, Flanagan 77.	
18	25.10	H	UL	Bamber Bridge	W	1-0	229	Dobie 69 (pen).	10
19	28.10	A	**ULCC 2**	Barrow	W	3-0	*658*	Dobie 15, Martin 25,. 71.	-
20	01.11	A	UL	Guiseley	L	1-2	*453*	Lancaster 50.	12
21	04.11	H	UL	Winsford United	D	1-1	153	Martin 71.	11
22	08.11	H	UL	Emley	D	2-2	239	Dobie 49, 52.	11
23	11.10	A	UL	Altrincham	L	0-1	*670*		
24	15.10	H	UL	Marine	W	3-2	232	Martin 20, Worthington 48, Cheal 78.	9
25	18.11	H	**ATS 1**	Skelmersdale United	W	2-0	121	Dobie 30, Leitch 37.	-
26	22.11	A	UL	Alfreton Town	D	1-1	*153*	Francis 61.	10
27	29.11	A	**FAT 3Q**	Tamworth	W	1-0	*618*	Dobie 31.	-
28	06.12	A	UL	Marine	L	0-2	*269*		11
29	09.12	A	UL	Runcorn	L	0-3	*220*		
30	13.12	H	UL	Leigh RMI	L	0-1	176		17
31	17.12	A	**ULCC 3**	Winsford United	L	0-1	*70*		-
32	20.12	A	UL	Bishop Auckland	L	1-3	*219*	Cheal 88.	18
33	27.12	H	UL	Barrow	L	0-2	1,119		18
34	01.01	A	UL	Barrow	L	0-1	*1,459*		19
35	10.01	H	**FAT 1**	Northwich Victoria	L	0-3	472		-
36	17.01	H	UL	Gainsborough Trinity	L	0-1	233		
37	20.01	H	**ATS 2**	Bacup Borough	W	3-0	81	Graham 36, OG (Ridley) 73, Martin 82.	-
38	24.01	H	UL	Accrington Stanley	W	3-2	342	Dobie 9, 64, McDonald 89.	18
39	31.01	A	UL	Bamber Bridge	W	1-0	*408*	Taylor 34.	18
40	03.02	H	**ATS 3**	Chorley	D	1-1*	217	Cheal 19.	-
41	07.02	A	UL	Spennymoor United	D	1-1	*166*	Dobie 74.	17
42	10.02	A	**ATS 3 R**	Chorley	W	2-1	*281*	Flannery 16, Dobie 70.	-
43	14.02	H	UL	Guiseley	W	3-2	339	Gelling 16, Boyd 43, McDumart 90.	16
44	21.02	H	UL	Blyth Spartans	D	1-1	208	Barker 89.	16
45	24.02	A	**ATS SF**	Morecambe	L	0-2	*1,442*		-
46	28.02	A	UL	Colwyn Bay	L	2-5	*269*	Henningan 7, McDonald 15.	17
47	21.03	A	UL	Gainsborough Trinity	L	1-2	*440*	Trainor 71.	18
48	28.03	H	UL	Bishop Auckland	W	1-0	219	OG (Waller) 89.	18
49	07.04	H	UL	Frickley Athletic	D	2-2	163	Taylor 8, Cheal 87.	18
50	13.04	A	Ul	Leigh RMI	L	0-2	*246*		18
51	18.04	H	UL	Hyde United	L	0-1	222		18
52	21.04	H	UL	Blyth Spartans	W	3-1	192	Jones 32, Cheal 41, Taylor 62.	17
53	23.04	A	UL	Leigh RMI	L	0-2	*246*		18
54	25.04	H	UL	Boston United	W	3-1	214	Cheal 28, Flannery 42, Taylor 90.	17

PLAYING SQUAD 1998

Goalkeepers: Mark Thornley (Morecambe, Fleetwood T, Matlock T, Stafford R,Alfreton T, Sutton T, Belper T, Alfreton T)

Defenders: Jimmy Graham (Guiseley, Hull C, Rochdale, Bradford C), Jay Flannery (Southport, Bamber Bridge), Stuart Phillips (Youth team), Neil Davies (Vauxhall GM, Netherfield, Lincoln C, Fleetwood T), Steve Hartley (Blackpool R)

Midfielders: Charlie Boyd (Bangor C, Caernarfon T, Winsford U, Northwich V,Droylsden, Runcorn, Chorley, Bristol R, Chesterfield, Liverpool), Grant Leitch (Bamber Bridge, Chorley, Altrincham, Halifax T, Blackpool), Stuart Gelling (Acc.Stanley, Lancaster C, Fleetwood T, Knowsley U, Liverpool), David Taylor (Workington, Gretna, Gillford Park), Darren Wilson (Workington, Carlisle U)

Forwards: Dave Lancaster (Bamber Bridge, Rochdale, Bury, Rochdale,Chesterfield, Blackpool, Colne D, Morecambe, Leyland Motors), Steve Trainor (Bamber Bridge, Lancaster C, Fleetwood T, Blackpool R, Fleetwood T, Runcorn,Fleetwood T, Blackpool), Mark Grugel (Barrow, Everton), Mark Dobie (Workington, Queen of the South, Barrow, Gretna, Darlington, Torquay U,Cambridge U, Gretna, Workington), Tony McDonald (Radcliffe B, Witton Alb,Chorley, Horwich RMI, Radcliffe B), Steve Creed (Workington, Lancaster C).

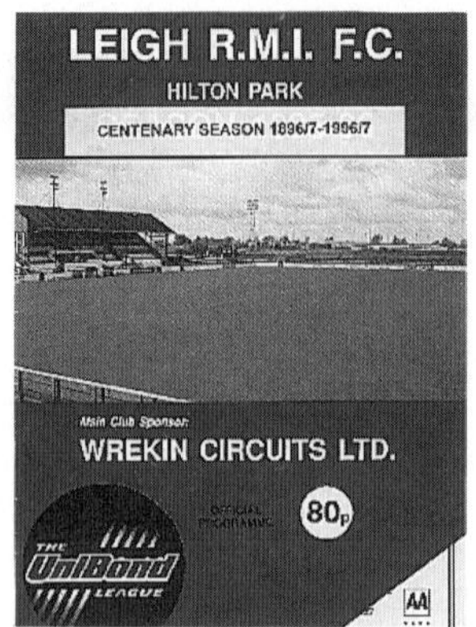

LEIGH R.M.I. F.C.
HILTON PARK
CENTENARY SEASON 1896/7-1996/7
WREKIN CIRCUITS LTD.
80p
UniBond
LEAGUE

PROGRAMME DETAILS:
Pages: 32 **Price:** £1
Editor: Stephen Culshaw
(01257 427144)

LEIGH R.M.I.

Colours: Red & white stripes/black/black **Formed:** 1896
Change colours: All Yellow **Nickname:** Railwaymen
Midweek home matchday: Tuesday **Sponsors:** Gosome Ltd
Reserve Team's League: Preston & District League
Local Press: Bolton Evening News.
Local Radio: Radio Lancs, Red Rose Radio, G.M.R.

Chairman: Chris Healey **President:** G H Fisher
Secretary: Alan Robinson, 55 Janice Drive, Fulwood, Preston, Lancs. PR2 9TY. 01772 719266 (H) 01942 743743 (Club)
Manager: Steve Waywell **Asst Manager/Coach:** Gerry Luska

GROUND Address: Hilton Park, Kirkhall Lane, Leigh. WN7 1RN. 01942 743743 (Office). **Directions:** From M61 at junction 5, follow the Westhoughton sign to r'about, then follow signs to Leigh. Keep on main road to the traffic lights, turn left into Leigh Road, carry on about 3 miles to the traffic lights. Turn left and first right to the next set of lights. Turn right onto Atheleigh Way, A579 at the first set of traffic lights, turn left (B & Q on right), at the next set of lights turn right (Leigh town centre), at the 2nd opening on right turn into Prescott St., carry on to top, turn right, ground on left.
Capacity: 8000 **Cover:** 4,000 **Seats:** 2,000 **Floodlights:** Yes
Clubhouse: Yes. **Club Shop:** Yes

PREVIOUS - **Name:** Horwich R.M.I. to 1995. **Ground:** Grundy Hill, Horwich to 1994. **Leagues:** Lancs Alliance 1891-97; Lancs 1897-1900; Lancs Comb 17-18, 19-39, 46-68; Cheshire County 68-82; North West Counties 82-83.

CLUB RECORDS - **Attendance:** 8,500 v Wigan Ath (at Horwich) Lancs Jnr Cup 54: 980 v Runcorn (at Leigh) FA Cup 4th Rd 96-97. **Win:** **Defeat:** 2-9 v Brandon Utd FA Cup. **Appearances:** **Goalscorer:** **Fee Paid:** £4,000 to Hyde Utd for Keith Evans 95-96. **Fee Received:** £10,000 for Marcus Hallows.

BEST SEASON - **FA Trophy:** Quarter Final 90-91 **FA Cup:** 1st Rd 28-29, 82-83. - **League clubs defeated:** None.

HONOURS - Premier Inter League (GMAC) Cup 87-88; Cheshire County Lg 78-79 (Challenge Shield 78-79); Lancs Combination 57-58 (R-up 29-30 55-56 66-67), Lg Cup 28-29 53-54 56-57 65-66, Div 2 R-up 48-49 50-51; West Lancs Lg 10-11 11-12; Lancs Junior Cup 24-25 29-30 (R-up 53-54 57-58 62-63 82-83); Lancs Floodlit Trophy 84-85 (R-up 83-84); Lancs FA Cup 84-85, NPL Div 1 R-up 96-97.

Players progressing to Football League: Harold Lea (Stockport 58), David Holland (Stockport 59), Jim Cunliffe (Stockport 60), Frank Wignall (Everton 58), Gary Cooper (Rochdale 73), Tony Caldwell (Bolton 83), Raymond Redshaw (Wigan 84), Tony Ellis (Oldham 86).

97-98 Captain: Mark Schofield **P.o.Y.:** Graham Hill **Top Scorer:** Keith Evans

Back Row (L-R); Derek Miles (Physio), Keith Evans, Lee Anderson, Ian McInerney, Peter McCrae, Dave Ridings, Ian Brady, Dave Felgate, Simon Kay, Terry Williams, Peter Smith, John Keary, Neil Smith (Kit Mgr). Front Row; Lee Cryer, Mark Schofield, Mick Wallace, Chris Shaw, Mick Higgins, Steve Waywell (Mgr), Eric Rostron, Martin James, Ian Barker, Stuart Locke.

LEIGH R.M.I. - Match Facts 97-98

ATS - Lancashire `ATS' Trophy

Match No.	Date	Venue H / A	Comp.	Opponents	Result & Score	Att.	Goalscorers	League Position
1	23.08	H	UL	Boston United	L 0-1	237		
2	25.08	A	UL	Runcorn	D 2-2	485	Evans 72, Ridings 88.	
3	30.08	A	UL	Spennymoor United	W 3-0	198	Shaw 32, Evans 56, 61.	9
4	02.09	H	UL	Radcliffe Borough	D 0-0	281		
5	09.09	A	UL	Bamber Bridge	D 1-1	341	Evans 82.	14
6	13.09	H	**FAC 1Q**	Accrington Stanley	W 1-0	343	Evans 7.	
7	16.09	H	UL	Barrow	L 0-1	246		15
8	20.09	A	UL	Blyth Spartans	W 1-0	490	Ridings 26.	9
9	23.09	H	UL	Accrington Stanley	W 1-0	243	Schofield 73.	5
10	27.09	A	**FAC 2Q**	Halifax Town	L 0-4	1,103		
11	30.09	A	**ULCC 1**	Workington	D 1-1	86	Ridings 82.	-
12	04.10	H	UL	Frickley Athletic	D 1-1	201	Cryer 37.	12
13	11.10	H	**ULCC 1 R**	Workington	W 3-1	85	Evans 40, Shaw 60, Wallace 73.	-
14	18.10	A	**FAT 1Q**	Frickley Athletic	D 1-1	171	Cryer 53.	-
15	21.10	H	**FAT 1Q R**	Frickley Athletic	W *2-1	86	Shaw 75, Evans 94.	-
16	25.10	A	UL	Bishop Auckland	L 2-3	174	Evans 55, Schofield 79.	18
17	28.10	A	**ULCC 2**	Radcliffe Borough	D 0-0	141		-
18	01.11	H	UL	Marine	W 1-0	201	Schofield 89.	16
19	08.11	A	**FAT 2Q**	Radcliffe Borough	D 1-1	267	Shaw 76.	-
20	11.11	H	**FAT 2Q R**	Radcliffe Borough	W 1-0	201	Brown 37.	-
21	15.11	H	UL	Bamber Bridge	**W 4-0**	236	Shaw 26, Rostron 52, 63, Cryer 84.	16
22	18.11	H	**ATS 1**	Marine	L 1-4	90	Brown 35.	-
23	22.11	A	UL	Hyde United	D 3-3	522	Cryer 82, 90, Evans 88.	15
24	25.11	A	**ULPC**	Altrincham	W 1-0	269	James 3.	-
25	06.12	A	UL	Barrow	W 1-0	1,012	Rostron 41.	16
26	08.12	A	**FAT 3Q**	Bradford P.A.	D 1-1	127	Rostron 11.	-
27	10.12	H	**FAT 3Q R**	Bradford P.A.	W 1-0	120	Cryer 40.	-
28	13.12	A	UL	Lancaster City	W 1-0	176	Locke 76.	14
29	16.12	H	**ULCC 2 R**	Radcliffe Borough	W 2-0	101	Ridings 69, Shaw 83.	-
30	20.12	H	UL	Emley	W 2-1	267	Ridings 7, Shaw 44.	12
31	06.01	A	UL	Altrincham	D 2-2	348	Shaw 67, Hill 80.	
32	10.01	A	**FAT 1**	Grantham	D 1-1	560	Shaw 11.	-
33	17.01	H	UL	Chorley	W 2-0	367	Evans 14, Shaw 45.	9
34	19.01	H	**FAT 1 R**	Grantham	D !0-0	171		(Lost 3-4 on penalties)
35	21.01	A	**ULCC 3**	Chorley	L 2-5	210	Evans 25, Shaw 56.	-
36	24.01	A	UL	Colwyn Bay	W 3-2	323	OG (Paton) 5, Cryer 75, 90.	9
37	31.01	A	UL	Marine	D 1-1	322	Rostron 87 (pen).	10
38	03.02	A	**ULPC 2**	Guiseley	D 0-0	137		-
39	07.02	H	UUL	Bishop Auckland	L 1-3	181	Shaw 48.	10
40	10.02	H	UL	Winsford United	W 2-0	171	Cryer 24, Evans 90.	7
41	14.02	A	UL	Emley	D 2-2	299	Cryer 65, Williams 86.	7
42	17.02	H	UL	Colwyn Bay	W 3-0	228	Brady 40, Cryer 53, 63.	6
43	21.02	H	UL	Blyth Spartans	D 1-1	208	Barker 89.	6
44	24.02	H	**ULPC 2 R**	Guiseley	L 0-3	146		-
45	28.02	A	UL	Guiseley	L 1-2	227	James 10.	8
46	03.03	A	UL	Radcliffe Borough	W 1-0	144	Ridings 44.	6
47	07.03	H	UL	Guiseley	D 0-0	201		6
48	14.03	A	UL	Accrington Stanley	W 3-1	1,461	Shaw 22, 61, Rostron 82 (pen).	6
49	17.03	H	UL	Gainsborough Trinity	W 1-0	133	Rostron 75.	
50	21.03	H	UL	Altrincham	D 2-2	449	Rostron 61 (pen), Cryer 75.	4
51	28.03	H	UL	Runcorn	D 2-2	319	Evans 61, 77.	5
52	01.04	A	UL	Winsford United	W 1-0	153	Ridings 79.	4
53	04.04	H	UL	Hyde United	W 2-1	251	Ridings 85, 89.	4
54	07.04	A	UL	Chorley	W 1-0	342	Cryer 15.	2
55	11.04	A	UL	Boston United	L 0-1	1,145		4
56	13.04	H	UL	Lancaster City	W 2-0	246	Smythe 13, Evans 70.	3
57	15.04	A	UL	Gainsborough Trinity	**L 0-3**	588		4
58	18.04	A	UL	Alfreton Town	L 2-3	130	McCrae 72, Hill 85.	4
59	21.04	H	UL	Spennymoor United	W 4-2	140	Evans 47, 90, Barber 32, Rostron 80.	4
60	25.04	A	UL	Frickley Athletic	D 0-0	138		3
61	02.05	H	UL	Alfreton Town	W 1-0	159	Evans 38.	3

PLAYING SQUAD 1998 - **Goalkeepers:** David Felgate (Wigan Ath, Chester C, Wolves, Bury, Bolton W,Grimsby T, Lincoln C, Bolton W, Blaenau Festiniog), John Ogden (Rochdale). **Defenders:** Graham Hill (Runcorn, Curzon Ashton, Atherton Coll), Mike Wallace (Netherfield, Chorley, Witton Alb, York C, Rochdale, Bury, Stockport Co,Manchester C), Stuart Locke (Leek T, Macclesfield T, Stalybridge C, Crewe Alex., Manchester C), Simon Kaye (Mossley, Oldham Ath), Ian Brady (Gateshead, Runcorn, Bootle, Heswall). **Midfielders:** Dave Ridings (Crewe Alex., Rochdale, Curzon Ashton, LincolnC, Halifax T, Curzon Ashton), Peter Smythe (Curzon Ashton, Altrincham, HorwichRMI, Manchester U), Martin James (Acc. Stanley, Rotherham U, Stockport Co,Preston NE), Gavin Oldham (Oldham Ath), Steve Pickford * (Glossop NE, LeighRMI, Glossop NE). **Forwards:** Lee Cryer (Atherton LR), Keith Evans (Hyde U, Ashton U, Curzon Ashton, Irlam T, Preston NE), Chris Shaw (Ashton U, Witton Alb, Ashton U, Oldham T, Radcliffe B), Phil Brown (Gt.Harwood T, Bamber Bridge), Ian McInerney (Halifax T, Runcorn, Stockport Co, Huddersfield T, Newcastle Blue Star), Dave Gardner *(Haslingden), Neil Matthews *(Guiseley, GainsboroughTrin, Dag & Red, Lincoln C, Stockport Co, Halifax T, Grimsby T), Ian Monk *(Morecambe, Macclesfield T, Ashton U, Clitheroe).

MARINE

Colours: White/black/black **Formed:** 1894
Change colours: All Yellow **Nickname:** The Mariners
Midweek matchday: Tuesday **Sponsors:** Johnsons the Cleaners
Reserve Team's League: Lancashire League Division One.
Local Press: Crosby Herald, Liverpool Echo, Daily Post
Local Radio: BBC, Radio Merseyside, Radio City.

Chairman: Tom Culshaw **President:** David Bryant.
Secretary: John Wildman, 4 Ashbourne Avenue, Blundellsands, Liverpool L23 8TX (0151 924 5248).
Manager: Roly Howard **Asst Mgr/Coach:** Roger Patience
Press Officer: David Wotherspoon **Physio:** John Bradshaw
GROUND Address: Rossett Park, College Road, Crosby, Liverpool (0151 924 1743). **Directions:** College Road is off main Liverpool-Southport road (A565) in Crosby. Ground ten minutes walk from Crosby & Blundellsands (Mersey Rail). Bus No. 92.
Capacity: 2,500 **Cover:** 1,900 **Seats:** 400 **Floodlights:** 210 lux
Clubhouse: Open daily. Concert Hall (250 seats), Members Lounge (100 seats). **Club Shop:** Sells replica kit, baseball caps, polo shirts, scarves, badges, mugs, pens/pencils, bookmarks, car stickers, combs, tax disc holders. (Dave Rannard 0151 924 0076

PROGRAMME DETAILS:
Pages: 24 **Price:** 80p
Editor: David Wotherspoon

PREVIOUS - **Leagues:** Liverpool Zingari; Liverpool Co. Comb.; Lancs Combination 35-39, 46-69; Cheshire County 69-79. **Name:** Waterloo Melville. **Ground:** Waterloo Park 1894-1903.

CLUB RECORDS - **Attendance:** 4,000 v Nigeria, Friendly 49. **Goalscorer:** Paul Meachin 200. **Appearances:** Peter Smith 952. **Win:** 14-2 v Rossendale United (A), Cheshire County League 25/2/78. **Defeat:** 1-7 v Dulwich Hamlet, FA Amateur Cup final at West Ham, 1932. **Fee Paid:** £6,000 for Jon Penman (Southport October 1995). **Fee Received:** £20,000 for Richard Norris (Crewe 96).

BEST SEASON - **FA Cup:** 3rd Rd 92-93 (lost 1-3 at Crewe Alexandra). **League clubs defeated in FA Cup:** Barnsley 75-76, Halifax Town 92-93.

HONOURS - FA Amtr Cup R-up 31-32 (SF 46-47); FA Trophy SF 83-84 91-92; Northern Prem Lg 94-95, R-up 85-86 91-92, Lg Cup 84-85 91-92 (R-up 80-81 85-86); Presidents Cup R-up 83-84 86-87; Cheshire Co. Lg 73-74 75-76 77-78 (R-up 72-73); Lancs Comb. R-up 46-47 (Lg Cup 46-47 63-64 68-69); Liverpool Comb. 27-28 30-31 33-34 34-35 (Lg Cup 30-31); Lancs Tphy 87-88 90-91; Lancs Jnr Cup 78-79; Lancs Amtr Cup (5); Liverpool Snr Cup 78-79 84-85 87-88 89-90 94-95; Liverpool Non-Lge Cup 68-69 75-76 76-77; Liverpool Chal. Cup 42-43 44-45 71-72.

Players progressing to Football League: A Sharrock, S Brooks (Southport 73 & 77), A Jones (Leeds 60), G Williams (Preston 72), J Lacy (Fulham & Spurs), P Beesly (Sheffield Utd), M Kearney (Everton 81), A Finlay (Shrewsbury 81), P Cook (Norwich), P Edwards (Crewe & Coventry), I Nolan (Tranmere), J McAteer (Liverpool), R Norris (Crewe 96).

Back Row (L-R); Andy Draper, David Oxton, Tom Barnicle, Adrian Rigolioso, Rick Bainbridge, Tony Rodwell, Ritchie Holden, Kevin O'Brian. Front Row; Steve Baines, Dave Richardson, Mark Nulty, Matthew Thompson (Mascot), Jon Gautrey (Capt), Andy Cavannagh, Eddie Murray

MARINE - Match Facts 97-98

ATS - Lancashire `ATS' Trophy
LSC - Liverpool Senior Cup

Match No.	Date	Venue H / A	Comp.	Opponents	Result & Score		Att.	Goalscorers	League Position
1	23.08	H	UL	Bishop Auckland	D	0-0	320		
2	25.08	A	UL	Barrow	W	1-0	*1,474*	Blackhurst 43.	
3	30.08	A	UL	Hyde United	D	1-1	*558*	Nulty 43.	6
4	02.09	H	UL	Bamber Bridge	W	3-1	302	Carberry 25, 67, Cavanagh 64.	4
5	07.09	H	UL	Blyth Spartans	L	1-2	301	Rodwell 80.	6
6	13.09	H	**FAC 1Q**	Ashton United	W	1-0	261	Blackhurst 76.	-
7	16.09	H	UL	Radcliffe Borough	L	1-2	235	Gautrey 8.	9
8	20.09	A	UL	Boston United	D	1-1	*884*	OG (Withe) 2	10
9	27.09	A	**FAC 2Q**	Bamber Bridge	W	3-1	*318*	**Daley 3** (8, 48, 66).	-
10	04.10	H	UL	Alfreton Town	W	2-0	297	Cavanagh 48, Daley 88.	14
11	07.10	A	UL	Colwyn Bay	L	1-4	*307*	Gautrey 48.	16
12	11.10	H	**FAC 3Q**	Lincoln United	D	1-1	265	Morgan 70.	-
13	15.10	A	**FAC 3Q R**	Lincoln United	L	*1-4	*262*	Gautrey 26 (pen).	-
14	18.10	A	UL	Guiseley	D	2-2	*458*	Morgan 18, Carson 29.	16
15	25.10	H	UL	Frickley Athletic	D	1-1	252	Doolan 3.	16
16	28.10	A	**ULCC 2**	Accrington Stanley	D	4-4	*266*	Proctor 35, Gautrey 42, Morgan 52, Carberry 88.	-
17	01.11	A	UL	Leigh RMI	L	0-1	*201*		18
18	08.11	H	UL	Runcorn	W	3-2	386	Daley 4, 75, Morgan 25.	16
19	11.11	H	**ULCC 2 R**	Accrington Stanley	W	2-0	190	Gautrey 3, Cardon 50.	-
20	15.11	A	UL	Lancaster City	L	2-3	*232*	Morgan 9, Nulty 58.	17
21	18.11	A	**ATS 1**	Leigh RMI	W	4-1	*90*	Daley 27, Bainbridge 32, Rodwell 40, Morgan 55.	-
22	22.11	H	UL	Altrincham	W	1-0	474	Gautrey 12 (pen).	16
23	25.11	A	**ULPC 1**	Barrow	**W**	**5-2**	*410*	Morgan 8, Rodwell 18, Cavanagh 64, Bainbridge 76, Baines 88.	-
24	29.11	H	**FAT 3Q**	Grantham	D	1-1	255	Draper 89.	-
25	02.12	A	**FAT 3Q**	Grantham	L	0-1	*326*		-
26	06.12	H	UL	Lancaster City	W	2-0	269	Morgan 43, 47.	17
27	09.12	H	UL	Accrington Stanley	W	3-1	238	Bainbridge 7, Gautrey 64 (pen), Pepper 90.	
28	13.12	A	UL	Emley	L	0-2	*245*		15
29	16.12	H	**ULCC 3**	Runcorn	W	1-0	187	Pepper 73.	-
30	20.12	A	UL	Altrincham	L	1-3	*687*	Pepper 32.	16
31	26.12	H	UL	Winsford United	D	0-0	405		16
32	10.01	A	UL	Bamber Brdge	W	2-1	*318*	Blackhurst 17, Draper 48.	13
33	13.01	A	**ATS 2**	Southport	L	0-4	487		-
34	17.01	H	UL	Colwyn Bay	W	1-0	341	Morgan 20.	10
35	24.01	A	UL	Bishop Auckland	W	4-2	*233*	Murray 10, Rodwell 30, Gautrey 42, Bainbridge 72.	10
36	27.01	A	UL	Winsford United	W	4-2	*148*	Morgan 24, Richardson 42, Bainbridge 45, Cavanagh 66.	
37	31.01	H	UL	Leigh RMI	D	1-1	322	Blackhurst 3.	6
38	03.02	H	**LSC 1**	Bootle	W	2-1	181	Blackhurst 18, Morgan 59.	-
39	07.02	A	UL	Alfreton Town	D	0-0	*178*		7
40	14.02	H	UL	Spennymoor United	**L**	**0-4**	277		9
41	17.02	A	**ULCC 4**	Blyth Spartans	L	0-2	*386*		-
42	21.02	A	UL	Accrington Stanley	D	1-1	*460*	Murray 63.	9
43	24.02	A	**ULPC 2**	Runcorn	L	1-2	*219*	Rodwell 43.	-
44	28.02	A	UL	Blyth Spartans	L	0-1	*446*		11
45	03.03	H	UL	Chorley	L	1-2	297	Bainbridge 90.	
46	07.03	A	UL	Frickley Athletic	D	1-1	*175*	Baines 52 (pen).	12
47	14.03	H	UL	Emley	L	3-5	332	Morgan 3, Gautrey 39, Bainbridge 75.	13
48	17.03	H	**LSC 2**	Liverpool	L	0-4	256		-
49	21.03	H	UL	Guiseley	L	0-1	113		14
50	28.03	A	UL	Radcliffe Borough	W	3-0	*204*	Townsend 48, 70, Morgan 82.	12
51	31.03	H	UL	Hyde United	L	0-2	267		
52	04.04	H	UL	Boston United	L	1-2	211	Donnell 46.	14
53	11.04	A	UL	Runcorn	L	0-3	*330*		14
54	13.04	H	UL	Barrow	W	1-0	539	Bainbridge 82.	13
55	18.04	A	UL	Gainsborough Trinity	L	0-2	*582*		14
56	21.04	A	UL	Chorley	W	3-0	*295*	Morgan 23, Rigoglioso 34, 87.	12
57	25.04	A	UL	Spennymoor United	W	2-1	*127*	Townsend 9, 80.	12
58	02.05	H	UL	Gainsborough Trinity	D	2-2	254	Bainbridge 53, Townsend 76.	11

PLAYING SQUAD 1998

Goalkeepers: Kevin O'Brien (Sth Liverpool, Chorley, Runcorn, Burscough, Rhyl,Maghull, Everton). **Defenders:** Keith Proctor (Youth team), Andy Draper (Local football), IanBaines (Southport, Knowsley U, Rhyl, Knowsley U, Southport, Kirkby T), MarkNulty (Youth team), Jimmy Carberry (Bangor C, Skelmersdale U, Macclesfield T,Wigan Ath, Everton), Danny Carr (Youth team), Alan Finley (Runcorn, StockportCo, Shrewsbury T, Marine). **Midfielders:** Jon Gautrey (Southport, Bolton W), John Doolan (Barrow, WiganAth, Knowsley U), Adriano Rigoglioso (Liverpool), Richard Holden (Chester C), Alex Chvalovsky (FK Chmel Blsany (Czech), Danny Gabrielson (Wigan Ath), DaveRichardson (Connah's Quay N, Holywell T, Marine), Chris Price (Clitheroe,Chester C, Oxford U, Everton), Tom Barnicle (Youth team), Tony Rodwell (Witton Alb, Scarborough, Blackpool, Colne D, Runcorn, Buxton, Southport). **Forwards:** Phil Daley (Bangor C, Southport, Lincoln C, Wigan Ath, Newton,Kirkby T), Richard Townsend (Cwmbran T, Everton), Jimmy Blackhurst (Southport, Sth Liverpool, Marine), Ricky Bainbridge (Local football), PaulCarden (Blackpool).

PROGRAMME DETAILS:
Pages: 32 **Price:** £ 1.20
Editor: Alex Keenan
01928 590425

RUNCORN

Colours: Yellow/green/yellow. **Formed:** 1918
Change colours: All red **Nickname:** The Linnets
Reserve's league: Northwest Alliance **Midweek matchday:** Tuesday
Youth's league: Altrincham & Dist
Local Press: Runcorn Weekley News, Liverpool Echo, Runcorn World, Manchester Evening News.
Local Radio: Radio Merseyside, GMR.

Chairman: Dr David Robertson **Vice Chairman:** Tony Bamber
Secretary: Chris Henshall, 58 Minerva Close, Warrington, Cheshire WA4 2XN. Tel. 01925 650311 (Home), Tel/Fax 01928 560076 (Sec office)
Asst Secretary: Rob Ellison, 24 Cross Lane, Grappenhall, Warrington, Cheshire WA4 2LR. Tel. 01925 266999 (Home), 0802 480313 (Mobile).
Manager: Derek Brownbill **Assistant Manager:** Alan Blair
GROUND Address: Canal Street, Wivern Place, Runcorn, Cheshire WA7 1RZ. Tel. 01928 560076. Fax 01928 560076.
Directions: From South: Leave M56 (junct 11). Follow A56 to Warrington for 1.5 miles. Turn left at roundabout onto A558 signposted Liverpool for 3 miles. Take left hand slipway sign posted Football Ground. From North: Leave M62 (junct 7). Travel via Widnes and over Runcorn bridge. Follow signs for Northwich for 1 mile. Take left hand slipway sign posted Football Ground.
Capacity: 3,928 **Cover:** 1,327 **Seats:** 499 **Floodlights:** Yes
Clubhouse: Open on matchdays. Light snacks available.
Club Shop: Selling usual club memorabilia. Contact Roy Pickering Tel. 01928 568665. **Metal Badges:** Yes

PREVIOUS - **Leagues:** Lancs Combination; Cheshire Co. Lg; Northern Prem. Lge. 68 -81; Alliance Premier (Conference) 81-96. **Names:** None. **Grounds:** None

CLUB RECORDS - **Attendance:** 10,111 v Preston - FA Cup 1938-39. **Goalscorer:** Alan Ryan (66 goals in 64 appearances 67-68). **Win:** 11-1 v Congleton Town 64-65. **Defeat:** 0-9 v Wellington 46-47. **Fee Paid:** £17,000 for Simon Rudge from Hyde United, 1989. **Fee Received:** £80,000 for Ian Woan from Nottingham Forest, 1990.

BEST SEASON - **FA Trophy:** Runners-up 85-86, 92-93, 93-94. **FA Cup:** Second Round Replay 85-86, 0-4 v Wigan Ath. (A), after 1-1. Second Round also 47-48, 67-68, 77-78, 86-87, 87-88, 88-89. **League clubs defeated:** Scunthorpe Utd., Notts. Co., Chester City, Wrexham.

HONOURS - Lancs Jnr Cup 1918-19; Cheshire Lg 1919-20, 36-37, 38-39, 39-40, 62-63; Cheshire Snr Cup 24-25, 35-36, 61-62, 64-65, 67-68, 73-74, 74-75, 84-89 (5 times), R-up 93-94; Cheshire Co. Bowl 37-38; Northern Premier Lg 75-76, 80-81 (R-up 74-75); NPL Chall Cup 74-75, 79-80, 80-81; NPL Challenge Shield 80-81, 81-82; Alliance Premier Lg 81-82, Gola Lg Championship Shield 82-83, 85-86; Bob Lord Trophy 82-83, 84-85, R-up 91-92. FA Trophy R-up 85-86, 92-93, 93-94.

Players progressing to Football League: Mark McCarrick, Eddie Bishop, Jim Cumbes, Graham Abel, Barry Knowles, Mark Jones, Don Page, David Pugh, Ian Woan, Gary Brabin, Paul Robertson, Mike Smith.
97-98 Captain: Carl Ruffer **P.o.Y.:** Carl Ruffer **Top scorer:** Liam Watson (41)

Back Row (L-R); Joey Dunn, Alan Blair (Asst Mgr), Aidan Warder, Neil Whalley, Paul McNally, Mark Morris, Peter Ellis, Matty Brooks, Darren Oliver, Tommy Ellis (Kit Mgr), Danny Worthington. Front Row; Paul Fleming, Gary Randles, Liam Watson, Carl Ruffer (Capt), Danny Salt, Tony Ward, Richard Irving. Photo: John Newton

RUNCORN - Match Facts 97-98

UCSC - Cheshire Senior Cup

Match No.	Date	Venue H / A	Comp.	Opponents	Result	& Score	Att.	Goalscorers	League Position
1	23.08	A	UL	Lancaster City	L	0-3	251		
2	25.08	H	UL	Leigh RMI	D	2-2	385	McNally 17, Lee 23.	
3	30.08	H	UL	Emley	W	1-0	362	McNally 67.	14
4	02.09	A	UL	Accrington Stanley	W	3-0	604	McNally 6, Watson 26, Whalley 44.	7
5	13.09	H	UL	Altrincham	W	1-0	670	Salt 19.	4
6	16.09	A	UL	Chorley	L	2-4	235	McNally 22, Watson 46.	5
7	20.09	H	UL	Hyde United	L	0-1	400		8
8	24.09	A	**U CSC 1**	Winsford United	D	1-1	168	Watson 44.	-
9	27.09	A	UL	Colwyn Bay	L	1-2	373	Salt 44.	14
10	30.09	H	**U CSC 1 R**	Winsford United	W	*2-1	156	Carragher Dunn.	-
11	04.10	H	UL	Bamber Bridge	W	4-2	327	McNally 3, Watson 30 (pen), Carragher 82.	13
12	08.10	A	UL	Winsford United	D	1-1	362	Dunn 83.	13
13	11.10	A	UL	Boston United	W	3-0	938	Watson 11 (pen), Heavey 65, 69.	8
14	14.10	H	UL	Radcliffe Borough	W	6-3	233	Heavey 3, 77, McNally 40, Watson **3** (46, 64, 81).	6
15	18.10	H	UL	Bishop Auckland	W	2-1	349	Watson 7 (pen), Heavey 11.	3
16	21.10	A	UL	Altrincham	L	1-2	704	Heavey 2.	3
17	25.10	H	**FAC 4Q**	Lincoln United	L	1-2	505	Heavey 19.	-
18	27.10	A	**ULCC 2**	Ashton United	W	2-1	190	McNally 5, Heavey 16.	-
19	01.11	H	UL	Blyth Sparatans	D	1-1	326	McNally 69.	4
20	08.11	A	UL	Marine	L	2-3	386	Salt 14, Watson 90.	5
21	11.11	H	UL	Barrow	L	0-1	373		5
22	15.11	A	UL	Alfreton Town	W	3-1	141	Watson 5, Carragher 66, Brooks 88.	5
23	18.11	H	**U CSC 2**	Stalybridge Celtic	W	3-0	195	Dunn 52, Watson 73, 78.	-
24	22.11	H	UL	Gainsborough Trinity	W	2-0	300	Brooks 20, 78.	5
25	25.11	H	**ULPC 1**	Radcliffe Borough	D	0-0	155		-
26	29.11	A	**FAT 3Q**	Accrington Stanley	W	5-0	402	McNally 6, 89, Whalley 14, Carragher 70, Brooks 86.	-
27	06.12	H	UL	Alfreton Town	W	3-1	295	Dunn 3, 88, Watson 86.	5
28	09.12	H	UL	Lancaster City	W	3-0	220	**Watson 3** (10 (pen), 57, 62).	
29	13.12	A	UL	Radcliffe Borough	D	0-0	178		3
30	16.12	A	**ULCC 3**	Marine	L	0-1	187		-
31	20.12	H	UL	Chorley	L	2-3	377	Watson 7, McNally 10.	4
32	06.01	H	**U CSC SF**	Vauxhall GM	D	2-2	192	Watson 31, 34.	-
33	17.01	H	UL	Frickley Athletic	W	2-4	278	McNally 48, Heavey 60.	4
34	19.01	A	**FAT 1**	Altrincham	L	2-3	555	Ruffer 23, McNally 88.	-
35	24.01	A	UL	Blyth Spartans	**W**	**4-0**	630	Salt 7, Watson 33, 60, Warden 87.	4
36	31.01	A	UL	Spennymoor United	W	1-0	161	Watson 39.	3
37	03.02	A	**U CSC SF R**	Vauxhall GM	W	3-1	201	Watson 44 (pen), 74, McNally 89 (pen).	-
38	07.02	H	UL	Accrington Stanley	W	3-0	345	McNally 38, Irvine 89, Brook 90 (pen).	3
39	10.02	H	**ULPC 1 R**	Radcliffe Borough	W	3-1	166	Salt 39, 51, Brooks 50.	-
40	14.02	A	UL	Bishop Auckland	W	2-1	200	McNally 43, Brooks 80.	3
41	21.02	H	UL	Boston United	W	3-0	475	Irvine 7, Salt 43, Watson 67.	3
42	24.02	H	**ULPC 2**	Marine	W	2-1	219	McNallyt 29, 38.	-
43	28.02	A	UL	Emley	**L**	**2-6**	238	Watson 33, 63.	3
44	10.03	A	**ULPC SF-1**	Blyth Spartans	L	1-2	294	Oliver 9. * No 2nd leg - Blyth expelled for playing an inelible player	-
45	14.03	A	UL	Bamber Bridge	W	3-1	297	Watson 14, 40, Ruffer 26.	2
46	17.03	H	UL	Colwyn Bay	D	0-0	285		2
47	21.03	H	UL	Spennymoor United	W	2-0	334	Irving 32, Watson 81.	2
48	24.03	N	**U CSC Final**	Macclesfield Town	L	0-1	995	Played at Northwich Victoria FC	
49	28.03	A	UL	Leigh RMI	D	2-2	319	Watson 22, 50.	2
50	31.03	H	UL	Guiseley	D	1-1	302	Randles 37.	2
51	04.04	A	UL	Barrow	L	0-1	1,743		3
52	11.04	H	UL	Marine	W	3-0	330	Watson 10, McNally 41, Randles 44.	3
53	13.04	A	UL	Guiseley	D	2-2	324	Salt 62, 73.	4
54	18.04	A	UL	Frickley Athletic	W	3-1	148	**Watson 3** (17(pen), 23, 47).	3
55	21.04	H	UL	Winsford United	D	2-2	246	Salt 12, Irvine 47.	3
56	25.04	A	**ULPC Final 1**	Guiseley	W	2-1	312	Watson 3, Brooks 18.	-
57	27.04	A	UL	Gainsborough Trinity	L	0-1	581		
58	30.04	H	**ULPC Final 2**	Guiseley	W	3-2	454	Watson 2, 3, Warder 76.	-
59	02.05	A	UL	Hyde United	W	2-0	747	McNally 31, Worthington 45.	4

PLAYING SQUAD 1998 - **Goalkeepers:** Mark Morris (Wrexham), Karl Williams (Curzon Ashton,Macclesfield T, Warrington T, Macclesfield T, Chester C). **Defenders:** Carl Ruffer (Everton), Danny Salt (Wigan Ath), Tony Ward (Chorley, Marine, Chorley, Wigan Ath, Everton), Peter Ellis (Knowsley U), Mark Ashton (Curzon Ashton, Warrington T, Mossley, Castleton Gabriels , Mossley), Paul Fleming (Chorley, Halifax T, Mansfield T, Halifax T), Darren Oliver (Stafford R, Caernarfon T, Barrow, Altrincham, Rochdale, Bolton W). **Midfielders:** Gray Randles (Curzon Ashton, Warrington T, Cosmo (USA),Warrington T, Avon Ath), Paul McNally (Marine, Warrington T, Southport,Stalybridge C, Runcorn, Oswestry T), Kevin Tyrrell (Wigan Ath), Matty Brooks (Atherton LR, Wigan Ath), Aiden Warder (Curzon Ashton, Runcorn, Warrington T,Sth Liverpool), Neil Whalley (Witton Alb, Altrincham, Preston NE, WarringtonT), Colin Rose * (Macclesfield T, Witton Alb, Crewe Alex), Dave Nolan * (HydeU, Barrow, Chester C, Bromborough Pool, Prescot). **Forwards:** Liam Watson (Witton Alb, Marine, Preston NE, Warrington T,Burscough, Maghull), Joey Dunn (Atherton LR, Curzon Ashton, Warrington T,Caernarfon T, Warrington T, Marine, Burscough, Altrincham, Formby, SthLiverpool, Earle), Richard Irving (Macclesfield T, Nottingham F, ManchesterU), Chris Lee (Congleton T, Runcorn, Curzon Ashton, Warrington T, Chorley,Knowsley U, Ford M), Paul Ireland (Nantwich T, Atherton LR, Chester C).

PROGRAMME DETAILS:
Pages: 44 **Price:** £1
Editor: Andy Potts
(0191 386 1439)

SPENNYMOOR UNITED

Club colours: Black & white stripes/black/white. **Founded:** 1904
Change colours: All red **Sponsors:** Rothmans (Spennymoor).
Midweek home matches: Tuesday **Nickname:** The Moors
Reserve Team: None
Local Press: Northern Echo; The Journal.

Chairman: Barrie Hindmarch **Vice Chairman:** J Norman
President: **Secretary:** Tom Metcalfe, 23 Tangmere, Spennymoor, County Durham DL16 6TY (01388 811561).
Manager: Matt Pearson **Asst Manager:** John Parnaby
Physio: Alan Jackson **Coach:** Managerial team.
Commercial Mgr: Des Beamson **Press Off.:** Chairman
GROUND Address: Brewery Field, Durham Road, Spennymoor, County Durham DL16 6JN (01388 811934). **Directions:** From South; A1(M), A167, A688, straight on at mini-r'bout, 3rd exit at next large r'bout (St Andrews church opposite), pass Asda on left, straight on at junction, pass Salvin Arms (Durham Rd), ground 200 yds on left. From A167 North - leave at Croxdale (N.E.S.S. factory), right at cemetary on left - this is Durham Rd - ground half mile on right. Nearest rail station is Durham - buses from there.
Seats: 300 **Cover:** 2,000 **Capacity:** 7,500 **Floodlights:** Yes
Clubhouse: (01388 814100) Open eves. 7-11pm, Sat 12-11pm (matchdays only), Sun 12-2 & 7-10.30pm. Bar snacks. Private functions. Tea bar in ground.
Club Shop: Sells replica kit, memorabilia, programmes etc. Contact Peter Fletcher (01388 814100).

PREVIOUS - **Leagues:** Northern 05-08 60-90; North Eastern 08-37 38-58; Wearside 37-38; Midland Counties 58-60; Northern Counties East 90-93. **Ground:** Wood Vue 1901-1904. **Names:** None.

CLUB RECORDS - **Attendance:** 7,202 v Bishop Auckland, Durham County Challenge Cup 30/3/57. **Win:** 19-0 v Eden Colliery, North Eastern Lge 6/2/37. **Defeat:** 0-16 v Sunderland 'A', Durham Snr Cup 4/1/02 (Half-time: 0-10). **Scorer:** Dougie Humble 200+. **Appearances:** Ken Banks 600+. **Fee Paid:** £3,500 for Don Prattie (Gretna) **Fee Received:** £20,000 for Michael Heathcote (Sunderland, 88).

BEST SEASON - **FA Trophy:** Semi Final 77-78. **FA Cup:** 3rd Rd 36-37 (lost 1-7 at West Bromwich Albion). **League clubs defeated in FA Cup:** Hartlepool 27-28, Southport 75-76.

HONOURS - Northern Premier Lg Cup 93-94 (Div 1 R-up 93-94); Northern Lg(6) 67-68 71-72 73-74 76-79 (R-up(3) 74-75 79-81), Lg Cup(5) 65-66 67-68 79-81 86-87; Turney Wylde Cup 80-81; J R Cleator Cup 80-81 86-87; Northern Counties (East) Lg 92-93 (Lg Cup 92-93); Durham Challenge Cup 29-30 44-45 45-46 53-54 62-63 67-68 72-73 73-74 74-75 75-76 78-79 82-83 93-94 94-95 95-96 97-98; Durham Benevolent Bowl 26-27 29-30 31-32 47-48 58-59 60-61; North Eastern Lg(4) 09-10 44-46 56-57 (Lg Cup 28-29).

Players progressing to Football League: Over fifty, including: H. Hubbick (Burnley, 3.25), T. Dawson (Charlton, 3.39), T. Flockett (Charlton, 4.49), J. Smallwood (Chesterfield, 12.49), J. Oakes (Aldershot, 5.54), J. Adams (Luton Town, 53), Alan Moore (Chesterfield), Michael Heathcote (Sunderland, 5.87), Jason Ainsley (Hartlepool, 94), Richie Alderson (York City 97), Graeme Paxton (Newcastle Utd 97).

97-98 Captain: Dave Robson **P.o.Y.:** Simon Bates **Top scorer:** Steve Preen

Back Row (L-R); Dion Raitt, Gary Cowell, Lee Innes, Adrian Swan, Gary O'Hara, Gary Lowes, Alan Jackson (Physio), Graham Pepper, Simon Bates, Wayne Edgecumbe, David Graham, Dave Hall (Coach), John Parnaby (Asst Mgr). Front Row; Richie Watson, Craig Veart, Dave Robson (Capt), Steve Preen, Matt Pearson (Mgr), Stephen Williamson (Mascot).

SPENNYMOOR UNITED - Match Facts 97-98

DSC - Durham Senior Cup

Match No.	Date	Venue H / A	Comp.	Opponents	Result & Score		Att.	Goalscorers	League Position
1	23.08	A	UL	Gainsborough Trinity	W	1-0	*481*	Alderson 41.	
2	25.08	H	UL	Bishop Auckland	D	1-1	454	Alderson 22.	
3	30.08	H	UL	Leigh RMI	L	0-3	198		15
4	02.09	A	UL	Lancaster City	L	2-3	*163*	Richardson 37, Robson 45.	18
5	09.09	H	UL	Emley	D	2-2	208	Alderson 13, Richardson 45.	17
6	13.09	H	**FAC 1Q**	Blyth Spartans	D	1-1	340	Bates 31.	-
7	16.09	A	**FAC 1Q R**	Blyth Spartans	L	0-1	*360*		-
8	20.09	H	UL	Chorley	W	2-0	190	Dia 10, Alderson 20.	16
9	23.09	A	UL	Blyth Spartans	W	3-2	*542*	Robson 4, Alderson 41, Cowell 58.	11
10	27.09	A	UL	Radcliffe Borough	W	2-0	*147*	Alderson 9, 44.	6
11	30.09	H	UL	Frickley Athletic	D	0-0	157		
12	04.10	A	UL	Barrow	W	2-1	*1,174*	Alderson 73, Robson 85.	4
13	11.10	H	UL	Bamber Bridge	L	0-3	192		4
14	14.10	H	UL	Blyth Spartans	W	2-1	314	O'Hara 51, Alderson 61.	3
15	18.10	A	**FAT 1Q**	Blakenall	W	3-2	*195*	Pepper 8, Innes 72, Cowell 78.	-
16	25.10	H	UL	Accrington Stanley	W	2-0	246	Alderson 76, 88.	3
17	28.10	H	**DCC 1**	South Shields	W	2-1	169	Richardson 58, Alderson 85.	-
18	01.11	A	UL	Colwyn Bay	L	0-2	*316*		6
19	08.11	A	**FAT 2Q**	Winsford United	L	0-1	*293*		-
20	12.11	A	**ULCC 2**	Whitby Town	W	1-0	*404*	Alderson 88.	-
21	15.11	H	UL	Hyde United	D	2-2	179	Veart 20, Richardson 53.	8
22	18.11	H	**DSC 2**	Sunderland Kennock Roker	W	5-0	79	**Richardson 3** (4, 54, 56), Veart 38, OG 52.	-
23	22.11	H	UL	Boston United	L	1-2	201	Innes 7.	11
24	29.11	A	UL	Guiseley	D	1-1	*296*	Robson 90.	17
25	02.12	H	**ULCC 3**	Boston United	L	1-3	76	Preen 73.	-
26	06.12	H	UL	Winsford United	D	1-1	169	Pepper 34.	10
27	13.12	A	UL	Chorley	L	1-4	*276*	Richardson 28 (pen).	12
28	15.12	A	UL	Hyde United	L	1-3	*232*	Robson 45, Cowell 80.	
29	20.12	A	UL	Accrington Stanley	L	0-3	*409*		15
30	06.01	H	**DSC QF**	Evenwood Twon	W	8-0	91	O'Hara 9, **Preen 3** (23,61,84), Edgcombe 38,68, Innes 45, Raitt 75.	-
31	10.01	A	UL	Frickley Athletic	W	3-2	*179*	Preen 8, Veart 54, Black 58.	14
32	17.01	H	UL	Radcliffe Borough	D	1-1	167	Veart 88 (pen).	16
33	24.01	A	UL	Alfreton Town	W	3-2	*208*	Innes 40, Cowell 61, Veart 90 (pen).	11
34	31.01	H	UL	Runcorn	L	0-1	161		13
35	07.02	H	UL	Lancaster City	D	1-1	166	Preen 52.	13
36	10.02	H	**DSC SF**	Bishop Auckland	D	*2-2	317	Cowell 29, Innes 108.	-
37	14.02	A	UL	Marine	**W**	**4-0**	*277*	Veart 22 (pen), OG (Draper) 42, Preen 74, Watson 88 (pen).	13
38	18.02	A	**DSC SF R**	Bishop Auckland	W	*3-1	*267*	Cowell 87, Preen 95, 102.	-
39	21.02	H	UL	Guiseley	L	1-3	248	O'Hara 28.	14
40	28.02	A	UL	Bamber Bridge	D	2-2	*254*	Preen 44, Veart 45.	14
41	07.03	A	UL	Boston United	W	3-1	*602*	Innes 24, 52, Preen 55.	13
42	14.03	H	UL	Alfreton Town	D	1-1	165	Black 78.	12
43	21.03	A	UL	Runcorn	L	0-2	*334*		13
44	25.03	A	UL	Bishop Auckland	D	1-1	*216*	OG (Roulston) 28.	13
45	28.03	H	UL	Colwuyn Bay	W	2-1	151	Bates 40, 83.	11
46	31.03	H	UL	Altrincham	W	2-1	159	Preen 43, Innes 72.	11
47	11.04	H	UL	Gainsborough Trinity	L	1-4	152	Preen 74.	12
48	13.04	H	**DSC Final**	Hartlepool United	W	2-1	443	Edgcumbe 23, OG 30.	-
49	18.04	A	UL	Winsford United	L	0-1	*134*		13
50	21.04	A	UL	Leigh RMI	L	2-4	*140*	Cowell 18, Irons 86.	13
51	23.04	A	UL	Emley	L	0-3	*171*		14
52	25.04	H	UL	Marine	L	1-2	127	Innes 78.	14
53	27.04	A	UL	Altrincham	**L**	**0-4**	*444*		15
54	02.05	H	UL	Barrow	W	3-2	370	Veart 39, Cowell 62, Preen 73.	14

PLAYING SQUAD 1998

Goalkeepers: Adrian Swan (Billingham T, Darlington).

Defenders: Terry Hird (Chester-le-Street), Richie Watson (Billingham T, BAuckland, Billingham T, Whitley Bay, Billingham T), Simon Bates (Evenwood T,Manchester U), Graham Flockett (Ferryhill Ath, Crook T, Whitby T, FerryhillAth), Mark Sunley (Stalybridge C, Halifax T, Darlington, Middlesbrough), Graham Pepper (Darlington, Newcastle U), Andy Purvis (Blackpool), Gary O'Hara (Port Vale, Leeds U).

Midfielders: Craig Veart (Gateshead, Ferryhill Ath, Middlesbrough), DavidRobson (Dunston Fed, Spennymoor U, Murton), Daniel Key (Gateshead, Darlington), C arl Black (Consett), Micky English (Whitley Bay, S Shields,Newcastle U), Gary Cowell (Ferryhill Ath), Carl Beasley (Evenwood T).

Forwards: Lee Innes (Consett, Spennymoor U, Darlington, Sheffield U), Dion Riatt (Darlington), Wayne Edgcumbe (Gateshead, Crook T, B Auckland, Crook T), Andy Sinclair (Dunston Fed, Tow Law T, Fleetwood T, Whitby T, Newcastle BlueStar, Ferryhill Ath, B Auckland, Consett, Gretna), Steve Preen (Tow Law T), Paul Richardson (Middlesbrough), Gary Lowes (W Auckland T, Whitley Bay, WAuckland T, Darlington).

STALYBRIDGE CELTIC

Club colours: Blue & white/blue/blue **Sponsors:** Manro Ltd.
Change colours: Green & white hoops/green/green **Formed:** 1909
Midweek home matchday: Tuesday **Nickname:** Celtic
Reserves' League: None
Local Newspapers: Manchester Evening News, Manchester Evening News Pink (Sat. eve.), Aston Reporter, Ashton Advertiser
Local Radio Stations: G.M.R. (BBC Manchester), Piccadilly Radio

Chairman: Peter Barnes **President:** Joe Jackson
Vice Chairman: Derek Wolstenholme
Football Secretary: Martyn Torr, c/o the club. Tel: 0161 628 3387 (H) 0161 338 2828 (B) 0161 338 8256 (Fax)
Commercial Manager: Keith Mogford Tel: 0161 338 2828 (B)
Press Officer: Keith Trudgeon Tel: 0161 331 4426 (B) 0161 304 8934 (H)
Manager: Brian Kettle **Asst. Man.:** Tommy Martin **Physio:** Dave Pover

PROGRAMME DETAILS:
Pages: 40 **Price:** £1.30
Editor: Nick Shaw
(0161 633 1117)

GROUND Address: Bower Fold, Mottram Road, Stalybridge, Cheshire SK15 2RT. Tel: 0161 338 2828 Fax: 0161 338 8256.
Simple Directions: M6 to A556 to M63 to M67; end of Motorway through roundabout to traffic lights, left; left at end into Molltram Road, up hill, down hill into Stalybridge, ground on left next to Hare & Hounds pub.
Capacity: 6,000 **Seats:** 1,300 **Cover:** 1,300
Clubhouse: Open matchdays and evenings during the week. Food available on matchdays.
Club Shop: Contact Keith Mogford for details (0161 338 2828)

PREVIOUS - **Leagues:** Lancashire Combination 1911-12, Central Lge 1912-21, Football Lge 1921-23, Cheshire Co. Lge 1923-1982, North West Co's 1982-87, Northern Prem. Lge 1987-92.
Grounds: None **Names:** None

CLUB RECORDS - **Attendance:** 9,753 v WBA - FA Cup replay - 22-23 **Win:** 16-2 twice; v Manchester NE 1/5/26; v Nantwich 22/10/32 **Defeat:** 0-6 v Northwich Victoria **Career appearances:** Kevin Booth 354 **Career goalscorer:** Not known **Goalscorer (in a season):** Chris Camden 45, 91-92 **Transfer fee paid:** £15,000 to Kettering Town for Ian Arnold 95 **Transfer fee received:** £3,000 for Martin Filson from Halifax Town

BEST SEASON - **FA Cup:** Second Round 93-94, 1-3 v Carlisle Utd.(A) **League clubs defeated:** None
FA Trophy: Third Round 1991-92, 0-1 v Witton Albion (A).

HONOURS - Northern Premier Lg Prem Div 91-92, R-up 90-91 (Div.1 R-up 87-88); Cheshire Cnty Lg 79-80 (R-up 77-78), Lg Cup 21-22 (R-up 46-47,81-82); Challenge Shield 77-78 (R-up 79-80), Res Div R-up 81-82; NW Co's Lg 83-84, 86-87 (Lge Cup R-up 83-84), Champions v Cup Winners Trophy 83-84; Lancs Comb Div 2 11-12; Cheshire Snr Cup 52-53 (R-up 54-55, 80-81); Manchester Snr Cup 22-23, Intermediate Cup 57-58, 68-69 (R-up 56-57, 67-68, 69-70); Challenge Shield 54-55, (Junior Cup 62-63); Lancs Floodlit Cup 88-89 (R-up 89-90); Reporter Cup R-up 74-75; Edward Case Cup 77-78.

Past players who progressed to the Football League: Too numerous to list.

Stalybridge Celtic

STALYBRIDGE CELTIC - Match Facts 97-98

Match No.	Date	Venue H / A	Comp.	Opponents	Result & Score		Att.	Goalscorers	League Position
1	16.08	H	VC	Kidderminster Harriers	W	2-1	1,013	Charles 80, Burke 90.	
2	19.08	A	VC	Telford United	L	0-1	*816*		
3	23.08	A	VC	Hednesford Town	L	0-1	*1,054*		16
4	25.08	H	VC	Leek Town	**W**	**6-1**	974	**Burke 3** (23, 47, 64), Powell 62, 63, Trees 85.	6
5	30.08	H	VC	Slough Town	L	0-1	809		12
6	07.09	A	VC	Welling United	L	0-1	*503*		18
7	13.09	H	VC	Hayes	D	1-1	545	Williams 53.	18
8	20.09	H	VC	Cheltenham Town	L	1-4	561	Sullivan 79.	18
9	27.09	A	VC	Hereford United	L	0-3	*2,312*		19
10	04.10	H	VC	Yeovil Town	W	3-2	590	**Burke 3** (24, 78, 90).	18
11	11.10	A	VC	Hayes	W	2-1	*691*	Trundle 18, Hine 56.	15
12	18.10	A	VC	Dover Athletic	L	1-3	*832*	Storey 31.	18
13	01.11	H	VC	Stevenage Borough	D	1-1	702	Bates 59.	17
14	08.11	A	VC	Woking	L	1-3	*2,829*	Trundle 53 (pen).	20
15	15.11	H	VC	Halifax Town	L	0-1	1,421		20
16	22.11	A	VC	Southport	L	2-4	*909*	Trundle 86, Burke 89.	20
17	29.11	H	VC	Hednesford Town	D	1-1	651	Thomas 89.	19
18	06.12	A	VC	Halifax Town	L	1-3	*2,453*		19
19	13.12	H	VC	Telford United	L	1-2	534	Ramsey 79	20
20	20.12	A	VC	Farnborough Town	**L**	**0-6**	*621*		21
21	26.12	A	VC	Northwich Victoria	L	0-1	*1,340*		21
22	29.12	H	VC	Southport	L	1-3	767	Burke 41	21
23	01.01	H	VC	Northwich Victoria	L	0-1	1,004		21
24	17.01	H	VC	Woking	L	0-3	710		21
25	24.01	A	VC	Leek Town	D	2-2	*781*	Trundle 20 (pen), 32.	21
26	07.02	H	VC	Dover Athletic	W	1-0	1,666	Trundle 14.	21
27	17.02	H	VC	Gateshead	D	2-2	605	Hall 32, Sullivan 90.	21
28	21.02	H	VC	Morecambe	W	3-1	756	**Sullivan 3** (20, 50, 73).	21
29	23.02	A	VC	Kidderminster Harriers	L	0-5	*1,666*		21
30	28.02	A	VC	Rushden & Diamonds	L	0-3	*2,470*		21
31	07.03	A	VC	Stevenage Borough	D	1-1	*2,273*	Burke 66.	21
32	14.03	A	VC	Yeovil Town	L	0-2	*1,862*		21
33	21.03	H	VC	Welling United	W	2-1	802	Jones 66, Trundle 67.	21
34	25.03	A	VC	Gateshead	D	3-3	*642*	**Burke 3** (32, 84, 88).	21
35	04.04	H	VC	Hereford United	L	2-3	795	Martin 50, Dolby 73.	22
36	11.04	A	VC	Kettering Town	L	1-3	*1,547*	Jones 25.	22
37	13.04	H	VC	Rushden & Diamonds	L	2-4	952	Burke 21, Highfield 90.	22
38	18.04	H	VC	Farnborough Town	D	1-1	505	Burke 58.	22
39	23.04	A	VC	Cheltenham Town	L	0-2	*1,093*		22
40	28.04	A	VC	Morecambe	L	1-3	*1,012*	Burke 18.	22
41	30.04	A	VC	Slough Town	L	0-4	*435*		22
42	02.05	H	VC	Kettering Town	L	3-4	565	Jones 4, Sullivan 47, Heath 79.	22

CUP COMPETITIONS

Date	Venue H / A	Comp.	Opponents	Result & Score		Att.	Goalscorers
25.10	H	**FAC** 4Q	Solihull Borough	D	3-3	570	Trundle 11, 43(pen), Sullivan 52.
29.10	A	4Q R	Solihull Borough	L	*3-4	402	Burke 81, 101, Sullivan 110.
10.01	H	**FAT** 1	Gateshead	L	2-4	524	Ord 25, Rowe 32, Bowey 63, Kitchen 70.
07.10	H	**SCC** 1	Halifax Town	W	3-1	489	Butler 23, Trees 57, Trundle 70.
25.11	H	2	Gateshead	L	*3-4	224	Burke 24, Sullivan 68, 118.

SCC - Spalding Challenge Cup

PLAYING SQUAD 1998 **Goalkeepers:** Chris Knowles* (Witton Alb, Northampton T, Hereford U, Chester C,Bury, Peterborough U)
Defenders: Leroy Dove (Southport, Buxton, Droylsden,Prestwich Heys), David Hall (Halifax T, Oldham Ath), Ian Patterson (Wigan Ath, Burnley, Sunderland), Lee Anderson* (Leigh RMI, Southport, Altrincham, Bury), Loz Greenhalgh* (Radcliffe B, Warrington T, Rossendale U, Bury), Paul Jones* (Souhtport,Stockport Co), Kevin Booth* (Winsford U, Radcliffe B, Leigh RMI, Flixton,Stalybridge C, Curzon Ashton, Stalybridge C, Bacup B, Stalybridge C)
Midfielders: Steve Jones (Leek T, Eastwood H., Stafford R, Stoke C), Mark Hine (Gateshead, Scunthorpe U,Peterborough U, Darlington, Grimsby T, WhitbyT), Brian McCord (Notts Co, Stockport Co, Barnsley, Derby Co), Dean Martin (Lancaster C,Halifax T Rochdale Scunthorpe U, Halifax T), Steve Quinn (Bolton W), Derek Hall * (Buxton,Hyde U,Rochdale,Hereford U, Halifax T,Southend U,Swindon T,Torquay U, Coventry C)
Forwards: Tony Sullivan (Prescot Cables), Lee Trundle (Chorley, Burscough,St.Dominics), Brendan Burke (Witton Alb, Mossley, Manchester U), Mark Highfield (Stocksbridge PS, Matlock T, Denaby U, Sheffield, Denaby U,Parkgate, Alfreton T), Chris Dolby (Alfreton T, Matlock T, Denaby U, BradfordC, Rotherham U), Sam Goodacre (Scunthorpe U, Sheffield U), Ian Lunt * (Radcliffe B, Curzon Ashton, Droylsden, Curzon Ashton, Winsford U, Witton Alb,Altrincham).

PROGRAMME DETAILS:
Pages: 24 **Price:** 80p
Editor: A Maylor
Tel: 01606 552763

WINSFORD UNITED

Colours: Royal/white/royal **Founded:** 1883
Change colours: Maroon/white/white. **Nickname:** Blues
Sponsors: Dickson Motors Ltd, Winsford (Ford).
Midweek home matchday: Monday.
Local Press: Winsford Chronicle, Winsford Guardian.
Local Radio: Signal, Piccadilly.

Chairman: M Morgan **President:** A Bayliss
Vice Chairman: D.Cotterill. **Secretary:** Peter Warburton, 3 Massey Avenue, Winsford, Cheshire CW7 3DU (01606 554295).
Manager: Dalton Steele **Asst Manager:** John Imrie

GROUND Address: Barton Stadium, Wharton, Winsford, Cheshire CW7 3EU (01606 593021).
Directions: From north; M6 junction 19, A556 towards Northwich to Davenham, then A5018 to Winsford. From south; M6 junction 18, A54 through Middlewich to Winsford. Ground quarter mile off main road in Wharton area of town. 1 mile from Winsford (BR).
Capacity: 6,000 **Cover:** 5,000 **Seats:** 250 **Floodlights:** Yes
Clubhouse: Mon-Sat 8-11pm, Sun 8-10.30pm
Club Shop: Yes - contact E Welch

PREVIOUS - **Leagues:** The Combination 02-04; Cheshire County 19-40, 47-82; North West Counties 82-87. **Name:** Over Wanderers (prior to 1914).

CLUB RECORDS - **Attendance:** 7,000 v Witton Albion 1947. **Goalscorer:** Graham Smith 66. **Appearances:** Edward Harrop 400. **Fee Paid:** Nil. **Fee Received:** £6,000 for Neville Southall from Bury.

BEST SEASON - **F.A. Cup:** 2nd Rd 1887-88. 1st Rd 1975-76 1991-92. **F.A. Trophy:** Qtr Finals 77-78. **League clubs defeated:** None.

HONOURS - Northern Premier Lg R-up 92-93, Div 1 R-up 91-92, Lg Cup 92-93, Presidents Cup 92-93, Div 1 Cup SF 89-90; Cheshire County Lg 20-21 76-77 (R-up 74-75 79-80), Lg Cup 49-50 55-56 59-60 76-77 78-79 79-80 80-81 (R-up 36-37 68-69 77-78); Cheshire Snr Cup 58-59 79-80 92-93; Mid-Cheshire Snr Cup 90-91 92-93 (R-up 88-89); Cheshire Amateur Cup 00-01 02-03; Lancs Comb/Cheshire County Inter-Lg Cup 62-63.

Players progressing to Football League: W Foulkes (Chester 48), C Marsh (Leeds U. 48), B Nicol (Rochdale 49), E Johnson (Coventry 52), W Hughes (Liverpool 54), R Lewis (Luton 54), W Heggie (Accrington 55), J Richardson (Birmingham C. 59), J Abbott (Crewe Alex. 61), R Walters (Shrewsbury 62), P Mullington (Rochdale 78), Neville Southall (Bury 80), Mark Came (Bolton Wanderers 84), Dave Bamber (Blackpool), Bob Sutton (West Ham U.), J Richardson (Sheffield U.), Stanley Wood (W.B.A.), R Pearce (Luton T.).

Winsford United FC

WINSFORD UNITED - Match Facts 97-98

UCSC - Cheshire Senior Cup

Match No.	Date	Venue H / A	Comp.	Opponents	Result & Score		Att.	Goalscorers	League Position
1	23.08	A	UL	Accrington Stanley	L	1-2	*549*	Steele 74.	
2	25.08	H	UL	Colwyn Bay	W	2-0	360	Shaughnessy 37, Steele 61.	
3	30.08	H	UL	Guiseley	W	2-1	260	Russell 59, 63.	3
4	02.09	A	UL	Colwyn Bay	**W**	**3-0**	*323*	Wheeler 13, Shaughnessy 50, Steele 62.	1
5	13.09	H	**FAC 1Q**	Leek Town	W	1-0	287	Wheeler 11.	-
6	16.09	A	UL	Altrincham	W	1-0	*621*	Birmingham 66.	4
7	20.09	H	UL	Frickley Athletic	W	2-1	232	Wheeler 52, 80.	1
8	24.09	H	**UCSC 1**	Runcorn	D	*1-1	168	Steele 78.	-
9	27.09	A	**FAC 2Q**	Whitby Town	W	4-1	*582*	Shaughnessy 33, 36, Steele 81, Doherty 86.	-
10	30.09	A	**UCSC 1 R**	Runcorn	L	*1-2	*156*	Steele 35.	-
11	04.10	A	UL	Blyth Spartans	W	1-0	*462*	Steele 90.	3
12	08.10	H	UL	Runcorn	D	1-1	362	Doherty 72.	3
13	11.10	H	**FAC 3Q**	Arnold Town	D	1-1	480	Wheeler 82.	-
14	14.10	A	**FAC 3Q R**	Arnold Town	D	!0-0	*250*		(Won 7-6 after penalties)
15	18.10	H	**FAT 1Q**	Ilkeston Town	W	2-0	287	Steele 56, Fearon 75 (og).	-
16	21.10	A	UL	Radcliffe Borough	W	2-1	*152*	Russell 36, Aspinall 64.	4
17	25.10	H	**FAC 4Q**	Penrith	W	2-0	611	Talbot 23, Dulson 75.	-
18	29.10	H	**ULCC 2**	Congleton Town	D	3-3	147	Obeng 7, Dulson 72, O'Handjanian 80.	-
19	01.11	A	UL	Gainsborough Trinity	W	2-0	*544*	Limber 50 (og), Steele 78.	3
20	04.11	A	UL	Lancaster City	D	1-1	*153*	Steele 62.	3
21	08.11	H	**FAT 2Q**	Spennymoor United	W	1-0	293	Doherty 43.	-
22	11.11	A	**ULCC 2 R**	Congleton Town	L	2-3	*181*	O'Handjanian 10, Dulson 47.	-
23	15.11	A	**FAC 1**	Chester City	L	1-2	*3,885*	Steele 11.	-
24	19.11	H	UL	Bamber Bridge	L	0-1	215		9
25	22.11	H	UL	Emley	L	0-1	278		9
26	25.11	A	UL	Chorley	L	0-2	*216*		9
27	29.11	A	**FAT 3Q**	Matlock Town	D	1-1	*231*	Steele 23.	-
28	03.12	H	**FAT 3Q R**	Matlock Town	D	!0-0	168		(Won 5-3 after penalties)
29	06.12	A	UL	Spennymoor United	D	1-1	*169*	Shaughnessy 40.	9
30	09.12	A	UL	Frickley Athletic	L	1-3	*119*		
31	13.12	A	UL	Barrow	W	2-1	*991*	Wheeler 3, Byrne 45.	8
32	17.12	H	**ULCC 3**	Lancaster City	W	1-0	70	Byrne 22.	
33	20.12	H	UL	Boston United	D	0-0	222		10
34	26.12	A	UL	Marine	D	0-0	*405*		8
35	01.01	H	UL	Altrincham	W	2-1	444	Thomas 52, Taylor 86 (og).	8
36	03.01	A	UL	Hyde United	L	3-4	*687*	Peel 4, 74, Wheeler 9.	8
37	10.01	A	**FAT 1**	Southport	L	0-3	*996*		-
38	17.01	H	UL	Hyde United	D	1-1	252	Peel 39	8
39	24.01	A	UL	Emley	W	2-0	*298*	Bettingham 15, Steel 23.	7
40	28.01	H	UL	Marine	L	2-4	148	Connor 23, Thomas 47.	
41	31.01	A	UL	Boston United	L	1-2	*938*	Came 51.	8
42	07.02	H	UL	Radcliffe Borough	D	2-2	184	Birmingham 63, 87.	8
43	10.02	A	UL	Leigh RMI	L	0-2	*171*		8
44	14.02	A	UL	Bamber Bridge	W	3-2	*292*	Wheeler 3, OG (Sculpher) 33, Steele 34.	6
45	17.02	A	**ULCC 4**	Chorley	D	0-0	*280*		-
46	21.02	H	UL	Bishop Auckland	D	0-0	168		8
47	24.02	H	**ULCC 4 R**	Chorley	L	0-1	132		-
48	28.02	A	UL	Bishop Auckland	**L**	**0-6**	*120*		9
49	11.03	H	UL	Alfreton Town	D	0-0	75		10
50	14.03	H	UL	Blyth Spartans	**W**	**3-0**	158	Aspinall 30, 46, Peel 74.	10
51	21.03	H	UL	Chorley	W	1-0	193	Shaughnessy 72.	10
52	24.03	H	UL	Barrow	D	0-0	213		9
53	28.03	A	UL	Alfreton Town	W	1-0	*160*	Talbot 57.	8
54	01.04	H	UL	Leigh RMI	L	0-1	153		
55	04.04	A	UL	Guiseley	W	2-0	*300*	Thomas 21, Steele 53.	6
56	18.04	H	UL	Spennymoor United	W	1-0	134	Wheeler 82 (pen).	8
57	21.04	A	UL	Runcorn	D	2-2	*246*	Aspinall 57, Talbot 90 (pen).	
58	23.04	H	UL	Lancaster City	W	3-0	120	Hussin 4, Sahughnessy 15, Thomas 37.	7
59	25.04	H	UL	Gainsborough Trinity	D	1-1	147	Shaughnessy 12.	7
60	02.05	H	UL	Accrington Stanley	**W**	**3-0**	200	Wheeler 38, Steele 51, Hibbert 72.	7

PLAYING SQUAD 1998 **Goalkeepers:** Andy Oakes (Witton Alb, Burnley), Steve Roberts (Droylsden,Flixton, Broadheath Central, Flixton, Winsford U, Acc.Stanley, Chorley,Altrincham). **Defenders:** Gary Talbot (Barnton, Wilmslow Alb, Rhyl), Mark Came (Exeter C,Chester C, Bolton W, Winsford U), Ray Moss (Acc.Stanley, Marine), Eddie Hussin (Northwich V, Everton), Phil Greenhalgh (Cemaes Bay, Marine), Steve Aspinall (Knowsley U, Caernarfon T, Poulton V), Andy Burns (Leigh RMI, Acc.Stanley,Curzon Ashton, Wythenshawe Am). **Midfielders:** David German (Macclesfield T, Halifax T, Sheffield U), WinfieldSteele (Bury), Gary Thomas (Stalybridge C, Chorley, Southport, Witton Alb,Winsford U), Jason Danskin (Northwich V, Winsford U, Witton Alb, Mansfield T,Everton), Joe Connor (Radcliffe B, Runcorn, Witton Alb, Hyde U, Mossley, HydeU, Stockport Co). **Forwards:** Steve Shaughnessy (Leigh RMI, Droylsden, Flixton, Acc.Stanley,Stalybridge C, Runcorn, Maine Road, Tranmere R), Paul Wheeler (Leigh RMI,Stalybridge C, Chester C, Stockport Co, Hereford U, Hull C, Cardiff C,Aberaman, Bristol R), Nathan Peel (Macclesfield T, Clitheroe, Burnley,Sheffield U, Preston NE), Michael Moore (Southport, Altrincham, Liverpool), Darryl Dickin (Congleton T, Grove U), Daniel Gee (Barnton).

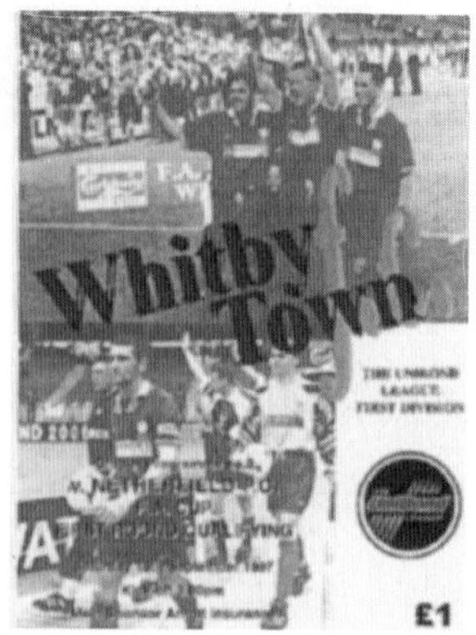

WHITBY TOWN

Colours: All Royal Blue
Change Colours: All white.
Midweek matchday: Tuesday
Reserve League: Teeside League
Local Newspapers: Whitby Gazette, Northern Echo.
Local Radio: Yorkshire Coast Radio

Formed: 1926
Nickname: Seasiders
Sponsors: Arnott Insurance

Chairman: Graham Manser. **President:** Brooks Mileson
Secretary: Charlie Woodward, 6 Westlands Ave, Whitby, North Yorks YO21 3DZ (01947 602312).
Manager: Harry Dunn **Asst Manager:** Mitch Cook
Press Officer: Secretary **Physio:** I Jackson

PROGRAMME DETAILS:
Pages: 40 **Price:** £1
Editor: C Woodward
(01947 602312)

GROUND Address: Turnbull Ground, Upgang Lane, Whitby, North Yorks (01947 604847). **Directions:** Take A174 road from town centre. Ground on offside travelling towards Sandsend.
Capacity: 3,200 **Cover:** 500 **Seats:** 300 **Floodlights:** Yes
Clubhouse: Mon-Fri 7-11pm, Sat 12-11pm, Sun 12-2 & 7-10.30.
Club Shop: Yes

PREVIOUS - **Leagues:** Northern League 1926-97. **Name:** Whitby United (pre 1950). **Grounds:** None

CLUB RECORDS - **Attendance:** 4,000 v Scarborough, N Riding Senior Cup 18/4/65 **Goalscorer:** Paul Pitman (364). **Appearances:** Paul Pitman (452). **Win:** 11-2 v Cargo Fleet Works 1950. **Defeat:** 3-13 v Willington 24/3/28. **Transfer Fee Paid:** £2,500 for John Grady (Newcastle Blue Star 90). **Received:** £5,000 for Graham Robinson (Gateshead 97)

BEST SEASON - **FA Vase:** Winners 97. **FA Amateur Cup:** Runner-up 1964-65 **FA Trophy:** Quarter Finals 1983-84 **FA Cup:** 2nd Round 83-84

HONOURS - NPL Div 1 97-98; Northern Lge 92-93 96-97 (R-up 27-28 63-64 67-68 81-82 82-83), Lg Cup 28-29 63-64 69-70 76-77 84-85 95-96; Rothmans National Cup 75-76 77-78; Nth Riding Snr Cup 64-65 67-68 82-83 89-90; N Riding Bene Cup 92-93; J R Cleator Cup 84-85 92-93 95-96 96-97; Mickey Skinner Trophy [5]

Players progressing to Football League: Malcolm Poskett (Hartlepool, Brighton, Watford, Sammy Kemp (Huddersfield), Jimmy Mulvaney (Hartlepool, Barrow, Stockport), Bobby Veart (Hartlepool), Derek Hampton & Trevor Smith & John Linacre & Phil Linacre (Hartlepool), Mark Hine (Grimsby). David Logan (Mansfield)

97-98 Captain: Neil Hodgson **P.o.Y.:** Andy Toman **Top scorer:** Paul Pitman (30)

Back Row (L-R); B Dewhirst (Coach), H Dunn (Mgr), D McGee, N Hodgson, G Williams, J Borthwick, D Goodchild, M Cook, B Hayes, K Goodrick, D Logan A Toman, C Hudson. Front Row; M Williams, P Hinton, J Francis, P Pitman, L Pearson, I Williams, D Ward, D Wheeler (Coach). Photo: Robert Townsend

WHITBY TOWN - Match Facts 97-98

NRSC - North Riding Senior Cup

Match No.	Date	Venue H/A	Comp.	Opponents	Result & Score		Att.	Goalscorers	League Position
1	23.08	H	UL	Workington	L	2-3	589	Toman 59, Fletcher 62.	
2	25.08	H	UL	Flixton	W	6-1	553	Pyle 21, Goodchild 29, Toman 32, 53, Pitman 58, OG (Ivison) 81.	
3	30.08	A	UL	Witton Albion	D	1-1	*506*	Fletcher 56.	6
4	09.09	A	UL	Workington	W	1-0	*193*	Fletcher 16.	7
5	13.09	H	**FAC 1Q**	Netherfield	W	6-2	560	**Pitman 3** (27,80(pen),86), Fletcher 56, OG(Holliday)68, Crawley 90(pen)	-
6	20.09	A	UL	Matlock Town	D	3-3	*322*	McGhee 56, Fletcher 67, 81.	11
7	24.09	A	UL	Bradford Park Ave.	D	1-1	*318*	Crawley 88.	12
8	27.09	H	**FAC 2Q**	Winsford United	L	1-4	582	Borthwick 3.	-
9	01.10	H	**ULCC 1**	Harrogate Town	W	6-1	297	Toman 12, 82, Fletcher 61, 76, Pitman 80, 90.	-
10	04.10	A	UL	Trafford	W	3-1	*237*	OG (Eaton) 60, Fletcher 81, Pitman 90.	9
11	08.10	H	UL	Bradford Park Ave.	W	5-2	515	Cook 23, Toman 28, Pitman 45, 53, Goodrick 71.	
12	11.10	H	UL	Whitley Bay	W	3-2	541	Pitman 28 (pen), Toman 37, Borthwick 51.	6
13	14.10	A	UL	Whitley Bay	W	3-1	*219*	Fletcher 6, Pitman 31, Goodrick 65.	5
14	18.10	A	**FAT 1Q**	Netherfield	D	1-1	*161*	Fletcher 44 (pen).	-
15	22.10	H	**FAT 1Q R**	Netherfield	D	3-3	481	Pitman 88, Goodrick 90, Toman 116. AET - Won 4-3 after pens.	-
16	25.10	H	UL	Belper Town	D	2-2	547	Logan 7, Cook 89.	5
17	29.10	A	UL	Farsley Celtic	W	2-1	*151*	Fletcher 26, Pyle 79.	
18	01.11	A	UL	Buxton	W	2-1	*213*	Crawley 37, McGhee 68.	4
19	04.11	A	**ULCC 2**	Spennymoor United	D	1-1	*178*	Young 65.	-
20	08.11	A	**FAT 2Q**	Hinckley United	L	1-3	*364*	Toman 11.	-
21	12.11	H	**ULCC 2 R**	Spennymoor United	L	0-1	404		-
22	15.11	H	UL	Matlock Town	W	1-0	479	Pitman 35.	4
23	19.11	H	**UFDC 1**	Whitley Bay	D	2-2	282	Baldwin 75, Currie 79.	-
24	22.11	A	UL	Congleton Town	W	2-1	*191*	Pitman 16, Hodgson 51.	4
25	25.11	A	**UFDC 1 R**	Whitley Bay	W	2-1	*138*	Pitman 5, Martin 35.	-
26	29.11	H	UL	Congleton Town	W	2-1	412	Hodgson 16, Pitman 81.	4
27	06.12	A	UL	Lincoln United	W	5-2	*141*	Currie 19, Goodrick 39, Pitman 46, Logan 66 (pen), Williams 70.	4
28	13.12	H	UL	Worksop Town	L	2-3	514	Pitman 29, Currie 31.	4
29	20.12	A	UL	Droylsden	W	3-2	*189*	Cook 10, Pearson 43, Borthwick 47.	3
30	27.12	H	UL	Harrogate Town	W	1-0	689	Pitman 85.	3
31	10.01	A	UL	Gretna	W	2-1	*132*	Pitman 44, Borthwick 77.	3
32	14.01	A	**NRSC 3**	Guisborough Town	W	1-0	*187*	Logan 112 (pen).	-
33	17.01	H	UL	Great Harwood Town	W	3-0	474	Cook 13, Borthwick 23, Pitman 45.	2
34	24.01	A	UL	Stocksbridge Park Steels	W	4-1	*287*	Cook 10, Pitman 56, 89, Borthwick 74.	2
35	31.01	H	UL	Gretna	W	2-0	596	Francis 4, Pitman 7.	2
36	04.02	A	**UFDC 2**	Bradford Park Avenue	L	0-2	*134*		-
37	07.02	A	UL	Worksop Town	W	3-1	*606*	**Toman 3** (16, 25, 53).	2
38	11.02	A	**NRSC 4**	Northallerton Town	W	6-0	170	Toman 13, Hinton 31, 87, Borthwick 36, 71, Cook 76.	-
39	14.02	A	UL	Great Harwood Town	**W**	**7-0**	*130*	**Borthwick 3** (6, 46, 89), Francis 9, 79, Pitman 22, Williams 74.	1
40	21.02	H	UL	Buxton	W	4-3	601	Hutson 22, Francis 26, Pitman 27, 48.	1
41	28.02	A	UL	Flixton	W	4-1	*231*	Pitman 49, 90, Logan 66, Williams 89.	1
42	04.03	H	UL	Netherfield	D	1-1	372	Goodchild 66.	1
43	07.03	H	UL	Ashton United	D	1-1	955	Borthwick 33.	1
44	14.03	H	UL	Trafford	W	2-1	573	Logan 61, Hinton 70.	1
45	21.03	A	UL	Eastwood Town	D	0-0	*201*		1
46	28.03	A	UL	Belper Town	W	1-0	*426*	Francis 28.	1
47	31.03	A	UL	Netherfield	W	1-0	*153*	Toman 1.	1
48	04.04	H	UL	Witton Albion	W	4-1	546	Toman 14, Hodgson 44, 73, Francis 48.	1
49	08.04	H	UL	Farsley Celtic	W	2-1	544	Borthwick 30, Francis 90.	1
50	13.04	A	UL	Harrogate Town	D	1-1	*532*	Goodchild 66.	1
51	18.04	H	UL	Droylsden	W	1-0	704	Toman 40.	1
52	22.04	H	UL	Lincoln United	**L**	**3-5**	616	G Williams 39, Borthwick 52, Cook 80 (pen).	1
53	25.04	H	UL	Eastwood Town	W	2-0	585	Pitman 31, Toman 55.	1
54	29.04	H	UL	Stocksbridge Park Steels	W	1-0	639	Goodchild 71.	1
55	02.05	A	UL	Ashton United	L	0-2	*403*		1
56	04.05	H	**NRSC 5**	Stockton	W	3-0			-

PLAYING SQUAD 1998 - **Goalkeepers:** David Campbell (Guisborough T, South Bank)
Defenders: Dave Goodchild (Nth Ormesby), Graeme Williams (Guisborough T,Aston Villa), Lawrie Pearson (Blyth Spartans, Gateshead, Darlington,Chesterfield, Bristol C, Hull C, Gateshead), Ian Williams (Shildon), DavidLogan (B Auckland, Northallerton T, Billingham Syn, Scarborough, Stockport Co,Halifax T, Northampton T, Mansfield T, Whitby T), Alan Martin (EasingtonColl), Chris Hudson (Pickering T), Mitch Cook (Scarborough, Guiseley,Blackpool, Darlington, Halifax T, Scarborough, Middlesbrough, Darlington,Scarborough), Paul Hobbs (Scarborough). **Midfielders:** Neil Hodgson (Guisborough T), Dean McGee (Billingham T,Guisborough T, Sunderland), Brian Crawley (Hibernians (Malta), Floriana(Malta), Whitby T, B Auckland, Whitby T, Guisborough T), Kenny Goodrick (Spennymoor U, Whitby T, Gretna, Ferryhill Ath), Lee Tucker (Guisborough T,Spennymoor U, Darlington, Middlesbrough), John Borthwick (Tow Law T, BAuckland, Gateshead, York C, Darlington, Hartlepool U, Owton Social). **Forwards:** Paul Pitman (Nth Shields, Easington CW), Andy Toman (Scarborough,Scunthorpe U, Darlington, Hartlepool U, B Auckland, Lincoln C, B Auckland), John Francis (Lancaster C, Guiseley, Farsley C, Halifax T, Scunthorpe U,Burnley, Cambridge U, Burnley, Sheffield U, Halifax T, Emley), Darren Ward (Tees Components)

PROGRAMME DETAILS:
Pages: 28-32 **Price:** £1
Editor: Mel Bradley
(01909 500491/500500)

WORKSOP TOWN

Colours: Amber & black/white/white **Formed:** 1861
Change colours: All white/amber/black trim **Nickname:** The Tigers
Midweek home matchday: Tuesday.
Reserve Team's League: Birmingham Prem.
Youth Team's Lge: U21's Central Mid, U18's Notts Imp.
Local Press: Worksop Guardian, Worksop Star, Nottingham Football Post.
Local Radio: Radio Sheffield, Radio Hallam, Radio Lincoln.

Chairman: Rick Knowles **Vice Chairman:** John Shuker
Club Secretary: Keith Illett, 2 Mount Avenue, Worksop, Notts (01909 487934)
General Manager: Paul Mitchell **Company Secretary:** Mel Bradley
Asst Manager: Danny Hague **Physio:** Graham Bacon
Press Officer: Mel Bradley **Commercial Manager:** Kevin Barratt

GROUND Address: Babbage Way, off Sandy Lane, Worksop, Notts S80 1UJ (01909 501911). **Directions:** M1 jct 31 (from north) jct 30 (from south), follow Worksop signs, join A57 and follow signs for Sandy Lane Industrial Estate - ground on left. 5 mins walk from station.
Capacity: 2,500 **Cover:** 1,000 **Seats:** 450 **Floodlights:** Yes.
Clubhouse: Tigers Club. Normal licensing hours. Pool, quiz nights, disco etc.
Club Shop: The Tigershop selling badges, scarves, magazines, programmes. 30 page catalogue from Steve Jarvis, 10 Wood End Drive, Ravenshead, Notts NG15 9EJ.

Sponsors: D.T.H. Engineers/Eyres of Worksop/Norwood Fisheries/Erriccsons

PREVIOUS - **Grounds:** Netherton Road, Bridge Meadow, Central Avenue (pre 1989), The Northolme (Gainsborough Trinity - shared) 89-92. **Leagues:** Midland (Counties) 1896-98 1900-30 49-60 61-68 69-74, Sheffield Assoc. 1898-99 1931-33, Central Comb. 33-35, Yorkshire 35-39, Central All. 47-49 60-61, Northern Premier 68-69, 74-

CLUB RECORDS - **Attendance:** 1,503 v Sheffield Utd, friendly. *Central Avenue: 8,171 v Chesterfield, FA Cup 1925.* **Goalscorer:** Kenny Clark, 287. **Appearances:** Kenny Clark 347. **Win:** 20-0 v Staveley, 1/9/1894. **Defeat:** 1-11 v Hull City Res., 55-56. **Fees Received:** £10,000 Martin Hardy, Boston U. 87.

BEST SEASON - **FA Cup:** 3rd Rd: 1907-08 v Chelsea (A) 1-9, 21-22 v Southend (H) 1-2, 22-23 v Spurs (A) 0-0 & 0-9, 55-56 v Swindon (A) 0-1. 2nd Rd: 25-26, 1st Rd: 20-21, 26-27, 61-62, 78-79. **League Clubs defeated:** Rotherham Town 1894-95, Grimsby Town 94-95, Nelson 1921-22, Chesterfield 22-23, Coventry City 25-26, Bradford City 55-56. **FA Trophy:** 2nd Rd replay 73-74.

HONOURS - N.P.L. Presidents Cup 85-86 95-96, Midland Cos Lg 21-22 65-66 72-73 (R-up 62-63 66-67 73-74), Sheffield Assoc. Lg 1898-99, Sheffield & Hallamshire Snr Cup 23-24 52-53 54-55 65-66 69-70 72-73 81-82 84-85 96-97, Mansfield Charity Cup 22-23.

Players progressing to Football League: J Brown (Sheff Wed), G Dale (Chesterfield 48), A Daley (Doncaster 50), K Wood (Grimsby 51), H Jarvis (Notts Co. 51), B Taylor (Leeds 51), S Rhodes 51, D Gratton 52, A Hodgkinson 53, J Harrison 67 (Sheffield Utd), S Lloyd & P Marshall (Scunthorpe 54), A Rhodes (QPR 54), R Moore (Rotherham 55), H Mosby (Crewe 1956), L Moore (Derby 1957), H Bowery (Nottm Forest 75), T Moore (Rochdale 84), S Adams (Scarborough 87), D Moss (Doncaster 93).

97-98 Captain: Darren Dye **P.o.Y.:** Jamie Holmshaw **Top scorer:**

Back Row (L-R); Rick Knowles (Chr), P Stafford, N Robinson, J Maybury, D Bonnington, J Holmshaw, T Morris, D Cutts, D Dye, A Womble, K Illett (Sec). Front Row; D Campbell, L Howard, T Harris, L Whitehead, S Johnson, D Scott, P Wood, G Townsend.

WORKSOP TOWN - Match Facts 97-98

S&HSC - Sheffield & Hallamshire Senior Cup

Match No.	Date	Venue H / A	Comp.	Opponents	Result & Score		Att.	Goalscorers	League Position
1	23.08	A	UL-1	Congelton Town	W	1-0	*181*	Womble.	
2	25.08	H	UL-1	Matlock Town	W	3-1	610	Johnson, Stafford, Walsh.	
3	30.08	A	**FAC Pre**	Guisborough Town	W	3-2	*216*	Howard, Stafford, Harris.	-
4	07.09	H	UL-1	Workington	W	3-0	401	Robinson, Wood, Walsh.	
5	09.09	H	UL-1	Trafford	D	1-1	408	Stafford.	
6	13.09	H	**FAC 1 Q**	Oldham Town	W	4-2	386	Townsend 2, Whitehead, Harris.	-
7	22.09	A	UL-1	Ashton United	L	1-2	*230*	Dye.	
8	27.09	A	**FAC 2 Q**	Brigg Town	D	1-1	*341*	Townsend.	-
9	30.09	H	**FAC 2 Q R**	Brigg Town	W	3-1	364	Whitehead 2, Robinson.	-
10	04.10	H	UL-1	Ashton United	L	1-2	418	Whitehead.	12
11	07.10	H	**ULCC 1**	Eastwood Town	L	1-4	333	Atkinson.	-
12	11.10	A	**FAC 3 Q**	Blyth Spartans	L	0-4	*596*		-
13	14.10	A	UL-1	Droylsden	L	0-1	*156*		16
14	18.10	A	**FAT 1 Q**	Whitley Bay	W	1-0	*173*	Hobson.	-
15	21.10	H	UL-1	Bradford Park Avenue	W	1-0	321	Campbell.	
16	25.10	H	UL-1	Harrogate Town	D	3-3	334	Walsh, Harris, Whitehead.	13
17	28.10	A	UL-1	Buxton	W	1-0	*229*	D Johnson	
18	04.11	H	**S&HSC 1**	Sheffield Bankers	W	5-1	176	Dye 2, Whitehead, Womble, Harris.	-
19	08.11	A	**FAT 2 Q**	Redditch	W	3-1	*277*	Hobson, Johnson, D Johnson.	-
20	12.11	A	UL-1	Bradford Park Avenue	W	3-2	*228*	Whitehead 2, D Johnson.	
21	15,11	H	UL-1	Flixton	W	3-0	349	Walsh, Townsend, Stafford.	9
22	18.11	H	UL-1	Belper Town	D	0-0	352		
23	22.11	H	UL-1	Netherfield	W	4-1	324	Atkinson, Johnson, Townsend, Howard.	7
24	24.11	A	**ULPC 1**	Ashton United	L	1-2	*133*	Wood.	-
25	29.11	A	**FAT 3 Q**	Bromsgrove Rovers	W	2-1	*517*	Stafford, D Johnson.	-
26	06.12	H	UL-1	Congleton Town	W	5-1	357	**Stafford 3,** Walsh, Wood.	7
27	09.12	H	**S&HSC 2**	Rossington Main	W	5-0	207	Howard, Whitehead, Wood, Womble, D Johnson.	-
28	13.12	A	UL-1	Whitby Town	W	3-2	*415*	D Johnson 2, Walsh.	6
29	16.12	A	UC 2	Stocksbridge Park Steels	L	0-1	*192*		-
30	20.12	H	UL-1	Great Harwood Town	W	3-0	370	Walsh, Hobson, D Johnson.	6
31	27.12	A	UL-1	Stocksbridge Park Steels	L	0-1	*610*		6
32	02.01	H	UL-1	Lincoln United	W	3-0	618	Walsh, Whitehead, D Johnson.	6
33	10.01	A	**FAT 1**	Barrow	D	1-1	*1,199*	Whitehead.	-
34	13.01	H	**FAT 1 R**	Barrow	L	2-4	1,044	Whitehead 2.	-
35	17.01	H	UL-1	Stocksbridge Park Steels	L	1-2	439	Howard.	6
36	20.01	A	**S&HSC 3**	Maltby Main	W	3-2	*200*	Whitehead 2, Stafford.	-
37	24.01	A	UL-1	Gretna	W	3-2	*120*	Johnson, D Johnson.	6
38	31.01	H	UL-1	Witton Albion	W	2-0	480	Johnson 2.	6
39	04.02	A	UL-1	Farsley Celtic	D	1-1	*155*	Whitehead.	
40	07.02	H	UL-1	Whitby Town	**L**	**1-3**	606	Whitehead.	7
41	14.02	A	UL-1	Netherfield	**W**	**6-2**	*123*	Harris 2, Johnson, Walsh, Stafford, Womble.	6
42	21.02	A	UL-1	Witton Allbion	W	2-1	*385*	Womble 2.	5
43	28.02	H	UL-1	Whitley Bay	W	2-0	405	Johnson, Townsend.	4
44	03.03	A	UL-1	Belper Town	W	4-0	*302*	Townsend 2, Whitehead, Stafford.	
45	07.03	H	UL-1	Farsley Celtic	W	2-0	439	Hirst, Johnson.	4
46	09.03	A	**S&HSC SF**	Emley	L	1-3	*305*	D Johnson.	-
47	14.03	A	UL-1	Whitley Bay	W	3-1	*224*	Johnson, D Johnson, Townsend.	3
48	21.03	A	UL-1	Flixton	D	1-1	*233*	Johnson.	3
49	24.03	H	UL-1	Eastwood Town	W	3-1	563	Stafford 2, Hirst.	
50	28.03	A	UL-1	Trafford	W	2-1	*251*	Whitehead, Townsend.	3
51	31.03	A	UL-1	Lincoln United	L	0-1	*339*		
52	04.04	H	UL-1	Droylsden	D	2-2	473	Hirst, Walsh.	3
53	11.04	A	UL-1	Workington	W	4-0	*270*	Whitehead 2, D Johnson, Howard.	2
54	13.04	A	UL-1	Matlock Town	W	2-1	*649*	Walsh, Harris.	2
55	19.04	H	UL-1	Gretna	W	3-2	903	Townsend 2, D Johnson.	2
56	21.04	A	UL-1	Eastwood Town	D	2-2	*361*	Johnson, Harris.	2
57	25.04	H	UL-1	Buxton	W	3-2	775	Todd, OG, Whitehead.	2
58	02.05	A	UL-1	Great Harwood Town	W	3-2	*350*	Whitehead, Jones, Walsh.	2

PLAYING SQUAD 1998 - **Goalkeepers:** Richard Harrison (Belper T, Matlock T, Farsley C, Frickley Ath,Sheffield U), Jamie Holmshaw (Gainsborough Trin). **Defenders:** Neil Beech (Harworth Cl, Alfreton T, Gainsborough Trin, SheffieldU), Tony Morris (Alfreton T, Worksop T), Lee Hobson (Frecheville Comm), Dave McNicholas (Matlock T, Goole T, Matlock T, Goole T, Barnsley), Tim Atkinson (Alfreton T, Rotherham U, Sheffield U), Darren Dye (Grantham T, Lincoln U,Lincoln Moorlands), David Cutts (Alfreton T, Matlock T, Boston U, Glapwell). **Midfielders:** Ryan Jones (Sheffield Wed), Linden Whitehead (Alfreton T,Worksop T), Matt Walsh (Alfreton T, Leek T, Alfreton T, Stafford R, BradfordC, Swansea C), Steve Johnson (Buxton, Matlock T, Alfreton T, Buxton, MatlockT), Ian Askey (Alfreton T, Sheffield Aurora), Mark Todd (Gainsborough Trin,Blyth S, Telford U, Stalybridge C, Rotherham U, Sheffield U, Manchester U), Lee Howard (Eastwood T, King's Lynn, Harworth Cl, Mansfield T, Nottingham F). **Forwards:** David Johnson (Altrincham, Lincoln C, Sheffield Wed), Phil Stafford (Alfreton T, Ashfield U, Sheffield Aurora, Sutton T, Frickley Ath, Denaby U,Sheffield, Goole T, Gainsborough Trin), Gavin Townsend (Youth team), Danny Campbell (Wombwell T, Sheffield Wed), Andy Womble (Belper T, Lincoln U,Gainsborough Trin, Belper T, Glapwell), Jamie Creaghan (Sheffield, Hucknall T,Hallam, Chesterfield), Dave Brocklehurst (Buxton, Staveley MW, Eastwood T,Sheffield U), Terry Harris (Grantham T, Bridlington T, Grantham T, KetteringT, Grantham T, Enfield, Sheffield U, Norseman, Enfield).

ALFRETON TOWN - Match Facts 97-98

Match No.	Date	Venue H / A	Comp.	Opponents	Result & Score		Att.	Goalscorers	League Position
1	23.08	H	UL-P	Frickley Athletic	W	2-1	162	Macrow 37, 68.	
2	27.08	A	UL-P	Boston United	L	0-2	*863*		
3	30.08	H	UL-P	Accrington Stanley	L	0-1	262		18
4	03.09	A	UL-P	Gainsborough Trinity	L	0-4	*474*		20
5	09.09	H	UL-P	Altrincham	L	0-3	324		21
6	13.09	A	**FAC 1Q**	Guiseley	L	0-3	*379*		-
7	16.09	H	UL-P	Guiseley	D	1-1	149	Hammond 61.	22
8	20.09	H	UL-P	Bamber Bridge	L	1-2	165	Weston 30.	22
9	23.09	A	UL-P	Frickley Athletic	L	1-2	*162*	Cunningham 70.	22
10	27.09	H	UL-P	Barrow	L	0-3	206		22
11	30.09	A	**ULCC 1**	Matlock Town	D	1-1	*281*	Dempsey 40.	-
12	04.10	A	UL-P	Marine	L	0-2	*297*		22
13	07.10	H	UL-P	Gainsborough Trinity	L	2-3	273	Dempsey 8, Brady 39.	22
14	11.10	H	**ULCC 1 R**	Matlock Town	L	1-3	223	Brady 90.	-
15	18.10	A	**FAT 1Q**	Buxton	W	1-0	*234*	Brady 65.	-
16	21.10	A	UL-P	Guiseley	W	2-1	*263*	Cunningham 3, Brady 11.	
17	25.10	H	UL-P	Radcliffe Borough	L	0-2	175		22
18	01.11	A	UL-P	Barrow	L	0-2	*938*		22
19	08.11	A	**FAT 2Q**	Solihull Borough	L	1-9	*188*	Adams 88.	-
20	15.11	H	UL-P	Runcorn	L	1-3	141	Brady 13.	22
21	22.11	H	UL-P	Lancaster City	D	1-1	153	Schofield 48.	22
22	29.11	A	UL-P	Chorley	L	0-2	*288*		22
23	07.12	A	UL-P	Runcorn	L	1-3	*295*	Adams 44.	22
24	09.12	H	UL-P	Hyde United	D	0-0	154		22
25	13.12	H	UL-P	Colwyn Bay	D	1-1	149	Dring 28.	22
26	20.12	A	UL-P	Hyde United	L	1-4	*364*	Bullivant 84.	22
27	27.12	H	UL-P	Bishop Auckland	L	2-6	279	Connerley 21, Dolby 61.	22
28	10.01	A	UL-P	Radcliffe Borough	D	1-1	*186*	Sissons 71.	22
29	13.01	H	**DSC 3**	Mickleover	W	1-0	89	Dempsey 86.	-
30	17.01	H	UL-P	Emley	D	1-1	354	Dempsey 34.	22
31	24.01	H	UL-P	Spennymoor United	L	2-3	208	Sisson 62, Pickering 70 (pen).	22
32	31.01	A	UL-P	Blyth Spartans	L	2-4	*467*	OG (Farrey) 20, Pickering 86 (pen).	22
33	07.02	H	UL-P	Marine	D	0-0	178		22
34	10.02	A	**DSC 4**	Glossop North End	L	0-3	*75*		-
35	14.02	A	UL-P	Altrincham	**L**	**0-5**	*612*		22
36	21.02	A	UL-P	Lancaster City	D	1-1	*275*	Ward 58.	22
37	28.02	H	UL-P	Chorley	D	1-1	165	Taylor 69.	22
38	07.03	H	UL-P	Blyth Spartans	L	0-3	195		22
39	11.03	A	UL-P	Winsford United	D	0-0	*75*		22
40	14.03	A	UL-P	Spennymoor United	D	1-1	*165*		22
41	21.03	A	UL-P	Colwyn Bay	L	0-3	*261*		22
42	28.03	H	UL-P	Winsford United	L	0-1	160		22
43	01.04	A	UL-P	Bishop Auckland	D	1-1	*88*	Ward 12.	22
44	04.04	A	UL-P	Emley	L	0-2	*243*		22
45	11.04	A	Ul-p	Bamber Bridge	L	1-4	*260*	Storey 33.	22
46	13.04	H	UL-P	Boston United	L	1-2	285	Stacey 46.	22
47	18.04	H	UL-P	Leigh RMI	**W**	**3-2**	130	Weston 48, Stacey 69, McCann 89.	22
48	25.04	A	UL-P	Accrington Stanley	D	1-1	*470*	Stacey 47.	22
49	02.05	A	UL-P	Leigh RMI	L	0-1	*159*		22

DSC - Derbyshire Senior Cup

RADCLIFFE BOROUGH - Match Facts 97-98

Match No.	Date	Venue H/A	Comp.	Opponents	Result & Score		Att.	Goalscorers	League Position
1	23.08	A	UL-P	Guiseley	L	1-4	*429*	McDonald 66.	
2	25.08	H	UL-P	Accrington Stanley	L	1-2	485	Connor 44.	
3	30.08	H	UL-P	Colwyn Bay	D	1-1	255	Whittle 38.	21
4	02.09	A	UL-P	Leigh RMI	D	0-0	*281*		21
5	07.09	A	UL-P	Boston United	D	2-2	*980*	Lunt 1, OG (Fee) 40.	20
6	13.09	H	**FAC 1Q**	Bishop Auckland	L	1-3	257	McCrory 40.	-
7	16.09	A	UL-P	Marine	W	2-1	*235*	Lunt 21, Allen 89.	17
8	20.09	H	UL-P	Bishop Auckland	L	1-2	182	Lunt 23.	11
9	23.09	A	UL-P	Barrow	L	0-3	*1,142*		20
10	27.09	H	UL-P	Spennymoor United	L	0-2	147		20
11	30.09	H	**ULCC 1**	Great Harwood Town	W	3-0	76	McCrory 60, Connor 61, Senior 80.	-
12	04.10	A	UL-P	Gainsborough Trinity	L	0-3	*506*		20
13	07.10	H	UL-P	Lancaster City	**W**	**6-2**	174	Whittel 1, Lunt 59, Connor 61, Astle 71, Lyons 83, McCrory 85.	19
14	11.10	A	UL-P	Lancaster City	W	1-0	*189*	Brierley 12.	18
15	14.10	A	UL-P	Runcorn	**L**	**3-6**	*233*	McCrory 17, 77, Connor 52.	18
16	21.10	H	UL-P	Winsford United	L	0-2	152		
17	25.10	A	UL-P	Alfreton Town	W	2-0	*175*	Lunt 65 (pen), Bean 70.	15
18	28.10	H	**ULCC 2**	Leigh RMI	D	0-0	141		-
19	01.11	H	UL-P	Boston United	D	1-1	244	Edwards 44.	17
20	08.11	H	**FAT 2Q**	Leigh RMI	D	1-1	267	Lunt 70.	-
21	11.11	A	**FAT 2Q R**	Leigh RMI	L	0-1	*201*		-
22	15.11	A	UL-P	Altrincham	L	0-3	*706*		19
23	18.11	H	**ATS 1**	Darwen	W	2-0	108	Connor 21, Lunt 86.	-
24	22.11	H	UL-P	Blyth Spartans	L	1-2	201	Lunt 9.	20
25	25.11	H	**ULPC 1**	Runcorn	D	0-0	155		-
26	29.11	A	UL-P	Bishop Auckland	L	0-3	*161*		21
27	06.12	H	UL-P	Chorley	L	1-2	218	Lunt 55.	21
28	13.12	H	UL-P	Runcorn	D	0-0	178		
29	16.12	A	**ULCC 2 R**	Leigh RMI	L	0-2	*101*		-
30	20.12	S	UL-P	Colwyn Bay	L	1-2	263	Russell 15.	21
31	26.12	H	UL-P	Hyde United	D	0-0	375		
32	01.01	A	UL-P	Accrington Stanley	D	2-2	*662*	Carroll 10, Bean 72.	21
33	10.01	H	UL-P	Alfreton Town	D	1-1	181	McHugh 43.	21
34	17.01	A	UL-P	Spennymoor United	D	1-1	*167*	Carroll 90.	21
35	21.01	H	**ATS 2**	Barrow	L	0-1	113		-
36	24.01	A	UL-P	Frickley Athletic	L	0-1	*142*		21
37	27.01	A	**MPC 2**	Oldham Town	W	1-0	*80*	Bean 73.	-
38	31.01	H	UL-P	Gainsborough Trinity	L	1-3	163	McHugh 71.	21
39	07.02	A	UL-P	Winsford United	D	2-2	*184*	Bean 76, Carroll 90 (pen).	21
40	10.02	A	**ULPC 1 R**	Runcorn	L	1-3	*166*	Whittle 63 (pen).	-
41	17.02	H	UL-P	Altrincham	L	0-1	334		21
42	23.02	A	UL-P	Emley	L	0-2	*185*		21
43	28.02	A	UL-P	Hyde United	W	1-0	*410*	Brown 45.	21
44	03.03	H	UL-P	Leigh RMI	L	0-1	144		21
45	10.03	A	**MPC SF**	Curzon Ashton	W	*2-1	*98*	Carroll 92, Whittle 118. AET	-
46	18.03	H	UL-P	Guiseley	L	0-2	113		21
47	21.03	A	UL-P	Blyth Spartans	L	0-1	*467*		21
48	28.03	H	UL-P	Marine	L	0-3	204		21
49	31.03	A	UL-P	Chorley	D	1-1	*239*	McCrory 90.	21
50	04.04	A	UL-P	Bamber Bridge	L	0-1	*374*		21
51	11.04	H	UL-P	Emley	L	1-2	228	Lunt 2.	21
52	15.04	H	UL-P	Barrow	L	1-2	254	Carroll 6.	21
53	21.04	H	UL-P	Bamber Bridge	W	3-0	143	Astley 20, Carroll 32, Levendis 60.	21
54	29.04	N	**MPC Final**	Glossop North End	L	0-1	*866*	Played at Manchester City FC.	-
55	02.05	H	UL-P	Frickley Athletic	D	1-1	137	Farrelly 85.	21

MSC - Manchester Sen. Cup ATS - Lancashire `ATS' Trophy

UNIBOND DIVISION ONE

Final League Table	P	HOME W	D	L	F	A	AWAY W	D	L	F	A	PTS	GD
1 Whitby Town	42	15	3	3	50	27	15	5	1	49	21	98	51
2 Worksop Town	42	14	4	3	49	21	14	3	4	44	23	91	49
3 Ashton United	42	16	2	3	50	24	10	7	4	43	19	87	50
4 Droylsden	42	13	3	5	39	25	11	5	5	31	24	80	21
5 Lincoln United	42	11	5	5	37	25	9	6	6	39	37	71	14
6 Farsley Celtic	42	11	6	4	41	28	9	4	8	31	38	70	6
7 Witton Albion	42	11	5	5	44	20	8	4	9	33	35	66	22
8 Eastwood Town	42	8	10	3	36	25	10	2	9	32	26	66	17
9 Bradford Park Ave.	42	9	5	7	37	24	9	6	6	25	22	65	16
10 Belper Town	42	10	2	9	37	38	8	5	8	31	28	61	2
11 Stocksbridge Park S.	42	10	5	6	38	29	7	4	10	30	34	60	5
12 Trafford	42	9	3	9	29	25	7	3	11	30	36	54	-2
13 Whitley Bay	42	7	6	8	32	30	7	6	8	28	33	54	-3
14 Matlock Town	42	10	4	7	44	28	4	7	10	24	36	53	4
15 Gretna	42	8	6	7	32	26	5	3	13	26	38	48	-6
16 Netherfield	42	8	2	11	32	42	4	9	8	23	33	47	0
17 Flixton	42	6	6	9	22	27	4	6	11	23	46	42	-28
18 Congleton Town	42	7	5	9	32	42	4	3	14	33	59	41	-36
19 Harrogate Town	42	4	8	9	26	34	4	6	11	31	46	38	-23
20 Great Harwood Town	42	2	8	11	21	43	6	4	11	20	45	36	-47
21 Workington	42	4	3	14	18	40	4	4	13	20	44	31	-46
22 Buxton	42	4	2	15	24	40	3	1	17	17	47	24	-56

FIRST DIVISION CUP 1997-98

FIRST ROUND

Belper Town 5 v 2 Congleton Town
Gretna 2 v 0 Workington
Matlock Town 1 v 2 Eastwood Town
Netherfield 0 v 2 Great Harwood Town
Whitley Bay 1 v 2 Whitby Town
After 2-2
Witton Albion 0 v 2 Trafford

SECOND ROUND

Belper Town 3 v 2 Buxton
Bradford Park Ave. 2 v 0 Whitby Town
Droylsden 4 v 2 Flixton
Eastwood Town 0 v 1 Farsley Celtic
Great Harwood Town 0 v 1 Ashton United
After 1-1
Harrogate Town 2 v 3 Lincoln United
Stocksbridge P.S. 1 v 0 Worksop Town
Trafford 2 v 0 Gretna

THIRD ROUND

Belper Town 1 v 2 Ashton United
Bradford Park Ave. 3 v 1 Droylsden
After 1-1
Farsley Celtic 0 v 3 Lincoln United
Stocksbridge P.S. 2 v 3 Trafford

SEMI-FINALS (Two legs)

Ashton United 2 v 4 Lincoln United
Lincoln United 0 v 1 Ashton United
Trafford 1 v 2 Bradford Park Ave.
Bradford Park Ave. 0 v 2 Trafford

FINAL (at Lincoln Utd. FC)

Lincoln United 1 v 3 Trafford
After Extra Time

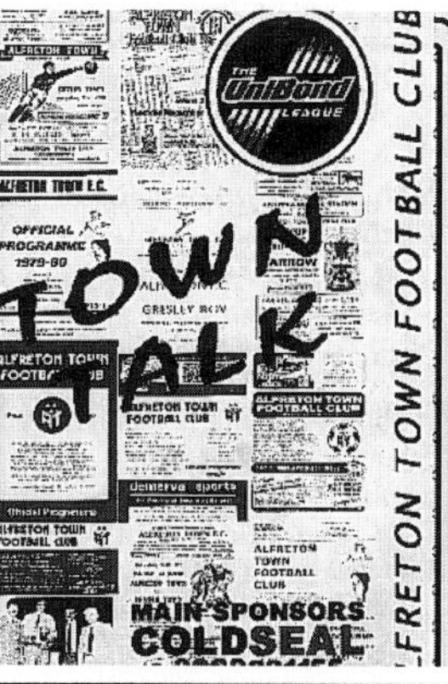

PROGRAMME DETAILS:
Pages: 32 **Price:** £1
Editor: Chris Tacey
(01302 722415)

ALFRETON TOWN

Colours: Red & white/red/red **Formed:** 1959
Change colours: Yellow/blue/yellow. **Nickname:** The Reds
Midweek home matchday: Tuesday **Sponsors:** Coldseal Windows
Reserve League: None, Under 13s & 12s
Local Press: Derbyshire Times, Derby Evening Telegraph, Chad, Ripley & Heanor News. **Local Radio:** Radio Derby.

Chairman: Sean Egan **Secretary:** Roger Taylor, 9 Priory Rd, Alfreton, Derbys. DE55 7JT (01773 835121).
Vice Chairman: Dave Gregory
Manager: Dave McCarthy
Coach: Russ Eagle **Physio:** Kevin Grundy

GROUND - Address: Town Ground, North Street, Alfreton, Derbyshire (01773 830277). **Directions:** M1 junction 28 and follow A38 towards Derby for 1 mile, left onto B600, right at main road to town centre and after half a mile turn left down North Street - ground on right. Half mile from Alfreton (BR) station. Buses 242 & 243 from both Derby and Mansfield.
Capacity: 5,000 **Cover:** 1,000 **Seats:** 350 **Floodlights:** Yes
Clubhouse: Clubhouse on ground for members. Hot & cold food & drinks available on ground. Supporters Club just outside ground open 11-4pm matchdays and 7-11pm evenings.
Club Shop: Sells programmes & club souvenirs. Contact Brian Thorpe, 13 Oakland St., Alfreton. (01773 836251)

PREVIOUS - **Leagues:** Central Alliance *(before reformation 21-25)* 59-61/ Midland (Counties) *25-27* 61-82/ Northern Counties (East) 82-87.

CLUB RECORDS: - **Attendance:** 5,023 v Matlock Tn, Central All 60. **Scorer:** J Harrison 303. **Appearances:** J Harrison 560. **Win:** 15-0 v Loughborough, Midland Lge. 69-70. **Defeat:** 1-9 v Solihull FA Trophy 97, 0-8 v Bridlington 92. **Fees - Paid:** £1,000 for R Mountain (Matlock). **Received:** £7,000 for Paul Eshelby (Ilkeston Tn 96-97)

BEST SEASON - **FA Trophy:** 1st Rd Proper 94-95. **FA Cup:** 1st Rd 3rd replay 69-70. Also 1st Rd 73-74. - **League clubs defeated:** Lincoln 24-25, but none since club's reformation in 1959.

HONOURS - Northern Counties (E) Lg 84-85 (Lg Cup 84-85); Midland Cou Lg 69-70 73-74 76-77 (R-up 71-72 80-81 81-82), Lg Cup 71-72 72-73 73-74; Derbyshire Sen Cup 60-61 69-70 72-73 73-74 81-82 94-95 (R-up 62-63 64-65 77-78 79-80 84-85 87-88 92-93) Div Cup (N) 64-65; Evans Halshaw Floodlit Cup 87-88 95-96; Cent All Lg. R-Up 63-64; NPL Div 1 R-Up 95-96.

Players progressing to Football League: M Wright (68), A Kowalski (73), A Henson (81), Philip Greaves (86) (All Chesterfield), A Woodward (Grimsby T. 70), A Taylor (Chelsea 72), R Greenhough Chester C. 85), K Smith (Exeter C. 89).

97-98 - Captain: Neil Pickering **Top Scorer:** A Brady (5) **P.o.Y.:** Neil Pickering

Back Row (L-R); Mark Dempsey, Matt Warren, Craig Weston, Duncan Roberts, Ian Dring, Martin Connelly, Wayne Adams, Neil Pickering, Andy Glenister, Russ Eagle. Front Row; Darren Schofield, John Noble, Dean Bartholomew, Jamie Bullivant, Aaron Brady, Andy Taylor Photo: Bill Wheatcroft

ASHTON UNITED

PRICE 80p
The Robins welcome you to Hurst Cross!
ASHTON
UNITED
FOOTBALL
CLUB
THE UniBond LEAGUE
"THE ROBINS"
SEASON
1997 - 1998
DIVISION ONE
OFFICIAL
MATCHDAY
PROGRAMME
ASHTON UNITED
v
FLIXTON
Unibond League Challenge Cup

PROGRAMME DETAILS:
Pages: 22 **Price:** £1
Editor: Debbie Quaile
Tel: 01457 834208 H
0161 200 4925 W

Colours: Red & white halves/black/red
Change colours: All yellow
Midweek matchday: Monday
Local Press: Ashton Reporter, Ashton Advertiser
Local Radio: GMR

Formed: 1878
Club Sponsors:
Nickname: Robins

Chairman: T N Styring **President:** D C N Jones
Vice Chairman: J Milne
Secretary: Debbie Quaile, 19 Quickwood, off Carrhill Road, Mossley, Lancs OL5 0SF (H 01457 834208, B 0161 200 4925, Mob 07970 175652)
Manager: John Coleman **Asst Manager:** Jimmy Bell
Press Officer: T Liversidge **Physio:** Chris Moseley
GROUND Address: Surrey Street, Hurst Cross, Ashton-u-Lyne OL6 8DY. Tel; 0161 339 4158. (office) 01613 301511 (Social Club). Fax 0161 339 4158.
Directions: M62 jct 20, A627(M) to Oldham, keep in righthand 2 lanes, leave at Ashton sign after 2 miles passing Belgrade Hotel, take A627 at next island, keep in left lane and take slip road signed Ashton-under-Lyme, at island follow Stalybridge/Park Road sign, go straight ahead for 3 miles to ground at Hurst Cross. BR to Charles Street (Ashton), or Stalybridge. Buses 331, 332, 337, 408 (Ashton-Stalybridge) all pass ground.
Seats: 250 **Cover:** 750 **Capacity:** 4,500 **Floodlights:** Yes
Clubhouse: Open 11am-11pm. Refreshment bar open matchdays.
Club Shop: Yes - contact Mr K Lee (0161 330 9800).

PREVIOUS - **Leagues:** Manchester; Lancs Comb 12-23, 48-64, 66-68; Midland 64-66; Cheshire Co. 23-48, 68-82; Nth West Count 82-92. **Name:** Hurst 1878-1947. **Ground:** Rose Hill 1878-1912.

CLUB RECORDS - **Attendance:** 11,000 v Halifax Town, FA Cup First Round 1952. **Scorer:** Mark Edwards, 37. **Appearances:** Micky Boyle, 462. **Win:** 11-3 v Staylbridge Manchester Interm Cup 55, **Defeat:** 11-1 v Wellington Town Cheshire Lge 46-47. **Fees Paid:** £9,000 for Andy Whittaker (Netherfield, 1994). **Fees Received:** £15,000 for Karl Marginson (Rotherham, March 1993).

BEST SEASON - **FA Trophy:** Qtr Final v Dagenham (0-1) (A0 96-97. **FA Cup:** 1st Rd replay 52-53, 1-2 v Halifax T (A), after 1-1. Also 1st Rd 55-56, 1-6 v Southport (A).

HONOURS - Northern Prem Lge Div 1 Cup 94-95; Manchester Sen Cup 1884-85 13-14 75-76 77-78; Manchester League 11-12; Lancs Comb. Div 2 60-61 (Lge Cup 62-63); Manchester Prem. Cup 79-80 82-83 92-93; North West Counties Lge 91-92; Challenge Cup 91-92, Div 2 87-88; Floodlit League 90-91; Challenge Shield 92-93; Manchester Chall Shield 35-36 38-39 49-50 53-54 (R-up 34-35 39-40), Manchester Interm Cup 58-59 62-63 65-66 (R-up 60-61 64-65); Manchester Jnr Cup(4) 1894-95 10-12 32-33; Unifilla Div 1 Cup 96-97.

Players progressing to Football League: A Ball (Blackpool), J Mahoney (Stoke C.), B Daniels (Manchester C.), R Jones (Rotherham U.), A Arrowsmith (Liverpool), N Stiffle (Crystal Palace), K Marginson (Rotherham U), P Wilson (Plymouth Argyle).

97-98 Captain: Paul Clowes **Top Scorer:** Eamonn Elliott/Jimmy Be **P.o.Y.:** John McKenna

Back Row (L-R); Darren Twigg, Brian Fairbrother, John Maquire, Karl Bell, Mick Fagan, David Pierce, John McKenna Steve Hollis, John Coleman (Pl/Mgr), Stewart Anderson, Jimmy Bell (Pl/Asst Mgr), David Burrows. Front Row; Mick Doherty, Mark Brennan, Dave Dickin, David Robinson, Paul Clowes (Capt), Eamonn Elliott, Steve Caswell, Lee Kissock

PROGRAMME DETAILS:
Pages: 28 **Price:** 70p
Editor: David Laughlin
Tel: 01773 856556

BELPER TOWN

Colours: Yellow/black/black & yellow **Formed:** 1883
Change colours: All white **Nickname:** Nailers
Midweek home matchday: Tuesday
Reserve's League: Midlands Reg All
Local Press: Belper News, Derby Evening Telegraph, Belper Express
Local Radio: BBC Radio Derby.

Chairman: Phil Varney **President:** Alan Benfield
Secretary: David Laughlin, Lorne Cottage, 1 Hagg Lane, Fritchley, Derbys DE56 2HJ (01773 856556).
Manager: Martin Rowe **Asst Manager:** Steve Dolby
Press Officer: Nigel Oldrini

GROUND Address: Christchurch Meadow, Bridge Street, Belper DE56 1BA (01773 856556). **Directions:** From M1 North, Jnct 28 onto A38 towards Derby, turn off at A610 (Ripley/Nottingham), then 4 exit at roundabout towards Ambergate. At junction with A6 (Hurt Arms Hotel) left to Belper. Ground on right past traffic lights. 400 yards from Belper (BR).
Capacity: 2,640 **Cover:** 1,000 **Seats:** 200 **Floodlights:** Yes
Clubhouse: Open matchdays, bar, hot & cold food available
Club Shop: Yes manager Andy Smithurst 01773 570967

PREVIOUS - **Leagues:** Central Alliance 57-61; Midland Co's 61-82. **Grounds:** Acorn Ground prior to 1951. **Names:** None

CLUB RECORDS - **Attendance:** 3,200 v Ilkeston Town, 1955. **Goalscorer:** Mick Lakin 231. **Appearances:** Gil Rhodes. **Transfer Fees - Paid:** Nil. **Received:** £700 for Brian Hall (Mansfield Town 59). **Biggest Victory:** 15-2 v Nottingham Forest 'A' 1956. **Biggest Defeat:** 0-12 v Goole Town 1965.

BEST SEASON - **FA Amateur Cup:** Not entered **FA Trophy:** 3rd Qual Rd 97-98 **FA Cup:** 1st Rd Prop 1887-88 (4th Qual. Rnd 1964-65). **FA Vase:** Semi-final 94-95

HONOURS - Northern Counties East Lge 84-85, Midland Counties Lg 79-80; Central Alliance Lge 58-59; Derbys Snr Cup 58-59 60-61 62-63 79-80

Players progressing to Football League: None
97-98 - Captain: Mark Townsend **P.o.Y.:** Carl Cunningham **Top scorer:** Paul Galloway

Back Row (L-R); Richard Cope, Paul Galloway, Ian Grostate, Tim Harrison, Dean Smith, Jon Webster. Front Row; Kevin Fowler, Mark Hurst, Brendan Morgan, Shaun Machin, Richard Harrison, Richard Walker, Steve Orr, Craig Smithurst.

BRADFORD PARK AVENUE

Colours: Green & white/white/green & white **Formed:** 1907
Change colours: Red, amber & black/black/black **Reformed:** 1988
Midweek Matches: Wednesday **Nickname:** Avenue
Reserve Team's league: Bolton Comb All
Local Press: Telegraph & Argus **Local Radio:** Radio Leeds

Chairman: Mike Firth **President:** Charlie Atkinson
Secretary: Alan Hirst, 24 Quarryfields, Mirfield, West Yorks WF14 0NT. Tel. 01924 480349 (H) 01924 474477 (B).
Manager: Trevor Storton **Asst Manager:** Bobby Barr
Res Team Manager: **Physio:** Ray Killick.
Press Officer: Tim Clapham. **Commercial Manager:** Garry Sawyer

GROUND Address: Horsfall Stadium, Cemetery Road, Bradford, West Yorks BD6 2NG. **Directions:** M62 Jct 26. Go along M606 to the end. At the roundabout go along the A6036 (signposted Halifax) and pass Odsal Stadium on left hand side. At next roundabout take the 3rd exit A6036 (Halifax), in approx. 1 mile turn left into Cemetery Road (by Kings Head Pub). Ground 150 yards on left.
Capacity: 5,000 **Cover:** 2,000. **Seats:** 1,247 **Floodlights:** Yes
Clubhouse: No
Club Shop: Yes - contact Trevor Hutchinson (01274 785657)
Sponsor: Ham Construction (Kit); Allied Colliods (Club)

PROGRAMME DETAILS:
Pages: 36 **Price:** £1.20
Editor: Tim Clapham
01274 598130

PREVIOUS - **Leagues:** Southern 07-08; Football 08-70; Northern Prem 70-74; West Riding County Amtr 88-89; Central Mids 89-90; N. W. Counties 90-95. **Grounds:** Park Ave 07-73; Valley Parade 73-74; Manningham Mills 88-89; Bramley R.L.F.C., McLaren Field 89-93; Batley 93-96.

CLUB RECORDS - **Attendance:** 1,007 v Bradford City 97 (Centenary Chall). *32,810 v Blackpool, War Cup 1944*
Win: 11-0 v Denby Dale FAC 1908 **Defeat:** 0-7 v Barnsley 1911
Scorer: Len Shackleton 171 1940-46 **Appearances:** Tommy Farr 542 1934-50
Fee Received: £ 34,000 for K Hector (derby County 1966)
Fee Paid: £ 24,500 for L Leuty (Derby County 1950)

BEST SEASON - **FA Vase:** 2nd Rd Prop 94-95 **FA Trophy:** 2nd Rd Prop 72-73 96-97 **FA Cup:** Qtr finals 12-13, 19-20, 45-46

HONOURS - Football Lge Div 2 R-up 1914; 3rd Div N 28; Yorkshire Lge 21, 23; Midland Lge 32; West Riding Snr Cup 11,13,25,27,32,36,51,53,63, County Cup 29, 90-91, N.W.C. Lg Champions 94-95, N.W.C. Carling Challenge Trophy 94-95.

97-98 Captain: Phil Sharpe **Top Scorer:** Stephen Ball **P.o.Y.:** Phil Sharpe

Back Row (L-R); Mark Price, Paul Green, Wayne Benn, Richard Harrison, Clive Freeman, Patrick Kenny, Lee Connor, Christian Annan, Joe Richardson. Front Row; David Blair, Neil Grayston, Stephen Ball, Phil Sharpe, Glen Lee, Dean Pritchard.

BURSCOUGH

Colours: Green/white/green.
Change colours: Yellow/blue/blue
Midweek Matches: Tuesday
Local Radio: Radio Lancs,Red Rose

Founded: 1946
Nickname: Linnets
Sponsors: Crown Computer Products.

Chairman: Frank Parr
Vice Chairman: Stuart Heaps
President: Ken Griffin
Secretary: Stan Strickland, 109 Redgate, Ormskirk, Lancs L39 3NW (H 01695 574722) (B 01695 574722)
Manager: John Davison
Asst Manager: Peter King.
Physio: Rod Cottam
Press Officer: S Strickland
Ground: Victoria Park, Mart Lane, Burscough, Ormskirk, Lancs L40 0SD (01704 893237).
Directions: M6 Jct 27, follow signs thru Parbold A5209, right into Junction Lane (signed Burscough & Martin Mere) to lights, right onto A59 to Burscough Village, 2nd left over canal bridge into Mart Lane to ground. 200 yards from Burscough Bridge BR station (Wigan-Southport line). Half mile from Burscough Junction (Ormskirk Preston line).
Seats: 220 **Cover:** 1,000 **Capacity:** 3,000
Club Shop: No **Floodlights:** Yes
Clubhouse: 'Barons Club' (privately owned, access outside grd). Mon-Thurs 7-11pm, Fri 4-11pm, Sat 1-11pm, Sun noon-3 & 7-10.30pm. No food.

PROGRAMME DETAILS:
Pages: 36 **Price:** 60p
Editor: Stan Strickland
(01695 574722)

PREVIOUS - Leagues: Liverpool County Comb. 46-53, Lancs Comb. 53-70, Cheshire Co. 70-82.
CLUB RECORDS - Attendance: 4,798 v Wigan Athletic,F.A.Cup 3rd Qual.Rd.1950-51. **Goalscorer:** Johnny Vincent 60 53-54. **Most Goals in Game:** Louis Bimpson 7. **Win:** 10-0 v Cromptons Recreation, Lancashire Combination 1947. 10-0 v Nelson, Lancashire Combination,1948-49. **Defeat:** 0-9 v Earlstown,Liverpool County Combination,1948-49. **Transfer fee paid:** Undisclosed for Arthur Green (Burton Albion, 1948). **Received:** £10,000 for Gary Martindale (Bolton Wanderers), & Kevin Formby (Rochdale).
BEST SEASON - FA Cup: 1st Rd 59-60 77-78 79-80 80-81.
HONOURS - Liverpool Challenge Cup 47-48 50-51,54-55; George Mahon Cup 47-48; Liverpool County Comb Div 1, 49-50 (Div 2 53-54, 67-68); Lancs Comb.Div 2 53-54; Lancs Comb Div 1 55-56 69-70; Lord Wavertree Cup Winners 67-68; Cheshire County League R-up 70-71, League Cup 74-75 (R-up 73-74); Lancs Jnr Cup 47-48 49-50 66-67; Liverpool Snr Cup 55/56, 71-72; Nth West Co's League 82-83 (League Cup 92-93 95-96(R-up 91-92), Challenge Shield 82-83, 95-96; Bill Tyrer Memorial Trophy 90; Liverpool Snr Non-League Cup Finalist 92-93, 95-96:
Players progressing to Football League: L Bimpson, B Parker (Liverpool 53), B Pilson (Stoke 53-54), A Green (Huddersfield), K Waterhouse (Preston), K Spencer (Everton), F Gamble (Derby 80), Tony Rigby (Bury), S Teale (Aston Villa), L Watson (Preston), K Formby A Russell (Rochdale 94), G Martindale (Bolton 94), S Perkins (Plymouth Arg 97).
97-98 - Captain: Ged Nolan **Top Scorer:** Lee Cooper **P.o.Y.:** Neil Hanson

Back Row (L-R); Darren Saint, Brian Holmes, Paul Dawson, Robbie Cowley, Paul Blasbery, Billy Knowles, Paul Lodge, Mark Wilde, Mick McDonough. Front Row; Simon Jennings, Neil Hanson, Ged Nolan, Andy Howard, Gary Anderson, John Quayle

PROGRAMME DETAILS:
Pages: 48 **Price:** 60p.
Editor: Ian Auty
01260 278552

CONGLETON TOWN

Colours: White & black flashes/black/black & white **Formed:** 1901
Change colours: All blue **Nickname:** Bears
Midweek home matchday: Tuesday.
Reserve Team: N/A.
Local Press: Congleton Chronicle, Staffs Evening Sentinel.
Local Radio: Radio Stoke, Signal.

Chairman: Peter Evans
Vice Chairman: Barry Machin
Secretary and Press Officer: David Wilcock, 4,Maxwell Rd., Congleton, Cheshire. CW12 3HY.(H) 01260 276347 or (W) 01260 270275.
Manager: Tommy Lawson **Asst Mgr:** Andy Gray **Physio:** Paul Kelly

GROUND Address: Booth Street Ground, Crescent Road, Congleton, Cheshire (0260 274460).
Directions: On approach to Congleton via Clayton bypass take second right after fire station, into Booth Street. Two miles from Congleton (BR).
Capacity: 5,000 **Cover:** 1,200 **Seats:** 250 **Floodlights:** Yes
Clubhouse: Open match days only.
Club Shop: Yes. Contact: Robert Fletcher.

PREVIOUS - **Leagues:** Crewe & Dist; North Staffs; Macclesfield; Cheshire 20-39, 46-65, 78-82; Mid Cheshire 68-78; Nth West Co 82-87. **Name:** Congleton Hornets *(prior to current club's formation in 1901).*

CLUB RECORDS - **Attendance:** 7,000 v Macclesfield, League 53-54. **Goalscorer:** Mick Biddle (150+). **Appearances:** Ray Clack (600+) & Graham Harrison (600+). **Fee Paid:** None. **Fee Received:** £5,000 for D Frost (Leeds).

BEST SEASON - **FA Trophy:** 3rd Qualifying Rd 89-90 90-91. **FA Vase:** 4th Rd 76-77 80-81. **FA Cup:** 1st Rd 89-90 (lost 0-2 at Crewe). **League clubs defeated:** None.

HONOURS - North West Counties League R-up 85-86; Cheshire County League R-up 20-21 21-22 (Div 2 81-82); Mid Cheshire League 73-74 75-76 77-78 (R-up 69-70 71-72 76-77, League Cup 71-72; Cheshire Senior Cup 20-21 37-38.

Players progressing to Football League: Ron Broad (Crewe 1955), Jack Mycock (Shrewsbury 1958), Steve Davies (Port Vale 1987), L Hamlet (Leeds), Jimmy Quinn (West Ham, N Ireland), Ian Brightwell (Man City).

97-98 Captain: Ray Birch **P.o.Y.:** Mark Winstanley **Top Scorer:** Graham Dodd

Back Row (L-R); Mark Ansell, Tommy Lawson (Mgr), Paul Wilson, Paul Abbey, Ian Marshall, Ian Owen, Steve Rothwell, Andy Grey (Asst Mgr), Paul Kelly (Physio), Simon Rudge. Front Row; Ray Birch, Peter Weston, Jay McComb, Mark Winstanley.

DROYLSDEN

Colours: Red & white/black/black **Formed:** 1892
Change colours: Green/white/green. **Nickname:** The Bloods
Midweek home matchday: Wednesday.
Reserve Team: None.
Local Press: Droylsden Reporter (0161 303 1910), Advertiser.
Local Radio: BBC Manchester.

Chairman: David Pace
Secretary: Bernard King, 22 Hart Street, Droylsden, Manchester M43 7AW. Tel. 0161 2855232 (Home), Fax 0161 3701426.
Manager: David Pace
Asst Manager: Alan Blair.

PROGRAMME DETAILS:
Pages: 20 **Price:** 80p
Editor: Martin Crookall

GROUND Address: The Butchers Arms Ground, Market Street, Droylsden, Manchester (0161 370 1426).
Directions: 4 miles east of Manchester via A662 Ashton New Road, behind Butchers Arms Hotel.
Capacity: 3,500 **Cover:** 2,000 **Seats:** 500 **Floodlights:** Yes
Clubhouse: Pub hours except atchdays. Pool and darts.
Shop: Yes **Metal Badges:** Yes.
Sponsors: Alpha Court Windows/ Hastings Taxis.

PREVIOUS - **Leagues:** Manchester; Lancs Com 36-39, 50-68; Cheshire County 39-50, 68-82; NW Counties 82-87.

CLUB RECORDS - **Attendance:** 4,250 v Grimsby, FA Cup 1st rd 1976. **Scorer:** E Gillibrand 78 (1931-32). **Win:** 13-2 v Lucas Sports Club. **Fee Received:** £11,000 for Tony Naylor (Crewe).

BEST SEASON - **FA Cup:** 2nd Rd 78-79. **League clubs defeated:** Rochdale 78-79.

HONOURS - Northern Prem Lge Div 1 R-up 89-90 (Div 1 Cup 87-88); NW Counties Lge Div 2 86-87; Cheshire County Lge R-up 39-40 45-46, Lge Cup 77-78 (R-up 76-77); Lancs Comb Div 2 R-up 55-56 58-59 62-63; Manchester Lge 30-31 32-33 (Lge Cup 23-24 33-34); Manchester Prem Cup 80-81 (R-up 83-84 90-91 93-94); Manchester Sen Cup 72-73 75-76 78-79 (R-up 72-73 75-76 78-79); Manchester Interm Cup 59-60 64-65 69-70; Manchester Chall Shield 46-47.

Players progressing to Football League: Albert Butterworth & F Letchford (Blackpool 1931), William Davies & Maurice Randall (Crewe 1947), William Mellor (Accrington 1950), Geoff Tonge (Bury 1960), David Campbell (WBA 1962), Kevin Randall (Bury 1965), Peter Litchfield (Preston 1979), Tony Naylor (Crewe 1990).

Back Row (L-R); Peter Orr (Asst Mgr), Ian Tunnicliffe, Andy Diggle, Richard Horner, Lee Williams, Dave Ashton, Aeon Lattie, Graham Hughes, David Pace (Chr & Mgr). Front Row; Physio, Billy O'Callaghan, Neil Rigby, Andy Loo, Neil Hull, Wes Kinney, Mick Jones, Dominic Morley

PROGRAMME DETAILS:
Pages: 24 **Price:** 50p
Editor: Jim McVea
01773 717745

EASTWOOD TOWN

Colours: Black & white stripes/black/black **Formed:** 1953
Change Colours: Yellow/blue/yellow. **Nickname:** The Badgers
Midweek home matchday: Wednesday **Sponsors:**
Local Press: Eastwood Advertiser, Nottingham Evening Post, Derby Telegraph.
Local Radio: Radio Nottingham, Radio Trent.

Chairman: George Belshaw **Vice Chairman:** Roy Cheatle
Secretary / Press Officer: Paddy Farrell, 7 Primrose Rise, Newthorpe, Notts NG16 2BB (Tel/Fax: 01773 715500). **President:** Franil Haynes
Manager: Bryan Chambers **Physio:** Derek Myatt.

GROUND Address: Coronation Park, Eastwood, Notts (01773 715823).
Directions: From North - M1 jct 27, follow Heanor signs via Brinsley to lights in Eastwood. Turn left then first right after Fire Station - ground entrance on Chewton Street. From South - M1 jct 26, A610 to Ripley, leave at 1st exit (B6010), follow to Eastwood, left at lights, first left at 'Man in Space' - ground entrance on Chewton Street. Nearest station - Langley Mill. Buses every 10 mins (R11, R12 or R13) from Victoria Centre, Nottingham - approx 40 mins.
Capacity: 5,500 **Cover:** 1,150 **Seats:** 200 **Floodlights:** Yes
Clubhouse: Social club open normal licensing hours (Sat 11am-11pm, midweek matches 6.30-11pm). Hot & cold food available. Steward; Richard James (01773 715823)
Club Shop: Sells programmes, mugs, scarves, badges etc. Contact R K Storer (0115 938 5239).

PREVIOUS - **Leagues:** Notts Alliance 53-61; Central Alliance 61-67; East Midlands 67-71; Midland Counties 71-82; Northern Counties East 82-87. **Names:** None - predecessors Eastwood Collieries disbanded in 1953. **Previous Ground:** Coronation Park 1953-65 - previous pitch now town bowling green.

CLUB RECORDS - **Attendance:** 2,723 v Enfield, FA Amateur Cup, February 1965. **Goalscorer:** Martin Wright. **Appearances:** Arthur Rowley, over 800 1st team games, but not a single booking, 1955-76. **Win:** 21-0 v Rufford Colliery 26/10/54 & Ilkeston Town 10/5/69. **Defeat:** 1-8 v Ransome & Marples 2/2/57 **Fee Paid:** £500 for Jamie Kay, Gainsborough Trinity 90-91. **Fee Received:** £72,500 for Richard Liburd (Middlesbrough 92-93).

BEST SEASON - **FA Amateur Cup:** Third Round replay 1967-68. **FA Trophy:** First Round 1978-79. **FA Cup:** Final Qual. Rd replay 75-76 (0-1 at Wycombe W.).

HONOURS - Northern Counties (East) Lg R-up 82-83 84-85; Midland Counties Lg 75-76 (R-up 74-75 77-78), Lg Cup 77-78 79-80; Central Alliance 63-64 (R-up 64-65); Notts Alliance 56-57 (R-up 53-54 54-55 55-56 57-58 58-59 59-60), Lg Cup 55-56; East Midlands Lg R-up 68-69; Notts Senior Cup 75-76 77-78 78-79 79-80 82-83 83-84 88-89 89-90 91-92 (R-up 57-58 63-64 65-66); Evans Halshaw Floodlit Cup 94-95 R-up 89-90 97-98; Notts Intermediate Cup 86-87; Ripley Hospital Charity Cup(6) 76-81.

Players progressing to Football League: J Butler (Notts County 57), A Woodcock A Buckley Andrew Todd (Nottm Forest), P Richardson (Derby), S Buckley (Luton), R Liburd (Middlesbrough 92-93), Martin Bullock (Barnsley 94-95), Neil Illman (Plymouth 95-96), Lee Marshall (Scunthorpe 97).

Back Row (L-R); Gavin Warboys, Richard Smith, Freddy Morgan, Shaun Browne, Richard Parkin, Glenn Kirkwood, Paul Gould, Gary Breach. Front Row; Gary Castledine, John Folwell, Owen Harvey, Martyn Chadbourne, Richard Cleugh.

FARSLEY CELTIC

THE UniBond LEAGUE
FARSLEY CELTIC
v
GT. HARWOOD TOWN
Unibond League First Division
Saturday 10th January
K.O. 3.00pm at Throstle Nest

PROGRAMME DETAILS:
Pages: 26 **Price:**
Editor: Keith Huggins.

Colours: Sky & navy/navy/navy **Formed:** 1908
Change colours: Yellow/yellow/navy & red **Nickname:** Villagers
Midweek home matchday: Wednesday
Reserve Team's League: Northern Counties (E) Reserve Div.
Local Press: Yorkshire Evening Post, Telegraph & Argus, Pudsey Times.
Local Radio: Radio Leeds, Radio Aire, Radio Pennine.

Chairman: John E Palmer **Vice Chairman:**
Secretary: Mrs Margaret Lobley, 29 Spring Bank Road, Farsley, Leeds, West Yorks LS28 5LS (01132 575675)
Manager: Martin Haresign **Coach:** Darren Foreman/Gary Chapman
Press Officer: **Physio:** Ian McGready
GROUND Address: Throstle Nest, Newlands, Farsley, Pudsey, Leeds LS28 5BE (01532 561517). **Directions:** From North East: A1 south to Wetherby, A58 to Leeds, at 1st island (approx 8 miles) take 3rd exit (A6120 ring-rd), follow Bradford signs to 12th r'bout (approx 12 miles) - 1st exit (B6157 Stanningley). From M62 jct 26, M606 (Bradford) to r'bout, 4th exit (A6177) passing McDonalds on left, continue on Rooley Lane - Sticker Lane passing Morrisons store on left to lights (approx 3 miles) - right onto A647 (Leeds) to 2nd r'bout, 2nd exit (B6157 Stanningley). Continue 800yds passing Police & Fire Stations on left. Turn left down New Street at Tradex warehouse before turning right into Newlands. Ground at bottom of road. 1 mile from New Pudsey (BR).
Capacity: 4,000 **Cover:** 1,000 **Seats:** 430 **Floodlights:** Yes
Clubhouse: Lounge, games room and committee room open every evening and Friday and weekend lunchtimes. New multi-purpose Leisure Centre available evenings and afternoons.
Club Shop: League & non-League programmes & magazines. Club badges, scarves, ties, sweaters, training suits, polo & T-shirts. Various souvenirs & photos. Contact Brian Falkingham, 27 Rycroft Ct., Leeds LS13 4PE. 0113 255 0749

PREVIOUS - **Leagues:** West Riding County Amateur; Leeds Red Triangle; Yorkshire 49-82; Northern Counties East 82-87. **Grounds:** Red Lane, Farsley; Calverley Lane, Farsley (prior to 1948).

CLUB RECORDS - **Attendance:** 11,000 (at Elland Road) v Tranmere Rovers, FA Cup 1st Rd 1974.

BEST SEASON - **FA Amateur Cup:** Third Round, 34-35. **FA Cup:** 1st Rd 74-75 (see above). Lost 0-2. **FA Vase:** Quarter Final 87-88.

HONOURS - West Riding County Cup 57-58 59-60 66-67 70-71 83-84 87-88 95-96 96-97; Yorkshire League 59-60 68-69 (R-up 57-58 58-59 70-71 71-72); Div 2 51-52; League Cup 62-63 63-64 66-67 96-97.

Players progressing to Football League: Barry Smith (Leeds 1951), Paul Madeley (Leeds 1962), William Roberts (Rochdale 1988), Stuart McCall (Bradford City, Everton, Scotland, Bradford City).

97-98 - Captain: Paul Stevenson **P.o.Y.:** Scot Jackson **Top scorer:** Scot Jackson

Back Row (L-R); Paul Allen, Chris Stabr, Steve Learoyd, Scott Jackson, Phil Robinson, Wayne Noteman, Paul Stevenson, Allan Roberts, Martin Haresign (Mgr). Front Row; Darren Foreman, Robbie Wellans, Billy Roberts, Phil Turner, Vince Brockie, Jason Day, Calvin Allan

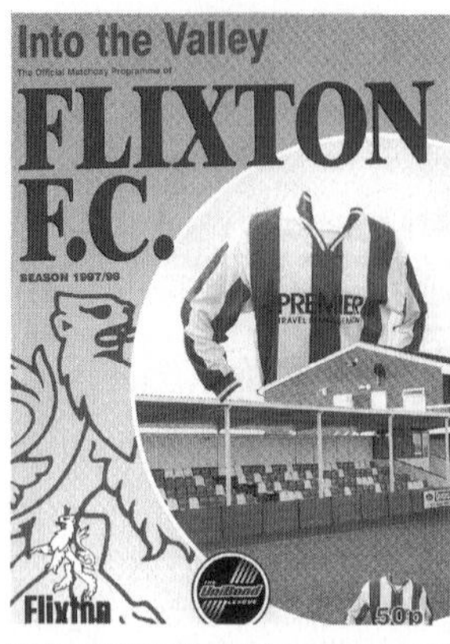

PROGRAMME DETAILS:
Pages: 36 **Price:** 50p
Editor: John Fradley

FLIXTON

Colours: Blue & white stripes/blue/blue **Formed:** 1960
Change Colours: Gold/black/black **Nickname:** Valley Roaders
Midweek home matchday: Tuesday
Reserve Team's league: North West Alliance

Chairman: John Mitchell **President:** F H Eadie
Secretary: Peter Rogers, 55 Benbecula Way, Davyhulme, Urmston, Manchester M41 7FW, (0161 445 2722)
Manager: David Morris **Asst Manager:** Chris Nicholson

GROUND Address: Valley Road, Flixton, Manchester M31 2RQ (0161 748 2903). **Directions:** M63 Jct 3, B5214 (signed Urmston), follow Trafford General Hosp. signs, at 4th r'bout take 3rd exit (Woodbridge Rd), ground at top. One and a quarter miles from Flixton BR station (trains from Manchester Oxford Rd) - turn right out of station onto Flixton Rd, left after quarter mile into Woodsend Rd, at r'bout after quarter mile take 2nd exit into Woodbridge Rd - ground at top. Take any bus from Manchester Picadilly bus station to Flixton and alight at Flixton Red Lion.
Capacity: 2,000 **Cover:** 650 **Seats:** 250 **Floodlights:** Yes
Clubhouse: Open daily 1.00pm-11pm. Sandwiches available most evenings.
Club Shop: No

PREVIOUS - **Leagues:** South Manchester & Wythenshawe 60-63; Lancs & Cheshire 63-73; Manchester 73-86; North West Counties 86-96

CLUB RECORDS - **Attendance:** 1,543 v Brigg Town FA Vase Semi-Final 95-96.
Goalscorer: John Mitchell.
Appearances: John Mitchell & Stan Matthews.
Win: 10-2 Irlam 94-95.
Defeat: 1-10 v Knowsley Utd 90-91.

BEST SEASON - **FA Cup:** 1st Qual. Rd replay 91-92 (lost 1-2 at Mossley after 1-1 draw. **FA Vase:** Semi-final 95-96 v Brigg Town.

HONOURS - N.W.Co Div I Champions & Cup 95-96, Div 2 94-95 Lg.Cup 94-95, (R-up 87-88), Div 3 R-up 86-87, Cup SF 86-87, Res. Chal. Cup 87-88 90-91 (R-up 88-89 89-90 91-92 92-93), Res. Div East 89-90, Res. Div Sth 92-93; Manc. Lg R-up 78-79 81-82 85-86, Div 1 77-78, Div 2(res) 82-83 85-86, Open Tphy 80-81; Lancs Amtr Cup 79-80 (R-up 80-81); Manc. Chal. Tphy 83-84 (R-up x2 84-86); Manc. Prem. Cup R-up 86-87 91-92; Manc. Amtr Cup R-up 88-89.

Flixton on the attack against Buxton Photo: Tim Lancaster

GREAT HARWOOD TOWN

Colours: All red
Change colours: All blue.
Midweek Matches: Monday.
Reserve Team's league: West Lancs Lge

Formed: 1978
Nickname: Robins
Club Sponsors: None

PROGRAMME DETAILS:
Pages: 20 **Price:** 20p
Editor: D Bennet.

Chairman: William Holden **Secretary:** Peter Birtwhistle, 23 Dryden Grove, Great Harwood, Blackburn BB6 7LW.(01254 886754)
Manager: M Crabbe **Asst Manager:** Dave Sargent
Press Officer: K Lambert **Commercial Manager:** Mark Smith
GROUND Address: The Showground, Wood Street, Great Harwood, Lancs (01254 883913). **Directions:** M66 from Manchester to Haslingden exit, A680 through Baxenden, Accrington to Clayton-le-Moors, left at the Hyndburn Bridge Hotel into Hyndburn Road and right into Wood Street to ground. Or M6 jct 31, Clitheroe/Skipton road to Trafalgar Hotel, A677 to Blackburn, left at Moat House Hotel and follow ring-road to M65 junction, A678 to Rishton, left at lights (B6536) to Gt Harwood, right at Town Gate into Queen Str., follow signs for Lomax Square, left into Park Rd, right into Balfour Street to ground. 3 miles from Rishton (BR), 6 miles from Blackburn (BR). Various buses from Heyes Lane & Park Road to Blackburn & Accrington.
Capacity: 2,500 **Cover:** 700 **Seats:** 200 **Floodlights:** Yes
Clubhouse: The Sportsman just outside ground. Normal licensing hours. Full bar facilities. Squash courts and gym. Hot & cold snacks & drinks on matchdays from tea bar in ground.
Club Shop: Sells programmes, badges, key rings, shirts. Contact: J McKay (c/o club).

PREVIOUS - **Name:** Great Harwood Wellington. **Leagues:** West Lancashire; Lancs Combination 79-82; North West Counties 82-92. **Ground:** Park adjacent to the Showground until demise of Great Harwood FC in 1978.

CLUB RECORDS - **Attendance:** 5,397 v Manchester Utd, 1980. **Scorer:** **Appearances:** **Fee Paid:** **Fee Received:** **Win:** 7-0 v Farsley Celtic (H), NPL Div. 1 92-93. **Defeat:** 0-6 v Spennymoor Utd (H), NPL Div. 1 94-95

BEST SEASON - **FA Cup:** 1st Qualifying Round replay 92-93 (lost 1-2 at home to Atherton LR after 1-1 draw). **FA Vase:** Quarter Finals 90-91 (lost 1-2 at Littlehampton Town).

HONOURS - North West Counties League R-up 91-92 (Div 2 90-91, Lamot Pils Tphy 89-90 (R-up 90-91), Tennents Floodlit Trophy 91-92), Lancs ATS Challenge Trophy 91-92 (R-up 90-91).

Gretna's Tony Fyfe had this shot saved by Great Harwood's keeper. Photo: Alan Watson

PROGRAMME DETAILS:
Pages: 28 **Price:** 80p
Editor: R MacGregor
(01387 811820)

GRETNA

Club colours: Black & white hoops/black/black & white
Change colours: All maroon (black & white trim) **Formed:** 1946
Midweek matchday: Tuesday **Nickname:** Black & whites
Reserve Team's league: None
Local Newspapers: Cumberland News/Evening News & Star
Local Radio: C.F.M.; Radio Cumbria
Chairman: Brian Fulton **President:** Thomas Kerr.
Secretary: Ron MacGregor, Brackenhurst, Lochmaben, Lockerbie, Scotland DG11 1QA (01387 811820).
Manager: Michael McCartney **Physio:** William Bentley

GROUND Address: Raydale Park, Dominion Rd., Gretna, Dumfriesshire (01461 337602). **Directions:** 8 miles north of Carlisle on A74. Take slip road to Gretna over border bridge, left at Crossways Inn for Township along Annan Rd for quarter of a mile, left into Dominion Rd, ground on right. Buses leave Carlisle on the half hour. Also trains from Carlisle.
Capacity: 2,200 **Cover:** 800 **Seats:** 385 **Floodlights:** Yes
Clubhouse: Bar, lounge, TV room, concert room. Cooked meals available. Open every day. Late bar at weekends.
Club Shop: Yes, contact Alan Watson 01387 251550, matchdays & postal sales
Club Sponsors: Home Kit; Ewart Engineering, Away Kit; North British Tours

PREVIOUS - **Leagues:** Dumfriesshire Amateur 46-47; Carlisle & District 47-51; Cumberland 51-52; Northern 83-92.

CLUB RECORDS - **Attendance:** 2,307 v Rochdale, F.A. Cup First Round Proper, 16/11/91. **Scorer:** Denis Smith **Appearances:** William Cross. **Win:** 20-0 v Silloth 62-63 **Defeat:** 0-6 v Worksop Town 94-95 **Transfer Fee Received:** £10,000 from Queen of the South for Derek Townsley 96

BEST SEASON - **FA Trophy:** 2nd Rd 84-85 88-89 90-91 93-94. **FA Cup:** 1st Rd Prop 91-92 (lost 1-3 in replay at Rochdale) & 93-94 (lost 2-3 to Bolton Wanderers). **FA Vase:** 2nd Rd 80-81 83-84.

HONOURS - Northern Lg 90-91 91-92 (Lg Cup 90-91); Cumberland Senior Cup (9); JR Cleator Cup 89-90 90-91 91-92; Craven Cup 91-92; Carlisle & Dist. Lg (28) (Charity Shield (25), Lg Cup (20); Benevolent Cup (15).

Players progressing to Football League: John Hamilton (Hartlepool United) 1982, Russell Black & Don Peattie (Sheffield United) 1984, Mark Dobie (Cambridge United).

97-98 Captain: Les Armstrong **Top Scorer:** Gary Milne
Supporters P.o.Y.: Tony Monaghan **Players P.o.Y.:** Tony Monaghan

Gretna v Rangers X1 at the occasion of the Mike McCartney Testimonial match 6/5/98. Mike McCartney lines up centre front with players of both teams.
Photo: Alan Watson

PROGRAMME DETAILS:
Pages: 32 **Price:** 60p
Editor: R Chambers/ T Moseley

HARROGATE TOWN

Colours: Yellow/black/yellow **Formed:** 1919
Change colours: All blue. **Nickname:** Town
Midweek home matchday: Tuesday **Club Sponsors:** Crystal Motors.
Reserve Team's Lge: Northern Co's (East) Reserve Div.
Local Press: Yorkshire Post, Harrogate Herald Advertiser.
Local Radio: Radio Leeds, Radio York, local hospital radio.

Chairman: George Dunnington **President:**
Managing Director: Alan Smith **General Secretary:** Roy Dalby, 123a Dene Park, Harrogate, North Yorkshire HG1 4JX (01423 567973).
Youth Development Coach: Malcolm Richardson **Coach:**

GROUND Address: Wetherby Road, Harrogate. 01423 883671 (880675-press). **Directions:** From Leeds turn right at traffic lights (Appleyard's) into Hookstone Road, continue to Woodlands Hotel (traffic lights) turn left into Wetherby Road, ground on the right. From Harrogate (BR), turn left and left again, cross road (Odeon Cinema), proceed for about 400yds to main road, cross over to The Stray (open land) using footpath which leads to Wetherby Rd, ground 200yds on left.
Capacity: 3,800 **Cover:** 600 **Seats:** 450 **Floodlights:** Yes
Clubhouse: On ground, open Tuesday, Thursday and every other Wednesday in addition to every matchday. Sandwiches available.
Club Shop: Sells scarves, ties, pens shirts and other common souvenirs.
Metal Badges: Yes

PREVIOUS - **Names:** Harrogate FC 26-34; Harrogate Hotspurs 36-50. **Ground:** Starbeck Lane 1919-20. **Leagues:** Yorkshire 20-21, 22-31, 51-82; Midland 21-22; Northern 31-32; Harrogate & District 36-46; West Yorkshire 46-51; Northern Counties East 82-87.

CLUB RECORDS - **Attendance:** 3,208 v Starbeck LNER (now Harrogate R.A.), Whitworth Cup final 1948. **Win:** 9-1 v Winsford. **Defeat:** 0-7 v Hyde Utd & v Lancaster City.

BEST SEASON - **FA Vase:** 4th Round 89-90. **FA Cup:** 3rd Qual. Rd 94-95 (0-3 at Bishop Auckland)

HONOURS - Northern Premier Lge Div 1 Cup 89-90; Northern Counties (East) Div 1 (Nth) R-up 84-85 (Reserve Div 85-86, Reserve Div Cup 86-87); Yorkshire League Div 1 26-27 (Div 2 81-82, Div 3 R-up 71-72 80-81); West Riding County Cup 62-63 72-73 85-86; West Riding Challenge Cup 24-25 26-27.

Players progressing to Football League: Tony Ingham (Leeds 47), Stewart Ferebee (York City 79), Tim Hotte (Halifax Town 85), Andy Watson (Halifax Town 88), Ian Blackstone (York City 95)

Harrogate's Lee Edmunds in action against Gretna's Mike Hodgson Photo: Alan Watson

HUCKNALL TOWN

Colours: Yellow/black/black **Founded:** 1987
Change colours: All red **Nickname:** The Town
Midweek matches: Tuesday **Sponsors:** Doff-Portland
Reserve League: Midlands Regional Alliance
Local Newspapers: Hucknall & Bulwell Dispatch/ Nottm Evening Post/ Nottm Football Post.

PROGRAMME DETAILS:
Pages: 72 **Price:** 50p
Editor: Simon Matters
(0115 956 1336

Chairman: John Coleman **Vice-Chairman:** John Beharall
President: Andy Stewart
Secretary: Brian Scothern, 95 Brookfield Ave., Shortwood Estate, Hucknall, Notts NG15 6FF (0115 956 3151)
Manager: John Ramshaw **Assistant Manager:** Billy Millar
Physio: Ken Burton.
Ground: Watnall Road, Hucknall, Notts NG15 7LP (0115 956 1253)
Directions: M1 jct 27, A608 to lights, right onto A611 to Hucknall, right at r'bout (new by-pass), over next r'bout, right at next r'bout into Watnall Rd - grd on right. From M1 jct 26 follow Nottm signs to lights on island, left onto A610, right at Three Ponds Pub onto B600 towards Watnall, 200 yds past Queens Head turn right signed Hucknall, follow over motorway and past Rolls Royce - ground on left. Nearest station Hucknall
Capacity: 3,000 **Seats:** 240 **Cover:** 1,100 **Floodlights:** Yes
Clubhouse: Every night and weekend lunchtimes **Club Shop:** Yes

PREVIOUS - **Leagues:** Bulwell & Dist. 46-59 60-65; Central All. 59-60; Notts Spartan 65-70; Notts All. 70-89; Central Midlands 89-92. **Ground:** Wigham Park 46-54 **Name:** Hucknall Colliery Welfare (until pit closure 1988)

CLUB RECORDS - **Attendance:** 1,305 v Macclesfield, FA Cup 2nd Qual 26/9/92. **Appearances:** Ted Mullane

HONOURS - Northern Counties (East) Lg Div 1 R-up 92-93 (Lg Cup 93-94 96-97) Presidents Cup 96-97; Central Mids Lg(2) 89-91 (R-up 91-92, Lg Cup(3) 89-92); Notts All.Sen (4) 76-78 87-89, Div 1 Div 1 72-73 80-81 86-87 Div 2 70-71; Intermediate Cup 72-73 78-81 84-84; Lge Cup 78-79; Notts Snr Cup 84-85 90-91 (R-up 83-84 85-86 87-88 89-90); FA Vase QF 85-86.

97-98 - Captain: Colin Thacker **P.o.Y.:** Dave McCarthy **Top Scorer:** P Tomlinson/M Edwards (30)

Hucknall Town 98/99

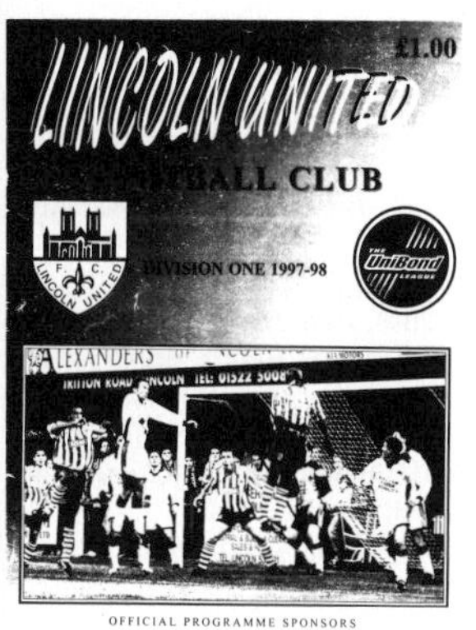

PROGRAMME DETAILS:
Pages: 40 **Price:** 50p
Editor: John Wilkinson
(01522 788880)

LINCOLN UNITED

Colours: All white
Formed: 1938
Change Colours: Red/Black.
Nickname: United
Midweek home matchday: Wednesday
Reserve team's League: Lincolnshire.
Local Press: Lincolnshire Echo, Lincoln Standard.

Chairman: K Roe
President: A Simpson
Vice Chairman: P Day
Commercial Manager: S Eastmead.
Secretary / Press Officer: Steve Eastmead, 23 Woodvale Avenue, Doddington Park, Lincoln LN6 3RD (01522 885112 H, 01522 696400 B)
Manager: Ged Creane/John Wilkinson
Physio: Anthony Adams

GROUND Address: Ashby Avenue, Hartsholme, Lincoln (01522 690674).
Directions: From Newark A46 onto Lincoln relief road (A446), right at 2nd r'bout for Birchwood (Skellingthorpe Rd), go for 1 mile passing lake and Country Park, 1st right 10yds after 30mph sign into Ashby Ave., ground entrance 200 yds, opposite Old Peoples home. From north follow A57 via Saxilby until reaching A46 Lincoln Relief Road - continue on this and turn left at r'bout signed Birchwood then as above. 3 miles from Loncoln Central (BR).
Capacity: 2,714. **Seats:** 400. **Covered:** 1,084. **Floodlights:** Yes
Clubhouse: Open every day normal licensing hours. Matchday snack bar - hot & cold food & drinks.
Club Shop: Yes. Contact Jane Eastmead (01522 885112)
Sponsors: Hykeham Forum Supplies/ City Tyre Experts.

PREVIOUS - **Leagues:** Lincs 45-48 60-67; Lincoln 48-60; Yorks 67-82; Northern Co's East 82-86, 92-95; Central Mids 82-92. **Grounds:** Skew Bridge (40s); Co-op Sports Ground (to mid 60s); Hartsholme Cricket Ground (to 82). **Name:** Lincoln Amateurs (until an ex-pro signed in 1954).

CLUB RECORDS - **Attendance:** 2,000 v Crook Town, FA Amateur Cup 1st Rd Proper, 1968. **Scorer:** Terry Nelson 189. **Appearances:** Brian Davies 439. **Win:** 12-0 v Pontefract Colls 95. **Defeat:** 0-7 v Huddersfield Town FA Cup 1st Round Proper 16-11-91. **Fee Paid:** £250 for Dean Dye (Sutton Town, 7.90) - only player ever bought. **Fee Received:** £3,000 for Dean Dye (Charlton Ath., 7.91).

BEST SEASON - **FA Cup:** First Round Proper 91-92 (0-7 at Huddersfield Town).

HONOURS - Northern Counties East - Prem Div. 94-95, Div 1 92-93, Div 1 Sth 82-83, Div 2 85-86, Presidents Cup 94-95; Yorks Lg 70-71 73-74 (Lg Cup 70-71); Lincs Lg 63-64; Lincs Snr 'A' Cup 72-73 85-86 95-96, R-up 91-92 94-95, 'B' Cup 63-64 70-71; Central Mids Lg 91-92 (Wakefield Cup 90-91); Evans Halshaw Floodlit Cup R-up 92-93; Lincs I'mediate Cup(7) 67-73 80-81; Blankney Hunt Inter Lge 95-96, Cup 95-96.

Back Row (L-R); Arthur Simpson (Pres), John Wilkinson (jt Mgr), Peter Day, Tony Adams (Physio), Rick Ranshaw, Rick Wright, Billy Heath, Mike Heath, Mike Trotter (Capt), Mark Rookyard, Steve Carter, Brendan McDaid, Steve Eastmead (Sec), Roy Parnham, Willy White. Front Row; Stuart Reddington, Ady Barker, Paul Casey, Darren Munton, Keith Roe (Chr), Andy Gray, Paul Farley, Baz Barker, Jamie Sayce, Ged Creane (jt Mgr).

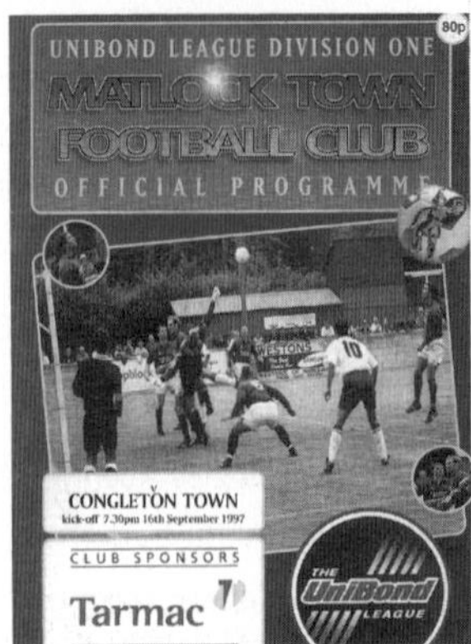

PROGRAMME DETAILS:
Pages: 40 **Price:** 80p
Editor: Ian Richardson
01629 56042

MATLOCK TOWN

Colours: Royal/white **Formed:** 1885
Chamge colours: All yellow **Nickname:** The Gladiators
Midweek home matchday: Tuesday
Reserve Team's league: Beauvale Mid All
Local Press: Matlock Mercury, Derbyshire Times, Derby Evening Telegraph, Chesterfield Express. **Local Radio:** Radio Derby.

Chairman: Donald T Carr **Vice Chairman:** G Michael Tomlinson
Secretary: Keith F Brown, 'Barncroft', 1 Malvern Gardens, Matlock, Derbyshire DE4 3JH. 01629 584231 (H) 01335 390301 (B).
Manager: Tommy Spencer **Physio:** Michael Cunningham
Press Officer: Ian Richardson 01629 56042 (H)
Commercial Manager: Tom Wright

GROUND Address: Causeway Lane, Matlock, Derbyshire (01629 583866 & Fax). **Directions:** On A615, 500 yds from town centre and Matlock (BR).
Capacity: 7,500 **Cover:** 2,000 **Seats:** 240 **Floodlights:** Yes
Clubhouse: Gladiators Social Club, on ground, open matchdays only.
Club Shop: Yes. Contact: Sue Tomlinson (01629 583866)
Sponsors: Westons of Wirksworth/ Panasonic/ Tarmac

PREVIOUS - **Ground:** Hall Leys (last century). **Leagues:** Midland Counties 1894-96; Matlock & District; Derbys Senior; Central Alliance 24-25 47-61; Central Combination 34-35; Chesterfield & District 46-47; Midland Counties 1961-69.

CLUB RECORDS - **Attendance:** 5,123 v Burton Albion, FA Trophy 1975. **Win:** 10 v 0 Lancaster (A) 74. **Defeat:** 1-8 v Chorley (A) 71. **Career Goalscorer:** Peter Scott. **Career Appearances:** Mick Fenoughty **Fee Paid:** £2,000 for Kenny Clarke 1996. **Fee Received:** £10,000 for Ian Helliwell (York).

BEST SEASON - **FA Trophy:** 74-75. **FA Cup:** 3rd Rd 76-77. 1st Rd 1885-86 86-87 86-87 87-88 1959-60 74-75 75-76 89-90. **League clubs defeated in FA Cup:** Mansfield Town 76-77.

HONOURS - Northern Prem Lge R-up 83-84, Lge Cup 77-78, Shield 78-79; Midland Counties Lge 61-62 68-69; Central All (North) 59-60 60-61, R-up 61-62 62-63, Div 1 Cup R-up 61-62, Div 2 59-60, Div 2 Cup 59-60 60-61; Derbyshire Sen Cup 74-75 76-77 77-78 80-81 83-84 84-85 91-92, R-up 60-61 72-73 73-74 75-76 80-81 81-82 82-83 89-90 93-94 97-98; Derbshire Div Cup (North) 61-62 R-up 62-63; Evans Halshaw Floodlit Cup 88-89 91-92; Anglo-Italian Non-League Cup 79.

Players progressing to Football League: Keith Haines (Leeds 1959), Wayne Biggins (Burnley 1984), Darren Bradshaw (Chesterfield 1987), Les McJannet (Scarborough 1987), Ian Helliwell (York 1987).
97-98 - Captain: Jimmy Flynn **Top Scorer:** Kenny Clarke **P.o.Y.:** Darrell Fox

Back Row (L-R); Andy Williams, Kenny Clark, Steve Curruthers, Neil Booker, Phil Robinson, Mark Smith, Jamie Evans, Darrell Fox, Robbie Clark, Tommy Spencer (Mgr). Front Row; Paul Burton, Chris Dolby (Physio), Jimmy Flynn (Capt), Lee Wainwright, John Stokes (Asst Mgr), Robbie Curtis. Photo: Mr N Thaler

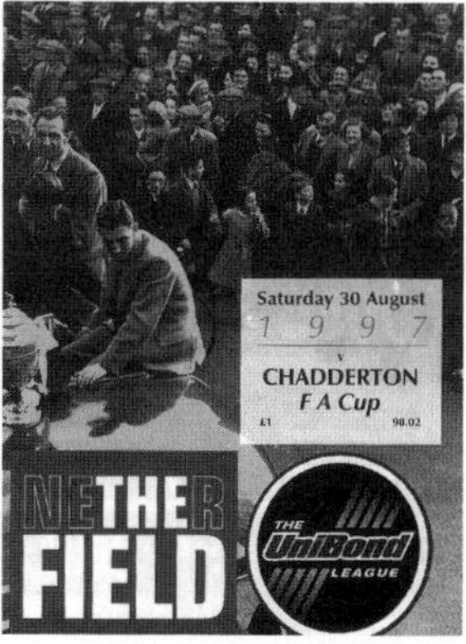

NETHERFIELD

Colours: Black & white stripes/black/black & white **Formed:** 1920
Change colours: Yellow/blue/yellow **Nickname:** The Field
Midweek home matchday: Tuesday **Sponsors:** T B A
Reserve Team's League: North West Alliance.
Local Press: Westmorland Gazette, Lancaster Evening Post.
Local Radio: Radio Cumbria, Red Rose.

Chairman: Ian Needham **President:** M Macklin
Secretary: Andrew Roe, 4 Lowther Park, Kendal, Cumbria LA9 6RS. 01539 731680 (H) 01524 582390 (B).
Match Secretary: Craig Campbell, 34 High Sparrowmire, Kendal Cumbria LA9 5PD 01539 725557 (H).
Manager: Stan Allan **Asst Manager:** Bruce Richardson
Press Officer: Peter Savage (01539 726488).
GROUND Address: Parkside Road, Kendal, Cumbria (01539 727472).
Directions: M6 junction 36, follow signs for Kendal (South), right at lights, left at r-bout to 'K' Village - Pa.kside Rd on right opposite factory main offices - ground 400 yds. A mile & a half from Oxenholme (BR) station - bus service to 'K' village, No 41 or 41A.
Capacity: 2,490 **Cover:** 1,000 **Seats:** 250 **Floodlights:** Yes
Clubhouse: The Park, open all matchdays. Pies & pasties available.
Club Shop: No.

PROGRAMME DETAILS:
Pages: 36 **Price:** 80p
Editor: Peter Savage
(01539 726488)

PREVIOUS - **Leagues:** Westmorland; North Lancs; Lancs Combination 45-68; Northern Premier 68-83; North West Counties 83-87.

CLUB RECORDS - **Attendance:** 5,184 v Grimsby Town, FA Cup 1st Rd 1955. **Goalscorer:** Tom Brownlee. **Win:** 11-0 v Great Harwood 22/3/47. **Defeat:** 0-10 v Stalybridge Celtic 1/9/84. **Fee Paid:** Undisclosed for Tom Brownlee (Bradford C., 66). **Fee Received:** £10,250 for Andy Milner (Man. City 95).

BEST SEASON - **FA Vase:** 3rd Rd 89-90. **FA Trophy:** 2nd Rd 80-81. **FA Cup:** 2nd Rd replay 63-64 (1-4 at Chesterfield after 1-1 draw). 2nd Rd 49-50, 1st Rd 45-46 48-49 52-53 54-55 55-56 64-65.

HONOURS - Lancs Comb. 48-49 64-65 (R-up 45-46 53-54 61-62 63-64, Lg Cup 55-56 60-61), Westmorland Snr Cup(12) 24-25 31-33 35-36 46-48 63-64 65-66 71-72 86-87 89-89 90-91.

Players progressing to Football League: John Laidlaw (Carlisle 1946), Louis Cardwell (Crewe 1947), Herbert Keen (Barrow 1953), Alec Aston (Preston 1955), Horace Langstreth (Torquay 1956), John Simpson (Lincoln 1957), Dennis Rogers (Accrington 1959), Tom Brownlee (Bradford City 1965), Peter McDonnell (Bury 1973), Keith Silken (Workington 1973), Roger Wicks (Darlington 1981), Andy Milner (Man City).

Netherfield AFC Photo: John Newton

PROGRAMME DETAILS:
Pages: 28 **Price:** 80p
Editor: Ian Hannay

RADCLIFFE BOROUGH

Colours: Blue/blue/white. **Formed:** 1949
Change colours: All white. **Sponsors:** Martin Darlington Transport
Midweek home matchday: Tuesday **Nickname:** Boro'
Reserve Team: Yes
Local Press: Radcliffe Times, Bolton Evening News, Manchester Evening News.
Local Radio: Greater Manchester Radio (GMR), Piccadilly.

Chairman: Bernard Manning Jnr **President:** A A Swarbrick
Vice Chairman: R Doyle
Company/Club Secretary: Graham E Fielding, c/o Radcliffe Borough
Manager: Kevin Glendon **Coach:** Frankie Bunn
Press Officer: **Physio:** Roy Davies

GROUND Address: Stainton Park, Pilkington Road, Radcliffe, Lancs M26 3PE (0161 724 5937-club), (0161-724-8346 Office), (Fax 0161 723 3178).
Directions: M62 junction 17 - follow signs for Whitefield and Bury. Take A665 to Radcliffe. Thro' town centre, turn right into Unsworth St. (opposite Turf Hotel). Ground on left half mile Colshaw Close East. 1/2 mile from Radcliffe (BR).
Capacity: 3,000 **Cover:** 1,000 **Seats:** 350 **Floodlights:** Yes
Clubhouse: (0161 724 5937) 'The Boro'- public house on ground. No food available.
Club Shop: Yes - contact Ryan Davies at ground.(0161-724-5937).

PREVIOUS - **Ground:** Bright Street 1949-70. **Leagues:** South East Lancs; Manchester 53-63; Lancs Combination 63-71; Cheshire County 71-82; North West Counties 82-87.

CLUB RECORDS - **Attendance:** 1,468 v Caernarfon Town, N.W.C. Lge 83. **Goalscorer:** Gary Haworth. **Appearances:** Chris Lilley. **Fee Paid:** £5,000 for Gary Walker (Buxton, 1991). **Fee Received:** £5,000 for Kevin Hulme (Bury, 1989).

BEST SEASON - **FA Trophy:** 3rd Rd v Gateshead 1995-96. **FA Cup:** 2nd Qual. Rd replay 75-76 (1-4 at Rossendale Utd after 2-2 draw). **FA Vase:** 4th Rd v Boston Town 93-94

HONOURS - Unibond Lge Div One Champ 96-97; North West Counties Lg 84-85 (Div 2 82-83); Lancs Combination Lg Cup 69-70; Manchester Lg R-up 55-56 (Lg Cup 58-59 joint); Manchester Prem Cup R-up 97-98.

Players progressing to Football League: Jim Hayman (Bury 50), Ian Wood (Oldham Athletic 65), Robert Hutchinson (Rochdale 74), Gary Haworth (Rochdale 84), Kevin Hulme (Bury 89).
97-98 - Captain: Laurence Greenhalgh **P.o.Y.:** David Bean **Top scorer:** Ian Luut

Radcliffe Borough at Maine Rd for Manchester Premier Cup Final Photo: John Newton

STOCKSBRIDGE PARK STEELS

STEELS REVIEW

Club Sponsors
ST CHRISTOPHERS MOTOR COMPANY LTD
Let us take care of you!

STOCKSBRIDGE PARK STEELS FOOTBALL CLUB

TODAYS VISITORS
- V -
BELPER TOWN
Tuesday 3rd February 1998

SEASON 1997/98 UNIBOND LEAGUE DIVISION 1

PROGRAMME DETAILS:
Pages: 28 **Price:** 80p
Editor: Edwin O'Sullivan (0114 2884218)

Colours: Yellow/blue/yellow **Formed:** 1986
Change colours: All blue **Nickname:** Steels
Midweek matches: Tuesday **Sponsors:** St Christophers Motor Company
Reserves' League: Beefeater County Senior.
Local Press: Sheffield Trader, Green'un, The Star

President: C D Sedgwick **Chairman:** A Bethel
Vice-Chairman / Secretary: Michael Grimmer, 48 Hole House Lane, Stocksbridge, Sheffield S36 1BT (0114 2886470).
Manager: Mick Horne **Asst Manager:** Trevor Gough
Physio: Sean Hird **Press Officer:** Edwin O'Sullivan
Commercial Manager: Andrew Horsley (0114 2883867)

GROUND Address Bracken Moor Lane, Stocksbridge, Sheffield (0114 2742 882045). **Directions:** M1 jct 35a (from S), 36 (from N), A616 to Stocksbridge. On arrival in Stocksbridge turn left into Nanny Hill under the Clock Tower and continue up the hill for about 500 yds - ground on left.
Capacity: 3,500 **Cover:** 700 **Seats:** 450 **Floodlights:** Yes
Clubhouse: Open seven days (lunchtime & evenings). No food, but separate food bar open for matches.
Club Shop: Yes, badges, mugs, shirts, programmes and scarves on sale.

PREVIOUS - **Ground:** Stonemoor 49-51 52-53. **Names:** Stocksbridge Works, Oxley Park; clubs merged in 1986. **Leagues:** Sheffield Amateur/ Sheffield Association/ Yorkshire 49-82.

CLUB RECORDS - **Attendance:** 2,000 v Sheffield Wed., Floodlight opening Oct '91. **Fee Received:** £15,000 for Lee Mills (Wolves, 1992). **Fee Paid:** Nil. **Win:** 5-0 v Warrington Town NPL 96-97. **Defeat:** 0-5 v Whitley Bay NPL 97-98. **Scorer:** Trevor Jones (145). **Appearances:** Not known.

HONOURS - Northern Co's East Prem Div 93-94, R-up 95-96, Div 1 91-92, Lg Cup 94-95; Sheffield Snr Cup 92-93 95-96; *Oxley Park FC: County Sen Div 1 85-86: Stocksbridge Works FC: Yorkshire Lge Div 1 51-52 54-55 55-56 56-57 57-58 61-62 62-63, Div 2 50-51 64-65, Div 3 70-71 74-75, Lge Cup 61-62; Sheffield Snr Cup 51-52.*

Players progressing to Football League: Peter Eustace (Sheffield Wednesday) 1960 *(from Stocksbridge Works)*, Lee Mills (Wolverhampton Wanderers) 1992.

97-98 - Captain: Sean Dunphy **P.o.Y.:** Simon Marples **Top Scorer:** Gary Hurlestone (24)

Back Row (L-R); W Fieldsend, J Newton, P Keeton, P Cartledge, C Appleby, P Kenny, D Sedgewick, S Hird (Physio), G Ingham, S Shutt, A Watson, E O'Sullivan, R Sellars, W Harlow, D Webster, P Birkinshaw, A Horsley, K Murphy, D Keeton, A Bethal (Chr). R Fidler, S Needham, D Brooke, P Sykes, S Marples, Trevor Jones, Mick Horne (Mgr), Trevor Gough (Asst Mgr), G Hurlstone, John Tesh, R Holmshaw, M Turner, S Dunphy, R Wake. Ground; Mascots Liam O'Sullivan, Christian Newton.

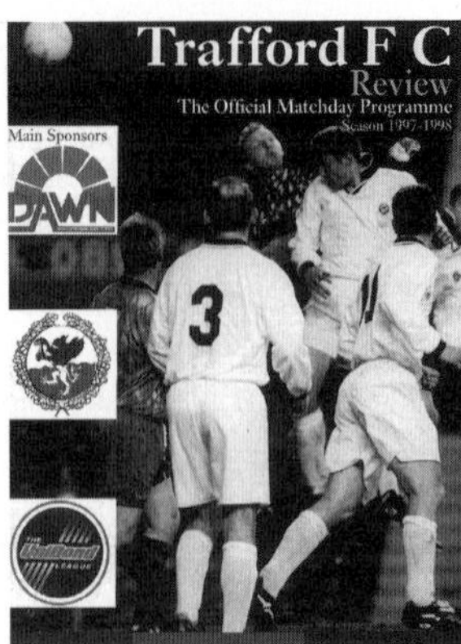

PROGRAMME DETAILS:
Pages: 44 **Price:** 75p
Editor: David Murray
(0161 775 7509)

TRAFFORD

Colours: All White
Sponsors: Dawn Processing Ltd
Change colours: Red/navy/red
Formed: 1990
Midweek Matchday: Tuesday
Nickname: The North
Reserve League: Mid Cheshire Div 2
Local Press: Stretford & Urmston Messenger, Manchester Evening News
Local Radio: GMR Talk, Piccadilly Radio

Chairman: David Brown **President:** K Illingworth
Secretary: Graham Foxall, 62 Grosvenor Road, Urmston M41 5AQ (0161 746 9726)
Manager: David Law **Asst Manager:** Mark Molyneaux
Coach: Dave Higgs

GROUND Address: Shawe View, Pennybridge Lane, Flixton, Urmston, Manchester M41 5DL (0161 747 1727) **Directions:** M60 jct 9, B5158 towards Urmston, at 1st r/about take 1st exit, 1st lights turn right into Moorside Road, at next r/about 2nd exit into Bowfell Rd, at next lights turn sharp left, then immediately right into Pennybridge Lane next to Bird-in-Hand Pub, parking on left 100 yds.
Capacity: 2,500 **Cover:** 732 **Seats:** 284 **Floodlights:** Yes
Clubhouse: Yes **Club Shop:** Yes

PREVIOUS - **Leagues:** Mid Cheshire 90-92; North West Counties 92-97. **Name:** North Trafford 90-94.

CLUB RECORDS - **Attendance:** 803 v Flixton (NPL Div 1 27/12/97) **Goalscorer:** Colin Small 74 **Appearances:** Jay McComb 237 **Win:** 10-0 v Haslingden St Mary's (Lancs Amt Shield 91) **Defeat:** 0-6 v Oldham Town (NWCL Div 2 93) **Transfer Fee Paid:** Undisclosed for Jock Russell (Radcliffe Borough). **Received:** Undisclosed for Mike Turner (Witton Albion).

BEST SEASON - **FA Vase:** 5th Rd 95-96 **FA Trophy:** 1st Qual Rd 97-98 (1st season) **FA Cup:** 2nd Rd Qual 95-96

HONOURS - Lamont Pils Trophy 93-94; NWCL Div 1 96-97, Div 2 R-up 93-94, Lge Chall Cup R-up 96-97; Res Div 93-94; Carling Chall Cup R-up 94-95; Manchester Prem Cup R-up 94-95, R-up 96-97, Res Div Champ 96-97, Cup 96-97; Manchester Amt Cup 96-97. Unifilla 1st Div Cup 97-98.

Players progressing to Football League: Anthony Vaughan (Ipswich)

97-98 **Captain:** Garry Vaughan **P.o.Y.:** Tom Murray **Top Scorer:** Chris Simms/Tom Murray (12)

Back Row (L-R); Darren Kelsey, Chris Patterson, Jim O'Donnell, Alan Pannett, Steve Raffell, Steve Burns, Chris Simms. Front Row; Tony Briffa, Tom Murray, Garry Vaughan (Capt), Chris Adams

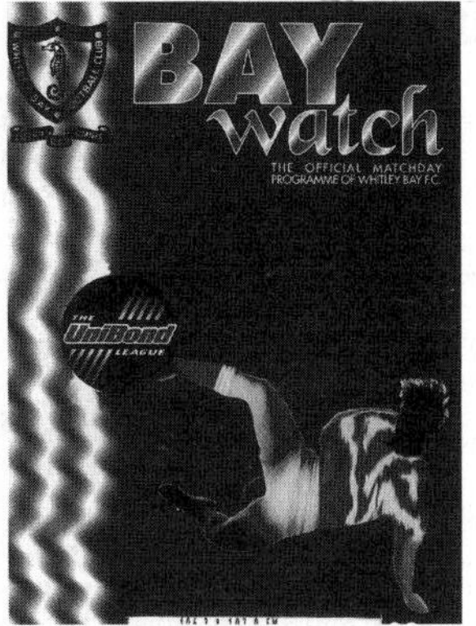

PROGRAMME DETAILS:
Pages: 24 **Price:** 80p
Editor: David Hunter
(0191 291 3637)

WHITLEY BAY

Colours: Blue & white stripes/blue/blue
Change colours: Yellow/sky blue
Midweek home matchday: Tuesday.
Local Press: The News, Guardian, Herald & Post.
Local Radio: Radio Newcastle, Metro.

Formed: 1897
Nickname: The Bay

Chairman: Colin Cameron
Vice Chairman: Peter Siddle
President: J Hedworth
Secretary: Derek Breakwell, 27 kings Road, Whitley Bay, Tyne And Wear, NE26 3BD (0191 252 7940).
Manager: Patrick Lowery
Asst Manager: Steve Kendal
Coach: Bill Charlton
Physio: Joe Jabs
Press Officer: David Hunter
Commercial Manager:

GROUND Address: Hillheads Park, Rink Way off Hillheads Road, Whitley Bay, Tyne & Wear NE25 8HR (0191 291 3637 Club) (Fax & matchday office 0191 291 3636).
Directions: 1 mile walk from bus station - leave St Pauls Church southward, turn right at r-about, ground 3rd left at rear of ice rink. Whitley Bay (25 mins from Newcastle) or Monkseaton metro stations, both 1 mile.
Capacity: 4,500 **Cover:** 650 **Seats:** 450 **Floodlights:** Yes
Clubhouse: Open 7-11pm, except Wed. Bar & concert room. Darts, pool.
Club Shop: Sells programmes, scarves, hats etc.
Contact Tom Moody (0191 291 1618) **Metal Badges:** Yes

PREVIOUS - **Name:** Whitley Bay Athletic 1950-58. **Leagues:** Tyneside 09-10, Northern Alliance 50-55, North Eastern League 55-58, Northern League 58-88.

CLUB RECORDS - **Attendance:** 7,301 v Hendon, FA Amateur Cup 1965. **Win:** 12-0 v Shildon 1961. **Defeat:** 1-8 v Bishop Auckland 1979. **Goalscorer:** Billy Wright 307. **Appearances:** Bill Chater 640. **Transfer Fee Paid:** £500 for Paul Walker from Blyth Spartans. **Received:** £ 10,000 for Kevin Todd from Berwick Rangers.

BEST SEASON - **FA Amateur Cup:** Semi Final 65-66 68-69. **FA Trophy:** 3rd Rd 86-87. **FA Cup:** 3rd Rd 89-90 (0-1 v Rochdale [A]). 2nd Rd 90-91 (0-1 v Barrow [H]). **League clubs defeated:** Scarborough, Preston North End 89-90.

HONOURS - Northern Premier Lg Div 1 90-91 (Div 1 Cup 88-89 90-91), Northern Lg 64-65 65-66 (R-up 59-60 66-67 68-69 69-70), Lg Cup 64-65 70-71 (R-up 67-68); Northern Alliance 52-53 53-54 (Lg Cup 52-53 53-54); Northumberland Senior Cup 52-53 60-61 63-64 64-65 67-68 68-69 69-70 70-71 72-73 86-87 (R-up 53-54 54-55 55-56 65-66 76-77 85-86 90-91).

Players progressing to Football League: W Dodd (Burnley 56), W Younger (Nottm Forest 57), R Brown (Blackpool 65), J Ritchie (Port Vale 65), John Brodie & A McCaffery (Carlisle 67 & 88), M Spelman (Wolves 69), T Harrison (Southport 77), M Miller (Gillingham 81), G Haire (Bradford City 83), S Ferebee (Darlington 87), David John Cullen (Hartlepool 97, Sheffield Utd), Kevin Todd (Berwick Rangers).

97-98 Captain: Gary Lurmor **P.o.Y.:** Andy Blower **Top scorer:** Martin Henderson

Action between Whitley's match v Gretna. Photo: Alan Watson

PROGRAMME DETAILS:
Pages: 32 **Price:** £1
Editor: Phil Chadwick.
(01606 44845)

WITTON ALBION

Colours: Red & white stripes — **Formed:** 1887
Change colours: All yellow — **Nickname:** The Albion
Midweek matchday: Tuesday — **Sponsors:**
Reserve League: None
Local Press: Northwich Guardian, Northwich Chronicle
Local Radio: BBC GMR, BBC Radio Stoke.

President: T Stelfox — **Chairman:** D T Lloyd
Secretary: Phil Chadwick, 29 Jack Lane, Davenham, Northwich, Cheshire CW9 8LF (01606 44845)
Manager: Kevin Tully — **Coach:** Rob Brown
Commercial Mgr: — **Physio:** John Bird

GROUND Address: Wincham Park, Chapel St, Wincham, Northwich (Tel/Fax: 01606 43008) **Directions:** M6 junc 19. A556 towards Northwich, after 3 miles turn onto A559 at beginning of dual carriageway, after 3/4 mile turn left opposite Black Greyhound Inn, grd 1/2 mile on left immediately after crossing Canal Bridge.
Capacity: 4,500 **Seated:** 650 **Cover:** 2,300 **Floodlights:** Yes

Clubhouse: Concert room and Vice-Presidents room open matchdays, Tuesday, Thursday, Friday and Sunday evenings. Food available for private functions. **Club Shop:** Yes

PREVIOUS - **Leagues:** Lancs Comb.; Cheshire County -79; Northern Premier 79-91, GMV Conference 91-94. **Grounds:** Central Ground, Witton Street, Northwich.

CLUB RECORDS - **Attendance:** 3,940 v Kidderminster Harriers - FA Trophy Semi-Final. **Win:** 6-0 v Stafford Rangers - 1992/93. **Defeat:** 0-5 v Welling United (H), GMV Conference 12/3/94. **Fee Paid:** £12,500 to Hyde Utd for Jim McCluskie 91. **Fee Received:** £11,500 for Peter Henderson from Chester City. **Goalscorer:** Frank Fidler 122. **Appearances:** John Goryl 652.

BEST SEASON - **FA Trophy:** Runners-up 91-92, Semi-Finals 90-91, 92-93. **FA Cup:** 91-92 Second Round 91-92, 1-5 v Preston North End (A). **League clubs defeated:** Halifax Town 91-92.

HONOURS - Northern Prem Lge 90-91; Cheshire County Lge 48-49 49-50 53-54 (R-up 50-51), Lge Cup 53-54 75-76; Cheshire County Sen Cup (7); FA Trophy R-up 91-92 (SF 90-91 92-93).

Players progressing to the Football League: P Henderson (Chester City), Chris Nicholl (ex-Southampton manager), Phil Power (Crewe), Neil Parsley & Mike Whitlow (Leeds).

97-98 - Captain: Mark Wright **Top Scorer:** Darren Washington **P.o.Y:** Brian Pritchard

Back Row (L-R); Bancroft, Washington, Boswell, Pritchard, Wright, Brenchley. Front Row; Gardner, Dowe, Gedman, Heeson, Carter, Roberts. Photo: Keith Clayton

NORTH WEST COUNTIES FOOTBALL LEAGUE

Founded: 1982

FEEDER TO: NORTHERN PREMIER LEAGUE

Chairman: J E Hinchliffe **Treasurer:** K H Dean
Secretary: M Darby,
87 Hillary Road, Hyde, Cheshire SK14 4EB
Tel/Fax: 0161 368 6243

Kidsgrove Athletic won the Championship but were not promoted. However it was a superb all round season in which they made many friends. They reached the FA Carlsberg Vase semi-final ?? ?? ?? Craig Walker on the attack for them against AFC Lymington in the Fifth Round.

Photo: Martin Wray

FINAL LEAGUE TABLES 1997-98

Division One

	P	W	D	L	F	A	Pts
Kidsgrove Athletic	42	32	3	7	127	50	99
Burscough	42	29	7	6	101	30	94
Newcastle Town	42	23	16	3	82	32	85
Vauxhall GM	42	24	9	9	91	52	81
St Helens Town	42	22	12	8	91	59	78
Citheroe	42	21	10	11	72	51	73
Prescot Cables	42	19	11	12	72	57	68
Glossop North End	42	19	7	16	78	69	64
Mossley	42	16	14	12	67	52	62
Nantwich Town	42	17	6	19	71	79	57
Maine Road	42	15	10	17	56	70	55
Chadderton	42	15	8	19	63	59	53
Rossendale United	42	15	6	21	61	80	51
Blackpool Rovers	42	13	9	20	68	84	48
Atherton LR	42	12	11	19	54	73	47
Haslngden	42	12	10	20	68	95	46
Ramsbottom United	42	12	9	21	58	85	45
Salford City	42	13	4	25	64	92	43
Warrington Town	42	10	10	22	56	72	40
Holker Old Boys	42	7	12	23	46	96	33
Darwen	42	6	13	23	42	93	31
Atherton Collieries	42	7	9	26	42	100	30

Division Two

	P	W	D	L	F	A	Pts
Oldham Town	40	27	8	5	118	49	89
Skelmersdale Utd	40	26	7	7	111	50	85
Leek CSOB	40	26	7	7	76	38	85
Cheadle Town	40	24	9	7	108	58	81
Woodley Sports	40	22	7	11	118	56	73
Formby	40	22	7	11	90	63	73
Bootle	40	19	15	6	82	60	72
Garswood United	40	19	10	11	98	62	67
Tetley Walker	40	19	9	12	98	62	66
Castleton Gabriels	40	18	7	15	86	59	61
Maghull	40	16	10	14	67	62	58
Fleetwood Freeport	40	15	11	14	73	55	56
Nelson	40	17	5	18	69	76	56
Bacup Borough	40	13	8	19	58	83	47
Squires Gate	40	11	9	20	72	88	42
Daisy Hill	40	11	9	20	60	86	42
Middlewich Athletic	40	11	8	21	48	90	41
Colne	40	8	7	25	48	91	31
Ashton Town	40	6	6	28	73	137	24
Stantondale	40	4	4	32	50	146	16
Blackpool Mechs	40	2	5	33	33	165	11

DIVISION ONE RESULTS CHART 1997-98

		1	2	3	4	5	6	7	8	9	10	11	12	13	14	15	16	17	18	19	20	21	22
1	Atherton C	X	0-0	0-1	0-1	2-2	0-2	2-2	1-1	2-2	2-0	0-2	2-1	0-0	3-5	1-3	1-2	1-1	1-5	0-3	2-3	1-2	1-1
2	Atherton LR	0-1	X	0-0	0-4	1-0	0-0	4-1	1-0	2-1	1-0	1-3	3-7	1-1	5-1	1-1	0-0	0-0	0-1	3-2	1-2	2-2	1-2
3	Blackpool R	2-0	2-3	X	0-4	0-2	2-2	2-0	2-1	5-2	1-1	1-6	1-3	2-1	3-0	1-2	1-2	5-3	1-0	1-1	3-1	1-2	2-3
4	Burscough	8-0	4-3	3-2	X	1-0	1-2	4-0	6-1	4-0	3-0	2-3	1-2	0-0	3-1	0-0	3-0	1-0	2-0	0-1	3-0	1-1	6-0
5	Chadderton	1-2	0-1	2-0	0-1	X	1-0	4-1	3-7	5-2	2-2	0-2	1-2	0-2	3-0	2-3	1-2	0-1	2-2	1-1	5-1	0-2	1-0
6	Citheroe	2-0	2-1	2-0	1-2	3-2	X	4-1	1-3	0-3	2-0	1-3	1-2	3-1	3-1	0-0	3-2	4-0	4-1	4-1	3-1	0-2	3-3
7	Darwen	1-0	1-3	0-4	0-1	0-0	3-1	X	3-3	1-1	0-2	0-5	0-3	2-0	2-0	2-2	1-2	2-5	3-5	1-1	1-0	2-2	2-1
8	Glossop NE	1-0	4-1	3-1	2-4	0-1	0-2	5-1	X	1-2	4-0	0-3	3-0	0-0	2-1	1-1	1-1	2-0	1-3	3-1	3-5	0-2	2-1
9	Haslingden	1-2	2-2	3-3	1-5	2-1	2-2	4-2	1-5	X	2-2	3-2	0-3	1-1	2-1	0-1	3-5	0-2	3-1	1-4	5-0	2-2	1-0
10	Holker OB	1-4	4-1	4-1	2-2	1-1	0-0	0-0	0-1	2-0	X	1-2	2-0	0-2	0-1	4-0	0-3	0-1	0-6	0-1	2-2	3-3	1-1
11	Kidsgrove A	5-0	3-2	3-0	1-1	3-1	3-1	5-0	5-1	4-0	4-0	X	5-2	4-3	2-1	3-2	1-3	2-0	7-0	7-2	4-1	1-3	3-0
12	Maine Road	3-0	1-0	0-3	0-2	0-3	2-2	1-1	1-3	0-1	1-0	3-1	X	2-1	0-2	1-4	2-0	2-2	1-4	0-3	2-1	3-2	0-0
13	Mossley	5-0	1-1	1-1	0-0	1-2	1-1	1-1	2-0	4-2	5-1	1-3	1-1	X	2-2	1-2	1-1	2-1	2-0	0-1	3-2	3-2	3-0
14	Nantwich T	2-2	3-4	4-2	0-1	1-0	0-1	4-1	1-1	4-2	4-0	1-6	1-1	1-1	X	0-2	0-4	4-1	2-1	1-4	3-2	3-0	3-2
15	Newcastle T	4-0	4-0	6-0	3-1	0-0	1-1	4-1	2-0	0-0	5-1	0-0	2-0	1-2	2-1	X	2-1	4-0	2-0	1-1	1-1	2-1	2-2
16	Prescot Cbl	1-0	2-0	0-0	0-1	1-1	2-1	1-0	0-0	3-4	7-1	2-2	3-0	0-2	0-4	1-1	X	1-2	4-1	3-3	1-1	0-1	2-1
17	Ramsbottom	4-2	2-1	2-1	0-3	5-3	1-2	1-1	1-3	3-1	0-0	1-2	0-0	3-2	2-0	0-3	3-4	X	2-2	0-5	1-2	3-3	1-4
18	Rossendale	3-0	1-0	1-1	0-5	2-1	0-1	1-0	2-6	1-1	4-1	1-0	3-1	1-3	0-1	0-2	1-2	1-1	X	1-3	0-0	0-3	1-0
19	St Helens T	4-2	3-0	4-4	1-1	1-2	0-0	2-2	3-1	4-2	6-1	4-2	1-1	0-1	2-3	0-0	1-1	3-2	5-0	X	1-0	2-1	3-2
20	Salford C	4-1	1-3	3-4	1-3	0-2	0-3	1-0	3-0	2-0	5-0	1-2	5-2	1-4	2-0	0-4	4-0	2-1	0-3	1-2	X	0-1	1-4
21	Vauxhall GM	6-0	3-0	2-1	2-1	1-3	3-1	2-0	1-2	2-1	4-4	1-2	0-0	3-0	2-3	0-0	1-0	3-0	3-2	3-0	4-1	X	5-2
22	Warrington	3-4	1-1	2-1	0-2	0-2	0-1	0-0	0-1	0-2	2-3	3-1	0-0	3-0	1-1	1-1	1-3	2-0	3-0	0-1	5-1	0-3	X

LEAGUE CHALLENGE CUP 1997-98

FIRST ROUND

Atherton LR	v	Warrington Town	0-2	Burscough	v	Tetley Walker	2-0
Cheadle Town	v	Prescot Cables	2-2 aet, 1-3	Clitheroe	v	Bacup Borough	3-2
Darwen	v	Glossop North End	1-7	Formby	v	Castleton Gabriels	1-2
Garswood Untied	v	Rossendale United	5-3 aet	Kidsgrove Athletic	v	Holker OB	3-2 aet
Maine Road	v	Atherton Collieries	3-2	Middlewich Athletic	v	Nelson	3-4 aet
Mossley	v	Chadderton	1-2	Nantwich Town	v	Maghull	0-0 aet, 3-3aet

SECOND ROUND

Burscough	v	Nelson	5-0	Castleton Gabriels	v	Glossop NE	2-3
Clitheroe	v	Vauxhall GM	0-2	Garswood United	v	Newcastle Town	5-0
Kidsgrove Athletic	v	Chadderton	2-0	Maine Road	v	Blackpool Rovers	1-2
Nantwich Town	v	Prescot Cables	1-0	Skelmersdale Utd	v	Warrington Town	3-1

THIRD ROUND

Blackpool Rovers	v	Vauxhall GM	1-3 aet	Garswood United	v	Glossop NE	2-2 aet, 0-2
Nantwich Town	v	Burscough	2-1	Skelmersdale Utd	v	Kidsgrove Athletic	3-4

SEMI-FINAL

Glossop NE	v	Vauxhall GM	1-3 Agg	Nantwich Town	v	Kidsgrove Athletic	1-8 Agg

FINAL

Kidsgrove Athletic v Vauxhall GM 1-0

FLOODLIT TROPHY 1997-98

SEMI-FINAL

Kidsgrove Athletic	v	Burscough	4-6 Agg	Vauxhall GM	v	St Helens Town	1-4 Agg

FINAL

Burscough v St Helens Town 2-1 aet

SECOND DIVISION TROPHY CUP 1997-98

SEMI-FINAL

Formby	v	Squires Gate	1-4 Agg	Garswood United	v	Tetley Walker	2-3 Agg

FINAL

Squires Gate v Tetley Walker 0-3

LEADING GOALSCORERS 1997-98 (DIVISION ONE)

53	Scott Dundas	Kidsgrove Athletic
49	Robbie Cowley	Burscough
47	Steve Pennington	St Helens Town
37	Gregg Blundell	Vauxhall GM
36	Paul Kiely	Kidsgrove Athletic
32	Mark Wilde	Burscough
26	Steve O'Neill	St Helens Town
24	Peter Cumiskey	Prescot Cables
24	Richard Batho	Kidsgrove Athletic
23	Dave Baron	Blackpool Rovers
22	John Burndred	Newcastle Town
22	Danny Hobby	Kidsgrove Athletic
21	Mark Walsh	Clitheroe
21	Nicky Young	Vauxhall GM
20	Gavin McDonald	Prescot Cables

NORTH WEST COUNTIES DIVISION ONE CLUBS 1998-99

ATHERTON COLLIERIES

Chairman: Steve Payne **Vice Chairman:** **President:** J Fielding
Secretary: Emil Anderson, 109 Douglas St, Atherton, Gtr Manchester M46 9EB (01942 87209 (H), 0161 288 6216 (B)
Manager: Tommy Harrison/Brian Smith **Physio:** Ernie Ackers
Ground: Atherton Collieries Football Ground, Atherton, Gt Manchester (01942 884649).
Directions: M61 Jct 5, follow sign for Westhoughton, left onto A6, right onto A579 (Newbrook Rd/Bolton Rd) into Atherton. At first set of lights turn left into High Street, 2nd left into Alder St. to ground. Quarter mile from Atherton Central (BR).
Seats: 300 **Cover:** 1,000 **Capacity:** 2,500 **Floodlights:** Yes **Founded:** 1916
Colours: Black & white stripes/black/black. **Change colours:** All blue **Nickname:** Colls
Reserves' Lge: NWTL Res Div **Record Attendance:** 3,300 in Lancs Combination, 1920's
Midweek Matches: Tuesday **Club Sponsors:** Kensite
Club Shop: No, but programmes, badges available
Programme: 40 pages, 60p **Editor:** Frank Anderson.
Previous Lges: Bolton Comb. 20-50 52-71, Lancs Comb. 50-52 71-78, Cheshire Co. 78-82.
Players progressing to Football League: J Parkinson (Wigan), Russell Beardsmore (Manchester Utd).
Clubhouse: Open Mon-Fri 7-11pm, Sat 11am-11pm, Sun noon-3 & 7-10.30pm. Hot & cold food on matchdays.
Captain 97-98: Simon O'Brien **P.o.Y.:** Scott Dowds **Top Scorer:** Alan Shawcross
Hons: BNWCFL 3rd Div Champ 86/87; Bridge Shield 85/86; Lancs County FA Shield 19/20, 22/23, 41/42, 45/46. 56/57, 64/65; Tennents F/lit Trophy Finalist 94/95; NWCFL Div 2 R/up 95/96

ATHERTON L. R.

President: **Chairman:** Brian Horsebury. **Treasurer:** Jack Hetherington
Secretary: Steve Hartle, 32 Greensmith Way, Westhoughton, Bolton BL5 3DR (01942 840906).
Manager: Gerry Luczha **Assistant Manager:** Ian Senior **Coach:** Steve Walton
Ground: Crilly Park, Spa Road, Atherton, Greater Manchester (01942 883950).
Directions: M61 to Jct 5, follow signs for Westhoughton, left onto A6, right onto A579 (Newbrook Rd/Bolton Rd) over the railway bridge, right into Upton Rd passing Atherton Central Station, left into Springfield Rd and left again into Hillside Rd into Spa Rd and ground.
Seats: 250 **Cover:** 3 sections **Capacity:** 3,000 **Floodlights:** Yes **Club Shop:** Yes
Programme: 48 pages 70p **Editor:** Mark Salt (01942 796256)
Formed: 1954 **Nickname:** The Panthers **Sponsors:** T B A
Colours: Yellow/royal/royal **Change colours:** Red & white/black/black **Midweek Matches:** Tuesday
Reserve Team's League: North West Alliance.
Previous - Leagues: Bolton Combination/ Cheshire County 80-82/ NWCL 82-94/ NPL 94-97. **Name:** Laburnum Rovers 54-79 **Grounds:** Laburnum Road 54-56/ Hagfold 56-66.
Clubhouse: Open normal licensing hours.
Club Records - Attendance: 1,856 v Aldershot Town, FA Vase Quarter-Final replay 5/3/94. **Goalscorer:** Shaun Parker **Appearances:** Jimmmy Evans. **Transfer Fee Paid:** £500 for Joey Dunn from Warrington Town **Received:** £1,500 for Stuart Humphries to Barrow
Best Season: FA Cup: 3rd Qual Rd 96-97, 0-2 v Bamber Bridge. **FA Vase:** Semi-Final replay 94-95 (1-2 v Diss Town). **FA Trophy:** 1st Qual Rd 96-97
Players progressing to Football League: Barry Butler (Chester), Lee Unsworth (Crewe).
Honours:: North West Counties Lge 92-93 93-94, Champions Trophy 92-93 93-94, F/Lit Trophy 93-94; Northern Premier Lge Div.1 Cup R-up 95-96

BLACKPOOL (Wren) ROVERS

Chairman: J Nolan **Manager:** Brian Wilson
Secretary: P Kimberley, 34 Priory Gate, South Shore, Blackpool FY4 2QE (H 01253 349853) (B 01253 737464)
Ground: Bruce Park, School Road, Marton, Blackpool, Lancs, (01253 760570)
Directions: M6 to M55, leave junc 4, left onto A583, sharp right at 1st lights (Whitehill Rd), follow signs for Airport. Ground approx 1.5 miles on right. 6 miles from Blackpool North BR station.
Seats: 500 **Cover:** 1000 **Capacity:** 1,500 **Floodlights:** Yes **Club Shop:** No.
Programme: 20 pages, 50p **Editor:** P Kimberley **Nickname:** Wrens
Colours: All red **Change colours:** All blue **Founded:** 1936
Midweek matchday: Tuesday **Reserve League:** West Lancs
Record Attendance: 1,011 v Manchester City, floodlight opener Oct 1991
Previous leagues: West Lancs, Lancs Comb 72-82 **Previous Name:** Wren Rovers
Clubhouse: Open matchdays
Honours: W Lancs Lg 69-70 70-71, (Lge Cup 70/71, 71/72); Lancs FA Shield 68-69 70-71; Lancs Comb 78-79 80-81, (R-up 77-78), Lge Cup 78-79.

BOOTLE

Chairman: Frank Doran. **Manager:** T.B.A.
Secretary: Paul Carr, 58 Orchard Hey, Old Roan, Bootle, Merseyside L30 8RY (H 0151 474 0153) (B 0151 951 4799)
Ground: Bucks Park, Northern Perimeter Road, Netherton, Bootle, Merseyside L30 7PT (0151 526 1850).
Directions: End of M57 & M58 follow signs to Bootle and Docks A5063. Turn right at next lights by Police station. Entrance 100 yds on right. Old Roan station 300yds. Bus 55 (150yds from grd), 302 341 345 350 (350yds).
Seats: 400 **Cover:** 1,400 **Capacity:** 5,000 **Floodlights:** Yes **Club Shop:**Yes.
Programme: 32 pages, 50p **Editor:** Secretary
Colours: All royal blue **Change colours:** Yellow/black/black
Sponsors: Taximex **Nickname:** Bucks **Founded:** 1953
Midweek matchday: Tuesday **Reserve League:** Liverpool Co. Combination.
Records - Attendance: 750 v Carshalton Athletic, FA Trophy 2nd Rd 31/1/81. **Win:** 9-1 v Glossop (H), North West Counties League 8/2/86 **Defeat:** 1-8 v Accrington Stanley (A), North West Counties League 83
Previous - Leagues: Liverpool Shipping, Liverpool County Comb., Lancs Comb. 74-78, Cheshire Lge 78-82. **Name:** Langton 53-73 **Grounds:** Edinburgh Park 53-73, Orrell Mount Park 73-78.
Players progressing to Football League: Graeme Worsley (Shrewsbury Town 89), Lee Steele (Shrewsbury 96).
Clubhouse: Normal pub hours. Darts & pool.
97-98 Captain: Billy Loughlin **Top Scorer:** Marcel Anzani & Ronnie Morgan 14.
P.o.Y: Ronnie Morgan
Club record appearances: Peter Cumiskey (almost 400).
Hons: North West Counties League Div 2 Runners-up 92-93 (Floodlit Trophy 93-94), Liverpool Challenge Cup 64-65 75-76 78-79, Liverpool Amtr Cup 65-66 67-68 73-74, Lancs Amtr Cup 69-70, Liverpool County Combination 64-65 65-66 67-68 68-69 69-70 70-71 71-72 72-73 73-74, George Mahon Cup 66-67 67-68 68-69 69-70 72-73 73-74, Lancs Combination 75-76 76-77 (League Cup 75-76), Cheshire County League Div 2 78-79.

CHEADLE TOWN

President: Freddie Pye **Chairman:** Chris Davies **Vice-Chairman:** Clive Williams
Secretary: Susan Burton, 2 Lavington Ave., Cheadle, Stockport, Cheshire SK8 2HH (0161 491 0823).
Manager: Peter Blundell. **Physio:** John Hornbuckle
Ground: Park Road Stadium, Park Road, Cheadle, Cheshire SK8 2AN (0161 428 2510).
Directions: M60 Jct 2, follow signs towards Cheadle (A560), first left after lights into Park Road, ground at end. 1 mile from Gatley (BR), buses from Stockport.
Seats: 300 **Cover:** 300 **Capacity:** 2,500 **Floodlights:** Yes **Club Shop:** No
Programme: 24 pages, 50p. **Editor:** Stuart Crawford **Press Officer:** Chris Davies (0161 428 2510).
Colours: White/black/black **Change colours:** All blue. **Founded:** 1961
Midweek Matches: Tuesday **Reserves' Lge:** NW Counties Lge
Club Records - Gate: 1,700 v Stockport County, August 94. **Goalscorer:** Peter Tilley **Appearances:** John McArdle
Previous Lges: Manc. (pre 1987).
Players progressing to Football League: Ashley Ward (Crewe), Steve Bushell (York), Dean Crowe (Stoke).
Clubhouse: Open every night. Food available.
97-98 Captain: Ian Henderson **P.o.Y.:** Tony McCombe **Top Scorer:** Steve Mallinson
Honours: Manchester Lg Div 1 79-80 (R-up 80-81 81-82); Manchester Amtr Cup 79-80; Lamot Pils R-up 90-91; NWCFL Div 2 Trophy R-up 95-96:

CLITHEROE

Chairman: S Rush **President:** Jer Aspinall
Secretary/Press Officer: Colin Wilson, 4 Moss Street, Clitheroe, Lancs BB7 1DP (01200 424370).
Manager: Denis Underwood/Gary Butcher **Coach:** **Physio:** Keith Lord.
Ground: Shawbridge, Clitheroe, Lancs (01200 423344).
Directions: M6 jct 31, A59 to Clitheroe (17 miles), at 5th r'bout continue for half a mile and turn left at Pendle Road. Ground one mile, behind Bridge Inn' on the right. 11 miles from Blackburn BR station
Seats: 300 **Cover:** 1200 **Capacity:** 2,000 **Floodlights:** Yes **Club Shop:**Yes.
Programme: 12 pages, 60p **Editor:** Ian Rimmer **Press Officer:** Colin Wilson
Formed: 1877. **Nickname:** The Blues
Colours: Blue & white stripes/blue/blue **Change colours:** All yellow
Midweek matchday: Monday **Reserves' Lge:** N.W.C.L.
Club Records - Attendance: 2,000 v Mangotsfield, FA Vase Semi/F 95-96. **Goalscorer:** Don Francis **Appearances:** Lindsey Wallace.
Previous Lges: Blackburn & Dist./Lancs Comb. 03-04 05-10 25-82.
Players progressing to Football League: Ray Woods (Leeds 1950), Chris Sims (Blackburn 1960), Lee Rogerson (Wigan Ath), Carlo Nash (Crystal Palace).
Clubhouse: Open during matches. Snacks available.
Hons: Lancs Comb. 79-80 (Lg Cup 34-35); Lancs Challenge Tphy 84-85; NW Co's Lg 85-86 (Div 2 84-85, Div 3 83-84; East Lancs Floodlit Trophy 94-95; FA Vase Finalists 95-96.

GLOSSOP NORTH END

Chairman: J Dillon **President:** C T Boak
Secretary: Peter Hammond, 15 Longmoor Road, Simmondley, Glossop, Derbys SK13 9NH, Tel: (H 01457 863852) (B 01457 854411)
Manager: Ged Coyne **Asst Manager:** Tommy Martin **Physio:** TBA.
Ground: Surrey Street, Glossop, Derbys (01457 855469).
Directions: A57 (Manchester-Sheffield) to Glossop town centre, turn into Shrewsbury Street, follow to top of the hill, left at T-junction for ground. 700 yds from Glossop (BR). Buses 236 & 237 from Manchester.
Seats: 209 **Cover:** 509 **Capacity:** 2,374 **Floodlights:** Yes **Club Shop:** Yes
Programme: 32 pages, 40p **Editor:** Mr P Heginbotham (0161 439 3932). **Press Officer:** Secretary.
Colours: Blue & white stripes/blue/blue **Change colours:** All gold.
Sponsor: Davis Blank Furniss Solicitors. **Nickname:** Hillmen. **Founded:** 1886
Midweek Matches: Tuesday **Reserve's League:** North Western Alliance.
Record Attendance: 10,736 v Preston North End, FA Cup 1913/14
Record transfer fee paid: £3,000 for Andy Gorton (Lincoln City, 1989).
Record transfer fee received: £3,000 for Andy Gorton (Oldham Athletic, 1990).
Previous Leagues: Midland 1896-98/ Football Lge 1898-1915/ Manchester Lge 15-56 66-78/ Lancs Combination 56-66/ Cheshire County 78-82.
Previous Names: Glossop North End 1886-1898/ Glossop FC 1898-1992.
Players progressing to Football League: Jimmy Rollands (Rochdale), Ray Redshaw (Wigan Athletic).
Clubhouse: Licensed bar. Hot & cold drinks and pies etc on matchdays.
Honours: Nth West Co's Lg Lamot Pils Trophy 90-91; Manchester Lg 27-28 (Gilgryst Cup 22-23 29-30 34-35 74-75); FA Amateur Cup QF 08-09.

HOLKER OLD BOYS

President: R Brady **Chairman:** Ron Moffatt **Vice Chairman:** Ray Sharp.
Secretary: Stewart Patton, 15 Bowfell Crescent, Barrow-in-Furness, Cumbria LA14 4PT (H 01229 832429) (B 019467 85600)
Manager: Des Johnson **Asst Manager:** Jim Capstick **Coach:** Jim Ballantyne.
Physio: Mark Hetherington **Comm. Manager:** Ged Woods **Press Officer:** John Taylor
Ground: Rakesmoor Lane, Hawcoat, Barrow-in-Furness, Cumbria (01229 828176).
Directions: M6 Jct 36, A590 to Barrow-in-Furness, on entering Barrow, continue across r'bout, 2nd right (Dalton Lane) to top of road, right into Rakesmoor Lane, ground on right.
Seats: 220 **Cover:** 500 **Capacity:** 2,500 **Floodlights:** Yes **Founded:** 1936
Colours: Green & yellow/green/yellow **Change colours:** Blue/red **Nickname:** Cobs.
Midweek Matches: Tuesday **Club Sponsors::** Kitchen Design Studio.
Previous Leagues: North Western/ Furness Premier/ West Lancs 70-91.
Previous Grounds: None.
Programme: 8 pages, 30p **Editor:** **Club Shop:** No.
Record Attendance: 1240 v Barrow ATS Tourny 95-96
Record win: 12-0 **Record defeat:** 1-8 v Newcastle T. (H) 91-92.
Clubhouse: Weekdays 8-11pm, Sat noon-11pm, Sunday normal licensing hours. Pies & peas on matchdays.
Club record scorer: Dave Conlin **Hons:** W Lancs Lg 86-87, R-up 85-86; Lancs Junior Shield 88-89 90-91.

KIDSGROVE ATHLETIC

Chairman: Leslie Wagg **President:** Ernie Langford
Secretary: Christine Osmond, 451 New Inn Lane, Trentham, Stoke-on-Trent, ST4 8BN (01782 644241).
Manager: Peter Ward **Coach:** Jack Heath **Physio:** Arthur Duckworth.
Ground: Clough Hall, Hollinwood Road, Kidsgrove, Stoke-on-Trent, Staffs (01782 782412).
Directions: M6 Jct 16, A500 towards Stoke, 2nd jctn onto A34 towards Manchester, turn right at 1st lights into Cedar Ave., 2nd right into Lower Ash Rd, 3rd left into Hollinwood Rd to ground. B R Kidsgrove (5mins)
Seats: 250 **Cover:** 600 **Capacity:** 4,500 **Floodlights:** Yes **Formed:** 1952
Colours: Blue/white/blue **Change Colours:**
Record Attendance: 538 **Clubhouse:** Yes
Previous Leagues: Staffordshire County, Mid Cheshire Lge.
Midweek Matches: Tuesday
Club Record Goalscorer: **Club Record Appearances:**
Honours: Mid Cheshire Lg 70-71 78-79 86-87 87-88, R-up 68-69 85-86; Lg Cup 67-68 69-70 85-86, R-up 84-85 86-87; Staffs Co. FA Vase 87-88 89-90; Staffs County Lge; Burslem & Tunstall Lge.

Clitheroe FC

Photo: John Newton

Glossop North End: Back Row (L-R); Micky Parr (Physio), Danny Wild, Mark Harries, Tony Dyzra, Kevin O'Connell, Chris Ringland, Mike Boyle, Kev Parr, Phil Hulme, Chris Bell, Sid White (Mgr). Front Row; Steve Smith, Steve Heaton, Steve Morgan, Dave Blow, Trev Smallwood, Paul Sunderland, Sid Pickford

Photo: John Newton

Mossley FC

Photo: John Newton

LEEK C.S.O.B. FC

Chairman: K J Hill, 11 Springfield Drive, Leek, Staffs ST13 (01538 371859)
Secretary: Stan Lockett, 5 Fitzherbert Close, Swynnerton, Stone, Staffs ST15 0PQ, (01782 796551 Mob 0802 301134)
Manager: Chris McMullen **Assistant Manager:** Andrew Walters **Physio:** Noel Carroll
Ground: Harrison Park, Macclesfield Road, Leek, Staffs, (01538 383734)
Directions: M6 south Junc 17, A534 to Congleton - follow signs for Leek (A54), carry on until junction with A523, turn right on to A523, this road is direct to Leek, ground is 8 miles, on right just into Leek.
Capacity: 6,000 **Seating:** 600 **Covered:** Whole Ground **Floodlights:** Yes
Colours: White & red/red/white **Change colours:** Black & white/black/white
Founded: 1945 **Midweek Matchday:** Wednesday
97-98 Captain: Steve Callear **Programme:** Yes **Editor:** Stan Leckett
Previous Leagues: Leek & Moorland Lge, Staffs County North, Refuge Midland Lge.
Honours: Refuge Midland Lge 95-96. Lge Cup 94-95 95-96; Leek Cup 94-95 95-96; Midland Ref Charity Shield 95-96; Sportsline Chall Cup 95-96.

MAINE ROAD

Chairman: Mr R Meredith **President:** Mr F G Thompson.
Secretary: Mr K Hunter, 157 Aston Ave., Fallowfield, Manchester M14 7HN (0161 226 9937).
Manager: G Whittingham **Asst Manager:** **Physio:** E Jenkinson.
Ground: Manchester Co. FA Grnd, Brantingham Rd., Chorlton-cum-Hardy, Manchester M21 0TT (0161 862 9619).
Directions: M63 Jct 7, A56 towards City Centre, right onto A5145 Chorlton/Stockport, through lights, left at next lights into Wilbraham Rd (A6010) to Chorlton, through lights for approx 1 mile. Left into Withington Rd, first left into Brantingham Rd, ground 300 yds on left. 2 miles from Stretford (Metrolink(tram)), 3 miles from Piccadilly and Victoria (BR). Buses 85 87 103 168 188 260 261 275
Seats: 200 **Cover:** 700 **Capacity:** 2,000 **Floodlights:** Yes **Club Shop:** No
Programme: 48 pages, 50p **Editor:** Mr R Price (0161 442 7269) **Press Officer:** P Ramsden
Colours: All blue **Change Colours:** All yellow
Sponsors: Surface Engineers **Nickname:** Blues **Founded:** 1955
Midweek matchday: Tuesday **Reserves League:** NW Co's Lge Reserve Division.
Club Records - Attendance: 875 v Altrincham, FA Cup 2nd Qual. Rd 29/9/90. **Goalscorer:** John Wright 140 **Appearances:** Gordon Woods 399. **Win:** 15-0 v Little Hulton 2/9/86 **Defeat:** 6-10 v Old Altrinchamians 22/9/79.
Best FA Cup year: 2nd Qual. 2nd replay 92-93. **Best FA Vase year:** 4th Rd 94-95.
Previous - Leagues: Rusholme Sunday 55-66/ Manchester Amtr Sunday 66-72/ Manchester 72-87. **Name:** City Supporters Rusholme **Grounds:** Hough End PF 55-73/ Ward Street O.B. 73-75/ Tootal Spts Ground 75-79/ Leesfield 79-80.
Clubhouse: Before/during/after games. Refreshment bar sells hot & cold drinks, pies, crisps, confectionary.
Honours: Manc. Prem. Lg(4) 82-86, Cup 82-83 83-84; Manc. County Prem. Cup 87-88, Chal. Cup(4) 82-83 84-87; NW Co's Lg Div 2 89-90 (R-up 88-89).

MOSSLEY

Chairman: Vacant **President:** J Wharmby
Secretary: Andrew Fenna, 254 Fairfied Rd., Droylsden, Manchester M43 6AN (0161 370 0508).
Manager: Benny Phillips **Coach:** **Physio:**
Ground: Seel Park, Market Street, Mossley, Lancs. (Grd 01457 832369), (Club 01457 836104).
Directions: From north; M62 Junc 20, A627M/A627 to Ashton-U-Lyne, A670 to Mossley- ground in town centre behind market place. From south; M6 Junc 19, A556, M56 to Junc 3, A5103 to manchester, then Mancunian Way (A57M) to A635. Follow Ashton signs 5 miles, the Mossley signs via A670 to town centre. Local station Mossley BR. Buses 153 from Manchester, 343 from Oldham, 350 from Ashton.
Capacity: 4,500 **Cover:** 1,500 **Seats:** 200 **Floodlights:** Yes **Club Shop:** Yes
Programme: 28 Pages 50p **Editor:** John A Cawthorne
Colours: White/black/black **Change colours:** Yellow/green/green.
Formed: 1903 **Nickname:** Lilywhites **Midweek home matchday:** Tuesday
Records - Attendance: 7,000 v Stalybridge, 50. **Fees - Paid:** £2,300 **Received:** £25,000 for Eamon O'Keefe (Everton, 79).
Best FA Cup season: 2nd Rd replay 49-50. Also 2nd Rd 80-81, 1st Rd 69-70 77-78 78-79 79-80 81-82 83-84.
League clubs defeated in FA Cup: Crewe Alexandra, 80-81.
Previous - Leagues: Ashton/ South East Lancs/ Lancs Combination 18-19/ Cheshire County 19-72, Northen Prem.
Names: Park Villa 03-04/ Mossley Juniors 04-09. **Ground:** Luzley.
Players progressing to Football League: J Wright (Blackpool 46), T Bell & A Wadsworth (Oldham 46/49), A Lomas (Rochdale 50), A Tyrer (Leeds 46), E Williams (Halifax 51), J Willis (A Villa 58), M Eckershall (Torquay 59), A Roberts (Bradford PA 69), G Pierce (Huddersfield 71), E O'Keefe (Everton 79), D Young (Wigan 83).
Clubhouse: Open nights and matchdays.
Honours: FA Trophy Runners-up 79-80; Northern Premier League 78-79 79-80 (R-up 80-81 81-82 82-83, Challenge Cup 78-79; NWCFL Floodlit Trophy Finalists 95-96;

NANTWICH TOWN

Chairman: R Tilley **Vice Chairman:** P Temmen **President:** J Davies
Secretary: Gary Wollaston, 68 Lunt Avenue, Crewe, CW2 7NA, (01270 668513)
Manager: Clive Jackson. **Asst Manager:** John Brydon. **Physio:** Keith Leigh.
Ground: Jackson Avenue, off London Road, Nantwich, Cheshire (01270 624098).
Directions: M6 Jct 16, A500 for Nantwich (about 8 miles), continue on A52 over railway crossing (London Rd), first right into Jackson Avenue. From Chester take A51. 3 miles from Crewe (BR).
Seats: 150 **Cover:** 555 **Capacity:** 1,500 **Floodlights:** Yes **Club Shop:** Yes
Programme: 18 pages, 65 **Editor:** Che Kerrin (01270 624098).
Colours: Black & white/black/black **Change colours:** All green.
Club Sponsors: Jim Barrie Plant Hire **Founded:** 1884 **Nickname:** Dabbers
Reserves' League: Refuge Assurance **Midweek matchday:** Tuesday.
Club Records - Attendance: 2,750 v Altrincham, Cheshire Senior Cup 66-67. **Goalscorer:** Gerry Duffy, 42 in 61-62.
Transfer fee paid: £4,000 from Stafford Rangers for D.Dawson. **Received:** £2,500 (P Mayman, Northwich).
Previous - Leagues: Shropshire & Dist./ The Combination 1892-94/ Lancs Comb. 12-15/ Cheshire Combination 19-38/ Manchester/ Mid-Cheshire/ Cheshire County 68-82. **Name:** Nantwich FC (pre 1973)
Clubhouse: Every night except Sunday 8pm-11pm. Hot pies available.
Hons: Cheshire Co. Lg 80-81; Ches. Snr Cup 75-76; Carling N.W. Co.Lg.Cup 94-95.

NEWCASTLE TOWN

Chairman: J W Walker **Vice-Chairman:** K G Walshaw **President:** K H Walshaw.
Secretary: John F Cotton, 293 Weston Road, Weston Coyney, Stoke-on-Trent, Staffs ST3 6HA (01782 333445)
Player/Manager: Ray Walker **Asst Manager:** Martin Smith **Physio:** Lee Arnold
Ground: 'Lyme Valley Parkway Stadium', Lilleshall Road, Clayton, Newcastle-under-Lyne, Staffs (01782 662351) (Club 01782 662350)
Directions: M6 jct 15, A500 for Stoke, left at r'bout A519 for Newcastle, right at 2nd r'bout into Stafford Ave., 1st left into Tittensor Road to ground. 3 miles from Stoke-on-Trent (BR).
Seats: 300 **Cover:** 1,000 **Capacity:** 4,000 **Floodlights:** Yes **Club Shop:** Yes
Programme: 40 pages, 50p **Editor:** Peter Tindall (01260 28093) **Press Officer:** Ray Tatton (01782 644916)
Colours: All Royal with red & white trim **Change colours:** All yellow
Club Sponsors: A.N.C.Ltd **Nickname:** Castle. **Founded:** 1964
Midweek Matches: Tuesday **Reserve Team:** Lycett's Burshlem & Newcastle Dist Lge
Records - Attendance: 3,948 v Notts County FA Cup Nov 96 **Goalscorer:** Shaun Wade 105 (NWCL only)
Appearances: Neil Pesteridge 275 (NWCL only). **Win:** 7-0 v Blackpool Mechanics, 8-1 v Holker Old Boys. **Defeat:** 0-5 v Eastwood Hanley (A).
Previous - Leagues: Hanley & Dist. Sunday/ North Staffs Sunday/ Potteries & Dist. Sunday/ Res Refuge Ass Mid/ Newcastle & Dist/ Staffs Co./ Mid Cheshire. **Names:** Parkway Hanley (founded 1964, later Clayton Park/ Parkway Clayton)/ Newcastle Town (founded 1980) - clubs merged in 1986. **Grounds:** Hanley Park 64-79/ Northwood Lane, Clayton 79-85.
Players progressing to Football League: C Beeston, G Shaw, P Ware, D Ritchie, D Hope, S Wade.
Clubhouse: Open Saturday matchdays noon-7.30pm and midweek 5-11pm. Hot & cold food always available.
97-98 - Captain: Andy Holmes **Top Scorer:** John Burndred (21) **P.o.Y.:** Neil Pesteridge
Hons: Nth West Co's Lg Div 1 R-up 95-96 96-97, Div 2 R-up 91-92, Challenge Cup 96-97, F/Lit Trophy R-up 96-97; Lamot Pils Tphy 91-92; Mid Cheshire Lg Div 1 85-86, R-up 86-78, Div 2 82-83, 90-91, Lge Cup 84-85; Walsall Snr Cup 93-94 94-95 R-up 95-96; Sentinel Cup 94-95; Tennents Floodlit Trophy 92-93 95-96; Staffs Snr Cup R-up 95-96; Staffs M/W F/Light Lge 94-95 R-up 95-96; Umbro Over 35 Chall Cup 94-95;

PRESCOT CABLES A.F.C.

President: Mr B F Taylor **Chairman:** Ted Mercer **Vice Chairman:** D J Lace
Secretary: Dot Lace, 20 Cable Road, Prescot, Merseyside (0151 426 6440).
Manager: Arthur McCumiskey **Asst Manager:** Derek Hughes
Commercial Manager: Arthur McCumiskey
Ground: Hoghton Road, Sutton, St Helens (01744 817225)
Directions: M62 Jct 7, take 4th exit (St Helens Linkway), exit Linkway at 3rd r/about (Sherdley) follow signs for Sutton, continue to Sutton Village, Ground just beyond St Helens Junc station 150 yards
Seats: 200 **Cover:** 550 **Capacity:** 4,400 **Floodlights:** Yes **Founded:** 1886
Record Gate: 8,122 v Ashton National, 1932 **Metal Badges:** Yes.
Colours: Gold/black/black **Change colours:** Blue/blue/gold **Nickname:** Tigers.
Previous - Leagues: Liverpool Co. Comb./ Lancs Comb. 1897-98 18-20 27-33 36-67/ Ches. Co. 33-36 78-82/ Mid Cheshire 67-78. **Names:** Prescot Athletic/ Prescot Cables 46-65 80-90/ Prescot Town 65-80.
Programme: 30 pages, 50p **Editor:** A McCumiskey **Club Shop:** No
Midweek Matches: Wednesday **Best FA Cup season:** 2nd Rd 57-58 59-60
Clubhouse: Refreshment bar, open matchdays/evenings for hot & cold refreshments.
Hons: Lancs Comb. 56-57 (Lg Cup 47-48); Ches. Lg Div 2 76-77; Mid Ches. Lg 76-77; L'pool Non-League Cup(4) 51-53 58-59 60-61; L'pool Chal. Cup(5) 28-30 48-49 61-62 77-78; George Mahon Cup 36-37.

Nantwich Town

Photo: John Newton

Newcastle Town: Back Row (L-R); Harry Walshaw (Coach), Trevor Brissett (Asst Mgr), Neil Posteridge, Simon Schwatz, Rob Wade, Chris Holmes, Andy Holmes, Albert Altonar, Michael Bates, Wayne Johnson. Front Row; Antony Buckle, Adrian Dunn, Dean Gillick, Richard Poxon, David Sutton, John Burndred.

Photo: Bill Wheatcroft

Ramsbottom United

Photo: John Newton

RAMSBOTTOM UNITED

Chairman: H Williams (01706 822799)
Secretary: John Maher, 75 Ramsbottom Road, Hawkshaw, Bury BL8 4JS. (01204 852742)
Ground: Riverside Ground, Acre Bottom, Ramsbottom. (01706 822799)
Directions: M66 (North) to junction 1, take A56 towards Ramsbottom. After 1 mile turn left Bury New Road. Turn left after Trinity paper Mill along the road running parallel with the East Lancs Railway.
Colours: Blue with white trim/blue/white **Formed:** 1966 **Floodlights:** Yes
Record Attendance: 464 v Haslingden NWCFL Div 2 29/3/97 **Midweek Matchday:** Wednesday
Previous Leagues: Bury Amateur League, Bolton Combination, Manchester Lge.
Honours: Bolton Comb. Div. One Champs 72-73; Bolton Comb. Prem Div. 76-77, 86-87; Manchester Lge Div. One Champs 90-91; Manchester Lge Div. 1 Cup Winners 90-91; Gilgryst Cup Winners 94-95; NWCFL Div 2 Champ 96-97, Trophy 95-96

ROSSENDALE UNITED

Chairman: J Feber **Vice-Chairman:** **President:**
Secretary: Wendy Ennis, 4 Brow Edge, Newchurch, Rossendale, Lancs BB4 7TT (01706 212634)
Manager: Mickey Graham **Coach:** John Hughes **Physio:**
Ground: Dark Lane, Staghills Rd, Newchurch, Rossendale, Lancs BB4 7UA (Grd 01706 215119; Club 213296)
Directions: M66 Junc 18, M66 north following signs for Burnley, then A682 to Rawstenstall, take 2nd exit sign Burnley A682, at 1st lights turn right into Newchurch Rd, 1.5 miles turn right into Staghills Rd, grd 800 yards right.
Capacity: 2,500 **Cover:** Yes **Seats:** 500 **Floodlights:** Yes **Club Shop:** T.B.A.
Programme: Yes **Editor:** Bill Howarth. **Press Officer:** Kevin Proctor
Colours: Blue & white/blue/blue **Change colours:** Yellow (blue sleeves)/blue/yellow
Sponsors: T.B.A. **Nickname:** Rossy **Founded:** 1898
Midweek matchday: Tuesday **Reserve Team's League:** NWCL Reserve Division.
Club Records - Attendance: 12,000 v Bolton Wanderers FA Cup 2nd Rd 71 **Goalscorer:** Bob Scott **Appearances:** Johnny Clarke 770, 47-65. **Win:** 10-0 v Wigan Rovers, Lancs Combination 69-70. **Defeat:** 0-14 v Morecambe, Lancs Comination 67-68. **Fees - Paid:** £3,000 for Jimmy Clarke (Buxton, 92) **Received:** £1,500 for Dave O'Neill (Huddersfield Town, 74).
Best FA Cup season: 2nd Rd 71-72 (1-4 v Bolton at Bury FC). Also 1st Rd 75-76 (0-1 at home to Shrewsbury Town).
Best FA Trophy/Vase Season: Vase 5th Rd 88-89; Tphy 2nd Rd 81-82.
Previous Leagues: North East Lancs Comb./ Lancs Comb. 1898-99 1901-70/ Central Lancs 1899-1901/ Cheshire County 70-82/ North West Counties 82-89/ Northern Premier 89-93.
Players progressing to Football League: T Lawton, G Smith (Bradford C 52), E Hartley & W O'Loughton (Oldham 56/60), C Blunt (Burnley 64), F Eyre (Bradford PA 69), D O'Neill (Huddersfield), C Parker (Rochdale 92).
Clubhouse: Evenings & matchdays. Hot snacks. Snooker room. Pool, darts, satellite TV, concert room.
Honours: North West Counties Lg Div 1 88-89 (R-up 87-88 93-94), Div 2 R-up 85-86; Carling Chall Cup 93-94

St HELENS TOWN

President: Mr J Jones. **Chairman/Press Officer:** J Barrett
Secretary: W J Noctor, 95 Sutton Park Drive, Marshalls Cross, St Helens WA9 3TR (01744 816182).
Manager: James McBride **Asst Manager:** G Walker **Coach:** John Neary
Ground: Hoghton Road, Sutton, St Helens, Merseyside (Grd 01744 817225) (Club 01744 812721)
Directions: M62 Jct 7, take 4th exit (St Helens Linkway), exit Linkway at 3rd r/about (Sherdley) follow signs for Sutton, continue to Sutton Village, Ground just beyond St Helens Junc station 150 yards
Seats: 200 **Cover:** 550 **Capacity:** 4,400 **Floodlights:** Yes **Club Shop:** Yes
Programme: 24 pages, 50p **Editor:** John McKiernan (01744 600612) **Nickname:** 'Town'
Colours: Blue & white/white/blue **Change colours:** All yellow **Founded:** 1946
Midweek Matches: Wednesday **Reserve League:**
Club Records - Attendance: 4,000 v Manchester City, Bert Trautmann transfer match, April 50. **Goalscorer:** S Pennington **Appearances:** Alan Wellens. **Win:** 10-4 v Everton 'B' 52 **Defeat:** 1-8 v Liverpool Res., L'pool Snr Cup 50.
Previous - Leagues: Lancs Comb. 03-14 49-75/ Liverpool County Combination 49-74/ Cheshire County 74-82.
Previous Grounds: Park Road 01-52/ City Road 52-53.
Players progressing to Football League: Bert Trautmann, John Connelly, John Quinn, Mike Davock, Billy Foulkes, Dave Bamber, Bryan Griffiths, Mark Leonard, Joe Paladino.
Clubhouse: Weekdays 8-11pm, Saturday matchdays 2-6.30pm.
97-98 Captain: G Lowe **Top Scorer:** Steve Pennington **P.o.Y.:** Mike Allison
Honours: FA Vase 86-87; Reserve Div R-up 94-95, Res Div Champions 94-95, R-Up 95-96; George Mahon Cup 49-50; Lancs Comb. 71-72, Div 2 50-51, Lg Cup R-up 70-71; Liverpool Snr Non Lge Cup R-up 76-77; Lancs Jnr Cup R-up 66-67; Bass Charrington Cup 73-74; Carling Chall Cup finalist 93-94; N.W.C. Floodlit Trophy finalist 97-98:

SALFORD CITY

Chairman: Harold Brearley **Manager:** Alan Lord. **Asst Manager:**
Secretary: Stephen Blake, 71 Blandford Road, Salford, M6 6BD (0161 737 0922)
Press Officer: Scott White **Commercial Manager:** Stevie Plant.
Ground: Moor Lane, Kersal, Salford, Manchester (0161 792 6287).
Directions: M62 jct 17, A56 Bury New Road to Manchester, continue thro' 4 sets of lights, right into Moor Lane, ground 500 left. 4 miles from Manchester Victoria (BR). Buses 96, 139, 94, 95 to Moor Lane.
Seats: 260 **Cover:** 600 **Capacity:** 8,000 **Floodlights:** Yes **Founded:** 1940
Midweek Matches: Tuesday **Record Attendance:** 3,000 v Whickham FA Vase 1981
Colours: Tangerine/white/white **Change colours:** Blue & white stripes/blue/blue.
Prev. Names: Salford Central 40-63/ Salford Amateurs 1963 until merger with Anson Villa/ Salford FC.
Previous Ground: Crescent, Salford **Previous Leagues:** Manchester 63-80/ Cheshire Co. 80-82.
Programme: 24 pages, 50p **Editor:** Scott White **Nickname:** Ammies.
Clubhouse: Open matchdays only. Hot snacks.
Honours: Lancashire Amateur Cup 72-73 74-75 76-77; Manchester Senior Cup, Manchester Challenge Cup, Manchester Lg 74-75 75-76 76-77 78-79.

Vauxhall Motors 97-98 *Photo: John Newton*

Workington AFC: Back Row (L-R); Derek WAlsh, John George, Lee Copeland, Ian Williamson, Stuart Williamson, Nigel Dustin, Simon Parry. Front Row; Kevin Rowntree, Lee Collins, Karl Fillingham, Jeff Henderson, George Corrie, Liam Armstrong, Lee Armstrong. *Photo: John Newton*

SKELMERSDALE UNITED

Chairman: D Tomlinson **Vice Chairman:** T Garner.
Secretary: Arthur Gore, 7 Hilltop Walk, Ormskirk, Lancs L39 4TH (01695 575643)
Manager: Russ Perkins **Asst Manager:** Alan Kershaw **Physio:** Billy Leigh
Ground: White Moss Park, White Moss Road, Skelmersdale, Lancs (01695 722123).
Directions: M58 Jct 3, at 2nd r'bout take 3rd exit towards Skelmersdale, continue for approx 1 mile, ground on the right. 4 miles from Ormskirk (BR).
Seats: 250 **Cover:** 1,000 **Capacity:** 10,000 **Floodlights:** Yes **Club Shop:** No
Programme: 20 pages, 50p **Editor:** Team effort **Press Officer:** Secretary
Colours: Blue & white/blue/blue **Change colours:** Red & white/red/red
Sponsors: **Nickname:** Skem **Founded:** 1882
Midweek Matches: Thursday **Record Attendance:** 7,000 v Slough FA Amat Cup 67
Best FA Cup year: 1st Rd 67-68 (0-2 at Scunthorpe), 68-69 (0-2 at Chesterfield), 71-72 (0-4 at Tranmere).
Previous Leagues: Liverpool County Combination, Lancashire Combination 1891-93 03-07 21-24 55-68 76-78, Cheshire County 68-71 78-82, Northern Premier 71-76.
Clubhouse: None, but matchday food bar sells hot drinks, soup, hot pies & pasties etc.
Hons: FA Amateur Cup 70-71 R-up 96-97; Ches. Co. Lg 68-69 69-70, Jubilee Cup 69-70; Lancs F'lit Cup 69-70; Lancs Jnr Cup 69-70 70-71; Ashworth Cup 70-71; Barassi Anglo-Italian Cup 70-71; Lancs Non-Lge Cup 73-74 74-75; North West Co's Lg Cup R-up 82-83.
97-98 - Captain: Gary Trewhitt **Top Scorer:** Frank Ryan **P.o.Y.:** Robbie Holcroft

VAUXHALL MOTORS

Chairman: Tony Woodley
Secretary: Stephen McInerney, 12 Merton Rd, Great Sutton, South Wirral L66 2SW (H 0151 356 0941) (B mobile 0385 343633)
Ground: Vauxhall Sports Ground, Rivacre Road, Hooton, Ellesmere Port, South Wirrall. (Grd 0151 327 1114) (Club 0151 327 2115)
Directions: M53 junction 5, take A41 to Chester, on reaching the first set of traffic lights turn left into Hooton Green, Left at the T-junction, right at the next T-junction into Rivacre Road, ground is 250 yards on the right.
Colours: All White **Club Sponsors:** James Edwards **Formed:** 1987
Midweek Matchday: Tuesday **Floodlights:** Yes
Record Attendance: 1,500 v English F.A. XI, 1987.
Previous Leagues: North West Counties League, West Cheshire League (to 1995)
Honours: B.N.W.C.F.L. 2nd Div Champ 88-89 95-96; Raab Karcher Chall Cup 90-91.

WORKINGTON

Formed: 1884 (reformed 1921) **Nickname:** Reds **Sponsors:** T.B.A.
Chairman: Bill Wilson **President:** Eric Fisher **Vice Chairman:** Jeff Tubman
Secretary: Tom Robson, 12 Derwent Bank, Seaton, Workington CA14 1EE (01900 65566).
Manager: Keith Hunton **Physio:** Peter Hampton **Press Officer:** Steve Durham (01946 61380)

GROUND Address: Borough Park, Workington, Cumbria CA14 2DT (01900 602871). **Directions:** A66 into town, right at 'T' junction, follow A596 for three quarters of a mile - ground is then visible and signposted. Ground is to north of town centre quarter of a mile from Workington (BR) station and half mile from bus station in town centre.
Capacity: 2,500 **Cover:** 800 **Seats:** 300 **Floodlights:** Yes
Clubhouse: Open matchdays and for private functions. Food on matchdays restricted menu.
Club Shop: Sells programmes, badges, magazines, pennants, photographs, replica kit, T-shirts. Contact Keith Lister (01900 812867).
Colours: All red **Change colours:** Blue/white/blue
Midweek matchday: Tuesday **Reserve's League:** West Cumberland.
PROGRAMME DETAILS: **Pages:** 36 **Price:** £1 **Editor:** Steve Durham (01946 61380)
PREVIOUS - Grounds: Various 1884-1921, Lonsdale Park 21-37. **Leagues:** Cumberland Association 1890-94, Cumberland Senior League 94-1901 03-04, Lancashire League 1901-03, Lancashire Combination 04-10, North Eastern 10-11 21-51, Football League 51-77.

CLUB RECORDS - Attendance: 21,000 v Manchester Utd, FA Cup 3rd Rd 4/1/58. **Goalscorer:** Billy Charlton 193. **Appearances:** Bobby Brown 419. **Win:** 17-1 v Cockermouth Crusaders, Cumberland Senior League 19/1/01. **Defeat:** 0-9 v Chorley (A), NPL Prem. Division, 10/11/87. **Fee Paid:** £6,000 for Ken Chisholm (Sunderland, 1956). **Fee Received:** £33,000 for Ian McDonald (Liverpool, 1974).
BEST SEASON - FA Cup: 4th Rd 33-34. 1st Rd - 53 occasions. **FA Trophy:** 1st Round replay 77-78.
Players progressing to Football League: Numerous, the best known being John Burridge.

HONOURS: Football League Cup QF 63-64 64-65, Football League: 5th in Div 3 65-66, 3rd Div 4 63-64, Northern Prem. Lge Presidents Cup 83-84, North Eastern Lge R-up 38-39 (Lge Cup 34-35 36-37 (R-up 37-38)), Cumberland County Cup 1886-91(x5) 95-99(x4) 1906-08(x2) 09-10 24-25 34-35 36-38(x2) 49-50 53-54 67-68 85-86 95-96 (R-up 1885-86 91-92 1899-1901(x2) 02-03 08-09 11-12 23-24 26-27 29-30 46-47 68-69 78-79).
97-98 - Captain: Derek Walsh **P.o.Y.:** Nigel Dustin **Top Scorer:** Lee Collins (4)

DIVISION TWO CLUBS 1998-99

ABBEY HEY

Secretary: Mr G Lester, 6 Newhaven Ave., Higher Openshaw, Manchester M11 1HU.
Colours: Red & navy/navy/navy **Ground:** Goredale Avenue, Gorton (0161 231 7147).
Directions: A57 towards Hyde, right into Woodland Avenue approx one & a half miles past Belle Vue junction, right again into Ryder Brow Rd, 1st left after bridge into Goredale Ave.

ASHTON TOWN

President: W Pomfrett **Chairman:** G Messer
Secretary: Chris Ashcroft, 8 Mason Close, Ashton-in-Makerfield, Wigan WN4 8SD (01942 203247).
Manager: Norman Hickson
Ground: Edge Green Street, Ashton-in-Makerfield, Wigan WN4 8SY (01942 510677).
Directions: M6 Jct 23, A49 to Ashton-in-M. Right at lights onto A58 towards Bolton. After 3/4 mile turn right at 'Rams Head' P.H. into Golbourne Rd. After 200 yds right into Edge Green Str. Ground at end.
Record Gate: 600 v Accrington Stanley 76-77 **Floodlights:** No **Founded:** 1965
Colours: Red with white trim/red/red **Change colours:** All sky blue
Best FA Vase season: Prelim. Rd 84-85
Previous Leagues: Warrington, Lancs Comb. 03-11 71-78, Ches. Co. 78-82.
Midweek Matches: Tuesday **Hons:** Warrington Lg Guardian Cup.

BACUP BOROUGH

President: W Shufflebottom **Chairman:** W Heywood **Vice Chairman:** D Whatmough
Secretary: Frank Manning, 38 Acre Avenue, Stacksteads, Bacup OL13 0HN (H 01706 877460) (B 01706 873177)
Manager: TBA **Asst Manager:** TBA **Commercial Mgr:**
Ground: West View, Cowtoot Lane, Blackthorn, Bacup, Lancashire (01706 878655).
Directions: From M62, M66 onto A681 through Rawtenstall to Bacup centre, left onto A671 towards Burnley, after approx 300 yds right (immed. before the Irwell Inn) climbing Cooper Street, right into Blackthorn Lane then first left into Cowtoot Lane to ground.
Seats: 500 **Cover:** 1,000 **Capacity:** 3,000 **Floodlights:** Yes **Founded:** 1875
Colours: Black & white stripes/black/black **Change colours:** All red
Previous league: Lancs Comb. 03-82. **Midweek Matches:** Tuesday.
Previous Name: Bacup FC. **Previous Grounds:** None
Programme: 12 pages, 30p **Editor:** D Whatmough (0706 875041) **Club Shop:** Not yet
Club Sponsors: Hoover Ltd **Record Gate:** 4,980 v Nelson 1947 **Nickname:** The Boro
Clubhouse: Open matchdays and private functions (for which buffets can be provided). Pies and sandwiches on matchdays.
Club record scorer: Jimmy Clarke
Honours: Lancs Jnr Cup 10-11 (R-up 22-23 74-75); Lancs Comb. 46-47 (Lg Cup R-up 46-47 80-81; NW Co's Lg Div 2 R-up 89-90.

BLACKPOOL MECHANICS

Chairman: Henry Baldwin **Vice Chairman:** John Sanderson **President:** Gregory Gregorio
Secrertary: William Singleton, C/O Club (H 01253 313444) (B 01253 761721)
Manager: Dave Rump **Asst Manager:** Gary Collings. **Physio:**
Coach: William Singleton. **Commercial Manager:** John Sanderson
Ground: Jepson Way, Common Edge Rd, Blackpool, Lancs FY4 5DY (01253 761721).
Directions: M6 to M55, follow Airport signs. Left at r'bout along A583 (Preston New Rd) to lights, right into Whitehill Rd, becomes School Rd, to lights. Straight over main road & follow signs for Blackpool Mechanics F.C. to ground. Rail to Blackpool North - then bus 11c from Talbot Rd bus station (next to rail station) to Shovels Hotel, Common Edge Rd.
Seats: 250 **Cover:** 1,700 **Capacity:** 2,000 **Floodlights:** Yes **Founded:** 1947
Club colours: Yellow & Green/green/green **Change colours:** All blue **Nickname:** Mechs
Programme: 10 pages, 50p **Editor:** John Barlow
Midweek home matchday: Tuesday **Club Sponsors:** Yates Wine Lodge, Talbot Rd, Blackpool.
Club Shop: Manager Andrew Sneddon (01253 729962). Ties, sweaters, old programmes, metal badges.
Record Gate: 1,200 v Morecambe, Lancs Comb, August 1968 **Prev. Ground:** Stanley Pk 47-49
Previous Leagues: Blackpool & Fylde Combination, West Lancs, Lancs Comb. 62-68.
Clubhouse: Match days, training nights. Dancehall. Matchday, hot food:
Honours: Lancs Comb Bridge Shield 72-73; NW Co's. Lg Div 3 85-86; W Lancs Lg 60-61 62-63; Lancs County FA Sheild 57-58 60-61:

CASTLETON GABRIELS

Chairman: T E Butterworth **Vice Chairman:** R Butterworth
Secretary: David Lord, 34 Fairway, Castleton, Rochdale OL11 3BU (01706 522719).
Manager/Coach:: Peter Freakes **Assistant Manager:** Dave Jones
Coach: Neil Mills **Press Officer:** Peter Wilson (01616 249602)
Ground: Butterworth Park, Chadwick Lane, off Heywood Rd., Castleton, Rochdale (01706 527103)
Directions: M62 Jct 20, A6272M to r'bout. Left towards Castleton (A664 Edinburgh Way) to next r'bout, keeping Tesco Superstore to the left, take 1st exit to next r'bout, take 2nd exit into Manchester Rd (A664), after just under mile turn right at 'Top House' P.H. into Heywood Rd., to end & ground on right.
Seats: 250 **Cover:** 500 **Capacity:** 1,500 **Floodlights:** Yes **Founded:** 1924
Colours: Royal/black/black. **Change colours:** Red/white/red. **Nickname:** Gabs.
Previous Name: St Gabriels (pre-1960s) **Previous Ground:** Park pitches/ Springfield Pk 60-81.
Previous Leagues: Rochdale Alliance 24-84/ Manchester 84-89.
Record Gate: 640 v Rochdale, pre-season friendly 1991.
Programme: 28 pages, 50p **Editor:** Peter Wilson (01616 249602) **Club Shop:** No
Club Sponsors: Dale Mill **Reserve Team's League:** N.W.Co.Res.Division
Record win: 8-0 v Squires Gate N.W.Co.Div 2 94 **Record defeat:** 1-10 v Blackpool Mechanics N.W.Co.Div 2 95
Players progressing to Football League: Dean Stokes (Port Vale) 92
Clubhouse: Open seven nights a night and all day Saturday. Pie & peas and sandwiches available matchdays (pie & peas only at Reserve matches).
Midweek home matchday: Tuesday **Club record scorer for a Season:** Tony Diamond 17.
96-97 Captain: **P.o.Y.:** **Top Scorer:**
Honours: Manc. Lg 86-87 (Murray Shield 86-87); Res Div Cup 95-96; Nth West Co's Lg Cup SF 91-92:

CHADDERTON

Chairman: Peter Evans **Vice Chairman:** Harry Mayall. **President:** Allison Elliott
Secretary: Ronald Manton, 42 Fife Avenue, Chadderton, Oldham, Lancs OL9 8AC, (0161 620 0368)
Manager: Dave Stewart **Asst Manager:** Paul Dixon **Physio:** Allison Elliott
Ground: Andrew Street, Chadderton, Oldham, Lancs (0161 624 9733).
Directions: M62 Jct 20, A627(M) to Oldham. Motorway then becomes dual carriageway. Turn left at first major traffic lights A669 (Middleton Road), then second left opposite 'Harlequin' P.H. into Burnley Street - Andrew Street 2nd left. 1 mile from Oldham Werneth (BR), buses 458 & 459 (Oldham-Manchester) stop at the Harlequin.
Seats: 200 **Cover:** 600 **Capacity:** 2,500 **Floodlights:** Yes **Club Shop:** No
Programme: 28-32 pages **Editor:** David Greaves **Press Officer:** John Fitton
Colours: All red. **Change colours:** White/Blue/White.
Sponsors: Royton Metals,Nationwide Building Society and Asda. **Nickname:** Chaddy **Founded:** 1947
Midweek Matches: Tuesday. **Reserves' Lge:** Carling NWCL Reserve Division.
Record Attendance: 1,500 v Guinness Exports 1969
Previous Leagues: Oldham Amateur, Manchester Amateur, Manchester 64-80, Lancs Comb. 80-82
Players progressing to Football League: David Platt (Crewe, Aston Villa, Bari, Juventus, Sampdoria,Arsenal), John Pemberton (Crewe, Crystal Palace, Sheffield Utd, Leeds), Graham Bell (Oldham, Preston), Paul Hilton (Bury, West Ham), Don Graham (Bury).
Clubhouse: Matchdays only. Hot & cold snack during & after games
97-98 Captain: Marl Paver **P.o.Y.:** Tony Lucas **Top Scorer:** Jimmy Gemmell
Club Record Appearances: Billy Elwell 750+ (64-90). **Club Record Goalscorer:**
Honours: Manchester Amat Lg 62-63 (North Div 55-56), Manchester Prem Cup R-up 82-83 (Challenge Tphy 71-72, R-up 72-73), Manchester Lg Div 1 66-67 (Div 2 64-65), Gilgryst Cup. 69-70, Murray Shield 65-66, Lancs Comb. Cup R-up 81-82, Alfred Pettit & Hulme Celtic Cup 61-62, Nth West Co's F/lit Tphy R-up 92-93 (Res Div 85-86, R-up 90-91), Res Cup 91-92 (R-up 90-91)), Manchester Yth Cup 59-60 (R-up 60-61).

COLNE

Chairman: D Blacklock (01282 696340)
Secretary: Jean Moore, 5 Haverholt Close, Colne, BB8 9SN (01282 868857)
Ground: Colne Dynamoes Stadium, Holt House, Colne, Lancs, (01282 862545)
Directions: Enter Colne from M65 to roundabout, keep left follow signs for Keighley. At next rounabout turn left, continue on Harrison Drive over mini roundabout & follow road to ground.
Seats: 50 **Cover:** 1000 **Capacity:** 1,800 **Floodlights:** Yes **Club Shop:** No
Colours: All red **Change colours:** All yellow **Formed:** 1996
Midweek Matchday: Wednesday **Record Gate:** 85 v Nelson 96-97
Programme: Yes **Editor:** Ray Moore **Press Officer:** Ray Moore
Clubhouse: No
Club record scorer: Geoff Payton **Club record appearances:** Nick Roscoe

CURZON ASHTON

Chairman: Harry Galloway **Chief Executive:** Harry Twamley **President:** Peter Mayo
Secretary: Graham Shuttleworth, 42 Southgate Road, Chadderton, Oldham, OL9 9PT. Tel: 0161 682 1137 (H)
Manager: Dave Denby **Physio:** Malcolm Liptrot. **Press Officer:** Barry Thorpe
Ground: National Park, Katherine Street, Ashton-under-Lyne OL7 6DA (0161 330 6033) **Directions:** Behind Ashton police station off Manchester Rd (A635), Ashton-under-Lyne, one and a half miles from Ashton-under-Lyne (BR).
Capacity: 5,000 **Cover:** 450 **Seats:** 350 **Floodlights:** Yes **Formed:** 1963
Clubhouse: Open every night. Food on matchdays. **Club Shop:** Yes, contact Roy Howe (0161 2208345)
Programme: 16pages 50p **Editor:** Robert Hurst (0161 775 3883) **Nickname:** Curzon
Colours: All blue **Change colours:** Yellow/green/yellow **Midweek matches:** Tuesday
PREVIOUS Leagues: Manchester Amateur; Manchester (until 1978); Cheshire Co. 78-82; North West Co's 82-87, Northern Prem. Lge. 87-97.
CLUB RECORDS - Attendance: 1,826 v Stamford, FA Vase SF 1980. **Goalscorer:** Alan Sykes. **Appearances:** Alan Sykes 620. **Win:** 7-0 v Ashton United. **Defeat:** 0-8 v Bamber Bridge. **Fee Paid:** £1,000 for Garry Stewart (Witton Albion, 1993). **Fee Received:** £3,000 for Keith Evans (Ashton Utd.).
BEST SEASON - FA Cup: 3rd Qual. Rd replay 89-90 (1-3 at Mossley after 1-1 draw). **FA Vase:** Semi-Final 79-80. **FA Trophy:** 2nd Qual. Rd 82-83 84-85.
Players progressing to Football League: Gordon Taylor (Bolton 1962), Steve Wigley (Nottm Forest 1981), Malcolm O'Connor (Rochdale 1983), Eric Nixon (Man. City 1983).
HONOURS: Cheshire Co. Lge Div 2 R-up 78-79 (Res. Div 81-82), Manchester Lge 77-78 (R-up 74-75 75-76), Lge Cup 77-78 (R-up 74-75 75-76), Murray Shield R-up 75-76, Manchester Amat. Lge 63-64 65-66 (R-up 64-65 79-80), Manchester Prem. Cup 81-82 83-84 85-86 86-87 89-90, Manchester Intermediate Cup 71-72 72-73 73-74 (R-up 70-71), Manchester Amat. Cup R-up 63-64, Ashton Chall. Cup 64-65 67-68, Philips F'lit Cup R-ups 77-78, NWC Res. Div 82-83 84-85 (R-up 83-84), Lge Cup 84-85 (R-up 83-84 85-86), Northern Comb. Supp. Cup 87-88 88-89, S.E. Lancs Lge Shield R-up 84-85.

DAISY HILL

Chairman: Tony Veitch
Secretary: Bob Naylor, 8 Bailey Fold, Westhoughton, Bolton, Lancs BL5 3HH (01942 813720).
Manager: Matty Wardrop **Asst Mgr:** Micky Gaynor **Physio:** Peter Rowbotham
Ground: New Sirs, St James Street, Westhoughton, Bolton, Lancs (01942 818544).
Directions: M61 Jct 5, A58 (Snydale Way/Park Rd) for 1.5 miles, left into Leigh Rd (B5235) for 1 mile, right into village then left between Church and School into St James St. Grd 250 yds on the left. Half mile from Daisy Hill (BR).
Seats: 200 **Cover:** 250 **Capacity:** 2,000 **Floodlights:** No **Club Shop:** No
Programme: 38 pages 50p **Editor:** **Press Officer:**
Colours: All royal blue. **Change:** Red & black stripes/black/black
Founded: 1894 **Reformed:** 1952
Midweek Matches: Tuesday **Reserves' Lge** CNWL Res Div.
Record Attendance: 2,000 v Horwich RMI, Westhoughton Charity Cup final May 1980.
Previous - Leagues: Westhoughton/ Bolton Comb./ Lancs Combination. 78-82. **Name:** Westhoughton Town
Grounds: Various - being researched
Players progressing to Football League: Barry Butler (Chester City via Atherton LR).
Clubhouse: Open normal licensing hours during any football activity. Snacks on matchdays.
Club Record scorer/appearances: Alan Roscoe, 300 goals. 450 games.
Honours: Bolton Comb Prem Div 62-63 72-73 75-76 77-78, Lg Cup 59-60 61-62 71-72 72-73; Lancs Shield 61-62 71-72 86-87:

DARWEN

President: E Devlin **Chairwoman:** Mrs K.Marah.
Secretary: Lynn Atkinson, 58 Harwood Str., Darwen, Lancs BB3 1PD (01254 761755).
Manager: S Wilkes **Asst Manager:** M Atkinson **Physio:** Mick Sharples
Ground: Anchor Ground, Anchor Road, Darwen, Lancs BB3 0BB, (01254 705627).
Directions: A666 Blackburn/Bolton road, 1 mile north of Darwen town centre, turn right at Anchor Hotel, ground 200 yds on left. One and a half miles from Darwen (BR), bus 51 to Anchor Hotel.
Seats: 250 **Cover:** 2,000 **Capacity:** 4,000 **Floodlights:** Yes **Founded:** 1875
Record Gate: *Anchor Grd* 10,000 v Fleetwood Lancs Jun Cup 1920 **Previous Ground:** Barley Bank.
Colours: Red & white/white/red **Change colours:** All blue
Prev. Lges: Football Alliance 1889-91, Football Lg 1891-99, Lancs Lg 99-03, Lancs Comb. 03-75, Ches. Co. 75-82.
Programme: 20 pages, 60p **Editor:** D.Marah. **Club Shop:** No
Sponsors: Prince Moran **Midweek Matches:** Tuesday.
Reserve Team's League: North West Counties
Clubhouse: Matchday only. **Best FA Cup season:** Semi Finals
Hons: Lancs Comb 31 32 73 75: Comb Cup 30 31 75; Lancs Jun Cup 73; Geo Watson Trophy 73; LFA Youth Cup 75; NWC Cup 83; Lancs F/Lit Trophy 90; NWCL Res Div Cup 94; Blackburn & Dist Youth Lge 94 95 97, Cup 94 95 97; NW All Chall Cup 96.

FLEETWOOD WANDERERS FC

Chairman: J Betmead
Secretary: Alan Birkett, 22 Warren Avenue South, Fleetwood, Lancs FY7 7AZ (01253 873779
Ground: Highbury Stadium, Highbury Avenue, Fleetwood, Lancs (01253 770702)
Directions: From M55 follow signs (A583) to Fleetwood. At Nautical Campos (on left) traffic island take first left, at second island take 6th exit. Stadium is 3/4 mile on left.
Colours: Red & white/black/red & white
Founded: 1997 **Floodlights:** Yes **Midweek Matchday:** Tuesday

FORMBY

Chairman: Chris Welsh **Managers:** Peter Hennerty + Mike Scott. **Physio:** Keith Johnson
Secretary: Paul Lawler, 13 Sefton Road, Formby, Merseyside L37 2JG (01704 878409).
Ground: Brows Lane, Formby, Merseyside (01704 833505)
Directions: A565 Liverpool-Southport, turn left for Formby at lights opposite Tesco into Altcar Rd, left at T junction to r'bout (opposite Blundell Arms Hotel), take 2nd exit then sharp left into Duke Street, 1st right into Elbow Lane, ground 50yds on left. Half a mile from Formby (BR), buses from Formby & Southport stations.
Seats: 200 **Cover:** 500 **Capacity:** 2,000 **Floodlights:** No **Founded:** 1919
Colours: Yellow/blue/yellow **Change:** White/black/black **Nickname:** Squirrels
Programme: 36 pages, 50p **Editor:** Paul Lawler, (01704 878409)
Club Shop: Sells programmes, badges & souvenirs. Contact Paul Lawler (01704 878409).
Clubhouse: Social club and offices sadly destroyed in fire in September 1990, and as yet unreplaced. However, matchday refreshment bar stocks hot food & drinks.
Club Sponsors: DKS Packaging. **Midweek Matches:** Wednesday.
Best Season - FA Cup: 1st Rd 73-74 (lost 0-2 at home to Oldham Athletic). **FA Trophy:** 1st Rd 73-74 (lost to Staylbridge Celtic) **FA Vase:** 2nd Rd 96-97 (lost to Tetley Walker)
Previous Leagues: Liverpool Co. Comb. 19-68/ Lancs Comb. 68-71, Ches. Co. 71-82.
Club Records - Gate: 2,500 v Oldham, FA Cup 1st Rd 24/11/73 **Win:** 11-1 v Earle (H) 18/10/52 **Defeat:** 0-10 v Irlam Town (H) 18/1/86. **Transfer fee paid:** Unknown **Received:** £1,000 for Geoff Twentyman (Chorley).
Honours: Liverpool Co. Comb. 48-49, R-up 64-65; Liverpool Senior Cup 77-78, R-up 84-85; Challenge Cup 52-53 63-64 67-68, R-up 64-65; Amtr Cup 29-30 47-48 48-49; Lamot Pils Trophy 94-95; George Mahon Cup 64-65, R-up 55-56 56-57; Lancs Co FA Amt Cup 34-35:

MAGHULL

Chairman: Les Jacques **Vice Chairman:** G Fisher **President:** M Latham.
Secretary: Danny Sherlock, 14 Alexander Drive, Lydiate, Merseyside L31 2NJ (0151 526 2306).
Manager: Frank O'Brien **Coach:** Derek McLatchey **Physio:** Fred Smith.
Ground: Old Hall Field, Hall Lane, Maghull, Merseyside (0151 526 7320).
Directions: M57 or M58 to end (Switch Island), A59 towards Preston (Northway) to lights at Hall Lane, turn right following signs for Maghull Station. Ground 200 yds on the left. Half mile from Maghull (Merseyrail).
Seats: None **Cover:** 75 **Capacity:** 500 **Floodlights:** No **Club Shop:** No.
Programme: 40 pages, 50p **Editor/Press Officer:** Andy Boyd (0151 526 2715).
Colours: Blue & red stripes/blue/blue **Change colours:** All yellow **Founded:** 1921
Sponsors: John McCabe **Midweek Matches:** Tuesday **Res' Lge:** Liverpool Co Comb.
Club Records - Attendance: 500 v Marine, L'pool Chal. Cup 82/83 **Goalscorer:** Bobby Prince **Appearances:** Bobby Prince.
Previous - Leagues: Liverpool Co. Comb./ Lancs Comb. 72-78/ Cheshire Co. 78-82. **Ground:** Pimbley Recreation Ground 1921-59.
Clubhouse: Fully licenced clubhouse & lounge open matchdays and midweek. Hot & cold food available.
Honours: Liverpool Co. Amtr Cup 34-35 62-63; Liverpool Co. Chal. Cup 79-80 85-86 93-94; Lancs FA Amtr Cup 48-49 57-58; Liverpool Co. Comb. 66-67; North West Co's Lg Div 2 92-93:

NELSON

Chairman: Ken Broom. **Vice-Chairman:** A Barnes.
Secretary: Cyril King, 1 Grange Ave, Barrowford, Nelson, Lancashire BB9 8AN (01282 695578)
Manager: Ian Britton. **Assistant Manager:** P Rigby.
Ground: Victoria Park, Lomeshaye Way, Nelson, Lancs (01282 613820).
Directions: M65 jct 13, 1st left (A6068 Fence), 2nd left (B6249 for Nelson), 2nd right sign Lomeshaye Village to grd.
Capacity: **Seats:** 60 **Cover:** 200 **Floodlights:** Yes **Club Shop:**
Sponsor: **Nickname:** Blues **Founded:** 1881
Colours: Blue & white stripes/black/blue **Change colours:** White/red
Midweek matchday: Wednesday **Reserve League:** North West Co's Reserve Div.
Best FA Cup season: FA Cup 2nd Rd Proper 30-31(replay)
Previous Leagues: Lancashire 1889-98 1900-01/ Football League 1898-1900/ Lancashire Combination 01-16 46-82/ Nth West Counties 82-88/ West Lancashire 88-92.
Clubhouse: Bar open matchdays
Honours: Lancs Lge 54-55; Lancs Comb. 1949-50 51-52; Lg Cup 49-50 50-51 59-60; Bridge Shield 75-76 81-82; Lancs Jnr Cup 54-55; NW Counties Div 2 Cup 96-97:

OLDHAM TOWN

Chairman: Ken Hughes **Manager:** T B A **Secretary:** To be Appointed
Ground: Whitebank Stadium, Whitebank Rd, Hollins, Oldham, Lancs OL8 3JH (0161 624 2689).
Directions: M62 jct 18, M66 to Heaton Pk, right on to A576, left at 2nd lights on to A6104, follow Victoria Ave. on to Hollinwood Ave. under bridge to roundabout take 2nd exit onto Hollins Road, follow Hollins Rd for one & a half miles to Fire Station, left on throughgate leading onto Elm Rd and follow to next left, Whitebank Rd on left.
Seats: 101 **Cover:** Yes **Capacity:** 1,000 **Floodlights:** Yes **Founded:** 1964
Programme: 16 pages, 50p **Editor:** Secretary
Colours: White/blue/white **Change Colours:**
Midweek Matches: Tuesday **Previous Leagues:** Manch. Amtr/ Lancashire Comb. 81-82.
Record Attendance: 325 v Flixton, NWCL Div 2 Championship decider May 95
Clubhouse: Open evenings and matchdays.
97-98 - Captain: Adrian Moran **Top Scorer:** Mike Bartholomew **P.o.Y.:**
Honours: Div 2 R-up 94/95; Div 3 R-up 85/86; Res Div R-up 94/95, Cup 94/95:

SQUIRES GATE

Chairman: P Mack **Vice President:** Brian Addison
Secretary: John Maguire, 2 Squires Court, Cairn Grove, Blackpool, Lancs FY4 2RA (01253 348512)
Manager: Paul Arnold **Assistant Manager:** John Chippendale.
Ground: School Road, Marton, Blackpool, Lancs (01253 798584).
Directions: M6 to M55 jct 4, left onto A583, right at 1st lights (Whitehall Rd) follow signs for airport. Grd 1.5milesright.
Seats: 2 rows **Cover:** One side **Capacity:** **Floodlights:** No **Formed:** 1948
Colours: Royal/black/royal **Midweek Matches:** Tuesday
Programee: 20 pages **Clubhouse:** Yes **Record Attendance:** 600 v Everton 95
Previous Leagues: W. Lancs (pre-1991) **Honours:** W. Lancs Lg Div 2 80-81, Richardson Cup 86-87

Tetley Walker FC: Back Row (L-R); Brian Gleave (Sec), Lee Webster, Robbie Preidt, Steve Hunt, Stuart Clay, Tony Plant, Lee Medland, Chris Coulson (Mgr), Chris Woodward. Front Row; Bobby Fitzpatrick, John Sanson, Kevin Dack, Mike Tandy, Steve Roberts, Tony Healey, Jimmy Drewery.

TETLEY WALKER

President: John Sixsmith **Chairman:** Bob McLaughlin **Treasurer:** Mark Fisher
Secretary: Brian Gleave, 8 Cossack Ave., Orford, Warrington, Cheshire WA2 9PB (01925 659559).
Manager Chris Coulson **Asst.Manager:** Jimmy Drewery
Physio: Harry Peacey **Press Officer:** Garry Clarke
Ground: Tetley Walker Club, Long Lane, Orford, Warrington, Cheshire WA2 9PB (01925 634904).
Ground: M6 Junc 21A to M62 Junc 9, follow signs to Warrington town centre on A49. After about one and a half miles turn left at 2nd r'bout (next to Coachmans pub), ground about 500yds on left. Nearest station Warrington Central
Capacity: 2,000 **Seats:** 40 **Cover:** 150 **Floodlights:** No **Founded:** 1974
Midweek matches: Tuesday **Reserves' Lge:** Warrington & D. **Nickname:** Walkers
Colours: Yellow/navy blue **Change Cols:** Red/blue
Programme: 40 pages 50p **Editor:** Garry Clarke **Sponsor:** Adobe Systems/Driwall/Spro Don Press
Clubhouse: Open noon-midnight. Food includes sandwiches & pies, (01925 634904) **Club Shop:** No
Best FA Vase Season: 4th Rd 96-97 **Previous League:** Warrington & District 1974-94.
Record Attendance: 200 v Durham FAV 96-97 **Record Appearances:** Ray Arnold
97-98 - Captain: Mike Tandy **Top Scorer:** Kevin Dack (37) **P.o.Y:** Lee Webster
Honours: NWC Div 2 Trophy 97-98; Guardian Cup 84-85 85-86 93-94 95-96 96-97; Jubilee Cup 84-85 93-94; Warrington Lge 86-87 93-94:

WARRINGTON TOWN

Chairman: TBA **Vice Chairman:** M P McShane
Secretary: Ian Dick, 53 Arlington Drive, Penketh, Warrington WA5 2QG. 01925 724421.
Manager: Alan Lord **Asst Manager:** Dave Entwhistle
Coach: Gary Bradley **Physio:** Lynda Roberts **Press Officer:** Colin Serjent
GROUND Address: Cantilever Park, Common Lane, Latchford, Warrington WA4 2RS 01925 631932 (Club), 01925-653044 (Office). **Directions:** M6 junction 20, then A50 towards Warrington. After 2 miles turn left immediately after swing bridge into Station Road, ground 600yds on left. From town centre travel 1 mile south on A49, left at lights into Loushers Lane, ground quarter mile on right. 2 miles from Warrington Bank Quay (BR).
Capacity: 2,000 **Cover:** 650 **Seats:** 350 **Floodlights:** Yes **Formed:** 1948
Colours: Blue & yellow/blue/blue **Change colours:** All purple. **Nickname:** The Town
Midweek matchday: Tuesday **Reserve's League:** Mid-Cheshire.
Clubhouse: Weekdays 1-11pm, Sat. 12-11pm, Sun. 12-3pm, 7-10.30pm. Lounge, concert room & Sports room. Rooms for hire for all occasions. Pools, darts, dominoes & indoor bowls. Traditional bar food on matchdays.
Club Shop: Sells badges, scarves, pennants, old & new League & non-League progs, fanzines. Contact Matthew Dale
PROGRAMME: Pages: 36 **Price:** 50p **Editor:** Rick Barker 01925 604101 Tel/Fax
PREVIOUS - Leagues: Warrington & Dist. 49-52/ Mid-Cheshire 52-78/ Cheshire Co. 78-82/ North West Co's 82-90/ Northern Prem 90-97. **Name:** Stockton Heath 1949-62. **Grounds:** London Road, Stockton Lane and Loushers Lane.
CLUB RECORDS - Attendance: 2,600 v Halesowen Town, FA Vase Semi Final 1st leg 85-86. **Goalscorer:** Steve Hughes 167. **Win:** 14-0 v Crosfields (H), Depot Cup 1951-52. **Defeat:** 0-10 v Eastwood (A), Mid-Cheshire Challenge Cup 1967-68. **Fee Paid:** £2,000 for - Paul McNally (Southport) 92 & Darren Schofield (Mossley) 93. **Fee Received:** £60,000 for Liam Watson (Preston N. E.) 92-93.
Best Season - FA Cup: 4th Qualifying Rd 94-95 (replay with Hyde Utd.). **FA Vase:** Finalists 86-87 (2-3 to St Helens Town). **FA Trophy:** Quarter-Finalists 92-93 (1-2 at Sutton United).
Players progressing to Football League: S Morris (Chester 51), J Green (Tranmere 58), R Hunt (Liverpool 59), J Richards (Wolves), J Bramhall (Tranmere 76), M Leonard (Everton), N Whalley & L Watson (Preston N.E.) 92-93.
HONOURS: N.W.C. Lge 89-90 (Lg Cup 85-86 87-88 88-89 (R-up 89-90), Div 2 R-up 86-87, Div 3 R-up 82-83, Res. Div West 89-90), Mid-Cheshire Lg 60-61 (R-up 57-58, Lg Cup 54-55 55-56) 11-12 72-73, Altrincham Amat. Cup 54-55, Warrington Yth Chall. Cup 94-95.

WOODLEY SPORTS FC

Chairman: Ian Campbell
Secretary: Ian Woodhouse, 4 Firethorn Drive, Godley, Hyde SK14 3SN (0161 351 1631 H, 0161 330 6837 B)
Ground: Lambeth Grove Stadium, Lambeth Grove, Woodley, Stockport (0161 494 6429)
Directions: M63 Junc 15, follow signs (A560) Bredbury, take left filter at lights which brings you onto A560 Stockport Road for approx 1 mile, turn left at pub, Lowes Arms into Mill Street which goes into Mill Lane. Over bridge take 2nd right into Woodlands Avenue, then 1st leftinto Lambeth Grove. Ground 200 yards ahead. Manchester A-Z page 121 G3, Edition 8
Colours: Red & royal blue/royal/white
Founded: 1970
Floodlights: No
Midweek Matchday: Wednesday
Record Attendance: 1,500 v Stockport County
Previous Leagues: Lancashire & Cheshire, Manchester League.

MANCHESTER FOOTBALL LEAGUE

President: P Morris

League Secretary: J A Warrington,
17 Broadacre, Mottram Rise, Stalybridge, Cheshire SK15 2TX
Tel: 01457 764427 (H) 01457 855993 (B/F) 0802 657593 (M)
E.mail: jameswarrington@compuserve.com

SPRINGHEAD TAKE THEIR FIRST CHAMPIONSHIP

The 1997-98 season was the start of a new era for the league with a new line up of officials following the retirement of the League President Albert Booth, and the Treasurer Norman Noden who had served the League for over 80 years between them. In addition the League Secretary Frank Fitzpatrick had died in March after a long illness so a new team had been formed to supervise and maintain the traditions of the league.

All the title battles in the Manchester League went to the wire with three of the four being settled on the last day of the season.

In the Premier Division Springhead led the division from the first day of the season when they scored a 10-0 victory at Stockport Georgians right to the end to win their first Championship. However, they did not clinch the title until the last day since Abbey Hey kept up the pressure right to the last match and had Springhead lost could have taken the title had they themselves not lost that day. This was Abbey Hey's last season with us as they move to the North West Trains League next season.

The promotion race in Division One was a fight right to the line. Old Alts led the division up until the last day but a victory by Urmston gave them the title with Failsworth clinching the runners-up spot on goal difference with a draw. This was a tremendous achievement for both clubs who had only joined the league at the commencement of the season. The other new club British Aerospace found life harder ending up having to seek re-election.

Atherton Town Reserves were runaway winners of Division Two with Springhead Reserves taking the second spot. Urmston Reserves took the Division Three title with New Mills clinching the runners-up spot on the last day of the season.

In the League Cup competitions Monton Amateurs won the Gilgryst Cup with a 1-0 victory over Tottington United. Gamesley took the Murray Trophy with a 2-1 victory over Willows whilst East Manchester Reserves took the Open Trophy with a 4-2 victory over Tottington United Reserves.

The league looks forward to next season with four new clubs having been elected into membership: Avro, Hindsford, Tintwistle Villa and Wilmslow Albion. This will bring the league strength back to 36 clubs.

FINAL LEAGUE TABLES 1997-98

Division Premier

	P	W	D	L	F	A	Pts
Springhead	30	21	3	6	80	32	66
Abbey Hey	30	19	4	7	81	44	61
Tottington Utd	30	15	7	8	58	43	52
Stand Athletic	30	14	9	7	60	36	*48
Atherton Town	30	14	6	10	50	43	48
Dukinfield Town	30	13	7	10	52	46	46
B.I.C.C.	30	13	5	12	71	59	44
Wythenshawe Am	30	12	8	10	46	41	44
Monton Amateurs	30	12	6	12	44	49	42
East Manchester	30	11	7	12	52	51	40
Little Hulton United	30	10	8	12	51	50	*37
Prestwich Heys	30	11	4	15	42	47	37
Elton Fold	30	8	7	15	47	65	31
Mitchell Shackleton	30	8	5	17	42	66	29
Stockport Georgians	30	5	8	17	38	75	23
Wythenshawe Town	30	6	2	22	36	103	20

* Indicates clubs with points adjustment

Division One

	P	W	D	L	F	A	Pts
Urmston	32	26	0	6	102	49	78
Failsworth Town	32	23	4	5	105	36	73
Old Alts	32	23	4	5	97	51	73
Willows	32	21	5	6	138	62	68
Gamesley	32	16	4	12	70	63	52
Pennington	32	15	4	13	66	58	49
Sacred Heart	32	15	3	14	72	71	48
Breightmet United	32	13	6	13	54	61	45
Whalley Range	32	13	4	15	64	90	43
New Mills	32	12	5	15	76	74	41
Milton	32	11	7	14	64	65	40
Hollinwood	32	12	3	17	57	65	39
Whitworth Valley	32	12	2	18	77	106	38
Ashton Athletic	32	11	4	17	54	66	37
Manchester Royal	32	8	10	14	56	57	34
GM Police	32	4	3	25	34	103	15
British Aerospace	32	1	4	27	37	146	7

Note: Abbey Hey resigned having been elected to the North West Trains League.
British Aerospace will be known as Lostock FC next season

CUP SUCCESSES

GILGRYST CUP FINAL

Monton Amateurs	1
Tottington United	0

MURRAY SHIELD FINAL

Gamesley	2
Willows	1

OPEN TROPHY FINAL

East Manchester Res	4
Tottington Utd Res	2

Springhead AFC: 1997-98 Manchester League Premier Champions
Back Row (L-R): P Lent, G Bird, G Burton, P Smith, A Revil, M Butterworth, R Van De Veer (Coach), M Coleman (Manager)
Front Row (L-R): G Crompton, A Bedford, A Heffernan, P Dowd (Captain), C Hipkin, A Yates, C Lawson, R Bailey

STOCKPORT GEORGIANS

Secretary: Ged Newcombe, 7 Chiltern Close, Hazel Grove, Stockport SK7 5BQ (0161 483 0004).
Colours: Purple/white/black **Ground:** Cromley Rd, Stockport, (0161 483 6581).
Directions: Follow A6 from Stockport centre, turn right at Cemetery into Branhall Lane. After 1 mile turn left at r/about into Woodsmoor Lane. Take 1st right Flowery Fields then right into Cromley Road

TOTTINGTON UNITED

Secretary: Vincent Holden, 6 Ash Grove, Holcombe Brook, Ramsbottom BL0 9RS (01204 884958)
Colours: Blue & black/blue/white **Ground:** St Annes Fields, Tottington
Directions: From Bury Town centre follow B6213 to Tottington. Turn right into Laurel Street at Cenotaph. Car park in Royds Street.

URMSTON

Secretary: Sean Brett, 3 Shuttleworth Close, Whalley Range, Manchester (0161 881 1962)
Colours: Royal & white/royal/royal **Ground:** Flixton Park, Flixton Road.
Directions: M63 junc 3 take Barton Rd to r/about. Then 3rd turning into Bayswater Rd. To r/about, take 2nd left Bowfell Rd, joins Flixton Rd, ground on left.

WYTHENSHAWE AMATEURS

Secretary: John Sobierajsh, 5 Wensley Drive, Withington, Manchester (0161 445 3415)
Colours: Blue & white stripes/blue/blue **Ground:** Longley Lane, Northenden (0161 998 7268).
Directions: Princess Parkway from Manchester to Post House hotel, via Palatine Rd & Moor End Rd to Longley Lane - ground entrance opposite Overwood Rd.

DIVISION ONE CLUBS 1998-99

ASHTON ATHLETIC

Secretary: Jimmy Whyte, 33 Eskdale Road, Ashton in Maker, Wigan (01942 205775)
Colours: Blue & yellow/blue/blue **Ground:** Brocstedes Park, Brocstedes Rd, N Ashton, Wigan (01942 716360).
Directions: A580 or M6 to Haydock Island, A49 to Ashton (Bryn Cross), left at lights onto Downall Green Rd, over M6, 2nd right, 2nd right is Brocstedes Rd.

AVRO

Secretary: Karen Birch, 99 Clough Road, Failsworth, Manchester (0161 688 0941)
Colours: Red/white/red **Ground:** Lancaster Club, Broadway, Failsworth
Directions: From Manchester take Oldham Rd A62, turn left into Broadway. Ground immed. on left

BREIGHTMET UNITED

Secretary: Raymond Walsh, 94 Hatherleigh Walk, Breightmet, Bolton (01204 435197)
Colours: Black & white/black/red **Ground:** Moss Park, Back Bury Rd, Breightmet, Bolton (01204 33930).
Directions: The ground is approx 2 miles from Bolton Centre on the A58 Bury Road, Entrance on right behind Hi-Speed Tyres

GAMESLEY

Secretary: Gary Weatherhead, 36 Winster Mews, Gamesley, Glossop (01457 866393)
Colours: Green & white/white/white **Ground:** Gamesley Community Centre, Melandra Castle Rd, Glossop
Directions: Follow A57 towards Glossop, at Dinting turn right at Plough Inn into Glossop Rd. Take 1st right into Cottage Lane to Melandra Castle Rd. Ground app 440 yards right.

GREATER MANCHESTER POLICE

Secretary: P Davidson, 2 Oakwood, Sale M33 5RH (0161 962 2327).
Colours: Yellow/blue/yellow **Ground:** Hough End Police Club (0161 856 1798).
Directions: Princess Parkway from central Manchester, right at Mauldeth Rd West, grd entrance half mile left.

HINDSFORD

Secretary: Peter Lowe, 13 Sunnybank Road, Astley, Tyldesley (01942 876987)
Colours: Red & white/red/red **Ground:** Squires Lane, Tyldesley
Directions: Take A580 from Manchester. Turn right at A577 signed Wigan. At end of Elliott St in Tyldesley str on past church to end. Ground at end Squires Lane

HOLLINWOOD

Secretary: K Evans, 20 Meadow Rise, High Crompton, Shaw, Oldham OL2 7QG (01706 840987).
Colours: Blue & red/blue/blue & red **Ground:** Lime Lane, Hollinwood (0161 681 3385).
Directions: Oldham Road (A62) from Manchester to Roxy Cinema, right into Hollins Rd, 1st right into Albert Street, left at junction with Roman Road, 1st right into Lime Lane for quarter mile.

LOSTOCK

Secretary: Peter Hoyle, 1 Wimbourne Close, Lostock, Bolton (01204 694132)
Colours: Black & white/black/black & white **Ground:** Lostock Spts Field, Lostock Lane, Horwich
Directions: Off A6027 (Horwich/M61 Link) into Lostock Lane. Turn left into works car park

MANCHESTER ROYAL

Secretary: N Kinvig, 3 Cranleigh Drive, Cheadle (0161 491 0824)
Colours: Red & black/black/black **Ground:** Barnes Hospital, Cheadle.
Directions: From Manchester, hospital entrance is on the left of Kingsway just after M63 jct 10. Keep left within hospital grounds, pitch is adjacent to motorway.

MILTON

Secretary: Andrew Cole, 7 Crossfield Close, Woodend Park Shaw, (01706 291973)
Colours: Green/green/yellow & green **Ground:** Athletic Stadium, Springfield Pk, Rochdale.
Directions: From Manchester via Middleton (A664) to Hollins, A6046 towards Heywood then A58 towards Rochdale - Park on left after one and a half miles.

NEW MILLS

Secretary: John Hackney, 46 Mellor Road, New Mills, Stockport, (01663 744546).
Colours: Amber/black/black **Ground:** Church Lane, New Mills (01663 747435).
Directions: A6 to Swan Hotel, left into Albion Rd, continue to Church Rd, left into Church Lane.

OLD ALTRINCHAMIANS

Secretary: Phil Lewis, 10 Woodfield Grove, Sale, M33 6JW (0161 973 7082)
Colours: Black & white/black/black **Ground:** Crossford Bridge P.F., Meadows Rd, Sale.
Directions: From Manchester via Stretford (A56), under M63, left at lights into Dane Rd/Meadows Rd, ground entrance at end.

PENNINGTON

Secretary: Joanne Hindley, 30 Sycamore Road, Atherton, Manchester (01942 897273)
Colours: Yellow/blue/yellow **Ground:** Jubilee Park, Leigh Rd, Atherton (01942 894703).
Directions: From Leigh centre B5215 Atherton Road, ground 1 mile on left directley opposite G.M.T. depot.

SACRED HEART

Secretary: Joe Devlin, 61 Buersil Ave., Balderstone, Rochdale, Lancs OL16 4TR (01706 660989)
Colours: Red/white/red **Ground:** Fox Park, Belfield Mill Lane, Rochdale.
Directions: From Manchester follow Bury Old Road A665 to Prestwich, turn right into Heywood Rd, then 3rd left into Mount Rd/Sandgate Rd ground on right

TINTWISTLE VILLA

Secretary: William Higginbottom, 61 West Drive, Tintwistle, Glossop (01457 852467)
Colours: Black & white/black/black **Ground:** West Drive, Tintwistle
Directions: M67 follow signs for Barnsley through Mottram & Hollingworth. At Tintwistle turn right at Bus Shelter into West Drive, ground at end on right.

WHALLEY RANGE

Secretary: R Lapsley, 8 Withnell Rd, Burnage, Manchester (0161 432 6158).
Colours: Red & black/black/black **Ground:** King's Rd, Chorlton (0161 881 2618).
Directions: Princess Parkway from Manchester, right at Wilbraham Rd, left at Withington Rd South, King's Rd is 1st right, ground entrance opposite Daventry Rd.

WHITWORTH VALLEY

Secretary: Mark Kirkham, 10 Hargate Avenue, Norden, Rochdale (01706 356055)
Colours: Black & white/black/black **Ground:** Rawstron Str, Whitworth (01706 853030).
Directions: Bacup road (A671) from Rochdale, after just over 2 miles turn left at Whitworth centre into Tonge Lane then 3rd right left into Crown Park Way.

WILLOWS

Secretary: Frank Miller, 11 Edmund Street, Salford, Manchester (0161 737 2411)
Colours: All red **Ground:** Salteye Park, Peel Green, Eccles
Direction: From Eccles Town centre take A57, pass under M63 at Peel Green r/about. After approx 400 yds turn left into lay-by. Ground behind Kara Cafe.

WILMSLOW ALBION

Secretary: Norma Winn, 236 Derbyshire Lane, Stretford, Manchester (0161 286 9520)
Colours: Red & blue/blue/blue **Ground:** Oakwood Farm, Styal Road, Wilmslow
Directions: M56 Junc 5 follow signs Wilmslow. Turn right at lights at end of Ringway Rd. Ground 3rd left approx 3/4 mile from lights. Opp Quarry Mill

WYTHENSHAWE TOWN

Secretary: Ray Pattison, 24 Rawpool Gardens, Royal Oak Est. Baguley (0161 374 3086)
Colours: All royal **Ground:** Ericstan Park, Timpson Rd, Baguley, Manchester (0161 998 5076).
Directions: Princess Parkway from Manchester, right into Altrincham Rd (A560), left into Southmoor Rd and 1st right into Timpson Rd - ground at end.

GREEN CONTRACT SERVICES MID-CHESHIRE LEAGUE

Founded 1948

President: R Atherton

League Secretary: E B Davies,
34 Ryebank Road, Firswood, Manchester, M16 0FP
Tel: 0161 881 5732

The 1997-98 season commenced when two clubs found themselves in difficulties prior to the first matches which kicked off on the 16th August 1997, Chorlton Town Reserves, who missed two fixtures before sorting out their problems, and Grove United Reserves, who missed four fixtures in the same division before having to resign. A further interruption of fixtures occurred due to the sad death of the Princess of Wales, all fixtures in the 6th September being cancelled.

Management sub-committees have been busy throughout the season helping to ensure that the Jubilee Book, ably researched by Paul Lavelle, to whom we are indebted and grateful, becomes a reality when published in August/September this year. A disappointment to the Management Committee was the apology from Roger Hunt, the principle guest at a Jubilee Dinner held at the end of the season, that he was unable to attend. Roger was a former player of Stockton Heath (now Warrington Town), long established members of this league, before his move to Liverpool.

A Jubilee Cup open to all 32 member teams was very successful despite the league's high flyers at the time being knocked out in the early rounds. Prior to the final, extra time was played in four matches with two going to penalties. The eventual winners were Chorlton Town who beat Cheadle Heath Nomads 2-1 in the final played at Wincham Park.

The League Cup competitions operated with the same rules with extra time and penalties settling the ties in both divisional cups. The decision to get the result settled on the day of the match was correct, as any replays together with the 79 games lost throughout the season due to the weather, replayed external competitions and various other reasons, would have caused chaos later in the season.

Garswood United Reserves and Padgate St Oswalds were the finalists in the Division Two Cup with the Warrington side taking the Cup with a 2-1 win. The Division One final was between the two top teams in that Division, Knutsford and Barnton, and in a close game Barnton retained the cup that they were defending, winning with a 1-0 scoreline. Both the finals were played at Barton Stadium and the league are grateful to Winsford United.

Both divisions of the league went to the last match of the season before the championships were decided, Garswood United beating Padgate St Oswalds in a title deciding last match by 3-1, Padgate had needed to win to take the title and promotion; both eluded them but they should be pleased with their first season in the league despite losing their promotion hopes to Pilkington who, together with Garswood United Reserves, Padgate St Oswalds and Chester Nomads, had been in the top five all season. The Division One title chase was an all season battle between Barnton, Knutsford and Linotype, each having spells at the top, but a bad second half of the season saw Linotype slip out of the race in mid April leaving founder members Knutsford and Barnton to play out the final stages of the season in first and second positions. Defeat for Knutsford in their final match and a victory for Barnton in their last match saw Barnton retain their title (a double double), a feat recorded twice previously in the 1951-53 seasons and in 1965-67 seasons, both by Lostock Graham. Mention must also be made of the efforts of Poynton, Bollington and Warrington Borough, who all had good seasons.

With Wilmslow Albion having finished in bottom spot resigning from the league, only one team was relegated, this

Chorlton Town, 1997-98 Jubilee Cup winners at Witton Albion

being Grove United. Due to the resignations of Alsager and Hanley Town neither of the bottom two teams had to apply for re-election and seven teams took part in a ballot for the four vacancies in Division Two for season 1998-99, resulting in Crewe FC, Ellesmere Port United FC, Trafford FC Reserves and Walker Sports & Social FC being elected.

Following difficulties experienced by both Garswood United and Middlewich Athletic (shortly to be renamed Town) with the NWCFL, the council were asked to consider support for both these clubs in their late applications to re-join the Division One of this league. A ballot resulted in both teams being accepted which automatically relegated Garswood United Reserves back to Division Two. Both divisions of the league will operate with seventeen teams for season 1998-99.

The annual inter-league fixture with the West Cheshire league resulted in a 2-2 draw. In outside competitions the league boasts successes in several areas, and congratulates the following: Chorlton Town, finalists, Manchester Junior Cup; Beeches, finalists, Liverpool Junior Cup; Whitchurch Alport, winners, Shropshire County Challenge Cup; Barnton, winners, Mid-Cheshire Sunday Cup; Bollington Athletic, winners, Macclesfield Senior Cup beating finalists, AFC Zeneca; Alsager, winners, Crewe & District Cup; and Linotype Reserves, winners, Altrincham & District Senior Cup. Overall the league can look back on a successful and enjoyable Jubilee Season.

FINAL LEAGUE TABLES 1997-98

DIVISION ONE	P	W	D	L	F	A	Pts
Barnton	30	23	4	3	95	30	73
Knutsford	30	22	4	4	91	27	70
Linotype	30	20	6	4	62	30	66
Poynton	30	14	10	6	69	48	52
Bollington Ath	30	13	7	10	54	61	46
Beeches	30	13	5	12	57	54	44
Warrington Boro	30	11	7	12	51	50	40
Chorlton Town	30	11	4	15	51	58	37
Rylands	30	10	7	13	46	61	37
Bramhall	30	11	4	15	63	79	37
Lostock Graham	30	10	5	15	47	61	35
Cheadle Hth N	30	10	4	16	52	74	34
Whitchurch Alp	30	8	8	14	37	51	32
AFC Zeneca	30	8	4	18	42	67	28
Grove United	30	5	8	17	40	74	23
Wilmslow Alb	30	5	5	20	48	80	20

DIVISION TWO	P	W	D	L	F	A	Pts
Garswood U Rs	28	19	5	4	52	24	62
Pilkington	28	18	4	6	92	35	58
Padgate St Os	28	16	8	4	87	38	56
Chester Nomads	28	15	6	7	49	37	51
Linotype Res	28	12	11	5	59	36	47
Malpas	28	13	6	9	60	49	45
Styal	28	13	5	10	66	65	44
Alsager	28	11	5	12	48	44	38
Poynton Res	28	10	7	11	55	51	37
Hanley Town	28	9	6	13	58	70	33
Rylands Res	28	10	2	16	45	62	32
Broadheath C	28	8	6	14	52	65	30
Littlemoor	28	7	2	19	48	85	23
Chorlton T Rs	28	5	5	18	37	78	20
Bollington A Rs	28	3	4	21	40	109	13

DIVISION ONE RESULTS CHART 1997-98

		1	2	3	4	5	6	7	8	9	10	11	12	13	14	15	16
1	AFC Zeneca	X	0-1	2-1	0-1	2-1	2-4	1-3	3-2	1-3	0-2	2-1	0-0	1-4	1-4	1-1	4-1
2	Barnton	3-2	X	5-2	8-2	4-1	4-0	1-1	2-1	1-0	3-0	2-2	4-2	6-1	5-1	2-1	1-0
3	Beeches	2-0	0-4	X	8-1	4-1	1-4	3-2	5-1	0-4	2-3	3-2	1-1	1-1	3-1	0-2	3-4
4	Bollington Ath	2-1	1-7	2-1	X	2-1	5-3	4-1	3-0	1-1	0-2	0-1	1-1	2-1	3-0	0-1	1-1
5	Bramhall	5-0	1-5	1-3	2-2	X	5-1	1-3	2-2	2-4	2-0	3-2	0-3	0-4	2-0	1-7	7-3
6	Cheadle Hth T	2-0	1-2	2-1	0-2	2-6	X	2-4	2-2	3-2	0-2	4-3	2-2	1-3	2-3	2-2	1-0
7	Chorlton Tn	4-1	3-2	1-2	1-3	2-0	0-1	X	3-3	0-2	2-5	0-1	0-1	2-3	1-4	1-1	2-0
8	Grove Utd	3-2	0-7	0-3	1-1	4-1	5-1	1-3	X	1-4	0-1	3-1	1-5	0-2	0-4	0-0	2-1
9	Knutsford	5-0	1-1	4-0	3-1	2-4	5-2	4-1	5-0	X	2-2	7-1	4-2	3-0	3-0	2-1	1-0
10	Linotype	3-0	0-2	1-1	2-2	1-0	1-0	3-3	2-0	1-0	X	4-0	3-1	1-1	1-1	5-1	3-1
11	Lostock Gra.	2-1	0-0	1-2	6-1	2-3	2-3	1-0	1-0	0-4	0-2	X	3-3	1-1	2-0	2-0	2-2
12	Poynton	2-2	2-1	3-1	3-1	2-3	4-0	4-0	2-2	2-3	3-2	2-0	X	1-1	0-0	1-2	3-2
13	Rylands	0-3	1-3	1-1	0-4	0-2	4-3	0-1	3-1	0-4	0-2	2-1	2-3	X	2-6	3-0	2-1
14	Warrington B	2-2	1-4	0-0	1-1	5-1	0-0	0-2	3-1	0-2	1-2	4-2	1-3	2-2	X	2-1	3-0
15	Whitchurch Al	0-3	2-1	0-1	2-3	2-2	0-1	1-0	2-2	0-0	-4	1-2	2-4	2-2	1-1	X	1-4
16	Wilmslow Alb	3-5	0-4	0-2	3-2	4-4	1-4	2-4	2-2	1-5	1-2	1-2	4-4	3-0	0-4	0-1	X

JUBILEE CUP 1997-98

SEMI-FINAL

Cheadle Heath Nom	v	Pilkington	1-0	Chorlton Town	v	Linotype	2-1 aet

FINAL

Cheadle Heath Nom v Chorlton Town 1-2 at Wincham Park

DIVISION ONE LEAGUE CUP 1997-98

SEMI-FINAL

Knutsford	v	Beeches	2-1	Poynton	v	Barnton	1-2

FINAL

Barnton v Knutsford 1-0 at Winsford United

DIVISION TWO LEAGUE CUP 1997-98

SEMI-FINAL

Linotype Reserves	v	Garsoeed UR	1-1 aet, 2p3	Padgate St Os	v	Malpas	4-1

FINAL

Garswood U Res v Padgate St Oswalds 1-2 at Winsford United

CLUBS DIRECTORY 1997-98

A F C ZENECA

Chairman: David Lea **Manager:** Chris Owen
Secretary: David Stubbs, 11 Petunia Grove, Macclesfield, Cheshire SK11 7YY (01625 423160)
Ground: Mulberries Leisure Centre, Zeneca Pharmaceuticals, (01625 514040)
Colours: All green **Change Colours:** Yellow/black/black

BARNTON

Chairman: William Perrin **Manager:** Terence Murphy
Secretary: Michael Webster, 29 Townfield Lane, Barnton CW8 4LH (01606 781119)
Ground: Townfield, Townfield Lane, Barnton.
Colours: Black & white stripes/black/black **Change Colours:** Amber/blue/blue

BEECHES

Chairman: Gordon Rigby **Manager:**
Secretary: David Corrigan, 7 Burrows Avenue, Haydock, St Helens WA11 0DE (01744 757273).
Ground: Cowley Fields, Wynne Road, St Helens
Colours: Red & blue/navy/navy **Change Colours:** Claret & blue/maroon/maroon

BOLLINGTON ATHLETIC

Chairman: A Hall **Manager:** Glynn Ingham
Secretary: Melanie Vaughan, 53 Broken Cross, Macclesfield, Cheshire SK11 8TU (01625 615274).
Ground: Rec Grd, Bollington. **Colours:** Green & white/black/black **Change:** Blue & white/blue/blue

BRAMHALL

Chairman: Mark Weaver **Manager:** Tim Wharmby
Secretary: Mrs Elaine Weaver, 25 Kimberley Street, Edgeley, Stockport SK3 8EB (0161 477 7273)
Ground: Lumb Lane, Bramhall. **Colours:** Black & red/black/black **Change Colours:** Yellow/blue/blue

BROADHEATH CENTRAL

Chairman: Ian Beresford **Manager:** Gerrard Pickering
Secretary: Graham Anderson, 1 Foxglove Dr, Broadheath, Altrincham WA14 5JX (0161 218 9093).
Ground: Viaduct Rd, Broadheath, Altrincham. (0161 928 5849)
Colours: Blue & White stripes/white/white **Change Colours:** Red & black/black/black

CHEADLE HEATH NOMADS

Chairman: Roy Welsh **Manager:**
Secretary: George Gibbons, 3 Hurley Drive, Cheadle Hulme, Stockport SK8 6DH (0161 485 1343)
Ground: The Heath, Norbreck Ave, Cheadle, Stockport (0161 282 6574)
Colours: Maroon & Sky/maroon/maroon **Change Colours:** Black & white/black/black

CHESTER NOMADS

Chairman: Phil Darlington **Manager:** Bob Delgardo
Secretary: Ritz Ritzema, 22 Cross Green Upton, Chester CH2 1QR (01244 379791)
Ground: Garrison Ground, Eaton Road, Handbridge, Chester
Colours: Amber/black/amber **Change Colours:** Grey/red/white

CHORLTON TOWN

Chairman: Bert Ennis **Manager:** TBA
Secretary: Jim Calderbank, 21 South Meade, Timperley, Altrincham WA15 6QL (0161 969 1156).
Ground: Machester County FA, Brantingham Road, Chorlton
Colours: Red & black stripes/white/white **Change Colours:** Yellow or blue/blue/red

CREWE

Chairman: Patrick Slack **Manager:** Ian O'Reilly
Secretary: Stephen Palin, 56 Vincent St, Crewe, Cheshire CW1 4AA (01270 585231)
Ground: Cumberland Sports Grd, Thomas St, Crewe (01270 537913)
Colours: White & blue/white/white **Change Colours:** Blue & white & red/navy/navy

ELLESMERE PORT UNITED

Chairman: Martin Maund **Manager:** P Rushton
Secretary: Walter Colderley, 27 Chorley Old Rd, Bolton BL1 3AD (01204 532149)
Ground: Ellesmere Port Stadium **Colours:** All blue **Change Colours:** All white

GARSWOOD UNITED RESERVES

Chairman: R Jones **Manager:** Alan Clarke
Secretary: John Richards, 45 Elm House, Egerton Rd, Prescot L34 3LZ (0151 292 6581)
Ground: Simms Lane Ends, Garswood Road, Garswood, Nr Wigan (01744 892258).
Colours: Blue & white halves/blue/blue **Change Colours:** All red.

GROVE UNITED

Chairman: Mark Boothby **Manager:**
Secretary: Bernard Jordon, 25 Bean Leach Road, Hazel Grove, Stockport SK7 4LD (0161 456 2542).
Ground: Half Moon Lane, Alfreton Rd, Offerton/Lisburne Lane, Stockport.
Colours: Red/black/black **Change Colours:** Maroon/white/white

KNUTSFORD

Chairman: **Manager:** Ken Harrison
Secretary: Keith Jones, 20 Townfields, Cheshire WA16 8DR (01565 755711)
Ground: Manchester Road, Knutsford.
Colours: Red & black/black/black **Change Colours:** White/blue/white

LINOTYPE

Chairman: Brian Hennis **Manager:** K Gardner
Secretary: John Tighe, 466 Wythenshawe Rd, Brooklands, Manchester M23 9DX (0161 374 1212)
Ground: British Airways Club, Clay Lane, Timperley, Altrincham (0161 980 7354).
Colours: White/black/black **Change Colours:** Red & black/white/white

LITTLEMOOR

Chairman: Arthur McClean **Manager:** Frank Saunders
Secretary: Stanley McQuarrie, 96 Mottram Towers, Mottram St, Hillgate, Stockport SK1 3NY (0161 474 0257)
Ground: Stockport Lads Club, Hempshaw Lane, Offerton
Colours: Black & white Stripes/black/black **Change Colours:** All blue

LOSTOCK GRALAM

Secretary: Richard Longworth, 6 Hope St, Castle, Northwich, Cheshire (01606 782747)
Chairman: Derek Washburn **Ground:** Rear Slow & Easy Hotel, Manchester Road, Lostock Gralam
Colours: All blue **Change Colours:** Green & yellow halves/black/black

MALPAS

Chairman: Robert Leslie **Manager:** Martin Holden
Secretary: Bernard Lloyd, 15 Springfield Avenue, Malpas, Cheshire SY14 8QD (01948 860812).
Ground: Malpas & District Sports Club, Oxheys, Wrexham Rd, Malpas, Cheshire (01948 860662).
Colours: White/blue/red **Change Colours:** Yellow & green/green/yellow

MIDDLEWICH TOWN

Chairman: Steven Morris **Manager:** David Twite
Secretary: Bernard Lycett, Rivington, Clay Lane, Haslington, Cheshire CW1 5SE (01270 584066)
Ground: Seddon Street, Middlewich (01606 835842)
Colours: Red/white/red **Change Colours:** Blue/white/blue

PADGATE ST OSWALDS

Chairman: Graham Millins **Manager:** Mick Armitage
Secretary: Brian Hughes, 13 Jubilee Avenue, Padgate, Warrington WA1 3JY (01925 490924)
Ground: Bennets Rec Grd, Station Rd, Padgate.
Colours: Black & white/black/red **Change Colours:** Blue & red

PILKINGTON AFC

Chairman: John Potter **Manager:** Paul Pinder
Secretary: Paul Pinder, 629 Eltonhead Road, Sutton Heath St Helens WA9 5SX (01744 816158)
Ground: Ruskin Drive, St Helens (01744 22893)
Colours: Green & black/black/black **Change Colours:** All Claret & blue

POYNTON

Chairman: David Coreovan **Manager:** Paul Cunningham
Secretary: Mark Warburton, 27 Alderley Close, Hazel Grove, Cheshire SK7 6BS (01625 873872)
Ground: London Rd North, Poynton (01625 875765).
Colours: Red & black/black/red & black **Change Colours:** Blue & white/blue/blue.

RYLANDS

Chairman: William Morris **Manager:** Terry Selby
Secretary: Ian Finchett, 31 Elizabeth Drive, Padgate, Warrington WA1 4JQ (01925 816911).
Ground: Gorsey Lane, Warrington (01925 35700).
Colours: Blue & black/black/black **Change Colours:** Red & royal/blue/red

STYAL

Chairman: Barry Green **Manager:** Frank Jones
Secretary: Alan Jones, 1 Oak Brow Cottages, Atrincham Road, Styal, Wilmslow SK(4JE (01625 530270)
Ground: Altrincham Road, Styal (01625 529303)
Colours: Yellow/blue/blue **Change Colours:** Blue/black/black

TRAFFORD FC RES

Chairman: David Brown **Manager:** Dave Norman
Secretary: Graham Foxall, 62 Grosvenor Road, Urmston, Manchester M41 5AQ (0161 746 9726)
Ground: Shawe View, Pennybridge Lane, Urmston M41 5DL (0161 747 1727)
Colours: All white **Change Colours:** Red/navy/red

WALKERS SPORTS & SOCIAL

Chairman: Thomas Tandy **Manager:** Ian Walsh
Secretary: Steven Harris, 4 Ackers Rd, Stockton Heath, Warrington, Ches WA4 2DH (01925 261929)
Ground: Tetley Walkers Social Club, Long Lane (01925 634904)
Colours: Yellow/blue/blue **Change Colours:** Blue & black/black/black

WARRINGTON BOROUGH

Chairman: Harry Boon **Manager:** Derek Holden
Secretary: Ian Dick, 53 Arlington Drive, Penketh, Warrington, Cheshire WA5 2QG (01925 653044)
Ground: Cantilever Park, Warrington (01925 724421)
Colours: Blue & yellow/blue/blue **Change Colours:** Navy & purple/navy/navy

WHITCHURCH ALPORT

Chairman: P Wainwright **Manager:** Alan Smith
Secretary: Robert Dutton, 7 Nessina Grove, Crewe, Cheshire CW2 8EL (01270 663015)
Ground: Yockings Park, Whitchurch, Shropshire. (01948 667415)
Colours: Red/black/red **Change:** Yellow/blue/blue

CARLSBERG WEST CHESHIRE A.F.L.

President: K Halsall **Chairman:** R Prescott

Hon. Secretary: L Bullock,
8 Cambridge Road, Bromborough, Wirral L62 7JA
Tel: 0151 334 3545

Season 1997-98 heralded the introduction of three points for a win, but, irrespective of the rewards, the Division One Championship went the way of the previous two campaigns. Poulton Victoria who defended their title with largely the same squad, possessed the all round strength and experience eventually to take them through - their hat trick by an eleven point margin. They were made to fight until the penultimate week of the season by three sides, Ashville, Stork and Shell who had spent most of the previous campaign at the wrong end of the table. At the other end of the table nothing went right for Moreton who failed to collect a win throughout and after a number of seasons flirting with danger were relegated to Division Two. Their place will be taken by General Chemicals who, having themselves been relegated at the end of the previous campaign, didn't make the best of starts in Division Two. However, 24 consecutive wins followed by two draws took them to a deserved title and an immediate return to the higher sphere.

The one trophy not to go to Poulton Victoria in recent years has been the Pyke Cup, but they made amends this time round by overcoming Heswall 1-0 in the final of this competition for Division One sides. The lower league sides do battle for the West Cheshire Bowl and Stork Reserves gained compensation for finishing Divisional runners up by lifting the Bowl following a 4-2 final success over Poulton Victoria Reserves.

Probably the most sought after trophy for our clubs is the Cheshire Amateur Cup with the 100th ever holding of this fine competition taking place this season. The league is understandably proud of its recent record in the "Cheshire" with April's Ashville v Poulton Victoria final being the seventh consecutive "all West Cheshire" affair. A tremendous tussle eventually went the way of young pretenders Ashville with their Wallasey neighbours suffering a rare final defeat. Vics gained some consolation a week later by winning the Northern Counties championships as representatives of the Cheshire FA having opened their trophy account at the start of the campaign by collecting the Bill Weight Memorial Trophy. As our only representatives in the Lancashire Amateur Cup, Merseyside Police did themselves proud by seeing off all opposition before overcoming Crawfords 2-1 in the final, after extra time.

In District competitions, having been regular holders during the 90's Christleton renewed acquaintance with the Chester Senior Cup after a gap of twelve months while Heswall avenged their Pyke defeat at the hands of Poulton Victoria when overcoming the same opponents, 4-2, in the Wirral Senior Cup final. In just their second season in the League New Brighton collected their first trophy when they edged out Heswall Reserves 2-1. The annual inter-league game with the Mid Cheshire league finished 2-2 while the Castlemaine XXXX shoot out was won by Mersey Royal.

In a historic change, season 1998-99 will see the West Cheshire League expand to three Divisions. This will be accomplished with the addition of new clubs along with the acceptance of reserve sides of current members.

Poulton Victoria - 1997-98 Carslberg West Cheshire AFL Division One Champions

FINAL LEAGUE TABLES 1997-98

Division One	*P*	*W*	*D*	*L*	*F*	*A*	*Pts*	*Leading Scorers*		*Most Man of Match Awards*
Poulton Victoria	30	24	3	3	100	27	75	N Dillon	14	P Connor
Ashville	30	19	7	4	56	27	64	A Robinson	12	A Robinson
Stork	30	18	7	5	67	39	61	P Wiggins	16	P Wiggins
Shell	30	15	10	5	71	37	55	L Oldfield	14	W Nicol
Cammell Laird	30	14	8	8	49	38	50	S Watterson	8	C Littlejohn
Heswall	30	15	4	11	67	48	49	J Pepper/M Brady	8	D Lepts
Christleton	30	13	5	12	56	40	44	C Reid	11	G Jones
Blacon YC	30	11	9	10	70	56	42	D Edwards	23	P Martin
Newton	30	11	9	10	47	50	42	M Forshaw	14	S Platt
Mersey Royal	30	11	8	11	38	44	41	D Carrington	7	J Thompson
Vauxhalls	30	10	9	11	62	66	39	G Washington	16	G Washington
Mond Rangers	30	10	4	16	57	60	34	K Thomas	16	K Patterson
Merseyside Pollice	30	9	5	16	53	65	32	D McCarthy	9	D McCarthy
Capenhurst	30	7	4	19	37	70	25	A Brown	6	J Dowd/S Sailes/C Davies
Brom. Pool	30	5	2	23	40	104	17	T Williams	17	T Williams
Moreton	30	0	2	28	29	128	2	D Cowdrey/R Murray	3	P Nugent

Division Two	*P*	*W*	*D*	*L*	*F*	*A*	*Pts*	*Leading scorer*		*Most Man of Match Awards*
Gen. Chemicals	34	26	5	3	126	43	83	M Quigley	25	P Houghton
Stork Reserves	34	25	5	4	113	45	80	B McHugh	28	B McHugh
Heswall Res	34	19	8	7	85	54	65	K Gore	18	K Gore
West Kirby	34	19	6	9	71	51	63	J Ward/M Andrews	17	M Andrews
Poulton Vics Res	34	18	7	9	96	48	61	C Hawitt	25	P Haddock
Ashville Res	34	17	10	7	84	56	61	J Stanhope	19	D Bennett/R Hawitt
New Brighton	34	19	4	11	89	55	61	P Parkhill	12	P Bowden
Christleton Res	34	15	10	9	63	47	55	A Tydd	12	C Vernall/P Hollifield
C Laird Res	34	15	8	11	79	68	53	J Edwards	16	J Edwards
Castrol Social	34	15	3	16	73	73	48	J Farrell	18	T Livens
Upton AA	34	13	6	15	73	72	45	M Thomson	11	J Cadwallader
Vauxhall Res	34	10	6	18	55	75	36	K Coles/J McNicholas	7	K Coles/J Battie
Shell Res	34	10	5	19	68	96	35	J Powell	14	J Powell
M Royal Res	34	10	5	19	52	98	35	S Jones/A Morgan/J Brunt	5	B Connelly
Capenhurst Res	34	8	6	20	56	90	30	N Walmsley	8	N Walmsley/M Collins
Willaston	34	8	2	24	54	107	26	I Smith	10	P Jones
Brom Pool Res	34	4	4	26	38	132	16	K Kelly	7	G Hand
Manor Ath	34	3	4	27	46	121	13	P McNay	7	G Carvell

DIVISION ONE RESULTS CHART 1997-98

		1	2	3	4	5	6	7	8	9	10	11	12	13	14	15	16
1	Ashville	X	1-0	2-1	0-0	2-1	2-1	2-0	1-0	5-1	3-1	5-1	0-0	0-2	0-0	2-0	2-1
2	Blacon YC	1-2	X	1-1	0-2	0-1	3-2	1-1	3-1	2-6	4-2	5-3	0-1	3-2	2-1	2-4	2-2
3	Bromboro P	0-2	2-2	X	2-6	3-1	1-6	1-8	0-2	2-3	2-7	3-2	0-0	1-6	1-0	2-4	1-5
4	Cammell Laird	1-2	1-1	2-1	X	3-1	0-2	4-1	0-0	5-3	1-0	3-2	2-0	0-3	3-2	1-0	4-0
5	Capenhurst	1-2	2-0	2-1	0-0	X	0-4	1-4	3-0	1-3	2-3	4-0	1-2	0-3	1-2	2-3	3-4
6	Christleton	0-3	6-1	2-0	1-1	2-0	X	2-1	2-2	2-1	3-0	6-0	0-2	0-2	0-1	1-2	3-1
7	Heswall	2-4	1-1	9-3	1-2	3-1	1-2	X	0-1	1-0	3-2	5-2	5-3	0-2	3-2	1-3	0-1
8	Mersey Royal	2-0	1-1	2-0	2-2	1-1	2-1	1-2	X	2-2	1-3	1-0	0-2	0-4	1-1	1-2	2-0
9	Mersey Police	0-2	1-2	2-3	1-0	4-2	1-1	1-3	1-2	X	2-4	4-1	2-4	0-2	2-8	2-2	1-2
10	Mond Rngrs	2-2	2-4	3-0	2-0	3-1	2-0	1-4	5-3	0-2	X	5-1	2-2	1-3	1-2	0-3	0-0
11	Moreton	1-4	0-4	1-4	1-3	0-1	1-1	0-2	1-3	1-3	0-4	X	2-2	1-7	1-6	1-9	0-7
12	Newton	1-3	0-7	3-1	2-0	2-3	1-0	1-1	1-8	0-2	1-1	4-2	X	4-5	1-3	6-0	0-3
13	Poulton Vic	3-2	3-0	4-0	5-1	7-0	3-1	3-2	1-2	1-0	3-1	11-0	1-1	X	3-0	3-2	2-2
14	Shell	1-1	4-1	5-1	2-0	2-2	1-1	2-0	3-1	4-1	2-0	6-2	6-0	1-1	X	0-1	3-3
15	Stork	1-1	1-1	3-1	0-0	5-3	5-2	1-0	2-0	1-1	3-1	4-1	1-1	2-1	0-0	X	3-2
15	Vauxhall M	1-2	1-15	4-2	2-1	2-1	0-2	1-3	0-1	1-1	3-2	3-1	2-2	0-4	4-4	4-1	X

1997-98 CUP FINALISTS

	Winners	*Runners up*
PYKE CUP	Poulton Victoria 1	Heswall 0
WEST CHESHIRE BOWL	Stork Reserves 4	Poulton Vic Res 2
CHESHIRE AMATUER CUP	Ashville	Poulton Victoria
LANCASHIRE AMATUER CUP	Merseyside Police	
CHESTER SENIOR CUP	Christleton	
WIRRAL SENIOR CUP	Heswall	Poulton Victoria
WIRRAL AMATEUR CUP	New Brighton	Heswall Reserves
RUNCORN SENIOR CUP		Mond Rangers
CASTLEMAINE XXXX SHOOT OUT	Mersey Royal 4	Blacon YC 2
Group winners	Christleton	Upton AA
BILL WEIGHT TROPHY	Poulton Victoria	Shell

MANAGER OF THE MONTH 1997-98

Aug	Terry Swanwick (C Laird R)
Sep	Kevin Mulville (Shell)
Oct	Terry Howells/Mick Fadden (New Brighton)
Nov	Alvin McDonald (Poulton Vics)
Dec	Keith Ravenscroft/Ian Killen (Stork Reserves)
Jan	Jimmy Williams (G.Chemicals)
Feb	Keith Bennoch/Paul Corbett (Willaston)
Mar	Dave Jones (Blacon YC)
Apr	Dave Anderson (Ashville)

CLUB DIRECTORY 1998-99

ASHVILLE FC

Secretary: Dave Walton, 15 Wellesley Road, Wallasey, Wirral, Merseyside, L44 5UR (0151 639 9196).
Ground: Villa Park, Cross Lane, Wallasey Village, Wallasey, (0151 638 2127)
Sponsor: Clinitex, Kelly Sports **Formed:** 1949 **Colours:** White/black/black

BLACON YOUTH CLUB FC

Secretary: Ron Paddock, 71 Blacon Avenue, Blacon, Chester, Cheshire CH1 5BB (01244 371240)
Ground: Cairns Crescent Playing Fields, Cairns Crescent, Blacon, Chester.
Sponsor: Acorn Glass **Formed:** 1964 **Colours:** Black & white/black/black

BROMBOROUGH POOL FC

Secretary: Trevor Patterson, 102 Princes Boulevard, Higher Bebington, Wirral L63 5LP (0151 645 1642)
Ground: Bromborough Pool Village, The Green, South View Road, Bromborough Pool.
Sponsor: **Formed:** 1884 **Colours:** All Blue

CAMMELL LAIRD FC

Secretary: Ray Steele, 46 Croft Ave, Bromborough, Wirral L62 2BR (0151 334 8998)
Ground: Kirklands, St Peters Road, Rock Ferry, Birkenhead (0151 645 5991)
Sponsor: Met Arc **Formed:** 1900 **Colours:** All blue

CAPENHURST FC

Secretary: Martin Williams, 157 Hope Farm Road, Great Sutton, South Wirral L66 2TJ (0151 339 8935)
Ground: Capenhurst Sports Ground, Capenhurst Lane, Capenhurst (0151 339 4101)
Sponsor: Atlantic Comm/Deeglass **Formed:** 1952 **Colours:** Sky & claret/claret/claret & sky

CASTROL SOCIAL FC

Secretary: Dave Bebbington, 490 Overpool Rd, Whitby, Ellesmere Port, South Wirral L66 2JJ (0151 357 1979)
Ground: Castrol Sports & Social Club, Chester Road, Whitby, Ellesmere Port (0151 355 1730)
Sponsor: Castrol/ Peninsula Restaurant **Formed:** 1954 **Colours:** Blue & white/black/black

CHRISTLETON FC

Secretary: Ken Price, 35 Canadian Ave, Hoole, Chester, Cheshire CH2 3HQ (01244 313513)
Ground: Little Heath, Christleton (01244 332153)
Sponsor: The Chester Evening Leader **Formed:** 1966 **Colours:** Red/black/red

GENERAL CHEMICALS FC

Secretary: Tony Riley, 171 Cotton Lane, Runcorn, Cheshire WA7 5JB (01928 565390)
Ground: Pavilions Club, Dandy Lane, Weston Point, Runcorn (01928 590508)
Sponsor: Maltacourt Ltd **Formed:** 1958 **Colours:** Yellow/l blue/yellow

HESWALL

Secretary: Jake Horan, 13 Reedville Road, Bebington, Wirral L63 2HS (0151 644 0459)
Ground: Gayton Park, Brimstage Road, Heswall, Wirral, (0151 342 8172)
Sponsor: Pyramids Shopping Centre **Formed:** 1891 **Colours:** Yellow/royal/yellow

MANOR ATHLETIC

Secretary: Stewart Galtress, 3 Centurion Close, Meols, Wirral L47 7BZ (0151 632 3211)
Ground: Octel Sports Club, Bridle Road, Bromborough
Sponsor: **Formed:** 1968 **Colours:** White/black/red

MERSEY ROYAL

Secretary: Dave Lawson, 7 Mount Park, Higher Bebington, Wirral L63 %rd (0151 608 2261)
Ground: Unilver Sports Ground, Bromborough
Sponsor: N S Glazier **Formed:** 1946 **Colours:** Black & green/black/black

MERSEYSIDE POLICE

Secretary: George Todd, 14 Crowther Street, St Helens, Merseyside WA10 4NH (01744 755845)
Ground: Police Club, Fairfield, Prescot Road, Liverpool L7 0JD (0151 228 2352)
Sponsor: Davies Ltd **Formed:** 1885 **Colours:** Green/black/black

MOND RANGERS

Secretary: Beverley Crilly, 26 Perrin Ave, Weston Point, Runcorn, Cheshire WA7 4BJ (01928 575938)
Ground: Pavilions Club, Sandy Lane, Weston Point, Runcorn (01928 590508)
Sponsor: Rocksavage Power Co Ltd **Formed:** 1967 **Colours:** Navy & azurte/navy/azure

MORETON FC

Secretary: Jeff Williams-Lloyd, 46 Burrell Drive, Moreton, Wirral L46 0TQ (0151 677 9840)
Ground: Elm Grove, Hoylake
Sponsor: Tilney & Co **Formed:** 1900 **Colours:** Red/black/black

NEW BRIGHTON

Secretary: Russell Holmes, 10 Rudgrave Square, Wallasey, Wirral L44 0EL (0151 638 9506)
Ground: Harrison Drive, Wallasey Village, Wallasey
Sponsor: George Major Skip Hire **Formed:** 1993 **Colours:** Red & white/white/red & white

NEWTON F C

Secretary: Alan Dabner, 41 St David Road, Claughton, Birkenhead L43 8SW (0151 653 2151)
Ground: Millcroft, Frankby Road, Greasby, Wirral (0151 677 8382)
Sponsor: Cory Bothers Shipping Ltd **Formed:** 1933 **Colours:** Gold/black/yellow

POULTON VICTORIA

Secretary: John McGraath, 1 Wernbrook Close, Noctorum, Wirral L43 9HY (0151 652 8043)
Ground: Victoria Park, Rankin Street, Wallasey (0151 638 3559)
Sponsor: Carlsberg & Bass **Formed:** 1935 **Colours:** All Royal Blue

SHELL FC

Secretary: Roy Jones, 5 Sycamore Drive, Whitby, Ellesmere Port, South Wirral L66 2PW (0151 200 1532)
Ground: Chester Road, Whitby, Ellesmere Port, South Wirral (0151 200 7080)
Sponsor: Portion Controls Ltd **Formed:** 1924 **Colours:** Yellow & blue/yellow/yellow

STORK FC

Secretary: Steve Carter, 7 Elm Road, Bebington, Wirral L63 8PF (0151 645 6697)
Ground: Unilever Sports Ground, Bromborough
Sponsor: The Village Leisure Hotel **Formed:** 1920 **Colours:** All green

UPTON ATHLETIC

Secretary: Bary Gaulton, 24 St Marks Crescent, Whitby, Ellesmere Port L66 2XD (0151 339 1504)
Ground: Cheshire County Council Sports & Social Club, Plas Newton Lane, Chester (01244 318367)
Sponsor: **Formed:** 1964 **Colours:** White/black/black

VAUXHALL MOTORS

Secretary: Carole Paisey, 26 South Road, West Kirby, Wirral L48 3HQ (0151 625 6936)
Ground: Vauxhall Sports Ground, Rivacre Road, Hooton, Ellesmere Port (0151 328 1114)
Sponsor: James Edwards/Lookers **Formed:** 1963 **Colours:** Maroon/sky/maroon

WILLASTON

Secretary: Peter Armstrong, 22 Deeside, Whitby, Ellesmere Port, South Wirral L65 6RQ (0151 200 2068)
Ground: Johnston Recreation Ground, Neston Road, Willaston, South Wirral
Sponsor: The Pollard Inn **Formed:** 1962 **Colours:** Yellow & royal/royal/royal

SGL SEAT CARS
WEST LANCASHIRE FOOTBALL LEAGUE

President: D Procter **Chairman:** W Carr

General Secretary: W Carr, 60 Selby Avenue, Blackpool, Lancashire FY4 2LZ
Tel: 01253 348450

Another page in the history of the league was turned when the clubs accepted a Management proposal that a third Senior Division be formed commencing season 1998-99. The league will now have a Premier, First and Second Divisions, while the two divisions for the reserve teams of member clubs will be unchanged, extending the League to 67 teams from 42 clubs.

As part of the re-formation it was agreed to reduce Divisions One and Two to sixteen teams each, (from eighteen and twenty respectively), this required six teams to be relegated from the Second Division to form a strong base for the new division.

Four new clubs were recruited - Fleetwood Anchor, Millom from Cumbria, and S.D.O. Rangers Barrow; also Coppull United returned after an absence of 70 years having been founder members and the first League Champions in 1906.

Charnock Richard, runners-up last season, became the League Champions for the first time since joining the league. Burnley United, last season's Richardson Cup winners, were runners up.

Vickers Sports Club were Division Two champions, returning at the first attempt to the senior division which they had graced since joining the league in 1962. Barnoldswick United unfortunately cannot join them as runners up as only one team is to be promoted as part of the arrangement to reduce the top two divisions to sixteen teams. Nevertheless, it was an excellent and rare performance

Barnoldswick United - West Lancashire League 1997-98

as newcomers to the league who battled to hold off strong challenges from Tempest United, BAC Preston and Garstang.

Fulwood Amateurs won the Richardson Cup beating champions Charnock Richard 2-0 at Accrington Stanley. Fulwood also won the Lancashire Challenge Shield by the same score against fellow leaguers and previous Shield winners, Kirkham & Wesham. It was the first time Fulwood had won the prestigious Trophy dominated in recent years by the West Lancashire League with a record of nine wins plus eight runners up in the past thirteen years.

Vickers Sports Club won the President's Cup as well as the Division Two Championship, but they were taken right to the wire by Milnthorpe Corinthians to win 2-1 at Lancaster City. The Reserve Division's Houston Cup was won by Charnock Richard beating their close rivals Leyland Motors on the County Ground.

Derrick Procter

FINAL LEAGUE TABLES 1997-98

Division One

	P	*W*	*D*	*L*	*F*	*A*	*Pts*
Charnock Richard	34	25	3	6	107	46	78
Burnley United	34	23	3	8	96	48	72
Leyland Motors Ath	34	20	5	9	85	41	65
Kirkham & Wesham	34	20	6	8	65	44	*63
Fleetwood Hesketh	34	18	5	11	70	62	59
Blackrod Town	34	18	2	14	67	61	56
Fulwood Amateurs	34	15	10	9	71	48	55
Lansil	34	14	5	15	85	82	47
Wyre Villa	34	14	5	15	62	68	47
Dalton United	34	13	5	16	72	74	44
Eagley	34	12	6	16	77	83	42
Feniscowles	34	11	9	14	54	69	42
Padiham	34	11	5	18	54	79	38
Springfields	34	10	6	18	55	71	*33
Freckleton	34	7	12	15	44	78	33
Thornton Cleveleys Int	34	9	5	20	58	91	32
Turton	34	8	7	19	50	77	31
Lancashire Constab.	34	7	3	24	52	102	*21

* Indicates clubs with points adjustment

Division Two

	P	*W*	*D*	*L*	*F*	*A*	*Pts*
Vickers S.C.	38	28	6	4	118	32	90
Barnoldswick United	38	23	8	7	86	58	77
Tempest United	38	23	5	10	96	47	74
B.A.C. Preston	38	24	6	8	98	56	*72
Garstang	38	22	4	12	89	73	70
Wigan College	38	20	9	9	91	53	69
Norcross & Warbreck	38	17	10	11	71	57	61
Milnthorpe Corinthians	38	17	7	14	81	67	58
Poulton Town	38	16	9	13	75	70	57
Hesketh Bank	38	13	13	12	88	75	52
Lytham St Annes	38	14	9	15	62	65	51
Whinney Hill	38	12	10	16	71	79	46
Haslingden St Marys	38	11	10	17	45	62	43
Preston West End	38	12	6	20	69	85	42
Glaxo	38	10	9	19	63	88	39
Blackpool Wren Rvrs		38	12	5	21	63	92
*38							
Bootle	38	9	6	23	62	105	33
BAE Canberra	38	8	9	21	66	94	*30
Carnforth Rangers	38	7	8	23	50	87	29

LEADING GOALSCORERS 1997-98

(ALL DIVISIONS)

L Chambers	BAC Preston	53
S Walker	Vickers SC	44
P Corrigan	Barnoldswick United	40
A Briggs	Leyland Motors Athletic	38
J Vargon	Wigan College	35
C Ward jun.	Springfields	31
D Willoughby	Garstang	31

EAST LANCASHIRE FOOTBALL LEAGUE

President: I W Bullock **Chairman:** M P Bibby

General Secretary: J Constable,
66 Dukes Meadow, Ingol, Preston PR2 7AT
Tel: 01772 727135

FINAL LEAGUE TABLES 1997-98

Division One

	P	W	D	L	F	A	Pts
Crosshills	22	15	4	3	66	38	49
Oswaldtwistle	22	14	4	4	73	44	46
Rimington	22	12	3	7	55	51	39
Trawden Celtic	22	11	4	7	65	48	37
Worsthorne	22	10	4	8	69	49	34
Settle United	22	10	4	8	57	40	34
Stacksteads St Jos	22	9	5	8	46	48	32
Gargrave	22	7	4	11	54	47	25
Colne United	22	7	1	14	54	79	22
Barnoldswick Utd Rs	22	6	3	13	35	55	21
Hurst Green	22	5	5	12	38	47	20
Mill Hill St Peters	22	5	1	16	24	90	16

Whalley Rangers w/d

Division Two

	P	W	D	L	F	A	Pts
Kelbrook	24	18	3	3	64	26	57
Langho	24	15	9	0	78	34	54
Sabden	24	17	3	4	71	33	54
Whinney Hill	24	12	4	8	54	43	40
Ribchester Rovers	24	11	4	9	64	43	37
Colne Reserves	24	11	3	10	46	49	36
Rolls Royce	24	10	5	9	63	59	35
Rock Rovers	24	9	3	12	69	50	30
Earby Town	24	9	3	12	41	62	30
Barnoldswick Pk Rs	24	8	4	12	37	41	28
Read United	24	7	2	15	43	78	23
Chatburn	24	3	3	18	35	100	*9
Oswaldtwistle Town	24	2	2	20	26	73	8

* 3 points deducted for playing ineligible player

FRANK ARMITT LIVERPOOL CITY FOOTBALL COMBINATION

DIVISION ONE

		P	W	D	L	F	A	Pts	GD
1	St Dominics	28	19	7	2	88	38	64	50
2	Crawfords UB	28	18	5	5	86	48	59	38
3	Waterloo Dock	28	17	4	7	78	42	55	36
4	Royal Seaforth	28	16	1	11	74	59	49	15
5	Plessey GPT	28	14	5	9	76	61	47	15
6	South Liverpool	28	13	8	7	43	31	47	12
7	Ayone	28	12	6	10	59	56	*39	3
8	Manweb	28	11	4	13	45	45	37	0
9	Ford Motors	28	9	8	11	54	55	35	-1
10	Mossley Hill	28	10	2	16	77	100	32	-23
11	Yorkshire CT	28	9	3	16	65	77	30	-12
12	Bootle Res	28	8	5	15	46	65	29	-19
13	Lucas Sports	28	8	4	16	49	77	28	-28
14	Stockbridge	28	6	7	15	42	66	25	-24
15	Crystal Villa	28	4	3	21	25	87	15	-62

DIVISION TWO

		P	W	D	L	F	A	Pts	GD
1	Speke	20	16	2	2	65	23	50	42
2	BRNESC	20	12	5	3	55	28	41	27
3	Cabin	20	13	3	4	58	30	*39	28
4	Cheshire Lines	20	11	5	4	48	27	38	21
5	Prescot BICC	20	6	8	6	41	45	26	-4
6	Rainhill Town	20	6	4	10	37	48	22	-11
7	Maghull Reserves	20	5	5	10	21	35	20	-14
8	Halewood Town	20	5	5	10	28	45	20	-17
9	Plessey GPT Res	20	5	3	12	34	51	18	-17
10	Manweb Reserves	20	3	7	10	33	68	16	-35
11	Mossley Hill Reserves	20	4	1	15	25	45	13	-20

DIVISION ONE
CLUB DIRECTORY 1998-99

BARNOLDSWICK UNITED

Secretary: Mrs L.James, 37 Long Inn Lane, Barnoldswick, Lancs BB8 6BJ (01282 815361).
Ground: West Close, Victory Park, Barnoldswick.
Colours: Blue & black/black/black **Change Colours:** Blue & yellow/blue/blue & yellow

COLNE UNITED

Secretary: Mr S Bannister, 26 Higgin St, Colne, Lancs.BB8 9RS (01282 711796)
Ground: Sough Park, Kelbrook, Earby, Colne.
Colours: Black and white/black/black **Change colours:** All claret

CROSSHILLS

Secretary: Mr P Smith, 72 North Parade, Skipton, N Yorks BD23 3SR (01756 799338)
Ground: Sutton Fields, Sutton-in-Craven, Keighley, West Yorkshire.
Colours: Red/black/red **Change colours:** All blue

GARGRAVE

Secretary: Mr P Watson, Saw Mill Cottage, Marton Road, Gargrave, Skipton N Yorks BD23 3NN (01756 749351)
Ground: Skipton Road, Gargrave
Colours: Claret & blue **Change Colours:** Blue & white

HURST GREEN

Secretary: Mr N Brown, 11 Chatburn Rd, Longridge, Preston, Lancs PR3 3FN (01772 785416)
Ground: off Smithy Row, Hurst Green
Colours: Black & white/black/black **Change colours:** Yellow & green/green/yellow

MILL HILL St PETERS

Secretary: Mr D Willacy, 15 Springfield Ave, Feniscowles, Blackburn, Lancs (01254 208347)
Ground: Mill Hill St Peters, Queen Victoria St, Mill Hill, Blackburn.
Colours: Blue & gold/black/black **Change colours:** Green & white

OSWALDTWISTLE TOWN

Ground: Heys Playing Field, Heron Way, Oswaldtwistle.
Secretary: Mrs M.Riley, 11A Polar Close, Oswaldtwistle, Lancs. BB5 3AY (01254 382830)
Colours: All green & yellow **Change colours:** All blue & black

RIMINGTON

Secretary: Mr L Whittaker, 2 Dorset Drive, Clitheroe, Lancs BB7 2BQ (01200 29112).
Ground: Coulthurst Jubilee Field, Back Lane, Rimington (behind Black Bull).
Colours: Tangerine/black/tangerine **Change colours:** Blue/red

SETTLE UNITED

Secretary: Mr J Dinsdale, 3 Goldielands Settle N Yorks (01729 823738)
Ground: Bridge End Ground, Goggleswick, Settle.
Colours: Yellow & black/black/black **Change Colours:** Black & white

STACKSTEAD ST JOSEPH'S

Secretary: Mr R Cronshaw, 16 Heathbourne Rd, Stacksteads, Bacup, Lancs (01706 873638)
Ground: Stacksteads Recreation Ground.
Colours: All Blue **Change Colours:** Yellow/black/black

TRAWDEN CELTIC

Secretary: M Timberlake, 191 Cotton Tree Lane, Colne, Lancs BB8 7BN (01282 868143)
Ground: Trawden Rec Ground, Rock Lane, Trawden
Colours: Black & white/black/black & white **Change colours:** Red & blue/blue/red

WORSTHORNE

Secretary: Mr J Carrington, 18 Rossendale Ave, Burnley, Lancs. BB11 5HF (01282 428273)
Ground: Bank Hall, Colne Rd, Burnley
Colours: Yellow & green/green/yellow **Change colours:** Claret & blue/claret/claret

NORTH WESTERN FINAL LEAGUE TABLES 1997-98

I ZINGARI LEAGUE

PREMIER DIV	P	W	D	L	F	A	Pts
East Villa	24	16	4	4	82	32	52
St Aloysius	24	17	2	5	91	38	*50
Aigburth PH	24	15	5	4	68	33	50
Quarry Bank OB	24	13	5	6	48	36	44
REMYCA Utd	24	11	4	9	59	45	37
Roma	24	10	7	7	50	50	37
Sacre Coeur FP	24	8	9	7	57	40	33
Stoneycroft	24	7	8	9	51	58	29
NELTC	24	7	3	14	29	72	24
St Marys COB	24	6	4	14	45	77	22
Kirkby Boulevard	24	4	9	11	39	70	*18
St Philomena's	24	3	8	13	43	68	17
Warbreck	24	3	4	17	31	74	13

I ZINGARI COMBINATION

DIVISION ONE	P	W	D	L	F	A	Pts
Aigburth PH	26	21	2	3	101	26	65
Quarry Bank OB	26	17	5	4	64	29	56
Liverpool Nalgo	26	17	3	6	79	40	54
REMYCA Utd	26	16	4	6	80	50	52
St Marys	26	15	4	7	93	59	*48
Sacre Coeur FP	26	13	1	12	55	56	40
Old Xaverians	26	10	4	12	62	69	34
Stoneycroft	26	11	1	14	54	73	34
Warbreck	26	8	6	12	55	50	30
Bluecoat OB	26	9	3	14	65	90	30
Aintree Villa	26	7	3	16	46	72	24
Essemmay OB	26	7	2	17	52	113	23
Leyfield	26	4	5	17	41	77	17
Sefton & District	26	4	3	19	36	79	15

ST HELENS COMBINATION

PREMIER DIV	P	W	D	L	Pts
Child	22	19	2	1	59
Owens Corn. Rav.	22	19	2	1	59
The Anchor	22	18	1	3	55
Gerard Arms	22	10	5	7	35
Holy Cross	22	11	2	9	35
Bold Cherry	22	9	4	9	31
Shoe	22	9	3	10	30
Pilkington Res	22	6	5	11	23
Rifle	22	6	2	14	20
Prescot BICC Rs	22	4	2	16	14
Globe	22	3	3	16	12
Beeches Res	22	1	3	18	6

SOUTHPORT & DISTRICT LEAGUE

DIVISION ONE	P	W	D	L	F	A	Pts
Birchfield	21	16	2	3	84	34	34
High Park	21	16	2	3	63	24	34
Crossens	21	14	3	4	85	40	31
Heathfield Athletic	21	12	3	6	62	59	27
Leisure Sports	21	7	3	11	50	64	17
Formby JSCOB	21	4	3	14	45	74	11
Blowick	21	5	1	15	35	85	11
Formby Dons	21	1	1	19	32	76	13

EAST CHESHIRE LEAGUE

PREMIER DIV	P	W	D	L	F	A	Pts
Mary Dendy	18	10	5	3	48	30	25
Puss In Boots	18	11	2	5	63	43	24
Wharf W	18	11	3	4	72	41	23
Ald St P A	18	8	4	6	61	42	20
Wilmslow A	18	8	4	6	47	44	20
AFC Zeneca	18	7	5	6	58	40	19
Lindow	18	7	5	6	46	53	19
Poynton A	18	6	2	10	33	63	14
O Alts A	18	3	4	11	27	53	10
Poynton	18	1	2	15	34	80	4

CARLISLE & DISTRICT LEAGUE

	P	W	D	L	F	A	Pts
Abbeytown	22	18	2	2	97	19	56
Hearts	22	15	2	5	89	37	47
Sporting Museum	22	13	5	4	82	39	44
Silloth	22	13	4	5	85	46	43
Northbank Res	22	13	2	7	85	42	41
Longtown	22	12	4	6	89	38	40
Wigton	22	12	3	6	74	54	40
Whitehaven	22	11	2	9	62	36	35
Carliston City	22	5	0	17	37	92	15
Dalston	22	2	2	18	36	112	8
Silloth Colts	22	2	1	19	31	131	7
Ingleswood	22	1	2	19	23	162	5

WESTMORLAND LEAGUE

DIVISION ONE	P	W	D	L	F	A	Pts
Kendal County	26	18	2	6	74	35	56
Sedburgh Wdrs	26	16	2	8	74	45	50
Burneside	26	15	4	7	67	43	49
Wetheriggs Utd	26	15	4	7	58	39	49
Coniston	26	14	4	8	59	35	46
Appleby	26	13	6	7	55	45	45
Keswick	26	13	4	9	55	45	43
Shap	26	9	6	11	54	55	33
Staveley Utd	26	9	6	11	40	43	33
Dent	26	10	3	13	65	69	33
Windermere SC	26	9	5	12	41	42	32
Kirkby Stephen	26	8	3	15	46	66	27
Ambleside Utd	26	5	6	15	39	59	21
Kirkoswald	26	0	1	25	18	124	1

LANCASHIRE AMATEUR LEAGUE

PREMIER DIV	P	W	D	L	F	A	Pts
Leigh Ath	26	17	4	5	77	39	55
Rochdale St C	26	17	3	6	72	36	54
Bury GSOB	26	17	3	6	66	35	54
Accrington	25	13	5	7	69	52	44
Burnley Bel	25	12	4	9	54	48	40
Lymm HSA	26	11	5	10	61	53	38
Walshaw SC	26	12	2	12	55	56	38
Chadderton	26	11	4	11	55	50	37
Tarleton Cors	26	9	7	10	42	52	34
Royton Town	24	9	6	9	52	52	33
Smithills	26	9	2	15	54	87	29
O Boltonians	26	8	4	14	54	71	28
Burnley	26	5	4	17	36	69	19
Mostonians	26	2	3	21	26	73	9

ASHTON SUNDAY LEAGUE

PREMIER DIV	P	W	D	L	F	A	Pts
Horseshoe	18	14	1	3	51	30	29
Robin Hood	18	11	1	6	62	31	23
Lark A	18	11	1	6	46	33	23
Junction R	18	9	3	6	56	30	21
Warwick Utd	18	8	4	6	44	34	20
K George A	18	8	4	6	33	24	20
Greyhound	18	4	5	9	28	47	13
Broadway	18	4	4	10	28	51	12
Rifle Range	18	5	2	11	33	66	12
H & Hounds	18	2	3	13	30	56	7

ALTRINCHAM & DISTRICT AMATEUR SUNDAY LEAGUE

PREMIER DIV	*P*	*W*	*D*	*L*	*F*	*A*	*Pts*
Nelson	20	17	2	1	66	20	53
J Boat	20	14	2	3	58	25	44
B Tap	20	10	5	5	44	44	35
Packet House	20	9	5	6	45	33	32
Portland	20	9	2	9	48	46	29
B Wolf Vale	20	8	3	9	38	44	27
Partington	20	8	5	7	38	43	26
Lisbon St A	20	5	4	11	37	43	19
Tatton Arms	20	5	1	14	39	60	16
Lord Nelson	20	4	4	12	26	50	16
Stam Lads	20	3	3	14	27	58	12

CITY OF MANCHESTER SUNDAY LEAGUE

DIVISION ONE	*P*	*W*	*D*	*L*	*Pts*
Feathers	27	24	1	2	73
Mauldeth	27	23	3	1	72
Church inn	27	18	5	4	59
A/C Rusholme	27	15	4	8	49
R Lion With	27	12	5	10	4
R Star Chorlton	27	11	2	14	35
Superstar	27	9	3	15	30
Barton Vale	27	8	2	17	26
Bass Eleven	27	3	0	24	9
Quadrant	27	0	0	27	0

UNOFFICIAL NORTH WEST PYRAMID FOR LEAGUES UNDERNEATH NORTH WEST COUNTIES LEAGUE

compiled by Alan Wilson

	1	2	3	4	5
A1	LIVERPOOL CO COMB	WEST CHESHIRE		MANCHESTER	
A2			MID-CHESHIRE		WEST LANCASHIRE
B	I ZINGARI LEAGUE		LANCASHIRE & CHESHIRE AMAT		LANCS AMAT PRESTON & DIST
C	ST HELENS COMB I ZINGARI COMB	SOUTH WIRRAL	WIGAN & DISTRICT WARRINGTON/DIST		
D	L'POOL C.M.S. L'POOL O.B.	BIRKENHD/WIRRAL CHESTER & DISTRICT			
C OR D			CREWE & DIST. EAST CHESHIRE	MANCHESTER AM E. LANCASHIRE STOCKPORT BOLTON COMBINATION	BLACKPOOL COMB BURNLEY & DIST

Notes about the Pyramid:

I have graded the leagues into 4 levels: Level A, with possible promotion to teh N.W.C.L., is divided by current playing standards based on recent County Cup performances.

Those leagues below D, I don't know enough about to grade them, but would guess they would be at level C or D.

Two other leagues I have known about during the '90s are the Altrincham Saturday, and the North Lancashire and District, yet I have not seen any tables for them during 1997-98. Altrincham would be placed at level C or D in columns 3 and 4, North Lancs the same, in column 5.

Two Liverpool leagues folded at the end of the season:

I Zingari Alliance	(11 clubs, founded 1912)
SSU Shipping	(10 clubs, SSU League founded 1910, Shipping League founded 1920, the two leagues amalgamated in 1991)

NORTHERN COUNTIES EAST FOOTBALL LEAGUE

FEEDER TO: NORTHERN PREMIER LEAGUE

Secretary: B Wood,
6 Restmore Avenue, Guiseley, Leeds LS20 9DG
Tel/Fax: 01943 874558

My review of the 1997-98 season takes a look at the playing records of our clubs outlining the successes and failures throughout that time.

The promotion/demotion system between the NCE and the Unibond League at the end of the 1996-97 season worked to the advantage of runners-up Belper Town as Champions Denaby United failed on ground grading and it was the Derbyshire club which moved ahead in the Pyramid. However, there was an initial problem with regard to the club moving down to us. As all three demotion candidates from the Unibond were located west of the Pennines it was necessary for Curzon Ashton to be transferred to us and this was confirmed after an FA hearing.

Only four defeats in a 38 match season indicates the strength of the team put together by John Ramshaw, manager of Premier Division Champions Hucknall Town and its consistency was shown by the remarkable undefeated run of League matches which stretched from 23rd September to their only other reversal at the end of March. Crucial to the team's success was the 4-1 win over challengers North Ferriby United in early April and the Humberside outfit had to be content with runners-up position. Also missing out on the honours were Ossett Albion who led the division for much of the season until both Town and United caught up their fixtures due to a good FA Vase run by each club. Both Glasshoughton Welfare and Brigg Town had good seasons and there was a special interest in how Curzon Ashton would fare after their relegation mentioned above. Recruitment of suitable quality players was a problem for them and they eventually finished in a relegation position for the second successive season and will be moving west to their preferred North West Counties League. Hatfield Main (the 1995-96 Champions) have had quite a reversal of fortune and their bottom position is scheduled to result in relegation with Liversedge escaping the drop with a final 0-0 draw at Armthorpe Welfare.

Hucknall Town have gained promotion to the Unibond League next season and we wish them every success whilst that League's bottom placed club, Buxton, are due to join our Premier Division.

The disappointment experienced by Garforth Town at the end of last season when promotion was denied due to ground problems only proved to be a spur to their fortunes this time. Indeed, they looked likely Champions from November onwards. So it proved and manager, Dave Parker, has now steered his club to the Premier Division as everyone is confident that their new 'Wheatley Park' Stadium will soon be completed. Pressing the Leeds team were Hall Road Rangers, newcomers from the Central Midlands League, Staveley MW, and Glapwell and it was down to matches on the very last Saturday of the season to determine the final runners-up position. This was claimed by Staveley MW who pipped the Rangers by 2 points by winning at Blidworth Welfare whilst the Hull side lost at Parkgate.

Yorkshire Amateurs will have to apply for re-election whilst the bottom club, Blidworth Welfare, are leaving to revert back to the Central Midlands League. The Mansfield club entered the League record books by failing to win a single League match with a goals tally of 8 for and 186 against. Their latest Secretary/Manager, Steve Fleming, took on a very difficult task and managed to keep them functioning until the season's end when they attracted plenty of local and national media coverage.

Whilst Ossett Albion's first team just missed out on the honours, their Reserve team took the Divisional title for the second season as they finished ahead of their rivals across Town, Ossett Town Reserves, by a seven point margin. Farsley Celtic Reserves ended their season in third position. Worsbrough Bridge MW Reserves who joined the Division at the start of the season have decided not to continue in the Division which will operate with 14 teams.

In our own NCE Cup Competitions Hucknall Town achieved the Cup and League double by defeating North Ferriby United by a narrow 1-0 margin in the League Cup Final at Hatfield Main - Darren Davis making a crucial strike just before the interval. The President's Cup was won by Glasshoughton Welfare who defeated Ossett Albion by a 7-2 aggregate and in the Wilkinson Sword Trophy our new side, Staveley MW, overcame a 2-3 reversal in the first Leg at home to romp through as overall 8-3 winners against Harrogate Railway. Their Reserve Division Cup Final was won by Farsley Celtic Reserves who prevented Ossett Albion Reserves from achieving a Cup and League double by winning 2-1 at Thackley's ground.

The last two seasons have proved very successful for NCE sides in the FA Vase with winners Brigg Town and losing finalists North Ferriby United but it was not to be third time lucky. However, both Hucknall Town and North Ferriby United reached Round Five before going out to Porthleven and Taunton Town respectively. Ferriby also reached the Fourth Qualifying Round of the FA Cup. The League also had four County Cup Winners: Derbyshire Senior Cup - Glapwell; East Riding Senior Cup - North Ferriby United; Notts Senior Cup - Hucknall Town; West Riding County Cup - Garforth Town, plus two losing finalists in Parkgate (Sheffield Senior Cup) and Liversedge (West Riding County Cup)

B Wood

FINAL LEAGUE TABLES 1997-98

Premier Division

	P	*W*	*D*	*L*	*F*	*A*	*Pts*
Hucknall Town	38	26	8	4	90	34	86
North Ferriby United	38	25	6	7	89	37	81
Ossett Albion	38	21	11	6	59	25	74
Brigg Town	38	20	10	8	76	40	70
Glasshoughton Welf.	38	17	9	12	66	64	60
Maltby Main	38	17	8	13	51	40	59
Ossett Town	38	17	7	14	67	53	58
Eccleshill United	38	16	9	13	64	58	57
Armthorpe Welfare	38	16	8	14	60	44	56
Selby Town	38	15	6	17	60	75	51
Thackley	38	12	12	14	48	55	48
Denaby United	38	14	6	18	55	68	48
Pontefract Collieries	38	13	9	16	60	76	48
Arnold Town	38	10	16	12	55	52	46
Sheffield	38	13	7	18	62	72	46
Pickering Town	38	12	8	18	56	68	44
Hallam	38	10	10	18	52	77	40
Liversedge	38	7	9	22	41	88	30
Curzon Ashton	38	7	8	23	42	75	29
Hatfield Main	38	6	5	27	46	98	23

Division One

	P	*W*	*D*	*L*	*F*	*A*	*Pts*
Garforth Town	28	23	3	2	77	17	72
Staveley MW	28	15	9	4	51	30	54
Hall Road Rangers	28	16	4	8	68	34	52
Glapwell	28	14	4	10	59	50	46
Parkgate	28	14	3	11	61	47	45
Louth United	28	14	2	12	73	50	44
Worsbro' Bridge MW	28	13	4	11	58	57	43
Borrowash Victoria	28	11	8	9	67	50	41
Rossington Main	28	11	4	13	41	46	37
Winterton Rangers	28	11	3	14	41	55	36
Harrogate Rail Ath	28	10	4	14	58	52	34
Brodsworth MW	28	8	9	11	53	43	33
Tadcaster Albion	28	8	6	14	56	46	30
Yorkshire Amateur	28	8	5	15	49	57	29
Blidworth Welfare	28	0	0	28	8	186	0

PREMIER DIVISION RESULTS CHART 1997-98

		1	2	3	4	5	6	7	8	9	10	11	12	13	14	15	16	17	18	19	20
1	Armthorpe Welfare	X	2-0	0-1	4-1	1-1	0-2	0-0	3-0	2-0	1-1	0-0	3-2	5-1	0-0	0-3	3-0	0-1	5-0	1-1	0-1
2	Arnold Town	2-2	X	3-0	1-1	5-2	2-0	4-2	1-1	3-1	1-1	2-0	1-1	1-2	0-2	0-2	1-1	4-1	2-2	3-0	0-2
3	Brigg Town	2-1	0-0	X	2-1	3-0	1-1	0-0	5-2	4-1	0-1	7-0	1-0	1-1	1-3	2-5	6-0	1-0	0-0	2-2	1-1
4	Curzon Ashton	3-2	2-2	0-5	X	1-1	2-3	1-2	1-1	1-2	0-2	1-2	0-0	0-1	0-0	3-2	3-0	1-3	2-0	3-1	1-2
5	Denaby United	1-2	2-0	1-2	4-1	X	1-1	2-0	4-1	1-5	0-1	2-0	1-2	0-3	0-2	0-2	1-0	0-4	3-0	1-2	4-0
6	Eccleshill United	2-0	3-1	1-4	1-0	2-1	X	2-2	1-2	3-2	1-3	2-1	1-2	0-2	0-1	1-1	1-2	4-0	3-0	2-2	0-2
7	Glasshoughton W.	3-2	2-2	0-4	3-1	3-0	2-2	X	4-2	2-1	2-4	1-2	2-0	0-2	0-1	1-3	1-0	1-1	7-0	3-1	2-0
8	Hallam	0-0	1-1	1-1	1-1	3-4	2-4	0-1	X	3-1	0-1	1-1	1-2	1-1	0-5	2-1	2-0	2-2	2-3	5-1	3-1
9	Hatfield Main	1-0	0-2	2-4	5-0	2-2	1-2	0-2	1-3	X	1-7	1-1	3-4	0-2	0-3	1-1	2-4	2-0	0-0	2-4	0-1
10	Hucknall Town	1-2	3-2	3-1	3-0	5-1	2-1	8-0	1-0	5-1	X	3-0	2-2	4-1	0-0	0-0	2-0	5-4	3-0	2-3	0-1
11	Liversedge	0-3	0-2	1-3	2-2	2-3	1-1	1-4	0-2	1-0	2-2	X	0-3	1-3	0-3	2-2	2-2	0-2	1-0	4-1	1-1
12	Maltby Main	0-1	0-0	1-0	1-0	1-0	0-2	1-2	0-2	4-0	0-2	4-1	X	1-2	0-0	2-1	0-1	4-0	0-3	2-0	0-0
13	North Ferriby United	3-1	1-1	1-0	1-0	1-2	3-1	5-1	5-0	9-0	0-2	4-1	1-0	X	0-2	3-1	3-0	7-0	4-0	3-0	1-1
14	Ossett Albion	1-0	0-0	0-1	1-0	1-2	3-0	1-1	0-0	2-1	0-1	2-3	2-1	1-1	X	3-0	2-1	2-2	2-2	1-2	1-1
15	Ossett Town	2-5	2-0	2-4	0-1	0-1	0-4	0-0	6-2	2-0	1-1	2-0	1-1	2-1	0-2	X	3-0	6-1	0-3	1-2	2-1
16	Pickering Town	1-2	2-0	2-2	3-2	3-1	2-3	1-3	5-0	2-2	0-0	3-2	1-3	2-1	3-2	0-2	X	0-2	5-0	0-0	2-2
17	Pontefract Colts	0-2	1-1	0-2	4-1	3-4	2-2	2-2	2-3	1-3	4-0	3-1	11	3-3	0-1	3-1	1-0	X	0-4	2-1	1-1
18	Selby Town	3-1	4-2	1-0	5-2	1-1	4-2	1-2	3-1	2-0	1-3	4-1	1-3	0-2	2-4	0-1	1-5	0-1	X	2-1	2-2
19	Sheffield	1-2	2-2	1-2	1-2	2-0	1-1	3-2	2-0	6-2	1-5	6-1	0-1	2-3	0-2	0-1	3-1	3-1	1-3	X	1-0
20	Thackley	3-2	2-1	1-1	2-1	1-1	1-2	4-1	2-0	3-0	0-1	1-3	1-2	0-2	0-1	1-6	2-2	1-2	1-3	2-2	X

LEAGUE CUP 1997-98

FIRST ROUND

Parkgate	v	Yorkshire Amateur	3-2	Staveley MW	v	Blidworth Welfare	3-2
Winterton Rangers	v	Louth United	2-0				

SECOND ROUND

Armthorpe Welfare	v	Selby Town	4-2	Borrowash Victoria	v	Tadcaster Albion	1-5
Garforth Town	v	Arnold Town	1-1, 31	Glapwell	v	Curzon Ashton	2-3
Glasshoughton Welf.	v	Thackley	2-1	Hall Road Rangers	v	Hallam	3-1
Harrogate Railway	v	Eccleshill United	3-2	Hatfield Main	v	Denaby United	0-3
Hucknall Town	v	Staveley MW	1-0	Maltby Main	v	Ossett Town	1-3
North Ferriby United	v	Sheffield	4-0	Parkgate	v	Brigg Town	0-1
Pickering Town	v	Worsbro Bridge MW	2-3	Pontefract Colls	v	Liversedge	5-1
Rossington Main	v	Ossett Albion	0-6	Winterton Rngrs	v	Brodsworth MW	1-2

THIRD ROUND

Armthorpe Welfare	v	Glasshoughton Welfare	1-0	Brodsworth MW	v	Brigg Town	2-1
Denaby United	v	Hall Road Rangers	1-2	Hucknall Town	v	Tadcaster Albion	4-0
North Ferriby United	v	Harrogate Railway	3-1	Ossett Town	v	Ossett Albion	0-1
Pontefract Collieries	v	Garforth Town	0-3	Worsbro Bridge	v	Curzon Ashton	0-3

FOURTH ROUND

Armthorpe Welfare	v	Ossett Albion	1-2	Curzon Ashton	v	Brodsworth MW	3-4
North Ferriby United	v	Garforth Town	1-0	Hucknall Town	v	Hall Road Rangers	4-0

SEMI-FINAL

Hucknall Town	v	Brodsworth MW	4-0	North Ferriby Utd	v	Ossett Albion	3-2

FINAL

Hucknall Town	v	North Ferriby United	1-0

PRESIDENT'S CUP 1997-98

FIRST ROUND

Blidworth Welfare	v	Hallam	1-5	Liversedge	v	Yorkshire Amateur	0-4
Ossett Town	v	Eccleshill United	1-2				

SECOND ROUND

Armthorpe Welfare	v	Sheffield	1-2	Borrowash Victoria	v	Glapwell	0-1
Brigg Town	v	Hatfield Main	3-2	Eccleshill United	v	Garforth Town	2-2, 1-7
Glasshoughton Welf.	v	Brodsworth MW	1-0	Hall Road Rngrs	v	Selby Town	4-2
Hallam	v	Arnold Town	4-5	Maltby Main	v	Pontefract Collieries	1-0
Ossett Albion	v	Curzon Ashton	5-3	Parkgate	v	Hucknall Town	3-6
Staveley MW	v	Louth United	3-1	Tadcaster Albion	v	Denaby United	4-0
Thackley	v	Pickering Town	3-0	Winterton Rngrs	v	North Ferriby United	1-4
Worsbrough Bridge	v	Rossington Main	0-1	Yorkshire Amateur	v	Harrogate Railway	3-0

THIRD ROUND

Brigg Town	v	Staveley MW	1-2	Glapwell	v	Arnold Town	1-3
Glasshoughton Welf.	v	Tadcaster Albion	4-1	Hall Road Rngrs	v	Ossett Albion	0-3
Hucknall Town	v	Rossington Main	3-1	Maltby Main	v	Sheffield	5-0
North Ferriby United	v	Yorkshire Amateur	4-0	Thackley	v	Garforth Town	3-2

FOURTH ROUND

Glasshoughton Welf.	v	North Ferriby United	2-0	Maltby Main	v	Hucknall Town	2-5
Staveley MW	v	Arnold Town	0-0, 3-1	Thackley	v	Ossett Albion	1-2

SEMI-FINAL

Glassboughton Welf.	v	Hucknall Town	2-0	Ossett Albion	v	Staveley MW	2-1

FINAL

Ist Leg				2nd Leg			
Ossett Albion	v	Glasshoughton Welf.	1-3	Glasshoughton W	v	Ossett Albion	4-1

Glasshoughton Welfare won 7-2 on aggregate

WILKINSON SWORD TROPHY 1997-98

FIRST ROUND

Brodsworth MW	v	Parkgate	2-3	Hall Road Rngrs	v	Tadcaster Albion	3-0
Harrogate Railway	v	Yorkshire Amateur	3-1	Louth United	v	Glapwell	1-0
Rossington Main	v	Blidworth Welfare	8-0	Staveley MW	v	Borrowash Victoria	3-1
Winterton Rangers	v	Garforth Town	3-0				

Bye: Worsbrough Bridge MW

SECOND ROUND

Hall Road Rngrs	v	Louth United	1-0	Parkgate	v	Worsbrough B MW	6-2
Rossington Main	v	Harrogate Railway	3-4	Staveley MW	v	Winterton Rangers	1-0

SEMI-FINAL

Hall Road Rangers	v	Harrogate Railway	1-2	Parkgate	v	Staveley MW	1-2

FINAL

Ist Leg				2nd Leg			
Staveley MW	v	Harrogate Railway	2-3	Harrogate Railway	v	Staveley MW	0-6

Staveley MW won 8-3 on aggregate

LEADING GOALSCORERS 1997-98

PREMIER DIVISION

A J Flounders	North Ferriby United	37	Cygan A	Selby Town	17
M Clough	Glasshoughton Welfare	26	Lawford C	Liversedge	17
G Briscoe	Hucknall Town	22	M Edwards	Hucknall Town	16
C Cheetham	Maltby Main	22	C A Gomersall	Ossett Albion	16
M Goddard	Hallam	22	C Maddison	Hucknall Town	16
K Hoy	Armthorpe Welfare	20	D A Morris	Ossett Albion	16
S S Johnson	Armthorpe Welfare	20	C Shaw	Ossett Albion	16
P Tomlinson	Hucknall Town	20	M A Tennison	North Ferriby United	16
Cygan G J	Pontefract Collieries	18	Stead N	Brigg Town	16

DIVISION ONE

R Blake	Louth United	30	M K Edeson	Hall Road Rangers	21
M Blythe	Tadcaster Albion	26	P Bilous	Rossington Main	18
D L Falk	Garforth Town	25	R Ramsden	Garforth Town	17
C G Sambrook	Brodsworth MW	24	W Gamble	Glapwell	15
D Wilson	Tadcaster Albion	24	D Pickering	Worsbrough Bridge MW	15
M Godber	Staveley MW	23			

RESERVE DIVISION

P Davies	Ossett Albion Reserves	37	V Nikolaidis	North Ferriby Utd Res.	15
A Rae	Eccleshill United Reserves	22	J Gill	Liversedge Reserves	14
L Lambert	North Ferriby Utd Res.	20	R Bloomfield	Ossett Albion Reserves	13
D Bray	Emley Reserves	15	J Sanderson	Farsley Celtic Reserves	13
A Hatfield	Ossett Albion Reserves	15			

PREMIER DIVISION CLUBS 1998-99

ARMTHORPE WELFARE

Chairman: Alan Bell, Tel: 01302 833882 (H) **Vice Chairman:** James Houston
Secretary: Maureen Cottam, The Orchards, Whiphill Lane, Armthorpe, Doncaster DN3 3JP. Tel: 01302 832514 (H)
Manager: Carl Leighton **Asst Manager:** John McKeown **Coach:** Steve Taylor.
Physio: Joey Johnson **Comm. Manager:** Peter Camm **Press Officer:** Sharon Morgan.
Ground: Welfare Ground, Church Str, Armthorpe, Doncaster DN3 3AG (0976 580597)
Directions: M18 junc 4, A630, left at r'bout then proceed to next r'bout and turn right. Ground 400yds on left behind Plough Inn. Two and a half miles from Doncaster (BR). Buses A2, A3 & 181 pass ground.
Seats: 200 **Cover:** 400 **Capacity:** 2,500 **Floodlights:** Yes **Nickname:** Wellie **Founded:** 1926
Clubhouse: No. Refreshments on ground. Wheatsheaf Hotel used after matches. **Club Shop:** No
Colours: White/navy/white **Change colours:** Navy/white/navy **Club Sponsors:** Houston Transport
Programme: 24 pages **Editor:** John Morgan, 01302 834475 (H) **Midweek matches:** Tuesday
Previous League: Doncaster Senior **Formed:** 1926 **Disbanded:** 1974 **Reformed:** 1976
Club Record: Att: 2,000 v Doncaster R., Charity match 85-86 **Goalscorer:** Martin Johnson **Appearances:** Gary Leighton. **Win:** 7-0 **Defeat:** 1-7
Honours: Northern Co's East Lg R-up 87-88 (Lg Cup R-up 91-92, Div 1 R-up 83-84, East Central Div 1 84-85); Doncaster & Dist. Lg 82-83 (Div 1 81-82, Div 2 79-80, Div 3 78-79; Lg Cup 79-80 80-81 81-82 82-83; Challenge Cup 82-83); West Riding Chall. Cup 81-82 82-83; Goole & Thorne Dist. Cup 82-83

ARNOLD TOWN

Back Row (L-R); John Scott, Gary Ricketts, Andy Elliott, Donavan Gethfield, Neil Walters, John Beale, Stuart Hammonds, Brett Williams, Iaim McCullock (Mgr). Front Row; Darren Bogan, Richard Flint, Bryan Gunn, Mark Clarke, Lee Wilson, Simon Osborne, Adrian Thorpe *Photo: Andrew Chitty*

President: Alan Croome **Chairman:** David Law **Vice-Chairman:** Roy Francis **General Manager:** Ray O'Brien
Secretary: Tony Beale, 6 Elms Gardens, Ruddington, Nottm NG11 6DZ (0115 921 1451).
Team Manager: Iain McCulloch **Asst Manager:** Bill Brindley **Physio:** John Scott
Ground: King George V Recreation Ground, Gedling Rd, Arnold, Notts (0115 926 3660).
Directions: From M1 jct 26, take A610 to B6004 (Stockhill Lane) 3 miles to A60, right at A60, immediate left (St Albans Rd), thru lights by Sainsburys, left at rear of Sainsburys, ground on right adjacent to market. From A1(M)/A614/A60 to lights (White Hart on right), 1st left thru lights, St Albans Rd then as above. Four miles from Nottingham Midland BR station. Buses 53, 55, 59 pass ground, buses 25, 40, 51, 57, 58, 90 stop within 200yds.
Capacity: 3,400 **Seats:** 150 **Cover:** 950 **Floodlights:** Yes **Nickname:** Eagles **Founded:** 1989
Clubhouse: Licensed bar open matchdays & training night. Also tea-bar on matchdays.
Club Shop: Yes, selling prog, scarves, badges, pennants etc, contact Rob Hornby (0115 974 6769)
Programme: 52 pages, 60p **Editor:** Rob Hornby **Sponsors:** Mapperley Sports/Neartone Printers
Colours: Yellow (blue trim)/blue/yellow **Change Colours:** All white (blue trim) **Midweek matches:** Tuesday
Reserves' Lge: Midland Reg. All. **Record Attendance:** 3,390, Arnold FC v Bristol R., FA Cup 1st Rd, 9/12/67.
Previous Leagues: Central Midlands 89-93. *Arnold FC: Bulwell & Dist, Nott Spartan, Notts Comb (pre 55), Central Alliance 55-63/ Midland 63-82/ Northern Co's East 82-86/ Central Mids 86-89. Kingswell: Notts Youth/ Notts Amateur/ Notts Spartan/ East Midlands Regional (pre'76)/Midland 76-82/ Northern Co's East 82-86/ Central Midlands 86-89.*
Player progressing to Football League: Devon White (Lincoln C 85), Chris Freestone (Middlesbrough 94)
97-98 - Captain: Bryn Gunn **Top Scorer:** Brett Williams (16) **P.o.Y.: Players & Supporters:** Bryn Gunn
Club Record - Scorer: Peter Fletcher 100 **Appearances:** Neil Waters 309 **Managers:** Adrian Thorpe
Honours (as Arnold FC + Arnold Town FC): Central Mids Lg 92-93 (R-up 88-89, Lg Cup 87-88 (R-up 90-91), F/lit Cup 89-90); Northern Co's East Lg 85-86 (R-up 83-84,94-95, Div 1 94-95); Presidents Cup 94-95; Notts Snr Cup 60-61 64-65 65-66 68-69 70-71 92-93 95-96 96-97,(R-up 69-70 74-75 75-76 76-77 84-85); FA Cup 1st Rd replay 77-78; Central All 62-63; FA Tphy 2nd Rd replay 71-72; Midland Co's Lg R-up 70-71 75-76, Lg Cup 74-75 (R-up 68-69 70-71 80-81).

BRIGG TOWN

President: B Robins **Chairman:** David Crowder, Tel: 01724 864742 (H)
Secretary: Robert B Taylor, 'Highfield House', Barton Rd, Wrawby, Brigg, N Lincs DN20 8SH. Tel: 01652 652284 (H).
Match Sec: John Martin. Tel: 01652 654526 (H) **Manager:** Ralph Clayton **Coach:** John Kaye
Ground: The Hawthorns, Hawthorn Avenue, Brigg (01652 652767).
Directions: From M180 Junc 4 Scunthorpe East, A18 through Brigg leaving on Wrawby Rd, left into East Parade/Woodbine Ave, follow houses on right into Hawthorn Ave. One mile from Brigg (BR).
Seats: 250 **Cover:** 2 Stands **Capacity:** 4,000 **Floodlights:** Yes **Formed:** 1864
Clubhouse: Licensed club open matchdays
Colours: Black & white stripes/black/red **Change colours:** Orange shirts **Nickname:** Zebras
Programme: 16 pages **Editor:** Match Secretary **Midweek Matchday:** Wednesday
Record Attendance: 2,000 v Boston U. 1953 (at Brocklesby Ox).
Previous Leagues: Lindsey; Lincs 48-76; Midland Counties 76-82
Previous Grounds: Manor House Convent, Station Rd (pre 1939); Brocklesby Ox 1939-59
Honours: F.A. Challenge Vase 95-96; Northern Co's East Lg Presidents Cup R-up 91-92 92-93, R-up 95-96; Lincs Lg 49-50 53-54 73-74 75-76 (Div 1 68-69 69-70 70-71 71-72, Lg Cup 49-50 65-66 68-69 69-70 72-73); Mids Co's Lg 77-78 (Lg Cup 77-78); Lincs 'A' Snr Cup 75-76 76-77 94-95; Lincs 'B' Snr Cup 54-55 56-57 66-67 68-69 84-85.

BUXTON

Buxton FC *Photo: Bill Wheatcroft*

Chairman: K Perrins **Vice Chairman:** M Baker
Secretary / Press Officer: J B Goodwin, 97 Tongue Lane, Fairfield, Buxton, Derbys. SK17 7LL. 01298 25068 (H).
Manager: Derek Hall **Asst Manager:** David Bainbridge **Physio:** Peter Walker
GROUND Address: The Silverlands, Buxton, Derbyshire (01298 24733).
Directions: 200 yards of Buxton Market Place, opposite County Police HQ. Half mile from Buxton (BR).
Capacity: 4,000 **Cover:** 2,500 **Seats:** 490 **Floodlights:** Yes **Club Shop:** Contact P Scott (01298 72159).
Clubhouse: (01298 23197). Open nightly + Sunday lunchtimes. licensed, no hot food.
Colours: Royal & white/royal/royal **Change colours:** All yellow with blue trim
Midweek matchday: Tuesday **Nickname:** The Bucks **Formed:** 1877
Sponsors: Eagle Hotel, Buxton **Programme:** 36 pages 60p **Editor:** A Tomlinson (01484 718907)
Previous - Lges: The Combination 1891-99; North Derbyshire; E Cheshire; Manchester 07-32; Cheshire County 32-73; NLP 73-98.
Club Records - Attendance: 6,000 v Barrow, FA Cup 1st rd 51-52. **Goalscorer:** Dave Herbert. **Appearances:** Mick Davis. **Transfer Fees - Paid:** £5,000 for Gary Walker (Hyde Utd 89). **Received:** £16,500 for Ally Pickering (Rotherham 89). **Best Season - FA Trophy:** Qtr Finals 70-71 71-72. **FA Cup:** 3rd Rd 51-52. 2nd Rd 58-59, 1st Rd 62-63.
Players progressing to Football League: Peter Robinson (Notts Co 50), John Higgins (Bolton 50), Maurice Brooks (Stockport 51), Ray Parker (Bradford City 51), Fred Marlow (Grimsby 51), Ian Greaves (Man Utd 53), John Brindley (Chesterfield 53), Les Ferriday (Walsall 54), John Good (Tranmere 55), Jimmy Anders (Bradford PA 56), William Haydock (Man City 59), Anthony Parkes (Blackburn 70), Andy Proudlove (Sheffield Wednesday 75), Graham Collier (York City 78), Harry Charlton (Darlington 79), Ally Pickering (Rotherham 90).
97-98 - Captain: C Martin **P.o.Y.:** D Bainbridge **Top scorer:** S Botchett
Honours: Northern Prem Lg Cup 90-91 (Presidents Cup 81-82); Cheshire County 72-73 (R-up 46-47 62-63, Lg Cup 56-57 57-58 68-69); Manchester Lg 31-32 (R-up 04-05 28-29 29-30 30-31, Lg Cup 25-26 26-27); Derbyshire Senior Cup 38-39 44-45 45-46 56-57 59-60 71-72 80-81 85-86 86-87.

DENABY UNITED

Back Row (L-R); Jack Bramhall (Physio), Adam Longden, Steve Evans, Stewart Evans, Tony Foster, Craig Davis, Jason Helliwell, Mel Sterland, Mark Thompson,Paul Cook, Gary Gillatt (Mgr). Front Row; Nathan Thorpe, Shaun Smith, Marcus Wood, Carl Kent, Craig Thompson. Photo: Mr Thaler

Chairman: J Gordon Westwood **Vice Chairman:** David Hough **President:** Alan Wilson
Secretary: Derek Mower, 60 Windmill Crescent, Mexborough, S Yorks S64 0EB. Tel: 01709 329338 (H)
Manager: David Lloyd **Asst Manager:** Dennis Hobson **Physio:** John Carver
Ground: Tickhill Square, Denaby Main, Doncaster (01709 864042).
Directions: From Conisbrough take first left in Denaby along Wadworth St. From Mexborough take first right after Reresby Arms, left on to Bolton St. then left on to Wheatley Street. Rail to Conisbrough.
Seats: 250 **Cover:** 350 **Capacity:** 6,000 **Floodlights:** Yes
Clubhouse: None **Club Shop:** Yes **Nickname:** None **Founded:** 1895
Programme: 64 pages 60p **Editor:** David Green (01709 862319) **Reserves' League:** Beefeater Co. Sen.
Colours: Red & white/red/red **Change colours:** White/blue/blue **Midweek matches:** Tuesday
Previous - Leagues: Sheffield Ass 1900-02 15-18 19-20 40-45; Midland 02-13 20-40 45-60 61-65; Doncaster & District 18-19; Central Alliance 60-61; Yorks 65-82. **Ground:** Denaby Recreation Ground 1895-1912.
Club Records - Attendance: 5,200 v Southport, FA Cup 1st Rd 27 **Record Win:** 20-0 v Shirebrook Colliery (A), Central Alliance 60-61. **Transfer fee paid:** £350 for Kevin Deakin (Mossley, 84). **Received:** £5,000 for Jonathan Brown (Exeter, 90).
Players progressing to Football League: Jack Barker (Derby & England), Keith Burkinshaw (Liverpool 1953), Andy Barnsley (Rotherham 1985), Chris Beaumont (Rochdale 1988), Jonathan Brown (Exeter 1990).
Honours: Yorks Lg R-up 67-68 (Div 2 R-up 66-67, Div 3 R-up 81-82, Lg Cup 71-72); Northern Counties East Div 1 South R-up 83-84; Midland Lg R-up 07-08; Sheffield & Hallamshire Snr Cup 32-33 35-36 86-87; Thorn EMI Floodlight Competition R-up 83-84; Sheffield Association Lg 40-41; Mexborough Montague Cup 14-15.

ECCLESHILL UNITED

Chairman: Keith Firth. Tel: 01274 787057 (H)
Secretary: Ian Gardiner, 14 Tivoli Place, Little Horton, Bradford BD5 0PQ. Tel: 01274 226052 (H)
Manager: Barry Gallagher **Physio:** Gordon McGlynn **Press Officer:** Bill Rawlings (01274 635753).
Ground: Plumpton Park, Kingsway, Wrose, Bradford BD2 1PN (01274 615739).
Directions: M62 jct 26 onto M606, right on Bradford Ring Road A6177, left onto A650 for Bradford at 2nd r'bout. A650 Bradford Inner Ring Road onto Canal Rd, branch right opposite Woodheads Builders Merchants into Kings Rd, fork right after 30mph sign to junction with Wrose Rd, across junction - continuation of Kings Rd, 1st left onto Kingsway - ground 200 yds on right. 2 miles from Bradford (BR). Buses 686 or 687 for Wrose.
Seats: 225 **Cover:** 225 **Capacity:** 2,225 **Floodlights:** Yes **Founded:** 1948 **Nickname:** Eagles
Clubhouse: Open normal licensing hours. Bar, lounge, games room, kitchen (hot & cold snacks), committee room
Club Shop: Yes, selling range of souvenirs. Contact Roy Maule Snr, 01274 662428.
Colours: Blue & white stripes/blue/blue **Change colours:** All yellow **Reserves' Lge:** NCE Res. Div
Programme: 24-28 pages, 50p **Editor:** Raymond Maule (01274 634317) **Midweek matches:** Tuesday
Previous - Leagues: Bradford Amat; W Riding Co Amat. **Ground:** Myers Lane **Name:** Eccleshill FC
Club Records - Attendance: 600 v Bradford City 90-91 **Goalscorer:** Paul Viner **Appearances:** Paul Viner **Win:** 7-1 v Yorkshire Main (H), N.C.E. Lge Div. 2 86-87. **Defeat:** 0-6 v Rossington Main (A), N.C.E. Lge Cup 2nd Rd 92-93, & v Gt. Harwood T. (A), FA Cup Prel. Rd 91-92.
Players progressing to Football League: Terry Dolan (Huddersfield, Bradford PA, Bradford City)
Honours: Northern Counties East Div 2 R-up 86-87 (Reserve Div 86-87 89-90 (R-up 87-88 94-95)); Bradford Amtr Lg Cup 61-62; Bradford & Dist. Snr Cup 84-85; Bradford & Dist. FA Snr Cup 85-86; West Riding County Amateur Lg 76-77

GARFORTH TOWN

President: Norman Hebbron **Chairman:** Stephen Hayle.
Secretary: Paul Bracewell, 24 Coupland Rd, Garforth, Leeds LS25 1AD (0113 286 3314).
Manager/Coach: Dave Parker. **Asst Manager:** Dave Harrison **Physio:** Jack Coup
Ground: Wheatley Park, Brierlands Lane, Aberford Road, Garforth, Leeds (0113 2864083).
Directions: From North, A642 from A1 to Wkefield/Garforth, follow signs to Garforth. Over r/about, top of hill turn sharp left, grd end of lane. From South, M1 to M18, north on A1, Left A63 Leeds at PH Boot & Shoe, at r/about right onto A656, next r/about left A642 Garforth. Top of hill turn left into lane. From West, M62 jct 30, A642 to Rothwell Follow to Garforth, thru Garforth on A642, ground on right 1 mile on from lights just past new housing developement & Indian restaurant.
Seats: 278 **Cover:** 200 **Capacity:** 3,000 **Floodlights:** Yes **Nickname:** The Miners **Founded:** 1964
Clubhouse: Full Licensing Hours **Club Shop:** Yes **Sponsors:** Aagrah Restaurants
Programme: 28 pages, 50p **Editor:** K Strangeway (0113 286 6500) **Press Officer:** Secretary
Colours: Red/black/red **Change colours:** Blue & yellow **Midweek matches:** Tuesday
Previous leagues: Leeds Sunday Comb 64-72; West Yorks 72-78; Yorks 78-82.
Previous names: Miners Arms 64-78, Garforth Miners 78-79
Club Records - Goalscorer: Vinnie Archer **Appearances:** Philip Matthews (82-93) **Attendance:** 817 v Leeds Utd, friendly 1987 **Win:** 11-0 v Blidworth Welf, N.C.E. Div. 1 97-98 **Defeat:** 1-7 v Lincoln Utd (A), N.C.E. Div. 1 92-93 97-98 **Captain:** Brendan Ormsby **P.o.Y.:** Brendan Ormsby **Top Scorer:** Darren Falk (31)
Honours: FA Vase QF 85-86; Northern Co's East Lg Div 1 97-98, R-up 96-97, Div 2 R-up 85-86; Yorks Lg Div 3 R-up 79-80; Barkston Ash Snr Cup 80-81 84-85 85-86 86-87 92-93 94-95; Wilkinson Sword Trophy 96-97; West Riding County FA Cup 97-98.

GLASSHOUGHTON WELFARE

President: R Rooker **Chairman:** Gordon Day, Tel: 01977 514178 (H)
Secretary: Eric Jones, 'Marrica', Westfields Ave, Cutsyke, Castleford WF10 5JJ. Tel: 01977 556257 (H)
Match Sec: Barry Bennett, Tel: 01977 682593 (H) **Manager:** Wayne Day **Asst Manager/Coach:** M Ripley
Ground: Glasshoughton Welfare, Leeds Rd, Glasshoughton, Castleford (01977 518981).
Directions: From M62 use either Junct. 31 or 32 towards Castleford. From Junction 32 the road comes into Glasshoughton. From Junction 31 turn right at 2nd roundabout at Whitwood Tech. College. The ground is on the left in Leeds Road. Car park on ground. 1 mile from Castleford (BR).
Seats: None **Covered:** 250 **Capacity:** 2,000 **Floodlights:** Yes **Founded:** 1964
Clubhouse: Bar & refreshment facilities. **Club Shop:** No
Club colours: Blue and white stripes/blue/blue **Change colours:** All yellow **Reserves' Lge:** N.C.E. Res. Div.
Programme: 20 pages, 20p **Programme Editor:** Nigel Lee (01977 516615) **Midweek Matchday:** Tuesday
Previous - League: West Yorkshire **Name:** Anson Sports 1964-76 **Ground:** Saville Park 1964-76
Honours: West Riding County Cup 93-94. **Record Att.:** 300 v Bradford C, 90

HALLAM

Chairman: Tony Scanlan, Tel: 01246 413548 (H) **Vice Chairman:** P Fuller **President:** A Cooper
Secretary: Richard L Groves, 22 Moorgate Crescent, Dronfield, Sheffield, S18 1YF. Tel: 01246 413548 (H)
Press Officer: Mark Radford, Tel: 0114 249 7287 (H) **Manager:** K Johnson **Physio:** P Fuller
Ground: Sandygate, Sandygate Road, Crosspool, Sheffield S10 (0114 230 9484)
Directions: A57 Sheffield to Glossop Rd, left at Crosspool shopping area signed 'Lodge Moor' on to Sandygate Rd. Ground half mile on left opposite Plough Inn. 51 bus from Crucible Theatre.
Seats: 100 **Cover:** 200 **Capacity:** 1,000 **Floodlights:** Yes **Club Shop:** Yes
Clubhouse: Licensed bar and meals in Plough Inn opposite. Hot & cold snacks on ground for matches.
Programme: Yes 50p **Editor:** Mark Radford (Press Off.) **Nickname:** Countrymen **Formed:** 1860
Colours: Blue & white hoops/white/blue **Change colours:** Red &black/black/red
Club Sponsors: S Peace & Son, Le Coq Sportib
PREVIOUS - Leagues: Yorks 52-82. **Midweek Matches:** Wednesday
CLUB RECORDS - Attendance: 2,000 v Hendon, FA Amtr Cup 3rd Rd 59 (13,855 v Dulwich at Hillsborough, FA Amtr Cup 55) **Goalscorer:** A Stainrod 46 **Appearances:** P Ellis 500+ **Win:** 7-0 v Hatfield Main (H) 92-93, & v Kiveton Park (H) 69-70. **Defeat:** 0-7 v Hatfield Main (A) 88-89
Players progressing to Football League: Sean Connelly (Stockport County 92-93), H Wilkinson (Sheffield Wed), L Moore (Derby County)
Honours: Northern Counties (East) Lg Div 1 R-up 90-91 94-95, Yorkshire Lg Div 2 60-61 (R-up 56-57), Sheffield & Hallamshire Snr Cup 50-51 61-62 64-65 67-68.

LIVERSEDGE

Chairman: Robert Gawthorpe **Manager:** Eric Gilchrist **Asst Mgr:** Tony Passmore
Secretary/Press Officer: Michael Balmforth, 2 Reform Street, Gomersal, Cleckheaton BD19 4JX (01274 862123).
Ground: Clayborn Ground, Quaker Lane, Hightown Rd, Cleckheaton, West Yorks (01274 862108).
Directions: M62 jct 26, A638 into Cleckheaton, right at lights on corner of Memorial Park, through next lights & under railway bridge, 1st left (Hightown Rd) and Quaker Lane is approx quarter mile on left and leads to ground. From M1 jct 40, A638 thru Dewsbury and Heckmondwike to Cleckheaton, left at Memorial Park lights then as above. Buses 218 & 220 (Leeds-Huddersfield) pass top of Quaker Lane.
Seats: 250 **Cover:** 750 **Capacity:** 2,000 **Floodlights:** Yes **Nickname:** Sedge **Founded:** 1910
Clubhouse: Matchdays, Tues, Thursday. Pool, TV. Pies + crisps **Club Shop:** No
Programme: 28 pages, 50p **Editor:** Secretary **Midweek Matches:** Tuesday
Colours: All blue **Change colours:** Yellow & black **Reserves League:** NCEL Res. Div.
PREVIOUS - **Leagues:** Spen Valley; West Riding County Amateur 22-72; Yorkshire 72-82.
Ground: Primrose Lane, Hightown. **Name:** None
Players progressing to Football League: Garry Briggs (Oxford), Martin Hirst (Bristol City).
96-97 - Captain: Richard Clarke **P.o.Y.:** Mick Oddy **Top Scorer:** Craig Lawford
Honours: West Riding Co. Chal. Cup 48-49 51-52 69-70; West Riding County Cup 89-90; North Counties East Lg Div 1 R-up 89-90 (Div 2 R-up 88-89); West Riding Co. Amtr Lg(6) 23-24 25-27 64-66 68-69 (Lg Cup 57-58 64-65).

MALTBY MAIN

Chairman: G McCormick **Vice Chairman:** M Richardson **President:** H Henson
Secretary: Nick Dunhill, 10 Conrad Drive, Maltby, Rotherham, Sth Yorks S66 8RS (01709 815676).
Manager: Dave McCarthy **Asst Manager:** Kevin Eley **Physio:** G Hally
Ground: Muglet Lane, Maltby (01709 812462 match days)
Directions: Exit M18 at junct 1 with A631. Two miles into Maltby, right at traffic lights at Queens Hotel corner on to B6427 Muglet Lane. Ground 3/4 mile on left. Bus 101 from Rotherham stops at ground. Bus 287 from Sheffield to Queens Hotel, then follow as above.
Seats: 150 **Cover:** 300 **Capacity:** 2,000 **Floodlights:** Yes **Club Shop:** No
Clubhouse: No, Miners Welfare Club opposite.
Programme: 12 pages, 50p **Editor:** Secretary **Press Officer:** Secretary
Colours: Black & white/black/black **Change colours:** Yellow/blue/yellow
Sponsors: Jack Green Sports, RJB Mining. **Nickname:** Miners
Midweek matchday: Tuesday **Reserve League:** None
PREVIOUS - Name: Maltby Main 1916-65 (disbanded); Maltby Miners Welfare 1970-96. **Leagues:** Sheffield County Senior; Yorkshire 73-82.
CLUB RECORDS - Attendance: 1,500 v Sheffield Wed., June 91-92 (friendly) **Win:** 6-0
940 v Thackley, Yorks Lg Cup 77-78. (competitive) **Defeat:** 0-5
Players progressing to Football League: Michael Williams (Sheffield Wednesday) 1991-92.
96-97 - **Captain:** Rob Moorwood **Top Scorer:** Richard Coleman
P.o.Y. - Players: Tim Willis **Supporters:** Craig Pinder
Honours: Sheffield & Hallamshire Snr Cup 77-78, Northern Counties East Lg Presidents Cup 92-93 (SF 90-91), Mexborough Montague Cup 76-77 80-81 90-91, Yorks Lg R-up 77-78, Sheffield Wharncliffe Cup 80-81.

NORTH FERRIBY UNITED

President: Jeff Frank **Chairman:** Les Hare **Vice Chairman:** Roy Wallis
Secretary: Stephen Tather, 16 Peasholme, Heads Lane, Hessle, E Yorks HU13 0NY (01482 642046).
Press Officer: Roy Wallis **Manager:** Brian France **Asst Mgr:** Bobby McNeil **Coach/Physio:** Colin Naylor
Ground: Grange Lane, Church Road, North Ferriby HU14 3AA (01482 634601).
Directions: Main Leeds-Hull road A63 or M62, North Ferriby is 8 miles west of Hull. Into North Ferriby, thru village past the Duke of Cumberland Hotel, right down Church Rd, ground half mile on left. One mile from North Ferriby (BR).
Seats: 250 **Cover:** 1,000 **Capacity:** 5,000 **Floodlights:** Yes **Nickname:** United **Founded:** 1934
Clubhouse: Bar, lounge, TV, pool - open every night **Club Shop:** Yes **Midweek matches:** Tuesday
Programme: 40 pages, 75p **Editor:** Jeff Frank (01482 633387). **Reserves League:** N Counties East Res Div
Colours: ALL green **Change colours:** All yellow **Sponsors:** Dransfield Developments
Previous leagues: East Riding Church/ East Riding Amateur/ Yorks 69-82.
Club Records - **Attendance:** 1,800 v Tamworth, FA Vase Semi-Final, 1989
Goalscorer: Andy Flounders 45, 97-98. **Appearances:** Richard Woomble, 74-94.
Win: 9-0 v Hatfield Main, N.C.E. Lge Prem 97-98. **Defeat:** 1-7 v North Shields, N.C.E. Lge Prem 91. **Transfer fee received:** £3,000 for Tim Hotte (Hull City, 1988).
Players moving to Football Lge: T Hotte (Hull) 88, I Ironside (Halifax) 88, D France, D Windass & M Matthews (Hull) 91.
97-98 Captain: Neil Buckley **P.o.Y.:** Andy Flounders **Top Scorer:** Andy Flounders 45
Honours: FA Vase Finalist 96-97, SF 88-89, QF 89-90, 5th Rd 87-88 97-98); Yorkshire Lg R-up 75-76 (Lg Cup 74-75) (Div 2 70-71), Northern Co's East Prem Div R-up 97-98, Div 1 85-86 (Lg Cup R-up) 90-91 97-98, Presidents Cup 90-91, Div 1 (North), R-up 82-83, Reserve Div R-up 90-91); East Riding Snr Cup 70-71 76-77 77-78 78-79 90-91 96-97 97-98; East Riding Church Lg 37-38.

Garforth Town: Back Row (L-R); Norman Hebbron (Pres), Paul Bracewell (Sec), Dave Harrison (Asst Mgr), Jack Coop (Physio), Richard Ramsden, Elliott Beddard, Hayden Lobley, Dave Bramhill, Dave Woodhead, Patrick Flaherty, Chris Sullivan, Dave Parker (Mgr), Stephen Hayle (Chr). Front Row; Andy Sibson, Scott Stirk, Darren Adams, Brendan Ormsby, Darren Fack, Richard Smith, Damian Holmes

Eccleshill United. *Photo: John Newton*

OSSETT ALBION

President: Miss Helen Worth **Chairman:** Neville A Wigglesworth **Vice-Chairman:** S B Garside
Secretary: David Chambers, 109 South Parade, Ossett, Wakefield, WF5 0BE. Tel: 01924 276004 (H)
Manager: Jimmy Martin **Physio:** John Hirst **Coach:** Peter Eaton
Commercial Mgr: D Riley (01924 240247) **Press Officer:** Neville Wigglesworth (01924 275630).
Ground: Dimple Wells, Ossett (01924 273618-club, 01924 280450-grd)
Directions: M1 jct 40. Take Wakefield road, right at Post House Hotel down Queens Drive. At end right then second left down Southdale Rd. At end right, then first left down Dimple Wells (cars only). Coaches take second left following the road for 200yds bearing left twice. Four miles from both Wakefield and Dewsbury BR stations. Buses 116 and 117.
Seats: 200 **Cover:** 500 **Capacity:** 3,000 **Floodlights:** Yes **Nickname:** Albion **Founded:** 1944
Clubhouse: 3 bars + function room, open 7 days per week - catering available.
Club Shop: Yes, selling various souvenirs & programmes. Contact chairman. **Sponsors:** Arco.
Colours: Old gold & black/black/gold **Change colours:** All white **Reserves' Lge:** NCEL Res Div
Programme: 44 pages, 50p **Editor:** N Wigglesworth (01924 275630). **Midweek matches:** Tuesday
Previous Leagues: Heavy Woollen Area 44-49; West Riding Co. Amtr 49-50; West Yorks 50-57; Yorks 57-82.
CLUB RECORDS - Attendance: 1,200 v Leeds Utd, floodlight opening 1986. **Goalscorer:** John Balmer **Appearances:** Peter Eaton, 800+ (22 yrs) **Win:** 12-0 v British Ropes (H), Yorkshire Lge Div. 2 6/5/59 **Defeat:** 2-11 v Swillington (A), W. Yorkshire Lge Div. 1 25/4/56
Players progressing to Football League: Gary Brook (Newport, Scarborough, Blackpool) 1987, Ian Ironside (Barnsley, Middlesbrough, Scarborough) 1980.
Honours: Yorks Lg 74-75 (R-up 59-60 61-62, Lg Cup 75-76, 76-77, Div 2 78-79, 80-81 (R-up 58-59)); Northern Co. East Div 1 86-87 (Lg Cup 83-84); West Yorks Lg 53-54 55-56 (Div 2 52-53, Lg Cup 52-53); West Riding County Cup 64-65 65-66 67-68; Wheatley Cup 56-57 58-59

OSSETT TOWN

President: Paul Jervis. **Chairman:** Graham Firth **Vice Chairman:** Bruce Saul
Secretary: Frank Lloyd, 27 Park Close, Mapplewell, Barnsley S75 6BY (01226 382415).
Manager: Trevor Best **Asst Manager:** Paul Murphy **Coach:** Mick Polli **Commercial Manager:** Peter Jessop
Ground: Ingfield, Prospect Road, Ossett, Wakefield WF5 8AN (01924 272960).
Directions: M1 jct 40, B6129 to Ossett, left into Dale Street, left again at lights opposite bus station on ring road, ground on left. Nearest stations Dewsbury or Wakefield Westgate - both three miles from. Buses 116, 117, 126 and 127 from Wakefield, buses 116, 126 and 127 from Dewsbury, buses 117, 118 or 216 from Leeds.
Seats: 360 **Cover:** 650 **Capacity:** 4,000 **Floodlights:** Yes **Founded:** 1936
Clubhouse: Open Fri & Sun lunchtimes, all day Sat and every evening. Pie & peas, chips, soup from tea bar.
Colours: All red **Change colours:** All sky **Midweek matches:** Tuesday **Sponsors:** Action Stations
Programme: 12 pages, 50p **Editor/Press Off.:** Bruce Saul, 01924 277652 **Reserves' League:** N.C.E. Res Div
Previous - Leagues: Leeds 36-39; Yorkshire 45-82 **Ground:** Fern House (pre-1958)
Club Records - Attendance: 2,600 v Manchester Utd, friendly 1988 **Win:** 10-1 v Harrogate RA (H), N.C.E. Lge Prem. Div. 27/4/93 **Defeat:** 0-7 v Easington Colliery, FA Vase 8/10/83 **Transfer fee received:** £1,350 for Derek Blackburn (Swansea 1957) **Appearances:** Steve Worsfold **Goalscorer:** Dave Leadbeater
Players progressing to Football League: Arnold Kendall (Bradford C.) 1949, Ron Liversidge (Bradford C.) 56, Derek Blackburn (Swansea) 57, Simon Lowe (Barnsley) 83, Gary Chapman (Bradford C.) 88, Mick Norbury (Scarborough) 1989, Mike Williams (Sheffield W.) 90.
96-97 Captain: Lloyd Fellows **96-97 P.o.Y.:** Lloyd Fellows **96-97 Top Scorer:** R Sayer
Honours: Northern Counties East - Lg Cup 89-90, Div 2 88-89, Res. Div 88-89, Res. Cup 87-88 88-89; West Riding County Cup 58-59 81-82.

PICKERING TOWN

Chairman: Anthony Dunning, Tel: 01751 473697 (H) **President:** S P Boak
Secretary: Steve Adamson, 16 Overgreen View, Burniston, Scarborough, N Yorks YO13 0HZ. Tel: 01723 870930 (H)
Manager: Nigel Tate **Asst Manager/Physio:** Michael Hudson **Coach:** Robbie Goodwill
Ground: Recreation Club, Mill Lane (off Malton Rd), Pickering, North Yorkshire (01751 473317)
Directions: A169 from Malton. On entering Pickering take 1st left past Police Station and B.P. garage into Mill Lane, ground 200 yards on right.
Seats: 100 **Cover:** 500 **Capacity:** 2,000 **Floodlights:** Yes **Founded:** 1888 **Nickname:** Pikes
Clubhouse: Open 1.30pm for Saturday games, 6pm for midweek games. Food available from Football Club Kitchen at half-time and after games. **Club Shop:** No **Club Sponsors:** Flamingoland
Programme: 32 pages, 50p **Editor:** Anthony Dunning (Chairman) **Midweek matches:** Tuesday
Colours: Royal/white/royal **Change colours:** Amber/black/amber **Reserves' League:** York & Dist.
Record Gate: 1,412 v Notts County, friendly, August 1991.
Previous leagues: Beckett; York & District; Scarborough & District; Yorkshire 72-82.
Players progressing to Football League: Chris Short (Scarborough & Notts Co.)
Craig Short (Scarborough, Notts Co, Derby Co, Everton.)
Honours: Northern Co's East Lg R-up 92-93 (Div 2 1987-88, Div 1 R-up 91-92), Yorks Lg Div 3 73-74, North Riding Snr Cup R-up 93-94 94-95, North Riding County Cup 90-91.

PONTEFRACT COLLIERIES

Chairman: Frank Carter, Tel: 01226 728428 (H)
Secretary: Frank Maclachlan, 188 Watling Road, Ferry Fryston, Castleford WF10 2QY 01977 512085 (H), 01977 601327 (B), 0410 586447 (M)
President: J Betts **Manager:** Jim Kenyon **Asst Mgr:** Frank Maclachlan **Physio:** Alan Dean
Ground: Skinner Lane, Pontefract, West Yorkshire (01977 600818)
Directions: M62 jct 32 towards Pontefract. Left at traffic lights opposite Racecourse entrance (travelling through Pontefract follow Racecourse/Leeds signs to traffic lights and turn right) - ground past Territorial Army unit. 1 mile from Monkhill (BR). All Leeds and Castleford buses stop near ground.
Seats: 300 **Cover:** 400 **Capacity:** 1,200 **Floodlights:** Yes **Nickname:** Colls **Founded:** 1958
Clubhouse: Fully licensed. Hot & cold snacks. Open before and after games **Club Shop:** No
Sponsors: John Betts Quality Used Cars
Programme: 16 pages, 50p **Editor/Press Officer:** Secretary **Reserve League:** N.C.E. Res. Div.
Colours: Blue & black/black/black **Change Colours:** White/blue/blue **Midweek Matches:** Tuesday
PREVIOUS - Leagues: West Yorkshire 58-79; Yorkshire 79-82.
CLUB RECORDS - Goalscorer: Gary Cygan **Appearances:** John Brown **Attendance:** 1,000 v Hull City, floodlight opening 1985.
Players progressing to Football League: David Penney to Derby County, 1985.
Honours: Northern Co's East Lg Div 1 83-84 95-96 (Div 2 R-up 82-83); Floodlit Comp 87-88 88-89; Yorks Lg Div 3 81-82; West Riding Co. Cup R-up 87-88 90-91; Embleton Cup 82-83 86-87 95-96; Castleford FA Cup 82-83 86-87,94-95; Wilkinson Sword 95-96

SELBY TOWN

Chairman: Ralf Pearse, Tel: 01757 703942 (H) **President:** A Carter
Secretary: Paul Atkin, 6 The Link, Carlton, Goole, E York DN14 9QE
Match Sec: David McGuire, 26 Leeds Road, Selby YO8 4HX Tel: 01757 702219.
Manager: B Lyon **Asst Manager:** **Coach:** P Dooley
Ground: Flaxley Road Ground, Richard Street, Scott Road, Selby, North Yorkshire YO8 0BS. (01757 210900)
Directions: From Leeds, left at main traffic lights in Selby down Scott Rd. then 1st left into Richard St. From Doncaster go straight across main traffic lights into Scott Road then 1st left. From York right at main traffic lights into Scott Rd, and 1st left. 1 mile from Selby (BR).
Seats: 220 **Cover:** 350 **Capacity:** 5,000 **Floodlights:** Yes **Nickname:** The Robins **Founded:** 1918
Clubhouse: Bar at ground open first and second team matchdays **Club Shop:** Yes
Programme: 30 pages, 50p **Editor:** Mark Fairweather, 01757 705376 (H) **Midweek Matches:** Tuesday
Colours: All red **Change colours:** Amber/black/amber **Sponsors:** Hazlewood Preserves
Reserves' League: N.C.E. Res. Div. **Players progressing to Football League:** Numerous
Previous - League: Yorkshire (1920-82) **Ground:** Bowling Green, James St. 1920-51
Record attendance: 7,000 v Bradford Park Avenue (FA Cup 1st Rnd 1953-54)
Best Season - FA Cup: Second Round Proper 54-55 **FA Vase:** Prel Round 89-90
Honours: Yorkshire Lg 32-33 34-35 35-36 52-53 53-54 (R-up 24-25 25-26 27-28 28-29 30-31 31-32 50-51 55-56, Div 3 R-up 74-75, Lg Cup 37-38 53-54 54-55 62-63); Northern Co. East Div 1 95-96, Div 2 R-up 89-90; West Riding Snr Cup 37-38; West Riding Co Cup 27-28 48-49; West Riding Chall. Cup 34-35 35-36

SHEFFIELD

Chairman: Peter Beeby Tel: 0114 251 2509 (B) **President / Press Officer:** Alan Methley
Secretary: Stephen Hall, 23 Regent Court, Bradfield Rd, Hillsborough, Sheffield S6 1BT 0114 233 4441 (H), 01246 450255 ext 300 (B).
Manager: John Pearson **Asst Manager:** Sam Saif **Commercial Manager:** John Pearson
Ground: Don Valley Stadium, Worksop Rd, Sheffield S9 3TL (0114 256 0607)
Directions: M1 Junc 33, turn onto dual carriageway sign City centre, take 2nd exit A57. Turn right at bottom of slip road, and at bottom of hill turn right again at lights. Left at lights at rear of Morrison's supermarket. Follow road passing under bridge, ground on right
Seats: 25,000 **Cover:** 13,000 **Capacity:** 25,000 **Floodlights:** Yes **Founded:** 1857 **Nickname:** The Club
Clubhouse: Licensed Bar **Club Shop:** No **Colours:** Red & black/black/black **Change:** All blue
Programme: 16 pages, 50p **Editor:** David Deans (0114 232 5901) **Club Sponsors:** Bumford Heating
PREVIOUS - League: Yorks 49-82 **Grounds:** Abbeydale Park, Dore (1956-1989); Sheffield Amateur Sports Club, Hillsborough Park 1989-91; Sheffield International (Don Valley) Stadium 1991-94; Sheffield Sports Stadium 94-97.
Record Gate: 2,000 v Barton Rovers, FA Vase SF 76-77. **Midweek matchday:** Wednesday
Player progressing to Football Lge: Richard Peacock, Hull 94-95.
96-97 Captain: J Eastwood **96-97 Top Scorer:** **96-97 P.o.Y.:** M Thomson
Honours: F.A. Amateur Cup 03-04; F.A. Challenge Vase Runners-up 76-77;
Northern Co's East Lg Cup 94-95 (Div 1 88-89 90-91); Yorkshire Lg Div 2 76-77.

Pontefract Colleries *Photo: Paul Watkins*

STAVELEY MINERS WELFARE

Chairman: Philip White, Tel: 01246 471702 (H) **Vice-Chairman:** Phil White
Secretary: Roy Berry, 11 Thorpleigh Rd, Woodthorpe, Chesterfield, Derbyshire S43 3BJ. Tel: 01246 281827 (H)
Ground: Inkersall Road, Staveley, Chesterfield, Derbyshire (01246 471441).
Directions: M1 jct 30, follow A619 Chesterfield - Staveley is 3 miles from jct 30. Turn left at GK Garage in Staveley town centre into Inkersall Rd - ground 200yds on right at side of Speedwell Rooms. Frequent buses (47, 70, 72, 75, 77) from Chesterfield stop in Staveley town centre - 3 mins walk to ground.
Capacity: 5,000 **Cover:** 200 **Seats:** 200 **Floodlights:** Yes **Nickname:** The Welfare **Founded:** 1989
Clubhouse: The Staveley Miners Welfare, 500yds from ground, is open before and after games.
Club Shop: Yes, contact Craig Cousins, 01246 475068.
Colours: All red **Change colours:** Yellow/blue/yellow **Midweek matches:** Tuesday
Programme: 16 pages, 30p **Editor:** Secretary **Reserves' League:** Central Midlands Res. Div.
Previous Leagues: Chesterfield & D. Amat 89-91; County Sen 91-93. **Club Records - Attendance:** 280 v Stocksbridge, Sheffield Snr Cup 22/1/94.
Goalscorer: Paul Nicholls **Appearances:** Shane Turner.
Honours: County Sen Lg Div 2 92-93, Div 3 91-92, Chesterfield & D. Amat Lg R-up 89-90 90-91, Byron (Lge) Cup 89-90, R-up 90-91.

THACKLEY

Chairman: John Myers **Treasurer:** Steven Paley **Press Officer:** Jamie Scott (01274 611520).
Secretary: Stewart Willingham, 3 Kirklands Close, Baildon, Shipley, West Yorks BD17 6HN (01274 598589).
Manager/Coach: John Boyle **Asst Manager:** Colin Smith. **Physio:** John Laider.
Ground: Dennyfield, Ainsbury Avenue, Thackley, Bradford (01274 615571). **Directions:** On main Leeds/Keighley A657 road, turn off at Thackley corner which is 2 miles from Shipley traffic lights and 1 mile from Greengates lights. Ainsbury Avenue bears to the right 200yds down the hill. Ground is 200yds along Ainsbury Avenue on the right. 3 miles from Bradford Interchange (BR), one and a half miles from Shipley (BR). Buses to Thackley corner (400 yds).
Seats: 300 **Cover:** 600 **Capacity:** 3,000 **Floodlights:** Yes **Founded:** 1930.
Clubhouse: Open Tue-Sun evenings, matchdays and w/e lunchtimes. Hot & cold snacks on matchdays.
Club Shop: Yes. Programmes, souvenirs. Metal badges available - £2.50 + s.a.e. Contact Jamie Scott (01274 61152).
Colours: Red & white/white/red **Change colours:** All white **Midweek matches:** Tuesday
Programme: 20 pages, 50p **Editor:** Secretary **Sponsors:** Diamond International Shipping
Previous - Leagues: Bradford Amateur, W. Riding County Amateur, W. Yorks, Yorks 67-82.
Name: Thackley Wesleyians 1930-39.
Record Attendance: 1,500 v Leeds Utd 1983 **Best FA Vase year:** 5th Rd 80-81 (01-2 v Whickham).
Players progressing to Football League: Tony Brown (Leeds, Doncaster, Scunthorpe, Rochdale), Ian Ormondroyd (Bradford City, Aston Villa, Derby, Leicester).
96-97 Captain: Warren Fletcher **96-97 Top Scorer:** Keith Sanderson **96-97 P.o.Y.:** Richard Wilson
Honours: Northern Co's (East) Lg R-up 94-95 (Lg Cup R-up 94-95), Yorks Lg Div 2 73-74, West Yorks Lg 66-67, West Riding Co. Amtr Lg 57-58 58-59 59-60, West Riding Co. Cup 73-74 74-75, West Riding Co. Chal. Cup 63-64 66-67,(R-Up 94-95) Bradford & Dist. Snr Cup(11) 38-39 49-50 55-56 57-60 65-67 78-79 87-88.94-95. .gap 5

Thackley *Photo: Tony Bills*

Northern Counties East Premier Division: Curzon Ashton v Ossett Albion, Neil Taylor of Curzon Ashton keeps a close eye on Ossett Albion's Perrin during a muddy 0-0 League encounter

Photo: Colin Stevens

DIVISION ONE CLUBS 1998-99

BORROWASH VICTORIA

Chairman: Ian Anderson **Vice Chairman:** Peter Erwin **Founded:** 1911 **Reformed:** 1963
Sec./Press Officer: Ian Collins, 30 Margreave Road, Chaddesden, Derby DE21 6JD (01332 739437).
Manager/Coach: Kevin Smith **Asst Manager:** Kevin Harrigan **Physio:** Geoff Woolley
Ground: Asterdale Bowl, Borrowash Road, Spondon, Derby (01332 668656).
Directions: M1 jct 25, A52 towards Derby, 3rd left off by-pass into Borrowash Rd, ground 400 yds on left. 2 miles from Spondon (BR). Nottingham to Derby buses pass nearby.
Capacity: 5,000 **Seats:** No **Covered:** 500 **Floodlights:** Yes **Nickname:** Vics
Clubhouse: Normal pub hours. Hot & cold food. **Club Shop:** No **Midweek matches:** Tuesday
Colours: Red & white/black/black **Change Colours:** Yellow/sky/yellow **Club Sponsors:** St Ivel
Programme: 16 pages, 50p **Editor:** Michael Smith 01332 573832 **Previous Ground:** Dean Drive, 11-84
Previous Leagues: Derby Sunday School & Welfare 52-57; Derby Comb.; Midland 79-82; Northern Co's East.
Club Records - **Win:** 11-1 **Defeat:** 3-8 **Goalscorer:** Paul Acklam **Appearances:** Neil Kellogg
Attendance: 2,000 v Nottingham Forest, floodlight opening 22/10/85.
Honours: Northern Co's East Lg Div 1 Sth 83-84 (R-up 84-85, Div 2 Sth R-up 82-83), Derby Comb. 77-78 (R-up(10) 65-66 68-74 75-77 78-79, Lg Cup 68-69 75-76 (R-up 63-64 66-67), Midland Co's Lg Div 80-81 (Div 1 Cup 80-81), Derbys Snr Cup R-up 90-91, Derbys Div. Cup 73-74 (R-up 70-71 72-73), Central Midlands Lg B E Webbe Cup R-up 88-89 (Reserves Cup 94-95), FA Cup 3rd Qual. Rd 91-92.

BRODSWORTH WELFARE

Chairman: Gordon Jennings Tel: 01302 781121 **Press Officer:** John Muldowney
Secretary: Robert Beswick, 75 Coniston Drive, Bolton-on-Dearne, Rotherham S63 8NE (01709 890913)
Manager: Neil Brandon **Physio:** J Bedford **Match Sec:** John Muldowney, Tel: 01302 721274 (H)
Ground: Welfare Ground, Woodlands, Nr. Doncaster (01302 728380).
Directions: From A1 take A638 to Doncaster, take left after Woodlands Pub into Welfare Road, ground 50yds on left. Regular bus service from North Bridge Bus Station, Doncaster.
Seats: No **Cover:** 250 **Capacity:** 3,000 **Floodlights:** Yes **Founded:** 1912
Clubhouse: Yes, Matchday drinks and snacks
Colours: Green & yellow stripes/yellow/yellow **Change colours:** All yellow
Club Shop: No **Nickname:** Brody **Midweek home matchday:** Tuesday
Previous Name: Brodsworth Main **Leagues:** Doncaster Snr/ Sheffield/ Yorks.
Programme: 20 pages, compiled Match Sec. **Editor:** Match Sec.
Record fee paid: Nil **Record fee received:** Barry Stobart, Wolves 60.
97-98 Captain: Colin Bishop **Top scorer:** Chris Sambrook (29)
Honours: Yorks Lg 24-25, Donc. & Dist. Lg 84-85 (Lg Cup 85-86, Div 2 78-79, Div 2 Cup 78-79), Sheffield Jnr Cup 83-84, Mexborough Montagu Cup 91-92 92-93.

HATFIELD MAIN

President: John Green **Chairman:** Peter Wright **Vice Chairman:** Russell Wright
Secretary: Bruce Hatton, 92 Ingram Rd, Dunscroft, Doncaster, Sth Yorks DN7 4JE (01302 841648).
Manager: Paul Morrell **Asst Manager:** Peter Wright **Coach:**
Physio: Anthony Hatton **Commercial Manager:** Russell Wright.
Ground: Dunscroft Welfare Ground, Dunscroft, Doncaster, Sth Yorks (01302 841326).
Directions: From Doncaster (A18) Scunthorpe Rd to Dunsville, left at Flarepath Hotel down Broadway. Ground half mile on right. Half mile from Stamforth & Hatfield (BR). Buses every fifteen minutes from Doncaster.
Seats: 200. **Cover:** 600 **Capacity:** 4,000 **Floodlights:** Yes **Founded:** 1936.
Programme: 25 pages, 50p **Editor:** Tony Ingram (01302 842795) **Club Shop:** Yes
Colours: All red **Change:** All blue **Nickname:** The Main
Previous League: Doncaster Dist, Yorkshire 55-82. **Clubhouse:** Full licensing hrs. Hot/cold drinks/snacks.
Record transfer fee received: £1,000 for Mark Hall (York C.)
Record Gate: 1,000 v Leeds, A Jones testimonial. Competitive: 750 v Bishop Auckland, FA Amtr Cup
Midweek home matchday: Tuesday **Reserve Team's League:** None
Sponsors: Manor Tyres, (Stainforth)
Players progresing to Football League: Mark Atkins (Scunthorpe, Blackburn), Mark Hall (York).
97-98 Captain: Phillip Hill **Top Scorer:** Phillip Hill **P.o.Y.:** Paul Evans
Club record appearances: Lal Dutt.
Honours: Northern Counties East Prem Div 95-96, R-up 88-89, Div One 94-95; Yorks Lge Div 1 R-up 65-66; W Riding Cup 61-62 63-64: .gap 5

GLAPWELL

Chairman: Roger Caton
Secretary: Ellen Caton, 111 The Hill, Glapwell, Chesterfield. S44 5LU. Tel: 01246 854648 (H)
Manager: Dave Waller
Ground: Hall Corner, Park Ave., Glapwell, Chesterfield, Derbyshire (01623 812213).
Directions: M1 Junc 29 A617 towards Mansfield, after Young Vanish Inn take filter lane left onto Bolsover Road, ground facing, use rear entrance next to garden centre
Colours: Black & white stripes/white/white **Change colours:** Red/black/black
Founded: 1980 **Floodlights:** Yes **Midweek matches:** Tuesday
Programme: 16 pages, 30p **Editor:** Club Secretary
Honours: Central Midlands Lg 93-94 (Floodlit Cup 93-94), Derbyshire Senior Cup SF 93-94.

HALL ROAD RANGERS

Chairman: Robert Smailes, 7 Cotterdale, Sutton Park, Hull, HU7 4AA. Tel: 01482 821354 (H)
Secretary: David J Simmons, 24 Gorton Road, Willerby. Hull HU10 6LT. Tel: 01482 658998 (H), 01482 224429 (B)
Manager: Mick Matthews **Asst Mgr:** Peter Smurthwaite **Coach:** Ian Davis
Ground: Dene Park, Dene Close, Beverley Rd, Dunswell, Nr Hull (01482 850101).
Directions: M62 to A63, turn left before Humber Bridge onto A164 to Beverley, after approx 5 miles turn right onto A1079. In 2 miles turn left at large roundabout to ground 20 yards on right.
Seats: 50 **Cover:** 750 **Capacity:** 1,200 **Floodlights:** Yes **Club Shop:** Yes
Clubhouse: Open all week for drinks and snacks. Bar snacks. Snooker, pool, darts.
Programme: 36 pages, 50p **Editor/Press Officer:** Secretary **Nickname:** Rangers
Colours: Blue & white hoops/blue/blue & white **Change colours:** Green & white hoops **Founded:** 1959
Midweek Matches: Wednesday **Reserve League:** East Riding Co. Lge. **Sponsor:** John Moore Security
Previous Leagues: East Riding; Yorks 68-82.
Previous ground: Hull Co-Op (until 1968)
96-97 - Top Scorer: Lee Collingwood **P.o.Y.:** Lee Collingwood
Club Records - Attendance: 400 v Manchester City Aug 93 **Scorer:** G James **Appearances:** G James
Players progressing to Football League: Gerry Ingram (Blackpool, Sheff Wed).
Honours: Northern Co's East Lg Div 2 90-91, Yorks Lg Div 3 72-73 79-80, East Riding Snr Cup 72-73 93-94.

HARROGATE RAILWAY ATHLETIC

President: J Robinson **Chairman:** Dennis Bentley **Commercial Mgr:** Wendy Rock (01423 883104)
Secretary: W Douglas Oldfield, 80 Stonefall Ave., Harrogate, Nth Yorks HG2 7NP (01423 540786).
Manager: A Vincent **Coach:** A Canham **Physio:** J Tope
Press Officer / Programme Editor: Gordon Ward, Tel: 01423 880423 (H)
Ground: Station View, Starbeck, Harrogate (01423 885539).
Directions: A59 Harrogate to Knaresborough road. After approx 1.5 miles turn left just before railway level crossing. Ground is 150 yds up the lane. Adjacent to Starbeck (BR). Served by any Harrogate to Knareborough bus.
Seats: 300 **Cover:** 600 **Capacity:** 3,000 **Floodlights:** Yes **Founded:** 1935
Clubhouse: Games, TV room, lounge, open during normal public house hours every day. Hot food available.
Club Shop: Yes **Midweek matchday:** Monday **Sponsors:** Crest Homes
Colours: Red & green/green/red **Change:** White/red/white **Nickname:** The Rail
Previous leagues: West Yorkshire; Harrogate District; Yorkshire 55-73 80-82.
Record Attendance: 1,400; 1962 FA Amateur Cup
96-97 Top Scorer: A Spence **96-97 Captain:** G Edmunds **96-97 P.o.Y.:** S Hampson
Honours: Northern Co's (East) Lg Cup 86-87

LOUTH UNITED

Chairman: George Horton **Vice-Chairman:** Andrew Sylvester **President:** Dave Fairburn
Secretary/Press Officer: Albany Jordan, 20d Upgate, Louth, Lincs. LN11 9ET. Tel: 01507 600694 (H)
Manager: Steve Newby **Coaches::** Nigel Fanthorpe/D Cole **Physio:** Kenny Vincent
Ground: Park Avenue, Louth, Lincs (01507 607351).
Directions: A16 To Louth Market Place, exit via Eastgate/Eastfield Rd, to Fire Station turn right into Park Avenue. Ground at bottom of avenue of prefabricated bungalows.
Capacity: 2,500 **Seats:** None **Cover:** 400 **Floodlights:** Yes **Nickname:** The Lions **Founded:** 1947
Clubhouse: Weekdays 6.30-11.45, Sat 12-11.45. Full bar facilities. Snacks available. **Club Shop:** No
Sponsors: Foxhall Plant Hire
Programme: 50p **Editor/Press Officer:** Albany Jordan (Sec.) **Midweek matches:** Tuesday
Colours: Royal with white stripes/royal/red **Change:** Red & black stripes **Reserves League:** Lincolnshire
Previous - Leagues: Lincs 47-75 82-88; Central Midlands 88-93. **Names:** Louth Nats & Louth Town - merged
Grounds: None
Club Records - Goalscorer: Peter Rawcliffe 39 **Appearances:** Gary Smith 476 **Attendance:** 2,500 **Transfer fee received:** £10,000 for Martyn Chalk (Derby County, 1990).
Players progressing to Football League: Terry Donovan (Grimsby), Paul Bartlett (Derby), Brian Klug (Ipswich), Glen Cockerill (Lincoln, Watford, Southampton), Peter Rawcliffe & Peter Green (Grimsby), Martin Chalk (Derby).
Honours: Lincs Lg Prem 72-73 85-86 86-87 (Div 1 57-58 66-67 67-68; Lg Challenge Cup 73-74 86-87; Lg Charity Cup 55-56 56-57 67-68; Central Mids Lg Cup R-up 92-93; Wakefield F'lit Cup R-up 91-92; Lincs Snr 'A' Cup 77-78.

PARKGATE

President: T L Dabbs **Chairman:** Albert T Dudill, Tel: 01709 524533 (H) **Vice Chairman:** Les Taylor
Secretary: Bruce Bickerdike, 2 Cardew Close, Rawmarsh, Rotherham S62 6LB (01709 522305 Fax: 01709 528583).
Press Officer: Secretary **Manager:** Gary Gillatt **Asst Manager:** Alan Smith **Physio:** Peter Wakefield
Ground: Roundwood Sports Complex, Green Lane, Rawmarsh, Rotherham (01709 826600).
Directions: From Rotherham A633 to Rawmarsh. From Doncaster A630 to Conisbrough, then A6023 through Swinton to Rawmarsh. Grd at Green Lane – right from Rotherham, left from Conisbrough at the Crown Inn. Grd 800yds right
Seats: 300 **Cover:** 300 **Capacity:** 1,000 **Floodlights:** Yes **Founded:** 1969
Clubhouse: Licensed bar, 2 lounges. Meals available lunchtime Mon-Sat. **Club Shop:** No.
Colours: All red **Change colours:** All sky **Nickname:** The Gate or The Steelmen **Midweek matches:** Tuesday
Programme: 20 pages, 50p **Editor:** Stuart Bisby (01709 817524) **Club Sponsors:** British Steel
Previous - Leagues: Rotherham Association; Whitbread County Senior; Yorkshire 74-82
Ground: None **Names:** BSC Parkgate (until mid-eighties); RES Parkgate (pre-1994).
Local Newspapers: Star/ Green'Un/ Rotherham Advertiser/ Sth Yorks Times/ Dearne Valley Weekender.
Senior Honours: None **Record attendance:** v Worksop 1982

ROSSINGTON MAIN

Chairman: Hugh Gibson, 16 Ludgate Close, Rossington, Doncaster DN11 0UP 01302 864995 (H)
Secretary: Gerald Parsons, 15 Seaton Gardens, Rossington, Doncaster DN11 0XA. Tel: 01302 867542 (H)
Joint Managers: D Ridley & L Ostle **Physio:** J White
Ground: Welfare Ground, Oxford Street, Rossington, Doncaster (01302 865524).
Directions: Enter Rossington and go over the railway crossings. Pass the Welfare Club on right, Oxford Street is next right - ground is at bottom. 8 miles from Doncaster (BR).
Seats: 200 **Cover:** 500 **Capacity:** 2,000 **Floodlights:** Yes **Nickname:** The Colliery **Founded:** 1920
Clubhouse: Evenings & matchdays, Sandwiches, rolls, satillite TV, pool. **Club Shop:** No
Programme: 50p **Editor:** Ian Wilson 01302 867221 (H)
Midweek matches: Tuesday **Sponsor:** RJB Mining
Colours: All white **Change colours:** Blue & black **Reserve League:** Beefeater County Sen
Previous Leagues: Doncaster Sen, Yorkshire Lge, Sheffield County Sen, Cent Mids.
Club Records - Attendance: 864 v Leeds United 8/91. **Goalscorer:** Mark Illman **Appearances:** Darren Phipps
Players progressing to Football League: Jim Harkin (Shrewsbury, Mansfield, Doncaster Rov),Shaw Bothers (WBA, Doncaster), Joe Leiversly (Arsenal), Dennis Leiversly/Ken Hardwicke/Brian Makepease/Jack Teasdale/Gary Jones (Doncaster), Ronnie Spence (York City), Reg Brian (Blackpool), Bob Forest/Brian Taylor (Leeds Utd), Malcolm Webster (Arsenal/Southend/Cambridge).
Honours: Sen Lge 44-45, Cup 44-45, CMFL Prem Lge 84-85, Cup 83-84 84-85, DDSAL Shield 90-91 R-up 89-90.

TADCASTER ALBION

Chairman: Michael R Burnett, Tel: 01937 832802 (H/Fax) **President:** Lord Edward Stourton
Secretary: Mrs Angela J Burnett, 6 Beech Grove House, Ouston Lane, Tadcaster LS24 8DP. Tel: 01937 832802 (H/Fax)
Manager: Ken Payne **Match Sec:** Howard Clarke, 01937 832887 (H/B)
Ground: The Park, Ings Lane, Tadcaster, LS24 9AY (01937 834119)
Directions: From West Riding and South Yorks, turn right off A659 at John Smith's Brewery Clock. From East Riding turn left off A659 after passing over river bridge and pelican crossing (New Street).
Colours: Red & blue/red/blue **Change colours:** White/black/black **Midweek Matchday:** Tuesday
Programme: 20 pages **Programme Editor:** Mrs Angela Burnett (Sec.) **Founded:** 1936

Action from Tadcaster Albion's match with Parkgate Photo: Ray Pruden

WINTERTON RANGERS

President: J W Hiles **Chairman:** G Spencer **Vice Chairman:** A Smith
Secretary/Press Officer: G Spencer, 2 Dale Park Ave., Winterton, Scunthorpe, N Lincs. DN15 9UY, 01724 732039 (H)
Manager: Martin Jacklin **Asst Manager/Coach:** Peter Lea
Ground: West Street, Winterton, Scunthorpe, South Humberside (01724 732628).
Directions: From Scunthorpe take A1077 Barton-on-Humber road for 5 miles. On entering Winterton take second right (Eastgate), third left (Northlands Road) and first right (West Street). Ground 200yds on left
Seats: 200 **Covered:** 200 **Capacity:** 3,000 **Floodlights:** Yes **Founded:** 1930
Colours: Navy & white/navy/navy **Change colours:** All red **Nickname:** Rangers
Midweek matches: Monday **Sponsors:** Finaction Ltd **Club Shop:** No.
Programme: 28-36 pages, 50p **Editor:** M Fowler (01724 734570)
Best FA Vase year: QF 76-77 **Best FA Cup year:** 4th Qual Rd replay 76-77 (lost 2-3 after 3-3)
Previous League: Scunthorpe & Dist. 45-65/ Lincs 65-70/ Yorkshire 70-82.
Previous Grounds: Watery Lane 1930-48.
Record attendance: 1,200 v Sheffield Utd - Official opening of floodlights, October 1978.
Record transfer fee received: £5,000 for Henry Smith (Leeds United, 1979).
Clubhouse: Open matchdays & evenings Mon-Sat, hot & cold food available on matchdays. Pool and snooker rooms.
Players progressing to Football League: Henry Smith (Leeds, Hearts), Keith Walwyn (Chesterfield, York, Carlisle), Rick Greenhough (Chester, York)
96-97 Captain: Steve Bell **96-97 P.o.Y.:** Tony McGrath **96-97 Top Scorer:** Grafme Ross
Honours: Lincs Jnr Cup 47-48 61-62; Lincs Snr 'B' Cup 69-70; Yorks Lg 71-72 76-77 78-79 (Lg Cup 80-81); Northern Co's East Lg Div 2 89-90; S'thorpe Lg & Cup many times; Philips National F'light 6-aside 76-77.

WORSBROUGH BRIDGE M.W. & ATHLETIC

Chairman: Mr J Wright **Press Officer:** Mr A Wright (01226 243418).
Secretary: Garry Wiggan, 9 Pantry Well, Worsbrough Bridge, Barnsley, S. Yorks S70 4SW (01226 247023)
Manager: K Paddon **Asst Manager:**
Ground: Park Road, Worsbrough Bridge, Barnsley (01226 284452).
Directions: On the A61 Barnsley-Sheffield road two miles south of Barnsley, 2 miles from M1 jnt 36 opposite Blackburns Bridge. Two and a half miles from Barnsley (BR). Yorkshire Traction run buses every 10 mins thru Worsbrough Bridge.
Seats: 175 **Cover:** 175 **Capacity:** 2,000 **Floodlights:** Due **Founded:** 1923
Colours: All red **Change colours:** Yellow/blue **Reformed:** 1947
Record attendance: 2,300 v Blyth Spartans, FA Amateur Cup 1971
Previous Leagues: Barnsley 52-61/ County Snr 62-70/ Yorks 71-82.
Midweek Matchday: Wednesday **Programme:** 20 pages, 20p **Editor:** Secretary
Honours: Northern Co's East Div 1 R-up 90-91 (Div 3 R-up 85-86); Sheffield Snr Cup R-up 72-73; County Snr Lg 65-66 69-70 (R-up 62-63, Lg Cup 65-66); Barnsley Lg 52-53 58-59 59-60, Lg Cup 56-57 58-59 (R-up 53-54), Beckett Cup 57-58.

YORKSHIRE AMATEUR

Chairman: William Ellis, Tel: 01405 839990 (H) **President:** Rayner Barker
Secretary: Charles Sharman, 44 Roxholme Place, Leeds LS7 4JQ (0113 293 8894 H & Fax).
Manager: Kevin Smith **Coach:** Dave Holmes **Physio:** Terry Davies
Ground: The Bracken Edge Football Ground, Roxholme Road, Leeds LS8 4DZ (0113 262 4093).
Directions: From South M1 to Leeds, then A58 Wetherby Road to Fforde Green Hotel, left at lights and proceed to Sycamore Ave. (on right). From East A1 to Boot & Shoe Inn then to Shaftesbury Hotel, turn right into Harehills Lane, then to Sycamore Avenue. Two and a half miles from Leeds (BR). Buses 2, 3 & 20 from Briggate to Harehills Ave.
Seats: 200 **Cover:** 160 **Capacity:** 1,550 **Floodlights:** Yes **Club Shop:** Yes
Clubhouse: Bar, tea bar, games, lounge. Every night 8.30-11, Sat matchdays 12-11, Sun 12-3.
Programme: 12 pages, 50p **Editor:** Secretary **Midweek Matches:** Tuesday **Founded:** 1919
Colours: White/navy/red **Change colours:** All red **Sponsors:** Screeching Parrot **Nickname:** Ammers
Previous League: Yorks 20-24 30-82. **Previous ground:** Elland Road 1919-20
Record Attendance: 4,000 v Wimbledon, FA Amateur Cup QF 1932.
Players progressing to Football League: Gary Strodder & Stuart Naylor (WBA), Peter Swan (Leeds), Brian Deane (Doncaster, Sheffield United, Leeds).
Honours: FA Amtr Cup SF 31-32; West Riding Co. Cup(3); Yorks Lg 31-32, Div 2 58-59 (R-up 52-53 71-72), Div 3 77-78, Lg Cup 32-33; Leeds & Dist. Snr Cup.

Ground grading? Of course we're ready!

REDFERNS INTERNATIONAL REMOVERS
CENTRAL MIDLANDS FOOTBALL LEAGUE

FEEDER TO: NORTHERN COUNTIES EAST LEAGUE

Chairman & General Secretary: F A Harwood,
103 Vestry Road, Oakwood, Derby DE21 2BN Tel: 01332 832372
Public Relations Officer: S Wilton,
Haven Holme, 57 Main Rd, Smalley, Ilkeston, Derby DE7 6DS Tel: 01332 880199

We can be proud of the achievements of the League both on and off the field. An excellent season for Gedling Town and newcomers Goole AFC. Both literally led their respective divisions from start to finish and were worthy champions. And from Gedling town's point of view it was disappointing that they did not achieve promotion to the Northern Counties East League due to failing ground grading requirements. Mickleover Sports, who finished third, also failed on the same requirement, whilst second placed Kimberley Town did not wish to leave the Central Midlands League.

For the first time in many years the League Cup Final was not played on a Football League ground but we thank Hucknall Town, one of our former clubs, who allowed us the use of their facilities and in an exciting final Dunkirk defeated Clipstone Welfare. Both of these sides being Nottinghamshire clubs, and this season has proved to be a tremendous one for clubs from that county. Of the fourteen honours available in the League Nottinghamshire clubs took ten. And most of the clubs came to the Central Midlands League via the Notts Alliance Football League. This is a credit to the best league in the Midlands outside the Pyramid System.

It is extremely pleasing that we go into a new season in excellent condition both on and off the field. With an increase in clubs in both the top divisions, and financially sound, having recovered from the "court" problems of a few years ago.

Frank Harwood

FINAL LEAGUE TABLES 1997-98

Travis Perkins Supreme Division

	P	*W*	*D*	*L*	*F*	*A*	*W*	*D*	*L*	*F*	*A*	*Pts*
Gedling Town	30	14	0	1	45	10	12	1	2	43	15	79
Kimberley Town	30	11	1	3	40	18	9	2	4	38	63	
Mickleover Sports	30	11	2	2	42	15	6	4	5	29	28	57
Dunkirk	30	10	3	2	40	19	7	1	7	24	19	55
Heanor Town	30	7	3	5	32	25	7	4	4	30	20	49
Nettleham	30	11	1	3	39	16	4	0	11	20	34	46
Clipstone Welfare	30	5	6	4	30	31	8	0	7	32	32	45
Collingham	30	6	4	5	26	24	5	3	7	23	28	40
Rossington	30	8	2	5	37	24	3	3	9	23	36	38
Graham Street Prims	30	8	2	5	34	31	3	3	9	15	32	38
Long Eaton United	30	7	2	6	29	25	4	0	11	19	32	35
Grimethorpe Miners Wel.	30	7	2	6	20	21	3	2	10	16	32	34
Harworth Colliery Inst.	30	4	3	8	17	29	4	4	7	21	29	31
Shirebrook Town	30	5	5	5	19	24	2	4	9	24	44	30
Sandiacre Town	30	6	0	9	21	34	3	3	9	17	31	30
Thorne Colliery	30	4	0	11	15	36	0	2	13	8	46	14

FINAL LEAGUE TABLES 1997-98

Premier Division

	P	W	D	L	F	A	W	D	L	F	A	Pts
Goole	32	14	1	1	60	9	13	3	0	41	9	85
Hucknall Rolls	32	11	3	2	44	16	12	1	3	45	19	73
Sneinton	32	10	2	4	45	21	11	2	3	51	23	67
Askern Welfare	32	9	1	6	54	24	12	2	2	46	15	*63
South Normanton Ath	32	9	2	5	32	22	8	1	7	29	27	54
Greenwood Meadows	32	10	2	4	42	18	6	2	8	28	41	52
Hemsworth Town	32	9	3	4	33	25	5	5	6	21	27	50
Selston	32	7	3	6	32	28	7	4	5	29	24	49
Radford	32	6	5	5	26	31	7	1	8	24	36	45
Holbrook	32	8	1	7	31	35	6	2	8	16	31	45
Shardlow St James	32	7	3	6	27	25	6	1	9	27	36	*42
Stanton Ilkeston	32	6	3	7	30	28	3	3	10	22	38	33
Sheepbridge	32	5	1	10	23	39	3	5	8	23	47	30
Mickleover RBL	32	3	4	9	23	43	3	6	7	23	33	28
Sheffield Hallam Univ.	32	3	2	11	25	37	5	0	11	23	38	26
Mexborough Athletic	32	2	2	12	9	31	3	2	11	28	53	19
Blackwell Miners Welf.	32	0	3	13	9	57	2	1	13	13	48	10

TRAVIS PERKINS SUPREME DIVISION RESULTS CHART 1997-98

		1	2	3	4	5	6	7	8	9	10	11	12	13	14	15	16
1	Clipstone Welfare	X	0-2	3-2	2-1	3-2	2-2	2-2	1-1	1-3	4-3	2-4	3-1	3-4	2-2	1-1	1-1
2	Collingham	0-3	X	4-2	2-3	1-1	1-3	0-1	1-1	4-1	2-0	2-2	2-0	1-0	1-3	3-3	2-1
3	Dunkirk	3-1	3-0	X	0-2	4-2	1-0	1-1	6-4	2-4	4-1	0-0	3-2	4-0	1-1	6-1	2-0
4	Gedling Town	6-0	2-0	2-1	X	7-0	2-0	2-0	1-2	6-1	2-1	2-1	1-0	3-1	1-0	4-2	4-1
5	Graham St Prims	3-2	2-4	0-3	0-4	X	2-0	5-3	2-2	1-4	4-2	2-2	0-2	2-1	4-2	4-0	3-0
6	Grimethorpe MW	1-3	2-0	0-4	0-4	1-0	X	1-0	0-1	0-0	1-0	1-1	1-2	4-2	1-2	3-2	4-0
7	Harworth CI	1-3	0-4	2-1	0-2	1-0	1-2	X	2-2	1-3	1-3	0-2	0-2	3-3	3-1	1-0	1-1
8	Heanor Town	4-2	2-3	0-1	2-2	3-1	1-0	2-2	X	1-2	2-1	1-2	5-3	1-1	2-1	3-4	3-0
9	Kimberley Town	2-0	3-1	2-0	2-3	2-1	6-2	3-1	0-1	X	1-0	6-0	2-1	1-3	2-1	4-4	4-0
10	Long Eaton United	1-2	1-2	1-1	2-5	0-0	4-0	2-3	1-0	1-2	X	3-2	2-3	3-2	1-0	4-2	3-1
11	Mickleover Sports	5-1	0-0	1-0	0-1	4-1	2-1	4-2	2-0	3-2	2-3	X	3-0	3-1	4-2	1-1	8-0
12	Nettleham	2-0	4-2	0-1	2-1	4-1	1-0	0-3	1-4	1-1	3-1	4-0	X	3-1	6-0	4-1	4-0
13	Rossington	1-3	1-1	2-0	2-3	1-2	4-1	1-1	2-1	3-4	3-0	2-3	5-1	X	3-1	3-1	4-2
14	Sandiacre Town	1-3	3-1	1-4	1-3	1-3	1-2	3-0	0-5	0-6	1-2	0-3	3-0	2-0	X	2-0	2-1
15	Shirebrook Town	2-5	1-1	0-1	0-5	0-0	1-1	2-0	0-1	4-3	0-1	2-1	3-2	3-3	0-0	X	1-0
16	Thorne Colliery	0-4	4-2	1-3	0-4	0-1	3-2	1-2	1-5	0-2	2-1	1-6	1-0	0-1	0-1	1-2	X

LEADING GOALSCORERS 1997-98

SUPREME DIVISION

R Orton	Gedling Town	28	L Vickers	Sandiacre Town	14
N Limb	Kimberley Town	24	P Vick	Clipstone Welfare	13
M Taplin	Mickleover Sports	15	E Marsh	Gedling Town	13
W Manners	Dunkirk	14	S Wiggins	Gedling Town	13
P Mable	Heanor Town	14	R Nelson	Rossington	13

PREMIER DIVISION

T Hattersley	Askern Welfare	29	J Evans	Radford	18
S Parker	Askern Welfare	28	D Short	Sth Normanton Athletic	18
W Miles	Greenwood Meadows	25	K Severn	Goole	15
S Sewell	Hucknall Rolls	19	P Cheetham	Hucknall Rolls	15
P Gibbon	Goole	18	J Staples	Radford	15

RESERVE DIVISION

M Nowak	Greenwood Meadows	25	N Woodward	Gedling Town	17
N Furber	Sandiacre Town	23	N Tideswell	Hucknall Rolls	16
G Smedley	Clipstone Welfare	20	A Lyons	Worksop Town 'A'	15
B Hudson	Mickleover Sports	19	R Clifton	Clipstone Welfare	14
P Smith	Staveley Miners Welfare	18	S Dillon	Clipstone Welfare	14

THE COX CENTRAL MIDLANDS LEAGUE CUP 1997-98

PRELIMINARY ROUND

Dunkirk	v	Goole	2-1

FIRST ROUND

Dunkirk	v	Nettleham	0-0, 3-1	Gedling Town	v	Blackwell MW	5-0
Harworth Coll. Inst	v	Clipstone Welfare	0-0, 1-5	Holbrook	v	Greenwood M	1-1, 2-2*, 4p3
Hucknall Rolls	v	Thorne Colliery	1-1, 3-2	Mexborough Ath	v	Collingham	0-2
Mickleover RBL	v	Grimethorpe MW	2-2, 0-3	Mickleover Sports	v	Kimberley Town	2-1
Rossington	v	Long Eaton Utd	2-1 v, 1-2	Sandiacre Town	v	Askern Welfare	1-2
Shardlow St James	v	Graham St Prims	0-0, 0-2	Sheepbridge	v	Selston	3-6
Sheffield Hallam U.	v	Heanor Town	1-6	Sneinton	v	Radford	1-0
Sth Normanton Ath	v	Hemsworth Town	3-0	Stanton Ilkeston	v	Shirebrook Town	1-1, 1-4

SECOND ROUND

Collingham	v	Clipstone Welfare	1-1, 0-2	Dunkirk	v	Askern Welfare	3-1
Gedling Town	v	Sth Normanton Ath	3-1	Graham St Prims	v	Sneinton	0-5
Heanor Town	v	Grimethorpe MW	3-2	Hucknall Rolls	v	Long Eaton United	1-4
Selston	v	Mickleover Sports	3-0	Shirebrook Town	v	Holbrook	1-1, 1-1*, 3p4

THIRD ROUND

Holbrook	v	Clipstone Welfare	1-6	Long Eaton Utd	v	Dunkirk	1-2
Selston	v	Heanor Town	1-2	Sneinton	v	Gedling Town	2-3

SEMI-FINAL

Clipstone Welfare	v	Gedling Town	3-1	Dunkirk	v	Heanor Town	2-1*
at Dunkirk FC				at Mickleover Sports FC			

FINAL

Clipstone Welfare	v	Dunkirk	0-2	at Hucknall Town FC

READY MIXED CONCRETE RESERVE LEAGUE CUP 1997-98

SECOND ROUND

Gedling Town	v	Clipstone Welfare	2-3	Greenwood M	v	Mickleover Sports	1-2
Shirebrook Town	v	Worksop Town 'A'	1-2	Stanton Ilkeston	v	Staveley MW	0-4

SEMI-FINAL

Worksop Town 'A'	v	Clipstone Welfare	2-1	Staveley MW	v	Mickleover Sports	5-2*
at Worksop Town FC				at Staveley MW FC			

NB. For playing an ineligible player Worksop Town 'A' were removed from the competition. Clipstone Welfare reinstated

FINAL

Clipstone Welfare	v	Staveley MW	2-0	at Glapwell FC

WAKEFIELD FLOODLIT CUP 1997-98

GROUP A

Collingham	v	Goole	2-1
Collingham	v	Nettleham	3-1
Goole	v	Harworth	2-0
Harworth	v	Collingham	0-3
Harworth	v	Nettleham	3-0
Nettleham	v	Goole	1-5
Collingham	v	Harworth	3-1
Goole	v	Collingham	1-1
Goole	v	Nettleham	1-0
Harworth	v	Goole	3-4
Nettleham	v	Collingham	2-2
Nettleham	v	Harworth	2-2

	P	*W*	*D*	*L*	*F*	*A*	*Pts*
Collingham	6	4	2	0	14	6	14
Goole	6	4	1	1	14	7	13
Harworth CI	6	1	1	4	9	14	4
Nettleham	6	0	2	4	6	16	2

GROUP B

Heanor Town	v	Mickleover Sports	1-0
Heanor Town	v	Selston	7-1
Mickleover Sports	v	Stanton	4-2
Stanton	v	Heanor Town	0-2
Stanton	v	Selston	3-2
Selston	v	Mickleover Sports	0-1
Heanor Town	v	Stanton Ilkeston	2-0
Mickleover Spts	v	Heanor Town	0-2
Mickleover Spts	v	Selston	6-1
Stanton	v	Mickleover Sports	0-0
Selston	v	Heanor Town	2-1
Selston	v	Stanton	0-1

	P	*W*	*D*	*L*	*F*	*A*	*Pts*
Heanor Town	6	5	0	1	17	6	15
Mickleover Sports	6	3	1	2	11	6	10
Stanton Ilkeston	6	2	1	3	9	12	7
Selston	6	1	0	5	6	19	3

GROUP C

Gedling Town	v	Dunkirk	1-1
Gedling Town	v	Sandiacre Town	2-2
Dunkirk	v	Long Eaton United	1-0
Long Eaton United	v	Gedling Town	1-6
Long Eaton United	v	Sandiacre Town	7-2
Sandiacre Town	v	Dunkirk	0-2
Gedling Town	v	Long Eaton Utd	3-1
Dunkirk	v	Gedling Town	0-5
Dunkirk	v	Sandiacre Town	1-0
Long Eaton Utd	v	Dunkirk	1-3
Sandiacre Town	v	Gedling Town	1-3
Sandiacre Town	v	Long Eaton Utd	1-4

	P	*W*	*D*	*L*	*F*	*A*	*Pts*
Gedling Town	6	4	2	0	20	6	14
Dunkirk	6	4	1	1	8	7	13
Long Eaton Utd	6	2	0	4	14	16	*3
Sandiacre Town	6	0	1	5	6	19	1

GROUP C

Shirebrook Town	v	Grimthorpe	2-0
Shirebrook Town	v	Hemsworth Tn	+
Grimethorpe	v	Kimberley Town	0-2
Kimberley Town	v	Shirebrook Town	0-3
Kimberley Town	v	Hemsworth Town	6-1
Hemsworth Town	v	Grimethorpe	0-1
Shirebrook Town	v	Kimberley Town	1-0
Grimethorpe	v	Shirebrook Town	0-3
Grimethorpe	v	Hemsworth Tn	5-0
Kimberley Town	v	Grimethorpe	3-5
Hemsworth Town	v	Shirebrook Town	3-3
Hemsworth Town	v	Kimberley Town	3-3

+ Game not played - awarded 1-0 victory to Shirebrook Town

	P	*W*	*D*	*L*	*F*	*A*	*Pts*
Shirebrook Town	6	5	1	0	13	4	12
Grimethorpe MW	6	3	1	2	14	10	10
Kimberley Town	6	1	2	3	14	15	*4
Hemsworth Town	6	0	2	4	4	15	1

SECOND ROUND

Goole	v	Shirebrook Town	2-7 Agg
Dunkirk	v	Heanor Town	6-4 Agg
Mickleover Sports	v	Gedling Town	2-5 Agg
Grimethorpe MW	v	Collingham	3-5 Agg

SEMI-FINAL

Collingham	v	Gedling Town	6-3 Agg
Dunkirk	v	Shirebrook Town	3-4 Agg

FINAL

Collingham	v	Shirebrook Town	1-5 Agg

LEADING CLUB GOALSCORERS 1997-98

Askern Welfare	T Hattersley	29	S Parker	28	M Illman	9
Blackwell MW	J Riley	6	M Baines	2	D Hopkinson	2
Clipstone Welfare	P Vick	13	P Shaw	10	D Hand	6
Collingham	W Stark	10	D Cooper	5	S Doughty	5
Dunkirk	W Manners	14	J Ward	8	A Brandy	6
Gedling Town	R Orton	28	E Marsh	13	S Wiggins	13
Goole	P Gibbon	18	K Severn	15	J Miller	14
Graham Street Prims	L Richards	10	P Davis	7	M CmQuilton	6
Greenwood Meadows	W Miles	25	S Ireland	10	B Marshall	8
Grimethorpe Miners Welfare	G Wilson	6	D Lodge	3	D Mills	3
Harworth Colliery Institute	S Goulding	9	S Stanley	7	C Whalley	7
Heanor Town	P Mable	14	P Tomlin	10	P Acklam	10
Hemsworth Town	K Mayne	12	R Stewart	9	S Robinson	5
Holbrook	V Hallsworth	8	M Houldsworth	8	J Fowell	7
Hucknall Rolls	S Sewell	19	P Cheetham	15	G Wright	10
Kimberley Town	N Limb	24	S Gordon	10	W Bennett	9
Long Eaton United	S Bull	12	G Stacey	7	R Pollard	7
Mexborough Athletic	M Hodgett	7	D Jones	5	R Whittingham	3
Mickleover Royal British Legion	C Shardlow	12	K Burden	6	K Baldwin	4
Mickleover Sports	M Taplin	15	M Ashford	11	C Parkins	11
Nettleham	D Hargreaves	12	D Dye	10	S Scargill	8
Radford	J Evans	18	J Staples	15	J Rush	3
Rossington	R Nelson	13	S Henderson	11	S Breen	8
Sandiacre Town	L Vickers	14	J Slinger	5	M Millward	2
Selston	L Widdowson	12	C Clement	6	M Bradley	5
Shardlow St James	N Day	7	J Webster	7	R Butcher	6
Sheepbridge	S Adams	15	C Evans	4	G Thurnham	3
Sheffield Hallam University	D Mulliner	8	K Jones	7	G Davis	6
Shirebrook Town	S Hill	7	N Booth	6	R Sharma	5
Sneinton	T Khan	15	T Brookbanks	13	G Chulan	12
South Normanton Athletic	D Short	18	M Brameld	8	M Drury	4
Stanton Ilkeston	I Trueman	14	W Freestone	10	P Boyle	4
Thorne Colliery	A Irwin	4	G Jones	3	K Sadd	2

SUPREME DIVISION CLUBS 1998-99

BLIDWORTH WELFARE

Chairman: Richard Paterson. Tel: 01623 27470 (H). **President:** Ray Hilton **Comm. Manager:** Chris Jukes
Secretary: Darrel Bailey, 220 Wharf Road, Pinxton, Notts. Tel: 01773 813432 (H) **Press Officer:** Pete Craggs
Match Secretary: Bill Deakin, 220 Brick Kiln Lane, Mansfield, Notts NG19 6LR. Tel: 01623 454071 (H).
Manager: Andy Brown **Asst Manager:** John Miller **Coach:** Shaun Hird
Ground: Welfare Ground, Mansfield Rd, Blidworth, Mansfield (01623 793361).
Directions: On B6020, Rainworth side of Blidworth. From M1 jct 27 take A608 to Kirby and Annesley Woodhouse, at lights follow A611 to Kirby then take B6020 through Ravenshead to Blidworth - thru village and ground at top of hill on right. From A1 follow A614 and A617 to Rainworth, left at lights then 1st right on to B6020 to Blidworth - ground on left at top of hill. Served by Mansfield-Nottingham buses.
Capacity: 3,000 **Seats:** 200 **Cover:** 700 **Floodlights:** Yes **Founded:** 1980
Clubhouse: Welfare Social Club built 199. Normal matchday hours. **Club Shop:** No
Programme: 32 pages, 50p **Editor:** Andy Brown, Tel: 01773 861176 (H) **Midweek matches:** Tuesday
Colours: Orange/black/orange **Change colours:** All yellow **Nickname:** Hawks
Prev. Lges: Notts All. 80-82; NCEL 82-86; Centrals Mids 86-94.

CLIPSTONE WELFARE

Secretary: Barry Clarke, 40 Church Road, Clipstone, Mansfield, NG21 9DG (01623 640829).
Manager: Carl Hanson **Midweek Matchday:** Tuesday or Wednesday
Ground & Directions: Clipstone Lido Ground Clipstone Road West, Mansfield, Notts (01632 655674). B6030 from Mansfield, between Forest Town & Clipstone, on left entering Clipstone.
Colours: Red & navy/navy/white **Change Colours:** Amber & navy/navy/amber
Honours: Notts Snr Cup 85-86 94-95, Notts Alliance 72-73 73-74 74-75 92-93 94-95 (Lg Cup 72-73 73-74 74-75 94-95 (R-up 92-93)), Notts I'mediate Cup 55-56.

COLLINGHAM

Secretary: Mr G Williams, 47 Dukes End, Collingham, Newark, Nottinghamshire NG23 7LD (01636 892189)
Manager: Paul Hyde **Midweek Matchday:** Tuesday
Ground & Directions: Collingham FC, Station Road, Collingham, Newark, Notts. (01636 892303) Take A46 Newark to Lincoln road (Newark bypass). Turn left into Collingham on the A1133 road. In village turn right at traffic lights. Ground 100 yards on left.
Colours: Amber & black/black/black **Change Colours:** Blue & white/blue/blue

DUNKIRK

Secretary: Steve Trossell, 24 Kingfisher Wharf, Castle Marina, Nottingham NG7 1GA (0115 947903)
Manager: Steve Hardie/Ian Upton **Midweek Matchday:** Tuesday
Ground & Directions: The Ron Steel Sports Ground, Trentside Farm, Clifton Bridge, Nottingham (0602 850803). Ring Road - Clifton Bridge (North End), Industrial Estate, Lenton Lane.
Colours: Red/white/red **Change Colours:** Black & white/black/red
Honours: FA Vase 5th Rd 93-94; Cen Mid Sup Div R-up 96-97, Prem Div R-up 95-96, KO Cup 97-98; Notts Alliance Div 1 84-85, Div 2 82-83, Lg Cup R-up 84-85; Notts I'mediate Cup 83-84.

GEDLING TOWN

Secretary: Paul Dobson, 26 Chevin Gardens, Top Valley Estate, Nottingham NG5 9ES (0115 9274790)
Manager: Everton Marsh/Jamie Brodie **Physio:** Trevor Wells/Pete Tyers
Ground & Directions: Riverside Ground, rear Ferry Boat Inn, Stoke Inn, Stoke Bardolph, Gedling, Nottm (01159 402145). A612 Nottingham-Lowdham-Southwell road. just before Burton Joyce turn right into Stoke Lane to Ferryboat Public House. Approx 1 1/2 miles. Ground rear of Ferry Boat Inn.
Capacity: 2,000 **Seats:** None **Cover:** 500 **Floodlights:** Yes **Shop:** No
Clubhouse: Matchdays only. Hot & cold food. Licensed bar.
Programme: 32 pages 50p **Editor:** Paul Dodson **Founded:** 1989 **Nickname:** None
Colours: Yellow & navy/navy/yellow **Change colours:** All red **Midweek Matchday:** Wednesday
Record Attendance: 250 v Arnold Town. **Goalscorer:** Robbie Orton 41, **Appearances:** Gary Ball 165. **Win:** 11-0 v Radford 91-92. **Defeat:** 2-5 v Staveley MW 93-94. **Best season FA Vase:** 3rd Rd 96-97
97-98 Captain: Jonathan Flint **P.O.Y.:** Matt Fisher **Top Scorer:** Robbie Orton 41
Honours: Central Mids Lg Prem 97-98 R-up 91-92, Div 1 90-91, (Res Prem 96-97 97-98); Wakefield Floodlit Trophy 92-93 R-up 95-96; Ken Marsland Cup(Res) 93-94; Notts Amtr Lg 89-90 (Snr Cup R-up 89-90).

GOOLE AFC

Secretary: M E Norman, 10 High Ash Drive, Leeds LS17 8QY (0113 266 4900)
Manager: John Reed **Midweek Matchday:**
Ground & Directions: Victoria Pleasure Grounds, Marcus St, Goole (01405 762794). M62 JUnc 36 follow signs town centre. Turn right at 2nd lights into Boothferry Rd, 300 yards right again into Carter St, ground at end of road.
Colours: White with black trim/black/black & white **Change Colours:** Gold/black/gold & black

GRAHAM STREET PRIM.

Secretary: David Wright, 6 Athol Close, Sinfin Moor, Derby DE24 9L2 (01332 606837)
Manager: S Woodings **Midweek Matchday:** Tuesday
Ground & Directions: Carriage & Wagon Welfare Club, Longbridge Lane, off Ascot Drive, Derby (01332 571376) M1 Junc 25, take A52 to Derby, turn left onto A5111 ring road, Raynesway. Take left at next island Ascot Drive and first right into Longbridge Lane
Colours: Red (white trim)/black/red **Change Colours:** Yellow/black/black

GRIMETHORPE MINERS WELFARE

Secretary: Arthur Gill, 7 Duke Street, Grimethorpe, Barnsley, Yorks S72 7NJ (01226 712863)
Manager: Stewart Barrowclough **Midweek Matchday:** Tuesday or Wednesday
Ground & Directions: Grimethorpe Miners Welfare, Cemetery Road, Grimethorpe. (01226 711544), A1M to A635 Hickleton to Thurnscoe, turn right to Houghton, At Robin Hood, turn left to Grimethorpe M1 junc 36. A628 to Shafton traffic lights, turn right to Grimethorpe.
Colours: All Blue & black **Change Colours:** All red

HARWORTH COLLIERY INSTITUTE

Secretary: Tom Brogan, 30 Lindsey Road, Harworth, Doncaster, Sth Yorks DN11 8QH (01302 750132).
Manager: Alan Needham **Midweek Matchday:** Wednesday
Ground & Directions: Recreation Ground, Scrooby Rd, Bircotes, Doncaster (01302 750614). Off A1(M) at Blyth, head towards Bawtry for approx 2 miles, take third left, ground in village at top of hill on left. Or, from Doncaster to Bawtry then head for A1(M) and turn left after caravan site - ground at top of hill.
Colours: Amber & black/black/amber & black **Change Colours:** Red & blue/red/red
Honours: Wharncliffe Charity Cup 62-63 74-75, Central Midlands League 87-88 (Runners-up 86-87, Challenge Cup 86-87 87-88, F'lit Cup 91-92 (Runners-up 89-90)), Sheffield Senior League 64-65 74-75, Sheffield & Hallamshire Senior Cup SF 87-88

HEANOR TOWN

Secretary: Keith Costello, 45 Stainsby Avenue, Heanor, Derbyshire DE75 7EL (01773 719446).
Manager: Bill Fossey **Midweek Matchday:** Wednesday
Ground & Directions: The Town Ground, Mayfield Avenue, Heanor (01773 713742/715815). M1 (J26), take A610 onto A608, ground 200yds from Market Square
Colours: White/black/black **Change Colours:** All red or all blue
Honours: Central Midlands League Cup 94-95 (Runners-up 86-87 92-93, B E Webbe Removals Cup 88-89), West Midlands Reg. League Runners-up 72-73; Midland Co's League Runners-up 65-66 67-68; Derbys Senior Cup(9) 1892-94 1946-47 65-69 70-71 78-79; FA Cup 1st Rd 58-59 63-64.

HUCKNALL ROLLS

Secretary: Peter Williams, 38 Tiverton Close, Hucknall, Nottingham NG15 6JT (0115 956 33691)
Manager: Roger Dawkins **Midweek Matchday:** Wednesday
Ground & Directions: Rolls Royce Sports & Social Club, Watnall Road, Hucknall Notts (0115 963 0134). M1 Junc 27. Follow sign A611 to Hucknall. Turn right on to by-pass. 2nd r/about turn right on to Watnall Road. Take 2nd left after fire station on R.R. Sports Ground
Colours: Blue & black/black/black **Change colours:** White/blue/white

KIMBERLEY TOWN

Chairman: George Giddens **Vice Chairman:** Reg Izzard **President:** Russell Penney
Match Secretary: Alan Jennings, 8 Watchwood Grove, Calverton, Nottingham NG14 6HX (0115 965 6100)
Manager: Andy Freeman **Gen Manager:** Brian Harrison **Press Officer:** Richard Jayes
Ground & Directions: Stag Ground, Nottingham Road, Kimberley (0115 9382788). Through Nuthall from M1 jct 26 to Kimberley, ground entrance 150 yds after Stag Inn.
Seats: None **Cover:** 150 **Capacity:** 2,500 **Floodlights:** Yes **Nickname:** Stags
Clubhouse: Evenings (Except Sun) & matchdays. Hot & cold snacks available
Programme: 40 pages 50p **Editor:** George Brown **Midweek Matchday:** Tuesday
Colours: Blue & white/white/red **Change colours:** Blue/white/white
Honours: Notts Amateur Lg Div 1 54-55, Central Alliance Div 2 R-up 57-58.

Long Eaton United — Photo: Martin Wray

Goole AFC

Hucknall Rolls Royce — Photo: Bill Wheatcroft

LONG EATON UNITED

Chairman: J C Fairley **Vice Chairman:**
Secretary: David Hampson, 4 Airedale Close, Long Eaton, Nottingham. NG10 3HW (0115-9726343.
Manager: John Bartlett **Physio:** John Burns
Ground & Directions: Grange Park, Station Road, Long Eaton, Nottingham (0115 9735700). M1 Junc 25, take A52 towards Nottingham, to island by 'Bardills Garden Centre', left onto B6003 to t/lights. Turn right A453 and take 2nd left into Station Rd. Entrance on left opposite the Speedway Stadium
Seats: None **Cover:** 500 **Capacity:** 5,000 **Floodlights:** Yes **Shop:** No
Clubhouse: Open matchdays, snacks available
Programme: 20 pages 50p **Editor:** G Whitehead **Press Officer:** Secretary
Sponsor: Beeston Suite Co **Nickname:** Blues **Founded:** 1956
Colours: Blue & black/black/black **Change colours:** Yellow/green/blue
Midweek Matchday: Tuesday **Record Attendance:** 2,000 1973 FA Cup
Honours: Derbys Snr Cup 64-65 75-76, Midland Co's Lg R-up 76-77, Central Alliance Div South 58-59, Northern Co's (East) Div 1 South 84-85.

MICKLEOVER SPORTS

Secretary: Tony Shaw, 80 Onslow Road, Mickleover, Derbyshire DE3 5JB (01332 512826)
Manager: Mark Kelsey **Midweek Matchday:** Wednesday
Ground & Directions: Mickleover Sports Ground, Station Rd, Mickleover, Derby (01332 521167). Derby ring road A38 to A52, turn off at Markeaton Park Island. Take turn to Ashbourne A52, 2nd left into Radbourne Lane. Take 3rd left into Station Road, ground on corner.
Colours: White/black/black **Change Colours:** All blue

NETTLEHAM

Secretary: John Wilson, 21 Chancer Drive, Lincoln LN2 4LN (01522 884051).
Manager: Ian Musson **Midweek Matchday:** Tuesday
Ground & Directions: Mulsanne Park, Field Close, Nettleham (01522 750007). A46 approx. 3 miles north of Lincoln, right at Brown Cow Pub, proceed past Church 2nd turning on right, ground at end
Colours: Blue/blue/yellow **Change Colours:** All Red
Honours: Central Mids Lg Premier Division Cup R-up 87-88, Village Tphy, Nursing Cup, Kelly Read Cup, Blankney Hunt Cup, Lincoln & Dist. Amtr Cup R-up, Joe Miller Tphy(2).

SANDIACRE TOWN

Secretary: Adie Barrow, 8 Gatcombe Grove, Sandiacre, Nottingham NG10 5PN (0115 949 1946)
Manager: Ged Le Blond **Asst Manager:**
Ground & Directions: St Giles Park, Stanton Road, Sandiacre, Nottingham NG10 5EP (0115 939 2880). M1 jct 25, follow signs to Sandiacre passing Post House Hotel on right, straight over crossroads into Rushy Lane and towards Stanton Rd, 1st right after 1000yds into Stanton Rd, ground at bottom after another 1000yds.
Seats: None **Cover:** 250 **Capacity:** 2,000 **Floodlights:** Yes **Shop:** No
Clubhouse: Members Club 8-11pm. Sunday lunchtimes, Saturday 3.45-11pm. Snacks available
Programme: 44 pages 50p **Editor:** Mel Williams (0115 917 4079) **Press Officer:** Josie Le-Blond
Founded: 1978 **Nickname:** Saints **Midweek Matchday:** Tuesday
Colours: Navy/red **Change colours:** Yellow/sky/yellow
97-98 Captain: Bob Parker **P.o.Y.:** Lee Beck **Top Scorer:** Leigh Vickers
Honours: Central Mids Lg Premier Div 92-93 (Lg Cup 92-93), Midlands Regional Alliance R-up 91-92, Central Mids Lge Cup R-up 95-96.

SHIREBROOK TOWN

Secretary: Steve Wall, 26 Carter Lane West, Shirebrook, Mansfield, Notts NG20 8NA (01623 747638).
Manager: S Greenwood, G Charlesworth **Midweek Matchday:** Tuesday
Ground & Directions: BRSA Sports Ground, Langwith Rd, Shirebrook, Mansfield (01623 742535). M1 jct 29, A617 to Mansfield, 2.5 miles, onto B6407 to Shirebrook, through town to Langwith Rd.
Colours: All Red & black **Change Colours:** Blue & black/blue/blue
Honours: Central Midlands League Reserve Prem Div 94-95 95-96.

SNEINTON

Secretary: Albert Graves, 32 Shelford Road, Gedling, Nottingham NG4 4HW (0115 9878185)
Manager: Tom Brookbanks/Neil Cooper **Midweek Matchday:** Tuesday
Ground & Directions: Stoke Lane Gedling, Nottingham, A612 Nottingham to Southwell Road. Stoke Lane is situated off A612 between Gedling & Burton Joyce (signed Stoke Bardolph). Ground 200 yards on left over level crossing
Colours: Blue & black/black/black **Change Colours:** Green & white/white & green/white

SOUTH NORMANTON ATHLETIC

Secretary: Bob Ravenhall. 6 Carter Lane West, South Normanton, Alfreton, Derbyshire DE55 2DX (01773 8612363
Manager: **Midweek Matchday:** Wednesday
Ground & Directions: South Normanton Athletic FC, Lees Lane, South Normanton, Derby (01773 581491). M1 Junc 28, B6019 towards South Normanton, right after 1 mile (in South Normanton) at Mobil garage into Market Street, after quarter mile turn left immediately after The Clock pub into Lees Lane, ground at bottom
Colours: Yellow/navy/yellow **Change colours:** Black & white/black/black

PREMIER DIVISION CLUBS 1998-99

ASKERN WELFARE

Secretary: Miss Lynn Sudworth, Hollycroft, Main St, Stillington, York YO6 1JU (01347 810038)
Manager: Ron Pounder **Midweek Matchday:** Wednesday
Ground & Directions: Askern Welfare Sports Ground, Doncaster Road, Askern, Doncaster (01302 700957). A1/A639 Pontefract. Follow sign for Askern/Campsall. At T-junction right. Left at Anne Arms, right at Supersave, ground on right.
Colours: White (navy trim)/navy/navy & white **Change Colours:** Orange/white/yellow

BLACKWELL MINERS WELFARE

Secretary: Robin Ward, 47 Gladstone Avenue, Blackwell, Alfreton, Derbys DE55 5JU (01773 811691).
Manager: Barrie Brady **Midweek Matchday:** Tuesday
Ground & Directions: Welfare Ground, Primrose Hill, Blackwell, Derbyshire DE55 5JE. (01773 811295). M1 Junc 28, A38 towards Mansfield, left onto B6406, left again at Hilcote Arms, ground 1 mile on left just past Miners Welfare.
Colours: Red & black stripes/black/red **Change colours:** Green/white/green

GREENWOOD MEADOWS

Secretary: Brain Hall, 34 Sullivan Close, Marmion Estate, St Ann's, Nottingham NG3 2HX (0115 958 2459)
Manager: G Walker **Midweek Matchday:**
Ground & Directions: Greenwood Meadows (0115 986 5913). M1 Junc 24 take A453 Nottingham-Clifton Bridge to Lenton Ind Estate. Left into Old Lenton Lane. Ground second on right on lane.
Colours: Green & white/green/green **Change Colours:** Red & black/black/black

HEMSWORTH TOWN

Secretary: Mike Pickering, 1 Sycamore Road, Hemsworth, Nr Pontefract, West Yorks WF9 4PD (01977 613974)
Manager: Sammy Waugh **Midweek Matchday:** Wednesday
Ground & Directions: Hemsworth Town FC, Sports Complex, Kirby Road, Hemsworth
Directions: M1 to M18 to A1M.North to A638 Wakefield Road, 3 miles turn off left. Signposted Langwaite Grange Ind Est (Netto). 2 miles on join B6422 Hemsworth. 2 miles further on in Hemsworth, ground 400 yards on left after Fina garage
Colours: Red/red/red & white **Change Colours:** All navy

HOLBROOK

Secretary: Stevan Broadhurst, 35 Laund Hill, Belper, Derbys. DE56 1FH (01773 821483)
Manager: Grant Woodside **Midweek Matchday:** Tuesday
Ground & Directions: The Welfare Ground, Shaw Lane, Holbrook, Derbyshire (01332 880259), From A38 take B6179 for Kilburn, turn left at lights for Belper. 1 mile on left at Bulls Head for Holbrook. 2 miles on turn right at Venture garage into Shaws Lane.
Colours: Blue & White/blue/blue & white **Change Colours:** Red & white/red/red

LINCOLN MOORLANDS

Secretary: Colin Edwards, 5 Lansdowne Ave, Lincoln LN6 7PU (01522 520857)
Manager: Gary Goddard **Midweek Matchday:**
Ground & Directions: Moorland Sports Ground, Newark Road, Lincoln (01522 520184). From Newark enter Lincoln on A1434, go past Forum Shopping Centre 500 yds. Ground on left sign Moorland Club.
Colours: Yellow & blue/yellow & blue/blue **Change colours:** White/black/black

MEXBOROUGH ATHLETIC (OAKHOUSE)

Secretary: Nev Wheeler, 15 Holmshaw Drive, Sheffield, South Yorkshire S13 8UJ (0114 2694142).
Manager: Nev Wheeler **Midweek Matchday:** Tuesday
Ground & Directions: Mexborough Athletic Club, New Oxford Road, Mexborough (01709 583426). M18 Junc 2, join A1 for 1 junc. Take Sheffield/Rotherham road to Conisborough, take right beside castle to Denaby. Go through Denaby to r/about at Mexborough, take right turn into Adwick Road, ground on left
Colours: All blue & white **Change colours:** Red and Navy/black/black.

MICKLEOVER ROYAL BRITISH LEGION

Secretary: Ray Taylor, 15 Inglwood Avenue, Mickleover, Derby DE3 5RT (01332 515047).
Manager: Kevin Morton **Midweek Matchday:** Tuesday
Ground & Directions: Mickleover RBL, Ypres Lodge, Western Road, Mickleover (01332 513548). On west side of Derby off A38, 1/2 mile from Mickleover Village centre.
Colours: Yellow/royal/royal **Change Colours:** Tangerine/black/black

RADFORD

Secretary: R W Thomas, 7 Warrener Grove, Heronbridge, Nottingham NG5 9BN (0115 955 3905)
Manager: Terry Lack **Midweek Matchday:** Tuesday
Ground & Directions: Radford Road, Radford, Nottm (0115 943250). M1 Junc 26, take A610 to Nottingham, at duel carriageway turn left. Move to right lane and go immediately right into Wilkinson St. At top turn right & right again at 2nd crossing.
Colours: Black & white/black/black **Change colours:** Blure & white/white/white

SELSTON

Secretary: Alan Jones, 6 Derwent Drive, Selston, Nott NG16 6QU (01773 580436)
Manager: Wayne Bradley **Midweek Matchday:**
Ground & Directions: Mansfield Hosiery Mills Sports Ground, Mansfield Road, Sutton in Ashfield, Notts (01623 552376). M1 junc 28, take A38 Mansfield, pass through 7 sets of lights to island (Kings Mill Hospital), ground oposite McDonalds on left
Colours: Black & white/black & blue/black & white **Change Colours:** Yellow & green/sky/yellow & green

SHARDLOW St JAMES

Secretary: Reg Symcox, 22 West End Drive, Shardlow, Derby DE7 2GY (01332 792733).
Manager: Dave Spencer **Midweek Matchday:** Wednesday
Ground & Directions: The Wharf, Shardlow, Derby. (01332 799135), M1 Junc 24, A6 Derby/Leicester, 6 miles out of Derby at Shardlow take next left after Shardlow church (on right), ground 100yds on left.
Colours: White & blue/white/white **Change colours:** Tangerine/black/tangerine

SHEEPBRIDGE

Secretary: D G Barnes, 22 Windsor Drive, Wingerworth, Chesterfield, Derbyshire S42 6TJ (01246 277445)
Manager: P Sindall/R Lilley **Midweek Matchday:** Wednesday
Ground & Directions: GKN Sports Ground, Newbold Road, Chesterfield, (01246 234282), M1 Junc 30, Follow signs to Chesterfield use bypass and on reaching island with Tesco store follow signs for Newbold. Ground on the Newbold Road.
Colours: Blue & white/blue/blue **Change colours:** Red & white/white/red

SHEFFIELD HALLAM UNIVERSITY

Secretary: Stephen Wright, 198 Holme Lane, Malin Bridge, Sheffield S6 4JZ (0378 481483)
Manager: John Warnock **Midweek Matchday:** Monday
Ground & Directions: Aurora Sports & Social Club, Bawtry Rd, Brinsworth, Rotherham (01709 372613), M1 junc 34, take A631 Bawtry Rd, ground 1 mile on right.
Colours: Red/black/red **Change Colours:** All blue

SOUTH NORMANTON ATHLETIC

Secretary: Bob Ravenhall. 6 Carter Lane West, South Normanton, Alfreton, Derbyshire DE55 2DX (01773 8612363
Manager: **Midweek Matchday:** Wednesday
Ground & Directions: South Normanton Athletic FC, Lees Lane, South Normanton, Derby (01773 581491). M1 Junc 28, B6019 towards South Normanton, right after 1 mile (in South Normanton) at Mobil garage into Market Street, after quarter mile turn left immediately after The Clock pub into Lees Lane, ground at bottom
Colours: Yellow/navy/yellow **Change colours:** Black & white/black/black

STANTON ILKESTON

Secretary: Mrs S Smedley, 4 Queens Avenue, Ilkeston, Derbyshire DE7 4DL (0115 9323772)
Manager: J Smedley/C Trueman **Midweek Matchday:** Monday or Wednesday
Ground & Directions: Hallam Fields Sports Ground, Stanton Club, Hallam Fields, Nr Ilkeston, Derbys (0115 9323244), M1 (J26), take A52 Nottingham, then A6002 for Ilkeston. Follow road through t/lights, turn right at next lights. Follow road to Rutland Windows. Turn left into Thurman St, to top turn left ground 200 yds right.
Colours: Blue & white/blue/blue **Change Colours:** Yellow/blue/blue

TEVERSAL GRANGE

Secretary: Kevin Newton, 8 Vere Ave., Sutton in Ashfield, Notts NG17 2ES (01623 511402).
Ground: Teversal Grange Country Inn, Carnarvon Street, Teversal, Notts **Colours:** Red & black/black

THORNE COLLIERY

Secretary: Glyn Jones, Top Town Social, Frederick Street, Grimsby DN31 1RG (01472 350554)
Manager: Paul Morrell
Ground & Directions: Miners Welfare, Grange Road, Moorends, Thorne, Doncaster. (01374 996474), M18 Junc 6, in THorne, turnat lights to Moorends, go almost through village, Grange Road on right.
Seats: Yes **Cover:** Yes **Floodlights:** No **Club Shop:** No
Colours: Green/black/black **Change Colours:** Yellow/green/yellow
Programme: 44 pages £1 incl entry **Editor:** Stuart Robinson, (01405 814441)
Sponsors: National Deposit Friendly Society Ltd **Midweek Matchday:** Tuesday
Previous Leagues: Yorkshire, NCEL, Doncaster Sen.
Clubhouse: No, but refreshments available on matchdays. Use Red Bear in Thorne.

WELBECK COLLIERY WELFARE

Secretary: Mr Ron Turner, 75 Hamilton Drive, Warsop, Mansfield, Notts NG20 0EY (01623 847738).
Ground: Elksley Road, Meden Vale (01623 842611) **Colours:** Black & yellow/black.
Hons: Notts Alliance Div 2 93-94 (Intermediate Cup 93-94), Chesterfield & District Lg 92-93.

YORKSHIRE MAIN

Secretary: Dennis Tymon, 22 Pamela Drive, Warmsworth, Doncaster DN4 9RP (01302 852455)
Manager: Derek Wynne **Midweek Matchday:**
Ground & Directions: Yorkshire Main Welfare, Edlington Lane, Edlington, Doncaster (01709 864075). A1M junc 36. Proceed on A630 towards Rotherham. At 1st lights turn on to B6376. Ground on left after Fire Station.
Colours: Red/black/red **Change colours:** All White

Sheepbridge FC Photo: Bill Wheatcroft

POWERLEAGUE
NOTTS FOOTBALL ALLIANCE

Founded 1894

Chairman: Alan Wright
10 Farady Road, Mansfield. NG18 4ES
Tel: 01623 624379 (H) 01623 553237 (B)

General Secretary & Treasurer: Godfrey Stafford
7 The Rushes, Gotham, Nottingham. NG11 0HY. Tel: 01509 820737

1997-98 HONOURS LIST

Senior Division	
Champions	**Boots Athletic**
Runners Up	**Welbeck C.W.**
First Division	
Champions	**Basford United**
Runners Up	**Bilsthorpe C.W.**
Second Division	
Champions	**Matrixgrade F.C.**
Runners Up	**Magdala Arms**
Senior Cup	
Champions	**Boots Athletic**
Runners Up	**Notts Police**
Intermediate Cup	
Champions	**Southwell City Res.**
Runners Up	**Matrixgrade F.C.**

SENIOR DIV.	P	W	D	L	F	A	Pts
Boots Athletic	30	27	1	2	88	29	82
Welbeck C.W.	30	22	3	5	75	37	69
Pelican F.C.	30	18	7	5	53	40	61
Notts Police	30	18	4	8	64	32	58
Rainworth M.W.	30	14	7	9	58	45	49
Linbyy C.W.	30	14	7	9	61	50	49
Southwell City	30	13	4	13	49	42	43
Attenborough F.C.	30	13	4	13	50	58	43
Ruddington Utd.	30	11	6	13	37	60	39
Ollerton Town	30	10	4	16	35	72	34
Keyworth Utd.	30	8	6	16	37	86	30
Thoresby C.W.	30	8	6	16	33	76	30
Wollaton F.C.	30	7	6	17	30	58	27
Cotgrave C.W.	30	6	7	17	28	88	25
Retford Utd.	30	6	4	20	46	62	22
Awsworth Villa	30	5	4	21	33	86	19

FIRST DIV.	P	W	D	L	F	A	Pts
Basford Utd.	30	20	6	4	74	32	66
Bilsthorpe C.W.	30	19	6	5	65	28	63
Kimberley M.W.	30	19	4	7	117	72	61
Abacus F.C.	30	19	3	8	88	34	60
Worth Simpson	30	17	4	9	89	44	55
Beeston Town	30	15	7	8	71	42	52
Bestwood M.W.	30	16	6	8	83	41	*51
Teversal Garage	30	14	5	11	70	58	47
Wollaton F.C. Res.	30	11	6	13	60	62	39
Boots Ath. Res.	30	12	3	15	63	67	39
Clifton F.C.	30	11	4	15	57	74	37
Radcliffe Olympic	30	10	5	15	47	56	35
Gedling M.W.	30	11	2	17	58	70	35
City & Sherwood	30	7	1	22	47	106	22
Rainworth M.W. Res.	30	6	0	24	42	117	18
Carlton D.C.	30	1	2	27	28	156	5

SECOND DIV.	P	W	D	L	F	A	Pts
Matrixgrade F.C.	28	21	5	2	95	26	68
Magdala Amateurs	28	17	4	7	72	40	55
Southbank F.C.	28	16	4	8	71	42	52
Chaffoteux F.C.	28	15	5	8	73	49	50
Calverton M.W.	28	14	4	10	57	51	46
Southewell C. Res.	28	13	6	9	59	40	45
East Leake Ath.	28	12	7	9	69	47	43
Pelican F.C. Res.	28	10	8	10	51	60	38
Worth Simp. Res.	28	10	4	14	43	72	34
Newark F.C.	28	9	6	13	56	67	33
Retford Utd. Res.	28	9	5	14	44	57	32
Basford Utd. Res.	28	9	5	14	41	76	32
Ruddington U. Res.	28	7	7	14	43	65	28
Attenborough Res.	28	7	4	17	38	72	25
Keyworth U. Res.	28	2	4	22	24	72	10

SENIOR DIVISION 1998-99

ATTENBOROUGH

Secretary: Terry Allen, 3 Firth Close, Arnold, Nottingham NG5 8RU (0115 920 0698)
Ground & Directions: The Village Green, The Strand, Attenborough, Beeston, Nottingham. Midway between Beeston & Long Eaton on A6005 - adjacent to Nature Reserve (via Attenborough Lane).
Colours: All blue **Change cols:** White/black/black.

BASFORD UNITED

Secretary: S Thompson, 2 Haddon Road, West Brdgford, Nottm NG12 6EQ (0115 914 1940)
Ground: Greenwich Avenue, Bagnall Road, Basford, Nottm (0115 942 3918).
Directions: M1 (J26) follow signs 'A610 Nottingham' then 'B6004 Arnold' into Mill Street.
Colours: Black, yellow & purple/black

BILSTHORPE COLLIERY WELFARE

Secretary: Les Lee, 18 The Hollies, Rainworth, Mansfield, (01623 490053)
Ground: Eakring Road, Bilsthorpe, Notts **Colours:** Red/black

BOOTS ATHLETIC

Secretary: Ian Whitehead, 21 Rosthwaite Close, West Bridgford, Nottingham NG2 6RA (01159 812830).
Ground: Lady Bay, West Bridgford, Nottingham (01159 822392). **Colours:** White/black.
Hons: Notts Alliance Div 1 91-92 (Lg Cup 91-92), Notts Snr Cup R-up 93-94, Notts Inter R-up 91-92.

COTGRAVE COLLIERY WELFARE

Secretary: Kevin Whitehead, 51 Cross Hill, Cotgrave, Nottinham. (0115 9894043)
Ground: Cotgrave Welfare. **Colours:** Yellow/black.

KEYWORTH UNITED

Secretary: M Simpson, 25 Waddington Drive, Wilford Hill, West Bridgford, Nottm NG2 7GT (0115 923 2921)
Ground: Platt Lane, Keyworth (0115 937 5998) **Colours:** Green/black

LINBY COLLIERY WELFARE

Secretary: Frank Taylor, 6 Beech Avenue, Hucknall, Nottingham, NG15 7FH (0115 952 9633)
Ground: Church Lane, Linby **Colours:** Red/White

NOTTINGHAMSHIRE POLICE

Secretary: John Beeston, 17 Alandene Ave, Watnall, Nottingham NG16 1HH (0115 938 2110)
Ground: Police Training Centre, Epperstone, Notts. **Colours:** White/navy.
Hons: Notts Snr R-up 91-92, Notts All. Div 1 & Lge Snr Cup R-up 85-86, PAAN Nat. K-O Comp 63-64.

OLLERTON TOWN

Secretary: Jack Graham, 73 Petersmith Drive, New Ollerton, Mansfield, Notts NG22 9SD (01623 863127)
Ground: Walesby Lane, New Ollerton, Notts
Colours: Red & black/black

PELICAN

Secretary: Dave Eastwood, 42 Chetwin Road, Bilborough, Nottm NG8 4HN (01159 138345).
Ground: Brian Wakefield Sports Ground, Lenton Lane, Nottm (0115 986 8255)
Colours: All Blue. **Hons:** Notts Alliance Lg Cup 90-91 (R-up 91-92 93-94).

RAINWORTH MINERS WELFARE

Secretary: Alan Wright, 10 Faraday Road, Mansfield NG18 4ES (01623 24379).
Ground: Kirklington Road, Rainworth, Notts
Directions: On A617 Mansfield - Newark Road. **Colours:** All White
Hons: Notts Alliance 77-78 78-79 79-80 80-81 81-82 82-83 (R-up 93-94, Lg Cup 81-82), Notts Snr Cup 80-81 81-82 (R-up 82-83 92-93), FA Vase R-up 82-82, Thorn EMI F'lit Cup R-up 82-83 83-84 84-85.

RETFORD UNITED

Secretary: Jeff Lamb, 18 Northumbria Drive, Retford, Notts, DN22 7PR (01777 705833)
Ground: Oaklands Lane (Off London Road), Retford. **Colours:** Black & white stripes/black

RUDDINGTON

Secretary: John Fisk, 3 Savages Road, Ruddington, Nottm NG11 6EW (0115 984 2552).
Ground & Directions: The Elms Park Ground, Loughborough Road, Ruddington (01159 844976. On A60 Nottm to Loughborough, 5 miles out of Nottingham.
Colours: Red & blue stripes/blue. **Honours:** Notts Comb. Lg 79-80 (Lg Cup 70-71 76-77 80-81).

SOUTHWELL CITY

Secretary: P K Johnson, 63 The Ropewalk, Southwell, Notts NG25 0AL (01636 812594).
Ground: War Memorial Ground, Bishops Drive, Southwell, Notts, (01636 814386)
Colours: Black & white stripes/black

THORESBY COLLIERY WELFARE

Secretary: Brian Wathall, 29 First Ave., Edwinstowe, Nr Mansfield NG21 9NZ (01623 823885).
Ground: Thoresby Colliery, Fourth Avenue, Edwinstowe, Nr Mansfield. **Colours:** Blue/white.

WOLLATON

Secretary: Andrew Moon, 150 Wollaton Vale, Wollaton, Nottm NG8 2PL (0115 928 1215).
Ground: Wollaton Cricket & Sports Club, Wollaton Village, Nottm (0115 928 9748).
Colours: Sky/maroon **Hons:** Notts All. Div 1 R-up 92-93 (Div 2 91-92 (I'mediate Cup R-up 91-92)).

DIVISION ONE CLUBS 1998-99

ABACUS

Secretary: Stephen Bingley, 6 Brisbane Close, Mansfield Woodhouse NG19 8QZ (01623 23072).
Ground: Sherwood Colliery Sports Ground, Debdale Lane, Mansfield Woodhouse, Notts.
Colours: Black & white stripes.

AWSWORTH VILLA

Secretary: Keith Slaney, 24 Attewell Road, Awsworth, Nottm NG16 2SY (0602 302514).
Ground: Shilo Park, off Attewell Road, Awsworth. **Colours:** Red & white & black/black

BEESTON TOWN

Secretary: Andy Meakin, 26 Redland Drive, Chilwell, Nottingham NG9 5LE (0115 967 7520
Ground: University Ground, Nottingham **Colours:** All white

BESTWOOD MINERS WELFARE

Secretary: Mrs Alana Jackson, 9 Derwent Drive, Hucknall, Nottm NG15 6DS (0115 953 8561)
Ground: Bestwood Workshops, Park Rd, Bestwood **Colours:** Navy & red/navy

CITY & SHERWOOD HOSPITALS

Secretary: Alan Bird, 72 Bilborough Rd, Nottm NG8 4DW (0115 928 5507)
Ground: M.O.D. Chilwell (0115 925 4811) **Colours:** All blue

CLIFTON

Secretary: Keith Elliott, 61 Greencroft, Clifton Est., Nottm NG11 8GJ (0115 921 5401)
Ground: Green Lane, Clifton Est., Nottm (0115 921 5113) **Colours:** All white

GEDLING MINERS WELFARE

Secretary: Mrs Maureen Chambers, 8 Fraser Road, Carlton, Nottm NG4 1NJ (0115 961 2994)
Ground: Gedling Colliery Welfare, Plains Road, Mapperley (0115 926 6300) **Colours:** Yellow & blue/blue

KIMBERLEY MINERS WELFARE

Secretary: Graham Rowley, 47 Noel Street, Kimberley, Nottingham NG16 2NF (0115 938 9151)
Ground: Didby Street, Kimberley, Nottingham **Colours:** Black & red/black

MAGDALA AMATEURS

Secretary: Alan Gilmour, 9 Adbolton Grove, West Bridgford, Nottingham NG2 5AR (0115 982 1071)
Ground: Civil Service Sports Ground, Wilford Lane, W Bridgford. **Colours:** Maroon & sky/sky/sky

RADCLIFFE OLYMPIC

Secretary: C Johnson, 2 The Firs, Holme Pierrepoint, Nottingham NG12 2LT (0115 933 3791)
Ground: Wharf Lane, Radcliffe-on-Trent, Nottingham **Colours:** Blue/red

SOUTHBANK

WORTHINGTON SIMPSONS

Secretary: Alan Allam, 11 Graham Close, Balderton, Newark, Notts NG24 3EW (01636 72430)
Ground: Lowfields Works, off Hawton Lane, Baldeton, Newark, Notts (01636 702672).
Colours: Yellow/black **Hons:** Notts Alliance Lg Cup (Intermediate Cup(res) 92-93 (R-up 93-94)).

This Division also includes the Reserve sides of: Boots Athletic, Rainworth MW, Wollaton.

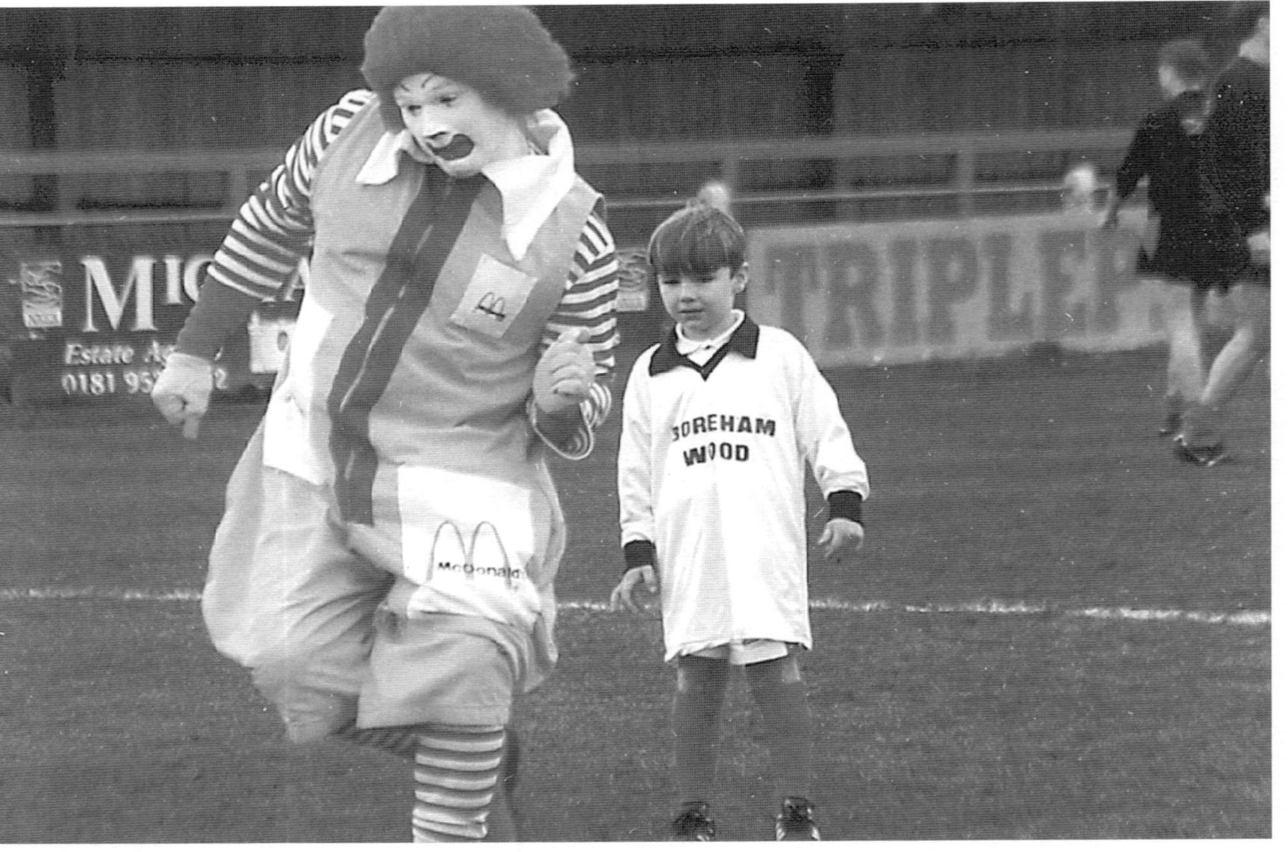

The Boreham Wood strike force had a good season last year
Photo: Clive S Butchins

EAST MIDLANDS FINAL LEAGUE TABLES 1997-98

EAST MIDLANDS ALLIANCE

PREMIER DIV	*P*	*W*	*D*	*L*	*F*	*A*	*Pts*
Corby Pegasus	22	19	3	0	81	21	60
Corby Danesholme	22	15	1	6	68	33	46
Kettering Nomads	22	14	1	7	51	29	43
Barton & Briars	22	10	3	9	50	54	33
Islip United	22	8	6	8	39	42	30
Corby Strip Mills	22	9	3	10	40	48	30
Corby St Brendans	22	8	2	12	40	44	26
Corby Darleydale	22	7	3	12	35	50	24
Weldon	22	6	5	11	45	53	23
Gretton	22	7	1	14	38	61	22
Kettering Generals	22	6	4	12	37	62	22
Corby Locomotive	22	6	2	14	36	63	20

MIDLAND FLOODLIT YOUTH LEAGUE

NORTHERN DIV	*P*	*W*	*D*	*L*	*F*	*A*	*Pts*
Leicester City	20	18	0	2	75	12	54
Burton Albion	20	16	1	3	79	18	49
Quorn	20	15	0	5	61	23	*42
Hinckley United	20	11	5	4	47	21	38
Barrow Town	20	10	1	9	45	39	31
Holwell Sports	20	7	5	8	25	33	26
Gresley Rovers	20	9	1	10	35	50	*25
VS Rugby	20	6	1	13	43	57	19
Ford Sports	20	3	3	14	19	66	12
Ibstock Welfare	20	2	4	14	21	65	10
Bardon Hill Spts	20	2	1	17	18	83	7

MIDLANDS (REGIONAL) ALLIANCE

PREMIER DIV	*P*	*W*	*D*	*L*	*F*	*A*	*Pts*
Siemans FC	34	21	7	6	78	44	70
Eastwood Tn Res	34	20	6	8	97	41	66
Matlock Tn Res	34	20	6	8	75	53	66
Santos FC	34	18	11	5	84	46	65
Arnold Tn Res	34	16	9	9	70	49	57
Hucknall Tn Res	34	15	8	11	65	58	53
Ilkeston Tn Res	34	14	9	11	93	62	51
Brailsford FC	34	13	8	13	59	58	47
Belper Tn Res	34	11	9	14	70	67	42
Littleover Irongate	34	10	12	12	48	72	42
Rowsley 86	34	10	11	13	62	62	41
Butterley Brick	34	11	8	15	55	57	41
Derby Rolls-Royce	34	11	8	15	68	86	41
Holbrook St M	34	11	7	16	55	63	40
Slack & Parr	34	10	7	17	51	79	37
Belper Utd	34	9	9	16	52	79	36
Borrowash V Res	34	8	8	18	43	75	32
Wirksworth Town	34	4	5	25	29	103	17

EAST MIDLANDS SENIOR LEAGUE

PREMIER DIV	*P*	*W*	*D*	*L*	*F*	*A*	*Pts*
Melbourne Dynamo	24	18	3	3	96	29	57
Royal Crown '96	24	16	4	4	70	34	52
Allestree	24	16	3	5	89	43	51
AFC Highfields	24	12	4	8	55	46	40
Allenton Ath	24	12	3	9	54	44	39
Findern	24	10	8	6	60	44	38
Grenville Ath	24	10	7	7	62	62	37
Alv & Boulton	24	11	1	12	61	62	34
TS Rail	24	8	4	12	53	56	28
FC Napier	24	7	3	14	32	61	24
Derventio	24	6	2	16	51	92	20
Stanley Common	24	4	1	19	55	104	13
Aston	24	3	3	18	32	93	12

P J MCGINTY & SONS SUFFOLK & IPSWICH LEAGUE

SENIOR DIVISION	*P*	*W*	*D*	*L*	*F*	*A*	*Pts*
Grundisburgh	30	22	2	6	79	29	46
Walton United	30	16	9	5	72	32	41
BS Fonnereau	30	13	11	6	68	50	37
Walshamle Wil	30	16	4	10	60	32	36
Haughley United	30	14	7	9	56	51	35
East Bergholt	30	12	7	11	53	47	31
Leiston Town	30	13	5	12	48	49	31
Stonham Aspal	30	13	4	13	44	50	30
Framlingham Tn	30	12	5	13	50	50	29
Ipswich Athleic	30	11	5	14	45	56	27
Achilles	30	11	4	15	45	65	26
Brantham & St	30	10	4	16	38	49	24
Westerfield Utd	30	8	8	14	37	55	24
BT Research	30	10	4	16	48	69	24
Kesgrave	30	9	5	16	32	49	23
Bramford Utd	30	6	4	20	37	79	16

TRAVIS PERKINS NORTHANTS COMBINATON

PREMIER DIV	*P*	*W*	*D*	*L*	*F*	*A*	*Pts*
Woodford United	28	26	1	1	136	30	79
Towcester Town	28	18	4	6	74	41	58
Pottersbury	28	15	8	5	93	54	53
Brixworth All St	28	14	4	10	67	49	46
Harpole	28	14	3	11	77	46	45
Kislingbury	28	14	3	11	77	46	45
Moulton-1	28	12	6	10	53	58	41
Northants Police	28	12	4	12	66	64	40
Weedon	28	12	4	12	49	54	40
Heyford Athletic	28	12	3	13	62	56	39
Spratton	28	10	6	12	48	50	36
West Haddon	28	9	5	14	40	52	32
Milton	28	5	6	17	41	82	21
Bugbrook St M A	28	3	6	19	37	92	15
Crick Athletic	28	2	1	25	23	157	7

BARRY FENTON & PARTNERS LINCOLNSHIRE LEAGUE

	P	*W*	*D*	*L*	*F*	*A*	*Pts*
Lincoln United	36	29	4	3	117	29	91
Barton Town OB	36	25	8	3	112	45	83
Grim & Imm Am	36	24	6	6	104	43	78
Sleaford Town	36	23	2	11	77	55	71
Linc Moorlands	36	22	6	8	97	39	69
Wyberton	36	19	6	11	84	64	63
Boston Utd Res	36	18	6	12	96	64	60
Bottesford Town	36	17	9	10	66	48	60
Limestone R	36	16	7	13	70	72	58
Louth Utd Amat	36	17	4	15	88	77	55
Grantham Tn Rs	36	16	6	14	78	77	54
Appleby Frod Ath	36	13	5	18	67	83	44
Ruston Sports	36	13	2	21	67	86	41
Skegness Town	36	11	5	20	64	81	38
Horncastle Tn	36	9	9	18	62	78	36
Epworth Tn LC	36	8	3	25	58	115	27
Hykeham Town	36	5	5	26	31	88	20
BRSA Retford	36	6	1	29	61	157	19
Nettleham Res	36	3	2	31	30	128	11

CAMBRIDGESHIRE LEAGUE

PREMIER DIV	*P*	*W*	*D*	*L*	*F*	*A*	*Pts*
Over Sports	28	19	3	6	68	25	60
Histon Res	28	19	2	7	66	33	59
Debden	28	16	4	8	63	40	52
Great Shelford	28	16	3	9	56	33	51
Girton United	28	15	4	9	54	44	49
Godmanchester Rv	28	14	4	10	76	61	46
Sawston United	28	13	6	9	71	52	45
Steeple Bumpstd	28	13	5	10	64	51	44
Newmarket T Rs	28	9	7	12	47	48	34
Waterbeach	28	8	5	15	52	75	29
Foxton	28	7	7	14	45	69	28
Cottenham Und	28	8	3	17	52	78	27
West Wratting	28	5	10	13	34	61	25
Cherry Hinton	28	7	3	18	36	78	24
Comberton Utd	28	5	6	17	31	66	21

PEARL ASSURANCE
PETERBOROUGH & DISTRICT

PREMIER DIV	*P*	*W*	*D*	*L*	*F*	*A*	*Pts*
Oundle Town	30	23	4	3	73	30	73
Moulton Harrox	30	20	6	4	94	29	66
Wisbech Town Rs	30	20	5	5	62	24	65
Ortonians	30	18	5	7	73	29	59
Deeping Rangers	30	16	5	9	76	41	53
Ryhall United	30	15	7	8	65	41	52
EyeUnited	30	14	6	10	49	38	48
Perkins Sports	30	15	1	14	58	56	45
Pinchbeek United	30	14	2	14	59	61	44
Hotpoint	30	10	4	16	39	62	34
Whittlesey United	30	9	6	15	51	61	33
Alconbury	30	7	7	16	47	68	27
Brotherhoods	30	8	4	18	35	65	27
Leverington Sports	30	5	5	20	32	74	20
Sford Belvedere	30	5	3	22	25	81	16
Pearl Assurance	30	3	6	21	41	109	14

TMS MOTOR GROUP LEICS & DISTRICT
VOLVO PREMIER DIVISION

	P	*W*	*D*	*L*	*F*	*A*	*Pts*
Thurmaston Town	24	20	2	2	101	18	62
Magna	24	16	3	5	64	26	51
Cosby United	24	14	5	5	73	40	47
GEC Spts & Social	24	15	1	8	54	27	46
Houghton Rangers	24	12	4	8	62	51	40
Beaumont Town	24	12	3	9	58	50	39
TWT Glenfield Tn	24	9	4	11	41	50	31
County Hill	24	8	6	10	40	62	30
Epworth	24	8	5	11	40	65	29
City Gas	24	6	2	16	30	65	20
Blaby Utd	24	6	1	20	24	53	19
Gynsill Lane	24	6	0	18	41	81	18
Lutterworth Ath	24	4	4	16	28	68	16

NORTHAMPTON TOWN FOOTBALL LEAGUE

PREMIER DIV	*P*	*W*	*D*	*L*	*F*	*A*	*Pts*
Roseberry Rangers	24	19	4	1	99	22	61
Queen Eleanor	24	18	3	3	111	24	57
Crusaders	24	18	3	3	87	30	57
Bective Wanderers	24	17	2	5	100	23	53
Wootton	24	15	2	7	74	32	47
Ashley Rovers	24	10	5	9	44	60	35
Kingsley Park	24	11	1	12	57	64	34
Kingsthorpe Wdrs	24	8	2	14	42	75	26
Dunston United	24	7	4	13	41	65	25
Northampton Pk	24	6	1	17	32	61	19
Kingsthorpe Nds	24	5	4	15	38	84	19
Pitsford Eagles	24	6	1	17	33	102	19
ON Chenecks A	24	0	0	24	17	133	0

DEMAGLASS
CHESTERFIELD & DISTRICT AMATEUR LEAGUE

PREMIER DIV	*P*	*W*	*D*	*L*	*F*	*A*	*Pts*
Holymoorside	22	18	2	2	89	21	56
Ashover	22	18	2	2	87	28	56
Marsh Lane	22	18	0	4	86	28	54
Mosborough	22	12	4	6	63	38	40
Killamarsh Jnrs	22	11	3	8	52	65	36
Broad Oaks	22	10	1	11	53	58	31
CSC	22	8	4	10	55	57	28
Unstone	22	7	3	12	44	66	24
Bookmakers	22	6	1	15	27	64	18
Renishaw	22	5	2	15	47	99	17
Mastin Moor	22	5	1	16	43	80	16
Creswell Park	22	2	1	19	38	79	7

Blunham FC - Bedford & District League (Premier) Champions and Brittania Cup Winners

Photo: Gordon Whittington

Shy? No - Neil Thaler comes from Whitby
Photo: K Rolfe

THE

ARNOTT Insurance

NORTHERN LEAGUE

Founded 1889

(The World's Second Oldest League)

FEEDER TO: NORTHERN PREMIER LEAGUE

President: George Courtney **Chairman:** Mike Amos

Hon Secretary & Treasurer: A Golightly

85 Park Road North, Chester-le-Street, Co Durham DH3 3SA

Tel: 0191 388 2056

The final paragraph of last season's Directory report was both optimistic and unequivocal. "The Vase final is on May 9 1998 and we anticipate a return" it said.

So, memorably, it proved. In all the happy years of the Vase, and of the FA Amateur Cup before it, there may never have been a story so memorable as Tow Law's, nor one that so perfectly captured the spirit of football at this level.

Tow Law, hitherto most famous for being just about the coldest spot in Britain, is a "town" of 2,200 people stuck perilously atop a west Durham ridge. The uncompromisingly named Ironworks Ground was built by striking workers, though both ironworks and coal mines have long gone.

Tow Law's spirit remained. In 1967 they beat Mansfield Town 5-1 in the FA Cup, drew with Shrewsbury in the second round and were drawn at home to Arsenal in the third. "The Gunners face a fate worse than death, Tow Law in winter" wrote Frank McGhee in the Daily Mirror. They didn't, the Lawyers lost the replay 6-2.

Bernard Fairbairn was club secretary in those days. He still is. Harry Hodgson and Harry Dixon both served 35 years as chairman and treasurer and were among the mass exodus to Wembley. The Northern League even won a famous victory before the match, persuading the FA at the highest level to overturn its ban on club mascot Sam Gordon leading out his heroes.

The ban had applied to all mascots in FA controlled games at Wembley; its lifting was equally universal. That there were also mascots in the FA Cup final - where the Northern League chairman shamelessly and stridently supported the Arsenal - was down to the Northern League and to Tow Law. The ban had attracted national publicity, and so, inevitably, did its removal: play it again, Sam.

Sadly the Lawyers lost to long time favourites Tiverton, 1-0 in a good, competitive game. Good luck to the winners, but they'd the advantage of warm weather training. . .

In the summer we had become the Arnott Insurance Northern League, a three year sponsorship from the Co Durham based, nationally expanding group. They have become active, interested sponsors and also presented a handsome new trophy for the League's player of the year - Trevor Laidler of Tow Law.

The League has also been much indebted to Darlington based North England newspapers, which met all the season's printing costs of Northern Ventures Northern Gains the much acclaimed League magazine - and has ensured that its cover price will remain at 30p for the foreseeable future. (Six issues £3.30, including postage: Don Warner, 18 The Riggs, Hunwick, Crook, Co Durham)

On the regional front, it was very much Bedlington Terriers' season. In the first division they led from the gun and won quite comfortably from Billingham Synthonia, celebrating their 75th anniversary. In the Northumberland Senior Cup - competing against several Unibond sides and against Newcastle United Reserves - Terriers won the trophy for the second successive season at St James Park.

At the League's annual dinner, they felt close enough to Scotland to turn up uniformly in full Highland dress, proved that whatever it is Scotsmen wear underneath their kilts in Bedlington they don't wear very much at all, and looked absolutely magnificent notwithstanding.

Neither of the first two had indicated a desire for promotion. None of our feeder league clubs was in a position to accept it, either. The new season's composition remains the same, therefore, with the exception that Ferryhill Athletic, whose 77 year membership had been suspended at the previous annual meeting, now leave the league.

It is a long, complicated and unsavoury story. A new committee had worked hard during the suspension to raise enough money to develop a new ground and to rekindle interest, but time ran out on them. Representatives accepted the inevitability of the annual meeting's decision: a new club, Ferryhill Athletic '98, will contest the re-formed Vaux Wearside League second division next season.

Other clubs, almost inevitably these day, have had difficulties. Murton, plagued more than most by the curse of vandalism, have survived both a blaze that destroyed their stand and a hammer gang that smashed their way into the generator room before destroying everything in sight. They continue, relegated to the second division, with a committee of two. Simultaneously, we applaud their resilience and wonder how long it can continue.

Whickham also had problems, largely of apathy. Their resignation, happily, was withdrawn before the annual meeting when other volunteers came forward.

Perhaps clubs both in the the Arnott Insurance Northern League and throughout the country may look at the example of Willington, one of the league's oldest clubs, which two seasons ago came perilously close to folding - again largely because of arson and vandal attacks.

Re-structured with a wide community base, the club's chairmen (we don't have chairs in this league) and secretary are both female, industrious and motivational. They lead a committee of 21, 16 more than two years ago and the biggest in the whole league, both in driving forward the football club and in a whole range of activities for the town's youngsters. A thoroughly inspirational example.

Inspiration also at Chester-le-Street, champions after just one season back in the second division, and at West Auckland who also made their second division stay as short as possible, Marske United, breezy newcomers, occupied the third promotion place. Northallerton and Durham City - on goal difference - join Murton in the relegation spots.

Dunston Federation won the League Cup over a leg weary Tow Law, Peterlee lifted the second division Craven Cup, against Hebburn.

At the beginning of the season we also instigated a campaign called Stamp Out Swearing, its object as self-evident as it was optimistic. Travellers (who may wish to be reminded that it is the League's re-union ground hoppers weekend at Easter 2002) tell us that the AINL is a veritable Church League compared to some. The League management committee still believed that too much casual swearing took place and tried to do something about it.

By and large the campaign has failed, so that the minority of referees who uphold the letter of the law - the laws of the game, not of the Northern league - are now the ones accused of inconsistency. It has got to the stage where many match officials seem wiling to accept abuse almost directly to their faces, so long as it's not suffixed by the word "referee". Perhaps it is that word to which they take such offence.

A yet more vigorous campaign may be needed if the proposal for a Conference second division is sanctioned at Lancaster Gate., Again it seems that football, - no matter what the level, no matter how much we tell ourselves that things are different here - is driven solely by the ugly principle of devil take the hindmost.

A conference second division, arbitrary in establishment and execution, would not only pillage and impoverish leagues at several levels below it, it would mean the end for some of them as meaningful members of the national League System.

Do we exist solely as cannon fodder for the avaricious? Has all the careful Pyramid building been just for this? How long before someone wants a third national division, or a fourth, before the whole thing implodes?

We and many others in the system look to the FA for a positive, long term declaration that football remains a democracy, not an exercise in the survival of the fattest. Perhaps they will remember the story of the mascot Sam.

The League chairman may also be embarking on something of a personal campaign against paying hard won money - usually cash in hand - to after dinner speakers, ex-professional players, with nothing funny or original to say, and no idea of how to say it.

That apart, there is much about which to be hopeful. The Arnott Insurance Northern League remains a fraternity, a regional community in which there is much fellow feeling and many friendships. Particularly we are proud of our football, and its skill level.

Whenever next year's Vase final may be, we anticipate a return.

Mike Amos

FINAL LEAGUE TABLES 1997-98

Division One

	P	*W*	*D*	*L*	*F*	*A*	*Pts*
Bedlington Terriers	38	29	3	6	120	32	90
Billingham Synthonia	38	23	9	6	82	36	78
Guisborough Town	38	23	6	9	84	53	75
Dunston FB	38	21	10	7	69	35	73
RTM Newcastle	38	20	5	13	92	70	65
Penrith	38	19	8	11	81	62	65
Morpeth Town	38	16	14	8	75	48	62
South Shields	38	15	19	4	65	39	*61
Shildon	38	16	7	15	78	87	55
Billingham Town	38	17	2	19	72	79	53
Tow Law Town	38	16	7	15	78	61	*52
Consett	38	13	11	14	60	62	50
Jarrow Roofing BCA	38	11	12	15	64	70	45
Crook Town	38	12	7	19	58	67	43
Seaham Red Star	38	12	7	19	60	83	43
Easington Colliery	38	13	6	19	77	97	*42
Stockton	38	10	10	18	54	65	*37
Durham City	38	10	7	21	55	67	*37
Northallerton	38	4	6	28	39	102	18
Murton	38	2	0	36	23	172	*3

Division Two

	P	*W*	*D*	*L*	*F*	*A*	*Pts*
Chester-le-Street	3629	3	4	105	27	90	
West Auckland	36	24	8	4	85	36	80
Marske United	36	24	5	7	78	30	77
Prudhoe Town	36	20	5	11	87	58	*62
Ashington	36	18	7	11	76	52	61
Willington	36	16	6	14	87	65	54
Peterlee Newton	36	16	7	13	60	55	*52
Evenwood Town	36	14	9	13	62	62	51
Alnwick Town	36	15	5	16	68	64	50
Norton & Stockton A	36	14	7	15	58	57	49
Shotton Comrades	36	13	8	15	66	61	47
Hebburn	36	12	10	14	57	43	46
Ryhope CA	36	12	10	14	60	63	46
Horden CW	36	12	8	16	58	67	44
Whickham	36	14	7	15	51	66	*43
Esh Winning	36	11	9	16	58	79	42
Brandon United	36	11	6	19	59	87	39
Eppleton CW	36	4	4	28	29	103	16
Washington	36	1	0	35	24	153	*0

* Denotes points deducted

DIVISION ONE RESULTS CHART 1997-98

		1	2	3	4	5	6	7	8	9	10	11	12	13	14	15	16	17	18	19	20
1	Bedlington Terriers	X	3-0	2-3	5-0	2-0	0-0	5-1	4-0	2-3	4-1	1-3	4-1	1-0	4-0	5-1	3-0	2-2	1-3	2-1	2-1
2	Billingham Synthonia	0-2	X	1-0	2-1	4-2	0-1	0-2	3-1	3-0	3-3	1-1	6-1	3-1	2-0	0-2	3-1	3-1	0-0	2-0	1-0
3	Billingham Town	3-10	2-1	X	1-2	3-2	0-1	2-1	4-3	0-3	3-4	4-2	1-0	2-0	1-2	2-1	0-1	2-1	0-2	1-2	1-2
4	Consett	2-0	0-2	2-1	X	2-1	3-0	1-1	2-1	2-3	0-0	2-4	3-0	4-1	1-3	2-4	1-1	1-2	4-4	0-2	1-0
5	Crook Town	0-1	2-2	2-0	1-0	X	1-4	0-1	0-1	1-1	1-0	0-0	7-1	4-0	2-1	3-0	2-2	1-4	0-3	3-2	0-5
6	Dunston Federation	0-1	1-1	1-2	3-1	1-1	X	0-0	4-2	3-2	0-0	2-0	2-1	3-1	3-0	2-5	3-3	3-0	0-1	2-0	1-3
7	Durham City	0-2	0-2	1-3	1-3	1-2	0-1	X	4-0	1-2	1-1	0-2	9-1	3-1	5-1	1-3	2-0	1-1	2-3	2-0	2-6
8	Easington Colliery	1-9	2-3	1-4	4-4	3-1	1-1	1-2	X	4-2	3-2	3-1	3-1	1-2	2-4	7-2	2-1	1-2	0-2	3-3	4-2
9	Guisborough	1-0	1-2	5-1	5-1	3-2	1-2	4-1	1-1	X	1-2	1-0	4-1	4-2	3-2	3-3	5-1	1-0	1-1	1-0	2-0
10	Jarrow	0-2	2-2	4-0	1-1	1-0	2-2	3-3	1-2	1-2	X	2-2	5-2	5-0	0-2	1-3	4-2	0-1	1-1	3-1	0-5
11	Morpeth	1-2	0-0	1-1	0-0	5-2	0-0	2-0	5-4	2-2	3-0	X	6-0	2-0	1-2	0-0	6-1	3-3	0-0	3-2	1-2
12	Murton	0-6	0-5	1-0	0-3	1-6	0-9	0-1	0-2	2-5	1-3	0-5	X	0-2	2-6	2-4	0-5	1-4	0-3	0-2	0-3
13	Northallerton	0-5	0-5	1-4	1-1	2-2	1-1	1-1	6-2	0-2	1-2	1-2	0-1	X	0-2	1-7	2-3	0-1	0-0	3-4	1-3
14	Penrith	1-6	2-3	3-2	2-1	2-0	0-1	1-0	3-2	0-0	3-0	2-0	8-1	5-0	X	5-2	1-1	2-2	1-1	0-1	3-1
15	RTM Newcastle	0-2	0-0	2-4	1-2	1-2	0-2	3-1	4-0	2-1	4-3	4-1	8-0	5-1	1-1	X	4-0	1-3	2-0	2-1	4-1
16	Seaham RS	0-2	1-6	0-3	3-1	3-0	0-2	2-0	2-2	0-1	3-1	1-1	7-1	2-0	1-4	2-3	X	3-2	2-2	2-1	0-4
17	Shildon	1-9	0-3	5-2	0-4	0-3	1-6	5-4	1-5	2-5	3-0	1-2	6-1	4-2	1-2	5-1	3-2	X	3-3	0-0	2-1
18	South Shields	1-1	0-0	2-0	2-2	2-0	1-0	0-0	1-3	3-1	1-1	1-1	6-0	3-1	2-2	2-0	3-0	2-4	X	0-0	1-1
19	Stockton	0-5	0-4	3-3	0-0	2-2	0-1	2-0	0-0	1-2	0-3	2-4	6-0	1-1	2-2	1-2	3-1	1-1	2-1	X	5-2
20	Tow Law Town	1-3	1-4	2-7	0-0	1-0	0-1	1-0	4-0	2-0	2-2	1-1	7-0	2-3	3-3	1-1	0-1	4-1	2-2	2-1	X

NORTHERN LEAGUE CUP 1997-98

FIRST ROUND

Alnwick	v	Whickham	1-1, 6p5	Marske United	v	Crook Town	2-1
Willington	v	Durham City	1-1, 3p4	Guisborough	v	Seaham RS	3-4
Chester le Street	v	Norton & SA	2-2, 4p2	Penrith	v	Murton	5-2
Easington Colliery	v	Morpeth Town	1-1, 5p3				

SECOND ROUND

Horden CW	v	Penrith	0-5	Stockton	v	Ryhope CA	2-2, 5p4
Northallerton	v	Shotton	2-0	Prudhoe Town	v	Marske United	1-0
B'ham Synthonia	v	Seaham RS	2-1	Hebburn	v	Alnwick	5-4
Shildon	v	West Auckland	1-3	Ashington	v	Durham City	1-0
Bedlington	v	Consett	1-2	Dunston	v	Washington	2-0
South Shields	v	Esh Winning	5-0	Easington	v	Eppleton CW	24
RTM Newcastle	v	Peterlee	7-1	Brandon Utd	v	Billingham Town	0-2
Tow Law Town	v	Jarrow Roofing	3-2	Evenwood Town	v	Chester le Street	6-2

THIRD ROUND

Easington Colliery	v	Billingham Town	3-2	Penrith	v	Stockton	1-0
Evenwood Town	v	West Auckland	4-2	Dunston Fed.	v	Consett	2-0
Ashington	v	Prudhoe	1-1, 3p5	South Shields	v	B'ham Synthonia	1-0
Hebburn	v	RTM Newcastle	2-1	Northallerton	v	Tow Law Town	1-4

FOURTH ROUND

South Shields	v	Prudhoe Town	3-0	Tow Law Town	v	Easington	1-0
Evenwood Town	v	Penrith	2-0	Hebburn	v	Dunston Fed	0-2

SEMI-FINAL

Evenwood Town	v	Tow Law Town	0-2	South Shields	v	Dunston Fed	2-2, 4p5

FINAL

Dunston Fed v Tow Law Town 3-2 at Durham City FC

CRAVEN CUP 1997-98

SECOND ROUND

Marske United	v	Brandon United	5-1	Norton & SA	v	Evenwood Town	0-2
Peterlee	v	Shotton Comrades	2-0	Washington	v	Willington	1-2
Ryhope CA	v	Hebburn	3-4	Whickham	v	Eppleton CW	2-0
Alnwick	v	Chester le Street	4-1	Horden CW	v	Prudhoe	0-1

THIRD ROUND

Alnwick	v	Hebburn	0-1	Peterlee	v	Marske United	3-2
Prudhoe Town	v	Whickham	0-3	Evenwood Town	v	Willington	1-3

SEMI-FINAL

Whickham	v	Peterlee	1-1, 3p4	Willington	v	Hebburn	0-3

FINAL

Peterlee v Hebburn 2-0 at South Shields FC

LEADING GOALSCORERS 1997-98

DIVISION ONE

Club	Player	Goals
Bedlington	Lee Ludlow	23
B'ham Synthonia	Anthony Wood	17
Billingham Town	Paul Rowntree	36 (1st)
Consett	Steven Robson	13
Crook Town	Bellamy/Shotton	8
Dunston Fed	Gary McDonald	21
Durham City	Derek Bell	11
Easington	Andrew McKenna	29 (3rd)
Guisborough	Carl Chillingsworth	25
Jarrow	Paul Thompson	20
Morpeth	Paul Symons	18
Murton	Stephen Burns	4
North Allerton	David Lawson	9
Penrith	Timothy Bell	16
RTM Newcastle	Andrew Morell	36 (1st)
Seaham	Victor Holt	20
Shildon	John Outhwaite	21
South Shields	Tim Wilson	13
Stockton	David Turner	8
Tow Law Town	Trevor Laidler	19

DIVISION TWO

Club	Player	Goals
Alnwick	Albert Straughan	25 (1st)
Ashington	Greg Peary	19
Brandon	Chris Heron	10
Chester le Street	Nicky Gray	19
Eppleton	Graeme Hutchinson	6
Esh Winning	John David Oliver	13
Evenwood	Keith Gorman	13
Hebburn	Paul Donaghy	20
Horden	Neville Johnson	13
Marske	Ben Thompson	16
Norton	Phillip Gordon	13
Peterlee	Stuart Hope	13
Prudhoe	Mark Drake	20
Ryhope	Christian Robson	21 (3rd)
Shotton	Chris Creamer	14
Washington	Andrew Nichols	3
West Auckland	Paul Adamson	14
Whickham	Kevin Guthrie	10
Willington	Brett Cummings	23 (2nd)

Tow Law Town
Back Row L-R: Tony Heslop (Assistant Manager); Michael Vasey; Lee Bennett; Paul Hague; Michael Bailey; Stuart Dawson; Sean Musgrave; Darren Darwent; Warren Pearson; Darren Watkins; Keith Young; Peter Quigley (Manager)
Front Row L-R: Tony Nelson; Billy Johnson; Keith Moorhead; Jorrod Suddick; Glen Moan; Michael Robinson; Trevor Laidler; Stephen Pickering; Tommy Mason; Jeff Hall

DIVISION ONE CLUBS 1998-99

BEDLINGTON TERRIERS

Chairman: David Perry. **Press Officer:** Secretary
Secretary: Eric Young, 6 Millbank Place, Bedlington, Northumberland NE22 5AT (01670 829196).
Manager: Keith Perry **Assistant Manager:** Steven Locker.
Coach: Tony Lowery **Physio:** Dave Robertson
Ground: Welfare Park, Park Rd., Bedlington, Northumberland (01670 825485).
Directions: Into Bedlington, turn left at 'Northumberland Arms' on Front St., then 2nd Right, ground on right 100 yds.
Seats: 150 **Cover:** 200 **Capacity:** 1,500 **Floodlights:** Yes **Formed:** 1949
Programme: 40 pages, 70p **Previous Leagues:** Northern Alliance. **Midweek Matches:** Wednesday
Colours: Red & white/white/white **Change colours:** All blue **Souvenir Shop:** No
Clubhouse: Open every evening, 11-11pm Sat. & Sun lunch. Pool, darts etc.
CLUB RECORDS - Win: 11-0 v West Auckland, (H) Lge 96-97. **Attendance:** 1,013 v Blyth Spartans, Northern Lg 85-86.
Previous Names: Bedlington Mechanics 49-53/ Colliery Welfare 53-56/ Mechanics 56-61/ Bedlington United 61-65/ Bedlington Colliery 65-68/ Bedlington Town 68-74.
97-98 Captain: Andy Gowens **P.o.Y.:** Warren Teasdale **Top Scorer:** John Milner (33)
Club record scorer: John Milner 33
Honours: Northern League Div 2 94-95 (R-up 84-85), Northern Alliance 66-67 (R-up 67-68 69-70 71-72, Lg Cup 57-58 66-67 69-70 81-82, Lge Chall Cup 96-97, Northumberland Sen Cup 96-97.

BILLINGHAM SYNTHONIA

Chairman: Don Beattie **Vice Chairman:** Stuart Coleby **President:** Frank Cook
Secretary: Graham Craggs, 2 Ribble Close, Billingham, Cleveland TS22 5NT (01642 535856).
Manager: Stuart Coleby **Physio:** Tommy Cushley. **Coach:** Lenny Gunn
Ground: The Stadium, Central Avenue, Billingham, Cleveland (Press Box 01642 532348).
Directions: Turn off A19 onto A1027 signposted Billingham, Norton (this applies from either north or south), continue straigh on along Central Avenue, ground on left opposite office block. 1 mile from Billingham (BR).
Seats: 370 **Cover:** 370 **Capacity:** 1,970 **Floodlights:** Yes **Club Shop:** No.
Programme: 12 pages (+ads), 50p **Editor:** Nigel Atkinson (01642 342469) **Press Officer:** Secretary
Colours: All white **Change colours:** All green
Nickname: Synners **Sponsors:** Teeside Park **Founded:** 1923
Midweek Matches: Wednesday **Previous League:** Teesside (1923-War).
CLUB RECORDS - Attendance: 4,200 v Bishop Auck. 6/9/58. **Goalscorer:** Tony Hetherington **Appearances:** Andy Harbron.
BEST SEASON FA Trophy: Quarter-final replay 93-94 (lost 1-2 after 1-1 draw at Woking). **FA Cup:** 1st Rd 48-49 51-52 56-57 57-58 87-88 89-90.
Players progressing to Football League: Peter Atkinson & Ken Harrison (Hull 1947), Ernie Wardle & John Murray (M'boro 1948 & 49), Richard Mulvaney (Blackburn 1964), Mike Hodgson (Hartlepool 1964), David Hockaday (Blackpool 1975), Terry Gaffney (Hartlepool 1977), Aidan Davidson (Notts County 1988).
Clubhouse: 200yds across car park. Normal club hours.
Honours: Northern Lg 56-57 88-89 89-90 95-96, R-up 49-50 50-51 51-52, Lg Cup 51-52 87-88 89-90, Div 2 86-87, Teesside Lg 36-37 (Lg Cup 34-35 38-39), Durham Challenge Cup 88-89 90-91, North Riding Snr Cup 66-67 71-72, North Riding Amateur Cup 38-39 56-57 62-63 63-64, FA Amateur Cup 4th Rd 48-49, FA Trophy QF replay 94-95.

BILLINGHAM TOWN

Chairman: Mr.P.Martin. **Hon.President:** Mr.F.Cook M.P. **President:** Mr G.A.Maxwell.
Secretary/Press Officer: Tom Donnelly, 36 Cumberland Crescent, Billingham, Cleveland TS23 1AY (01642 555332).
Manager: Trevor Arnold **Asst Manager/Coach:** Neal Granycome
Ground: Bedford Terrace, Billingham, Cleveland. (01642 560043)
Directions: Leave A19 on A1027 (signed Billingham). Turn left at 3rd r/bout, over bridge 1st left, 1st left again to grd.
Seats: 176 **Cover:** 600 **Capacity:** 3,000 **Floodlights:** Yes **Founded:** 1967
Colours: All Blue **Change colours:** Yellow/green/yellow
Programme: 28 pages, 50p. **Editor:** Alex Matthews (01642 653621) **Souvenir Shop:** No
Clubhouse: Open matchdays. Hot & cold food. **Nickname:** The Social.
Midweek Matches: Tuesday **PREVIOUS - Lges:** Stockton & Dist. 68-74/ Teesside 74-82.
Name: Billingham Social Club (pre-1982). **Ground:** Mill Lane (pre-1974).
Best FA Cup season: 1st Rd Proper 55-56. **Reserves' Lge:** Stockton & Dist Sunday
Players progressing to Football League: Gary Pallister (Middlesbrough & Manchester Utd), Gerry Forrest (Southampton), Dave Robinson (Halifax), Tony Barratt (Hartlepool), Mark Hine (Grimsby & Darlington), Tony Hall (Middlesbrough), Graham Hall (Arsenal).
Club Records - Attendance: 1,500 v Manchester City, FA Youth Cup 85. **Goalscorer:** Paul Rowntree 100 **Appearances:** Darren Marsh, 250 in Northern League.
Honours: Durham Amateur Cup 76-77 77-78, Teesside Lg 77-78 81-82, Nth Riding Snr Cup R-up 76-77 81-82, Stockton & Dist. Lg(3).

CHESTER-LE-STREET TOWN

Chairman: John Tomlinson **Vice Chairman:** Jack Thornback **President:** John Holden.
Secretary: Melvin Atkinson, 1 St Marys Close, Chester-le-Street, Co Durham DH2 3EG (0191 388 3664).
Manager: Paul Bryson **Asst Mgr/Coach:** Stuart Sherwood **Physio:** Ray Hartley
Commercial Manager: Paul Days **Press Officer:** Jack Thornback (0191 3883554).
Ground: Moor Park, Chester Moor, Chester-le Street, County Durham (0191 388 3363).
Directions: Ground lies approx 2 miles south of town on A167 (C.-le-S. to Durham road). Regular buses from C.-le-S. and Durham pass ground. Railway station 2 miles distant in town centre.
Seats: 200 **Cover:** 1,500 **Capacity:** 4,000 **Floodlights:** Yes **Founded:** 1972
Midweek Matches: Tuesday **Shop:** No, but old programmes available from editor.
Colours: Blue & white hoops/white/white **Change colours:** All yellow.
Programme: 40 pages, 50p **Editor/Press Officer:** Keith Greener **Nickname:** Cestrians
Clubhouse: Open matchdays, Wed, Thurs & Sun. Wed/Thurs 7-10.30pm, Sun 12-2pm, midweek matches 6.30-10.30pm, Sat 12-10.30pm.
Previous Leagues: Newcastle City Amtr 72-75/ Washington 75/ Wearside 77-83.
Record Gate: 893 v Fleetwood FA Vase 18/2/85, (3000 Sunderland v Newcastle, Bradford appeal match 85).
Players progressing to Football League: Dave Atkinson (Sunderland 86), Peter Ward (Huddersfield 87), Paul Kitson (West Ham), Todd Lumsden (Stirling Albion)
97-98 Captain: Colin Wake **P.o.Y.:** Grey Bainbridge **Top Scorers:** M Carroll (24)
Club record scorer: **Club record appearances:** Dean Ferry 219 (+38 subs)
Honours: FA Vase 4th Rd 91-92; Northern Lg Div 2 83-84 97-98; Wearside Lg 80-81 (R-up 82-83); Monkwearmouth Cup 80-81 81-82; Washington Lg; Durham Minor Cup; Washington AM Cup.

CONSETT

Chairman: Jack Kay. **Vice Chairman:** I Hamilton. **President:** D McVickers
Secretary: Ian Hamilton, 29 Grange Street, Delves Lane, Consett, Co. Durham DH8 7AG (01207 509366).
Manager: Colin Carr **Physio:** Joe Darroch **Press Officer:** Andrew Pearson (01207 506194)
Ground: Belle Vue Park, Ashdale Road, Consett, County Durham (01207 503788)
Directions: Quarter of mile north of town centre - along Medomsley Rd, left down Ashdale Rd, ground 100m yards on left. Follow signs for Sports Centre and Baths.
Seats: 400 **Cover:** 1,000 **Capacity:** 4,000 **Floodlights:** Yes **Founded:** 1899
Colours: Red with black & white trim/black/red **Change colours:** Sky blue/dark blue/sky blue
Previous Leagues: Northern Alliance 19-26 35-37/ North Eastern 26-35 37-58 62-64/ Midland 58-60/ Northern Counties 60-62/ Wearside 64-70.
Programme: 16 pages, 30p **Programme Editor:** Colin French **Souvenir Shop:** No
Record Gate: 7,000 v Sunderland Reserves, first match at Belle Vue, 1950. **Nickname:** Steelmen
Best FA Cup season: 1st Rd 58-59 (lost 0-5 at Doncaster Rovers).
Players progressing to Football League: Tommy Lumley (Charlton), Alan Ellison (Reading), Laurie Cunningham (Barnsley), Jimmy Moir (Carlisle), Jackie Boyd (West Bromwich Albion).
Clubhouse: Matchdays, and evenings on request. Darts & pool. **Midweek Matches:** Wednesday
Honours: North Eastern Lg 39-40 (Div 2 26-27, Lg Cup 50-51 (jt) 53-54), Durham Challenge 5, (R-up 2), Northern Lg R-up 76-77 (Div 2 88-89, Lg Cup 78-79 80-81), Northern Counties Lg 61-62, Sunderland Shipowners Cup 67-68, Monkwearmouth Charity Cup 67-68, Wearside Lg R-up 68-69 69-70, FA Trophy 2nd Rd 78-79.

CROOK TOWN

Chairman: Bob Emerson **Vice-Chairman:** Brian Lowe **President:** Sir Tom Cowie O.B.E.
Secretary: Alan Stewart, The Wardens Flat, 47 Grasmere Grove, Crook, Co Durham DL15 8NX (01388 763425)
Managers: Paul Cross/Kevan Smith **Physio:**Jimmy Vipond **Coach:**
Ground: Millfield Ground, West Road, Crook, County Durham (01388 762959).
Directions: 400 yds west of town centre on Wolsingham Road (A689). Nearest BR station is Bishop Auckland (5 miles). Buses 1A & 1B from Bishop Auckland or X46 & X47 from Durham.
Seats: 400 **Cover:** 300 **Capacity:** 3,500 **Floodlights:** Yes **Club Shop:** Yes
Programme: Yes **Editor:** Jeff Paterson (01388 450335) **Press Officer:** Secretary
Colours: Amber/black/black **Change colours:** All White
Sponsors: Vaux Breweries **Formed:** 1889 **Nickname:** Black & Ambers
Midweek Matches: Wednesday **Reserve's League:** Auckland & Dist
Record Attendance: 17,500 v Walton & Hersham, FA Amateur Cup quarter-final 24/02/52.
BEST SEASON - FA Trophy: 3rd Rd 76-77. **FA Vase:** 2nd Rd 93-94, 95-96 **FA Cup:** 3rd Rd (v Leicester) 31-32. 2nd Rd(4), 1sr Rd.(10).
Previos Leagues: Auckland & District 1894-96/ Northern 1896-28 29-30/ Durham Central 28-29/ North Eastern 30-36/ Wartime Durham & Northumberland League 40-41/ Durham Cen 41-45.
Players progressing to Football League: Since 1960; F Clark (Newcastle 62), K Bowron (Berwick 63), A Coates & W Rougnley (Q.o.t.S 63 64), P Garbutt (Carlisle 64), R Snowball (Darlington 64), W Hepplewhite (Carlisle 65), C Neal (Darlington 67), D Attlee (Seattle Sounders 75), T Turnbull (Hartlepool 76), G Whetter (Darlington 86).
Clubhouse: Lic Bar open matchdays. Hot & Cold Food available from Shop
97-98 Captain: David Neil **Top Scorer:** David Bellamy/David Pither (8) **P.o.Y.:** Ian McGraghan
Club Record Scorer: Ronnie Thompson 118, 52-62 **Club Record appearances:** Jimmy McMillan 505, 51-68
Honours: FA Amtr Cup 00-01 53-54 58-59 61-62 63-64 (SF 48-49 57-58 59-60); Northern Lg 5, (R-up 4), Lg Cup 3, (R-up 4); Durham Challenge Cup 26-27 31-32 54-55 59-60; Durham Benevolent Bowl 5; Ernest Armstrong Mem Trophy 97.

DUNSTON FEDERATION BREWERY

Chairman: Malcolm James. **Vice-Chairman:** Fred Fowles **President:** Norman Rippon.
Secretary: Bill Montague, 12 Dundee Close, Chapel House, Newcastle-upon-Tyne NE5 1JJ (0191 2672250).
Manager: Peter Quigley **Asst Manager:** Steve Kendal **Physio:** Glen Martin.
Press Officer: Ian McPherson (0191 4205583) **Commercial Secretary:** Malcolm James.
Ground: Federation Park, Wellington Road, Dunston, Gateshead (0191 493 2935).
Directions: Dunston/Whickham exit off A1(M), ground 400 yds north along Dunston Rd on left. 1 mile from Dunston or Metrocentre stations. Buses from Gateshead & Metrocentre stop outside ground.
Seats: 80 **Cover:** 200 **Capacity:** 2,000 **Floodlights:** Yes **Founded:** 1975
Colours: All blue (white trim) **Change:** Green/white. **Nickname:** The Fed
Programme: 28 pages, 30p **Editor:** Ian McPherson (0191 420 5583) **Souvenir Shop:** No
Record Attendance: 1,550 - Sunderland Shipowners Cup Final 1/4/88.
Best F.A. Vase season: Quarter-Finals 92-93 (lost 0-2 at Gresley Rovers).
Best F.A. Cup season: 3rd Qualifying Rd 92-93 (lost 0-3 to Northallerton Town).
Sponsors: Federation Brewery **Clubhouse:** Matchdays only. Hot & cold snacks, darts, pool.
Midweek home matchday: Tuesday **Reserve team:** None.
Club record scorer: Paul King **Club record appearances:** Paul Dixon.
Hons: Northern Lg Div 2 92-93, Northern Amtr Lg 77-78 (R-up 2), Lg Cup 77-78 78-79 (R-up 75-76), Lg Shield 78-79 79-80), Wearside Lg 88-89 89-90 (R-up 90-91, Lg Cup 90-91), Northern Comb. 86-87 (R-up 3), Lg Cup 83-84 86-87 (R-up 3), Sunderland Shipowners Cup 87-88, Durham County Tphy 81-82 (R-up 2), Minor Cup 79-80 (R-up 78-79)), Gateshead Charity Cup 77-78 80-81, Heddon Homes Cup 80-81.

EASINGTON COLLIERY

Chairman: Fred Wellburn **Vice-Chairman:** Charlie Dodds.
Secretary: Alan Purvis, 12 Wark Crescent, Jarrow, Tyne & Wear, NE32 4SH (0191 489 6930)
Manager: Vin Pearson **Asst Mgr/Coach:** John Cullen
Ground: Easington Colliery Welfare Ground, CW Park, Easington, Co Durham. (0191 527 3047)
Directions: A19 Easington turn-off, B1284 thru Easington till Black Diamond PH (next to zebra crossing), grd right
Seats: 175 **Cover:** 475 **Capacity:** 2,450 **Floodlights:** Yes **Club Shop:** No
Programme: Yes **Editor:** Charlie Dodds **Press Officer:** Alan Purvis
Colours: Green & white stripes/green/green **Change colours:** Yellow/black/yellow
Sponsors: Middleton Maintenance **Nickname:** The Colliery. **Founded:** 1913
Midweek Matches: Tuesday **Reserves:** None.
Record Attendance: 4,500 v Tranmere Rovers, FA Cup 1st Round 1955.
Previous Leagues: Wearside 13-37 39-64 73-88 **Best FA Cup season:** 1st Rd Proper 55-56
Players progressing to Football League: Ron Greener (Newcastle 1951), Frank Wayman (Darlington 1957), John Langridge (Hartlepool 1982).
Clubhouse details: Normal licensing hours. Pies, soup and sandwiches available.
97-98 Captain: John Bendel **P.o.Y.:** Mark Taylor **Top Scorer:** Andrew McKenna
Club record scorer: Andrew McKenna **Club record appearances:** David Howard.
Honours: FA Trophy 2nd Qualifying Rd replay 88-89, FA Vase 4th Rd replay 82-83. Northern Lg Div 2 R-up 85-86; Wearside League 29-30 31-32 32-33 47-48 48-49, R-up 28-29 46-47 73-74, Lg Cup 32-33 45-46 61-62; Monkwearmouth Cup 30-31 47-48 75-76; Sunderland Shipowners Cup 74-75 79-80;

GUISBOROUGH TOWN

Chairman: Keith Watson **Vice Chairman:** Paul Beeforth **President:** Vacant
Secretary: Keith Smeltzer, 55 Thames Ave., Guisborough, Cleveland TS14 8AR (01287 638993).
Manager: Mark Forster **Asst Manager:** Steve Corden **Physio:** Steve Carter
Ground: King George V Ground, Howlbeck Rd, Guisborough, Cleveland (01287 636925).
Directions: From west: bear left at 2nd lights, left into Howlbeck Rd 1/4 mile, grd at end. Buses from Middlesbrough.
Seats: 150 **Cover:** 400 **Capacity:** 3,500 **Floodlights:** Yes **Club Shop:** Yes
Programme: 32 pages, 40p **Editor:** M Hollinworth (01287 637737) **Press Officer:** K Smeltzer/K Watson
Colours: Red & white stripes/Black/Red. **Change colours:** Yellow
Sponsors: Henson Windows & Conservatories **Nickname:** Priorymen **Founded:** 1973.
Midweek home matchday: Wednesday **Reserve Team's League:** Teesside Strongarm.
RECORDS - Gate: 3,112 v Hungerford, FA Vase SF, 80 *(at Middlesbrough FC - 5,990 v Bury, FA Cup 1st Rd 88).*
Goalscorer: Mark Davis 323 **Appearances:** Mark Davis 551
Best FA Cup season: First Round Proper 1988-89 (lost 0-1 to Bury).
Previous Leagues: Middlesbrough & District/ South Bank/ Northern Alliance 77-80/ Midland Counties 80-82/ Northern Counties (East) 82-85.
Players progressing to Football League: Frank Harrison (Middlesbrough 1982), Steve Holmes (Preston 93).
Clubhouse: Evenings & weekends. Darts & pool. Hot & cold snacks and drinks from kitchen on matchdays.
97-98 Captain: Anthony Wyke **P.o.Y.:** Sean Robins **Top Scorer:** Carl Chillingworth
Honours: FA Vase R-up 79-80, Northern Lg Cup 87-88 (Div 2 R-up 86-87), Northern Alliance 79-80 (R-up 78-79, Lg Cup 78-79), North Riding Senior Cup 89-90 90-91 91-92 92-93 94-95, FA Trophy 1st Rd Proper 90-91 91-92 92-93. FA Vase Semi finalist 96-97.

Chester-Le-Street

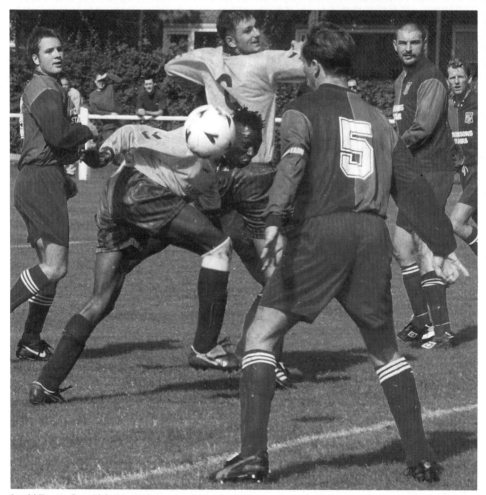

Arnold Town's Gary Ricketts gets in a powerful header as team mate John Beale and Shildon's defenders look on
Photo: Andrew Chitty

JARROW ROOFING BOLDON C.A.

Chairman: Richard McLoughlin. **Press Officer/Treasurer:** Rose McLoughlin.
Secretary/Manager: Richard McLoughlin, 8 Kitchener Terrace, Jarrow NE32 5PU (0191 489 9825).
Coach: Kevin Arnott **Physio:** Fred Corner/Alan Leslie
Ground: Boldon CA Sports Ground, New Road, Boldon Colliery (0191 519 1391)
Seats: 150 **Cover:** 800 **Capacity:** 3,500 **Floodlights:** Yes **Club Shop:**Yes
Programme: 20 pages, free with entry **Editor:** Brian Marshall (0191 455 1190)
Colours: All blue with red trim **Change colours:** Claret & blue
Sponsors: Jarrow Roofing Co. **Nickname:** Roofing. **Founded:** 1987.
Midweek matchday: Wednesday **Record Attendance:** 500 v South Shields
Previous Leagues: Mid-Tyne/ Tyneside Amtr 88-91/ Vaux Wearside
Clubhouse: Open nights and weekend lunchtimes. Chips, hotdogs, burgers etc available from tea bar on matchdays.
96-97 Captain: **96-97 Top Scorer:** **96-97 P.o.Y.:**
Club Record Appearances: Mick Haley **Club Record Goalscorer:** Lee Young
Honours: Wearside Lg Div 2 R-up 91-92 95-96; Sunderland Shipowners Cup R-up 93-94, 94-95; Tyneside Amtr Lg R-up 90-91, Chal. Shield 90-91 (R-up 89-90); Bill Dixon Cup 90-91; Mid-Tyne Lg 87-88; Fred Giles Cup R-up 87-88; Gateshead Charity Cup SF 90-91; Monkwearmouth Cup 94-95; Craven Cup 96-97:

MARSKE UNITED

Chairman: John Hodgson **Vice Chairman:** John Corner. **President:** Raymond Jarvis
Secretary: Ian Rowe, 19 High Row, Loftus, Saltburn By The Sea, Cleveland. TS13 4SA (01287 643440 H, 01642 230546 B, 01642 241273 Fax)
Manager: Charlie Bell **Asst Manager:** Stephen Dowling **Physio:** Barry Schollay
Coach: Charlie Bell/Stephen Dowling/Jackie O'Reilly
Commercial Manager: Chris Sharratt/Steve Davies
Ground: Mount Pleasant, Mount Pleasant Ave., Marske, Redcar (01642 471091).
Directions: From A19 take A174 exit marked Yarm, Teesport, Redcar, Whitby and head east towards Teesport until Quarry Lane r/about. Take 1st left exit (A1085) into Marske, take 1st right (Meadow Rd) then 1st left (Southfield Rd), then 1st left again Mount Pleasant Ave directly into carpark.
Seats: 169 **Cover:** 300 **Capacity:** 2,500 **Floodlights:** Yes **Founded:** 1956
Programme: 32 pages 50p **Editor:** John Hodgson (01642 484006).
Colours: Yellow/royal/white **Change:** Royal/sky/yellow
Sponsors: Arnott Insurance **Nickname:** The Seasiders.
Club Shop: Yes, contact Pat Hodgson (01642 484006) **Midweek matchday:** Tuesday
Previous Leagues: Cleveland, South Bank & Dist, Teesside, Vaux Wearside.
Clubhouse: Open every night and weekend lunchtimes. Food served after all games.
CLUB RECORDS - Goalscorer: Chris Morgan 212 **Appearances:** John Hodgson. **Win:** 16-0 **Defeat:** 3-9
Honours: N Riding Sen Cup 94-95; N Riding County Cup 80-81 85-86; Teesside Lg 80-81 84-85; Wearside Lg 95-96, (R-up 93-94 94-95 96-97), Cup 92-93 94-95 95-96; M/mouth Charity Cup 93-94 95-96; Sunderland Ship. Cup 95-96 96-97.

MORPETH TOWN

Chairman: Ken Beattie. Tel.: 01670 515271 (H), 01670 520565 (B). **Press Officer:** Secretary
Secretary: Joe Hobin, 23 Princes Gardens, Malvins Close, Blyth, Northumberland. NE24 5HJ. (01670 360820).
Ground: Craik Park, Morpeth Common, Morpeth, Northumberland. (01670 513785).
Directions: Morpeth is signed off the A1 onto A197. Take the B6524, right at Mitford sign, then right after about a mile into the ground, next to Morpeth Common.
Colours: Yellow & black stripes/black/black. **Change colours:** All red with white trim.
Previous Leagues: Northern Alliance. (pre 1994). **Previous Ground:** Storey Park, Morpeth. (pre 1992).
Honours: Northern Alliance 83-84, 93-94 (R-up 37-38, 65-66, 73-74, 81-82, 84-85); Challenge Cup Winners 38-39, 85-86, 93-94 (R-up 36-37, 62-63, 73-74).

NEWCASTLE BLUE STAR

Chairman: Tom Brash **Vice-Chairman:**
Secretary: Jim Anderson, 7 Whitbeck Rd, Statyford, Newcastle-upon-Tyne NE5 2XA (0191 243 1025)
Manager/Coach: T Mitchell **Asst Manager:** B Latty **Physio:** T Grady
Ground: Wheatsheaf Sports Ground, Woolsington, Newcastle-upon-Tyne. NE13 8DF. (0191 286 0425).
Directions: From central station follow airport signs for 7 miles - ground next to Wheatsheaf Hotel on left, approximately 800yds before airport. Callerton Parkway metro station is 400yds from ground.
Seats: 300 **Cover:** 300 **Capacity:** 2,000 **Floodlights:** Yes **Club Shop:** Yes
Programme: 12 pages, 30p **Editor:** Secretary **Press Officer:** Secretary.
Colours: Blue/white/blue **Change colours:** Red/black/red **Founded:** 1930
Sponsors: RTM **Nickname:** 'Star' **Midweek matchday:** Monday
RECORDS - Gate: 1,800 v Almondsbury Greenway, FA Vase SF 77-78. **Appearances & Goalscorer:** Ian Crumplin.
Best FA Cup season: 1st Rd 84-85 (lost 0-2 at York C.).
Best FA Trophy season: Qtr-finals 88-89 (lost 1-4 at home to Telford Utd)
Previous Leagues: Newcastle Business Houses 32-38/ North East Amateur/ Tyneside Amateur/ Northern Combination/ Wearside 75-85.
Players progressing to Football League: Ian Crumplin & Tony Robinson (Hartlepool 1976 & 1986), Barry Dunn (Darlington 1979), Ian McInerney (Huddersfield Town 1988).
Clubhouse: Matchdays only. Hotdogs, soup, sandwiches available.
Honours: FA Vase 77-78 (SF 81-82); FA Trophy QF 88-89; Northern Lg R-up 87-88, Lg Cup 85-86, R-up(1), Div 2 85-86; Wearside Lg 73-74 75-76 82-83 83-84 84-85, R-up 74-75 77-78 79-80, Lg Cup 76-77 79-80 80-81 82-83 83-84; Sunderland Shipowners Cup 82-83 84-85; Monkwearmouth Charity Cup 74-75 79-80 82-83 88-89; Northern Comb. 62-63 68-69, Lg Cup 66-67 71-72; Northumberland Snr Cup 76-77 82-83 85-86 87-88, R-up 74-75 78-79 80-81, Minor Cup 64-65; J R Cleator Cup 86-87.

PENRITH

Chairman: Walter Brogden **Vice Chairman:** M Robson
Secretary: John Balmer, 58 Castle Hill Road, Penrith, Cumbria (01768 866736)
Manager: Geoff Byers **Physio:** Les Cornwell.
Ground: Southend Road Ground, Penrith, Cumbria (01768 863212).
Directions: M6 Jct 40, onto dual carriageway to Appleby & Scotch Corner, turn first left at next r'bout, approx half a mile into Penrith on A6 into town, take 1st left for ground. Three quarters of a mile from Penrith (BR).
Seats: 200 **Cover:** 1,000 **Capacity:** 4,000 **Floodlights:** Yes **Club Shop:** No
Programme: 24 pages, 50p **Editor/Press Officer:** J Bell (01768 63898)
Colours: Blue/white/blue **Change colours:** White/red/white
Sponsors: British Gypsum **Nickname:** Blues. **Founded:** 1894
Midweek Matches: Wednesday **Reserve team:** None
Record Attendance: 2,100 v Chester 1981. **Best FA Cup season:** 2nd Rd 81-82
Previous leagues: Carlisle & Dist., Northern 48-82, NW Co's 82-87, 90-97, Northern Prem. 87-90.
Players progressing to Football League: K Sawyers, G Fell, G Mossop (all Carlisle).
Clubhouse: Open Thurs-Fri 9.30pm-2am, Sat 2-6pm & 9.30pm-2am, Wed match nights 6.30-10.30pm.
Club Record Goalscorer: C Short **Club Record Appearances:** Lee Armstrong
Hons: Northern Lg R-up 61-62; NW Co's Lg R-up 83-84; NW Co's F/Light Trophy 95-96 96-97; Cumberland Snr Cup [12], 46-48 50-51 60-66 70-71 72-73 74-75

SEAHAM RED STAR

Chairman: Reg Atkinson **President:** Michael English.
Secretary: John McBeth, 29 Frederick Street, Seaham, County Durham SR7 7HX (0191 581 5712).
Manager: Chris Copeland **Asst Manager:** Paul Walker.
Physio: Allan Jackson **Press Officer:** John Campbell (0191 581 4308).
Ground: Seaham Town Park, Stockton Road, Seaham, County Durham (0191 581 2540).
Directions: From Tyne Tunnel: A19 Teeside approx 8 miles; B1404 Seaham slip road, left at top of slip road. Right at traffic lights & first left past school into ground.
Seats: 60 **Cover:** 200 **Capacity:** 4,000 **Floodlights:** Yes **Year Formed:** 1973
Colours: All Red **Change colours:** All blue **Nickname:** The Star
Programme: 20 pages **Editor:** David Copeland (0191 581 8514) **Club Shop:** No.
Record Attendance: 1,500 v Guisborough, Wearside Lg/ v Sunderland, floodlight opener 1979.
Previous Leagues: Sunday football/ Houghton & District 73-74/ Northern Alliance 74-79/ Wearside 79-83.
Players progressing to Football League: Bobby Davison (Huddersfield 1980), Nigel Gleghorn (Ipswich 1985), Billy Stubbs (Nottm Forest 1987), Paul Nixon (Bristol Rovers (1989), Mick Smith (Hartlepool).
Midweek home matchday: Wednesday **Reserve team's League:** Banks Youth League.
Clubhouse: Mon-Sat 11am-11pm, Sun 12-2, 7-10.30pm. Large function room, snooker, pool, Restuarant & Bars.
Club record scorer: Tom Henderson **Club record appearances:** Michael Whitfield.
Honours: Northern Lg Cup 92-93, Phillips F'lit Tphy 78-79, Durham Chal. Cup 79-80, Wearside Lg 81-82 (Lg Cup 81-82, Div 2 R-up 87-88, Monkwearmouth Charity Cup R-up 79-80), FA Vase 5th Rd 78-79, FA Tphy 2nd Rd 89-90.

Shildon AFC: Back Row (L-R); Ray Gowan (Mgr), Neil Hoban, Neil Emmerson, Matt Sowden, John Outhwaite, Phil Owers, Nigel Bolton, John Harlane, Terry Stones, Lee Stewart, Jimmy Smalls (Physio). Front Row; Trevor Bygate, Chris Emmerson, Alex Degioreis, Steve Ritchie, Ross Christie, Chris Crowe, Darren Slater, Matt Myers

Towlaw Town 97-98. *Photo: John Newton*

Paul Hodgson (Jarrow Roofing) and Scott Garrett (South Shields). *Photo: Alan Watson*

SHILDON

Chairman: Bill Aisbitt **Vice Chairman:** George Elliott **President:** John Atkinson.
Secretary: Mike Armitage, 22 Hambleton Ct, Byerley Park, Newton Aycliffe, Co. Durham DL5 7HR (01325 316322).
Manager: Ray Gowan **Asst Manager:** Phil Owers **Physio:** Jimmy Smalls
Ground: Dean Street, Shildon, County Durham (01388 773877).
Directions: In the town centre 1 mile from BR station and 300yds from Darlington-Bishop Auckland bus stop.
Seats: 400 **Cover:** 500 **Capacity:** 4,000 **Floodlights:** Yes **Club Shop:** No
Programme: 48 pages, 50p **Editor:** Neil Bennett (01325 332310) **Press Officer:** Secretary
Colours: Red & green **Change colours:** All blue. **Midweek Matches:** Wednesday
Sponsors: Atkinsons Stairs **Nickname:** Railwaymen. **Founded:** 1890
Record Attendance: 13,000 - Leeholme v Perkinsville, schoolboys game, 1920s. For Shildon game; 11,000 Shildon v Ferryhill Athletic, Durham Senior Cup 1922.
Best FA Cup season: 2nd Rd 36-37. Also 1st Rd 27-28 29-30 34-35 36-37 55-56 59-60 61-62.
Previous Leagues: Auckland & District 1892-96/ Wearside 96-97/ North Eastern 07-32.
Players progressing to Football League: Ken Whitfield (Wolves 47), James Smith (Chelsea 51), Mike Peacock, Philip Shute, Nigel Bolton (Darlington 60, 84, 95), Kevin Stonehouse (Blackburn 79), Alan White (Middlesbrough 83).
Clubhouse: Open every evening 7.30-11pm (open earlier on matchnights), 1pm onwards on Satrurday matchdays. Bar, pool & darts.
97-98 Captain: Neil Emmerson **P.o.Y.:** Phil Owers **Top Scorer:** John Outwaite (20)
Club Record Appearances: Bryan Dale **Club Record Goalscorer:** Jack Downing, 61 (1936-37).
Honours: Northern Lg 33-34 34-35 35-36 36-37 39-40 (R-up 32-33 38-39, Lg Cup 33-34 34-35 37-38 38-39 39-40 52-53), Durham Challenge Cup 07-08 25-26 71-72, Durham Amateur Cup 01-02 02-03, Durham Benevelopment Bowl 24-25, FA Trophy 3rd Qualifying Rd 74-75, FA Amateur Cup 4th Rd 58-59, FA Vase 1st Rd 86-87.

SOUTH SHIELDS

Chairman: John Rundle **Vice Chairman:** George Scott **President:**
Secretary/Press Officer: David Fall, 50 Basil Way, South Shields NE34 8UD (0191 426 2135)
Manager: Bobby Graham **Asst Manager:** Keith Tweddle **Physio:** Jim Wilkinson
Ground: Mariners Club, Filtrona Park, Shaftesbury Avenue, Jarrow, Tyne & Wear NE34 9PH.(0191 4279839)
Directions: From A1 (M) take A194(M) to South Shields, A194 town centre road for 5 miles, ignore A1300 (Sunderland & coast) & turn left at next lights beside Co-op store into Simonside Ind. Est. (Shaftesbury Ave.), grd at bottom
Seats: 150 **Cover:** 400 **Capacity:** 2,500 **Floodlights:** Yes **Founded:** 1974
Colours: Claret & blue/white/white **Change:** All white **Nickname:** Mariners
Previous Leagues: Northern Alliance 74-76. **Previous Ground:** Jack Clarke Park 74-92.
Record Attendance: 1,500 v Spennymoor, Durham Challenge Cup Final 94-95
Programme: 40p **Editor:** Steve Leonard **Club Shop:** Yes
Midweek matchday: Tuesday **Reserve team:** None.
Clubhouse: Two function suites, club kitchen.
96-97 Captain: M Irwin **96-97 Top Scorer:** **96-97 P.o.Y.:** Marc Irwin
Honours: FA Vase QF 75-76, Northern Lge Div 2 R-up 95-96, Northern Alliance 74-75 75-76, Wearside Lg 76-77 92-93 94-95, Monkwearmouth Charity Cup 86-87 (R-up 94-95), Shipowners Cup 92-93 (R-up 83-84)), Durham Chal. Cup 76-77 R-up 94-95.

STOCKTON

Chairman: Lol Lyons
Secretary: Peter Morris, 20 Wheatear Lane, Ingleby Barwick, Stockton-on-Tees, Cleveland TS17 0TB (01642 760779)
Manager: Alan Robinson **Asst Mgr:** Michael Watson. **Coach:** Peter May.
Press Officer: Gary Stephenson (01642 713355)
Ground: Teesdale Park, Acklam Road, Thornaby, Stockton-on-Tees TS17 8TZ (01642 606803).
Directions: A19 to Thornaby turn off, ground half mile on right. One mile from Thornaby BR station. Any Stockton-Middlesbrough bus - stop at Acklam Rd, Thornaby.
Seats: 150. **Cover:** 350. **Capacity:** 5,000 **Floodlights:** Yes **Formed:** 1980
Club colours: Red & black stripes/black/red **Change colours:** All sky.
Programme: 24 pages, 30p **Editor:** Alan Reddy (01642 585625). **Club Shop:** No.
Reserves' Lge: Teesside **Midweek Matches:** Tuesday.
PREVIOUS - Leagues: Stockton & District 80-81/ Wearside 81-85. **Names:** Stockton Cricket Club 65-80. **Grounds:** Grangefield Youth & Community Centre, Stockton 80-82/ Tilery Sports Centre 82-83.
Clubhouse: 150+ seater social club with concert room, pool/games room and bar. Open every night and Sunday lunchtimes and all day Saturday. Sandwiches available in bar, canteen in ground sells pies, burgers, soup, drinks etc.
Best FA Cup season: 4th Qual. Rd replay 92-93 (lost 1-2 at home to Blyth after 1-1 draw).
CLUB RECORDS - Attendance: 3,000 v Middlebrough, pre-season friendly August 1986. **Appearances:** Michael Watson. **Win:** 11-0 v Horden C.W.(H) Buchanan Cup 94-95.
Hons: Northern Lg Div 2 87-88 91-92, Nth Riding Co. Cup 85-86, FA Vase 2nd Rd, FA Tphy 1st Rd.Inaugral winners of Craven Cup(Northern Div 2 clubs)94-95.

TOW LAW TOWN

Chairman: John Flynn
Secretary: Bernard Fairbairn, 3 Coppice Walk, Mowden Park, Darlington, County Durham DL3 9DP (01325 350743).
Manager: Stuart Leeming **Assistant Manager:** Terry Kirkbride. **Press Officer:** John Flynn (01325 730525)
Ground: Ironworks Road, Tow Law, Bishop Auckland (01388 731443).
Directions: Just of High Street in Tow Law town centre.
Founded: 1890 **Seats:** 200 **Cover:** 300 **Capacity:** 6,000 **Floodlights:** Due
Colours: Black & white stripes/black/black & white **Change colours:** Red & white
Previous leagues: None **Programme:** Yes. **Club Shop:** Yes
Midweek Matches: Tuesday **Record Gate:** 5,500 v Mansfield Town, FA Cup 1967.
Best F.A. Cup season: 2nd Rd replay 67-68. Also Competition Proper 68-69 84-85 89-90.
League Clubs defeated in F.A. Cup: Mansfield Town 67-68. **Nickname:** Lawyers.
Players progressing to Football League: Reuben Cook & Ralph Guthrie (Arsenal 1951 & 53), Gordon Hughes & Terry Melling & Chris Waddle (Newcastle 1956 & 65 & 80), Eric Johnstone & Kevin Dixon (Carlisle 1963 & 83), Keith Adamson (Barnsley 1966), Tom Henderson (Bradford PA 1969), Vincent Chapman (Huddersfield 1988).
Clubhouse: Every evening 8.30 -10.30.
Honours: Rothmans National Cup 1977, Northern Lg 23-24 24-25 Federation Brewery Northern League Champions 94-95, (R-up 28-29 88-89, Lg Cup 73-74, Rothmans Overseas Cup 76-77), Durham Chal. Cup 1895-96, Durham Amtr Cup 1892-93, FA Amtr Cup 3rd Rd rep. 70-71, FA Tphy 2nd Rd rep. 82-83.

WEST AUCKLAND TOWN

Chairman: Jim Polfreyman
Sec/Press Officer: Allen Bayles, 11 Edith Terrace, West Auckland, Co.Durham. DL14 9JT (011388 833783).
Manager: Dale Swainston **Ass.Manager:** Paul Anderson **Coach:** Robin Gill
Ground: Darlington Road, West Auckland, Co.Durham (011388 834403)
Directions: Leaving West Auckland take A68-ground on right before leaving village. Bus route via Bishop Auckland fron Newcastle or Darlington.
Founded: 1892 **Seats:** 250 **Cover:** 250 **Capacity:** 3,000 **Floodlights:** Yes
Colours: All white **Change Colours:** Black & amber/black/black **Nickname:** West **Club Shop:** No
Midweek Matches: Tuesday **Sponsors:** Tenwick Transport,Hathaway Roofing,Southend Builders.
Previous League: Auckland & District **Previous Names:** St Helens Utd(1919 only),West Auck Town.
Record Gate: 6,000 v Dulwich Hamlet, FA Amateur Cup 58-59. **Best F.A. Cup season:** 1st Rd 58-59,61-62.
Clubhouse: None-use local working mans club five minutes walk away. Thomas Lipton Trophy on display within). On ground reception room for visiting officials and snack bar
96-97 Captain: Gary Lowes **96-97 P.o.Y.:** **96-97 Top Scorer:** Paul Adamson
Honours: F.A.Amateur Cup Finalists 60-61 (QF 59-60) Northern League Champions 59-60,60-61 Div 290-91,Lg Cup 59-60,62-639r-UP;48-49,61-62,63-64) Durham Challenge Cup 63-64 Durham Benevolent Bowl 62-63 Best F.A.Trophy 3rd Rd.77-78 Sir Thomas Lipton Trophy 'First World Cup'(as featured in a television play 'The Captains Tale'1909,+1911

FA Vase 2nd Rd Qual. Jarrow Roofing's Ralph Cooling shots with Horden CW's Keith Evans

Photo: Ray Pruden

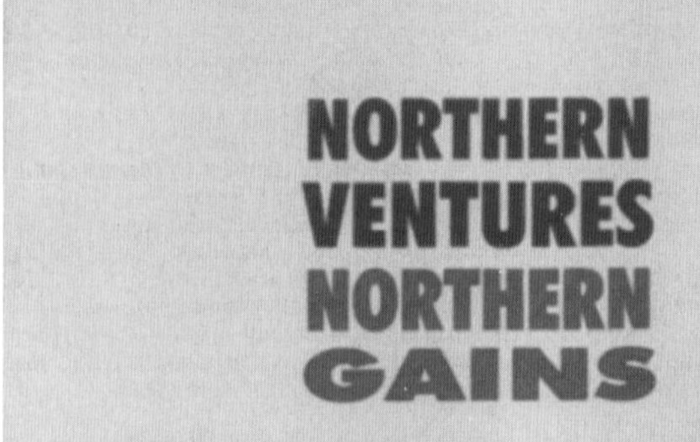

Northern Ventures Northern Gains is published six times a season - seven when an Arnott Insurance Northern League side reaches Wembley.

For ten years the cover price has been held at 30p.

Subscriptions; £3.30 including postage from Don Warner, 18 The Riggs, Hunwick, Crook, Co Durham DL15 0JQ

DIVISION TWO CLUBS 1998-99

ALNWICK TOWN

Chairman: John Common **Press Officer:** Secretary
Secretary: R Miller, 2 Beech Grove, Alnwick NE66 1EB (01665 606169)
Manager: D Clark **Assistant Manager:** Dave Williamson.
Ground: St James' Park, Alnwick, Northumberland (01665 603162).
Directions: 35 miles north of Newcastle on A1, take the slip road to Alnwick, then first left. At roundabout turn left, ground is then on your left.
Seats: 100 **Cover:** 200 **Capacity:** 2,500 **Floodlights:** Yes **Founded:** 1879
Colours: Black & white stripes/black/black **Change colours:** All yellow
Midweek Matches: Tuesday **Reserve Team's League:** North Northumberland
Programme: 20 pages, 25p **Programme Editor:**
Previous Leagues: Northern Alliance 35-39 46-64 64-82.
Record Attendance: 600 v Bedlington Terriers, Northern Alliance 1971.
Best FA Cup season: 3rd Qual. Rd 51-52 (3-4 at Blyth), 57-58 (4-6 at Easington Colliery).
Players progressing to Football League: George Turnbull (Grimsby 1950), Brian Pringle (1973).
Honours: Northern Lg Div 2 R-up 88-89, Northern Alliance 37-38 62-63 63-64 65-66 67-68 68-69 69-70 70-71 71-72 (R-up 59-60 61-62 66-67 72-73, Lg Cup 61-62 65-66 67-68 68-69 70-71, Subsidiary Cup 80-81), Durham Central Lg Cup 64-65, Northumberland Benevolent Bowl 86-87, Northumberland SNR Cup R-up 61-62, Northumberland Amtr Cup 71-72, FA Trophy 3rd Qualifying Rd 90-91.

ASHINGTON

Chairman: T Reed **Joint Predidents:** Sir Bobby Charlton and Jackie Charlton OBE
Secretary: Brian Robinson, 80 Milburn Rd, Ashington, N/thumberland NE63 0PG (01670 852832 H, 01670 521212 B)
Manager: Keith Grant. **Asst.Manager:** Colin Stocks. **Physio:** Brian Hogg
Ground: Portland Park, Ashington NE63 9XG (01670 811991 Social Club)
Directions: 200 yds north at traffic lights in centre of town.
Seats: 350 **Cover:** 2,200 **Capacity:** 4,000 **Floodlights:** Yes **Club Shop:** No
Programme: Yes, 50p **Editor:** A.Marchett (01670 854585) **Press Officer:** Brian Bennett (01670 856606)
Club colours: Black & white stripes/black/white **Change colours:** Yellow with black trim.
Midweek Matches: Tuesday. **Sponsors:** Furst Renault Garage. **Formed:** 1883 **Nickname:** The Colliers.
Best F.A. Cup season: 3rd Rd 26-27. **Record Attendance:** 13,199 v Rochdale, FA Cup 2nd Rd 9/12/50.
Previous Leagues: Northern Alliance 1892-93 1902-14 69-70/ Football League/ North Eastern 14-21 29-58 62-64/ Midland 58-60/ Northern Counties 60-62/ Wearside 64-65/ Northern Premier 68-69.
Players progressing to Football League: Tony Lowery (W.B.A./Mansfield T), Les Mutrie (Colchester), R Cummins (Aberdeen/Newcastle U). David Walton (Sheff Utd./Shrewsbury T.)
Clubhouse: Open normal licensing hours in evenings & from 11.0 a.m. on Tuesdays (market days). Pool, darts, jukebox, snacks etc. Jumpers, baseball caps etc. available behind bar.
Honours: FA Amateur Cup SF 73-74, Northumberland Snr 20-21 32-33 38-39 49-50 55-56 56-57 61-62 66-67 79-80, Northumberland Challenge Bowl 12-13 21-22 22-23 23-24 25-26 33-34, Midland Lg 58-59, North Eastern Lg Cup 33-34(jt with Sunderland Reserves) 39-40 (Div 2 26-27(Res)), Northern Alliance 13-14 24-25(Res) 39-40(Res) 55-56(Res) (R-up 05-06 10-11 11-12 22-23(Res) 54-55(Res) 56-57(Res), Lg Cup 47-48(Res)).

BRANDON UNITED

Chairman: Neil Scott **Vice Chairman:** Joe Cutmore. **President:** Terry Jacques
Secretary: Brian Richardson, Flat 2, 30 Commercial St, Brandon, Durham DH7 8PL (0191 378 1373).
Manager: John Carey **Asst Mgr:** Roli Bell **Physio:** Bev Dougherty
Ground: Welfare Ground, rear of Commercial Street, Brandon, Durham (0191 378 2957).
Directions: A690 - 3 miles west of Durham City. Buses 49 & 49A from Durham.
Seats: 200 **Cover:** 300 **Capacity:** 3,000 **Floodlights:** Yes **Club Shop:** No
Programme: 40 pages, 30p. **Editor:** Keith Nellis (0191 378 0704) **Press Officer:** Secretary.
Colours: All red **Change colours:** All blue. **Founded:** 1968.
Sponsors: Bramble Down Lanscapes **Nickname:** United **Midweek Matches:** Wednesday
Club Records - Gate: 2,500, FA Sunday Cup SF. **Goalscorer:** Tommy Holden **Appearances:** Derek Charlton.
Best FA Cup season: 1st Rd replay 88-89 (lost to Doncaster). Also 1st Rd 79-80.
Previous Lges: Durham & Dist. Sunday 68-77/ Northern All. 77-80/ Northern Amtr 80-81/ Wearside 81-83.
Players progressing to Football League: Bryan Liddle & Dean Gibb (Hartlepool 1984 & 86), Paul Dalton (Manchester Utd 1988), Neil Richardson (Rotherham).
Clubhouse: Open every day, lunch & evening. Pool & juke box. Entertainment at weekends.
97-98 Captain: Colin Myers **Top Scorer:** Chris Heron **P.o.Y.:**
Honours: FA Sunday Cup 75-76, FA Vase QF 82-83 83-84, Northern Lg Div 2 84-85 (Lg Cup R-up 92-93), Northern All.(2) 77-79 (R-up 79-80, Lg Cup 77-78 79-80 (R-up 78-79)), Sunderland Shipowners Cup 81-82, Durham Co. Sunday Cup 73-74 75-76 76-77, FA Tphy 3rd Qual. Rd 87-88 89-90, Durham & Dist Sunday Lg(4) 73-77 (Div 2 69-70, Div 3 68-69), Staffieri Cup 75-76.

DURHAM CITY

Chairman: David Asbery **Vice Chairman:** A Thompson **President:** G Newton.
Secretary: Bob Major, 11 Sherwood Close, Glebe Village, Washington Tyne & Wear NE38 7RJ (0191 416 8679 H, 0191 477 1011 Ext 3105 B)
Manager: B Cruddas **Asst Manager/Coach:** T Harrison
Physio: Joanne Dowson **Commercial Manager:** D Willis. **Press Officer:** Secretary
Ground: New Ferens Park, Belmont Durham (0191 386 9616)
Colours: Gold/navy/gold **Change colours:** Red/black/red. **Reformed:** 1949.
Programme: 30 pages **Editor:** Dave Asberry (0191 386 6469) **Nickname:** City
Midweek Matches: Wednesday. **Club Sponsors:** Key Windows
Previous Leagues: Victory 18-19/ N Eastern 19-21 28-38/ Football Lge 21-28/ Wearside 38-39 50-51.
Prev. Grounds: Garden House Park 18-21/ Holliday Park 21-38/ Ferens Park 49-94. *Nb club disbanded in 1938.*
Best FA Cup season: 2nd Rd 25-26 57-58 (Also 1st Rd 27-28 55-56).
Players progressing to Football League: Harry Houlahan (Newcastle 51), Derek Clark (Lincoln 51), Leo Dale & David Adamson (Doncaster 54/70), Stan Johnstone (Gateshead 54), Dennis Coughlan (Barnsley 57), John Wile (Sunderland 66), Brian Taylor (Coventry 68), Paul Malcolm (Rochdale 84).
Club record appearances: Joe Raine, 552.
Hons: Northern Lg 94-95 (R-up 70-71, Div 2 R-up 30-31 91-92), FA Vase QF 87-88, Durham Benevolent Bowl 55-56, FA Amtr Cup 2nd Rd rep. 57-58, FA Tphy 1st Rd 83-84, Durham Challenge Cup R-up(2).

EPPLETON COLLIERY WELFARE

Chairman: Ralph Lawson **Vice Chairman:** **President:** Mr F Hartis.
Secretary: John Gibson, Avondene, Houghton Road, Hetton-le-Hole, Tyne & Wear DH5 9PH (0191 526 3782)
Manager: Alan Hurst **Asst Manager:** Stuart Gooden **Physio:**
Commercial Mgr: Secretary **Press Officer:** Secretary.
Ground: Eppleton Welfare Park, Park View, Hetton-le-Hole, Tyne & Wear (0191 5261048).
Directions: Situated behind Front Street Post Office & directly behind Hetton swimming baths, Hetton-le-Hole on A182. Buses 194, 535, 231, X5, X94 in Front Street. 8 miles from Durham BR statio; buses 154 and 254 from Durham.
Seats: 250. **Cover:** 500 **Capacity:** 2,500 **Floodlights:** Yes **Founded:** 1929.
Colours: Black & sky/black/black **Change:** Yellow/green/green
Record Attendance: 1,250 - Monkwearmouth Charity Cup Final 1987-88.
Previous - Leagues: Wearside 51-65 74-92/ Houghton & District 65-74. **Grounds:** None **Names:** None (merged with Natcobos, early 70's).
Programme: 16 pages, 20p **Editor:** **Nickname:** Welfare
Club Shop: Club sweaters, polo shirts, metal lapel badges available
Club Sponsors: E & N Ritchie **Midweek home matchday:** Wednesday
Clubhouse: Bar & lounge on ground. Normal opening hours. Whitbread beers.
Honours: Northern Lg Div 2 R-up 92-93, Wearside Lg 90-91 91-92 (Lg Cup 74-75 78-79 87-88, Sunderland Shipowners Cup 47-48 85-86 90-91 (R-up 91-92), Monkwearmouth Charity Cup 89-90 90-91 91-92), Durham Challenge Cup 89-90.

ESH WINNING

Chairman: Charles Ryan **Vice Chairman:** Billy Hall **President:** Jack Lumsden
Secretary: Alan Morton, 20 Durham Road, Esh Winning, Durham (0191 373 3611).
Manager: T.B.A.. **Physio:** T.B.A.
Ground: West Terrace, Waterhouses, Durham (0191 373 3872).
Directions: Durham to Ushaw Moor, to Esh Winning; ground 1 mile further at Waterhouses.
Seats: 160 **Cover:** 160 **Capacity:** 3,500 **Floodlights:** Yes **Club Shop:** No
Programme: 20 pages, 50p **Editor/Press Officer:** Ian Fish (0191 373 0641)
Colours: Yellow/green/yellow & green **Change colours:** Purple & Black.
Club Sponsors: Renault Trucks (North East). **Formed:** 1967 **Nickname:** 'Esh'
Midweek Matches: Tuesday **Club Records - Gate:** 900 v Liverpool Fantail, FA Sunday Cup 1982.
Goalscorer: Paul Ward 31 **Appearances:** Paul Hewitson 40. **Win:** 9-0 v Langley Park (H) **Defeat:** 0-8 v Dunston FB (A). **Transfer fee paid:** Nil **Received:** £400 for Derek Middleton (Easington Colliery).
Best FA Cup season: 2nd Qual Rd 90-91 **Best FA Vase season:** 2nd Round 83-84.
Previous - Leagues: Durham & Dist Sunday/ Northern Alliance 81-82. **Grounds:** None **Names:** Esh Winning Pineapple (pre-1982).
Clubhouse: Open daily. Snacks served
Honours: Durham & District Sunday Lg 78-79 79-80, Durham County Sunday Cup R-up 78-79, Staffieri Cup 74-75, Guards Cup 72-73, North Durham Youth Lg 94-95, Auckland Yth Lge 94-95.

EVENWOOD TOWN

Chairman: Matt Robinson **President:** N Colegrove
Secretary: Jim Coates, 19 Wellgarth, Evenwood, Bishop Auckland, Co Durham DL14 9QU (01388 833035)
Manager: Dr Graeme Forster **Press Officer:** G Forster (0191 373 5143)
Ground: Welfare Ground, Stones End, Evenwood, County Durham (01388 832281).
Directions: In village centre by Sports & Social club in Stones Rd.
Seats: 32 **Cover:** 200 **Capacity:** 3,500 **Floodlights:** Yes **Founded:** 1890
Sponsors: C A Roofing **Midweek Matches:** Wednesday **Programme:** None
Club colours: All blue **Change:** Red (white sleeves)/white/red (white hoops).
Nickname: The Wood. **Clubhouse:** Open lunch & evening every day.
Best FA Cup season: 1st Rd 1936. **Record Gate:** 9,000 v Bishop Auckland, FA Amtr Cup 1931.
Previous Names: None **Players progressing to Football Lge:** Too numerous to record.
Previous Leagues: Barnard Castle & District 1894-95/ Auckland & District 1894-96 1903-04 08-23 28-31/ Wear Valley 1896-99 1904-06 24-25/ Gauntlett Valley 06-07/ South Durham 27-28.
96-97 Captain: **96-97 Top Scorer:** **96-97 P.o.Y.:**
Honours: Northern Lg 48-49 69-70 70-71 (Lg Cup 35-36), Durham Challenge Cup 69-70.

HEBBURN

Chairman: Bill Laffey **Vice-Chairman:** Brian Lowe.
Secretary: Tom Derrick, 63 Staneway, Felling, Gateshead, NE10 8LS. (0191 442 1563)
Manager: Tony Robinson **Assistant Manager:** Dennis Melia **Physio:**
Ground: Hebburn Sports & Social Ground, Victoria Road West, Hebburn (0191 483 5101).
Directions: On the main road through the town about 1 mile from railway station. Hebburn lies on the Metroline - excellent bus service from Heworth Metro.
Seats: 153. **Cover:** 420. **Capacity:** 2,000 **Floodlights:** Yes **Club Shop:** No
Programme: 24 pages, 30p **Editor:** Steve Newton. **Press Officer:** Alan Armstrong (0191 430 0078).
Colours: Yellow & black trim/royal/yellow **Change colours:** All red
Midweek Matches: Wednesday **Nickname:** Hornets. **Founded:** 1912
Club Records - Attendance: 503 v Darwen, FA Cup Preliminary Round replay 7/9/91. **Goalscorer:** Keith Carter
Appearances: **Win:** 10-1 **Defeat:** 3-10.
Best FA Vase season: 2nd Round 91-92.
Best FA Cup season: 2nd Qualifying Rd replay 89-90 (lost 0-3 at South Bank).
Previous Leagues: Jarrow & Dist. Jnr 12-14/ South Shields Comb. 19-22/ Tyneside Comb. 22-27/ Tyneside 27-39/ Northern Comb. 41-44 45-59/ North Eastern 44-45 59-60/ Wearside 60-89.
Previous Grounds: None
Previous Names: Reyrolles/ Hebburn Reyrolles (pre-1988).
Clubhouse: Open 7-11pm weekdays, Sat 11am-1pm, Sun noon-2.30pm. Pool, darts etc.
Honours: Shields Gazette Cup 91-92, Wearside Lg 66-67 (Monkwearmouth Charity Cup 68-69), Durham Challenge Cup 42-43 91-92, Tyneside Lg 38-39, Northern Comb. 43-44, Gateshead Charity Cup 35-36 37-38, Palmer Hospital Cup 27-28, Hebburn Aged Miners Cup 35-36, Heddon Homes Cup 42-43, Hebburn Infirmary Cup 35-36 36-37 37-38 38-39.

HORDEN COLLIERY WELFARE

Chairman: John McCoy **Press Officer:** Karl Henson (01915 842479)
Secretary: Robert Wood, 29 Morpeth Str., Horden, Peterlee, County Durham SR8 4BE (0191 586 8802).
Ground: Welfare Park Ground, Park Road, Horden, Peterlee, County Durham (0191 518 2692 Club)
Directions: A19 to Peterlee, signposted from there.
Seats: 300 **Cover:** 400 **Capacity:** 4,500 **Floodlights:** Yes **Reformed:** 1980
Colours: Red/black/red **Change colours:** Blue/black/blue
Midweek Matches: Tuesday **Programme:** 10 pages, 20p **Nickname:** Colliers
Previous Lges: Wearside 07-35 63-75/ N. Eastern 35-58 62-64/ Midland (Co's) 58-60/ Northern Co's 60-62.
Best FA Cup year: 2nd Rd 38-39 (2-3 at home to Newport Co.). Also 1st Rd 25-26 52-53 53-54 54-55 81-82.
Previous Names: Horden Athletic. **Record Attendance:** 8,000 - FA Cup 1937.
Players progressing to Football League: Paul Dobson (Hartlepool United).
Clubhouse: Normal licensing hours. Hot & cold snacks, darts, pool.
Honours: Durham Challenge Cup 35-36 63-64 80-81 81-82, Durham Benevolent Cup 33-34, Wearside Lg 11-12 12-13 13-14 33-34 64-65 67-68 69-70 70-71 71-72 72-73 (Lg Cup 33-34 49-50, Monkwearmouth Charity Cup 12-13 23-24 32-33 69-70 72-73, Sunderland Shipowners Cup 65-66 72-73), North Eastern Lg 37-38 63-64 ('Non-Reserve' Medal 50-51).

MURTON

Chairman: Tom Torrence **Vice Chairman:** J Hudson **President:** John Hellens.
Secretary: T Turnbull, 15 Dalton Terrace, Murton, Seaham, Co Durham SR7 9BZ (0191 526 6488 H, 0191 581 9874 B)
Manager: Jeff Cranson **Asst Mgr:** Brian Burlinson **Coach:** Richie Madden.
Physio: Vince Symmonds **Press Officer:** James Hudson (0191 526 0283) **Commercial Mgr:** T Carr.
Ground: Recreation Park, Church Lane, Murton, County Durham (0191 517 0814).
Directions: Exit A19 onto B1285 heading west into Murton - Church Lane on left opposite catholic church.
Seats: 100 **Cover:** 320 **Capacity:** 3,500 **Floodlights:** Yes **Founded:** 1904
Colours: All white with red trim **Change colours:** Red/black/red **Nickname:** Gnashers
Programme: 12 pages, 30p **Programme Editor:** Stuart Upperton **Club Shop:** No.
Club Sponsors: John Hellyns **Midweek home matchday:** Wednesday
Record Gate: 3,500 v Spennymoor Utd, Durham Challenge Cup 1951.
Previous Grounds: Fatton Pasture 04-28. **Players progressing to Football League:** Numerous.
Previous Names: Murton Red Star 04-28/ Murton Colliery Welfare 28-88.
Previous Leagues: Wearside 13-46 51-88/ North East Counties 46-51.
Record win: 17-1 v Thornley **Record defeat:** 0-14 v South Shields (H).
Clubhouse: 'The International' 300 yards from ground on B1285. Normal pub hours. Restaurant upstairs. Function room for 100. Open plan downstairs with horse shoe bar. Matchday snacks at ground.
Club record scorer: **Club record appearances:** Robert Welch 500 (1962-78).
Honours: Northern Lg Div 2 89-90, Wearside Lg 28-29 36-37 59-60 (Lg Cup 58-59 70-71), Sunderland Shipowners Cup 59-60 69-70 70-71, Monkwearmouth Charity Cup 21-22 28-29 34-35 35-36 63-64 70-71 87-88, Durham Chall. Cup 92-93, Durham Jnr Cup 50-51.

NORTHALLERTON

Chairman: **Vice Chairman:** Keith Alderson **President:** Ian Butler
Secretary: David Watson 26 Bilsdale Close, Romanby, Northallerton, N Yorks (01609 783818 H, 01609 772418 B)
Manager: John Woods/Mike Sell **Physio:** Andrew Garson **Press Officer:** Secretary
Ground: Ainderby Rd, Romanby, Northallerton, North Yorks (01609 772418)
Directions: Leave A1 at Leeming Bar (A684) follow signs to Northallerton, approaching town take B1333 signed Romanby - ground 250yds on left. Three quarters of a mile from Northallerton BR station - local bus from town centre (one and a half miles) passes ground.
Seats: 150 **Cover:** 500 **Capacity:** 3,000 **Floodlights:** Yes **Founded:** 1994
Clubhouse: Mon-Fri 7.30-11pm, Sat noon-7.30pm, Sun 12-2 & 7.30-10.30pm.
Midweek home matchday: Wednesday **Club Shop:** Yes, Contact Mark Walker (01609 780837)
Colours: All black & white **Change colours:** Yellow/blue/yellow. **Nickname:** Town
Previous Leagues: Allertonshire (now defunct)/ Vale of Mowbray (defunct)/ Ripon & Dist./ Teesside/ North Yorks (defunct)/ Darlington & Dist./ Harrogate & Dist.
Previous Ground: Bluestone Ground (pre-1975).
Previous Names: Northallerton Alliance/ Northallerton Town (pre-1994).
Programme: 16 pages, 50p **Programme Editor:** Ian Bolland
Club Sponsors: TBA **Reserve Team's League:** None
Club Records - Gate: 671 v Farnborough, FA Tphy 3rd Rd 20/2/93. **Goalscorer:** John Woods **Appearances:** Lee Wasden. **Win:** 11-0 v Ferryhill (A) **Defeat:** 9-1 v Ryhope CA (A)
Best FA Cup year: 4th Qual. Rd 92-93 **Best FA Trophy year:** 3rd Rnd 92-93
Players progressing to Football League: Andy Toman (Hartlepool, Darlington, Scarborough).
Honours: Northern Lg Cup 93-94 (Div 2 R-up 89-90), North Riding Snr Cup R-up 83-84, Harrogate & Dist. Lg, Richmond Cup, Bedale Cup, Millbank Cup, Orde Powlett Cup, Harrogate Invitation Cup, Alverton Trophy.

NORTON & STOCKTON ANCIENTS

Chairman: Stephen Warnes **President:** Barry Lee **Press Officer:** Secretary
Secretary: Andrew Boynton, 37 Wollaton Road, Billingham, TS23 3AU (01642 862039)
Ground: Station Road, Norton, Stockton-on-Tees, Cleveland (01642 530203).
Directions: Norton village 2 miles from Stockton centre, turn into Station Road on outskirts of village.
Seats: 200 **Cover:** Yes **Capacity:** 2,000 **Floodlights:** Yes **Formed:** 1959
Colours: Amber, white & black/black & amber/black **Change colours:** White with amber trim
Programme: 12 pages with entry **Editor:** **Nickname:** Ancients
Midweek Matches: Wednesday **Record Attendance:** 1,430 v Middlesbrough, Friendly 88
Previous - Leagues: Teesside (pre-1982). **Name:** Norton & Stockton Cricket Club Trust.
Best F.A. Cup season: 1st Qual Rd(4) 88-89 90-93
Clubhouse details: Full bar facilities, 150 yds from ground.
Honours: Northern Lg Cup 81-82.

PETERLEE NEWTOWN

Chairman: Carl Paylor **Vice-Chairman:** Bill Burnett. **President:** David Brown
Secretary: Danny Cassidy, 23 Melbury Str, Seaham, County Durham SR7 7NF (0191 581 4591).
Manager: Tommy Smith **Asst Manager:** Eddie Freeman **Physio:** Ron Lamdrel.
Ground: Eden Lane, Peterlee, County Durham (0191 586 3004).
Directions: From town centre Fire Station, turn left into Edenhill Rd, then right into Robson Ave. Left at the next junction and ground is on the right.
Seats: 50 **Cover:** 200 **Capacity:** 6,000 **Floodlights:** Yes **Formed:** 1976
Colours: Sky/navy/sky **Change colours:** Yellow/black/yellow **Club Shop:** No.
Programme: 10 pages, 30p **Editor:** Secretary **Press Officer:** Ray Matthews (0191 587 0727)
Sponsors: Artix Ltd **Previous lges:** Northern Alliance 76-79/ Wearside 79-82.
Nickame: Newtowners. **Record Attendance:** 2,350 v Northern, Hillsborough Fund match 1989.
Midweek Matches: Wednesday. **Best FA Cup season:** 4th Qual. Rd replay 85-86
Players progressing to Football Lge: Keith Fairless (Scarborough) 1986, Brian Honour (Hartlepool) 1988).
Clubhouse: Open normal licensing hours. Sandwiches etc available.
Club record scorer: Keith Fairless **Club record appearances:** Keith Bendelow.
Honours: Northern Lg Div 2 82-83, North Eastern F'lit League, 4th Qual Rd FA Cup

PRUDHOE TOWN

Chairman: Alex Waters
Secretary: Brian Tulip, 12 Orchard Close, Prudhoe NE42 5LP (01661 833169).
Manager: Terry Hunter **Asst Manager:** Kenny Barton **Physio:** Ernie Goodfellow
Ground: Kimberley Park, Broomhouse Road, Prudhoe, Northumberland NE42 5EH (Tel/Fax: 01661 835900).
Directions: Approach Prudhoe along A695, turn right at 'Falcon' Inn, 200 yds down Eastwood Rd., turn left into Broomhouse Rd., ground on right.
Seats: 150 **Cover:** Yes **Capacity:** 5,000 **Floodlights:** Yes **Founded:** 1959
Colours: Purple & jade/purple/purple. **Change:** White & blue chevrons/navy/sky.
Programme: 8 pages, 20p **Editor:** J Smith **Press Officer:** Ken Barton (0191 273 4640)
Sponsors: Swinton Insurance **Midweek Matches:** Wednesday **Nickname:** Citizens
Previous Leagues: Hexham & Dist 59-69/ Newcastle & Dist 69-71/ N. Comb./ N. Amtr/ Northern All. 84-88.
Previous Names: Ovington 1969-75/ Prudhoe East End 75-94.
Previous Grounds: Farm field, Ovington 59-68/ Mickley Welfare 68-69.
Record Attendance: 2,500 v Blyth, Northumberland Snr Cup 1981.
Clubhouse: Open every evening plus Sat/Sun lunchtimes
Honours: Hexham & Dist. Lg 68-69 (Lg Cup 68-69), Newcastle & Dist. Lg 69-70 70-71 (Lg Cup 69-70, Charity Shield 69-70 70-71), Northern Comb. 79-80, Northerm Amtr Lg 71-72, Clayton Charity Cup 68-69, Northumberland Minor Cup 78-79, Northumberland Benevolent Bowl 79-80, Heddon Homes Charity Cup 81-82.

RYHOPE COMMUNITY ASSOCIATION

Chairman: David Lawson **Press Officer:** Secretary
Secretary: Bob Lewins, 7 Belsay Gardens, St.Gabriels Estate, Sunderland. SR4 7SZ (01915 141725)
Ground: Meadow Park, Stockton Road, Ryhope, Sunderland (0191 523 6555)
Directions: From Sunderland follow signs for A19 South, ground adj to Cherry Knowle Hopital in Ryhope
Seats: 150 **Cover:** 200 **Capacity:** 2,000 **Floodlights:** Yes **Founded:** 1988.
Colours: Red & white/black/red & white **Change colours:** All Blue
Previous Leagues: Sporting Club Vaux: Tyne & Wear/ North Eastern Amateur.
Previous Names: Ryhope Colliery Welfare (founded 1898, previously Ryhope Villa) merged with Sporting Club Vaux (founded in 1968 as Monkwearmouth, later Bishopwearmouth, South Hetton) in 1988/ Sunderland Vaux Ryhope Colliery Welfare 88-93.
Previous Grounds: Sporting Club Vaux: Glenesk Road (pre-1988)
Record Gate: 2,000; Ryhope Colliery Welfare v Workington, FA Cup 1967.
Players progressing to Football League: Alan Harding (Lincoln, Darlington, Hartlepool), Kenny Ellis (Hartlepool, Darlington, Belgian clubs), Kenny Mitchell (prof. Icelandic club), Robert Malt (Leeds), Brian Smiles (Chelsea), Ron Robinson (Ipswich, Leeds), Nigel Staddington (Doncaster, Sunderland).
Honours *(Sporting Club Vaux hons italicised)* Wearside Lg 61-62 62-63 63-64 65-66 (Lg Cup 63-64 77-78), Durham Challenge Cup 77-78, Monkwearmouth Charity Cup 09-10 65-66 66-67, Sunderland Shipowners Cup 61-62 *86-87*, FA Cup 1st Rd Proper 67-68, FA Vase 1st Rd 81-82.

SHOTTON COMRADES

Chairman: J Maddison **Vice Chairman:** T.Robindon. **President:** G Taylor.
Secretary: Billy Banks, 30 Hamilton Court, Shotton Colliery, Durham DH6 2NL (0191 526 7134)
Manager: B.Huntingdon. **Asst Manager:** **Physio:** W.Banks.
Ground: Shotton Recreational Ground, Station Road, Shotton Colliery, Co. Durham (0191 526 2859).
Directions: A19 to Peterlee to Shotton, right at War Mem. t-junction, follow round 800yds, ground on right.
Seats: 80 **Cover:** 400 **Capacity:** 1,700 **Floodlights:** No **Formed:** 1973
Colours: Black & white/black/black **Change colours:** All orange.
Sponsors: T.B.A. **Midweek home matches:** Wednesday **Nickname:** Coms
Programme: 12 pages, 20p **Editor:** Mr E A Jones **Press Officer:** Secretary
Previous Leagues: Peterlee Sunday 74-76/ Houghton & District 76-80/ Northern Alliance 80-83.
Previous Grounds: None **Reserves' Lge:** Banks u-19 Yth **Club Shop:** No
Club Records - Attendance: 1,726 v Dennis Waterman XI. **Goalscorer:** Keith Willets 50 **Appearances:** J Cudlip.
Win: 8-0 v Bedlington Ter. (H), '92 **Defeat:** 1-7 v Brandon Utd (A), F.A. Cup Prel. Rd 91-92. **Transfer received:** £500 for G Gudlip (Shildon)
Best F.A. Cup season: 2nd Qualifying Rd 85-86 (lost 0-2 at home to Wingate). **Clubhouse:** No.
Honours: Houghton & District Lg 78-79 (Lg Cup(2)), Northern Alliance Lg Cup SF, Hetton Charity Cup 78-79, Peterlee Sunday Lg 75-76 (Div 2 74-75), FA Vase 1st Rd 86-87 90-91, Durham Challenge Cup QF 78-79 (Minor Cup QF 78-79).Northern Lg.Div 2 Cup R-Up. 94-95.

WASHINGTON IKEDA HOOVER

Chairman: Derek Armstrong **Press Officer:** Ray Lish (0191 415 7071)
Secretary: George Abbott, 14 Grosvenor Street, Southwick, Sunderland SR5 2DG (0191 549 1384).
Ground: Albany Park, Spout Lane, Concord, Washington (0191 417 7779).
Directions: Ground situated behind the cinema opposite bus station.
Seats: 25 **Cover:** Yes **Capacity:** 3,000 **Floodlights:** No **Founded:** 1949
Colours: All red **Change colours:** All blue **Midweek Matches:** Wednesday
Programme: 8 pages, 10p **Editor:** Mr Bull (0191 4164618) **Club Shop:** No
Nickname: Mechanics **Previous Leagues:** Washington Amateur/ Northern Alliance 67-68/ Wearside 68-88.
Previous Ground: Usworth Welfare Park **Record Gate:** 3,800 v Bradford Park Avenue, FA Cup 1970.
Clubhouse: Open normal licensing hours, with live entertainment, pool etc.

WHICKHAM

Chairman: Tommy Thompson **Manager:** Billy Hodgson **Press Officer:** Ray Graham (0191 477 3633)
Secretary: Harry Hodgson, 18 Deepdale Close, Whickham, Newcastle upon Tyne, NE16 6SN (0191 488 2493)
Ground: Glebe Ground, Rectory Lane, Whickham (0191 420 0186)
Directions: A692 (Consett) from A69. Left at r'bout signed Consett/Whickham. Up hill and right at mini-r'bout. Continue along & turn left into Rectory Lane (by Lloyds Bank) for about 500 yds, clubhouse on right
Seats: 100 **Cover:** Yes **Capacity:** 4,000 **Floodlights:** Due **Founded:** 1944
Colours: All black & white **Change colours:** All white
Programme: 20p **Souvenir Shop:** No **Midweek Matches:** Wednesday
Previous Leagues: Derwent Valley -55/ Northern Comb. 55-57 59-74/ Tyneside Amtr 57-59/ Wearside 74-88.
Previous Ground: Rectory Rec. Field
Record Gate: 3,165 v Windsor & Eton, F.A. Vase SF 81 **Best F.A. Cup season:** 1st Qual. 89-90
Players progressing to Football League: Nigel Walker (Newcastle 1977), David Norton (Hartlepool 1981), Mike Carroll (Chesterfield 1981).
Clubhouse: Mon-Fri. 12-3 & 7-11, Sat.11-11, Sun. 12-2, 7.30-11
Honours: FA Vase 80-81, Wearside Lg 77-78 87-88 (R-up 80-81 84-85, Lg Cup 86-87, Monkwearmouth Charity Cup 76-77, Sunderland Shipowners Cup 77-78 80-81), Northern Comb. 69-70 72-73 73-74 (Lg Cup 60-61 73-74).

WILLINGTON

Chairman: Anne Robson **Vice-Chairman:** Jack Snowdon **President:** Hilary Armstrong
Secretary/Press Officer: Bob Nichols, 46 Cavendish Court, Brandon, Durham DH7 8UW
Player/Manager: Dave Taylor **Asst.Mgr:** Les Ryder **Physio:** T B A
Ground: Hall Lane, Hall Lane Estate, Willington, County Durham (01388 746221).
Directions: Willington is on A690 7 miles west of Durham City & 2 miles east of Crook. Off main through road at 'The Black Horse Tavern' corner turn off Commercial St, then into Hall Lane after 100yds. Northern Bus Co. operates a service through Willington from Crook or Durham City.
Seats: 350 **Cover:** 400 **Capacity:** 2,680. **Floodlights:** Yes **Founded:** 1906.
Programme: 40p **Editor:** Keith Stephenson **Club shop:** Occasionally
Colours: Blue & white stripes/blue/blue **Change colours:** Yellow/green/yellow.
Sponsor: Rackwood Park Drift Mine **Nickname:** Blue & Whites **Midweek Matches:** Wednesday
Youth League: Auckland & Dist League. **Youth (U18)'s League:** Auckland & district League.
Club Records - Attendance: 10,000 v Bromley, FA Amateur Cup 2nd Rd 24/1/53. **Goalscorer:** J 'Boxer' Taylor 55-69. **Appearances:** S Rutherford 47-61. **Win:** 13-3 v Whitby (H), 1928 **Defeat:** 0-11 v Dunston (H), 5/9/92 - both Northern Lge. **Transfer fee paid:** £300 for Geoff Young (Durham City) 1998. **Received:** £550 for Dominic Dimambro (Whitby Town) 1988.
Best FA Cup season: 1st Rd replay 73-74 (lost 1-6 at Blackburn after 0-0 draw). Also 1st Rd 45-46 50-51.
Previous - Leagues: Auckland & Dist. 1906-11. **Grounds:** West End Ground 1906-11. **Names:** Willington Temperance 1906-11.
Players progressing to Football League: George Tweedy (Grimsby) 33, Andy Graver (Newcastle) 47, Brian Ronson (Fulham) 53, Martin Burleigh (Newcastle) 69, Wally Hindmarsh (Portsmouth) 45.
Clubhouse: Open evenings 7-11pm at Saturday matchdays 1-11pm. Bar facilities. Tea shop on matchdays.
97-98 Captain: Dave Edwards **Top Scorer:** Brett Cummings **P.o.Y.:** Ryan Murray
Honours: FA Trophy 3rd Rd 75-76; FA Amateur Cup 49-50, R-up 38-39, SF 27-28, Northern League 13-14 25-26 29-30, R-up 12-13 57-58 75-76, League Cup 24-25 25-26 27-28 56-57 30-31 31-32 48-49 74-75; Durham Benevolent Cup 48-49 50-51 57-58.

Jarrod Suddick scores the semi-final winner for Tow Law Town against Taunton . . .

. . . and celbrates

Photos: Neil Thaler

Wembley - What a feeling
Photo: Neil Thaler

It's great to be here
Photo: Colin Stevens

Action at both ends for Tow Law Town

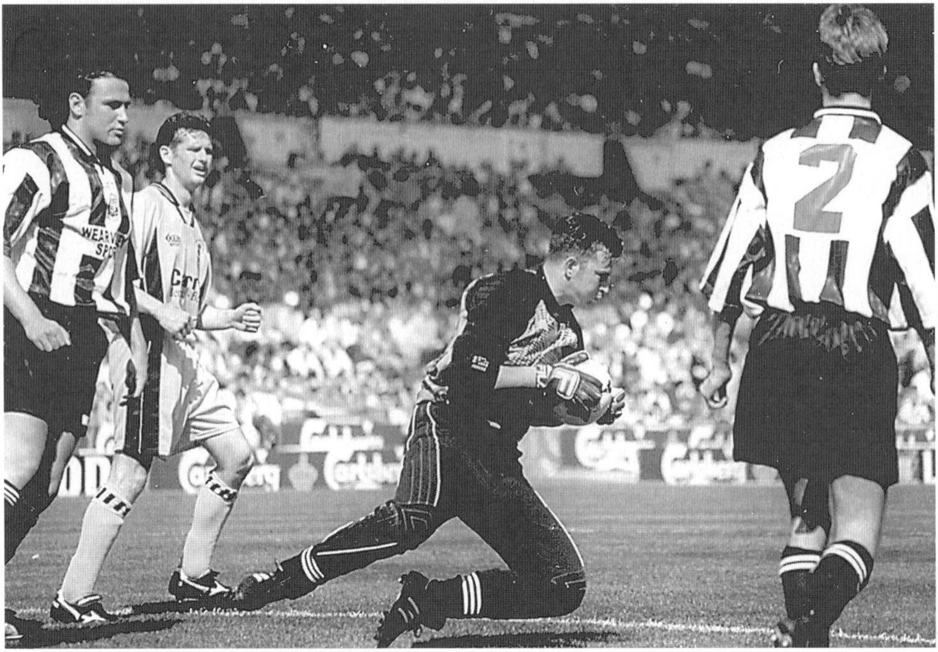

Tow Law keeper Stuart Dawson shows determination and confidence in his area Photo: Neil Thaler

A last gasp effort by Tow Law Town is tipped over the bar by Tiverton Town keeper Paul Edwards
Photo: Colin Stevens

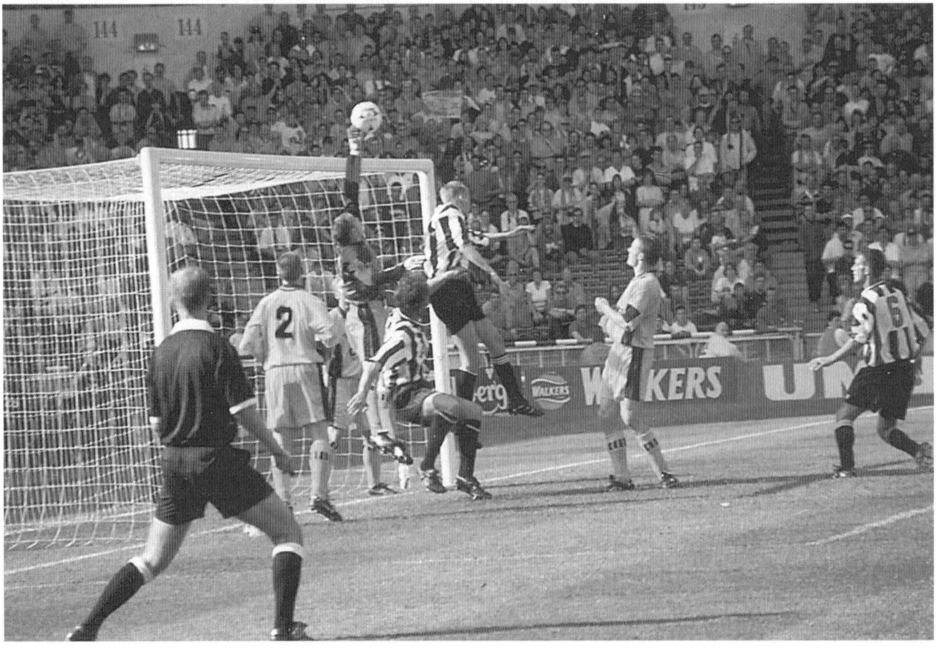

VAUX WEARSIDE LEAGUE

Founded: 1892
FEEDER TO: ARNOTT INSURANCE NORTHERN LEAGUE

President: J C Thomas **Chairman:** P J Maguire
Hon. Secretary & Treasurer: Bill Robson
12 Deneside, Howden-le-Wear, Crook, Co Durham DL15 8JR

DIVISION ONE FINAL LEAGUE TABLE 1997-98

	P	*W*	*D*	*L*	*F*	*A*	*Pts*
Annfield Plain	36	26	3	7	121	43	81
Sunderland KR	36	23	8	5	103	44	77
Birtley Town	36	25	3	8	103	49	75
Gateshead Res	36	22	5	9	106	53	71
Ryhope Coll. W	36	19	6	11	80	47	63
Washington Nis.	36	17	11	8	80	54	62
Boldon CA	36	19	6	12	90	79	62
S Shields Cl. SC	36	18	7	11	71	49	61
Windscale	36	17	5	14	98	66	66
S Tyneside Utd	36	14	9	13	90	76	61
N Shields Ath	36	14	7	15	67	71	49
Stanley Utd	36	14	6	16	98	91	48
Hart'pool BWOB	36	13	9	14	67	70	48
Wolviston	36	14	4	18	71	77	46
Herton & W. CW	36	11	8	17	67	95	41
Jarrow	36	6	7	23	56	95	25
Whitehaven Am	36	7	4	25	65	133	25
South Bank	36	7	2	27	42	118	23
Horden Ath D	36	1	1	34	26	191	4

		1	2	3	4	5	6	7	8	9	10	11	12	13	14	15	16	17	18	19
1	Annfield Plain	X	5-1	3-1	1-2	4-0	3-0	10-1	6-2	3-1	1-3	5-1	3-2	4-1	6-1	1-2	1-3	8-0	2-1	2-2
2	Birtley Town	3-1	X	2-4	2-2	2-2	3-1	10-1	2-1	4-1	2-1	5-1	6-0	6-1	5-0	4-1	3-0	4-2	2-4	2-1
3	Gateshead Res	1-2	5-0	3-1	X	4-0	2-3	8-1	5-2	2-1	0-0	6-0	2-0	8-2	5-3	3-2	1-0	9-0	2-0	1-1
4	Hartlepool BWOB	0-1	0-2	1-0	2-0	X	1-2	3-1	1-1	1-1	4-0	4-0	1-2	0-4	5-3	2-3	2-3	2-2	2-1	5-4
5	Horden Athletic	1-2	0-4	2-4	1-7	0-3	2-2	X	0-4	0-3	0-1	0-1	1-5	0-7	1-9	0-4	1-6	1-3	1-3	1-6
6	Jarrow	1-3	1-4	0-5	2-2	1-2	0-1	8-0	X	2-2	3-1	4-0	3-1	3-3	1-2	3-3	0-2	2-6	0-8	2-0
7	North Shields Athletic	4-2	0-2	1-3	1-3	1-2	2-0	5-1	1-0	X	2-4	3-2	2-2	1-3	3-2	0-6	1-2	4-1	0-4	3-0
8	Ryhope Colliery Welfare	1-1	0-2	3-1	4-0	4-3	2-0	7-0	4-0	0-1	X	6-0	2-2	1-1	1-1	1-1	2-3	4-1	2-0	3-0
9	South Bank	0-5	2-6	1-2	0-1	2-1	2-0	1-2	2-2	0-4	2-0	X	0-2	2-4	0-8	0-5	0-4	4-0	1-0	0-2
10	Sth Shields Cleadon SC	0-1	1-1	3-2	2-1	2-2	3-0	3-0	3-2	2-0	2-0	2-1	X	2-0	2-3	2-1	3-1	9-0	1-1	2-0
11	South Tyneside United	0-5	1-0	2-3	4-2	2-0	2-2	8-0	5-1	2-2	0-1	4-1	0-2	X	2-2	0-2	1-1	6-0	1-1	2-5
12	Stanley United	3-2	0-1	1-4	2-5	1-2	1-2	3-0	4-1	2-2	1-4	0-7	2-1	2-6	X	1-1	3-3	9-1	6-2	2-0
13	Sunderland Kennek R.	1-7	2-0	1-2	4-2	1-1	5-1	6-1	3-0	2-2	3-1	5-2	2-1	3-0	5-1	X	4-0	4-0	2-2	5-0
14	Washington Nissan	0-0	1-2	4-0	1-3	2-0	4-4	7-1	2-1	0-3	3-0	2-2	1-1	2-1	4-0	1-1	X	5-1	1-1	1-1
15	Whitehaven Amateurs	1-5	1-2	0-5	1-2	3-3	1-4	9-1	0-0	2-4	1-4	6-2	0-3	4-3	2-1	0-2	2-2	X	1-0	1-2
16	Windscale	0-1	2-1	7-1	3-1	2-4	4-2	16-0	2-1	4-0	2-4	5-0	4-1	1-2	3-3	0-2	2-1	5-0	X	0-1
17	Wolviston	0-5	3-0	0-5	2-1	2-2	2-4	5-0	4-1	3-2	4-1	5-1	1-0	3-5	1-3	0-2	1-2	6-2	2-3	X

SUNDERLAND SHIPOWNERS CUP 1997-98

Semi-Final

Jarrow Roof. Boldon	v	Chester le Street Tn	3-2
Sunderland Ken Rok.	v	Consett	0-1

FINAL

CONSETT	v	JARROW/BOLDON	3-0

LEAGUE CUP 1997-98

Semi-Final

Annfield Plain	v	Wolviston	3-2
Stanley United	v	Birtley Town	0-2

FINAL

BIRTLEY TOWN	v	ANNFIELD PLAIN	2-1

MONKWEARMOUTH CHARITY CUP 1997-98

Semi-Final

Annfield Plain	v	South Tyneside Utd	2-3
Windscale	v	Washington Nissan	5-2

FINAL

S TYNESIDE UTD	v	WINDSCALE	2-3

STAN SEYMOUR CUP 1997-98

Semi-Final

Coxlodge Social Club	v	Newcastle Benfield P	5-2
Ponteland United	v	Carlisle City	1-2

FINAL

COXLODGE SC	v	CARLISLE CITY	0-5

DIVISION ONE CLUBS 1998-99

ANNFIELD PLAIN

Chairman: Frank Ross **Manager:** D Longstaff **Press Officer:** Frank Ross
Secretary: M Lawson, 24 Northgate, Anfield Plain, Stanley, Co. Durham DH9 7UY (01207 235879).
Ground: Derwent Park, Annfield Plain. **Directions:** On A693 road to Consett, 200 yds west of junction with A6067. Ground behind new housing estate. 6 miles from Durham (BR). Buses from Sunderland, Newcastle & Durham.
Seats: 20 **Cover:** 200 **Capacity:** 6,000 **Floodlights:** No **Founded:** 1890.
Colours: Claret/white/white **Change colours:** All blue. **Programme:** 16 pages, 20p
Hons: Wearside Lg 84-85 (Monkwearmouth Charity Cup 92-93), FA Cup 1st Rd 26-27 28-29 64-65.

BIRTLEY TOWN

Chairman: J Heslington **Vice-Chairman:** J Grainger. **Manager:** Barry Fleming
Secretary: Kevin McConnell, 8 Leyburn Place, Birtley, DH3 1PL (0191 4100495)
Asst Manager: David Smith **Coach:** Malcolm Thompson **Commercial Manager:** Ray Stafford.
Ground: Birtley Sports Complex. **Directions:** (From Durham) Off A1 (M) signpsted for Chester-le-Street, take 2nd turn off r-bout signed Birtley, take last turn off next r-bout (still signed Birtley), after one and a half miles take 1st left after AEI Cables - ground at rear of sports complex.
Seats: None **Cover:** None **Capacity:** **Floodlights:** No. **Founded:** 1890
Colours: Green/white/white **Change colours:** Yellow/blue/red. **Reformed:** 1986
Midweek matches: Wednesday **Sponsors:** C & C Coachworks **Clubhouse:** Matchdays only
Hons: Wearside Lg 45-46 (Lg Cup 35-36), Northern Alliance 23-24 (R-up 13-14).

BOLDON COMMUNITY ASSOCIATION

Chairman: R A O Shepherd. **Vice Chairman:** G Smith **President:** A Brewster.
Sec./Press Off./Comm Mgr: George Pollard, 126 Horsley Hill Road, South Shields (0191 4546821).
Manager: Bill Newham **Asst Manager:** P Quinn **Coach:** Tommy Frazer.
Ground: Boldon Community Association, New Road, Boldon Colliery.
Directions: A19 to junc A184 Sunderland/Newcastle. Follow signs to Boldon Asda stores, then to North Road Social Club (SHACK). Ground behind. 800 yds from East Boldon (BR). Buses 533, 531, 319, 528.
Seats: 100 **Cover:** 400 **Capacity:** 3,500 **Floodlights:** No **Founded:** 1892.
Colours: Blue & white/blue/blue & white **Change:** Scarlet & black **Nickname:** Villa.
Clubhouse: Matchdays only. Bar snacks **Sponsors:** Tyne Dock Engineering Co., South Shields.
Hons: Wearside Lg 3, (Lg Cup 3), M/mouth Char Cup 2, Shipowners Cup 6.

HARTLEPOOL BOYS WELFARE OLD BOYS

Chairman: Tom Harvey **Treasurer:** Derek Stephens
Secretary: Phillip Jordan, 473 Catcote Road, Hartlepool TS25 2RA (01429 870015)
Manager: Jimmy Costello **Asst Manager:** Wilf Constantine **Physio:** Tony Metcalfe.
Ground: Grayfields Enclosure, Jesmond Road, Hartlepool.
Directions: Leave A19 on A179 signed Hartlepool, right for Throston Grange at 1st r'bout, left at 1st lights into Jesmond Road, ground 400yds on left.
Seats: None **Cover:** No **Capacity:** **Floodlights:** No **Founded:** 1952.
Colours: All yellow **Change colours:** White/red/red **Nickname:** None.
Programme: 10 pages, 50p **Editor:** Secretary **Clubhouse:** No.
Hons: FA Vase 3rd Rd, Wearside Lg Div 2 92-93, Hartlepool Church Lg(2)(Lg Cup(3)), Hartlepool Mem. Shield, Durham Amat Cup 2, Hartlepool & Dist. Lg(3)(Lg Cup(3)), Teesside Lg 73-74 85-86 (R-up 3).

JARROW

Chairman: Paul Thu **Treasurer:** Jimmy Kane
Secretary: Calum McAuley, 156 Beaconside, Cleadon Village, South Shields (0191 4555924).
Ground: Perth Green Community Centre. **Directions:** From A19 or A1(M) follow drections to South Shields, right onto John Reid Road. First slip road onto Brockley Whinns Estate, follow road past Red Hackle pub, third left left onto Inverness Road, then right into Perth Green Community Centre.
Colours: Blue & white/blue/blue **Change:** Green/black/green **Founded:** 1980.
Hons: Sth Tyne Lg & Lg Cup, Washington Lg R-up 89-90 (Lg Cup 90-91, Aged Peoples Tphy R-up 90-91), Gateshead Charity Cup 90-91, Durham Tphy R-up 90-91.

NORTH SHIELDS

Chairman: Alan Matthews. **Manager:** Bob Weir. **Coach:** Wilf Keilty.
Secretary: Dave Thompson, 38 Barnstable Road, North Shields, (0191 2590249)
Ground: Ralph Gardner Park, West Percy Rd., N.Shields, Tyne & Wear,NE29 OES
Directions: A19 northbound through Tyne Tunnel. Take 1st slip round to 1st r/about & take 3rd exit & over next r/about. Take 3rd exit again at next r/about into Waterville Rd. Over another r/about and 2nd left into Silkey's Lane. 1st right into West Percy Rd, grd on right.
Colours: All red **Change colours:** Blue & black/black/black
Sponsors: Wilkinson Stores **Nickname:** New Robins **Founded:** 1896 **Clubhouse:** None
Hons: Nthn Cnt E, Champ/Cup/Presidents Cup 91-92. FA Amt Cup 68-69, N Lge 68-69.

RYHOPE C W

Chairman: David Lawson **Press Officer:** Secretary
Secretary: George McKitterick, 8 Kilburn Close, Ryhope Village, Sunderland. SR2 0QU (0191 523 8436)
Ground: Ryhope Recreation Park, Ryhope Street, Ryhope, Sunderland (0191 521 2843).
Directions: Take A19 (3 miles south of Sunderland centre) to Ryhope village, at Village Green turn into Evelyn Terrace/Ryhope Street and carry on up bank past Presto's for 600 yds - ground appears on left. 3 miles from Sunderland Central (BR), bus every 10 minutes from Sunderland centre.
Seats: No **Cover:** No **Capacity:** 1,000 **Floodlights:** Yes **Founded:** 1988.
Colours: Yellow/black/black & red **Change colours:** Red/white/red & white
Honours: Wearside Lg 4, (Lg Cup 2), Durham Chall Cup 77-78, M/mouth Charity Cup 3, S/land Shipowners Cup 2.

SOUTH SHIELDS CLEADON SOCIAL CLUB

Chairman: Gordon Ferries **Vice-Chairman/Press Off./Manager:** David Wood (0191 4554607).
Secretary: Mr Charlie Appleby, 49 Tynedale Rd, South Shields (0191 454 5724).
Asst Manager: Steve Duguid **Commercial Manager:** Joan Wood **Coach:** Andy Wilkinson
Ground: Jack Clarke Park, South Shields.
Directions: Enter South Shields on A194 to r'bout taking you on to A1300 John Reid Rd. 2nd left at 3rd r'bout into King George Rd then Sunderland Rd, right at lights into Grosvenor Rd, left into Horsly Hill Rd. Ground on right
Colours: Amber/black/amber **Change:** All red **Club Shop:** No
Midweek matches: Wednesday **Sponsors:** Cleadon & Dist. Soc. Club **Nickname:** The Club
Clubhouse: Cleadon Social Club, Fulwell Avenue, South Shields. Normal pub hours except Saturday.
Hons: Wearside Lg Div 2 90-91, Shields & Dist. Lg, Washington Lg 77-78 84-85

SOUTH SHIELDS COUNTY KITCHENS

Chairman: Barry Raper **Treasurer:** Susan Raper.
Secretary: Barry Raper, 59 Priestley Court, South Shields NE34 9NQ (0191 5363087)
Ground: Monkton Stadium, Dene Terrace, Jarrow. **Directions:** From A1 north straight onto Jarrow slip road, then left nto York Ave, take 6th left into Dene Terrace. ground on left
Colours: All Yellow & black **Change colours:** Green & white/black/green & white

SOUTH SHIELDS HARTON & WESTOE

Chairman: Ronald Wightman **Treasurer:** Steven Camm
Secretary: Graham Bass, 76 Stanhope Road, South Shields NE33 4BS (0191 4544798)
Ground: Harton Colliery Welfare.
Directions: A1M at Whitemare Pool take A194 to South Shields for 2 1/2 miles. At third roundabout turn right onto A1300. At 2nd roundabout turn left onto Boldon Lane. Ground 50 yards on right
Colours: Royal & white/royal/blue & white **Change colours:** All red

STANLEY UNITED

President: A Westgarth **Vice-President:** B Waiting.
Secretary: V Kirkup, 9 Brookes Rise, Regents Green, Langley, Durham DH7 8XY (0191 3780921)
Asst Manager/Coach: K Finnegan **Physio:** J Burn.
Ground: High Road, Stanley, near Crook (nicknamed Hill Top Ground).
Directions: Teeside on A689 to Bishop Auckland and onto Crook, turn left at Market Place then 1st right for Tow Law to Billy Row and Stanley, right at top of bank then 1st left, grd 250 yards on left.
Colours: Red & white stripes/black/red **Change colours:** Sky/navy/navy **Nickname:** The Nops
Sponsors: Company Cars Direct **Clubhouse:** Open matchdays. **Club Shop:** No
Honours: Northern Lg 3, R-up 62-63), Lg Cup 3, FA Cup 1st Rd 53-54, FA Amtr Cup SF 19-20.

SUNDERLAND KENNEK ROKER

Chairman: J Broadbent **Treasurer:** Keith Hunter **Press Officer:** Les Dodds
Secretary: Tom Clark, 55 Vicarage Close, New Silksworth, Sunderland SR3 1JF (0191 521 1242)
Ground: Silksworth Welfare Park. **Directions:** Behind Lord Seaham Public House. Blind Lane Silsworth
Colours: Red & white stripes/black/red **Change:** Navy & orange/navy & orange/navy
Hons: Wearside Lg Cup 91-92 (Shipowners Cup 89-90 (R-up 80-81), M/mouth Charity Cup R-up 80-81).

WASHINGTON NISSAN

Chairman: A Hill **Treasurer:** P Bevington **Press Officer:** Secretary
Secretary: Harry English, 193 Newcastle Road, Fulwell Mill, Sunderland SR5 1NR (0191 548 7194)
Manager: Stan Fenwick **Assistant Manager:** Keith Robertson. **Coach:** Darren Ward
Ground: Nissan Sports Complex.
Directions: North along A1 (M) use A690 (sign post Sunderland) connect with A19, north on A19, after passing the A1231 turn off, plant on the left. Past plant & follow signs 'Nissan Offices'.
Colours: Blue & yellow/ blue/blue **Change colours:** Red & black/black/black **Founded:** 1988
Clubhouse: Open Mon-Fri 5-11pm, Sat 11am-11pm, Sun noon-3 & 7-10.30pm
Hons: Wearside Lg Div 1 93-94 (Lg Cup R-up 91-92, Div 2 Cup 92-93 93-94), Nissan European Tphy 3.

WHITEHAVEN AMATEURS

Chairman: D Polkey **Press Officer:** Secretary
Secretary: Harry Upton 14 Foxhouses Road, Whitehaven CA28 8AF (01946 61750)
Manager: Ian Green **Assistant Manager:** Ian Atkins.
Ground: Whitehaven County Ground, Coach Road, Whitehaven
Directions: Barrow on A595, ignore branch to town centre at B.P. garage turn right at t/lights on A5094. 1/2 mile turn left at Esso garage into Coach Rd. Narrow lane ent immed after l/ crossing to grd behind Rugby Lge Stadium.
Colours: Yellow/blue/blue **Change colours:** White/navy/white
Honours: Cumberland Cup 90-91, County League 87-88 88-89, Wearside Lg Div 2 Cup R-up 93-94.

WINDSCALE

Chairman: R Napier **Press Officer:** Secretary **Treasurer:** A Barwise
Secretary: Geoff Turrell, 65 Leathwaite, Loop Road South, Whitehaven, Cumbria CA28 7UG (01936 62229)
Ground: Falcon Field, Egremont. **Directions:** A66 to Bridgefoot. A595 Barrow, bottom of hill approaching Egremont take 3rd turn off island (signed) Smithfield/Gillfoot, grd in housing estate
Colours: Purple/navy/navy **Change:** Blue & white/royal/royal **Founded:** 1950
Hons: Furness Snr Cup 85-86

WOLVISTON

Chairman: Eddie Poole **Vice Chairman:** Derek Stockton **President:** Bob Smith
Sec./Press Officer: Keith Simpson, 14 Lodore Grove, Acklam, Middlesbrough TS5 8PB (01642 823734).
Manager: John Johnson **Asst Manager:** Kevin Smith **Coach:** Alan Lucas
Ground: Metcalfe Way, Wynyard Road, Wolviston, Billingham, Cleveland TS22 5NE.
Directions: On Wynyard Road between Thorpe Thewles & Wolviston. A19 onto A689 into Wolviston village, take Wynyard Road heading towards Thorpe Thewles, grd left before Sir John Halls Estate.
Seats: None **Cover:** 200 **Capacity:** 2,000 **Floodlights:** No **Founded:** 1910
Colours: Royal/white/white **Change:** Red & white/red/white **Nickname:** Wolves
Sponsors: R.C.I. Industrial Cleaners **Rec. Gate:** 500 v Middlesbrough 27/7/93 **Club Shop:** No.
Clubhouse: Licensed bar. Hot & cold meals. Open 11am-11pm on matchdays.
Hons: Wearside Lg Div 2 89-90 (Lg Cup R-up 92-93), Teesside Lg R-up 84-85 (R T Raine Cup 86-87), Durham FA Trophy R-up 89-90, Stockton & District Lg 3, (Lg Cup 3), Lg Charity Cup 79-80).

JPL WADE
NORTHERN FOOTBALL ALLIANCE

FEEDER TO: NORTHERN LEAGUE

President: Sir John Hall **Chairman:** G F Dobbins
Secretary: J H McLackland, 92 Appletree Gardens, Walkerville, Newcastle upon Tyne NE6 4SX Tel: 0191 2621636
Press Officer: Bill Gardner **Tel/Fax:** 0191 4883422

West Allotment Celtic claimed their fourth Northern Alliance title in style. After starting with three draws and a defeat last August the Celtic lads went on to put a record-breaking run together - they won all of their remaining twenty-four matches!

The title success placed another notch in the managerial gun of Ken Scott who joined Celtic after guiding his previous club Seaton Delaval to three championships. Scott in fact has guided his last two clubs to nine major league honours in the last decade. And player loyalty was a major factor in his latest success. Several ex-Delaval stalwarts joined their boss at West Allotment's shared Whitley Bay base.

Lemington Social, the previous season's champions, finished second this time around but they finished nine points adrift and after only one campaign in charge ex-Newcastle United stalwart John Connolly has moved on to take charge at Ashington in the Arnott Insurance Northern League. His post at the Tavern Ground has been taken over by Derek Bell whose latest clubs as a player were Whitley Bay, Gateshead and Durham City.

After finishing third (they were runners-up in 1996-97), Ponteland United are becoming known as the "near miss club". Despite figuring in numerous cup finals in recent years and being among the front runners in several title races, United have yet to claim their first major honour in the Northern Alliance. But manager Barrie Wardrobe is a well-respected optimist who is staying put with his assistant Steve Baxter and eventual success must be on the cards.

Ryton got through their first Premier Division season despite being dogged by off-the-field problems. They were forced to ground-share with Swalwell while awaiting a move to their new ground at Crawcrook. But next term they will be installed at their Kingsley Park base which boasts a purpose-built club house on two floors with lavish dressing rooms and ample car parking space. Up-and-coming Ryton also have the backing of ten sponsors for the 1998-99 campaign.

Shankhouse are one of the oldest football clubs in the country and it was nice to see them crowned as 1997-98 champions in the league's First Division. New Boss Gary Kirkup's newly-promoted outfit will be sharing with Seaton Delaval at Wheatridge Park before moving back to a renovated base at Dudley.

Cumbrians Northbank gave Shankhouse a run for their money and edged Heaton Stannington out of the second promotion slot in the First Division. The Carlisle-based club have gained promotion for the second season running - a feat only previously accomplished by Spittal Rovers who unfortunately ended the season by propping up the other teams in the Premier Division.

Champions Coxlodge and Morpeth Town 'A' won promotion from the Second Division but, as in previous campaigns, there were also some casualties.

Hartlepool United 'A' resigned from the Alliance's top flight and in the First Division Longbenton decided to call it a day. And Swalwell, who finished bottom of the middle division and Gateshead Schooner who have struggled in the Second Division were another two clubs to drop out.

Also in the lower division Whitley Bay Snooker finished with the worst playing record in England and they disbanded after management committee advice to try their luck in one of the Northern Alliance's feeder competitions.

For the 1998-99 campaign the league's strength will be reduced to forty-two clubs (six short of a full complement) and three new clubs have been admitted from feeder leagues. They are Chopwell, Shiremoor and Amble Vikings.

Bill Gardner, League Press Officer

FINAL LEAGUE TABLES 1997-98

PREMIER DIVISION

	P	*W*	*D*	*L*	*F*	*A*	*Pts*
West Allotment C	28	24	3	1	80	30	75
Lemington Social	28	21	3	4	79	31	66
Ponteland United	28	19	2	7	87	41	59
Hartlepool U 'A'	28	15	6	7	72	45	51
Carlisle City	28	13	8	7	51	29	47
Ryton	28	11	3	14	56	69	36
Benfield Park	28	10	4	14	39	61	34
Winlaton Hallgarth	28	8	7	13	37	57	31
Walker Ledwood	28	7	9	12	35	43	30
St Columbas	28	8	6	14	42	76	30
Hebb Reyrolle	28	8	7	13	54	53	28
Seaton Delaval A	28	7	6	15	43	60	27
Gillford Park	28	7	6	15	34	52	27
Walker Cent	28	5	10	13	33	51	19
Spittal Rovers	28	5	4	19	31	75	19

DIVISION ONE

	P	*W*	*D*	*L*	*F*	*A*	*Pts*
Shankhouse	26	22	1	3		25	82
Northbank Carl.	26	21	2	3			65
Heaton Stann'ton	26	20	1	5	99		61
Heddon Institute	26	16	3	9	82		
Amble Town	26						
Newcastle Univ.	26						
Newbiggin CW	26						
Percy MA	26						
Gosforth Bohem.	26						
Hexham Swinton	26						
Procter & Gamble	26						
Longbenton	26						
Ashington H P	26						
Swalwell	26						

PREMIER DIVISION RESULTS CHART 1997-98

		1	2	3	4	5	6	7	8	9	10	11	12	13	14	15
1	Carlisle City	X	0-1	1-1	4-2	0-3	2-0	3-1	3-0	2-1	5-1	3-0	0-0	1-1	1-2	1-1
2	Carlisle G. Park	2-3	X	2-4	1-1	0-1	0-2	1-2	0-2	3-1	2-0	0-0	1-1	1-2	1-3	1-4
3	Hartlepool U 'A'	1-2	5-2	X	3-2	0-6	7-1	2-1	1-2	3-0	2-0	2-2	2-0	1-0	4-0	2-2
4	Hebburn Reyrolle	1-3	0-0	0-4	X	0-1	3-0	6-0	1-2	5-1	4-0	6-2	2-2	-0	0-0	2-2
5	Lemington Social	0-0	1-1	0-4	2-1	X	7-2	2-2	3-2	2-2	3-0	4-0	3-1	5-0	1-2	5-1
6	Newcastle Ben Pk	0-5	2-2	4-1	2-3	1-2	X	2-0	1-4	2-3	2-1	3-2	2-0	1-0	1-1	1-1
7	N Shields St Col	1-3	1-3	0-3	1-4	2-3	1-3	X	3-1	2-3	1-1	3-0	2-2	0-0	1-5	2-1
8	Ponteland Utd	2-5	2-0	1-2	2-2	0-3	3-0	4-0	X	7-1	1-0	7-0	3-1	1-1	1-2	2-0
9	Ryton	1-1	1-0	2-1	4-0	0-3	3-0	3-5	1-2	X	3-4	8-1	2-2	1-3	2-4	3-0
10	Seaton Del Am	2-1	6-2	3-3	2-0	0-1	4-0	1-3	3-5	2-3	X	1-1	2-2	1-0	0-2	0-4
11	Spittal Rovers	2-1	1-2	2-1	0-2	1-2	2-2	0-1	2-5	1-1	4-1	X	4-0	0-2	1-4	0-2
12	Walker Central	0-0	1-0	2-2	2-1	2-1	0-2	1-2	2-3	1-2	1-1	2-0	X	0-0	0-3	3-0
13	Walker Led Fosse	0-0	0-1	3-3	2-2	3-5	1-3	1-1	1-2	3-1	2-5	0-1	4-2	X	2-3	1-0
14	West Allot Celtic	2-1	5-3	5-0	2-1	3-2	2-0	2-2	1-0	4-0	2-2	5-1	4-1	2-0	X	3-2
15	Winlaton Hallgarth	1-0	1-2	0-8	3-3	1-3	1-0	0-2	2-5	1-1	1-0	3-1	3-2	0-0	0-4	X

PREMIER DIVISION CLUBS 1998-99

CARLISLE CITY

Chairman: J Ewbank **Manager:** W Armstrong.
Secretary: D Ivison, 40 Skiddaw Road, Carlisle CA2 5OS (01228 31654).
Ground: The Sheepmount Sports Complex, Carlisle (01228 26569).
Directions: B6264 Brampton-Carlisle road & follow Workington signs, dual-c'way down hill (Carlisle Castle on right), where road intersects double back on yourself and take turning left just before castle, follow down hill keeping left until ground.
Colours: All Sky **Change colours:** White/red

CARLISLE GILLFORD PARK

Chairman: R Wilson **Manager/Coach:** R Rutherford/D Graham.
Secretary: Paul McMullen, 154 Blackwell Road, Currrock, Carlisle (01228 22983).
Ground: Gillford Park, Carlisle (01228 26649).
Directions: A69 to Rose Hill r'bout, straight over & 2nd left into Eastern Way, 1 mile to lights, left, 1st right Petrill Bank Rd, right at bridge, ground 200yds up this road.
Colours: All red **Change colours:** White/black.

HEBBURN REYROLLE

Chairman/Press Officer: Alan Graham **Manager/Coach:** Norman Dryden
Secretary: Gordon Taylor, 29 Crawley Avenue, Hebburn, Tyne & Wear NE31 2LT (0191 4834537)
Ground: Hebburn Sports Ground, Victoria Road West, Hebburn, Tyne & Wear.
Directions: From Newcastle & Gateshead via the Felling Bypass travel to Heworth r/about, take A195 signed Hebburn/Jarrow. Ground approx 2 miles on left.
Colours: Red & blue/blue **Change colours:** Green & navy/navy

LEMINGTON SOCIAL

Chairman: R Craven **Manager:** John Connolly
Secretary: R M Alsop, 11 Allerdene Close, West Denton Park, Newcastle, NE15 8RN (0191 267 5072).
Ground: Cowgate New Tavern Sports Ground, Ponteland Rd, Cowgate, Newcastle-upon-Tyne.
Directions: Kenton turn off A1, over Kenton r'bout & next 2 r'bouts, ground on right before garage and behind Co-op dairy.
Colours: Red & black/black **Change colours:** White/navy

NEWCASTLE BENFIELD PARK

Chairman: J Rowe **Manager:** Tom Sword
Secretary: Danny Gates, 5 Winship Terrace, Byker, Newcastle-upon-Tyne (0191 276 3049).
Ground: Benfield Park, Benfield Rd, Newcastle-upon-Tyne.
Directions: From Newcastle towards coast take 2nd exit after Corner House pub lights, right into Benfield Rd, ground on left opp. Walkergate Hosp. & adjacent to school.
Colours: Blue/white **Change colours:** White/blue

NORTH SHIELDS St COLUMBAS

Chairman: N Hooper **Manager/Coach:** J Wall.
Secretary: A J Baird, 23 Balkwell Ave., North Shields, Tyne & Wear NE29 7JN (0191 258 0833).
Ground: Purvis Park, St John's Green, Percy Main, North Shields.
Directions: From Tyne Tunnel take N Sdields road past Duke Of Wellington, after 1/2 mile take 2nd left, ground on right.
Colours: All white **Change colours:** Black & white/black

NORTHBANK CARLISLE

Chairman: Kenny Brown **Manager:** Richard Sendall
Secretary: Bob Lancaster, 25 South Street, Carlisle, Cumbria CA1 2EW (0860 680482)
Ground: Sheepmount Sports Complex, Carlisle
Directions: B6264 from Bampton to Carlisle, follow Workington sign, past Carlisle Castle on right. Where dual carriageway intersects take next right and travel back towards Castle. Turn left before castle & keeping left follow the road to Complex
Colours: Red & white/navy **Change colours:** Yellow & navy/white

PONTELAND UNITED

Chairman: F W Smith **Manager:** B Wardrobe/S Baxter
Secretary: L McMahon, 1 Wardle Drive, Annitsford, Cramlingham NE23 7DB (0191 250 0463).
Ground: Ponteland Leisure Centre, Ponteland (01661 25441).
Directions: Left at lights entering Ponteland from N'castle, ground 100m on left adjacent to Leisure Centre.
Colours: Black & white stripes/black **Change colours:** All white.

RYTON

Chairman: Philip Hall **Manager/Coach:** Alan Patterson/Stephen Murray
Secretary: Les Robson, 31 Park View Gardens, Runhead, Ryton, Tyne & wear NE40 3JD (0191 413 7628)
Ground: Avenue Ground, Old Hexham Road, Swalwell, Tyne & Wear.
Directions: From Newcastle, cross the Tyne via Redheugh Bridge & take A1 Western bypass past the Metro Centre. Take the 1st left sliproad past the Metro Centre. Turn right at r/about and follow for half mile. Ground on right just past Fewsters.
Colours: Blue & black/black **Change colours:** Orange/black

SEATON DELAVAL AMATEURS

Chairman: T Ashburn **Manager/Coach:** I Watts
Secretary: V Donnelly, 6 Hollymount Square, Bedlington (01670 829464).
Ground: Wheatridge Park, Seaton Delaval.
Directions: A189 from Newcastle, at Annitsford r'bout A190 to Seaton Delaval, left at r'bout entering village, ground 450yds on right next to Deal Garage and behind Market Garden. 3 miles from Cramlington BR station. Bus 363 from Newcastle passes ground.
Colours: Sky/black **Change colours:** Yellow/blue

SHANKHOUSE

Chairman: George Davison **Manager:** Gary Kirkup
Secretary: Syd Ramsey, 6 Brinkburn Ave, Cramlington, Northumberland NE23 6TB (01670 715943)
Ground: Dudley Welfare Ground, Dudley, Cramlington.
Directions: From Newcastle follow the Morpeth Rd as far as the Seaton Burn flyover. Take the A19 south exit sign Tyne Tunnel, first slip rd to Dudley, ground opposite the Owen Pugh site
Colours: Yellow/blue **Change colours:** White/blue

SPITTAL ROVERS

Vice Chairman: Paul Renton **Manager/Coach:** Steven Roughead
Secretary: G Burn, 7 Sea Road, Spittal, Berwick-on-Tweed TD15 1RN (01289 306049).
Ground: Newfields, Berwick-on-Tweed.
Directions: From south take Berwick by-pass to 3rd r'bout. Safeway Store on right - pitch reached by taking 2nd left on r'bout.
Colours: Black & white stripes/black **Change colours:** Red/black

WALKER CENTRAL

Chairman: R T McClellan **Manager/Coach:** A Bell.
Secretary: Mr B Mulroy, 31 Dalton Cres., Byker Wall, Newcastle-upon-Tyne NE6 2DA (0191 265 7803).
Ground: Monkchester Recreation Ground, Walker, Newcastle.
Directions: From City: Shields Rd to Union Rd, to Welbeck Rd, right into Monkchester Rd, left into pitch (between houses) opposite Norbury Grove.
Club colours: Blue & yellow/blue **Change colours:** Red & white/red

WALKER LEDWOOD FOSSE

Chairman: W A Callanan **Manager/Coach:** T Lunn.
Secretary: K Slade, 59 Moorland Cres., Walkergate, Newcastle-upon-Tyne NE6 4AT (0191 276 1519)
Ground: Miller's Dene, Walkergate, Newcastle-upon-Tyne.
Directions: Miller's Dene Fosseway from Newcastle, travel through Byker to the r'bout at the top of Shields Rd, turn right & continue to next r'bout, left at B & Q store & continue down Fosseway. The ground is the second one down the Fosseway past Fire Station on left.
Colours: All white **Change colours:** Green & black/black

WEST ALLOTMENT CELTIC

Chairman: J Mather **Manager/Coach:** Ken Scott
Secretary: J T Jackson, 4 Rosewood Crescent, Seaton Sluice, Whitley Bay NE26 4BL (0191 237 0416).
Ground: Hillheads Park, Whitley Bay
Directions: From Newcastle take A1058 to Tynemouth Baths, turn left roundabout on A192 to Foxhunters Pub. Turn right follow A191 to Ice Rink on right, ground beside.
Colours: Black & white stripes/black **Change colours:** Red/blue.

WINLATON HALLGARTH

Chairman: R Young **Manager/Coach:** K Rides/S Breen.
Secretary: Sid Batey, 6 Wylam View, Winlaton, Tyne & Wear NE21 4RJ (0191 414 7970).
Ground: Shibdon Park, Shibdon Road, Blaydon-on-Tyne, Tyne & Wear.
Directions: From north, over A1 Tyne Bridge to 1st slip road, take Swalwell and Consett road to r'bout, right, Blaydon Baths car park and ground 400yds on right.
Colours: Green & white/white **Change colours:** Yellow & black/black

TEESSIDE STRONGARM FOOTBALL LEAGUE

FEEDER TO: NORTHERN LEAGUE

President: K P Moore **Chairman:** L Crossman
Secretary: R D Marsay, 12 Aislaby Court, Wilton Lane,
Guisborough, Cleveland TS14 6TG
Tel: 01287 637087

FINAL LEAGUE TABLE 1997-98

	P	W	D	L	F	A	Pts
Acklam SW	32	25	4	3	91	30	*76
Thornaby YC	32	18	9	4	68	41	63
New Marske	32	18	5	9	67	51	59
Carlin H WMC	32	17	6	9	77	57	57
Tess Comp	32	15	9	8	69	49	54
Beads FC	32	14	8	10	59	50	*47
Whitby Town Rs	32	14	3	15	65	60	45
Grangetown BC	32	14	5	13	69	60	*44
BSC Redcar	32	13	8	11	62	63	*44
Cargo Fleet	32	12	3	17	70	78	39
Stokesley SC	32	11	6	15	55	78	39
Richmond Town	32	11	8	13	55	54	*38
Dormans Ath	32	13	5	14	68	75	*38
Nunthorpe Ath	32	8	7	17	52	67	*28
Fishburn Park	32	7	7	18	44	61	28
Thornaby	32	8	5	19	58	87	*26
Guisb Town Rs	32	4	2	26	48	117	14

* Points deducted

MACMILLAN BOWL 1997-98

Preliminary Round

Richmond Town	v	Cargo Fleet SC	5-0

First Round

Fishburn Park	v	Tees Comp	2-1 aet
Whitby Town Res	v	Grangetown BC	3-6 aet
Richmond Town	v	BSC Redcar	2-1
Dormans Ath	v	Crlin How WMC	1-3
Thornaby YC	v	Thornaby FC	2-0
Acklam SW	v	Beads FC	3-2
Stokesley SC	v	New Marske SC	1-0
Guisboro Tn Res	v	Nunthorpe Ath	0-6

Second Round

Stokesley SC	v	Nunthorpe Ath	1-0
Grangetown BC	v	Fishburn Park	1-0
Acklam SW	v	Richmond Town	3-2
Thornaby YC	v	Carlin How	1-0

Semi-Final

Thornaby YC	v	Stokesley SC	1-0
Grangetown BC	v	Acklam SW	0-1

FINAL

ACKLAM SC	v	THORNABY YC	3-1

R T RAINE TROPHY 1997-98

Preliminary Round

New Marske SC	v	Whitby Town Res	1-0 aet

First Round

New Marske SC	v	Beads FC	2-1
Tees Components	v	BSC Redcar	3-0
Guisboro Town	v	Dormans Athletic	0-3
Cargo Fleet	v	Thornaby	4-1

Semi-Final

Cargo Fleet	v	Tees Components	3-2
Dormans Athletic	v	New Marske SC	1-0

FINAL

CARGO FLEET	v	DORMANS ATH	1-3

CLUB DIRECTORY

ACKLAM STEELWORKS

Secretary: Peter Conley, 53 Roseberry Road, Longlands, Middlesbrough, Cleveland TS4 2LJ (01642 224266)
Ground: Acklam Steelworks Club, Park Road South, Middlesbrough (01642 818717)
Directions: Marton Road A172, follow route to Middlesbrough centre, follow signs to County Sports Stadium, entrance opposite Sports Stadium.
Sponsor: Upsall Vending
Colours: Red/blue/red **Change Colours:** Blue & black/black/blue

B.E.A.D.S.

Secretary: Dave Kane, 27 Edgeworth Court, Hemlington, Middlesbrough, Cleveland TS8 9EP (01642 596559)
Ground: Beechwood & Easterside SC, Marton Road, Middlesbrough. (01642 311304)
Directions: Follow A172 into Middlesbrough centre down Marton Road, ground behind Social Club.
Sponsor: Classic Trophies UK
Colours: Red & black/black/black **Change Colours:** Yellow/blue/blue

BEDALE ATHLETIC & SPORTS ASSC.

Secretary: Mike Allen, 1 Sycamore View, Nosterfield, Bedale, N Yorks DL8 2QR (01677 470739)
Ground: B.A.S.A. Leyburn Road, Bedale (01677 422085)
Directions: Follow route to Northallerton, then signs Bedale. At Town centre turn right to Leyburn, past church & golf course, ground on right
Sponsor: Halls Fish & Chips/Kings Head
Colours: Orange/orange/white **Change Colours:** White/red/white

BRITISH STEEL S & S CLUB

Secretary: David Collins, 23 Welland Road, Redcar, Cleveland TS10 1NR (01642 491547)
Ground: BSC Sports & Social Club, Dormanstown, Redcar (01642 486691)
Directions: Approaching Redcar from Middlesbrough, enter Dormanstown at BSC Steel House Works rounabout, turn 1st right then 1st left, ground behind club.
Sponsor: Area Electrical Projects
Colours: Sky/black/black **Change Colours:** White/black/black

CARGO FLEET SC

Secretary: M Coonorton, 84 Durham Road, Eston, Middlesbrough, Cleveland TS6 9LZ (01642 467327)
Ground: Pallister Park, Middlesbrough
Directions: Head towards M'bro (A171) Oremesby Bank, onto Cargo Fleet Lane, turn first left aftyer Cargo Fleet Club onto Homerton Rd, turn right at end of Homerton Road. Ground 100 yards on right.
Sponsor: Cargo Fleet Social Club/Sam Smiths Brewery.
Colours: Red & black/black/black. **Change Colours:** Navy/blue/yellow

CARLIN HOW WMC

Secretary: Neil Townend, 32 Westray Street, Carlin How, Saltburn, Cleveland TS13 4EL (01287 643741)
Ground: Kilton Lane, Carlin How.
Directions: From M'bro follow A173/174 towards Loftus. When entering Carlin How, turn right just before traffic lights/Loftus Bank, onto Maynard St. Follow road 200 yards, ground on right passed club.
Sponsor: Carlin How & Dist WMC Institute Ltd
Colours: All red **Change Colours:** Black & amber/black/black

DORMANS ATHLETIC

Secretary: Don Hall, 52 Westbourne Road, Linthorpe, Middlesbrough, Cleveland TS5 5BJ (01642 879603)
Ground: Dormans Athletic Club, Oxford Road, Middlesbrough. (01642 817099)
Directions: Follow the A1032 down Acklam Road towards Middlesbrough Centre, turn right onto Oxford Road, ground on right before the garage.
Sponsor: MSV Technics
Colours: Blue & black/black/black **Change Colours:** All red

FISHBURN PARK

Secretary: Karen Hutton, 24 Abbots Road, Whitby, N Yorks YO22 4EB (01947 602537)
Ground: Showfield Ground, White Leys Rd, Whitby
Directions: Follow A171 to Whitby, at 1st r/about turn left. End of road, fork right, ground 3rd right.
Sponsor: Saxonville Hotel/Landers Butchers
Colours: All green **Change Colours:** White/blue/blue

GRANGETOWN BOYS CLUB

Secretary: Kevin Larkin, 19 Braemar Grove, Teesville, Middlesbrough, Cleveland TS6 0AN (01642 452095)
Ground: Grangetown YCC, Trunk Road, Grangtown, Midlesbrough (01642 455435)
Directions: Follow the trunk road into Redcar from M'bro, ground on right after roundabout leading over bridge.
Sponsor: M & H Plant Hire
Colours: Black & Amber/black/black **Change Colours:** All royal blue

GUISBOROUGH TOWN RESERVES

Secretary: Keith Smeltzer, 55 Thames Avenue, Guisborough, Cleveland TS154 8AR (01287 638993)
Ground: King George V Playing Fields, Howlbeck Road, Guisborough (01287 636925)
Directions: Follow A171 into Guisborough, turn left at 2nd traffic lights opposite Moorcock Hotel, turn 3rd left follow signs for swimming baths.
Sponsor: Hensons
Colours: Red & white/black/red
Change Colours: All yellow

NEW MARSKE SPORTS CLUB

Secretary: Peter Whitaker, 28 High Street, Marske, Redcar, Cleveland TS11 7BE (01642 486770)
Ground: New Marske Sports Club, New Marske, Redcar (01642 479808)
Directions: From M'bro A174 to rounabout junc with Longbeck Lane turn right, ground on left.
Sponsor: Car Care
Colours: Yellow/blue/yellow
Change Colours: White & red/black/black

NUNTHORPE ATHLETIC

Secretary: Kevin Levitt, 131 Burlam Road, Middlesbrough, Cleveland, TS5 5AX (01642 824332)
Ground: Recreation Ground, Guisborough Road, Nunthorpe (01642 313251)
Directions: Leaving Middlesbrough on A172, turn left into Nunthorpe ground 300 yards on right.
Sponsor: Val Reeve & Chis Elvin at Paws
Colours: Blue & black/black/black
Change Colours: Red & white/blue/red & white

RICHMOND TOWN

Secretary: Linda Blackburn, 14 Westfields, Richmond, N Yorks DL10 4DD (01748 824919)
Ground: Earls Orchard Playing Fields, Sleegill, Richmond
Directions: Entering Richmond on A6108, over 2 roundabouts turn right at third, 2nd left follow downhill and cross Green Bridge on road to Hudswell village, ground on left immediately after bridge.
Sponsor: Property Management Services/Turf Hotel
Colours: Blue & yellow/blue/blue
Change Colours: Blue & black/black/blue & black

STOKESLEY SC

Secretary: Peter Grainge, 77 Darnton Drive, Easterside, Middlesbrough, Cleveland TS4 3RF (01642 316691)
Ground: Stokesley Sports Club, Broughton Road, Stokesley (01642 710051)
Directions: Follow signs for Stokesley. Take B1257 to Great Broughton at roundabout junc A172/A173, ground on left next to cricket field.
Sponsor: The Stokesley Sports Shop
Colours: All red
Change Colours: White & blue/blue/blue

THORNABY FOOTBALL CLUB

Secretary: Susan Gardner, 25 Brotton Rd, Thornaby, Stockton, Cleveland TS17 8EP (01642 646032)
Ground: Teesdale Park, Acklam Road, Thornaby.
Directions: Leave A19 at Thornaby interchange, follow road through traffic lights towards Stockton centre, turn right when in dip at sign for Teesdale Park
Sponsor: Scott Bros
Colours: Claret/claret/sky
Change Colours: Blue/black/black

THORNABY YOUTH CLUB

Secretary: Geoffrey Kirk, 9 Tipton Close, Thornaby, Stockton, Cleveland TS17 9QF (01642 676516)
Ground: Dene School, Baysdale Road, Thornaby.
Directions: Leave A19 at Thornaby interchange. turn left at the Roundel Pub onto Mitchell Ave, proceed towards Thornaby Town centre, turn right at Baysdale Road, follow road round to entrance.
Sponsor: Thornaby Youth Club/Market Tavern
Colours: Claret/white/white
Change Colours: Blue & black/black/black

WHITBY TOWN RESERVES

Secretary: Charlie Woodward, 6 Westlands Avenue, Whitby, N Yorks YO21 3DZ (01947 602312)
Ground: Turnbull Ground, Upgang Lane, Whitby.
Directions: Entering Whitby by A169 or A171, take 1st fork and follow signs for West Cliff
Sponsor: Whitby Tanks Ltd/Harrison's Garage Ltd
Colours: All blue
Change Colours: White/black/white

BRITISH INDUSTRIAL RECLAMATION
SHEFFIELD COUNTY SENIOR LEAGUE

President: M Matthews **Chairman:** F Wright
Secretary: Roy Beadsworth,
32 Cockayne Place, Norton Lees, Sheffield S8 9DG
Tel/Fax: 0114 255 1275

FINAL LEAGUE TABLES 1997-98

PREMIER DIVISION

	P	*W*	*D*	*L*	*F*	*A*	*Pts*
Phoenix	26	18	1	7	67	42	55
Frecheville CA	26	17	3	6	53	24	54
Ecclesfield R Rose	26	16	3	7	59	36	51
Worksop Town	26	14	4	8	53	32	46
Mexborough MS	26	13	7	6	54	39	46
Caribbean Sports	26	11	3	12	59	56	36
Stocksbridge PS	26	9	7	10	37	41	34
Parkgate	26	9	6	11	61	60	33
Denaby United	26	8	8	10	45	45	32
Penistone Church	26	8	5	13	37	59	29
Wombwell Town	26	8	4	14	51	64	28
High Green Villa	26	7	6	13	27	44	27
A.B.M.	26	6	5	15	37	75	23
Swinton Athletic	26	4	6	16	26	49	18

DIVISION ONE

	P	*W*	*D*	*L*	*F*	*A*	*Pts*
The Wetherby	24	17	4	3	76	30	55
Wombwell Main	24	14	5	5	55	31	47
Sheffield Lane Top	24	14	4	6	62	45	46
Hallam	24	14	3	7	48	39	45
Oughtibri WMSC	24	11	5	8	50	38	38
Parramore Sports	24	10	4	10	38	48	34
Treeton Welfare	24	9	4	11	54	54	31
NCB Maltby MW	24	8	5	11	43	45	29
Avesta Sheffield	24	9	1	14	41	61	28
Wickersley	24	6	7	11	47	53	25
Sheffield Bankers	24	6	7	11	41	47	25
Grapes Roy Hanc.	24	5	5	14	64	89	20
Davy	24	3	6	15	24	63	15

PREMIER DIVISION RESULTS CHART 1997-98

		1	2	3	4	5	6	7	8	9	10	11	12	13	14
1	A.B.M.	X	1-4	4-1	3-2	1-3	3-2	1-4	0-8	2-1	0-4	0-0	2-0	4-4	0-3
2	Caribbean Sports	3-1	X	4-4	0-2	1-5	1-1	0-2	2-0	1-1	5-3	2-1	2-0	3-0	3-1
3	Denaby United	0-0	5-1	X	1-3	0-0	4-0	0-0	1-1	2-1	0-1	1-2	1-0	1-0	4-0
4	Ecclesfield RR	4-0	2-1	7-1	X	2-0	1-0	3-2	3-3	2-0	1-1	3-0	3-0	2-4	1-0
5	Frecheville CA	4-1	4-2	2-2	0-1	X	2-0	4-1	3-2	2-1	2-1	1-2	3-0	4-0	3-1
6	High Green Villa	2-0	1-6	2-0	1-2	1-0	X	1-1	2-1	2-1	1-2	2-2	0-1	0-2	1-1
7	Mexborough MS	8-2	3-2	1-0	1-1	0-1	1-1	X	2-3	2-1	3-1	0-0	***	6-1	0-1
8	Parkgate	6-2	5-4	1-9	3-2	2-0	1-3	2-4	X	1-1	3-4	4-0	2-2	3-1	1-3
9	Penistone Church	3-2	3-2	3-1	0-3	1-3	0-1	2-2	2-1	X	2-9	1-0	0-0	0-7	0-4
10	Phoenix	2-1	4-2	2-0	4-2	1-0	2-1	1-2	4-3	0-1	X	1-0	4-3	4-2	1-3
11	Stocksbridge PS	2-2	2-0	1-1	3-1	1-1	2-1	2-3	2-0	3-1	2-6	X	2-1	1-3	1-1
12	Swinton Athletic	2-2	4-3	2-3	0-3	0-3	0-0	1-3	2-2	1-2	0-3	0-3	X	4-0	1-2
13	Wombwell Town	2-1	0-2	3-3	4-0	0-1	2-1	3-3	2-2	3-6	1-2	4-3	1-2	X	1-2
14	Worksop Town	1-2	1-3	4-0	4-3	0-2	6-0	5-0	0-1	3-3	2-0	1-0	0-0	4-1	X

*** Match awarded to Mexborough Main Street

BRITISH INDUSTRIAL RECLAMATION
COUNTY SENIOR LEAGUE CUP 1997-98

First Round

Yorkshire Main	v	Old Edwardians	6-1
Frecheville CA	v	Norton Woodseats	3-2
ABM	v	Parkgate	0-1
Wombwell Town	v	Denaby United	0-3
Caribbean Sports	v	Woodhouse West E	4-2
Hare & Hounds	v	Stocksbridge Park S	2-0
Wickersley	v	Rossington Main	2-0
Avesta Sheffield	v	Penistone Ch Res	4-1
Harworth CI	v	Grapes Roy Han.	2-3
High Green Villa	v	Brinsworth Athletic	3-0
Parramore Sports	v	Ecclesfield Red R.	1-2

Second Round

Hallam	v	Yorkshire Main	0-2
Swinton Athletic	v	Treeton Welfare	3-2
Frecheville CA	v	Avesta Sheffield	3-1
Parkgate	v	Grapes Roy Hancock	3-4
Queens Hotel	v	Sheffield Bankers	1-2
High Green Villa	v	Sheffield	4-1
Caribbean Sports	v	Thorpe Hesley	0-1
Wombwell Main	v	Phoenix	2-0
Athersley Rec.	v	NCB Maltby	5-1
Wickersley	v	Penistone Church	3-1
Wath Saracens	v	Oughtibridge	1-2
Sheffield Centralians	v	Denaby United	0-3
Davy	v	Sheffield Lane Top	0-2
The Wetherby	v	Worksop Town	1-2
Elsecar Market H.	v	Ecclesfield R. Rose	1-6
Mexborough Main	v	Hare & Hounds	2-0

Third Round

Yorkshire Main	v	Athersley Rec.	0-3
Frecheville CA	v	Oughtibridge	0-1
Sheffield Bankers	v	Sheffield Lane Top	1-2
Thorpe Hesley	v	Ecclesfield Red Rose	0-2
Swinton Athletic	v	Wickersley	3-2
Grapes Roy H.	v	Denaby United	2-1
High Green Villa	v	Worksop Town	2-1
Wombwell Main	v	Mexborough Main	3-1

Fourth Round

Athersley Rec.	v	Swinton Athletic	2-0
Sheffield Lane Top	v	High Green Villa	1-2
Oughtibridge	v	Grapes Roy H.	3-2
Ecclesfield R.R.	v	Wombwell Main	4-1

Semi-Final

Athersley Rec.	v	Oughtibridge	3-2
High Green Villa	v	Ecclesfield R.R.	2-3

FINAL

ATHERSLEY REC v ECCLESFIELD RR

PREMIER DIVISION CLUBS 1998-99

CARIBBEAN SPORTS

Secretary: Ashley Richards, 34 Louth Road, Sheffield S11 7AW (0114 268 5314)
Ground: The Common, Ecclesfield, Sheffield S30 3WL
Sponsor: Neville Roe **Colours:** All Red

DENABY UNITED RESERVES

Secretary: Barney Randall, 30 Tickhill Square, Denaby Main, Doncaster DN12 4AW (01709 866763)
Ground: Ticknell Square, Denaby Main, Doncaster
Sponsor: David's School of Motoring **Colours:** Black & white/black/black

ECCLESFIELD RED ROSE

Secretary: Alf Goodison, 202 High Street, Ecclesfield, Sheffield S35 9XF (0114 246 8286)
Ground: Civil Service Ground, Green Lane, Ecclesfield.
Sponsor: Windsor Frozen Foods **Colours:** All scarlet & black & white

FRECHEVILLE COMMUNITY ASSOCIATION

Secretary: David Taylor, 75 Gleadless Ave, Sheffield S12 3QG, (0114 264 9754)
Ground: Silkstone Road, Frecheville, Sheffield
Sponsor: E.S.P. **Colours:** Amber & black/black/amber

MEXBOROUGH MAIN STREET

Secretary: Tony Hough, 4 Cranswick Way, Conisborough, Doncaster DN12 3AY (01709 866479)
Ground: Hampden Road, Mexborough
Sponsor: Ideal Travel **Colours:** Claret & blue/claret/claret

PARKGATE RESERVES

Secretary: Fred Powell, 4 Landseer Court, Flanderswell, Rotherham S66 2NH (01709 548283)
Ground: Roundwood Sports Complex, Green Lane, Rawmarsh, Rotherham
Sponsor: **Colours:** White & black/black/black

PENISTONE CHURCH

Secretary: Mr D Hampshire, 36 Park Avenue, Penistone, Sheffield S30 6DN (01226 764689)
Ground: Church View Road, Penistone
Sponsor: Shearcut Engineering **Colours:** Black & white/black/black

PHOENIX

Secretary: Trevor Cottam, 41 Pleasant Road, Sheffield S12 2BD (0114 239 0897)
Ground: Phoenix Sports Complex, Brinsworth
Sponsor: Canada Life **Colours:** Green & white/green/green

SHEFFIELD LANE TOP

Secretary: Des Barlow, 29 Strawberry Avenue, Sheffield S5 9GP (0114 245 5265)
Ground: Forgemasters S & SC, Shirecliffe Rd, Sheffield S5 8XD
Colours: Yellow/purple/yellow **Change colours:** Blue/black/blue

STOCKSBRIDGE PARK STEEL RESERVES

Secretary: M Grimmer, 48 Hole House Lane, Stocksbridge, Sheffield S30 5BP (0114 288 6470)
Ground: Bracken Moor Lane, Stocksbridge, Sheffield
Sponsor: St Christopher Motor Co **Colours:** Yellow/blue/blue

THE WEATHERBY

Secretary: Ron Lyne, 18 Ashley Grove, Aston, Sheffield S31 0AB (0114 287 6483)
Ground: Swallownest Miners Welfare, Swallownest Nr Sheffield
Sponsor: Manship Electrical **Colours:** Maroon/navy/maroon

WOMBWELL MAIN

Secretary: Ian Woodall, 15 Loxley Avenue, Wombwell, Barnsley S73 8NU (01226 756744)
Ground: Wombwell Main Cricket Club, Windmill Road, Wombwell, Barnsley
Sponsor: Vulcan Tanks Ltd & Hazeldens **Colours:** All Red

WOMBWELL TOWN

Secretary: Gary Mallender, 1 Redcliffe Close, Redbrook, Barnsley S75 2RU (01226 236276)
Ground: Wombwell Sporting Centre, Station Road, Wombwell, Barnsley
Sponsor: **Colours:** All red

WORKSOP TOWN RESERVES

Secretary: Keith Ilett, 2 Mount Avenue, Worksop, Notts S81 7JL (Worksop 487934)
Ground: Sandy Lane, Worksop
Sponsor: DTH **Colours:** Black & amber/black/black

THE WEST YORKSHIRE ASSOCIATION FOOTBALL LEAGUE

Founded 1928

President: J Hill **Chairman:** B Chaplin
League General Secretary: Kevin Parkinson
Tel: 0113 204 2130 (B) 01924 825461 (H)

There was a new format to the league competitions which incorporated the first teams of clubs competing in separate divisions from reserve teams. The overall feedback has been most favourable indicating that this change has been a success.

With the season having just commenced, our attention to the the game of football was tragically deflected following the death of Diana, Princess of Wales. In respect, the League cancelled its weekend fixtures, a decision made prior to and in line with a subsequent notification from footballing authorities.

As the season progressed, this has led to as open a competition for many years as clubs sought Championship honours and election to the higher division. The teams who reaped ultimate success are worthy Champions indeed but other clubs deserve much praise for their contribution to the League during the season.

Despite announcements at this time last year and the offer to be of assistance, one of the most regrettable and significant factors of the Cup Competitions was the expulsion of some clubs. In the main, this was due to the playing of ineligible players and serves to remind all that the same decision will apply next season. Club Secretaries must ensure they are aware of the squad of players legitimately available and team managers must be instructed accordingly.

In our annual representative match with the West Riding County Amateur Football League, our inability to turn chances into goals resulted in a narrow defeat. On a positive note, all those involved are worthy of the highest praise for their contribution in the honour to represent the League.

The list of clubs gaining honours in District and County FA competitions is again a lengthy one and all are to congratulated. At all times, it is important that we project ourselves as exemplary ambassadors of the League which will endorse the high regard that we hold with these football organisations.

Continued sponsorship for our Premier Division Cup Competition has been received from Briggsports who have additionally supported the Divisional Golden Boot Awards. Our clubs have been able to benefit from the competitive products and services that are readily made available.

The Fair Play League results are a good measure of the discipline, or the lack of it and this does transmit a message. Those teams who feature in the lower reaches should look at the on field root causes and would do well to take the appropriate action. In this number game, those teams with a low score are worthy of recognition and praise.

K Parkinson

PREMIER DIVISION FINAL LEAGUE TABLE 1997-98

	P	*W*	*D*	*L*	*F*	*A*	*Pts*
Wakefield	30	19	8	3	51	19	64
Whitkirk Wndrs	30	19	5	6	86	44	62
Nestle Rowntrees	30	19	2	9	79	55	59
Beeston St Anthony's	30	17	7	6	74	40	58
Rothwell Athletic	30	17	6	7	78	42	57
Carlton Athletic	30	16	4	10	78	50	52
Horbury Town	30	16	4	10	68	41	52
Knaresborough Town	30	14	8	8	65	41	50
Bramley	30	13	4	13	55	58	43
York RI	30	11	6	13	60	71	39
Nostell Miners Welfare	30	11	2	17	52	76	35
Bardsey	30	6	10	14	40	56	28
Barwick	30	7	6	17	46	73	27
Swillington Miners Welfare	30	5	3	22	40	95	18
Robin Hood Athletic	30	3	8	19	32	69	17
Magnet Sports	30	4	3	23	30	104	15

PREMIER DIVISION RESULTS CHART 1997-98

		1	2	3	4	5	6	7	8	9	10	11	12	13	14	15	16
1	Carlton	X	3-2	0-1	2-2	2-3	1-3	5-0	4-1	0-2	4-1	2-0	4-0	12-2	2-1	3-1	3-3
2	Whitkirk Wanderers	4-0	X	1-1	1-2	1-0	3-1	2-1	3-1	2-1	4-1	3-1	5-2	4-0	5-1	3-1	7-2
3	Wakefield	1-0	1-1	X	1-2	3-1	1-0	1-2	2-0	1-0	3-0	7-1	3-2	4-1	1-0	2-1	1-0
4	Nestle Rowntree	1-3	1-4	1-3	X	2-3	1-4	3-2	3-0	1-2	0-2	5-3	1-1	4-3	4-2	9-0	5-2
5	Knaresborough	2-2	2-2	2-0	2-3	X	1-1	1-0	0-2	2-2	2-1	1-2	1-0	5-1	4-1	4-0	4-1
6	Beeston	3-2	2-1	0-2	1-4	1-1	X	3-5	2-0	1-0	1-1	4-1	2-0	7-0	2-2	4-1	2-1
7	Rothwell Athletic	2-2	2-2	0-0	1-2	3-0	3-0	X	6-0	4-2	1-3	6-1	3-1	6-0	1-0	1-4	2-0
8	Bardsey	2-0	2-1	0-0	1-2	1-1	2-2	0-1	X	2-3	1-1	0-1	4-0	2-2	1-2	1-4	2-2
9	Horbury	4-2	2-3	0-1	2-0	3-1	3-3	2-2	3-3	X	4-1	1-2	6-0	3-0	3-2	6-1	0-1
10	Barwick	4-6	1-4	0-3	0-1	0-7	3-0	0-0	3-3	0-2	X	2-4	2-1	1-1	5-1	5-3	1-0
11	York RI	1-3	2-5	0-0	2-3	1-1	2-4	0-3	1-1	2-1	4-3	X	1-2	5-0	1-1	6-1	3-3
12	Nostell	4-1	5-2	1-4	3-5	1-5	1-5	2-6	0-0	3-2	5-2	1-3	X	1-0	3-1	3-2	3-1
13	Magnet	0-4	1-4	0-1	0-5	1-4	1-3	0-3	2-1	2-3	2-1	0-4	2-1	X	2-1	3-3	0-1
14	Robin Hood Athletic	0-1	1-1	1-1	1-3	1-1	0-5	2-5	1-2	0-4	0-0	1-1	2-1	4-3	X	1-2	0-1
15	Swillington	0-3	1-4	1-1	0-2	0-3	0-2	0-5	2-4	0-2	3-1	1-4	1-4	2-1	2-2	X	2-3
16	Bramley	0-2	3-2	1-1	4-2	3-1	0-6	1-2	2-1	1-2	3-1	6-1	0-1	5-0	2-0	3-1	X

FAIR PLAY LEAGUE 1997-98

	A	*B*	*C*	*D*	*TOTAL*
Carlton Athletic	50	300		10	360
Bramley	100	275			375
Beeston St Anthony's		425			425
Nestle Rowntrees	100	350			450
Nostell Miners Welfare		475			475
Robin Hood Athletic	150	375			525
Wakefield	50	450	40	20	560
York R I	50	550			600
Whitkirk Wanderers	100	550			650
Magnet Sports		625	40		665
Knaresborough Town	150	525			675
Swillington Miners Welfare	100	525	40	10	675
Barwick	100	600			700
Horbury Town	100	600	20		720
Rothwell Athletic	150	975			1125
Bardsey	300	925		20	1245

LEGEND

A	DISMISSAL	50 points	B	CAUTION	25 points
C	REGISTRATION FINE	20 points	D	LEAGUE FINE	10 points

HONOURS 1997-98

	CHAMPIONS	*Runners-up*	**CUP WINNERS**	*Runners-up*	**FAIR PLAY**	*Runners-up*
Premier Div.	Wakefield	Whitkirk W.	Horbury Tn	Knaresbro' T.	Carlton Ath	Bramley
Division One	Sandy Lane	Armley Ath.	Pontefract L.	Sandy Lane	Featherstone	U. Armley OB
Division Two	Mount St M.	Rothwell S.	Mount St M.	Hartshead S.	E. Leeds Trin.	Adel
Prem. Res. Div	Carlton Ath.	Bardsey	Bardsey	Beeston St A.	Wakefield	Barwick
Reserve Div.	Whitkirk W. 'A'	Armley Ath.	Featherstone	Whitkirk W 'A'	Rothwell A. 'A'	Dewsbury M A

GOLDEN BOOT AWARD

Premier Division	John Fletcher	Horbury Town	35
Division One	Billy Ingleson	Armley Athletic	22
Division Two	Lee Parker	Churwell Lions	45
Premier Res.	Rod Christopher	Bardsey	27
Reserve Div.	Oliver Escreet	Armley Athletic	35

PREMIER DIVISION FOR SEASON 1998-99

Secretary: Kevin Parkinson Tel: 0113 204 2130 (B) 01924 825461 (H)

Wakefield
Whitkirk Wanderers
Beeston St Anthony's
Rothwell Athletic
Nestle Rowntrees
Horbury Town
Carlton Athletic
Knaresborough Town
York R.I.
Nostell Miners Welfare
Bardsey
Barwick
Swillington Miners Welfare
Horsforth St Margarets
Sandy Lane
Aberford Albion

WEST RIDING COUNTY AMATEUR FOOTBALL LEAGUE

Founded 1922

President: D H Humpleby
Secretary: Mr S Mitchell
24 Burnsall Road, Liversedge, West Yorkshire WF15 6QF
Tel: 01924 404684

LEAGUE HONOURS LIST 1997-98

PREMIER DIVISION

Champions:	Marsden
Runners-up:	Storthes Hall
Cup Winners:	Hemsworth Miners Welfare
Relegated:	Farnley and Altofts

DIVISION ONE

Champions:	Phoenix
Runners-up:	Pontefract Borough
Cup Winners:	Campion
Relegated:	Morley Town and Lower Hopton

DIVISION TWO

Champions:	Hall Green United
Runners-up:	Littletown
Cup Winners:	Littletown
Relegated:	Bowling Celtic and Dynamoes

DIVISION THREE

Champions:	Phoenix Reserves
Runners-up:	Dudley Hill Rangers
Cup Winners:	Tyersal Reserves

DIVISION FOUR

Champions:	Westbrook Wanderers Reserves
Runners-up:	Ventus/Yeadon Reserves
Cup Winners:	Hemsworth Miners Welfare Res.

COUNTY FA CHALLENGE CUP

Winners:	Storthes Hall
Runners-up:	Aberford Albion

FINAL LEAGUE TABLES 1997-98

PREMIER DIVISION

	P	*W*	*D*	*L*	*F*	*A*	*Pts*
Marsden	26	16	6	4	60	24	38
Storthes Hill	26	18	1	7	56	37	37
Wibsey	26	14	8	4	58	28	36
Hemsworth	26	14	5	7	75	45	33
Field	26	14	5	7	54	41	33
Brighouse Town	26	12	8	6	49	31	32
Ovenden WR	26	11	5	10	62	43	27
Aberford Albion	26	11	4	11	51	52	26
Crag Rd Utd	26	7	9	10	39	44	23
Golcar Utd	26	8	6	12	48	67	22
Halifax Irish	26	6	6	14	46	64	18
Tyersal	26	6	4	16	51	75	16
Altofts	26	4	5	17	37	89	13
Farnley	26	3	4	19	32	73	10

DIVISION ONE

	P	*W*	*D*	*L*	*F*	*A*	*Pts*
Phoenix AFC	30	23	5	2	90	23	51
Pontefract Boro	30	21	1	8	86	43	43
Campion AFC	30	16	11	3	75	40	43
Greetland AFC	30	14	5	11	65	56	33
Overthorpe SC	30	11	11	8	53	47	33
Bay Athletic	30	15	2	13	65	57	32
Otley Town	30	13	5	12	53	44	31
Pudsey Liberal	30	13	4	13	70	72	30
Salts AFC	30	13	4	13	58	63	30
Ardsley Celtic	30	10	6	14	54	60	26
Dudley Hill Athletic	30	9	8	13	50	66	26
Rawdon Old Boys	30	9	6	15	54	67	24
Eastmoor AFC	30	9	5	16	36	50	23
Ventus/Yeadon C.	30	7	9	14	46	73	23
Lower Hopton	30	6	8	16	46	75	20
Morley Town	30	3	6	21	39	104	12

NORTH EASTERN FINAL LEAGUE TABLES 1997-98

BARNSEY & DISTRICT FOOTBALL ASSOCIATION

PREMIER DIV	P	W	D	L	F	A	Pts
Athersley Recr FC	20	18	1	1	66	19	55
Barnsley Trades FC	20	16	2	2	69	26	50
Kendray WMC FC	20	13	0	7	64	38	39
Houghton Main FC	20	11	3	6	56	30	36
Thurnscoe Butchers	19	10	2	7	39	39	32
Kingstone Unt WMC	20	10	0	10	46	39	30
Lundwood Lane End	20	9	0	11	37	44	27
Darfield Cross Keys	20	6	2	12	28	53	20
New Lodge WMC FC	20	5	1	14	46	71	16
Squires FC	19	4	1	14	34	47	13
Dodworth M/Wel	20	1	0	19	17	96	3

THE SHEFFIELD SPORTS ATHLETIC SATURDAY FOOTBALL LEAGUE

PREMIER DIV	P	W	D	L	F	A	Pts
Earl Fullflow	18	17	0	1	77	26	51
Fighting Cock	18	12	1	5	64	42	37
Waleswood Hotel	18	12	0	6	58	32	36
Boynton Sports	18	11	0	7	67	46	33
The Springwood	18	7	4	7	57	55	25
Elm Lane Fisheries	18	5	4	9	49	55	19
Rose Inn	18	5	4	9	47	59	19
Golden Plover	18	4	6	8	40	59	18
Vine Tavern	18	5	3	10	43	64	18
Norwich Union	18	1	0	17	40	104	3

CRAVEN FOOTBALL LEAGUE

PREMIER DIV	P	W	D	L	Pts
Embsay	22	16	4	2	36
Bulldogs	22	16	3	3	35
Oxenhope Rec	22	12	5	5	29
Keighley	22	13	3	6	29
Haworrth	22	11	4	7	26
Cross Hills R	22	12	5	5	29
Addingham	22	9	3	10	21
Cononley Spts	22	6	7	9	19
Colne CC	22	7	4	11	18
Cowling	22	4	5	13	13
Skipton LMS	22	4	1	17	9
Skipton Town	22	2	2	18	6

WEST YORKSHIRE FOOTBALL LEAGUE

PREMIER DIV	P	W	D	L	F	A	Pts
Wakefield	30	19	8	3	51	19	64
Whitkirk Wanderers	30	19	5	6	86	44	62
Nestle Rowntrees	30	19	2	9	79	55	+59
Beeston st Anthonys	30	17	7	6	74	40	58
Rothwell Athletic	30	17	6	7	78	42	57
Carlton Athletic	30	16	4	10	78	50	52
Horbury Town	30	16	4	10	68	41	52
Knaresborough Town	30	14	8	8	65	41	50
Bramley	30	13	4	13	55	58	43
York R I	30	11	6	13	60	71	39
Nostell Miners W	30	11	2	17	52	76	35
Bardsey	30	6	10	14	40	56	28
Barwick	30	7	6	17	46	73	27
Swillington Min W	30	5	3	22	40	95	18
Robin Hood Athletic	30	3	8	19	32	69	17
Magnet Sports	30	4	3	23	30	104	15

HARROGATE LEAGUE

PREMIER DIV	P	W	D	L	F	A	Pts
Bedale	22	18	2	2	69	19	56
Boroughbrige RES	22	12	5	5	73	37	41
Pateley Bridge	22	12	5	5	48	31	*40
Beckwithshaw	22	11	5	6	57	44	38
Spa Athletic	22	11	4	7	52	54	37
Otley Town R	22	9	5	8	44	49	32
H/Gate Railway Res	22	8	7	7	50	36	31
Kirkby Malzeard	22	6	8	8	47	49	26
Kirk Deighton	22	8	2	12	49	54	26
Bramham	22	4	5	13	56	75	17
St John Fisher	22	4	4	14	30	73	16
Ripon City Magnets	22	2	2	18	21	75	8

*Points Deducted

YORKSHIRE OLD BOYS FOOTBALL LEAGUE

	P	W	D	L	F	A	Pts
Leeds Univ Union	20	13	3	4	61	33	42
O.Modernians	20	13	1	6	50	26	40
Yorkshire Bank	20	12	2	6	64	41	38
Matthew Murray F.P.	20	11	4	5	60	35	37
Roundhegians	20	9	4	7	38	44	31
Wakefield CitY	20	7	2	11	43	51	23
O.Centralians	20	5	5	10	35	57	20
Almondburians	20	4	3	13	34	54	15
Abbey Grange O.B.	20	2	3	15	24	52	9
Sandal Wanderers	20	1	4	15	26	87	7

SOUTH YORKSHIRE AMATEUR LEAGUE

PREMIER DIV	P	W	D	L	F	A	Pts
Elm Tree	22	21	0	1	67	19	69
Hillsborough	22	13	4	5	65	33	46
Market Inn	22	12	5	5	56	35	41
Hollinsend Alb	24	11	7	6	64	53	40
SWD City Surv	23	11	2	10	49	48	38
Burncross	22	10	3	9	53	44	36
Davy	24	10	5	9	50	48	35
SH. Centralians	24	7	4	13	37	49	25
The Cumberland	21	7	3	11	36	47	24
Gate 13	23	6	5	12	56	59	23
Phoenix	24	8	1	15	39	74	*22
De La Salle O.B.	23	6	3	14	37	69	21
Oughtibridge	22	3	4	15	28	59	13

SPEN VALLEY LEAGUE

PREMIER DIV	P	W	D	L	F	A	Pts
Fountain Roberttown	18	14	2	2	56	21	44
Howden clough	18	10	4	4	53	25	34
White Horse	18	9	5	4	54	35	*29
Bulls Head Walkers	18	8	3	7	33	41	27
Saviletown Youth	18	8	2	8	56	44	26
Low Side W.M.C.	18	5	6	7	44	41	21
Lord Nelson	18	5	5	8	40	51	20
Airedae Celtic	18	5	4	9	38	54	19
Barclays F.C.A.	18	5	3	10	28	47	18
Overthorpe s.v. R	18	2	4	12	20	63	10

NORTH EASTERN FINAL LEAGUE TABLES 1997-98

BARNSEY & DISTRICT FOOTBALL ASSOCIATION

PREMIER DIV	P	W	D	L	F	A	Pts
Athersley Recr FC	20	18	1	1	66	19	55
Barnsley Trades FC	20	16	2	2	69	26	50
Kendray WMC FC	20	13	0	7	64	38	39
Houghton Main FC	20	11	3	6	56	30	36
Thurnscoe Butchers	19	10	2	7	39	39	32
Kingstone Unt WMC	20	10	0	10	46	39	30
Lundwood Lane End	20	9	0	11	37	44	27
Darfield Cross Keys	20	6	2	12	28	53	20
New Lodge WMC FC	20	5	1	14	46	71	16
Squires FC	19	4	1	14	34	47	13
Dodworth M/Wel	20	1	0	19	17	96	3

THE SHEFFIELD SPORTS ATHLETIC SATURDAY FOOTBALL LEAGUE

PREMIER DIV	P	W	D	L	F	A	Pts
Earl Fullflow	18	17	0	1	77	26	51
Fighting Cock	18	12	1	5	64	42	37
Waleswood Hotel	18	12	0	6	58	32	36
Boynton Sports	18	11	0	7	67	46	33
The Springwood	18	7	4	7	57	55	25
Elm Lane Fisheries	18	5	4	9	49	55	19
Rose Inn	18	5	4	9	47	59	19
Golden Plover	18	4	6	8	40	59	18
Vine Tavern	18	5	3	10	43	64	18
Norwich Union	18	1	0	17	40	104	3

CRAVEN FOOTBALL LEAGUE

PREMIER DIV	P	W	D	L	Pts
Embsay	22	16	4	2	36
Bulldogs	22	16	3	3	35
Oxenhope Rec	22	12	5	5	29
Keighley	22	13	3	6	29
Hawortth	22	11	4	7	26
Cross Hills R	22	12	5	5	29
Addingham	22	9	3	10	21
Cononley Spts	22	6	7	9	19
Colne CC	22	7	4	11	18
Cowling	22	4	5	13	13
Skipton LMS	22	4	1	17	9
Skipton Town	22	2	2	18	6

WEST YORKSHIRE FOOTBALL LEAGUE

PREMIER DIV	P	W	D	L	F	A	Pts
Wakefield	30	19	8	3	51	19	64
Whitkirk Wanderers	30	19	5	6	86	44	62
Nestle Rowntrees	30	19	2	9	79	55	+59
Beeston st Anthonys	30	17	7	6	74	40	58
Rothwell Athletic	30	17	6	7	78	42	57
Carlton Athletic	30	16	4	10	78	50	52
Horbury Town	30	16	4	10	68	41	52
Knaresborough Town	30	14	8	8	65	41	50
Bramley	30	13	4	13	55	58	43
York R I	30	11	6	13	60	71	39
Nostell Miners W	30	11	2	17	52	76	35
Bardsey	30	6	10	14	40	56	28
Barwick	30	7	6	17	46	73	27
Swillington Min W	30	5	3	22	40	95	18
Robin Hood Athletic	30	3	8	19	32	69	17
Magnet Sports	30	4	3	23	30	104	15

HARROGATE LEAGUE

PREMIER DIV	P	W	D	L	F	A	Pts
Bedale	22	18	2	2	69	19	56
Boroughbrige RES	22	12	5	5	73	37	41
Pateley Bridge	22	12	5	5	48	31	*40
Beckwithshaw	22	11	5	6	57	44	38
Spa Athletic	22	11	4	7	52	54	37
Otley Town R	22	9	5	8	44	49	32
H/Gate Railway Res	22	8	7	7	50	36	31
Kirkby Malzeard	22	6	8	8	47	49	26
Kirk Deighton	22	8	2	12	49	54	26
Bramham	22	4	5	13	56	75	17
St John Fisher	22	4	4	14	30	73	16
Ripon City Magnets	22	2	2	18	21	75	8

*Points Deducted

YORKSHIRE OLD BOYS FOOTBALL LEAGUE

	P	W	D	L	F	A	Pts
Leeds Univ Union	20	13	3	4	61	33	42
O.Modernians	20	13	1	6	50	26	40
Yorkshire Bank	20	12	2	6	64	41	38
Matthew Murray F.P.	20	11	4	5	60	35	37
Roundhegians	20	9	4	7	38	44	31
Wakefield CitY	20	7	2	11	43	51	23
O.Centralians	20	5	5	10	35	57	20
Almondburians	20	4	3	13	34	54	15
Abbey Grange O.B.	20	2	3	15	24	52	9
Sandal Wanderers	20	1	4	15	26	87	7

SOUTH YORKSHIRE AMATEUR LEAGUE

PREMIER DIV	P	W	D	L	F	A	Pts
Elm Tree	22	21	0	1	67	19	69
Hillsborough	22	13	4	5	65	33	46
Market Inn	22	12	5	5	56	35	41
Hollinsend Alb	24	11	7	6	64	53	40
SWD City Surv	23	11	2	10	49	48	38
Burncross	22	10	3	9	53	44	36
Davy	24	10	5	9	50	48	35
SH. Centralians	24	7	4	13	37	49	25
The Cumberland	21	7	3	11	36	47	24
Gate 13	23	6	5	12	56	59	23
Phoenix	24	8	1	15	39	74	*22
De La Salle O.B.	23	6	3	14	37	69	21
Oughtibridge	22	3	4	15	28	59	13

SPEN VALLEY LEAGUE

PREMIER DIV	P	W	D	L	F	A	Pts
Fountain Roberttown	18	14	2	2	56	21	44
Howden clough	18	10	4	4	53	25	34
White Horse	18	9	5	4	54	35	*29
Bulls Head Walkers	18	8	3	7	33	41	27
Saviletown Youth	18	8	2	8	56	44	26
Low Side W.M.C.	18	5	6	7	44	41	21
Lord Nelson	18	5	5	8	40	51	20
Airedae Celtic	18	5	4	9	38	54	19
Barclays F.C.A.	18	5	3	10	28	47	18
Overthorpe s.v. R	18	2	4	12	20	63	10

SELBY & DISTRICT LEAGUE

FIRST DIVISION	P	W	D	L	F	A	Pts
Kellingley Welf	18	15	3	0	79	20	48
Riccall Colliery	18	12	0	6	65	45	36
NormantonComrades	18	10	4	4	50	38	34
Fox Inn	18	9	1	8	44	44	28
Redhill s.s.	18	7	3	8	37	36	24
Hensall Athletic	18	7	3	8	36	56	24
Kippax Welfare	18	5	6	7	37	38	21
Drax P.S.	18	6	3	9	41	51	21
Thorpe United	18	4	1	13	30	64	13
Real Cliffe	18	1	2	15	34	70	5

HUDDERSFIELD & DISTRICT LEAGUE

DIVISION ONE	P	W	D	L	F	A	Pts
Britannia Sp	22	14	3	5	71	43	31
Brackenhall	22	10	5	7	44	26	25
Honley	22	10	5	7	50	39	25
Skelmanthorpe	22	9	7	6	46	38	25
Slaithwaite	22	9	4	9	41	41	22
Almondbury	22	8	6	8	33	34	22
Kirkburton	22	8	6	8	43	46	22
Scholes	22	7	6	9	36	47	20
Heywood Sp	22	7	5	10	38	40	19
Hepworth	22	6	7	9	34	55	19
Wooldale	22	7	4	11	43	53	18
Storthes Hill Res	22	7	2	13	41	58	16

HUDDERSFIELD WORKS & COMBINATION LEAGUE

DIVISION ONE	P	W	D	L	F	A	Pts
Zeneca	16	13	0	3	77	20	26
Leeds Road U	16	12	1	3	54	26	25
Plover	16	12	0	4	81	28	24
Forestrs	16	9	1	6	58	41	19
Berry Brow A	16	7	1	8	48	47	15
Ossett Panthers	16	7	1	8	26	49	15
Hepworth U Res	16	4	2	10	37	57	10
Botham Hall	16	3	1	12	24	66	7
Dr Browns	16	1	1	14	23	96	3

ROTHERHAM & DISTRICT LEAGUE

PREMIER DIV	P	W	D	L	F	A	Pts
Lord Conyers	18	15	1	2	99	22	31
ABS Kilnhurst	18	10	4	4	62	33	24
Queens Rawmarsh	18	9	5	4	51	43	23
Oaktree 95	18	8	6	4	51	46	22
New Life	18	9	2	7	57	40	20
Maltby Sheppey	18	5	5	8	53	55	15
Brinsworth WMC	18	5	3	10	39	69	13
Langold OB	18	5	2	11	36	61	12
Silverwood	18	5	1	12	50	61	11
Treeton Welfare	18	4	1	13	35	103	9

DRIFFIELD & DISTRICT LEAGUE MULTISERVE PREMIER

	P	W	D	L	F	A	Pts
Nafferton	18	8	1	0	65	19	33
Hilderthope	18	8	0	1	74	27	29
Crown Atc	18	8	1	0	67	29	28
Pack Horse	18	6	2	1	63	28	25
Middleton Rovers	18	5	3	1	58	43	20
Bridlington Rovers	18	1	3	5	39	49	12
Hornsea Town	18	3	1	5	38	64	12
Brid Labour Club	18	3	0	6	39	81	9
Drittield E.I.	18	1	1	7	26	67	7
Atc Brid George	18	1	0	8	23	85	62

WAKEFIELD & DISTRICT LEAGUE

PREMIER DIV	P	W	D	L	F	A	Pts
Stanley Utd	25	18	5	2	111	44	59
Crofton Arms	26	18	5	3	81	30	59
Walton SSC	26	18	1	7	92	54	55
Wrenthorpe AFC	26	14	7	5	79	50	49
Snydale Ath	26	15	3	8	82	52	48
Nostell MW	26	15	3	8	67	46	48
Shepherds Arms	26	12	3	11	70	56	39
Waterloo FC	26	11	3	12	67	70	36
Bay Horse Wdrs	26	10	4	12	78	88	34
Flanshaw Hotel	26	8	6	12	69	70	30
Crown FC	26	6	4	16	54	85	22
Wakefield Awaaz	25	5	2	18	44	120	17
Fieldhead Hosp	26	3	4	19	36	86	13
Eastmoor AFC	26	2	2	22	25	104	8

BRADFORD GRATTAN LEAGUE

PREMIER DIV	P	W	D	L	F	A	Pts
Woodend Rgrs	18	16	0	2	103	33	45
Fagley	18	12	3	3	63	38	39
Red Ginn	18	11	3	4	88	47	36
Wibsey 'A'	18	10	3	5	56	49	33
Queensbury	18	9	3	6	55	36	30
Mail Coach	18	7	6	5	43	33	27
U-Save DIY	18	4	6	8	39	59	18
Station	18	2	4	12	29	93	10
Royds United	18	1	5	12	49	77	8
Wibsey Park Utd	18	1	3	14	30	90	6

BRADFORD SUNDAY ALLIANCE LEAGUE

PREMIER DIV	P	W	D	L	F	A	Pts
Oakenshaw	22	19	2	1	75	30	59
Hudsons	22	13	6	3	66	39	45
Bolton woods	22	11	3	8	40	28	36
East Bowling Unity	22	9	4	9	50	45	31
Albion Sports	22	9	4	9	40	39	31
Sandy Lane	22	9	2	11	53	46	29
Brown Cow Wyke	22	9	2	11	36	64	29
Ventus Utd	22	6	5	11	44	46	*26
Fairweather Green	22	7	5	10	47	51	26
Bradford Moor	22	8	2	12	55	63	26
Green Man	22	7	4	11	45	50	25
West Bowling	22	4	3	15	36	86	+12

+Three points deducted *Three points awarded

CLARO LEAGUE SUNDAY LEAGUE

DIVISION ONE	P	W	D	L	F	A	Pts
Atlanta	18	14	4	0	56	26	46
Sherwood	18	12	3	3	59	21	39
H/Gate Catholic Club	18	8	6	4	37	30	30
Boroughbridge	18	8	3	7	58	49	27
Garforth Miners	18	7	3	8	39	46	24
Prince Of Wales	18	6	2	10	35	66	20
Scholes	18	6	1	11	47	48	19
Coach and Horses	18	5	3	10	49	53	18
Dishforth	18	5	2	11	28	50	17
Darley	18	4	3	11	42	61	15

DEE JAYS SCUNTHORPE SUNDAY LEAGUE

DIVISION ONE	P	W	D	L	F	A	Pts
Britannia Inn Brigg	16	10	5	1	52	17	35
Broughton Town	16	10	3	3	54	30	33
Burton Ath	16	10	3	3	39	26	33
Keadby Club	16	6	4	6	26	21	22
Queen Bess	16	6	4	6	31	31	22
Beacon	16	5	5	6	27	33	20
Ashby Star	16	3	5	8	19	31	14
George & Dragon	16	4	0	12	20	52	12
Poachers	16	3	1	12	27	53	10
Broughton FC			RESIGNED				

Starting young!
Photo: K Rolfe

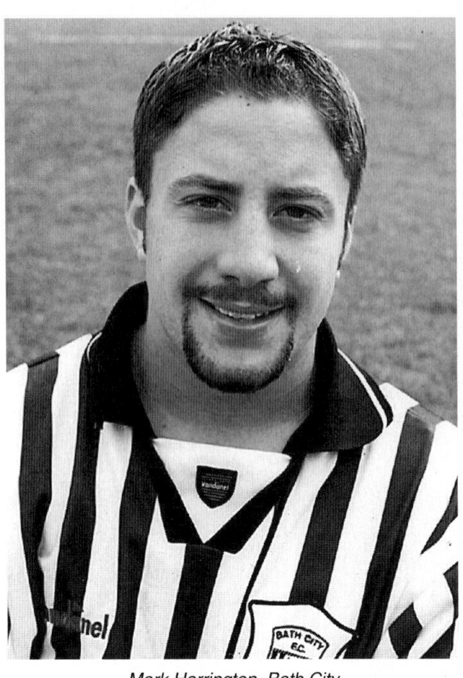

Mark Harrington, Bath City

Nick Ashby, Burton Albion
Photo: Dave West

Jason Hollman, Kings Lynn
Photo: Roger Turner

Adie Mings, Gloucester City
Photo: Peter Barnes

SOUTHERN LEAGUE

PYRAMID SECTION

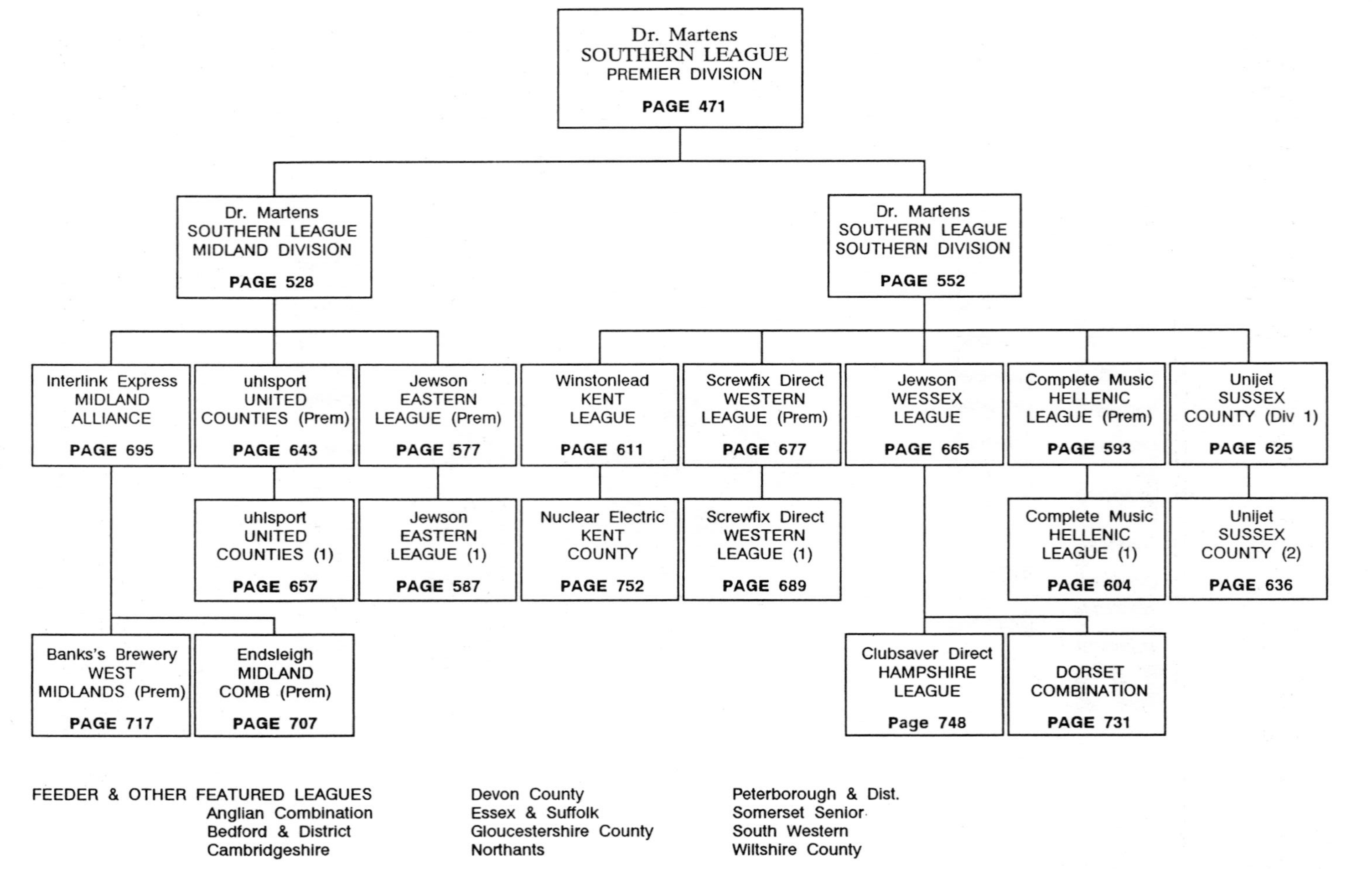

FEEDER & OTHER FEATURED LEAGUES

Anglian Combination
Bedford & District
Cambridgeshire
Devon County
Essex & Suffolk
Gloucestershire County
Northants
Peterborough & Dist.
Somerset Senior
South Western
Wiltshire County

Dr Martens League

President G E Templeman

Chairman D S R Gillard

Vice-Chairman K J Allen

Secretary & Treasurer D J Strudwick
11 Welland Close, Durrington, Worthing, West Sussex BN13 3NR
Tel: 01903 267788 (H) Fax: 01903 830500 Mob: 0860 445125

Rovers Return, League-head Revisited or simply Twin Peakes, whichever way you look at it Forest Green Rovers have won successive Championships. Last year it was the Southern Division; this year it's the big one. Forest Green Rovers are the Premier Division champions of the Southern Football League.

Don't be deceived, however, into thinking that winning a Southern League Championship is easy (ask the five clubs who, in recent seasons, have all finished in Premier Division relegation positions immediately after being relegated from the Football Conference). Every Championship/Runner-up position this year went 'to the wire', so they say, the final day of term. Whoever won the clash of the titans (Forest Green or Merthyr Tydfil), in the final midweek of the season, still needed to win their last game to clinch the title. Rovers won the meeting between the top two on the 29th April and then defeated Bath City on the 2nd May to wrest the honours.

To win the Midland Division Grantham Town needed at least a draw against Stourbridge in their final match. Failure would have let in Ilkeston Town, who had amassed 123 goals in 40 League games. And, although Weymouth needed only one point from their final match at Baldock Town to make absolutely certain of the Southern Division title, it had taken a fifteen match winning sequence starting on the 2nd March to put them in that position!

Forest Green's performance in their first season in the Premier Division was truly remarkable. They topped the table until the 11th October and were never out of the top three throughout the whole season. Such was Forest's prominence in the Division (they won 27 of their 42 League matches) that their record absorbed defeats against close rivals Merthyr Tydfil, Burton Albion (twice), Dorchester Town and Halesowen Town. A ten match unbeaten run at the start of the season was followed by three consecutive defeats. But nine consecutive wins, in a twelve game undefeated run from mid-December, ensured that Rovers were seldom far from the driver's seat. And whilst Burton, Dorchester, Halesowen, Bath, Worcester, King's Lynn and Atherstone United all threatened to challenge, only Merthyr Tydfil were able to keep pace with Rovers. Indeed, Merthyr enjoyed their own unbeaten run of fourteen matches and at no time during the season did the Martyrs suffer consecutive defeats. The Championship was only conceded on the final Saturday when Forest Green's victory over Bath City rendered Merthyr's result at Ashford Town academic. The real damage had been done three days earlier when Forest felled Merthyr 4-2. I feel sure that many pundits did not anticipate Forest Green maintaining their early season pace. Rover's bite, however, proved worse than their bark.

At the foot of the table, St. Leonards Stamcroft immediately felt the heat in the Premier Division kitchen. The team promoted from the Southern Division with Forest Green, at the end of last season, never really recovered from an opening gambit of eight straight defeats and a further eight without a win. Ashford Town, who avoided relegation last season when Sudbury Town withdrew, failed to escape the trap-door this year, in spite of new management. After a 'helter-skelter' season Sittingbourne occupied twentieth spot, despite a rally in March that produced eight points. And victory on the last day could not prevent Bromsgrove Rovers from joining Fisher Athletic, Nuneaton Borough, Stafford Rangers and Weymouth amongst the list of clubs to finish in the Premier Division relegation zone after falling out of the Football Conference just twelve months earlier.

In the Midland Division newcomers Blakenall and Wisbech Town, along with Bilston Town, Moor Green, Raunds Town and Solihull Borough all made an early impression on the leader board. I mean to offend no one, however, by commenting that the Division had become a virtual 'two horse race' by the New Year. Grantham Town and Ilkeston Town had broken away by ten points and four points, respectively, from Solihull Borough. Thereafter, neither were seriously challenged.

Grantham Town were undefeated in fifteen outings during a spell between mid-December and Easter Saturday. The run produced twelve straight wins but was brought to a close on Easter Monday by closest rivals Ilkeston Town, 3-2. Although the triumph still left the Robins trailing the Gingerbreads by six points, it appeared momentarily to shake the confidence of the South Kesteven side. Ten points were collected from their remaining six matches whilst Ilkeston mustered a maximum from their last five fixtures. It was almost enough to pull the Robins abreast of Grantham. Only one point separated the teams at 4.45 on the 2nd May.

Corby Town finished at the foot of a table that had been depleted by Dudley Town's withdrawal on the eve of the season. The Steelmen had to wait until the 25th October before gaining their first victory, a tally which they could only double by May 2nd. Corby's first win was against Evesham United, the team that eventually finished just one place above them in the table despite gaining sixteen more points.

Bashley, Chelmsford, Fisher Athletic, the two Newports and Weymouth were the main contenders for the Southern Division title during most of the campaign. Bashley and Chelmsford got off to flyers with eight and six straight wins, respectively. These two teams largely dominated the leader board during the opening third of the season with Weymouth and Newport A.F.C. breaking into second spot at the expense of Bashley. For the most part Chelmsford set the pace. City led the table by as much as ten points at times despite undergoing the trauma of losing their New Writtle Street home early in September. They were obliged to fulfil their home fixtures on three different grounds during the season. Manager Gary Bellamy must take much credit for the controlled manner with which he sustained the focus of his team upon the football, in the face of obvious distractions.

The tale of the championship's eventual destiny also revolved around a manager. After a variable start under the guidance of Matthew McGowan, and then John Crabbe, the Terras found themselves managerless. Crabbe resigned. Former Merthyr Tydfil and Shrewsbury Town boss, Fred Davies, was then appointed. In the 25 League matches that followed Davies' appointment defeat was conceded on only four occasions. On the 14th February Weymouth embarked on a winning run of fifteen consecutive matches that took them through the chasing pack and brought them the champonship, three points ahead of Chelmsford City. All that after losing their opening two fixtures.

At the foot of the table Cinderford and Yate Town found things pretty tough for most of the season. Between them only eleven victories were won (Cinderford six and Yate five) and both endured fourteen match runs without a win. Tonbridge Angels flirted with the foot of the table for an unfamiliar length of time before collecting fourteen wins to earn respectability. Baldock Town, Cirencester Town and Weston-Super-Mare also found themselves in alien territory before climbing into the comfort zone. Baldock collected valuable points at the end of the season to finish twelve points clear of Cinderford Town, who were a point ahead of Yate Town.

The League's Challenge Cup threw up its usual quota of surprises. Not one Premier Division club reached the semi-final stage of the competition! Gloucester existed at the Quarter Final stage in a replay at Redditch 4-1; Dorchester crashed to Bashley in similar circumstances 2-0 and Margate defeated Cambridge City. In earlier rounds Clevedon cut down Forest Green 4-1, Margate K.O.'d St. Leonards Stamcroft 4-0 and Newport I.O.W. defeated Bath 2-1. Moor Green beat Burton 3-1, Bashley thumped Salisbury 6-1, Margate beat Hastings 2-1 and Bedworth beat Worcester 1-0, Bromsgrove, Halesowen, King's Lynn, Atherstone, Rothwell and Nuneaton Borough had all lost their places in the first round of the tournament to First Division clubs.

When the competition reached its sharp end Margate and Bashley met in the Semi-Final. Margate exacted revenge for a Trophy defeat earlier in the season by ending Bashley's hopes of winning the League Cup's famous Worcester Vase. Margate's opponents in the Final were to be Redditch United who, amid a growing fixture list, eliminated the Midland Division's Runners-up Ilkeston Town.

In the First Leg of the Final at Hartsdown Park, Margate took advantage of home privilege when Paul Sykes scored in the fifth minute. A further goal in the 74th minute, this time by Mark Munday, increased Redditch's task for the Second Leg. Despite battling bravely in the second encounter, Redditch's only reward was a bizzare 'own goal' which was credited to Margate's goalkeeper, Lee Turner. Margate had mastered the inclement weather and playing conditions better than their opponents over the two games and were deserving victors. In defeat, however, Redditch merited every ounce of the praise heaped upon them for having climbed a mountainous fixture programme.

The English climate regularly invokes a muesli of fixtures at the end of each season. So, when rain clouds dropped their unwelcome load in record proportions during April, several clubs had to scurry through a serial of late re-arrangements. Redditch, though became embroiled in a veritable porridge of games in the final nine days of the campaign, a fixture list of Himalayan proportions. But without complaint or whine the Valley Stadium club fulfilled eight Midland Division League games and the Final of the Birmingham Senior Cup in as many days!

In the country's premier knock-out competition, the F.A. Cup, thirteen Dr. Martens League clubs reached the Fourth Qualifying Round. At the end of the day's play on Saturday 25th October eight clubs tuned in to 'B Sky B' for the First Round Draw. Amid the elation at still being 'in the hat' at this stage of the tournament hopes are always high for a draw that will offer either a realistic chance of going further, a home draw against a Fooball League club when financial reward may sweeten an unwanted result, or that increasingly more frequent phenomenon - a 'giant-killing'.

The magnificent eight was reduced to six when Sittingbourne lost in a replay at Hereford United and Gloucester City fell to colleagues Wisbech Town. Solihull Borough defeated Stalybridge Celtic, also in a second attempt. Margate, Bromsgrove Rovers, King's Lynn and Ilkeston Town had all 'holed out in one' against Staines, Romford, Salisbury City and Hyde United, respectively.

The First Round presented Margate with a home encounter against Fulham. The West London club had recently undergone a change of ownership and the new regime had appointed former England International Kevin Keegan as the club's manager. The tie attracted 6,000 spectators and Sky Television. Live coverage of the match earned £60,000 for each club. Whilst this naturally pleased the Treasurer, Margate's manager Chris Kinnear will almost certainly look to the injury sustained by leading scorer Martin Buglione as being the real influencing factor in his club's 2-1 defeat.

Solihull Borough also drew opposition from the Football League. Despite falling behind in the first minute, Borough held Darlington to a 1-1 draw at Feethams. The fireworks were, however, saved for the replay. The teams produced a 3-3 thriller before Darlington won 4-2 on penalties. Then came the real banger. The Quakers left Solihull Borough quaking in their shoes with an accusation that a club delegate had been seen passing money to the match referee after the first game. At an F.A. inquiry, no evidence was provided to support the indictment and the charge was dismissed.

In an all Dr. Martens tie, King's Lynn defeated their Premier Division colleagues from Bromsgrove 1-0. Ilkeston Town dispatched Boston United of the Northern Premier League 2-1 and Wisbech Town took the scalp of Billericay Town with a fine 3-2 away victory.

A few years ago having three clubs in the Second Round of the F.A. Cup would have attracted a 'Box 2 Appraisal - performance above expectation'. These days it is not unusual for any of the Pyramid League to have such representation. Dreams of Wembley's Towers can, though, be awakened by sharp realism. King's Lynn were uncompromisingly knocked out at Rotherham United 6-0 and Wisbech Town battled bravely before being robbed by the Pirates from Bristol Rovers 2-0. Ilkston Town's journey to Glanford Park, Scunthorpe, was more fruitful. The Robins earned a 1-1 draw. In the replay a crowd of more than 2,100 saw the Irons win 2-1. Visions of Wembley were gone. But there's always next year.... unless the Trophy proffered better hopes.

With fourteen Dr. Martens club partaking in the First Round Proper, there was room for optimism. Unfortunately, though, only six survived and worse was to come. On this occasion the 'ill-luck' of the draw paired each member together.

Grantham Town pulled off a great result at Bath City, beating the Romans 3-2. After Margate's exploits in the F.A. Cup, Bashley were delighted to leave Hartsdown Park 2-1 to the good. Gloucester City and Burton Albion battled out successive 1-1 and 2-2 draws before the Tigers downed the Brewers 5-4 on penalties.

Gloucester were then taken to a replay in Round Three. After appearing to have completed the difficult job of holding Stevenage Borough on their own patch 1-1, City succumbed at home 2-1. 'On a Roll' Bashley took high hopes to Hayes who were having a hard time in the Football Conference. It was not without a little surprise that the New Foresters were eliminated 2-0. But Grantham's success against foes from higher echelons continued. In front of a record crowd for the South Kesteven Stadium the Gingerbreads undermind the Pitmen from Hednesford 2-1.

A home draw against Southport in Round Four guaranteed another attendance record; 3,695, the biggest crowd at this particular stage of the competition, turned up to watch Grantham hold their rivals from the Conference 1-1. The eventual Finalists, though, took early control in the replay at the windswept Haig Avenue Stadium. Grantham were never allowed to settle into their cultured passing game orchestrated by David Harbottle. Despite a late rally by Grantham, Southport won 3-1 and Grantham's disappoitment at having missed a place in the Semi-Final was obvious and understandable. It was, nevertheless, misplaced after such an excellent run.

Talking of runs (or probably walks in this case), the Dr. Martens list of Referees has had a highly successful year. Three of the League's referees have been promoted to the National list of Referees, six more have achieved National list Assiatant Referee status and four other have been promoted to the Panel List of Referees. A successful season in anyone's language. Just reward to the League's Match Officials Association ably led by chairman Laurance Jones and steered by secretary Steve Tincknell. It is also, a worthy reflection of the League's investment in the Association's Training Programme and just return for Jim Hill and his merry band of Assessors.

So another successful season has been enjoyed by the Dr. Martens Football League. Combat within the League and the League Cup was fierce, as usual. Not one League title or Runner-up spot was decided before the last day of the season. A dramatic climax to the end of a year's campaign. The Competition remains the envy of all similar Leagues and still boasts of being the best supported League outside of the Football Conference.

But such a vibrant competition doesn't just happen. Each member club plays its part and sound impartial control by the Management Committee is an essential ingredient. This latter aspect is willingly supplied by the elected members of the Management Committee who operate under the guidance of their impeccably honest and hardworking chairman, Doug Gillard. In this memorable season, his courage and integrity could well have provided the catalyst for the realignment of soccer beneath the Football Conference. Time will tell. Meanwhile, fortunately for Doug (and the league), the Competition's No. 2, the ubiquitous Keith Allen, has the same talents in equal abundance. Well done Gentlemen.

The backbone of the League's management structure is sound. Sponsorship, however, enhances the way in which the management can operate and brings obvious benefits to the member clubs. The Southern Football League's Sponsors are fantastic.

Through the offices of Andrew Borge, Dr. Martens Airwair has advanced the profile of the League whilst enabling nearly £200,000 of cash funding to be distributed amongst the clubs during the past two years. Thank you Max and Steven Griggs.

To conclude the good news, I congratulate the winning clubs and send my best wishes to Forest Green Rovers for their venture into the Football Conference. I commiserate with all the clubs who have not fared so well, particularly those who will not be with us next season. I extend the hand of typical Dr. Martens League friendship to the new faces that join us - Boston United (Northern Premier League), Andover (Wessex League), Bloxwich Town (Midland Alliance), Folkestone Invicta (Kent League) and Stamford (United Counties League). I hope our League will provide you with the vehicle to fulfil all your hopes and ambitions.

For me, football reflects the tapestry of life very accurately indeed. So having recorded the 'highs' an objective Annual Report must also reflect the 'lows'. The only certainty in life .... dealt its usual set of dark cards with which we must cope. This year we have had to contend with the passing of Mrs. Templeman, the lady of our wonderful president. We have also lost Bob Griffiths of Margate, and Eddie Jones of Racing Clubs Warwick. But how can we ever fully overcome the tragic loss of Burton Albion's Simon Redfern who left our world in the prime of his life. I intend no offence to any other friends that we will miss during the coming years. Instead, I propose the names of these four lovely people, on everyone's behalf, as the focal point of my condolences.

My conclusion is, as usual, reserved for the clubs. Thanks for making 1997/98 another memorable season. Thanks to everyone who has helped me, and have made a courteous, friendly contrbution to the League's affairs.

DR. MARTENS PREMEIR DIVISION

Final League Table

		HOME					AWAY							Leading Goalscorers (these include all goals as reported in the league bulletin)		
	P	W	D	L	F	A	W	D	L	F	A	PTS	GD			
Forest Green Rovers	42	16	3	2	51	20	11	5	5	42	35	89	38	29 Hunt	17 Smart	13 Sykes
Methry Tydfil	42	16	4	1	51	16	8	8	5	29	26	84	38	30 Mitchell	11 Griffiths	10 Summers
Burton Albion	42	12	4	5	39	19	9	4	8	25	24	71	21	18 Garner	10 Cotter	9 Holmes
Dorchester Town	42	11	7	3	41	18	8	6	7	22	20	70	25	21 Shepherd	10 Richardson	7 Killick
Halesowen Town	42	14	4	3	46	18	4	11	6	24	20	69	32	26 Piearce	24 Wright	13 Crisp
Bath City	42	12	8	1	42	14	7	4	10	30	37	69	21	21 Colbourne	20 Davis	13 Paul
Worcester City	42	15	4	2	34	15	4	8	9	20	29	69	10	16 Bowan	7 Griffiths & Harding	
King's Lynn	42	11	7	3	34	22	7	4	10	30	43	65	-1	20 Hudson	20 Williams	18 McNamara
Atherstone United	42	8	8	5	30	22	9	4	8	25	27	63	6	11 Middleton	10 Warner	8 Green
Crawley Town	42	9	6	6	31	23	8	2	11	32	37	59	3	10 Garland	10 Warden	9 Reilly
Gloucester City	42	10	5	6	33	25	6	6	9	24	32	59	0	18 Mainwaring	16 Fergusson	13 Mings
Nuneaton Borough	42	12	3	6	39	22	5	3	13	29	39	57	7	13 Straw	11 King	10 Street & Thomas.
Cambridge City	42	9	4	8	31	28	7	4	10	31	42	56	-8	30 Harris	11 Cogger	7 Bennett
Hastings Town	42	9	6	6	42	32	5	6	10	25	38	54	-3	30 Browne	17 Dent	7 Beard & Fox
Tamworth	42	10	4	7	43	30	4	7	10	25	35	53	3	20 Piggott	16 Smith	12 Hunter
Rothwell Town	42	7	8	6	30	33	4	8	9	25	40	49	-18	12 Kirkup	10 McGuire	6 Bullimore
Gresley Rovers	42	9	4	8	39	33	5	2	14	20	44	48	-18	12 Murphy	12 Pitt	5 Alsopp
Salisbury City	42	9	5	7	30	31	3	7	11	23	41	48	-19	13 Chalk	9 Bright	9 Puckett
Bromsgrove Rovers	42	11	6	4	41	23	2	0	19	26	62	45	-18	18 Whitehouse	9 Payne	6 Mainwaring & Smith
Sittingbourne	42	9	4	8	30	30	3	4	14	17	36	44	-19	12 Plank	10 Rowland	9 Overton
Ashford Town	42	5	4	12	18	32	3	1	17	16	53	29	-51	5 Scott	4 Harrison & Lough	3 by 5 players
St. Leonards Stamcroft	42	4	3	14	32	50	1	7	13	16	47	25	-49	14 Miles	7 Ruddy	4 Flanagan & Norman

Results 1997-98

		1	2	3	4	5	6	7	8	9	10	11	12	13	14	15	16	17	18	19	20	21	22	
1	Ashford Town	X	2-0 (403)	0-1 (289)	3-0 (326)	1-3 (441)	1-2 (302)	0-1 (382)	0-4 (443)	0-1 (389)	0-1 (318)	1-0 (397)	0-5 (433)	1-2 (456)	0-3 (447)	2-2 (448)	2-1 (378)	1-1 (420)	1-1 (339)	0-1 (536)	2-0 (563)	1-1 (374)	0-2 (499)	1
2	Atherstone United	2-1 (282)	X	2-0 (267)	2-1 (302)	3-0 (346)	0-1 (283)	3-0 (252)	0-0 (270)	1-1 (364)	2-2 (317)	2-3 (472)	0-0 (212)	2-2 (242)	0-0 (259)	0-2 (302)	2-2 (2101)	3-1 (171)	0-3 (221)	2-1 (304)	4-0 (267)	0-0 (645)	0-2 (206)	2
3	Bath City	3-0 (619)	0-0 (571)	X	3-1 (603)	0-0 (727)	2-2 (474)	2-1 (455)	0-0 (611)	1-1 (1019)	1-0 (704)	0-0 (547)	1-3 (544)	4-2 (503)	2-0 (719)	3-0 (1280)	5-0 (786)	1-1 (711)	5-0 (513)	1-0 (523)	4-0 (572)	3-3 (1026)	1-0 (571)	3
4	Bromsgrove Rovers	3-0 (456)	0-1 (414)	3-1 (568)	X	1-2 (860)	3-0 (585)	1-1 (578)	0-2 (488)	2-1 (356)	3-1 (1061)	5-3 (622)	2-2 (1370)	1-1 (465)	1-1 (750)	0-0 (731)	3-1 (693)	0-2 (567)	2-2 (369)	3-2 (745)	4-0 (504)	1-0 (827)	3-0 (769)	4
5	Burton Albion	4-0 (705)	0-1 (720)	0-3 (790)	5-1 (760)	X	1-3 (868)	5-2 (690)	2-2 (543)	4-1 (609)	2-1 (731)	1-0 (2189)	0-0 (880)	0-1 **(528)**	0-0 (849)	3-0 (1001)	1-0 (864)	3-0 (628)	1-2 (751)	2-0 (696)	2-1 (464)	1-1 (1012)	2-0 (588)	5
6	Cambridge City	2-0 (323)	1-2 (257)	0-1 (290)	4-0 (325)	0-1 (369)	X	3-2 (480)	1-2 (334)	1-2 (282)	1-1 (284)	1-0 (316)	0-0 (393)	0-2 (239)	2-0 (668)	0-3 (410)	2-0 (491)	3-3 (310)	3-1 (322)	2-1 (325)	2-1 (358)	2-2 (379)	1-4 (3270	6
7	Crawley Town	1-2 (963)	3-0 (1003)	1-0 (806)	4-2 (1240)	0-0 (1381)	3-2 (1135)	X	0-1 (1162)	2-2 (2163)	3-1 (1178)	0-1 (930)	0-0 (1570)	0-0 (1573)	2-0 (911)	1-2 (1370)	1-2 (858)	2-2 (1104)	1-0 (1314)	0-0 (1028)	2-1 (1382)	3-2 (1281)	2-3 (1040)	7
8	Dorchester Town	5-1 (575)	0-0 (570)	2-1 (513)	4-0 (441)	3-1 (517)	1-1 (540)	0-1 (612)	X	1-1 (560)	3-0 (830)	2-2 (485)	2-0 (537)	3-0 (641)	3-4 (676)	1-1 (885)	3-1 (600)	2-3 (581)	1-0 (1088)	2-0 (222)	1-1 (669)	2-0 (712)	0-0 (504)	8
9	Forest Green Rovers	3-0 (449)	3-1 (364)	2-0 (1678)	2-1 (693)	1-3 (461)	2-0 (342)	3-2 (428)	1-0 (530)	X	1-1 (1333)	0-1 (569)	2-0 (701)	5-2 (371)	4-2 (418)	3-1 (2891)	4-2 (402)	2-0 (365)	3-2 (865)	3-0 (534)	2-2 (485)	5-0 (548)	0-0 (402)	9
10	Gloucester City	2-3 (375)	1-2 (660)	4-0 (978)	4-2 (518)	4-2 (562)	3-5 (678)	0-0 (556)	1-2 (648)	1-4 (1095)	X	1-0 (606)	1-0 (718)	1-1 (711)	3-0 (608)	1-0 (823)	1-0 (649)	0-1 (582)	1-1 (328)	2-1 (555)	1-1 (612)	1-0 (519)	0-0 (758)	10
11	Gresley Rovers	2-0 (565)	2-0 (718)	2-2 (462)	4-2 (408)	2-0 (1752)	0-1 (348)	3-1 (501)	0-1 (504)	1-5 (557)	2-3 (566)	X	1-1 (695)	1-2 (391)	2-4 (575)	2-0 (601)	0-1 (859)	5-2 (416)	1-1 (418)	2-1 (508)	5-1 (513)	0-3 (636)	2-2 (563)	11
12	Halesowen Town	1-0 (645)	3-1 (715)	2-1 (355)	3-1 (1074)	1-1 (648)	1-1 (737)	0-1 (663)	2-1 (609)	3-0 (749)	0-1 (681)	5-0 (631)	X	2-1 (713)	4-1 (907)	2-2 (1225)	3-0 (913)	1-3 (739)	4-1 (447)	3-1 (638)	3-0 (759)	1-1 (927)	2-0 (1543)	12
13	Hastings Town	4-1 (683)	3-1 (444)	2-2 (629)	3-2 (482)	0-1 (472)	4-5 (431)	1-2 (761)	0-0 (413)	0-1 (469)	1-1 (436)	4-1 (334)	2-2 (465)	X	3-2 (419)	0-1 (392)	2-4 (467)	3-1 (441)	2-0 (446)	1-1 (530)	2-1 (1672)	2-2 (537)	3-1 (307)	13
14	King's Lynn	2-1 (893)	1-4 (1005)	3-1 (943)	3-2 (866)	2-1 (777)	2-1 (1122)	2-0 (1007)	2-0 (924)	2-2 (814)	1-2 (483)	1-0 (585)	0-0 (908)	1-1 (1014)	X	1-1 (1446)	1-1 (1180)	2-0 (939)	3-0 (731)	0-1 (739)	1-1 (889)	2-1 (813)	2-2 (690)	14
15	Merthyr Tydfil	3-0 (715)	1-1 (675)	2-3 (671)	4-2 (1005)	2-1 (661)	3-1 (676)	2-1 (727)	4-0 (863)	4-0 (1930)	1-0 (635)	3-0 (602)	2-1 (615)	4-2 (648)	4-0 (743)	X	1-0 (869)	2-2 (537)	0-0 (619)	0-0 (527)	4-0 (697)	3-1 (687)	2-1 (1089)	15
16	Nuneaton Borough	2-1 (610)	0-1 (1113)	3-3 (1603)	2-1 (1376)	0-1 (1115)	0-1 (889)	4-2 (1534)	2-2 (1155)	2-1 (1560)	3-1 (526)	6-0 (1605)	2-1 (1107)	2-0 (940)	0-1 (902)	0-1 (1203)	X	3-0 (816)	2-1 (1174)	3-1 (1009)	1-1 (652)	0-2 (1573)	2-0 (1091)	16
17	Rothwell Town	1-2 (225)	2-2 (287)	1-4 (224)	2-0 (253)	1-0 (327)	2-1 (236)	1-2 (283)	0-0 (230)	2-5 (224)	1-1 (252)	1-0 (253)	1-1 (271)	5-1 (221)	1-2 (402)	1-1 (288)	1-6 (657)	X	2-2 (202)	1-1 (372)	1-1 (204)	1-0 (314)	2-1 (246)	17
18	Salisbury City	0-0 (315)	2-1 (294)	1-0 (403)	2-0 (343)	0-2 (301)	1-1 (246)	2-6 (685)	0-3 (472)	0-2 (506)	2-3 (434)	1-0 (574)	1-0 (306)	2-0 (375)	2-3 (408)	2-5 (324)	2-2 (371)	0-0 (430)	X	4-0 (221)	2-0 (204)	3-2 (347)	1-1 (280)	18
19	Sittingbourne	3-2 (678)	0-2 (379)	4-2 (451)	2-0 (432)	0-2 (571)	3-1 (556)	2-1 (448)	1-0 (457)	4-5 (436)	2-0 (467)	2-3 (419)	0-0 (454)	2-1 (427)	2-2 (441)	1-2 (462)	1-0 (447)	0-0 (277)	0-3 (417)	X	1-3 (539)	0-1 (459)	0-0 (446)	19
20	St. Leonards Stamcroft	4-1 (508)	1-2 (486)	1-2 (427)	2-4 (404)	0-2 (444)	5-1 (254)	0-2 (432)	0-2 (373)	1-2 (418)	0-0 (351)	1-3 (324)	2-5 (264)	1-4 (1579)	2-4 (537)	0-0 (489)	1-5 (501)	3-2 (426)	6-2 (436)	0-4 (332)	X	1-2 (354)	1-1 (302)	20
21	Tamworth	4-0 (519)	0-2 (1410)	1-2 (647)	2-4 (631)	1-1 (786)	4-1 (670)	2-1 (615)	3-0 (863)	1-2 (467)	1-3 (730)	6-3 (710)	0-2 (909)	1-0 (492)	3-0 (478)	2-4 (715)	2-1 (1242)	1-1 (801)	1-1 (453)	4-1 (582)	1-1 (491)	X	3-0 (703)	21
22	Worcester City	2-1 (768)	2-1 (599)	1-1 (1035)	2-0 (1201)	2-1 (914)	1-0 (692)	1-3 (706)	1-0 (812)	2-3 (816)	2-1 (1010)	1-0 (851)	1-1 (1206)	0-0 (707)	3-1 (907)	1-1 (1301)	1-0 (964)	3-0 (540)	2-0 (713)	1-0 (616)	2-0 (559)	3-1 (1819)	X	22

DR MARTENS LEAGUE CUP 1997-98

PRELIMINARY ROUND

Weston super Mare	0 v 3	Gloucester City
Tamworth	6 v 5	Gresley Rovers

FIRST ROUND

(aggregate scores)

Margate	4 v 0	Tonbridge Angels
Baldock Town	0 v 4	Hastings Town
Crawley Town	8 v 6	Sittingbourne
St Leonards S'croft	4 v 3	Erith & Belvedere
Fisher Athletic Lon.	7 v 3	Dartford
Ashford Town	3 v 5	Chelmsford City
Shepshed Dynamo	3 v 6	Cambridge City
Hinckley United	4 v 1	VS Rugby
Havant Town	3 v 1	Weymouth
Fareham Town	2 v 7	Dorchester Town
Clevedon Town	6 v 3	Cirencester Town
Merthyr Tydfil	1 v 3	Forest Green Rvrs
Yate Town	1 v 3	Bath City
Newport IoW	4 v 3	Waterlooville
Salisbury City	6 v 6	Trowbridge Town
Bashley	5 v 1	Fleet Town
Redditch United	4 v 1	Bromsgrove Rovers
Bilston Town	3 v 1	Halesowen Town
Paget Rangers	3 v 4	Solihull Borough
Stourbridge	6 v 0	Evesham United
Bedworth United	3 v 1	Nuneaton Borough
Worcester City	6 v 5	Stafford Rangers
Witney Town	2 v 5	Newport AFC
Cinderford Town	0 v 5	Gloucester City
Raunds Town	9 v 1	Rothwell Town
Grantham Town	5 v 1	Wisbech Town
Corby Town	3 v 2	Brackley Town
Ilkeston Town	4 v 3	Kings Lynn
Tamworth	1 v 3	Burton Albion
Atherstone United	4 v 6	Moor Green
Sutton Coldfield Town	4 v 3	Racing C. Warwick
Bye: Blakenall	and	Dudley Town

SECOND ROUND

Margate	2 v 1	Hastings Town
Crawley Town	0 v 1	St Leonards Stam.
Fisher Athletic Lon.	2 v 0	Chelmsford City
Cambridge City	1 v 0	Hinckley United
Havant Town	0 v 3 (after 1-1)	Dorchester Town
Clevedon Town	4 v 1	Forest Green Rvrs
Bath City	1 v 2	Newport IoW
Salisbury City	1 v 6	Bashley
Redditch United	1 v 0	Bilston Town
Solihull Borough	0 v 1 (after 0-0)	Stourbridge
Bedworth United	1 v 0	Worcester City
Newport AFC	1 v 2 (after 2-2)	Gloucester City
Raunds Town	3 v 1 (after 3-3)	Grantham Town
Corby Town	1 v 2	Ilkeston Town
Burton Albion	1 v 3	Moor Green
Sutton Coldfield Tn	4 v 0	Blakenall

THIRD ROUND

Margate	4 v 0	St Leonards Stam.
Fisher Athletic Lon.	3 v 4	Cambridge City
Dorchester Town	4 v 1	Clevedon Town
Newport IoW	0 v 3	Bashley
Redditch United	1 v 0	Stourbridge
Bedworth United	0 v 3	Gloucester City
Raunds Town	0 v 3	Ilkeston Town
Moor Green	1 v 0	Sutton Coldfield Tn

FOURTH ROUND

Margate	2 v 1	Cambridge City
Dorchester Town	0 v 2 (after 1-1)	Bashley
Redditch United	4 v 1 (after 2-2)	Gloucester City
Ilkeston Town	4 v 0 (after 3-3)	Moor Green

SEMI FINALS (Two Legs)

Margate	3:1 v 0:2	Bashley
Redditch United	3:0 v 1:1	Ilkeston Town

FINAL (Two Legs)

Margate	2:0 v 0:1	Bashley

Dr MARTENS LEAGUE Premier Division Ten Year Records

	88/9	89/0	90/1	91/2	92/3	93/4	94/5	95/6	96/7	97/8
Alvechurch	14	21	-	-	-	-	-	-	-	-
Ashford Town	18	19	-	-	-	-	-	-	19	21
Atherstone United	-	6	15	13	15	4	15	17	11	9
Baldock Town	-	-	-	-	-	-	-	18	20	-
Bashley	-	-	10	4	9	21	-	-	-	-
Bath City	9	2	-	-	-	-	-	-	-	6
Bedworth United	22	-	-	-	-	-	-	-	-	-
Bromsgrove Rovers	10	10	5	1	-	-	-	-	-	19
Burton Albion	8	4	7	10	8	11	3	16	6	3
Cambridge City	5	8	3	5	14	17	9	19	18	13
Chelmsford City	-	18	18	18	12	6	15	12	22	-
Cheltenham Town	-	-	-	-	2	2	2	3	2	-
Corby Town	16	20	-	14	3	9	22	-	-	-
Crawley Town	12	15	19	17	=6	5	11	9	17	10
Dartford	2	3	13	6	-	-	-	-	-	-
Dorchester Town	13	14	11	11	18	18	6	13	15	4
Dover Athletic	6	1	4	2	1	-	-	-	-	-
Fareham Town	19	-	-	-	-	-	-	-	-	-
Farnborough Town	-	-	1	-	-	1	-	-	-	-
Fisher Athletic	-	-	-	21	-	-	-	-	-	-
Forst Green Rovers	-	-	-	-	-	-	-	-	-	1
Gloucester City	-	9	2	12	13	10	4	4	3	11
Gosport Borough	7	22	-	-	-	-	-	-	-	-
Gravesnd & Northfleet	-	7	21	22	-	-	14	11	14	-
Gresley Rovers	-	-	-	-	-	14	8	5	1	17
Halesowen Town	-	-	8	8	10	3	13	2	4	5
Hastings Town	-	-	-	-	16	12	12	8	16	14
Hednesford Town	-	-	-	-	4	13	1	-	-	-
Ilkeston Town	-	-	-	-	-	-	-	20	-	-
Kings Lynn	-	-	-	-	-	-	-	-	5	8
Leek Town	-	-	-	-	-	-	7	-	-	-
Leicester United	20	-	-	-	-	-	-	-	-	-
Merthyr Tydfil	1	-	-	-	-	-	-	7	9	2
Moor Green	15	11	16	9	19	19	-	-	-	-
Newport A F C	-	-	-	-	-	-	-	14	21	-
Nuneaton Borough	-	-	-	-	-	22	-	-	7	12
Poole Town	-	-	17	20	-	-	-	-	-	-
Redditch United	21	-	-	-	-	-	-	-	-	-
Rothwell Town	-	-	-	-	-	-	-	-	-	16
Rushden Town	-	-	14	-	-	-	-	-	-	-
Rushden & Diamonds	-	-	-	-	-	-	5	1	-	-
Salisbury	-	-	-	-	-	-	-	15	12	18
Sittingbourne	-	-	-	-	-	8	20	-	8	20
Solihull Borough	-	-	-	-	=6	6	19	-	-	-
St Leonards	-	-	-	-	-	-	-	-	-	22
Stafford Rangers	-	-	-	-	-	-	-	21	-	-
Sudbury Town	-	-	-	-	-	-	18	10	11	-
Trowbridge Town	-	-	-	7	5	7	21	-	-	-
Tamworth	-	-	-	-	-	-	-	-	-	15
V.S. Rugby	3	5	9	3	20	-	17	22	-	-
Waterlooville	17	16	20	15	11	20	-	-	-	-
Wealdstone	11	12	12	19	-	-	-	-	-	-
Weymouth	-	17	22	-	21	-	-	-	-	-
Worcester City	4	13	6	16	17	15	10	6	10	7
No of Clubs Competing	22	22	22	22	21	22	22	22	22	22

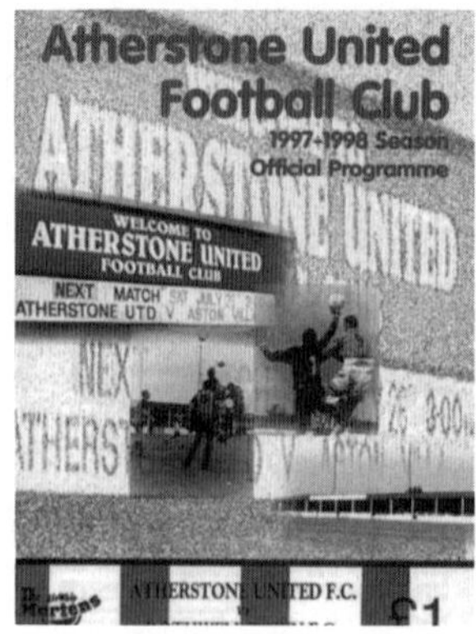

PROGRAMME DETAILS:
Pages: 28 **Price:** £1
Editor: Brian Stephenson
01827 715067

ATHERSTONE UNITED

Colours: Red & white stripes/red/red **Formed:** 1979
Change colours: Yellow & blue/blue/blue **Nickname:** The Adders
Midweek home matchday: Monday 7.30pm **Club Sponsors:** T.B.A.
Reserve's Lge: Midland Comb. Reserve Div.
Local Press: Tamworth Herald, Evening News, Atherstone Herald, Coventry Telegraph.
Local Radio: Mercia Sound, CWR.

Chairman: Ku Akeredolu **President:** C Culwick
Secretary: Neil Dykes, 18 Greendale Close, Atherstone, Warwickshire CV9 1PR, (01827 714326)
Manager: Ron Bradbury 01203 382548 **Asst Manager:** R Stockley
Physio: S Welch **Commercial Manager:** T Jago

GROUND Address: Sheepy Road, Atherstone, Warwickshire. CV9 1HG. 01827 717829
Directions: Half mile north of town centre on B4116 Twycross/Ashby road.
Capacity: 3,500 **Cover:** 1,000 **Seats:** 373 **Floodlights:** Yes
Clubhouse: Open during normal licensing hours, all usual facilities.
Club Shop: Yes. Programmes, magazines, souvenirs etc. Contact Alan Hewitt, (01827 715799). **Metal Badges:** Yes

PREVIOUS - **Leagues:** West Midlands 1979-87

CLUB RECORDS - **Attendance:** 2,873 v V.S. Rugby, F.A. Cup 1st Round Proper 1987-88 **Win:** 12-2 v Tipton Town (H), West Midlands (Regional) League Premier Division 86-87. **Defeat:** 1-7 v Rushden & Diamonds, Beazer League Premier Division 94-95. **Goalscorer:** Alan Bourton **Appearances:** Lee Spencer **Fee Paid:** £4,500 to Gloucester City for Gary Bradder, 1989. **Fee Received:** £40,000 for Andy Rammell from Manchester United, September 1989.

HONOURS - Southern Lge Midland Div 88-89; West Midlands Lge 81-82 86-87 (Lge Cup 81-82, Premier Div Cup 86-87, Div 2 Cup (Reserves) 86-87); Walsall Senior Cup 83-84; Midland Combination Reserve Division 87-88; Birmingham Senior Cup R-up 89-90.
FA Cup: 2nd Rd Proper 1990-91 (lost 0-1 at Crewe Alexandra)
FA Trophy: 1st Round 88-89 91-92.

Players progressing to The Football League: Andy Rammell (Manchester United).

97-98 - Captain: Robin Judd **P.o.Y.:** Lee Middleton **Top scorer:** Lee Middleton

Back Row (L-R); Rob Higgs, Paul Olner, Bob Stockley (Asst Mgr), Gary Redgate, Owen Wright, Ashley Warner, David Hart, Kim Green. Front Row; Steve Welch (Physio), Boyd Young, Mark Albrighton, Scott Blair, Robin Judd, Craig Dean, Danny Martin, Lee Middleton

ATHERSTONE UNITED - Match Facts 1997-98

Match No.	Date	Venue H / A	Comp.	Opponents	Result & Score		Att.	Goalscorers	League Position
1	16.08	A	DM	St Leonards Stamcroft	W	2-1	486	Middleton 81(pen), Martin 84.	
2	23.08	H	DM	King's Lynn	D	0-0	259		14
3	25.08	A	DM	Halesowen Town	L	1-3	715	Murphy 13.	9
4	30.08	H	DM	Salisbury City	**L**	**0-3**	221		19
5	02.09	A	DM	Rothwell Town	D	2-2	287	Middleton 43, Young 74.	
6	07.09	A	DM	Sittingbourne	W	2-0	379	Ellison 14, Albrighton 90.	13
7	14.09	A	**FAC 1Q**	Knypersley Victoria	L	0-1	250		
8	20.09	H	DM	Bromsgrove Rovers	W	2-1	302	Murphy 63(pen), 78.	13
9	22.09	A	DM	Worcester City	L	1-2	599	Middleton 88.	
10	27.09	H	DM	Crawley Town	W	3-0	252	Murphy 23, Middleton 30(pen), Green 90.	11
11	30.09	H	**DMC 1-1**	Moor Green	L	1-4	102	Olner 74.	-
12	04.10	H	DM	Hastings Town	D	2-2	242	Martin 28, Murphy 49.	11
13	07.10	H	**BSC 1-1**	Halesowen Harriers	W	4-1	102	Warner 18, 84, Murphy 60, Green 48.	-
14	11.10	A	DM	Cambridge City	W	2-1	257	Warner 5, Redgate 90.	7
15	17.10	A	**FAT 1Q**	Moor Green	L	0-1	161		-
16	25.10	H	DM	Merthyr Tydfil	L	0-2	302		10
17	28.10	A	**DMC 1-2**	Moor Green	W	3-2	70	Martin 24, Judd 49, Green 90.	-
18	01.11	A	DM	Burton Albion	W	1-0	720	Olner 5.	8
19	04.11	H	DM	Halesowen Town	D	0-0	212		-
20	08.11	A	DM	Gresley Rovers	L	0-2	608		10
21	11.11	H	**MIC 2**	Kings Heath	**W**	**4-0**	94	Hart 34, 75, Warner 49, 83.	-
22	15.11	H	DM	Bath City	W	2-0	267	Middleton 25, 42.	7
23	18.11	H	DM	Rothwell Town	W	3-1	171	Ellison 63, Martin 45, Green 90.	
24	22.11	A	DM	Forest Green Rovers	L	1-3	364	Albrighton 71.	7
25	25.11	H	**BSC 2**	Worcester City	W	2-0	101	Albrighton 67, Middleton 70.	-
26	06.12	A	DM	Bromsgrove Rovers	W	1-0	414	Martin D 23.	5
27	13.12	H	DM	St Leonards Stamcroft	**W**	**4-0**	267	Redgate 33, Green 38, Warner 75, Olner 85.	4
28	16.12	H	DM	Worcester City	L	0-2	206		7
29	26.12	H	DM	Nuneaton Borough	D	2-2	2,101	Warner 57, Green 81.	
30	28.12	A	DM	King's Lynn	W	4-1	1,005	**Judd 3** (30, 52 80),OG (Lewis) 50.	7
31	01.01	A	DM	Tamworth	W	2-0	1,410	Ellison 20, Warner 89.	7
32	13.01	H	**MIC 3**	Bloxwich Town	D	*1-1	100	Warner 48. *A.E.T. Won 5-4 after penalties.	-
33	17.01	H	DM	Dorchester Town	D	0-0	270		8
34	20.01	H	**BSC 3**	Redditch United	L	1-2	183	Hart 80.	-
35	24.01	A	DM	Gloucester City	W	2-1	660	Blair 62, Ellison 88.	7
36	27.01	H	DM	Burton Albion	W	3-0	346	Warner 3, Middleton 45 (pen), Dean 70.	
37	31.01	H	DM	Sittingbourne	W	2-1	304	Middleton 15 (pen), Albrighton 47.	3
38	07.02	H	DM	Gresley Rovers	L	2-3	472	Green 30, Albrighton 54.	3
39	14.02	A	DM	Merthyr Tydfil	D	1-1	675	Judd 4.	3
40	21.02	A	DM	Hastings Town	L	1-3	444	OG (Playford) 78.	7
41	22.02	A	DM	Ashford Town	L	0-2	403		7
42	03.03	A	**MIC 4**	Hinckley United	D	*1-1	151	Ward 30. *A.E.T. Won 2-1 after penalties.	-
43	07.03	H	DM	Ashford Town	W	2-1	282	Hart 30, Warner 32.	7
44	14.03	A	DM	Dorchester Town	D	0-0	570		7
45	21.03	A	DM	Salisbury City	L	1-2	294	Albrighton 45.	9
46	28.03	H	DM	Gloucester City	D	2-2	317	Middleton 23 (pen), Green 90.	9
47	04.04	A	DM	Bath City	D	0-0	571		9
48	11.04	H	DM	Tamworth	D	0-0	645		14
49	13.04	A	DM	Nuneaton Borough	W	1-0	1,113	Green 53.	9
50	18.04	H	DM	Cambridge City	L	0-1	283		9
51	20.04	H	**MIC SF**	Stafford Rangers	W	4-0	192	Middleton 16 (pen), 47, Judd 60, Green 85 (pen).	-
52	25.04	H	DM	Forest Green Rovers	D	1-1	364	Middleton 51 (pen).	9
53	29.04	H	**MIC Final**	Blakenall	W	1-0	190	Albrighton 37.	-
54	02.05	A	DM	Crawley Town	**L**	**0-3**	1,003		9

BSC - Birmingham Senior Cup **MIC** - Midland Invitation Cup

PLAYING SQUAD 1998

Goalkeepers: Craig Glover * (Coleshill T)

Defenders: Gary Redgate (Hinckley T, VS Rugby, Burton Alb, VS Rugby, Atherstone U), Matt Wileman (Bedworth U, Atherstone U, Stoke C), Boyd Young (Corby T, Hinckley T,VS Rugby, Hinckley Ath, Tamworth, St.Mirren, Coventry C), Mark Allbrighton (Nuneaton B), Richard Barrett (Youth), Nick Glover (Tividale), Danny Martin (Nuneaton B, VS Rugby, Nuneaton B, Stoke C)

Midfielders: Paul Olner (Hinckley T, VS Rugby, Gloucester C, VS Rugby, Atherstone U), Lee Middleton (Cambridge U, Swindon T, Coventry C), Robert Higgs (Solihull B), Robin Judd (Solihull B, Atherstone U, Redditch U, Mile Oak R, Kidderminster H, Birmingham C), David Hart (Nuneaton B), Gary Rice (Youth), Craig Dean (Nuneaton B, Hinckley T, Tamworth, Manchester U)

Forwards: Robbie Ellison (Hednesford T, Atherstone U, Tamworth, Mile Oak R), Ashley Warner (Rothwell T, Corby T, VS Rugby, Gloucester C, Peterborough U, VS Rugby,Hinckley T, VS Rugby, Friar Lane OB, Hillcroft, Anstey T, Coventry C), Kim Green (VS Rugby, Solihull B, Hednesford T, VS Rugby, Atherstone U, Nuneaton B,VS Rugby, Coventry Sporting, M.S.A.), Wayne Pulford (Daventry F. S.), Leon Kelly (Massey Ferguson)

BATH CITY

Midweek home matchday: Tuesday **Founded:** 1889
Ladies Team: Yes **Nickname:** Romans & The City
Club colours: Black & white striped/black shorts/black & white
Change colours: Red & white stripe/red/red & white
Youth League: South West Co, Somerset Youth Floodlit.

Chairman: Stephen Hall **Vice Chairman:**
Directors: J Turner, R Brimson, A Kerslake, S Skinner, P Evans, R Shepheard, K Loach.
Secretary: Jason Turner, c/o the club. 01179 325921 (H), 01225 423087 (B)
Commercial Manager: S Hall/P Bodin
Manager: Paul Bodin **Physio:** Steve Tregale
Safety Officer: J Watt **Press Officer:** J Turner
GROUND Address: Twerton Park, Twerton, Bath Avon BA2 1DB. (01225 423087/313247 Fax: 01225 481391)
Directions: Twerton Park is situated on the A4/A36 Lower Bristol Road - on the Bristol side of Bath City Centre (Approx 2.5 miles). The area is serviced by J18 on the M4. From the centre of Bath the bus route is No.5 - Twerton High Street.
Capacity: 8,840 **Seated:** 1,017 **Covered Terracing:** 4,800
Clubhouse: Several bars open all week and full service with menu on matchdays catering for up to 250 people.
Club Shop: Contact Mr K Sellick.

PROGRAMME DETAILS:
Pages: 36 **Price:** £1
Editor: Chris Stillman
Tel: 01225 423087

PREVIOUS - **Grounds:** The Belvoir Ground, Lambridge - 1889-1932. **Leagues:** Beazer Homes (Southern League), Vauxhall Conference

CLUB RECORDS - **Attendance:** 18,020 v Brighton & Hove Albion, FA Cup. **Defeat:** 9-0 Yeovil Town 46-47. **Career goalscorer:** Paul Randall. **Career appearances:** David Mogg (530). **Transfer fee paid:** £15,000 for Micky Tanner from Bristol City. **Transfer fee received:** £80,000 for Jason Dodd from Southampton.

BEST SEASON - **FA Cup:** 63-64, 93-94 **FA Trophy:** 89-90, 4th Rd

HONOURS - Southern League Champions 59-60, 77-78; R-up 29-33, 61-62, 89-90; Southern League Cup 78-79; Somerset Premier Cup 51-52, 52-53, 57-58, 59-60, 65-66, 69-70, 77-78, 80-81, 81-82, 83-84, 84-85, 85-86, 88-89, 89-90, 93-94, 94-95; Anglo-Italian Cup R-up 76-77, 77-78.

Past players who progressed to the Football League: Alan Skirton (Arsenal), Tony Book (Plymouth A.), Kenny Allen (Bournemouth), Peter Rogers (Exeter C.), R Bourne (Torquay), Dave Wiffil (Manchester C.), Stan Mortensen (Blackpool), Brian Wade (Swindon Town), Jeff Meacham (Bristol R.), Martin Hirst (Bristol C.), Paul Bodin (Swindon), Graham Withey (Coventry), Jason Dodd (Southampton), Paul Adcock (Torquay).

97-98 - Captain: Nicky Brooks **Top scorer:** Mike Davis **P.o.Y.:** I Hedges

Back Row (L-R); R Skidmore, G Wotton, M Hervin, J Matthews, M Paul, P Tovey. Middle Row; J Turner (Sec), D Hazlehurst, C Towler, P Hirons, S James, G Colbourne, M Wyatt, I Hedges, N Brooks (Capt), S Penny (Player/Coach), J Forster (Grd/Kit). Front Row; S Tregale (Physio), P Chenoweth, M Davis, A Gill, S Millard (Mgr), M Harrington, N Reeves, E Randall (Coach).

BATH CITY - Match Facts 1997-98

Match No.	Date	Venue H / A	Comp	Opponents	Result & Score		Att	Goalscorers	League Position
1	16.08	H	DM	Rothwell Town	D	1-1	711	Brookes 49.	
2	19.08	A	DM	Bromsgrove Rovers	L	1-3	*568*	Colbourne	
3	23.08	A	DM	Burton Albion	W	3-0	*790*	Brookes 45, Harrington 75, Davis 88.	8
4	25.09	H	DM	Dorchester Town	D	0-0	611		11
5	30.08	H	DM	Cambridge City	D	2-2	474	Harrington 20, James 35.	13
6	02.09	A	DM	Merthyr Tydfil	W	3-2	*671*	Davis 28, Colbourne 89, Paul 90.	
7	08.09	A	DM	Nuneaton Borough	D	3-3	*1,601*	Hedges 78, OG (Crowley) 81, Colbourne 87.	9
8	13.09	A	**FAC 1Q**	Bideford	W	2-0	*214*	Davis 29, Paul 82.	-
9	20.09	H	DM	Hastings Town	W	4-2	503	Paul 43, **Colbourne 3** (51, 73, 89).	6
10	23.09	H	DM	Gloucester City	W	1-0	704	Paul 52.	3
11	27.09	A	**FAC 2Q**	Basingstoke Town	D	1-1	*488*	Davis 4.	-
12	30.09	H	**FAC 2Q R**	Basingstoke Town	L	1-3	388	Paul 20	-
13	04.10	A	DM	Gresley Rovers	D	2-2	*462*	Paul 14 (pen), Davis 45.	7
14	07.10	A	**DMC 1-1**	Yate Town	W	1-0	*210*	Haynes 5.	-
15	11.10	H	DM	Crawley Town	W	2-1	455	Hedges 83, James 85.	4
16	18.10	A	DM	St Leonards Stamcroft	W	2-1	*427*	Hedges 42, Paul 75.	5
17	28.10	H	**DMC 1-2**	Yate Town	W	2-1	244	Colbourne 67, Hirons 85.	-
18	01.11	H	DM	Worcester City	W	1-0	571	Colbourne 26.	3
19	04.11	A	DM	Dorchester Town	L	1-2	*513*	Colbourne 80.	
20	08.11	A	DM	King's Lynn	L	1-3	*943*	Hirons 85	4
21	15.11	A	DM	Atherstone United	L	0-2	*267*		6
22	18.11	H	**SSC 1**	Wellington	W	7-0			-
23	22.11	H	DM	Nuneaton Borough	**W**	**5-0**	786	James 32, Towers 36, Colbourne 49, Davis 61, 76.	6
24	29.11	A	**FAT 3Q**	Harrow Borough	W	3-1	*270*	Colbourne 43, Davis 60, 66.	-
25	06.12	A	DM	Rothwell Town	W	4-1	*224*	Colbourne 34, Davis 65, 72(pen), Chenowith 86.	5
26	13.12	H	DM	Burton Albion	D	0-0	727		
27	16.12	H	**DMC 2**	Newport IOW	L	1-2	179	Wyatt 45.	-
28	20.12	A	DM	Tamworth	W	2-1	*647*	Davis 3, 41.	6
29	26.12	H	DM	Merthyr Tydfil	W	3-0	1,280	Brooks 9, Chenoweth 58, Davis 63 (pen).	
30	28.12	A	DM	Hastings Town	D	2-2	*629*	Hedges 80, Paul 81.	4
31	01.01	A	DM	Gloucester City	**L**	**0-4**	*978*		
32	03.01	H	DM	Ashford Town	W	3-0	619	Paul 42, Skidmore 61, Towler 69.	4
33	10.01	H	**FAT 1**	Hastings Town	D	0-0	662		-
34	13.01	A	**FAT1 R**	Hastings Town	W	1-0	*481*	Colbourne 84.	-
35	17.01	A	DM	Worcester City	D	1-1	*1,035*	Davis 53.	5
36	24.01	H	DM	St. Leonards Stamcroft	W	4-0	572	**Paul 3** (14, 49, 65), Davis 30.	5
37	27.01	H	DM	Salisbury City	**W**	**5-0**	513	**Colbourne 4** (9, 26, 65, 72), Davis 87.	4
38	31.01	H	**FAT 2**	Grantham Town	L	2-3	832	Colbourne 25, Davis 46 (pen).	-
39	09.02	A	**SSC**	Clevedon Town	L	*2-3	*352*	Paul 90 (pen), Lester 104.	-
40	14.02	A	DM	Sittingbourne	L	2-4	*451*	Hedges 36, Harrington 62.	7
41	17.02	H	DM	Halesowen Town	L	1-3	544	Towler 89.	
42	21.02	H	DM	Sittingbourne	W	1-0	523	Wyatt 32.	5
43	28.02	H	DM	Gresley Rovers	D	0-0	547		7
44	07.03	A	DM	Salisbury City	L	0-1	*403*		8
45	14.03	H	DM	Forest Green Rovers	D	1-1	1,019	Hedges 59.	8
46	21.03	A	DM	Tamworth	D	3-3	*1,026*	Davis 1 (pen), 38, Hedges 35.	8
47	28.03	A	DM	Ashford Town	W	1-0	*289*	Colbourne 15.	8
48	04.04	H	DM	Atherstone United	D	0-0	571		8
49	13.04	H	DM	Bromsgrove Rovers	W	3-1	603	Colbourne 52, Chenoweth 80, Wyatt 90.	8
50	18.04	A	DM	Crawley Town	L	0-1	*806*		8
51	21.04	A	DM	Cambridge City	W	1-0	*290*	Brooks 21.	
52	25.04	H	DM	King's Lynn	W	2-0	719	Colbourne 6, Chenoweth 14.	5
53	30.04	A	DM	Halesowen Town	L	1-2	*355*	Chenoweth	5
54	02.05	A	DM	Forest Green Rovers	L	0-2	*1,678*		6

SSC - Somerset Senior Cup

PLAYING SQUAD 1998

Goalkeepers: Mark Hervin (Frome T, Forest Green R, Mangotsfield U, Yeovil T, Bristol R)

Defenders: Colin Towler (Yate T, Mangotsfield U), Rob Skidmore (Forest Green R, ClevedonT, Bristol C), Gary Wotton (Hayes, Cheltenham T, Weston-S-M, Liskeard Ath,Dorchester T, Yeovil T, Reading, Plymouth A), Paul Bodin (Reading, Swindon T,Crystal Palace, Swindon T, Newport Co, Bath C, Cardiff C, Newport Co, Chelsea)

Midfielders: Nicky Brooks (Clevedon T, Mangotsfield U, Barnstaple T, Bristol C), Paul Chenoweth (Cheltenham T, Bath C, Bristol R), Danny Hazlehurst (Southampton), Mark Harrington (Paulton R, Bristol R), Stuart James (Swindon T), Wayne Noble (Clevedon T, Weston-S-M, Clevedon T, Cinderford T, Salisbury C, Cheltenham T,Trowbridge T, Clevedon T, Bath C, Gloucester C, Yeovil T, Bristol R), Gareth Loyden (Bristol C)

Forwards: Martin Paul (Doncaster R, Bristol R), Mike Davis (Bristol R, Yate T), Mike Wyatt (Bristol R, Bristol C), Graham Colbourne (Paulton R, Radstock T), Mark Stevens (Oxford U), Denny Mundee (Salisbury C, Dorchester T, Brighton,Brentford, AFC Bournemouth, Swindon T, QPR), Alex Kiratzoglou (Oldham Ath), Steve White * (Cardiff C, Hereford U, Swindon T, Bristol R, Charlton Ath, LutonT, Bristol R, Mangotsfield U)

BOSTON UNITED

Colours: Amber/black/amber
Change colours: White/green/navy
Midweek matchday: Wednesday
Newsline: 0898 121 539.
Reserve League: Lincolnshire League.

Founded: 1934
Nickname: The Pilgrims
Sponsors: TBA

Chairman: S.Burgess **President:** Mr A E Bell
Vice-Chairman: B R James
General Manager / Secretary / Commercial Manager: John Blackwell, 14-16 Spain Place, Boston, Lincs PE26 6HN 01205 364406 (office).
Manager: Gregg Fee **Asst Manager:** Chris Cook
GROUND Address: York Street, Boston, Lincs (0205 364406-office, 365524/5-matchday no., 354063-fax).
Directions: A1 to A17 Sleaford-Boston, over rail crossing, bear right at Eagle pub to lights over Haven Bridge, thru lights opposite New Store, right into York Street. Ground just off town centre.
Capacity: 8,771 **Cover:** 8,771 **Seats:** 1,826 **Floodlights:** Yes
Clubhouse: (0205 362967) Open every day except Tuesday. Live entertainment Saturday, pool, darts, dominoes, Sunday football teams.
Club Shop: At club office (as secretary's address, above) not ground.
Metal Badges: Yes (2 types)

PROGRAMME DETAILS:
Pages: 44 **Price:** £1
Editor: Secretary

PREVIOUS - **Leagues:** Midland 21-58 62-64; Southern 58-61; Central Alliance 61-62; United Counties 65-66; West Midlands (Regional) 66-68; Northern Premier 68-79, 93-98; Alliance Premier (Conference) 79-93. **Names:** Boston Town; Boston Swifts. **Grounds:** None.

CLUB RECORDS - **Attendance:** 10,086 v Corby Tn, floodlit inauguration 1955. **Scorer:** Chris Cook (181). **Appearances:** Billy Howells, 500+. **Win:** 14-0 v Spilsby Tn, Grace Swan Cup, 92-93. **Transfer Fee Paid:** £14,000 for Micky Nuttell (Wycombe Wanderers). **Transfer Fee Received:** £25,000 for Gary Jones (Southend Utd 93)

BEST SEASON - **FA Trophy:** Runners-up 84-85 **FA Cup:** Third Round replay 73-74, 1-6 V Derby County (H), after 0-0. **League clubs defeated:** Derby 55-56, Southport 70-71, Hartlepool 71-72, Crewe 82-83.

HONOURS - Northern Prem Lg 72-73 73-74 76-77 77-78 (R-up 71-72 95-96), Lg Cup 73-74 75-76 (R-up 77-78), Challenge Shield 73-74 74-75 76-77 77-78; Lincs Snr Cup 34-35 36-37 37-38 45-46 49-50 54-55 55-56 76-77 78-79 85-86 87-88 88-89; E Anglian Cup 60-61; Central All 61-62 (Lg Cup 61-62); Utd Counties Lg 65-66 (Lg Cup 65-66); W Mids (Reg) Lg 66-67 67-68, Eastern Professional Floodlit Cup 71-72 (R-up 76-77); Non-League Champion of Champions Cup 72-73 73-74 76-77 77-78; Midland Lg R-up 55-56.

Players progressing to Football League: Jim Smith (Colchester), Steve Thompson (Lincoln), Brendon Phillips (Mansfield), Gordon Simmonite (Blackpool), Simon Garner (Blackburm), John Froggatt & Bobby Svarc (Colchester), David Gilbert, Neil Grayson, Jamie Pascoe, Robbie Curtis, Dean Trott (Northampton), Tim Dalton (Bradford C.), Gary Jones (Southend).

97-98 Captain: Martin Hardy **P.o.Y.:** Steve Appleby **Top scorer:** Steve Charles

Back Row (L-R); Paul Creasey (Scout), Chris Cook, Leroy Chambers, Simon Buckley, Andrew Stanhope, Adam Sollitt, Glen Maddison, Paul Watts, Greg Fee (Player/Mgr), Mark Shackleton (Res Mgr). Front Row; Jim Woods (Physio), Joe Vaughan, Phil Brown, Mark Lovelace, Richard Mason, Steve Appleby, Mark Melson, Paul Cavell.
Photo: Courtesy A & K Markham

BOSTON UNITED - Match Facts 1997-98

Match No.	Date	Venue H / A	Comp.	Opponents	Result & Score		Att.	Goalscorers	League Position
1	23.08	A	UL	Leigh RMI	W	1-0	*237*	Chambers 87.	
2	27.08	H	UL	Alfreton Town	W	2-0	863	Hardy 47, Cowshall 69.	
3	30.08	H	UL	Chorley	D	1-1	1,080	Watts 87.	2
4	02.09	A	UL	Guiseley	D	1-1	*403*	Cowshall 52.	3
5	07.09	H	UL	Radcliffe Borough	D	2-2	980	Marshall 40, Chambers 44.	4
6	09.09	A	UL	Frickley Athletic	L	0-1	*268*		
7	13.10	A	UL	Colwyn Bay	W	3-0	*283*	Stanhope 6, Chambers 86, Cook 90.	5
8	17.10	H	UL	Hyde United	D	1-1	751	Cowshall 87.	3
9	20.10	H	UL	Marine	D	1-1	884	Chambers 6.	3
10	24.09	A	UL	Bishop's Auckland	W	2-0	*202*	Charles 52, Chambers 53.	
11	27.10	A	UL	Altrincham	W	2-1	*630*	Chambers 21, Charles 77.	2
12	04.10	A	UL	Accrington Stanley	D	1-1	*527*	Charles 49.	2
13	08.10	H	UL	Emley	W	3-2	769	**Chambers 3** (18, 37, 69).	1
14	11.10	H	UL	Runcorn	**L**	**0-3**	938		2
15	13.10	A	UL	Emley	D	0-0	*289*		2
16	18.10	H	UL	Lancaster City	W	2-0	869	Chambers 25, Cowshall 41.	2
17	25.10	A	**FAC 4Q**	Knypersley Victoria	W	1-0	*575*	Cavell 55.	-
18	29.10	H	**ULCC 2**	Emley	W	1-0	398	Cavell 51.	-
19	01.11	A	UL	Radcliffe Borough	D	1-1	*244*	Chambers 6.	2
20	08.11	H	UL	Barrow	L	0-2	1,239		2
21	15.11	A	**FAC 1**	Ilkeston Town	L	1-2	*2,504*	Cavell 61.	-
22	22.11	A	UL	Spennymoor United	W	2-1	*201*	Marshall 11, Cook 90.	2
23	26.11	H	**ULPC 1**	Bradford Park Avenue	W	1-0	306	Watts 78.	-
24	29.11	A	**FAT 3Q**	Belper Town	W	5-1	*502*	Chambers 8, **Charles 3** (25, 63, 76), Cowshall 84.	-
25	02.12	A	**ULCC 3**	Spennymoor United	W	3-1	*76*	Curtis 2, Watts 47, 70.	-
26	06.12	A	UL	Blyth Spartans	W	1-0	*375*	Marshall 64.	3
27	13.12	H	UL	Bamber Bridge	D	1-1	806	Cavell 75.	4
28	20.12	A	UL	Winsford United	D	0-0	*222*		5
29	26.12	A	UL	Gainsborough Trinity	W	1-0	*1,295*	Charles 40.	3
30	01.01	H	UL	Gainsborough Trinity	W	1-0	1,730	Charles 9.	3
31	10.01	A	**FAT 1**	Hyde United	L	1-2	*792*	Charles 55.	-
32	17.01	H	UL	Bishop Auckland	W	1-0	905	Charles 18.	2
33	2101	H	**ULPC 2**	Blyth Spartans	D	3-3	348	OG (McGargle) 48, Armstrong 71, Cavell 73.	-
34	24.01	A	UL	Chorley	W	2-0	*431*	Mason 23, OG (Jones) 60.	2
35	31.01	H	UL	Winsford United	W	2-1	938	Charles 3, Appleby 85.	2
36	03.02	A	**ULPC 2 R**	Blyth Spartans	L	2-4	*303*	Hardy 46 (pen), Cook 71.	-
37	07.02	H	UL	Blyth Spartans	D	2-2	956	Mason 7, 21.	2
38	09.02	H	**ULCC 4**	Altrincham	D	1-1	378	Melson 85.	-
39	14.02	A	UL	Hyde United	W	2-0	*526*	OG (Wilson) 5, Mason 25.	2
40	21.02	A	UL	Runcorn	**L**	**0-3**	*475*		2
41	24.02	A	**ULCC 4 R**	Altrincham	L	1-2	*283*	Cook 88.	-
42	28.02	H	UL	Accrington Stanley	L	1-3	752	Withe 61.	2
43	07.03	H	UL	Spennymoor United	L	1-3	602	Cavell 90.	2
44	21.03	A	UL	Bamber Bridge	D	2-2	*281*	Cavell 36, Appleby 61.	3
45	28.03	H	UL	Guiseley	W	2-1	652	Filson 11, Charles 74 (pen).	3
46	01.04	H	UL	Frickley Athletic	W	3-0	485	**Charles 3** (45, 66, 90 (pen)).	
47	04.04	A	UL	Marine	W	2-1	*211*	Cooke 16, Charles 90 (pen).	2
48	11.04	H	UL	Leigh RMI	W	1-0	1,145	Appleby 65.	2
49	13.04	A	UL	Alfreton Town	W	2-1	*285*	Cook 29, 31.	2
50	18.04	H	UL	Colwyn Bay	W	1-0	1,010	Filson 90.	2
51	21.04	A	UL	Barrow	L	0-1	*2,765*		2
52	25.04	A	UL	Lancaster City	L	1-3	*214*	Appleby 24.	2
53	02.05	H	UL	Altrincham	W	1-0	1,077	Appleby 66.	2

PLAYING SQUAD 1998

Goalkeepers: Paul Bastock (Kettering T, Cambridge U, Coventry C). **Defenders:** Greg Fee (Mansfield T, Sheffield Wed, Boston U, Kettering T, Bradford C), JodyCowshall (Lincoln C), Martin Hardy (Matlock T, Boston U, Worksop T, NottsCo), Simon Askey (WBA), Chris Withe (Shrewsbury T, Mansfield T, Bury, NottsCo, Bradford C, Newcastle U), Martin Filson (Leek T, Caernarfon T, Dag & Red,Halifax T, Stalybridge C, Rhyl, Blackpool, Wrexham, Tranmere R), Lennie Curtis (Stalybridge C, Matlock T, Shamrock R)

Midfielders: Steve Charles (Stalybridge C, Scarborough, Mansfield T, Wrexham, Sheffield U), Ross Hewson (Notts Co), Steve Appleby (Bourne T, Boston U, Bourne T,Kettering T, Bourne T), Danny Marshall (Chesterfield, Notts Co), Richard Mason (Hednesford T, Boston U, Sheffield Wed), Andy Stanhope (King's Lynn,Peterborough U), Mark Melson (Youth team), Chris Aitken (Lincoln C)

Forwards: Paul Cavell (Purfleet, Macclesfield T, Gateshead, Dag & Red, Boston U,Stafford R, Worksop T), Chris Cook (Boston FC, Boston U, King's Lynn, BostonU), Joe Vaughan (Youth), Mark Lovelace (Youth), Paul Watts (Youth), Darren Munton * (Lincoln U, Boston U, King's Lynn, Boston U, Bourne T,Pedigree Petfoods, Melton T, Oakham U).

BROMSGROVE ROVERS
Football Club
ATHERSTONE UNITED
Premier Division
Bromwich

BROMSGROVE ROVERS

Colours: Green & white stripes/black/green. **Formed:** 1885
Change colours: All red. **Sponsors:** All Saints Masterfit (Bromsgrove).
Midweek matchday: Tuesday **Nickname:** Rovers or Greens
Reserves' league: Central Conference.
Newsline: 0891 88 44 96.

Chairman: Keith McMaster **President:** Charles W Poole
Secretary: Eddie Million, c/o Bromsgrove Rovers FC
Commercial Manager: Rebecca O'Neill
Manager: Brian Kenning **Trainer:** Stewart Pinfold**Physio:** Paul Sunners

GROUND Address: Victoria Ground, Birmingham Road, Bromsgrove, Worcs, B61 0DR (01527 876949). **Directions:** Ground is situated on the north side of Bromsgrove on the Birmingham Road, off the A38 Bromsgrove by pass. The M5 and M42 join the A38 to the north of the town making it easy to get to the ground without having to go into town. The 144 Midland Red bus runs from New Street Station Birmingham and passes the ground.
Capacity: 4,893 **Seated:** 394 **Covered Terracing:** 1,344
Clubhouse: Victoria Club (01527 878260) - Serves hot & cold food. Big screen TV, pool table & darts. Open matchdays and week-day evenings.
Club Shop: Selling replica clothing & souvenirs. Contact Doug Bratt (01527 874997).

PROGRAMME DETAILS:
Pages: 40 **Price:** £1.20
Editor:
Brian Perry 0121 628 6009
Alan Saunders 01527 833838

PREVIOUS - **Leagues:** Birmingham Lge 1898-08, Birmingham Combination 1908-53, Birmingham 53-65, West Midlands 65-72, Southern League - Northern Div. 73-79, Midland Div. 79-1986, Premier Div. 86-92, GMVC 92-97. **Grounds:** Old Station Road 1885-87, Recreation Ground 87-88, Churchfields 88-97, Well Lane 1897-1910.

CLUB RECORDS - **Attendance:** 7,389 v Worcester City - 1957. **Win:** 11-0 - v Hinckley Ath. 1970, v Halesowen Town 'A' 1939. **Defeat:** 0-12 v Aston Villa 'A' 1939. **Career goalscorer:** Chris Hanks 238, 1983-84. **Career appearances:** Shaun O'Meara 763, 1975-94. **Transfer fee paid:** £3,000 for Recky Carter (Solihull B.) 93-94. **Transfer fee received:** Undisclosed for Scott Cooksey (Peterborough) Dec. 93.

HONOURS - Vauxhall Conference R-up 92-93, Lge Cup 94-95 95-96; Bob Lord Trophy 94-95; Spalding Cup 95/96; Southern Lge Prem 91-92, R-up 86-87, Cup 92-93, R-up 86-87, Midland Div 85-86, Merit Cup 85-86, Cup 85-86, R-up 73-74 87-88; Bill Dellow Cup 85-86; Worcester Sen Cup (8), R-up (10); Birmingham Sen Cup 46-47, R-up 47-48 88-89; W Mid Lge R-up 67-70, Cup 67-68 70-71; Birminham Lge 59-60, R-up 04-05 56-57 60-61; Birmingham Comb 46-47, R-up 49-50 50-51; Hereford Charity Chall Cup 46-47, R-up 47-48.

Past players who progressed to the Football League: M McKenna (Northampton 46), R Hartle (Bolton 52), A McLean (Bury 53), A Smith (A.Villa 54), M Deakin (C Palace 54), B Puster (Leicester 58), Tom Smith (Sheff Utd 1978), Malcolm Goodman (Halifax 1979), Steve Smith (Walsall 1980), Gary Hackett (Shrewsbury 1983), Bill McGarry, Martyn O'Connor (C Palace 1992), Scott Cooksey (Peterborough 1993), Steve Taylor (Crystal Palace 1995).

Bromsgrove Rovers

BROMSGROVE ROVERS - Match Facts 1997-98

Match No.	Date	Venue H / A	Comp.	Opponents	Result & Score	Att.	Goalscorers	League Position
1	16.08	A	DM	King's Lynn	L 2-3	*866*	Peters 63, Payne 72.	
2	19.08	H	DM	Bath City	W 3-1	568	Skelding 23 (pen), Burgher 55, Whitehouse 69.	
3	23.08	H	DM	St Leonards Stamcroft	**W 4-0**	504	Gardiner 21, 85, Whitehouse 67.	4
4	25.08	A	DM	Forest Green Rovers	L 1-2	*693*	Grocutt 1.	
5	30.08	H	DM	Gresley Rovers	W 5-3	622	Amos 18, Smith 36, Skelding 52, Gardner 74, Simpson 78.	5
6	09.09	A	DM	Rothwell Town	L 0-2	*253*		11
7	13.09	A	**FAC 1Q**	Tamworth	W 2-1	*725*	Elms 75, OG 90.	-
8	16.09	H	DM	Worcester City	W 3-0	769	Grocutt 42, Smith 43, Whitehouse 62.	10
9	20.09	A	DM	Atherstone United	L 1-2	*302*	Mainwaring 90.	10
10	23.09	A	DM	Tamworth	W 4-2	*631*	Burgher 2, Grocutt 55, Amos , Mainwaring .	6
11	27.09	A	**FAC 2Q**	Sudbury Wanderers	D 1-1	*227*	Mainwaring 37.	-
12	30.09	H	**FAC 2Q R**	Sudbury Wanderers	W 2-0	408	Elms, Skelding.	-
13	04.10	H	DM	Cambridge City	W 3-0	585	Amos 25, Whitehouse 31, 75.	4
14	07.10	A	**DMC 1-1**	Redditch United	L 1-2	*411*	Payne 41.	-
15	11.10	H	**FAC 3Q**	Rocester	W 2-1	612	Whitehouse 74, 79.	-
16	18.10	H	DM	Burton Albion	L 1-2	860	Smith 29.	8
17	21.10	H	DM	Forest Green Rovers	W 2-1	356	Smith 23, 84.	
18	25.10	H	**FAC 4Q**	Romford	W 2-0	820	Whitehouse 41, Grocutt 43.	-
19	28.10	H	**DMC 1-2**	Redditch United	L 0-2	492		-
20	01.11	H	DM	Crawley Town	D 1-1	578	Whitehouse 73.	7
21	08.11	A	DM	Sittingbourne	L 0-2	*432*		9
22	15.11	A	**FAC 1**	King's Lynn	L 0-1	*2,847*		-
23	18.11	A	DM	Gloucester City	L 2-4	*518*	Whitehouse 89, Mainwaring 51.	
24	22.11	A	DM	Hastings Town	L 2-3	*482*	Softley 31, Gardner 70.	13
25	29.11	H	**FAT 3Q**	Worksop Town	L 1-2	517	Mainwaring 75.	-
26	06.12	H	DM	Atherstone United	L 0-1	414		15
27	13.12	H	DM	Salisbury City	D 2-2	369	Mainwaring 50, Whitehouse 54.	16
28	20.12	A	DM	St Leonards Stamcroft	W 4-2	*404*	Smith 1, Carter 16, 46, Whitehouse 72.	13
29	26.12	H	DM	Halesowen Town	D 2-2	1,370	Whitehouse 33, Grocutt 68.	
30	28.12	A	DM	Burton Albion	**L 1-5**	*760*	Whitehouse 38.	15
31	01.01	A	DM	Nuneaton Borough	L 1-2	*1,376*	Carter 52.	
32	03.01	H	DM	Tamworth	W 1-0	827	Whitehouse 59.	14
33	10.01	H	DM	Merthyr Tydfil	D 0-0	731		13
34	17.01	A	DM	Crawley Town	L 2-4	*1,240*	Whitehouse 3, 5 (pen).	14
35	20.01	A	DM	Gresley Rovers	L 2-4	*408*	Lamorte 38, Peters 67.	
36	24.01	A	DM	Ashford Town	L 0-4	*326*		15
37	27.01	H	**WSC**	Halesowen Town	L 1-2	382	Wardle 15.	-
38	31.01	H	DM	Dorchester Town	L 0-2	488		15
39	14.02	A	DM	Cambridge City	L 0-4	*325*		16
40	21.02	H	DM	Rothwell Town	L 0-2	567		
41	28.02	A	DM	Worcester City	L 0-2	*1,201*		18
42	10.03	A	DM	Dorchesrter Town	L 0-4	*441*		19
43	14.03	H	DM	King's Lynn	D 1-1	750	Bennett 12.	20
44	21.03	A	DM	Halesowen Town	L 1-3	*1,074*	Taylor 41.	20
45	24.03	H	DM	Ashford Town	W 3-0	456	Purdie 16, Davis 44, Payne 52.	
46	28.03	H	DM	Hastings Town	D 1-1	465	Payne 7.	19
47	04.04	A	DM	Salisbury City	L 0-2	*343*		20
48	11.04	H	DM	Nuneaton Borough	W 3-1	693	Taylor 5, Payne 27, 76.	20
49	13.04	A	DM	Bath City	L 1-3	*603*	Payne 31.	20
50	18.04	H	DM	Sittingbourne	W 3-2	745	Payne 29, Peters 48, Taylor 75.	19
51	25.04	A	DM	Merthyr Tydfil	L 2-4	*1,005*	Payne 55, Ashley 71 (pen).	20
52	02.05	H	DM	Gloucester City	W 3-1	1,061	Carter 11, 73, Payne 86.	19

WSC - Worcestershire Senior Cup

PLAYING SQUAD 1998

Goalkeepers: Derek Dudley (Telford U, Halesowen T, WBA, VS Rugby, Worcester C, Stourbridge,Sutton Coldfield T, Aston Villa)

Defenders: Paul Wardle (Gresley R, Bromsgrove R, Belper T, Denaby U), Kevin Ashley (Telford U, Peterborough U, Wolves, Birmingham C), Richard Gardner (Youth), John Hickman (Aston Villa), Mark Bowater * (Bloxwich T, Bilston T,Willenhall T, Mile Oak R, Rushall O, Shrewsbury T), Shaun Davies (Westfields,Hereford U), Jason Darkes (Boldmere St .M., Paget R, Sutton Coldfield T,Worcester C, Paget R, Everton)

Midfielders: Steve Taylor (Telford U, Bromsgrove R, Hednesford T, Crystal Palace,Bromsgrove R, Rushall Olympic), Dean Bennett (WBA), Nick Amos (Rushall Olympic, Hornchurch, Rainham T), Robert Elms (Boldmere St.Michaels, NorhfieldT), Jon Purdie (Telford U, Kidderminster H, Cheltenham T, Worcester C,Shrewsbury T, Brentford, Oxford U, Wolves, Arsenal)

Forwards: Stuart Payne (Halesowen Harriers, Blakenall, Stourbridge, Lye T, Halesowen T,Lye T), Karl Payne (Burton Alb, Chesterfield), John Hunt (Sutton Coldfield T,Paget R), Recky Carter (Solihull B, Kettering T, Bromsgrove R, Solihull B,Malvern T, Worcester C, Kidderminster H, Fairfield Villa, Northfield T)

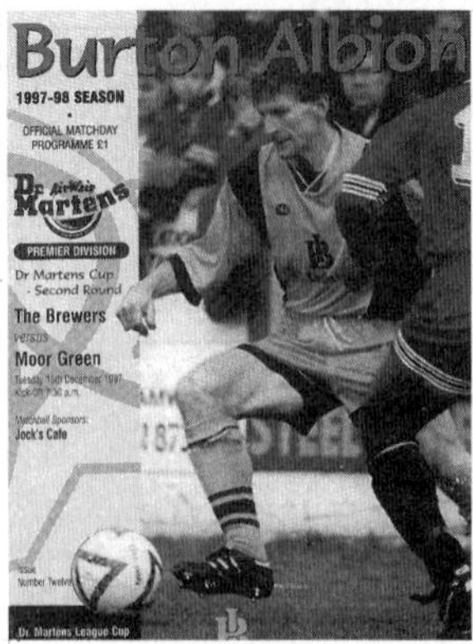

PROGRAMME DETAILS:
Pages: 48 **Price:** £1
Editor: David Twigg
(01283 562013)

BURTON ALBION

Colours: Yellow with black trim. **Formed:** 1950
Change colours: Sky blue, black trim **Nickname:** Brewers
Midweek matchday: Tuesday **Sponsors:** B.I. Industries.
Local Press: Burton Daily Mail (01283 43311)
Local Radio: Radio Derby

Chairman: C B Robinson 01283 813943 (H) **Vice Chairman:**
Secretary: Tony A Kirkland, 40 Hurst Drive, Stretton, Burton-on-Trent DE13 0ED 01283 536510 (H). 0374 102485 (Mobile)
Manager: John Barton **Assistant Manager:** John Newman
Commercial Man: Peter Alcock **Physio:** Matt Brown
Press Officer: David Twigg (01283 562013)

GROUND Address: Eton Park, Princess Way, Burton-on-Trent DE14 2RU (01283 565938. **Directions:** From south - M1 jct 22, A50 (Ashby) follow to Burton over Trent bridge, thru 3 sets of lights, right at mini-r'bout (Derby Turn Pub), left at next island - ground on left: From M42 - A38 (Lichfield), follow signs for Burton, take 2nd turn for Burton (A5121), right at island - ground on left: From M6 north - jct 15 and follow A50 for Stoke and Uttoxeter, follow A50 signs to Burton, continue under bypass, left into Shakespeare Rd after canal bridge (opp. Navigation Inn), ground at end.
Capacity: 4,500 **Cover:** 2,500 **Seats:** 400 **Floodlights:** Yes
Clubhouse: 'The Football Tavern' - open normal pub hours. Full hot & cold menu. **Steward:** Graham Frost
Club Shop: Yes **Metal Badges:** Yes

PREVIOUS - **Leagues:** West Midlands 1950-58/ Southern 58-79/ Northern Premier 79-87 **Ground:** Wellington Street 50-57.

CLUB RECORDS - **Attendance:** 5,860 v Weymouth, Southern Lg Cup Final 2nd leg, 1964 *(22,500 v Leicester City, F.A. Cup 3rd Rd 1984 - played at Derby County F.C.).* **Goalscorer:** Ritchie Barker, 157. **Appearances:** Phil Annable, 567. **Fee Paid:** £21,000 to for R Jones and J Pearson (Kidderminster). **Fee Received:** £60,000 for Darren Carr (C Palace 89).

BEST SEASON - **FA Trophy:** R-up 86-87 (SF 74-75). **FA Cup:** 3rd Rd Prop 55-56, 84-85. 1st Rd 9 times

HONOURS - Sth Lg Cup 63-64 96-97 (R-up 88-89), Div 1 (Nth) R-up 71-72 73-74; Nth Prem Lg Chall Cup 82-83 (R-up 86-87), Presidents Cup R-up 85-86 (SF 86-87); Birmingham Snr Cup 53-54 70-71 (R-up 86-87); FA Trophy R-up 86-87 (SF 74-75); GMAC Cup SF 86-87; Bass Charity Vase 81-82 85-86, Challenge Cup 84-85; Wt Mids Lg R-up 53-54; Staffs Sen Cup 55-56.

Players progressing to Football League: L Green & T Parry & S Aston (Hartlepool 65/66), G Hunter (Lincoln 65), D Jones (Newport 68), R Barker & J Bourne & T Bailey (Derby 67/69/70), M Pollock & S Buckley (Luton 74), P Ward (Brighton 75), Tony Moore (Sheffield Utd 79), C Swan & G Clayton (Doncaster 80 & 86), R Jobson (Watford 82), P Haycock (Rotherham 86), A Kamara (Scarborough 87), P Groves (Leicester City 88), S Cotterill & J Gayle (Wimbledon 89), D Carr (Crystal Pal. 89), D Smith & D Roberts (Wolves 90 & 92).

Back Row (L-R); John Newman (Asst Mgr), Dave Titterton, Martin Devaney, David Holmes, Mark Blount, Emeka Ejiofor, Darren Acton, Matthew Smith, Darren Stride, Richard Smith, Charlie Palmer, Alex Hook, Steve Spooner, Matt Brown (Physio). Front Row; Tony Marsden, Alan Davies, Les Hornby, Pat Lyons, John Barton (Mgr), Simon Redfern, Nick Ashby, Dave Benton, Andy Marlow

BURTON ALBION - Match Facts 1997-98

Match No.	Date	Venue H / A	Comp.	Opponents	Result & Score		Att.	Goalscorers	League Position
1	05.08	A	**DM Ch S**	Gresley Rovers	L	1-2	*858*	Holmes 7.	
2	16.08	A	DM	Sittingbourne	W	2-0	*571*	Marsden 44, Marlow 71.	
3	19.08	H	DM	King's Lynn	D	0-0	849		
4	23.08	H	DM	Bath City	**L**	**0-3**	790		13
5	25.08	A	DM	Worcester City	L	1-2	*914*	Lyons 54.	17
6	30.08	A	DM	Ashford Town	W	3-1	*441*	Devaney 27, 50, Lyons 86.	9
7	02.09	H	DM	Halesowen Town	D	0-0	880		
8	07.09	H	DM	Hastings Town	L	0-1	528		12
9	12.09	A	**FAC 1Q**	Solihull Borough	L	0-2	*323*		-
10	20.09	A	DM	Dorchester Town	L	1-3	*517*	Hornby 72.	16
11	23.09	A	DM	King's Lynn	L	1-2	*777*	Spooner 73.	17
12	04.10	H	DM	Sittingbourne	W	2-0	696	Marsden 82, Devaney 88.	16
13	07.10	A	**DMC 1-1**	Tamworth	W	2-0	*520*	Marsden 24, Garner 60.	
14	11.10	A	DM	Forest Green Rovers	W	3-1	*461*	Cotter 30, Stride 58, 73.	10
15-	14.10	H	DM	Worcester City	W	2-0	588	Spooner 8, Cotter 54.	
16	18.10	A	DM	Bromsgrove Rovers	W	2-1	*860*	Spooner 55, Garner 59.	7
17	25.10	H	DM	Cambridge City	L	1-3	868	Cotter 4.	8
18	01.11	H	DM	Atherstone United	L	0-1	720		9
19	04.11	H	**DMC 1-2**	Tamworth	D	1-1	364	Garner 68.	-
20	08.11	A	DM	Salisbury City	W	2-0	*301*	Holmes 26, Garner 69 (pen).	8
21	15.11	H	DM	Tamworth	D	1-1	1,012	Garner 63.	8
22	18.11	A	DM	Halesowen Town	D	1-1	*648*	Cotter 56.	
23	22.11	A	DM	Crawley Town	D	0-0	*1,381*		10
24	29.11	A	**FAT 3Q**	Halesowen Town	W	2-1	*733*	Benton 4, Holmes 81.	-
25	01.12	A	**BSC 2**	Walsall	D	1-1	162	Spooner 32.	-
26	06.12	H	DM	Forest Green Rovers	W	4-1	609	Cotter 20, Garner 23, 68, Marlow 82.	10
27	13.12	A	DM	Bath City	D	0-0	*727*		9
28	16.12	H	**DMC 2**	Moor Green	L	1-3	228	Garner 68 (pen).	-
29	20.12	H	DM	Dorchester Town	D	2-2	543	Cotter 47, Spooner 80.	10
30	26.12	A	DM	Gresley Rovers	L	0-2	*1,752*		
31	28.12	H	DM	Bromsgrove Rovers	**W**	**5-1**	760	Holmes 18, Cotter 38, 89, Garner 45, 69.	
32	01.01	H	DM	Gresley Rovers	W	1-0	2,189	OG 32.	10
33	10.01	H	**FAT 1**	Witton Albion	W	2-1	735	Stride 37, Holmes 83.	-
34	14.01	H	**BSC 2 R**	Walsall	L	0-2	203		-
35	17.01	H	DM	Ashford Town	W	4-0	705	Garner 20, Holmes 58, Blount 73, Cotter 78.	11
36	24.01	A	DM	Rothwell Town	L	0-1	*327*		-
37	27.01	A	DM	Atherstone United	L	0-3	*346*		11
38	31.01	A	**FAT 2**	Gloucester City	D	1-1	*963*	Smith 37.	-
39	03.02	H	**FAT 2 R**	Gloucester City	D	*2-2	701	Stride 16, Spooner 63. * A.E.T. Lost 6-7 after penalties.	
40	07.02	H	DM	St Leonards Stamcroft	W	2-1	464	Lyons 27, Ashby 85.	11
41	14.02	H	DM	Crawley Town	W	5-3	690	**Garner 3** (36, 64(pen), 77), Stride 66, Blount 71.	10
42	24.02	A	DM	Merthyr Tydfil	L	1-2	*661*	Holmes 42.	
43	28.02	A	DM	St Leonards Stamcroft	W	2-0	*441*	Lyons 7, Stride 74.	10
44	07.03	H	DM	Gloucester City	W	2-1	731	Garner 67, Marlowe 75.	10
45	14.03	A	DM	Hastings Town	W	1-0	*472*	Stride 85.	9
46	21.03	A	DM	Nuneaton Borough	W	1-0	*1,115*	Spooner 70.	7
47	28.03	H	DM	Nuneaton Borough	W	1-0	864	Holmes 8.	7
48	04.04	A	DM	Gloucester City	L	2-4	*562*	Garner 19, Ejiofor 62.	7
49	11.04	H	DM	Rothwell Town	W	3-0	628	Lyons 52, Garner 77, 79.	6
50	13.04	A	DM	Cambridge City	W	1-0	*369*	Blount 80.	3
51	18.04	H	DM	Merthyr Tydfil	W	3-0	1,001	Grocutt 15, Cotter 56, Lyons 81.	3
52	25.04	A	DM	Tamworth	D	1-1	*786*	Holmes 45.	3
53	02.05	H	DM	Salisbury City	L	1-2	751	Garner 29 (pen).	3

BSC - Birmingham Senior Cup

PLAYING SQUAD 1998

Goalkeepers: Nicky Goodwin (Gresley R, Telford U, Burton Alb, Corby T, Kettering T,Shepshed Chart, Kettering T, Graham St.Prims)

Defenders: David Benton (Worcester C, Kidderminster H, Birmingham C), Nick Ashby (Rushden & D, Kettering T, Aylesbury U, Rushden T, Nottingham F), Allan Davies (Manchester C), Pat Lyons (WBA, Derby Co), Mark Blount (Gresley R,Peterborough U, Sheffield U, Gresley R, Derby Co), Matthew Smith (Cork C,Plymouth A, Derby Co)

Midfielders: Tony Marsden (Gresley R, Grantham T, Belper T, Burton Alb), Steve Spooner (Rushden & D, Chesterfield, Blackpool, Mansfield T, Rotherham U, York C,Hereford U, Chesterfield, Halifax T, Derby Co), Darren Grocutt (Bromsgrove R,Burton Alb, Evesham U, Moor Green, Northfield T), Matt Gooderick (Youth), Brendan Hackett * (Rushden & D, Hednesford T, Telford U, Gloucester C,Worcester C, Dudley T, Stourbridge, Redditch U, Bilston T), Craig Smith * (Derby Co)

Forwards: David Holmes (Gloucester C, Gresley R, Scarborough), Andy Garner (Gresley R,Blackpool, Derby Co), Emeka Ejiofor (Youth), Micky Cotter (Gravesend,Dover Ath, Erith & B, Welling U), Darren Stride (Youth)

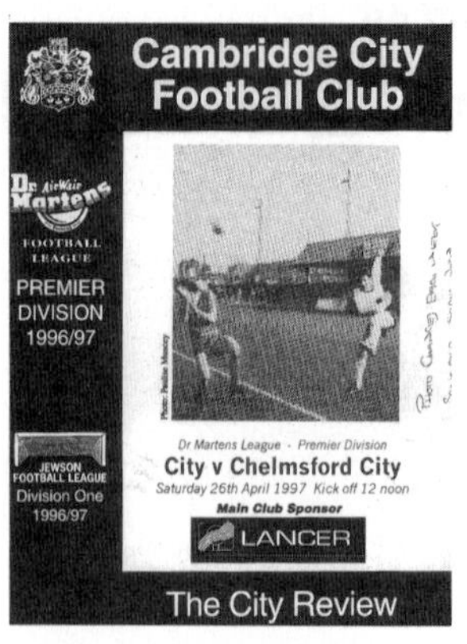

Cambridge City
Football Club
PREMIER
DIVISION
1996/97
City v Chelmsford City
Saturday 26th April 1997 Kick off 12 noon
Main Club Sponsor
LANCER
The City Review

PROGRAMME DETAILS:
Pages: 24 **Price:** £1.00
Editor: David Crane
(01223 233057)

CAMBRIDGE CITY

Colours: White & black halves/black/white & blck hoops **Formed:** 1908
Change colours: All sky blue. **Nickname:** Lilywhites
Midweek matchday: Tuesday **Sponsors:** Lancer UK
Reserve Team's League: Jewson Eastern Counties.
Local Press: Cambridge Evening News 35877
Local Radio: BBC Radio Cambridge

Chairman: Dennis Rolph **President:** Sir Neil Westbrook, CBE MA FRICS
Secretary: Stuart Hamilton, 55 Crowhill, Godmanchester, Huntingdon, Cambs (01480 382675).
Manager: Graham Daniels **Asst Manager:** Steve Low
Press Officer: Secretary **Physio:** John Aves, Collin Pettit
General Manager: W E Leivers

GROUND Address: City Ground, Milton Road, Cambridge CB4 1UY (0223 357973). **Directions:** 50 yards on left from start of A1309, Cambridge to Ely Rd. 30 mins walk Cambridge BR
Capacity: 5,000 **Cover:** 1,400 **Seats:** 400 **Floodlights:** Yes
Clubhouse: 11am-11pm Mon-Sat, 12-3pm & 7pm-10.30pm Sun. Bingo, Dances, Pool, Stag nights, Darts.
Club Shop: Sells programmes, club history, badges, scarves, pennants, replica shirts etc. Contact Neil Harvey (01223 235991).

PREVIOUS - **Name:** Cambridge Town 1908-51. **Leagues:** Bury & Dist. 08-13 19-20, East Anglian 08-10, Southern Olympian 11-14, Southern Amateur 1913-35, Spartan 35-50, Athenian 50-58.

CLUB RECORDS - **Attendance:** 12,058 v Leytonstone, FA Amateur Cup 1st Rd, 1949-50. **Scorer:** Gary Grogan. **Appearances:** Mal Keenan. **Fee Paid:** £8,000 for Paul Coe (Rushden + Diamonds). **Fee Received:** £15,500 for Kevin Wilkin (Northampton Tn 91).

BEST SEASON - **FA Amateur Cup:** Semi Final 27-28. **FA Trophy:** 2nd Rd. 86-87 87-88. **FA Cup** 1st Rd; v Ashford 66, v Swindon 46, v Walthamstow Ave. 48, v Hereford 93.

HONOURS - Southern Lg 62-63 (R-up 70-71, Southern Div 85-86, Div 1 R-up 69-70, Champ Cup 62-63; E Anglian Cup (9); Eastern Prof Floodlit Lg 65-66 72-73, Cambs Prof Cup (6); Cambs Invitation Cup (7); Spartan Lg 47-48 48-49 (R-up 49-50); Eastern Div Champs 45-46); Southern Amat Lg 20-21 27-28 28-29 30-31 31-32; Bury & Dist. Lg (4); E Anglian Lg (6); AFA Snr Cup 30-31 46-47 47-48(shared) 48-49 49-50; AFA Invitation Cup 50-51; Hunts Prem Cup 62-63 64-65; Suffolk Sen Cup 09-10; Addenbrookes Hosp Cup 87-88; The Munns Youth Cup 82-83 83-84 84-85; Chiltern Youth Lge Cup R-up 75-76; South Mids Lg Youth Trophy 82-83; Robinson Cup 87-88 89-90; Jim Digney 89-90; Essex & Herts Youth Lg 89-90.

Players progressing to Football League: K Wright (West Ham 46), A Gallego (Norwich 47), A Stokes (Watford 61), D Weddle (Middlesbrough 61), D Hicksen (Bury 62), B Harvey (Blackpool 62), R Whitehead (Darlington 62), G Cummins (Hull 62), R Pearce (Peterborough 63), A Banks (Exeter 63), T Carroll (Ipswich 66), Dominic Genovese (Peterborough 88), Roy Jones (Swindon), Winston Dubose (Oldham), K Wilkin (Northampton Tn 91), S Flack (Cardiff City 95), D Hedcock (Sheffield Wed 96).

Cambridge City FC

CAMBRIDGE CITY - Match Facts 1997-98

Match No.	Date	Venue H / A	Comp.	Opponents	Result & Score		Att.	Goalscorers	League Position
1	16.08	A	DM	Forest Green Rovers	L	0-2	*342*		
2	19.08	H	DM	Tamworth	D	2-2	379	Ullathorne 41, Gawthorp 81.	
3	23.08	H	DM	Salisbury City	W	3-1	322	Adams 6, Harris 50, Ullathorne60.	10
4	25.08	A	DM	King's Lynn	L	1-2	*1,122*	Taylor 89.	13
5	30.08	A	DM	Bath City	D	2-2	*474*	Adams 28, Harris 75.	15
6	02.09	H	DM	Sittingbourne	W	2-1	325	Harris 14, Taylor 88.	
7	07.09	H	DM	Merthyr Tydfil	L	0-3	410		14
8	13.09	A	**FAC 1Q**	Shepshed Dynamo	W	3-0	*221*	Cogger 43, 76, Harris 48.	-
9	20.09	A	DM	Worcester City	L	0-1	*692*		17
10	23.09	H	DM	Rothwell Town	D	3-3	310	**Harris 3** (5, 8, 28).	16
11	27.09	A	**FAC 2Q**	Kettering Town	D	1-1	*921*	Harris 17.	-
12	30.09	H	**FAC 2Q R**	Kettering Town	L	*2-4	498	Harris 36, 57.	-
13	04.10	A	DM	Bromsgrove Rovers	L	0-3	*585*		17
14	07.10	A	**DMC 1-1**	Shepshed Dynamo	D	3-3	*130*	Bennett 15, 19, Ullathorne 46.	-
15	11.10	H	DM	Atherstone United	L	1-2	257	Harris 25.	18
16	14.10	H	DM	Hastings Town	L	0-2	239		
17	18.10	H	**FAT 1Q**	Maidenhead United	W	2-1	216	Pincher 33, Harris 67.	-
18	25.10	A	DM	Burton Albion	W	2-1	*868*	Adams 67, Harris 76, Cogger 78.	18
19	28.10	H	**DMC 1-2**	Shepshed Dynamo	W	3-0	207	Bennett 23, Cogger 25, 65.	
20	01.11	A	DM	Tamworth	L	1-4	*670*	Cogger 6.	18
21	08.11	H	**FAT 2Q**	Dartford	D	1-1	328	Harris 62.	-
22	12.11	A	**FAT 2Q R**	Dartford	W	1-0	*260*	Harris 88.	-
23	19.11	A	DM	St Leonards Stamcroft	**L**	**1-5**	*254*	Harris 90 (pen).	
24	22.11	H	DM	Gresley Rovers	W	1-0	316	Pincher 65.	20
25	29.11	A	**FAT 3Q**	Merthyr Tydfil	D	2-2	*469*	McCannon 28, Lockhart 42.	-
26	03.12	H	**FAT 3Q**	Merthyr Tydfil	W	*6-3	200	**Harris 3** (27, 81, 93), Darton 100, Ullathorne 102, 108.	-
27	06.12	A	DM	Nuneaton Borough	W	1-0	*889*	Adams 85.	20
28	13.12	A	DM	Dorchester Town	D	1-1	*540*	Cheetham 68.	19
29	16.12	H	**DMC 2**	Hinckley United	W	1-0	126	Smith 53.	-
30	20.12	H	DM	Worcester City	L	1-4	327	Bennett 83.	19
31	26.12	A	DM	Sittingbourne	L	1-3	*556*	Cheetham 63	
32	27.12	H	DM	Forest Green Rovers	L	1-2	282	Cogger 73.	20
33	01.01	H	DM	Crawley Town	W	3-2	480	Reader 53, Adams 62, Taylor 84.	18
34	10.01	H	**FAT 1**	Hayes	L	2-3	533	Harris 27, Byatt 90.	-
35	17.01	H	DM	Gloucester City	D	1-1	284	Cogger 46.	18
36	24.01	A	DM	Hastings Town	W	5-4	*431*	OG (Morris) 9, McCurren 13, 53, Cheetham 37, Harris 68.	18
37	27.01	A	**DMC 3**	Fisher Athletic London	W	4-3	*97*	**Harris 3** (34, 62, 83), Cogger 86.	-
38	03.02	A	**DMC 4**	Margate	L	1-2	*168*	Lockhart 90 (pen).	-
39	07.02	A	DM	Crawley Town	L	2-3	*1,135*	Cogger 53, McParlane 87.	19
40	14.02	H	DM	Bromsgrove Rovers	**W**	**4-0**	325	Harris 11, 77, Reeder 45, Stock 71.	18
41	21.02	A	DM	Salisbury City	D	1-1	*246*	Harris 65.	19
42	28.02	A	DM	Merthyr Tydfil	L	1-3	*676*	Cogger 74.	19
43	07.03	H	DM	Halesowen Town	D	0-0	393		20
44	10.03	A	DM	Rothwell Town	L	1-2	*236*	Harris 73.	20
45	14.03	H	DM	Ashford Town	W	2-0	323	Harris 23, McCammon 72.	18
46	21.03	H	DM	St. Leonards Stamcroft	W	2-1	358	Harris 2, Cheetham 20.	18
47	24.03	H	DM	King's Lynn	W	2-0	668	Pincher 34 (pen), Reeder 74.	16
48	28.03	A	DM	Halesowen Town	D	1-1	*737*	Pincher 40.	16
49	04.04	H	DM	Dorchester Town	L	1-2	334	Bennett 31.	17
50	07.04	A	DM	Ashford Town	W	2-1	*302*	McDougald 26, Pincher 72 (pen).	15
51	13.04	H	DM	Burton Albion	L	0-1	369		15
52	18.04	A	DM	Atherstone United	W	1-0	*283*	McDougald 36.	15
53	21.04	H	DM	Bath City	L	0-1	290		15
54	25.04	A	DM	Gloucester City	W	5-3	*578*	McDougald 23, 59, Bennett 53, Cheetham 57, Chattoe 88.	15
55	28.04	A	DM	Gresley Rovers	W	1-0	*348*	Bennett 78.	14
56	02.05	H	DM	Nuneaton Borough	W	2-0	491	McDougald 35, Brown 88.	13

PLAYING SQUAD 1998 - **Goalkeepers:** Danny Kelly (Kettering T, Notts Co, Tottenham H). **Defenders:** Steve Gawthrop (Youth), Dave Hercock (Ilkeston T, Kettering T, SheffieldWed, Cambridge C, Boston T, Lincoln C), Jason Carter (Diss T, Sudbury T, DissT, King's Lynn, Colchester U), Mark Adams (Sudbury T, Peterborough U), AndyJeffrey (Cambridge U, Cambridge C, Leicester C), Steve Holden * (Stevenage B,Rushden & D, Kettering T, Carlisle U, Leicester C), James Saddington (Kettering T, Millwall, Cambridge C, Newmarket T), Richard Chattoe (Baldock T,Weston-S-M, Bristol R), Andy Taylor (Sudbury T, Bury T, Long Melford), Marvin Harriott (Cardiff C, Enfield, Grays Ath, Leyton Orient, Bristol C, Barnsley,Oldham Ath, West Ham U), Richard McPartland (Youth). **Midfielders:** Mike Cheetham (Sudbury T, Colchester U, Chesterfield, Cambridge U, Ipswich T), Keith Lockhart (Sudbury T, Cambridge C, Hartlepool U, Wolves, Cambridge U), Andy Pincher (Cambridge U), Aaron Rutter (Cambridge U), Russell Stock (King's Lynn, Kettering T, Cambridge U), Mickey Bennett (Leyton Orient,Cambridge C, Cardiff C, Millwall, Charlton Ath, Brentford, Wimbledon, Charlton Ath), Mark Reeder (Youth). **Forwards:** Neil Cogger (Haverhill R), Wes Byrne (Stotfold, Histon, Stotfold), Ian Brown (Sudbury T, Northampton T, Bristol C, Chelmsford C, Harwich & P, Stowmarket T,Sudbury T, Felixstowe T, Colchester U, Birmingham C), Junior McDougald (FCToulon (Fr), Rotherham U, Brighton, Tottenham H)

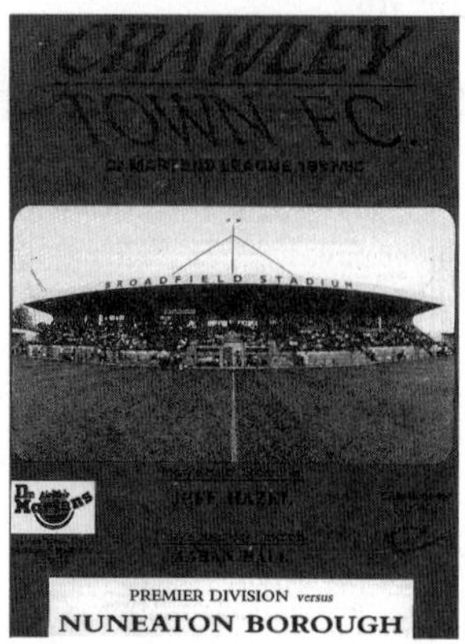

PROGRAMME DETAILS:
Pages: 40 **Price:** £1
Editor: Ian Hands

CRAWLEY TOWN

Colours: All red **Formed:** 1896
Change colours: Blue & black/black/black **Nickname:** The Reds
Midweek matchday: Tuesday **Sponsors:** Eurobell
Reserves' League: Suburban.
Local Press: Crawley Observer, Crawley News, The Argus
Local Radio: Fame 1521

Chairman: John Maggs **President:** Ken Symons
Secretary: Dave Haining, 20 Irving Walk, Tilgate, Crawley RH10 5BQ (01293 535683).
Manager: Billy Smith **Asst Man:** John Broughton
Physio: Richard Massimo **Commercial Manager:** Andy Bell

GROUND Address: Broadfield Stadium, Brighton Road, Crawley RH11 9RX (01293 410000). **Directions:** M23 exit 11, 2nd exit off r/about, A23, towards Crawley, turn left at next r/about into ground.
Capacity: 4,800 **Cover:** 4,200 **Seats:** 1,080 **Floodlights:** Yes
Clubhouse: Weekdays 11-3 & 6-11pm, Sat 11-11pm, Sun noon-10.30pm, Bank Hols 11-11. Snacks available.
Club Shop: Sells programmes, metal badges, hats, scarves, mugs, replica kits.

PREVIOUS - **Leagues:** Sussex County 1951-56/ Metropolitan 56-63. **Grounds:** Malthouse Farm 1896-1914 38-40/ Victoria Hall + Rectory Fields 18-38/ Yetmans Field 45-49, Town Mead 49-53 54-97, Ilfield Rec Grd 53-54

CLUB RECORDS - **Attendance:** 4,104 v Barnet, FA Cup 2nd Rd 4/12/93. **Goalscorer:** Phil Basey 108.(68-72). **Appearances:** John Maggs 652.(63-73 75-79). **Win:** 10-0 v Chichester United, Sussex County League Division Two 17/12/55. **Defeat:** 0-10 v Arundel (A), Sussex County Lge 9/2/52. **Fee Paid:** £5,000 for David Thompson (Wokingham, May 92) **Fee Received:** £50,000 for Craig Whitington (Scarborough 93).

BEST SEASON - **FA Trophy:** 2nd Rd 85-86 87-88. **FA Cup:** 3rd Rd Proper 91-92 (lost 0-5 at Brighton). - **League Clubs defeated:** Northampton Town 91-92.

HONOURS - Sussex Snr Cup (2) 89-91 (R-up 58-59 95-96); Sussex Intermediate Cup 26-27; Sussex Prof. Cup 69-70; Southern Lg Southern Div R-up 83-84; Merit Cup 70-71; Sussex Floodlit Cup (3) 90-93; Sussex Lg Div 2 R-up 55-56; Gilbert Rice Floodlit Cup 79-80 83-84; Southern Co's Comb. Floodlit Cup 85-86; Metropolitan Lg Chal. Cup 58-59; Mid-Sussex Snr 02-03; Montgomery Cup 25-26.

Players progressing to Football League: Ray Keeley, Graham Brown (Mansfield 68), Andy Ansah (Brentford 87), Craig Whitington (Scarborough 93).

Back Row (L-R); Justin Gregory, John Richardson, Billy Smith (Mgr), John Mackie, Colin Hunwick, Phil Barber, Jon Warden, Marc Pullan, Wesley O'Connor, Jon Broughton (Asst Mgr). Front Row; Ron Wilson (Coach), Ryan Andtrews, Andy Riley, Ben Abbey, Ian Payne, Dave Stevens, Lee Richardson,Simon Ullathorne, Richard Massimo (Physio).

CRAWLEY TOWN - Match Facts 1997-98

Match No.	Date	Venue H / A	Comp.	Opponents	Result & Score		Att.	Goalscorers	League Position
1	16.08	A	DM	Worcester City	W	3-1	*706*	Warden 28, Garland 68, Hawthorne 89.	
2	23.08	H	DM	Gloucester City	W	3-1	1,178	Warden 18, Garland 35, Reilly 66 (pen).	5
3	25.08	A	DM	Salisbury City	**W**	**6-2**	*685*	Warden 11, Reilly 61, Eriemo 66, 90, Garland 80, Hawthorne 83.	3
4	30.08	A	DM	Nuneaton Borough	L	2-4	*1,534*	Hawthorne 30, 39.	6
5	02.09	H	DM	St Leonards Stamcroft	W	2-1	1,382	Maikie 75, Davey 56.	
6	07.09	H	DM	Halesowen Town	D	0-0	1,570		3
7	13.09	A	**FAC 1Q**	Whyteleafe	L	2-3	*380*	Garland 69, Reilly 83 (pen).	-
8	16.09	A	DM	Ashford Town	W	1-0	*382*	Warden 68.	2
9	20.09	H	DM	Tamworth	W	3-2	1,281	Reilly 62 (pen), Jones 88, Garland 90.	2
10	23.08	A	DM	Hastings Town	W	2-1	*761*	Warden 52, Garland 62.	2
11	27.09	A	DM	Atherstone United	L	0-3	*252*		2
12	04.10	H	DM	Forest Green Rovers	D	2-2	2,163	Garland 25, Warden 66.	2
13	07.10	H	**DMC 1-1**	Sittingbourne	D	3-3	730	Reilly 2 (pen), Jones 64, Garland 88.	-
14	11.10	A	DM	Bath City	L	1-2	*455*	Garland 84.	4
15	14.10	H	DM	Sittingbourne	D	0-0	1,028		3
16	18.10	H	**FAT 1Q**	Kingstonian	W	2-1	1,587	Mackie 73, Reilly 82 (pen).	-
17	25.10	A	DM	Tamworth	L	1-2	*615*	Warden 6.	3
18	01.11	A	DM	Bromsgrove Rovers	D	1-1	*578*	Whittington 79.	4
19	05.11	A	**DMC 1-2**	Sittingbourne	W	*5-3	*201*	**Abbey 4** (35, 58, 69, 100), Payne 119.	-
20	08.11	H	**FAT 2Q**	Bishop's Stortford	L	1-2	1,255	Whittington 63.	-
21	15.11	H	DM	Rothwell Town	D	2-2	1,104	OG (Bullimore) 10, Garland 49.	5
22	18.11	A	DM	Dorchester Town	W	1-0	*612*	Hawthorne 70.	
23	22.11	H	DM	Burton Albion	D	0-0	1,381		5
24	24.11	A	**SSC 2**	Bognor Regis Town	L	0-1	*450*		-
25	29.11	A	DM	Gresley Rovers	L	1-3	*501*	Warden 46.	6
26	02.12	H	**DMC 2**	St Leonards Stamcroft	L	0-1	278		-
27	06.12	H	DM	Worcester City	L	2-3	1,040	Payne 39, Gregoryy 43.	9
28	13.12	H	DM	Merthyr Tydfil	L	1-2	1,370	Gregory 23.	10
29	20.12	A	DM	Gloucester City	D	0-0	*556*		11
30	26.12	H	DM	Hastings Town	D	0-0	1,573		
31	01.01	A	DM	Cambridge City	L	2-3	*480*	Abbey 10, Richardson 17.	
32	03.01	H	DM	Salisbury City	W	1-0	1,314	Ullathorne	11
33	10.01	A	DM	Rothwell Town	W	2-1	*283*	Richardson 33, Ullathorne 86.	9
34	17.01	H	DM	Bromsgrove Rovers	W	4-2	1,240	OG (Elms) 6, Reilly 29 (pen), Abbey 36, Warden 63.	9
35	24.01	A	DM	King's Lynn	L	0-2	*1,007*		10
36	31.01	A	DM	Forest Green Rovers	L	2-3	*428*	Hawthorne 2, Richardson 52.	
37	07.02	H	DM	Cambridge City	W	3-2	1,135	Abbey 15, OG (Carter) 19, Moore 86.	10
38	14.02	A	DM	Burton Albion	**L**	**2-5**	*690*	Warden 17, Andrews 39.	11
39	21.02	H	DM	Dorchester Town	L	0-1	1,162		11
40	28.02	H	DM	Nuneaton Borough	L	1-2	858	Barber 54.	11
41	07.03	A	DM	Sittingbourne	L	1-2	*448*	Payne 74.	11
42	21.03	H	DM	Gresley Rovers	L	0-1	930		12
43	28.03	A	DM	Merthyr Tydfil	L	1-2	*727*	Riley 69 (pen).	14
44	04.04	H	DM	King's Lynn	W	2-0	911	Gregory 49, Ullathorne 82.	13
45	11.04	A	DM	St Leonards Stamcroft	W	2-0	*432*	Mackie 16, Hawthorne 42.	13
46	13.04	H	DM	Ashford Town	L	1-2	963	Mackie 75.	13
47	18.04	H	DM	Bath City	W	1-0	806	Riley 44 (pen).	12
48	25.04	A	DM	Halesowen Town	W	1-0	*663*	Abbey 89.	12
49	02.05	H	DM	Atherstone United	W	3-0	1,003	Richardson 24, Riley 80 (pen), Barber 86.	10

SSC - Sussex Senior Cup

PLAYING SQUAD 1998

Goalkeepers: Colin Hunwick (Napier City R (NZ), Coventry C)

Defenders: Dave Stevens (Croydon, Tooting & Mitcham U, Carshalton Ath, Kingstonian,Carshalton Ath, Crystal Palace), Wes O'Connor (Bromley, Slough T), Solomon Eriemo (Hendon, Carshalton Ath, Aldershot T, Kingstonian, Wealdstone, Leyton-Wingate, Walthamstow Ave, Leytonstone & Ilf), John Mackie (Arsenal), Marc Pullan (Peacehaven & Telscombe), Andy Riley (Sutton U, Kingstonian,Carshalton Ath, Leatherhead, Whyteleafe, Malden Vale)

Midfielders: John Richardson (Hendon, Enfield, Slough T, Chesham U, Papatoetoe (NZ),Chalfont St.Peter, Chesham U, Amersham T), Lee Richardson (Arsenal), MarkHawthorne (Hayes, Torquay U, Walsall, Sheffield U, Crystal Palace), Joel Kirkland (Crystal Palace), Jon Warden (Bromley, Kingstonian, Carshalton Ath,Tooting & Mitcham U, Croydon), Phil Barber (Dover Ath, Bristol C, Millwall,Crystal Palace, Aylesbury U)

Forwards: Craig Whitington (Huddersfield T, Scarborough, Crawley T, Worthing), Ian Payne (Vancouver 86ers (Can), Plymouth A), Ben Abbey (Maidenhead U, Osterley), Simon Ullathorne (Cambridge C, Hastings T, Gloucester C, Sittingbourne, Gravesend,Croydon, Cleator Moor Celtic, Workington, Windscale U).

PROGRAMME DETAILS:
Pages: 32 **Price:** 80p
Editor: David Martin
(011305 264740)

DORCHESTER TOWN

Colours: Black & white stripes/black/black **Formed:** 1880
Change colours: Sky blue/white/sky blue **Nickname:** The Magpies
Midweek games: Tuesday **Sponsors:** Winterbourne Hospital
Newsline (Magpies Hotline): 0839 664412.
Reserves' League: Dorset Comb
Local Press: Dorset Evening Echo, Western Gazette, Western Daily Press.
Local Radio: Two Counties Radio, Wessex FM .

Chairman: C E Clark **President:**
Vice Chairman: K Mitchell **Comm Mgr:** Keith Kellaway (01305 262451)
Secretary: Albert Miller, 29 Shaston Crescent, Dorchester DT1 2EB (01305 264843)
Manager: Stuart Morgan **Physio:** Geoff Dine

GROUND Address: Avenue Stadium, Weymouth Avenue, Dorchester DT1 2RY (01305 262451). **Directions:** situated at the junction of the town bypass (A35) and the Weymouth road (A354). Nearest station: Dorchester South.
Capacity: 7,210 **Cover:** 4,000 **Seats:** 710 **Floodlights:** Yes
Clubhouse: Dorchester Lounge Club - access via main entrance to stadium. Cold food and snacks
Club Shop: Sells replica shirts, badges, mugs, etc.

PREVIOUS - **Grounds:** Council Recreation Ground, Weymouth Avenue 1880-1929/ The Avenue Ground, Weymouth Avenue 29-90. **Leagues:** Dorset/ Western 1947-72.

CLUB RECORDS - **Attendance:** 4,000 v Chelsea, official ground opening 1990. Competitive: 3,027 v Weymouth, Southern Lge Prem Div 92. **Goalscorer:** Dennis Cheney 61 (in one season). **Appearances:** Derek (Dinkie) Curtis 458 50-66. **Win:** 7-0 v Canterbury (A), Southern Lge Southern Div 86-87. **Defeat:** 0-13 v Welton Rovers Western Lge 66. **Fee Paid:** £12,000 for Chris Townsend (Gloucester City, 1990). **Fee Received:** £35,000 for Trevor Senior (Portsmouth, 1981)

BEST SEASON - **FA Trophy:** 3rd Rd replay 71-72, 96-97. **FA Cup:** 2nd Rd Replay 81-82 (1-2 v A.F.C. Bournemouth after 1-1 draw). 2nd Rd 54-55 57-58, 1st Rd 7 times.

HONOURS - Southern Lg 85-85, R-up 79-80 (Div 1 Sth R-up 77-78), Lg Cup 86-87 (R-up 91-92); Western Lg 54-55 (R-up 60-61, Div 2 R-up 49-50), Lge Cup 54-54; Dorset Snr Cup 50-51 60-61 67-68 68-69 71-72 93-94 94-95; Dorset Lg 37-38.

Players progressing to The Football League: Len Drake (Bristol Rovers 57), David Noake (Luton 59), Mike Turner (Swindon 61), Trevor Senior (Portsmouth 81), David West (Liverpool 83), Mike Squire (Torquay 84), Jeremy Judd (Torquay 84), Anthony White (Bournemouth 85), Graham Roberts (Spurs, Chelsea, Rangers, England) who progressed via Weymouth. Darren Garner (Rotherham U, 95), Craig Taylor (Swindon).

Back Row (L-R); Martyn Sullivan, Martin Shepherd, Kevin Maloy, Ellis Laight, Mark Lisk. Middle Row; Paul Wilkinson, Tommy Killick, Ian Symons, Andy Harris, Dave Lovell, Steve Richardson, Chris Myers. Front Row; William Stringer, Ryan Cross, Geoff Dine (Physio), Brian Benjafield (Asst), Stuart Morgan (Mgr), Pete Peavoy (Kit), Toby Redwood, Neil Coates

DORCHESTER TOWN - Match Facts 1997-98

Match No.	Date	Venue H / A	Comp.	Opponents	Result & Score		Att.	Goalscorers	League Position
1	16.08	A	DM	Tamworth	L	0-3	*863*		
2	19.08	H	DM	Forest Green Rovers	D	1-1	560	Richardson 61.	
3	23.08	H	DM	Halesowen Town	W	2-0	537	Redwood 14, Shepherd 85.	12
4	25.08	A	DM	Bath City	D	0-0	*611*		12
5	30.08	H	DM	Worcester City	D	0-0	504		14
6	06.09	A	DM	Salisbury City	W	3-0	*492*	Myers 53, Shepherd 58, Richardson 66.	
7	06.09	A	DM	Gresley Rovers	W	1-0	*504*	Shepherd 53.	7
8	13.09	A	**FAC 1Q**	Oxford City	D	1-1	*217*	Shepherd 87.	-
9	16.09	H	**FAC 1Q R**	Oxford City	W	1-0	353	Lisk	-
10	20.09	H	DM	Burton Albion	W	3-1	517	Richardson 68, Shepherd 77, 89.	3
11	24.09	A	DM	Forest Green Rovers	L	0-1	*530*		5
12	27.09	H	**FAC 2Q**	Forest Green Rovers	W	1-0	652	Shepherd 82.	-
13	04.10	A	DM	Ashford Town	W	4-0	*443*	Shepherd 51, Myers 69 (pen), Killick 74, Redwood 83.	4
14	08.10	A	**DMC 1-1**	Fareham Town	W	4-1	*116*	Laight 37, 60, Killick 40, Lovell 57.	-
15	11.10	H	**FAC 3Q**	Tiverton Town	L	0-1	1,171		-
16	18.10	A	DM	Gloucester City	W	2-1	*648*	Shepherd 27, Redwood 52.	6
17	25.10	H	DM	Gresley Rovers	D	2-2	485	Bundy 73, Shepherd 82.	6
18	28.10	H	**DMC 1-2**	Fareham Town	W	3-1	215	**Shepherd 3** (3, 44, 67).	-
19	01.11	A	DM	Nuneaton Borough	D	2-2	*1,155*	Myers 8 (pen), Richardson 74.	6
20	04.11	H	DM	Bath City	W	2-1	513	Richardson 27, Laight 86.	
21	08.11	A	DM	St Leonards Stamcroft	W	2-0	*373*	OG (Jones) 25, Richardson 73.	3
22	15.11	H	DM	Ashford Town	**W**	**5-1**	575	Shepherd 42, 65, Bundy 57, Richardson 61, Harris 78.	2
23	18.11	H	DM	Crawley Town	L	0-1	612		
24	22.11	A	DM	King's Lynn	L	0-2	*924*		3
25	29.11	H	**FAT 3Q**	Worthing	W	3-0	1,026	Lisk 13, Killick 73, Legg 88.	-
26	06.12	A	DM	Halesowen Town	L	1-2	*609*	Laight 87.	4
27	10.12	A	**DMC 2**	**Havant Town**	**D**	**1-1**	***101***	Lovelll 64.	-
28	13.12	H	DM	Cambridge City	D	1-1	540	Laight 74.	5
29	16.12	H	DM	Sittingbourne	W	2-0	222	Lisk 4, OG Haylock) 78.	
30	20.12	A	DM	Burton Albion	D	2-2	*543*	Redwood 60, Killick 90.	5
31	26.12	H	DM	Salisbury City	W	1-0	1,088	Killick 7.	
32	03.01	H	DM	Gloucester City	W	3-0	830	Cross 8, Sullivan 52, Myers 82 (pen).	3
33	06.01	H	**DMC 2 R**	Havant Town	W	3-0	229	Lovell 49, DSullivan 58, LKillick 70.	-
34	10.01	A	**FAT 1**	Kettering Town	L	0-1	*1,341*		-
35	17.01	A	DM	Atherstone United	D	0-0	*270*		4
36	24.01	H	DM	Tamworth	W	2-0	712	Richardson 52, Shepherd 61.	4
37	27.01	H	**DMC 3**	Clevedon Town	W	4-1	280	Shepherd 6, 18, Sullivan 31, Richardson 46.	-
38	31.01	A	DM	Bromsgrove Rovers	W	2-0	*488*	Lisk 73, Sullivan 84.	4
39	03.02	H	**DMC 4**	Bashley	D	1-1	534	Richardson 14.	-
40	07.02	H	DM	King's Lynn	L	3-4	676	OG (Spearing) 25, Killick 41, Harris 75.	
41	09.02	A	**DMC 4 R**	Bashley	L	0-2	*407*		-
42	14.02	A	DM	Rothwell Town	D	0-0	*230*		5
43	21.02	A	DM	Crawley Town	W	1-0	*1,162*	Shepherd 24.	4
44	28.02	H	DM	Hastings Town	W	3-0	641	Lisk 31, Harris 45, Myers 75.	3
45	07.03	A	DM	Worcester city	L	0-1	*812*		4
46	10.03	H	DM	Bromsgrove Rovers	W	4-0	441	O'Hagan 12, 20, Coates 35, O'Brien 90.	3
47	14./03	H	DM	Atherstone United	D	0-0	570		3
48	17.03	A	DM	Merthyr Tydfil	**L**	**0-4**	*843*		3
49	28.03	H	DM	Rothwell Town	L	2-3	581	Shepherd 9, O'Hagan 57.	3
50	04.04	A	DM	Cambridge City	W	2-1	*334*	O'Hagan 43, Cross 67.	4
51	11.04	H	DM	Merthyr Tydfil	D	1-1	885	Lovell 37.	3
52	13.04	A	DM	Hastings Town	D	0-0	*413*		4
53	18.04	H	DM	Nuneaton Borough	W	3-1	600	O'Hagan 12, 30, Lovell 42.	4
54	25.04	A	DM	Sittingbourne	L	0-1	*457*		4
55	02.05	H	DM	St Leonards Stamcroft	D	1-1	669	Shepherd 2.	4

PLAYING SQUAD 1998

Goalkeepers: Kevin Maloy (Cheltenham T, Weston-S-M, Taunton T, Blackpool, Exeter C, TauntonT)

Defenders: Mark Lisk (Bashley, AFC Lymington, Eastleigh), Ryan Cross (Sligo R, Bury,Hartlepool U, Plymouth A), Mark Sullivan (Plymouth A, Torrington), Toby Redwood (Exeter C), Neil Coates (Yeovil T, Dorchester T, Yeovil T, AFCBournemouth, Watford), Darren Tallon (Truro C, Dorchester T, Plymouth A), Ray O'Brien (AFC Bournemouth, Wigan Ath, Arsenal), Mark Carr (Weymouth, Erith T,Welling U)

Midfielders: Simon Cooper * (Gloucester C, Cheltenham T), Dave Lovell (Moreton, Puddleton), Ian Symons (Bideford T, Plymouth A), Chris Myers (Exeter C, Scarborough,Wrexham, Dundee U, Torquay U, Barnstaple T, Torquay U), John Cross (Cardiff C,QPR)

Forwards: Tommy Killick (Wimborne T, Bashley, Wimborne T, Swanage, Poole T), Ellis Laight (Bideford, Torquay U), Martin Sheppard (Weymouth, Trowbridge T,Westlands Sports), Andy Harris (Weymouth, Bridport, Dorchester T, Bridport), Danny O'Hagan (Weston-S-M, Plymouth A).

GLOUCESTER
CITY
Dr Martens League
Premier Division
Forest Green Rovers
City Stadium, Meadow Park
Saturday 7th February 1998
Kick Off 3.00pm
OMP
Official Match Day Programme £1.00

PROGRAMME DETAILS
Pages: 44 **Price:** £1
Editor: Mike Dunstan
Tel: 01242 250087

GLOUCESTER CITY

Colours: Yellow & black/black/black. **Formed:** 1889
Change colours: Red & white/white/red **Nickname:** The Tigers
Midweek games: Tuesday **Sponsors:** Hartland Renault
Local Press: Gloucester Citizen, Western Daily Press
Local Radio: Severn Sound, BBC Radio Gloucestershire

Chairman: Rob Thomas **President:** R F Etheridge
Vice-Chairman: Michael Tuck **Chief Executive:** Rob Thomas
Secretary: Ken C Turner, 24 Ladysmith Road, Cheltenham, Glos. GL52 5LQ. 01242 522514 (H) 0374 999839 (mobile).
Manager: Leroy Rosenior (0973 766797) **Asst Manager:** Brian Hughes
Press Officer: Jason Mills (01452 387049) **Physio:** Adrian Tandy
General Manager: Mike Bullingham 01452 421400

GROUND Address: Meadow Park, Sudmeadow Road, Hempsted, Gloucester GL2 6HS (01452 421400). **Directions:** From North: A40 then then A4301 towards City Centre & Historic Docks, right into Severn Road over swingbridge, right into Llanthony Road/Hempsted Lane, 2nd right into Sudmeadow Road, ground 50yds on left.
Capacity: 5,000 **Cover:** 3,000 **Seats:** 560 **Floodlights:** Yes
Clubhouse: Meadow Park Sports & Social Club at entrance to ground. Normal licensing hours. H & C food available. **Club Shop:** Yes

PREVIOUS - **Grounds:** Longlevens 1935-65, Horton Road 65-86. **Name:** Gloucester Y.M.C.A. **Leagues:** Bristol & Dist. (now Western) 1893-96, Gloucester & Dist. 97-1907, Nth Glos. 07-10, Glos. Nth Snr 20-34, Birmingham Comb. 1935-39.

CLUB RECORDS - **Attendance:** 4,000 v Dagenham & Redbridge, FA Trophy S-F 2nd Leg, 12.4.97. **Win:** 9-0 v Gosport Borough 13/5/90. **Defeat:** 1-12 v Gillingham 9/11/46. **Goalscorer:** Reg Weaver, 250. **Appearances:** Stan Myers & Frank Tredgett in 1950s. **Fee Paid:** £25,000 for S Fergusson (Worcester City), and D Holmes (Gresley R.) **Fee Received:** £25,000 Ian Hedges (AFC Bournemouth, 1990).

BEST SEASON - **FA Cup:** 2nd Rd 89-90. **FA Trophy:** Semi-Final 1996-97.

HONOURS - Southern Lg R-up 90-91 (Lg Cup 55-56 (R-up 81-82), Midland Div 88-89), Glos Nth Sen Lg 33-34, Glos Sen. Cup 37-38 49-58 65-66 68-69 70-71 74-75 78-79 79-80 81-82 82-83 83-84 90-91 92-93, Sen Amat Cup (Nth) 31-32).

Players progressing to The Football League: Numerous including William Teague (61) & Rod Thomas (64) to Swindon, John Layton (Hereford 74), Ian Main (Exeter 78), Mike Bruton (Newport 79), Mel Gwinnett (Bradford C. 84), Steve Talboys (Wimbledon 91).

97-98 - Captain: Chris Burns **P.o.Y.:** Gary Thorne **Top scorer:** Andy Mainwaring

Back Row (L-R);Phil Preedy, Ian Howell, Steve Mokler, Andy Hoskins, Jon Holloway, Adie Mings. Middle Row; Adrian Tandy (Physio), Paul Adcock, Dave Webb, Rob Thomas (Chr), Will Steadman, Andy Tucker, David Johnson, Mike Heather (Grd/Kit Mgr). Front Row; Gary Thorne, Gary Kemp, Leroy Rosenior (Mgr), Chris Burns (Capt), Steve Fergusson, David Elsey, Simon Cooper.

GLOUCESTER CITY - Match Facts 1997-98

GSC - Glos. Sen. Cup

Match No.	Date	Venue H / A	Comp.	Opponents	Result & Score	Att.	Goalscorers	League Position
1	16.08	H	DM	Hastings Town	D 1-1	711	Webb 60.	
2	23.08	A	DM	Crawley Town	L 1-3	1,178	Mings 71.	19
3	25.08	H	DM	Merthyr Tydfil	W 1-0	823	Adcock 52.	15
4	30.08	H	DM	Rothwell Town	L 0-1	582		17
5	01.09	A	**DMC P-1**	Weston-super-Mare	W 2-0	220	Mings 33, Hoskins 71.	-
6	05.09	A	DM	Tamworth	W 3-1	730	Adcock 29, Hoskins 72, Mings 84.	15
7	09.09	H	**DMC P-2**	Weston-super-Mare	W 1-0	306	Webb 32.	-
8	13.09	H	**FAC 1Q**	Mangotsfield Town	W 3-0	532	Burns 5, 81, Hoskins 71.	-
9	16.09	A	DM	Halesowen Town	W 1-0	681	Fergusson 54.	10
10	20.09	H	DM	St Leonards Stamcroft	D 1-1	612	Fergusson 1.	12
11	23.09	A	DM	Bath City	L 0-1	704		13
12	27.09	H	**FAC 2Q**	Newport (I.o.W.)	W 2-1	582	Burns 82, Fergusson 86.	-
13	30.09	A	**DMC 1-1**	Cinderford Town	W 3-0	260	Rosenior 3, Adcock 21 (pen), Preedy 89.	-
14	04.10	H	DM	King's Lynn	W 3-0	608	Thorn 67, Fergusson 77, Burns 85.	12
15	11.10	H	**FAC 3Q**	Waterlooville	W 2-0	558	Elsey 36, Fergusson 67.	-
16	14.10	A	DM	Merthyr Tydfil	L 0-1	635		
17	18.10	H	DM	Dorchester Town	L 1-2	648	Fergusson 28.	16
18	25.10	H	**FAC 4Q**	Wisbech Town	D 1-1	911	Holloway 27.	-
19	28.10	A	**FAC 4Q R**	Wisbech Town	L 2-3	1,094	Fergusson 10 (pen), Mings 33.	-
20	01.11	A	DM	Rothwell Town	D 1-1	252	Hoskins 3.	17
21	04.11	A	**GSC 1**	Cinderford Town	W 1-0	139	Holloway 75.	-
22	08.11	H	DM	Halesowen Town	W 1-0	718	Fergusson 19 (pen).	15
23	10.11	H	**DMC 1-2**	Cinderford Town	W 2-0	187	Burns 65, D Smith 84.	-
24	15.11	A	DM	Hastings Town	D 1-1	436	Mings 85.	15
25	18.11	H	DM	Bromsgrove Rovers	W 4-2	518	Mings 4, Tucker 45, Adcock 70, 81.	
26	22.11	A	DM	Sittingbourne	L 0-2	467		15
27	25.11	A	**GSC 2**	Forest Green Rovers	L 1-2	439	Kemp 47.	-
28	27.11	H	**DMC 2**	Newport AFC	D 2-2	253	Thorne 15, Holloway 45.	-
29	02.12	H	DM	Salisbury City	D 1-1	328	Smith 73.	
30	06.12	A	DM	St Leonards Stamcroft	D 0-0	351		13
31	13.12	A	DM	Worcester City	L 1-2	1,010	Burns 72.	14
32	16.12	A	DM	Nuneaton Borough	L 1-3	526	Mings 18.	15
33	20.12	H	DM	Crawley Town	D 0-0	556		15
34	26.12	A	DM	Forest Green Rovers	D 1-1	1,333	Mainwaring 73.	
35	27.12	H	DM	Gresley Rovers	W 1-0	606	Tucker 22.	12
36	01.01	H	DM	Bath City	**W 4-0**	978	Mainwaring 60, 78, Mings 64, Burns 88.	
37	03.01	A	DM	Dorchester Town	**L 0-3**	830		12
38	10.01	A	**FAT 1**	Basingstoke Town	W 1-0	715	Mings 15.	-
39	14.01	A	**DMC 2 R**	Newport AFC	W 2-1	302	Mainwaring 87, Adcock 90.	-
40	17.01	A	DM	Cambridge City	D 1-1	284	Smith 72.	13
41	20.01	H	DM	Tamworth	W 1-0	519	Mings 14.	12
42	24.01	H	DM	Atherstone United	L 1-2	660	Fergusson 32.	13
43	27.01	A	**DMC 3**	Bedworth United	W 3-0	82	Fergusson 65, Mainwaring 72, Holloway 90 (pen).	-
44	31.01	H	**FAT 2**	Burton Albion	D 1-1	963	Kemp 67.	-
45	03.02	A	**FAT 2 R**	Burton Albion	D *2-2	701	Burns 34, Fergusson 83. Won 6-7 after penalties.	-
46	07.02	H	DM	Forest Green Rovers	L 1-4	1,095	Tucker 46.	13
47	10.02	H	**DMC 4**	Redditch United	D 2-2	302	Mainwaring 42, Burns 86.	-
48	14.02	A	DM	Gresley Rovers	W 3-2	566	Mainwaring 42, Keeling 48, Fergusson 74 (pen).	12
49	17.02	H	DM	Ashford Town	L 2-3	375	Mainwaring 45, Fergusson 82 (pen).	12
50	21.02	A	**FAT 3**	Stevenage Borough	D 1-1	2,835	Fergusson 62 (pen).	-
51	24.02	H	**FAT 3 R**	Stevenage Borough	L 1-2	1,540	Webb 75.	-
52	28.02	H	DM	Sittingbourne	W 2-1	555	Keeling 27, Thorne 88.	12
53	02.03	A	**DMC 4 R**	Redditch United	L 1-4	170	Keeling 46.	-
54	07.03	A	DM	Burton Albion	L 1-2	731	Mainwaring 23.	12
55	14.03	H	DM	Nuneaton Borough	W 1-0	649	Mainwaring 64.	11
56	21.03	A	DM	Ashford Town	W 1-0	318	Mainwaring 17.	11
57	28.03	A	DM	Atherstone United	D 2-2	317	Mings 48, Mainwaring 75.	11
58	04.04	H	DM	Burton Albion	W 4-2	562	**Mainwaring 3** (23, 43, 53), Webb 72.	11
59	11.04	H	DM	Worcester City	D 0-0	758		11
60	13.04	A	DM	Salisbury City	W 3-2	434	Mings 11 Mainwaring 45, Tucker 90.	10
61	18.04	A	DM	King's Lynn	W 2-1	483	Burns 35, Mainwaring 55.	10
62	25.04	H	DM	Cambridge City	L 3-5	678	Mings 40, Fergusson 68, 84 (both pens).	10
63	02.05	A	DM	Bromsgrove Rovers	L 1-3	1,061	Mainwaring 7.	11

PLAYING SQUAD 1998 - **Goalkeepers:** Steve Mokler (Sudbury T, Harwich & P, Newmarket T, Harwich & P, Thetford T). **Defenders:** Gary Kemp (Almondsbury T), Jon Holloway (Swindon T), Dave Elsey (CheltenhamT, Fairford T, Weston-S-M, Gloucester C, Swindon T), Gary Thorne (Swindon T), Andy Tucker (Cheltenham T), Will Steadman (Youth team), Martyn Rowntree (Burton Alb), Steve Powell (Ledbury T). **Midfielders:** Chris Burns (Northampton T, Swansea C, Portsmouth, Cheltenham T), Steve Fergusson (Worcester C, Telford U, Gloucester C, Worcester C, Redditch U,Alvechurch, Redditch U, Bromsgrove R), David Webb (Trowbridge T, Gloucester C,Stroud, Devizes T, Wantage T, Supermarine). **Forwards:** Adie Mings (Bath C, Chippenham T), Andy Hoskins (Cinderford T, Forest GreenR, Tuffley R), Andy Mainwaring (Bromsgrove R, Cwmbran T, Inter Cardiff,Everton), Robbie Colwell (Ledbury T, Worcester C, Ledbury T), Darren Keeling (Weymouth, Bristol C).

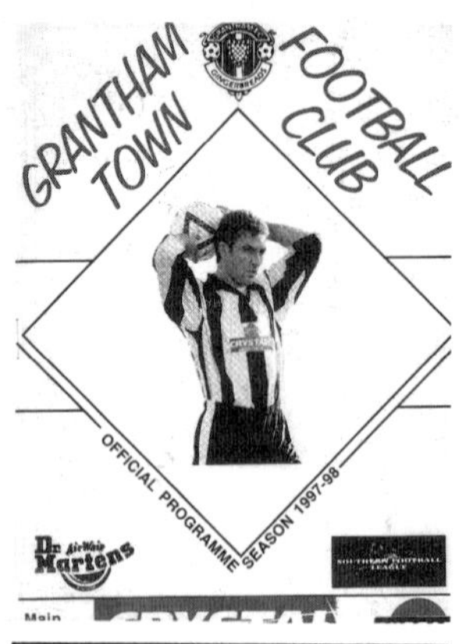

GRANTHAM TOWN

Colours: Black & white stripes/black/black **Formed:** 1874
Change colours: Blue/blue or black/blue or black
Midweek matchday: Tuesday **Nickname:** Gingerbreads
Reserves' League: Lincolnshire **Sponsors:** Crystal Motors.
Local Press: Grantham Journal, Nottingham Evening Post, Melton & Grantham Trader, Grantham Citizen, Lincolnshire Echo.
Local Radio: Radio Lincolnshire, Lincs FM.

Chairman: Alan Prince **President:** Baroness Thatcher of Kesteven.
Secretary: Mr Pat Nixon, 72 Huntingtower Road, Grantham, Lincs NG31 7AU (01476 564408).
Manager: Gary Mills **Asst Mgr:** Paul Buckthorpe **Physio:** Nigel Marshall

GROUND Address: The South Kesteven Sports Stadium, Trent Road, Grantham, Lincs (01476 562177)
Directions: Midway between A1 and A52 on edge of Earlesfield Industrial Estate; from A1 take A607 to Earlsfield Ind. Est and continue into Trent Rd.
Capacity: 7,500 **Cover:** 1,950 **Seats:** 750 **Floodlights:** Yes
Clubhouse: (01476 593506) Open evenings and weekends. Bar, darts, pool etc. Frequent live entertainment. Available for functions.
Club Shop: Sells programmes and a wide range of souvenirs. Contact Paul Wilson (01476 562177).

PROGRAMME DETAILS:
Pages: 36 **Price:** 70p
Editor: M Koranski

PREVIOUS - **Leagues:** Mid Amat All, Central All. 11-25 59-61, Midland Co's 25-59 61-72, Southern Lge 72-79, Northern Prem. 79-85. **Names:** Grantham FC, pre-80. **Grounds:** London Rd up to 90.

CLUB RECORDS - **Attendance:** 1,402 v Ilkeston Town, FA Cup Preliminary Rd 91-92 **Win:** 13-0 v Rufford Colliery (H), FA Cup Preliminary Rd 15/9/34. **Defeat:** 0-16 v Notts County Rovers (A), Midland Amateur Alliance 22/10/1892. **Career Goalscorer:** Jack McCartney 416 **Career Appearances:** Chris Gardiner 664 **Transfer fee paid:** £1,000 for Gary Jones (Doncaster Rovers, 1989) **Transfer fee received:** £20,000 for Gary Crosby (Notts Forest 87)

BEST SEASON - **FA Cup:** 3rd Rd 1883-84 86-87 1973-74. Comp Proper on 23 occasions **FA Trophy:** Quarter Final 1971-72 **FA Vase:** **FA Amateur Cup:**

HONOURS - Southern Lg R-up 73-74 (Div 1 Nth 72-73 78-79, Merit Cup 72-73), Midland Co's Lg(3) 63-64 70-72 (R-up 37-38 64-65 69-70, Lg Cup 68-69 70-71), Midland Amtr Lg 10-11 (Lg Cup R-up 10-11), Central All. 24-25 (Southern Div R-up 59-60), Lincs Snr Cup 1884-85 1936-37 (R-up(5) 34-36 39-40 45-47), Lincs Co. 'A' Cup(3) 53-54 60-62 (R-up 49-50 52-53 57-58), Lincs Co. Snr Cup 71-72 82-83 (R-up 80-81).

Players progressing to Football League: E Morris (Halifax 50), P Thompson/R Cooke (Peterborough 64/80), J Rayner (Notts County 64), D Dall (Scunthorpe 79), N Jarvis/H Wood (Scunthorpe 80), D White (Bristol Rvrs 86), T Curran (Grimsby 87), G Crosby (Nottm Forest 87), A Kennedy (Wrexham 87), R Wilson (Lincoln 87).

Action from Grantham's match against Hednesford in the FA Trophy.

GRANTHAM TOWN - Match Facts 1997-98

LSC - Lincs Sen. Cup

Match No.	Date	Venue H / A	Comp.	Opponents	Result & Score		Att.	Goalscorers	League Position
1	23.07	A	**LSC 1**	Gainsborough Trinity	W	1-0	*265*	Speed.	-
2	02.08	A	**LSC 2**	Lincoln United	L	0-3	*201*		-
3	16.08	A	DM-M	Brackley Town	W	2-1	*251*	OG, King.	
4	19.08	H	DM-M	Paget Rangers	W	3-0	314	King 2, D Harbottle.	
5	23.08	H	DM-M	Moor Green	W	2-1	347	King 2.	1
6	25.08	A	DM-M	Hinckley United	W	2-1	*467*	Taylor 2.	1
7	30.08	A	DM-M	Bedworth United	W	3-1	*332*	King 2, D Harbottle.	1
8	02.09	H	DM-M	V. S. Rugby	W	2-1	530	King, Taylor.	1
9	06.09	A	DM-M	Bilston Town	W	2-1	*110*	King, Taylor.	1
10	13.09	A	**FAC 1Q**	Halesowen Harriers	W	1-0	*142*	Taylor.	-
11	20.09	H	DM-M	Blakenall	W	2-0	436	M Harbottle (pen), Glasser.	1
12	24.09	A	DM-M	Paget Rangers	W	4-3	*125*	Dakin 2, Glasser, D Harbottle.	1
13	27.09	A	**FAC 2Q**	Solihull Borough	L	1-2	*234*	D Harbottle.	-
14	04.10	H	DM-M	Raunds Town	W	1-0	455	King.	1
15	07.10	H	**DM-M C 1-1**	Wisbech Town	W	1-0	362	Taylor.	-
16	11.10	A	DM-M	Shepshed Dynamo	W	2-0	*279*	King, D Harbottle.	1
17	14.10	H	DM-M	Hinckley United	D	1-1	395	King.	1
18	18.10	A	DM-M	Stourbridge	L	0-2	*158*		1
19	25.10	A	DM-M	V. S. Rugby	W	3-1	*354*	King, D Harbottle, Parkinson.	1
20	01.11	A	DM-M	Corby Town	W	4-1	*259*	JKing, M Harbottle, D Harbottle.	1
21	05.11	A	**DM-M C 1-2**	Wisbech Town	W	4-1	*457*	Hare 2, Taylor, King.	-
22	15.11	A	DM-M	Sutton Coldfield Town	L	0-1	*204*		1
23	22.11	H	DM-M	Solihull Borough	D	2-2	573	Dakin, D Harbottle.	1
24	29.11	A	**FAT 3Q**	Marine	D	1-1	*255*	D Harbottle.	-
25	02.12	H	**FAT 3Q R**	Marine	W	1-0	326	Taylor.	-
26	06.12	A	DM-M	Raunds Town	**L**	**0-3**	*151*		1
27	09.12	H	**DMC 2**	Raunds Town	D	3-3	169	M Harbottle (pen), Hare, King.	-
28	13.12	H	DM-M	Corby Town	W	6-5	302	Speed, King 2, Hare, Taylor 2.	1
29	20.12	A	DM-M	Stafford Rangers	W	2-0	*650*	Speed, D Harbottle.	1
30	26.12	A	DM-M	Wisbech Town	D	1-1	*429*	Hare.	1
31	01.01	H	DM-M	Shepshed Dynamo	W	4-0	608	Glasser 2, Dakin, D Harbottle.	1
32	10.01	H	**FAT 1**	Leigh R.M.I.	D	1-1	560	Thorpe.	-
33	14.01	A	**DMC 2 R**	Raunds Town	L	1-3	*80*	Taylor.	-
34	17.01	H	DM-M	Bedworth United	W	2-0	409	D Harbottle, Taylor.	1
35	19.01	A	**FAT 1 R**	Leigh R.M.I.	D	*0-0	*171*	A.E.T. Won 4-3 after penalties.	-
36	24.01	H	DM-M	Stafford Rangers	W	1-0	497	Speed.	1
37	31.01	A	**FAT 2**	Bath City	W	3-2	*832*	Taylor 2, King.	-
38	07.02	H	DM-M	Brackley Town	W	3-1	448	D Harbottle, Taylor, King.	1
39	14.02	H	DM-M	Sutton Coldfield Town	W	1-0	479	King.	1
40	21.02	H	**FAT 3**	Hednesford Town	W	2-1	2,214	King, Taylor.	-
41	28.02	A	DM-M	Redditch United	W	2--0	*266*	Wilson 2.	1
42	03.03	H	DM-M	Ilkeston Town	**W**	**6-0**	2,191	Glasser, OG, **M Harnbottle 3** (3 pens), Taylor.	1
43	07.03	H	DM-M	Evesham United	W	1-0	659	Taylor.	1
44	14.03	H	**FAT 4**	Southport	D	1-1	3,695	M Harbottle (pen).	-
45	17.03	A	**FAT 4 R**	Southport	L	1-3	*1,707*	King.	-
46	21.03	A	DM-M	Evesham United	W	2-0	*131*	Taylor 2.	1
47	28.03	H	DM-M	Bilston Town	W	3-1	635	Taylor, Speed, Wilson.	1
48	01.04	A	DM-M	R. C. Warwick	W	1-0	*226*	Robinson.	1
49	11.04	H	DM-M	Wisbech Town	W	3-2	732	Dakin, Wilson 2.	1
50	13.04	A	DM-M	Ilkeston Town	L	2-3	*1,275*	Speed, D Harbottle.	1
51	16.04	H	DM-M	Redditch United	W	1-0	498	King.	1
52	18.04	H	DM-M	R.C. Warwick	L	1-2	523	Taylor.	1
53	21.04	A	DM-M	Moor Green	L	1-2	*172*	Thorpe.	1
54	25.04	A	DM-M	Blakenall	W	3-1	*225*	Ramsey, Taylor, M Harbottle (pen).	1
55	28.04	A	DM-M	Solihull Borough	W	5-0	*152*	**Taylor 3,** Robinson, Bailey.	1
56	02.05	H	DM-M	Stourbridge	D	1-1	1,082	M Harbottle (pen).	1

PLAYING SQUAD 1998 - **Goalkeepers:** Steve Sutton (Birmingham C, Derby Co, Nottingham F). **Defenders:** Steve Fraser (Lincoln C, Grimsby T), Adrian Speed (Holbeach U, PeterboroughU), Emeka Nwadike * (Shrewsbury T, Wolves), Craig Clark (Arnold T, Ilkeston T,Dunkirk, Radcliffe Olympic), Dave Robinson (Gresley R, Ilkeston T, Heanor T), Mark Pennant (Ilkeston T, Gainsborough Trin, Sutton T, Eastwood T, Sutton T,Oakham U), Simon Dakin (Arnold T, Hull C, Derby Co). **Midfielders:** Paul Ramsey (Rothwell T, CPV (Fin), Merthyr Tydfil, Torquay U, Telford U,St.Johnstone, Cardiff C, Leicester C), Neil Glasser (Ilkeston T, Bromsgrove R,Notts Co, Nottingham F), Mark Corbett (Shepshed Dynamo, Hucknall T, Arnold T), Dave Harbottle (Lincoln U, Ilkeston T, Gedling T, Sutton T, Dunkirk, Notts Co,Scarborough), Nigel Baily (Lincoln U, Ilkeston T, Hucknall T, Dunkirk), Adrian Thorpe (Arnold T, Kettering T, Instand Dict (HK), Northampton T, Walsall,Notts Co, Bradford C, Heanor T, Mansfield T). **Forwards:** Dave King (Shepshed Dynamo, Rocester, Shepshed Alb, Sandiacre T, Ilkeston T,Sutton T, Heanor T, Gresley R, Derby Co), Dave Taylor (Ilkeston T, Gresley R,Ilkeston T, Arnold T, GPT Plessey, Ilkeston T, Dunkirk), Mark Hurst (Belper T,Gresley R, Leicester U, Grantham T, Huddersfield T, Sheffield U), Wayne Hallcro (Stamford, Cotgrave), Steve Hare (Shepshed Dynamo, Arnold T, Hucknall T), Kirk Jackson * (Chesterfield, Scunthorpe U, Sheffield Wed).

GRESLEY ROVERS
FOOTBALL CLUB
Main Club Sponsor
BM
Warehousing
Dr. Martens
Football
League
Premier
Division
Gresley Rovers
Versus
Burton Albion

PROGRAMME DETAILS:
Pages: 36 **Price:** £1.00
Editor: Brian Spare
(01332 862812)

GRESLEY ROVERS

Colours: Red & white/red/red **Formed:** 1882
Change colours: Light blue & navy/navy/navy **Nickname:** The Moatmen
Midweek matchday: Tuesday **Sponsors:**
Reserves' League: Midland Comb (Res. Div.)
Local Press: Derby Evening Telegraph, Burton Mail, Burton Trader, Swadlincote Times
Local Radio: BBC Radio Derby

Chairman: Peter Hall **President:** Gordon Duggins
Vice Chairman: Dennis Everitt
Secretary / Press Officer: Neil Betteridge, 34 Thorpe Downs Road, Church Gresley, Swadlincote, Derbys DE11 7PG (01283 226229).
Manager/Coach: Garry Birtles **Asst Manager:** Paul Fitzpatrick
Commercial Director Barrie Morton **Physio:** Gordon Ford.
GROUND Address: Moat Ground, Moat Street, Church Gresley, Swadlincote, Derbys DE11 9RE (01283 216315).
Directions: To A444 via either the A5, A38, A5121 or M42 North to Appleby Magna. On reaching A444 head for Castle Gresley. Turn onto A514 to Derby; at island 2nd exit (Church St), then 2nd left (School St) then 1st left into Moat St. 5 miles Burton-on-Trent (BR). Buses from Swadlincote and Burton.
Capacity: 2,000 **Cover:** 1,200 **Seats:** 400 **Floodlights:** Yes
Clubhouse: Inside ground, open Mon, Tues & Thurs eves & matchdays.
Club Shop: Sells merchandise, programmes, metal badges etc. Contact Kath Southern (01283 221898)

PREVIOUS - **Leagues:** Burton Lge 1892-95 97-01 09-10 43-45, Derbyshire Sen 1895-97 02-03, Leics Sen 1890-91 98-99 08-09 10-12 15-16 35-42 45-49, Notts 01-02, Midland 03-06, Central All 11-15 19-25 49-53 59-67, Birmingham Comb 25-33 53-54, Birmingham (now West Mids) 54-59 75-92, Central Comb 33-35, East Mids 67-75 **Grounds:** Mushroom Lane, Albert Village 1882-95, Church Str., Church, Gresley. 1895-1909.

CLUB RECORDS - **Attendance:** 3,950 v Burton Albion, Birmingham (now West Mids) Lg Division One, 57-58. **Win:** 23-0 v Holy Cross Priory, Leics Jun Cup 1889-90. **Defeat:** 1-15 v Burton Crusaders, 1886-87. **Career Goalscorer:** Gordon Duggins 306. **Career Appearances:** Dennis King 579. **Transfer fee received:** £30,000 for Justin O'Reilly (Port Vale 1996). **Transfer fee paid:** £2,500 for David Robinson (Ilkeston Town 97)

BEST SEASON - **FA Vase:** Runners-up 90-91, (SF 92-93). **FA Trophy:** Qtr Finals 95-96. **FA Cup:** 1st Rd Proper: 30-31 (1-3 at York City), 94-95 (1-7 at Crewe Alex.) **League clubs defeated:** None.

HONOURS - Southern Lge Champ 96-97; FA Vase R-up 90-91; West Mids Lg 90-91 91-92 (R-up 85-86 88-89); Lg Cup 88-89 R-Up. 86-87 91-92; Southern Lg Mid Div R-up 92-93; Derbys Snr Cup (7), (R-Up (2); Leics Snr Cup 1898-99 46-47 (R-Up 1899-90 45-46); Leics Sen Lg 00-01 46-47 47-48 R-Up (7); Coalville Charity Cup 46-47; Derby Senior Cup (S) (2) R-Up 00-01; Bass Vase (6); Cent All 64-65 66-67 R-Up (3) (Lg Cup 52-53); East Mids Reg Lg (2) R-Up (2); Dr.Martens (S Lge) Cup Fin 93-94.

Players progressing to Football League: Phil Gee (Derby County 85), Mark Blount (Sheffield Utd 94), Colin Loss (Bristol City 94), Justin O'Reilly (Port Vale 96)

97-98 Captain: Richard Denby **P.o.Y.:** Stuart Ford **Top scorer:** Ian Pitt

Back Row (L-R); Gordon Ford (Physio), Paul Fitzpatrick, Richard Denby, Will Davies, Gez Murphy, Andy Simpson, Brian Horseman, David Robinson, Stuart Ford, Garry Birtles (Mgr). Front Row; Gareth Jennings, Graeme Fowkes, Richard Wardle, Ian Pitt, Dave Puttnam, Andy Cheetham

GRESLEY ROVERS - Match Facts 1997-98

DSC - Derbyshire Sen. Cup

Match No.	Date	Venue H / A	Comp.	Opponents	Result & Score		Att.	Goalscorers	League Position
1	05.08	H	**DM ChS**	Burton Albion	W	2-1	858	Simpson 6, Pitt 20.	
2	16.08	A	DM	Salisbury City	L	0-1	*574*		
3	19.08	H	DM	Halesowen Town	D	1-1	695	Fowkes 23.	
4	23.08	H	DM	Sittingbourne	W	2-1	508	Simpson 7, Pitt 14.	11
5	25.08	A	DM	Nuneaton Borough	**L**	**0-6**	*1,605*		19
6	30.08	A	DM	Bromsgrove Rovers	L	3-5	*622*	Jenkins 10, Farmery 44, 51.	20
7	02.09	A	**DMC P-1**	Tamworth	L	3-4	*626*	Garner 4, 56, Pitt 36.	-
8	07.09	H	DM	Dorchester Town	L	0-1	504		20
9	09.09	H	**DMC P-1**	Tamworth	D	2-2	666	Alsopp 50, Jennings 81 (pen).	-
10	13.09	A	**FAC 1Q**	Holbeach United	W	6-3	*173*	Simpson 6, 59, Powell 31, Pitt 43, Turner 56, Grant 89.	-
11	20.09	H	DM	Forest Green Rovers	L	1-5	557	Pitt 66 (pen).	21
12	23.09	A	DM	Halesowen Town	L	0-5	*631*		21
13	27.09	A	**FAC 2Q**	Knypersley Victoria	L	1-3	*280*	Alsopp 1.	-
14	04.10	H	DM	Bath City	D	2-2	462	Wardle 1, Horseman 25.	21
15	11.10	H	DM	Rothwell Town	W	5-2	496	Jennings 13, Gyatt 15, Cotterill 54, Alsopp 55, Fowkes 59.	19
16	14.10	H	DM	Nuneaton Borough	L	0-1	859		
17	18.10	A	DM	Sittingbourne	W	3-2	*419*	Fowkes 38, Robinson 55, Davis 62.	17
18	25.10	A	DM	Dorchester Town	D	2-2	*485*	Cotterill 52, Grant 82.	
19	01.11	A	DM	Ashford Town	L	0-1	*397*		19
20	04.11	A	DM	King's Lynn	l	0-1	*585*		
21	08.11	H	DM	Atherstone United	W	2-0	718	Murphy 49, 73.	18
22	15.11	H	DM	St Leonards Stamcroft	**W**	**5-1**	513	Davis 30, Fitzpatrick52 (pen), Wilson 74, Alsopp 82, Grant 89.	17
23	18.11	A	DM	Tamworth	L	3-6	*710*	Robinson 41, Batchelor 43 (og), Pitt 79.	
24	22.11	A	DM	Cambridge City	L	0-1	*316*		18
25	29.11	H	DM	Crawley Town	W	3-1	501	Murphy 29, 86, Cotterill 90.	16
26	13.12	H	DM	Ashford Town	W	2-0	365	Murphy 30, 82.	15
27	20.12	A	DM	Merthyr Tydfil	L	0-3	*602*		17
28	26.12	H	DM	Burton Albion	W	2-0	1,752	Gyatt 61, Jennings 86.	
29	27.12	A	DM	Gloucester City	L	0-1	*606*		17
30	01.01	A	DM	Burton Albion	L	0-1	*2,189*		17
31	10.01	H	**FAT 1**	Leek Town	D	4-4	638	Pitt 19, Guyett 31, 87, Turner 88.	-
32	14.01	A	**FAT 1R**	Leek Town	L	1-3	*324*	Robinson 52.	-
33	17.01	H	DM	King's Lynn	L	2-4	575	Murphy 51, 86.	17
34	20.01	H	DM	Bromsgrove Rovers	W	4-2	408	**Murphy 3** (14, 24, 50), Fearon 45.	16
35	24.01	A	DM	Worcester City	L	0-1	*851*		
36	27.01	H	**DSC 3**	Belper Town	L	1-3	283	Pitt 48.	-
37	07.02	A	DM	Atherstone United	W	3-2	*472*	Pitt 14, Murphy 43, Fowkes 77.	15
38	14.02	H	DM	Gloucester City	L	2-3	566	Allsop 66, Pitt 77.	15
39	21.02	H	DM	Merthyr Tydfil	W	2-0	601	Lonergen 46, Simpson 88.	15
40	28.02	A	DM	Bath City	D	0-0	*547*		15
41	07.03	A	DM	Forest Green Rovers	W	1-0	*569*	Pitt 88.	13
42	17.03	H	DM	Hastings Town	L	1-2	391	Lonergan 16.	
43	21.03	A	DM	Crawley Town	W	1-0	*930*	Lonergan 55.	13
44	28.03	H	DM	Worcester City	D	2-2	563	Horsman 22, OG (Greenman) 47.	15
45	04.04	A	DM	Hastings Town	L	1-4	*334*	Lonergan 71.	15
46	13.04	A	DM	Rothwell Town	L	0-1	*253*		16
47	18.04	H	DM	Salisbury City	D	1-1	418	Fitzpatrick 81 (pen).	17
48	25.04	A	DM	St Leonards Stamcroft	W	3-1	*324*	**Pitt 3** (38, 52, 61).	16
49	28.04	H	DM	Cambridge City	L	0-1	348		16
50	02.05	H	DM	Tamworth	L	0-3	636		17

PLAYING SQUAD 1998

Goalkeepers: Stuart Ford (Scarborough, Doncaster R, Bury, Scarborough, Rotherham U)

Defenders: Brian Horseman (Notts Co), Will Davies (Gainsborough Trin, King's Lynn, DerbyCo), John Cottrell (Hednesford T, Wolves), Richard Denby (Alfreton T,Huthwaite, Sutton T, Boston U, Chesterfield, Nottingham F), Paul Fitzpatrick (Forest Green R, Corby T, RC Warwick, Forest Green R, Rushden & D, NorthamptonT, Hamilton Ac, Rotherham U, Leicester C, Carlisle U, Bristol C, Bolton W,Preston NE, Liverpool, Tranmere R)

Midfielders: Richard Wardle (Tamworth), Graeme Fowkes (Weymouth, Birmingham C, NottinghamF), Mike Lonergan (Argyle Sports, Rocester, Shepshed Dynamo, Newhall U,Stapenhill, Burton Alb), Terry Wilson (Ilkeston T, Rushden & D, Nottingham F), Andy Simpson (Derby Co), Darren Turner (Nottingham F)

Forwards: Gareth Jennings (Hednesford T, Gresley R, Sutton Coldfield T, Stoke C), Ian Pitt (Newhall U, Shepshed Dynamo, Heanor T, Shepshed Dynamo, Stapenhill,Heanor T, Stapenhill, Burton Alb).

PROGRAMME DETAILS:
Pages: 44 **Price:** £1
Editor: R Pepper

HALESOWEN TOWN

Colours: White with black & yellow trim
Change colours: All Blue & White trim
Midweek home matchday: Tuesday
Reserve's League: None.
Formed: 1873
Nickname: Yeltz
Sponsors: Hamer Ford.
Newsline: 0930 555818.
Local Press: Sports Argus, Express & Star, Birmingham Mail, Halesowen News, Stourbridge & Halesowen Chronicle.
Local Radio: B.R.M.B., BBC West Midlands, Beacon.

Chairman: Ron Moseley **President:** Laurence Wood
Vice Chairman: Nigel Pitt **Secretary:** Stewart Tildesley, 83 Bloomfield Street, Halesowen B63 3RF (0121 550 8443).
Manager: Stewart Hall **Asst Manager:** Colin Brookes
Physio: Gavin Blackwell **Commercial Manager:** Nigel Pitt
Press Officer: Paul Floud (0121 550 8999)

GROUND Address: The Grove, Old Hawne Lane, Halesowen, West Midlands B63 3TB (0121 550 2179). **Directions:** M5 jct 3, A456 (signed Kidderminster) to 1st island turn right (signed A459 Dudley), left at next island (signed A458 Stourbridge), at next island take 3rd left into Grammar School Lane, then Old Hawne Lane - ground 400 yds on left.
Capacity: 5,000 **Cover:** 1,420 **Seats:** 420 **Floodlights:** Yes
Clubhouse: (0121 602 2210) 12-2.30 & 7-11pm daily (closes 10.30pm on Sundays). Cold snacks served.
Club Shop: Sells replica strips, T-shirts, waterproof tops, coats, scarves, programmes, badges etc.

PREVIOUS - **Leagues:** West Mids 1892-1905 06-11 46-86, Birmingham Comb. 11-39.

CLUB RECORDS - **Attendance:** 5,000 v Hendon F.A. Cup 1st Rd Proper 1954, *(18,234 v Southall, 1986 FA Vase Final at Wembley).* **Goalscorer:** Paul Joinson 369. **Appearances:** Paul Joinson 608. **Win:** 13-1 v Coventry Amateurs, Birmingham Senior Cup, 1956. **Defeat:** 0-8 v Bilston, West Midlands League, 7/4/62. **Fee Paid:** £7,250 for Stuart Evans (Gresley 1996) **Fee Received:** £40,000 for Jim Rodwell (Rushden & Diamonds 96)

BEST SEASON - **FA Vase:** Winners 84-85, 85-86 R-up 82-83. **FA Cup:** 1st Rd 9 times: 54-55 then each season from 84-85 to 91-92. **FA Trophy:** 3rd Round Proper 94-95.

HONOURS - Southern Lg Premier Div R-up 96, Southern Lg Midland Div 89-90, W Mids Lg(5) 46-47 82-85 85-86 (R-up 64-65, Lg Cup 82-83 84-85), Birmingham Snr Cup 83-84 (R-up 51-52 67-68), Staffs Snr Cup 88-89 (R-up 83-84), FA Vase(2) 84-86 (R-up 82-83), Worcs Snr Cup 51-52 61-62 (R-up 87-88), Midland Comb. Res Div 89-90.

Players progressing to Football League: Arthur Proudler (Aston Villa), Cyril Spiers (Aston Villa), Billy Morris (Wolves), Dean Spink (Aston Villa), Stuart Cash (Nottm Forest), Andrew Pearce & Tim Clarke & Sean Flynn (Coventry), Dean Stokes (Port Vale), Frank Bennett (Southampton), Julian Alsop (Bristol Rovers).

97-98 - Captain: John Snape **P.o.Y.:** Steven Piearce **Top scorer:** Steven Piearce (29)

Back Row (L-R); Colin Brookes (Gen Mgr), Steven Piearce, Jason Owen, John Snape, Stuart Evans, Ross Collins, Paul Beswick, Daniel McDonnell, Phillip Wood, Matthew Gardiner, Kevin Harrison, Stuart Skidmore, Jeff Jones, Tony Hacket. Front Row; Stewart Hall (Mgr), Lee Brown, Evran Wright, Simon Swallow, Richsrd Crisp, Andrew Bradley, John Sharpe, Paul Harding, Ian Reed, Adrian Cooper, Ryan Robinson-Little.

HALESOWEN TOWN - Match Facts 97-98

BSC - Birmingham Sen. Cup
WSC - Worcs. Sen. Cup

Match No.	Date	Venue H / A	Comp.	Opponents	Result & Score		Att.	Goalscorers	League Position
1	16.08	H	DM	Ashford Town	W	1-0	645	Pierce 17.	
2	19.08	A	DM	Gresley Rovers	D	1-1	*695*	OG (Davies) 68.	
3	23.08	A	DM	Dorchester Town	L	0-2	*537*		14
4	25.08	H	DM	Atherstone United	W	3-1	715	Evans 25,Sharpe 41, Pierce 74.	6
5	30.09	H	DM	St Leonards stamcroft	W	3-0	759	Pierce 34, Harrison 45, Cooper 56.	3
6	02.09	A	DM	Burton Albion	D	0-0	*880*		
7	07.09	A	DM	Crawley Town	D	0-0	*528*		6
8	13.09	A	**FAC 1Q**	Felixstowe Port & Town	W	5-2	*253*	Pierce 13, Harrison 15, 43, Crisp 17 (pen), Sharpe 28.	-
9	16.09	H	DM	Gloucester City	l	0-1	681		7
10	20.09	A	DM	King's Lynn	D	0-0	*908*		7
11	23.09	H	DM	Gresley Rovers	**W**	**5-0**	631	Cooper 1, Harrison 23, Pierce 37, Crisp 52, Yates 77.	6
12	27.09	A	**FAC 2Q**	Rothwell Town	D	1-1	*350*	Evans 63.	-
13	30.09	H	**FAC 2Q R**	Rothwell Town	W	*4-1	489	Harrison 16, Gardiner 105, Pierce 114, Yates 116.	-
14	04.10	A	DM	Merthyr Tydfil	L	1-2	*615*	Bradley 70.	8
15	07.10	A	**DMC 1-1**	Bilston Town	L	1-3	*151*	Pierce 38.	-
16	11.10	H	**FAC 3Q**	Redditch United	D	2-2	702	Crisp 20, Gardiner 83.	-
17	14.10	A	**FAC 3Q R**	Redditch United	W	3-0	*512*	Bradley 30, Crisp 44, Pierce 72.	-
18	25.10	H	**FAC 4Q**	Northwich Victoria	L	0-2	1,206		-
19	28.10	H	**DMC 1-2**	Bilston Town	D	0-0	402		-
20	01.11	H	DM	Sittingbourne	W	3-1	638	Wright 34, Pierce 58, OG (Hodge) 87.	10
21	04.11	A	DM	Atherstone United	D	0-0	*212*		
22	08.11	A	DM	Gloucester City	L	0-2	*718*		11
23	15.11	H	DM	Forest Green Rovers	W	3-0	749	Pierce 3, Wright 24, 57.	10
24	18.11	H	DM	Burton Albion	D	1-1	648	OG (Benson) 55.	
25	22.11	A	DM	Tamworth	W	2-0	*909*	Yates 80, Reed 88.	8
26	25.11	H	DM	Salisbury City	W	4-1	447	**Wright 3** (1, 55, 73), Pierce 77.	
27	29.11	H	**FAT 3Q**	Burton Albion	L	1-2	773	Wright 27.	-
28	03.12	H	**BSC 2**	Aston Villa	D	0-0	271		-
29	06.12	H	DM	Dorchester Town	W	2-1	609	Wright 47, Snape 89.	3
30	13.12	A	DM	Rothwell Town	D	1-1	*271*	Pierce 90.	3
31	20.12	H	DM	Hastings Town	W	2-1	713	Pierce 65, Cooper 88.	4
32	26.12	A	DM	Bromsgrove Rovers	D	2-2	*1,370*	Yates 14, Wright 81.	
33	01.01	H	DM	Worcester City	W	2-0	1,543	Wood 31, Wright 54.	
34	10.01	H	DM	King's Lynn	W	4-1	907	Pierce 44, 72, Reed 64, Wright 69.	3
35	13.01	A	**BSC 2 R**	Aston Villa	W	*7-4	*402*	Piearce 2,49, Crisp 30 pen),10, Cooper 71, Reed 108, Yates 119.	-
36	17.01	A	DM	Nuneaton Borouugh	L	1-2	*1,107*	Wright 78.	3
37	24.01	H	DM	Merthyr Tydfil	D	2-2	1,225	Piearce 34, Crisp 63.	6
38	27.01	A	**WSC 2**	Bromsgrove Rovers	W	2-1	*382*	Cooper 11, Yates 13.	-
39	31.01	A	DM	Salisbury City	L	0-1	*306*		9
40	03.02	H	**BSC 3**	Tamworth	D	2-2	405	Reed 60, Crisp 68 (pen).	-
41	07.02	H	DM	Rothwell Town	**L**	**1-3**	739	Wright 62.	9
42	09.02	A	**BSC 3 R**	Tamworth	D	*2-2	*356*	Crisp 24, Piearce 90. Won 3-2 after penalties	-
43	14.02	A	DM	Ashford Town	**W**	**5-0**	*433*	Piearce 40, Wright 42, 89, Cooper 48, 60.	9
44	17.02	A	DM	Bath City	W	3-1	*544*	**Piearce 3** (13, 73, 77).	
45	21.02	H	DM	Nuneaton Borough	W	3-0	913	Cooper 34, Evans 51, Crisp 83 (pen).	3
46	28.02	H	DM	Tamworth	D	1-1	927	Piearce 84 (pen).	5
47	03.03	*A	**BSC 4**	Paget Rangers	D	1-1	302	Wright 31.	-
48	07.03	A	DM	Cambridge City	D	0-0	*393*		6
49	12.03	A	**WSC S-F**	Kidderminster Harriers	L	0-1	*558*		-
50	18.03	A	DM	St Leonards Stamcroft	W	5-1	*264*	Crisp 32 (pen), 89, Wright 41, Piearce 58, 84.	
51	21.03	H	DM	Bromsgrove Rovers	W	3-1	1,074	Wright 29, Crisp 44, Evans 61.	3
52	24.03	H	**BSC 4 R**	Paget Rangers	W	1-0	322	Piearce 12.	-
53	28.03	H	DM	Cambridge City	D	1-1	737	Wright 9.	4
54	04.04	A	DM	Sittingbourne	D	0-0	*454*		3
55	06.04	H	**BSC S-F**	Birmingham City	W	*3-2	681	Wright 35, Sharpe 58, Cooper 92. * A.E.T.	-
56	13.04	A	DM	Worcester City	D	1-1	*1,206*	Wright 82.	6
57	18.04	A	DM	Forest Green Rovers	L	0-2	*701*		6
58	25.04	H	DM	Crawley Town	L	0-1	663		7
59	27.04	H	**BCS Final**	Redditch United	W	3-1	904	Snape 10, Sharpe 48, Harrison 89.	-
60	30.04	H	DM	Bath City	W	2-1	355	Wright 71, 89.	6
61	02.05	A	DM	Hastings Town	D	2-2	*465*	Wright 62, Bradley 85.	5

PLAYING SQUAD 1998

Goalkeepers: Danny McDonnell (Lye T, Stourbridge, Lye T). **Defenders:** Matt Gardiner (Stourbridge, Moor Green, Torquay U), Andy Bradley (Tividale), Phil Wood (Pelsall Villa, Bilston T, Dudley T, Bilston T, Rushall Olympic,Bilston T). **Midfielders:** Adrian Cooper (Dudley T, Stourbridge, Halesowen T, Dudley T, Halesowen Harriers), Richard Crisp (Telford U, Aston Villa), Mark Peters * (BromsgroveR, Mansfield T, Peterborough U, Norwich C, Manchester C), Carlos de Azevedo (Club Athletico Lisbon (Port), Simon Swallow (Tividale), Paul Harding (Worcester C, Cardiff C, Birmingham C, Notts Co, Barnet, Enfield, DulwichHamlet, Carshalton Ath, Epsom & Ewell, Sutton U, Whyteleafe), John Sharpe (Exeter C, Manchester C), Neil Smith * (Hednesford T, Rushden & D, CheltenhamT, Lincoln C, Redditch U, Shrewsbury T). **Forwards:** Steve Piearce (Doncaster R, Wolves), Ian Adams (Youth team), Tim Langford * (Telford U, Wycombe W, Telford U, Halesowen T).

PROGRAMME DETAILS:
Pages: 64 **Price:** £1
Editor: David Bealey
Tel: (01797 253310)

HASTINGS TOWN

Colours: All white **Sponsors:** Alsford Timber
Change colours: Red/black **Newsline:** 0930 555 879.
Midweek matchday: Tuesday **Nickname:** The Town
Reserves' League: Winstonlead Kent Div 2. **Formed:** 1894
Local Press: Hastings Observer & News, Evening Argus.
Local Radio: Radio Sussex, Southern Sound, Arrow FM

Chairman: Mark Gardiner
Vice Chairman: Terry Avann **President:** David Harding
Secretary / Press Officer: R A Cosens, 22 Baldslow Road, Hastings TN34 2EZ 01424 427867 (H) 01424 444635 (B).
Team Manager: Terry & Dean White
Asst Manager: **Physio:** Ray Tuppen

GROUND Address: The Pilot Field, Elphinstone Road, Hastings TN34 2AX (01424 444635). **Directions:** From A21 turn left at 1st mini-r'bout into St Helens Rd, left after 1 mile into St Helens Park Rd, this leads into Downs Rd, at end of Downs Rd (T-junction) turn left, ground 200yds on right. From town centre take Queens Road (A2101). Right at roundabout into Elphinstone Road - ground 1 mile on right. One and a half miles from Hastings BR station - infrequent bus service from town centre to ground.
Capacity: 4,050. **Cover:** 1,750 **Seats:** 800 **Floodlights:** Yes
Clubhouse: Open matchdays, Tues, Thurs and Fri evenings from 7pm, and Sundays from 12 noon.
Club Shop: Sells replica kits, scarves, programmes, pens, key-rings, badges etc.

PREVIOUS - Leagues: South Eastern 04-05, Southern 05-10, Sussex County 21-27 52-85, Southern Amateur 27-46, Corinthian 46-48. **Name:** Hastings & St Leonards Amateurs **Ground:** Bulverhythe Rec Gd (pre 76)

CLUB RECORDS - Attendance: 4,888 v Notts Forest, friendly 23/6/96. *Competitive: 1,774 v Dover Athletic, Southern Lge Prem. Div. 12/4/93.* **Goalscorer:** (Season) Stafford Browne (29). **Transfer Fee Paid:** £8,000 for Nicky Dent from Ashford. **Received:** £50,000 for Paul Smith from Notts Forest.

BEST SEASON - FA Cup: 4th Qual. Rd 85-86, 2-3 v Farnborough Town (A). **FA Amateur Cup:** 3rd Rd. 38-39. **FA Vase:** 5th Rd. rep. 90-91.

HONOURS - Southern Lg Cup 94-95, Southern Div 91-92, Div 2 R-up 08-09, Div 2(B) 09-10; Sussex Co Lg R-up 21-22 25-26, Lg Cup 80-81, Div 2 79-80 (R-up 59-60), Div 2 Cup 79-80; Sussex Sen Cup 35-36 37-38 95-96 97-98; AFA Snr Cup 37-38; Gilbert Rice F/lit Cup 89-90.

Players progressing to Football League: Peter Heritage (Gillingham), Paul Smith (Nottm Forest)

97-98 - **Captain:** Mat Ball **P.o.Y.:** Stuart Playford **Top scorer:** Stafford Browne (29)

Back Row (L-R); Simon Fox, James Creed, Steve Willard, Steve Yates, Liam Barham, Nicky Dent, Simon Beard. Front Row; Ray Tuppen, Stafford Browne, Stuart Playford, Mat Ball, Danny Simmonds, Andy Larkin, Phillip Henderson

HASTINGS TOWN - Match Facts 97-98

SSC - Sussex Sen. Cup

Match No.	Date	Venue H / A	Comp.	Opponents	Result & Score		Att.	Goalscorers	League Position
1	16.08	A	DM	Gloucester City	D	1-1	*711*	Browen 65.	
2	19.08	H	DM	Sittingbourne	D	1-1	530	Rowland 84.	
3	23.08	H	DM	Nuneaton Borough	L	2-4	467	Playford 62, Browne 74.	18
4	25.08	A	DM	St Leonards Stamcroft	**W**	**4-1**	*1,579*	Dent 5, Browne 8, Paine 65, Fox 89.	9
5	30.08	H	DM	Tamworth	D	2-2	537	Browne 46, 76.	11
6	02.09	H	DM	Ashford Town	**W**	**4-1**	683	Dent 14, Browne 32 (pen), Payne 59, OG (O'Brien) 69.	
7	07.09	A	DM	Burton Albion	W	1-0	*528*	Beard 33.	5
8	13.09	A	**FAC 1Q**	Burnham Ramblers	W	1-0	250	Dent 80.	-
9	20.09	A	DM	Bath City	L	2-4	*503*	Browne 86, Fox 90.	11
10	23.09	H	DM	Crawley Town	L	1-2	761	Symonds 31.	12
11	27.09	A	**FAC 2Q**	Bognor Regis Town	L	1-2	439	Browne 49.	-
12	04.10	A	DM	Atherstone United	D	2-2	*242*	Browne 75, Dent 88.	14
13	08.10	A	**DMC 1-1**	Baldock Town	W	1-0	89	Dent 46.	-
14	11.10	H	DM	Merthyr Tydfil	L	0-1	392		15
15	14.11	A	DM	Cambridge City	W	2-0	*239*	Dent 21.	
16	18.10	A	DM	Salisbury City	L	0-2	*375*		14
17	25.10	H	DM	Rothwell Town	W	3-1	441	Playford 10, Symonds 48 (pen), Browne 90.	
18	28.10	H	**DMC 1-2**	Baldock Town	W	3-0	231	Fox 43, Playford 45, 75.	-
19	01.11	A	DM	Forest Green Rovers	L	2-5	*371*	Willard 31, 38.	11
20	08.11	A	**FAT 2Q**	Tonbridge Angels	W	3-0	577	Symonds 62, Playford 64, Smith 82.	13
21	15.11	H	DM	Gloucester City	D	1-1	436	Browne 8.	13
22	19.11	A	DM	Sittingbourne	L	1-2	*427*	Dent 67.	
23	22.11	H	DM	Bromsgrove Rovers	W	3-2	482	Ball 28, Browne 60, Barham 87.	12
24	25.11	H	**SSC 2**	Horsham	W	2-1	213	Fox 38, Smith 79.	-
25	29.11	H	**FAT 3Q**	Haybridge Swifts	W	3-2	532	Playford 65, Browne 66, 86.	-
26	06.12	A	DM	Tamworth	L	0-1	*492*		14
27	13.12	H	DM	King's Lynn	W	3-2	419	Playford 77, Browne 89, Fox 90.	13
28	16.12	H	**DMC 2**	Margate	L	1-2	182	Smith 64.	
29	20.12	A	DM	Halesowen Town	L	1-2	*713*	Browne 50.	14
30	26.12	A	DM	Crawley Town	D	0-0	*1,573*		
31	28.12	H	DM	Bath City	D	2-2	629	Browne 78, 88.	14
32	01.01	H	DM	St Leonards Stamcroft	W	2-1	1,672	Browne 19, 90.	13
33	10.01	A	**FAT 1**	Bath City	D	0-0	662		-
34	13.01	H	**FAT 1 R**	Bath City	L	0-1	481		-
35	17.01	A	DM	Merthyr Tydfil	L	2-4	*648*	Fox 13, Beard 72.	15
36	20.01	H	**SSC 3**	Horsham YMCA	W	9-1	168	Browne 12, 46, Willard 50, Simmonds 59 (pen), Beard 67, 83, Payne 71, OG (Burdon) 72, Dent 74.	-
37	24.01	H	DM	Cambridge City	L	4-5	431	Browne 7, 88, Tuppenny 36, Dent 69.	14
38	31.01	A	DM	Nuneaton Borough	L	0-2	*940*		15
39	07.02	H	DM	Salisbury City	W	2-0	446	Browne 7, Dent 29.	14
40	14.02	A	DM	King's Lynn	D	1-1	*1,014*	Tuppenny 7.	14
41	17.02	A	**SSC 4**	Shoreham	W	2-0	203	Browne 35, Beard 69.	-
42	21.02	H	DM	Atherstone United	W	3-1	444	**Dent 3** (26, 49, 67).	13
43	28.02	A	DM	Dorchester Town	L	0-3	*641*		14
44	04.03	N	**SSC S-F**	Worthing	W	1-0	333	Simmonds 34 (pen). Played at Langney Sports.	-
45	14.03	H	DM	Burton Albion	L	0-1	472		15
46	17.03	A	DM	Gresley Rovers	W	2-1	391	Fox 3, White 41.	
47	21.03	H	DM	Forest Green Rovers	L	0-1	469		15
48	24.03	H	DM	Worcester City	W	3-1	307	White 43, Beard 64, 90.	
49	28.03	A	DM	Bromsgrove Rovers	D	1-1	465	Browne 89.	12
50	04.04	H	DM	Gresley Rovers	**W**	**4-1**	334	Dent 41, White 50, Simmonds 51 (pen), Fox 53.	12
51	11.04	A	DM	Ashford Town	W	2-1	456	Dent 35, 82.	12
52	13.04	H	DM	Dorchester Town	D	0-0	413		12
53	18.04	A	DM	Rothwell Town	**L**	**1-5**	221	Browne 86.	13
54	25.04	A	DM	Worcester City	D	0-0	707		13
55	02.05	H	DM	Halesowen Town	D	2-2	465	Browne 46, 80.	14
56	04.05	N	**SSC Final**	Burgess Hill Town	W	2-1	1,256	Yeats 12, Simmons 65 (pen). Played at Crawley Town FC.	-

PLAYING SQUAD 1998

Goalkeepers: James Creed (Faversham T, Hastings T)

Defenders: Phil Henderson (Eastbourne U, Wivenhoe T, Northampton T), Paul Tuppenney (Stamco, Hastings T), Mark Morris (Brighton, AFC Bournemouth, Sheffield U,Watford, Wimbledon), Matthew Ball (Worthing, Bexhill T), Danny Simmonds (Brighton), Spencer Mintram * (Farnborough T, Worthing, Lewes, Brighton)

Midfielders: Simon Beard (Sittingbourne, West Ham U), Stuart Myall (Brentford, Brighton), Justin Gregory (Crawley T, Hastings T, Worthing, Shoreham), Steve Yates (Local football), Terry White (St.Leonards Stamcroft, Hastings T, Hythe T,Hastings T, Bexhill, Millwall, Charlton Ath), Laim Barham (Wealdstone,Hastings T, Grays Ath, Kingstonian, VV Veendam (Holl), Dover Ath, Dunstable,Windsor & Eton, Dunstable, Hastings U, Brighton)

Forwards: Lee McRobert * (Millwall, Sittingbourne, Ashford T), Stafford Browne (Horsham,Lewes, Ringmer), Simon Fox (Brighton), Stuart Playford (Rye U), Nicky Dent (Ashford T, Sing Tao (HK), Dover Ath, Poole T, Yeovil T, Bristol C, Bristol Manor Farm)

Ron Brooks
ILKESTON TOYOTA

PROGRAMME DETAILS:
Pages: 32 **Price:** £1
Editor: Mic Capill
J.Shiels,D.Payne.

ILKESTON TOWN

Colours: Red/black/red **Re Formed:** 1945
Change colours: All purple. **Nickname:** The Robins
Midweek matchday: Tuesday **Sponsors:** Ron Brooks Ilkeston Toyota
Reserves' League: Midland Comb.

Chairman: Paul Millership **President:** Robert Lindsay
Secretary: Tony Cuthbert, 8 Darwin Road, Long Eaton, Nottingham NG10 3NW (0115 9731531). **Commercial Manager:** Midland Sports Promotions
Manager / Coach: Keith Alexander **Asst Manager:** Gary Simpson

GROUND Address: New Manor Ground, Awsworth Rd, Ilkeston (0115 9324094). **Directions:** M42 to M1 junc 23A, continue on M1 to junc 26, exit left onto A610 towards Ripley, take 1st exit signed Awsworth and Ilkeston (A6096), follow bypass signed Ilkeston A6096. Turn right after 1/2 mile signed Cotmanhay. Ground 200 yards on left
Capacity: 3,500 **Seats:** 270. **Cover:** 1,100. **Floodlights:** Yes
Clubhouse: Open Wed-Fri 7-11pm, Sat-Sun noon-3 & 7-11pm, and Mon or Tue if there is a match. Snacks behind bar. Large tea bar open matchdays 2-5pm (6.30-9pm for night games).
Club Shop: Sells wide range of souvenirs & programmes + 'Team Talk'. Contact Manager (0115 9305 622) or club secretary

PREVIOUS - **Leagues:** Midland 1894-1902 25-58 61-71/Notts and Derby Senior Lg.1945-47/ Central Alliance 47-61/Midland CountiesLg.1961-71/Southern League 1971-73/ Midland Co.Lg.1973-82/ Northern Co.East Lg.1982-86/ Central Midlands 86-90/ West Midlands (Regional) 90-94. **Ground:** Manor Ground, Manor Rd (1945-92).

CLUB RECORDS - **Attendance:** 2,504 v Boston United FA Cup 1st Rd 15/11/97. **Win:** 14-2 v Codnor M.W 46-47: 13-0 v Swanwick OB 46-47. **Defeat:** 1-11 v Grantham T. 47-48: 0-10 v VS Rugby 85-86. **Career Goalscorer:** Jackie Ward 141. **Career Appearances:** Terry Swincoe 377. **Season Goalscorer:** Barry Jepson 62, 1952-53. **Transfer fee paid:** £7,000 for Paul Eshelby (Alfreton Tn 96-97). **Transfer fee received:** £25,000 for Francis Green (Peterborough Utd).

BEST SEASON - **FA Cup:** 2nd Rd 1-1, 1-2 v Scunthorpe Utd 97-98. **FA Trophy:** 3rd Round 82-83 1-5 v Enfield, 94-95 2-2, 1-2 v Kidderminster H. **FA Vase:** 4th Round 88-89 1-2 v Tamworth.

HONOURS - Southern Lge, Midland Div 94-95, (R-up 97-98); West Mids (Regional) Lg 93-94, Lg Cup 93-94, Div 1 91-92, Lg Cup 91-92; Central Mids Lg Cup 87-88; Midland Lg 67-68 (R-up 1898-99); Midland Co Lg 67-68; Central All 51-52 52-53 53-54 54-55 (R-up 47-48 55-56).

97-98 - Captain: John Knapper **Top Scorer:** Christian Moore **P.o.Y.:** Gary Middleton

Back Row (L-R); Nicky Law, Dean Fearon, John Knapper, Garry Middleton, Malcolm Rigby, Dale Wright, Paul Eshelby, Scott Huckerby, Tony Simpson Front Row; Christian Moore, Darren Ball, Ian Robinson, Matt Carmichael

ILKESTON TOWN - Match Facts 1997-98

DSC - Derbys. Sen. Cup

Match No.	Date	Venue H / A	Comp.	Opponents	Result & Score		Att.	Goalscorers	League Position
1	16.08	H	DM-M	Solihull Borough	W	2-1	475	Knapper, Moore.	
2	19.08	A	DM-M	Blakenall	L	1-2	*120*	Knapper	
3	23.08	A	DM-M	Sutton Coldfield Town	W	4-1	*241*	Eshelby, Robinson, Carmichael 2.	
4	25.08	H	DM-M	Stafford Rangers	W	2-1	653	Eshelby, Carmichael.	4
5	30.08	A	**FAC Pre**	Buxton	W	1-0	*303*	Carmichael.	-
6	02.09	H	DM-M	Bilston Town	W	6-0	448	Fearon, Robinson, Carmichael 2, Moore, Wright.	
7	07.09	A	DM-M	Bedworth United	W	3-0	*318*	Carmichael, Moore, Wright.	2
8	13.09	H	**FAC 1Q**	Rossendale United	W	3-0	390	Eshelby, Carmichael, Wright.	-
9	20.09	A	DM-M	Wisbech Town	W	5-2	*582*	**Carmichael 3,** Simpson 2.	2
10	23.09	H	DM-M	Blakenall	L	0-1	553		3
11	27.09	H	**FAC 2Q**	RTM Newcastle	W	7-1	394	**Moore 3,** Thompson 2, Eshelby, Middleton.	-
12	04.10	H	DM-M	Brackley Town	W	5-1	545	**Carmichael 3,** Fearon, Eshelby.	3
13	07.10	H	**DMC 1-1**	King's Lynn	W	2-1	357	Carmichael, Knapper.	-
14	11.10	A	**FAC 3 Q**	Chorley	W	3-1	*477*	Fearon, Robinson, Moore.	-
15	14.10	A	DM-M	Stafford Rangers	D	2-2	*364*	Robinson, Moore.	3
16	18.10	A	**FAT 1 Q**	Winsford United	L	0-2	*287*		-
17	25.10	H	**FAC 4 Q**	Hyde United	W	3-2	1,232	Fearon 2, Middleton.	-
18	28.10	A	**DMC 1-2**	King's Lynn	D	2-2	*555*	Ludlum, Simpson.	-
19	01.11	A	DM-M	Stourbridge	W	5-1	*218*	Moore 2, Carmichael, Knapper, Fearon.	3
20	08.11	H	DM-M	Paget Rangers	W	5-0	503	Carmichael 2, Robinson, Eshelby, Fearon.	2
21	15.11	H	**FAC 1**	Boston United	W	2-1	2,504	Carmichael 2.	-
22	18.11	A	DM-M	Bilston Town	D	2-2	*104*	Carmichael, Simpson.	
23	25.11	H	DM-M	Shepshed Dynamo	W	1-0	484	Huckerby.	3
24	29.11	H	DM-M	Sutton Coldfield Town	W	3-0	422	Knapper, Robinson 2.	2
25	06.12	A	**FAC 2**	Scunthorpe United	D	1-1	*1,187*	Robinson.	-
26	13.12	H	DM-M	Bedworth United	W	3-1	1,084	Fearon 2, Eshelby.	2
27	17.12	H	**FAC 2 R**	Scunthorpe United	L	1-2	2,109	Moore.	-
28	20.12	A	DM-M	Evesham United	W	5-0	*124*	**Moore 3,** Knapper, Eshelby.	2
29	26.12	A	DM-M	Corby Town	W	5-1	*147*	**Moore 3,** Ball, Robinson.	2
30	01.01	H	DM-M	Wisbech Town	D	3-3	939	Ball, Eshelby, Moore.	2
31	07.01	A	**DMC 2**	Corby Town	W	2-1	*72*	Carmichael, OG.	-
32	10.01	A	**DSC 3**	Stapenhill	W	7-0	*135*	Knapper, Eshelby, Robinson, Atkinson 2, Simpson, Wright.	-
33	17.01	H	DM-M	Raunds Town	W	3-0	622	Carmichael, Moore, OG.	2
34	21.01	A	**DMC 3**	Raunds Town	W	3-0	*114*	Fearon, Eshelby, Atkinson.	-
35	24.01	A	DM-M	Solihull Borough	W	4-0	*292*	Moore 2, Carmichael, OG.	2
36	31.01	H	DM-M	Hinckley United	W	3-0	667	Moore, Ball, Simpson.	2
37	03.02	A	**DMC 4**	Moor Green	D	3-3	*142*	Huckerby 2, Wright.	-
38	07.02	A	DM-M	Redditch United	D	1-1	*294*	Simpson.	2
39	10.02	A	**DSC 4**	Staveley M.W.	W	4-1	*155*	Knapper, Eshelby 2, Green.	-
40	14.02	H	DM-M	Evesham United	W	8-1	681	**Moore 3,** Carmichael 2, Fearon, Ball, Huckerby.	2
41	17.02	H	**DMC 4 R**	Moor Green	W	4-0	518	**Moore 3,** Robinson.	-
42	21.02	A	DM-M	Brackley Town	W	2-0	*244*	Moore, Huckerby.	2
43	28.02	A	DM-M	R. C. Warwick	D	0-0	*239*		2
44	03.03	A	DM-M	Grantham Town	**L**	**0-6**	*2,191*		2
45	07.03	H	DM-M	Corby Town	W	3-0	587	Fearon, Knapper, Eshelby.	2
46	10.03	H	**DMC S-F 1**	Redditch United	W	1-0	422	Huckerby.	-
47	14.03	H	DM-M	Stourbridge	W	3-1	662	Moore 2, Huckerby.	2
48	17.03	A	**DSC S-F**	Glapwell	L	0-2	*180**	* estimated crowd.	-
49	21.03	A	DM-M	Raunds Town	L	0-1	*127*		2
50	24.03	A	**DM C S-F 2**	Redditch United	L	1-3	*272*	Knapper.	-
51	27.03	A	DM-M	Paget Rangers	L	0-1	*193*		--
52	31.03	A	DM-M	Moor Green	D	2-2	*184*	Law, Moore.	2
53	04.04	H	DM-M	R. C. Warwick	W	2-0	534	Huckerby, Wright.	2
54	11.04	A	DM-M	Shepshed Dynamo	W	2-1	*393*	Allsop, Huckerby.	2
55	13.04	H	DM-M	Grantham Town	W	3-2	1,275	**Huckerby 3.**	2
56	18.04	H	DM-M	V. S. Rugby	**W**	**11-1**	753	Knapper, **Simpson 3, Eshelby 3,** Middleton, Robinson, Allsop, Carmichael.	2
57	22.04	A	DM-M	V. S. Rugby	W	8-0	*233*	**Huckerby 3,** Eshelby, Moore, Knapper, Shay.	2
58	25.04	A	DM-M	Hinckley United	W	4-3	*421*	Wright, Huckerby, Allsop, Law (pen).	2
59	29.04	H	DM-M	Redditch United	W	2-0	529	Simpson, Huckerby.	2
60	02.05	H	DM-M	Moor Green	W	1-0	782	Moore.	2

PLAYING SQUAD 1998

Goalkeepers: Malcolm Rigby (Nottingham F, Notts Co). **Defenders:** Craig Ludlam (Matlock T, Sheffield Wed), Darren Ball (Youth team), Gary Middleton (Arnold T, Matlock T, Gainsborough Trin, Belper T, Barnsley,Rotherham U), Lee Saunders (Leicester U, Doncaster R), Dean Fearon (Emley,Rotherham U, Barnsley), Matt Simpson (Stapenhill, Belper T, Burton Alb). **Midfielders:** John Knapper (Eastwood T, Belper T), Ian Robinson (Mansfield T), Dale Wright (Nottingham F), Tony Simpson (Nuneaton B, Tamworth, Nuneaton B, Grantham T,Nottingham F), Ben Smith (Sheffield Wed), Tony Dennis (Giansborough Trin,Lincoln C, Colchester U, Cambridge U, Slough T, Taunton T, Bideford, Exeter C,Plymouth A), Dean Randall * (Notts Co). **Forwards:** Ian Helliwell * (Doncaster R, Burnley, Stockport Co, Rotherham U, Scunthorpe U,York C, Matlock T), Christian Moore (Forest Green R, Leicester U, Belper T,Gresley R, Nuneaton B, Stockport Co, Leicester C), Kevin Allsop (Gresley R,Stapenhill, Harrstad (Nor), Hinckley T), Paul Eshelby (Alfreton T,Scarborough, Exeter C, Endcliffe U).

PROGRAMME DETAILS
Pages: 24 **Price:** £1.20
Editor: Secretary.

KING'S LYNN

Colours: Royal Blue with gold trim/Blue/Blue & Gold hoops **Formed:** 1879
Change colours: All red **Nickname:** The Linnets
Midweek home matchday: Tuesday **Sponsors:** Eastern Group
Reserves' League: None
Local Press: Lynn News & Advertiser, Eastern Daily Press.
Local Radio: KLFM

Chairman: John Scales. **President:** Jim Chandler.
Secretary: Martin Davis, 158 Lynn Road, Wisbech, Cambs PE13 3EB (01945 583567 H & B) **Manager:** Tony Spearing
Asst Man/Coach: Darren Bloodworth **Physio:** Dave Edgeley
GROUND Address: The Walks Stadium, Tennyson Road, King's Lynn PE30 5PB (01553 760060). **Directions:** At mini r-about arriving from A10/A47 take Vancouver Avenue. Ground on left after a half mile. Quarter mile from King's Lynn (BR), half mile from bus station.
Capacity: 8,200 **Cover:** 5,000 **Seats:** 1,200 **Floodlights:** Yes
Clubhouse: Normal licensing hours, with extension on matchdays.
Club Shop: Sells metal badges and other merchandise

PREVIOUS - **Leagues:** Norfolk & Suffolk/Eastern C'ties 35-39 48-54/UCL 46-48/Midland C'ties 54-58/ NPL 80-83. **Name:** Lynn Town. **Ground:** None.
CLUB RECORDS - **Attendance:** 12,937 v Exeter, FA Cup 1st Rd 50-51. **Win:** 17-0 v Beccles 29/30 **Defeat:** 0-11 v Aston Villa FA Cup 1905/6 **Career Appearances:** Mick Wright 1,152 (British Record). **Career Goalscorer:** Malcolm Lindsay 321. **Transfer Fee Paid:** G Jones, **Received:** Andy Hunt
BEST SEASON - **FA Cup:** 3rd Rd 61-62 (0-4 at Everton). Competition Proper on 14 occasions; 05-06 37-38 49-50 51-52 58-63 64-65 68-69 71-72 73-74 84-85. Rd 2 97-98. **League clubs defeated:** Aldershot 59-60, Coventry 61-62, Halifax 68-69. **FA Trophy:** 2nd Rd 78-79. **FA Vase:** 5th Rd 94-95 (0-2 at Diss Town). **FA Amateur Cup:** R-up 1900-01.
HONOURS - FA Amateur Cup R-up 1900-01, Southern Lg R-up 84-85 (Div 1 R-up 63-64), NPL Presidents Cup 82-83, Eastern Co's Lg 53-54 (R-up 49-50 52-53 (Lg Cup 53-54), Norfolk & Suffolk Lg(8)(R-up(6)), E Anglian Lg R-up(2), Norfolk Snr Cup(19)(R-up(20), Norfolk Invitation Cup 94-95, Norfolk Premier Cup 68-69(jt) 73-74, East Anglian Cup(4)(R-up(3), Eastern Prof Floodlit Lg 68-69, Southern Lg Midland R-up 95-96.
Players progressing to Football League: N Rowe (Derby 1949), B Taylor & P Ward (Bradford P. A. 54 & 55), T Reynolds (Darlington 54), G Reed (Sunderland 55), P McCall (Bristol C 55), J Neal (Swindon 57), T Dryburgh (Oldham 57), J Hunter (Barrow 59), J Stevens (Swindon), G Catleugh (Watford), George Walters (Chesterfield 64), P McNamee (Notts County 1966), W Biggins (Burnley), Jackie Gallagher (Peterborough 80), Andy Higgins (Rochdale 83), Neil Horwood (Grimsby 86), Darren Rolph (Barnsley 87), Mark Howard (Stockport 88), Andy Hunt, Malcom Lindsay.
97-98 - Captain: Colin Hoyle **P.o.Y.:** Tony Spearing **Top scorer:** Ian Williams/Lee Hudson (20)

Kings Lyn celebrating the FA Cup 1st Rd win over Bromsgrove Rovers.

KING'S LYNN - Match Facts 97-98

Match No.	Date	Venue H / A	Comp.	Opponents	Result & Score		Att.	Goalscorers	League Position
1	16.08	H	DM	Bromsgrove Rovers	W	3-2	866	Williams 10, Matthews 60, Skelly 88 (pen).	
2	19.08	A	DM	Burton Albion	D	0-0	*849*		
3	23.08	A	DM	Atherstone United	D	0-0	*259*		6
4	25.08	H	DM	Cambridge City	W	2-1	1,122	Williams 52, Skelly 58.	4
5	30.08	A	DM	Forest Green Rovers	L	2-4	*418*	McNamara 6, 16.	7
6	02.09	H	DM	Nuneaton Borough	D	1-1	1,180	Pascoe 43.	
7	07.09	A	DM	St Leonards Stamcroft	W	4-2	*537*	Hudson 29, 60, Williams 83, McNamara 85.	8
8	13.08	A	**FAC 1Q**	Bourne Town	W	3-1	450	Hudson 45, Mead 47, McNamara 84.	-
9	20.08	H	DM	Halesowen Town	D	0-0	908		8
10	23.09	H	DM	Burton Albion	W	2-1	777	Hudson 39, 44.	7
11	27.09	A	**FAC 2Q**	Bilston Town	W	2-1	196	Hudson 18, Skelly 74.	-
12	04.10	A	DM	Gloucester City	L	0-3	*608*		9
13	07.10	A	**DMC 1-1**	Ilkeston Town	L	1-2	357	Cambridge 83 (pen).	-
14	11.10	H	**FAC 3Q**	V. S. Rugby	W	4-3	1,508	Hudson 47, McNamara 29, Williams 73, 85.	-
15	18.10	A	DM	Merthyr Tydfil	**L**	**0-4**	*743*		15
16	25.10	H	**FAC 4Q**	Salisbury City	W	5-0	1,346	McNamara 31, 65, Williams 14, 15, Hudson 29.	-
17	28.10	H	**DMC 1-2**	Ilkeston Town	D	2-2	555	Williams 58, Delicate 79.	-
18	01.11	A	DM	Salisbury City	W	3-2	*408*	Hudson 7, Hoyle 45, Wright 80.	12
19	04.11	H	DM	Gresley Rovers	W	1-0	585	Hoyle 13.	
20	08.11	H	DM	Bath City	W	3-1	943	McNamara 26, 82, Williams 60.	6
21	15.11	H	**FAC 1**	Bromsgrove Rovers	W	1-0	2,847	Hudson 26.	-
22	18.11	A	DM	Nuneaton Borough	W	1-0	*902*	Hudson 63.	
23	22.11	H	DM	Dorchester Town	W	2-0	924	Williams 65, Hudson 71.	4
24	29.11	H	**FAT 3Q**	Chelmsford City	L	1-4	1,014	Matthews 90.	-
25	06.12	A	**FAC 2**	Rotherham United	L	0-6	5,883		-
26	13.12	A	DM	Hastings Town	L	2-3	*419*	McNamara 45, 48.	8
27	20.12	H	DM	Forest Green Rovers	D	2-2	814	Hudson 35, Williams 85.	9
28	26.12	A	DM	Rothwell Town	W	2-1	*402*	Williams 52, 65.	-
29	28.12	H	DM	Atherstone United	L	1-4	1,005	Hudson 10.	9
30	01.01	H	DM	Rothwell Town	W	2-0	939	Hoyle 6, Williams 82.	9
31	10.01	A	DM	Halesowen Town	L	1-4	*907*	Williams 90.	10
32	13.01	A	DM	Gresley Rovers	W	4-2	*575*	Hopkins 9, Williams 12, McNamara 52, 90.	10
33	24.01	H	DM	Crawley Town	W	2-0	1,007	McNamara 62, Hopkins 85.	9
34	31.01	H	DM	Ashford Town	W	2-1	893	Skelly 74, Hudson 89.	8
35	07.02	A	DM	Dorchester Town	W	4--3	*676*	Williams 11, Mead 17, Hudson 63, 84.	7
36	14.02	H	DM	Hastings Town	D	1-1	1,014	McNamara 42.	6
37	18.02	A	DM	Sittingbourne	D	2-2	*441*	Cotterill 17, Mead 30.	
38	21.02	H	DM	St Leonards Stamcroft	D	1-1	869	Roberts 82.	6
39	28.02	A	DM	Ashford Town	**W**	**3-0**	*447*	Cotterill 17, Williams 50, Hudson 70.	4
40	07.03	H	DM	Merthyr Tydfil	D	1-1	1,446	McNamara 45 (pen).	5
41	14.03	A	DM	Bromsgrove Rovers	D	1-1	*750*	Paul 84.	5
42	17.03	H	DM	Tamworth	W	2-1	813	Matthews 4, Paul 90.	
43	21.03	A	DM	Worcester City	L	1-3	*907*	Williams 6.	6
44	24.03	A	DM	Cambridge City	L	0-2	*668*		
45	28.03	H	DM	Salisbury City	W	3-1	731	Williams 12 (pen), Hudson 43, Norfolk 67.	3
46	04.04	A	DM	Crawley Town	L	0-2	*911*		6
47	11.04	H	DM	Sittingbourne	L	0-1	739		7
48	13.04	A	DM	Tamworth	L	0-3	*478*		7
49	18.04	H	DM	Gloucester City	L	1-2	483	McNamara 85.	7
50	25.04	A	DM	Bath City	L	0-2	*719*		8
51	02.05	H	DM	Worcester City	D	2-2	690	Hudson 1, McNamara 42.	8

PLAYING SQUAD 1998

Goalkeepers: James Hollman (Ipswich T), Duncan Roberts (Mansfield T), Steve Lewis (Cambridge U).

Defenders: Tony Spearing (Peterborough U, Plymouth A, Leicester C, Norwich C), Colin Hoyle (Notts Co, Bradford C, Barnsley, Arsenal), Leo Cotterell (Rushden & D,AFC Bournemouth, Ipswich T), Matthew Wright (Torquay U, Great Yarmouth T).

Midfielders: Jason Pascoe (Northampton T, Boston U, Ashfield U, Worksop T, Sutton T, OakhamU), Simon Mead (Warboys T), Lee Norfolk (Ipswich T), Julian Delicata (Tottenham H), Glyn Roberts (Chelmsford C, Rotherham U, Norwich C).

Forwards: Dave Puttnam * (Gresley R, Barry T, Gresley R, Swansea C, Gillingham, LincolnC, Leicester C, Leicester U).

PROGRAMME DETAILS:
Pages: 32 **Price:** £1.00
Editor: Anthony Hughes (01685 359921)

MERTHYR TYDFIL

Colours: White & black/black/black
Change colours: All amber
Midweek home matchday: Tuesday
Reserves' League: None

Formed: 1945
Nickname: The Martyrs
Sponsors: Hoover PLC

Chairman: Ken Gunter **Football Secretary:** Peter Hunt.
Joint Presidents: The Archbishop of Cardiff, His Grace John Aloysious Ward, The Lord Bishop of Llandaff, The Right Rev. Roy Davies.
Manager: Colin Addison **Physio:** Ken Davey
Press Officer: Anthony Hughes **Commercial Manager:** Howard King.

GROUND Address: Penndarren Park, Merthyr Tydfil, Mid Glamorgan
Tel: 01685 384102.
Directions: South A470 Express Way to Merthyr through Town Centre to Pontmorlais (traffic lights) turn left then first right, first right at Catholic Church and right again into Park Terrace to ground. North Heads of the Valley road to Town Centre, to Pontmorlais (traffic lights) turn right, then as above.
Capacity: 10,000 **Seats:** 1,500 **Cover:** 5,000. **Floodlights:** Yes
Clubhouse: Open Monday to Sunday 6.30 to 11.00pm. Two club cafes open on match days for hot food.
Club Shop: Sells replica kits, club souvenirs & programmes. Contact Mel Jenkins 01443 692336.

PREVIOUS - **Leagues:** Southern League, Beazer Homes (Mid. Div.), Beazer Homes (Prem. Div.), G M Conference.

CLUB RECORDS - **Attendance:** 21,000 v Reading FA Cup 2nd Rnd 1949/50 **Win:** 11-0 **Defeat:** 9-2
Transfer fee paid: £ 10,000 to Cardiff City for Robbie James 1992
Transfer fee received: £12,000 for Ray Pratt from Exeter City 1981).

BEST SEASON - **FA Trophy:** 3rd Rd v Northwich Vic 95-96

HONOURS - Welsh FA Cup 48-49, 50-51, 86-87; Southern League 47-48, 49-50, 50-51, 51-52, 53-54; Southern League (Midland) 87-88; Southern League (Premier) 88-89; Southern League Cup 47-48, 50-51.

Past players who progressed to the Football League: Syd Howarth (Aston Villa), Cyril Beech, Gilbert Beech, Bill Hullet, Ken Tucker (Cardiff City), Nick Deacy (Hereford United), Gordon Davies (Fulham), Ray Pratt (Exeter City), Peter Jones, Paul Giles (Newport County).

L-R - Back Row: Colin Loss, Tony Rees(now EbbwVale), Dean Clarke, Ian French, Neil O'Brien, Gary Wager, Shaun Chapple, David Barnhouse, Anthony Rivett, Chris Summers, Colin Addison (manager). Front: Anthony Jenkins, Ian Mitchell, Cohen Griffiths, Gareth Abraham, Roger Gibbins, Roy Jordan, Terry Green, Darren Poretta.

MERTHYR TYDFIL - Match Facts 97-98

FAWIC - FAW Invitation Cup

Match No.	Date	Venue H / A	Comp.	Opponents	Result & Score		Att.	Goalscorers	League Position
1	16.08	A	DM	Nuneaton Borough	W	1-0	1,203	Bowen 55.	
2	19.08	H	DM	Salisbury City	D	0-0	619		
3	23.08	H	DM	Tamworth	W	3-1	6687	**Bowen 3** (6, 30, 71 (pen)).	2
4	25.08	A	DM	Gloucester City	L	0-1	823		5
5	30.08	A	DM	Sittingbourne	W	2-1	462	Simmons 47, 90 (pen).	4
6	02.09	H	DM	Bath City	L	2-3	671	Rees 14, Mitchell 87.	
7	07.09	A	DM	Cambridge City	W	3-0	410	Summers 31, Rees 67, Griffiths 77.	4
8	13.09	H	**FAC 1Q**	Brockenhurst	W	7-2	516	Griffiths 31, Rees 45, 77, Rivers 48, Summers 56, Mitchell 68, 88.	-
9	20.09	H	DM	Rothwell Town	D	2-2	537	French 63, Griffiths 65.	5
10	24.09	A	DM	Salisbury City	W	5-2	324	Abrahams 7, Mitchell 29, 35, Griffiths 54, Bowen 58.	3
11	27.09	H	**FAC 2Q**	Cheltenham Town	L	0-2	830		-
12	04.10	H	DM	Halesowen Town	W	2-1	615	O'Brien 26, Griffiths 38.	3
13	09.10	H	**DMC**	Forest Green Rovers	D	0-0	311		-
14	11.10	A	DM	Hastings Town	W	1-0	392	Barnhouse 90.	2
15	14.10	H	DM	Gloucester City	W	1-0	635	Griffiths 84.	2
16	18.10	H	DM	King's Lynn	**W**	**4-0**	743	Abrahams 52, Porteta 74, Mitchell 79, Bowen 80.	1
17	25.10	A	DM	Atherstone United	W	2-0	302	Mitchell 45, Griffiths 58.	1
18	28.10	A	**DMC**	Forest Green Rovers	L	1-3	309	Rees 7.	-
19	01.11	A	DM	St Leonards Stamcroft	D	0-0	489		1
20	08.11	H	DM	Nuneaton Borough	W	1-0	869	Mitchell 64 (pen).	1
21	11.11	H	**FAWIC**	Newtown	L	1-2	554	Mitchell 77.	-
22	22.11	H	DM	Ashford Town	W	3-0	715	Griffiths 60, Chapple 80, Mitchell 90.	1
23	25.11	A	**FAWIC**	Wrexham	L	1-5		Mitchell 25.	-
24	29.11	H	**FAT 3Q**	Cambridge City	D	2-2	469	Jenkins 7, 70.	-
25	02.12	A	**FAT 3Q R**	Cambridge City	L	*3-6	200	Jenkins 14, 30, Griffiths 105.	-
26	06.12	H	DM	Sittingbourne	D	0-0	527		1
27	09.12	A	**FAWIC**	Newtown	D	!2-2	100	Clarke 34, O'Brien 76.	-
28	13.12	A	DM	Crawley Town	W	2-1	1,370	Mitchell 37, 65.	1
29	16.12	H	**FAWIC**	Cardiff City	D	0-0	542		-
30	20.12	H	DM	Gresley Rovers	W	3-0	602	O'Brien 10, Abrahams 61, Rees 90.	1
31	26.12	A	DM	Bath City	**L**	**0-3**	1,280		
32	27.12	H	DM	Worcester City	W	2-1	1,089	Abrahams 75, Summers 90.	1
33	10.01	A	DM	Bromsgrove Rovers	D	0-0	731		1
34	17.01	H	DM	Hastings Town	W	4-2	648	Barnhouse 1, Mitchell 22, 87, Williams 24.	1
35	20.01	H	**FAWIC**	Wrexham	L	0-2	473		-
36	07.02	A	DM	Tamworth	W	4-2	715	Wigley 10, 84, Griffith 20, Chappel 35.	2
37	09.02	H	**FAWIC**	Cardiff City	L	0-1	1,055		-
38	114.02	H	DM	Atherstone United	D	1-1	675	Abraham 65.	2
39	21.02	A	DM	Gresley Rovers	L	0-2	601		2
40	24.02	H	DM	Burton Albion	W	2-1	661	Summers 6, Clark 40.	2
41	28.02	H	DM	Cambridge City	W	3-1	676	Mitchell 33 (pen), 90, Loss 89.	2
42	07.03	A	DM	King's Lynn	D	1-1	1,446	Summers 56.	2
43	14.03	H	DM	St Leonards Stamcroft	**W**	**4-0**	697	Mitchell 9, Summers 26, 89, Porretta 66.	1
44	17.03	H	DM	Dorchester Town	**W**	**4-0**	843	Summers 6, Abrahams 15, Mitchell 72, 81.	1
45	21.03	A	DM	Rothwell Town	D	1-1	288	Evans 18.	1
46	28.03	H	DM	Crawley Town	W	2-1	727	Mitchell 71 (pen), 73.	1
47	04.04	A	DM	Worcester City	D	1-1	1,301	Mitchell 49.	1
48	07.04	H	**FAWIC SF 1**	Cardiff City	L	0-4	1,302		-
49	11.04	A	DM	Dorchester Town	D	1-1	885	Jenkins 59.	2
50	13.04	H	DM	Forest Green Rovers	**W**	**4-0**	1,930	O'Brien 1, Evans 75, Jenkins 76, Mitchell 84 (pen).	1
51	18.04	A	DM	Burton Albion	L	0-3	1,001		2
52	21.04	A	**FAWIC SF 2**	Cardiff City	L	1-3	1,031	Mitchell 16.	-
53	25.04	H	DM	Bromsgrove Rovers	W	4-2	1,005	Griffiths 37, 40, Evans 44, Mitchell 66.	1
54	29.04	A	DM	Forest Green Rovers	L	1-3	2,891	Mitchell 89.	2
55	02.05	A	DM	Ashford Town	D	2-2	448	Evans 6, Mitchell 63.	2

PLAYING SQUAD 1998

Goalkeepers: Gary Wager (Bridgend T)

Defenders: Gareth Abrahams (Hereford U, Cardiff C), Neil O'Brien (Inter Cardiff,Aberystwyth T, Llanelli), David Barnhouse (Swansea C), Anthony Rivett (Westfields), Terry Green (Pegasus Juniors)

Midfielders: Ian Mitchell (Chesham U, Hereford U, Merthyr Tydfil, Newport Co), Shaun Chapple (Swansea C), Roger Gibbins (Cwmbran T, Cardiff C, Torquay U, NewportCo, Swansea C, Cardiff C, Cambridge U, New England Tea Men (USA), Norwich C,Oxford U, Tottenham H), Colin Loss (Ebbw Vale, Merthyr Tydfil, Barry T,Merthyr Tydfil, Bristol C, Gresley R, Derby Co, Norwich C), Greg Milsom (Cardiff C), Darren Porretta (Newport AFC, Cardiff Corries)

Forwards: Tony Rees (WBA, Grimsby T, Barnsley, Birmingham C, Aston Villa), Cohen Griffiths (Inter-Cable Tel, Barry T, Cardiff C, Kettering T, Leicester U), Chris Summers (Ton Pentre, Inter Cardiff, Barry T, Hereford U, Cardiff C), Paul Evans (Newport AFC, Ebbw Vale, Merthyr Tydfil, Ton Pentre, MerthyrTydfil, Barry T, Auckland (NZ), Barry T, Bridgend T, Newport Co, Brecon Corries, Ferndale Ath, Barry T, Cardiff C), Richard Evans (Worcester C,Trowbridge T, Yeovil T, Bristol R, Weymouth), Anthony Jenkins (Inter-CableTel, Merthyr Tydfil, Chesham U).

NUNEATON BOROUGH

Colours: All blue & white **Formed:** 1937
Change colours: All yellow & green **Nickname:** The Boro
Midweek matchday: Tuesday, 7.45pm **Sponsors:** Pailton Engineering
Reserves' League: Ansells Midland Comb.

Chairman: Howard Kerry
Secretary: Peter Humphreys, 29 Amington Rd, Shirley, Solihull, West Mids B90 2RF (0121 745 2031). **Manager:** Brendan Phillips
Press Officer: Gordon Chislett (01203 222106)
1st Team Coach: Steve Burr **Physio:** Richie Norman
Commercial Manager: Phil Wright (01203 385738)

GROUND Address: Manor Park, Beaumont Road, Nuneaton, Warks CV11 5HD (01203 342690/385738. Fax: 342690).
Directions: A444 to Nuneaton from M6 junction 3, 2nd exit at 1st roundabout, 2nd exit at 2nd r'about, left at 3rd r'bout, 2nd right into Greenmoor Rd, turn right at the end, grd on left. Parking 100 cars Manor Park Schl, Beaumont Rd, 50p each. Grd 1 mile Nuneaton Trent Valley (BR).
Capacity: 6,500 **Cover:** 3,500 **Seats:** 520 **Floodlights:** Yes
Clubhouse: Open every evening, weekend lunchtimes and matchdays
Club Shop: Sells souvenirs, progs etc. Contact Andy Pace (01203 374043).

PROGRAMME DETAILS:
Pages: 40 **Price:** £1
Editor: Editorial team (contact Comm Mgr

PREVIOUS - **Leagues:** Central Amateur 37-38/ B'ham Comb 38-52/ West Mids (B'ham) 52-58/ Southern 58-79 81-82/ GM Conference (Alliance Premier & Gola) 79-81 82-87.

CLUB RECORDS - **Attendance:** 22,114 v Rotherham, FA Cup 3rd Rd 1967 **Transfer fee paid:** £9,500 for Richard Dixey (Scarborough, 1981) **Transfer fee received:** £60,000 for D Bullock (Huddersfield Tn 93) **Win:** 11-1 (45-46 & 55-56) **Defeat:** 1-8 (55-56 & 68-69). **Goalscorer:** Paul Culpin 201 (Career), 55 (Season - 92/93) **Career Appearances:** Alan Jones 545 (62-74)

BEST SEASON - **FA Cup:** 3rd Rd rep. 66-67. 1st Rd 19 times. **FA Trophy:** Qtr final 76-77(rep), 79-80, 86-87.

HONOURS - Alliance Prem Lge R-up(2) 83-85; Southern Lg R-up 66-67 74-75, Sth Lg Cup Win 95-96, Midland Div 81-82 92-93, Champ 95-96, Lg Cup R-up 62-63, Merit Cup 92-93(jt); Birmingham Lg 55-56 (Nth Div 54-55); Birmingham Comb. R-up 3; Birmingham Snr Cup 6, R-up 3

Players progressing to Football League: A Morton (Fulham 70), R Edwards Port Vale 72), K Stephens (Luton 78), T Peake (Lincoln 79), P Sugrue (Man City 80), M Shotton & T Smithers (Oxford 80), D Thomas (Wimbledon 81), P Richardson (Derby 84), P Culpin (Coventry 85), R Hill/T Morley/E McGoldrick/A Harris (Northampton 85/86), D Bullock (Huddersfield 93).

97-98 Captain: David Crowley **Top Scorer:** Rob Straw **P.o.Y.:** David Crowley

Back Row (L-R); Jon Symonds, Richard Quailey, Jon Hassell, Paul Hayward, Ian King, Kevin Wilkin, Richie Norman (Physio). Middle Row; Derek Brown, Gary Statham, Brendan Phillips (Mgr), Howard Kerry (Chr), Colin Welsh (Asst Mgr), Rob Straw, Tyron Street. Front Row; Lee Everitt, Warren Donald, David Crowley, Richard Bailey, Carl Lawrence.

NUNEATON BOROUGH - Match Facts 97-98

BSC - Birmingham Sen. Cup

Match No.	Date	Venue H / A	Comp.	Opponents	Result & Score		Att.	Goalscorers	League Position
1	16.08	H	DM	Merthyr Tydfil	L	0-1	1,203		
2	19.08	A	DM	Rothwell Town	W	6-1	*657*	King 7, Straw 38, 53, **Wilkin 3** (12, 59, 88).	
3	23.08	A	DM	Hastings Town	W	4-2	*467*	Wilkin 41, King 45, Drewitt 61, Straw 88.	3
4	25.08	H	DM	Gresley Rovers	**W**	**6-0**	1,605	Street 8, Bailey 14, Drewitt 38(pen), 48, King 67, Straw 75.	2
5	30.08	H	DM	Crawley Town	W	4-2	1,534	Brown 12, King 52, 85, Street 62.	2
6	02.09	A	DM	King's Lynn	D	1-1	*1,180*	Drewitt 79.	
7	08.09	H	DM	Bath City	D	3-3	1,603	Street 34, Straw 45, 79.	2
8	13.09	A	**FAC 1Q**	Bury Town	W	2-1	*502*	Straw 12 (pen), Everitt.	-
9	20.09	A	DM	Ashford Town	L	1-2	*378*	Street 23.	4
10	27.09	A	**FAC 2Q**	Bedworth United	D	1-1	*2,100*	Williams 5.	-
11	30.09	H	**FAC 2Q R**	Bedworth United	W	6-0	1,960	Street 2, Straw, Crawley, Bailey, Drewitt.	-
12	04.10	A	DM	St Leonards Stamcroft	W	5-1	*501*	Bailey 14, Straw 24, 52, Statham 57, Donald 80.	6
13	07.10	A	**DMC 1-1**	Bedworth United	D	1-1	*486*	Bailey 20.	-
14	11.10	H	**FAC 3Q**	Stourbridge	W	4-1	1,411	Brown 23, Bailey 45, Straw 54, Street 88.	-
15	14.10	A	DM	Gresley Rovers	W	1-0	*859*	Straw.	-
16	18.10	H	DM	Forest Green Rovers	W	2-1	1,560	Street 5, King 10.	4
17	21.10	A	DM	Tamworth	L	1-2	*1,342*	Bailey 68.	
18	25.10	H	**FAC 4Q**	Emley	L	2-3	1,960	King 14, Williams 29.	-
19	28.10	H	**DMC 1-2**	Bedworth United	L	0-2	568		-
20	01.11	H	DM	Dorchester Town	D	2-2	1,155	Street 31, 42.	5
21	08.11	A	DM	Merthyr Tydfil	L	0-1	*869*		7
22	15.11	H	DM	Salisbury City	W	2-1	1,174	Williams 37, Straw 79 (pen).	7
23	18.11	H	DM	King's Lynn	L	0-1	902		
24	22.11	A	DM	Bath City	**L**	**0-5**	*786*		9
25	29.11	H	**FAT 3Q**	Altrincham	L	0-2	903		-
26	06.12	H	DM	Cambridge City	L	0-1	889		11
27	13.12	A	DM	Forest Green Rovers	L	2-4	*402*	Furnell 10, Bailey 59.	12
28	16.12	H	DM	Gloucester City	W	3-1	526	Bailey 64, Burnell 81, King 87.	
29	20.12	H	DM	Rothwell Town	W	3-0	816	Furnell 67, Thomas 81, 87.	8
30	26.12	A	DM	Atherstone United	D	2-2	*2,101*	Thomas 21, 87 (2 pens).	
31	27.12	H	DM	Sittingbourne	W	3-1	1,009	Peeks 28, Thomas 56, Furnell 66.	8
32	01.01	H	DM	Bromsgrove Rovers	W	2-1	1,376	Statham 63, King 75.	8
33	10.01	H	DM	Tamworth	L	0-2	1,573		8
34	14.01	A	**BSC 2**	Solihull Borough	L	0-3	*120*		-
35	17.01	H	DM	Halesowen Town	W	2-1	1,107	Furnell 67, 90.	6
36	24.01	A	DM	Salisbury City	D	2-2	*371*	Healey 36, Thomas 37.	8
37	26.01	A	DM	Worcester City	L	0-1	*964*		8
38	31.01	H	DM	Hastings Town	W	2-0	940	Furnell 54, King 71.	7
39	07.02	A	DM	Sittingbourne	L	0-1	*447*		8
40	14.02	H	DM	Worcester City	W	2-0	1,091	Thomas 55, 90.	8
41	21.02	A	DM	Halesowen Town	L	0-3	*913*		9
42	28.02	A	DM	Crawley Town	W	2-1	*858*	Thomas 42, King 80.	8
43	14.03	A	DM	Gloucester City	L	0-1	*649*		10
44	21.03	H	DM	Burton Albion	L	0-1	1,115		10
45	28.03	A	DM	Burton Albion	L	0-1	*864*		10
46	04.04	H	DM	St Leonards Stamcroft	D	1-1	652	Christie 63.	10
47	11.04	A	DM	Bromsgrove Rovers	L	1-3	*693*	Christie 10.	10
48	13.04	H	DM	Atherstone United	L	0-1	1,113		11
49	18.04	A	DM	Dorchester Town	L	1-3	*600*	Thomas 14.	11
50	25.04	H	DM	Ashford Town	W	2-1	610	OG (Ross) 5, Yates 24.	11
51	02.05	A	DM	Cambridge City	L	0-2	*491*		12

PLAYING SQUAD 1998

Goalkeepers: Richard Williams * (Atherstone U, Hednesford T, Atherstone U, Birmingham C), Robert Wood (Bedworth U)

Defenders: Gary Statham (VS Rugby, Hinckley T, Shepshed Alb, Hinckley FC, Barlestone St.Giles, Barwell), Barry Williams (Redditch U, Ely C, Alvechurch), Leigh Everitt (Evesham U, Atherstone U, Nuneaton B), Kevin Elvin (RC Warwick,Nuneaton B), Danny Green (Youth), John Woodhouse (Youth)

Midfielders: Dave Crowley (Stafford R, Bedworth U, Coventry C), Paul White (Birmingham C), Brett Healy (Coventry C), Matthew Dyer (Youth).

Forwards: Kevin Wilkin (Rushden & D, Northampton T, Cambridge C, Histon), Ian Drewitt (Stafford R, Merthyr Tydfil, Weymouth, Ton Pentre, Ferndale Ath), Rob Straw (Bedworth U, Tamworth, Bedworth U, Nuneaton B, Stafford R, Derby Co), Malcolm Christie (Local football), Anton Thomas (Worcester C, Kettering T, Corby T,Leicester U, Bedworth U, Northampton T), Shaun Wray * (Stafford R, ShrewsburyT).

PROGRAMME DETAILS:
Pages: 48 **Price:** 90p
Editor: Mark Southon
(01162 774877)

ROTHWELL TOWN

Colours: Blue, red + white trim/blue/blue **Founded:** 1895
Change Colours: Red, white trim/red/red **Nickname:** The Bones
Midweek matchday: Tuesday **Sponsors:** Forester Health
Newsline: 0930 555 829.
Reserve Team's League: United Counties Lge Res Div
Local Press: Northants Evening Telegraph, Chronicle & Echo, Herald & Post.
Local Radio: BBC Radio Northants, KCBC.

Chairman: Stuart Andrews **Vice-Chairman:** Jeremy Freestone
President: Ken Cheney
Secretary: Roger Barratt, 18 Norton Street, Rothwell, Northants NN14 2DE (01536 507744).
Press Officer/Comm Mgr: Peter Bradley (01536 710925).
Manager: Jack Murray **Physio:** Graham Simmonds
Asst Manager: Graham Simmonds **Coach:** Kim Davies

GROUND Address: Cecil Street, Rothwell, Northants NN14 2EZ (01536 710694). **Directions:** A14/A6 to Rothwell. At town centre roundabout turn into Bridge Street (right if northbound, left if southbound), take 3rd left into Tresham Street, ground is at top on left. Three miles from Kettering (BR); Rothwell is served by Kettering to Market Harborough buses.
Capacity: 3,500 **Seats:** 264 **Cover:** 1,264 **Floodlights:** Yes
Clubhouse: Rowellian Social Club, open every evening and weekend lunchtimes. Crisps and rolls available on matchdays (hot food and drinks available in ground). 'Top of the Town Ballroom', lounge seats 200.
Club Shop: Yes **Metal Badges:** Yes

PREVIOUS - **Leagues:** Northants 1896-1911 21-33, Kettering Amateur 11-21 33-48, Leics. Senior 48-50, United Counties 50-56 61-94, Central Alliance 56-61. **Grounds:** Harrington Rd, Castle Hill. **Name:** Rothwell Town Swifts.

CLUB RECORDS - **Attendance:** 2,508 v Irthlingborough Diamonds, United Counties League 1971.
Win: 17-0 v Stamford, FA Cup Preliminary Round replay 1927.
Defeat: 1-10 v Coalville Town, Leicestershire Sen Lge 1949.
Transfer fee paid: Undisclosed for Andy Wright (Aylesbury 1992).
Transfer fee received: Undisclosed for Matty Watts (Charlton 1990).

BEST SEASON - **FA Cup:** Second Qualifying Round. **FA Trophy:** Second Round Proper 94-95. **FA Vase:** Fifth Round 92-93 (1-2 v Bridlington Town).

HONOURS - United Counties Lg 92-93 94-95 (R-up 69-70 70-71 87-88 89-90 90-91, KO Cup 55-56 70-71 71-72 91-92 92-93 (R-up 77-78 79-80 82-83), Div 2 52-53 53-54, Div 2 Cup 52-53 53-54, Benevolent Cup 92-93 94-95 (R-up 89-90 90-91)), Northants Lg 1899-1900 (R-up 1895-96 96-97 97-98), Northants Snr Cup 1899-1900 23-24 59-60 88-89 95-96 (R-up 24-25 71-72 87-88), Dr Martens Mid Div R-up 96-97.

Players progressing to Football League: Lee Glover (Nottingham Forest) 1987, Matty Watts (Charlton Ath.) 1990.

Rothwell Town FC

ROTHWELL TOWN - Match Facts 1997-98

DCC - Daventry Charity Cup

Match No	Date	Venue H / A	Comp	Opponents	Result & Score		Att	Goalscorers	League Position
1	16.08	A	DM	Bath City	D	1-1	711	McGuire 60.	
2	19.08	H	DM	Nuneaton Borough	**L**	**1-6**	657	Kirkup 65.	
3	23.08	H	DM	Forest Green Rovers	L	2-5	224	McGuire 3, Warner 42.	21
4	25.08	A	DM	Tamworth	D	1-1	801	Kirkup 54.	21
5	30.08	A	DM	Gloucester City	W	1-0	582	Bullimore 61.	16
6	02.09	H	DM	Atherstone United	D	2-2	287	Warner 30 (pen), 52.	18
7	09.09	H	DM	Bromsgrove Rovers	W	2-0	253	Orton 7, Kirkup 23.	12
8	13.09	H	**FAC 1Q**	Corby Town	W	2-1	209	Coe 15, 63.	-
9	20.09	A	DM	Merthyr Tydfil	D	2-2	537	Kirkup 33, Lord 90.	15
10	23.09	A	DM	Cambridge city	D	3-3	310	McGuire 23, 28, Kirkup 36.	14
11	27.09	H	**FAC 2Q**	Halesowen Town	D	1-1	350	McGuire 42.	-
12	30.09	A	**FAC 2Q R**	Halesowen Town	L	*1-4	489	Kirkup 34. A.E.T.	-
13	04.10	H	DM	Worcester City	W	2-1	246	Foley 67, McGuire 90.	13
14	08.10	A	**DMC 1-1**	Raunds Town	L	1-6	144	Lord 41.	-
15	11.10	A	DM	Gresley Rovers	L	2-5	496	Kirkup 21, McGuire 51.	14
16	14.10	H	DM	Tamworth	W	1-0	314	Kirkup 29.	
17	18.10	A	**FAT 1Q**	Evesham United	W	2-1	89	Beazeley 2, Lord 40.	-
18	25.10	A	DM	Hastings Town	L	1-3	441	Beazeley 49.	12
19	28.10	H	**DMC 1-2**	Raunds Town	L	0-3	104		-
20	01.11	H	DM	Gloucester City	D	1-1	252	Lord 13.	14
21	08.11	A	**FAT 2Q**	Romford	L	1-5	257	Coe 49.	-
22	15.11	A	DM	Crawley Town	D	2-2	1,104	McGuire 45, Beazeley 57.	16
23	18.11	A	DM	Atherstone United	L	1-3	171	Foley 15.	
24	22.11	H	DM	St Leonards Stamcroft	D	1-1	204	McGuire 62.	16
25	29.11	A	DM	Worcester City	L	0-3	540		17
26	06.12	H	DM	Bath City	L	1-4	224		18
27	13.12	H	DM	Halesowen Town	D	1-1	271	Marshall 55.	18
28	20.12	A	DM	Nuneaton Borough	L	0-3	816		18
29	26.12	H	DM	King's Lynn	L	1-2	402	McGuire 73.	
30	27.12	A	DM	Ashford Town	D	1-1	420	Bullimore 34.	18
31	01.01	A	DM	King's Lynn	L	0-2	939		19
32	10.01	H	DM	Crawley Town	L	1-2	283	Beazeley 73.	19
33	17.01	A	DM	Forest Green Rovers	L	0-2	365		19
34	24.01	H	DM	Burton Albion	W	1-0	327	Moffat 61.	19
35	31.01	A	DM	St Leonards Stamcroft	L	2-3	426	OG (Flanagan) 19, Foley 81 (pen)	19
36	03.02	H	**DCC 3**	Northampton Spencer	W	3-1	90	Jowett 4, Orton 44, 70.	-
37	07.02	A	DM	Halesowen Town	W	3-1	739	Bullimore 65, Finlay 83, 85.	19
38	14.02	H	DM	Dorchester Town	D	0-0	230		19
39	21.02	A	DM	Bromsgrove Rovers	W	2-0	567	Kirkup 7, 75.	17
40	28.02	H	DM	Salisbury City	D	2-2	202	Moffatt 21 (pen), Jowett 80.	17
41	04.03	A	DM	Sittingbourne	D	0-0	277		17
42	10.03	H	DM	Cambridge City	W	2-1	236	Foley 14, Kirkup 23.	
43	21.03	H	DM	Merthyr Tydfil	D	1-1	288	Jowett 23.	17
44	28.03	A	DM	Dorchester Town	W	3-2	581	Finlay 29, Bullimore 36, Jowett 63.	17
45	04.04	H	DM	Ashford Town	L	1-2	225	Bullimore 82.	18
46	11.04	A	DM	Burton Albion	L	0-3	628		17
47	13.04	H	DM	Gresley Rovers	W	1-0	253	Foley 43.	17
48	18.04	H	DM	Hastings Town	**W**	**5-1**	221	Spencer 17, Finlay 39, Bullimore 69, Kirkup 72, Jowett 88.	16
49	29.04	A	DM	Salisbury City	D	0-0	430		16
50	02.05	H	DM	Sittingbourne	D	1-1	372	Lord 70.	16

PLAYING SQUAD 1998

Goalkeepers: John Parsons (Sutton Coldfield T, Bilston T, Halesowen T, Rocester, Tamworth,Sutton Coldfield T, Willenhall T)

Defenders: Derek Brown (Nuneaton B, Rothwell T, Corby T, Buckingham T, Newport PagnellT), Dean Foley (S & L Corby, Desborough T, Raunds T, Corby T, Leicester C), Gary Torrance (Desborough T, Raunds T, Stamford, Desborough T, Corby T,Kettering T, Leicester C), Glyn Davies (Nuneaton B, Rothwell T), Andy Bullimore (Grantham T, Melton T), Dougie Keast (Burton Alb, Rushden & D,Corby T, Kettering T, Shepshed Chart, Hibernian).

Midfielders: Gary Pick (Shepshed Dynamo, Brackley T, Kettering T, Newport AFC, CheltenhamT, Worcester C, Cambridge U, Hereford U, Stoke C, Leicester U), Steve Coates (Stoke C, Leicester U), Ben Lord (Highan T, Irthlingborough D), Marc Orton (Leicester U, Rothwell T, Leicester U, Grimsby T), Dave Beazley (S & L Corby,Corby T, Barrow T, S & L Corby, Cottingham T, Corby T, Wellingborough T,Rushden T)

Forwards: Andy Kirkup (Gloucester C, Rushden & D, Wellingborough T, Rushden T, Corby T,Rushden T), Wayne Spencer (Corby T, Hinckley U, King's Lynn, Corby T,Buckingham T, Milton Keynes C, Dunstable, Leighton T), Richard Jowatt (Nuneaton B, Ilkeston T, Attenborough, Sandiacre T, Stanton Ilkeston, GPTPlessey), Danny Finlay (Sutton Coldfield T, Evesham U, Ford Sports, RCWarwick, Atherstone U, VS Rugby), Paul Wagstaff (VS Rugby, Raunds T,Northampton T).

SALISBURY CITY

Colours: White/black/white **Formed:** 1947
Change colours: All Blue. **Nickname:** The Whites
Midweek matchday: Wednesday **Sponsors:** Tintometer Glass
Reserve Team's League: None.
Club Line: 'City Line' 0930 555 864
Local Press: Salisbury Journal, Evening Echo & Sports Echo, Western Daily Press. **Local Radio:** Wiltshire Sound, Spire F.M.

PROGRAMME DETAILS:
Pages: 48 **Price:** £1.20
Editor: Kevin Gover

Chairman: P R McEnhill **Vice-Chairmam:** R Brocksom
Secretary: Sean Gallagher, 1 Tempest Road, Beamont Park, Amesbury, Wilts SP4 7UE (01980 626855 H & Fax).
Press Officer: David Macey (01264 773765)
Youth Dev. Off.: Simon Pickett **Commercial Manager:** Geoff Butler
Manager: Geoff Butler **Physio:** Kim Sturgess/Eric Simpson
GROUND Address: The Raymond McEnhill Stadium, Partridge Way, Old Sarum, Salisbury SP4 6PU. Tel: 01722 333988/326454, Fax 01722 323100.
Directions: The Stadium is situated off the main A345 (Salisbury - Amesbury) road on the northern edge of the city some two miles from the City centre. Continue on this road, turn right onto A338 signed Old Sarum Business Park, Partridge Way & ground on left.
Capacity: 4,000 **Cover:** 3,062 **Seats:** 462 **Floodlights:** Yes
Clubhouse: On ground, open matchdays only. Hot & cold snacks available.
Club Shop: Sells replica shirts, memorabilia, programmes, scarves, metal badges, souvenirs. Contact Commercial Office (01722 326454)

PREVIOUS - **Leagues:** Western 47-68. **Name:** Salisbury FC, 47-92. **Ground:** Hudson Field 47-48, Victoria Park 48-97.

CLUB RECORDS - **Attendance:** 8,902 v Weymouth, Western League 48. **Win:** 9-0 v Westbury United (H), FA Cup 1st Qual. Rd 72. **Defeat:** 0-7 v Minehead, Southern League 1975. **Career Goalscorer:** Royston Watts 180 (59-65). **Career Appearances:** Barry Fitch 713 (63-75). **Transfer fee paid:** £5,750 for Peter Loveridge (Dorchester Town, 90). **Transfer fee received:** £16,000 for Ian Thompson (AFC Bournemouth, 83).

BEST SEASON - **FA Trophy:** 2nd Rd 96-97 (lost to Dorchester Town). **FA Amateur Cup:** 2nd Rd 49-50 (lost to Hendon). **FA Cup:** 2nd Rd 59-60 (lost to Newport County)

HONOURS - Southern Lg Southern Div Champ 94-95, R-up 85-86 92-93; Western Lg 57-58 60-61, R-up 58-59 59-60 61-62 66-67 67-68; Hants Senior Cup 61-62 63-64; Wilts Premier Shield 56-57 59-60 61-62 66-67 67-68 70-71 77-78 78-79 95-96.

Players progressing to Football League: Eric Fountain (Southampton 48), Cyril Smith (Arsenal & Southampton 48), Tony Alexander (Fulham 65), John Evans (Stockport County 67), Graham Moxon (Exeter 75), Eric Welch (Chesterfield 76), Ian Thompson (Bournemouth 83), Trevor Wood (Port Vale, Walsall, Hereford 88), Denny Mundee (B'mouth Brentford, Brighton 88), Matthew Carmichael (Lincoln 90), Shaun Brookes (Barnet & Orient 91), Andrew Dungey (Exeter City 97), Andrew Sargent (Plymouth Argyle 97).

97-98 - Captain: Roger Emms **P.o.Y.:** David Mogg **Top scorer:** Ian Chalk

Back Row (L-R); Geoff Butler (Mgr), Conrad Parrott (Trainer), Sandy Baird (Player/Coach), Lee Webb, Danny Rofe, Simon Browne, Joe McCormack, Paul Gadsby, Gavin Sandrey, Kevin Braybrook, Andy Barham, Matthew Lovell, Dave Wakefield (Jt Res Mgr). Front Row; Gary Fletcher, Reza Sotoudeh, Robbie Harbutt, Matthew Parkin, Ian Chalk, Dave Puckett, Jon Preston, Eric Simpson (Physio).

SALISBURY CITY - Match Facts 1997-98

WPS- Wiltshire Prem. Shield

Match No.	Date	Venue H / A	Comp.	Opponents	Result & Score		Att.	Goalscorers	League Position
1	16.08	H	DM	Gresley Rovers	W	1-0	574	Chalk 82.	
2	19.08	A	DM	MerthyrTydfil	D	0-0	*619*		
3	23.08	A	DM	Cambridge City	L	1-3	*322*	Harbut 84.	15
4	25.08	H	DM	Crawley Town	L	2-6	685	Chalk 17, Browne 38.	18
5	30.08	A	DM	Atherstone United	W	3-0	*221*	Webb 21, Pickett 58, Preston 78.	10
6	03.09	H	DM	Dorchester Town	L	0-3	472		
7	08.08	A	DM	Worcester City	L	0-2	*713*		16
8	13.09	H	**FAC 1Q**	Chard Town	W	3-0	274	Puckett 7, Webb 68, Browne 83.	
9	20.09	A	DM	Sittingbourne	W	3-0	*417*	Sandrey 20, Puckett 49, OG (Smith) 53.	13
10	24.09	H	DM	Merthyr Tydfil	L	2-5	324	Chalk 44, Findlayson 90.	15
11	27.09	H	**FAC 2Q**	Weston-super-Mare	D	2-2	305	Harbut 31, 54.	-
12	29.09	A	**FAC 2Q R**	Weston-super-Mare	D	!2-2	210	Browne 7 (pen), Fletcher 82.	-
13	04.10	H	DM	Tamworth	W	3-2	347	Whale 43, Finlayson 58, Braybrook 85.	15
14	08.10	H	**DMC 1-1**	Trowbridge Town	L	2-3	273	Browne 52 (pen), Winter 59.	-
15	11.10	H	**FAC 3Q**	Taunton Town	W	3-0	403	Puckett 15, Chalk 37, Preston 45.	-
16	14.10	A	DM	Ashford Town	D	1-1	*339*	Chalk 39.	
17	18.10	H	DM	Hastings Town	W	2-0	375	Whale 47, Findlayson 78.	10
18	25.10	A	**FAC 4Q**	King's Lynn	L	0-5	1,356		-
19	29.10	A	**DMC 1-2**	Trowbridge Town	W	4-3	141	OG (Bird) 48, Harbut 75, Puckett 80, 87.	-
20	01.11	H	DM	King's Lynn	L	2-3	408	Holmes 14, Braybrook 31.	15
21	08.11	H	DM	Burton Albion	L	0-2	301		17
22	15.11	A	DM	Nuneaton Borough	L	1-2	*1,174*	Houseley 30.	18
23	22.11	H	DM	Worcester City	D	1-1	280	Holmes 10.	17
24	25.11	A	DM	Halesowen Town	L	1-4	*447*	Chalk	
25	27.11	A	**FAT 3Q**	Berkhamsted Town	L	1-2	112	Chalk 56.	-
26	02.12	A	DM	Gloucester City	D	1-1	*328*	Bartlett 86.	
27	06.12	H	DM	Ashford Town	D	0-0	315		17
28	10.12	H	**DMC 2**	Bashley	L	1-6	137	Harbut 79.	-
29	13.12	A	DM	Bromsgrove Rovers	D	2-2	*369*	Puckett 55, Houseley 76.	17
30	20.12	H	DM	Sittingbourne	**W**	**4-0**	221	Emms 9, Preston 15, Browne 34, 72.	16
31	26.12	A	DM	Dorchester Town	L	0-1	*1,088*		
32	27.12	H	DM	St Leonards Stamcroft	W	2-0	413	Puckett 8, Whale 52.	16
33	01.01	H	DM	Forest Green Rovers	L	0-2	506		
34	03.01	A	DM	Crawley Town	L	0-1	*1,314*		16
35	14.01	A	**WPS 2**	Warminster Town	W	6-0	97	Chalk 17, 75, Puckett 37, Holmes 41, Sotoudeh 65, 90.	-
36	17.01	A	DM	St Leonards Stamcroft	L	2-6	*436*	Bright 37, Chalk 38.	16
37	24.01	H	DM	Nuneaton Borough	D	2-2	371	Bright 25, Braybrook 40.	17
38	27.01	A	DM	Bath City	**L**	**0-5**	*513*		
39	31.01	H	DM	Halesowen Town	W	1-0	306	Chalk 86.	16
40	07.02	A	DM	Hastings Town	L	0-2	*446*		17
41	14.02	H	DM	Cambridge City	D	1-1	246	Whale 48.	17
42	28.02	A	DM	Rothwell Town	D	2-2	*202*	Bright 19, Holmes 25.	16
43	07.03	H	DM	Bath City	W	1-0	403	Harbutt 81.	16
44	11.03	H	**WPS S-F**	Trowbridge Town	W	2-1			
45	14.03	A	DM	Tamworth	D	1-1	*453*	Bright 6.	16
46	21.03	H	DM	Atherstone United	W	2-1	294	Chalk 41, Bright 59.	16
47	28.03	A	DM	King's Lynn	L	0-3	*731*		18
48	04.04	H	DM	Bromsgrove Rovers	W	2-0	343	Bright 26, Chalk 77.	16
49	10.04	A	DM	Forest Green Rovers	L	2-3	*865*	Bright 30, Thompson 61.	
50	13.04	H	DM	Gloucester City	L	2-3	434	Browne 36, Hobson 89.	18
51	18.04	A	DM	Gresley Rovers	D	1-1	*418*	Bright 24.	18
52	29.04	H	DM	Rothwell Town	D	0-0	430		18
53	02.05	H	DM	Burton Albion	W	2-1	751	Thompson 14, Bright 45.	18
54	05.05	N	**WPS Final**	Melksham	D	0-0		A.E.T. Lost 3-5 after penalties.	

PLAYING SQUAD 1998

Goalkeepers: David Mogg (Forest Green R, Bath C, Gloucester C, Cheltenham T, Bath C,Atvidaberg (Swe), Bristol C), Nick Flower (Fareham T, Newport IOW, Bashley,Wimborne T, Bashley, Havant T, Salisbury C, Bashley, Swindon T)

Defenders: Matt Parkin (Bournemouth Sports), Gavin Sandrey (Fareham T, Weymouth,Dorchester T, Weymouth, Swindon T, Weymouth), Roger Emms (Andover, Newbury T,Swindon Ath, Devizes T), Matt Lovell (Cheltenham T, Moss IFK (Nor), AFCBournemouth), Sandy Baird (Bashley, Gosport B, Basingstoke T, Weymouth,Horndean, Fareham T, Horndean, Fareham T)

Midfielders: Danny Rofe (Yate T, Bristol R), Chris Male (Newport IOW, Weymouth,Waterlooville, Stoke C, Portsmouth), Ryan Bushby (Plymouth Argyle), DannyHolmes (Aldershot T, Farnborough T, AFC Bournemouth), Robbie Harbut (Bashley,Southampton), Jon Preston (Bournemouth Sports), Gary Fletcher (Bashley,Wimborne T, Poole T, Wimborne T, Salisbury C, Brockenhurst, Bashley, Newbury T,Basingstoke T, Portals Ath), Tyrone Bowers * (Fareham T, AFC Bournemouth).

Forwards: Ian Chalk (Warminster T, Bemerton Ath, Swindon T, Peterborough U, Wrexham), Leroy Whale (Fareham T, Yeovil T, Enfield, Bashley, Basingstoke T, Rotherham U, Southampton), David Bright (Clevedon T, Mangotsfield U, Clevedon T, PaultonR, Mangotsfield U), Kevin Braybrook (Yeovil T, Portsmouth), Lee Webb (PooleT, Salisbury C, Westbury U, Trowbridge T, Westbury U, Devizes T).

PROGRAMME DETAILS:
Pages: 28 **Price:** £1
Editor: Brian & Theresa Whitehouse

TAMWORTH

Colours: Red/red/black **Formed:** 1933
Change colours: All blue **Sponsors:** Nissan - Polesworth Garage
Midweek home matchday: Tuesday **Nickname:** Lambs or Town
Reserves' League: Midland Comb. Res Div
Local Press: Tamworth Herald, Tamworth Times
Local Radio: Extra AM.

Chairman: Bob Andrews **Vice Chairman:** Tony Reeves
President: Len Gendle.
Secretary: Rod A Hadley, 38 Godolphin, Riverside, Tamworth B79 7UF (01827 66786 & Fax).
Manager: Paul Hendrie **Asst Man.:** Andy Dwyer **Physio:** TBA
Press Officer: Mark Maybury **Commercial Manager:** Steve Shaw

GROUND Address: The Lamb Ground, Kettlebrook, Tamworth, Staffs B77 1AA (01827 65798). **Directions:** Follow the signs for Town Centre / Snowdome, then for Kettlebrook.The entrance to the ground and car parks is in Kettlebrook Road, 50yards from the traffic island by the railway viaduct.
Capacity: 3,410 **Cover:** 1,191 **Seats:** 402 **Floodlights:** Yes
Clubhouse: Club on ground - open matchdays, training nights and tote night (Monday) only.
Club Shop: Sells replica kit, scarves, stickers pens & metal badges.

PREVIOUS - **Leagues:** Birmingham Combination 33-54, West Midlands (initially Birmingham Lg) 54-72 84-88, Southern 72-79 83-84, Northern Premier 79-83. **Grounds:** Jolly Sailor Ground 33-34.

CLUB RECORDS - **Attendance:** 4,920 v Atherstone Tn, Birm Comb 48. **Win:** 14-4 v Holbrook Institute (H), Bass Vase 34. **Defeat:** 0-11 v Solihull (A), Birmingham Comb. 40. **Career Goalscorer:** Graham Jessop 195 **Season Goalscorer:** Percy Vials 64 (36-37) **Career Appearances:** Dave Seedhouse 869 **Transfer fee paid:** £5,000 for Steve Cartwright (Colchester Utd, 88). **Transfer fee received:** £7,500 for Martin Myers (Telford Utd, 90).

BEST SEASON - **FA Cup:** 2nd Rd 69-70 (0-6 at Gillingham). **Trophy:** Qtr Final. **FA Vase:** Winners 88-89

HONOURS - FA Vase 88-89, West Mids Lg 63-64 65-66 71-72 87-88 (R-up(2) 67-69, Div 2 55-56, Lg Cup(5) 64-66 71-72 85-86 87-88 (R-up 70-71)), Birmingham Snr Cup 60-61 65-66 68-69 (R-up 36-37 63-64), Staffs Snr Cup 58-59 63-64 65-66 (R-up 55-56 66-67 70-71), Midland F'lit Cup R-up 71-72 72-73, Camkin Cup 71-72 (R-up 70-71),

Players progressing to Football League: P Hilton (WBA 49), A Godridge (Swansea 50), W Ealing (Doncaster), Higgins (Fulham), P Weir (Cardiff), S Fox (Wrexham), S Cartwright (Colchester 88), S Ryder (Walsall), D Williams (Brentford).

97-98 - Captain: Willie Batchelor **P.o.Y.:** Tim Steele **Top scorer:** Gary Piggott

Back Row (L-R); Paul Hendrie (Mgr), Chris Keogh, Jon Howard, Gary Piggott, Mark Phillips, Tony Rowe, Willie Batchelor, Adrian Baddams, Michael Crawford, Tim Steele, Andy Dwyer (Asst Mgr). Front Row; Derek Bond (Asst Mgr), Lee Wilson, Paul Hunter, Ian Bennett, Gary Smith, Shaun Bedward, Peter Smith (Physio).

TAMWORTH - Match Facts 1997-98

BSC - Birmingham Sen. Cup
SSC - Staffs Senior Cup

Match No.	Date	Venue H / A	Comp.	Opponents	Result & Score	Att.	Goalscorers	League Position
1	16.08	H	DM	Dorchester Town	W 3-0	863	Howard 35, Piggott 59, Baddams 86.	
2	19.08	A	DM	Cambridge City	D 2-2	*379*	Wilson 36, Baddams 77.	
3	23.08	A	DM	Merthyr Tydfil	L 1-3	*687*	Shaw 88.	
4	25.08	H	DM	Rothwell Town	D 1-1	801	Bennett 29.	10
5	30.08	A	DM	Hastings Town	D 2-2	*537*	Hunter 21, Piggott 67.	12
6	02.09	H	**DMC** P-1	Gresley Rovers	W 4-3	626	Hunter 5, Foy 35, Wilson 81, Baddams 90.	-
7	05.09	H	DM	Gloucester City	L 1-3	730	Howard 7.	17
8	09.09	A	**DMC** P-1	Gresley Rovers	D 2-2	666	Shaw 37, Hunter 53.	-
9	13.09	H	**FAC** 1Q	Bromsgrove Rovers	L 1-2	725	Wilson 58.	-
10	20.09	A	DM	Crrawley Town	L 2-3	*1,281*	Baddams 39 (pen), Piggott 71.	19
11	23.09	H	DM	Bromsgrove Rovers	L 2-4	631	Howard 52, Batchelor 61.	
12	04.10	A	DM	Salisbury City	L 2-3	*347*	Burchell 34, Batchelor 38.	19
13	07.10	H	**DMC** 1-1	Burton Albion	L 0-2	520		-
14	11.10	H	DM	Ashford Town	**W 4-0**	519	Smith 29, 49, Hunter 68, Wilson 89.	17
15	14.10	A	DM	Rothwell Town	L 0-1	*314*		
16	18.10	H	**FAT** 1Q	Congleton Town	W 5-1	489	Baddams 36, Smith 40, Piggott 49, 85, Hunter 89.	-
17	21.10	H	DM	Nuneaton Borough	W 2-1	1,242	Gray 28, Piggott 84.	17
18	25.10	H	DM	Crawley Town	W 2-1	615	Smith 25, 82.	16
19	01.11	H	DM	Cambridge City	W 4-1	670	Piggott 24, 67, Smith 59, Bennett 85.	13
20	04.11	A	**DMC** 1-2	Burton Albion	D 1-1	364	OG (Benton) 41.	-
21	08.11	H	**FAT** 2Q	Moor Green	W 4-3	602	Howard 51, Foy 79, Smith 84, 86.	-
22	15.11	A	DM	Burton Albion	D 1-1	*1,012*	Hunter 47.	14
23	18.11	H	DM	Gresley Rovers	W 6-3	710	Piggott 16, 45, Hunter 44, Smith 38, Bennett 87.	
24	22.11	H	DM	Halesowen Town	L 0-2	909		14
25	25.11	H	**SSC** 1	Stafford Rangers	W *7-2	459	**Piggott 3** (50, 77, 95), Baddams 105, 110, Whitehead 116, Hunter 118.	
26	29.10	H	**FAT** 3Q	Lancaster City	L 0-1	618		-
27	06.12	H	DM	Hastings Town	W 1-0	492	Adams 26 (pen).	12
28	09.12	A	**BSC** 2	Wednesfield	W 3-0	78	Wilson 34, Bennett 48, Piggott 82.	-
29	13.12	A	DM	Sittingbourne	W 1-0	*459*	Smith 90.	11
30	20.12	H	DM	Bath City	L 1-2	647	Smith 89.	12
31	26.12	A	DM	Worcester City	L 0-2	1,819		13
32	01.01	H	DM	Atherstone United	L 0-2	1,410		15
33	03.01	A	DM	Bromsgrove Rovers	L 0-1	*827*		15
34	10.01	A	DM	Nuneaton Borough	W 2-0	*1,573*	Hunter 58, Piggott 68.	14
35	17.01	H	DM	Sittingbourne	W 4-1	582	Foy 25, Batchelor 53, Hunter 54, 86.	12
36	20.01	A	DM	Gloucester City	L 0-1	*519*		
37	24.01	A	DM	Dorchester Town	L 0-2	*712*		13
38	31.01	H	DM	Worcester City	W 3-0	703	Piggott 36, 82, Shaw 45.	12
39	03.02	A	**BSC** 3	Halesowen Town	D *2-2	405	Smith 38, Fox 90.	A.E.T.
40	07.02	H	DM	Merthyr Tydfil	L 2-4	715	Smith 62, Crawford 71.	12
41	09.02	H	**BSC** 3 R	Halesowen Town	D *2-2	356	Shaw 13, Bennett 60.	A.E.T. - Lost 2-3 after penalties
42	17.02	A	**SSC** 2	Newcastle Town	W 1-0	154	Smith 28	-
43	21.02	A	DM	Forest Green Rovers	**L 0-5**	*548*		14
44	28.02	A	DM	Halesowen Town	D 1-1	*927*	Piggott 45.	13
45	07.03	H	DM	St Leonards Stamcroft	D 1-1	491	Bennett 55.	14
46	14.03	H	DM	Salisbury City	D 1-1	453	Piggott 54.	13
47	17.03	A	DM	King's Lynn	L 1-2	813	Piggott 19.	14
48	21.03	A	DM	Bath City	D 3-3	1,026	Piggott 7, Smith 41, Bennett 90.	14
49	24.03	H	**SSC** SF	Leek Town	D *3-3	410	Bennett 7, 17, Smith 22. A.E.T.	-
50	28.03	A	DM	St Leonards Stamcroft	W 2-1	354	Steele 67, Batchelor 69.	13
51	04.04	H	DM	Forest Green Rovers	L 1-2	467	Crawford 15.	14
52	07.04	A	**SSC** SF R	Leek Town	W 3-1	301	Piggott 6, Shaw 31, Bennett 64.	-
53	11.04	A	DM	Atherstone United	D 0-0	645		14
54	13.04	H	DM	King's Lynn	W 3-0	478	Howard 23, Batchelor 48, Piggott 88.	14
55	18.04	A	DM	Ashford Town	D 1-1	374	Bennett 20.	14
56	21.04	H	**SSC** Final 1	Bilston Town	L 0-1	576		-
57	25.04	H	DM	Burton Albion	D 1-1	786	Bennett 66.	14
58	28.04	A	**SSC** Final 2	Bilston Town	D 1-1	560	Shaw 5.	-
59	02.05	A	DM	Gresley Rovers	W 3-0	636	Baddams 23, Foy 29, Batchelor 77.	15

PLAYING SQUAD 1998 - **Goalkeepers:** Tony Rowe (Monica Star, Halesowen T, Worcester C, Northfield T). **Defenders:** Willie Batchelor (Barry T, Inter Cardiff, Sandwell B, Barry T, Worcester C,Highgate U), Darren Shaw (Wolves), David Foy (Stafford R, Scunthorpe U,Birmingham C), Denis Mulholland (Redditch U, Tamworth, Chelmsley T,Kidderminster H, Nuneaton B, Solihull B, Highgate U, Sutton Coldfield T, PagetR, Moor Green, Grimsby T), Jon Howard (Wolves), Chris Keogh (Hinckley T,Nuneaton B, Sutton Coldfield T, Tamworth, Sutton Coldfield T, Nuneaton B,Burton Alb, Redditch U, Aston Villa), Richard Clark * (Evesham U, Cheltenham T,Forest Green R, Moreton T, Cheltenham T, Port Val, Cheltenham T). **Midfielders:** Tim Steele (Exeter C, Hereford U, Bradford C, Wolves, Shrewsbury T), Mike Crawford (Youth team), Brendan Devery (Solihull B, Bromsgrove R, Moor Green,Birmingham C), Mark Rufo (Youth team), Michael Gray (Rushden & D, BromsgroveR), Nick Colley * (Telford U, Halesowen T, Chasetown). **Forwards:** Ian Bennett (Leicester U, Paget R, Armitage, Rushall Olympic, Armitage,Bilston T, Armitage, Bury), Gary Smith (Worcester C, Sutton Coldfield T, PagetR), Warren Haughton (Sutton Coldfield T, VS Rugby, Stafford R, Stourbridge,Leicester C), Liam Dixon * (Evesham U, Moreton T, Forest Green R, Gloucester C,Happy Valley (HK), Swindon T).

WEYMOUTH
OFFICIAL MATCHDAY PROGRAMME 1997-1998
THE DR. MARTENS LEAGUE Southern Division
THE TERRAS
MAIN SPONSOR PARK ENGINEERING
£1

PROGRAMME DETAILS:
Pages: 36 **Price:** £1
Editor: Ian White
(01305 785558)

WEYMOUTH

Colours: Claret & sky/claret & sky.
Formed: 1890
Change colours: White with terra cotta trim
Nickname: The Terras
Midweek matchday: Tuesday
Sponsors: Park Engineering
Reserves' League: Wessex Comb.
Local Press: Dorset Evening Echo.
Local Radio: Wessex FM.

Chairman: Peter Shaw **Vice Chairman:** Mike Archer
Secretary: Terry Northover, 2 Stoke Rd, Weymouth, Dorset DT4 9JF (01305 771480).
Manager: Fred Davies
Asst Manager: **Physio:** Bob Lucas.
GROUND Address: Wessex Stadium, Radipole Lane, Weymouth, Dorset DT4 9XJ (01305 785558).
Directions: Arriving from Dorchester on A354, turn right following signs to Granby Industrial Estate at Safeway r'bout - ground on right as you enter estate.
Capacity: 10,000 **Cover:** All sides **Seats:** 900 **Floodlights:** Yes
Clubhouse: Matchdays & functions. Hot & cold food available.
Club Shop: Open matchdays only. Progs & souvenirs. During week contact Amanda (01305 815752)

PREVIOUS - **Leagues:** Dorset Lge, Western 1907-23 28-49, Southern 23-28 49-79, Alliance Premier 79-89. **Ground:** Recreation Ground (until 1987).

CLUB RECORDS - **Attendance:** 4,995 v Manchester Utd, ground opening, 21/10/87. **Career Goalscorer:** W Farmer, Haynes. 275. **Career Appearances:** Tony Hobson 1,076. **Transfer fee paid:** £15,000 for Shaun Teale (Northwich). **Transfer fee received:** £100,000 for Peter Guthrie (Spurs, 1988)

BEST SEASON - **FA Amateur Cup:** First Round 1900. **FA Trophy:** Fourth Round replay 1976-77. **FA Cup:** Fourth Round 61-62, 0-2 v Preston N.E. (A). 1st rd on 29 occasions. - **League clubs defeated:** Merthyr 24-25, Aldershot 49-50, Shrewsbury Town 56-57, Newport County 61-62, Cardiff City 82-83.

HONOURS - All Prem Lg R-up 79-80 (Lg Cup 81-82); Prem Inter Lg Cup R-up 87-88 (QF 90-91); Sth Lg 64-65 65-66 (R-up 54-55 77-78), Lg Cup 72-73 (R-up 5), Sthn Div R-up 91-92; Wstn Lg 22-23, Div 2 33-34 36-37, (R-up 35-36 47-48); Dorset Sen. Cup (25); Mark Frowde Cup (12).

Players progressing to Football League: A Smith (Accrington 61), G Bond/T Spratt/A Donnelly/M Cave (Torquay 61/65/67/68), P Leggett (Swindon 62), R Fogg (Aldershot 63), B Hutchinson (Lincoln 65), A Wool (Reading 71), A Beer (Exeter 74), B Iles (Chelsea 78), G Roberts (Spurs 80), T Gulliver/R Hill/N Townsend/P Morrell/J Smeulders (Bournemouth 66/67/79/83/84), T Agana (Watford), A Townsend/D Hughes (Southampton), S Claridge (C Palace), B McGorry/S Teale (Bournemouth), T Pounder/R Evans (Bristol Rvrs), R Pethick (Portsmouth 93)

97-98 - Captain: Alex Browne **P.o.Y:** David Laws **Top scorer:** David Laws (41)

Back Row (L-R); A Dyke (Dir), K Puttock (Dir), S Bick (Dr), M Thomas (Sec), T Greaves (Dir), T Bennett (Dir), G Tempelman (Dr Martens Pres), D Stevens (Pres), M Archer (Dir), T Hayne (Dir), B Lucas (Physio), T Northover (Sec). Middle Row; J Waldock, N Flory, M Jackson, Fred Davies (Mgr), A Browne (Capt), P Shaw (Chr), A Mason, N Housley, P Adcock, I Hutchinson. Front Row; P Dennis (Kit), S Heath, M Robinson, D Laws, M Gammon, D Powell, L Bradford, P Myers, M Boulton.

WEYMOUTH - Match Facts 1997-98

Match No.	Date	Venue H / A	Comp.	Opponents	Result & Score		Att.	Goalscorers	League Position
1	16.08	H	DM-S	Fleet Town	L	2-3	751	Bradford, Laws.	16
2	19.08	A	DM-S	Trowbridge Town	L	1-3	*343*	Bradford.	19
3	23.08	A	DM-S	Dartford	W	3-2	*261*	Powell, Laws 2.	14
4	25.08	H	DM-S	Havant Town	W	5-0	755	**Laws 3,** Webb, Hutchinson.	10
5	30.08	A	**FAC Pre**	Tiverton Town	L	0-2	*785*		-
6	02.09	H	DM-S	Newport I.o.W.	W	1-0	620	Hutchinson.	10
7	20.09	H	DM-S	Witney Town	L	1-2	636	Clarke.	11
8	23.09	H	DM-S	Trowbridge Town	W	3-1	533	Hutchinson, Laws, Greeno.	8
9	27.09	A	DM-S	Cirencester Town	W	4-0	*150*	Robinson 2, Hutchinson, Boulton.	6
10	04.10	H	DM-S	Chelmsford City	W	2-1	870	Robinson, Jackson.	4
11	11.10	A	DM-S	Weston-super-Mare	W	2-1	*281*	Browne, Laws.	3
12	15.10	A	**DMC 1-1**	Havant Town	D	1-1	*174*	Robinson.	-
13	18.10	A	**FAT 1Q**	Uxbridge	D	2-2	*208*	Browne, Laws.	-
14	21.10	H	**FAT 1Q R**	Uxbridge	L	1-2	492	Robinson.	-
15	25.10	H	DM-S	Tonbridge Angels	W	4-1	721	Lovell 2, Laws, Housley.	3
16	01.11	H	DM-S	Fisher Athletic London	**L**	**2-4**	727	Robinson, Browne.	4
17	04.11	H	**DMC 1-2**	Havant Town	L	0-2	253		-
18	08.11	A	DM-S	Fleet Town	W	2-0	*156*	Laws 2.	3
19	15.11	A	DM-S	Cinderford Town	W	2-0	*172*	Robinson, Jackson.	3
20	22.11	H	DM-S	Baldock Town	W	3-1	709	Browne, Mason, Robinson.	2
21	03.12	A	DM-S	Fareham Town	D	3-3	*207*	Powell, Browne.	3
22	06.12	H	DM-S	Margate	D	1-1	652	Laws.	4
23	14.12	A	DM-S	Chelmsford City	W	3-0	*671*	Housley 2, Hutchinson.	4
24	20.12	H	DM-S	Clevedon Town	W	2-0	749	Robinson, Laws.	2
25	26.12	A	DM-S	Bashley	**L**	**2-4**	*629*	Robinson, Boulton.	4
26	27.12	H	DM-S	Dartford	W	2-0	1,090	Laws 2.	4
27	01.01	H	DM-S	Waterlooville	L	0-1	1,127		4
28	10.01	A	DM-S	Havant Town	W	2-1	*236*	Laws 2.	2
29	17.01	H	DM-S	Yate Town	W	4-2	813	Laws 2, Mason, Robinson.	2
30	24.01	A	DM-S	Margate	L	0-2	*329*		3
31	31.01	H	DM-S	Weston-super-Mare	W	4-0	795	Laws 2, Boulton, Bradford.	2
32	07.02	A	DM-S	Witney Town	L	1-2	*201*	Laws.	3
33	14.02	H	DM-S	Fareham Town	W	2-1	757	Gammon, Laws.	2
34	21.02	H	DM-S	Newport AFC	W	3-2	1,003	Gammon, Laws, Housley.	2
35	01.03	A	DM-S	Erith & Belvedere	W	2-0	*233*	Boulton, Laws.	2
36	14.03	H	DM-S	Erith & Belvedere	W	1-0	832	Housley.	3
37	17.03	A	DM-S	Newport I.o.W.	W	2-1	*254*	Mason, Laws.	2
38	21.03	A	DM-S	Yate Town	W	3-1	*223*	**Robinson 3.**	2
39	28.03	A	DM-S	Newport AFC	W	3-1	*812*	Laws 2, Gammon.	2
40	04.04	H	DM-S	Cinderford Town	**W**	**9-0**	1,109	**Gammon 3**, Hale, Powell, Hutchinson, **Laws 3.**	1
41	07.04	A	DM-S	Tonbridge Angels	W	4-2	*311*	Laws 2, Robinson, Hutchinson.	1
42	11.04	A	DM-S	Waterlooville	W	3-2	*380*	Hale, Powell, Laws.	1
43	13.04	H	DM-S	Bashley	W	4-1	2,852	Hale, Hutchinson, Laws, OG.	1
44	18.04	A	DM-S	Fisher Athletic London	W	2-0	*346*	Hutchinson, Laws.	1
45	25.04	H	DM-S	Cirencester Town	W	3-1	2,087	Laws 2, Adcock.	1
46	28.04	A	DM-S	Clevedon Town	W	3-0	*626*	Hutchinson, Adcock, Laws.	1
47	02.05	A	DM-S	Baldock Town	W	2-1	*499*	Browne, Laws.	1

PLAYING SQUAD 1998

Goalkeepers: Paul Myers (Cogenhoe U, Northampton Spencer, Cambridge U)

Defenders: Alex Browne (Youth team), Gary Rice (Exeter C), John Waldock (Sunderland), Nick Flory (Chard T, Yeovil T), Simon Browne * (Salisbury C, Dorchester T,Swanage & H, Weymouth), Mark Kenway (Youth team), Andy Flory (Trowbridge T,Bridport, Yeovil T), Mark Gammon (Truro C)

Midfielders: Darren Powell (Bashley, Dorchester T, Poole T, AFC Bournemouth), Ian Hutchinson (Halifax T, Gillingham, Halifax T), Mark Boulton (Bournemouth FC,Dorchester T, Trowbridge T, Salisbury C, Yeovil T), Andy Mason (Thame U,Wallingford T, Manchester C), Mark Robinson (Gravesend, Whitstable T), NeilHousley (Trowbridge T, Yeovil T)

Forwards: David Laws (B Auckland, Murton, Waikato (NZ), Seaham Red Star, Ed ThompsonFC), Aaran Watkins (Youth team), Mark Jackson (Whitstable T), Mick Ward (Wrexham, Shrewsbury T), Paul Adcock * (Gloucester C, Bath C, Torquay U, BathC, Plymouth Argyle)

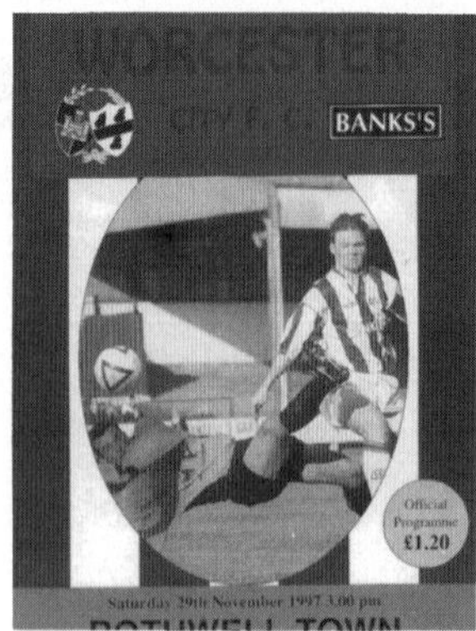

WORCESTER CITY

Colours: Blue & white/black/white **Formed:** 1902
Change colours: Red/white/red **Nickname:** The City
Midweek matchday: Monday **Sponsors:** Banks's
Reserve Lge: Mid Comb/Central Conf **Newsline:** 0930 555 810
Local Press: Berrows Journal, Worcester Evening News.
Local Radio: Radio Wyvern & BBC Hereford & Worcester

Chairman: Dr Michael Sorenson **Vice Chairman:** L Brown
Secretary: Steve Bond, 4 Ferry Close, Worcester, Worcs WR2 5PQ (01905 423120/25427).
Manager: George Rooney **Chief Coach:** Graham Selby
Physios: Peter O'Connell

GROUND Address: St Georges Lane, Barbourne, Worcester WR1 1QT (01905 23003 Fax: 26668)
Directions: M5 jct 6 (Worcester North), follow signs to Worcester, right at first lights, St Georges Lane is 3rd left. 1 mile from Foregate Street (BR) station.
Capacity: 3,443 **Cover:** 2,000 **Seats:** 1,223 **Floodlights:** Yes
Clubhouse: Open every evening and Saturday and Sunday daytime. Cold snacks available.
Club Shop: Sells programmes and souvenirs. Contact Sarah Bushell c/o club.

PROGRAMME DETAILS:
Pages: 36 **Price:** £1.20
Editor: Julian Pugh
(01905 723234)

PREVIOUS - **Leagues:** West Mids (Birmingham) 1902-38, Southern 38-79, Alliance Premier 79-85. **Names:** Worcester Rovers, Berwick Rangers. **Grounds:** Severn Terrace, Flagge Meadow.

CLUB RECORDS - **Attendance:** 17,042 v Sheff Utd (lost 0-2), FA Cup 4th Rd 24/1/59. **Win:** 18-1 v Bilston, Birmingham League 21/11/31. **Defeat:** 0-10 v Wellington, Birmingham League 29/8/20. **Career Goalscorer:** John Inglis 189 (1970-77). **Career Appearances:** Bobby McEwan 596 (1959-75). **Transfer fee paid:** £8,500 for Jim Williams (Telford United, 1981). **Tranmsfer fee received:** £27,000 for John Barton (Everton, 1979).

BEST SEASON - **FA Cup:** 4th Rd 58-59. 1st Rd (10) 05-06 25-26 28-29 50-51 57-58 60-61 78-79 82-84 87-88. **FA Trophy:** QF 69-70 73-74 80-81 81-82.

HONOURS - Southern Lg 78-79, Div 1 67-68, Div 1 Nth 76-77, Lg Cup R-up 45-46 59-60, Chal. Cup 39-40, Champs Cup 78-79; West Mids (B'ham) Lg(4) 13-14 24-25 28-30 (R-up(3) 31-34); Worcs Snr Cup (26) 07-14 28-30 32-33 45-46(jt) 48-49 55-59 60-61 62-63 64-65 69-70 77-78 79-80 81-82 83-84 87-88 96-97; B'ham Snr Cup 75-76; Staffs Snr Cup 76-77; Inter Lg Champs Cup 78-79; Welsh Cup SF 78-79.

Players progressing to Football League: A Awford (Portsmouth 91), P King/K Ball (Cardiff City), J Williams/M Gayle (Walsall 60/6579/91), J Fairbrother (Peterborough 65), D Tennant (Lincoln 66), R Davies (Derby 71), N Merrick (Bournemouth 74), J Barton (Everton 79), A Preece (Wrexham 90), D Lyttle (Swansea 92).

97-98 Captain: Chris Greenman **P.o.Y:** Jason Burnham **Top Scorer:** Sam Bowen

Worcester's Jason Burnham attempts to hold off St Leonards David Ndunduma.

WORCESTER CITY - Match Facts 1997-98

WSC - Worcs. Senior Cup

Match No.	Date	Venue H / A	Comp.	Opponents	Result & Score		Att.	Goalscorers	League Position
1	16.08	H	DM	Crawley Town	L	1-3	706	Harding 65.	
2	23.08	A	DM	Ashford Town	W	2-0	*499*	Harding 10, 37.	16
3	25.08	H	DM	Burton Albion	W	2-1	914	Harding 14, Malloy 85.	8
4	30.08	A	DM	Dorchester Town	D	0-0	*504*		8
5	01.09	H	DM	Forest Green Rovers	L	2-3	816	Richards 13, 40.	
6	08.09	H	DM	Salisbury City	W	2-0	713	Thomas 73, 85.	10
7	13.09	H	**FAC 1Q**	AFC Lymington	W	3-2	673	Woods 7, Hemstock 41, Cottrill 64.	-
8	16.09	A	DM	Bromsgrove Rovers	**L**	**0-3**	*769*		
9	20.09	H	DM	Cambridge City	W	1-0	692	Power 41.	9
10	22.09	H	DM	Atherstone United	W	2-1	599	Heeley 11, Thomas 80.	3
11	27.09	H	**FAC 2Q**	Yeovil Town	L	1-2	1,250	Heeley 34.	-
12	30.09	A	**BSC 1**	Oldbury United	W	3-1	*96*	Harding 59, 60, Thomas 74.	-
13	04.10	A	DM	Rothwell Town	L	1-2	*246*	Thoams 57.	10
14	06.10	H	**DMC 1-1**	Stafford Rangers	W	6-3	420	Harding 28, Greenman 44 (pen), **Woods 4** (54, 66, 79, 89).	-
15	08.10	H	**MIC 1**	Boleshall Swifts	W	3-0	86	Thomas 20, Hallam 27, Benbow 35.	-
16	14.10	A	DM	Burton Albion	L	0-2	*588*		13
17	18.10	A	**FAT 1Q**	Brackley Town	D	2-2	*292*	Hallam 2, 70.	-
18	21.10	H	**FAT 1Q R**	Brackley Town	W	5-0	423	Hallam 11, Heeley 59, Malloy 61, Rouse 62, Benbow 72.	-
19	25.10	H	**MIC 2**	Stourport Swifts	W	5-1	205	Burnham 34 (pen), Benbow 28, 44, Hibberd 63, Hallam 85.	-
20	28.10	A	**DMC 1-2**	Stafford Rangers	L	0-2	*315*		-
21	01.11	A	DM	Bath City	L	0-1	*571*		16
22	03.11	H	DM	St Leonards Stamcroft	W	2-0	559	Richards 84, Greenman 89 (pen).	13
23	08.11	A	**FAT 2Q**	Berkhamstead Town	L	2-3	*245*	Greenman 81 (pen), Hallam 89.	-
24	15.11	H	DM	Sittingbourne	W	1-0	616	Benbow 39.	12
25	19.11	A	DM	Forest Green Rovers	D	0-0	*402*		
26	22.11	A	DM	Salisbury City	D	1-1	*280*	Kelly 58.	11
27	25.11	A	**BSC 2**	Atherstone United	L	0-2	*101*		
28	29.11	H	DM	Rothwell Town	W	3-0	540	**Bowan 3** (27, 58, 60).	10
29	02.12	A	**DMC 2**	Bedworth United	L	0-1	*85*		-
30	06.12	A	DM	Crawley Town	W	3-2	*1,040*	Burnham 59, Griffiths 64, Cottrill 90.	8
31	13.12	H	DM	Gloucester City	W	2-1	1,010	Bowan 7, 31.	
32	16.12	A	DM	Atherstone United	W	2-0	*206*	Bowan 60, Griffiths 90.	2
33	20.12	A	DM	Cambridge City	**W**	**4-1**	*327*	Griffiths 48, Taylor 68 (og), Richards 70, Bowan 75.	2
34	26.12	H	DM	Tamworth	W	3-1	1,819	Greenman 62 (pen), Griffiths 65, Findlayson 88.	
35	27.12	A	DM	Marthyr Tydfil	L	1-2	*1,089*	Bowan 68.	3
36	01.01	A	DM	Halesowen Town	L	0-2	*1,543*		3
37	17.01	H	DM	Bath City	D	1-1	1,035	Mackay 88.	7
38	24.01	H	DM	Gresley Rovers	W	1-0	851	Cotterill 31.	5
39	28.01	H	DM	Nuneaton Borough	W	1-0	964	Bowan 5.	
40	31.01	A	DM	Tamworth	**L**	**0-3**	*703*		6
41	07.02	H	DM	Ashford Town	W	2-1	768	Malloy 48, 85.	3
42	09.02	H	**WSC 2**	Moor Green	D	0-0	302		-
43	14.02	A	DM	Nuneaton Borough	L	0-2	*1,091*		4
44	24.02	A	**WSC 2 R**	Moor Green	W	3-1	*93*	Bowan 49, 88, Burnham 70 (pen).	-
45	28.02	H	DM	Bromsgrove Rovers	W	2-0	1,201	Bowan 27, Griffiths 65.	6
46	02.03	H	**MIC 3**	Stourbridge	L	1-2	201	Bowan 51.	-
47	07.03	H	DM	Dorchester Town	W	1-0	812	Griffiths 90.	3
48	14.03	A	DM	Sittingbourne	D	0-0	*446*		4
49	21.03	H	DM	King's Lynn	W	3-1	907	Owen 9, Burnham 33 (pen), Griffithhs 62.	4
50	24.03	A	DM	Hastings Town	L	1-3	*307*	Griffiths 31.	
51	28.03	A	DM	Gresley Rovers	D	2-2	*563*	Owen 45, 47.	5
52	30.03	H	**WSC S-F**	Solihull Borough	L	1-3	338	Burnham 77 (pen).	-
53	04.04	H	DM	Merthyr Tydfil	D	1-1	1,301	Bowan 19.	5
54	11.04	A	DM	Gloucester City	D	0-0	*758*		4
55	13.04	H	DM	Halesowen Town	D	1-1	1,206	Griffiths 84.	5
56	18.04	A	DM	St Leonards Stamcroft	D	1-1	*302*	Bowan 14.	5
57	25.04	H	DM	Hastings Town	D	0-0	707		6
58	02.05	A	DM	King's Lynn	D	2-2	*690*	Bowan 47, 88.	7

PLAYING SQUAD 1998 - **Goalkeepers:** Paul Moore (Barrow, Bangor C, Inglewood Kiev (Aust), Witton Alb, Worcester C,Southport, Morecambe, Alvechurch, Worcester C, Rhyl). **Defenders:** Steve Hillman (Bloxwich T, Bloxwich Strollers, Oxford U), Jason Burnham (Chester C, Northampton T), Chris Greenman (Bromsgrove R, Peterborough U,Coventry C), Carl Heeley (Sutton Coldfield T, Bilston T, Dudley T, Bilston T,Alvechurch, Gt Wyrley), Dave Richards (Walsall), Mark Burrow (Youth). **Midfielders:** Paul Molloy (Redditch U, Stafford R, Redditch U, Bromsgrove R), Ian Cottrill (Nuneaton B, Worcester C, Bromsgrove R, Worcester C), Shaun Rouse (TrowbridgeT, Forest Green R, Witney T, Gloucester C, Weston-S-M, Carlisle U, Weston-S-M,Bristol C, Glasgow Rangers), Mark Kelly (Merthyr T., Hereford U,Huddersfield T, Worcester C), Roy Jordan (Merthyr T., Hereford U), Ray Woods (Nuneaton B, Telford U, Shrewsbury T, Coventry C, Wigan Ath, Colne D,Caernarfon T, Runcorn, Northwich V, Bangor C, Tranmere R). **Forwards:** Sam Bowen (Merthyr T., Westfields, Moor Green, Westfields), Mark Owen (Willenhall T, Bloxwich Strollers, Wolves), Michael Griffiths (Sutton Coldfield T, Boldmere St. M.), Kieran Hemstock (Youth), Mark Benbow (Pegasus Jnrs), Evran Wright * (Halesowen T, Telford U, Halesowen T, BilstonT, Stafford R, Barry T, Walsall, Halesowen T, Stourbridge, Oldbury U,Stourbridge, Springvale-Tranco).

In view of the unusual amount of movement which took place within the Dr Martens League structure this close season we have outlined below how the 1998-99 make-up of the divisions has occurred. In response to a suggestion regarding incomplete records we have given the match details of the three clubs relegated from the Premier Division, at the end of last season, on the following three pages.

PREMIER DIVISION

Club	
Atherstone United	
Bath City	
Boston United	Transferred from Unibond Prem.
Burton Albion	
Bromsgrove Rovers	
Cambridge City	
Crawley Town	
Dorchester Town	
Gloucester City	
Grantham Town	Promoted from Midland Div.
Gresley Rovers	
Halesowen Town	
Hastings Town	
Ilkeston Town	Promoted from Midland Div.
King's Lynn	
Merthyr Tydfil	
Nuneaton Borough	
Rothwell	
Salisbury City	
Tamworth	
Weymouth	Promoted from Southern Div.
Worcester City	

MIDLAND DIVISION

Bedworth United	
Bilston Town	
Blakenall	
Bloxwich Town	Promoted from Midland Alliance
Cinderford Town	Transferred from Southern Div.
Clevedon Town	Transferred from Southern Div.
Evesham United	
Hinckley United	
Moor Green	
Newport AFC	Transferred from Southern Div.
Paget Rangers	
R C Warwick	
Redditch United	
Shepshed Dynamo	
Solihull Borough	
Stafford Rangers	
Stamford	Promoted from United Counties
Stourbridge	
Sutton Coldfield Town	
V S Rugby	
Weston-s-Mare	Transferred from Southern Div.
Wisbech Town	

SOUTHERN DIVISION

Andover	Promoted from Wessex League
Ashford Town	Relegated from Premier Div.
Baldock Town	
Bashley	
Brackley	
Cirencester Town	
Chelmsford City	
Corby Town	
Dartford	
Erith & Belvedere	
Fisher Athletic (London)	
Fleet Town	
Folkestone Invicta	Promoted from Kent League
Havant & Waterlooville	Merged 1998
Margate	
Newport I.o.W.	
Raunds Town	
St Leonards Stamcroft	Relegated from Premier Div.
Sittingbourne	Relegated from Premier Div.
Tonbridge Angels	
Witney Town	
Yate Town	

CLUBS LEAVING THE LEAGUE SINCE LAST SEASON - **Forest Green Rovers** Promoted to Conference. **Fareham Town** Transferred to Wessex League. **Trowbridge Town** - Finished.

ASHFORD TOWN - Match Facts 1997-98

Match No.	Date	Venue H / A	Comp.	Opponents	Result & Score	Att.	Goalscorers	League Position
1	16.08	A	DM	Halesowen Town	L 0-1	*645*		
2	19.08	H	DM	St Leonards Stamcroft	W 2-0	563	Griffiths 35, Scott 71.	
3	23.08	H	DM	Worcester City	L 0-2	499		17
4	25.08	A	DM	Sittingbourne	L 2-3	*678*	Griffiths 26, Parks 63.	20
5	30.08	H	DM	Burton Albion	L 1-3	441	OG (Davies) 30.	21
6	02.09	A	DM	Hastings Town	L 1-4	*683*	Parks 26.	
7	05.09	A	DM	Forest Green Rovers	L 0-3	*449*		21
8	16.08	H	DM	Crawley Town	L 0-1	382		21
9	20.09	H	DM	Nuneaton Borough	W 2-1	378	White 35 (pen), Bower 50.	20
10	04.10	H	DM	Dorchester Town	L 0-4	443		20
11	07.10	H	**DMC 1-1**	Chelmsford City	W 2-1	254	Harrison 42, White 72.	-
12	11.10	A	DM	Tamworth	L 0-4	*519*		21
13	14.10	H	DM	Salisburyy City	D 1-1	339	Donn 31.	21
14	18.10	H	**FAT 1Q**	V. S. Rugby	W 2-1	397	Harrison 8, Parks 64.	-
15	25.10	A	**FAC 4Q**	Heybridge Swifts	L 2-5	*515*	Bower 46, Scott 74.	-
16	27.10	A	**DMC 1-2**	Chelmsford City	L *1-4	*302*	OG (Girling) 85.	-
17	01.11	H	DM	Gresley Rovers	W 1-0	397	Jones 71.	20
18	08.11	H	**FAT 2Q**	Raunds Town	L 1-2	434	Scott 15.	-
19	15.11	A	DM	Dorchester Town	L 1-5	*575*	Donn 72.	21
20	22.11	A	DM	Merthyr Tydfil	L 0-3	*715*		21
21	25.11	H	**KSC 1**	Dartford	L 0-1	265		-
22	06.12	A	DM	Salisbury City	D 0-0	*315*		21
23	13.12	A	DM	Gresley Rovers	L 0-2	*565*		21
24	26.12	A	DM	St Leonards Stamcroft	L 1-4	*508*	Eeles 62.	21
25	27.12	H	DM	Rothwell Town	D 1-1	420	Eeles 27.	21
26	03.01	A	DM	Bath City	L 0-3	*619*		21
27	10.01	H	DM	Forest Green Rovers	L 0-1	389		21
28	17.01	A	DM	Burton Albion	L 0-4	*705*		22
29	24.01	H	DM	Bromsgrove Rovers	**W 3-0**	326	Wilson 5 (pen), White 42, Griffin 77.	21
30	31.01	A	DM	King's Lynn	L 1-2	*893*	Bower 17.	22
31	07.02	A	DM	Worcester City	L 1-2	*768*	O'Brien 72.	22
32	14.02	H	DM	Halesowen Town	**L 0-5**	433		22
33	17.02	A	DM	Gloucester City	W 3-2	*375*	Porter 36, OG (Elsey) 59, Chambers 89.	22
34	22.02	H	DM	Atherstone United	W 2-0	403	Chambers 6, 87.	21
35	28.02	H	DM	King's Lynn	L 0-3	447		21
36	07.03	A	DM	Atherstone United	L 1-2	*282*	Scott 83.	21
37	14.03	A	DM	Cambridge City	L 0-2	*323*		21
38	17.03	H	DM	Sittingbourne	L 0-1	536		21
39	21.03	H	DM	Gloucester City	L 0-1	318		21
40	24.03	A	DM	Bromsgrove Rovers	L 0-3	*456*		21
41	28.03	H	DM	Bath City	L 0-1	289		21
42	04.04	A	DM	Rothwell Town	W 2-1	*225*	Wilson 54, Harrison 78.	21
43	07.04	H	DM	Cambridge City	L 1-2	302	Lough 19.	21
44	11.03	H	DM	Hastings Town	L 1-2	456	Harrison 63.	21
45	13.04	A	DM	Crawley Town	W 2-1	*963*	Lough 37, O'Brien 66.	21
46	18.04	H	DM	Tamworth	D 1-1	374	Lough 38.	21
47	25.04	H	DM	Nuneaton Borough	L 1-2	610	Lough 64.	21
48	02.05	H	DM	Merthyr Tydfil	D 2-2	448	O'Brien 51, Scott 68.	21

ST LEONARDS STAMCROFT

SSC - Sussex Senior Cup

Match No.	Date	Venue H / A	Comp.	Opponents	Result & Score		Att.	Goalscorers	League Position
1	16.08	H	DM	Atherstone United	L	1-2	486	White 11 (pen).	
2	19.08	A	DM	Ashford Town	L	0-2	*563*		
3	23.08	A	DM	Bromsgrove Rovers	L	0-4	*504*		22
4	25.08	H	DM	Hastings Town	L	1-4	1,579	Lambert 56.	22
5	30.08	A	DM	Halesowen Town	L	0-3	759		22
6	02.09	A	DM	Crawley Town	L	1-2	*325*	Rowland 76.	22
7	07.09	H	DM	King's Lynn	L	2-4	537	Brady 65, Miles 89.	22
8	13.09	H	**FAC 1Q**	Bishop's Stortford	W	1-0	408	Miles 40.	-
9	17.09	H	DM	Sittingbourne	L	0-4	332		22
10	20.09	A	DM	Gloucester City	D	1-1	*612*	N'Duduma 52.	22
11	27.09	H	**FAC 2Q**	Canvey island	W	2-0	463	Ruddy 63, Lambert 85.	-
12	04.10	H	DM	Nuneaton Borough	**L**	**1-5**	501	Adams 56.	22
13	12.10	H	**FAC 3Q**	Camberley Town	L	1-3	440	Gatting 87.	-
14	18.10	H	DM	Bath City	L	1-2	427	Ruddy 46.	22
15	22.10	H	**DMC 1-1**	Erith & Belvedere	L	2-3	178	Burt 12, Ruddy 45.	-
16	25.10	A	DM	Forest Green Rovers	D	2-2	*301*	Tydeman 29, Ruddy 38.	22
17	29.10	A	**DMC 1-2**	Erith & Belvedere	W	2-0	*63*	Ruddy 57, Miles 66.	-
18	01.11	H	DM	Merthyr Tydfil	D	0-0	489		22
19	03.11	A	DM	Worcester City	L	0-2	*559*		22
20	08.11	H	DM	Dorchester Town	L	0-2	373		22
21	15.11	A	DM	Gresley Rovers	**L**	**1-5**	*513*	Miles 40.	22
22	19.11	H	DM	Cambridge City	W	5-1	254	Parris 16, Magee 70, 76, Brown 74, Norman 88.	22
23	26.11	H	**SSC 2**	Saltdean United	W	2-1	176	Tydeman 45, Rose 90.	-
24	29.11	A	**FAT 3Q**	Yeading	L	1-2	*120*	Phillips 85.	-
25	02.12	A	**DMC 2**	Crawley Town	W	1-0	*278*	Flanagan 83.	-
26	06.12	H	DM	Gloucester City	D	0-0	351		22
27	13.12	A	DM	Atherstone United	L	0-4	*267*		22
28	20.12	H	DM	Bromsgrove Rovers	L	2-4	404	Norman 8, O.G. 57.	22
29	26.12	H	DM	Ashford Town	W	4-1	508	**Brown 3** (25, 70, 82), Parris 57.	22
30	27.12	A	DM	Salisbury City	L	0-2	*413*		22
31	01.01	A	DM	Hastings Town	L	1-2	*1,672*	Miles 45 (pen).	22
32	06.01	A	**DMC 3**	Margate	L	0-4	*128*		-
33	17.01	H	DM	Salisbury City	**W**	**6-2**	436	Miles 4, 60, Burt 56, 75, Hunter 54, 86.	21
34	24.01	A	DM	Bath City	L	0-4	*572*		22
35	27.01	A	**SSC 3**	Selsey	W	3-1	*118*	Norman 58, Flanagan 84, Willard 86.	-
36	31.01	H	DM	Rothwell Town	W	3-2	426	Miles 50, 70, Flanagan 30.	21
37	07.02	A	DM	Burton Albion	L	1-2	*464*	Miles 86.	21
38	10.02	A	**SSC 4**	Wick	L	1-2	*160*	Atkinson 72.	-
39	14.02	H	DM	Forest Green Rovers	L	1-2	418	Willard 42.	21
40	21.02	A	DM	King's Lynn	D	1-1	*889*	Ruddy 52.	21
41	28.02	H	DM	Burton Albion	L	0-2	444		22
42	07.03	A	DM	Tamworth	D	1-1	*491*	Miles 67.	22
43	14.03	A	DM	Merthyr Tydfil	L	0-4	*697*		22
44	18.03	H	DM	Halesowen Town	L	2-5	264	Norman 44, Burt 71.	22
45	21.03	A	DM	Cambridge City	L	1-2	*358*	Gatting 16.	22
46	28.03	H	DM	Tamworth	L	1-2	354	Miles 43 (pen).	22
47	04.04	A	DM	Nuneaton Borough	D	1-1	*652*	Flanagan 1.	22
48	11.04	H	DM	Crawley Town	L	0-2	432		22
49	13.04	A	DM	Sittingbourne	W	3-1	*539*	Nduma 9, Ruddy 22, Ramsden 40.	22
50	18.04	H	DM	Worcester City	D	1-1	302	O'Callaghan 74.	22
51	25.04	H	DM	Gresley Rovers	L	1-3	324	Miles 20 (pen).	22
52	02.05	A	DM	Dorchester Town	D	1-1	*669*	Norman 58.	22

SITTINGBOURNE

KSC - Kent Senior Cup

Match No.	Date	Venue H / A	Comp.	Opponents	Result & Score		Att.	Goalscorers	League Position
1	16.08	H	DM	Burton Albion	L	0-2	571		
2	19.08	A	DM	Hastings Town	D	1-1	*530*	Rowland 84.	
3	23.08	A	DM	Gresley Rovers	L	1-2	*508*	Walker 56.	20
4	25.08	H	DM	Ashford Town	W	3-2	678	Haylock 37, 59, Miller 87.	16
5	30.09	H	DM	Merthyr Tydfil	L	1-2	462	Hume 24 (pen).	18
6	02.09	A	DM	Cambridge City	L	1-2	*325*	Rowland 76.	
7	07.09	H	DM	Atherstone United	L	0-2	379		19
8	13.09	H	**FAC 1Q**	Molesey	W	5-0	404	Planck 3, 81, Miller 18, Ponsford 78, Pavey 84.	-
9	17.09	A	DM	St Leonards Stamcroft	**W**	**4-0**	*332*	**Planck 3** (43, 75 (pen), 88), Rowland 75 (pen).	
10	20.09	H	DM	Salisbury City	L	0-3	417		18
11	27.09	H	**FAC 2Q**	Purfleet	W	2-1	420	Rowland 30, Pavey 89.	-
12	04.10	A	DM	Burton Albion	L	0-2	*696*		18
13	07.10	A	**DMC 1-1**	Crawley Town	D	3-3	730	Miller 18, Planck 37, Overton 66.	-
14	11.10	H	**FAC 3Q**	Langney Sports	W	2-1	498	Planck 24, Miller 42.	-
15	14.10	A	DM	Crawley Town	D	0-0	*1,028*		
16	18.10	H	DM	Gresley Rovers	L	2-3	419	Ponsford 53 (pen), M Miller 75.	20
17	25.10	H	**FAC 4Q**	Hereford United	D	2-2	1,011	OG (Mathewson) 53, Miller 56.	-
18	28.10	A	**FAC 4Q R**	Hereford United	L	0-3	2,054		-
19	01.11	A	DM	Halesowen Town	L	1-3	*638*	Walker 64.	21
20	05.11	H	**DMC 1-2**	Crawley Town	L	*3-5	201	Walker 5, Pavey 14, Overton 56.	
21	08.11	H	DM	Bromsgrove Rovers	W	2-0	432	Pavey 6, Haylock 80.	20
22	11.11	A	**KSC 1**	Gravesend & Northfleet	L	0-5	393		-
23	15.11	A	DM	Worcester City	L	0-1	*616*		20
24	19.11	H	DM	Hastings Town	W	2-1	427	Overton 15, 51.	
25	22.11	H	DM	Gloucester City	W	2-0	467	Walker 70, Rowland 84.	19
26	29.11	H	**FAT 3Q**	Abingdon Town	D	1-1	369	Seagar 34.	-
27	02.12	A	**FAT 3Q R**	Abongdon Town	W	*2-1	88	Pavey 14, Sinden 104.	-
28	06.12	A	DM	Merthyr Tydfil	D	0-0	527		19
29	13.12	H	DM	Tamworth	L	0-1	459		20
30	16.12	A	DM	Dorchester Town	L	0-2	*222*		20
31	20.12	A	DM	Salisbury City	**L**	**0-4**	*221*		20
32	26.12	H	DM	Cambridge City	W	3-1	556	Rowland 44, 90, Planck 69.	19
33	27.12	A	DM	Nuneaton Borough	L	1-3	*1,009*	Rowland 7.	19
34	10.01	A	**FAT 1**	St Albans City	D	0-0	475		-
35	14.01	H	**FAT 1 R**	St Albans City	L	0-1	450		
36	17.01	A	DM	Tamworth	L	1-4	*582*	Ponsford 13.	20
37	24.01	H	DM	Forest Green Rovers	L	4-5	436	Smith 47, Walker 78, Overton 83, Planck 90.	20
38	31.01	A	DM	Atherstone United	L	1-2	*304*	Ponsford 60 (pen).	20
39	07.02	H	DM	Nuneaton Borough	W	1-0	447	Owen 79.	20
40	14.02	H	DM	Bath City	W	4-1	418	Owen 14, Overton 18, Planck 27, 32..	20
41	18.02	H	DM	King's Lynn	D	2-2	441	Smith 15, Overton 65.	20
42	21.02	A	DM	Bath City	L	0-1	*523*		20
43	28.02	A	DM	Gloucester City	L	1-2	*555*	Clout 6.	20
44	04.03	H	DM	Rothwell Town	D	0-0	277		20
45	07.03	H	DM	Crawley Town	W	2-1	448	Rowland 61, Sinden 63.	18
46	14.03	H	DM	Worcester City	D	0-0	446		19
47	17.03	A	DM	Ashford Town	W	1-0	536	Rowland 87.	19
48	28.03	A	DM	Forest Green Rovers	L	0-3	534		20
49	04.04	H	DM	Halesowen Town	D	0-0	454		19
50	11.04	A	DM	King's Lynn	W	1-0	739	Smith 10.	18
51	13.04	H	DM	St Leonards Stamcroft	L	1-5	539	Overton 23.	19
52	18.04	A	DM	Bromsgrove Rovers	L	2-3	745	Planck 43 (pen), Overton 59.	20
53	25.04	H	DM	Dorchester Town	W	1-0	457	Hume 89.	19
54	02.05	A	DM	Rothwell Town	D	1-1	372	Rowland 83.	20

MIDLAND DIVISION

FINAL LEAGUE TABLE 1997-98

			Home			*Away*						
		P	*W*	*D*	*L*	*W*	*D*	*L*	*F*	*A*	*GD*	*Pts*
1	Grantham Town	40	16	3	1	14	1	5	87	39	48	94
2	Ilkeston Town	40	18	1	1	11	5	4	123	39	84	93
3	Solihull Borough	40	11	4	5	11	5	4	81	48	33	75
4	Raunds Town	40	13	3	4	7	5	8	73	44	29	68
5	Wisbech Town	40	12	2	6	8	5	7	79	57	22	67
6	Moor Green	40	12	4	4	8	3	9	72	55	17	67
7	Bilston Town	40	13	1	6	7	4	9	69	57	12	65
8	Blakenall	40	10	8	2	7	5	8	66	55	11	64
9	Stafford Rangers	40	9	2	9	9	4	7	57	56	1	60
10	Redditch United	40	7	7	6	9	4	7	59	41	18	59
11	Stourbridge	40	11	3	6	5	6	9	57	55	2	57
12	Hinckley United	40	10	4	6	5	7	8	59	56	3	56
13	Brackley Town	40	9	1	10	6	6	8	45	57	-12	52
14	Bedworth United	40	7	4	9	8	1	11	50	73	-23	50
15	Racing C. Warwick	40	6	8	6	5	1	14	49	56	-7	42
16	Shepshed Dynamo	40	4	10	6	5	4	11	55	74	-19	41
17	Sutton Coldfield Tn	40	4	8	8	5	4	11	42	68	-26	39
18	Paget Rangers	40	6	4	10	3	8	9	40	75	-35	39
19	VS Rugby	40	3	8	9	5	4	11	53	93	-40	36
20	Evesham United	40	4	3	13	3	6	11	47	94	-47	30
21	Corby Town	40	1	4	15	1	4	15	41	112	-71	14

MIDLAND DIVISION RESULTS CHART 1997-98

		1	2	3	4	5	6	7	8	9	10	11	12	13	14	15	16	17	18	19	20	21
1	Bedworth Utd	X	4-0	0-0	1-0	0-0	1-2	1-3	1-3	0-3	0-1	1-1	1-0	0-2	3-2	2-1	1-4	0-1	3-1	3-0	3-3	2-5
2	Bilston Town	3-1	X	1-0	3-0	6-0	1-0	1-2	1-0	2-2	2-1	3-1	2-0	3-2	0-3	1-2	1-0	2-3	2-0	3-1	3-4	0-1
3	Blakenall	1-1	2-1	X	1-1	4-2	5-0	1-3	2-2	2-1	2-1	2-2	2-0	1-3	1-1	4-3	2-2	4-1	3-3	2-2	3-1	1-0
4	Brackley Town	0-2	2-0	4-1	X	3-1	1-1	0-2	0-2	0-2	2-5	0-1	0-1	2-1	1-0	2-1	0-2	1-2	2-1	2-0	3-1	4-6
5	Corby Town	2-4	2-2	1-2	0-2	X	4-4	1-4	0-1	1-5	1-2	2-2	2-1	1-1	0-3	1-3	1-7	1-2	1-2	2-3	1-3	0-1
6	Evesham Utd	1-2	1-5	2-4	2-0	0-1	X	0-2	3-1	0-5	0-2	1-1	2-1	1-0	0-2	0-0	1-1	1-2	2-3	2-4	1-3	0-1
7	Grantham Tn	2-0	3-1	2-1	3-1	6-5	1-0	X	1-1	6-0	2-1	3-0	1-2	1-0	1-0	4-0	2-2	1-0	1-1	1-0	2-1	3-2
8	Hinckley Utd	2-0	4-1	1-2	0-1	0-0	4-1	1-2	X	3-4	2-1	1-0	2-1	1-1	0-4	3-2	2-2	0-0	3-0	1-3	2-1	3-1
9	Ilkeston Town	3-1	6-0	0-1	5-1	3-0	8-1	3-2	3-0	X	1-0	5-0	2-0	3-0	2-0	1-0	2-1	2-1	3-1	3-0	11-1	3-3
10	Moor Green	2-0	0-0	1-3	0-1	2-1	2-0	2-1	3-1	2-2	X	2-4	1-0	3-0	2-0	4-0	0-3	4-3	1-1	3-0	2-2	3-2
11	Paget Rangers	3-2	0-4	2-2	1-1	2-1	0-0	3-4	1-3	1-0	0-3	X	2-3	1-5	0-2	1-3	0-3	3-1	0-0	2-0	1-0	0-3
12	RC Warwick	2-0	0-2	0-0	0-2	1-1	4-0	0-1	2-2	0-0	4-1	3-0	X	2-2	0-2	2-2	0-3	0-1	1-0	5-1	1-1	2-2
13	Raunds Town	7-1	3-2	2-0	0-0	3-0	4-0	3-0	2-1	1-0	2-1	1-1	1-2	X	1-2	6-0	2-1	1-2	0-0	1-0	0-2	4-1
14	Redditch Utd	0-2	0-1	0-1	1-1	3-3	3-1	0-2	3-1	1-1	1-1	0-0	2-0	0-1	X	3-2	1-2	0-0	3-1	5-1	3-0	0-0
15	Shepshed D'mo	0-1	0-4	4-1	2-0	2-0	1-1	0-2	1-1	1-2	1-3	0-0	1-1	1-5	2-1	X	3-3	0-0	0-0	0-0	2-2	2-2
16	Solihull Boro	3-0	1-2	1-0	1-1	1-0	2-0	0-5	0-0	0-4	3-2	1-3	2-1	1-1	1-2	3-1	X	2-0	3-1	2-2	4-1	4-0
17	Stafford Rngrs	1-2	3-1	1-0	0-1	6-0	2-5	0-2	0-0	2-2	1-3	2-0	3-1	2-1	0-1	1-2	2-1	X	5-1	0-3	3-2	0-2
18	Stourbridge	4-1	0-2	1-2	2-0	5-0	2-3	2-0	1-0	1-5	1-1	0-0	1-0	4-1	3-3	3-1	0-1	1-2	X	1-0	4-0	1-0
19	Sutton Coldfield	1-2	0-0	0-0	1-2	3-2	3-3	1-0	0-2	1-4	0-1	1-0	3-1	1-1	0-0	2-2	0-2	1-1	0-2	X	1-3	1-1
20	VS Rugby	0-1	1-1	0-0	1-1	3-0	2-2	1-3	1-1	0-7	3-3	4-1	0-4	0-1	1-1	0-5	1-3	2-0	0-1	1-1	X	0-3
21	Wisbech Town	4-0	2-0	2-1	1-0	5-0	4-3	1-1	4-2	2-5	3-0	3-0	3-1	0-1	2-1	2-2	1-3	0-1	0-1	0-1	4-1	X

Dr MARTENS LEAGUE Midland Division Ten Year Records

	88/9	89/0	90/1	91/2	92/3	93/4	94/5	95/6	96/7	97/8
Alvechurch	-	-	20	21	-	-	-	-	-	-
Armitage '90	-	-	-	-	-	22	22	-	-	-
Atherstone United	2	-	-	-	-	-	-	-	-	-
Banbury United	16	21	-	-	-	-	-	-	-	-
Barri (ex Barry Town)	-	5	6	4	4	-	-	-	-	-
Bedworth United	-	15	13	5	6	17	13	3	5	14
Bilston Town	13	17	14	12	14	8	13	12	7	7
Blakenall	-	-	-	-	-	-	-	-	-	8
Brackley Town	-	-	-	-	-	-	-	-	-	13
Bridgnorth Town	17	12	17	17	16	12	5	22	-	-
Buckingham Town	-	-	-	-	-	-	6	9	-	-
Bury Town	-	-	-	-	-	-	-	21	-	-
Clevedon Town	-	-	-	-	-	5	-	-	-	-
Corby Town	-	-	2	-	-	-	-	20	20	21
Coventry Sporting	20	-	-	-	-	-	-	-	-	-
Dudley Town	9	9	19	22	17	14	11	10	15	-
Evesham United	-	-	-	-	15	10	14	19	18	20
Forest Green Rovers	12	10	18	19	19	15	18	-	-	-
Gloucester City	1	-	-	-	-	-	-	-	-	-
Grantham Town	5	14	9	13	13	11	21	14	4	1
Gresley Rovers	-	-	-	-	2	-	-	-	-	-
Halesowen Town	4	1	-	-	-	-	-	-	-	-
Hednesford Town	15	16	3	2	-	-	-	-	-	-
Hinckley Town	-	-	11	15	20	18	15	17	16	12
Ilkeston Town	-	-	-	-	-	-	2	-	3	2
King's Lynn	19	13	8	14	21	20	9	2	-	-
Leicester United	-	11	15	16	12	19	20	16	w/d	-
Mile Oak Rovers & Youth	22	-	-	-	-	-	-	-	-	-
Moor Green	-	-	-	-	-	-	4	4	8	6
Newport AFC	-	-	7	10	5	4	1	-	-	-
Nuneaton Borough	6	3	5	6	1	-	7	1	-	-
Paget Rangers	-	-	-	-	-	-	-	5	14	18
Racing Club Warwick	-	19	16	18	22	13	10	18	11	15
Raunds Town	-	-	-	-	-	-	-	-	10	4
Redditch United	-	18	10	20	9	6	19	15	13	10
Rothwell Town	-	-	-	-	-	-	8	8	2	-
Rushden & Diamonds	-	-	-	-	3	1	-	-	-	-
Rushden Town	17	2	-	8	-	-	-	-	-	-
Sandwell Borough	14	22	-	-	-	-	-	-	-	-
Shepshed Dynamo	-	-	-	-	-	-	-	-	12	16
Solihull Borough	-	-	-	1	-	-	-	7	6	3
Spalding United	8	6	22	-	-	-	-	-	-	-
Stafford Rangers	-	-	-	-	-	-	-	-	9	9
Stourbridge	18	8	1	9	7	9	16	11	17	11
Sutton Coldfield Town	10	7	12	3	8	16	17	13	21	17
Tamworth	3	4	4	7	10	7	3	6	1	-
V S Rugby	-	-	-	-	-	2	-	-	19	19
Wellingborough Town	21	-	-	-	-	-	-	-	-	-
Weston Super Mare	-	-	-	-	11	3	-	-	-	-
Willenhall Town	11	20	21	-	-	-	-	-	-	-
Wisbech Town	-	-	-	-	-	-	-	-	-	5
Yate Town	-	-	-	11	18	21	-	-	-	-
No of Clubs Competing	22	22	22	22	22	22	22	22	22	21

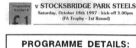

BEDWORTH UNITED

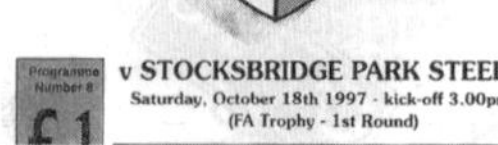

v STOCKSBRIDGE PARK STEELS
Saturday, October 18th 1997 - kick-off 3.00pm
(FA Trophy - 1st Round)
£1

PROGRAMME DETAILS:
Pages: 18 **Price:** £1
Editor: Jamie Home
(01203 354000)

Colours: Green & white/white/white **Formed:** 1947
Change colours: Yellow & green. **Nickname:** Greenbacks
Midweek matchday: Tuesday **Sponsors:** 'D' Drill
Reserves' League: Midland Floodlit Youth League.
Local Press: Heartland Evening News, Weekly Tribune, Bedworth Echo, Coventry Evening Telegraph
Local Radio: Mercia Sound, BBC CWR.

Chairman: Peter Randle **Vice Chairman:**
Secretary: Alan Aucott, 26 Hall Lane, Witherley, Nr Atherstone, CV9 3LT (01827 718736).
Press Officer: Jamie Home
Manager: Billy Hollywood **Asst Mgr:** None **Physio:** John Roberts.

GROUND Address: The Oval, Miners Welfare Park, Coventry Road, Bedworth CV12 8NN (01203 314302). **Directions:** M6 jct 3, into Bedworth on B4113 Coventry to Bedworth road, ground 200yds past past Bedworth Leisure Centre on this road. Coaches should park at this Leisure Centre. Buses from Coventry and Nuneaton pass ground.
Capacity: 7,000 **Cover:** 300 **Seats:** 300 **Floodlights:** Yes
Clubhouse: Social club open every day 7.30-11pm and weekend lunchtimes noon-3pm. Hot and cold bar food, pool, darts.
Club Shop: Selling a wide range of souvenirs & programmes. Contact Tom Ison-Jacques (01203 314884).

PREVIOUS - **Leagues:** Birmingham Comb. 47-54; West Mids (at first Birmingham) Lg 54-72.
Name: Bedworth Town 47-68
Ground: British Queen Ground 11-39.

CLUB RECORDS - **Attendance:** 5,127 v Nuneaton Borough, Southern Lg Midland Division 23/2/82.
Win: 11-0 **Defeat:** 1-10
Career Goalscorer: Peter Spacey (1949-69)
Career Appearances: Peter Spacey
Transfer fee paid: £1,750 for Colin Taylor (Hinckley Town, 1991-92)
Transfer fee received: £30,000 for Richard Landon (Plymouth Argyle, January 1994).

BEST SEASON - **FA Trophy:** Second Round 80-81.
FA Cup: 4th Qualifying Rd 1983/89/90

HONOURS - Birmingham Comb.(2) 48-50, Birmingham Snr Cup(3) 78-79 80-82, Midland Floodlit Cup 81-82 92-93.

Players progressing to Football League: Phil Huffer (Derby County 1953), Geoff Coleman (Northampton Town 1955), Ian Hathaway (Mansfield Town 1989), Richard Landon (Plymouth Argyle 1994).

Back Row (L-R); John Halford (Asst Mgr), Colin White (Sponsor), Marcus Green, Martin Rabone, Craig Dutton, Nick Kirk, Andy Dale, Wayne Starkey, Guy Sanders, Mark Adams, Rob Jones, Ade Gregory, Steve Brown, John Roberts (Physio), Peter White (Sponsor). Front Row; Gareth King, Jai Stanley, Robbie Beard, Billy Hollywood (Mgr), Scott Rose, John Halford jnr, Paul Bedder, Chris Goodman.

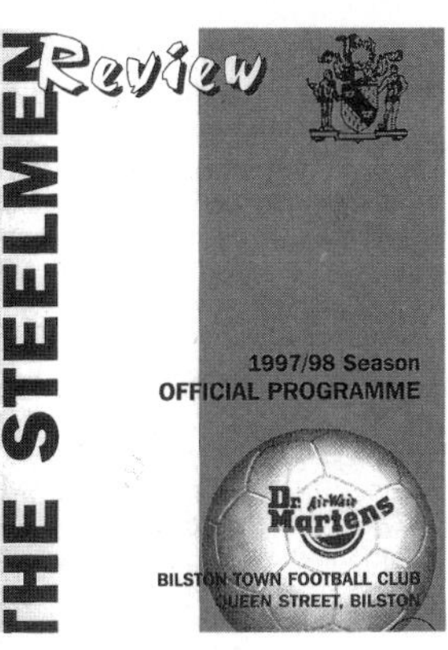

BILSTON TOWN

Colours: Orange/white/white **Formed:** 1895
Change colours: White/black/orange **Nickname:** Steelmen or Boro
Midweek matchday: Tuesday **Sponsors:** Stowlawn Ltd and Second City.
Reserves' League: No reserve team
Local Press: Expess & Star, Evening Mail.
Local Radio: Radio West Mids, WABC, Beacon, BRMB.

PROGRAMME DETAILS:
Pages: 24 **Price:** 70p
Editor: Secretary
(01902 491799)

Chairman: I K Wymer **Vice-Chairman:** A K Hickman
President: Dennis Turner MP **Press Officer:** Mr A Owen.
Secretary: Jeff Calloway, 4 Mervyn Rd, Bradley, Bilston, West Midlands WV14 8DF (01902 491799).
Manager: Ian Painter **Asst Manager:** Alan Potts
Coach: I Painter/B Pope **Physio:** Reg Pickering
GROUND Address: Queen Street, Bilston WV14 7EX (01902 491498).
Directions: M6 junction 10, A454 towards Wolverhampton then pick up A563 towards Bilston and turn left into Beckett Street after a little over a mile, ground at bottom. 3 miles from Wolverhampton (BR), bus 45 from bus station passes ground. Buses 78 and 79 from Birmingham stop within quarter of a mile of ground.
Capacity: 4,000 **Cover:** 350 **Seats:** 350 **Floodlights:** Yes
Clubhouse: Open evenings and weekend lunchtimes (normal pub hours). Usual club activities.
Club Shop: Sells a range of souvenirs and programmes. Contact Paul Galloway, 4 Mervyn Rd, Bradley, Bilston, West Mids WV14 8DF.

PREVIOUS - **Names:** Bilston Utd 1895-1932, Bilston. **Ground:** Pounds Lane 1895-1921. **Leagues:** Birmingham Comb. 07-21 48-54, (Birmingham) West Mids 21-32 54-85.

CLUB RECORDS - **Attendance:** 7,500 v Wolverhampton Wanderers, floodlight opening 1953. *Competitive: 7,000 v Halifax Town, F.A. Cup First Round 1968.* **Win:** 12-2 v Tipton Town **Defeat:** 0-8 v Merthyr Tydfil. **Career Goalscorer:** Ron McDermott 78. **Career Appearances:** **Transfer fee paid:** for Steve Gloucester. **Transfer fee received:** From Southend United for Ron Poutney, 1975.

BEST SEASON - **FA Trophy:** 2nd Round 70-71, 74-75. **FA Vase:** Quarter Finals 92-93. **FA Cup:** 2nd Rd replay 72-73 (0-1 at Barnet after 1-1 draw). Also 1st Rd 68-69. **League clubs defeated:** None.

HONOURS - West Mids Lg 60-61 72-73 (R-up 22-23 70-71 73-74 74-75 75-76 84-85, Lg Cup 72-73 (R-up 65-66), Div 2 56-57), Birmingham Comb R-up 07-08 53-54, Staffs Senior Cup 57-58 59-60 60-61 61-62 (R-up 56-57 64-65 85-86), Birmingham Junior Cup 1895-96, Wednesbury Charity Cup 1981-81 81-82 82-83 84-85 (R-up 83-84).

Players progressing to Football League: R Ellows (Birmingham), James Fletcher (Birmingham 1950), Stan Crowther (A Villa 1955), Ron Pountney (Southend 1975), K Price (Gillingham), Campbell Chapman (Wolves 1984).

Bilston Town FC

PROGRAMME DETAILS:
Pages: 52 **Price:** 70p
Editor: Russell Brown
Tel: 01902 822522

BLAKENALL

Colours: Blue with white trim/blue/blue with white trim **Founded:** 1946.
Change colours: Red & Black/black/black & white **Nickname:** Nall.
Midweek Matchday: Tuesday **Sponsor:** Castlemore Securities
Local Press: Express & Star, Walsall Chronicle, Walsall Advertiser, Walsall Observer, Sunday Mercury, Sports Argus
Local Radio: BBC West Midlands, BRMB, Beacon Radio.

Chairman: P Langston **Vice Chairman:** D Cotterill
President: J Bridgett
Secretary: David Birch, 64 Wimperis Way, Great Barr, Birmingham B43 7DF (0121 360 3574)
Manager: Bob Green **Asst Manager:** Gary Webb
Coach: Malcom Hazlewood **Commercial Manager:** Jeff Husted (01922 400600)
Press Officer: Russell Brown (01902 822522)
GROUND Address: Red Lion Ground, Somerfield Rd, Leamore, Walsall, West Mids (01922 405835). **Directions:** M6 jct 10, follow signs for Walsall centre. At 1st lights turn left (about 200yds from Motorway junction) into Bloxwich Lane. Keep following this lane to the 'T' junction and turn right into Leamore Lane, at this island turn left into Somerfield Road. Ground is approx. 400yds on the right.
Seats: 250 **Cover:** 250 **Capacity:** 2,500 **Floodlights:** Yes
Clubhouse: Open 7-11 (Mon-Sun), 1-11 (Sat). Food available matchdays
Club Shop: No

PREVIOUS - **Names:** None. **Leagues:** Bloxwich Comb./ Staffs County/ Midland Comb. 60-79/ W Midlands Reg Lge 79-95/ Midland All 95-97

CLUB RECORDS - **Attendance:** 1,550 v Halesowen Town 85-86. **Win:** 11-0 v Bilston United 26/4/95. **Defeat:** 0-7 v Macclesfield Town (Staffs Sen Cup) 31/1/95. **Fee Received:** £10,000 for Darren Simkin (Wolverhampton Wanderers, 1992).

BEST SEASON - **FA Trophy:** Prelim Rd 97-98. **FA Vase:** 2nd Rd Proper 91-92

HONOURS - Midland Football Alliance 96-97, R-up 95-96; Industrial Rewinds Lge Cup 95-96; Midland Invitation Triangular Cup 94-95, R-up 97-98; West Midlands Reg Prem Div 88-89, R-up 94-95, Prem div Lge Cup 94-95; Walsall Sen Cup 63-64 74-75 75-76 76-77 80-81 88-89 95-96 97-98; Midland Comb 76-77.

Players progressing to Football League: Darren Simkin (Wolverhampton Wanderers).

97-98 - Captain: Darren Simkin **P.o.Y.:** John Muir **Top scorer:** Les Palmer (24)

Blakenall

PROGRAMME DETAILS:
Pages: 30 **Price:** 50p
Editor: Phil Bradburn
Tel: 0121 554 7266

BLOXWICH TOWN

Colours: Blue & white/white/blue **Founded:** 1972.

Change Colours: Red & Black/Black/Black. **Nickname:** Kestrels

Midweek Matches: Tues/Thurs **Sponsors:** Alvin Amario/Rough & Ready

President: M M Ross **Chairman:** Veejay Thaper

Secretary: Kevin Edwards, 149 Coalpool Lane, Walsall WS3 1QL (01922 868608)

Manager: M Folland/P Knox **Coach:** Jim Skidmore.

Physio: Steve Hooper

Ground: Abbey Park, Glastonbury Crescent, Bloxwich, Walsall. (01922 477640)

Directions: A34 Walsall-Bloxwich, then west onto A4124. Ground 2-3 miles on right, s.p. Mossley Estate.

Capacity: 1,000 **Seats:** 200 **Covered:** 400 **Floodlights:** Yes

Clubhouse: Yes **Club Shop:** No.

PREVIOUS - **Leagues:** Midland Combination (Prem, Div 1). **Names:** Bloxwich AFC.

CLUB RECORDS - **Atendance:** 252. **Win:** 8-1 v Alvechurch. **Defeat:** 9-0 v Shepshed Dynamo **Career Goalscorer:** Mark Holdcroft. **Career Appearances:** Stephen Hillman

BEST SEASON - **FA Vase:** 3rd Rd Proper 97-98. **FA Cup:** 97-98 First Season. **League Clubs Defeated:** None

HONOURS - Midland Alliance 97-98, League Cup R-up 97-98; Bloxwich Comb.(2), Staffs Co. Lg Div 1, Walsall Snr Cup 96-97 R-up 86-87, Invitation Cup 89-90, Midland Combination Premier Div. 95-96 R-Up.94-95. Midland Combination Div 1 89-90, Alan Peck Cup (3), Carlsberg Challenge Cup 95-96, Industrial Rewinds Lge Cup R-up 96-97.

Players progressing to Football League: Martin O'Connor (Crystal Palace & Walsall).

97-98 **Captain:** Mark Bowater **Top Scorer:** Mark Holdcroft (36) **P.o.Y.:** Mark Bowater

Bloxwich Town, pictured after receiving the Midland Alliance Championship Shield.

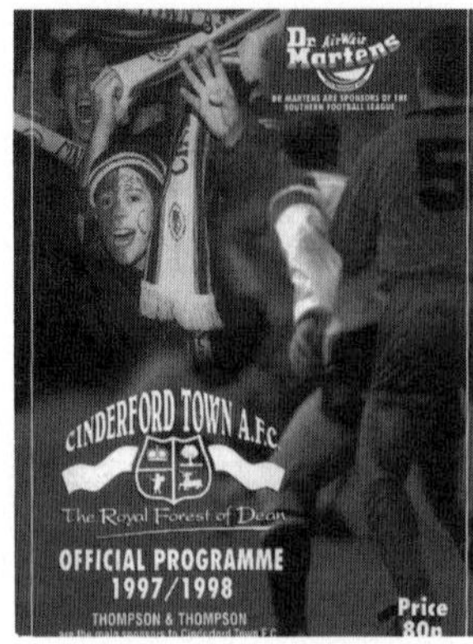

PROGRAMME DETAILS:
Pages: 50 **Price:** 80p
Editor: Mike Bradley
Tel: 01594 824566

CINDERFORD TOWN

Club colours: White & Black. **Formed:** 1922
Change colours: All Red. **Nickname:** Town
Midweek matchday: Tuesday. **Sponsors:** Thompson & Thompson
Reserves' League: No reserve team

Chairman: David Gettings **President:** S Watkins
Vice Chairman: Brian Cook
Secretary: Chris Warren, 9c Tusculum Way, Mitcheldean, Glos GL17 0HZ. 01594 543065 (H) 01594 542421 x 2360 (B)
Press Officer: B Cook
Manager: Brian Godfrey (01453 826901) **Physio:** Keith Marfell
Asst. Manager: Andy Beattie
GROUND Address: The Causeway, Hilldene, Cinderford, Glos (01594 827147 or 822039). **Directions:** From Gloucester take A40 to Ross-on-Wye, then A48 - Chepstow. In 8 miles turn right at Elton garage onto A4151 signed Cinderford, thru Littledean, up steep hill, right at crossroads, second left into Latimer Rd. Ground 5 mins walk from town centre.
Capacity: 2,500 **Cover:** 1,000 **Seats:** 250 **Floodlights:** Yes
Clubhouse: Open every day. 2 bars, kitchen, 2 skittle alleys, darts, dancehall, committee room.
Club Shop: Souvenirs, club badges (£2.50), ties, mugs etc. Programme exchanges welcome - contact secretary.

PREVIOUS - **Leagues:** Glos Northern Snr 22-39 60-62, Western 46-59, Warwickshire Comb 63-64, West Midlands 65-69, Gloucestershire County 70-73 85-89, Midland Comb. 74-84, Hellenic 90-95. **Names:** None **Grounds:** Mousel Lane, Royal Oak

CLUB RECORDS - **Attendance:** 4,850 v Minehead, Western League, 1955-56. **Win:** 13-0 v Cam Mills 38-39. **Defeat:** 0-10 v Sutton Coldfield 78-79. **Career Appearances:** Russell Bowles 516. **Career Goalscorer:** Unknown.

BEST SEASON - **FA Cup:** 2nd Rd v Gravesend 95-96. **FA Trophy:** 2nd Qual Rd **FA Vase:** 2nd Rd 91-92 **FA Amateur Cup:** 3rd Qual Rd 52

HONOURS - Hellenic Lg Premier Champions 94-95, Premier Lg.Cup 94-95, Floodlit Cup 93-94, Div 1 90-91; Glos Northern Snr Lg Div 1 38-39 60-61, R-up (6); Nth Glos Lg Div 1 38-39 60-61; Glos Snr Amtr Cup (Nth) (6), R-up (3); Western Lg Div 2 56-57; Warwickshire Comb. 63-64; W Mids Lg Prem Div Cup 68-69; Glos Jnr Cup (Nth) 80-81; Midland Comb. 81-82; Glos Co. Lg R-up 69-70 71-72 73-74; Glos FA Trophy R-up 92-93; Hungerford Cup 94-95.

97-98 - Captain: Gareth Howells **Top Scorer:** Bradley Thomas **P.o.Y.:** Adie Harris

Cinderford Town

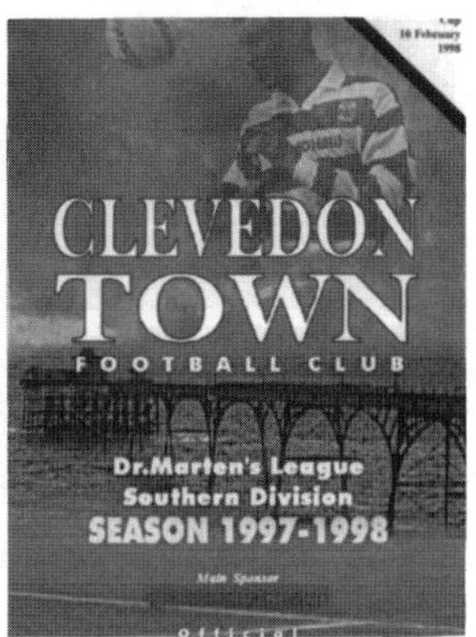

PROGRAMME DETAILS:
Pages: 40 **Price:** 80p
Editor: Steve Small
Tel: 01275 875612 (H)

CLEVEDON TOWN

Colours: Blue & white stripes/blue/blue
Change colours: All yellow or all green
Midweek Matches: Tuesday
Local Radio: Radio Bristol
Local Press: South Avon Mercury

Formed: 1880
Nickname: The Seasiders
Sponsors:

President: **Chairman:** John Croft
Secretary: Mike Williams, 34 Robinia Walk, Whitchurch, Bristol BS14 0SH (01275 833835).
Manager: Steve Fey **Asst. Manager:**
Coach: Jeff Meacham **Physio:** T Banks
GROUND Address: Hand Stadium, Davis Lane, Clevedon (01275 341919 ground 341641 office).
Directions: M5 Jct 20 - follow signs for Clevedon Town Sports Complex; first left into Central Way (at island just after motorway), 1st left at mini-r'bout into Kenn Rd, 2nd left Davis Lane; ground half mile on right. Or from Bristol (B3130) left into Court Lane (opposite Clevedon Court), turn right after 1 mile, ground on left. Nearest BR station: Nailsea & Backwell. Buses from Bristol.
Capacity: 3,650 **Seats:** 300 **Cover:** 1,600 **Floodlights:** Yes
Clubhouse: Open every day and evening. Separate function suite & lounge bar. Hot food available. Matchday refreshment bar within ground sells confectionary, teas & hot food.
Club Shop: Sells all types of souvenirs, programmes and replica kit. Exchanges welcome. Contact J Anderson.

PREVIOUS - **Leagues:** Weston & District, Somerset Senior, Bristol Charity, Bristol & District, Bristol Suburban, Western 74-93. **Grounds:** Dial Hill (til early 1890's)/ Teignmouth Road (til 1991). **Names:** Clevedon FC, Ashtonians (clubs merged in 1974).

CLUB RECORDS - **Attendance:** 1,295 v Tiverton Town, Western League Premier Division 17/4/93 *(At Teignmouth Road: 2,300 v Billingham Synthonia, FA Amateur Cup, 52-53).* **Win:** 18-0 v Dawlish Town (H), Western League Premier Division 24/4/93. **Defeat:** 13-3 v Yate YMCA (A), Bristol Comb 67-68

BEST SEASON - **FA Cup:** 3rd Qual. Rd 2nd replay 92-93 v Newport AFC, 2-4 after two 1-1. **FA Amateur Cup:** 3rd Round Proper, 52-53. **FA Vase:** 6th Round 87-88, v Sudbury (A). **FA Trophy:** 95-96

HONOURS - Western League 92-93 (R-up 91-92, League Cup R-up 92-93), Bristol Charity League, Somerset Snr Cup 01-02 04-05 28-29 76-77, Somerset Snr League Div 1(reserves) 92-93.

97-98 - Captain: Steve Lester **P.o.Y.:** I Harvey **Top scorer:** M Rawlins (27)

Back Row (L-R); J Meacham (Coach), L Jefferies, I Harvey, D Bright, S Weaver, N De-Long, A Bird, T Cook, S Fey (Mgr). Front Row; S Andrews, L Cogan, M Rawlins, M Micciche, S Lester, P Searjent, D Haines, W Noble.

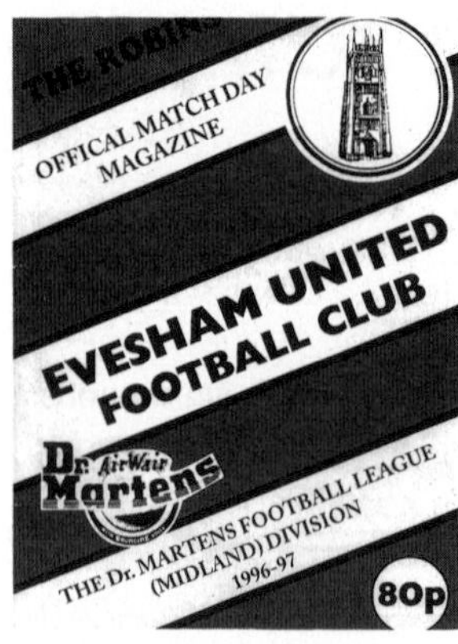

PROGRAMME DETAILS:
Pages: 36 **Price:** £1
Editor: Mike Peplow
(01905 425993)

EVESHAM UNITED

Formed: 1945 **Nickname:** The Robins
Midweek matches: Tuesday **Colours:** Red & white/white/white
Reserves' League: No reserve team. **Change Colours:** All blue
Local Press: Evesham Journal, Worcester Evening News, Gloucester Echo.
Local Radio: Radio Wyvern, BBC Hereford & Worcester.

Chairman: Jim Cockerton **Vice Chairman:** Steve Lane
President: M E H Davis **Treasurer:** Dave Wright.
Secretary: Mike J Peplow, 68 Woodstock Rd, St Johns, Worcester WR2 5NF (01905 425993).
Press Officer: M Peplow (01905 425993) **Manager:** Chris Robinson
Asst Manager: Martin Bewell **Physio:** Paul Ross

GROUND Address: Common Road, Evesham, Worcestershire WR11 4PU (01386 442303).
Directions: From Evesham High Street turn into Oat St, and join one-way system, turn right between Willmotts factory called Conduit Hill into Common Rd, ground 200yds down on right just before railway bridge. 5 minutes walk from Evesham BR station.
Capacity: 2,000 **Seats:** 350 **Cover:** 600 **Floodlights:** Yes
Clubhouse: Open matchdays and training nights. Cold food available in club, and hot food from tea hut on matchdays.
Club Shop: Contact John Hawkins c/o the club. **Sponsors:** Safeway

PREVIOUS - **Leagues:** Worcester, Birmingham Combination, Midland Combination 51-55 65-92, West Midlands Regional 55-62. **Name:** Evesham Town **Ground:** The Crown Meadow (pre-1968).

CLUB RECORDS - **Attendance:** 2,338 v West Bromwich A., friendly 18/7/92. **Win:** 11-3 v West Heath United. **Defeat:** 7-2 v Tamworth. **Career Goalscorer:** Sid Brain **Career Appearances:** Rob Candy. **Transfer fee paid:** £1,500; to Hayes for Colin Day, 1992. **Transfer fee received:** £5,000 for Simon Brain (to Cheltenham Town).

BEST SEASON - **FA Vase:** Quarter Finals 1991-92. **FA Amateur Cup:** Runners-up 1923-24. **FA Trophy:** 3rd Qual Rd 96-97. **FA Cup:** 2nd Qual Rd 96-97

HONOURS - FA Amateur Cup R-up 23-24, Worcestershire Snr Urn(2) 76-78 (R-up 90-91), Midland Comb.(6) 52-53 54-55 65-66 67-69 91-92 (Chal. Cup 53-54 87-88 91-92 (R-up(5) 54-55 71-72 83-84 88-90)), Worcestershire Comb. 52-53 54-55; B'gham Combination R-up 30-31, Evesham Hosp. Cup 89-90, Tony Allden Mem. Cup 1973 1988 1992.

Players who have progressed to Football League: Billy Tucker, Gary Stevens (Cardiff 77), Kevin Rose (Lincoln 78), Andy Preece (Northampton 86), Simon Brain (Hereford, via Cheltenham Town), Billy Turley (Northampton Tn).

97-98 - **Captain:** Eric Smith **P.o.Y:** Jason Percival **Top Scorer:** Jason Percival

Evesham United 1997-98

PROGRAMME DETAILS:
Pages: 44 **Price:** £1
Editor: Alan Mason

HINCKLEY UNITED

Colours: Red & blue/blue/red **Formed:** 1997
Change colours: Amber & black/black/amber
Midweek matchday: Tuesday
Reserves' League: Endsleigh Mid Comb Res Div
Local Radio: BBC Radio Leicester.
Local Press: Heartland Evening Echo, Hinckley Times, Leicester Mercury, Coventry Evening Telegraph

Chairman: Kevin Downes **Vice Chairman:** Rob Mayne
Commercial Director: Mick Voce
Secretary: Stuart Millidge, 25 Elizabeth Rd, Hinckley, Leics. LE10 OQY (01455 635808) **Manager:** John Hanna/Dean Thomas **Coach:** Bill Nally.
Physio: Julie Hayton **Press Officer:** Andy Gibbs (01455 233483)

GROUND Address: Middlefield Lane, Hinckley, Leics. LE10 0RB 01455 613553/615012. **Directions:** From M69 junction 1 take A5 north to Dodwells Island, then A47 (sign Leicester). At 3rd r/about turn right (Stoke Road) then first right (Tudor Road), until crossroads. Turn left (Middlefield Lane), ground at end of lane on left.
Capacity: 5,000 **Cover:** 1,000 **Seats:** 320 **Floodlights:** Yes
Clubhouse: Social club with lounge, games room and concert hall.
Club Shop: Sells programmes, books, vidoes, badges, mugs.

Hinckley Town Records & *Hinckley Athletic Records*

PREVIOUS - **Names:** Westfield Rovers 58-66, Hinckley Town 66-97. **Grounds:** Westfield Playing Field 58-60/ Coventry Rd Rec Grd 60-68/ Leicester Rd 68-97. **Leagues:** Town; S Leicester & Nuneaton Amat, Leics Snr 72-86, Central Mids 86-88, West Mids 88-90. *Athletic; Leicestershire & Northants/ Leicestershire Senior/ Birmingham Combination 14-39 47-54/ West Midlands (Regional) 54-59 64-94/ Southern 63-64.*

CLUB RECORDS - **Attendance:** Town: 2,000 v Real Sociedad 86. *Athletic: 5,410 v Nuneaton Boro 49.* **Win:** Town; 10-0 v Kettering Tn Res, Central Mid Lge B.E. Webbe Cup. **Defeat:** Town: 0-10 v Barry Town, Southern Lge Mid Div. **Career Goalscorer:** Town: Paul Purser. *Athletic: M Hodgkins.* **Career Appearances:** *Athletic: Steve Markham 455 86-96.* **Fee paid:** Town: £1,600 for John Lane (V.S. Rugby). **Fee received:** Town: £1,750 for Colin Taylor (Bedworth Utd).

BEST SEASON - **FA Vase:** Town: 3rd Rd 85-86. *Athletic: 5th Rd 89-90 93-94.* **FA Trophy:** *Athletic: 1st Qual. Rd 69-70 72-73 73-74.* **FA Cup:** Town: 4th Qual Rd v Welling 88-89. *Athletic: 2nd Rd v Queens Park Rangers 54-55*

HONOURS - Town; West Midlands (Regional) Lg 89-90, Central Midlands Lg 86-87 (R-up 87-88, B E Webbe Cup R-up 86-87 87-88, Gerry Mills Cup R-up 87-88), Leics Senior Lg R-up 83-84 (Div 2 72-73, Div 2 Cup 72-73), Leicestershire Challenge Cup 89-90 (R-up 90-91 93-94), Leics Senior Cup (Jelson Holmes) R-up 87-88, Leics Senior Cup 88-89, Midland Floodlit Cup 88-89 (R-up 91-92 93-94). *Athletic; Leics Snr Cup 1899-1900 00-01 09-10 82-83, Leics Snr Lg 1896-97 97-98 99-1900 08-09 09-10 13-14, Birmingham Comb. 23-24 26-27 (R-up 22-23), West Mids (Reg.) Lg R-up 82-83, Birmingham Snr Cup 54-55(jt with Brush Sports), Leics Challenge Cup 57-58 58-59 59-60 60-61 61-62 67-68.*

Players progressing to Football League: *Athletic: John Allen (Port Vale), Keith Scott (Wycombe, Swindon, Stoke, Norwich), Gary Pick (Hereford), Mike Love (Wigan).*

Hinckley United FC

Dr. Martens League
Midland Division

Tuesday, 28th October, 1997
v
ATHERSTONE UNITED
Dr. Martens League Cup
1st Round-2nd Leg

£1.00

PROGRAMME DETAILS:
Pages: 52 **Price:** £1
Editor: Michael Mulryan
(0121 608 7078)

MOOR GREEN

Colours: Light & dark blue halves/navy/light blue **Formed:** 1901
Change colours: Jade & lime/jade **Nickname:** The Moors
Midweek matchday: Tuesday **Sponsors:** Bradstocks Insurance
Reserve League: No reserve team
Local Press: Solihull News, Solihull Times, Birmingham Post & Mail, Express & Star.
Local Radio: Radio WM, BRMB.

Chairman: Ian Childs **Vice-Chairman:** John Bassford
Secretary: Nigel Collins, 7 The Morelands, West Heath, Birmingham B31 3HA (0121 243 3661 H, 0121 475 0240 B)
Press Officer: Peter Clynes (0121 745 3262)
Commercial Manager: Commercial Dept.(0121 777 8961)
Manager: Bob Faulkner **Physio:** Steve Shipway.
Coach: Doug Griffiths/Kim Casey
GROUND Address: 'The Moorlands', Sherwood Rd., Hall Green. B28 OEX. 0121 624 2727. **Directions:** Off Highfield Rd, which is off A34 (B'ham to Stratford). Hall Green & Yardley (BR) half mile.
Capacity: 3,250 **Cover:** 1,200 **Seats:** 250 **Floodlights:** Yes
Clubhouse: Two bars, dance floor. Open nightly & weekend lunch.
Club Shop: Selling scarves, mugs, stickers, programmes etc.

PREVIOUS - **Leagues:** (friendlies only 1901-21) Birmingham & Dist. A.F.A. 1908-36/ Central Amateur 36-39/ Birmingham Comb 45-54/ West Mids 54-65/ Midland Comb 65-83.
Grounds: Moor Green Lane 1901-02/ numerous 02-22/ Windermere Road 1910-30.

CLUB RECORDS - **Attendance:** 5,000 v Romford, FA Amtr Cup 51 **Career Goalscorer:** Phil Davies 221 **Appearances:** Michael Hawkins 800 **Transfer fee paid:** £1,000 for Adrian O'Dowd (Alvechurch) **Transfer fee received:** £90,000 for Ian Taylor (Port Vale.

BEST SEASON - **FA Cup:** 1st Rd Proper 79-80 (lost 2-3 Stafford Rgs). **FA Trophy:** 1st Rd Prop 90-91 lost 3-0 Burton Albion; 96-97 lost 5-3 Ashton United

HONOURS - Sthn Lg Mid Div R-up 87-88, Mids Comb 80-81 (R-up(4) 74-76 79-80 82-83, Div 1 85-86, Presidents Cup(2) 66-68 78-79), Mids Comb Chall Cup 80-81 (R-up 69-70 82-83), Lord Mayor of B'ham Charity Cup 90-91, Mids F'lit Cup(2) 90-92, Tony Allden Tphy 81-82, B'ham Snr Cup 57-58, Worcs Snr Cup R-up 86-87, B'ham Jnr Cup 66-67, Worcs Jnr Cup 85-86, Solihull Charity Cup 85-86, Smedley Crook Memorial Cup 87-88, Cent Amat Lg 36-37 37-38 38-39, Verviers (Belg) Tphy 32-33 36-37, AFA Chall Cup 38-39, AFA Snr Cup 26-27 35-36, Mids F'lit Yth Lg Cup R-up 87-88, B'ham County Yth Lg Cup R-up 83-84.

Players progressing to Football League: H Smith/R Jefferies (Aston Villa 47/50), F Pidcock (Walsall 53), P Woodward/B Mack (W B Abion 54), S Cooper (Birmingham City 83), K Barnes (Manchester City), P Brogan (Mansfield Town), I Taylor (Pt Vale 92), S Talbot (Pt Vale 94), D Busst (Coventry 92)
97-98 - Captain: Guy Russell **Topscorer:** G Russell (19) **Supp P.o.Y.:** G Russell **Mgrs P.o.Y.:** Michael Hayde

Back Row (L-R): Bob Faulkner (Mgr), Charlie Palmer, Richard Softley, Darren Heyes, Paul Jones, Nigel Brown, Mark Shepherd, Wayne Dyer, Chris Adamson, Stuart Hamilton, Matt Warren, Gavin Bassford, Doug Griffiths (Coach), Michael Mulryan. Front Row: Jamie Wills, Chris Pearce, Michael Hayde, Guy Russell, Chris Gillard, Mark Whitehouse

NEWPORT A.F.C.

Colours: Amber with black stripe. **Formed:** 1989
Change colours: Green with white stripe **Nickname:** The Exiles
Midweek matchday: Wednesday **Sponsors:** Cable Tel
Youth League: South West Counties Youth
Local Press: South Wales Argus, South Wales Echo.
Local Radio: Red Dragon.

PROGRAMME DETAILS:
Pages: 42 **Price:** £1.00
Editor: Wallace Brown
(01633 265500)

Chairman: David Hando **President:** Brian Toms, MBE.
Vice-Chairman / Press Officer: Wallace Brown (01633 265500)
Secretary: Mike Everett, 43 Downing Street, Newport. NP9 0JL (01633 669572)
Club Headquarters: The King, 76 Somerton Road, Newport. NP9 0JX (01633 662262, Fax 01633 271771).
Community Director: Ray Taylor (01443 237545).
Manager: Tim Harris **Asst Manager:** Chris Hyde
Physios: T Gilbert & D Williams **Trainer:** David Williams
Football in the Community Off: Derek Brazil
GROUND Address: Newport Stadium, Spytty Park, Langland Way, Newport, South Wales. 01633 280802. **Directions:** From Severn Bridge on M4 take 1st exit signed Newport (jct 24), 1st left at r'bout follow signs for industrial area, left at r'bout after 2 1/2 miles, over 2 r'bouts, next left for ground. Ample free parking available at ground.
Capacity: 3,300 **Cover:** 1,236 **Seats:** 1,236 **Floodlights:** Yes.
Clubhouse: Club HQ is a pub less than 1 mile from stadium. Private members' club only at ground. Refreshments, hot & cold snacks available at ground.
Club Shop: Open matchdays, sells a wide selection of souvenirs & programmes.

PREVIOUS - **Leagues:** Hellenic 89-90. **Grounds:** London Road, Moreton-in-Marsh 89-90; Somerton Park, Newport 90-92; Gloucester City FC 92-94 *(period in exile due to dispute with FAW over the League of Wales).* **Names:** None. Newport AFC were formed after the demise of Newport County in 1988-89.

CLUB RECORDS - **Attendance:** 2,475 v Redditch United, Beazer (Midland) 24.8.94. **Win:** 9-0 v Pontlottyn Blast Furnace (A), Welsh Cup First Round 1/9/90. **Defeat:** 1-6 v Stafford Rangers (A) BHL 6/1/96 **Career Goalscorer:** Chris Lilygreen 93. **Career Appearances:** Mark Price 274 (222 Lg + 52 cup) **Transfer fee paid:** £3,700 for Mark Williams from Merthyr Tydfil **Transfer fee received:** Not disclosed

BEST SEASON - **FA Cup:** 4th Qualifying Rd 92-93. **FA Trophy:** 2nd Rd Proper 95-96. **FA Vase:** N/A

HONOURS - Hellenic Lge Prem Div 89-90 (Lge Cup 89-90); Gloucs Sen Cup Winners 93-94; Southern League Mid Div Champ 94-95, Merit Cup Jnt Win 94-95; Gwent FA Sen. Cup Winners 96-97.

97-98 - Captain: Derek Brazil **Top scorer:** Paul Evans (24)
P.o.Y.: Bradley Thomas **Players P.o.Y.:** Derek Brazil

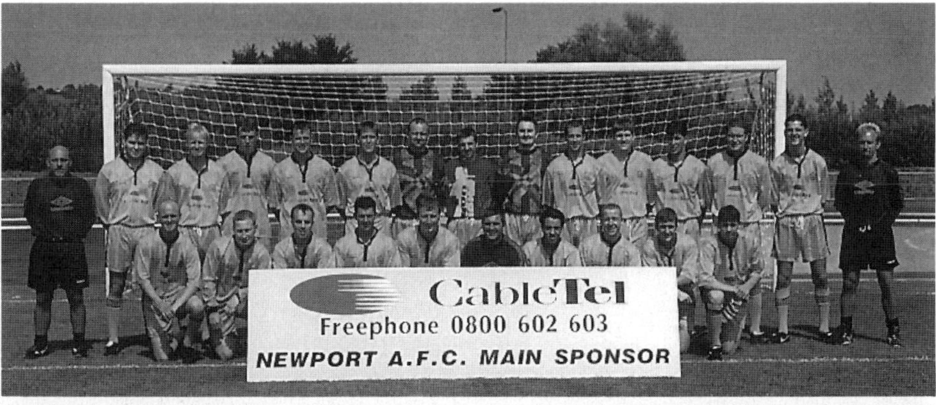

Back Row (L-R); Tony Gilbert (Physio), Martin Boyle, Jason Donovan, Keith Holmans, Paul Evans, Phil Coyne, Neil Hards, Paul Rowlands, Jon Roberts, Danny Hunt, Leigh Hall, Darren Porretta, Derek Brazil, Simon Truman, Chris Hyde (Asst Mgr). Front Row; Paul Burton, Andrew Ford, Chris Smith, Mark Williams, Norman Parselle, Tim Harris (Mgr), Samir Misbah, Carl Vowles, Robbie Painter, Lee Brown.

PROGRAMME DETAILS:
Pages: **Price:** 80p
Editor: Paul Vanes
Tel: 0121 770 9835

PAGET RANGERS

Colours: Gold/black/gold. **Formed:** 1938
Change colours: All red **Nickname:** The 'Bears'
Midweek matchday: Wednesday **Sponsors:** Delaware Communications
Reserves' League: No reserve team
Local Press: Sutton Coldfield News, Sutton Observer.
Local Radio: Radio WM, BRMB.
Chairman: R R Ruddick **Vice-Chairman:** Derek Culling
Secretary: Ian T Price, 80 Ward Grove, Lanesfield, Wolverhampton. WV4 6PQ (01902 679223)
Press Officer: Chris Inman
Commercial Manager: Rob Wilkinson (0121 686 3919)
Manager/Physio: Eddie Caulfield
Asst Manager: Paul Edwards **Coach:** Chris Sharpe

GROUND Address: Central Ground, Coles Lane, Sutton Coldfield B72 1NL. 0121 354 2997/0121 355 5475. **Directions:** A5127 into Sutton, right at Odeon cinema (Holland Road), then first right into Coles Lane - ground 150 yds on left. 10 mins walk from Sutton Coldfield (BR), bus 104 from Birmingham.
Capacity: 4,500 **Cover:** 500 **Seats:** 200 **Floodlights:** Yes
Clubhouse: Open daily, brick built lounge and concert room, fully carpeted and extensively decorated. Food available
Club Shop: No, metal badges available from chairman or secretary.

PREVIOUS - **Leagues:** Birmingham Suburban/Central Amateur/Midland Combination 50-81/Southern 86-88/West Midlands (Regional) 88-94/ Interlink Midland Alliance 94-95.
Grounds: Pype Hayes Park 38-46/ Springfield Road, Walmley 46-93

CLUB RECORDS - **Attendance:** 2,000 v Aston Villa, F'light opening 1971. **Win:** 24-1 v Evesham Town 1949. **Defeat:** 1-6 v Gloucester 87/Halesowen Town 87/Moor Green 88. **Career Appearances:** Gary Williams 512. **Career Goalscorer:** Unknown. **Transfer fee paid:** No transfer fee paid for any player. **Transfer fee received:** John Gittens (Southampton) £10,000

BEST SEASON - **FA Cup:** Third Qual Round 94-95. **FA Vase:** Fourth Rd 88-89, 0-1 v Wisbech. **FA Trophy:** First Rd 95-96, 0-2 v Winsford

HONOURS - West Mids Lg R-up 91-92 (Lg Cup 91-92); Midland Comb.(6) 59-61 69-71 82-83 85-86 (R-up 77-78, Lg Cup 59-60 66-67, Div 1 Cup 70-71, Div 3 82-83(res)); B'ham Jnr Cup 51-52; Walsall Snr Cup 85-86; Midland Alliance 94-95; Lord Mayor Birmingham Charity Cup 94-95; Staffs Sen Cup R-up 94-95.

Players progressing to Football League: John Gittens (Southampton)

Paget Rangers

RACING CLUB
WARWICK F.C.
FOUNDED 1919
BEAZER HOMES LEAGUE
(MIDLAND DIVISION)
Official Programme 1993/94 Season

PROGRAMME DETAILS:
Pages: 20 **Price:** 80p
Editor: Robin Lamb
Tel: 01926 774255

RACING CLUB WARWICK

Colours: Gold/black/black (Ajax Style) **Formed:** 1919
Change colours: Red/white/white **Nickname:** Racers
Midweek matchday: Wednesday
Youth's League: Mid F/Lit Yth Lge
Local Press: Warwick Advertiser, Leamington Courier, Coventry Evening Telegraph.
Local Radio: BBC Radio Coventry, Bear Radio

Chairman: **Secretary:** Pat Murphy 01926 612675
Commercial Manager: K Shirley 01926 831333
Manager: K Billington 01926 770267 **Asst Mgr:** B Powell 01676 535569
GROUND Address: Townsend Meadow, Hampton Road, Warwick CV34 6JP (01926 495786). **Directions:** On the B4095 Warwick to Redditch road (via Henley in Arden) next to owners' & trainers' car park of Warwick Racecourse. From M40 jct 15 (one and a half miles) take A429 into Warwick, left into Shakespeare Ave., straight over island, right at T-junction into Hampton Rd, ground 300yds on left. 2 miles from Warwick BR station.
Capacity: 1,000 **Cover:** 200 **Seats:** 250 **Floodlights:** Yes
Club Shop: Scarves, mugs, badges, programmes - contact Robin Lamb, 01926 774855
Clubhouse: 01926 495786 Open every evening & Fri, Sat, Sun & Mon lunchtimes.

PREVIOUS - **Leagues:** Birmingham & West Midlands Alliance, Warwickshire Combination, West Midlands (Regional) 67-72, Midland Combination 72-89. **Name:** Saltisford Rovers 1919-68, Warwick Saltisford 68-70. **Grounds:** Coventry Road.

CLUB RECORDS - **Attendance:** 1,000 v Halesowen Town, FA Cup 1987. **Transfer fee paid:** £1,000 for Dave Whetton (Bedworth United). **Transfer fee received:** £2,000 for Ian Gorrie (Atherstone Utd). **Win:** 9-1 v Knowle. **Defeat:** 0-6 v Tamworth. **Career Goalscorer:** Steve Edgington 200. **Career Appearances:** Steve Cooper 600.

BEST SEASON - **FA Vase:** 4th Round 77-78, **FA Cup:** 3rd Qual Rd 92-93.

HONOURS - Midland Combination 87-88 (R-up 88-89); Warwick Lg 33-34 34-35 35-36; Birmingham & West Mids Alliance 48-49; Birmingham & Dist Alliance Senior Cup 49-50; Leamington & Dist Lg 37-38 45-46 46-47 47-48; Leamington Hospital Cup 37-38 46-47; Warwick Cinderella Cup 35-36 36-37 37-38 38-39 46-47; T G John Cup 36-37; Leamington Junior Cup 38-39 46-47.

Players progressing to the Football League: None

97-98 - Captain: K Sullivan **P.o.Y.:** Kerion Sullivan **Top scorer:** Brian Agar

Back Row (L-R); Jason Caddon, Kevin Ellkin, Keith Brown, Mick Shearer, Peter McBean, Mark Smith, Sean McGrory, Ritchie Antiss, Adam Munday. Front Row; Chris Hammond, Tim Warner, Kieran Sullivan, Paul Eden, Martin Mier, Owen Johnson. Photo: Keith Clayton

REDDITCH UNITED

Colours: All red **Formed:** 1900
Change colours: All royal blue **Nickname:** The Reds
Midweek matchday: Tuesday
Reserves' League: Midland Comb. Res Div.
Local Press: Redditch Indicator, Redditch Advertiser, Birmingham Evening Mail, Redditch Weekly Mail.
Local Radio: BBC Hereford & Worcester.

Chairman: Keith Broom **President:** Bob Thompson
Secretary: M A Langfield, 174 Harport Road, Redditch, Worcs B98 7PE (01527 526603)
Commercial Manager: Dave Roberts
Press Officer: R Newbold (0527 27516)
Manager: Mick Tuohy **Asst Manager:** Ivor Chambers
Coach: **Physio:** Ginger Jordan

GROUND Address: Valley Stadium, Bromsgrove Road, Redditch B97 4RN (0527 67450). **Directions:** Access 7 on town centre ring-road takes you into Bromsgrove Road (via Unicorn Hill) - ground entrance 400yds past traffic lights on right. Arriving from Bromsgrove take first exit off dual carriageway. Ground 400 yds from Redditch BR station and town centre.
Capacity: 9,500 **Cover:** 2,000 **Seats:** 400 **Floodlights:** Yes
Clubhouse: Large clubroom and lounge boardroom. Open matchdays and for private hire. Food availsable on matchdays; hot dogs, burgers, chips etc.
Club Shop: No.

PREVIOUS - **Leagues:** Birmingham Combination 05-21 29-39 46-53, West Midlands 21-29 53-72, Southern 72-79, GMV Conference (then Alliance Premier League) 79-80.
Name: Redditch Town
Ground: HDA Spts Ground, Millsborough Rd.

CLUB RECORDS - **Attendance:** 5,500 v Bromsgrove, league match 54-55.
Transfer fee paid: £3,000 for Paul Joinson
Transfer fee received: £42,000 for David Farrell (Aston Villa, 1991).

BEST SEASON - **FA Cup:** 1st Rd replay 71-72 (lost 0-4 at P'boro after 1-1 draw). Also 1st Rd 71-72.
League clubs defeated: None.
FA Trophy: 1st Round 1978-79

HONOURS - Southern Lg Div 1 Nth 75-76 (Midland Div R-up 85-86), West Mids (B'ham) Lg Southern Sect. 54-55, Birmingham Comb. 13-14 32-33 52-53 (R-up 06-07 14-15 51-52), Staffs Snr Cup 90-91, Birmingham Snr Cup 24-25 31-32 38-39 76-77, Worcs Snr Cup 1894-95 1930-31 74-75 76-77 (R-up 1888-89 1929-30 52-53 73-74), Worcs Jnr Cup 90-91

Players progressing to Football League: Hugh Evans (Birmingham 1947), Trevor Lewes (Coventry 1957), David Gilbert (Chesterfield 1960), Mike Tuohy (Southend Utd 1979), Neil Smith (Liverpool), David Farrell (Aston Villa 1992).

Redditch United
Football Club
Season 1997-1998
Members of:
The Dr. Martens Southern Football League
Official Programme 80p
Main Sponsor: Protex (Fasteners) Ltd.

PROGRAMME DETAILS:

Pages: 48
Price: £1.00
Editor: Roger Newbold
(01527 27516)

SHEPSHED DYNAMO

Colours: Black & white/black/black
Change colours: Blue/white/blue
Midweek matchday: Tuesday
Reserves' League: None

Formed: 1890
Nickname: The Raiders
Sponsors: None

Chairman: Michael Voce **President / Vice Chairman:** TBA
Secretary: Peter Bull, 17 Welland Rd, Barrow-on-Soar, Leicestershire LE12 8NA (01509 413338).
Press Officer: Maurice Brindley (01509 267922)
Commercial Manager: Paul Mitchell
Manager: Mark O'Kane
Assistant Manager: Keith Milner **Physio:** John Watson

GROUND Address: The Dovecote, Butthole Lane, Shepshed, Leicestershire (01509 502684). **Directions:** M1 junction 23, A512 towards Ashby, right at first lights, right at garage in Forest Street, right into Butthole Lane opposite Black Swan. Five miles from Loughborough (BR).
Capacity: 5,000 **Cover:** 1,500 **Seats:** 209 **Floodlights:** Yes
Clubhouse: Accomodates 120 in main room, 50 in others.
Club Shop: No

PROGRAMME DETAILS:
Pages: **Price:**
Editor:
Tel:

PREVIOUS - **Leagues:** Leicestershire Senior 07-16 19-27 46-50 51-81, Midland Counties 81-82, Northern Counties (East) 82-83, Southern 83-88, Northern Premier 88-93, Midland Combination 93-94. **Grounds:** Ashby Road (pre-1897), Little Haw Farm. **Names:** Shepshed Albion 1890-1975 91-94, Shepshed Charterhouse 75-91.

CLUB RECORDS - **Attendance:** 1,672 **Win:** Unknown **Defeat:** Unknown **Career Goalscorer:** Jeff Lissaman **Career Appearances:** Austin Straker 300 **Transfer fee paid:** £2,000 for Doug Newton **Transfer fee received:** £10,000 for John Deakin from Birmingham City

BEST SEASON - **FA Vase:** Semi-Finalists 78-79 **FA Trophy:** 1st Rd Replay 85-86 89-90. **FA Cup:** 1st Rd 82-83 (lost 1-5 at Preston North End). **FA Amateur Cup:**

HONOURS - Southern League Midland Division Runners-up 83-84, Northern Counties (East) League 82-83 (League Cup 82-83), Midland Counties League 81-82 (League Cup 81-82), Leicestershire Senior League 10-11 20-21 78-79 79-80 80-81 (Runners-up 21-22, Div 2 53-54 65-66 77-78, Div 2 Cup 77-78), Leicestershire Senior Cup 77-78 79-80 81-82 83-84 84-85 85-86 87-88, FA Vase SF 78-79, Loughborough Charity Cup 92-93.

Players progressing to Football League: Neil Grewcock (Burnley 1984), Gordon Tucker (Huddersfield 1987), Devon White (Bristol Rovers 1987), John Deakin (Birmingham City).

Back Row (L-R); Dave Williams, Paul Robilliard, Michael McCarnon, Pat Clarke, Jason Woodley, Richard Selby, Richard Hill, John Hanna (Mgr). Front Row; Sven Sindon, Lee McGlanchey, Darren Robinson, Ibraham Bah, Steve Adams, Mark Hodgkins.

SOLIHULL BOROUGH

Colours: Red/white/red **Formed:** 1951
Change colours: Yellow/black/yellow **Nickname:** Boro
Midweek matchday: Wednesday **Sponsors:** Carling Black Label
Reserve's League: Midland Combination Reserve Division
Local Press: Solihull Times, Solihull News, Sunday Mercury, Sports Argus.
Local Radio: Radio WM, BRMB.

PROGRAMME DETAILS:
Pages: 52 **Price:** £1
Editors: Jonathon Morgan & Clare Anker 0121 357 8878

Chairman: John Hewitson **President:** Joe McGorian
Vice Chairman: Trevor Stevens **Commercial Man.:** Roger Lucas
Secretary: John A France, 22 Swallows Meadow, Shirley, Solihull B90 4QB (0121 733 6584) **Press Officer:** Richard Crawshaw (01564 702746)
Manager: Paul Dyson **Reserve Manager:** Kevin Sweeney
Coach: Robert Hopkins **Physio:** Dave Smith

GROUND Address: Ground Share at Redditch Utd.
Valley Stadium, Bromsgrove Road, Redditch B97 4RN (0527 67450).
Directions: Access 7 on town centre ring-road takes you into Bromsgrove Road (via Unicorn Hill) - ground entrance 400yds past traffic lights on right. Arriving from Bromsgrove take first exit off dual carriageway. Ground 400 yds from Redditch BR station and town centre.
Capacity: 9,500 **Cover:** 2,000 **Seats:** 400 **Floodlights:** Yes
Clubhouse: Large clubroom and lounge boardroom. Open matchdays and for private hire. Food availsable on matchdays; hot dogs, burgers, chips etc.
Club Shop: Yes

PREVIOUS - **Leagues:** Mercian; Midland Combination 69-91.
Name: Lincoln FC **Grounds:** Widney Stadium, Solihull 65-88

CLUB RECORDS - **Attendance:** 2,135 v Darlington FA Cup 1st Rd replay. *At previous ground: 400 v Moor Green, Midland Combination Division Two, 1971.* **Win:** 9-1 v Alfreton Town FA Trophy 1st Rd 97-98. **Defeat:** 1-7 v VS Rugby (A), Birmingham Senior Cup. **Career Goalscorer:** Joe Dowling **Career Appearances:** Darrel Houghton **Transfer fee paid:** £15,000 for Recky Carter, from Kettering Town **Transfer fee received:** £30,000 for Andy Williams (to Coventry)

BEST SEASON - **FA Cup:** 1st Rd 97-98; 1-1,3-3 (2-4pen) v Darlington **FA Vase:** 5th Rd 74-75 **FA Trophy:** 1st Rd Prop 97-98

HONOURS - Southern Lg Midland Div 91-92; Midland Comb. R-up 90-91, Chall Cup R-up 74-75 90-91, Presidents Cup R-up 69-70; Lord Mayor of Birmingham Charity Cup 91-92 92-93 94-95 96-97; Worcs Senior Cup R-up 92-93 96-97 97-98; Birmingham Senior Cup 94-95.

Players to Football League: Kevin Ashley (Birmingham C.), Andy Williams (Coventry C.), Geoff Scott (Leicester C.), Danny Conway (Leicester C.), Alan Smith (Leicester C.), Dean Spink (Aston Villa), John Frain (Northampton T.)

97-98 - Captain: Paul Brogan **P.o.Y.:** Andy Penny **Top scorer:** N Dowling

Solihull's Ian Mitchell lets fly against Shepshed. Photo: Keith Clayton

PROGRAMME DETAILS:
Pages: 40 **Price:** £ 1.00
Editor: Peter Wall
Tel. 01785 602430

STAFFORD RANGERS

Colours: White & black/black/black **Formed:** 1876
Change colours: Maroon/green/maroon **Nickname:** The Boro
Midweek matchday: Tuesday
Reserves' League: No reserve team
Local Press: Staffordshire Newsletter, Express & Star, Evening Sentinel
Local Radio: Radio Stoke, Beacon Radio, Signal Radio.

Chairman: John Downing **Vice-Chairmam:** TBA
Secretary: Peter Wall, c/o Stafford Rangers FC (01785 602430)
Manager: I Painter **Physio:** B. Whittaker
Coach: A King **Press Officer:** Chris Godwin
GROUND Address: Marston Road Stafford ST16 3BX (01785 602430) (Fax 01785 602431) **Directions:** From M6 junction 14, A34 (Stone) to roundabout, straight over into Beaconside, take third right into Common Road, ground one mile ahead. From Town Centre, follow signs for B5066 (Sandon) turn left by Lotus shoe factory. Two miles from railway station.
Capacity: 6,000 **Cover:** 3,000 **Seats:** 426 **Floodlights:** Yes
Clubhouse: Yes - Open every day. Food available
Club Shop: Two shops, one old programmes and one souvenirs run by Jim & Irene Dalglish.

PREVIOUS - **Leagues:** Shropshire 1891-93, Birm 1893-96, 21-40, N Staffordshire 1896-1900, Cheshire 00-01, Birm Comb 00-12, 46-52, Cheshire Cnty 52-69, Nthn Prem 69-79, 83-85, Alliance Prem 79-83, GMVC 85-95. **Grounds:** Lammascotes, Stone Rd, Newtown, Doxey (until 1896)

CLUB RECORDS - **Attendance:** 8,536 v Rotherham Utd FA Cup 3rd Rd 75. **Win:** 11-0 v Dudley Town FA Cup 6.9.58. **Defeat:** 0-12 v Burton Town Birmingham Lge 13.12.30. **Career Goalscorer:** M Cullerton 176 **Career Appearances:** Jim Sargent. **Transfer fee paid:** £13,000 for S Butterworth from VS Rugby 90 **Transfer fee received:** £100,000 for Stan Collymore from Crystal Palace 1990

BEST SEASON - **FA Trophy:** Winners 1971-72 & 78-79. R-up 75-76. **FA Cup:** 4th Rd 74-75. **League Clubs Defeated in FA Cup:** Halifax, Stockport, Rotherham

HONOURS - Birm Comb Champ 12-13; Birm Lge Champ 25-26; Nthn Prem Lge Champ 71-72, 84-85; FA Trophy Win 71-72, 78-79, R-up 75-76; Bob Lord Trophy 85-86; Wednesday Charity Cup 20-21; Mid F/light Cup 70-71; NPL Champ Shield 84-85; Jim Thompson Shield 86-87; Staffs Sen Cup 54-55 56-57 62-63 71-72 77-78 86-87 91-92.

Players progressing to Football League: M Aleksic (Plymouth/Luton/Spurs), J Arnold (Blackburn/Everton/Port Vale), R Williams/M Cullerton/T Bailey (Port Vale), K Barnes (Man City), A Lee (Tranmere), E Cameron (Exeter), W Blunt (Wolves), G Bullock (Barnsley), K Mottershead (Doncaster), McIlvenny (WBA), S Collymore (C Palace), P Devlin (Notts County), R Price (Birmingham City).

97-98 - Captain: D Humphreys **P.o.Y.:** S Jones **Top scorer:** S Wray

Back Row (L-R); Tyrone Mintus, Richard Mitchell, Steven Round, Farrell Kilburn, Peter Whiston (Sam Garry Mascot), Mark Deegan, Mark Perry, Dan Page, Adam Beazeley. Front Row; (Jack Kerry, Mascot), Shaun Wray, (Clifford West, Mascot), Stephen Jones, Delwyn Humphreys, Darren Bonghey, Neil Cartwright.

PROGRAMME DETAILS:
Pages: 36 **Price:** 80p
Editor: Andrew Eason
Tel:

STAMFORD

Colours: Red & white
Founded: 1896
Change Colours: Blue & white
Nickname: Daniels
Midweek matchday: Tuesday
Sponsors: Newflame
Reserves League: UCL Res Div 2
Local Newspapers: Stamford Mercury, Peterborough Evening Telegraph, Herald & Post.

Chairman: Arthur Twiddy **Vice-Chairman:** Bill Warrington
President:
Secretary: Lewis Lee, 3 Cromarty Road, Stamford, Lincs. PE9 2TQ (01780 756373)
Manager: Steve Evans. **Asst Manager:** Patrick O'Keeffe
Physio: Gerard Evans **Press Officer:** Andrew Eason
Ground: Wothorpe Road, Stamford, Lincs (01780 763079).
Directions: Off A43 Kettering Rd, 1 mile east of A1. 200 yds from station.
Capacity: 5,000 **Seats:** 250 **Cover:** 1,250 **Floodlights:** Yes
Clubhouse: Open matchdays, Sunday lunchtimes & evenings (bingo). Food available matchdays - hot and cold.
Club Shop: Wide range of Lge + non-Lge progs & club souvenirs. Contact Dave Salisbury (01780 752377)

PREVIOUS - **Grounds:** None **Leagues:** Peterborough/ Northants (UCL) 08-55/ Central Alliance 55-61/ Midland Co's 61-72/ UCL 72-98.

CLUB RECORDS - **Attendance:** 4,200 v Kettering, FA Cup 3rd Qual Rd 53. **Win:** 13-0 v Peterborough Reserves, Utd Co's Lge 29-30. **Defeat:** 0-17 v Rothwell, FA Cup 27-28. **Appearances:** Dick Kwiatkowski **Goalscorer:**: Bert Knighten

HONOURS - FA Vase 79-80 (R-up 75-76 83-84); Utd Co's Lg 75-76 77-78 79-80 80-81 81-82 96-97 97-98 (KO Cup 51-52 75-76 79-80 81-82 85-86); Northants Lg 11-12; Lincs Snr 'A' Cup 78-79 82-83; Lincs Snr 'B' Cup 51-52 53-54; William Scarber Mem. Cup 70-71 82-83 85-86 88-89 94-95; Stamford Chal. Cup 89-90; Lincs Jnr Cup 48-49.

Players to progress to Football League: A Birchenall (Chelsea, C/Palace, Leicester), R Chester (Aston Villa), T Tye (Chelsea), G Fell (Brighton, Southend, Torquay, York), C Chapman (Wolves), S Collins (Peterborough), K Alexander (Grimsby, Stockport, Lincoln), A Tillson (Grimsby, QPR, Bristol Rovers), B Stubbs (Notts Co.), D Genovese (Peterborough).

97-98 - Captain: Dean Elston **P.o.Y.:** Steve Kuhne **Top Scorer:** Steve Kuhne

Stamford AFC, celebrate after winning the United Counties Football League Premier Division to gain promotion to the Doc Martins League

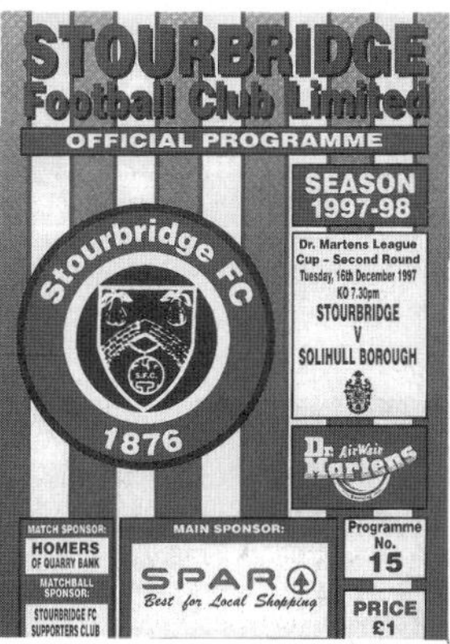

PROGRAMME DETAILS:
Pages: 28 **Price:** £1
Editors:
Hugh Clark & Nigel Gregg

STOURBRIDGE

Colours: Red & white stripes **Formed:** 1876
Change colours: Yellow & blue. **Nickname:** The Glassboys
Midweek matchday: Tues **Sponsors:** Spar, Wordsley Green/Carlsberg
Reserves' League: Midland Comb
Local Press: Stourbridge News & County Express, Express & Star, Dudley Evening Mail.
Local Radio: Radio West Wids, B.R.M.B., Beacon.

Managing Director: Steve Daniels **Chairman:** Larry Homer
Vice Chairman: Ray Cooper
Secretary / Press Officer: Hugh Clark, 10 Burnt Oak Drive, Stourbridge, West Mids DY8 1HL (01384 392975).
Manager: Steve Daniels **Coach:** Mick Guest **Physio:** Steve Ball
GROUND Address: War Memorial Athletic Ground, High Street, Amblecote, Stourbridge DY8 4HN (01384 394040).
Directions: Take A491, signposted Wolverhampton, from Stourbridge ring-road - ground 300yds on left immediately beyond traffic lights and opposite 'Royal Oak' pub. Buses 311, 313 from Dudley, and 256 from Wolverhampton, pass ground. One mile from Stourbridge Town (BR).
Capacity: 2,000 **Cover:** 1,250 **Seats:** 250 **Floodlights:** Yes
Clubhouse: Open every evening from 8pm and Sunday lunchtimes.
Club Shop: Programmes & souvenirs. Contact Nigel Gregg.

PREVIOUS - **Leagues:** West Midlands (previously Birmingham) 1892-1939 54-71, Birmingham Combination 45-53. **Grounds:** None. **Name:** Stourbridge Standard

CLUB RECORDS - **Attendance:** 5,726 v Cardiff City, Welsh Cup final 1st leg 74 (post war); 14,000 v W.B.A. Res 1901-02 Birm Lge (pre war). **Career Goalscorer:** Ron Page 269. **Career Appearances:** Ron Page 427. **Transfer fee received:** £20,000 for Tony Cunningham (Lincoln C 79). **Transfer fee paid:**

BEST SEASON - **FA Cup:** 4th Qual Rd: v Arnold 67-68, v V.S. Rugby 84-85 & 85-86. **FA Trophy:** Qtr Final 70-71

HONOURS - Welsh Cup R-up 73-74; Southern Lg Midland Div 90-91 (Lg Cup 92-93), Div 1 North 73-74, Merit Cup 73-74; West Mids (prev. Birmingham) Lg 23-24 (R-up 4); Birmingham Comb. R-up 51-52; Birmingham Snr Cup 49-50 45-46 75-76 (R-up 3); Worcs Snr Cup 9, (R-up 12); Herefordshire Snr Cup 54-55; Camkin Cup R-up 69-70; Camkin Presidents Cup 70-71; Albion Shield 43-44; Keys Cup 37-38 62-63, Worcs Comb. R-up 27-28; Worcester Jnr Cup R-up 27-28; Tillotson Cup R-up 39-40, Brierley Hill Lg R-up 44-45 (Lg Cup R-up 44-45); Brierley Hill Yth Lg Coronation Cup 56-57.

Players progressing to Football League: P Clark (Stockport Cnty 65), K Ball (Walsall 72), P Freeman (W B A 68), C Bates/R Haywood (Shrewsbury Tn 74), L Lawrence (Shrewsbury Tn 75), S Cooper (Torquay 78), T Cunningham (Lincoln 79), M Gwinnet (Peterborough 81).

97-98 - Captain: J Horne **Top scorer:** Toby Hall (23)
Supporters P.o.Y.: John Horne **Players P.o.Y.:** Steve Wilkinson

Back Row (L-R); Albert Johnson, Steve Wilkinson, Toby Hall, Gary Bruce, Steve Johnson, Rob Grant, Steve Ingram. Front Row; Richard Parker, Tim Nicholls, John Horne, Andy Wright, Adam Bastable, Gary Hackett.

PROGRAMME DETAILS:
Pages: 20 **Price:** 80p
Editor: Peter Young
Tel.

SUTTON COLDFIELD TOWN

Colours: Blue & white/blue/blue & white **Formed:** 1897
Change colours: Red & black/red/red & black **Nickname:** Royals
Midweek matchday: Tuesday
Reserves' League: No reserve team
Local Press: Sutton Coldfield News, Sutton Observer.
Local Radio: BRMB, Radio WM.

Chairman: Kevin Holt
Secretary: Fred Rought, 25 Lebanon Grove, Chase Terrace, Burntwood, Staffs. WS7 8BE (01543 685029).
Press Officer: Brian Turner **Commercial Manager:** Peter Young.
Manager: Gary Bradder **Asst Man:** Alan Hampton **Physio:** Reg Brassington

GROUND Address: Central Ground, Coles Lane, Sutton Coldfield B72 1NL (0121 354 2997/0121 355 5475).
Directions: A5127 into Sutton, right at Odeon cinema (Holland Road), then first right into Coles Lane - ground 150 yds on left. 10 mins walk from Sutton Coldfield (BR), bus 104 from Birmingham.
Capacity: 4,500 **Cover:** 500 **Seats:** 200 **Floodlights:** Yes
Clubhouse: Brick built lounge and concert room, fully carpeted and extensively decorated. Open daily, food available.
Club Shop: Selling metal badges, scarves, hats, pens, rosettes, progs. Contact Paul Vanes (0121 770 9835).

PREVIOUS - **Leagues:** Central Birmingham, Walsall Senior, Staffs County, Birmingham Combination 50-54, West Mids (Regional) 54-65 79-82, Midlands Combination 65-79. **Grounds:** Meadow Plat 1879-89/ Coles Lane (site of current ambulance station) 90-1919. **Name:** Sutton Coldfield FC 1879-1921.

CLUB RECORDS - **Attendance:** 2,029 v Doncaster Rovers, F.A. Cup 80-81 (Receipts £2,727). **Win:** **Defeat:** **Career Goalscorer:** Eddie Hewitt 288 **Career Appearances:** Eddie Hewitt 465 **Fee paid:** £1,500 twice in 1991, for Lance Morrison (Gloucester) & Micky Clarke (Burton A.) **Fee received:** £25,000 for Barry Cowdrill (WBAl 1979).

BEST SEASON - **FA Cup:** 1st Rd 80-81 (lost 0-1 to Doncaster), 92-93 (1-2 at Wanderers). **FA Trophy:** 1st Round replay 1989-90 **FA Amateur Cup:** 2nd Round 1970-71.

HONOURS - Southern Lg Midland Div R-up 82-83, West Mids Lg 79-80 (Lg Cup 80-81 81-82), Midland Comb.(2) 77-79 (R-up(2) 69-71, Lg Cup 69-70), Walsall Senior Lg 46-47, Walsall Sen. Cup(3) 77-80 (R-up 80-81), Staffs Sen. Cup R-up 89-90 (SF 84-85 86-87), Lord Mayor of Birmingham Charity Cup 95-96, R-up 93-94, Worcs Sen. Cup SF 88-89, Walsall Challenge Cup R-up 46-47 47-48, Sutton Charity Cup 46-47 65-66 71-72 86-87 89-90 90-91, Express & Star Cup 44-45.

Players progressing to Football League: Arthur Corbett (Walsall 1949), Paul Cooper (Manchester City), Noel Blake (Leeds), Steve Cooper (Barnsley), Peter Latchford (WBA & Celtic), Mark Smith (Wolves), John Barton (Everton), Barry Cowdrill (WBA 1979), Colin Dryhurst (Halifax 1979), Dale Belford (Notts County 1987), Ellis Laight (Torquay 1992).

Sutton Coldfield Town

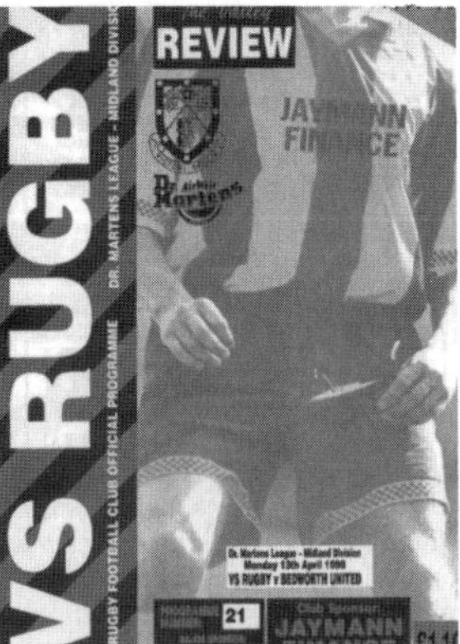

PROGRAMME DETAILS:
Pages: 36 **Price:** £1
Editor: Terry Coley
Tel: 0121 240 4521

V.S. RUGBY

Colours: Navy & sky/navy/sky
Change colours: All White
Midweek matchday: Wednesday
Club Newsline: 0891 10 19 99
Reserves' League: No reserve team
Local Press: Rugby Advertiser, Coventry Evening Telegraph, Rugby Observer
Local Radio: Mercia Sound, CWR

Formed: 1956
Nickname: The Valley
Sponsors: Jaymann Finance

Chairman: Peter Kilvert **Commercial Manager:** Ray Dickenson
Secretary: Doug Wilkins, 298 Rocky Lane, Great Barr, Birmingham B42 1NQ 0121 681 1544 H & Fax)
Press Officer: Alun Turner (01788 567181)
Manager: Alan Lewer **Coach:**
Asst Manager: Darren Heyes **Physio:** Alan Cooke

GROUND Address: Butlin Road, Rugby, Warks CV21 3ST (01788 543692).
Directions: The ground is situated off Clifton (B5414) on the north side of Rugby. 1 mile walk from the station.
Capacity: 6,000 **Cover:** 1,000 **Seats:** 240 **Floodlights:** Yes
Clubhouse: Open every night and weekend lunchtimes. Entertainment Saturday nights. Excellent facilities include Long Alley Skittles, darts and pool.
Club Shop: Yes

PREVIOUS - **Name:** Valley Sports, Valley Sports Rugby. **Leagues:** Rugby & District 1956-63, Coventry & Partnership, North Warks 63-69, United Counties 69-75, West Midlands 75-83

CLUB RECORDS - **Attendance:** 3,961 v Northampton FA Cup 1984 **Win:** 10-0 v Ilkeston Tn FA Trophy 4/9/85 **Defeat:** 8-0 v Shepshed, Midland F/Lit Lge 23/12/87 **Career Goalscorer:** Danny Conway, 124 **Career Appearances:** Danny Conway, 374 **Transfer fee paid:** £3,500 R Smith, I Crawley, G Bradder **Transfer fee received:** £15,000 T Angus (Northampton)

BEST SEASON - **FA Cup:** 2nd round 87-88, plus 1st Rd 84-85 85-86 86-87 94-95 **League clubs defeated:** None

HONOURS - Southern Lg Midland Div 86-87 (R-up 94-95, Lg Cup 89-90), FA Vase 82-83, Midland F'lit Cup 84-85 89-90 (R-up 86-87), Birmingham Snr Cup 88-89 91-92, Utd Co's Lg Div 3 Cup 69-70. (all-time record FA Trophy win; 10-0 away to Ilkeston Town, Preliminary Rd 85-86).

Players progressing to Football League: S Storer (Birmingham 1985), S Bicknell (Leicester), S Norris (Scarborough), T Angus (Northampton Town), Ashley Walker (Peterborough), Ian King (Stoke City).

V S Rugby

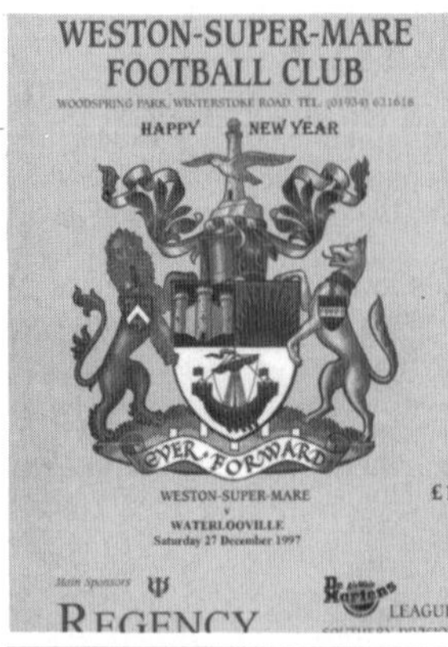

PROGRAMME DETAILS:
Pages: 32 **Price:** £1
Editor: Secretary
Tel. 01934 635665

WESTON-SUPER-MARE

Colours: White/blue/blue **Formed:** 1899
Change colours: All yellow **Nickname:** Seagulls
Midweek matches: Monday **Sponsors:** Regency
Reserves' League: None
Local Press: Bristol Evening Post, Western Daily Press.
Local Radio: Somerset Sound, Radio Bristol.

President: D A Usher **Chairman:** Paul T Bliss
Secretary / Press Officer: Keith Refault, c/o Weston Super Mare FC, 01934 635665 **Manager:** Len Ashurst
Asst Manager: John Relish **Physio:** Dave Lukins

GROUND Address: Woodspring Park, Winterstoke Road, Weston-super-Mare BS23 2YG 01934 6355665/621618. **Directions:** M5 Jct 21. A370 along dual carriageway to 4th roundabout. First left and immediately right at roundabout, club on right. From South: M5 Jct 22, follow Weston signs for approx 7 miles, right at first r'bout (by Hospital), left at next r'bout, ground 1 mile on left. 20 mins. walk from Weston-super-Mare (BR).
Seats: 250 **Cover:** 1,000 **Capacity:** 2,000 **Floodlights:** Yes
Clubhouse: Mon-Fri 7-11pm, Sat 12-11pm, Sun 12-3 & 7-11pm. 2 skittle alleys, 2 bars. Bar meals and hot meals everyday.
Club Shop: Selling a wide range of souvenirs & programmes. Contact Mr Geoff Milsom, 12 Greenland Road, Milton, Weston-s-Mare BS22 8JP (01934 413059).

PREVIOUS - **League:** Western 1900-92. **Name:** Borough of Weston-super-Mare. **Grounds:** The Great Ground, Locking Road 48-55, Langford Road 55-83.

CLUB RECORDS - **Attendance:** 2,623 v Woking, FA Cup First Round Proper replay 23/11/93. *At Langford Road: 2,500 v Bridgwater Town, FA Cup First Round Proper replay 1961-62.* **Win:** 11-0 v Paulton Rovers. **Defeat:** 1-12 v Yeovil Town Reserves. **Career Goalscorer:** Matthew Lazenby, 180. **Career Appearances:** Harry Thomas, 740. **Transfer fee paid:** None. **Transfer fee received:** £20,000 Stuart Jones from Sheffield Wednesday 98.

BEST SEASON - **FA Cup:** 1st Rd Proper replay 61-62 (lost 0-1 after 0-0 draw at Bridgwater Town) 94-95 (lost 0-1 after 2-2 draw at Woking). **FA Vase:** Do not enter. **FA Trophy:** 1st Rd 86-87 89-90 92-93 93-94

HONOURS - Somerset Snr Cup 23-24 26-27; Western Lg Champions 91-92 (R-up 76-77), Lg Cup 76-77 (R-up 89-90), Merit Cup 76-77 77-78; Somerset Snr Lg (Reserves) Div 1 87-88 (R-up 90-91), Div 2 R-up 85-86, Div 3 84-85.

Players progressing to Football League: Shaun Rouse (Carlisle United 94), Ian Maine, John Palmer, Wayne Brown, Stuart Jones (Sheffield Wed 98).

97-98 - Captain: Andy Llewellyn **P.o.Y.:** Ryan Souter **Top scorer:** Gareth Morgan (12)

Back Row (L-R); Dave Lukins (Physio), Lee Rogers, Tim Malessa, Lee Jones, Mark Price, Neil Fitzgerald, Dave Bell. Front Row; James Holt, Steve Lowndes, Andy Llewellyn, Leigh White, Linden Jones, Craig Dann.
Photo: Andrew Chitty

PROGRAMME DETAILS:
Pages: 40 **Price:** £ 1
Editor: Gordon Smith
Tel: 01945 581767

WISBECH TOWN

Colours: All red. **Founded:** 1920.
Change colours: Yellow/green/yellow **Nickname:** Fenmen.
Midweek Matchday: Wednesday **Newsline:** 0930 555 865.
Local Press: Fenland Citizen, Wisbech Standard
Local Radio: Radio Cambridgeshire

Chairman: Eddie Anderson **Vice Chairman:** John Petch
President: J W A Chilvers
Secretary: John Petch, 34 Walton Road, Wisbech, Cambs PE13 3EN, (01945 584333 & Fax)
Manager: Gary Childs **Coach:** Alex Irvine
Physio: P Ward **Press Officer:** R Green
GROUND Address: Fenland Park, Lerowe Road, Wisbech, Cambs (01945 584176).
Directions: Follow A47 bypass to the West Walton turn off roundabout where there is a Little Chef, turn left for Wisbech, Lerowe Road is first left after 30mph sign. Entering town from north along A1101 cross Freedom Bridge, at roundabout go straight over sign Walsoken/West Walton.
Seats: 258 **Cover:** 1,000 **Capacity:** 3,800 **Floodlights:** Yes
Clubhouse: Open every day. Matchday food & drink; Tea, coffee, cold drinks, confectionary, burgers, hotdogs, soup, sandwiches, rolls.
Club Shop: Yes, selling replica shirts, caps, pennants, pens, scarves etc. Contact Club Secretary.

PREVIOUS - **Names:** **Leagues:** Peterborough/ Utd Co's 35-50/ Eastern Co's 50-52 70-97/ Midland 52-58/ Southern 58-70. **Grounds:** Wisbech Park 20-21/ Waisoken Rectory 21-22/ Harecroft Rd 22-47.

CLUB RECORDS - **Attendance:** 8,004 v Peterborough United, Midland League 25/8/57. **Goalscorer:** Bert Titmarsh 246 (31-37). **Appearances:** Jamie Brighty (731). **Win:** 18-1 v Rushden 45-46. **Defeat:** 1-10 v Brighton FA Cup 65-66. **Fee Paid:** None. **Fee Received:** £3,000.

BEST SEASON - **FA Trophy:** 3rd Qual Rd. **FA Vase:** SF 84-85, 85-86. **FA Cup:** 2nd Rd 57-58, 97-98. **League clubs defeated:** Colchester

HONOURS - Southern Lg Div 1 61-62; Utd Co's Lg (4) 46-48 49-50 61-62 (res) (R-up 48-49, Lg Cup 35-36 (R-up 46-47); Midland Lg R-up 57-58; Eastern Co's Lg 71-72 76-77 90-91 (R-up 70-71 73-74 83-84 92-93 96-97), Lg Cup 50-51 70-71 71-72 (R-up 73-74 76-77 86-87); Cambs Invit Cup(8) 52-53 55-56 57-58 74-76 81-83 91-92; E Anglian Cup 87-88 (R-up 40-41 48-49); Peterborough Lg 24-25 27-28 28-29 31-32 32-33; Peterborough Snr Cup 32-33 76-77 89-90 97-98.

Players progressing to Football League: Chris Watts/Robert Taylor (Norwich City), Bryan Harvey/Terry Marshall (Newcastle), Jackie Callagher (Peterboro), Paul Scott (Blackpool), Peter Dobson (Ipswich).

97-98 - Captain: Andy Moore **P.o.Y.:** Peter Munns **Top scorer:** Ian Williams

Back Row (L-R); Joe Green, Alex Irvine (Coach), Matthew Heaton, Jason Bowler, Warren Ward, Lee Bray, Shaun Keeble, Paul Agnew, Andy Moore, Ian Williams. Front Row; Phil Ward (Physio), Tom Watson, Gary Childs (Player/Mgr), Phil Marshall, Peter Munns, Kevin Topliss, Chris Dear.

SOUTHERN DIVISION

FINAL LEAGUE TABLE 1997-98

			Home			Away						
		P	*W*	*D*	*L*	*W*	*D*	*L*	*F*	*A*	*GD*	*Pts*
1	Weymouth	42	16	1	4	16	1	4	107	48	59	98
2	Chelmsford City	42	17	1	3	12	7	2	86	39	47	95
3	Bashley	42	19	2	0	10	2	9	101	59	42	91
4	Newport IoW	42	12	5	4	13	4	4	72	34	38	84
5	Fisher Ath London	42	13	4	4	12	1	8	87	50	37	80
6	Margate	42	14	3	4	9	5	7	71	42	29	77
7	Newport AFC	42	12	3	6	9	3	9	83	65	18	69
8	Witney Town	42	13	3	5	7	6	8	74	58	16	69
9	Clevedon Town	42	8	6	7	12	1	8	57	55	2	67
10	Waterlooville	42	12	2	7	5	5	11	69	64	5	58
11	Dartford	42	11	3	7	6	4	11	60	60	0	58
12	Havant Town	42	6	8	7	7	6	8	65	70	-5	53
13	Fleet Town	42	10	3	8	6	2	13	63	83	-20	53
14	Tonbridge Angels	42	8	7	6	6	3	12	49	55	-6	52
15	Trowbridge Town	42	9	1	11	5	5	11	55	69	-14	48
16	Erith & Belvedere	42	8	6	7	3	7	11	47	68	-21	46
17	Fareham Town	42	8	5	8	4	4	13	75	87	-12	45
18	Cirencester Town	42	6	5	10	6	2	13	63	88	-25	43
19	Weston super Mare	42	7	2	12	5	3	13	49	86	-37	41
20	Baldock Town	42	7	1	13	3	4	14	53	81	-28	35
21	Cinderford Town	42	1	4	16	5	1	15	40	112	-72	23
22	Yate Town	42	3	4	14	2	3	16	44	97	-53	22

SOUTHERN DIVISION RESULTS CHART 1997-98

		1	2	3	4	5	6	7	8	9	10	11	12	13	14	15	16	17	18	19	20	21	22
1	Baldock T	X	1-2	0-2	3-2	1-4	1-3	3-1	1-2	3-1	1-2	5-0	1-2	0-3	0-2	0-3	2-1	0-1	2-2	2-1	1-2	2-3	2-0
2	Bashley	2-0	X	3-2	6-1	2-1	2-0	2-2	6-2	5-0	2-1	2-1	2-0	3-1	2-2	2-1	2-1	4-1	3-0	2-1	4-2	2-0	2-1
3	Chelmsford	1-0	3-1	X	3-0	4-1	2-0	1-4	6-0	1-0	2-0	5-0	3-2	2-1	0-2	1-1	1-0	1-0	1-0	4-0	0-3	1-0	3-1
4	Cinderford	1-1	0-4	0-3	X	2-5	1-2	2-0	1-2	3-3	1-2	0-1	1-1	0-4	2-3	0-2	2-4	0-2	2-2	1-4	0-2	1-3	0-2
5	Cirencester	1-0	2-3	1-2	1-2	X	0-1	1-1	1-1	1-0	2-1	2-2	3-4	2-1	0-0	2-3	0-2	1-1	0-1	1-2	0-4	2-1	3-1
6	Clevedon	0-0	0-4	1-1	4-1	2-4	X	1-3	1-1	2-0	1-0	3-0	0-2	2-2	2-4	1-1	1-0	2-3	2-1	1-0	0-3	0-0	2-0
7	Dartford	2-1	2-0	0-1	0-3	0-3	0-1	X	2-1	3-1	0-2	0-2	0-0	1-0	4-2	0-0	1-0	2-0	4-0	3-3	2-3	2-0	5-2
8	Erith & Belv.	1-2	0-3	2-2	0-1	4-0	2-1	2-1	X	1-1	1-0	2-1	0-0	1-1	0-2	1-2	0-0	0-2	5-2	2-0	0-2	1-1	1-0
9	Fareham T	6-6	5-2	2-2	7-0	5-1	0-2	1-3	0-0	X	0-2	6-1	2-1	0-3	3-1	0-5	2-3	0-1	1-2	1-0	3-3	1-1	4-1
10	Fisher Ath	5-1	5-2	1-1	4-1	2-2	1-2	2-1	3-0	3-0	X	2-1	2-1	1-2	2-3	2-1	1-0	2-0	1-1	5-2	0-2	3-3	1-0
11	Fleet Tn	2-1	1-2	2-2	2-3	4-1	2-0	3-2	2-1	2-2	2-5	X	2-2	0-2	1-0	0-1	1-2	2-1	2-1	1-4	0-2	2-1	2-0
12	Havant Tn	5-3	0-2	1-1	2-0	3-1	0-3	0-1	2-2	0-2	3-2	1-1	X	2-2	2-3	0-2	2-2	1-0	1-1	3-3	1-2	4-3	2-2
13	Margate	2-0	0-2	2-2	4-0	2-0	3-1	1-1	3-1	1-2	1-0	2-1	2-0	X	2-1	0-1	1-0	1-1	2-1	2-0	2-0	3-0	1-2
14	Newport AFC	3-1	1-1	1-2	2-1	2-3	3-2	3-1	2-1	7-1	4-2	1-0	0-1	3-0	X	2-2	1-0	5-1	2-0	1-2	1-3	0-1	2-2
15	Newport IoW	2-1	4-2	1-4	2-1	3-1	0-2	3-0	2-1	2-1	0-0	4-0	0-0	1-2	2-0	X	1-0	0-0	1-0	1-1	1-2	1-1	5-0
16	Tonbridge A	1-0	1-1	0-2	3-0	1-0	0-2	2-1	1-1	1-1	0-2	1-3	2-1	1-1	2-1	0-1	X	1-1	1-1	2-1	2-4	3-1	0-0
17	Trowbridge	2-0	3-1	1-2	0-0	5-1	1-3	1-2	1-2	2-0	1-2	1-0	2-3	0-1	3-2	0-2	1-4	X	0-3	4-0	3-1	0-1	2-1
18	Waterlooville	2-1	1-2	1-2	3-1	3-1	0-1	2-1	5-0	4-2	0-1	4-1	3-2	1-0	1-1	1-4	2-3	4-0	X	1-0	2-3	1-1	5-1
19	Weston SM	1-2	2-1	0-3	0-2	1-3	0-0	0-0	1-0	0-4	1-4	0-3	0-5	1-3	4-1	0-1	2-0	3-2	4-2	X	1-2	0-4	2-0
20	Weymouth	3-1	4-1	2-1	9-0	3-1	2-0	2-0	1-0	2-1	2-4	2-3	5-0	1-1	3-2	1-0	4-1	3-1	0-1	4-0	X	1-2	4-2
21	Witney Tn	0-0	4-0	0-1	3-0	4-2	5-1	3-1	1-1	3-1	0-4	3-2	1-2	1-4	2-3	2-0	2-0	1-1	2-0	3-1	2-1	X	2-1
22	Yate Town	0-1	0-5	2-3	2-1	2-2	0-2	0-1	2-2	1-3	0-3	2-5	1-1	3-0	1-2	0-3	1-1	5-3	0-2	0-1	1-3	2-3	X

Dr MARTENS SOUTHERN DIVISION Ten Year Records

	88/9	89/0	90/1	91/2	92/3	93/4	94/5	95/6	96/7	97/8
Andover	18	18	9	7	20	-	-	-	-	-
Ashford Town	-	-	5	9	8	6	5	2	-	-
Baldock Town	6	10	4	11	13	7	2	-	-	20
Bashley	-	1	-	-	-	-	7	16	13	3
Braintree Town	-	-	-	4	9	13	14	5	-	-
Buckingham Town	16	3	1	5	12	12	-	-	22	-
Burnham	5	11	11	10	16	16	22	-	-	-
Bury Town	4	9	12	17	22	22	18	-	-	-
Canterbury City	13	15	18	21	17	20	-	-	-	-
Chelmsford City	1	-	-	-	-	-	-	-	-	2
Cinderford Town	-	-	-	-	-	-	-	14	17	21
Cirencester Town	-	-	-	-	-	-	-	-	16	18
Clevedon Town	-	-	-	-	-	-	11	17	11	9
Corinthian	22	21	21	-	-	-	-	-	-	-
Dartford	-	-	-	-	-	-	-	-	14	11
Dunstable	15	4	17	16	21	18	-	-	-	-
Erith & Belvedere	17	20	19	20	7	19	19	21	21	16
Fareham Town	-	12	20	19	15	14	21	20	12	17
Fisher 93	-	-	-	-	19	17	17	15	10	5
Fleet Town	-	-	-	-	-	-	-	19	20	13
Folkstone Town	11	17	w/d	-	-	-	-	-	-	-
Forest Green Rovers	-	-	-	-	-	-	-	8	1	-
Gosport Borough	-	-	15	22	-	-	-	-	-	-
Gravesend & Northfleet	2	-	-	-	4	1	-	-	-	-
Hastings Town	7	8	7	1	-	-	-	-	-	-
Havant Town	-	-	-	3	5	5	3	7	3	12
Hounslow	8	19	-	-	-	-	-	-	-	-
Hythe Town	-	6	8	13	-	-	-	-	-	-
Margate	20	16	10	14	10	9	13	11	5	6
Newport AFC	-	-	-	-	-	-	-	-	-	7
Newport Isle of Wight	-	-	14	15	18	8	9	4	9	4
Poole Town	3	2	-	-	14	15	20	22	-	-
Ruislip	22	-	-	-	-	-	-	-	-	-
Salisbury	9	5	3	12	2	4	1	-	-	-
Sheppey United	19	22	-	-	-	-	-	-	-	-
Sittingbourne	-	-	-	6	1	-	-	1	-	-
St Leonards Stamcroft	-	-	-	-	-	-	-	-	2	-
Sudbury Town	-	-	13	8	6	2	-	-	-	-
Tonbridge Angels	21	-	-	-	11	-	12	18	8	14
Trowbridge Town	10	7	2	-	-	-	-	9	18	15
Waterlooville	-	-	-	-	-	-	4	3	15	10
Wealdstone	-	-	-	-	11	21	15	-	-	-
Weston Super Mare	-	-	-	-	-	-	6	13	4	19
Weymouth	-	-	-	2	-	10	8	6	7	1
Witney Town	14	14	16	18	3	3	10	12	6	8
Yate Town	-	13	6	-	-	-	16	10	19	22
No of Clubs Competing	22	22	21	22	22	22	22	22	22	22

ANDOVER

Colours: Red & black/black/red
Change cols: Blue & white/white/white
Midweek matchday: Tuesday
Reserve Team's League: None.

Founded: 1883.
Nickname: The Lions.
Sponsors:

Chairman: Mick Burford **President:** R Coleman
Secretary: Chris Jeremy, 23 Stubbs Court, Artists Way, Andover, Hants SP10 3QR (01264 361973)
Manager: Ken Cunningham-Brown **Asst Manager:** Mike Burford
Physio: Chris Burford
Ground: Portway Stadium, West Portway Industrial Estate, Andover SP10 3LF (01264 333052).
Directions: From the Andover By-pass A303 follow the signs to Portway Industrial estate. On exiting the A303 turn right at r/about and over bridge, bear off left at next mini r/about and after 150yards turn right onto estate. head straight on until you enter Hopkinson Way, ground on left 400/500 yards.
Capacity: 3,000 **Cover:** 250 **Seats:** 250 **Floodlights:** Yes
Clubhouse: Open matchdays & private functions
Club Shop: No. **Metal Badges:** Yes.
PROGRAMME DETAILS: Pages: 50 **Price:** 50p

PREVIOUS - **Leagues:** Salisbury & D./ Hants 1896-98, 1899-1901, 02-62; Southern 1898-99, 1971-93; Western 1962-71.

CLUB RECORDS - **Attendance:** 1,100 v Leicester, ground opening. *(3,484 v Gillingham at Walled Meadow, previous ground).* **Goalscorer:** T Randall 73 **Appearances:** P Pollard 469

BEST SEASON - **FA Cup:** 1st Rd 62-63 (lost 0-1 to Gillingham).
FA Trophy: 3rd Qual Rd 69-70, 70-71.
FA Vase: 4th Rd 94-95 (lost 1-3 at Falmouth Town)

HONOURS - Wessex Lg R-up 94-95, R-up 69-70 70-71; Hants Lg 13-14 24-25 33-34 44-45 48-49 50-51 61-62 (R-up 42-43), Northern Div 13-14, Div 2 R-up 37-38; Salisbury & Dist Lg 1894-95 95-96 96-97 99-1900 03-04 07-08 12-13; Hants Sen Cup 48-49 50-51 55-56 64-65; Russell Cotes Cup 23-24 31-32 37-38 44-45 52-53 58-59 60-61 61-62; Pickfords Cup 50-51; Hants Interm Cup 59-60 60-61; Hants Junior Cup 19-20 (R-up 1894-95 1910-11 12-13).

Players progressing to Football League: Keith Wilson (Soton 1959), Nigel Spackman (B'mouth 1980), Colin Court (Reading 1981), A Kingston (Soton), P Brown (Soton, Walsall), Emeka Nwajiobi (Luton).

L-R, Back Row: Chris Burford (physio), Paul Clarkson, John Wilson, Hedley Winter, Jamie-Lee Harris, David Hunt, Sean Saunders (player-coach), Scott Tarrant, Joey Collins, Phil Tye. Front Row: Paul Odey, Paul Atkins, Lee Abbott, John Scott, Tony Long, Robbie Trim, Alan Kennedy, Guy Dipper. Photo courtesy of Andover Advertiser.

PROGRAMME DETAILS:
Pages: 32 **Price:** £ 1.00
Editor: Elaine Orsbourne

ASHFORD TOWN

Colours: All Green **Formed:** 1930
Change colours: All White **Nickname:** Nuts & Bolts
Midweek home matchday: Tuesday
Reserve Team's League: No Reserve team
Local Press: Kentish Express
Local Radio: Radio Kent, Invicta Radio

Chairman: Ernie Warren **President:** Ashley M Batt
Secretary/Press Officer: A Lancaster, 128 Kingsnorth Rd, Ashford, Kent TN23 2HY (01233 621325). **Vice Chairman:** Peter Barton
Manager: Nigel Donn **Asst Manager:** None
Coach: Nicky Sparks **Physio:** George Sargeant
Commercial Director: Ernie Warron, (01233 634125)
GROUND Address: The Homelands, Ashford Road, Kingsnorth, Ashford, Kent TN26 1NJ (01233 611838).
Directions: M20 jct 10, follow A2070 signs towards Brenzett & Lydd airport, dual carriageway to junction of old A2070, ground one mile on left through village of Kingsnorth. 4 miles south of Ashford
Capacity: 3,200 **Cover:** 1,250 **Seats:** 500 **Floodlights:** Yes
Clubhouse: Open matchdays and for special functions. Licensed bar, function room. Limited food - sandwiches & simple snacks.
Club Shop: Sells old progs, pennants, scarves, badges etc. Contact Alan Bird (01233 662680)

PREVIOUS - **Names:** Ashford United, Ashford Railway, Ashford F.C. **Leagues:** Kent 30-59. **Ground:** Essella Park, Essella Rd 30-87.

CLUB RECORDS - **Attendance:** 6,525 (at Essella Park, previous ground), v Crystal Palace, FA Cup 1st Rd 1959. 3,363 (at current ground), v Fulham FA Cup 1st Round 1994. **Goalscorer:** Dave Arter 197. **Appearances:** Peter McRobert 765. **Win:** 10-1 v Bury Town, February 1964. **Defeat:** 0-8 v Crawley Town, November 1964. **Fee Paid:** £7,000 for J Ross & D Arter (Sittingbourne, March 94). **Fee Received:** £25,000 for Jeff Ross & Dave Arter (Hythe Tn, 90). *Individually: £20,000 for Lee McRobert (Sittingbourne, 93).*

BEST SEASON - **FA Trophy:** Semi Final 72-73, 96-97 2nd Rd **FA Cup:** 2nd Rd 61-62 (0-3 v QPR [H]), 66-67 (0-5 v Swindon [A]). 1st Rd 7 times. - **League clubs defeated:** None.

HONOURS - FA Trophy SF 72-73; Southern Lg Southern Div R-up 86-87 95-96; Kent Lg 48-49 (R-up 31-32), Lg Cup 38-39; Kent Senior Cup 58-59 62-63 92-93 95-96

Players progressing to Football League: Ollie Norris (Rochdale 61), Howard Moore (Coventry 66), Tony Godden (WBA 75), Lee McRobert (Millwall 94)

97-98 - Captain: **P.o.Y.:** Dave Scott **Top scorer:** Dave Scott/Stuart Harrison (5)

Back Row (L-R); Mike Perfect (Dir), Peter McRobert, Dave Scott, Maurice Mundon, Stuart White, Ian Ross, Matt Bower, George Sergeant (Physio), Bert Sutton (Dir), Sue Warren, Pat Earl (Dir). Front Row; Lee Lough, Graham Porter, Stuart Harrison, Paul Wilson, Tony Reynolds, Paul Obrien, Nigel Donn (Player/Mgr), Mascots Philip & Gemma May

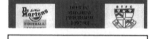

PROGRAMME DETAILS:
Pages: 48 **Price:** £1
Editor: TBA

BALDOCK TOWN

Colours: All red **Formed:** 1889
Change colours: All white **Nickname:** Reds
Midweek home matchday: Wednesday
Reserve Team's League: No reserve team.
Local Press: Comet, Gazette.
Local Radio: Radio Bedfordshire, Chiltern.

Joint Chairmen: Mike Watson-Challis & Ray Childerstone
Secretary: Cyril T Hammond, 2 Elmwood Court, High Str., Baldock, Herts SG7 6AY. 01462 894253 (H) 01462 895449 (B).
General Manager: B Williams
Team Manager: Robbie O'Keefe **Physio:** Fred Day.
Press Officer: David Hammond (01462 892797)

GROUND Address: Norton Road, Baldock, Herts SG7 5AU (01462 895449).
Directions: Off A1(M) at Letchworth/Baldock sign, left to 3rd island, A505 to Baldock, Norton Road is left off A505, left past Orange Tree pub, ground on right after railway bridge. From North or East turn left into town, Hitchin Street, right into Norton then proceed as above. From Baldock station (Kings Cross to Royston line) - left down Ickneild Way and right into Norton Road.
Capacity: 3,000 **Cover:** 1,250 **Seats:** 250 **Clubhouse:** Members' bar and separate function room. Food available.
Club Shop: No. **Metal Badges:** Yes
Supporters Club: Phil Rosendale (01462 223135)

PREVIOUS - **Ground:** Bakers Close (until 1982). **Leagues:** South Midlands 25-39 47-54 63-83, Parthenon 54-59, London 59-63, United Counties 83-87.

CLUB RECORDS - **Attendance:** 1,588 v Stevenage Boro. FA Cup 2nd Prelim 96-97
Goalscorer: Unknown. **Appearances:** Keith (Paddy) Stanton 550. **Fee Paid:** £2,000; for Colin Hull (Bishop's Stortford); for Glen Russell (Braintree 1993). **Fee Received:** £30,000 for Kevin Phillips (Watford F.C.).

BEST SEASON - **FA Vase:** 5th Round 83-84. **FA Trophy:** 2nd Qual. Round 90-91. **FA Cup:** 4th Qual. Round replay (0-1 v Halesowen Town [A] after 1-1 draw) 91-92.

HONOURS - United Counties Lg R-up 83-84 86-87, South Mids Lg 27-28 65-66 67-68 69-70 (R-up 53-54 82-83, Lg Cup 65-66 69-70, Div 1 49-50, Reserve Div 1 66-67), Herts Charity Cup 91-92 94-95, Herts Charity Shield 57-58 69-70, Wallspan Floodlit Cup 85-86, Hinchingbrooke Cup 86-87, TSI Floodlit Cup 88-89, Woolwich E.B.S. Cup 83-84, Herts Intermediate Cup 86-87. Southern Lge R-up 94-95. Southern Lge Cup Dr Martens 95-96

Players progressing to Football League: Ian Dowie (Luton & West Ham), Alan Stewart (Portsmouth), Kevan Phillips (Watford).

Back Row (L-R); Roy Ryall (Physio), Jay Thomas, Danny Power, Zema Abbey, David Walton, Adam Turner, Gary Simpson, Danny Swaile. Front Row; Danny Howell, Stuart Strange, Steve Cook, Ray Kilby, Neil Ryan, Marcelle Bruce.

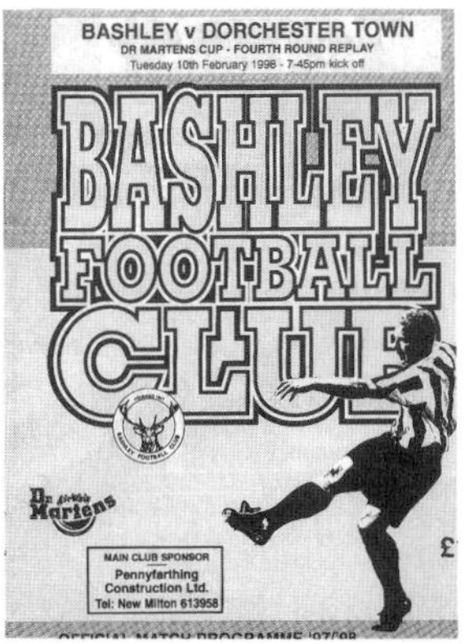

PROGRAMME DETAILS:
Pages: 36 **Price:** £1
Editor:

BASHLEY

Colours: Yellow & black **Formed:** 1947
Change colours: Blue & white. **Nickname:** The Bash
Midweek matchday: Tuesday **Sponsors:** Jacksons Mercedes
Reserves' League: Wessex Comb.
Local Press: Bournemouth Echo, Southern Pink, New Milton Advertiser.
Local Radio: 2CR Solent, Ocean Sound.

Chairman: R J Pinney **President:** Ian Hassell
Vice Chairman: Frank Whitman
Secretary: Ian Hassell, 35 Freshwater Road, Christchurch, Dorset BH23 4PD.
Commercial Manager: Mary Whitman
Press Officer: Terry Collett
Manager: Jimmy Case **Asst Manager/Coach:** Barry Blankney
Physio: Chris Lovegrove
GROUND Address: Recreation Ground, Bashley, Hampshire BH25 5RY. Tel: 01425 620280. **Directions:** A35 Lyndhurst towards Christchurch, turn left down B3058 towards New Milton, ground on left in Bashley village. Half hour walk from New Milton (BR) station
Capacity: 4,250 **Cover:** 1,200 **Seats:** 200 **Floodlights:** Yes
Clubhouse: Usual licensing hours. Snacks available.
Club Shop: Open matchdays - contact Anna Keegan

PREVIOUS - **Leagues:** Bournemouth 50-83/ Hants 83-86/ Wessex 86-89.

CLUB RECORDS - **Attendance:** 3,500 v Emley, F.A. Vase S.F. 1st Leg 87-88 **Win:** 21-1 v Co-operative (A), Bournemouth League, 64. **Defeat:** 2-20 v Air Speed (A), Bournemouth League, 57. **Career Goalscorer:** Colin Cummings (128) **Career Appearances:** John Bone (829) **Transfer fee paid:** £7,500 for J Stagg from Andover **Transfer fee received:** £7,500 for Darren Powell from Weymouth 95

BEST SEASON - **FA Cup:** 2nd Rd Proper, 1994-95 (0-1 v Swansea City) **FA Vase:** Semi Final 87-88, Qtr Final 88-89 **FA Trophy:** 2nd Round 91-92

HONOURS - Southern Lg Southern Division 89-90 (Lg Cup SF 89-90), Wessex Lg 86-87 87-88 88-89, Hants Lg Div 3 84-85, Hants Lg Combination 88-89, Russell Cotes Cup 88-89 90-91 92-93.

Past Players who have progressed into The Football League: Wayne Brown (Bristol City, 1994).

97-98 **Captain:** Dave Morris **P.o.Y.:** **Top scorer:**

Bashley FC. Photo: Eric Marsh

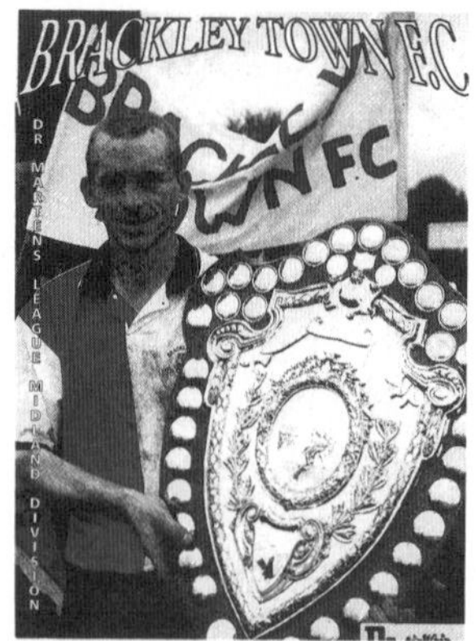

BRACKLEY TOWN

Colours: Red & white/black/white
Formed: 1890
Change colours: Yellow/blue/white
Nickname: Saints
Midweek home matchday: Tuesday
Reserve Team's League:
Local Press: Brackley Advertiser, Banbury Guardian, Herald & Post, Milton Keynes Citizen.
Local Radio: Fox FM
Chairman: Clive Lomax **President:** Miss C Billingham
Secretary/Press Officer: Pat Ashby, 17 Manor Rd, Woodford Halse, Daventry, Northants. NN11 3QP (01327 262955).
Manager: TBA **Asst Manager:** TBA
Coach: TBA **Physio:** TBA
GROUND Address: St James Park, Churchill Way, Brackley, Northants NN13 7EJ (01280 704077).
Directions: Churchill Way, east off A43, south end of town
Capacity: 3,500 **Cover:** 150 **Seats:** 300 **Floodlights:** Yes
Clubhouse: Lounge & main hall. Fully licensed. Food available. Open all week.

PROGRAMME DETAILS:
Pages: **Price:** £1
Editor: Geoff Lines
Tel: 01295 261017

PREVIOUS - **Names:** None **Leagues:** Banbury & District/ North Bucks/ Hellenic 77-83/ United Counties 83-94/ Hellenic 94-97. **Ground:** Banbury Road, Manor Road, Buckingham Road (up to 1974).

CLUB RECORDS - **Attendance:** 600 v Kettering, Northants Senior Cup 1989. **Transfer Fee Paid:** None **Received:** £ 2,000 for Phil Mason from Oxford City 98

BEST SEASON - **FA Trophy:** 1st Qual Rd 97-98. **FA Cup:** 2nd Qual Rd 97-98. **League clubs defeated:** None

HONOURS - UCL R-up 88-89 (Div 1 83-84); N'hants Snr Cup R-up 88-89; Buck'ham Charity Cup (3); Hellenic Lg Prem 96-97, Div 1 Cup 82-83.

Players progressing to Football League: Jon Blencowe (Leicester)

97-98 - Captain: Jess Mansfield **P.o.Y.:** Jason Allen **Top Scorer:** Jason Allen

Back Row (L-R); Mark Snazell, John Corbett, Darren Reynolds, Ian Moores, Tery Muckelberg, Jason Allen, James Baskerville, Phil Mason. Front Row: Steve Jenkins, Gary Pick, Karlton Stratford, Jess Mansfield, Mark Sherlock, Mark Thomas.
Photo: Andrew Chitty

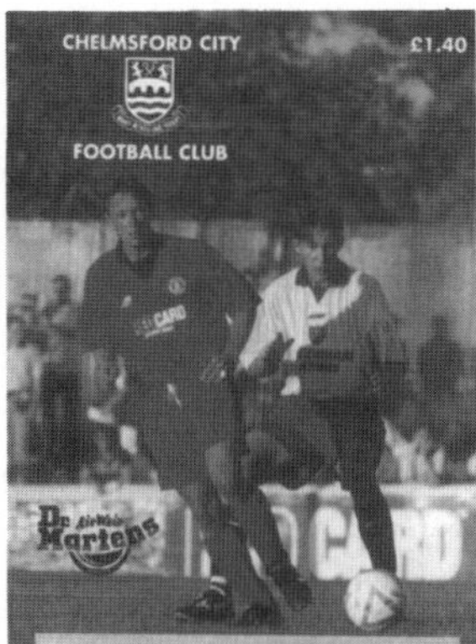

CHELMSFORD CITY

Colours: Claret, white trim/claret/claret. **Formed:** 1938
Change colours: Sky blue/navy/sky blue. **Nickname:** City
Midweek home games: Tuesday **Sponsors:** Britvic UK
Local Press: Essex Chronicle, Chelmsford Weekly News, East Anglian Daily Times, Evening Gazette.
Local Radio: Essex Radio/Breeze AM, BBC Essex.

Chairman: Trevor Wright (01245 356840 H, 0850 468403 Mob)
Secretary: David Clarke, 4 Homestead Cottages, Nighingale Road, Lowestoft NR33 7BZ. Tel 01502 514718 H.
Manager: Roy McDonough **Asst Manager:** Paul Roberts
GROUND Address: Ground Share with Billericay Town
New Lodge, Blunts Wall Road, Billericay CM12 9SA (01277 652188).
Directions: From Shenfield (A129) right at 1st lights then 2nd right. From Basildon (A129) over 1st lights in town, then left at next lights and 2nd right. Half mile from Billericay (GER) station (London Liverpool St. - Southend line). Ground 5 mins walk from buses 222, 251, 357, 255, 551.
Capacity: 3,500 **Seats:** 424 **Cover:** 600 **Floodlights:** Yes
Clubhouse: Open every evening 8-11pm (except Monday)(1pm-11pm Sat) and weekend lunchtimes noon-2.30pm. Discos, live entertainment.
Club Shop: Sells progs, badges, scarves, mugs etc. Contact Helen Williams via club.

PROGRAMME DETAILS:
Pages: 32 **Price:** £1.20
Editor: Trevor Smith
(01245 353052)

PREVIOUS - **Name:** None (Brentwood Town were incorporated in 1970). **Leagues:** None. **Grounds:** New Whittle Street 38-97

CLUB RECORDS - **Attendance:** 16,807 v Colchester, Southern League 10/9/49. **Goalscorer:** Tony Butcher, 287 (1957-71). **Appearances:** Derek Tiffin, 550 (1950-63). **Win:** 10-3 v Billericay Town (H), Essex Senior Cup, 4/1/93. **Defeat:** 2-10 v Barking (A), FA Trophy, 11/11/78. **Fee Paid:** £10,000 for Tony Rogers (Dover Athletic, 1992). **Fee Received:** £50,000 for David Morrison (Peterborough 94).

BEST SEASON - **FA Cup:** 4th Rd, 1938-39 (v Birmingham City). 1st Rd 25 times. **FA Trophy:** Semi-final 69-70 v Telford Utd.

HONOURS - Southern Lg 45-46 67-68 71-72 (R-up 48-49 60-61 63-64 65-66); Southern Div 88-89, R-up 97-98, Lg Cup 45-46 59-60 (R-up 60-61); Merit Cup 71-72; Southern Lg War-Time (East) 39-40); Essex Prof Cup 5; Essex Snr Cup 85-86 88-89 92-93; Non-League Champs Chall Cup 71-72; E Anglian Cup 48-49; Eastern Co's Lg(3) 46-49 (Lg Cup 59-60); Eastern Floodlit Comp 6, (Cup 72-73 74-75); Metropolitan Lg 67-68, Lg Prof Cup 67-68, Autumn Shield 70-71; Essex Snr Lg Cup 84-85; Harry Fisher Memorial Tphy 88-89.

Players progressing to Football League: G Merton (Watford 48), G Adams (Orient 49), W O'Neill (Burnley 49), B Farley/S McClellan/L Dicker/P Collins (Spurs 49/49/51/68), O Hold (Everton 50), R Marden (Arsenal 50), C McCormack (Barnsley 50), D Sexton (Luton 51), W Bellet & R Mason & A Nicholas (Orient 61 & 63 & 65), R Gladwin (Norwich 66), B King (Millwall 67), J O'Mara (Bradford City 74), N Spink (Aston 77), M Dziadulewicz (Wimbledon 79), M Cawston (Southend 84), P Coleman (Exeter 84), J Keeley & A Owers (Brighton 86 & 87), I Brown (Bristol C 93), D Morrison (Peterborough 94).

97-98 Captain: Chris Tovey **Top Scorer:** Wayne Goddard **P.o.Y:** Brett Girling

Back Row (L-R); G Bellamy (jt Mgr), Lee Edwards, John Monteath, Wayne Goddard, Danny Groom, Lee Ballard, Paul Dennis, Neal Docking, Mark Pacey, Sean Campbell, John Rothon, Brian Honeywood (Dir of Football). Front Row; Ian Butcher (Kit), Jamie Reilly, Mark Kinsley, Brett Girling, Chris Tovey, Colin Norman (jt Mgr), Liam Nash, Lee Guiver, Garry Kimble, Danny Roberts, Paul Smith (Physio). Photo: Courtesy The Essex Chronicle

PROGRAMME DETAILS:
Pages: Yes **Price:** £1
Editor: Margaret Marsh
Tel. 01258 645783

CIRENCESTER TOWN

Colours: Red & black/ black/ red **Founded:** 1889
Change colours: Blue/ black/ blue **Nickname:** Ciren
Midweek Matchday: Tuesday **Sponsors:** P.H.H./Cheltenham Windows
Reserves' League: Cirencester & District
Local Press: Standard, Western Daily Press.
Local Radio: BBC Radio Gloucester, Severn Sound.

Chairman: Stephen Abbley, 17 Dianmer Close, Hook, Swindon. SN4 8ER. Tel: 01743 853293 (H) 01793 884900 (B).
Secretary: Jim Saunders, 35 Chesterton Park, Cirencester, Glos. GL7 1XS 01258 659002 (H)
Commercial Manager: Margaret M **Press Officer:** Jim Saunders
Manager: Ray Baverstock 01242 260619
Coach: Mark Boyland **Physio:** Steve Slaughter
GROUND Address: The Stadium, Smithsfield, Chesterton Lane, Cirencester (01285 645783).
Directions: Follow signs on by-pass to Bristol & West. At roundabout where Sports Centre is situated, follow road 'up the hill' and take first left and then immediately right. 3 miles from Kemble (BR).
Seats: 236 **Cover:** 500 **Capacity:** 3,000 **Floodlights:** Yes
Clubhouse: Open Tuesday - Friday evenings & Saturday. Snacks are available on matchdays. **Club Shop:** None.

PREVIOUS - **Leagues:** Hellenic League **Names:** None. **Grounds:** None

CLUB RECORDS - **Attendance:** 2,600 v Fareham 1969. **Win:** Unknown. **Defeat:** Unknown. **Career Goalscorer:** Unknown. **Career Appearances:** Unknown. **Transfer fee paid:** None. **Transfer fee received:** None.

BEST SEASON - **FA Trophy:** 1st Qual. Round 1996-97 (1st season in comp.) **FA Vase:** Never past the 1st Round. **FA Cup:** 3rd Preliminary Round, 1996-97

HONOURS - Gloucestershire Senior Amateur Cup 89-90; Hellenic League Div One Challenge Cup 90-91; Hellenic League Prem Div 95-96, Legaue Cup 95-96; Gloucestershire County Cup 95-96.

Players progressing to the Fooball League: None

Cirencester Town

PROGRAMME DETAILS:
Pages: 32 **Price:** £1
Editor: C Smith
(01536 522159)

CORBY TOWN

Colours: White & black/black/white **Formed:** 1948
Change colours: All yellow. **Nickname:** The Steelmen
Midweek matchday: Wednesday **Sponsor:** Commision for New Towns.
Reserves' League: United Counties Res Div
Local Press: Northampton Evening Telegraph.
Local Radio: BBC Radio Northampton, Hereward, KCBC.

Chairman: James Kane **President:** H Hatterley.
Secretary: Roger Abraham, 68 Cornwall Rd, Kettering, Northants NN16 8PE (01536 522159).
Manager: Ian Benjamin **Coach:** Simon Mason
Physio: Mick Mackie.

GROUND Address: Rockingham Triangle Stadium, Rockingham Road, Corby NN17 2AE (01536 406640).
Directions: On northern outskirts of town at junction of A6003 and A6116, opposite entrance to Rockingham Castle grounds. One and a half miles from Corby (BR).
Capacity: 3,000 **Cover:** 1,150 **Seats:** 960 **Floodlights:** Yes
Clubhouse: VP Lounge open matchdays and during the week.
Club Shop: Sells badges, programmes etc. Contact C Woolmer (01536 260900).

PREVIOUS - **Leagues:** United Counties 35-52, Midland 52-58.

CLUB RECORDS - **Attendance:** 2,240 v Watford, pre-season friendly 86-87. At Old Ground; 10,239 v Peterborough Utd, FA Cup 3rd Qual. Rd 52-53. **Win:** 14-0 v Gainsborough Trinity, 56-57. **Defeat:** 0-10 v Paget Rangers, 95-96. **Career Goalscorer:** David Hofbauer 141 (84-95). **Career Appearances:** Derek Walker 600 (78-92). **Transfer fee paid:** £2,700 for Elwyn Roberts (Barnet, 81). **Transfer fee received:** £20,000 for Matt Murphy (Oxford Utd 93).

BEST SEASON - **FA Trophy:** 3rd Rd, 1986-87. **FA Cup:** 3rd Rd 65-66 (lost to Plymouth). 1st Rd on five occasions; 54-55 63-66 67-68. - **League clubs defeated:** Luton Town 65-66.

HONOURS - UCL 50-51 51-52 (R-up 37-38), Midland Lg R-up 52-53, Southern Lg Midland Div R-up 90-91 (Merit Cup 63-64 90-91), Northants Snr Cup 6; Maunsell Cup 83-84, Daventry Charity Cup 94-95, Midland Floodlit Cup 74-75, Evans Halshaw F'lit Cup 91-92, Anglia Floodlit Trophy 68-69 72-73, Chelmsford Invitation Cup 63-64 64-65 65-66(joint), Kettering & Dist Samaritan Cup 60-61 (joint) 68-69, Wellingborough Charity Cup 50-51, Desborough Nursing Cup 48-49 50-51 (joint), Bob Cumning Cup 6:

Players progressing to Football League: A McCabe (Chesterfield 55), L Clalmers (Leicester City 56), K Brown (Nottm Forest 56), P Kearns (Aldershot 62), N Dean (Southampton 63), H Curran (Millwall 64), D McNeil/A McGowan/G Reilly (Northampton 69/75/76), P Chard (Peterborough 79), T Morley (West Ham), J Flower (Sheffield Utd, Aldershot), M Murphy (Oxford Utd 93), C McKenzie (Hereford 94).

Back Row (L-R): Mike Mackie (Physio), John Neal, Stuart Robinson, Lee Harriman, Kevin Budge, Chris Tonge, Kevin Fox, Ossie Mintus, Michael Coles, Mark Wood, Danny Liquorish (Coach). Front Row; Peter Dowsing (Mgr), Paul Tiffney, Andy Coleman, Tim Griffin, John Caine, Jamie Mason, Aaron Bailey, Lee Adam (Asst Mgr). Photo: David Tilley

DARTFORD

Colours: White & black/black/black
Change colours: Red/white/red
Midweek home matchday: Monday.
Reserves' League: Winstonlead Kent Div 1
Local Press: Dartford Times, Kent Today
Local Radio: Radio Kent, Millennium Radio.

Formed: 1888
Nickname: The Darts

Chairman: David Skinner **Vice-Chairman:** Norman Grimes
Secretary: Mike Brett-Smith, 83 Wellcome Avenue, Dartford, Kent DA1 5JL. Tel. 01322 277243.
Commercial Man.: TBA **Press Officer:**
Manager: Gary Julians **Coach:Asst-Manager:** Bob Glozier
Physio: Peter Lucia-Hennis/Terry Skelton

GROUND Address: Purfleet FC, Thurrock Hotel, Ship Lane, Grays, Essex (01708 868901)
Directions: M25 North; through Dartford Tunnel 1st exit, at roundabout take Ship Lane exit (sign Purfleet FC), ground 100 yards on right beside Thurrock Hotel
Capacity: 4,500 **Cover:** 1,000 **Seats:** 300 **Floodlights:** Yes
Club Shop: Open matchdays. Mail Order: Norman Grimes 01474 815236.

PROGRAMME DETAILS:
Pages: 40 **Price:** £1
Editor: Mike Brett-Smith
Tel: 01322 277243

PREVIOUS - **Leagues:** Kent 1894-96, 97-98, 99-1902, 09-14, 21-26, 93-96/ Southern Lg 1896-98, 99-1900, 27-81, 82-84, 86-92/ GMVC 1981-82, 84-86. **Grounds:** The Brent/Westgate House, Potters Meadow, Engleys Meadow, Summers Meadow, Watling St, Cray Wanderers, Erith & Belverdere.

CLUB RECORDS - **Attendance:** 11,004 v Leyton Orient FA Cup 48 **Career Appearances:** Steve Robinson 653 **Win:** 11-1 v Faversham Tn Kent Snr Cup 65. **Defeat:** 0-10 v Guildford City Southern Lge 46 **Transfer fee paid:** £6,000 for John Bartley (Chelmsford 88) **Received:** £25,000 for Andy Hessenthaler (Watford via Redbridge F).

BEST SEASON - **FA Trophy:** R-up 74. **FA Vase:** 2nd Qual Rd 95/96 **FA Cup:** 3rd Rd Prop 35-36 & 36-37. - **League clubs defeated:** Cardiff (1935), Exeter (1961), Aldershot (1968).

HONOURS - Southern Lg 1930-31, 31-32, 73-74, 83-84, R-up 87-88, 88-89, Eastern Div 30-31, 31-32, Southern Div 80-81, Southern Lg Div 2 1896-97, Lg Cup 76-77, 87-88, 88-89, Championship Shield 83-84, 87-88, 88-89; Kent Lg 1995-96, Lg Cup 24-25, Kent Snr Cup 29-30, 34-35, 38-39, 69-70, Snr Trophy 95-96, Inter Lg Chall 1974; FA Trophy R-up 1974.

Players progressing to Football League: Idris Hopkins (Brentford 32), Fred Dall (West Ham 36), Riley Cullum/Fred Alexander/Ted Croker (Charlton 47/48/48) Frank Coombs (Bristol C 49), James Kelly (Gillingham 51), Tom Ritchie (Grimsby 58), Dave Underwood (Watford 60), Derek Hales (Luton 72), Andy Hessenthaler (Watford via Redbridge F).
97-98 - Captain: Paul Sawyer **P.o.Y.:** Colin Lewington **Top Scorer:** Glenn Payne

[illegible]
Danny Evans, Lee Jones, Paul Sawyer, Glenn Payne, Ricky Bennett
Photo: Andrew Chitty

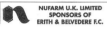

ERITH & BELVEDERE F.C.
FOUNDED 1922
"PARK VIEW"
LOWER ROAD, BELVEDERE, KENT DA17 6DF
TEL: 0181 311 4444

PROGRAMME DETAILS:
Pages: 30 **Price:** 50p
Editor: Mike Tarrant
Tel: 01322 275766

ERITH & BELVEDERE

Colours: Blue & white/blue/white
Change colours: All red
Midweek home matchday: Tuesday
Reserves' League: None.
Local Press: Kentish Times, Kentish Independant.
Local Radio: Radio Kent, Radio Mellenium.

Formed: 1922
Nickname: Deres

Chairman: John McFadden **President:** L O'Connell
Vice Chairman: Peter Bird
Secretary: Miss Kellie Discipline, 30 Chatsworth Road, Dartford, Kent DA1 5AT. 01322 275766
Press Officer/Commecial Manager: Martin Tarrant
Manager: Mike Acland 01322 225594
Asst Manager / Coach: Dave Hough **Physio:** Rob Couldwell
GROUND Address: Park View, Lower Road, Belvedere, Kent DA17 6DF (0181 311 4444). **Directions:** From Dartford bridge follow signs for Crayford to Erith and follow A206. Ground half mile from Erith Blackwall tunnel: head for Abbey Wood and on to Belvedere. Entrance in Station Road, adjoining Belvedere (BR) station. Bus No. 469.
Capacity: 1,500 **Cover:** 1,000 **Seats:** 500 **Floodlights:** Yes
Club Shop: Sells programmes, badges and pens.
Clubhouse: Licensed social club open matchdays and weekends. Cold snacks available available, separate canteen provides hot food on matchdays.

PREVIOUS - **Leagues:** Kent 22-29 31-39 78-82, London 29-31, Corinthian 45-63, Athenian 63-78. **Names:** Belvedere & District FC (Formed 1918, restructured 1922)

CLUB RECORDS - **Attendance:** 5,573 v Crook Colliery Welfare Amt Cup 3rd Rd 1949. **Win:** 14-2 v Royal Marines, Kent Lge 18/11/33. (16-2 v RAF Friendly 4/9/41). **Defeat:** 0-15 v Ashford, Kent Lge 28/4/37. **Career Appearances:** Dennis Crawford 504, 56-71. **Career Goalscorer:** Colin Johnson 284, 61-71.

BEST SEASON - **FA Amateur Cup:** Runners-up 1923-24, 37-38. **FA Trophy:** Third Qualifying Round second replay 89-90. **FA Vase:** Third Round 76-77. **FA Cup:** 4th Qual Rd 1924-25 (Equiv to 1st Rd Prop). **League clubs defeated:** None.

HONOURS - FA Amat Cup R-up 23-24 37-38; Athenian Lge Div 1 R-up 70-71 (Lge Cup 73-74), Memorial Shield 67-68; Corinthian Lge R-up 62-63, (Lge Cup 47-48 48-49 49-50); Kent Lge 81-82, (Lge Cup R-up 81-82); London Sen Cup 44-45 (R-up 38-39); Kent Amat Cup 6, (R-up 4); Kent F/lit Lge R-up 67-68; Kent Interm Cup R-up 90-91; Kent Jun Cup 67-68; Kent County Yth Lge 90-91; Kent Yth Cup 87-88. Bromley Hosp Cup 38-39; Essex & Herts Border Comb Cup 73-74;

Players progressing to Football League: John Coshall (West Ham 28), Fred Ford/Cyril Hammond/Keith Peacock (Charlton 36, 46, 62), Tommy Ord (Chelsea 72), Sean Devine (Barnet 95).

97-98 - Captain: Paul Roberts **P.o.Y.:** Danny Harwood **Top scorer:** Micky Clarke

Back Row (L-R); Danny Harwood, Tim Bealey, Robert Bird, Paul Roberts, Aaron Barnett, Micky Cloake, Paul Gurr. Front Row; Paul Bares, Tony Young, Darren Gowler, Ray Oboagye, Robert Hawley, Scott Liddell, Gary Ware.
Photo: Andrew Chitty

FISHER
ATHLETIC·LONDON·FC
BOREHAMWOOD F.C.
Tuesday 29th October 1996
London Challenge Cup-1st Round
K.O.
7.45pm
OFFICIAL PROGRAMME
SEASON 96/97
Price 70p

FISHER ATHLETIC (LONDON)

Colours: Black & white stripes/white/white.
Change colours: Blue/white/white
Midweek matchday: Tuesday
Reserves' League: Suburban Premier
Local Press: Southwark News, South London Press
Local Radio: Capital & Capital Gold

Formed: 1908
Nickname: The Fish
Sponsors: Alex Neil

President: Barry Albin-Dyer **Life President:** Lord Mellish
Chairman: Chris Georgiou **Vice Chairman:** Dave Wilding
Secretary: Mr John Leyden c/o Club.
General Manager: Cheryl Stepton
Manager: Micky Stead **Coach:** Chris Hiscock **Physio:** Joe Miller
Fitness Trainer: Ann Aris

PROGRAMME DETAILS:
Pages: 32 **Price:** £1
Editor: Cheryl Stepton

GROUND Address: The Surrey Docks Stadium, Salter Road, London SE16 1LQ (0171 231 5144. Fax: 0171 2520060).
Directions: 8 minutes walk from Rotherhithe (tube), 2 miles from London Bridge (main line). Buses 188, P11, P14.
Capacity: 5,300 **Cover:** 4,283 **Seats:** 400 **Floodlights:** Yes
Clubhouse: 0171 252 0590. Luxury clubhouse. Bar open 11am-11pm.

PREVIOUS - **Leagues:** Parthenon, West Kent, Kent Amateur, London Spartan 76-82, Southern 82-87, GMV Conference 87-91. **Names:** Fisher Athletic 08-93, Fisher'93 93-96. **Ground:** London Road, Mitcham.

CLUB RECORDS - **Attendance:** 4,283 v Barnet, GMV Conference 4/5/91. **Win:** 7-0 v Lewes Sept 95, FA Cup **Defeat:** 0-6 v Salisbury, 21/8/93. **Career Goalscorer:** Paul Shinners 205 **Career Appearances:** Dennis Sharp 720. **Transfer fee paid:** £500 each for Sean Devine & Jamie Kempster (Erith & Belvedere 1995) **Transfer fee received:** £45,000 for Paul Gorman (Charlton 1991)

BEST SEASON - **FA Cup:** 1st Rd 84-85 (0-1 at home to Bristol City), 88-89 (0-4 at Bristol Rovers). **FA Trophy:** Third Round replay 87-88 **FA Vase:** Second Round replay 82-83

HONOURS - Southern Lg 86-87 (R-up 83-84, Southern Div 82-83, Lg Cp 84-85, Championship Cup 87-88, Merit Cup), London Spartan Lg 80-81 81-82 (R-up 78-79, Senior Div 77-78, Div 2 R-up 76-77), Parthenon Lg 61-62 (Lg Cup 63-64 65-66), Kent Amateur Lg 73-74 74-75 (R-up 72-73), London Senior Cup 84-85 87-88 88-89, London Intermediate Cup 59-60 (R-up 75-76), Kent Senior Cp 83-84, Kent Senior Trophy 81-82 82-83, Surrey Intermediate Cup 61-62.

Players progressing to The Football League: John Bumstead (Chelsea), Trevor Aylott (Bournemouth), Paul Shinners (Orient 84), Dave Regis (Notts County - via Barnet), Paul Gorman (Charlton 91), Sean Devine (Barnet via Okonia Nicossia), George Barry (Leyton Orient), Dean Martin (West Ham Utd), Jason Lee (Charlton), Ken Charlery (Barnet)

97-98 - Captain: Paul Collins/Tim Hambley **P.o.Y.:** Matt Middleton **Top scorer:** Steve Watts

Back Row (L-R); Barry Albin-Dyer (Pres), Tony Issacs (Kit), Mickey Roberts, Paul Collins (Capt), Kelly Haag, Matt Middleton, Lewis Nightingale, Ray Power, Steve Watts, Jimmy Jones, Mickey Stead (Mgr), Chris Georgiou (Chr). Front Row; Dave Wilding (Vice Chr), Brian Lee, Paul Manning, Tim Hambley, Anthony Turner, Neil Thurgood, Matt Woolf, John Brunning, Phil O'Neil, Joe Miller (Physio).

PROGRAMME DETAILS:
Pages: 20 **Price:** 50p
Editor: Steve Beagley
Tel:

FLEET TOWN

Colours: Navy & sky/sky/navy & sky
Change colours: Yellow & red/yellow & red/yellow
Midweek Matches: Tuesday
Reserves' League: Suburban
Local Press:
Local Radio:

Founded: 1890.
Formed: 1947
Nickname: The Blues
Sponsors: Hart Dist Council

Chairman: Anthony Cherry **President:** Les Hocking
Vice Chairman: Colin Sturgess
Secretary: Dave Grenham, 149 Aldershot Road, Church Crookham, Fleet, Hants GU13 0JS. Tel. 01252 623021
Commercial Manager: **Press Officer:**
Manager: Trevor Norris **Assistant Manager:** Jess Bone
Coach: Clive Talentire **Physio:** Steve Hyde
GROUND Address: Calthorpe Park, Crookham Road, Fleet, Hants (01252 623804).
Directions: Leave the M3 at Junction 4A. Follow signs to Fleet via A3013. At 5th roundabout (a T-junction), turn left over railway bridge. Carry on past 'Oatsheaf' pub on the right - ground is 1/4 mile further on right.
Seats: 200 **Cover:** 250 **Capacity:** 2,000 **Floodlights:** Yes
Clubhouse: Yes. Hot & cold food served.
Club Shop: Yes.

PREVIOUS - **Leagues:** Wessex, Hants 61-77, Athenian, Combined Co's, Chiltonian.

CLUB RECORDS - **Attendance:**
Win: 7-0
Defeat:
Transfer fee received:
Transfer fee paid: £1,500 to Farnborough, 1991
Career Goalscorer: John Smith
Career Appearances: Steve Hodge / Paul Dear

BEST SEASON - **FA Cup:**
FA Vase:
FA Trophy:
FA Amateur Cup:

HONOURS - Wessex Lg 93-94, Lg Cup R-up 92-93, Hants Lg Div 2 R-up 61-62 (Div 1 R-up 60-61), Aldershot Snr Cup 92-93, Simpsonair Challenge Shield 1993, Hants Yth Lg Div 3 92-93.

Players progressing to the Football League:
97-98 - Captain: **P.o.Y.:** **Top scorer:** John Smith.

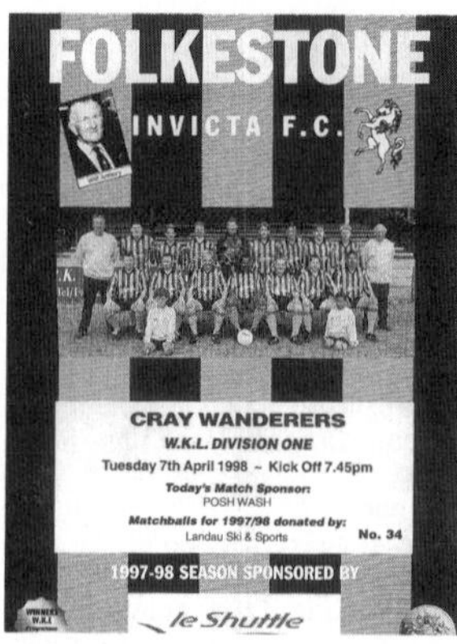

PROGRAMME DETAILS:
Pages: 60 **Price:** £1
Editor: Neil Pitcher
Tel: 01303 245066

FOLKESTONE INVICTA

Colours: Amber & black stripes/black/amber. **Founded:** 1936.
Change Colours: Blue & green stripes/blue/blue. **Nickname:**
Midweek matchday: Tuesday **Sponsors:** Eurotunnel(Le Shuttle).
Reserve's League: Winstonlead Kent Div 2
Local Press: Folkstone Herald
Local Radio: Neptune Radio, Radio Light

Chairman: Tommy Guiver. **President:** Bill Hewson
Secretary: Neil Pilcher, 25 Pavilion Road, Folkestone, Kent. CT19 5RW (01303 245066)
Manager: Neil Cugley **Asst Manager:** Dave Williams
Physio: Frank Clarke
Ground: The New Pavilion, Cheriton Road, Folkestine, Kent CT20 5JU (01303 257461).
Directions: On the A20 behind Safeway foodstore, midway between Folkestone Central & West BR stations.
Seats: 900 **Cover:** 3,500 **Capacity:** 6,500. **Floodlights:** Yes
Clubhouse: Yes, Stripes Club & Invicta Club
Club Shop: Yes

PREVIOUS - **Ground:** South Rd, Hythe (pre-1991).Kent County Lg matches were played on council pitches. **Leagues:** Kent County (pre-1991- 98). **Name:**

CLUB RECORDS - **Attendance:** 2,332 v West Ham Utd Friendly Nov 96 **Ground Record:** 7,881 Folkestone Town v Margate, Kent Snr.Cup 1958. **Win:** 9-0 v Crockenhill WHL Div 1 **Defeat:** 0-7 v Crockenhill WHL Div 1

BEST SEASON - **FA Vase:** Last sixteen 97-98. **FA Cup:** 2nd Qual Rd 95-96. **Leagues Clubs Defeated:** None

HONOURS - (since joining Winstonlead Kent League) Plaaya Kent Senior Trophy R-Up 93-94, 94-95.

97-98 - Captain: Carlton Wynter **P.o.Y.:** Andy Pearson **Top Scorer:** Dave Arter.

Back Row (L-R); Neil Cugley (Mgr), Tim Hulme, James Wootton, Andy Morris, Kevin Hudson, Nick Hopkin, Ogan Stone, Aaron O'Leary, Rob Beasley, Frank Clarke (Physio). Front Row; Jeff Ross, Dave Ward, Andy Pearson, Carlton Wynter, Malcom Smith, Tim Dixon, Steve Lawrence.

HAVANT & WATERLOOVILLE

Colours: White & yellow & navy/navy/navy **Formed:** 1998
Change colours: Red & black/black/red **Nickname:** Borough
Midweek matchday: Tuesday **Sponsors:** TBA
Local Press: News (Portsmouth) **Local Radio:** Ocean Sound, Radio Solent.
PROGRAMME DETAILS: Pages: 32 **Price:** £1 **Editor:** Adrian Gardiner

Chairman: Peter Faulknes **President:** Arthur Saitch, Maurie Hibb **Vice Chairman:** Derek Pope
Directors: Trevor Brock, Ray Jones, John Caster, Peter Dermott, Sandy Peters, Adrian Gardiner.
Secretary: Trevor Brock, 2 Betula Close, Waterlooville, Hampshire. PO7 8EJ (01705 267276)
Manager: Billy Gilbert **Asst Manager:** Mick Jenkins **Physio:** Phil Ashwell

GROUND Address: West Leigh Park, Martin Road, West Leigh, Havant PO9 5TH (0705 470918).
Directions: Take B2149 to Havant off the A27 (B2149 Petersfield Rd if coming out of Havant). 2nd turning off dual carriageway into Bartons Road then 1st right into Martins Road. 1 mile from Havant BR station.
Capacity: 6,000 **Cover:** 1,500 **Seats:** 240 **Floodlights:** Yes **Club Shop:** Sells various souvenirs & progs.
Clubhouse: Open every day, lunchtime and evening. 2 bars, function suites, hot & cold food available.
PREVIOUS - (Havant) **Leagues:** Portsmouth 58-71/ Hants 71-86/ Wessex 86-91. **Names:** Leigh Park/ Havant & Leigh Park/ Havant **Grounds:** Front Lawn 1958-83. (Waterlooville) **Leagues:** Waterlooville & District, Portsmouth 38-53, Hants 1953-71. **Grounds:** Convent Ground 10-30, Rowlands Avenue Recreation Ground 30-63, Jubliee Park 63-98
CLUB RECORDS - (Havant) **Attendance:** 3,500 v Wisbech Town, FA Vase QF 85-86.
Win: 10-0 three times; v Sholing Sports (H), FA Vase 4th Rd 85-86, v Portsmouth Royal Navy (H), Wessex League 90-91; v Poole Town, Southern League Southern Division 94-95. **Defeat:** 1-7 v Camberley Town (H), FA Vase 3rd Rd 88-89.
Career Goalscorer: Unknown. **Career Appearances:** Tony Plumbley. **Transfer fee paid:** £5,750 for John Wilson (Bashley, 90) **Received:** £7,000 for Steve Tate (Waterlooville, 1993). (Waterlooville) **Transfer fee paid:** £6,000 for Steve Tate (Havant Town, 93) **Received:** £6,000 for Dave Boyce (Gravesend & Northfleet, 93).
BEST SEASON - (Havant) **FA Cup:** 3rd Qual Rd 92-93 (2-3 at Sittingbourne). **FA Vase:** Qtr Final 85-86: (Waterlooville) **FA Trophy:** 2nd Rd 76-77 **FA Amateur Cup:** 1st Rd 59-60 **FA Cup:** 1st Rd 2nd replay 83-84, 0-2 v Northampton T. (A) after two 1-1 draws.
HONOURS - (Havant): FA Sunday Cup 68-69, Wessex Lg 90-91 (R-up 88-89), Hampshire Lg Div 3 72-73 (Div 4 71-72), Hampshire Senior Cup R-up 91-92 94-95, Hampshire Intermediate Cup, Hampshire Junior Cup, Russell Cotes Cup 91-92, Portsmouth Senior Cup 83-84 84-85 91-92, Gosport War Memorial Cup 74-75 91-92 92-93 94-95, Southern Counties Floodlit Cup R-up 91-92, Hampshire Floodlit Cup 85-86, Portsmouth Lg. (Waterlooville): Southern Lg Div 1 Sth 71-72 (Lg Cup 86-87, R-up 82-83), Hants Lg R-up 69-70 (Div 2 59-60 64-65, Div 3 (East) R-up 53-54), Hants Snr Cup 69-70 72-73 84-85 (R-up 75-76 90-91), Russell Cotes Cup 88-89, Portsmouth Lg 49-50 50-51 51-52 (Div 2 46-47, Div 3 38-39), Portsmouth Snr Cup 68-69, Portsmouth Victory Cup 59-60 69-70
Players progressing to Football League: (Havant); Bobby Tambling (Chelsea). (Waterlooville); Phil Figgins (Portsmouth 73), Paul Hardyman (Portsmouth 83), Guy Whittingham (Portsmouth via Yeovil Town 88), Paul Moody (Southampton 91).

Last ever photo of Havant 97-98

Last ever photo of Waterlooville 97-98 *Both Photos: Andrew Chitty*

PROGRAMME DETAILS:
Pages: 44 **Price:** 80p
Editor: Keith Smith
Tel. 01843 293220

MARGATE

Colours: Blue & white/blue & white **Formed:** 1896
Change colours: Maroon/white **Nickname:** The Gate
Midweek matchday: Tuesday **Sponsors:** Link Music Limited
Reserves' League: Winstonlead Kent Lg. Div 2 **Newsline:** 0891 800 665.
Local Press: Isle of Thanet Gazette, Thanet Times, Thanet Extra.
Local Radio: Radio Kent, Invicta Radio.

Chairman: Keith Piper **President:** Mr R W Griffiths
Vice Chairman: Richard Piper **Press Officer:** Chairman
Secretary: K E Tomlinson, 65 Nash Road, Margate CT9 4BT (01843 291040).
Manager: Chris Kinnear

GROUND Address: Hartsdown Park, Hartsdown Road, Margate CT9 5QZ (01843 221769).
Directions: A28 into Margate, turn right opposite Dog & Duck P.H. into Hartsdown Road, proceed over crossroads and ground is on left. Ten mins walk from Margate (BR).
Capacity: 6,000 **Cover:** 3 sides **Seats:** 400 **Floodlights:** Yes
Clubhouse: Flexible hours, private functions, matchday facilities. Steward: Pam & Mark Weatherly.
Club Shop: Contact Paul Turner 01843 293056.

PREVIOUS - **Grounds:** Margate College/ Dreamland, Northdown Rd/ Garlinge. **Leagues:** Kent 11-23 24-28 29-33 37-38 46-59/ Southern 33-37. **Name:** Thanet Utd 1981-89

CLUB RECORDS - **Attendance:** 14,500 v Spurs, FA Cup 3rd Rd 73. **Win:** 8-0 v Tunbridge Wells (H) 66-67 & v Chatham Town (H) 87-88 **Defeat:** 11-0 v AFC Bournemouth (A), FAC 1st Rd. 20.11.71 **Career Goalscorer:** Dennis Randall 66 (season 66-67). **Career Appearances:** Bob Harrop. **Transfer fee paid:** £5,000 for Steve Cuggy (Dover Ath 93) **Transfer fee received:** Undisclosed for Martin Buglione (St Johnstone 92-93).

BEST SEASON - **FA Trophy:** Third Round replay 78-79. **FA Amateur Cup:** Never entered
FA Cup: 3rd Rd 72-73 (0-6 to Spurs), 36-37 (1-3 at Blackpool).
League clubs defeated: Gillingham 29-30, Queens Park Rangers, Crystal Palace 35-36, Bournemouth & Boscombe Athletic 61-62, Swansea 72-73.

HONOURS - Southern Lg 35-36 (Lg Cp 67-68 (R-up 61-62 74-75), Div 1 62-63 (R-up 66-67), Div 1 Sth 77-78, East Div R-up 33-34, Merit Cp 66-67 77-78, Midweek Sect. 36-37), Kent Lg (4), (R-up 5, Div 2 4, Lg Cp 4), Kent Snr Cup (4), Kent Snr Shield (8), Kent F'lit Cp 62-63 66-67 75-76.

Players progressing to Football League: Over 40 including J Yeomanson (West Ham 47), D Bing/G Wright (West Ham 51), T Bing (Spurs 56), S Foster (C Palace 61), J Fraser (Watford 62), R Walker (Bournemouth 65), K Bracewell (Bury 66), T Jenkins/R Flannigan (Reading 69-70), M Blyth (Millwall 78), M Buglione (St Johnstone 92).

97-98 - Captain: Tony Dixon **P.o.Y.:** Bill Edwards **Top scorer:** Martin Buglione

Margate's Paul Sykes gets in a cross before the challange from Witney's Andy Martin. Photo: Alan Coomes

Newport I.W.
Football Club
97-98
Season
Welcome
to
St Georges
Park
Dr Martens
NEWPORT FC V WITNEY TOWN
Saturday December 13th, 1997

PROGRAMME DETAILS:
Pages: 28 **Price:** £1
Editor: Mark Major
(01983 525027)

NEWPORT I.O.W.

Colours: Gold & royal blue trim/gold/gold & royal trim **Formed:** 1888
Change colours: All purple **Nickname:** The Port
Midweek matchday: Tuesday
Reserves' League: Isle of Wight League
Local Press: Portsmouth Evening News, I.O.W. County Press, Southampton Evening Echo. **Local Radio:** Solent, Isle of Wight Radio, Ocean Sound.

Chairman: Bill Manuel **Vice Chairman:** TBA
President: W H J Bunday. **Commercial Manager:** Dave Hiscock.
Secretary/Press Off.: Chris Cheverton, 60 St Davids Road, East Cowes, Isle of Wight PO32 6EF (01983 281789).
Manager: Tony Mount **Physio:** Chris Cheverton

GROUND Address: St George's Park, St George's Way, Newport, Isle of Wight PO30 2QH (01983 525027). **Directions:** Roads from all ferry ports lead to Coppins Bridge R-about at eastern extremity of town. Take Sandown/Ventnor exit, proceed to small r-about, St George's way is first exit (straight on), ground immediately visible on left. Five minute walk from Newport bus station; along Church Litten (past old ground), turn left then right at r-about.
Capacity: 5,000 **Cover:** 1,000 **Seats:** 300 **Floodlights:** Yes
Club Shop: Sells souvenirs & programmes. Contact Ken Barnes at ground.
Clubhouse: Open normal licensing hours. 2 bars, full range of hot and cold bar snacks. Buffet inside ground.

PREVIOUS - **Leagues:** Isle of Wight 1896-1928; Hants 28-86; Wessex 86-90.
Ground: Church Litten (previously Well's Field) 1888-1988.

CLUB RECORDS - **Attendance:** 2,217 FA Cup 1st Rd Nov 1994 v Aylesbury U., (6,000 v Watford, FA Cup 1st Rd 56-57, at Church Litten). **Win:** 14-1, v Thornycroft Athletic (H), Hampshire Lge Div. One, 22.12.45. **Defeat:** 2-10, v Basingstoke Town (H), Hampshire Lge Div. One, 12.10.68. **Career Goalscorer:** Eddie Walder. **Career Appearances:** Jeff Austin 540 (69-87). **Fee paid:** £3,000 for Stuart Ritchie (Bashley, May 1991). **Fee received:** £2,250 for Mick Jenkins (Havant, March 1992).

BEST SEASON - **FA Trophy:** 1st Qual Rd each year. **FA Vase:** Fifth Round 91-92, 93-94. **FA Cup:** 2nd Rd 35-36 45-46. 1st Rd another eight times; 45-46 52-55 56-59 94-95 95-96. - **League clubs defeated:** Clapton Orient 45-46.

HONOURS - Wessex Lg R-up 89-90, Comb. 91-92 (res.); Hants Lg (11), R-up(7), Div 2 R-up 70-71, Hants Snr Cup(8); Russell Cotes Cup (3); Pickford Cup (4); Isle of Wight Snr (Gold) Cup (32); Hants F'lit Cup 76-77 77-78; Isle of Wight Lg(4) 07-10 23-24; Hants I'mediate Cup 31-32 96-97; Hants Comb. Cup 38-39.

Players progressing to Football League: Gary Rowatt (Cambridge City, Everton).

97-98 - Captain: John Price **P.o.Y.:** Gary Sperry **Top scorer:** Eurshell Fearon

Back Row (L-R); Eurshell Fearon, Clint Webbe, Clifton Soares, Tony White, David Graham, Mark Atkinson, Gary Green, Graeme Gee, Pete Tage, Stuart Ritchie, Chis Cheverton (Physio), Keith Leigh (Asst Mgr). Front Row; Steve Leigh, Gary Sperry, Leigh Cole, John Price, Tony Stephens.

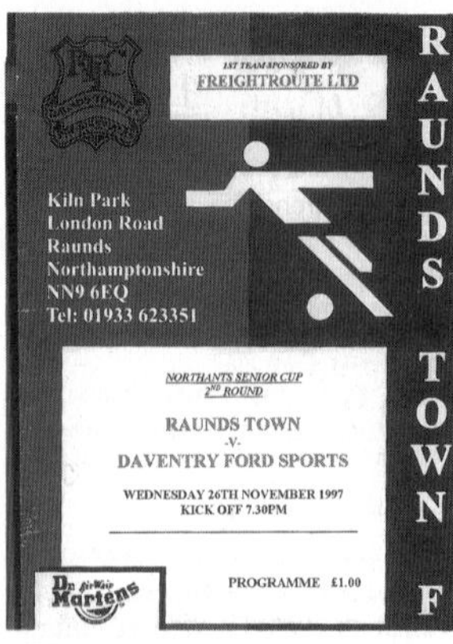

PROGRAMME DETAILS:
Pages: 68 **Price:** 50p
Editor: Mick Jones
(01933 625429)

RAUNDS TOWN FC

Colours: Red & black **Formed:** 1946
Change Colours: Yellow **Nickname:** Shopmates
Midweek matchday: Tuesday **Sponsors:** Jubilee Enterprises
Reserves' League: UCL Reserve Division One.
Local Press: Northants Evening Telegraph, Wellingborough Post, Chronicle & Echo. **Local Radio:** Northants Radio, KCBC

Chairman: George Hagan **President:** Jim Perera
Secretary: Mick Jones, 14 Welland Close, Raunds, Northants. NN9 6SQ. 01933 625429. **Press Officer:** Mick Jones (Secretary)
Commercial Manager: Ralph Maloney 01933 622036
Manager: Keith Burt **Asst Manager:** Glen Burdett

GROUND Address: Kiln Park, London Road, Raunds, Northants NN9 6EQ (01933 623351), Matchdays 01933 460941.
Directions: Take Raunds turning at roundabout on A45 and ground is first left. Nearest station; Wellingborough. Bus services local
Capacity: 3,000 **Seats:** 250 **Cover:** 600 **Floodlights:** Yes
Clubhouse: On ground, open every day
Club Shop: Yes Open matchdays, selling shirts, books programmes, contact Malc York, c/o club.

PREVIOUS - **Leagues:** Rushden & District, Central Northants Combination, United Counties League Prem Div. **Grounds:** Greenhouse Field (until 1948), The Berristers (1948-91).

CLUB RECORDS - **Attendance:** 1,500 v Crystal Palace, ground opening 23/7/91. **Win:** 9-0 v Potton 95, 11-2 v Brackley 93. **Defeat:** 0-6 v Baldock 83, v Buckingham 84-85. **Career Goalscorer:** Shaun Keeble 208. **Career Appearances:** Martin Lewis 355 (+29 subs). **Transfer fee paid:** £1,000 to Gloucester City for David Johnson 97. **Transfer fee received:** None

BEST SEASON - **FA Cup:** 3rd Qual Rd, 92-93 (0-4 at Nuneaton Borough), 93-94 (0-4 v Telford United). **FA Vase:** Semi-final v Arlesey Tn 94-5. **FA Trophy:** 1st Rd v Welling Utd 96-97, 1st Rd v Bashley 97-98.

HONOURS - UCL Prem Champions 95-96, UCL Div 1 82-83 (R-up 91-92), KO Cup 90-91, (R-up 83-84 93-94), Res Div 1 88-89 95-96 (R-up 86-87 87-88 89-90 90-91 91-92), Reserve KO Cup 84-85 88-89 93-94; Northants Snr Cup 90-91; Hunts Premier Cup R-up 92-93; Daventry Charity Cup R-up 83-84; Northants Jnr Cup 82-83 91-92(res) 92-93(res).

Players to progress to Football League: Greg Downs (Norwich, Coventry, Birmingham, Hereford).

Back Row (L-R); Ashley Carr, Darrell Page, John Fowler, Willie Staiton. Middle Row; Peter Scanlon (Physio), Simon Dunlop, Paul York, Kevin Fox, Gareth Johnson, Robert Gould, Richard Preston, Garry Harrison, Glenn Burdett (Asst Mgr). Front Row; Jimmy Simpson, Shaun Keeble, Keith Burt (Mgr), Ian Pearce, Kevin Slinn.

St LEONARDS

PROGRAMME DETAILS:
Pages: 60 **Price:** £1
Editor: Peter High
(01424 431482)

Colours: Blue/white/blue **Formed:** 1971
Change colours: White/navy/white **Nickname:** Saints or Blues
Midweek Matchday: Wednesday. **Sponsors:** Newlite Windows
Reserves' League: Kent Midweek **Clubcall Line:** 0930 555 804
Local Press: Hastings Observer, Evening Argus
Local Radio: Arrow FM, BBC Southern Counties Radio, Southern FM

Chairman: John Cornelius **President:** Mrs K Shepperdson
Vice-Chairman: Michael James
Secretary: Peter High, 1A Upper Maze Hill, St Leonards-on-Sea, East Sussex TN38 0LA (01424 431482)
Commercial Manager: John Huggett (01424 434755)
Manager: Andy Thomson **Asst Manager:** Gary Wilson

GROUND Address: The Firs, Elphinstone Rd, Hastings, East Sussex (01424 434755). Matchday Office (01424 716362). **Directions:** From M25 & London approach Hastings on the A21. immediately after the junct with the A28 on the northern borough boundary, turn right into Junction Rd. At T junct with B2093 turn right onto The Ridge. After 2 miles turn right, opposite the cemetary, into Elphinstone Rd, grd 600yards down hill on left. Nearest station; Ore (Connex South East), 1 mile uphill (no bus or taxi). Hastings (Connex South East) 1.5 miles. Bus service from town centre to grd.

Capacity: 3,768 (Day), 3,015 (Even) **Seats:** 251 **Cover:** 1,000 **Floodlights:** Yes
Clubhouse: Licensed bar open normal pubhours. Hot food matchdays. Hot food from tea bar.
Club Shop: Yes, selling leisure & sports wear, souvenirs & publications, open matchdays.

PREVIOUS - **Leagues:** Eastbourne & Hastings 71-82, Southern Counties Comb 82-88, Sussex County 88-96. **Grounds:** Council pitches 71-73, Pannel Lane, Pett 73-93. **Names:** Stamco (71-96), St Leonards Stamcroft 96-98

CLUB RECORDS - **Attendance:** 1,798 v Tiverton Town, FA Vase 4th Rd. 15/1/95. At old ground: 527 v Hastings Town, Sussex Senior Cup 2nd Rd 5/12/92. **Record win:** 10-1 v Portfield (H), Sussex County League Div One 4/12/93. **Record defeat:** 1-6 v Hailsham Town (A) League Cup 23/9/92. **Career appearances:** Wayne Farrier (290 92-97). **Career goalscorer:** Keith Miles (99 1995-98). **Transfer fee paid:** None. **Transfer fee received:** £8,000 for Jon Magee (Margate)

BEST SEASON: **FA Cup:** 3rd Qual Rd 96-97 97-98. **FA Vase:** 5th Rd 94-95. **FA Trophy:** 3rd Rd 96-97

HONOURS - Sussex Sen Cup 96-97; Sussex RUR Charity Cup R-up 94-95; Hastings Snr Cup 89-90 95-96 96-97, R-up 92-93 97-98; Dr Martens Lge Southern Div R-up 96-97, Merit Cup 96-97; Sussex County Div 1 R-up 94-95 95-96, Div 2 R-up 92-93, Cup R-up 89-90 90-91, Div Three R-up 88-89, Cup R-up 88-89

Player progressing to Football League: Sasha Ilic (Charlton Ath 97)

97-98 - Captain: Keith Miles **Top Scorer:** Keith Miles **P.o.Y.:** Keith Miles

Back Row (L-R); Mick James (Physio), Steve Gatting, Tony Burt, Peter Montgomery, Barry Gartell, Adam Flanagan, Gavin Ramsden, Steve Ferguson, George Parris, Andy Thomson (Mgr). Front Row; David Ndunduma, Mick O'Callaghan, Keith Miles, Neil Phillips, Paul Ruddy, Steve Norman, Jimmy Joines (Team Attend).

PROGRAMME DETAILS:
Pages: 28 **Price:** £1
Editor: William Rickson
(c/o the club)

SITTINGBOURNE

Colours: Red & black stripes/black/red **Formed:** 1881
Change colours: All yellow **Nickname:** Brickies
Midweek matchday: Wednesday **Sponsors:** Medway Galvanising.
Newsline: 0891 333 027
Reserves' league: Winstonlead Kent
Local Press: East Kent Gazette, Kent Today, Kent Messenger Extra, Sittingbourne & Sheppy Adscene.
Local Radio: Invicta Supergold, BBC Radio Kent, Invicta FM.

Chairman: B.Bright **President:** E H Bennett.
Secretary: Mrs M Bratton, c/o Sittingbourne F.C.
Manager: Alan Walker **Coach:** Paul Haylock **Physio:** Kevin Manser
Commercial Manager: Barry Bright

GROUND Address: Central Park, Eurolink, Sittingbourne, Kent ME10 3SB (01795 435077. Fax: 01474 814501).
Directions: Through Sittingbourne on main A2, club signposted clearly and regularly from both east and west. 1 mile from Sittingbourne BR station.
Capacity: 8,000 **Cover:** 3,300 **Seats:** 2,000 **Floodlights:** 420 lux
Clubhouse: The Cabin (Club's Tel No.)
Club Shop: Sells a wide selection of souvenirs etc. Open matchdays or contact Ann Morrison (01795 664436) or Clive Phillips (01795 477108).

PREVIOUS - **Names:** Sittingbourne United 1881-86. **Leagues:** Kent 1894-1905 09-27 30-39 46-59 68-91, South Eastern 05-09, Southern 27-30 59-67. **Grounds:** Sittingbourne Recreation Ground 1881-90, Gore Court Cricket Ground 90-92, The Bull Ground 1892-1990.

CLUB RECORDS - **Attendance:** 5,951 v Tottenham Hotspur, friendly 26/1/93. **Transfer fee paid:** £20,000 to Ashford Town for Lee McRobert, 1993. **Transfer fee received:** £210,000 from Millwall for Neil Emblen and Michael Harle, 1993.

BEST SEASON - **FA Cup:** 2nd Rd 25-26 (0-7 at Swindon Town), 28-29 (1-2 at Walsall), plus 1st Rd 26-27 30-31 62-63. **FA Trophy:**

HONOURS - Southern Lg Southern Div 92-93 95-96; Kent Lg 1897-98 1902-03 57-58 58-59 75-76 83-84 90-91 (Lg Cup 25-26 58-59 73-74 80-81, Div 2 Cup 54-55 57-58 83-84 86-87 87-88); Kent Senior Cup 01-02 28-29 29-30 57-58; Kent Senior Shield 25-26 27-28 53-54; Kent Senior Trophy 89-90; Thames & Medway Cup 55-56 58-59; Thames & Medway Comb 02-03 07-08 11-12 24-25 25-26; Chatham Charity Cup 03-04 19-20; Kent Midweek Lg(res) 91-92 (Lg Cup 90-91).

Players progressing to Football Lge: Jason Lillis (Walsall 93), Neil Emblen & Michael Harle & Steve Forbes & Lee McRobert (Millwall 93/93/94/95, Jimmy Case (Brighton 93), Lee Harper (Arsenal 94).

Back Row (L-R); Paul Haylock, Ricky Pearson, Andy Hough, Lloyd Hume, Peter Overton, Lynden Rowland. Front Row; Ben Taylor, Darren Smith, Damien Hodge, Shane Davies, Tommy Plance.

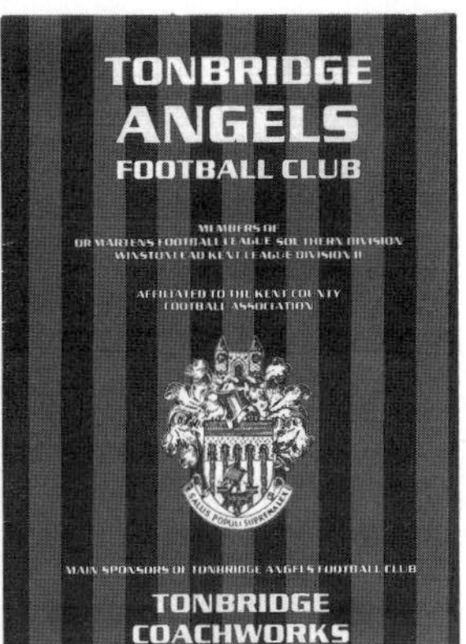

PROGRAMME DETAILS:
Pages: 38 **Price:** £1
Editor: Roger Alder
c/o Club

TONBRIDGE ANGELS

Colours: Black & blue/black/black **Founded:** 1948
Change Colours: All green **Nickname:** The Angels
Midweek matchday: Tuesday **Sponsors:** Tonbridge Coachworks
Reserves' League: Winstonlead Kent Division Two.
Local Press: Kent Messenger, Courier, Sevenoaks Leader.
Local Radio: Invicta, Radio Kent.

Chairman: Nigel Rimmer **Vice Chairman:**
Secretary: Ken Jarrett, 8 Farraday Ride, Tonbridge, Kent. TN10 4RL. (01732 351856)
Press Officer: Simon Piper **Commercial Manager:** Mark Goodier
Manager: Bill Roffey **Physio:** Peter Battell/Chris Dunk

GROUND Address: Longmead Stadium, Darenth Avenue, Tonbridge, Kent TN10 3JW (01732 352417). **Directions:** From Tonbridge BR station, through High Street, north up Shipbourne Rd (A227 Gravesend road) to 2nd mini-r'bout ('The Pinnacles' pub), left into Darenth Avenue, ground at bottom of Avenue, far side of car park
Seats: 202 **Cover:** 400 **Capacity:** 5,000 **Floodlights:** Yes
Clubhouse: Open Mon-Sat evenings and Sunday lunchtimes. Hot food on matchdays from burger bar.
Club Shop: Yes, progs, replica kits etc, contact Peter Jeffrey 01732 350692.

PREVIOUS - **Leagues:** Southern 48-89, Kent 89-93. **Ground:** The Angel 48-80. **Names:** Tonbridge Angels, Tonbridge F.C., Tonbridge A.F.C.

CLUB RECORDS - **Attendance:** 1,463 v Yeovil Town, FA Cup 4th Qualifying Round 26/10/91. *At the Angel Ground: 8,236 v Aldershot, FA Cup 1st Round 1951.* **Win:** 11-1 v Worthing FA Cup 1951 **Defeat:** 2-11 v Folkstone, Kent Sen Cup 1949 **Career Goalscorer:** Unknown **Career Appearances:** Mark Gillham, 520 to date. **Transfer fee paid:** **Transfer fee received:** £7,500 for Paul Emblen (Charlton Ath 97)

BEST SEASON - **FA Cup:** First Round (proper) 50-51 51-52 52-53 67-68 72-73.

HONOURS - Kent League 94-95 (League Cup (2)), Southern League Cup Runners-up (2) (SF (1)), Kent Senior Cup 64-65 74-75 (Runners-up (2)), Kent Senior Shield 51-52 55-56 57-58 58-59 63-64.

Players progressing to Football League: R Saunders, M McMcDonald, T Burns, I Seymour, G Moseley, T Morgan, Neil Emblen.

97-98 - Captain: Alan Tutton **P.o.Y.:** Paul Emblen **Top scorer:** Craig Wilkins

Back Row (L-R); Steve Lovell, Dave Walker, Colin Blewden, Jody Cole, Joe Radford, Andy Garrett, Brian Frampton, Jamie Rogers, Julian Taylor, Dean Harpley. Front Row; Grant Styles, Tim Marshall, Wayne Balmer, Ian Gibbs, Matt Le Moine, Matt Broadway, Ollie Scrivenor, Cliff Cunningham.

PROGRAMME DETAILS:
Pages: 40 **Price:** £1
Editor:
A Bircher & K Bushnell
(01993 200913)

WITNEY TOWN

Colours: All Yellow **Formed:** 1885
Change colours: Green/white/green **Nickname:** The Blanketmen
Midweek matchday: Tuesday **Sponsors:**
Reserves' League: None
Newsline: 0930 555 901
Local Press: Witney Gazette, West Oxon Standard, Oxford Mail & Oxford Times. **Local Radio:** Thames Valley FM, Fox (FM) Oxford.

Chairman: Brian Constable **President:** Sir Peter Parker
Vice-Chairman: Vacant **Press Officer:** Kieran Bushnell 01993 703622
Secretary: Adrian Bircher, 13 Colwell Drive, Witney, Oxon. OX8 7NJ (01993 200913, Mob 041 007 3207) **Commercial Man / P.R.O.:** Dermot Gallagher
Manager: Andy Lyne **Asst Manager**: Gary Ackling
Coach: Peter Bridgewater/Paul Holden **Physio:** Paul Sunners

GROUND Address: Marriott Stadium, Downs Rd, Witney, Oxon OX8 7LY. (01993 702549). **Directions:** From West on A40; take B4047 at island past Burford, follow signs for Witney West & N.W. Industrial Estates, thru Minster Lovell to West Witney, right into Downs Rd, ground on right. From the East on A40, 2nd turn off to Witney and follow signs for South & S.W. Industrial Estates, right at r'bout to traffic lights, left and proceed to r'bout, straight over, signs to West Witney Industrial Estate, left at lights onto B4047, left into Downs Rd, ground on right. Nearest BR station is Oxford 12 miles away.
Capacity: 3,500 **Cover:** 2,000 **Seats:** 280 **Floodlights:** Yes
Club Shop: Selling programmes and souvenirs. Contact secretary.
Clubhouse: Members bar open seven days a week 6.30-11pm. Open all day Saturday. Hot food on matchdays.

PREVIOUS - **Name:** Witney F.C. **Leagues:** Reading & Dist., Oxfordshire Senior, Hellenic 53-73. **Ground:** Marriotts Close, Welch Way (pre-1992).

CLUB RECORDS - **Attendance:** 3,167 v Chelsea 16/11/98 Stand Opening. Competitive: 734 v Wealdstone 8/10/92. **Career Goalscorer:** Kenny Clarke 145. **Career Appearances:** Kevin Alder 402 (+6 sub). **Transfer fee paid:** £3,000 for Steve Jenkins (Cheltenham Town). **Transfer fee received:** £5,000 for John Bailey (Worcester City).

BEST SEASON - **FA Trophy:** Second Rd 78-79. **FA Amateur Cup:** Second Rd replay - 3 times, 66-67, 71-72, 72-73. **FA Cup:** 1st Rd 71-72 (lost 0-3 at home to Romford).

HONOURS - Southern Lg Div 1 Nth 77-78; Hellenic Lg (8) 54-55 57-58 64-67 70-73 (R-up 53-54 67-68 69-70), Lg Cup (6), Prem Div Benevolent Cup 59-60 63-64; Oxon Snr Lg (5); Oxon Snr Cup (12).

Players progressing to Football League: Herbert Smith, Frank Clack (Birmingham City), Arthur Hall (Bristol Rovers 1959), David Moss (Swindon 1969), Jack Newman.

97-98 - Captain: Steve Tavinor **Top scorer:** Tom Pegler (20)
Players P.o.Y.: Andy Martin **Supporters P.o.Y.:** Kevin Alder

Back Row (L-R); Kevin Alder, Andy Martin, Steve Tavinor, Shaun Wimble, Gary Ackling (Asst Mgr), Roger Alder (Physio). Middle Row; Matthew McDonnell, Steve Ovens, Craig Dore, Geoff Neville, Tom Pegler. Front Row; Andy Lyne (Mgr), Andy Leach, Chris Organ, Lee Keyes, Terry Merriman, Eddie Denton, Paul Holden (Coach/Scout).

YATE TOWN

Colours: White/navy/navy. **Formed:** 1946
Change colours: Tangerine/white/white **Nickname:** The Bluebells
Midweek home matchday: Tuesday **Sponsors:** Homeworld.
Reserve Team's League: Bristol Suburban.
Local Press: Bristol Evening Post, Western Daily Press, North Avon Gazette.
Local Radio: GWR, Radio Bristol.

PROGRAMME DETAILS:
Pages: 40 **Price:** £1
Editor: Bob Chester
c/o Club

Chairman: R G Hawkins **President:** R Hewetson
Vice Chairman: D A Phillips
Secretary: Terry Tansley, 1 Tyning Close, Yate, Avon. BS17 4PN, 01454 324305
Press Officer / Commercial Manager: Bob Chester 01179 563674
Manager: John Freegard **Asst Manager:** Phil Purnell
Coach: Phil Purnell **Physio:** Steve Britton

GROUND Address: Lodge Road, Yate, Bristol BS17 5LE (0454 228103).
Directions: M4 jct 18, A46 towards Stroud, then A432 to Yate. Turn right at top of railway bridge into North Road, first left past traffic lights. Five miles from Bristol Parkway BR main line station, half mile from Yate BR station. Buses 329, X68 and 328.
Capacity: 2,000 **Cover:** 236 **Seats:** 236 **Floodlights:** Yes
Clubhouse: Open every night and weekend lunchtimes. Skittles, darts, pool, live entertainment.
Club Shop: Selling programmes & usual souvenirs. Contact: Bob Chester 0117 956 3674

PREVIOUS - **Leagues:** Gloucestershire County 68-83, Hellenic 83-89. **Name:** Yate YMCA 1946-70. **Grounds:** Yate Aerodrome 50-54, Newmans Field 54-60, Sunnyside Lane 60-84.

CLUB RECORDS - **Attendance:** 2,000 for Bristol Rovers v Bristol Rovers Past, Vaughan Jones testimonial 90. **Win:** 13-3 v Clevedon, Bristol Premier Comb 67-68. **Career Goalscorer:** Kevin Thaws. **Career Appearances:** Gary Hewlett. **Transfer fee paid:** None. **Transfer fee received:** £15,000 for Mike Davis (Bristol Rovers 93).

BEST SEASON - **FA Vase:** Fifth Round 1991-92

HONOURS - Hellenic Lg(2) 87-89 (Div 1 R-up 84-85, Lg Skol Cup R-up 87-88), Glos Chal. Tphy 88-89 (R-up 78-79), Glos Snr Amtr Cup Sth 77-78 91-92(res) 92-93(res), Glos Snr Chal. Cup (Nth) R-up 89-90 92-93 94-95, Stroud Charity Cup R-up 74-75 81-82 84-85 (Sect. A Winners(6) 76-78 79-80 82-83 87-89), Berkeley Hosp. Prem. Cup(3) 73-75 80-81, S.W. Co's Sutton Vase 85-86.

Players progressing to Football League: Richard Thompson (Newport County & Exeter City), Phil Purnell (Bristol Rovers), Darren Tilley (York City), Steve Winter (Walsall), Mike Davis (Bristol Rovers) 1993.

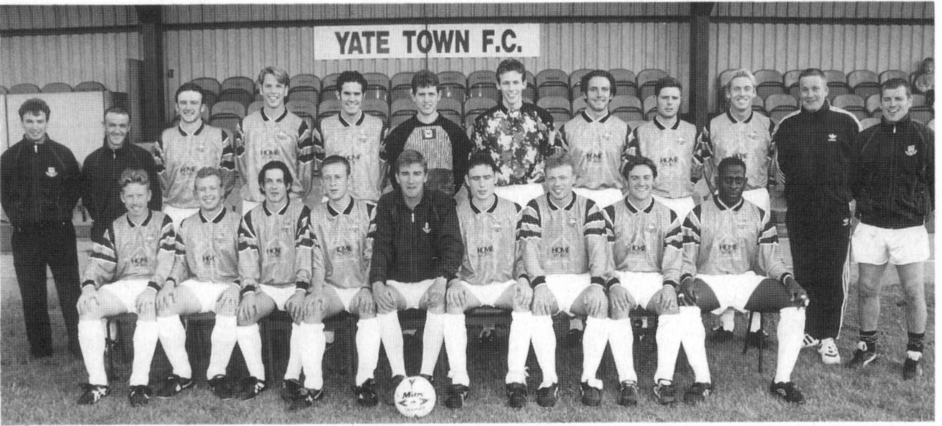

Back Row (L-R); Phil Purnell, Kris Lee, Steve Tucker, Steve Peters, David Hope, Chris Bright, Shane Cook, Andy Hogg, Mark Madge, Paul Murgatroyd, Steve Britton (Physio), Marcus Bray (Asst Mgr). Front Row; Micky Airs, Marcus Jefferies, Alan Theobald, Danny Iddles, John Freegard (Mgr), Mark Lippiatt, Alex Stocker, Darren Hunt, Kevin Thompson

Perhaps stripes would have been better
Photo: Kevin Rolfe

Jewson

EASTERN COUNTIES LEAGUE

FEEDER TO: Dr MARTENS FOOTBALL LEAGUE

FOUNDED: 1935

Hon. Patron: Derek Needham **President:** Roger Pauley

Secretary: Colin Lamb, 3 Land Close, Clacton-on-Sea, Essex CO16 8UJ (01255 436398)

Premier Division League Table 1997-98

	P	W	D	L	F	A	Pts
Wroxham	42	30	7	5	80	26	97
Ely City	42	29	8	5	91	43	95
Histon	42	27	7	8	102	48	88
Sudbury Wanderers	42	25	4	13	100	55	79
Great Yarmouth Town	42	21	8	13	80	60	71
Sudbury Town	42	19	13	10	81	43	70
Halstead Town	42	19	8	15	80	64	65
Felixstowe Port & Tn	42	20	4	18	58	43	64
Lowestoft Town	42	18	10	14	82	70	64
Fakenham Town	42	18	9	15	66	61	63
Newmarket Town	42	18	7	17	68	52	61
Woodbridge Town	42	15	14	13	74	71	50
Stowmarket Town	42	17	4	21	63	81	55
Gorleston	42	14	12	16	62	63	54
Soham Town	42	16	5	21	66	66	52
Warboys Town	42	10	4	22	71	76	52
Diss Town	42	13	10	19	64	78	48
Bury Town	42	13	0	21	56	71	47
Harwich & Parkeston	42	12	7	23	61	65	43
Watton United	42	7	7	28	44	128	28
Clacton Town	42	6	8	28	46	140	26
Tiptree United	42	3	8	31	46	123	17

(Soham Town Rangers deducted 1pt)

Premier Division Results Grid 1997-98

HOME TEAM	1	2	3	4	5	6	7	8	9	10	11	12	13	14	15	16	17	18	19	20	21	22
1. Bury Town	*	4-0	1-0	0-2	3-2	0-2	0-0	0-4	1-2	1-0	0-3	2-4	1-0	2-1	2-2	0-3	0-3	3-1	1-1	1-2	1-2	0-1
2. Clacton Tn	3-2	*	3-3	0-4	2-1	0-3	0-1	0-2	1-6	1-3	0-2	2-1	1-1	0-1	1-5	0-2	2-1	2-2	0-5	1-2	5-5	1-6
3. Diss Town	0-3	5-0	*	1-3	1-2	0-2	3-2	1-0	2-3	0-2	1-1	0-2	0-1	6-2	3-2	0-0	2-0	3-0	4-2	3-4	0-0	2-0
4. Ely City	3-2	4-0	2-2	*	1-0	1-0	2-0	2-1	2-1	3-0	2-2	2-3	2-1	4-3	1-1	1-1	3-1	5-1	3-0	1-0	1-2	5-1
5. Fakenham T	1-1	3-0	3-3	0-2	*	4-1	2-1	2-0	2-3	4-2	0-3	0-0	1-0	3-1	1-2	1-1	2-1	2-0	1-3	4-0	2-2	0-0
6. Felixstowe T	0-2	2-1	0-0	1-0	2-0	*	0-1	1-3	0-1	1-2	3-1	2-2	0-0	1-0	4-0	1-3	0-2	2-0	1-2	1-2	2-1	0-1
7. Gorleston	3-1	3-2	2-3	3-0	0-0	0-2	*	1-2	1-1	1-1	0-0	4-0	1-2	3-2	2-1	1-1	2-4	1-1	3-0	9-1	1-2	0-0
8. Gt Yarmouth	1-0	4-3	1-0	0-3	0-1	1-0	1-1	*	1-5	8-3	1-2	1-0	1-3	3-2	1-2	1-0	4-2	4-1	5-1	3-3	2-0	0-0
9. Halstead Tn	5-4	3-0	4-0	1-2	0-2	1-4	6-0	4-2	*	0-2	2-2	1-1	0-1	2-2	4-1	2-2	1-4	2-1	0-1	1-0	1-1	0-3
10. Harwich & P	2-2	1-1	1-1	1-3	5-1	0-5	2-0	1-2	1-2	*	1-3	4-2	1-0	0-3	1-2	1-1	1-2	2-2	1-3	3-0	1-2	0-4
11. Histon	3-2	5-0	3-1	0-3	5-1	2-0	6-0	1-0	2-1	2-0	*	3-4	1-2	5-1	2-0	1-1	3-0	4-1	1-0	6-0	3-1	0-2
12. Lowestoft	3-4	8-0	3-2	1-2	0-2	0-1	2-2	1-3	2-0	1-1	1-1	*	1-0	5-3	2-1	0-4	0-1	4-1	2-0	3-0	2-1	0-2
13. Newmarket	1-2	6-0	4-0	1-1	2-3	3-2	1-4	0-0	0-1	3-0	2-4	0-0	*	1-0	1-2	3-2	2-3	5-1	2-1	6-0	0-0	1-0
14. Soham Tn R	1-4	5-6	2-3	2-3	2-1	2-1	3-1	1-1	1-2	4-2	2-1	1-1	1-1	*	1-2	1-0	3-3	2-4	4-2	2-3	4-1	0-1
15. Stowmarket	2-1	5-1	0-1	1-2	1-1	0-1	0-1	3-2	2-3	0-3	0-2	1-2	2-0	0-3	*	1-0	0-8	4-1	2-4	3-1	0-3	0-0
16. Sudbury Tn	0-0	1-1	2-1	1-1	2-2	0-1	3-1	3-1	2-0	1-0	3-0	2-2	2-3	3-2	6-2	*	2-1	4-1	1-0	4-1	1-0	0-3
17. Sudbury Wd	1-1	6-0	0-1	0-1	1-2	2-0	1-0	2-3	2-1	1-0	0-1	3-0	2-1	4-1	5-1	2-1	*	4-0	3-1	2-2	3-2	1-2
18. Tiptree Utd	0-1	1-3	3-1	1-3	0-5	0-2	0-3	1-1	2-5	2-3	1-5	2-2	1-3	0-5	1-3	1-2	2-4	*	0-2	0-1	1-1	0-1
19. Warboys Tn	1-0	5-0	2-2	1-1	3-0	0-5	4-0	0-3	1-0	4-1	2-2	3-4	1-0	1-3	0-2	0-3	1-2	1-4	*	1-2	4-1	0-1
20. Watton Utd	1-1	2-2	2-2	1-2	0-2	0-1	1-3	1-4	1-1	1-3	1-2	0-7	2-3	1-4	0-3	0-8	2-2	2-2	1-6	*	0-3	0-1
21. Woodbridge	3-0	1-1	2-1	3-3	3-2	1-1	0-0	2-2	2-2	4-2	1-5	2-3	2-1	0-2	1-2	2-1	2-2	3-3	6-2	2-0	*	1-0
22. Wroxham	4-2	3-0	5-0	2-0	2-0	2-0	0-0	1-1	1-0	2-1	3-1	4-1	3-1	3-1	2-0	1-1	0-4	2-0	1-0	3-1	2-1	*

League Cup 1997-98

First Round

Bury Town	v	Lowestoft Town	0-2
Ely City	v	Stanway Rovers	2-1
Harwich & Park	v	Histon	0-2
Sudbury Town	v	Somersham Town	1-0
Tiptree United	v	Clacton Town	2-1
Woodbridge Town	v	Cambridge City	4-3
Ipswich Wanderers	v	Needham Market	1-0
Norwich United	v	Brightlingsea	4-0
Diss Town	v	Haverhill Rovers	8-1
Gorleston	v	Cornard United	2-1
March Town United	v	Swaffham Town	1-0
Sudbury Wanderers	v	Gt Yarmouth Town	2-4
Warboys Town	v	Wroxham	2-1
Chatteris Town	v	Newmarket Town	2-1
Stowmarket Town	v	Thetford Town	1-4
Mildenhall Town	v	Hadleigh United	1-5

Second Round

Chatteris Town	v	Ely City	1-2
Thetford Town	v	Diss Town	1-3
Hadleigh United	v	Gorleston	0-4
Sudbury Town	v	Norwich United	2-0
Ipswich Wanderers	v	Swaffham Town	3-4
Gt Yarmouth Town	v	Warboys Town	0-4
Lowestoft Town	v	Histon	0-1
Tiptree United	v	Woodbridge Town	1-3

Quarter Finals

Diss Town	v	Swaffham Town	1-0
Gorleston	v	Woodbridge Town	2-3
Ely City	v	Histon	1-3
Sudbury Town	v	Warboys Town	1-2

Semi Finals

Diss Town	v	Woodbridge Town	0-2
Warboys Town	v	Histon	4-2

Final Warboys Town v Woodbridge Town 2-4 (at Soham Town Rangers)

Division One League Table 1997-98

	P	W	D	L	F	A	Pts
Ipswich Wanderers	34	29	2	3	100	35	89
Maldon Town	34	26	2	6	84	29	80
Swaffham Town	34	21	7	6	67	20	70
Needham Market	34	17	7	10	53	39	58
Stanway Rovers	34	16	9	9	64	37	57
Cambridge City Res	34	16	8	10	63	44	56
Chatteris Town	34	16	8	10	56	53	56
Norwich United	34	16	3	15	51	46	51
Whitton United	34	14	8	12	66	55	50
Haverhill Rovers	34	14	7	13	54	56	49
Mildenhall Town	34	10	12	12	48	57	47
Downham Town	34	10	7	17	50	72	37
Thetford Town	34	9	5	20	47	74	32
Cornard United	34	8	8	18	41	71	32
March Town United	34	7	7	20	34	75	28
Hadleigh United	34	6	8	20	32	60	26
Brightlingsea United	34	5	7	22	30	67	22
Somersham Town	34	4	9	21	46	88	21

Division One Results Grid 1997-98

HOME TEAM	1	2	3	4	5	6	7	8	9	10	11	12	13	14	15	16	17	18
1. Brightlingsea	*	2-1	0-1	0-3	0-2	0-0	0-0	0-1	0-3	2-0	0-0	1-3	0-1	1-2	0-0	1-1	1-2	2-3
2. Cambridge City	2-1	*	1-0	2-2	1-3	4-2	2-0	1-2	3-2	3-1	4-1	0-2	2-1	5-1	2-2	1-1	1-1	7-1
3. Chatteris Tn	5-0	1-0	*	2-2	3-2	1-1	2-1	1-6	2-4	4-1	0-1	1-1	4-1	2-1	2-1	0-1	1-0	2-7
4. Cornard Utd	3-1	0-1	2-2	*	3-2	1-0	1-3	0-3	0-2	2-2	1-1	2-0	1-2	3-0	0-0	0-0	0-1	1-1
5. Downham Tn	0-3	0-0	1-1	6-0	*	2-1	3-3	1-4	1-2	1-2	1-1	1-4	1-0	1-1	0-4	1-3	1-0	1-2
6. Hadleigh Utd	2-1	2-1	0-1	1-2	1-1	*	4-1	1-2	0-1	1-1	0-0	1-2	0-1	0-0	2-7	2-1	1-0	1-4
7. Haverhill Rov	1-1	0-0	4-0	2-1	3-3	1-0	*	1-3	0-4	2-1	1-1	3-2	3-2	4-0	0-1	0-1	3-0	2-2
8. Ipswich Wand	7-0	4-1	5-0	3-1	4-1	4-0	0-5	*	2-1	4-0	3-0	4-0	2-0	4-2	1-0	0-2	3-2	3-2
9. Maldon Town	2-1	2-0	2-1	6-1	2-1	4-0	6-0	2-3	*	2-0	1-0	2-1	3-0	5-2	2-0	0-1	6-0	3-0
10. March Tn Utd	2-1	0-0	1-3	2-1	4-1	3-1	0-3	2-3	0-2	*	0-1	2-2	0-3	2-2	0-2	2-4	2-1	1-5
11. Mildenhall Tn	5-0	0-4	1-5	2-1	0-2	0-0	3-0	0-6	2-3	4-0	*	0-2	2-2	4-3	2-2	0-1	2-2	4-3
12. Needham Market	2-0	2-1	1-1	3-1	0-2	0-2	1-0	2-2	1-0	5-0	2-0	*	1-3	1-0	1-1	0-2	2-2	1-0
13. Norwich Utd	4-0	3-1	0-3	1-0	2-1	2-1	3-2	1-2	0-1	3-1	1-2	1-2	*	2-0	2-2	0-2	3-0	0-0
14. Somersham Tn	3-1	1-2	0-1	6-1	2-4	4-3	2-3	3-3	1-1	0-0	2-2	1-1	2-3	*	0-5	0-4	1-3	2-4
15. Stanway Rov	0-0	0-2	1-1	3-4	6-0	4-0	2-0	0-1	3-0	0-1	0-3	2-1	1-0	5-2	*	2-0	3-0	0-0
16. Swaffham Tn	0-3	3-2	2-2	5-0	2-0	0-0	2-0	2-1	1-3	0-0	3-0	0-1	1-0	5-0	6-0	*	7-0	2-2
17. Thetford Tn	2-5	1-4	0-2	4-1	7-0	2-1	0-1	1-3	2-2	3-0	2-2	1-3	1-4	2-0	2-4	0-1	*	2-1
18. Whitton United	4-2	2-2	2-0	3-0	1-3	2-1	1-2	0-2	0-1	6-1	0-0	0-3	2-0	1-1	0-1	3-1	3-1	*

PREMIER DIVISION CLUBS 1998-99

BURY TOWN

Chairman: Colin Hurley **Vice Chairman:** Russel Ward **President:** Cyril Elsey.
Secretary: Mrs Wendy Turner, 64 Winthrop Rd., Bury-St-Edmunds, Suffolk. IP33 3UF (01284 753688)
Manager/Coach: Tony Godden **Asst Manager:** Keith Vince **Physio:** John Chandler
Ground: Ram Meadow, Cotton Lane, Bury St Edmunds, Suffolk IP33 1XP, (01284 754721).
Directions: Leave A14 at sign to central Bury St Edmunds, follow signs to town centre at exit r'bout, at next r'bout 1st exit into Northgate St, left at 'T' junct (lights) into Mustow St, left immediately into Cotton Lane - grd 350 yds on right, through 'Pay & Display' car park. 10 mins from station.
Capacity: 3,500 **Cover:** 1,500 **Seats:** 300 **Floodlights:** Yes **Club Shop:** Yes
Clubhouse: Members'/Public Bars open at matchdays
Programme: 40 pages 80p **Editor:** Mrs Wendy Turner **Press Officer:**
Colours: All blue **Change colours:** All red. **Sponsors:** The Flying Fortress
Midweek matchday: Tuesday **Formed:** 1872 **Nickname:** The Blues
Best Season - FA Cup: 1st Rd replay 68-69 (lost 0-3 at AFC Bournemouth after 0-0 draw). **FA Vase:** Qtr Finals 88-89. **FA Trophy:** 2nd Rd 70-71
Previous - Leagues: Norfolk & Suffolk/ Essex & Suffolk Border/ Eastern Co's 35-64 76-87/ Metropolitan 64-71.
Names: Bury St Edmunds 1895-1902/ Bury Utd 02-06. **Ground:** Kings Road 1872-1978.
Players progressing to Football League: D Lewis (Gillingham, Preston), L Carberry (Ipswich), T Bly (Norwich 56, Peterborough), T Pearce (Ipswich), G Stevens (Brighton, Spurs), S Milton (Ipswich 90)
97-98 - Captain: M Wales **P.o.Y.:** D Vince **Top scorer:** D Vince
Records - Goalscorer: Doug Tooley 58. **Appearances:** Doug Tooley. **Attendance:** 2,500 v Enfield, FA Cup 3rd Qualifying Rd 1986. **Fees - Paid:** £1,500 for Mel Springett (Chelmsford 1990). **Received:** £5,500 for Simon Milton (Ipswich).
Honours: Eastern Counties Lg 63-64, R-up 37-38, Lg Cup 61-62 63-64; Metropolitan Lg 65-66, R-up 67-68 70-71, Lg Cup 67-68, Professional Cup 65-66; Suffolk Premier Cup (9); Suffolk Senior Cup 36-37 37-38 38-39 44-45 84-85.

DISS TOWN

Chairman: Des Tebble **President:** R A Gooderham **Treasurer:** Noel Mullenger.
Secretary: Richard Upson, Bamburgh House, Brewers Green Lane, Diss, Norfolk IP22 3QP (01379 642923).
Manager: Paul Chick **Asst Manager:** Donnie Pye **Physio:** Peter Etheridge
Ground: Brewers Green Lane, Diss (01379 651223).
Directions: Just off B1066 Diss-Thetford road, near Roydon School. One and a half miles from Diss (BR).
Seats: 280 **Cover:** Yes **Capacity:** 2,500 **Floodlights:** Yes **Club Shop:** Yes
Clubhouse: Open evenings (except Sunday), Sat/Sun lunchtimes, and matchdays.
Programme: 16 pages, 50p **Editor:** G Enderby (01953 455979)
Colours: Tangerine/navy/tangerine **Change colours:** White/navy/tangerine.
Founded: 1888. **Nickname:** Tangerines. **Sponsors:** Diss Fasteners
Midweek Matches: Tuesday **Reserve's League:** Anglian Combination.
Previous Leagues: Norwich & District/ Norfolk & Suffolk 35-64/ Anglian Combination 64-82.
Players progressing to the Football League: A Thurlow (Man City), M Cawston (Norwich), T Whymark (Ipswich), C Stafford, P Gibbs (Colchester)
97-98 - Captain: Sean Trail **Top Scorer:** Stuart Jopling **P.o.Y.:** Sean Trail
Record Attendance: 1,731 v Atherton LR, FA Vase SF 1st leg 19/3/94
Honours: FA Vase 94-95 (QF 91-92), Eastern Co's Lg Div 1 91-92, Anglian Comb. 76-77 78-79 (R-up 74-75, Div 1 67-68 73-74, Lg Cup 67-68 79-80 81-82), Norfolk & Suffolk Lg R-up 55-56 (Applegate Cup 56-57 57-58(joint)(R-up 55-56)), Norfolk Snr Cup 74-75 95-96, Norfolk Jnr Cup 1891-92, Jewson Prem Lge R-up 95-96.

ELY CITY

Chairman: Brian Jordan **Manager:** David Pinkowski & Tony Lyes
Secretary: Derek Oakey, 11 Frederick Talbot Close, Soham, Nr Ely, Cambs CB7 5EY (01353 722141).
Ground: Unwin Sports Ground, Downham Road (01353 662035).
Directions: A10 Ely by-pass turn off for Downham. 3 miles (approx) from Ely (BR).
Seats: 150 **Cover:** 350 **Capacity:** 1,500 **Floodlights:** Yes **Founded:** 1885
Clubhouse: Open matchdays, refreshments available
Colours: All red **Change colours:** Jade/black/jade **Nickname:** Robins
Programme: 20p **Editor:** John Lawson **Midweek Matches:** Tuesday
Previous Lges: Peterborough/ Central Alliance 58-60.
Record Gate: 260 v Soham, Eastern Co's Lg Div 1, 12/4/93. *At old ground: 4,260 v Torquay, FA Cup 56-57*
Honours: Cambs Snr Cup 47-48, Eastern Co's Lg R-up 69-70 (Lg Cup 79-80), FA Cup 1st Rd 56-56 (2-6 v Torquay).

FAKENHAM TOWN

Chairman: Tony Fisher **President:** G Middleditch **Manager:** Ian Jones
Secretary: Eddie Linnell, 40 Warren Avenue, Fakenham, Norfolk NR21 8NP (01328 855445).
Ground: Clipbush Lane, Fakenham (01328 856222).
Directions: Corner of A148 & Clipbush Lane
Seats: 264 **Cover:** 500 **Capacity:** 3,000 **Floodlights:** Yes **Founded:** 1884
Clubhouse: Bar, TV. Refreshments available **Club Shop:** Yes
Colours: Amber & black/black/amber **Change colours:** Red/white/red
Programme: 32 pages, 50p **Editor:** John Cushion
Midweek Matchday: Tuesday **Sponsors:** T.B.A. **Nickname:** Ghosts
Previous Leagues: N Norfolk 1884-1910/ Norwich & Dist 10-35/ Norfolk & Suffolk 35-64/ Anglian Comb 64-87.
Reserves' League: Anglian Comb. **Record Gate:** 1,000 v Norwich City, floodlight inauguration.
Players progressing to the Football League: Nolan Keeley (Scunthorpe & Lincoln).
Honours: Norfolk Snr Cup 70-71 72-73 73-74 91-92 93-94 94-95; Eastern Co's Lg Div 1 R-up 91-92; Anglian Comb. Cup 78-79.

FELIXSTOWE PORT & TOWN

Chairman: Dave Ashford **Manager:** Paul Adams **Fixture Sec:** Mike Gosling (01394 279758)
Secretary: Steve Page, 11A Lonsdale Close, Ipswich, Suffolk IP4 4HB (01473 712613).
Ground: Dellwood Avenue, Felixstowe (01394 282917).
Directions: A45 to Felixstowe. Turn right at 3rd r'bout then 1st left - ground 100 yds on left. 5 mins from Felixstowe (BR) and town centre.
Seats: 200 **Cover:** 200 **Capacity:** 2,000 **Floodlights:** Yes **Founded:** 1890.
Clubhouse: Bar, snack bar, TV, darts, pool table. Snacks available
Colours: White/blue/gold. **Change:** Blue/white/yellow & blue **Nickname:** Seasiders.
Programme: 16 pages, 30p **Editor:** Phil Griffiths **Club Shop:** Yes
Prev. Leagues: Essex & Suffolk Border/ Ipswich & Dist. **Midweek Matches:** Wednesday
Record Attendance: 1,500 v Ipswich Town, floodlight inauguration 25/1/91.
Honours: Suffolk Senior Cup 66-67 74-75.

GORLESTON

Chairman: Kevin Antcliffe **President:** Jimmy Jones **Manager:** M.Hubble & Steve Foyster
Secretary: A Ottley, 60 Peterhouse Ave., Gorleston, Gt Yarmouth, Norfolk NR31 7PZ (01493 603353).
Ground: Emerald Park, Woodfarm Lane, Gorleston, Great Yarmouth (01493 602802).
Directions: On Magdalen Estate - follow signs to Crematorium, turn left and follow road to ground. Five and a half miles from Great Yarmouth Vauxhall (BR).
Seats: 250 **Cover:** 4,000 **Capacity:** 5,000 **Floodlights:** Yes **Club Shop:** Yes
Clubhouse: Bar, colour TV, pool table, darts, snacks. Matchday Tea, coffee, cold drinks, burgers, hotdogs, rolls.
Programme: 56/60 pages 70p **Editor:** Brian Bunn (01493 843114) **Nickname:** Greens.
Colours: All Green. **Change colours:** All white. **Founded:** 1884.
Midweek Matchday: Tuesday. **Record Attendance:** 4,473 v Orient, FA Cup 1st Rd 29/11/51.
Previous Leagues: Gt Yarmouth & Dist/Norfolk & Suffolk/ Anglian Comb.
Past players progressing to the Football League: J Joblins (Norwich), M Bailey (Wolves), D Stringer (Norwich), R Carter (Aston Villa), D Carter (Man City), A Brown (Charlton), S Morgan (Cambridge), P Gibbs (Colchester).
Honours: Eastern Co's Lg 52-53 72-73 79-80 80-81; Lge Cup 55-56; Norf. Snr Cup(13)(R-up 25); Anglian Comb. 68-69, Norf. & Suf. Lg (7); E Anglian Cup (3); Jewson Lge Div 1 95-96; FA Cup 1st Rd 51-52 57-58:

GREAT YARMOUTH TOWN

Chairman: Colin Smith **General Manager:** Dale Gordon **Manager:** Paul Tong
Secretary: Brian Smith, The Bungalow, Humberstone Farm, Cobholm, Great Yarmouth, Norfolk NR31 0AZ. 01493 656099
Ground: Wellesey Recreation Ground, Wellesey Road (01493 842936).
Directions: Just off Marine Parade, 200 yds north of Britannia Pier. Half a mile from Vauxhall (BR).
Seats: 500 **Cover:** 2,100 **Capacity:** 3,600 **Floodlights:** Yes **Club Shop:** No.
Clubhouse: (01493 8443373). Dancehall, Committee Room, darts, pool. Hot & cold food available
Programme: 20 pages, 80p **Editor:** Gerry Brown **Nickname:** Bloaters.
Colours: Amber & black stripes/black/black. **Change colours:** All red.
Midweek Matches: Tuesday **Previous Leagues:** Norfolk & Suffolk **Founded:** 1897.
Players progressing to the Football League: R Hollis (Norwich), M Blyth & N Keeley (Scunthorpe), S Davy (West Ham), K Ready (Aston Villa), G Butcher (Blackburn).
97-98 - Captain: Mark Vincent **Top Scorer:** Stewart Roach **P.o.Y.:** Craig Lewis
Record Attendance: 8,944 v Crystal Palace, FA Cup 1st Rd 52-53.
Honours: Eastern Co's Lg 68-69 (R-up 56-57 67-68 77-78 78-79), Lg Cup 37-38 74-75 80-81; East Anglian Cup(3); Norfolk Snr Cup (12) (R-up(22); Norfolk Premier Cup (2jt); Norfolk & Suffolk Lg 13-14 26-27 27-28; FA Vase SF 82-83; FA Cup 2nd Rd(2) (1st Rd 1); Anglian Comb. Cup 65-66(res); E Anglian Lg 56-57(res).

Ipswich Wanderer's captain Cameron Smith being presented with Jewson League Division One Team of Month award for February 1998.
Back Row (L-R): S Head, A Harris, S Buckle, P Keys, J McKenna, C Osborne, D Head, J Keys. Front Row: J Coupe, N Barker, K Morrisey, A Howell, D Cattermole.

Sudbury Wanderers FC *Photo: Eric Marsh*

HALSTEAD TOWN

Chairman: Mick Coe **Vice-Chairman:** John Theedom **President:** Mr E J R McDowell
Secretary: Stephen Webber, 12 Ravens Ave, Halstead, Essex CO9 1NZ (01787 476959).
Manager: Steve Parnell **Physio:** B Dunster.
Ground: Rosemary Lane, Broton Ind Est, Halstead, Essex CO9 2HR (01787 472082).
Directions: A131 Chelmsford to Braintree - follow signs to Halstead. In Halstead, 1st left after Police Station, then 1st right, and first left to ground.
Seats: 312 **Cover:** 400. **Capacity:** 2,000 **Floodlights:** Yes **Founded:** 1879.
Clubhouse: Open evenings and matchdays.
Colours: White/black/white **Change colours:** Red/white/red
Programme: 50p **Editor:** Paul Downes **Midweek Matches:** Tuesday
Previous Leagues: Nth Essex/ Halstead & Dist./ Haverhill/ Essex & Suffolk Border/ Essex Snr 80-88.
Players progressing to the Football League: Steve Allen (Wimbledon Physio).
Record Attendance: 4,000 v Walthamstow Avenue, Essex Senior Cup 1949.
Honours: Eastern Co's Lg 94-95 95-96, R-up 93-94 (Div 1 R-up 89-90), Cup 95-96; Essex Senior Trophy 94-95 96-97; Knight Floodlit Cup R-up 90-91; Essex & Suffolk Border Lg 57-59 77-78 94-95(res), (R-up 49-50 54-55 60-61), Div 1 (res) 94-95); Essex Snr Lg Cup R-up 79-80; Essex Jnr Cup 01-02 46-47 (R-up 00-01).

HARWICH & PARKESTON

Chairman: Graham Firth **President:** J Whitmore **Manager:** Steve Wright/Jimmy Minter
Secretary: Andy Schooler, 21 The Vineway, Harwich, Essex CO12 4AX
Assistant Manager: **Physio:** **Press Officer:** Carl Allan
Ground: Royal Oak, Main Road, Dovercourt, Harwich CO12 4AA (01255 503649).
Directions: On main road into Dovercourt. 600 yds from Dovercourt (BR).
Seats: 350 **Cover:** 1,000 **Capacity:** 5,000 **Floodlights:** Yes **Founded:** 1875.
Clubhouse details: Open every day. Dances, bingo, darts, pool, function room. **Club Shop:** Yes
Colours: White & black/black/black **Change colours:** Mauve & white/white/mauve **Nickname:** Shrimpers.
Programme: 28 pages, 50p **Editor:** Carl Allen **Midweek Matches:** Tuesday
Reserve Lge: Essex & Suffolk Border Prem. Div.
Previous Leagues: Eastern Co's 35-37 38-64/ Essex County 37-38/ Athenian 64-73 83-84/ Isthmian 73-83.
Players progressing to the Football League: I Gillespie (C Palace, Ipswich), G Waites, K Sanderson, I Brown (Bristol City 91)
Record Attendance: 5,649 v Romford, FA Amat Cup 4th Rd 1938
Honours: FA Amateur Cup R-up 1898-99 52-53; FA Vase QF 90-91; Eastern Counties Lg 35-36(jnt) (Lg Cup 35-36 36-37 96-97); Essex County Lg 37-38; Athenian Lg Div 1 R-up 65-66 (Div 2 64-65, Lg Cup 64-65); Essex Senior Cup 1898-99 36-37; Essex Senior Trophy 89-90; AFA Senior Cup 35-36 36-37; Worthington Evans Cup 80-81.

HISTON

Chairman: Gareth Baldwin **President:** G P Muncey **Manager:** Andy Beattie
Secretary: Gareth Baldwin, 5 Caxton Lane, Foxton, Cambridge CB2 6SR (01223 872246).
Ground: Bridge Road, Impington, Cambridge (01223 232301).
Directions: Leave A14 northern Cambridge bypass on B1049 (signposted Histon and Cottenham). Ground half a mile on right. 5 miles from Cambridge (BR). Bus No. 104.
Seats: 250 **Cover:** 200 **Capacity:** 3,100 **Floodlights:** Yes **Founded:** 1904.
Clubhouse details: Bar/lounge open Tues-Sun evenings, Sun lunctimes and matchdays. Snacks available
Programme: 16 pages, 50p. **Editor:** Lisa Whybrow **Record Attendance:** 2,400 v K. Lynn, FA Cup.
Colours: Red and black/black/black. **Change colours:** All blue & white **Midweek Matches:** Tuesday
Previous Leagues: Cambridgeshire 04-48/ Spartan 48-60/ Delphian 60-63/ Athenian 63-65.
Honours: Eastern Co's Lg Div 1 R-up 96-97, Cup 90-91; Cambridge Invitation Cup 77-78 79-80 96-97 (R-up 50-51 52-53 53-54); Spartan Lg Div 1 (East) 50-51; Cambs Chall Cup; Cambs Lg Section; Kershaw Prem Lge R-up 97-98, Sen Lge A 96-97, Cup 96-97; Auto Trader Lge & Cup (U18) 96-97.

IPSWICH WANDERERS

Chairman: A.Haste. **President:** P.Emmerson. **Manager:** Alan Dilloway
Secretary: Martin Head, 246 Sidelate Lane, Ipswich, Suffolk. IP4 3DH (01473 273811)
Ground: Humberdoucey Lane, Ipswich, Suffolk (01473 728581).
Directions: Take Woodbridge Road out of Ipswich,then left fork into Playford Road.Take first left into Humberdoucy Lane Ground 300yds on right.
Seats: 50 **Cover:** Yes **Capacity:** 2,000 **Floodlights:** Yes **Founded:** 1983.
Clubhouse: Bar, Tea, coffee, cold drinks, confectionary, burgers, hotdogs, sandwiches, rolls.
Programme: Yes. **Editor:** Alan Haste (01473 711877) **Sponsors:** Car Glass & Trim.
Colours: Royal & white/blue/blue & white **Change colours:** Red & black/black/red & black
Midweek Matches: Wednesday **Previous Leagues:** Little David Sunday **Nickname:** Wanderers.
Record Attendance: 335 v Woodbridge, ECL Div 1 4/4/94.
Honours: Eastern Lge Div 1 97-98.

LOWESTOFT TOWN

Chairman: Shaun Cole **President:** Roy Harper **Manager:** Michael Chapman
Secretary: Terry Lynes, 156 Denmark Road, Lowestoft, Suffolk NR33 2EL (01502 564034).
Ground: Crown Meadow, Love Rd, Lowestoft (01502 573818). **Directions:** Just off A12, 10 mins from Lowestoft (BR).
Seats: 466 **Cover:** 500 **Capacity:** 1,850 **Floodlights:** Yes **Founded:** 1890.
Clubhouse: Pub hours, Snacks available **Club Shop:** Yes
Colours: Royal/white/royal **Change colours:** All red **Nickname:** Blues.
Programme: 20 pages, 60p **Editor:** Rachel Harrod **Midweek Matches:** Tuesday
Sponsors: Odebrecht BLS **Reserves' Lge:** Anglian Combination **Previous League:** Norfolk & Suffolk 1897-1935
Best Season - FA Cup: 1st Rd 26-27 38-39 66-67 77-78.
Players progressing to Football League: Eddie Spearitt (Ipswich 1965), Nigel Cassidy (Norwich 1967), Richard Money (Scunthorpe 1973), Graham Franklin (Southend 1977).
Record - Attendance: 5,000 v Watford, FA Cup 1st Rd 67. **Goalscorer:** M Tooley 383. **Appearances:** C Peck 629.
Honours: Eastern Co's Lg(8) 35-36(jnt) 37-38 62-63 64-65 67-68 69-71 77-78, Lg Cup(7) 38-39 54-55 65-67 68-69 75-76 83-84; Norf. & Suffolk Lg(8) 1897-99 1900-04 28-29 30-31; Suffolk Prem. Cup(5) 66-67 71-72 74-75 78-80; Suffolk Snr Cup(10) 02-03 22-24 25-26 31-32 35-36 46-49 55-56; E Anglian Cup(10); Anglian Comb. (Reserves) 77-78 79-80 (Lg Cup 76-77); E Anglian Lg (Reserves) 57-58 63-64.

MALDON TOWN

Chairman: Bob Large. **Manager:** Ben Embery.
Secretary: B D Lloyd, 46 Maldon Road, Great Totham, Maldon, Essex CM9 8PR (01621 893148)
Ground: Wallace Binder Ground, Park Drive, Maldon CM9 5XX (01621 853762).
Seats: Yes **Cover:** Yes **Capacity:** 2,500 **Floodlights:** Yes **Founded:** 1946.
Colours: Blue & white/blue/blue & white **Change colours:** Red & black/black/red
Programme: Yes **Editor:** T Wynne **Midweek Matchday:** Tuesday
Previous - Leagues: Eastern Counties, Essex & Suffolk Border. **Ground:** Fambridge Road (pre-1994).
Honours: Essex Snr Lg 84-85 (Sportsmanship Award 87-88,88-89,94-95, Reserve Shield 93-94), Reserve Cup:94-95, Essex & Suffolk Border Lg 55-56 (Cup 64-65), Essex Intermediate Cup 51-52, Tolleshunt D'Arcy Cup 93-94.

NEWMARKET TOWN

Chairman: Alf Collen **President:** M J Nicholas **Manager:** John Wright
Fixture Secretary: Terry Osborne, 1 Falmouth Street, Newmarket CB8 0LE (01638 601310).
Ground: Cricketfield Road, off New Cheveley Road, Newmarket (01638 663637).
Directions: 400 yds Newmarket (BR) - turn right into Green Rd, right at cr/rds New Cheveley Rd, grd at top on left
Seats: 144 **Cover:** 150 **Capacity:** 1,750 **Floodlights:** Yes **Founded:** 1877.
Clubhouse: Matchdays only. Refreshments available
Programme: 50p **Editor:** Tony Pringle (01638 669438) **Midweek Matches:** Tuesday
Colours: Yellow & navy/navy/navy **Change Colours:** Maroon & blue/maroon/maroon **Nickname:** Jockeys.
Previous League: Bury Snr/ Ipswich Snr/ Essex & Suffolk Border/ Utd Co's 34-37/ Eastern Co's 37-52.
Best F.A. Cup year: 4th Qualifying Rd 92-93 (lost 0-2 at home to Hayes).
Players progressing to the Football League: Mick Lambert (Ipswich), M Wright (Northampton), G Tweed (Coventry), R Fuller (Charlton), Colin Vowden (Camb.Utd.)
97-98 - Captain: Dave Brown **Top Scorer:** Jerry Rose **P.o.Y.:** Andy Eady
Record Attendance: 2,701 v Abbey Utd (now Cambridge Utd), FA Cup 1st Qualifying Rd 1/10/49.
Honours: Suffolk Snr Cup 34-35 93-94; Cambs Invitation Cup 58-59; Cambs Challenge Cup 21-22 26-27; Cambs Snr Lg, 19-20; Ipswich Snr Lg 30-31 31-32 32-33 33-34; Peterborough Lg 57-58; Suffolk Premier Cup 93-94 94-95 96-97.

SOHAM TOWN RANGERS

Chairman: M Robinson **President:** J Mann
Secretary: Mrs Wendy Gammon, 32 Broad Piece, Soham, Cambs CB7 5EL (01353 722139).
Manager: R Goodjohn **Coach:** Mick Drury
Ground: Julius Martins Lane, Soham, Cambs (01353 720732). **Directions:** A142 between Newmarket and Ely
Seats: 200 **Cover:** 1,500 **Capacity:** 2,000 **Floodlights:** Yes **Shop:** Yes
Clubhouse: General bar, Stud Bar, Lounge Bar. **Midweek Matchday:** Wednesday
Programme: 50p **Editor:** Graham Eley **Founded:** 1947. **Nickname:** Town or Rangers.
Colours: Green & white/white/white **Change colours:** Blue/black/black
Sponsors: Clark & Butcher & Able Acess Ltd **Reserves League:** Cambs Prem. B.
Record Attendance: 3,000 v Pegasus, FA Amateur Cup 1963. **Previous Leagues:** Peterborough & Dist.
Honours: Eastern Co's Lg Div 1 R-up 92-93; P'boro. Lg(3).

STOWMARKET TOWN

Chairman: Derek Barnard. **President:** John Bultitude **Fixture Sec:** Christine Gillingham (01449 674507)
Secretary: Colin Davies, 15 Winchester Close, Stowmarket, (01449 615632)
Manager: Trevor Wardlaw **Coach:** David King **Physio:** John Chandler
Ground: Green Meadows Stadium, Bury Road, Stowmarket (01449 612533). **Directions:** About 800 yds from Stowmarket BR station - turn right at 1st lights and head out of town over r'bout into Bury Road - ground on right.
Seats: 200 **Cover:** 450 **Capacity:** 2,000 **Floodlights:** Yes **Club Shop:** Yes
Clubhouse: Bar open 6.30pm onwards Mon-Fri, weekends 12.0pm onwards. Matchday food available.
Programme: 20 pages, 50p **Editor:** John Gillingham (01449 674507). **Founded:** 1883.
Colours: Gold/black/black **Change colours:** All Red **Nickname:** Stow
Reserves' Lge: Essex & Suffolk Border **Record Attendance:** 1,200 v Ipswich Town, friendly July 1994.
Midweek Matches: Wednesday **Previous Leagues:** Ipswich & Dist./ Essex & Suffolk Border 25-52.
Players progressing to Football League: Craig Oldfield (Colchester), Les Tibbott, Ted Phillips & Brian Klug (Ipswich).
97-98 - Captain: Nigel Vincent **P.O.Y.:** Ian Gedny **Top Scorer:** Ian Gedny
Honours: Eastern Co's Lg R-up 91-92, Suffolk Premier Cup(4), Suffolk Snr Cup(10), Suffolk Jnr Cup.

SUDBURY TOWN

Chairman: Phil Turner **President:** H D J Yallop.
Secretary: David Webb, 6 Melford Road, Sudbury, Suffolk CO10 6LS (01787 372352).
Manager: Paul Grimsey **Asst Manager:** T.B.A. **Physio:** Tony Brightwell
Ground: Priory Stadium, Priory Walk, Sudbury, Suffolk (01787 379095).
Directions: Take Friars Street from town centre, pass cricket ground and continue to the 'Ship & Star'. Left into Priory Walk and continue to ground. Half mile and three quarters of a mile from bus and rail stations respectively.
Capacity: 5,000 **Cover:** 1,000 **Seats:** 300 **Floodlights:** Yes **Founded:** 1885
Clubhouse: Open on matchdays and for functions. Pool, darts & dancehall. (01787 379095)
Colours: All yellow **Change colours:** Red & black/black/black **Shop:** Yes
Programme: 48 pages £1. **Editors:** Darren Witt/Kalvin Sargeant/Nick Morsley
Sponsors: Fairview Homes & Wheelers (Timber & Building). **Nickname:** The Borough
Previous Lges: Suffolk & Ipswich/ Essex & Suffolk Border/ Eastern Co 55-90/ Southern 91-94/ Southern Prem 95-97
Midweek matchday: Tuesday **Record Attendance:** 4,700 v Ipswich Town, testimonial 1978.
Best Season - F.A.Vase: R-up 88-89. **F.A.Trophy:** 3rd Rd.Proper 95-96. **FA Cup:** 2nd Rd Proper 96-97.
Players progressing to Football League: Gilbert Dowsett (Tottenham Hotpur 52), John Taylor (Cambridge Utd 88), Steve McGavin (promoted with Colchester Utd 92).
Hons: Beazer Champ 93-94; Southern Lg Cup 93-94 (Southern Div R-up 93-94), Eastern Counties Lg (7), R-up (6), Lg Cup (6), Suffolk Premier Cup (13), R-up(7), Suffolk Senior Cup (1); East Anglian Cup 85-86 91-92, R-up 83-84 95-96; Essex & Suffolk Border Lg (5); E.S.B.L.Cup Winners 49-50, R-Up 46-47; Eastern Floodlit Group 93-94 94-95; Southern Lge Cup R-up 96-97.

SUDBURY WANDERERS

Chairman: Nick Smith **Manager:** Mick Mills.
Secretary: Brian Tatum, 4 Beaconsfield Close, Sudbury, Suffolk CO10 6JR (01787 375840).
Ground: Brundon Lane, Sudbury, Suffolk (01787 376213).
Directions: From Sudbury centre follow Halstead/Chelmsford signs for about 1 mile. Take 1st right after railway bridge at foot of steep hill, and 1st right after sharp lefthand bend.
Seats: 200 **Cover:** 150 **Capacity:** 2,500 **Floodlights:** Yes **Founded:** 1958
Clubhouse: Matchdays/ training nights.
Colours: Yellow/blue/blue **Change Colours:** All Red
Programme: With entry **Editor:** P Scott (01787 379123) **Nickname:** Wanderers
Midweek Matchday: Tuesday **Record Attendance:** 248 v Woodbridge Town, 20/4/93.
Honours: Eastern Co's Lg Div 1 92-93, Ess. & Suff. Border Lg(2) 89-91 (R-up 88-89), Suffolk Snr Cup 90-91.

WARBOYS TOWN

Chairman: Richard Kelly. **President:** **Manager:** Robbie Cook.
Secretary: Brian Lewis, 29 Vinery Court, Ramsey, Cambs, PE17 1JZ (01487 710653)
Ground: Sports Field, Forge Way, off High Street, Warboys, Cambs (01487 823483).
Directions: Access through Forge Way, half way along south side of High Street.
Seats: 50 **Cover:** 200 **Capacity:** 2,000 **Floodlights:** Yes **Founded:** 1885.
Clubhouse: Bar, lounge, function hall. Open every evening & Sunday lunchtime. Entertainment, drinks & snacks
Colours: Red & white/black/red. **Change colours:** White/maroon/maroon. **Nickname:** Witches.
Programme: 12 pages, 40p **Editor:** Martin England **Midweek Matches:** Tuesday
Previous Leagues: Peterborough & District 46-48 56-88/ Utd Co's 50-56/ Huntingdonshire 48-50.
Past Players progressing to Football League: Alex Chamberlain (Ipswich, Everton, Colchester).
Record Attendance: 500 v Ramsey Town, Hunts Senior Cup Semi Final.
Honours: Utd Co's Lg Div 2 R-up 54-55, P'boro Lg R-up(2) 59-60 61-62, P'boro Snr Cup 63-64, Hunts Snr Cup 26-27 28-29 31-32 32-33,94-95. (R-up 92-93), Hunts Scott Gatty Cup 30-31. Reserves: Hunts Benevolent Cup 57-58, Hunts Junior Cup 24-25 27-28 52-53, Hunts Lower Junior Cup 75-76 77-78. .gap 3

Ely City's Martin Pammentor scores opening goal in their 2-0 win over Gorleston *Photo: Mike Joss*

Penalty taken by Ely City, which is second goal against Gorleston *Photo: Mike Joss*

WATTON UNITED

Chairman: Dick Jessup **Vice-Chairman:** Phil Scott **President:** Malcolm Warner.
Secretary: Lesley Barnard, 15 Churchill Close, Watton, Thetford, Norfolk IP25 6BB (01953 881337).
Manager: **Physio:** M Kay. **Fixture Sec:** Nigel Tilford (01953 881441)
Ground: Watton Sports Centre, Dereham Road, Watton, Norfolk (01953 881281).
Directions: On A1075 towards Dereham about half a mile from junction with B1108.
Seats: 50 **Cover:** 150 **Capacity:** 2,000 **Floodlights:** Yes **Founded:** 1888.
Clubhouse: Drinks, sweets & snacks **Club Shop:** No.
Colours: White/white/green **Change colours:** Green/black/green **Nickname:** Brecklanders.
Midweek Matchday: Tuesday. **Previous Lges:** East Anglian/ Anglian Combination.
Sponsors: Style Windows **Reserve's League:** Anglian Combination.
Programme: 25p **Editor:** Secretary
Players progressing to Football League: Chris Watts (Norwich), Robert Taylor (Leyton Orient, Brentford).
Record Gate: 1,200 v Norwich City, floodlight inauguration 1985.
Honours: Anglian Combination 66-67 67-68 85-86 (Lg Cup 66-67 69-70).

WOODBRIDGE TOWN

Chairman: Keith Dixon **President:** G Shemmings
Fixture Sec: John Bennett, (01394 385973)
Secretary: Eric Smy, 25 Queens Avenue, Woodbridge, Suffolk IP12 4AQ (01394 384213)
Manager: David Hubbick **Commercial Manager:** David Leech
Ground: Notcutts Park, Seckford Hall Road, Woodbridge, Suffolk (01394 385308)
Directions: Turning into Woodbridge off last r'bout from Lowestoft, or 1st r'bout from Ipswich. Take 1st turning left and 1st left again. Drive to ground at end of road on left.
Seats: 50 **Cover:** 200 **Capacity:** 3,000 **Floodlights:** Yes **Founded:** 1885.
Clubhouse: Visitors bar, lounge bar, function hall.Matchday Tea, coffee, cold drinks, hotdogs, soup, burgers, sandwiches, rolls. Also cooked meals after match.
Programme: 36p Free with entry **Editor:** D Crowley
Colours: Black & white/black/black **Change colours:** All blue
Sponsors: Posh Windows & Doors **Nickname:** The Woodpeckers. **Midweek Matcheday:** Tuesday.
Previous Leagues: Suffolk & Ipswich **Reserves League:** Essex & Suffolk Border
96-97 - **Captain:** Jason Burman **Top Scorer:** Simon Fryatt **P.o.Y.:** Mark Bailey
Record Attendance: 3,000 v Arsenal, floodlight opener 2/10/90.
Honours: Suffolk Sen Cup(4), Jun Cup (4); Eastern Co Lg Cup 93-94, Lge Div 1 R-up 93-94; Ipswich Sen Lge (2).

WROXHAM

Chairman: Tom Jarrett **President:** L King
Secretary: Chris Green, 24 Keys Drive, Wroxham, Norfolk NR12 8SS (01603 783936 H, 01603 683675 B)
Manager: Bruce Cunningham **Asst Manager:** Marty Hubble **Physio:** G Christmas
Ground: Trafford Park, Skinners Lane, Wroxham, Norfolk (01603 783538)
Directions: Arriving from Norwich turn left at former Castle PH and keep left to ground. One and a half miles from Wroxham + Hoveton (BR). Buses 722, 724 and 717.
Seats: 50 **Cover:** 250 **Capacity:** 2,500 **Floodlights:** Yes **Club Shop:** No.
Clubhouse: Bar, pool, darts etc. Drinks, hot & cold food
Programme: 20 pages **Editor:** Ray Bayles **Press Officer:** Secretary
Colours: Royal & white/blue/blue **Change colours:** Red & black/black/red & black
Founded: 1892. **Nickname:** Yachtsmen.
Midweek Matchday: Tuesday. **Reserve Team's League:** Anglian Comb Prem Div
Players progressing to Football League: Matthew Metcalf (Brentford) 93, Paul Warne 97.
Previous Leagues: Norwich City/ East Anglian/ Norwich & Dist./ Anglian Comb. 64-88.
Records - Attendance: 1,011 v Wisbech Town, Eastern Counties League Premier Division 16/3/93.
Goalscorer: Matthew Metcalf. **Appearances:** Mark Halsey.
Honours: Eastern Co's Lg 91-92 92-93 93-94 96-97 97-98, R-Up 94-95, (Lg Cup 92-93, R-up 90-91), Div 1 88-89; Norfolk Snr Cup 92-93 96-97 97-98; Anglian Comb (6) (Lg Cup(7); Reserves completed the double in 94-95.

DIVISION ONE CLUBS 1998-99

BRIGHTLINGSEA UNITED

Chairman: Graham Steady **Manager:** Graham Warren
Secretary: H J Beere, 108 Regent Road, Brighlingsea, Essex CO7 0NZ (01206 303122).
Ground: North Road, Brightlingsea, Essex (01206 304199).
Directions: B1027 Colchester-Clacton, B1029 from Thorrington Cross - follow Church Road into town, left into Spring Road, left into Church Road. Nearest station; Colchester then bus 78 to Brighlingsea.
Seats: 50 **Cover:** 250 **Capacity:** 2,000 **Floodlights:** Yes **Club Shop:** Yes.
Clubhouse: Open matchadays & every evening except Sunday. Matchday tea, coffee, & snacks
Colours: Red & black/black/red & black **Change colours:** Black & white/black/black & white
Programme: 24 pages, 30p **Editor:** Kim Lay (01206 305797) **Founded:** 1887
Previous Leagues: Tendring Hundred, Essex & Suffolk Border, Essex Senior 1972-90.
Record Gate: 1,200 v Colchester, friendly 68-69. **Midweek Matches:** Tuesday. **Nickname:** Oystermen.
Honours: Essex Snr Lg 88-89 89-90 (Harry Fisher Mem. Tphy 89-90 (R-up 88-89), Lg Cup R-up 78-79), Eastern Co's Lg Div 1 R-up 90-91, Essex & Suffolk Border Lg Prem. Div Cup 71-72, Harwich Charity Cup 87-88, Worthington Evans Cup 76-77 77-78 78-79.

CHATTERIS TOWN

Chairman: Jimmy Gill **President:** J Chambers **Manager:** Steve Taylor and Ian Edwards
Secretary: Jimmy Gill, 3 West End Close, Chatteris, Cambs PE16 6HW (01354 693690).
Ground: West Street, Chatteris (01354 692139).
Directions: Entering Chatteris on A141 from Huntingdon turn right into West Street after by-pass roundabout.
Seats: 250 **Cover:** 400 **Capacity:** 2,000 **Floodlights:** Yes **Founded:** 1920.
Clubhouse: Bar & tea bar. Matchday drinks & snacks available
Colours: White/blue/white **Change colours:** Red & black/black/black. **Nickname:** Lillies.
Previous League: Peterborough **Midweek Matches:** Wednesday
Programme: 12 pages, 20p **Record Gate:** 2,000 v March Town Utd, League 5/5/88.
Players progressing to Football League: Andy Rogers (Reading, Southend, Plymouth), Dave Gregory (Plymouth).
Honours: Eastern Counties Lg Cup 67-68, Peterborough Premier Lg(3).

CLACTON TOWN

Chairman: Ron Ayton **President:** **Manager:** John Herbert & David Lowe
Secretary: Mrs Sandra Harris, 57 Coopers Lane, Clacton-on-Sea, Essex CO15 2BY (01255 476133).
Ground: The Rushgreen Bowl, Rushgreen Road, Clacton-on-Sea (01255 432590).
Directions: A133 to Clacton, at r'bout right into St Johns Rd, 4th left Cloes Lane, 3rd right Rushgreen Rd, ground approximately half mile on right. From B1027 take main Jaywick turn off (Jaywick Lane), then 2nd left (after about a mile) into Rushgreen Rd. Ground 400 yds. 2 miles from Clacton (BR), buses 3, 5 or 5a to Coopers Lane/Rushgreen Rd.
Seats: 200 **Cover:** Yes **Capacity:** 2,500 **Floodlights:** Yes **Founded:** 1892.
Clubhouse: Licensed club. Open 7-11pm Mon-Sat, 12-3pm Sat-Sun. Refreshments & snacks available.
Colours: All Royal blue **Change colours:** All red **Shop:** Yes
Programme: 40 pages, 50p **Editor:** Larry Warren (01255 475182)
Midweek Matches: Tuesday **Nickname:** Seasiders.
Previous Leagues: Eastern Co's 35-37 38-58/ Southern 58-64.
Players progressing to Football League: Vivian Woodward (Spurs, Chelsea, England), Mick Everitt (Arsenal, Northampton), Christian McLean (Bristol Rovers).
Record Attendance: 3,505 v Romford, FA Cup 1st Qualifying Rd 1952 (at Old Road).
Honours: Southern Lg Div 1 59-60; Eastern Co's Lg R-up 36-37 53-54 64-65 74-75 (Lg Cup 73-74); Eastern F/lit Cup 95-96: East Anglian Cup 53-54; Worthington Evans Cup 56-57 67-68 74-75; FA Cup 1st Rd (v Southend) 60-61.

CORNARD UNITED

Chairman: Chris Symes **Vice-Chairman:** Mike Ford **President:** Jim French
Secretary: Chris Symes, 22 Greenacres, Mile End, Colchester, Essex CO4 (01206 851489)
Manager: Chris Symes. **Asst Manager:** Jason Stacker **Physio:** Mike Ford.
Ground: Blackhouse Lane Sportsfield, Great Cornard, Suffolk (01787 376719).
Directions: Left off r'bout on A134 coming from Ipswich/Colchester into Sudbury, follow signs for Country Park - ground is immediately opposite along Blackhouse Lane.
Seats: 250 **Cover:** 500 **Capacity:** 2,000 **Floodlights:** Yes **Club Shop:** No.
Clubhouse: Open matchdays & Sunday lunchtimes. Matchday Tea, coffee, cold drinks, & snacks.
Programme: 16 pages **Editor:** Secretary
Colours: Blue & white/white/blue **Change colours:** White/navy/white
Sponsors: Angelo Smith. **Nickname:** Ards. **Founded:** 1964.
Midweek Matches: Tuesday **Reserve League:** Essex & Suffolk Border.
Previous - Leagues: Sudbury S/day 64-65/Bury St Edmunds & Dist 65-72/Colchester 71-78/ Essex Suffolk Bord 78-89. **Grounds:** Cornard Rec 64-71/ Great Cornard Upper School 71-85.
96-97 - Captain: Andy McLargin **Top Scorer:** Dave Gipp **P.o.Y.:** Bob Seivey
Record - Appearances: Malcolm Fisher. **Goalscorer :** Andy Smiles. **Attendance:** 330 v Sudbury Town, Eastern Floodlit League 4/2/92. **Win:** 18-2 v St Peters House, Colchester League 14/9/72. **Defeat:** 4-10 v Finningham, Bury League 7/2/68.
Honours: Eastern Co's Lg Div 1 89-90 (Lg Cup R-up 92-93), Essex & Suffolk Border Lg 88-89 (Lg Cup 88-89), Suffolk Snr Cup 89-90, Suffolk Jnr Cup R-up 84-85.

DOWNHAM TOWN

Chairman: John Fysh **President:** T G Barker **Manager:** Steve Tyres.
Secretary: F.Thorne, 6 Maple Rd., Downham Market, Norfolk, PE38 9PY. (01366 382563)
Ground: Memorial Field, Lynn Road, Downham Market, Norfolk (01366 388424).
Directions: One and a quarter miles from Downham Market (BR) - continue to town clock, turn left and ground is three quarters of a mile down Lynn Road.
Seats: None **Cover:** Yes **Capacity:** 1,000 **Floodlights:** Yes **Founded:** 1881.
Clubhouse: Open matchdays, refreshments & snacks available
Programme: Yes, with entry **Editor:** Steve Penny (01553 810392)
Colours: Red & white/red/red **Change colours:** Sky/Navy/sky. **Nickname:** Town
Midweek Matches: Wednesday. **Previous Leagues:** Peterborough
Record Attendance: 292 v Diss Town, Jewson League Division One 1991/92.
Honours: P'boro Lg(5) 62-63 73-74 78-79 86-88, Norfolk Senior Cup 63-64 65-66 (R-up(3) 66-69).

HADLEIGH UNITED

President: H Claireaux **Chairman:** Dave Petts **Manager:** Louis Newman
Secretary: Peter Hutchings, 3 Mowlands, Capel St Mary, Ipswich, Suffolk IP9 2XB (01473 311093).
Ground: Millfield, Tinkers Lane, Duke Street, Hadleigh, Suffolk (01473 822165).
Directions: Turn off A12 approx halfway between Ipswich & Hadleigh. Take B1070 & follow signs to Hadleigh. Duke Street is off the High Street - turn left by Library.
Seats: 250 **Cover:** 500 **Capacity:** 3,000 **Floodlights:** Yes **Founded:** 1892.
Clubhouse: Open matchdays, Fridays & Sunday lunchtimes.
Colours: White & navy/navy/red **Change colours:** All yellow **Nickname:** Brettsiders.
Programme: 12 pages, 50p **Editor:** Peter Hutchings (01473 311093) **Sponsors:** Willhire Ltd
Reserves' Lge: Essex & Suff. Border **Player progressing to Football Lge:** Perry Groves (Arsenal).
Midweek Matches: Tuesday. **Record Gate:** 518 v Halstead Town,F.A.Vase Replay 17.1.95
Record win: 8-1 v Chatteris(A) 17/1/95.
Record defeat: 0-7 v Harwich & Parkston (H) 12/10/96, & Wisbech (H) 26/4/97
Previous - Leagues: Suffolk & Ipswich (prev. Ipswich & D.)(pre-1991). **Grounds:** Grays Meadow, Ipswich Roa.
Honours: Ipswich & Dist./Suffolk & Ipswich Lg 53-54 56-57 73-74 76-77 78-79 (Mick McNeil Lg Cup 76-77 80-81 81-82 86-87)), Suffolk Senior Cup 68-69 71-72 82-83.Eastern Co.Lg Champions 93-94.

HAVERHILL ROVERS

Chairman: Terry McGerty **President:** N Haylock **Manager:** Alan Bailey
Secretary: Chris Rice, 23 Ovington Place, Haverhill, Suffolk. CB9 0BA. (01440 712396)
Asst Mgr: Neil Farlie **Physio:** Chris Rice **Press Officer:** Ray Esdale
Ground: Hamlet Croft, Haverhill, Suffolk (01440 702137).
Directions: Centre of Haverhill.
Seats: 200 **Cover:** 200 **Capacity:** 3,000 **Floodlights:** Yes **Founded:** 1886.
Clubhouse: Open matchdays and functions. Snacks available
Colours: All red **Change colours:** All blue **Nickname:** Rovers.
Programme: 24 pages, 40p **Editor:** Ray Esdale (01440 704670) **Midweek Matches:** Tuesday
Previous League: Essex & Suffolk Border. **Players progressing to Football League:** R Wilkins (Colchester).
Record Attendance: 1,537 v Warrington Town, FA Vase QF 86-87.
Honours: Eastern Co's Lg 78-79 (Lg Cup 64-65); E & S Border Lg 62-63 63-64; East Anglian Cup 90-91; Suffolk Sen Cup 96-97.

MARCH TOWN UNITED

Chairman: Geoff Allen. **President:** D Wilkinson **Manager:**
Secretary: R S Bennett, 47 Ellingham Ave, March, Cambs PE15 9TE (01354 653271)
Ground: GER Sports Ground, Robin Goodfellows Lane, March (01354 653073).
Directions: 5 mins from town centre, 10 mins from BR station.
Seats: 500 **Cover:** 2,000 **Capacity:** 4,000 **Floodlights:** Yes **Founded:** 1885.
Clubhouse: On ground, seating 150. Light refreshments available
Club colours: Yellow & blue/blue/yellow. **Change colours:** Black & white/black/black.
Programme: 30p **Editor:** R Bennett **Nickname:** Hares
Previous - Leagues: Peterborough/ Isle of Ely/ Utd Co's 48-54. **Ground:** The Avenue (prior to 1946).
Midweek Matches: Tuesday **Record Gate:** 7,500 v King's Lynn, FA Cup 1956.
Honours: Eastern Co's Lg 87-88 (Lg Cup 60-61), Utd Co's Lg 53-64, FA Cup 1st Rd 53-54 77-78, Cambs Invitation Cup 54-55, East Anglian Cup 53-54 (jt with Barking).

MILDENHALL TOWN

Chairman: Brian Brigden **Manager:** Steve Hubbard **Fixture Sec:** Colin Marchant (01842 812123)
Secretary: Brian Hensby, 14 Sanderling Close, Mildenhall, Suffolk IP28 7LE (01638 715772).
Ground: Recreation Way, Mildenhall, Suffolk (01638 713449).
Directions: Next to swimming pool/car, quarter of a mile from town centre.
Seats: None **Capacity:** 2,000 **Founded:** 1890. **Nickname:** Town or Yellows.
Clubhouse: Open matchdays & functions. Light refreshments available
Colours: Amber/black/black. **Change colours:** All white
Programme: Free with admission **Editor:** F Marshall **Midweek Matchday:** Tuesday
Previous Leagues: Bury & District/ Cambs Lg 2B, 1B & Premier.
Record Attendance: 350 v Norwich City, friendly 22/7/89.
Honours: Suffolk Junior Cup 1899-1900.

NEEDHAM MARKET

Chairman: P Coleman **Managers:** Jim Fitzgerald & Wayne Leggett
Secretary: D Bloomfield, 33 Quinton Road, Needham Market, Suffolk IP6 8DA (01449 720693)
Fixture Secretary: I Croft, (01449 676517)
Ground: Bloomfields, Quinton Road, Needham Market, Suffolk (01449 721000)
Directions: Quinton Road is off Barretts Lane which inturn is off Needham Market High Street.
Colours: All Green & White **Change Coloures:** White/navy/navy
Floodlights: Yes **Midweek Matchday:** Wednesday
Programme: Yes **Editor:** Alan Spivey (01449 775118)

NORWICH UNITED

Chairman: John Hilditch **Vice-Chairman:** J Cubitt **President:** Michael Miles
Secretary: M Barber, Plantation Park, Blofield, Norwich NR13 4PL (01603 716963)
Manager: S Rushbrook **Physio:** Mike Chapman.
Ground: Plantation Road, Blofield, Norwich, Norfolk NR13 4PL (01603 716963).
Directions: Half a mile from Blofield village - coming from Norwich on Yarmouth Rd turn left in Blofield at Kings Head pub & follow to Plantation Rd (grd on right after bridge over bypass). 1/2 hour Brundall BR (Norwich-Yarmouth line).
Seats: 100 **Cover:** 1,000 **Capacity:** 3,000 **Floodlights:** Yes **Founded:** 1903.
Clubhouse: Matchday food & drink: Tea, coffee, cold drinks, hotdogs, burgers, soup, sandwiches, rolls.
Programme: 24 pages, 50p **Editor:** Secretary
Colours: Yellow/blue/yellow **Change colours:** All red
Nickname: Planters. **Midweek Matches:** Tuesday
Previous Ground: Gothic Club, Heartsease Lane, Norwich (until end of 90-91).
Club Record Goalscorer: M Money **Club Record Appearances:** Tim Sayer.
Record Attendance: 401 v Wroxham, League match, 2/10/91.
Honours: Eastern Co's Lg Div 1 90-91 (R-up 89-89, Lg Cup 91-92), Anglian Combination 88-89.

SOMERSHAM TOWN

Chairman: Alan Bailey **Vice-Chairman:** Norman Burkett **President:** Jack Marjason
Secretary: Norman Burkett, 6 West Leys, St Ives, Cambs. PE17 4DS (01480 464695)
Managers: Norman Hudson **Coach:** Bob Barnett **Physio:** Alan Magnus
Ground: West End Ground, St Ives Road, Somersham, Cambs (01487 843384).
Directions: On A604 St Ives to Somersham on right as you enter town.
Seats: None **Cover:** 200 **Capacity:** 1,500 **Floodlights:** Yes **Club Shop:**
Clubhouse: Open Friday, Sat/Sun lunchtimes.
Programme: 76 pages, 30p **Editor/Press Officer:** Dave Hardy (01487 840441)
Colours: All old gold **Change colours:** Sky/maroon/sky
Sponsors: Rapidtech (UK) Ltd. **Nickname:** Westenders **Founded:** 1893.
Midweek Matchday: Tuesday. **Reserve League:** Kershaw Senior A.
Record Attendance: 538 v Norwich City, f/light inauguration 91 **Previous League:** Peterborough & Dist.
Club Record Goalscorer & Appearances: Terry Butcher
Honours: Hunts Snr Cup 72-73 94-95, Peterboro Snr Cup 84-85, Hinchingbrooke Cup 53-54, Cambs Lg Premier B Div 94-95(reserves).

STANWAY ROVERS

Chairman: Brian Peachey. **President:** Richard Deguille
Secretary: Alan Brierley, 19 Barley Way, Stanway, Colchester, Essex CO3 5YD (01206 572439 + Fax).
Manager: Phil Bloss. **Physios:**
Ground: 'Hawthorns', New Farm Road, Stanway, Colchester, Essex (01206 578187).
Directions: Take turn off marked Stanway off A12. Turn right and go over flyover to Tollgate r'bout, 1st right into Villa Rd, after 25 yards turn left into Church Rd, 200 yards on left into New Farm Rd, ground 400 yards on left. Nearest BR station is Colchester North.
Seats: None **Cover:** 200 **Capacity:** 1,500 **Floodlights:** Yes **Founded:** 1955
Clubhouse: 6.45-11pm evenings, noon-11pm Sats. Rolls, soup, tea, coffee etc available matchdays.
Colours: Gold/black/black **Change colours:** White/gold/gold **Shop:** Pennants & ties
Programme: 12 pages, 50p **Editor:** Alan Brierley
Midweek matchday: Wednesday **Sponsors:** Collier & Catchpole. **Nickname:** Rovers.
Previous - Leagues: Colchester & E Essex/ Essex & Suff. Border (pre-1992). **Ground:** Stanway Secondary School, Winstree Road (20 years).
Reserves' Lge: Essex & Suff. Border **Record Gate:** 166 v Sudbury Town FA Vase 4/10/97.
Record win: 8-1 v Swaffham Town (H), Eastern Counties League Division One 26/3/94.
Record defeat: 0-10 v Sudbury Townt (A), E.C.L. Cup.
Players progressing to Football League: Andy Farrell (Colchester,Burnley,Wigan)
Honours: Essex Intermediate Cup R-up 89-90 90-91, Essex & Suffolk Border Lg R-up 91-92 (Div 1 86-87, Div 2 81-81 85-86), Essex Junior Cup R-up 74-75 (QF 73-74).

SWAFFHAM TOWN

Chairman: Stephen Choppen. **President:** J Smith. **Manager:** Mick Simmons.
Secretary: David Ward, 2 Princes Street, Swaffham, Norfolk PE37 7BX (01760 722516).
Ground: Shoemakers Lane, Swaffham, Norfolk (01760 722700).
Seats: None **Cover:** **Capacity:** 2,000 **Floodlights:** Yes **Founded:** 1892.
Clubhouse details: Open Tuesday, Thursday, Saturday & Sunday lunchtimes & evenings. Drinks, sweets etc
Colours: Black & white/black/black. **Change:** Blue/blue/yellow. **Nickname:** Pedlars
Programme: 36 pages, 30p **Editor:** Secretary
Midweek Matchay: Tuesday. **Previous Leagues:** Dereham, Anglian Combination
Record Attendance: 250 v Downham Town, Jewson Eastern Co's League Cup 3/9/91.
Honours: Norfolk Snr Cup(2), Anglian Comb. 89-90 (Div 1 88-89).

Swaffham Town FC *Photo: Martin Wray*

THETFORD TOWN

Chairman: Michael Bailey **Vice-Chairman:** B Richards
Secretary: John Wordley, 4 Claxton Close, Thetford, Norfolk IP24 1BA (01842 762530).
Manager: Ben Moyle **Coach:** Stuart Williams
Ground: Mundford Road, Thetford, Norfolk (01842 766120).
Directions: Turn off bypass (A11) at A143 junction - ground 800yds next to sports ground
Seats: 400 **Cover:** 400 **Capacity:** 2,000 **Floodlights:** Yes **Founded:** 1884.
Clubhouse: Bar, teas, refreshments, light meals & snacks
Programme: 48p with entry **Editor:** Graham Mills (01480 385425). **Press Officer:** Mick Burgess.
Colours: Claret & blue/sky/blue **Change:** All yellow **Sponsors:** Sportscene
Midweek Matches: Wednesday **Reserves League:** Anglian Comb. **Club Shop:** No.
Players progressing to Football League: Dick Scott (Norwich City, Cardiff City), Kevin Seggie (Leeds United), Simon Milton (Ipswich Town).
Record Attendance: 394 v Diss Town, Norfolk Snr Cup 91 **Previous Leagues:** Norfolk & Suffolk
Honours: Eastern Co's Lg R-up 89-90, Norfolk & Suffolk Lg 54-55, Norfolk Snr Senior Cup 47-48 90-91.

TIPTREE UNITED

Chairman: Frederick Byles **President:** Len Foakes **Manager:**
Secretary: Peter G Fidge, 77 Chelmer Road, Chelmsford, Essex CM2 6AA (01245 353667)
Ground: Chapel Road, Tiptree, Essex (01621 815213).
Directions: Enter town on B1023 - Chapel Road is left at second crossroads, ground 200yds on left. 3 miles from Kelverdon (BR). Served by Eastern National Colchester to Maldon bus.
Seats: 150 **Cover:** 300 **Capacity:** 2,500 **Floodlights:** Yes **Founded:** 1933. **Shop:** No.
Clubhouse: Large bar, two snooker tables, pool, darts, netball, badminton, pigeon club, bingo. Dance hall seats 180, small hall seats 60. Open daily 7-11pm (all day Fri & Sat) and noon-2.30, 7-10.30 Sun.
Colours: Red/black/black **Change colours:** All white. **Nickname:** Strawberries.
Programme: 30 pages, 30p **Editor:** Secretary **Sponsors:** S Smith (Transport)
Previous Lges: Essex & Suffolk Border/ Essex Snr 78-84 **Reserves' League:** Essex & Herts Comb.
Midweek Matchday: Tuesday. **Record Attendance:** 1,210 v Spurs, floodlight inauguration Dec 1990.
Honours: Essex Snr Tphy 80-81, Eastern Co's Lg 81-82 (Lg Cup 81-82 84-85), Essex Snr Lg R-up 75-76 77-78, Harwich Charity Cup(4).

WHITTON UNITED

Chairman: John Watkins **President:** Russell Woodward
Secretary: David Gould, 7 Karen Close, Ipswich, Suffolk IP1 4LP (01473 253838)
Manager: Colin Macrow **Fixture Sec:** Mark Woodward (01473 742805)
Ground: King George V Playing Field, Old Norwich Road, Ipswich, Suffolk. (01473 464030)
Directions: Turn off A14, junction A1156 approx 3 miles west of A12/A14 junction.
Seats: No **Cover:** 100 **Capacity:** 600 **Floodlights:** Yes **Club Shop:** No
Clubhouse: Licensed Bar. Hot & Cold Food available.
Programme: Yes **Editor/Press Officer:** Ian Vernau
Colours: Green & white/green/green **Change colours:** All orange
Sponsors: Lindacre **Formed:** 1926 **Nickname:** None
Midweek Matches: Tuesday **Youth's League:** U18 Eastern Jun Alliance
Previous Leagues: Suffolk & Ipswich **Players progressing to Football League:** None known
Record - Attendance: 528 v Ipswich Town 29/11/95; League 244 v Ipswich Wanderers 13/1/96.
Honours: Suffolk Senior Cup 58-59 62-63 92-93; Suffolk & Ipswich League 46-47 47-48 65-66 67-68 91-92 92-93, Jewson Fairplay Trophy 96-97.

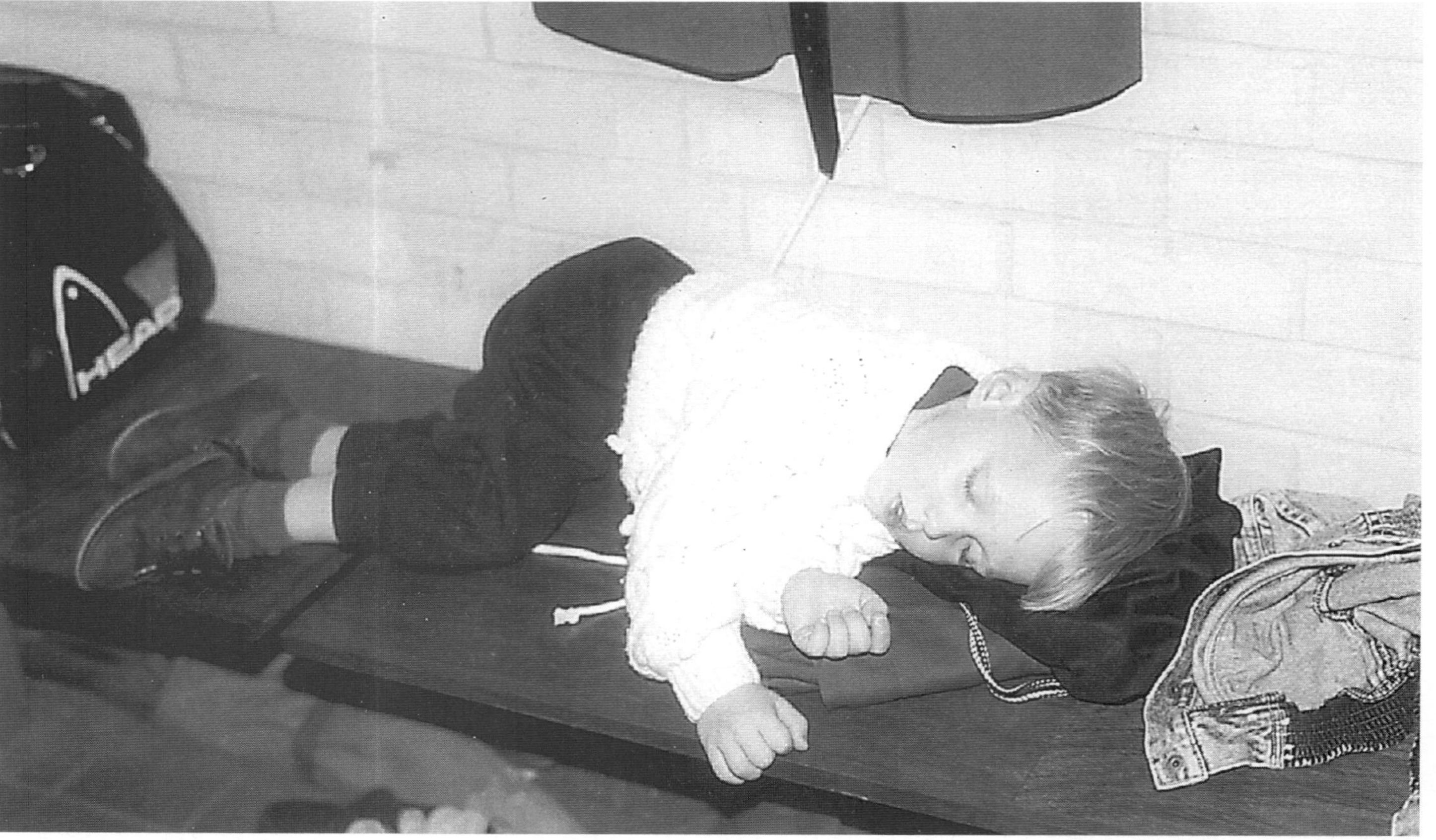

Football is a very exciting game!
Photo: Eric Marsh

THE COMPLETE MUSIC HELLENIC FOOTBALL LEAGUE

FEEDER TO: DR MARTENS LEAGUE

President: Norman Matthews **Chairman:** Michael Broadley
Secretary: Brian King, 83 Queens Road, Carterton, Oxon OX18 3YF
((H)01993 843870 (W) 01793 464620)
Press Officer: T G Cuss

NEWS FROM THE HELLENIC LEAGUE

For the 45th Season of the League's activities The Complete Music Group who are independent Music Publishers provided generous sponsorship for the League, an arrangement which will continue for Season 1998-99.

The season was tinged with sadness in the loss of playing members of the league with Marc Edwards of Bicester FC and Peter Jamieson of North Leigh FC sustaining fatal injuries due to road traffic accidents. As the season drew to a close another stalwart of Hellenic League Football from its inception was taken from us, Charlie Rawlings of Bicester Town FC died on May 5th at the age of 87.

Representative Football matches were played against The Southern Football League (0-0 at Burnham FC), The Chiltonian Football League (0-0 at Abingdon United FC) and The Combined Counties Football League (3-2 at Ashford, Middlesex). The team was managed by Mick Woolford.

The Premier Division Championship was won by Swindon Supermarine FC who secured the title in their final match of the season after an entertaining and exhausting final 2 weeks which saw Endsleigh FC as runners-up. Both Clubs displayed a level of consistency losing only 4 League games each, with Swindon Supermarine conceding only 20 goals whilst Endsleigh conceded 24. Neither Club were able to be considered for promotion through the Pyramid to the Southern Football League. Swindon Supermarine also secured The Complete Music Hellenic League Norman Matthews Floodlight Cup after a penalty shoot-out with North Leigh FC. The Cherry Red Records Senior Division Challenge Cup Final saw Didcot Town FC winning a furiously contested encounter by 4 goals to 2 with Carterton Town FC.

The Red Oak Press Division One Challenge Cup Final saw Ardley United FC successful once more, the fourth time running that the Club have won this competition and this time by 3 goals to 1 against Pegasus Juniors FC. The Division One Championship was a three horse race between Ardley United FC, new arrivals Cirencester Football Academy and Cheltenham Saracens FC who finished in that order with 1995-96 Champions Purton FC finishing in fourth position. Ardley United won the title for a second successive season by a 5 point margin and losing only 4 League games in the process. Sadly the Club will not be able to take their place in the Premier Division due to their inability to meet ground grading requirements. Cirencester Football Academy will be able to take their place in the Premier Division due to their ground sharing arrangement with Cirencester Town FC of The Doc Martens Southern League.

The Reserve Section was run as a two Division Competition with promotion and relegation at stake. The Reserve Division One title was won with a 2 point margin by Abingdon United FC with Swindon Supermarine FC in the runners-up spot. Reserve Division Two saw Ardley United FC secure the Championship from Didcot Town FC who finished in second place, both Clubs securing 46 points but Ardley United FC having a superior goal difference. The Anagram Records Reserve Section Challenge Cup was once again won by Swindon Supermarine FC who beat Kidlington FC in the Final by 3 goals to 1.

In National Competitions the level of success was disappointing. Didcot Town FC and Endsleigh FC were beaten at the first time of asking in The FA Challenge Cup Preliminary Round with Banbury United FC, Burnham FC, Carterton Town FC and Tuffley Rovers FC going one round further before being beaten in the first qualifying rounds. The FA Challenge Vase saw early exits in the qualifying rounds but 8 Clubs progressed to Round One with only Burnham FC and Endlsleigh FC surviving to the Second Round. Both Clubs fell in the Second Round, Endsleigh falling 0-2 to Cowes while Burnham FC after a 2-2 draw at Avely, lost 0-2 at home in the replay.

Hellenic League Clubs faired very well in the various County Cup Competitions. Abingdon United FC retained the Berks & Bucks Senior Trophy, Cirencester Football Academy secured the Gloucestershire Senior Cup and Ross Town FC won the Herefordshire Senior Cup. The Wiltshire Senior Cup was an all Hellenic League affair at the home of Swindon Town FC when Highworth Town FC triumphed 2-1 over Purton FC after extra time.

Season 1997 attracted the Sponsorship of Complete Music in a one year deal with an option for further sponsorship depending on the success of the initial term. The monies in the first year were set for maximum return to Member Clubs. The League have been very grateful to The Complete Music Group for their sponsorship and in particular for the Group's interest in The Hellenic Football League.

The forthcoming season will see the admission of Forest Green Rovers Reserves into League Division One. That Club's First Team have brought great honour to this League having progressed now to the Football Conference via the pyramid system having been this League's Champions in season 1981-82 and having been FA Vase Winners whilst members of the League.

Trevor G Cuss, Hon Press Liaison Officer

FINAL LEAGUE TABLES 1997-98

PREMIER DIVISION

	P	W	D	L	F	A	Pts
Swindon Super.	34	27	3	4	83	20	84
Endsleigh	34	26	4	4	75	24	82
Burnham	34	18	10	6	65	35	64
Banbury Utd	34	17	7	10	69	42	58
Almondsbury T	34	17	4	13	51	37	55
Tuffley Rovers	34	16	7	11	57	49	55
Highworth Tn	34	14	7	13	52	56	49
North Leigh	34	13	8	13	51	46	47
Fairford Town	34	13	8	13	54	53	47
Abingdon Utd	34	12	10	12	60	57	46
Wantage Tn	34	12	4	18	45	72	40
Didcot Town	34	9	12	13	48	49	39
Carterton Tn	34	9	10	15	50	57	37
Shortwood U	34	10	6	18	57	78	36
Hallen	34	9	6	19	39	57	33
Harrow Hill	34	8	7	19	38	70	31
Bicester Tn	34	7	8	19	43	73	29
Kintbury Rgrs	34	6	5	23	32	94	*20

DIVISION ONE

	P	W	D	L	F	A	Pts
Ardley United	32	23	5	4	104	36	74
Cirenceste Ac	32	21	9	2	66	22	*69
Cheltenham S	32	21	6	5	71	41	69
Purton	32	18	6	8	71	44	60
Kidlington	32	16	8	8	71	49	56
Easington Sp	32	15	5	12	60	56	50
Pegasus Jun	32	14	6	12	62	50	48
Clanfield	32	14	5	13	64	56	47
Ross Town	32	13	6	13	56	57	45
Wootton Bass	32	12	6	4	67	58	42
Cirencester U	32	11	7	14	51	57	40
Bishops Cleeve	32	12	3	17	42	63	39
Watlington	32	11	3	18	42	59	36
Headington Am	32	9	7	16	47	56	34
Letcombe	32	8	3	21	40	82	27
Milton United	32	6	4	22	37	82	22
Yarnton	32	2	3	27	29	112	9

* 3 Points deducted

TOP ATTENDANCES 1997-98 - PREMIER DIVISION

231	Banbury United	v	North Leigh
207	Almondsbury Town	v	Hallen
167	Shortwood United	v	Banbury United
160	Highworth Town	v	Fairford Town
215	Hallen	v	Almondsbury Town
167	Bicester Town	v	Banbury United
165	Highworth Town	v	Swindon Supermarine

TOP SCORERS 1997-98

PREMIER DIVISION

34	Mark McGregor	Endsleigh
25	Tate Hulbert	Swindon Sup.
23	Jody McKay	Banbury U
21	Julian Freeman	Shortwood U
	Alan Tatton	Endsleigh
19	Nigel Mott	Abingdon Utd
	Matthew Ellis	North Leigh
	Darren Deeley	Banbury Utd
16	Philip Rodney	Carterton T
	Chris Panter	North Leigh
14	Jason Titcombe	Fairford Town
13	Andrew Bradley	Fairford Town
	Shane Small	Burnham
	Damon York	Swindon Sup
	Nicky Hughes	Swindon Sup
11	Michael Preedy	Endsleigh
	Stuart Morse	Swindon Sup
	Jason Dee	Tuffley Rvrs
	Carl Woodroffe	Harrow Hill
	Steven Lockhart	Burnham
10	Neil Donovan	Banbury U
	Tony Goodwin	Tuffley Rvrs
	Steven Bunce	Burnham
	Gary Wright	North Leigh
	Andy Wollen	Swindon Sup

DIVISION ONE

28	Paul Darch	Ardley Utd
25	Keith Holmes	Ardley Utd
22	Leigh Harris	Pegasus J
20	Graham Jones	Ross Town

SWINDON SUPERMARINE - Complete Music Hellenic League Premier Division Champions

L-R, Back Row: Don Rogers (Joint Manager), Peter Farrow, Andy Wollen, Darren Baldwin, Steve Maggs, Mick Casey, Lee Hartshorn, Martin Tompson, Rob Etherington, John Fisher (Joint Mnager). Front Row: Martin Wheeler, Gary Horgan, Steve Mannion, Paul day, Richard Morgan, Nicky Hughes.

League sponsor Ian McNay of Complete Music, presenting the Premier Division Championship Shield to Alan Dyton, general manager of Swindon Supermarine.

PREMIER DIVISION CLUBS 1998-99

ABINGDON UNITED

Chairman: John Blackmore **President:**
Secretary: Terry Hutchinson, 41 Austin Place, Dunmore Farm Estate, Abingdon, Oxon OX14 1LT (01235 559019)
Manager: R Hayward **Coach:** P Storey **Physio:** G Corcoran
Press Officer: W Fletcher (01235 203203)
Ground: Northcourt Road, Abingdon OX14 1PL (01235 203203).
Directions: From north (Oxford) leave A34 at Abingdon north sign and Northcourt Rd is 1st major turning after r'bout. From South/East/West leave Abingdon on A4183 and turn left into Northcourt Rd after 1 mile. 2 miles from Redley (BR)
Seats: 52 **Cover:** 120 **Capacity:** 2,000 **Floodlights:** Yes **Founded:** 1946
Colours: All yellow **Change colours:** White/red or blue/white **Nickname:** The U's
Reserves' Lge: Hellenic Res section **Previous league:** North Berks **Prev. Grnds:** None
Programme: 30p **Editor:** W Fletcher, ACJI (0235 20255).
Midweek matchday: Tuesday **Record Gate:** 1,500 v Oxford Utd 1994.
Clubhouse: Two bars, food available. Open normal pub hours every day.
Club record appearances: D Webb.
Honours: N Berks Lg 53-54 (Lg Cup R-up 53-54), Charity Shield 52-53; Hellenic Prem R-up 96-97, F/Lit Cup 96-97, Div 1 R-up 76-77 81-82 (Lg Cup R-up 89-90), Div 1 Cup 65-66 81-82 (R-up 66-67, Reserve Cup R-up 93-94); Berks & Bucks Snr Cup R-up 83-84, Snr Tphy R-up 93-94 96-97.

ALMONDSBURY TOWN

Chairman: F David Pick **President:** Peter Howarth
Secretary: D W Winstone, 30 Cherington, Yate, Bristol BS17 4UZ (01454 323877)
Manager: Nick Tanner **Coach:** Nigel Hawkins **Physio:** Steve Watkins
Ground: Oakland Park, Almondsbury, Bristol (01454 612220).
Directions: Adjacent to M5 junction 16 - follow A38 Thornbury - ground first left. 4 miles from Bristol Parkway (BR). County bus services to Thornbury, Stroud and Gloucester.
Seats: None **Cover:** No **Capacity:** 2,000 **Floodlights:** Yes **Founded:** 1897
Colours: Sky/navy/navy **Change colours:** All yellow
Record Gate: Hellenic Cup Final replay 89-90.
Previous Leagues: Bristol Weslyan/ Bristol Suburban/ Bristol Premier Comb./ Glos Co.
Previous Ground: Almondsbury Rec. (until 1986). **Programme:** 20 pages 25p
Nickname: Almonds. **Midweek Matchday:** Tuesday
Clubhouse: 7 days, all sports, refreshments, function room, entertainment, skittles.
Honours: FA Vase R-up 78-79 (SF 77-78), Glos Co. Lg(4) 76-78 79-81 (R-up 75-76 81-82), GFA Chal. Tphy 78-79 (R-up 80-81), Avon Prem. Comb. 74-75, Glos Snr Amtr Cup 87-88, Hellenic Lg 83-84 (R-up 82-83, Lg Cup(2) 83-85).

BANBURY UNITED

Chairman: Paul Saunders **Vice Chairman:** B Kay **President:** David Jesson
Secretary: B Worsley, c/o Sol Systems, Unit 4 Mallorie Hse, Beaumont Rd, Banbury, OX16 7RH (01295 265638 H, 01295 255536 B)
Manager: Phil Lines **Coach:** Brian Robinson **Physio:** John Source
Ground: The Stadium, off Station Rd, Banbury, Oxon (01295 263354).
Directions: M40 jct 11, follow signs for Banbury then BR station, turn right down narrow lane before entering station forecourt; eastern end of town.
Seats: 50 **Cover:** 500 **Capacity:** 6,500 **Floodlights:** Yes **Club Shop:** Yes
Programme : 24 pages 60p **Editor:** Kevin Hicklin **Press Officer:** Barry Worsley.
Colours: Red & gold/red/red **Change colours:** White & blue/white/white
Midweek matches: Tuesday. **Reserves' Lge:** Hellenic Res. section **Nickname:** Puritans.
Founded: 1933 **Reformed:** 1965 **Club Sponsors:** Timms Homes.
Club Records - Attendance: 7,160 v Oxford City, FA Cup 3rd Qualifying Round, 30/10/48. **Goalscorer:** Dick Pike (1935-48), Tony Jacques (65-76) - both 222. **Appearances:** Dave Matthews.
Best FA Cup season: 1st Rd replay 73-74 (Also 1st Rd 47-48 61-62 72-73).
Best FA Trophy year: 3rd Rd 70-71 73-74.
Prev. Lges: Banbury Jnr 33-34/ Oxon Snr 34-35/ Birmingham Comb. 35-54/ W. Mids 54-66/ Southern 66-90.
Players progressing to Football League: Ollie Kearns (Reading), Kevin Wilson & Richard Pratley (Derby), Mick Kearns & Terry Muckleberg (Oxford), Martin Singleton (Coventry).
Clubhouse: Match days & week-ends. Mid-week on hire. Hot food available during aftermatches.
97-98 Captain: Martin Singleton **P.o.Y.:** Jody McKay **Top Scorer:** Jody McKay (28)
Honours: Oxon Snr Cup 78-79 87-88 (R-up 6); Birmingham Comb. R-up 47-48; Oxon Prof. Cup 52-53(jt) 70-71 (jt) 72-73 77-78 79-80(jt); Hellenic Lg.Cup R-Up 91-92; Birmingham Snr Cup R-Up 48-49 59-60 (S.F.46-47); Oxon Snr Lg. 34-35 39-40 47-48(res); Oxon Hosp. Cup 46-47 (R-up 45-46); Oxon Benev. Cup R-up 77-78 80-81 82-83; Daventry Charity Cup 88-90; Smiths Mem. Cup 68-70 (R-up 66-68); Hitchin Centenary Cup 68-69 (R-up 67-68); Leamington Charity Cup 51-52; Warks Comb. R-up 57-58 60-61, Presidents Cup R-up 60-61; Midland Floodlit Cup 67-68; Wallspan Comb. 85-86.

Banbury United FC *Photo: D Nicholson*

Bicester Town

Carterton Town FC: Back Row (L-R); J Butt, P Fox, D Hutt, P Hedges, C Rodney, M Balmer, A Cummings, C Griffin, M McLennon. Front Row; N Radbone, C McGregor, M Delaney, D Kew, A Henry, C Tyrell

BICESTER TOWN

Chairman: Bill Hammond. **Vice Chairman:** Ray Honour. **President:** Mike Staniford.
Secretary/Press Officer: Phil Allen, 38 Bassett Avenue, Bicester OX6 7TZ (01869 252125).
Manager: Barry Grant **Coach:** Barry Grant **Physio:** Ray Huntley
Ground: Sports Ground, Oxford Rd, Bicester (01869 241936)
Directions: From Oxford; past Tescos on outskirts of Bicester - ground on right. From Aylesbury; turn left at first island on outskirts of Bicester onto bypass, right at next island, pass Tescos & ground on right.
Seats: 250 **Cover:** 550 **Capacity:** **Floodlights:** Yes **Founded:** 1876
Colours: Red & black/black/black **Change:** Green & white/green/green
Previous Lge: Oxon Senior **Reserve team's league:** Hellenic Lge Reserve Division.
Programme: With entry **Editor:** Secretary **Midweek Matchday:** Tuesday
Nickname: Foxhunters **Previous Name:** Slade Banbury Road (pre-1923).
Clubhouse: One bar **Record Attendance:** 955 v Portsmouth, floodlight inauguration 1/2/94.
Honours: Hellenic Lg 60-1 77-78 (Lg Cup 90-91 (R-up 92-93), Div 1 76-77).

BURNHAM

Chairman: Malcolm Higton **Vice Chairman:** M.A.Beavis. **President:**
Secretary: Alan King, 41 Underwood Road, High Wycombe, Bucks HP13 6YD (01494 523920)
Manager: Shane Chandler **Coach:** John Griffith **Physio:** Mark Green
Ground: The Gore, Wymers Wood Road, Burnham, Slough SL1 8JG (01628 602467/602697).
Directions: North west of village centre, 2 miles from Burnham BR station, 2 miles from M4 junction 7, 5 miles from M40 junction 2, 100yds north of Gore crossroads - fork right into Wymers Wood Rd and ground is immediately on right.
Capacity: 2,500 **Cover:** 250 **Seats:** 250 **Floodlights:** Yes **Club Shop:** Yes
Press Officer: Secretary **Programme:** 30 pages **Editor:** Cliff Sparkes
Colours: Blue & white/blue/white **Change colours:** Yellow/yellow/black
Midweek matchday: Tuesday **Reserve Team's Lge:** Suburban.
Sponsors: Caflon International
Club Records - Attendance: 2,380 v Halesowen Town, FA Vase 2/4/83. **Goalscorer:** Fraser Hughes 65, 69-70 **Win:** 18-0 v High Duty Alloys, 70-70 **Defeat:** 1-10 v Ernest Turners Sports, 63-64.
Best FA Cup season: 3rd Qualifying Rd. **Best FA Trophy season:** Third Qualifying Rd replay 89-90.
Previous - Leagues: Sth Bucks & East Berks/ Maidenhead Interm/ Windsor, Slough & Dist./ Gt Western Comb. 48-64/ Wycombe Comb. 64-70/ Reading Comb. 70-71/ Hellenic 71-77/ Athenian 77-84/ London Spartan 84-85.Southern 85-95. **Name:** Burnham & Hillingdon 85-87 **Ground:** Baldwin Meadow (until 20's).
Players progressing to Football League: D Hancock (Reading), R Rafferty (Grimsby Town, Portsmouth), D Payne (Barnet, Southend United, Watford, Peterborough Utd).
Clubhouse: Open every evening and weekend lunchtimes. Darts and pool, two bars, usual matchday food.
97-98 - Captain: Paul Brett **P.o.Y.:** Jamie Furmage **Top Scorer:** Shane Small (14)
Honours: FA Vase SF 82-83 (QF 77-78), Athenian Lg R-up(2) 78-80, Hellenic Lg 75-76 (Div 1 R-up 72-73, Lg Cup 75-76, Div 1 Cup 71-72), London Spartan Lg 84-85 (Lg Cup 84-85), Reading Comb. Lg Cup 70-71 (All Champions Cup 70-71), Wycombe Comb. R-up(4) 65-67 68-70, various local cup competitions.

CARTERTON TOWN

President: Mr G Fox **Chairman:** Mr G Maxwell **Match Secretary:** Glyn Yates
Secretary: Mrs Cath Bulley, 58 Ashfield Road, Carterton, Oxfordshire, OX18 (01993 842704).
Manager: Jim Flynn **Physio:** Ady Cooper
Coach: Mark Haining **Press Officer:**
Ground: Kilkenny Lane, Carterton, Oxfordshire (01993 842410)
Directions: Enter Swinbrook Rd which off the Burford-Carterton road, proceed into Kilkenny Lane (one track road), ground car park 200yds on left before sharp corner. Hourly buses to Carterton from Oxford.
Seats: 50 **Cover:** 100 **Capacity:** 1,500 **Floodlights:** Yes **Founded:** 1922
Colours: Black & white/black/black **Change colours:** Yellow/blue/blue **Reformed:** 1946/1983
Previous Leagues: Witney & District **Record Gate:** 600 v Oxford Utd, Oxon Snr Cup 93-94.
Programme: 20 pages with admission **Editor:** Jenny Maxwell (01993 212803)
Sponsors: **Reserve League:** Hellenic Reserve section.
Midweek matches: Tuesday **Club record goalscorer:** Tim Dorrington.
Clubhouse: Lounge & fully licensed bar open every day 7.30-11pm, Sat & Sun noon-2pm, Sat 4-6pm. Snacks & meals available.
Honours: Oxon Junior Shield 85-86; Oxon Snr Cup R-up 90-91 96-97; Witney & Dist. Lg 65-66 (Div 1 84-85 76-77); Hellenic Lg Div 1 89-90 93-94 (Reserve Div 1989-90 (R-up 93-94)); Oxon Intermediate Cup R-up 93-94(res.)

CIRENCESTER FOOTBALL ACADEMY

Chairman: Tony Bedwell **President:** **Press Officer:** Steve Slattery
Secretary: Keith Ryan, 11 Pinehurst Road, Swindon, Wilts SN2 1QE (01793 526059)
Manager: Pat Slattery **Coach:** John Freeth **Physio:** Steve Slattery
Ground: Tetbury Road, Cirencester (01285 654783)
Directions: Follow by pass towards Bristol. THe ground is on left approx 1/2 mile from town centre.
Colours: Red & black/black/red **Change colours:** Black & blue/blue/blue
Midweek Matchday: Variable **Nickname:** Academy **Record Attendance:**

DIDCOT TOWN

President: **Chairman:** John Bailey
Secretary: Jon Gardner, 18 Drake Avenue, Didcot, Oxon. OX11 0AD (01235 210396 H, 0976 353998 B).
Manager: Robert Dodd **Coach:** Barry Cooper **Physio:** Mark Roberts
Ground: Station Road, Didcot (01235 813212).
Directions: Midway down Station Rd, Didcot, on right quarter mile from Railway Station towards town centre.
Seats: 50. **Cover:** 200 **Capacity:** 5,000 **Floodlights:**Yes. **Founded:** 1907
Colours: All red & white **Change colours:** All blue
Previous Leagues: Hellenic 53-57/ Metropolitan 57-63.
Nickname: Railwaymen. **Midweek Matchday:** Tuesday
Record Attendance: 550 v Wycombe Wanderers, 1956.
Programme: 50p **Editor:** Peter Swain.
Clubhouse: Every evenings and Sunday lunchtimes.
Honours: Hellenic Lg 53-54,Lg Cup 1965-66 66-67 92-93 Div 1 76-77,Div1 Cup 76-7

ENDSLEIGH

Chairman: Michael Alcock
Secretary: Graham Ayers, 7 Oakbrook Drive, The Reddings, Cheltenham, Glos GL51 6SB (01452 548556)
Manager: Mark Ratcliffe **Match Secretary:** Chris Hawkins (01242 692332) **Press Officer:** Stephen White
Ground: Cheltenham Town FC, Whaddon Road, Cheltenham (01242 521974)
Directions: M5 Junc 10, follow signs to town, the A46 (Winchcombe & Broadway). Grd just off Prestbury Rd.
Capacity: 5,000 **Seats:** 1,000 **Cover:** 4,000 **Floodlights:** Yes **Formed:** 1974
Colours: Blue/blue/white **Change colours:** All white. **Nickname:** Super Owls
Record Attendance: 83 v Bridgwater Town 95
Previous Ground: The Folley, Swindon Road, Cheltenham (pre-1993)
Previous Leagues: Glos Northern Snr (pre'93) **Midweek Matchday:** Wednesday
Honours: Glos Northern Snr Lg 92-93 (Div 1 91-92).

FAIRFORD TOWN

Chairman: M B Tanner **President:** B W Wall
Secretary: W Beach, 33 Park Cross, Fairford, GL7 4LF (01285 712136).
Ground: Cinder Lane, London Road, Fairford, Cirencester (01285 712071).
Manager: Gerry Kelly **Coach:** Rob Simpson **Physio:** C Tye
Directions: Entering Fairford on A417 from Lechlade turn left down Cinder Lane 150yds after 40mph sign. From Cirencester on same road, follow thru village and turn right down Cinder Lane 400yds after Railway Inn. Buses from Swindon, Lechlade and Cirencester.
Seats: 100 **Cover:** 150 **Capacity:** 2,000 **Floodlights:** Yes **Club Shop:** No.
Programme: 20 pages with admission **Editor/Press Officer:** Chairman
Colours: Red/white/red **Change colours:** White/blue/blue
Club Sponsors: Jewson **Founded:** 1891 **Nickname:** Town.
Midweek matchday: Wednesday **Reserve Team's League:** Hellenic Reserve section.
Record Attendance: 1,500 v Swindon Town, friendly 93
Club Record Goalscorer: Pat Toomey. **Club Record Appearances:**
Record win: 9-0 v Moreton T. **Record defeat:** 0-9 v Sharpness.
Previous Leagues: Cirencester & District (pre-1946)/ Swindon & District 46-70.
Previous Grounds: None
Clubhouse: Open each evening, weekend lunches & before and after all games
Honours: Glos Challenge Trophy 79-80 (R-up 82-83); Hellenic Lg R-up 78-79 79-80 90-91 94-95, (Premier Div Cup 78-79, Div 1 71-72, Div 1 Cup 71-72); Glos Jnr Cup 62-63; Swindon & Dist Lg 64-65 68-69.

HALLEN

Chairman: Barry Phillips **President:** Ken Naish
Secretary: Charmaine Phillips, 145A Station Road, Henbury, Bristol BS10 7LZ (0117 9501754)
Manager: Steve Brundson **Physio:** Tammy Mullan
Ground: Hallen Playing Fields, Moorhouse Lane, Hallen, Nr Bristol (0272 504610).
Directions: M5 jct 17, A4018 to Henbury r'bout, right, right again at junction, next right to Station Road, left into Avonmouth Road at r'bout. One mile to Hallen, ground first left, then right into lane to ground.
Seats: No **Cover:** No **Clubhouse:** Yes **Programme:** No **Founded:** 1949
Colours: Royal & black/black/black **Change Colours:** Green, black & red/red/red
Previous Names: Lawrence Weston Athletic (80's), Lawrence Weston Hallen (pre-1991).
Midweek Matchday: Wednesday **Previous League:** Glos County (pre-1993)
Honours: Glos County Lg 92-93, Glos Snr Trophy 92-93.

HARROW HILL

Chairman: Reg Taylor **President:** Ken Jones **Manager/Coach:** R White
Secretary: Geoff Tuffley, 19 Westfield Court, Heywood Road, Cinderford GL14 2RU (01594 542421)
Match Sec: Roger Partridge, (01594 825360) **Physio:** R Taylor
Ground: Larksfield Road, Harrow Hill (01594 543873)
Directions: Take A40 west out of Gloucester, follow A40 for 8 miles then take A4136 to Longhope, pass by on the outskirts of Michealdean, up steep hill (plump Hill), then second turn on the right signed Harrow Hill. At phone box on the left turn right into Larksfield Road, ground on right at top of hill.
Colours: Claret & blue/sky/sky **Change Colours:** Black & white/black/black
Record Gate: 350 v Cinderford Town 92 **Midweek Matchday:** Tuesday **Nickname:** Harry Hill

HIGHWORTH TOWN

President: Alan Vockins **Chairman:** Steven Leppard **Press Officer:** David Evans.
Secretary: Fraser Haines, 222 Windrush, Highworth, Swindon SN6 7EB (01793 861109).
Manager: Gary Goodwin **Coach:** Joe Matano **Physio:** Graham Ashby
Ground: Elm Recreation Ground, Highworth. (01793 766263)
Directions: Enter on A361 from Swindon, past Simpsons Garage, straight over island, next sharp left into Green by Vet's Surgery - ground & car park 60yds on left next to Sports Hall.
Seats: 50 **Cover:** 250 **Capacity:** 2,000 **Floodlights:** Yes **Founded:** 1894.
Colours: Red & white/black/red **Change colours:** Blue & white/black/blue **Club Shop:** No.
Programme: 16 pages, 60p **Editor:** Dave Evans (01793 764712)
Nickname: Worthians **Previous Leagues:** Wilts/Swindon & Dist.
Midweek matchday: Wednesday **Sponsors:** Smart Movers. **Reserves Lge:** Hellenic Reserve Div.
Club Records - Attendance: 1,862 v QPR opening Floodlights **Goalscorer:** Kevin Higgs **Appearances:** Rod Haines
Win: 12-0 v Beeches, Arthur Shipway Cup 92 **Defeat:** 2-8 v Milton United, Hellenic Lge Div One, 87
Clubhouse: Sat 12-2.30 & 4.30-11pm. Mon, Wed & Fri 7-11pm. Rolls & Hot food.
Honours: Wilts Snr Cup 63-64 72-73 95-96 (R-up 88-89), Hellenic Div 1 Cup 88-89, Arthur Shipway Cup 88-89 93-94, Swindon & District Lg 63-64 64-65 65-66 68-69.

Highworth's winning goal against Bicester. *Photo: G Whittington*

KINTBURY RANGERS

President: **Chairman:** A Keith Plank
Secretary: A K Plank, 26 Kennet Road, Kintbury, Hungerford, RG17 9XW (01488 658460).
Manager: Darren Angell **Coach:** D Ingram/J Smyth **Physio:** Gary Murphy
Ground: Recreation Ground, Inkpen Road, Kintbury (0488 57001).
Directions: Turn off A4 (signed Kintbury) between Newbury/Hungerford. 2nd left after level crossing into Inkpen Road, entrance 200yds on right by Jubilee Centre. Half mile from Kintbury (BR).
Seats: None **Cover:** No **Capacity:** 1,000 **Floodlights:** Yes **Founded:** 1890
Colours: Amber/black/amber **Change colours:** White/blue/white
Nickname: Rangers **Reformed:** 1943.
Reserves' Lge: Hellenic Res. sect. **Previous Leagues:** Newbury District/ Nth Berks.
Programme: 16 pages, 50p **Programme Editor:** Colin Godfrey (0635 874209)
Record Gate: 550 v Newport AFC, 1990. **Midweek Matchday:** Wednesday
Clubhouse: Open every nightl 7.30-11. Hot & cold meals matchdays.
Club record appearances: Nigel Llewellyn.
Honours: Nth Berks Lg 77-78 81-82, Hellenic Lg Div 1 R-up 87-88, Berks & Bucks I'mediate Cup 60-61 (R-up 87-88).

NORTH LEIGH

President: Mrs C Smith **Chairman:** Peter King. **Vice Chairman:** B.Shepperd.
Secretary: Mr P J Dix, 8 Windmill Close, North Leigh, Nr Witney, Oxon OX8 6RP (01993 881199).
Manager: A Buckingham/P Hutter **Asst Manager:** Mr P King **Physio:** Mr R Keen
Ground: Eynsham Hall Park Sports Ground, North Leigh, nr Witney, Oxon (0993 881427).
Directions: Ground is situated off A4095 Witney to Woodstock road 3 miles east of Witney. Entrance to ground is 300yds east of Main Park Entrance.
Seats: 100 **Cover:** 200 **Capacity:** 2,000 **Floodlights:** Yes **Club Shop:** No.
Programme: 20 pages, £1 with entry **Editor:** J Fogg **Press Officer:** B Norton (01993 881777).
Colours: Sky/navy/navy **Change colours:** White/navy/red
Club Sponsors: Various **Founded:** 1908 **Nickname:** None.
Midweek matches: Wednesday **Previous Leagues:** Witney & District 08-89.
Clubhouse: Bar open matches. Snacks available.
Club record scorer: P Coles **Club record appearances:** P King.
Honours: Hellenic Lg Div 1 R-up 92-93 (Reserves Cup 93-94), Oxon Jnr Shield 56-57 83-84, Oxon Charity Cup 84-85 88-89, Witney & Dist. Lg(13) 50-57 84-90 (Lg Cup(10) 47-48 51-52 53-55 56-57 81-82 85-89), Oxon Yth Cup 93-94 94-95, Oxon Yth u-17 Lg & Cup 93-94. Oxford Senior Cup R-Up 94-95. Marriott Cup 95-96.

SHORTWOOD UNITED

Chairman: Peter Webb **Vice C'men:** W Stratford, W Lewis **President:** R T Tanner
Secretary: Mark Webb, 1 The Bungalow, Shortwood, Nailsworth, Stroud, Glos GL6 0SD (01453 833204).
Manager: Brian Godfrey **Coach:** Tony Lewis/Brian Godfrey **Physio:** Alan Gough
Ground: "Meadow Bank", Shortwood, Nailsworth, Gloucestershire (01453 833936).
Directions: In Nailsworth turn into Spring Hill then first left. Continue past shop and and keep left past "Britannia" (signposted Shortwood) - continue to end for ground. 4 miles from Stroud (BR).
Seats: 50 **Cover:** 150 **Capacity:** 5,000 **Floodlights:** Yes **Club Shop:** No.
Programme: 18 pages, 30p **Editor:** Keith Sheppard **Press Officer:** Ashley Loveridge
Colours: Red & white **Change:** Blue/blue or white/blue or white
Sponsors: Springfast (Gloucester) **Nickname:** The Wood. **Founded:** 1900
Midweek matchday: Wednesday **Reserves' League:** Glos Northern Snr
Club Records - Attendance: 1,000 v Forest Green Rovers, FA Vase 5th Rd 81-82. **Goalscorer:** Peter Grant
Appearances: Peter Grant. **Win:** 11-0 **Defeat:** 0-9 **Transfer fee received:** Paul Tester (Cheltenham, 80-81).
Previous Leagues: Stroud/ Glos Northern Snr/ Glos Co.
Previous Grounds: Table Land, Wallow Green
Clubhouse: Mon-Sat 7-11pm, Sun noon-12 & 7-10.30pm. Crisps etc in bar, hot food kitchen on matchdays.
97-98 **Captain:** Julian Freeman **P.o.Y.:** Craig Lewis **Top Scorer:** Julian Freeman
Honours: Glos.Co.Lg 81-82 (R-up 80-81), Glos Tphy 83-84 91-92,94-95,(R-up 79-80), Hellenic Lg 84-85 91-92 (R-up 85-86 89-90 94-95, Div 1 R-up 83-84, Div 1 Cup 83-84), Prem Lge Cup R-up 95-96, Hungerford Merit Cup, Glos Snr Amtr Cup 85-86 (R-up 79-80), Stroud Charity Cup 91-92 92-93 94-95 (R-up 95-96), Stroud Lg 27-28 (Div 2 26-27 64-65(res), Div 3 25-26 49-50(res) 62-63(res)), Glos Northern Snr Lg R-up 67-68 91-92(res)(Div 2 62-63 80-81(res) 90-91(res)), Arthur Shipway Cup 78-79 79-80.

SWINDON SUPERMARINE

Chairman: Steve Moore **President:** Cliff Puffit
Secretary: Eric Stott, 43 Stanier Street, Swindon, Wilts SN1 5QU (01793 521301).
Manager: John Fisher **Coach:** Glynn Dubber **Physio:** Alan Jennings
Ground: Highworth Road, South Marston, Swindon (01793 824824)
Directions: On A361 Swindon/Highworth road, adjoining Marston Industrial Estate. 6 miles from Swindon (BR) - buses in direction of Highworth, Fairford & Lechdale. If lost ask for Vickers Sports Ground.
Seats: 75 **Cover:** 120 **Capacity:** 1,000 **Floodlights:** Yes **Founded:** 1992.
Colours: Blue & white/blue/blue **Change colours:** Yellow/navy/yellow **Programme:** Yes
Previous Leagues: Wilts. **Midweek Matchday:** Wednesday
Previous Names: Supermarine (prev. Vickers Armstrong 46-81), Swindon Athletic (prev. Penhill Yth Centre 70-84/ Penhill 84-84-89) amalgamated in 1992.
Previous Ground: Supermarine: Vickers Airfield (until mid-1960s), *Swindon Ath.: Merton 70-84/ 'Southbrook', Pinehurst Road 84-92.*
Honours: Wilts Snr Cup R-up 93-94, Hellenic Lg Reserve Section 93-94. As Supermarine: Wilts Snr Cup 85-86 (R-up 74-75 84-85), Hellenic Div 1 R-Up 82-83 (Res Section West R-up 84-85 (Challenge Cup 83-84), Wilts Comb Snr 75-76, Swindon & District Lg Div 3 55-56, Dr Elliott Cup(5), Faringdon Thursday Memorial Cup(3). *Swindon Ath.: Wilts Snr Cup 82-83 86-87 89-90 (R-up 83-84 85-86 90-91), Hellenic Lg Div 1 85-86 86-87, Wilts Co. Lg 82-83 83-84).*

TUFFLEY ROVERS

President: A W Purdy **Chairman:** Tony Newport
Secretary: Graham Moody, 50 Giles Cox, Quidgley, Gloucester GL2 4YL (01452 724083).
Manager: D Foxwell. **Coach:** C Gardner **Physio:** S Tracey
Ground: Glevum Park, Lower Tuffley Lane, Gloucester (01452 423402).
Directions: Follow Gloucester city ring-rd to r'bout signed M5 South & Bristol, take 4th exit signed Hempsted & city centre, after 200yds turn right (McDonalds on corner) into Lower Tuffley Lane, ground 400yds on left.
Seats: 50 **Cover:** Yes **Capacity:** **Floodlights:** Yes **Founded:** 1929
Colours: Claret & blue/white/claret **Change colours:** Yellow/claret/blue **Nickname:** Rovers
Previous Grounds: Stroud Rd, Gloucester/ Randwick Park, Tuffley. **Club Shop:** No.
Previous Leagues: Stroud/ Glos Northern Senior/ Glos County (pre-1991).
Record Attendance: 150 v Cinderford Town 94-95
Midweek Matchday: Wednesday
Programme: approx 10 pages with entry **Editor:** Mr A Purdy, 43 Ermin Park, Brockworth.
Club Sponsors: Ermin Plant. **Reserve League:** Glos.Northern Senior Stroud Lge.
Clubhouse: 800 yds from ground. Open before & after matches, and normal pub hours at other times. Snacks.
Honours: Hellenic Lg Div 1 92-93 (Div 1 Cup 92-93), Glos Co. Lge 90-91, Glos Snr Amtr Cup 87-88, Stroud Lg 72-73,94-95, Glos Northern Senior Lg. Div 1 87-88 Div2 79-80.

WANTAGE TOWN

Chairman: A Woodward **President:** Ernie Smart **Match Secretary:** Colin Blunsden
Secretary: Alan Parker, Little Orchard Road, Wantage, OX12 8DW. (01235 763842).
Manager: Derek Bint **Coach:** Kevin O'Hanlon **Physio:** Ian Howard
Ground: Alfredian Park, Manor Park, Wantage, Oxon (01235 764781).
Directions: Take Hungerford Road from Wantage, ground signposted on right oppsite recreation ground.
Seats: 50 **Cover:** 300 **Capacity:** 1,500 **Floodlights:** Yes **Club Shop:** No
Programme: 28 pages, 50p **Editor:** Andy Wells (01235 767291).
Colours: Green & white hoop/white/white **Change colours:** All White
Sponsors: Broadway Motors **Nickname:** Alfredians **Founded:** 1892
Midweek Matchday: Wednesday **Record Attendance:** 500 v Newport AFC 89
Club Record Goalscorer: A Rolls **Club Record Appearances:**
Record win: 11-1 v Amersham Tn (A), Hellenic Lge 60-61. **Record defeat:** 0-14 v Thame Utd (A), 20/1/62.
Previous Leagues: Swindon & Dist. 1901-12 30-35 47-56/ N Berks 12-22 38-40 46-47/ Reading & D. 22-30 35-38.
Previous Grounds: Challow Park (pre-1922)
Players progressing to Football League: Roy Burton and Colin Duncan (both Oxford United).
Clubhouse: Mon-Fri 7.30-11pm, Sat noon-2.30, 4-7pm.
Honours: Hellenic Lg R-up 81-82, Div 1 80-81 (R-up 69-70 87-88 91-92 95-96), Div 1 Cup R-up 91-92; Oxon Snr Cup 82-83; Berks & Bucks Intermediate Cup 54-55; Swindon & District Lg 07-08 33-34 52-53 55-56.

The League Representative XI for the match against against the Southern League

Left to Right - Back Row: M Woolford (Manager), A McKinness (EFC Cheltenham), D York (Swindon Supermarine), P Noble (Didcot Town), M Ellis (North Leigh), T Hulbert (Swindon Supermarine), D Dyson (Burnham), P Brett (Burnham), A Wollen (Swindon Supermarine) (Captain), B Haydon (Physio).
Front Row: M Preddy (EFC Cheltenham), M McGregor (EFC Cheltenham), G Reece (Burnham), J Freeman (Shortwood United), J Furmage (Burnham), D Guthrie (Swindon Supermarine).

ARDLEY UNITED F.C. - Complete Music Hellenic League (Red Oak Press) Division One Cup Winners

Left to Right - Back Row: Peter Foley (Manager), Fraser Gills, Leigh Bastable, Michael Faulkner, Matthew Cresswell, Robert Wild, Stephen Ayris, Paul Darch, Keith Holmes, Paul Spittle, Stuart Neal.
Front Row: Tony Blossom, Andy Parsons, Lee Durrant, Kevin Eldred, Paul Harwood, Paul Wright.

DIVISION ONE CLUBS 1998-99

ARDLEY UNITED

Chairman: Norman Stacey **Match Secretary:** Alan Mitchell (01869 346854)
Secretary: Nigel Adams, 35 Forsythia Close, Bicester, Oxon, OX6 9GA (01869 325734)
Manager: Peter Foley **Coach:** **Physio:** Norman Stacey
Press Officer: Ron Jones (01869 246717)
Ground: Ardley Sports Ground (01869 346429)
Directions: M40 junc 10 take A43 towards Middleton Stoney on the right after 1/2 mile.
Colours: Sky/navy/sky **Change colours:** Yellow/black/black
Midweek matchday: Tuesday **Previous Leagues:** Oxon Snr (pre-1993)
Honours: Oxon Snr Lg R-up 92-93 (Pres. Cup R-up 90-91 91-92).

BISHOPS CLEEVE

President: John Davies **Chairman:** David Lewis
Secretary: Phil Tustain, 7 Dale Walk, Bishops Cleeve, Glos GL52 4PQ (01242 674968).
Manager: David Lewis **Coach:** G Samuels **Physio:** Philip Tustain
Ground: Stoke Rd, Bishops Cleeve (01242 676257)
Directions: 3 miles north of Cheltenham on A435. 3rd left in village into Stoke Rd - ground on right. 4 miles from Cheltenham (BR); served by Cheltenham to Tewkesbury buses.
Seats: None **Cover:** 50 **Capacity:** 1,500 **Floodlights:** No **Founded:** 1892.
Colours: Green & black/black/black **Change colours:** Blue/white/red.
Midweek Matchday: Wednesday **Nickname:** Skinners
Previous Leagues: Cheltenham, Nth Glos **Record Gate:** 1,000 v Newport AFC.
Previous Grounds: The Skiller (pre-1913), Village Field (pre-1950)
Clubhouse: Full facilities, bar, dance area **Honours:** Hellenic Lg Cup R-up 90-91.

CHELTENHAM SARACENS

Chairman: J Utteridge **Manager:** Ian Ford
Secretary: R Attwood, 179 Arle Road, Cheltenham GL51 8LJ (01242 515855).
Match Sec: Terry Coates **Coach:** Kevin Barry **Physio:** Jim Utteridge
Press Officer: Terry Coates (01242 692320).
Ground: Petersfield Park, Tewkesbury Road, Cheltenham (01242 584134).
Directions: 1 mile from Cheltenham centre on A4019 Tewksbury Road (next to B & Q) - 1st left over railway bridge, 1st left and follow service road.
Seats: None **Cover:** 100 **Capacity:** 2,000 **Floodlights:** No **Founded:** 1964.
Colours: All blue **Change colours:** Black & white/black/black
Club Shop: No **Nickname:** Saras. **Midweek Matchday:** Wednesday
Prog.: 20 pages, 50p (Ed: Secretary) **Previous League:** Cheltenham 1964-86.
Reserve Team's League: Hellenic Reserve section.
Players progressing to Football League: S Cotterill (Wimbledon, B/mouth) 88, K Knight (Reading) 89.
Honours: Glos Snr Cup 91-92. **Clubhouse:** 2 mins away at 16-20 Swindon Rd, Cheltenham.

CIRENCESTER UNITED

President: A Day **Chairman:** J Austin **Vice Chairman:** Paul King.
Secretary/Press Officer: G Varley, 95 Vaisey Rd, Cirencester, Glos GL7 2JW (01285 657836).
Manager: A Smith **Coach:** T Dryden **Physio:** P Messenger
Ground: Four Acres P.F., Chesterton Lane (01285 885460)
Directions: Dual carriageway towards Bristol, under footbridge, first left after Cirencester Town F.C., ground 200yds on left hand side.
Seats: None **Cover:** No **Programme:** Yes **Floodlights:** No **Founded:** 1970
Colours: Red & black/black/red **Change colours:** Green & yellow/green/green
Nickname: Herd. **Previous Grounds:** None **Previous Name:** The Herd (pre-1990)
Previous Leagues: Cirencester & District (4 years)/ Cheltenham (8 years).
Programme: 40 pages, 50p **Editor:** N Warriner (01285 656187) **Club Shop:** No.
Midweek Matchday: Wednesday **Sponsors:**
Clubhouse: Training nights & matchdays. Rolls & sundries available.
Club record scorer: M Day **Club record appearances:** A Smith.
Honours: Glos Snr Amtr Cup R-up 86-87 89-90; Cirencester Lg 72-73 74-75 (Div 2(3) 71-73 74-75, Lg Cup 74-75, Res. Cup 74-75); Cheltenham Lg 76-77 83-84 (Div 2 75-76, Lg Cup 83-84 (R-up 86-87), Snr Charity Cup 86-87); Stroud Charity Cup 86-87 (Section A 82-83 83-84); Arthur Shipway Cup 86-87 (R-up 87-88 92-93); Fairford Hospital Cup R-up(4) 83-85 90-91 92-93; Hellenic Res Div 95-96, Cup 96-97.

CLANFIELD

President: B Wallis **Chairman:** J Osborne
Secretary: J Osborne, 70 Lancut Road, Witney, Oxon OX8 5AQ (01993 771631).
Manager: Bill Pirie/Mark Light **Physio:**
Ground: Radcot Road, Clanfield, Oxon (01367 810314)
Directions: On A4095 8 miles west of Witney & 4 miles east of Faringdon on south side of Clanfield. Buses from Witney - contact Thames Transit for details.
Seats: No **Cover:** 300 **Capacity:** 2,000 **Floodlights:** No **Club Shop:** No.
Colours: Red & white **Change colours:** Yellow & Black/black/black
Programme: 8 pages, with admission **Editor:** Secretary
Sponsors: Morelands Brewery **Nickname:** Robins **Founded:** 1890
Previous Leagues: Nth Berks/ Witney & Dist. **Reserves' League:** Hellenic League Reserve section.
Clubhouse: Every evening & Sat/Sun lunch
Honours: Oxon Jnr Shield 32-33, Oxon I'mediate Cup 67-68, Witney & Dist. Lg 66-67 (Div 1 65-66, Div 2 64-65), Hellenic Lg Div 1 69-70 (Premier Div Cup 72-73, Div 1 Cup 69-70 85-86), Jim Newman Mem. Tphy 83-84 87-88, Faringdon Thursday Memorial Cup 69-70 71-72.

EASINGTON SPORTS

Chairman: Jim Hay **President:** Terry Horley
Secretary: Terry Horley, 65 Grange Road, Banbury, Oxon OX16 9AT (01295 254950).
Manager/Coach: Jim Hay **Physio:** Alan Gardner **Press Officer:** T Horley
Ground: Addison Road, Easington Estate, Banbury, Oxon (01295 257006).
Directions: From Oxford A423. After passing under flyover on the outskirts of Banbury take first turning left into Grange Road then third right into Addison Rd. Ground at top on left. One and a half miles from Banbury (BR).
Seats: 50 **Cover:** 100 **Capacity:** 1,000 **Floodlights:** No **Founded:** 1946
Colours: Red & white/black/black **Change colours:** Blue & white/blue/blue. **Programme:** Yes, 25p
Midweek Matchday: Wednesday **Record Gate:** 250 v Witney Town 68
Previous Ground: Bodicote. **Previous Leagues:** Banbury Jnr/ Oxon Snr/ Warkwick Combination.
Reserves' League: Hellenic Res. section **Clubhouse:** Changing rooms, showers, bar facilities and food.
Honours: Oxon Snr Cup R-up, Oxon Intermediate League & Cup, Oxon Snr Lg.

FOREST GREEN ROVERS Reserves

Chairman: Trevor Horsley **President:** E G Smith
Secretary / Managing Director: Colin Peake, Club Admin Office, Unit 14 Springfield Bus. Centre. Stonehouse, Gloucester GL10 3SX (01453 791232, Fax 791305)
Press Officer: Heather Cook (01453 823281, Mob 0385 940981)
Manager: Frank Gregan **Asst Manager:** Tommy Callinan **Physio:** Dave Tyrrell
GROUND Address: 'The Lawn', Nympsfield Road, Forest Green, Nailsworth, Glos. GL6 0ET (01453 834860).
Directions: About 4 miles south of Stroud on A46 to Bath. In Nailsworth turn into Spring Hill off mini r'bout - ground approximately half mile up hill on left. The nearest BR station is Stroud.
Capacity: 3132 **Cover:** 980 **Seats:** 332 **Floodlights:** Yes
Clubhouse: (01453 833295). Bar and lounge, open every night.
Club Shop: Open matchdays. **Sponsors:** Daymac Graphics **Nickname:** Rovers
Programme: Yes **Editor:** Julie Davis **Formed:** 1890

HEADINGTON AMATEURS

President: John Dunne **Chairman:** Donald Light **Press Officer:** Paul Sammons
Secretary: C Barrett, 6 Holland Place, Wood Farm, Headington, Oxford OX3 8QT (01865 750828).
Manager: J Light. **Coach:** B McCrae **Physio:** J Taylor
Ground: Barton Rec., Barton Village Road, Barton, Oxon (01865 60489).
Directions: From Green Rd r'bout, Headington, (on A40) take Barton/Islip exit (1st exit coming from Witney, last coming from London), turn left into North Way, follow road for half mile - ground at bottom of hill on left.
Seats: None **Cover:** None **Floodlights:** No **Founded:** 1949. **Nickname:** A's.
Colours: All red **Change:** Blue/blue/white **Midweek matchday:** Tuesday
Club Records - Goalscorer: Tony Penge **Appearances:** Keith Drackett. **Win:** 6-0 v Carterton (H) 91 **Defeat:** 1-8 v Banbury United (A), February 1994.
Previous Leagues: Oxford City Junior 49-66/ Oxford Senior 67-88.
Previous Ground: Romanway, Cowley (pre-1990).
Programme: 8 pages, £1 with entry **Editor:** Stan Hawkswood (01865 65546) **Club Shop:** No.
Sponsors: Oxford Marquees **Reserves' Lge:** Hellenic Res. sect.
Player progressing to Football Lge: James Light (Oxford) 1970s.
Clubhouse: Open Tues & Thurs 6-11pm, Sat matchdays 4.45-11pm. Rolls, chips, burgers, hot dogs, sweets etc.
Honours: Oxon Snr League(4) 72-74 75-77 (R-up 71-72 74-75 77-78 81-82 84-85, Div 1 68-69, Presidents Cup(2) 72-74 (R-up 71-72 77-78 84-85)), Oxon Charity Cup 75-76 (Intermediate Cup 88-89), Hellenic League Div 1 R-up 87-88 (Res. Sect. 92-93, Res. Cup 91-92).

KIDLINGTON

President: Gordon Norridge. **Chairman:** Peter Walton.
Secretary: Peter Walton, 3 Azalea Ave, Kidlington, Oxon. OX5 1HQ (01865 377226)
Manager: K Grossman **Coach:** M O'Connell **Physio:** S Dickens
Ground: Yarnton Rd, Kidlington, Oxford (01865 375628)
Directions: From Kidlington r'bout (junction of A4260 & A34) A423 north to Kidlington; after 1st lights take 2nd left (Yarnton Road), ground is 200yds on the left.
Colours: Green & black/black/green **Change colours:** Red & black/black/red **Floodlights:** No
Programme: 20 pages, 20p **Editor:** M A Canning **Founded:** 1920
Midweek Matchday: Wednesday **Previous League:** Oxon Snr 47-54.
Record Attendance: 2500 v Showbiz XI 1973 **Clubhouse:** Two bars open after matches
Honours: Oxon Snr Lg 53-54 (R-up 47-48), Hellenic Lg Cup 74-75 (R-up 68-69 73-74 74-75, Div 1 R-up 63-64 78-79), Oxon Intermediate Cup 52-53 84-85 (R-up 68-69 73-74 74-75), FA Vase 5th last sixteen 76-77.

LETCOMBE

Letcombe FC *Photo: Gordon Whittington*

President: Dave McDowell. **Chairman:** Dennis Stock **Vice-Chairman:** G Delacoze
Secretary: Desmond Williams, 8 Larkdown, Wantage OX12 8HE (01235 764130).
Manager/Coach: Graham Foster **Commercial Manager:** R Stock.
Ground: Bassett Road, Letcombe Regis, Wantage, Oxon (012357 68685).
Directions: B4507 Swindon road from Wantage, left for Letcombe Regis, follow road thru Letcombe Regis; ground on right on far side of village.
Seats: No **Cover:** No **Floodlights:** No **Nickname:** None **Founded:** 1960.
Colours: Yellow/blue/yellow. **Change colours:** White/blue/blue
Sponsors: Autotype/ D McDowell **Previous Lges:** North Berks 60-90/ Chiltonian 90-93.
Programme: £1 with entry **Editor:** R.Stock (01235 762387) **Club Shop:** No.
Reserves' Lge: Hellenic Res. sect. **Midweek Matchday:** Wednesday
Clubhouse: Open evenings except Monday. Rolls & hot food sold.
Record scorer: R Taylor **Record appearances:** P Davies.
Honours: Chiltonian Lg Div 1 90-91, North Berks Lg 89-90 (Lg Cup 87-88, War Memorial Cup 89-90, A G Kingham Cup 89-90.

MILTON UNITED

Chairman: Mr K Tull **President:** Mr J Cannon **Match Secretary:** Sid Tindall
Secretary: Sue Walker, 122 High Street, Sutton Courtney, Abingdon, OX14 4AX. (01235 847158)
Ground: The Sportsfield, High Street, Milton, Abingdon, Oxon (01235) 832999
Directions: Use A34 bypass approx 10 miles north of M4 jct.13 & 10 miles south of Oxford. Leave A34 at Milton Hill roundabout and follow signs to Milton Park.
dabout follow road over railway bridge, take 1st left, ground immediately on left.
Capacity: **Seats:** None **Cover:** None **Floodlights:** No **Club Shop:** No.
Programme: Yes **Editor/Press Officer:** David Taylor(01235 816376)
Colours: Sky & maroon/white/white **Change colours:** All white
Sponsors: Morlands Brewery **Founded:** 1926
Midweek matchday: Tuesday **Reserve Team's League:** Hellenic Lge Res sect
Record Attendance: 500 v Almondsbury Picksons, Hellenic Lg 90-91.
Clubhouse: On ground, open matchdays.
Club Record Goalscorer: Nigel Mott **Club Record Appearances:**
Honours: Hellenic Lg 90-91 (Div 1 89-90 R-Up.94-95)), Nth Berks Lg(4) 85-86 87-89 (R-up 84-85 86-87, Lg Cup(3) 84-86 88-89, Div 2 80-81, Charity Shield(4) 84-86 87-89 (R-up 82-83), Nth Berks War Mem. Cup(3) 83-85 87-88, Berks & Bucks I'mediate Cup 90-91.

PEGASUS JUNIORS

President: Peter Hill **Chairman:** R W Pasley
Secretary: Brian James, 7 Loder Drive, Hereford HR1 1DS (01432 274982).
Manager/Coach: M.Williams. **Physio:** D Smith.
Ground: Essex Arms, Widemarsh St, Hereford. (0432 268705)
Directions: A49 Ross Road over Greyfriars Bridge, Victoria Street to end of Edgar Street, turn right, straight over mini-r/about, ground 50 yards on left.
Seats: None **Cover:** None **Capacity:** **Floodlights:** No. **Founded:** 1955
Programme: 50p **Editor:** K Bishop
Colours: All red. **Change colours:** Blue & white/blue/blue.
Previous Leagues: Leisure Centre.
Clubhouse: 48 Stowens Street. **Midweek Matchday:** Tuesday
Honours: Herefordshire Snr Amtr Cup 71-72, Herefordshire Co. Chal. Cup(5) 81-83 84-85 87-88 89-90 (R-up 93-94), Worcs Snr Urn 85-86, Hellenic Lg Div 1 84-85 (R-up 93-94, Div 1 Cup R-up 93-94).

PURTON

President: Graham Price **Chairman:** John Hayden **Press Officer:** Alan Eastwood
Secretary: Nick Webb, 4 Glevum Close, Purton, Swindon, Wilts SN5 9HA (01793 770242).
Ground: The Red House, Purton (01793 770262 - Saturday afternoons only).
Directions: Purton is on B4041 Wootton Bassett to Cricklade Road. Ground near village hall.
Seats: **Capacity** **Cover:** **Floodlights:** No **Founded:** 1923
Colours: All red **Change colours:** White & blue/blue/blue
Programme: 40 pagesp **Editor:** Alan Eastwood (01793 694036).
Sponsors: Courtoulds. **Nickname:** The Reds **Midweek Matchday:** Wednesday
Clubhouse: Open after matches
96-97 Captain: **96-97 Top Scorer:** **96-97 P.o.Y.:**
Honours: Wilts Lg 48-49 85-86 (Div 2 83-84, Div 3 86-87), Wilts Snr Cup(6) 38-39 48-49 50-51 54-55 87-89, Wilts Yth Cup 77-78 85-86 88-89, Fairford Hosp. Cup(3) 87-89 93-94.

ROSS TOWN

Patron: Dave Sexton **Chairman:** Geoff Jones **Press Officer:** Chris Parsons (01989 750691)
Secretary: Tim Barnard, Apsley House, Whitchurch, Ross-on-Wye, HR9 6DJ (01600 890722)
Manager: Phil Davies **Coach:** Martin Thomas **Physio:** Alan Bridges
Ground: Cinderford Town FC, Causeway Ground, Hilldene, Cinderford (01594 822039)
Directions: From Gloucester take A40 to Ross-on-Wye, then A48 - Chepstow. In 10 miles turn right at Elton garage onto A4151 signed Cinderford, thru Littledean, up steep hill, right at crossroads, second left into Latimer Rd. Ground 5 mins walk from town centre.
Capacity: 3,500 **Cover:** 1,000 **Seats:** 250 **Floodlights:** Yes
Colours: Red & white/red/red & white **Change colours:** Yellow & sky/black/yellow
Midweek Matchday: Various **Nickname:** Riversiders
Record Attendance: 147 v Harrow Hill 26/3/97
96-97 Captain: Chad Harris **96-97 Top Scorer:** Graham Jones **96-97 P.o.Y.:** Chad Harris
Honours: Hereford Lge 94-95, Charity Shield 95-96; Hereford FA Charity Bowl 94-95; Worcester & Dist Lge 95-96, Baylis Cup 95-96; Hereford FA County Chall Cup R-up 95-96; Pershore Hospital Charity Cup R-up 95-96.

WATLINGTON TOWN

Chairman: Bill Strong **President:** C Coles **Press Officer:** Kevin House
Secretary: Steven Muir, 91 Shirburn Street, Watlington, Oxford OX9 5BU (0411 132309)
Manager: Brian House **Coach:** Brian House **Physio:** Steven Muir
Ground: Shirburn Road, Watlington, Oxford.
Directions: From Oxford take A40/M40 east to junc 6, take B4009 towards Watlington. Ground is on right after 2 miles.
Colours: Red & black/black/red & black **Change colours:** Tangerine/white/tangerine
Midweek Matchday: Tuesday **Record Attendance:**

WOOTTON BASSETT TOWN

Chairman: Paul Harrison **President:** Keith Lodge
Sec./Press Officer: Mr R Carter, 14 Blackthorn Close, Wootton Bassett, Swindon, Wilts SN4 7JE (01793 851386).
Manager: Dave Warren **Coach:** Tony Lockyear **Physio:** Geoff Hawkins
Ground: Gerard Buxton Sports Ground, Rylands Way, Wootton Bassett, Swindon (0793 853880).
Directions: M4 jnct 16 to Wootton Bassett (A3102), left at 2nd r'bout (Prince of Wales pub on right), 2nd left into Longleaze (just after Mobil garage) and Rylands Way is 3rd right by shops, ground 100yds on right. Coming from Calne/Devizes proceed thru town centre and turn right into Longleaze after Shell petrol station on right - Rylands Ave. is 3rd left. Coming from Malmesbury take last exit off r'bout by Prince of Wales pub and Longleaze is 2nd left.
Seats: None **Cover:** 350 **Capacity:** 4,000 **Floodlights:** Due **Founded:** 1882
Colours: All Blue **Change colours:** All Red
Programme: 12 pages, free **Editor:** T.B.A. **Club Shop:** No.
Record Gate: 2,103 v Swindon T., friendly 91. **Previous Grounds:** None
Record scorer: Brian (Toby) Ewing **Record appearances:** Steve Thomas.
Record win: 11-2 **Record defeat:** 0-9
Sponsors: Cathy Moore Recruitment **Previous Leagues:** Wilts (pre-1988).
Midweek matchday: Wednesday **Reserve team's League:** Wiltshire.
Clubhouse: Open every matchdays, usual opening hours. Usual type of bar food available together with filled rolls. Tea & coffee available over bar. Matchday refreshments - teas, coffees, soups with light snacks.
Hons: Hellenic Lg Div 1 Cup 89-90 93-94, Wilts Lg 87-88 (Div 2 84-85, Subsidiary Cup 78-79), Wilts Snr Cup R-up 02-03 03-04 87-88, Ghia Snr 83-84, Ghia Jnr Cup R-up 88-89, FA Amateur Cup QF 26-27.

Ardley's Paul Darch heads in a goal against Letcombe *Photo: G Whittington*

Cray Wanderer's Paul McCarthy (left) is well tackled by Corinthian's Daniel Horsey in front of goal
Photo: Alan Coomes

Greenwich striker Paul Turner beats Thamesmead keeper Micky Orme to put Boro 1-0 up
Photo: K Gillard

FEEDER TO: DR MARTENS LEAGUE

President: D D Baker **Chairman:** P C Wager **Vice Chairman:** E V Ward

Hon. Secretary: A R Vinter, The Thatched Barn

Catt's Wood Road, Lower Hardress, Canterbury CT4 5PG (01227 700108)

During the past 1997-98 season in the Winstonlead Kent League, we had all the "thrills and spills" that you would expect, which provided many talking points, but the excitement of the Championship being decided in the final game was missing this year. In the previous two seasons, we have had the Dartford - Furness championship showdown and, last year, Herne Bay's three away wins in four days that saw them collect the coveted award. Herne Bay won the League Championship for the second successive season but their dream of a second "League and Cup double" was shattered in the Final when they lost to Greenwich Borough, who collected the Plaaya Kent Senior Trophy as well. In Division Two, Thamesmead Town Reserves provided the excitement in the Cup Final whilst Sittingbourne secured the League title.

At the start of the campaign, back in August, the League welcomed VCD Athletic, who were Champions of the Nuclear Electric Kent County League, and with nobody being promoted, the League constitution was at its maximum, twenty two clubs. It became apparent that Sheppey United would be "ground sharing" with Sittingbourne at Central Park, nearer to their natural home, and, in the months that followed, Chatham Town were to have problems with their ground. The Winstonlead Kent League Challenge Shield was won by Herne Bay, they defeated Ramsgate by a goal to nil, which saw them collect their fourth trophy in as many months, the prelude to the long and hard season ahead. The outcome of the League Championship, at this early stage, is always difficult to predict with many clubs having, during the close season, collected strong squads including Folkestone Invicta, Cray Wanderers, Sheppey United and, of course, Herne Bay. It was the South Coast side, under the guidance of the new manager, Neil Cugley, who began well with nine straight wins but they were not able to sustain the momentum, two home defeats against Whitstable Town and Chatham Town came as a shock. After two consecutive wins, Herne Bay suffered a home defeat against Greenwich Borough, a result that was to have a bearing on the proceedings later in the campaign. Ramsgate, last season's runners-up, started well with four wins and a draw but they were unable to maintain the form of the previous year. After a slow start, three draws and a loss in their first four outings, Sheppey United began to assert themselves. Two other sides, Greenwich Borough and Whitstable Town, also began their campaign well, 'Borough' were undefeated in their first eleven games whilst Whitstable suffered only one loss in their first fifteen outings.

As the months progressed, the League Table and Form Guide were taking shape, it became evident that Corinthian, Crockenhill and Canterbury City were all suffering from poor results. These three clubs eventually filled the bottom three positions. Corinthian, unfortunately, gained their first win at the thirty fifth attempt whilst Crockenhill suffered a run of twenty consecutive defeats and Canterbury City, in the first half of the season, had gained only three wins, all at home. The mid-table battle was always an interesting affair, places kept changing with every result and, at one point, with only a few points separating twelve or so clubs, the results were looked upon each week with interest from everyone. Chatham Town, during the season, had no fewer than four home grounds after their Maidstone Road ground was declared unfit. Their neighbours, Gillingham Football Club, helped out and several of the 'Chat's' home games were played at the Priestfield Stadium, they also played at the Garrison, at Slade Green and Maidstone Road, when fit. This unrest reflected in Chatham's final League position, seventeenth, their worst for six years. Erith Town, renamed from Woolwich Town, completed their season in nineteenth place. In between Chatham and Erith in eighteenth were Faversham Town whose position would have been higher but for irregularities which saw them lose eight points in the season.

Deal Town had their worst finish for ten years whilst Slade Green, Thamesmead Town, Tunbridge Wells and Lordswood all improved from last season's final positions. Tunbridge Wells improved dramatically to finish in eleventh place whilst Lordswood, at one point in December and January, put together an unbeaten twelve match run that saw them climb to fifth in the table, they eventually finished in tenth.

In the top half of the table, VCD Athletic were making good progress in their inaugural season with some good results, many of them draws, and they eventually finished in a creditable ninth place. Whitstable Town suffered a mid-season lapse which saw them slip to a final position of eighth, Beckenham Town produced some good results. One defeat in fourteen, during the latter half of the campaign, saw them end up in seventh place, their best place for four years. Earlier, I spoke about Cray Wanderers putting together a good squad and so it proved with their best placing for seven years, only two defeats in their last thirteen games went a long ways to securing sixth. After their good start, Greenwich fell by the wayside suffering consecutive defeats in the League but with one loss in their last nine they managed a fifth place, their best finish since 1990. The top four, Herne Bay, Folkestone Invicta, Sheppey United and Swanley Furness (formerly Furness) had been battling it out all season. Swanley, who had finished in the top three for the past four years, were never able to keep pace with the others and eventually finished fourth which left the others to fight it out.

During March, Herne Bay met Folkestone twice in "title deciders". At Winch's Field, the match ended in a draw whilst the return saw the reigning Champions secure victory in the last minute in front of the season's highest attendance, 1004, the best since the 1055 that watched the Dartford-Furness Championship decider two years ago. That win virtually assured Herne Bay of the Championship. It was confirmed on Easter Bank Holiday Monday when they gained the point needed and their second successive title. Earlier I mentioned about Herne Bay losing at home to Greenwich Borough, well since that loss in August Herne Bay put together an unbeaten run of thirty five League games which included fifteen consecutive away wins, a record in modern times. They also passed the 100 mark, points wise, with ease. Folkestone's, who finished as runners-up, cause was not helped when they surprisingly lost at home to Crockenhill and, in the last game, to Canterbury City. Sheppey, who played some sterling football which saw them lose only two of their last seventeen games, ended their campaign in a creditable third, they also have the accolade of being the only team to beat Herne Bay twice during the season, both games came after 'Bay' had won the title though.

In the Cup competitions, Deal Town shone in the FA Littlewoods Cup by reaching the Third Qualifying Round. They did it the hard way by playing six matches, three draws and three wins, in the earlier rounds before meeting Margate at Hartsdown Park. Victory by the odd goal in three, in front of 625 people, saw the Southern League side go through. In the FA Carlsberg Vase, Folkestone Invicta ended up by playing seven matches from the Preliminary Round to reach the Fourth Round, where they were beaten by Great Wakering Rovers. Herne Bay, after last year's success, also reached the Fourth Round but they lost to a very good Taunton Town by five goals to two. The one talking point from the Vase came when Slade Green met Whitehawk three times. The first match was a draw, Green won the replay but then after it was found out that Slade Green's pitch was too short and the replay was replayed! Slade Green won that one as well. The Plaaya Kent Senior Trophy and Winstonlead Kent League Division One Cup always creates a lot of interest. In the Trophy, Greenwich Borough and Folkestone Invicta battled their way to the Final, played at Ashford Town's ground. In a close match, 'Borough' won by the only goal. The Division One Cup saw some good matches, Sheppey's win at Tunbridge Wells by seven goals to three after extra time springs to mind, before Greenwich made it to their second Final of the season where they met the holders, Herne Bay. 'Bay' were in with a chance of an unprecedented second "League and Cup double" but it was Greenwich who took the honours with their second Cup success of the season when they won thanks to a Phil Turner strike.

In Division Two of the Winstonlead Kent League, Sittingbourne secured the Championship with only four defeats all season. It was a close affair as Tonbridge, the reigning Champions, finished just a point behind the 'Brickies'.The one unfortunate event to occur during the season was the withdrawal of Faversham Town which meant their earlier matches being expunged from the records. Thamesmead Town won the Division Two Cup after a thrilling Final with Herne Bay at Whitstable Town's Belmont Road ground. With the scores level after extra time, the South East London side eventually won five four on penalties. Fisher Athletic collected the Kent Intermediate Cup after beating Lordswood by the odd goal in seven in another thrilling encounter.

Overall the attendances for Division One games has been good and we have seen an improvement on last season by over 12 per cent, all the facts and figures appear later in the statistics along with the keenly contested Winstonlead Kent League Golden Boot Award and other facts. The season has been a good one for many clubs and now to the future. It has been announced in recent weeks that Folkestone Invicta's bid to join the Dr Martens Southern League has been accepted, we wish them well in their quest in the higher level. Since joining the league, after Folkestone Town's demise, they have made it known all along that Southern League Football should come back to the Town, they have achieved this and good luck to them. Next season we shall also see a big step made in the history of the Kent League as floodlights will become the criteria for entry into the new Premier Division of the Winstonlead Kent League. The decision for this was made some time ago and some clubs, Beckenham Town and Lordswood to name two, will have new lights installed at their grounds for next season. Others will probably seek a "groundshare" arrangement with other clubs until their lights are installed. This progression can only be good for the League, it will be good for the clubs and the supporters as well.

On behalf of the Kent League I would like to thank Winstonlead for their continued support and sponsorship of the League, and I look forward to next season.

Paul Rivers, Winstonlead Kent League Press Officer

FINAL LEAGUE TABLES 1997-98

DIVISION ONE

	P	W	D	L	F	A	Pts
Herne Bay	34	5	3	105	29	107	42
Folkestone Inv	42	31	4	7	127	42	97
Sheppey Utd	42	27	10	5	110	63	91
Swanley Furn.	42	22	9	11	86	50	75
Greenwich Boro	42	21	11	10	83	42	74
Cray Wndrs	42	20	11	11	70	50	71
Beckenham Tn	42	21	7	14	67	54	70
Whitstable Tn	42	19	11	12	72	54	68
VCD Athletic	42	17	14	11	88	62	65
Lordswood	42	18	9	15	70	64	63
Tunbridge Wells	42	17	6	19	73	76	57
Thamesmead T	42	15	9	18	69	70	54
Ramsgate	42	14	9	19	80	85	51
Hythe United	42	15	5	22	75	103	50
Slade Green	42	12	13	17	58	67	49
Deal Town	42	15	4	23	76	97	49
Chatham Tn	42	12	12	18	56	66	48
Faversham Tn	42	14	12	16	62	68	*46
Erith Town	42	12	6	24	48	86	42
Canterbury C	42	8	6	28	45	96	30
Crockenhill	42	6	2	34	31	133	20
Corinthian	42	2	5	35	36	130	11

DIVISION TWO

	P	W	D	L	F	A	Pts
Sittingbourne	36	25	7	4	105	35	82
Tonbridge	36	24	9	3	93	34	81
Thamesmead T	36	22	6	8	67	40	72
Swanley Furn.	36	20	5	11	79	45	65
Folkestone Inv	36	20	5	11	69	57	65
Dartford	36	21	7	8	75	49	*64
Dover Athletic	36	19	6	11	85	49	63
Lordswood	36	17	8	11	71	51	59
Herne Bay	36	17	7	12	75	57	58
Margate	36	16	7	13	60	59	*52
Hastings Town	36	14	7	15	85	69	49
Chatham Town	36	10	10	16	47	61	40
Ramsgate	36	11	4	21	60	94	37
Whitstable Tn	36	10	5	21	59	89	35
Hythe United	36	11	2	23	62	103	35
Corinthian	36	9	5	22	47	74	32
Beckenham T	36	7	6	23	40	86	27
Crockenhill	36	7	5	24	38	95	26
Deal Town	36	5	3	28	43	110	18

* Points deducted

GOLDEN BOOT AWARD

DIVISION ONE

Simon Bryant	(Deal Town)	37
Scott Appleton	(Herne Bay)	37
Simon Elliott	(Tunbridge Wells)	33
Dave Arter	(Folkestone Invicta)	29
Steve Hearn	(Whitstable Town)	29
Dean Bowey	(VCD Athletic)	28

DIVISION TWO

Ernie Batten	(Herne Bay)	28
Matt Quinlan	(Dartford)	23
Duncan Jones	(Hastings Town)	23
Steve Gibbons	(Tonbridge)	23

DIVISION ONE RESULTS CHART 1997-98

	1	2	3	4	5	6	7	8	9	10	11	12	13	14	15	16	17	18	19	20	21	22
1 Beckenham T	X	1-0	0-3	2-1	0-2	5-1	2-0	1-2	6-1	2-3	1-1	0-1	1-1	2-1	3-2	0-1	1-0	0-1	3-1	1-0	1-1	1-1
2 Canterbury C	0-3	X	0-0	3-2	1-2	2-1	3-2	1-4	1-1	0-2	2-1	0-7	3-2	0-2	1-1	2-4	1-3	2-1	2-4	0-0	1-3	1-4
3 Chatham T	1-2	3-0	X	2-0	1-3	1-0	2-1	0-1	2-2	1-1	2-1	1-3	2-2	0-2	2-2	0-3	4-4	1-1	1-2	3-1	1-2	0-2
4 Corinthian	1-4	1-1	0-2	X	0-4	0-2	0-3	3-2	1-1	1-5	0-1	0-4	1-4	2-3	1-4	2-3	1-1	0-6	1-3	2-3	0-3	1-3
5 Cray Wndrs	0-1	4-0	2-0	3-1	X	3-0	0-4	4-0	2-1	2-0	0-2	1-1	2-4	2-0	3-0	1-1	2-0	3-1	1-1	2-1	1-1	2-2
6 Crockenhill	0-3	2-1	2-0	1-5	1-3	X	0-3	1-2	0-0	0-9	0-3	0-3	0-2	0-2	0-3	0-3	1-2	0-3	1-5	0-2	0-7	1-3
7 Deal Town	1-2	2-1	2-3	5-1	1-1	8-0	X	2-0	2-6	1-3	1-1	0-2	3-1	3-1	1-3	2-3	2-0	4-5	1-1	0-2	3-2	2-2
8 Erith Town	2-1	2-1	1-3	4-0	1-3	0-1	1-2	X	0-1	2-3	2-2	0-2	1-4	0-3	0-4	1-4	0-1	2-0	4-0	3-2	1-5	2-2
9 Faversham T	1-0	1-0	0-0	3-0	1-1	2-2	3-2	0-0	X	2-3	1-3	1-3	2-0	0-0	2-0	2-2	3-2	2-1	2-0	2-3	3-1	0-0
10 Folkestone I	3-0	0-1	1-2	6-1	1-1	2-3	4-1	5-0	3-1	X	1-0	0-1	6-0	8-1	3-0	4-0	3-0	4-2	5-1	4-1	3-2	1-2
11 Greenwich B	0-0	1-0	2-3	1-0	3-0	7-1	4-0	1-1	3-0	3-2	X	0-1	3-2	4-0	6-0	1-1	4-2	0-1	1-1	2-2	2-2	0-1
12 Herne Bay	2-2	1-0	3-0	3-0	3-0	4-1	6-0	2-0	2-1	1-1	0-3	X	5-1	2-1	3-0	2-3	1-0	3-0	3-0	3-2	3-0	2-0
13 Hythe Utd	1-3	2-4	3-1	2-1	1-2	4-2	1-0	2-0	3-4	0-4	1-3	0-1	X	3-1	3-2	1-3	1-4	3-3	1-2	2-0	1-0	2-3
14 Lordswood	2-0	2-2	1-0	3-0	2-2	4-1	2-0	7-0	1-0	0-2	1-0	1-2	1-2	X	1-1	0-4	1-1	1-2	2-1	1-2	0-0	0-2
15 Ramsgate	3-4	2-0	3-1	7-0	2-1	5-1	2-4	0-2	4-1	0-2	1-4	1-3	2-2	1-3	X	1-3	1-1	3-2	1-1	2-1	1-1	2-1
16 Sheppey U	0-3	4-2	2-1	6-0	1-1	2-1	5-2	2-0	4-2	2-2	2-1	4-3	6-2	1-1	6-2	X	4-0	0-3	4-1	1-2	1-1	1-0
17 Slade Grn	0-1	5-2	1-1	2-1	3-1	5-0	0-1	1-1	2-0	0-3	1-2	0-2	1-1	2-2	2-1	2-2	X	1-1	0-2	2-4	0-3	0-0
18 Swanley F	2-0	3-0	2-2	3-0	1-0	2-1	5-0	4-1	1-1	0-2	1-2	0-4	10-1	3-1	1-1	1-1	1-0	X	2-0	1-0	1-1	2-1
19 Thamesmead	1-1	3-2	2-1	1-1	1-1	0-1	5-0	1-3	3-1	2-3	2-3	1-2	3-2	2-3	4-2	1-2	1-1	0-1	X	0-2	0-0	1-2
20 Tunbridge W	1-2	4-1	2-1	2-2	3-1	5-0	3-1	0-0	2-4	1-2	1-0	2-4	3-1	0-3	2-2	3-4	2-3	0-6	0-1	X	2-1	1-0
21 VCD Athletic	5-1	2-1	2-2	7-2	2-0	3-1	8-2	2-0	2-1	1-4	1-1	1-1	1-2	2-4	1-5	3-3	2-2	0-0	0-3	3-1	X	2-0
22 Whitstable T	4-1	2-1	0-0	2-0	0-1	5-1	1-2	3-0	1-0	1-4	1-1	1-1	4-2	3-3	2-1	4-2	0-1	2-0	1-5	3-3	1-2	X

LEAGUE DIVISION ONE CUP 1997-98

HOLDERS: HERNE BAY

First Round

Swanley Furness	v	Folkestone Invicta	3-2	Deal Town	v	Erith Town	1-2
Thamesmead Town	v	Canterbury City	2-1	Faversham Town	v	Tunbridge Wells	0-3
Beckenham Town	v	Lordswood	1-3	Sheppey United	v	Crockenhill	4-1

Second Round

Hythe United	v	Greenwich Borough	3-5	Chatham Town	v	VCD Athletic	0-1
Cray Wanderers	v	Slade Green	5-0	Swanley Furness	v	Whitstable Town	1-0
Herne Bay	v	Ramsgate	3-0	Erith Town	v	Corinthian	3-1
Thamesmead Town	v	Tunbridge Wells	1-2	Lordswood	v	Sheppey United	1-2

Quarter-Final

Greenwich Borough	v	VCD Athletic	2-1	Cray Wanderers	v	Swanley Furness	1-0
Herne Bay	v	Erith Town	5-2	Tunbridge Wells	v	Sheppey United	3-7

Semi-Final

Greenwich Borough	v	Cray Wanderers	7-1 agg	Herne Bay	v	Sheppey United	6-1 agg

Final

Greenwich Borough v Herne Bay 1-0

WINNERS: GREENWICH BOROUGH

MISCELLANEOUS TRIVIA

DIVISION ONE

Best Home Win
- 10-1 Swanley F v Hythe United
- 8-0 Deal Town v Crockenhill

Best Away Win
- 9-0 Folkestone Invicta at Crockenhill
- 7-0 Herne Bay at Canterbury City
- 7-0 VCD Athletic at Crockenhill

Highest Match Goals
- 11 Swanley F 10-1 Hythe United

Most Goalless Draws
- 5 Faversham Town

Fastest Goals
- 15 Seconds Phil Hancock (Hythe United)
- 40 Seconds Paul Gayle (Beckenham T)
- 56 Seconds Roly Graham (Herne Bay)

Scoring Feats (Most Goals in a Match)
- 6 Dave Arter (Folkestone Inv)
- 5 Simon Bryant (Deal Town)
- 4 Dave Arter (Herne Bay)
- 4 Simon Bryant (Herne Bay)
- 4 Scott Appleton (Herne Bay)
- 4 Phil Turner (Greenwich B)

Hat-tricks - 4 Simon Elliott (3 League, 1 FA Cup)

Steve Cuggy & Steve Lawrence (both Folkestone I) & Steve Hearn (Whitstable T) netted 2 hat-tricks during the year. There were 19 other hat-tricks netted during the season in Division One matches.

DIVISION TWO

Best Home Win
- 10-0 Dover Athletic v Hythe United

Best Away Win
- 7-0 Swanley Furness at Crockenhill
- 7-0 Tonbridge at Crockenhill
- 8-2 Dartford at Whitstable Town

Highest Match Goals
- 10 Dover Athletic 10-0 Hythe United
- 10 Whitstable Town 2-8 Dartford

Most Goalless Draws
- 3 Chatham T, Dartford, Margate & Thamesmead T

Fastest Goals
- 20 Seconds Julian Brazier (Hythe United)

Scoring Feats (Most Goals in a Match)

Karl Smith netted seven for Ramsgate when they defeated Faversham Town 15-0 but the record was expunged as was Smith's feat.

Matt Quinlan netted four goals in one match but with many games in Division Two having no recorded scorers this record could have been bettered.

ATTENDANCE FIGURES SUMMARY

HOME MATCHES Aggregate	Average	% Difference		TOTAL MATCHES Aggregate	Average	% Difference
2448	116.57	down 1.74%	Beckenham Town	4225	100.59	down 0.80%
1512	72	up 72.25%	Canterbury City	3447	82.07	up 24.16%
2646	126	up 1.94%	Chatham Town	4884	116.28	up 3.45%
1069	50.9	up 5.82%	Corinthian	2958	70.43	up 6.23%
1982	94.38	up 0.19%	Cray Wanderers	4324	102.95	up 8.03%
1919	91.38	down 1.42%	Crockenhill	3921	93.36	down 1.21%
2838	135.14	down 2.07%	Deal Town	4666	111.09	down 6.01%
1294	61.62	up 39.10%	Erith Town	3326	79.19	up 16.28%
1526	72.67	up 24.22%	Faversham Town	3477	82.78	up 7.88%
6799	323.76	up 90.34%	Folkestone Invicta	10468	249.24	up 79.96%
2038	97.05	up 39.23%	Greenwich Borough	4267	101.59	up 28.59%
3705	176.43	down 3.96%	Herne Bay	7606	181.09	up 12.34%
2031	96.71	down 12.16%	Hythe United	4412	105.05	up 1.89%
1892	90.09	down 6.84%	Lordswood	3954	94.14	up 0.90%
2001	95.29	down 13.45%	Ramsgate	4225	100.6	down 8.55%
2439	116.14	up 90.39%	Sheppey United	4571	108.83	up 32.88%
2138	101.81	up 5.07%	Slade Green	4503	107.21	up 17.55%
1547	73.67	down 0.44%	Swanley Furness	4091	97.4	up 9.80%
1152	54.88	down 22.48%	Thamesmead Town	3393	80.79	down 0.01%
2166	103.14	up 0.43%	Tunbridge Wells	4585	109.17	up 14.43%
2616	124.57	N/A	VCD Athletic	4672	111.24	N/A
2881	137.19	down 3.99%	Whitstable Town	5303	126.26	down 1.97%

Total Attendance for 1997-98 Season (462 matches) - 50639 Average - 109.61 Up 12.33%

PREMIER DIVISION CLUBS 1998-99

BECKENHAM TOWN

Chairman: T.B.A. **Vice Chairman:** B Hollaway.
Secretary: Peter Palmer, 107 Wentworth Rd, West Croydon, Surrey CR0 3HZ (0181 689 2134).
Manager: Kevin Sugrue **Asst Manager:**J.Moore.
Ground: Eden Park Avenue, Beckenham, Kent (0181 650 1066).
Directions: M25, A21 to Bromley then follow signs to Beckenham. Ground 1 mile west of town off A214, 2 mins walk from Eden Park (BR) station - trains from London Bridge. Bus 264.
Seats: 120 **Cover:** 120 **Capacity:** 4,000 **Floodlights:** Yes **Reformed:** 1971.
Colours: Red & white/red/white **Change Colours:** Yellow/black/black. **Nickname:** Reds.
Midweek matchday: Tuesday. **Record Gate:** 720 v Berkhamstead F.A.Cup 94-95
Previous Leagues: South East London Amtr 71-73/ Metropolitan 73-75/ London Spartan 75-82.
Programme: 8 pages, 50p **Editor:** Bob Chilvers (0181 301 2624) **Shop:** Yes
Clubhouse: All day opening at weekends. Hot & cold food, teas, etc. Bar & dance area. Pool & fruit machines.
Honours: London Spartan Lg Cup R-up 77-78 78-79, Kent Snr Tphy R-up 81-82 93-94, Kent Lg Cup R-up 84-85 92-93 (Div 2 Cup R-up 90-91).

CANTERBURY CITY

Back Row (L-R); Brian Ball (Physio), Gary Miller, Simon Tutt, Darren Hare, Mark Rees, Barry Gethin, Julian Taylor, Steve Parlett, Darren Watson (Asst Mgr). Front Row; Gary Allen (Player/Mgr), Lee Jones, Mark Baker, Kevin Parry, Karl Rolls, Julian Beal, Gavin Theze, Gary Pullen *Photo: Courtesy Canterbury Times*

Chairman: Tony Roberts **Vice Chairman:** TBA **President:** V H Heslop.
Secretary: Keith J Smith, 7 Knight Ave, London Rd Est, Canterbury, Kent CT2 8PZ (01227 456116).
Manager: Meirion George/Simon Tutt **Physio:** David Chapman-Jones **Comm Manager:** Geoff Roberts
Ground: Kingsmead Stadium, Kingsmead Road, Canterbury CT2 7PH (01227 457245)
Directions: A28 out of city centre into Military Road. At 1st r-about turn left into Tourtel Rd, proceed to next r-about and head straight over into Kingsmead Rd - stadium on right opposite Canterbury swimming pool. Half mile from Canterbury West (BR). Bus service 624 or 625 from Canterbury bus station
Capacity: 5,000 **Cover:** 200 **Seats:** 200 **Floodlights:** Yes **Club Shop:** Yes
Programme: 32 pages, 50p **Editor:** Keith Smith (01227 456116) **Press Officer:** TBA
Colours: Green & white/white/green & white **Change:** Red & black/black/red
Nickname: The City. **Sponsors:** Gladwish Land **Founded:** 1947.
Midweek matchday: Wednesday **Reserve's League:** Kent Lge Div 1
Club Records - Attendance: 3,542 v Chelsea, Friendly 97. **Goalscorer:** Wilf Heathcote 113 (48-51) **Appearances:** John Carragher 627 (60-70) **Win:** 10-0 v Deal Town (H), Southern League 30/1/65. **Defeat:** 0-9 v Corby Town (A), Southern League 16/9/63. **Fees - Paid:** £2,000 for Graham Knight (Maidstone Utd) **Received:** £2,000 for Dave Wiltshire (Gillingham).
Best FA Cup season: 1st Rd 64-65 (lost 0-6 to Torquay), 68-69 (lost 0-1 to Swindon).
Previous - Leagues: Kent 47-59/ Metropolitan 59-60/ Southern 60-94. **Name:** Canterbury Waverley **Grounds:** Wincheap Grove, Bretts Corner 47-58.
Players progressing to Football League: R Gawler (Southend 49), A Hughes (Grimsby 54), A Nugent (Darlington 56), J Richardson (Southport 56), T Horsfall (Cambridge Utd), J Murray (Wolves), K Hill, M Weatherley (Gillingham), T Norton (Brighton), P Hilton (Brighton 73), D Wiltshire (Gillingham 74), G Pugh (Torquay 84)
Clubhouse: Lounge bar open on matchdays. Snack bar, burgers, hot-dogs, pies, chips, tea, coffee, etc
97-98 - Captain: Barry Gethin **Top scorer:** Lee Jones (16)
P.o.Y.: Julian Beal **Supporters' P.o.Y.:** Lee Jones
Honours: Kent Lg Div 2 Cup 49-50 89-90, Div 1 Cup 49-50; Kent Senior Cup 53-54; Kent Senior Trophy 79-80; Kent Intermediate Cup 73-74; Kent Messenger Trophy 74-75; Frank Norris Memorial Shield 88-89 89-90; Kent League Div 2 Champ Res 90-91.

CHATHAM TOWN

Chairman: P Enright **President:**
Secretary: Brian Burcombe, 4 Hallwood Close, Parkwood, Rainham, Kent ME8 9NT (01634 363419).
Manager: John Adams **Asst Manager:**
Ground: Maidstone Road Sports Ground, Maidstone Road, Chatham, Kent (01634 812194).
Directions: M2, A229 Chatham turn-off, follow signs to Chatham, ground one and a half miles on right opposite garage. 1 mile from Chatham (BR).
Seats: 500 **Cover:** 1,000 **Capacity:** 5,000 **Floodlights:** Yes **Founded:** 1882.
Colours: Red & black halves/black/black. **Change Colours:** Yellow & green **Nickname:** Chats.
Midweek matchday: Tuesday **Record Gate:** 5,000 v Gillingham, 1980.
Previous Lges: Southern (several spells)/ Aetolian 59-64/ Metropolitan 64-68/ Kent (Sev. spells).
Programme: 12 pages, 50p **Editor:** Trevor Busby **Sponsors:** Topps Scaffolding
Clubhouse: Matchdays and functions
Honours: Kent Lg(9) 1894-95 03-05 24-25 26-27 71-72 73-74 76-77 79-80 (R-up 02-03 23-24 25-26 70-71 74-75 80-81, Lg Cup 71-72 76-77 (R-up(3)), Thames & Medway Comb.(5) 1896-97 04-06 19-20 23-24, FA Cup QF (beat Nottm Forest 2-0 en route) 1888-89, FA Tphy 3rd Rd 70-71, Kent Snr Cup 1888-89 1904-05 10-11 18-19, Kent Snr Shield 19-20.

CRAY WANDERERS

Chairman: Gary Hillman **President:** Bill Faulkner
Secretary: Mr Kerry Phillips, 15 Watling Street, Bexleyheath, Kent DA6 7QJ (01322 554108).
Director of Football: Frank Maloney **1st Team Manager:** John Roseman
Manager: Alan Hudson. **Asst Manager:** Charlie Pooley **Coach:** Peter Little
GROUND Address: (Ground share with Bromley) Hayes Lane, Bromley, Kent BR2 9EF (0181 460 5291 or 0181-313-3992). **Directions:** One mile from Bromley South (BR). Buses 316, 146 and 119 pass ground. Junction 4 off M25, then A21 towards London.
Capacity: 5,000 **Cover:** 2,500 **Seats:** 1,300 **Floodlights:** Yes **Club Shop:** Yes
Programme: 24 pages, 50p **Editor/Press Officer:** Greg Mann (H 0181-318 9604) (W 0171 500 4493)
Colours: Amber & black **Change Colours:** Purple & white
Sponsors: N.Hillman & Sons **Founded:** 1860. **Nickname:** Wands.
Midweek matchday: Tuesday
Record Gate: 1,523 v Stamford, F.A. Vase QF 79-80.
Previous Leagues: Kent 1894-1903 6-7 9-14 34-38/ W Kent 03-06 07-09/ London 20-34 51-59/ Kent Amtr 38-39 46-51/ S London All 43-46/ Aetolian 59-64/ Gtr London 64-66/ Metropolitan 66-71/ London Metropolitan 71-75/ London Spartan 75-78.
Clubhouse: Open pub hours (freehouse). Hot & cold food available.
Club Record Goalscorer: Ken Collishaw, 272. **Club Record Appearances:** John Dorey c500, 61-72
Honours: London Lg(2) 56-58 (Lg Cup 54-55), Aetolian Lg 62-63 (Lg Cup 63-64), Gtr London Lg 65-66 (Lg Cup(2) 64-66), Metropolitan Lg Cup 70-71 (Amtr Cup(2) 66-68), London Spartan Lg(2) 76-78, Kent Lg 01-02 80-81 (R-up 79-80 90-91, Lg Cup 83-84), Kent Snr Tphy 92-93, Kent Amtr Cup(4) 30-31 62-65.

CROCKENHILL

President: Mr H Miller **Chairman:** Chris Otterway **Vice-Chairman:** Brian Perfect
Secretary: Brian Perfect, 30 Tylers Green Road, Crockenhill, Swanley, Kent BR8 8LG (01322 663638)
Manager: Nick Elia **Asst Manager:** Carl Edyman **Coach:** Nick Elia
GROUND Address: (Ground Share with Erith & Belvedere) Park View, Lower Road, Belvedere, Kent DA17 6DF (0181 311 4444). **Directions:** From Dartford bridge follow signs for Crayford to Erith and follow A206. Ground half mile from Erith Blackwall tunnel: head for Abbey Wood and on to Belvedere. Entrance in Station Road, adjoining Belvedere (BR) station. Bus No. 469.
Capacity: 1,500 **Cover:** 1,000 **Seats:** 500 **Floodlights:** Yes
Colours: Red & white/black/black **Change Colours:** Black & white/black/black & blue **Nickname:** Crocks.
Record Gate: 800 v Maidstone, Kent Amtr Cup 1948. **Shop:** Yes
Programme: 8 pages + cover/ads **Editor:** Ruth Perfect
Midweek matchday: Tuesday **Reserve Lge:** Kent League Div 2
Previous Leagues: Kent Amtr 46-59/ Aetolian 59-64/ Gtr London 64-68
Players progressing to Football League: T Cascarino (Gillingham 82), Paul Gillcrest (Southampton)
Clubhouse: Open matchdays, Sunday lunchtimes, many evenings. Wide range of food always available.
Honours: Kent Lg 82-83 (R-up 84-85), Kent Snr Tphy 80-81, Kent Jnr Cup R-up 48-49, West Kent Amtr Cup 56-57, Sevenoaks Charity Cup 48-49, Kent Amtr Lg 56-57 (R-up 54-55, Prem Div 53-54 (R-up 52-53), Div 1 48-49 (R-up 46-47), Snr Div Cup R-up 56-57, Div 1 Cup R-up 46-47).

DEAL TOWN

Deal Town FC *Photo: Eric Marsh*

Chairman: Roy Smith. **Vice-Chairman:** Graham Jones
Secretary: Miss Lynne Fox, 32 Manor Road, Deal, Kent CT14 9BX (01304 361163).
Fixture Sec: Colin Adams (01304 372784) **Manager:** Tommy Sampson **Asst Manager:** Keith Lissenden
Ground: Charles Sports Ground, St Leonards Road, Deal, Kent (01304 375623).
Directions: A258 through Walmer, left into Cornwell Road, continue into Hamilton Road, veer left into Mill Rd, follow round to right into Manor Road, right into St Leonards Road, ground 100 yards on right. 1 mile from both Walmer and Deal BR stations. Local buses stop near ground.
Seats: 150 **Cover:** 500 **Capacity:** 2,000 **Floodlights:** Yes **Club Shop:** No
Programme: 32 pages, 50p. **Editor:** Colin Adams (01304 372784)
Press Officer: Tommy Sampson (01622 891784)
Colours: Black & white hoops/white/black & white hoops **Change Colours:** Yellow & Blue halves/blue/blue.
Founded: 1908. **Nickname:** Town. **Sponsors:** Mencare Ltd
Midweek matchday: Tuesday **Reserves' Lge:** Winstonlead Div 2
Record Gate: 4,000 v Billy Wright showbiz XI, Feb '61.
Previous Leagues: Kent 09-59/ Aetolian 59-63/ Southern 63-66/ Gtr London 66-71
Player progressing to Football Lge: Danny Wallace (Southampton)
Clubhouse: Matchdays & functions. Bar. Tea bar with hot & cold food.
97-98 - Captain: Colin Gilmore **Top Scorer:** Simon Bryant 40 **P.o.Y.:** Simon Bryant
Club Record Scorer: Joe Brayne 175. **Club Record Appearances:** Alan Barrow 544 (recent times).
Honours: Kent Lg 53-54 (R-up 88-89, Lg Cup 57-58 81-82 (R-up 94-95, SF 88-89 89-90), Kent Snr Tphy 94-95 R-up 82-83 90-91, Gtr London Lg Cup 67-68, Aetolian Lg R-up 59-60.

ERITH TOWN

Chairman: Phillip Legg **Vice Chairman:** **President:**
Secretary: J R Kelly, 88 Hook Lane, Welling, Kent DA16 2DP (0181 303 8977)
Manager: Ian Birrell **Asst Manager:** Alan Whitehead **Coach:** Peter Little
Ground: (Shared with Greenwich Borough), Harrow Meadow, Eltham Green Rd, Eltham, London SE9 (0181 850 5360).
Directions: S Circular (A205) to McDonalds, grd opposite. 1 mile from both Eltham and Kidbrooke BR stations.
Seats: 50 **Cover:** 50 **Capacity:** 2,500 **Floodlights:** Yes
Colours: Red & blue/black/black **Change Colours:** Yellow/black/black
Midweek matchday: Tuesday **Record Gate:**
Previous Ground: Flamingo Park, Sidcup (pre 1994) **Previous Leagues:**
Clubhouse:
Honours:

Erith Town FC: Back Row (L-R); Alan Whitehead (Asst Mgr), Martyn Panting, Dean Griffin, James Blyther, Dave Fennimore, Craig Clark, Simon Creasy, Kevin Holt, Richard Franklin, Ian Birrell (Mgr). Front Row; Peter Little (Coach), James Davie, John Reisel, Peter Brown, Peter Ellison, Lee Putnam, Scott Smith, Steve McAlphine.

Photo: Alan Coomes

FAVERSHAM TOWN

Chairman: Sal Aisani **Vice-Chairman:** **President:** Cris Aisani
Secretary: Reg Parr,
Manager: John Glover **Coach:** Bob Mason **Commercial Mgr:** Terry Whitehead
Ground: New Stadium, Salters Lane, Faversham, Kent (01795 532738).
Directions: On A2 (Canterbury road) just west of town.
Seats: 350 **Cover:** 1,500 **Capacity:** 2,000 **Floodlights:** Yes **Founded:** 1901.
Colours: White/blue/red **Change Colours:** Red/white/blue **Nickname:** Town.
Midweek matchday: Tuesday **Sponsors:**
Previous - Leagues: Aetolian 59-64/ Metropolitan 64-71/ Athenian 71-76. **Grounds:** Ashford Rd 1901-46/Gordon Square 46-58
Programme: 16 pages, 40p **Editor:** Quiram Aisani
Reserves' League: Kent Lg Div 2 **Club Records - Gate:** 1,400 v Sheppey Utd, 1949. **Goalscorer:** Tony Rudd 43.
Appearances: Bob Mason. **Win:** 8-0 v Greenwich B., Aug'89 **Defeat:** 0-9 v Sittingbourne, Jan '82.
Clubhouse: Open matchdays (Sat/Sun/Tues) Wed/Thurs. Snacks sold.
Honours: Kent Lg 69-70 70-71 77-78 89-90 (R-up 87-88, Lg Cup 70-71 90-91 (R-up 82-83)), Kent Snr Tphy 76-77 77-78 (R-up 87-88 88-89), Kent Amtr Cup 56-57 58-59 71-72 72-73 73-74.

GREENWICH BOROUGH

President: R Moore **Chairman:** P Meagan
Secretary: Ms Denise Richmond, 7 Castlecombe Rd, Mottingham, London SE9 6BA (0181 289 8956).
Manager: Dave Mehmet **Asst Manager:** R Dowling
Ground: Harrow Meadow, Eltham Green Rd, Eltham, London SE9 (0181 850 5360).
Directions: S Circular (A205) to McDonalds, grd opposite. 1 mile from both Eltham and Kidbrooke BR stations.
Seats: 50 **Cover:** 50 **Capacity:** 2,500 **Floodlights:** Yes **Founded:** 1928.
Colours: All Red **Change Colours:** All black **Nickname:** Boro.
Midweek matchday: Tuesday **Record Gate:** 2,000 v Charlton, floodlight opening, 1978.
Sponsors: **Programme:** 16 pages, 50p **Editor:** Keith Harmer
Previous - Leagues: South London Alliance/ Kent Amateur/ London Spartan 77-84. **Ground:** Erith & Belvedere F.C. 1992-93. **Name:** London Borough of Greenwich.
Record defeat: 0-8 v Faversham Town, August 1989.
Clubhouse: Yes.
Honours: London Spartan Lg 79-80 (Lg Cup 82-83), Kent Lg 86-87 87-88 (Lg Cup 84-85 86-87), Kent Snr Tphy 84-85, FA Vase 5th Rd 89-90.

HERNE BAY

Chairman: J Bathurst **Vice Chairman:** W Dordoy **President:** J Hodkinson
Secretary: L Gladwish, 41 Strangers Lane, Canterbury, Kent CT1 3XJ, (01227 451529)
Manager: Geoff Record **Asst Manager:** Gary Allen **Physio:** J Hodkinson.
Coach: K Lissenden **Press Officer:** Roy Twyman/ Doug Smith.
Commercial Manager: Roy Twyman (01227 375774).
Ground: Winch's Field, Stanley Gardens, Herne Bay, Kent (01227 374156).
Directions: Leave new Thanet Way at Herne Bay/Canterbury exit. Follow signs to Herne Bay via Canterbury Road. After railway bridge (1/2 mile), take first left into Spencer Road, then first left into Stanley Gardens, Ground on left.
Seats: 200 **Cover:** 1,500 **Capacity:** 4,000 **Floodlights:** Yes **Club Shop:** Due.
Programme: 36 pages, 70p **Editor/Press Officer:** Doug Smith, (01227 742182)
Colours: Blue & white halves **Change Colours:** Red & black halves
Sponsors: **Nickname:** The Bay. **Founded:** 1886.
Midweek matchday: Tuesday **Reserve Team's League:** Kent Lge Div Two.
Club Records - Attendance: 2,303 v Margate, FA Cup 4th Qual. Rd 70-71 **Win:** 15-1; v Canterbury Gas & Water, Kent Amateur Lge 52 **Defeat:** 0-11 v RAF Manston, Kent Amateur Lge 35 **Transfer fee received:** £3,000 for Mark Munday (Gravesend) 94.
Previous - Leagues: East Kent, Faversham & Dist, Canterbury & Dist, Kent Amateur, Kent 53-59, Aetolian 59-64, Athenian 64-74. **Ground:** Memorial Park 1886-1953.
Clubhouse: Open matchdays.
97-98 - Captain: Terry Martin **P.o.Y.:** Efrem Ebbli **Top Scorer:** Scott Appleton 40
Honours: Kent Lg 91-92 94-95 96-97 97-98, (R-up 92-93), Div 2 62-63 63-64, R-up 92-93(res) 94-95(res), Lg Cup 96-97, R-up 78-79 97-98, Div 2 Cup 53-54; Kent Snr Tphy 78-79, Kent Amtr Cup 57-58 (R-up 58-59 63-64 68-69 72-73); Aetolian Lg Div 2 62-63 63-64 (Lg Cup R-up 62-63), Div 2 Cup 62-63 63-64; Athenian Lg Div 2 70-71 (Lg Cup 66-67); Kent Amtr Lg Cup 53-54 54-55; Thames & Medway Comb. Cup R-up 61-62; Plaaya Kent Sen Trophy 96-97; FA Cup 4th Cup Qual. Rd 70-71 86-87.

HYTHE UNITED (1992)

Chairman: Tony Zapp **President:** Rt Hon Michael Howard QC
Secretary: Mr M R Giles, 21 Wych Elm Way, Hythe, Kent. CT21 6QE
Manager: Michael Dix **Asst Manager:** Dave Linstrem **Physio:** Tony Griggs
Ground: Reachfields, Fort Rd, Hythe (01303 264932)
Directions: On A259 west out of Hythe, turn left after light railway lights (Fort Road), entrance at end
Capacity: 3,000 **Seats:** 400 **Cover:** 2,400 **Floodlights:** Yes **Club Shop:** No
Programme: 50p **Editor:** Matt Blomfield **Press Officer:** M R Giles
Colours: All Red **Change Colours:** All blue
Sponsor: H V Wooding Ltd **Nickname:** **Founded:** 1992
Midweek Matchday: Tuesday **Youth League:** Kent Youth
Record Attendance: 1,655 v Crystal Palace 97-98
Previous Leagues: Nuclear Elec Kent Lge
Clubhouse: Bar open weekends/matchdays & training nights
97-98 - Captain: Kevin Clifford **Top Scorer:** Phil Hancock **P.o.Y.:** Phil Hancock
Honours: None as Hythe United

LORDSWOOD

Chairman: D Sims **Vice Chairman:** D Caulfield **President:**
Secretary: Steve Lewis, Sunnybrook, Gorsewood Road, Hartley, Longfield, Kent DA3 7DF (01474 708233 H, 01474 708233 B
Manager: B Zilwood **Asst Manager:** **Physio:**
Ground: Lordswood Sports & Social Club, North Dane Way, Walderslade, Chatham, Kent ME5 9XX (01634 669138)
Directions:
Capacity: 425 **Seats:** 125 **Cover:** No **Floodlights:** No **Club Shop:** No
Colours: Orange/black/black **Change Colours:** All green
Programme: Yes **Editor:** D Harman **Press Officer:** D Harman
Sponsor: **Nickname:** Lords **Founded:** 1968
Midweek Matchday: Tuesday/Thursday **Reserve or Youth League:** Both
Record Attendance: 386
Previous Leagues: Kent County Lge
Clubhouse: Yes

RAMSGATE

Chairman: R Lawson **Vice Chairman:** C Payne **President:** Tom Pendry
Secretary/Press Officer: Steve Lancaster. 66 Park Avenue, Birchington, Kent (01843 597703).
Manager/Coach: Lennie Lee **Asst Manager:** Dave Bostock **Physio:** John Burroughs
Ground: Southwood Stadium, Prices Avenue, Ramsgate, Kent (01843 591662).
Directions: From London on A229, A253 into Ramsgate - left into Netherhill at r'bout, right into Ashburnham Rd, right into Southwood Rd. 15 mins walk from Ramsgate BR station; walk thru Warre Recreation Ground, along St Lawrence High Str., left at 'White Horse', follow Southwood Rd and turn right into Prices Avenue.
Seats: 400 **Cover:** 600 **Capacity:** 5,000 **Floodlights:** Yes **Founded:** 1946.
Colours: Red & white. **Change Colours:** White/blue/blue **Nickname:** Rams.
Midweek matchday: Tuesday **Record Gate:** 5,200 v Margate, 56-57.
Sponsors: Hoverspeed. **Reserve Team's League:** Winstonlead Kent Div. Two.
Programme: 28 pages. **Editor:** Steve Redford (01843 596138). **Club Shop:** No.
Previous Leagues: Southern 59-75. **Previous Name:** Ramsgate Athletic
Club Record Scorer: Mick Williamson. **Record win:** 9-1 v Crockenhill, Kent League Cup 22/1/94.
Clubhouse: Open matchdays & private functions. Two bars, two pool tables, darts. Hot & cold food on matchdays.
Honours: Kent Lg 49-50 55-56 56-57 (Lg Cup 48-49 92-93 93-94 94-95)
Kent I'mediate Cup 54-55, Kent Snr Cup 63-64, Thames & Medway Cup 60-61, Kent Snr Shield 60-61, Kent Floodlit Tphy 69-70, Kent Snr Tphy(2) 87-89.

SHEPPEY UNITED

Chairman: Peter Sharrock **Manager:** Mal Watkins
Secretary: Mr Barry H Bundock, Dunedin, 104 Southsea Ave., Minster, Sheerness, Kent ME12 2NH (01795 876025) (0374 112834 Mobile)
Ground: (Ground sharing with Sittingbourne) Central Park, Eurolink, Sittingbourne, Kent ME10 3SB (01795 435077. Fax: 01474 814501).
Directions: Through Sittingbourne on main A2, club signposted clearly and regularly from both east and west. 1 mile from Sittingbourne BR station.
Capacity: 8,000 **Cover:** 3,300 **Seats:** 2,000 **Floodlights:** 420 lux **Founded:** 1890.
Colours: Red & white/white **Change colours:** Blue & white stripes
Midweek matchday: Wednesday **Nickname:** Islanders or Ites.
Previous Name: Sheppey Athletic/Ites **Programme:** 20 pages, 50p
Previous Ground: Botany Road, St Georges Avenue, Sheerness (pre-1992).
Record Gate: 4,000 v Sittingbourne, Kent Senior Trophy 1927 (at Botany Road).
Previous Leagues: Southern 1894-1901 84-91/ Kent 01-27 32-59 72-84/ Aetolian 59-64/ Gtr London 64-65/ Metropolitan Lg 65-71.
Players progressing to Football League: E C Harper (England, Blackburn, Spurs, Preston).
Hons: Kent Lg(6) 05-07 27-28 72-73 74-75 78-79 94-95, (R-up 03-04 04-05 77-78 83-84, Lg Cup 75-76 78-79, Div 2(reserves) 32-33 84-85 (R-up 1894-95 1979-80); Thames & Medway Comb. 08-09 12-13 22-23 25-26 28-29 55-56; Kent Amtr Cup 45-46 51-52; Kent Snr Shield 77-78; Kent Snr Cup R-up(3); Gtr London Lg 64-65; FA Cup 6th Qual. Rd 19-20; FA Tphy 1st Rd Proper 85-86.

SLADE GREEN

Chairman: Brian Smith. **President:** William Dudley
Secretary: Bruce Smith, 15 Gumping Rd, Orpington, Kent BR5 1RX (01689 858782).
Joint Managers: M Watts/T Carley. **Coach:** Tony Pruce. **Physio:** Alan Martin.
Ground: The Small Glen, Moat Lane, Slade Green, Erith, Kent (01322 351077).
Directions: Off A206 between Erith & Dartford. 400 yards from Slade Green BR station. Buses 89 & B13.
Capacity: 3,000 **Seats:** 150 **Cover:** 400 **Floodlights:** Yes **Club Shop:**
Programme: 30 pages, with admission **Editor/Press Officer:** Robert Smith (01322 287982).
Colours: White & green **Change Colours:** All yellow
Sponsor: Kingsway Furniture **Founded:** 1946. **Nickname:** The Green
Midweek matchday: Tuesday **Reserve League:**
Club Records - Attendance: 3,000 v Millwall, friendly 25/7/92. **Goalscorer:** Colin Dwyer **Appearances:** Colin Dwyer. **Win:** 14-0 v Island Social, Kent Amtr Lge 53. **Defeat:** 1-9 v Whitstable Greater London 64-65
Previous Leagues: Dartford 46-52/ Kent Amateur 52-62/ Greater London 62-70.
Previous Name: Slade Green Athletic 46-86.
Players pogressing to Football League: Roy Dwight (Nottm Forest), Alan Clark (Charlton), Fred Lucas (Charlton).
Clubhouse: Yes; Hall, Directors Lounge & Canteen
Honours: Kent Snr Tphy 91-92 (R-up 80-81); Kent Lg Cup 82-83; Kent Amtr Lg 52-53 53-54 60-61 (Lg Cup 60-61); Kent Intermediate Cup 61-62; Kent Benevolent Cup 46-47; West Kent 60-61 65-66; Dartford Lg R-up 48-49 (Lg Cup 47-48 (R-up 46-47)); Erith Hospitals Cup 46-47 48-49; Gtr London Lg R-up 68-69; Plumstead Challenge Cup 48-49.

THAMESMEAD TOWN

Chairman: Brian Morris. **Vice Chairman:** Keith Dunsmore. **President:**
Secretary: Albert Panting, 97 Sydney Road, Bexleyheath Kent DA6 8HQ (0181 303 1350)
Manager: Terry Hill. **Coach:** Keith Gurr. **Physio:** Shaun Edwards
Ground: Bayliss Avenue, Thamesmead, London SE28 8NJ (0181 311 4211).
Directions: From Abbey Wood (BR) north east along Harrow Manor Way, into Crossway at 3rd r'bout, Bayliss Av. is 3rd right (Bexley bus 272 stops in Crossway near Bayliss Av. By road: From Dartford tunnel A2 to London, exit Danson Interchange and follow signs for Thamesmead and Abbey Wood. From Blackheath tunnel exit on south side and follow signs to Woolwich, to Plumstead and then to Thamesmead.
Seats: 125 **Cover:** 125 **Capacity:** 400 **Floodlights:** Yes **Club Shop:**
Programmes: Yes. 50p **Ediotor:** **Press Officer:** Matthew Panting.
Colours: Green & black **Change Colours:** All red
Sponsors: Courage Brewery **Nickname:** The Mead. **Founded:** 1970.
Midweek matchday: Tuesday. **Reserves League:** Winstonlead Kent D2
Club Records - Attendance: 400 v Wimbledon, ground opening 88. **Appearances:** Delroy D'Oyley. **Win:** 9-0 v Kent Police, Kent League 19/4/94.
Previous - Leagues: London Spartan 80-91. **Ground:** Meridian Sports Ground, Charlton.
Clubhouse: Mon-Fri 6-11pm, Sat 12-11pm, Sun 12-3 & 7-10.30pm. Double bar, lounge, dance-floor, children's games room, video machines, hot & cold food. New members Bar.
Honours: Spartan Lg Div 3 79-80 (Lg Cup 84-85 86-87; I'mediate champs 85-86); Kent I'mediate Cup 83-84 94-95; 4 promotions, and 9 trophies (inc London FA and Kent FA Cups) in progress thru Spartan I'mediate Divs, 1980-87; Winstonlead Kent Div 2 94-95, Div 2 Cup 94-95.

TUNBRIDGE WELLS

Chairman: M Higgs **Vice Chairman:** P C Wager.
Secretary: P C Wager, 46 Mereworth Rd, Tunbridge Wells, Kent TN4 9PL (01892 524182).
Manager: Bill Tucker **Asst Manager:** **Coach:** Jack Whitely
Ground: Culverden Stadium, Culverden Down, Tunbridge Wells, Kent TN4 (01892 520517).
Directions: Leaving town on main Tonbridge rd (A26), turn left opposite 'Spanner in the Works' pub - grd half mile. 1 mile from Tunbridge Wells Central (BR). Served by any Tunbridge Wells-Tonbridge bus - to St Johns.
Seats: 350 **Cover:** 1,000 **Capacity:** 3,750 **Floodlights:** Yes **Club Shop:** Yes
Programme: 20 pages, 50p **Editor:** Secretary. **Press Officer:**
Colours: Red/White/Red. **Change Colours:** Yellow/navy/navy.
Sponsors: **Nickname:** Wells. **Founded:** 1886. **Reformed:** 1967.
Midweek Matchday: Tuesday **Reserve League:**
Previous - Names: None. *predecessors: T. Wells FC 1886-1910 47-50/ T. Wells Rgrs 03-09 63-67/ T. Wells Utd 51-62.*
Grounds: Down Lane 1906/ Combley Park 06-10/ Swiss Cottage 06-14/Down Farm 19-39/ St Johns 47-50/ Eridge Road 50-51.
Club Records - Attendance: 967 v Maidstone United, FA Cup 1969. **Goalscorer:** John Wingate 151 **Appearances:** Tony Atkins 410. **Win:** 10-0 v Deal (H), May'86 **Defeat:** 1-11 v Deal Town (H), 20/2/93.
Clubhouse: Open matchdays and as required.
Honours: Kent Lg 84-85 (R-up 68-69, Lg Cup 74-75 77-78 85-86 87-88), Kent Snr Tphy R-up 85-86 91-92.

Crockenhill's goalkeeper Peter McAuliffe makes a brave save at the feet of Lordwood's Stuart Johnson
Photo: Alan Coomes

VICKERS CRAYFORD, DARTFORD ATHLETIC

Secretary: Brian Norris 47 Oxenden Wood Road, Chelsfield Park, Orpington, Kent BR6 6HP (01689 854302)
Fixture Secretary: Mr Gary Dillon, 5 Ladds Way, Swanley, Kent BR8 8HN (01322 669057)
Ground: (Ground Sharing with Thamesmead Tn) Bayliss Avenue, Thamesmead, SE28 8NJ (0181 311 4211).
Directions: From Abbey Wood (BR) north east along Harrow Manor Way, into Crossway at 3rd r'bout, Bayliss Av. is 3rd right (Bexley bus 272 stops in Crossway near Bayliss Av. By road: From Dartford tunnel A2 to London, exit Danson Interchange and follow signs for Thamesmead and Abbey Wood. From Blackheath tunnel exit on south side and follow signs to Woolwich, to Plumstead and then to Thamesmead.
Seats: 125 **Cover:** 125 **Capacity:** 400 **Floodlights:** Yes
Colours: Green & white/white/white **Change Colours:** Yellow/blue/blue
Midweek matchday: Tuesday **Previous Ground:** Flamingo Park, Sidcup (pre 1994)

WHITSTABLE TOWN

Chairman: Joe Brownett **Vice Chairman:** Trevor Rapley **President:** George Gifford.
Secretary: Mrs Sylvia J Davis, 5 Old Bridge Rd, Whitstable, Kent CT5 1RJ (01227 265646).
Manager: Simon Kay/Doug Bosson **Asst Manager:** John Crabbe **Physio:** Tony Pattenden
Ground: Belmont Road, Belmont, Whitstable, Kent (01227 266012).
Directions: From Thanet Way (A299), left at Tescos r'bout and down Millstrood Rd - ground at bottom of road, 400yds from Whitstable (BR) station. Car park at Grimshall Rd entrance.
Capacity: 2,000 **Cover:** 1,000 **Seats:** 500 **Floodlights:** Yes **Club Shop:** Yes
Programme: 48 pages, 50p **Editor/Press Officer:** Trevor Myhill (01227 277297).
Colours: Red/white/red **Change colours:** Yellow/blue
Club Sponsors: D & J Tyres **Shirt Sponsor:** McDonalds **Founded:** 1885.
Nickname: Oystermen, Reds, Natives **Midweek matchday:** Tuesday
Club Records - Gate: 2,500 v Gravesend & Northfleet, FA Cup 3rd Qual Rd, 19/10/87. **Goalscorer:** Barry Godfrey **Appearances:** Frank Cox 429 (50-60). **Win:** 18-0 v Greenstreet (H), Faversham & District Lge 20-21. **Defeat:** 0-10 v Sittingbourne (A), FA Cup 1st Qual Rd 62-63.
Previous - Leagues: E. Kent 1897-1909/ Kent 09-59/ Aetolian 59-60/ Kent Amtr 60-62 63-64/ Seanglian 62-63/ Gtr London 64-67/ Kent Premier 67-68 (also in New Brompton, Thanet and Faversham & Dist. Lges over the years).
Names: Whitstable Utd (pre-1886)/ Whitstable Swifts 93-95/ Whitstable Town 95-1905/ Whitstable FC 08-66.
Grounds: Saddleston's Field 1885-94/ Westmeads (Cromwell Rd) 94-95/ Joy Lane 95-1908/ Church Rd 08-09.
Clubhouse: Social & recreation purposes, open all matchdays. Bar. Hot food & drinks at tea-bar.
97-98 - Captain: Meirion George **P.o.Y.:** Steve Hearn **Top Scorer:** Steve Hearn
Honours: Kent Lg Div 2 27-28 33-34 49-50 (Lg Cup 79-80 (R-up 89-90 91-92)), Kent Amtr Lg East 60-61, Kent Amtr Cup 28-29, Kent Snr Tphy R-up 78-79 89-90 92-93, Gtr London Lg Cup R-up 65-66, Kent Amtr Cup 28-29, Kent Midweek Lg Cup 92-93.

A jubilant Greenwich Borough squad celebrate their winning the Winstonlead Kent League Cup after the final at Folkstone
Photo: Francis Short

Herne Bay striker Scott Appleton gets in a header on the Greenwich goal *Photo: Francis Short*

Lordswood's Stuart Johnson is beaten to this corner by Crockenhill's Alan Everest *Photo: Alan Coomes*

Greenwich Borough's Trevor Booker gets in a shot, whilst Ramgate's defenders Scott Forbes (left) and Adrian Burroughs can only watch — *Photo: Alan Coomes*

Action from the match between Ramsgate and Slade Green

Action from VCD Athletic first match of the season against Eltham Town — *Photo: Martin Wray*

UNIJET SUSSEX COUNTY LEAGUE

FEEDER TO: BEAZER HOMES LEAGUE

FOUNDED 1920

President: P H Strange **Chairman:** Peter Bentley

Secretary: Peter Wells, 37 Bewley Road, Angmering, BN16 4JL (01903 771146)

Burgess Hill at Sudbury Wanderers, FA Vase

Photo: Eric Marsh

When Burgess Hill town started the season with home defeats in two trophy matches - to St Leonards Stamcroft in The Roy Haydon Trophy (0-2) and to Wick in the Norman Wingate Trophy - eyebrows were raised and the turf accountants offered generous odds against them retaining any of the major prizes.

However, when the season ended this was shown to be a false dawn for the opposition as the club retained their hard-won Unijet League Division One title by a comfortable five point margin over second club Littlehampton Town and in the process the only blips in a 38-match programme were five draws and four defeats. The 105-34 goals situation was a clear additional indication of their superiority with Ashley Carr (23) and Daren Newman (21) leading the goalscorers.

Littlehampton (promoted in 1996-97) were their only serious challengers with Wick sliding back slightly from the previous season's near miss, although this was softened by success in the SCFA RUR Charity Cup with a 3-2 win over Shoreham in the final. The actual SCFA Senior Cup was won by Hastings Town, who beat Burgess Hill in the final at Crawley (2-1), while the latter completed a double by landing the John O'Hara League Challenge Cup as the result of a narrow 3-2 victory over Portfield in the final.

With the leading clubs so dominant most of the others had to settle for respectable mid-table security and two of the relegation issues were decided early, Arundel and Peachehaven & Telscombe finishing well adrift of the others to be joined in the drop by luckless Mile Oak.

Their replacements were East Preston, impressive Division Two Champions by an eleven point margin over Eastbourne United, who were also promoted along with Broadbridge Heath, whose four extra goals meant that Sidley United again had to settle for fourth place.

Division Three was won by Lingfield by a single point from Storrington and they replace Bexhill Town and Midhurst & Easebourne in the higher league, but as usual one must spare a thought for the bottom club - in this case Bosham, who only won twice and drew six matches in a 30-game programme, but they bravely completed their fixtures.

Burgess Hill's domination was completed by top place in the Division One Merit Table by ten points from Littlehampton Town, while Mile Oak's consolation for being relegated was a meritorious but useless equal sixth place in that table plus success for their reserves in the Premier section.

In national cup competitions there were few outstanding efforts with Langney Sports proceeding farthest in the FA Cup - to the Third Qualifying Round - and Burgess Hill going out bravely by a lone goal in the Fifth Round of the FA Vase at Sudbury Wanderers.

With Brighton & Hove Albion struggling to survive in the Football League through eccentric boardroom decision-making Sussex is not at the moment a very high profile county, but things can only improve - at least we all hope that they will!

DIVISION ONE RESULTS CHART 1997-98

		1	2	3	4	5	6	7	8	9	10	11	12	13	14	15	16	17	18	19	20
1	Arundel	X	2-4	2-1	1-1	3-1	3-3	3-1	1-3	0-4	1-1	1-3	0-0	1-5	1-3	1-3	1-2	2-5	2-1	1-5	0-1
2	Burgess Hill Town	9-0	X	4-1	2-0	4-3	4-0	5-1	4-1	3-0	3-2	3-0	6-1	2-0	1-3	0-0	4-1	0-0	2-0	1-0	0-2
3	Chichester City	5-2	1-2	X	0-1	7-1	2-2	1-1	0-1	1-1	2-3	0-2	2-0	0-1	1-1	2-3	4-2	2-2	3-2	2-3	0-2
4	Eastbourne Town	6-1	1-5	1-3	X	2-1	3-1	3-1	2-3	0-2	1-1	1-0	5-0	2-6	2-1	2-3	0-4	2-1	2-3	0-0	0-0
5	Hailsham Town	3-0	1-3	2-4	4-2	X	0-1	2-0	3-1	1-5	4-1	0-2	2-1	1-3	0-4	1-1	2-4	0-3	0-2	3-0	0-2
6	Hassocks	6-0	1-1	1-1	2-1	4-0	X	4-0	1-2	0-4	2-2	2-0	0-0	1-1	1-2	1-2	1-2	2-0	3-2	0-0	2-1
7	Horsham YMCA	3-1	0-1	3-1	1-2	1-3	6-1	X	3-1	3-2	3-1	1-0	0-0	2-4	1-2	3-3	2-2	2-3	3-1	2-4	1-2
8	Langney Sports	4-1	2-1	9-1	1-1	3-2	1-0	2-0	X	3-1	4-1	0-1	8-0	1-0	2-1	1-1	1-2	1-2	0-3	2-2	2-2
9	Littlehampton Town	5-2	2-0	3-1	4-3	5-2	3-0	5-5	1-0	X	3-1	1-0	7-2	5-1	7-1	1-2	1-1	1-0	2-0	2-0	1-1
10	Mile Oak	1-1	1-2	3-2	1-1	3-2	3-1	0-2	0-1	1-3	X	2-3	3-1	2-4	0-0	0-0	1-0	1-2	0-2	1-2	1-3
11	Pagham	1-0	0-3	0-2	0-2	0-2	2-0	3-2	0-0	2-2	3-0	X	0-0	1-1	0-2	1-0	1-1	0-0	2-3	1-1	1-3
12	Peacehaven & Tels.	4-1	1-4	0-2	4-1	0-2	1-1	1-4	0-2	0-3	4-1	0-2	X	2-3	2-1	0-2	2-3	1-2	3-1	0-2	0-2
13	Portfield	0-3	0-4	1-1	2-1	3-4	2-1	0-4	1-5	0-4	1-1	0-1	2-3	X	0-3	1-2	1-4	1-1	1-3	0-0	2-1
14	Redhill	8-0	0-0	0-1	3-0	4-1	2-1	1-2	2-0	3-4	1-2	0-1	2-0	1-2	X	3-0	10-0	3-1	2-0	2-0	0-3
15	Ringmer	4-2	2-2	1-1	1-2	4-0	4-1	5-1	0-3	1-4	1-0	2-3	1-3	4-2	2-3	X	1-3	2-2	0-1	1-2	0-4
16	Saltdean United	3-0	1-2	2-1	4-1	3-2	1-2	3-1	1-2	0-2	1-1	1-1	1-1	5-3	2-1	1-4	X	2-0	4-2	2-0	1-2
17	Selsey	3-1	3-4	3-1	2-0	5-1	0-1	3-2	3-0	1-2	0-0	0-0	1-1	3-3	1-1	0-2	0-2	X	3-1	4-0	1-1
18	Shoreham	2-1	0-4	0-0	3-0	2-1	1-1	0-3	0-1	2-1	0-1	1-1	3-1	4-0	0-2	1-1	1-0	1-0	X	0-0	2-2
19	Whitehawk	2-1	1-4	4-1	0-0	3-1	2-1	2-1	0-1	1-2	2-1	2-2	1-1	1-1	0-5	1-1	3-4	0-0	4-1	X	0-1
20	Wick	4-1	0-2	5-2	2-0	1-2	1-1	6-1	2-3	1-3	3-1	1-1	5-0	1-0	3-2	0-1	3-1	5-0	2-4	1-0	X

DIVISION ONE ATTENDANCES CHART 1997-98

		1	2	3	4	5	6	7	8	9	10	11	12	13	14	15	16	17	18	19	20
1	Arundel	X	68	57	38	25	49	52	50	104	40	64	37	42	48	53	66	57	75	55	47
2	Burgess Hill Town	204	X	163	209	188	643	210	416	268	237	168	127	157	278	264	148	163	223	273	319
3	Chichester City	125	165	X	64	90	105	75	80	195	105	215	140	145	88	145	113	145	105	110	90
4	Eastbourne Town	103	102	131	X	311	81	81	405	180	65	102	92	107	121	131	31	96	115	82	105
5	Hailsham Town	145	235	153	135	X	105	135	507	219	75	105	146	107	163	231	120	135	146	153	151
6	Hassocks	83	289	65	80	80	X	113	111	78	156	64	161	95	152	101	85	110	76	107	141
7	Horsham YMCA	102	108	50	80	60	40	X	100	104	56	60	50	70	60	103	63	95	75	60	124
8	Langney Sports	238	355	204	527	258	206	187	X	226	159	183	162	204	278	215	144	205	224	168	289
9	Littlehampton Town	185	145	85	148	85	82	125	153	X	93	145	85	110	132	146	134	174	97	112	255
10	Mile Oak	112	175	60	55	84	78	71	95	89	X	76	75	73	94	94	73	65	115	150	83
11	Pagham	101	151	73	63	115	122	89	120	200	127	X	110	153	115	107	85	310	87	87	130
12	Peacehaven & Tels.	81	211	124	142	160	81	140	102	104	117	65	X	51	134	131	262	143	104	178	131
13	Portfield	47	58	130	51	40	75	53	65	54	48	31	53	X	67	60	38	76	68	58	86
14	Redhill	110	211	148	162	136	104	125	142	162	119	103	126	104	X	135	97	80	107	88	155
15	Ringmer	74	351	77	101	148	96	90	238	96	64	103	88	74	74	X	113	78	108	106	102
16	Saltdean United	83	193	119	79	189	89	89	163	116	89	89	189	83	93	33	X	123	173	166	133
17	Selsey	72	146	142	72	102	102	92	94	143	121	155	110	175	72	94	48	X	92	58	128
18	Shoreham	73	182	51	84	109	81	107	144	111	122	106	86	63	106	91	80	77	X	185	85
19	Whitehawk	58	75	55	70	70	90	65	110	75	80	90	80	80	75	60	120	70	85	X	110
20	Wick	140	240	102	150	119	102	100	136	270	129	92	115	120	150	1..	116	123	213	128	X

DIVISION ONE MERIT TABLE 1997-98

		No of Games	Wins	Wins by 5 Goals +	Clean Sheets	Clean Games	Cautions	Send Offs	Total
1	Burgess Hill Town	38	145	20	80	110	-120	-20	215
2	Littlehampton Tn	38	135	30	65	105	-110	-20	205
3	Wick	38	115	20	70	115	-115	-40	165
4	Whitehawk	38	60	5	35	120	-85	-20	115
5	Hassocks	38	55	5	45	125	-125	0	105
6	Mile Oak	38	40	0	25	125	-85	-40	65
=	Redhill	38	105	15	75	80	-130	-80	65
8	Langney Sports	38	115	15	55	65	-185	-20	45
9	Hailsham Town	38	60	0	30	105	-120	-40	35
=	Ringmer	38	80	5	35	95	-160	-20	35
11	Horsham YMCA	38	65	10	25	100	-110	-60	30
12	Pagham	38	70	0	70	80	-170	-20	30
13	Selsey	38	70	10	45	70	-155	-60	-20
14	Shoreham	38	80	0	50	90	-150	-100	-30
15	Eastbourne Town	38	60	10	35	65	-175	-40	-45
16	Arundel	38	30	0	10	90	-135	-60	-65
17	Saltdean United	38	100	5	25	45	-265	-60	-150
18	Portfield	38	55	10	10	55	-210	-100	-180
19	Chichester City	38	50	10	25	50	-250	-80	-195
20	Peacehaven & Tels	38	35	0	20	50	-215	-120	-230

MERIT TABLE POINTS

5 POINTS
for every win

5 POINTS
for every win, scoring 5 goals or more

5 POINTS
for every game with no goals conceded

5 POINTS
for every game with no cautions or send offs

-5 POINTS
for every caution

-20 POINTS
for every sending off

JOHN O'HARA LEAGUE CHALLENGE CUP 1997-98

First Round

Crowborough Athletic	v	Burgess Hill Town	2-9
Newhaven	v	Eastbourne Town	0-1
Three Bridges	v	Ringmer	1-2
Mile Oak	v	Worthing United	1-0
Shoreham	v	Withdean	2-1
Whitehawk	v	Crawley Down Vlge	1-0

Second Round

Broadbridge Heath	v	Langney Sports	1-3
East Preston	v	Hassocks	5-2
Hailsham Town	v	Lancing	1-3
Mile Oak	v	Burgess Hill Town	1-9
Pagham	v	Bexhill Town	4-0
Portfield	v	Sidlesham	1-0
Saltdean United	v	Eastbourne United	3-1
Whitehawk	v	Shoreham	2-1
East Grinstead Tn	v	Arundel	0-3
Eastbourne Town	v	Ringmer	0-2
Littlehampton Town	v	Southwick	4-1
Oakwood	v	Horsham YMCA	0-3
Peacehaven & Tels	v	Midhurst & Ease.	2-0
Redhill	v	Shinewater Assoc.	1-2
Sidley United	v	Selsey	1-2*
Wick	v	Chichester City	4-2*

Third Round

Burgess Hill Town	v	Whitehawk	3-1
Langney Sports	v	Selsey	3-1
Pagham	v	Peacehaven & Tels	2-0
Ringmer	v	Saltdean United	0-4
Lancing	v	East Preston	2-7
Littlehampton Tn	v	Shinewater Assoc.	3-0
Portfield	v	Horsham YMCA	4-1
Wick	v	Arundel	2-0*

Fourth Round

East Preston	v	Langney Sports	2-3
Portfield	v	Pagham	3-0
Littlehampton Town	v	Burgess Hill Town	1-3
Wick	v	Saltdean United	0-2

Semi-Final

Burgess Hill Town	v	Saltdean United	3-1
Langney Sports	v	Portfield	0-1

Final

Burgess Hill Town	v	Portfield	3-2

WINNERS: BURGESS HILL TOWN

P.G. CUNNINGHAM SPORTSMANSHIP TROPHY 1997-98

Horsham YMCA	78.68
Eastbourne United	76.47
Shinewater Association	75.88
Sidley United	74.71
Hailsham Town	74.47
Crowborough Athletic	73.53
Broadbridge Heath	72.94
Worthing United	72.12
Whitehawk	71.89
East Preston	71.76
Hassocks	71.58
Crawley Down Village	71.18
Redhill	71.05
Newhaven	70.59
Eastbourne Town	70.53
Mile Oak	70.53
Selsey	70.29
Burgess Hill Town	70.26
Littlehampton Town	70.00
Three Bridges	69.71
Arundel	69.19
Langney Sports	69.19
Chichester City	68.95
Withdean	68.44
Shoreham	67.30
Lancing	67.19
East Grinstead Town	66.18
Southwick	65.76
Bexhill Town	65.59
Ringmer	65.43
Midhurst & Easebourne	64.55
Oakwood	64.55
Sidlesham	63.53
Pagham	63.42
Peacehaven & Telscombe	62.63
Saltdean United	61.58
Portfield	60.53

LEADING (LEAGUE) GOALSCORERS 1997-98

Ansty Rangers	Richard Tilford	23
	Stuart Tippler	12
Arundel	Matthew Russell	13
Bexhill Town	Gareth Thacker	9
Bosham	Kelvin Fletcher	4
	Kevin Gibbins	4
Broadbridge Hth	Matthew Kelly	17
	Ricky Hart	10
Burgess Hill Tn	Ashley Carr	23
	Daren Newman	21
	Paul Boxall	11
Buxted	Andy Payne	11
Chichester City	Stuart Chandler	10
Crawley Down V.	Doug Cashman	21
Crowborough Ath	Sean Muggeridge	11
East Grinstead	Matthew Duffield	10
East Preston	Eamonn Searle	23
	Chris Jack	22
	Terry Withers	19
Eastbourne Tn	Ben Carrington	14
Eastbourne Utd	John Snelgrove	27
	Stephen Loughton	23
Forest	Gavin Pritchard	4
Franklands Vlge	Steve Hards	11
	Mark Ormanroyd	27
Hailsham Town	Paul Spencer	8
Hassocks	Robbie Kitchen	14
	Andrew Burt	10
Haywards Hth Tn	Liam Tucknott	10
Horsham YMCA	Andy Price	14
	Rob Grim	10
Hurstpierpoint	Danny Bryan	14
Ifield	Marc Allen	12
Lancing	Dale Brunton	15
Langney Sports	Sid Harman	18
Lingfield	Stewart Small	18
	Stephen Crawford	13
Littlehampton Tn	Clinton More	28
	Steve Guille	25
	Wayne Wren	10
Midhurst & Ebne	Martin George	10
Mile Oak	Justin Simmons	9
Newhaven	Micky Dorrill	5
	Simon Know	5
	Lee Martin	5
Oakwood	Nigel Brake	13
	Lee Butcher	12
	Danny Cousins	10
Oving S.C.	Michael Godolphin	16
	Justin Turnill	11
Pagham	Lee Hammond	8
P'haven & Tels.	Jon Lockhart	11
Portfield	Hugh Howden	14
Redhill	Jake Hutchinson	22
	Justin Jones	10
Ringmer	Leighton Allen	19
	Daniel Merry	10
Royal & Sun A	Andrew Taylor	16
	Richard Latham	11
Saltdean United	Tommy Pattenden	10
Selsey	Paul Lee	25
	Dominic Shepherd	14
Shinewater Ass.	Robbie Warner	19
Shoreham	John Byrne	13
Sidlesham	Darran Atkins	25
	Richard Elms	11
	Clive Muller	10
Sidley United	Gerard Moyse	18
	Peter Heritage	10
Southwick	Moray Forest	19
	Derren Woods	15
	Martin O'Donnell	12
St Francis Hosp.	James Laing	18
Steyning Town	Paul Tait	12
Storrington	Ben Whitby	20
	Gavin Bridle	11
	Miles Scerri	10
Three Bridges	Jim Fenton	24
Uckfield Town	Andy Potter	13
Westfield	Peter Baker	38
	Dominic Scott	19
Whitehawk	Roy Agyei	6
Wick	Phil Churchill	18
	Mark Vickers	12
Withdean	Lewis Claydon	6
	Richard Lacey	6
Worthing Utd	Nigel Waller	16
	Howard Albon	15
	Steve Gurney	10

DIVISION ONE CLUBS 1998-99

BROADBRIDGE HEATH

Chairman: Keith Soane **President:** G W Manketelow
Joint Managers: Gary Croydon, Martin Gander
Secretary: Andy Crisp, 19 Church Rd, Broadbridge Heath, Horsham, West Sussex RH12 3LD (01403 252273).
Ground: Broadbridge Heath Sports Centre, Wickhurst Lane, Horsham (01403 265871).
Directions: Alongside A24, Horsham north/south bypass.
Seats: 300 **Cover:** 300 **Capacity:** 1,300 **Floodlights:** Not full **Founded:** 1919
Programme: Yes **Editor:** Roy Neilson(01403 218318) **Admission:** £1.50.
Colours: All royal blue **Change colours:** All red **Nickname:** Bears
Sponsors: Mark Woodham, Painter &Decorator **Midweek matches:** Tuesday.
Previous Leagues: Horsham, West Sussex, Southern Co's Comb. **Record Attendance:** 240
Clubhouse: Bar. Kitchen serving meals, pool, darts, social club etc.

BURGESS HILL TOWN

Chairman: Jim Collins. **President:** Jack Lake **Manager:** Alan Pook
Secretary: Martin Waner, 26 Hamilton Close, Mile Oak, Brighton BN41 2WY (01273 439849) (Mobile 0378 148853)
Ground: Leylands Park, Burgess Hill, West Sussex RH15 8AW (01444 242429).
Directions: Turn east from A273 London Road into Leylands Road, take 4th left (signposted) Leyland Park. Nearest station Wivelsfield
Seats: 100 **Cover:** Yes **Capacity:** 2,000 **Floodlights:** Yes **Club badges:**Yes
Programme: Yes **Editor:** **Sponsors:** None
Colours: Yellow/white/black **Change colours:** All red
Nickname: Hillians **Founded:** 1882 **Midweek matchday:** Tuesday
Record Gate: 854 v Clitheroe, FA Vase 4th Rd (H) **Previous Lges & Grounds:** None
Clubhouse: Bar & social facilities. Tea bar.
97-98 - Captain: Daren Newman **Top Scorer:** Ashley Carr **P.o.Y.:** Daren Newman
Honours: Sussex County Lg 75-76 96-97, Lg Cup 73-74 79-80 97-98 (R-up 90-91), Div 2 74-75 (Cup 73-73), F/lit Cup 96-97, Reserve Section 76-77 77-78 91-92, Reserve Sect. East 77-78 82-83 84-85, Reserve Cup 82-83; Yth Sect. West 91-92 East 95-96, North 96-97 97-98; Sussex Fives 80; Mid-Sussex Lg 00-01 03-04 39-40 46-47 56-57 (Div 2 03-04(res), Div 3 20-21 36-37, Div 4(res) 56-57; Mid Sussex Snr Cup 94-95 96-97; Montgomery Cup 39-40 56-57; Mowatt Cup 45-46; Sussex RUR Charity Cup 91-92; Sussex I'mediate Cup 76-77; Sussex Yth Lge 96-97 97-98, Cup 91-92 97-98.

CHICHESTER CITY

Chairman: Tony Muncaster **Match Secretary:** Peter Harding
Company Sec: John F Hutter, 28 Stockbrigde Gdns, Donnington, Chichester, W Sussex PO19 2QT (01243 785839).
Manager: Adrian Girdler **Physio:** **Press Officer:** T Wallis (01705 464438).
Ground: Oaklands Park, Chichester (01243 785978).
Directions: Half mile north of city centre adjacent to Festival Theatre. Turn into Northgate car park from Oaklands Way and entrance is beside Tennis and Squash club. 1 mile from Chichester (BR) - walk north through city centre.
Seats: 50 **Cover:** 500 **Capacity:** 2,500 **Floodlights:** Yes **Founded:** 1873
Colours: White/black/white **Change colours:** All red **Nickname:** Lilywhites
Programme Editor: T Wallis **Club Shop:** No **Midweek matchday:** Wednesday
Previous Lgs: Chichester/ West Sussex 1886-1920 **Record Gate:** 2,500 v Dorchester, FA Cup 1960
Clubhouse: Licensed, open matchdays and some evenings. Tea bar.
Club record scorer: David Green **Club record appearances:** Neal Holder.
Honours: Sussex Co. Lg(5) 59-61 67-68 72-73 79-80 Invitation Cup 47-48 54-55 56-57 63-64, Div 2 Cup 84-85 87-88 90-91, Sussex Snr Cup 25-26, Sussex RUR Charity Cup 60-61 (jt with Brighton & HA) 63-64, Sussex I'mediate Cup 67-68.

EAST PRESTON

President: Greg Stanley **Chairman:** Brian Harwood **Vice-Chairman:** Don Pryke.
Secretary: Keith Freeman, 41 Ambersham Cres., East Preston, West Sussex BN16 1AJ (01903 771158).
Manager: Ian Cole **Asst Manager:** Brett Torode **Physio:**
Ground: Roundstone Recreation Ground, East Preston, West Sussex (01903 776026).
Directions: Less than a mile from Angmering (BR) station. A259 from Worthing to Roundstone Hotel (6 miles), turn south over railway crossing, left past Centurion garage, right into Roundstone Drive.
Seats: None **Cover:** 40 **Capacity:** **Floodlights:** Yes **Reformed:** 1966
Colours: Black & white/black/black **Change:** Red/white/red **Nickname:** None
Programme: Yes **Editor:** Andy Mott (01903 726097) **Sponsors:** Roundstone Garage
Previous Lges: Worthing / W Sussex **Reserve's League:** Sussex Co. Res. Div (Prem).
Clubhouse: Licensed bar open Mon-Fri evenings, Sat noon-11pm, Sun noon-11pm. Kitchen serves light refreshments on matchdays.
Honours: Sussex Co. Lg Div 3 83-84, (R-up 90-91), Div 3 Cup 87-88 (R-up 89-90); West Sussex Lg 77-78 80-81 81-82 82-83 (Malcolm Simmonds Cup 80-81 82-83), Div 2 Sth 81-82, Div 3 Sth 79-80, Div 5 Sth 82-83; Chichester Cup 87-88; Boreham Tphy 77-78 90-91 (R-up 93-94); Vernon Wentworth Cup 80-81 89-90; Worthing Lg 67-68 (Div 2 68-69(res); Benev. Tphy 66-67 68-69; Worthing Charity Cup 68-69.

Burgess Hill *Photo: Eric Marsh*

EASTBOURNE TOWN

Chairman: Kevin Moore **Manager:** Pete Cherry
Secretary: Ann Moore, 27 Chesterton Drive, Seaford. BN25 3RJ (01323 897369)
Ground: The Saffrons, Compton Place Road, Eastbourne, East Sussex (01323 723734).
Directions: Turn south west off A22 into Grove Road (opposite BR station), ground 1/4 mile on the right.
Seats: 200 **Cover:** Yes **Capacity:** 3,000 **Floodlights:** Yes **Founded:** 1882
Clubhouse: Fully licensed bar. Board room. Tea bar.
Colours: Yellow/blue/blue **Changes:** Blue & black/black/black
Programme Editor: Chris Backhurst (01323 505062) **Nickname:** 'Bourne'
Previous Leagues: Southern Amtr 07-46/ Corinthian 60-63/ Athenian 63-76.
Sponsor: Eastbourne Car Auctions **Record Attendance:** 7,378 v Hastings Utd 53
Honours: Sussex County Lg 76-77, Sussex Snr Cup (12) 1889-91 93-95 98-1901 02-03 21-22 31-33 52-53, Sussex RUR Charity Cup 32-33 47-48 49-50; Souhtern Amt Lge (2); AFA Snr Cup 21-22 24-25 (R-up 22-23 23-24); AFA Invitation Cup 69-70 (R-up 56-57 68-69 70-71)

EASTBOURNE UNITED

Chairman: I Botting **Vice-Chairman:** B Winter **President:** N Mansell.
Secretary: M Stevens, 21 Brookside Ave, Polegate, BN26 6DL (01323 484644)
Manager: M French **Asst Manager:** **Physio:** G Bishop
Ground: The Oval, Channel View Rd, Eastbcurne, East Sussex (011323-726989)
Directions: To seafront and turn left. Turn left into Channel View Rd at Princess Park and ground 1st right. 2 miles from Eastbourne (BR).
Seats: 160 **Cover:** 160 **Capacity:** 3,000 **Floodlights:** Yes **Club Shop:**
Programme: 36 pages **Editor:** R.Adcock. **Press Officer:** M Stevens
Colours: White/black/white **Change colours:** Blue/black/black
Sponsors: **Nickname:** The 'Us' **Founded:** 1894
Midweek Matchday: Tuesday **Reserve League:** Sussex County Res. Div. (East).
Record Attendance: 11,000 at Lynchmere
Previous Leagues: Sussex Co. 21-28 35-56/ Metropolitan 56-64/ Athenian 64-77/ Isthmian 77-92.
Players progressing to Football League: B Salvage, T Funnell, M French.
Clubhouse: Bar, lounge, dancefloor, stage, tea bar, board room.
Honours: Sussex Co. Lg 54-55, Sussex Snr Cup(5) 60-61 62-64 66-67 68-69 (R-up 89-90), Sussex RUR Charity Cup 55-56, Metropolitan Lg Cup 60-61, Athenian Lg Div 2 66-67 (Div 1 R-up 68-69), Sussex I'mediate Cup 65-66 68-69.

HAILSHAM TOWN

President: J Whippy **Chairman:** Barry Taylor **Manager:** Jeff Dyson
Secretary/Press Officer: Derek York, 59 Anglesey Avenue, Horsebridge, Hailsham BN27 3BQ (01323 848024).
Ground: The Beaconsfield, Western Road, Hailsham, East Sussex (01323 840446).
Directions: A22 to Arlington Road, turn east, then left into South Road - left into Diplocks Way until Daltons. Four miles from Polegate (BR - Brighton-Eastbourne line); regular bus service from Eastbourne.
Seats: None **Cover:** 300 **Capacity:** 2,000 **Floodlights:** Yes
Programme: Yes **Editor:** Secretary **Admission:** £2.50
Colours: Green & yellow/green/yellow **Change colours:** All white
Founded: 1885 **Nickname:** None **Midweek matchday:** Tuesday.
Record Gate: 1,350 v Hungerford, FA Vase Feb '89 **Previous League:** E Sussex, Southern Comb.
Clubhouse: Hot and cold snacks. Open every evening, matchdays and Sundays, tea bar.
97-98 Captain: P Comber **P.O.Y.:** M Cable **Top Scorer:** L Sale (16)
Club Record Goalscorer: H Stevens 51, 95-96 **Club Record Appearances:** P Comber 650
Honours: FA Vase 5th Rd 88-89, Sussex County Lg Div 2 R-up 80-81, Southern Co's Comb. 74-75, Sussex RUR Charity Cup, Sussex I'mediate Cup, Hastings Snr Cup, Sussex Jnr Cup, E Sussex Lg Cup, Hailsham Charity Cup, John O'Hara Cup 95-96.

HASSOCKS

President: Maurice Boxall **Chairman:** Jim Goodrum
Secretary: Bob Preston, 65 Oakhall Park, Burgess Hill, West Sussex RH15 0DA (01444 245695).
Manager: Dave John **Press Off.:** Dave Knight (01273 842023) **Physio:**
Ground: The Beacon, Brighton Rd, Hassocks (01273 846040)
Directions: Off A273 Pyecombe Road to Burgess Hill, 300yds south of Stonepound crossroads (B2116) to Hurstpierpoint or Hassocks.
Seats: None **Cover:** 100 **Capacity:** 1,500 **Floodlights:** Yes **Founded:** 1902
Colours: Red/white/red **Change colours:** All blue
Programme: 24 pages, 50p **Editor:** Dave Knight **Nickname:** The Robins
Sponsors: Icon **Midweek Matchday:** Tuesday/Wednesday
Previous Leagues: Mid Sussex/ Brighton Hove & Dist./ Southern Co's Comb.
Previous Ground: Adastra Park, Hassocks (pre-1992).
Record Gate: 610 v Burgess Hill Town, Sussex County Lge 96-97.
Clubhouse: Clubroom, bar, kitchen.
Honours: Sussex County Lg Div 3 91-92, Div 2 R-up 94-95, Res. Sect. East R-up 92-93; Southern Counties Comb. 76-77, Lg Cup R-up 79-80; Brighton Hove & Dist. Lg 71-72; Sussex Intermediate Cup 74-75 (R-up 80-81).

HORSHAM YMCA

Chairman: Robert Knight **Match Secretary:** Robin Bishop (01903 746332)
Secretary: Robin Bishop, 6 Brook Close, Storrington, RH20 3NT (01903 746332, 0996 202955)
Manager: John Suter **Asst Mgr:** **Physio:** Robin Bishop
Ground: Gorings Mead, Horsham (01403 252689).
Directions: Approaching Horsham fron East on A281 Brighton Road, the ground is on left & signposted opposite Gorings Mead
Seats: 100 **Cover:** 200 **Capacity:** 800 **Floodlights:** Yes **Founded:** 1898
Colours: White/black/red **Change colours:** All Red **Nickname:** YM's
Sponsors: Principal Copiers **Midweek Matchday:** Tuesday
Previous Leagues: Horsham & Dist/Brighton & Hove/Mid Sussex **Record Attendance:** 600 v Horsham FA Cup
Previous Grounds: Lyons Field, Kings Road
Honours: Sussex Co Lge Div 2 65-66 82-83 R-up 94-95 (Lg Cup 81-82, Invitation Cup 66-67 67-68, Div 2 Invit. Cup 59-60 61-62 94-95)

LANGNEY SPORTS

Chairman: Len Smith **President:** J Stonestreet
Secretary: Mrs Myra Stephens, 7b Erica Close, Langney, Eastbourne, East Sussex BN23 6HY (01323 766050).
Manager: Steve Richardson **Physio:** T.B.A.
Ground: Langney Sports Club, Priory Lane, Eastbourne, East Sussex (01323 766265).
Directions: A22 to Polegate, A27 to Stone Cross, right onto B32104 to Langney Shopping Centre, then left and first right. One mile from Pevensey & Westham (BR). Buses from Eastbourne.
Seats: **Cover:** 1,000 **Capacity:** 2,500 **Floodlights:** Yes **Club Shop:** Yes
Programme: Yes **Editor:** Mike Spooner (01323 461003)
Colours: All red **Change:** Sky & navy/navy
Sponsors: Nobo Group Plc. **Nickname:** None **Founded:** 1966
Previous League: Eastbourne & Hastings **Midweek Matchday:** Tuesday
Previous Grounds: Princes Park, Wartling Rd, Eastbourne/ Adjacent pitch.
Record Attendance: 1,000+ v Crystal Palace, f'light opener 90-91.
Clubhouse: Open every evening & lunchtime with adjoining sports hall, board room, matchday tea bar.
Club Record Goalscorer: Nigel 146 **Club Record Appearances:** Steve Dell 386.
Honours: Sussex Co. Lg R-up 91-92 (Div 2 87-88, Lg Cup 89-90, Div 3 86-87, Div 3 Cup 86-87, 5-aside comp. 1990), Sussex I'mediate Cup 85-86, Eastbourne Challenge Cup 85-86 86-87.

LITTLEHAMPTON TOWN

President: Ian Cunningham **Chairman:** Ian Cunningham **Manager:** Carl Stabler
Secretary: John Savage, 66 Nelson Road, Worthing. BN12 6EN. (01903 502850)
Ground: The Sportsfield, St Flora's Road, Littlehampton (01903 713944)
Directions: 10 minutes walk from Littlehampton station (BR) - turn left along Terminus Rd, continue through High Street and Church Rd to junction with St Flora's Rd (left).
Seats: 260 **Cover:** 260 **Capacity:** 4,000 **Floodlights:** Yes **Founded:** 1894
Colours: Gold/black/black. **Change:** Blue/white/white **Nickname:** Marigolds
Programme Editor: M Bennett (01903 785371) **Midweek Matches:** Tuesday
Record Gate: 4,000 v Northampton, FA Cup 1st Rd Proper 90-91
Clubhouse: Sportsman (Private Club). Separate board room & tea bar.
Honours: FA Vase SF 90-91, FA Cup 1st Rd 90-91, Sussex Co. Lg 58-59(jt with Shoreham) 75-77 84-85 90-91 96-97, Sussex Snr Cup 73-74.

Broadbridge Heath Photo: Roger Turner

Eastbourne United's keeper Alex Burns makes a great save to thwart East Preston's Marco Ceccarelli.
Photo: Graham Cotterill

PAGHAM

Chairman: Graham Peach **Vice-Chairman:** A Skeites **President:** A Peirce
Secretary: Alan Seal, 6 Greenlea Ave, Pagham, West Sussex PO21 3LH (01243 262944 Mobile: 0850 707932)
Manager/Coach: Graham Peach **Asst Manager:** S Booker **Press Officer:** Ken Randall (01243 555415)
Ground: Nyetimber Lane, Pagham, West Sussex (0243 266112).
Directions: Turn off A27 Chichester by-pass (signposted A259 Pagham). Ground in village of Nyetimber. Three miles from Bognor (BR). Buses 260 & 240.
Seats: 200 **Cover:** 200 **Capacity:** 2,000 **Floodlights:** Yes **Founded:** 1903
Colours: White/black/black **Change colours:** Yellow/green **Nickname:** Lions.
Midweek Matchday: Tuesday **Reserve's League:** Unijet Sussex Co. Reserve Div.
Programme: 12 pages, 50p **Editor:** Secretary **Club Shop:** No.
Record Gate: 1,200 v Bognor, 1971. **Sponsors:** City Saes Centre
Previous Leagues: Chichester 1903-50/ West Sussex 50-69.
Clubhouse: Bar open matchdays and some evenings. Hot food, pool, darts, satellite TV. Tea bar.
Club Record Scorer: Mark Vickers/ R Deluca.
Record win: 10-1 v Seaford Town (A), Sussex County League Division Two, 1970.
Record defeat: 0-7 v Newport IOW (H), FA Amateur Cup, mid-1970s.
Honours: Sussex Co. Lg R-up 80-81 87-88 88-89 92-93 (Div 2 78-79 86-87, Lg Cup 88-89, Div 2 Cup 71-72 85-86, Res. Sect. West 80-81, Res Section Cup 77-78 80-81 87-88 88-89 90-91 96-97; Sussex F'lit Cup R-up 88-89; Sussex RUR Charity Cup 88-89 (R-up 93-94); West Sussex Lg 65-66 68-69 69-70; Malcolm Simmonds Cup 67-68; Sussex I'mediate Cup 66-67.

PORTFIELD

President: S Kenny **Chairman:** Terry Rustell **Manager:** Richie Reynolds
Secretary: Gary Rustell, 102 Churchwood Drive, Tangmere, Nr Chichester, West Sussex PO20 6GB (01243 537978)
Ground: Church Road, Portfield, Chichester, West Sussex PO19 4HN (01243 779875)
Directions: A27 from Arundel to Chichester, take road to signposted city centre then 1st left (Church Rd) after supermarket r'bout. 1 mile from Chichester (BR).
Seats: 60 **Cover:** 200 **Capacity:** 2,000 **Floodlights:** Yes **Club Shop:** Badges
Programme: Yes **Editor:** TBA **Admission:** £2.00 & £1
Colours: Amber/black/amber. **Change colours:** All Blue
Sponsors: Swinton **Founded:** 1896 **Nickname:** Field.
Midweek Matchday: Tuesday **Record Attendance:** Unknown **Previous League:** West Sussex.
Clubhouse: 2 bars, pool, snooker, seating for 100, dance floor, darts, and tea bar selling hot & cold food.
Honours: Sussex Co. Lg Div 2 72-73 83-84 91-92 (Div 2 Cup 70-71 72-73, Res Sect Prem Lge 94-95, Cup 91-92), W Sussex Lg 46-47 48-49 (Malcolm Simmonds Cup 46-47), Sussex Jnr Cup 45-46, Benevolent Cup 46-47.

REDHILL

Chairman: Nick Creasey **Vice-Chairman:** Alan Thurlbeck **President:** Malcolm Chatfield
Secretary: Neil Hoad, 2b Earlswood Rd, Redhill, Surrey RH1 6HE (01737 213847).
Manager: Peter Burdett. **Asst Manager:** Dave Gellatley. **Coach:** Ricky Kidd
Ground: Kiln Brow, Three Arch Road, Redhill, Surrey (01737 762129).
Directions: On left hand side of A23, two and a half miles south of Redhill.
Seats: 150 **Cover:** 150 **Capacity:** 2,000 **Floodlights:** Yes **Club Shop:** Yes
Programme: 36 pages, 50p **Editor:** Neil Hoap **Press Officer:** Tim Reynolds
Colours: Red & white stripes/red/red. **Change colours:** White/black.
Sponsors: McDonalds (Redhill) **Nickname:** Reds/Lobsters **Founded:** 1894
Midweek matchday: Tuesday. **Reserve League:** Unijet Sussex Co.Lg.
Record Attendance: 1,200 v Crystal Palace & All Star XI, Brian Medlicott Testimonial 1989
Record win: 9-0; v Crown & Manor (H), London Spartan League 3/10/87; v Little Common Albion (H), Sussex County League Division Two 25/9/93.
Record defeat: 1-7 v Peacehaven & Telscombe (H), Sussex County League Cup 9/2/93.
Previous Leagues: E & W Surrey/ Spartan 09-10/ Southern Sub/ London 21-23/ Athenian 23-84/ Spartan 84-88.
Previous Grounds: Memorial Sports Ground, London Road 1894-1986.
Clubhouse: Social club, bar, canteen, board room, club shop, tanoy, toilets.
Club Record Goalscorer: Steve Turner 119 **Club Record appearances:** Brian Medlicott 766.
Honours: FA Amtr Cup SF 25-25, FA Cup 1st Rd 57-58, Athenian Lg 24-25 83-84 (Lg Cup 69-70 70-71),East & West Surrey Lg. 1902-03,Southern Suburban Senior West Lg. 1902-03,, Surrey Snr Cup 28-29 65-66 , Gilbert Rice F'lit Cup 80-81, Sussex County Lg Div 2 Cup 91-92, Southern Co's Comb. Cup 90-91.

Portfield FC *Photo: Eric Marsh*

RINGMER

President: Sir G Christie **Chairman:** Richard Soan
Secretary: Chris Christoff, 17 Babylon Way, Ratton, Eastbourne, (01323 501618)
Manager: Gary Allen. **Press Officer:** Alan Harper (01323 764263)
Ground: Caburn Ground, Anchor Field, Ringmer (01273 812738).
Directions: From Lewes road turn into Springett Avenue opposite Ringmer village green. Anchor Field first left. Three miles from Lewes (BR).
Seats: 100 **Cover:** Yes **Capacity:** 1,000 **Floodlights:** Yes **Founded:** 1906.
Colours: Sky & navy/navy/navy **Change colours:** All yellow **Nickname:** None
Programme: Yes **Editor:** Martin BUrke (01797 260260). **Admission:** £2.50
Previous League: Brighton **Record Gate:** 1,200 in FA Cup **Midweek Matchday:** Tuesday
Clubhouse: 2 bars, function room, boardroom, tea bar.
Honours: FA Cup 1st Rd Proper 70-71; Sussex Co. Lg 70-71, Div 2 68-69, Invit Cup 66-67; Res. Sect. East 79-80 80-81 (R-up 89-90), Yth Section 87-88, Yth Section East 87-88; Sussex Snr Cup 72-73 (R-up 80-81); Sussex Jnr Cup 25-26; Sussex Express Sn Charity Cup 94-95.

SALTDEAN UNITED

Chairman: Mike Walker **Vice Chairman:** Rod Flavell **President:** Jim Bower
Secretary: Iain Fielding, 40 Rowan Way, Rottingdean, Brighton BN2 7FP (01273 304995).
Manager: Tommy Hamilton **Asst Manager:** Mark Hammond **Physio:** Keith Gray
Ground: Hill Park, Combe Vale, Saltdean, Brighton (01273 309898).
Directions: A259 coast road east from Brighton to Saltdean Lido, left into Arundel Drive West, and Saltdean Vale to bridle path at beginning of Combe Vale. Club 200yds along track.
Seats: 50 **Cover:** Yes **Capacity:** 2,000 **Floodlights:** Yes **Club Shop:**
Programme: Yes **Editor:** Bob Thomas (01273 309898) **Press Officer:** Julian Appleton.
Colours: Red & black/black/black **Change colours:** Blue & yellow
Sponsors: Marat **Nickname:** Tigers **Founded:** 1966.
Record Attendance: 250 **Previous League:** Brighton Hove & Dist.
Clubhouse: Licensed bar, lounge, juke box, video games, board room, tea bar. Pool table.
Honours: Sussex Co. Lg Div 3 88-89, Div 2 95-96.

SELSEY

Chairman: Roger Slade **Manager:** John Davies/Dave Kew **President:** Roy Glew
Secretary: Denny Lee, 29 Malthouse Cottages, West Wittering, Chichester, W Sussex PO20 8QJ (01243 513788)
Ground: High Street Ground, Selsey, Chichester, West Sussex (01243 603420)
Directions: Through Selsey High Street to fire station. Take turning into car park alongside the station. Entrance is in the far corner. Regular buses from Chichester.
Seats: 50 **Cover:** Yes **Capacity:** 2,250 **Floodlights:** Yes **Founded:** 1923
Colours: Blue/white/blue **Change colours:** White/red/red **Nickname:** Blues
Programme Editor: Mrs D Hayers (0243 604013) **Press Officer:** Mr P Emms.
Record Gate: 750-800 v Chichester or Portfield, 50's **Midweek Matchday:** Wednesday
Sponsors: Allslade Welding & Fabrications Ltd **Previous Leagues:** Chichester & Dist./ West Sussex.
Clubhouse: Bar, hospitality room, lounge, toilets, kitchen.
Honours: Sussex Co. Lg R-up 89-90 (Div 2 63-64 75-76 (R-up 86-87), Div 2 Cup 86-87 (R-up 84-85), Div 2 Invitation Cup 63-64, Sussex 5-aside 88-89), Sussex Snr Cup R-up 63-64, Sussex I'mediate Cup 58-59, Sussex Jnr Cup(Reserves) 76-77, West Sussex Lg 54-55 55-56 57-58 58-59 60-61 (Malcolm Simmonds Cup 55-56 56-57 57-58 58-59).

Barton Rover's keeper Stuart Smith in command against Hassocks in a FA Cup Preliminary Round
Photo: Francis Short

Littlehampton Town's Clinton Moore scores in his sides win over Southen Manor in a FA Cup Preliminary Round
Photo: Dennis Nicholson

SHOREHAM

President: Alf Bloom **Chairman:** John Bell.
Secretary: Mrs Anne Harper, 66 Willow Crescent, Worthing. BN13 2SX (01903 267672).
Manager: John Prees **Press Officer:** Michael Wenham (01273 596009).
Ground: Middle Road, Shoreham-by-Sea, West Sussex (01273 454261).
Directions: Half mile from Shoreham-by-Sea (BR) - east across level crossing, up Dolphin Road, ground 150yds on right. Or, A27 to Shoreham. At Southlands Hospital turn left down Hammy Lane, left at end, ground opposite.
Seats: 20 **Cover:** 1 stand **Capacity:** 1,500 **Floodlights:** Yes **Founded:** 1892
Colours: Blue/white/blue. **Change colours:** Red & white **Nickname:** Musselmen
Programme: Yes **Editor:** Michael Wenham **Record Gate:** 1,342 v Wimbledon (f/lt opening 86)
Previous League: West Sussex **Midweek Matchday:** Wednesday **Sponsors:** Len German Wholesalers.
Previous Ground: Buckingham Park (pre-1970)
Clubhouse: Seats 70. Bar, pool, darts, tea bar.
Honours: Sussex Co. Lg 51-53 77-78 (R-up 34-35, Div 2 61-62 76-77 84-85 93-94, Div 2 Cup 74-75 82-83, Invitation Cup 57-58), Sussex Snr Cup 01-02 05-06, Sussex F'lit Cup R-up 89-90, Sussex RUR Charity Cup 02-03 05-06, Vernon Wentworth Cup 86-87.

WHITEHAWK

President: Ron Wiltshire **Chairman/Comm Mgr:** Ken Powell **Match Sec:** Fred Moore
Secretary: John Rosenblatt, 25 Arundel Street, Brighton BN2 5TH (01273 680322).
Manager: Paul Hubbard **Asst Manager:** Vic Standen **Coach:** Paul Hubbard.
Ground: The Enclosed Ground, East Brighton Park (01273 609736).
Directions: Follow Brighton seafront road towards Newhaven, turn inland (Arundel Road) opposite Marina, 3rd right into Roedean Road, 1st left into Wilson Avenue. Three miles from Brighton (BR); take Newhaven, Eastbourne or Saltdean bus to Marina, then as above.
Seats: None **Cover:** 500 **Capacity:** 3,000 **Floodlights:** Yes **Founded:** 1945
Colours: All red **Change colours:** All blue **Nickname:** Hawks
Programme: £2 with admission **Editor:** Tony Kelly (0273 698203) **Midweek Matchday:** Wednesday
Previous League: Brighton Hove & Dist. **Sponsors:** Brighton Co-operative Society.
Previous Grounds: None
Previous Name: Whitehawk & Manor Farm Old Boys (until 1958).
Record Gate: 2,100 v Bognor Regis Town, FA Cup 4th Qualifying Rd replay 88-89.
Clubhouse: Licensed bar, pool, darts. Board room. Tea bar.
Club record scorer: Billy Ford **Club record appearances:** Ken Powell 1,103.
Honours: Sussex Co. Lg 61-62 63-64 83-84 (Div 2 67-68 80-81, Lg Cup 82-83 93-94, Invitation Cup 60-61 69-70, Div 2 Cup 80-81), Sussex Snr Cup 50-51 61-62, Sussex RUR Charity Cup 54-55 58-59 90-91, Sussex I'mediate Cup 49-50, Sussex Jnr Cup 48-49 51-52, Brighton Charity Cup 51-52 59-60 61-62 82-83 87-88 88-89, Worthing Charity Cup 82-83, FA Vase 5th Rd 93-94.

WICK

Chairman: Norman Cairns. **Vice-Chairman:** J Burnett **President:** B Wadsworth
Secretary: Paul Beard, 2 Van Gogh Place, North Bersted, Bognor Regis, West Sussex PO22 9BG (01243 822063).
Manager: Jimmy Quinn. **Asst Manager:** Jim Thompson
Ground: Crabtree Park, Coomes Way, Wick, Littlehampton, West Sussex (01903 713535).
Directions: A27 to Crossbush, left at traffic lights signed Littlehampton, after 1 mile cross level crossing, turn left into Coombes Way next to Locomotive PH - ground at end. One and a half miles from Littlehampton (BR).
Seats: 50 **Cover:** 200 **Capacity:** 2,000 **Floodlights:** Yes **Founded:** 1892
Programme: Yes **Editor/Press Officer:** Thomas Cairns (01903 501857)
Colours: Red & black/black/black **Change colours:** All white. **Nickname:** Wickers
Midweek Matchedays: Tuesday **Reserve League:** Unijet Sussex Co. Reserve Div.
Sponsors: Swandean **Record Attendance:** 900. **Previous League:** West Sussex
Prev. Grounds: Southfields Rec.
Clubhouse: First floor. Capacity 120. Tea bar.
Honours: Sussex Snr Cup 92-93; Sussex Co. Lg 89-90 93-94, Lg Cup 87-88 96-97 (R-up 93-94 94-95), Div 2 81-82 85-86, Div 2 Cup R-up 81-82; Norman Wingate Tphy 88-89 90-91, Res. Sect West 87-88 90-91 94-95; Sussex 5-aside R-up 85-86; Sussex RUR Charity Cup 89-90 97-98; Gilbert Rice F'lit Cup R-up 80-81 81-82; Sussex Jnr Cup 59-60; Brighton Charity Cup 85-86; Sussex Floodlit Cop R-Up 94-95.

DIVISION TWO CLUBS 1998-99

ARUNDEL

Chairman: Peter Wells **Vice Chairman:** S Brennan.
Secretary: Doug Feest, 342 Goring Road, Worthing. BN12 4PD (01903 249276)
Manager: Mike Rowland
Ground: Mill Road, Arundel (01903 882548).
Directions: A27 from Worthing to Arundel over railway bridge to roundabout. Second exit into Queen Street to town centre, turn right over bridge. Car park leading to ground 100yards right.
Seats: 100 **Cover:** 200 **Capacity:** 2,200 **Floodlights:** 206 lux **Founded:** 1889
Colours: Red & white halves/white/red **Change colours:** Jade & black **Nickname:** Mulletts
Programme: 8 pages, free **Editor:** P Wells **Sponsors:** Warwick Davis (Kit), Mill Road Leisure Sports (Balls)
Record Gate: 2,200 v Chichester, League 67-68 **Midweek matchday:** Tuesday.
Previous Lge: West Sussex 1896-1975 **Reserves' Lge:** Sussex Co. Res Div (West)
Players progressing to Football League: John Templeman (Brighton & Hove Albion 1966).
Clubhouse: 2 bars, kitchen, toilets, telephone, pool, darts, Sky TV. Normal pub hours. No food.
Record Scorer: Paul J Bennett **Record appearances:** 537, Paul Bennett (goalkeeper).
97-98 - Captain: Jody Rowland **P.o.Y.:** Mark Frost
Honours: Sussex County Lg 57-58 58-59 86-87 (Lg Cup 86-87, Div 2 Cup 76-77, Reserve Section 78-79, Reserve Section Cup 78-79, Merit Table winners 80-81, Sussex Fives 1984 1987), Sussex RUR Charity Cup 68-69 72-73 78-79 79-80, Sussex Jnr Cup 07-08, West Sussex Lg (Reserves) 70-71 (Malcolm Simmonds Cup 70-71).

CRAWLEY DOWN VILLAGE

Chairman: Andrew Watkins **Manager:** Graham Standen, Alan Watson
Secretary: Stuart Frier, 30 Squires Close, Crawley Down, Surrey. RH10 4JQ (01342 714507 or 0181 667 2752 (B)).
Ground: The Haven Sportsfield, Hophurst Lane, Crawley Down. (01342 717140)
Directions: From B2028, follow signpost for village to War Memorial, turn left into Hophurst Lane, ground 100 yards on left. From A22, Felbridge, left into Crawley Down Road, ground 2 miles uphill on right.
Colours: All red

CROWBOROUGH ATHLETIC

President: Mr Peter Taylor **Chairman:** Barry J Sykes
Secretary: David Mackellow, 38 Eridge Drive, Crowborough,TN6 2TJ (01892 653122)
Manager: Tony Atkins. **Press Officer:** Peter Crisp (01892 655470).
Ground: Alderbrook Recreation Ground, Fermor Road, Crowborough (01892 661893).
Directions: Turn east off A26 at Crowborough. Cross traffic lights, through High Street, right into Croft Rd, continue into Whitehall Rd and Fermor Rd, Alderbrook is second right after mini-r'bout.
Seats: None **Cover:** 200 **Capacity:** 1,000 **Floodlights:** Yes. **Founded:** 1894
Colours: Blue & white/blue/blue **Change colours:** All red. **Nickname:** Crows.
Programme Editor: Bert Collick (01892 655565) **Sponsors:** Blackden Enterprises Ltd.
Previous League: Brighton **Midweek Matchday:** Tuesday
Record Gate: 439 v Stamco, Sussex County League Division Two 1/5/93.
Clubhouse: Bar facilities & tea bar on matchdays
Honours: Sussex Co. Lg Div 1 92-93 (Div 2 Cup 77-78, Div 3 R-up), Sussex Intermediate Cup 86-87.

EAST GRINSTEAD TOWN

Chairman: Paul O'Donnell **Vice-Chairman:** **President:** Colin Dixon
Secretary: How Roberts, 37 Parham Road, Ifield, Crawley, West Sussex RH11 0ET (01293 526805)
Manager: Kevin Moyse **Gen Manager:** **Physio:** Janette Brown
Ground: East Court, East Grinstead (01342 325885)
Directions: A264 Tunbridge Wells road (Moat Road) until mini-r'bout at bottom of Blackwell Hollow, turn immediately right by club sign then 1st left, ground 200yds down lane past rifle club on right.
Seats: None **Cover:** 400 **Capacity:** 3,000 **Floodlights:** Yes **Club Shop:** No
Programme: 36 pages, 50p **Editor/Press Officer:** Bruce Talbot (01293 543809).
Colours: Gold/black/black **Change colours:** Navy & L/blue
Sponsors: Rydon Group. **Nickname:** Wasps **Founded:** 1890
Midweek Matchday: Tuesday. **Reserves League:** Sussex County Reserve Div East
Record Attendance: 2,006 v Lancing, FA Amateur Cup 8/11/48
Previous Leagues: Mid-Sussex 1900-15 35-37/ Sussex County 20-32/ Southern Amateur League 32-35.
Players progressing to Football League: None
Clubhouse: Open 1.30-10.30 matchdays (6-11 midweek matches). Available for hire. Darts, pool, satellite TV. Hot food available Saturdays matcdays, hot snacks rolls etc available at midweek matches.
Club record appearances: Guy Hill in 19 seasons - 1977-94.
Honours: Sussex RUR Charity Cup (R-up 74-75); Sussex Co. Lg Invitation Cup 51-52; Sussex Jnr Cup (jointly) 07-08; Sussex Youth Cup 86-87; Southern Amtr Lg Snr Div 3 31-32; Mid-Sussex Lg(6),Lg Cup(7); Brighton Lg(3),Lg Cup(3);

LANCING

Chairman: John Brown **President:** R G Steele **Match Sec:** Mike Peters
Secretary: J Chisnall, 25 Amberley Court, Freshbrook Road, Lancing, West Sussex BN15 8DS (01903 763913)
Manager: Frank Phythian **Physio:** Peter Towell.
Ground: Culver Road, Lancing, West Sussex (01903 764398).
Directions: From A27 turn south at Lancing Manor r'about into Grinstead Lane, 3rd turning on right North Farm Rd. Turn left then immed. right into Culver Rd. From railway station take 3rd turning on left heading north.
Seats: 350 **Cover:** 350 **Capacity:** 2,400 **Floodlights:** Yes **Club Shop:**
Programme: Yes **Editor/Press Officer:** Len Ralph (01903 763913)
Colours: Yellow/blue/yellow **Change colours:** All red
Sponsors: Gold Arts **Nickname:** Yellows **Founded:** 1941
Midweek Matches: Wednesday **Previous - League:** Brighton Hove & Dist. **Name:** Lancing Athletic **Ground:** Croshaw Rec, Sompting.
Record Attendance: 2,591 v Tooting, FA Amtr Cup 22/11/47. At Culver Road: 2,340 v Worthing 25/10/52.
Clubhouse: Open matchdays & training nights. Sep tea bar.
97-98 - Captain: Jim Downey **Top Scorer:** Dale Brunton (25) **P.o.Y.:** Malcom Gammon
Honours: Sussex Co. Lg R-up 49-50 64-65 (Div 2 57-58 69-70 (R-up 82-83), Div 2 Cup 81-82 92-93, Invitation Cup), Sussex RUR Charity Cup 65-66, Brighton Lg 46-47 47-48, Sussex Intermediate Cup 46-47, Brighton Charity Cup 83-84 84-85 86-87.

LINGFIELD

Secretary: Ian Tomsett, 8 Orchard Cottage, St Piers Lane, Lingfield, Surrey. RH7 6PN. (01342 835089)
Ground: Godstone Road, Lingfield, Surrey. (01342 834269).
Directions: A22, 4 miles north of E Grinstead, to Mormon Temple r'about, take exit Lingfield (B2028) Newchapel Rd. for 1 1/2 miles. Left at T junction into Godstone Rd. (B2029) & ground 1/2 mile on left.
Manager: Ali Rennie **Colours:** Red & yellow/black/yellow

MILE OAK

Chairman: Geoff Kerly **President:** D Bean **Manager:** Tony Gratwicke
Secretary: Colin Brown, 19 The Crescent, Southwick, West Sussex BN42 4LB (01273 591346).
Ground: Mile Oak Recreation Ground, Graham Avenue, Mile Oak (01273 423854)
Directions: From A27 take Mile Oak Road or Locks Hill & Valley Road to Chalky Road, ground 500yds on right along Graham Avenue which runs up valley from centre of Chalky Road.
Seats: None **Cover:** Yes **Capacity:** **Floodlights:** Yes. **Founded:** 1960
Colours: Tangerine/black/tangerine **Change colours:** All white **Nickname:** The Oak
Programme: Yes **Editor:** C Tew (01273 416036) **Admission:** £1.50
Previous Leagues: Southern Counties Combination/ Brighton Hove & District
Previous Ground: Victoria Rec., Portslade.
Record Gate: 186 **Midweek Matchday:** Tuesday
Clubhouse: Mile Oak Pavillion; Hall and tea bar.
Honours: Sussex Co.Lg.Div 2 Champions, Div 3 R-up 91-92 (Div 2 Cup R-up 92-93), Southern Counties Combination 86-87, Brighton Hove & District Lg 80-81, Vernon Wentworth Cup 85-86, Sussex Intermediate Cup R-up 88-89.

NEWHAVEN

Chairman: Mick Godden **Manager:** Martin Langley
Secretary: Frank D Dixon, 39 Southdown Avenue, Peacehaven, East Sussex BN10 8RX (01273 585514).
Ground: Fort Road, Newhaven, East Sussex (01273 513940).
Directions: A275 from Lewes, or A259 coast rd, to Newhaven 1-way system. 1 mile from Newhaven Town (BR).
Seats: 50 **Cover:** Yes **Capacity:** 4,000 **Floodlights:** Yes **Founded:** 1887
Colours: Red & amber/red/red. **Change colours:** Yellow/green **Nickname:** Dockers
Programme: Yes **Editor:** S.Cox. **Admission:** £1.50
Previous Leagues: None (founder members of SCFL) **Record Gate:** 3,000
Previous Name: Newhaven Town.
Previous Ground: None (Lewes FC temporarily 90-91)
Midweek Matchday: Tuesday **Clubhouse:** Being redeveloped **Sponsors:** Long Dis Cabs.
Honours: Sussex County Lg 53-54 (Div 2 71-72 90-91, Invitation Cup 48-49, Lg Cup R-up 92-93, Reserve Section East R-up 92-93), Sussex Snr Cup R-up 53-54, Sussex RUR Charity Cup 93-94.

Sidley United

Photo: Roger Turne

Oakwood

Photo: Roger Turne

Shinewater Association

Photo: Roger Turne

OAKWOOD

Chairman: Alf Bridges
Secretary: Gerry Martin, Singlegate, Tinsley Green, Crawley RH10 3NS (01293 882400).
Manager: Bryn Marshall **Physio:** Ms S Widy **Press Officer:** Simon Milham
Ground: Tinsley Lane, Three Bridges, Crawley, West Sussex (01293 515742).
Directions: From A23 to Gatwick, take 1st set of lights into Manor Royal, pass next lights, over r'bout to warehouse marked Canon, turn right signposted Oakwood. Last clubhouse down lane. Two miles north of Three Bridges (BR).
Seats: 20 **Cover:** Yes **Capacity:** 3,000 **Floodlights:** Yes **Founded:** 1966
Colours: Red & black/black/black **Change colours:** Blue/black/black **Nickname:** Oaks
Programme: 24 pages **Editor:** Simon Milham (01293 615043) **Club Shop:** Yes
Previous Lgs: Crawley & Dist., Southern Co's Comb. **Previous Ground:** Park pitches.
Record Gate: 367 **Midweek Matchday:** Tuesday
Sponsors: Linden Plc. **Reserve's League:** Sussex County Reserve section.
Clubhouse: Pool tables, multidart boards, large bar area. Board room & tea bar.
Record appearances: Peter Brackpool
Honours: Sussex Snr Cup R-up 92-93, Sussex Co. Lg Div 2 R-up 89-90 (Div 2 Cup 89-90, Div 3 84-85), Southern Comb. Cup 83-84.

PEACEHAVEN & TELSCOMBE

Chairman: Jim Edwards **Manager:** Gerry Green **Match Sec:** Fred Parris
Secretary: Mrs Margaret Edwards, 87 Ambleside Ave, Peacehaven, E. Sussex BN10 7LN (01273 583022)
Ground: Piddinghoe Avenue, Peacehaven, East Sussex (01273 582471).
Directions: Arriving from Brighton on A259, cross r'bout and Piddinghoe Avenue is next left after 2nd set of lights - ground at end. From Newhaven Piddinghoe Avenue is first right after first set of lights. Three miles from Newhaven (BR). Peacehaven is served by Brighton to Newhaven and Eastbourne buses.
Seats: None **Cover:** 250 **Capacity:** 3,000 **Floodlights:** Yes **Founded:** 1923
Programme: Yes **Editor:** Secretary **Press Officer:** Secretary
Colours: All white **Change colours:** All sky
Sponsors: Anchor Garage **Nickname:** The Tye **Midweek Matches:** Wednesday
Record Gate: 1,420 v Littlehampton, Lge 91 **Previous Leagues:** Lewes/ Brighton
Clubhouse: Bar open evenings and weekends, pool darts, hot and cold food available. Tea bar.
Honours: Sussex Co. Lg 78-79 81-82 82-83 91-92 92-93 94-95 95-96 (R-up 77-78 80-81 90-91, Lg Cup 91-92 92-93, Div 2 R-up 75-76, Div 2 Cup 75-76, Norman Wingate Tphy 82-83 91-92 92-93, Hayden Tphy 82-83 92-93, Div 2 Invitation Cup 69-70, Res. Sect. 83-84 92-93 (R-up 91-92), Res Sect. Cup 81-82 83-84 85-86 86-87 87-88, Res Sect East R-up 90-91), Sussex Snr Cup R-up 81-82 92-93, Sussex RUR Charity Cup 77-78 81-82 92-93 (R-up 80-81 89-90 90-91 94-95 95-96), Brighton Charity Cup 91-92 92-93 93-94, Vernon Wentworth 91-92 92-93, FA Cup 4th Qual. Rd 90-91, FA Vase 5th Rd 92-93, Qtr Fin 95-96.

SHINEWATER ASSOCIATION

Chairman: John Pinyoun **Manager:** Alan Walsh
Secretary: Brian Dowling, 79 Harebeating Drive, Hailsham BN27 1JE (01323 442488)
Ground: Shinewater Lane (01323 765880)
Directions: A27, take B2104 to Eastbourne. At Stone Cross go under railway bridge, 1st right into Larkspur Drive, 1st left into Milfoil Drive, 3rd left into Shinewater Lane
Colours: Navy & sky/navy/navy

SIDLESHAM

Chairman: Roy Parker **Manager:** Petyer Cleverley
Secretary: Pete Turner, 64 Hawthorn Road, Bognor Regis, West Sussex PO21 2DD (01243 822860)
Ground: Sidlesham Recreation Ground, (01243 641538)
Directions: Signposted Hunston/Selsey B2145 from roundabout travel towards Selsey for 4 miles, ground on right between houses
Colours: Green & yellow/green/green

SIDLEY UNITED

President: Tibby Adams **Chairman:** Bryn Sayers **Manager:** Dickie Day
Secretary: Rob Green, 4 Robin Hill, Little Common, Bexhill-on-Sea, TN39 4QS (01424 846220)
Ground: Gullivers Sports Ground, Glovers Lane, Sidley, Bexhill-on-Sea (01424 217078).
Directions: From Brighton on A259 to Bexhill bypass traffic lights, left into London Road, continue into Sidley, right into Glovers Lane and 1st left into North Road. One mile from Bexhill (BR).
Seats: None **Cover:** 150 **Capacity:** 1,500 **Floodlights:** No **Founded:** 1906
Colours: Navy & sky/navy/navy & sky **Change colours:** All red **Nickname:** Blues
Programme: Yes **Editor:** Peter Snow **Sponsors:** J Burke
Previous Leagues: East Sussex/ Hastings & District
Record Attendance: 1,300 in 1959 **Midweek Matchday:** Tues/ Weds
Clubhouse: Large bar area & function room. Tea bar.
Honours: Suss. Co. Lg Div 2 58-59 64-65 (Div 2 Invit. Cup 57-58), Suss. I'mediate Cup 47-48, Suss. Jnr Cup 24-25.

SOUTHWICK

Chairman: Roy Pollard **Vice-Chairman:** Dave Cook **President:** Dr D W Gordon.
Secretary: Peter Hallett, 10 Hawkins Close, Shoreham-by-Sea, West Sussex BN43 6TL (01273 700474)
Manager: John Dedman **Asst Manager:** Dennis Nicholl **Coach:** Paul Croft
Ground: Old Barn Way, off Manor Hall Way, Southwick, Brighton BN43 4NT (01273 701010).
Directions: Five minutes walk from either Fishergate or Southwick BR stations. By A27 from Brighton take 1st left after 'Southwick' sign to Leisure Centre. Ground adjacent.
Seats: 220 **Cover:** 1,220 **Capacity:** 3,500 **Floodlights:** Yes
Programme: Yes **Editor/Press Officer:** Paul Symes (01273 594142).
Colours: Red & black stripes/black/red **Change Colours:** White/black/white
Sponsors: Guildcare Nursing Homes **Nickname:** Wickers **Founded:** 1882
Midweek matchday: Tuesday **Record Attendance:** 3,200 v Showbiz side 1971
Reserve League: Sussex Co. Res Div **Best FA Cup season:** 1st Rd Prop 74-75 (lost 0-5 Bournemouth)
Best FA Amtr Cup season: 3rd 28-29 **Best FA Vase season:** 3rd Rd 79-80 85-86
Previous Leagues: West Sussex 1896-1920/ Sussex County 20-52 54-84/ Metropolitan 52-54/ Combined
Previous Grounds: Croft Avenue/ The Green/ Oldfield Crescent.
Players progressing to Football League: Charles & William Buttenshaw (Luton 1948).
Clubhouse: Weekdays noon-3 & 6-11pm, all day Saturday, normal hrs Sunday. Members bar & boardroom with bar. Snacks on matchdays from tea bar.
Honours: Isthmian Lg Div 2 Sth 85-86, Sus. Co. Lg 25-26 27-28 29-30 47-48 68-69 74-75 (R-up(9) 23-24 28-29 36-37 39-40 70-71 76-77 78-80 82-83, Lg Cup 77-78, Div 1 Invit. Cup 65-66, Div 2 R-up 65-66), Combined Co's Lg R-up 84-85, Sus. Snr Cup 1896-97 1910-11 12-13 24-25 27-28 29-30 30-31 36-37 47-48 67-68, Sus. RUR Charity Cup(10) 1896-97 08-09 10-11 24-26 27-30 37-38 76-77, W. Sus. Lg 1896-97 97-98 1908-09 10-11, Sus. Jnr Cup 1891-92.

STORRINGTON

Secretary: Keith Dalmon, 4 End Cottages, Storrington Rd., Amberley. BN18 9LX. (01798 831887)
Ground: Recreation Ground, Storrington. (01903 745860).
Directions: Turn west on A283 (off A24). Ground opposite pond to west of village centre.
Manager: Malcolm MacMichael **Colours:** All blue.

THREE BRIDGES

President: Jim Steele **Chairman:** Alan Bell
Secretary: Martin Clarke, 18 Mannings Close, Pound Hill, Crawley RH10 3TX (01293 883726), (0585 662940 Mob).
Manager: Barry Hunt **Match Sec:** Secretary **Press Officer:** Alf Blackler
Ground: Jubilee Field, Three Bridges, Crawley, West Sussex (01293 442000)
Directions: From West Three Bridges station, turn second right into Three Bridges Road and first left 75 yds down, opposite the Plough Inn.
Seats: None **Cover:** 400 **Capacity:** 3,500 **Floodlights:** Yes **Founded:** 1901
Colours: Amber & black/black/black **Change colours:** Blue & white/blue/w**Nickname:** Bridges
Programme: Yes **Editor:** Andy West (01293 883163) **Sponsors:** Canon
Previous Lgs: Mid Sussex/ Redhill & District **Midweek Matchday:** Tuesday
Clubhouse: Bar, dance floor, pool, darts **Record Gate:** 2,000 v Horsham, 1948
Honours: Sussex Co. Lg R-up 85-86 87-88 88-89 (Div 2 54-55, Invitation Cup 70-71, Div 2 Invitation Cup 62-63), Sussex RUR Charity Cup 82-83.

WITHDEAN

Chairman: Phil Bond **President:** Graham Spicer **Manager:** Paul Norland
Secretary: Simon Pattenden, 37 Stanmer Road, Brighton. BN1 7JL. (H 01273 507128 B 01273 541102)
Ground: Withdean Stadium, off Valley Drive, Brighton (01273 542100)
Directions: Off main London - Brighton road.
Seats: 100. **Cover:** 1,000. **Capacity:** 10,000 **Floodlights:** No **Founded:** 1984.
Colours: Green & black/black/black **Change Colours:** All white **Club Shop:** No.
Programme Editor: Dave Bull **Previous Leagues:** Brighton Hove & District
Sponsors: Computer & Network Consultants Ltd. **Clubhouse:** Pub on ground
Honours: Sussex Co. Lg Div 3 92-93 (Div 3 Cup 91-92).

Three Bridges celebrate with Sussex County League Division Two Challenge Cup. *Photo: Roger Turner*

WORTHING UNITED

President: Ken Higson **Chairman:** Len Killpatrick
Secretary: Malcolm Gamlen, 1 Westbourne Ave., Worthing, West Sussex BN14 8DE (01903 263655).
Manager: Tony Elliot **Press Officer:** Brian Woolmer.
Ground: The Robert Albon Memorial Grd, Lyons Way, Worthing (01903 234466)
Directions: From west past Hill Barn roundabout to 2nd set of lights, turn left into Lyons Way. From east 1st set of lights at end of Sompting bypass turn right into Lyons Way
Seats: 100 **Cover:** 500 **Capacity:** 1,000 **Floodlights:** No **Founded:** 1988
Colours: Sky & white/navy/white **Change colours:** All white **Nickname:** None
Programme: Yes **Editor:** N Woolmer (0903 772698) **Sponsors:** Tinsley Robor.
Record Gate: 180 v Northwood, FA Vase 3rd Rd 91-92.
Previous Names: Wigmore Athletic (founded 1948) merged with Southdown in 1988.
Previous Grounds: Harrison Road, Worthing.
Clubhouse: Bar (capacity 80), refreshment facilities (tea bar).
Honours: *As Wigmore Athletic prior to 1988.* Sussex Co. Lg Challenge Cup 74-75 (Invitation Cup 59-60, Div 2 52-53, Div 2 Invitation Cup 59-60, Div 3 89-90, Reserve Section West 92-93, 5-aside comp. R-up 1993), Sussex Jnr Cup 49-50.

DIVISION THREE CLUBS

ANSTY RANGERS

Secretary: Tina Darbyshire, 6 Faulkners Way, Burgess Hill. RH15 8SB. (01444 233030)
Ground: Deaks Lane, Ansty (01444 454010) **Directions:** Take A272 for Ansty/Haywards Heath, to Ansty prior to mini r/about turn left into Deaks Lane.
Manager: **Colours:** Red & black/black/black

BEXHILL TOWN

Secretary: Mrs Leigh Quinn, 37 Colebrook Road, Bexhill-on-Sea. TN39 3PX (01424 214197).
Ground: The Polegrove, Brockley Rd, Bexhill-on-Sea, East Sussex (01424 220732) **Directions:** At Little Common r'bout take 3rd exit to Cooden Sea Rd, left into Cooden Drive for one and a half miles, Brockley Rd on the right. Three quarters of a mile from Bexhill Central (BR).
Colours: Green & white/white/white **Change colours:** Black & white

BUXTED

Secretary: Peter J Durrant, 'Haven', Station Road, Isfield. TN22 5XB. (01825 750449)
Ground: Buxted Recreation Ground, Buxted. (01825 763593) **Directions:** A272 to Buxted, 1st right, Framfield Rd., opposite Buxted Inn, ground 500 yds. on right.
Manager: Peter Coleman **Colours:** Red & Black/black/red & black.

FOREST

Secretary: Gill Hultquist, 117 Ifield Drive, Ifield. RH11 0EA. (01293 522846)
Ground: Roffey Sports & Social Club, Spooners Rd., Roffey. (01403 210221) **Directions:** Spooners Rd. is off the main Crawley road, 100 yds from the 'Star' PH, towards Crawley.
Manager: Russell Pentecost. **Colours:** Claret/blue/white.

FRANKLANDS VILLAGE

Secretary: Mrs Linsey Worsfold, 151a Franklands Village, Haywards Heath. RH16 3RF. (01444 416475)
Ground: Hardy Memorial Playing Field, Franklands Village. (01444 440138) **Directions:** A272 (Haywards H. to Uckfield). Left at Princess Royal Hosp. r'about. 2nd left & ground at rear of social club.
Manager: Chris Snelling **Colours:** All Royal blue

HAYWARDS HEATH TOWN

HURSTPIERPOINT

Secretary: Daniel Cleaveley, 10 St Christophers Road, Hurstpierpoint BN6 9UX (01273 835665)
Ground: Fairfield Recreation Ground, Cuckfield Road. ((01273 834783) **Directions:** At Hurstpierpoint crossroads, proceed north into Cuckfield Road (B2117) for 1km. Entrance to ground between houses nos. 158 & 160.
Manager: Steve Marchant. **Colours:** Blue & black/black/blue.

IFIELD

Secretary: Robert Anderson, 1 Old Orchards, Church Rd, Worth, Crawley. RH10 7QA. (01293 886215).
Ground: Ifield Sports Club, Ifield Green, Rusper Road. (01293 536569) **Directions:** From A23 Crawley by-pass going north, left at r'about signed Charlwood. Third left into Ifield Green, first right past Royal Oak (PH) into Rusper Rd.
Manager: Alan Wormull **Colours:** Red/black/red.

MIDHURST & EASEBOURNE

Secretary: Ted Dummer, 14 Nine Acres, June Lane, Midhurst, West Sussex GU29 9EP (01730 813887).
Ground: Rotherfield, Dodsley Lane, Easebourne, Midhurst, West Sussex (01730 816557) **Directions:** Ground one mile out of Midhurst on London Road (A286) opposite BP Garage. Ample car parking. Buses pass ground every hour.
Colours: All royal blue **Change colours:** Red/black/black

OVING SOCIAL CLUB

Secretary: Peter Hall, St Bruno, Prinsted Lane, Emsworth, Hants PO10 8HR (01243 372652)
Ground: Village Playing Fields, Highfield Lane, Oving, Nr Chichester **Directions:** Into Oving past the Gribble Inn, turn left into housing estate. Ground sign posted.
Manager: Paul Gilbert **Colours:** Black & white/white/white

ROYAL & SUN ALLIANCE

Secretary: Steve Jenkins, 33 Owlcastle Close, Horsham RH12 5YA (01403 256697)
457726)
Ground: Sunallon Sports Club, North Heath Lane, Horsham (01403 253814) **Directions:** Heading into Horsham on Warnham road, turn left at 1st lights, over mini-r/about to North Heath Lane, grd on left
Manager: Dix Roberts **Colours:** Yellow/blue/blue

ST. FRANCIS HOSPITAL

Secretary: Colin Mansbridge, 9 Pinehurst, Burgess Hill. RH15 0DG. (01444 244197)
Ground: St. Francis Hospital, Colwell Lane, Haywards Heath. (01444 441881) **Directions:** Enter through main entrance of Princess Royal Hospital on Lewes road, A272 Haywards Heath. Follow signs to Sports Complex.
Manager: Mark Leaney **Colours:** Green & white/white/green.

STEYNING TOWN

Secretary: Gina Barnes, 36 Shooting Fields, Steyning BN44 3RQ (01903 815387)
Ground: The Shooting Field, Steyning (01903 812228) **Directions:** Entering Steyning from west, take 1st left into High St, follow into Shooting Field estate, ground is 4th rurn left.
Manager: Alf Ford **Colours:** Red /white/red

UCKFIELD TOWN

Secretary: Craig Rome, Flat 3, 26 Newtown, Uckfield. TN22 5DD. (01825 764171)
Ground: Victoria Pleasure Grounds, Uckfield. (01825 769400) **Directions:** Take Eastbourne road (old A22) south of Uckfield town centre. Entrance to ground 1/2 mile on right (just after Police station).
Manager: George Nimmo **Colours:** Red/black/black.

WEALDEN

WESTFIELD

Secretary: Mrs Jenny Drinkwater, 28 Churchfields, Westfield TN35 4SN (01424 754032)
Ground: Parish Field. Westfield (01424 751011) **Directions:** Off A21 onto A28 Ashford Road.
Manager: Steve Booth **Colours:** Yellow & green/black/black

uhlsport
UNITED COUNTIES LEAGUE

FEEDER TO: DR MARTENS LEAGUE

FOUNDED 1895

Chairman: Geoff Paul

Hon. Secretary: R J Gamble, 8 Bostock Avenue, Northampton 01604 637766 (H)

Press Liaison Officer: J Biggs 01780 763048

The 1997-98 season was a particularly memorable one for Stamford and Higham Town, who ended the campaign as respective champions of the Premier and First Divisions.

Stamford retained their Premier Division title, only the second club to do so in 16 years, while Higham, five times runners-up in Division One in the nineties, at last made the breakthrough to land the championship and secure their first UCL honours in 75 years!

In the Premier Division Stewarts & Lloyds topped the table for three weeks or so before Ford Sports spent seven days in pole. On 22 September Stamford moved to the top, and they were never headed again - in complete contrast to their success twelve months before when they made a late run through the pack to win the title. Early in the campaign Stamford were a class apart, completing a half century of goals in just 13 games, their winning sequence including 6-0 away wins over Northampton Spencer and Spalding who were to finish in the next two places to them in the final table.

The likes of Desborough and St Neots were still in touch in mid-season but it was Stotfold who looked the main challengers to Stamford, who kicked off 1998 with some indifferent results after suffering their first home defeat against local rivals and tittle outsiders Mirrlees Blackstone on Boxing Day. Stamford exited three cup competitions in the early weeks of the new year, and also lost the services of star men Ian McInerney and Jason Bowler. The cup exits, with hindsight perhaps proved a blessing, while the return to fitness of Milton Graham after a lengthy absence kept Stamford on course for league honours. The former Football League star formed the league's most seasoned strike partnership with Mick Bennett, but their experience more than compensated for the duo's lack of pace. With Steve Kuhne scoring goals galore from midfield, the chasing pack had their work cut out to stay with Stamford.

Ford Sports and St Neots both faded out of contention, Desborough dropped too many points at home, while Stotfold's challenge faltered after Wes Byrne departed to Cambridge City. He later returned to Roker, but the Eagles never seemed quite the same once manager Ian Allinson announced his decision to leave Roker at the end of the campaign. The spring brought new challengers for honours - Northampton Spencer's combination of youth and experience gelled after a poor start. The Millers lost their first four games and eight of their first fourteen, but their next 21 matches brought 58 points, enabling Spencer to emerge as the main challengers to the reigning champions. Goalscoring midfielder Carl Holmes, Stuart Smeathers and Sammy Dale, all enjoying their first full seasons of Premier Division football, proved to be some of the brightest young talents around the league while the experience of the likes of Tim Agutter and Peter Green brought the best out of their team mates. Defeat at Stamford on Easter Saturday all but killed off Spencer's challenge, and two days later the Daniels' venerable strikeforce of Graham and Bennett clinched Stamford's title with a 2-0 win across town at Mirrlees. The spring had seen Stamford's Wothorpe Road ground change beyond recognition, enabling the Daniels to move up to Dr Martens League football at season's end.

As for Spencer, they still had work to do to get second as Spalding mounted a late bid for a second successive set of runners-up medals, a late season win at their final match at home to Boston to take second, they came back from a goal down to take the necessary points. Desborough enjoyed a good season to finish fourth, just ahead of Stewarts & Lloyds, who finished the season with seven successive clean sheets for Richard Lavin and his defensive colleagues.

At the other end of the table Kempston won just two matches in a season which saw them kick off with the division's oldest side and finish it with the youngest, after a mid-season managerial change which saw Bedford Eagles chief Neil Rodney take the Hillground's helm. For most of the season Bourne were favourites to join the Walnut Boys in the bottom two - the Wakes had also undergone a mid-season change at the top with Mick Bloodworth being replaced by Dave McNish. The former Rothwell Corinthians manager's injection of new blood did the trick as Bourne produced a fine finish to move clear of Eynesbury. Peter Schofield's collection of former reserves, local league recruits and battle scarred veterans had fared better than many pundits had expected early on, but a chronic shortage of goals proved their undoing - Eynesbury failed to score in their final eight matches of the seasons as they slid into the bottom two.

In the top flight Burton Park and relegated Newport Pagnell were among the early pacesetters before a hugely experienced Cottingham team moved to the top. The Berryfield Road club were unbeaten until their 10th game when surrendering their record to Harrowby, another experienced squad which looked well capable of a title challenge.

All in all the division looked very open. Blisworth had emerged from years in the doldrums under the guidance of returning manager Brian Oldham, Bugbrooke's new look side were again contenders under their new chief Chris Goodchild, while St Ives appeared rejuvenated by their managerial change which saw Mick O'Donovan take the reins at the end of August.

Meanwhile Higham had made a poor start, winning just four of their first nine matches. They were to remain undefeated in their 25 thereafter. Harrowby had displaced Cottingham at the top on 24 January, but they suddenly lost their form and were in turn toppled by Higham on 16 February. After that the championship race was as good as over as the Lankies pulled away, eventually winning the crown with nine points to spare. The Lankies were a strong side in all departments, their defence was the meanest in the league conceding just a club record 23 goals, player boss Aidy Mann was a class act in midfield and up front 38 goal Jon Ogden was unchallenged in the scoring stakes.

Elsewhere Newport's challenge faded in the new year, Daventry and Blisworth ran out of steam clearing fixture backlogs, while St Ives proved too inconsistent. Bugbrooke finished fourth, pipping neighbours Blisworth on goal difference, much improved Harrowby finished third, their best placing in years, while Cottingham had to settle for second despite adding the likes of Kevin McDonald, Ian Walker and Pat Rayment to their squad late in the campaign.

The Knockout Cup brought another near miss for Northampton Spencer - they lost in the final for the second season running. Spencer's dismay was Ford Sports' delight as they captured their first major trophy on a 3-2 aggregate. At Kingsthorpe Mill Carl Holmes' opener for Spencer was matched by a Martin Jennings leveller for the Motormen, at Royal Oak Way Fords were quickly ahead through Barry Wilcox before their lead was doubled by a hotly disputed Martin Flear goal. Spencer piled on the pressure in the second half, but could only muster a solitary Peter Green reply. Higham flew the flag for Division One in this competition too, beating Wellingborough and Mirrlees Blackstone en route to a single goal defeat at Spencer in the semi. A best ever year for Division One clubs also saw Daventry claim two higher grade scalps - Bourne and Eynesbury, plus further giant killings from Thrapston, Whitworths and Newport Pagnell.

Spalding again shone on the national stage, the Tulips were our most successful club in both FA Cup and FA Carlsberg Vase for the second season running. Ronnie Fortune played a starring role for Spalding in the FA Cup, scoring eight goals in four ties as the Tulips reached the 3rd Qualifying Round before suffering a surprise defeat at Knypersly. Three of Fortune's goals came in a 4-2 win at Raunds, the best victory by a member club in the 1997-98 competition. In the Vase the Tulips were one of three member clubs to reach the last 32. That 4th Round hurdle saw surprise exits for Stamford and Stotfold who failed to make the most of ground advantage against Potters Bar and Porthleven respectively. Spalding edged past Birstall in extra time and then beat Billingham Town 2-0 in Round 5, before going out 2-1 at home to eventual winners Tiverton in the quarter final. Some consolation was a Halley Stewart crowd of 2,038, the best in the competition apart from the final.

Spalding ended the season without any silverware to show for their efforts, they lost to Stamford in the final of the Lincolnshire Senior Cup 'A' in that cruellest of deciders, a penalty shootout. Extra time had failed to separate the sides who finished 1-1. Stamford also won the Hinchingbrooke Cup for the first time in 90 years, a single goal deciding the issue against competition debutants Stotfold. St Neots lifted the Huntingdonshire Senior Cup for the 34th time, but their first since reformation, beating holders Ortonians 1-0 to give Guy Loveday a trophy just a couple of months after replacing Gary Pilsworth in the Rowley Park hot seat.

The league continued to hold sway in the Northants Junior Cup, Northampton Vanaid, in winning the silver for the third time in five years, became our 16th consecutive winner. Familiar opponents - Oundle - were shot down by a familiar matchwinner - Matt Sanderson - as the Vans won by the only goal.

County cup football also brought its share of disappointments. A last minute goal condemned St Ives to a 2-1 Hunts Premier Cup final reverse against Biggleswade, the second successive final defeat for the Saints. It was the same story in the Bedfordshire Senior Cup, Potton going down 4-0 to Barton Rovers. Earlier Potton had beaten Barton to reach the South Midlands Floodlight Cup final - but they lost that one too, and extra time penalty giving Potters Bar the silverware.

Other cup winners were Buckingham, who beat Bicester 2-1 to lift the Buckingham Charity Cup, Desborough, who beat Cottingham 2-0 to retain the Desborough Charity Cup, and Stotfold, who battled back from two goals down to get the better of Biggleswade Town to win the North Beds Charity Cup by a 3-2 score. Holbeach, who had been long odds underdogs, became the league's first Evans Halshaw Floodlit Cup winners, defeating Eastwood Town 1-0 in the final.

At reserve level it was a memorable season for Rothwell. Andy Pawluk's side won the Reserve Division One and Reserve Knockout Cup double, edging out fellow heavyweights Raunds in the championship and easing to a 5-0 aggregate defeat of Northampton Vanaid in the Cup. Long Buckby and Bourne were relegated from Reserve Division One, their places go to St Neots and Yaxley who are promoted from the lower grade. Goal difference alone separated the Huntingdonshire pair with the Saints taking the title. St Neots' second string also enjoyed cup success, winning the Hunts Benevolent Cup. Also enjoying cup glory, but on a double scale, were Stotfold Reserves, they won the Bedfordshire Intermediate Cup and the Biggleswade Knockout Cup, the double success no doubt strengthening manager Phil Pateman's claims to take over from departing first team boss Ian Allinson.

The end of the season saw us bid farewell to Huntingdon United, whose second season in the competition proved a nightmare from start to finish. The pre-season exit of manager Andy Rossi to March left the Sapley Park club in disarray, and just when new boss John Scarborough seemed to be turning things round, news broke that the club's proposed relocation to Kings Ripton Road had fallen through. That prompted the further departure of Scarborough and many of the club's better players. Senior player Kenny Shields took up the reins and ensured that the club was able to complete its Division One fixures, no mean feat as the inexperienced squad plunged to no fewer than thirteen morale denting double figure defeats! No fewer than 93 players donned Huntingdon colours at first team level, perhaps it was no surprise that they could only muster a single point and conceded a record 173 goals. They will now regroup in the East Midlands Alliance and it is to be hoped that the efforts of John Hope and his committee to keep the club going are rewarded. Replacing Huntingdon in Division One next term are Woodford United who were runaway winners of the Northants Combination, they enjoyed an earlier spell in membership of the league in the seventies. The newcomers have made their intentions clear from the outset by recruiting Daventry manager Darren Foster as their new chief.

Jeremy Biggs, Press Liaison Officer

Right - Treble winners - Stamford AFC pictured after being presented with the Uhlsport United Counties Football League championship trophy which was retained and added to by successes in the Licolnshire Senior 'A' Cup and Hinchingbrooke Cup.
Top L-R: Gerard Evans (trainer), Paddy O'Keefe (player/coach), Meil Miller, Hamish Curtis, Dennis Rhule, Nicky Conroy, Mick Bennett, Steve Kuhne, Andy Gray, Trevor Quow, Graeme Archer, Milton Graham Ben Stimpson
Bottom L-R: Scott Kent, Paul Bryant, David Norris, Steve Evans (manager), Dean Elston (capt), Paul Hill, Al Lenihan (reserve team manager)

Photo: Andrew Eason

Left - Higham Town, Uhlsport UCL Division One Champions

FINAL LEAGUE TABLES 1997-98

PREMIER DIVISION

	P	*W*	*D*	*L*	*F*	*A*	*Pts*
Stamford	40	29	6	5	113	55	93
Northampton Sp	40	27	2	11	105	59	83
Spalding Utd	40	24	10	6	77	47	82
Desborough Tn	40	23	9	8	89	49	78
Stewart & Lloyds	40	24	6	10	68	39	78
Ford Sports Dav	40	22	10	8	74	38	76
Boston Town	40	23	6	11	82	48	75
Stotfold	40	21	9	10	89	60	72
Mirrlees Blackst.	40	20	7	13	69	50	67
St Neots Town	40	20	3	17	67	60	63
Buckingham Tn	40	18	7	15	58	49	61
Cogenhoe Utd	40	17	9	14	68	53	60
Long Buckby AFC	40	14	8	18	64	68	50
Potton United	40	11	10	19	46	62	43
Wellingborough Tn	40	11	5	24	46	77	38
Holbeach United	40	10	8	22	39	76	38
Wootton Blue Cr	40	9	6	25	53	99	33
Yaxley	40	9	3	28	57	102	30
Bourne Town	40	8	5	27	48	96	29
Eynesbury Rvrs	40	6	10	24	29	72	28
Kempston Rvrs	40	2	5	33	18	110	11

DIVISION ONE

	P	*W*	*D*	*L*	*F*	*A*	*Pts*
Higham Town	34	26	4	4	91	23	82
Cottingham	34	23	4	7	84	40	73
Harrowby United	34	20	4	10	94	61	64
Bugbrooke St M	34	18	7	9	90	47	61
Blisworth	34	19	4	11	73	54	61
Wellinboro Whit's	34	17	5	12	78	55	56
Daventry Town	34	16	5	13	87	66	53
St Ives Town	34	15	7	12	66	57	52
Newport Pagnell T	34	16	4	14	61	56	52
Rothwell Corinth	34	14	8	12	77	58	50
Olney Town	34	15	5	14	65	55	50
Northampton Van	34	14	5	15	90	54	47
Thrapston Town	34	12	7	15	74	59	43
Burton Pk Wndrs	34	13	3	18	58	71	42
Northampton ONC	34	10	8	16	54	61	38
Irchester Utd	34	7	5	22	43	85	26
Sharnbrook AFC	34	6	4	24	64	82	22
Huntingdon Utd	34	0	1	33	22	273	1

PREMIER DIVISION RESULTS CHART 1997-98

		1	2	3	4	5	6	7	8	9	10	11	12	13	14	15	16	17	18	19	20	21
1	Boston	X	5-0	0-0	1-0	3-1	3-1	2-1	3-0	3-1	3-2	2-3	2-2	7-1	3-0	0-1	2-0	2-0	1-0	1-0	2-0	1-2
2	Bourne	1-3	X	0-1	1-2	3-2	3-3	0-1	0-0	4-2	2-4	0-0	0-3	2-1	0-2	1-3	3-5	1-2	2-3	3-2	1-2	2-1
3	Buckingham	1-0	3-0	X	1-2	0-2	3-0	0-4	4-1	1-0	2-1	2-5	1-3	3-0	1-2	1-2	2-1	2-0	2-2	0-1	2-2	2-1
4	Cogenhoe	1-2	5-0	1-0	X	3-1	4-0	0-0	2-2	1-0	1-1	2-0	0-3	1-0	0-2	1-1	2-2	0-4	4-3	1-1	3-2	4-1
5	Desborough	5-0	6-1	2-0	2-2	X	4-2	0-2	3-0	6-0	1-3	1-0	2-4	1-1	3-1	0-0	3-0	2-1	0-2	2-3	2-1	2-1
6	Eynesbury	0-2	0-1	0-1	0-0	1-2	X	1-3	0-1	1-1	1-0	1-0	0-3	0-1	2-3	0-1	1-5	0-2	0-5	0-0	2-1	3-0
7	Ford Sports	2-2	0-3	1-2	1-0	2-2	3-1	X	3-0	3-0	1-0	2-1	1-4	2-2	2-0	0-1	1-1	1-0	4-3	0-0	3-1	6-0
8	Holbeach	2-1	2-1	1-1	1-6	0-1	1-2	1-0	X	1-2	1-2	0-3	2-0	2-0	1-0	1-2	1-4	2-3	0-4	0-3	0-2	2-2
9	Kempston	0-2	1-1	0-6	1-1	1-4	2-4	0-3	1-1	X	0-2	0-4	0-1	0-4	0-3	0-1	0-5	0-1	0-5	1-0	1-1	0-1
10	Long Buckby	0-3	0-2	2-2	1-2	3-3	1-0	0-1	1-1	2-0	X	1-1	1-3	1-0	0-4	2-1	1-3	0-1	2-2	2-1	8-2	1-1
11	M Blackstone	3-1	1-0	1-0	2-1	1-1	3-0	0-2	1-1	3-1	2-3	X	3-2	3-1	3-2	0-0	0-2	1-1	1-2	3-1	4-2	0-1
12	N Spencer	2-1	2-1	1-2	3-2	1-3	4-0	2-1	3-1	6-1	1-0	2-0	X	3-1	5-2	2-3	0-6	1-2	2-3	3-0	9-1	3-2
13	Potton	0-0	2-0	1-0	0-3	1-2	0-0	1-1	3-1	2-0	2-0	1-1	3-2	X	2-2	0-1	1-2	1-1	1-1	3-0	0-0	1-2
14	St Neots	0-3	1-0	3-0	2-1	0-3	0-0	0-4	4-0	3-0	3-2	1-0	1-2	3-1	X	0-2	0-2	0-2	1-3	2-1	0-1	1-0
15	Spalding	2-2	5-2	2-0	2-0	0-0	1-1	4-1	1-1	3-1	4-1	4-0	1-1	0-3	1-4	X	0-6	2-2	2-0	1-2	1-0	3-2
16	Stamford	3-1	4-2	2-1	1-0	1-1	3-0	1-1	2-1	3-1	4-2	0-3	2-0	4-1	2-2	4-3	X	0-1	5-3	4-0	3-0	5-0
17	S & L	2-0	4-1	0-0	1-0	0-5	0-0	0-2	1-0	5-0	1-1	2-1	2-1	1-0	5-0	0-1	0-3	X	1-2	3-1	3-0	3-0
18	Stotfold	3-1	7-0	1-1	0-0	1-3	1-1	1-1	3-0	2-0	2-1	2-5	1-3	3-2	1-0	1-1	0-0	2-5	X	1-2	5-3	3-1
19	Wellingborough	2-2	1-0	2-5	3-5	2-3	2-0	0-0	1-3	2-0	0-2	1-2	1-6	0-1	0-6	0-3	1-2	0-1	1-2	X	1-2	3-0
20	Wootton	1-6	2-2	0-1	2-1	0-0	2-1	1-4	1-3	3-0	2-4	0-1	1-2	4-0	1-2	3-8	3-3	1-3	0-2	1-2	X	1-4
21	Yaxley	2-4	3-2	0-2	2-4	2-3	0-0	1-4	0-1	6-0	2-4	2-4	3-5	3-0	1-5	2-3	1-7	3-2	1-2	1-3	0-1	X

MANAGER OF THE MONTH AWARDS 1996-97

	PREMIER DIVISION	DIVISION ONE
Aug/Sep	Steve Evans (Stamford AFC)	Rob Dunion (Cottingham)
Oct	Steve Evans (Stamford AFC)	Barry Shaw (Harrowby United)
Nov	Gary Sargent (Northampton Spencer)	Barry Shaw (Harrowby United)
Dec	Ian Allinson (Stotfold)	Aidy Mann (Higham Town)
Jan	Mike Emms (Long Buckby AFC)	Adam Sandy (Northampton Vanaid)
Feb	Darren Wood (Buckingham Town)	Aidy Mann (Higham Town)
Mar	Gary Sargent (Northampton Spencer)	Chris Goodchild (Bugbrooke St Michaels)
Apr/May	Alan Day (Spalding United)	Rob Dunion (Cottingham)

uhlsport UNITED COUNTIES LEAGUE 1997-98

PREMIER DIVISION	PLAYER OF THE YEAR	MOST APPEARANCES		LEADING SCORERS	
Boston Town	Richard Shaw (S & P)	Lee Rippin	43	Ian Shooter	20
Bourne Town	Tony Joynes (C)	Michael Cox	36		
Buckingham	Graham Bott (S), Richard Chaffer (P)	Graham Bott	42		
Cogenhoe United	Rob Powell (P), Jeff Gilmour (S)	Paul Smith	40		
Desborough Town	Bryan Jeffery (C & P)	Des Elliott	41	Shaun McPolin	21
		Shaun McPolin	41		
Eynesbury Rovers	Ray Stanley (P & S)	Ray Stanley	45		
Ford Sports	Barry Wilcox (S), Lee McBain (M)	Shane Geary	47	Mark Rosegreen	22
	Adam Stevens (P)	Adam Stevens	47		
Holbeach United	Steve Barnes (P), Martin Cundy (M)	Steve Barnes	38		
Kempston Rovers	Dave McArthur (C)	Steve Fox	40		
Long Buckby	Mark Coleman (M), Darren Jameson (P)	Mark Coleman	40	Craig Baker	17
		Darren Jameson	40		
Mirrlees Blackstone	Ian Pledger (P & S), Gavin Smith (M)	Ian Pledger	45	Dominic Genovese	20
Northampton Spencer	Carl Holmes (P & S), Peter Green (M)	Tim Agutter	44	Carl Holmes	27
		Jon Inwood	44		
Potton United	Darren Green (P), Gary Houghton (M),	Pete Saunders	40		
	Keeley Thake (S)	Keeley Thake	40		
St Neots Town	Gerald Sylvester (M & P), Andy Jakes (S)	Gerald Sylvester	40		
Spalding United	Tuncay Korkmaz (S, P & M)	Craig Wilson	40	Tuncay Korkmaz	15
Stamford	Steve Kuhne (P & S)	Paul Hill	43	Steve Kuhne	29
		Steve Kuhne	43		
Stewarts & Lloyds	Dennis Robertson (C)	Richard Lavin	40	Dave Torrance	15
Stotfold	Dave Cook (C), Mark Oakley (P)	Keith Coughlin	43	Wes Byrne	28
Wellingborough Town	Stuart Knight (C)	Paul James	38	Gary Fitzhugh	17
Wootton Blue Cros	Darek Jozwiak (P), Chris Hyde (S)	Andy Watt	41	Dark Jozwiak	18
Yaxley	Lee Minett (P), Stan Hardy (S)	Chris George	40		

uhlsport UNITED COUNTIES LEAGUE KNOCKOUT CUP 1997-98

Preliminary Round

Mirrlees Blackstone	v	Cottingham	4-2
Spalding	v	Thrapston	0-1
Newport Pagnell	v	Harrowby	4-2
Huntingdon	v	Stotfold	0-5
Potton	v	Eynesbury	1-1 aet, 0-1
Cogenhoe	v	Desborough	2-0
Stewarts & Lloyds	v	Stamford	1-2

First Round

Boston	v	St Ives	2-0
Thrapston	v	Sharnbrook	3-0
Newport Pagnell	v	Long Buckby	1-0
Stotfold	v	St Neots	4-1
Mirrlees Blackstone	v	Blisworth	6-0
Bugbrooke	v	ON Chenecks	1-2
Irchester	v	Eynesbury	0-3
Northampton Spencer	v	Olney	3-2
Wootton	v	Cogenhoe	1-0
Whitworths	v	Holbeach	5-1
Northampton Vanaid	v	Burton PW	1-3
Ford Sports	v	Yaxley	3-0
Higham	v	Welingborough	6-3
Kempston	v	Buckingham	2-3
Stamford	v	Rothwell Corinthians	4-2
Bourne	v	Daventry	1-2

Second Round

Newport Pagnell	v	Northampton Spencer	2-6
Stotfold	v	Mirrlees Blackstone	1-3
Stamford	v	Burton PW	3-1
Wootton	v	Thrapston	8-2
Ford Sports	v	Buckingham	4-0
ON Chenecks	v	Higham	2-5
Daventry	v	Eynesbury	1-1 aet, 3-1
Boston	v	Whitworths	6-1

Third Round

Mirrlees Blackstone	v	Higham	0-0 aet, 0-2
Boston	v	Northampton Sp	2-2 aet, 0-3
Ford Sports	v	Stamford	3-0
Daventry	v	Wootton	2-4

Semi-Final

Wootton	v	Ford Sports	3-3 aet, 0-3
Northampton Spencer	v	Higham	1-0

Final

First Leg

Northampton Spencer v Ford Sports 1-1

Second Leg

Ford Sports v Northampton Spencer 2-1

Ford Sports won 3-2 on aggregate

Teams

Northampton Spencer: Crick, Mann, Tansley, Andrews, Jelley, Tebbutt, Holmes, Pepperell, Green, Inwood, Smeathers
Subs: Dale, Cook
2nd leg: Agutter and Hodges replaced Tansley and Tebbutt. Subs: Tansley, Dale

Ford Sports: Bulliman, Stevens, Simpson, Fuller, Jennings, Wilcox, Geary, Stringer, Flear, Rosegreen, McBain
Subs: Watts, Coates
2nd leg: Rule for Stringer. Subs: Smith, I Morgan, Miller

THE uhlsport UNITED COUNTIES FOOTBALL LEAGUE HONOURS 1997-98

UNITED COUNTIES FOOTBALL LEAGUE HONOURS

Premier Division	Winners	Stamford AFC	Runners Up	Northampton Spencer
Division One	Winners	Higham Town	Runners Up	Cottingham
Reserve Division One	Winners	Rothwell Town	Runners Up	Raunds Town
Reserve Division Two	Winners	St Neots Town	Runners Up	Yaxley
Premier Division/Division One KO Cup	Winners	Ford Sports Daventry	Runners Up	Northampton Spencer
Reserve Divisions KO Cup	Winners	Rothwell Town	Runners Up	Northampton Vanaid
Benevolent Cup	Winners	Yaxley	Runners Up	Stamford AFC
Highest Aggregate of Goals		Stamford AFC		
Fair Play Awards Premier/Division One:		Cogenhoe United		
Fair Play Awards Reserve Divisions:		Spalding United		

COUNTY HONOURS

Bedfordshire Senior Cup	Runners Up	Potton United
Bedfordshire Intermediate Cup	Winners	Stotfold Reserves
Huntingdonshire Senior Cup	Winners	St Neots Town
Huntingdonshire Premier Cup	Runners Up	St Ives Town
Huntingdonshire Benevolent Cup	Winners	St Neots Town Reserves
Lincolnshire Senior Cup 'A'	Winners	Stamford AFC
	Runners Up	Spalding United
Northamptonshire Junior Cup	Winners	Northampton Vanaid

WINNERS IN OTHER COMPETITIONS

Biggleswade Knock Out Cup	Stotfold Reserves
Buckingham Charity Cup	Buckingham Town
Desborough Charity Cup	Desborough Town
Evans Halshaw Floodlit Cup	Holbeach United
Hinchngbrooke Cup	Stamford AFC
North Beds Charity Cup	Stotfold

PREMIER DIVISION CLUBS 1998-99

BLACKSTONE

President: Darren Laughton **Chairman:** Bill Sewell
Secretary: Ian McGillivry, 20 New Road, Ryhall, Stamford, Lincs PE9 4HL (01780 762263 H, 01733 67474 x2898) 332074).
Manager: Dominic Genovese **Press Officer:** Kevin Boor. **Asst Manager:** John Musgrove
Ground: Lincoln Road, Stamford (01780 757335).
Directions: A6121 Stamford to Bourne road, 2nd left past MB works.
Capacity: 1,000 **Seats:** 100 **Cover:** Yes **Floodlights:** Yes **Founded:** 1920.
Programme: 32 pages with entry **Editor:** Kevin Boor (01780 754584)
Colours: All yellow & royal **Change Colours:** All red
Clubhouse details: Open evenings, lunchtimes & matchdays.
Sponsors: Ideal Interiors **Midweek matchday:** Tuesday **Nickname:** Stones
Record Gate: 700 v Glinton. **Previous Leagues:** Peterborough Works/ Peterborough/ Stamford & District.
Previous Names: Rutland Ironworks/ Blackstone (until 1975).
Players to progress to Football League: Craig Goldsmith (Peterborough, Carlisle), Alan Neilson (Newcastle & Wales).
Club record scorer (in one game): A Dunn; 6 v Brackley Town, 22/1/94.
Honours: UCL Div 1 R-up 87-88 (Benevolent Cup R-up), Lincs Snr Cup 'A' 92-93.

BOSTON TOWN

Chairman: Mick Vines **Vice Chairman:** J Rose. **Treasurer:** J Rose
Secretary: A Crick, Daisy Cottage, Shore Rd, Freiston, Boston, Lincs PE22 0LU (01205 760162. Fax:760162).
Manager: Bob Don-Duncan **Asst Manager:** Shaughan Farrow. **Physio:** Don Mitchell
Ground: Tattershall Road, Boston, Lincs (01205 365470).
Directions: A52 Grantham-Sleaford ,2nd left into Brotherton Rd.,Argyle St.to bridge,immediately over left into Tattersall road,ground 3/4 mile on left.
Capacity: 6,000 **Seats:** 450 **Cover:** 950 **Floodlights:** Yes **Club Shop:** Yes.
Programme: 40 pages, 50p **Editor/Press Officer:** Bob Whitaker (01205 368445)
Colours: Blue & white/white/blue **Change:** All yellow
Sponsors: Tempests of Stickney/Keystone Fabricators **Nickname:** Poachers **Founded:** 1963.
Midweek Matchday: Tuesday **Reserves League:** None 94-95.
Record Attendance: 2,700 v Boston Utd, FA Cup 3rd Qual. Rd 1970.
Best FA Cup season: 1st Rd Proper 76-77 (lost 1-3 at Barnsley)
Best FA Trophy season: Second Round 79-80 (lost 3-6 at Mossley after 0-0 draw).
Best FA Vase season: Semi-Finals 94-95 (lost 0-2 on aggregate to Taunton Town).
Previous Leagues: Lincs 63-65/ Central Alliance 65-66/ Eastern Co's 66-68/ Midland 68-82/ Northern Co's East 82-87/ Central Midlands 87-91.
Players progressing to Football League: Julian Joachim (Leicester City), Neil Mann (Hull City).
Clubhouse: Open evenings (except Sunday), matchdays & functions. Bar & Lounge. Darts & pool.
Club Record Goalscorer (in a season): Carl Smaller 48, 1994-95.
Honours: Midland Co's Lg 74-75 78-79 80-81 (Lg Cup 76-77); Lincs Snr 'A' Cup (5) 73-74 79-82 89-90 (Snr 'B' Cup 65-66); Central Mids Lg 88-89; Central All 65-66; Lincs Lg 64-65; Hereward Spts Unt.Co.Lg.Prem Div Champ 94-95.

BOURNE TOWN

Chairman: Derek Bontoft **Vice-Chairman:** **President:** Jim Ashton
Secretary: Roger Atkins, 106 Stephenson Way, Bourne, Lincs PE10 9DD (01778 424882)
Manager: Dave McNish **Asst Manager:** **Physio:**
Ground: Abbey Lawn, Abbey Road, Bourne, Lincs (01778 422292). **Directions:** In market place take A151 Spalding Road, ground 500 yds on right. Public transport from Peterborough, Stamford and Grantham.
Capacity: 3,000 **Seats:** 300 **Cover:** 750 **Floodlights:** Yes **Club Shop:** Contact sec
Programme: 50 pages, 50p **Editor:** Melvin Ashton (01778 570976)**Press Officer:** Secretary
Colours: Maroon & sky/sky/maroon **Change Colours:** White & sky/white & sky/sky
Sponsors: Jaychem **Nickname:** Wakes **Founded:** 1883.
Midweek matchday: Wednesday **Reserves' Lge:** HSUCL Res Div 1
Record Attendance: 3,000 v Chelmsford, FA Tphy 1970
Previous Leagues: Peterborough/ UCL 47-56/ Central Alliance 58-61/ Midland Counties 61-63.
Previous Ground: Adjacent cricket field after WW2 until 1947.
Players to progress to Football League: Peter Grummit (Nottm Forest), Shaun Cunnington (Wrexham, Grimsby, Sunderland), David Palmer (Wrexham).
Clubhouse: Small, open matchdays and specific events. Food, confectionary available.
Club Record Goalscorer: David Scotney
Honours: Utd Co's Lg 68-69 69-70 71-72 90-91 (KO Cup 69-70, Benevolent Cup 90-91, Res Div 2 94-95), Lincs Snr 'A' Cup 71-72 (R-up 92-93), Central Alliance Division 1 South 59-60, Lincs Intermediate Cup 85-86.

BUCKINGHAM TOWN

Managing Director: **Vice Chairman:** Bryn Pond
Secretary: Peter Holman, 5 Greenway Walk, Buckingham, Bucks (01280 812787)
Team Manager / Coach: Darren Wood **Assistant Manager / Physio:** Tim Chamberlain
Ground: Ford Meadow, Ford Street, Buckingham (01280 816257).
Directions: From town centre take Aylesbury (A413) road and turn right at Phillips Garage after 400yds. By public transport: train to Milton Keynes, then bus to Buckingham.
Capacity: 4,000 **Cover:** 420 **Seats:** 420 **Floodlights:** Yes **Club Shop:** Yes
Colours: All red **Change colours:** All white
Sponsors: Wipac. **Formed:** 1883 **Nickname:** The Robins
Midweek Matchday: **Reserves' League:** No reserve team
Previous Leagues: Aylesbury & Dist, Nth Bucks, Hellenic 53-57, Sth Mids 57-74, Utd Co's 74-86, Southern Lge 86-97.
Record Attendance: 2,451 v Orient, FA Cup 1st Rd 84-85.
Best Season FA Cup: 1st Round 1984-85, **FA Vase:** Quarter Finals 1990-91 & 92-93.
Programme: Yes **Editor:**
Clubhouse: Open evenings 6.30-11.00 (12.00-11.00 Sat & Sun) Rolls etc available on matchdays. Bingo, dominoes, darts & pool. Concert room with stage for hire, capacity 150.
96-97 Captain: Paul Lamb **96-97 P.o.Y.:** Robin Tucker **96-97 Top scorer:** Tony Hamilton
Honours: Southern Lg Southern Div 90-91, Utd Co's Lg 83-84 85-86 (Div 1 R-up 75-76, Div 2 R-up 74-75, Lg Cup 83-84, Div 2 Cup R-up 74-75), Nth Bucks Lg 24-25 28-29 33-34 35-37 38-39 48-50(2) Aylesbury & Dist. Lg 02-03, Berks & Bucks Snr Cup 83-84, Berks & Bucks Jnr Cup 02-03 48-49 (R-up 38-39 72-73), Berks & Bucks Minor Cup 32-33, Buckingham Snr Charity Cup 32-33 35-36 37-38 47-50 52-55 72-73 75-77 78-79 80-81 83-87 97-98 (R-up 31-32 36-37 39-40 73-74 81-82).

COGENHOE UNITED

Chairman: Derek Wright **Vice Chairman:** Bob Earl **President:** Steve Brockwell
Secretary: Sue Wright, 6 Braefield Road, Cogenhoe, Northants NN7 1ND (01604 890737 H, 01604 890277 B, 01604 890641 Fax).
Manager: Steve Forbes **Asst Man.:** **Physio:** Ian Blair.
Ground: Compton Park, Brafield Rd, Cogenhoe, Northants (01604 890521).
Directions: Turn off A428 at Brafield-on-the-Green, first turn right to Cogenhoe or A45 to Billing Aquadrome. Carry on, take second Cogenhoe turn on left.
Capacity: 5,000 **Seats:** 100 **Cover:** 200 **Floodlights:** Yes **Founded:** 1967
Programme: 32 pages with Admission **Editor:** Paul Smith
Colours: All royal **Change:** Black & white/white/white **Club Shop:** No.
Midweek matchday: Tuesday **Nickname:** Cooks.
Sponsors: Supertrucking **Previous League:** Central Northants Combinatiom 1967-84.
Reserves' Lge: UCL Res. Div 1 **Record Gate:** 1,000 v Eastenders XI, Charity match 8/7/90.
Players to progress to Football League: Darren Bazeley (Watford 1989), Darren Harmon (Notts Co., Shrewsbury, Northampton 1989), Matt Murphy (Oxford Utd 1993), Gary Leonard (Northampton 1978).
Clubhouse: Open Tues-Fri 7-11pm, Sat 12-3 & 4-11pm, Sun 12-3 & 7-10.30pm. Snacks. Hot food on matchdays.
96-97 Captain: Neil Heslop **Record scorer & appearance maker:** Tony Smith.
Hons: UCL Div 1 R-up 86-87 (Reserve Div 2 88-89), Knockout Cup 96-97; Daventry Charity Cup 91-92 95-96, (R-up 79-80); Central Northants Comb 80-81 82-83 83-84 (R-up 81-82, Prem Div Cup 82-83 (R-up 78-79), Div 1 Cup R-up 77-78, Charity Shield 82-83 83-84).

DESBOROUGH TOWN

Chairman: Ernie Parsons **President:** Bryan Walmsley
Secretary: John Lee, 85 Breakleys Road, Desborough, Northants NN14 2PT (01536 760002).
Manager: Derek Maddox **Asst Manager:** Dave McHuchinson **Physio:** Steve Booth
Ground: Waterworks Field, Braybrooke Rd, Desborough (01536 761350).
Directions: Half a mile west of A6 following signs for Braybrooke.
Capacity: 8,000 **Seats:** 250 **Cover:** 500 **Floodlights:** Yes **Club Shop:**
Programme: 40 pages with entry **Editor:** Ernie Parsons **Press Officer:** John Lee
Colours: Blue & white/blue/blue **Change Colours:** Red & white/black/black **Previous Leagues:** None.
Sponsors: **Nickname:** Ar Tarn **Founded:** 1896.
Midweek matchday: Tuesday **Record Attendance:** 8,000 v Kettering Town.
Players progressing to Football League: Wakeley Gage (Northampton, Chester, Peterborough and Crewe), Jon Purdie & Campbell Chapman (Wolves), Andy Tillson (Grimsby, QPR & Bristol Rvrs).
Clubhouse: Lounge & main hall, 2 bars, games room. Open every evening, weekend lunchtimes.
97-98 - Captain: Jim Handley **P.o.Y.:** Bryan Jeffrey **Top Scorer:** Shaun McPolin
Honours: Utd Co's (Prev. Northants) Lg 00-01 01-02 06-07 20-21 23-24 24-25 27-28 48-49 66-67 (R-up 02-03 10-11 19-20 22-23 79-80), Div 2 10-11 (Res) 28-29(Res), R-up 09-10(Res) 26-27(Res) 51-52(Res), KO Cup 77-78 96-97; Northants Snr Cup 10-11 13-14 28-29 51-52; Desborough Charity Cup 97-98

EYNESBURY ROVERS

Chairman: Brian Abraham **Vice Chairman:** Mike Preece **President:** Bill Stephenson
Secretary: Derek Irons, 12 Hadleigh Close, Bedford MK41 8JW. (01234 268111)
Manager: Peter Schofield **Asst Manager:** Steve White
Ground: Hall Road, Eynesbury, St Neots (01480 477449).
Directions: Approx 2 miles from A1, on South side of St Neots urban area, near Ernulf School.
Capacity: 3,000 **Seats:** 270 **Cover:** 500 **Floodlights:** Yes **Founded:** 1897
Programme: 28 pages, 50p **Editor:** Graham Mills **Club Shop:** Dave Crisp
Colours: Royal & white/royal/royal **Change Colours:** Yellow/black/yellow **Nickname:** Rovers.
Clubhouse: Large bar, capacity 150, committee room **Midweek matchday:** Tuesday
Sponsors: National Power **Reserve Team's League:** United Counties Reserve Div. One.
Record Gate: 5,000 v Fulham 1953 **Previous Lges:** Sth Mids 34-39/ UCL 46-52/ Eastern Co's 52-63.
Best FA Vase season: 2nd Rd 85-86 88-89 **Best FA Cup season:** 4th Qual. Rd 54-55 (1-3 at Camb. Utd)
Players to progress to Football Lge: Chris Turner (P'boro, Luton, Cambridge), Denis Emery (P'boro)
Hons: UCL Div 1 76-77; Hunts Snr Cup 13-14 46-47 48-51 54-55 56-57 69-70 84-85 90-93 95-96; Hunts Premier Cup 50-51 90-91 95-96; Hinchingbrooke Cup (7) 46-47 48-52 57-58 66-67; Cambs Invitation Cup 61-62; E Anglian Cup R-up 90-91 91-92; Hunts Scott Gatty Cup 35-36 56-57 84-85 89-90 (R-up 93-94 res); Hunts Jnr Cup 21-22 26-27.

FORD SPORTS

Chairman: John Bailham **Vice Chairman:**
Secretary: Dave Hirons, 53 Arnull Cres., Daventry, Northants NN11 5AZ (01327 871461 H, 01455 550555 x376 B)
Managers: Richard Green & Kevin Flear **Physio:** Dave Bull
Ground: Royal Oak Way South, Daventry, Northants (01327 709219).
Directions: Enter Daventry on A45 or A361 and follow signs for Royal Oak Way
Capacity: 1,000 **Seats:** Yes **Cover:** Yes **Floodlights:** Yes **Founded:** 1968
Programme: 12 pages **Reserves' Lge:** UCL Res Div 2 **Clubhouse:** Yes
Colours: Blue/white/blue **Change colours:** Red & black/black/red & black **Nickname:** Motormen
Prev. Lge: Central Northants Comb **Sponsors:** Ford Sports & Social Club
Player progressing to Football League: Martin Aldridge (Northampton).
Honours: UCL Div 1 92-93, 95-96, Knockout Cup 97-98, Benevolent Cup R-up 92-93; Highest Aggregate Goalscoring Trophy 92-93; Northants Sen Cup R-up 96-97.

A perfect penalty, St Neot's Frank Atkins beats Eynesbury keeper Ray Stanley in their Boxing Day clash
Photo: Gordon Whittington

HOLBEACH UNITED

President: John King **Chairman:** Anton Louth
Secretary: Paul Beeken, 36 West End, Holbeach, Lincs PE12 7HA (01406 425355)
Manager: Jan Czarnecki **Asst Manager:** Jimmy Jackson
Ground: Carters Park, Park Road, Holbeach (01406 424761) **Directions:** Second left at traffic lights in town centre, 220 yds down road on left. From King's Lynn; sharp right at traffic lights.
Capacity: 4,000 **Seats:** 200 **Cover:** 450 **Floodlights:** Yes **Founded:** 1929.
Programme: 44 pages, 50p **Editor:** Alan Wright **Club Shop:**
Colours: Old gold & black/black/black **Change Colours:** White/blue/blue **Nickname:** Tigers
Reserves' Lge: Peterborough **Clubhouse:** Large bar, lounge & kitchen, open every night.
Midweek matchday: Tuesday **Record Gate:** 4,094 v Wisbech 1954. **Sponsors:** Kings Quality Homes
Previous Leagues: Peterborough/ Utd Co's 46-55/ Eastern Co's 55-62/ Midland Co's 62-63.
Players progressing to Football League: Peter Rawcliffe (Lincoln).
Best FA Cup season: 1st Rd Proper 82-83 (lost 0-4 v Wrexham at Peterborough).
Best FA Trophy season: 2nd Qualifying Round 69-70 71-72.
Best FA Vase season: 5th Round 88-89 (lost 2-4 v Wisbech Town).
Honours: Utd Co's Lg 89-90 (KO Cup 64-65 89-90), Benevolent Cup, Evans Halshaw Cup 97-98; Lincs Snr Cup 'A' 83-84 84-85 86-87 (Senior Cup 'B' 57-58)

KEMPSTON ROVERS

President: H Gilbert **Chairman:** Mark Salsbury **Vice-Chairman:** Russell Shreeves
Press Officer/Secretary: Alan Scott, 26 King William Rd, Kempston, Bedford MK42 7AT (01234 854875).
Manager: Neil Rodney **Asst Manager:** Steve Rigby
Ground: Hillgrounds Leisure, Hillgrounds Rd, Kempston, Bedford (01234 852346). **Directions:** M1 jct 13, A421 to Kempston, Hillgrounds Rd is off the B531 main Kempston-Bedford road. Entrance to Hillgrounds Road is opposite Sainsburys on the B531 - ground can be found just over twi miles from Sainsburys entrance. British Rail to Bedford Thameslink/Midland then bus No.103 from Bedford town centre stops outside ground.
Capacity: 2,000 **Seats:** 100 **Cover:** 250 **Floodlights:** Yes **Founded:** 1884.
Programme: 24 pages, 40p **Editor:** Richard Coop
Colours: Red & white/black/black **Change Colours:** All yellow.
Nickname: Walnut Boys **Club record scorer:** Doug Jack.
Midweek matchday: Wednesday **Club Sponsors:** Audi Vindis Bedford
Record Attendance: unknown **Previous League:** Sth Mids 27-53.
Previous Grounds: Bedford Rd 1900s-1973/ Hillgrounds Road 74-86 *(three grounds in same road!).*
Reserves's Lge: Bedford & Dist **Club Shop:** No, but old programmes available from clubhouse.
Players progressing to Football League: Ernie Fenn (WBA, Aston Villa), Matthew Woolgar (Luton 1994).
Clubhouse: Open 7-11pm every evening except Monday and weekend lunctimes noon-3pm. Sky TV, pool, fruit machines, hot pies & pasties.
Hons: Utd Co's Lg 73-74 (R-up 56-57 59-60 (Div 1 57-58 85-86, Div 2 55-56 (R-up 67-68), KO Cup 55-56 57-58 59-60 74-75 76-77), Beds Senior Cup 08-09 37-38 76-77 91-92 (R-up 92-93).

LONG BUCKBY

President: Alister Bruce **Chairman:** Ted Thresher
Secretary: Dean O'Grady, 6 Harry Close, Long Buckby, Northants NN6 7YU (01327 843726)
Manager: Ashley Alexander **Asst Manager:** **Physio:** Mick Deacon
Ground: Station Rd, Long Buckby (01327 842682).
Directions: On Daventry - Long Buckby road. 400 yds from station (Northampton - Rugby line).
Capacity: 1,000 **Seats:** 200 **Cover:** 200 **Floodlights:** Yes **Founded:** 1945
Programme: 8 pages **Editor:** Rod Pryor. **Sponsors:** Northampton Elec Dist
Colours: All blue **Change colours:** All red **Nickname:** Bucks
Reserves' Lge: HSUCL Res Div 1 **Clubhouse:** Bar & concert room. Open matchdays.
Midweek matchday: Tuesday **Record Gate:** 750 v Kettering, Northants Snr Cup Final 1984.
Previous Lges: Rugby & D./ Central Northants Comb. (pre-1968).
Prev. Name: Long Buckby Nomads 1936.
Best FA Vase season: 2nd Rd 85-86 **Best FA Cup season:** 1st Qualifying Rd 92-93..
Players progressing to Football League:
Gary Mills (Nottingham Forest, Derby, Notts County, Leicester), Vince Overson (Burnley, Birmingham), Des Waldock (Northampton), Steve Norris (Scarborough, Carlisle, Halifax, Chesterfield).
Honours: UCL KO Cup 84-85, UCL Div 2 70-71 71-72, Div 2 KO Cup 71-72, Div 3 69-70; Northants Snr Cup R-up; Daventry Charity Cup 96-97.

NORTHAMPTON SPENCER

President: J Sampson **Chairman:** Graham Wrighting
Secretary: D Ling, 26 Pritchard Close, Rectory Farm, Northampton (01604 407124).
Manager: Gary Sargent **Asst Manager:** Keith Bowen
Ground: Kingsthorpe Mill, Studland Rd, Northampton NN3 1NF (01604 718898).
Directions: Turn off Kingsthorpe Rd at traffic lights into Thornton Rd, 1st right into Studland Rd, ground at end.
Capacity: 2,000 **Seats:** 100 **Cover:** 350 **Floodlights:** Yes **Founded:** 1936
Programme: 48 pages, 50p **Editor/Press Officer:** Andy Goldsmith (01604 412382)
Colours: Yellow/green/yellow **Change Colours:** All red **Nickname:** Millers
Midweek matchday: Wednesday **Clubhouse:** Lounge and bar, open normal licensing hours.
Sponsors: Park Lans Windows **Record Gate:** 800 v Nottm F., dressing-room opener 1993.
Previous Lge: Northampton Town 36-68 **Reserves' Lge:** UCL Res. Div. One
Previous - Name: Spencer School Old Boys. **Grnds:** Dallington Park 1936-70, Duston High School 70-72.
Best FA Cup year: 1st Qual. Rd 93-94, 96-97. **Best FA Vase year:** 4th Round 87-88 (lost 1-2 v Gresley Rovers)
Players to progress to Football League: Paul Stratford (Northampton), Wakeley Gage (Northampton, Chester, Peterborough, Crewe)
Hons: United Counties Lg 91-92 (R-up 92-93 97-98), Div 1 84-85, KO Cup 88-89 93-94 (R-up 87-88 96-97 97-98), Benevolent Cup 91-92; Northants Snr Cup R-up 90-91 93-94.

POTTON UNITED

President: Peter Hutchinson. **Chairman:** Nigel Westhorp
Secretary/Press Officer: Derek Inskip, 16 Sheffield Close, Potton, Beds SG19 0NY (01767 260355).
Manager: Martin Humberstone **Asst Manager:** Martin Rowland
Ground: The Hollow, Biggleswade Road, Potton (01767 261100).
Directions: Outskirts of Potton on Biggleswade Road (B1040). Three and a half miles from Sandy (BR). United Counties buses from Biggleswade.
Capacity: 2,000 **Seats:** 200 **Cover:** 250 **Floodlights:** Yes **Founded:** 1943
Programme: 28 pages, 50p **Editor:** Bev Westhorpe **Club Sponsors:** Darlows
Colours: Blue & white/blue/blue **Change Colours:** Red/white/red **Nickname:** Royals
Midweek matchday: Tuesday **Previous Lges:** Sth Mids 46-55/ Central Alliance 56-61
Prev. Grnd: Recreation Grnd pre-1947
Reserves' Lge: UCL Res. Div. Two **Record Attendance:** 470 v Hastings Town, FA Vase 1989
Best Season - FA Trophy: 3rd Qualifying Round 71-72 72-73. **FA Vase:** 5th Round 89-90 (lost 1-2 to Billericay Town).
FA Cup: 3rd Qualifying Round 74-75 (lost 1-2 to Bedford Town).
Clubhouse details: Large (capacity for 100), opened 1985.
Hons: Utd Co's Lg 86-87 88-89, KO Cup 72-73, Benevolent Cup 88-89; Beds Snr Cup(5) 47-49 63-64 75-76 77-78 (R-up 94-95 96-97); Wallspan Floodlit Cup 87-88; Hinchingbrooke Cup 51-52 84-85 89-90 90-91 91-92; Hunts Premier Cup 89-90 91-92 94-95(joint) 96-97; Beds I'mediate Cup 43-44; Southern Comb. Cup 92-93; Nth Beds Charity Cup (12); East Anglian Cup 96-97; Jess Pigott Trophy 96-97.

ST NEOTS TOWN

Chairman: Bob Page **Press Officer:** Neil Holmes (01480 383382)
Secretary: Graham Izzard, 73 The Ridgeway, Eynesbury, St Neots, Cambridge, PE19 2PZ (01480 395576)
Manager: Guy Loveday **Asst Manager:** Mark Humphrey **Coach:**
Ground: Rowley Park, Cambridge Rd, St Neots, Cambs (01480 470012).
Directions: Through town centre, under railway bridge, 1st left.
Capacity: 3,000 **Seats:** TBA **Cover:** 250 **Floodlights:** Yes **Founded:** 1879
Programme: Yes **Editor:** Mike Birch **Nickname:** Saints
Reserves' Lge: UCL Res Div 2 **Clubhouse:** Built 1994. **Sponsors:** TBA
Club colours: Sky & navy/navy/navy **Change colours:** All white
Record Gate: 2,000 v Wisbech, 1966 **Best FA Cup year:** 1st Rd 66-67 (lost 0-2 at Walsall).
Best FA Vase year: 3rd Rd 78-78 **Best FA Trophy year:** Second Qualifying Round 69-70 72-73.
Previous Lges: South Midlands 27-36 46-49/ United Counties 36-39 51-56 66-69 73-88/ Metropolitan 49-51 60-66/ Central Alliance 56-60/ Eastern Counties 69-73/ Huntingdonshire 90-94.
Previous Ground: Shortsands **Previous Name:** St Neots & District 1879-1957.
Players progressing to Football League:
Frank Atkins (Cambridge), John Gregory (Aston Villa) and Matthew Oakey (Southampton).
Honours: Hunts Snr Cup(34), UCL 67-68 (KO Cup 67-68 68-69), Metropolitan Lg 49-50 (Lg Cup 79-80), South Midlands Lg 32-33, Huntingdonshire Lg 90-91 92-92 92-93 94-95.

SPALDING UNITED

Back Row (L-R): Andrew Lodge, Brendan Blythe, Glen Beech, Darren Cundy, Lee Wilkinson, Nick Keeble, Craig Wilson, Tuncay Korkmaz, Steve Graham. Front Row: Darren Rowley, Martin Rowbottom, Kevin Cross, Ronnie Fortune, Paul Langford, Darren Edey, Richard Cooper

Chairman: Mick Clare **President:** John Chappell
Secretary: Howard Williamson c/o EPH Supplies Ltd, West Elloe Ave, Spalding, Lincs PE11 2BJ (01775 711165)
Manager: Alan Day **Asst Manager:** Glenn Beech **Physio:** Alan Todd
Ground: Sir Halley Stewart Field, Winfrey Avenue, Spalding (01775 713328).
Directions: Town centre off A16, adjacent to bus station. 250 yds from Spalding (BR) station.
Capacity: 7,000 **Seats:** 350 **Cover:** 2,500 **Floodlights:** Yes **Shop:** Yes
Programme: 36 pages, 50p **Editor:** Richard Walton **Press Officer:** Ray Tucker
Colours: Tangerine & black/black/tangerine **Change:** All Blue
Sponsors: Foremost Supplies **Nickname:** Tulips **Founded:** 1921
Midweek matchday: Wednesday **Reserve League:** Utd Counties Lge Res Div Two.
Record Attendance: 6,972 v Peterborough, FA Cup 1952.
Previous Leagues: Peterborough/ Utd Co's 31-55 68-78 86-88/ Eastern Co's 55-60/ Central Alliance 60-61/ Midland Co's 61-68/ Northern Co's (East) 82-86/ Southern 88-91.
Best Season - FA Cup: 1st Round 57-58 (1-3 at Durham City), 64-65 (3-5 at Newport County). **FA Trophy:** 2nd Qualifying Round 69-70 70-71 71-72 74-75 76-77 81-82. **FA Vase:** Quarter-Finals 89-90 (lost 1-3 to Guiseley).
Players progressing to Football League: Carl Shutt (Sheffield Wednesday, Bristol City, Leeds).
Clubhouse: Open matchdays, and events.
Honours: Utd Co's Lg 54-55 74-75 87-88 (R-up 50-51 51-52 52-53 72-73 75-76 96-97); KO Cup 54-55 94-95; Northern Co's East Lg 83-84; Lincs Snr Cup 52-53; Lincs Snr 'A' Cup 87-88, R-up 97-98; Snr 'B' Cup 50-51; Evans Halshaw F'lit Cup 89-90.

STEWARTS & LLOYDS

Chairman: Peter Webb **Vice Chairmen:** Gordon Hall, Harry Nelson
Secretary: Dave Foster, 29 Tettenhall Close, Corby, Northants NN198 9PJ (01536 742358)
Manager: Elwyn Roberts. **Asst Manager:** Andy McGowan **Physio:** Roger White
Ground: Recreation Ground, Occupation Road, Corby (01536 401497).
Directions: On Occupation Rd at rear of Stewart & Lloyds Leisure Club, next to old Corby Town F.C. ground.
Capacity: 1,500 **Seats:** 100 **Cover:** 200 **Floodlights:** Yes **Club Shop:**
Programme: 12 pages with admission **Editor/Press Officer:** Dave Foster
Colours: Yellow/blue/yellow **Change Colours:** All red
Sponsor: Weldon **Nickname:** None **Formed:** 1935
Midweek matchday: Tuesday **Previous Leagues:** Kettering Amateur
Players to progress to Football League: Andy McGowan (Northampton), Willie Graham (Brentford)
Clubhouse: Licensed bar.
Club Record Goalscorer: Joey Martin 46 (92-93).
Honours: UCL R-up 85-86, Div 1(2) 73-75; UCL KO Cup, Prem 95-96, Div 1 Cup(2) 73-75, Div 2 KO Cup(2) 75-77)

STOTFOLD

Chairman: John Talbot **Vice Chairman:** Tom Peacock **President:** David Chellow
Secretary: W Clegg, 12 Common Rd, Stotfold, Hitchin, Herts SG5 4BX (01462 730421).
Manager: Phil Pateman **Asst Manager:** Dick Newman/Gary Winn
Physio: Nobby Kearns **Press Officer:** Bill Clegg
Ground: Roker Park, The Green, Stotfold, Hitchin, Herts (01462 730765).
Directions: A507 from A1, right at lights, right at T-jct. A507 from Bedford via Shefford, left at lights, right at T-jct.
Capacity: 5,000 **Seats:** 300 **Cover:** 300 **Floodlights:** Yes **Nickname:** Eagles
Programme: 22 pages with entry **Editor:** John Talbot **Founded:** 1904.
Colours: Amber/black/black **Change Colours:** All Sky blue **Reformed:** 1945.
Midweek matchday: Tuesday **Reserve Team's League:** UCL Reserve Division One.
Club Sponsors: Motorola **Record Attendance:** 1,000 v Letchworth Town, FA Amtr Cup.
Previous Leagues: Biggleswade & District/ North Herts/ South Midlands 51-84.
Clubhouse details: Clubroom, bar, refreshment bar, dressing rooms, physio room.
Record scorer: Roy Boon **Record appearances:** Roy Boon/Dave Chellew.
Hons: Utd Co's Lg R-up 93-94, KO Cup R-up 91-92, Res Div 1 87-88; Sth Mids Lg 80-81 (R-up 55-56 57-58 58-59 59-60 63-64 65-66 77-78), Div 1 53-54, Chal. Tphy 81-82; Beds Snr Cup 64-65 93-94; Beds Premier Cup 81-82; Beds I'mediate Cup 58-59; Nth Beds Charity Cup 55-56 56-57 61-62 81-82 87-88 90-91 97-98; Beds Colts Lg 88-89; Southern Comb Cup 94-95 95-96 96-97; Hinchingbrooke Cup R-up 97-98.

WELLINGBOROUGH TOWN

Chairman: Corville Brown. **President:**
Secretary: Mike Walden, 5 Fernie Way, Wellingborough, Northants NN8 3LB (01933 279561).
Manager: Brian Knight. **Coach:** Joe Kiernan/Graham Felton **Physio:** Tif Felton
Ground: Dog & Duck, London Road, Wellingborough, Northants (01933 223536).
Directions: 200yds off A45 by-pass, by Dog & Duck PH. 1 mile from Wellingborough (BR).
Capacity: 5,000 **Seats:** 300 **Cover:** 500 **Floodlights:** Yes **Club Shop:** No
Programme: 16 pages 30p **Editor:** Secretary **Press Officer:** Secretary
Colours: White/blue/white **Change Colours:** All red.
Sponsors: Overstone Park School **Nickname:** Doughboys **Founded:** 1867
Midweek matchday: Tuesday **Reserve League:** HSUCL Res. Div. Two
Record Attendance: 4,013 v Kettering Town.
Best FA Cup season: 1st Round 28-29 (v Bristol Rovers) 65-66 (1-2 v Aldershot Town).
Best FA Trophy season: 1st Round 71-72 (lost 0-3 to Dartford after 1-1 and 0-0 draws).
Best FA Vase season: 95-96.
Previous Leagues: Midland 1895-97 98-1901/ Southern 01-05 71-89/ Northants (Utd Co's) 19-34 36-56 61-68/ Central Alliance 56-61/ Metropolitan 68-70/ West Midlands Regional 70-71.
Players progressing to Football Lge: Phil Neal (N'hampton, L'pool & Eng.), Fanny Walden (Spurs & Eng.)
Clubhouse: Full facilities. Open evenings & Sat lunchtimes.
Club Record Goalscorer: S Hill **Club Record Appearances:** P Hayes 165, 1985-89.
Honours: Utd Co's Lg 10-11 62-63 64-65, Metropolitan Lge 69-70, Northants Snr Cup 1896-97 1901-02 02-03 33-34 47-48 49-50 81-82, Maunsell Cup 20-21 21-22.

Stotfold's Roy Boon steers the ball home in their match against Potton Utd. *Photo: Gordon Whittington*

Wooton Blue Cross's Andy Carey opens the score over Kempston *Photo: Gordon Whittington*

WOOTTON BLUE CROSS

Back Row (L-R): Shaun Staplehurst (jt Mgr), Christopher Hyde, Mark Emery, Martyn Taylor, Colin Roy, Tony Brittain, Martin Baker. Front Row: Mark Hall, John Hislop, Sam Brown, Darren Marsh (jt Mgr), Andrew Watt, Darek Jozwiak, Andrew Casey
Photo: Gordon Whittington

President: J Clarke. **Chairman:** D Peters
Secretary: Trevor Templeman, 3 Pollys Yard, Newport Pagnell, Bucks MK16 8YU
Manager: Shaun Staplehurst/Darren Marsh **Physio:** Trevor Templemen
Press Officer: Secretary
Ground: Weston Park, Bedford Road, Wootton (01234 767662).
Directions: Four miles south of Bedford on main road through village at rear of Post Office.
Capacity: 2,000 **Seats:** 50 **Cover:** 250 **Floodlights:** Yes **Founded:** 1887
Programme: 24 pages **Editor:** Secretary. **Club Shop:**
Colours: Blue & white/blue/blue **Change:** All yellow **Sponsors:** Vision Blinds
Nickname: Blue Cross. **Reserve's League:** United Counties Reserve Div 1
Midweek matchday: Tuesday **Record Gate:** 838 v Luton, Beds Prem. Cup 1988.
Best FA Vase year: 3rd Rd 74-75 **Best FA Cup year:** 2nd Qual. Rd 50-51 (3-4 v Hitchin (H)).
Previous Leagues: Bedford & District/ South Midlands 46-55.
Previous Grounds: Recreation Ground, Fishers Field, Rose & Crown, Cockfield.
Players progressing to Football Lge: Tony Biggs (Arsenal).
Clubhouse details: Main hall, bar, darts, pool, bingo. Open every evening and weekend lunchtimes.
97-98 - Captain: Chris Hyde **P.o.Y.:** Darak Jozwiak **Top Scorer:** Darak Jozwiak
Honours: Utd Co's Lg Div 2 67-68 69-70 (KO Cup 82-83, Div 2 Cup 64-65), South Midlands Lg 47-48 (R-up 49-50), Beds Senior Cup 70-71, Hinchinbrooke Cup(5).

YAXLEY

President: John Dowse **Chairman:** Malcom Whaley **Vice Chairman:** Geoff Heathcote
Secretary: Malcom Larrington, 70 Main Street, Yaxley, Peterborough PE7 3DB (01733 243276)
Manager: Dave Willis **Asst Manager:** Stuart Keir **Coach:**
Ground: Holme Road, Yaxley (01733 244928).
Directions: A1, then A15 at Norman Cross up to traffic lights, turn right then immediately right, follow road approx. 1 mile turn right into Holme Rd., ground approx. 200 yards on left.
Capacity: 1,000+ **Seats:** 150 **Cover:** Yes **Floodlights:** Yes **Founded:**
Programme: Yes **Editor:** Robin Peel **Sponsor:** Reads Removals
Colours: All blue **Change colours:** All tangerine **96-97 Captain:** Stuart Keir
Prev. Lge: Peterborough & District, Jewson Huntingdonshire, West Anglia.
Honours: UCL Div 1 96-97, Benevolent Cup 97-98; Hunts Senior Cup (4); Peterborough League (2); Peterborough Senior Cup (2); West Anglia League; Scott-Gatty Cup.

DIVISION ONE CLUBS 1998-99

BLISWORTH

Chairman: Pete Edwards **President:** L Piggott.
Secretary: Peter Edwards, 31 Windmill Ave, Blisworth, Northants NN7 3EQ (01604 858171 H, 0585 369933 B)
Manager: Brian Oldham **Assistant Manager:** Gary Edwards/Steve Paul. **Physio:** Elaine Johnson
Ground: Blisworth Playing Field, Courteenhall Road, Blisworth (01604 858024).
Directions: Courteenhall Road off A43.
Capacity: 1,000 **Seats/Cover:** No **Floodlights:** No **Clubhouse:** Yes **Programme:** No.
Colours: White/black/black & white **Change colours:** Black, white & red/black/black **Founded:** 1890.
Sponsors: Target Furniture, JB King Plant Hire **96-97 Captain:** Andy Johnson
Reserves' Lge: UCL Res. Div. 2 **Previous Lge:** Central Northants Combination 1978-87.
Player progressing to Football Lge: Dave Johnson (N'pton 83-84)
Hons: Northants Junior Cup 88-99

BUGBROOKE St MICHAELS

Chairman: Tom Treacy. **President:** John Curtis
Secretary: Roger Geary, 31 Kislingbury Rd, Bugbrooke, Northampton NN7 3QG (01604 831678).
Manager: Chris Goodchild **Asst Manager:** Mark Panter **Press Officer:** Rose Harris.
Ground: Birds Close, Gayton Road, Bugbrooke (01604 830707).
Directions: A45 Northampton to Daventry road, onto B4525 (Banbury Lane) at Kislingbury, left into Gayton Road, ground on left.
Capacity: 1,500 **Seats:** None **Cover:** Yes **Floodlights:** Yes **Founded:** 1929
Reserves' Lge: UCL Res. Div. 1 **Clubhouse:** Yes - normal licensing hours.
Programme: Eight pages. **Editor:** Rose Harris **Nickname:** Badgers
Club colours: Black & white/black/black **Change colours:** Blue & yellow/blue/blue **Record Gate:** 1,156
Previous Ground: School Close **Previous Lge:** Central Northants Combination 1952-87.
Players progressing to Football League: Kevin Slinn (Watford), Craig Adams (Northampton).
Sponsors: M C Builders. **96-97 Captain:** Dale Williams
Club Record Scorer: Vince Thomas **Club Record Appearances:** Jimmy Nord.
Honours: Northants Junior Cup 89-90; Central Northants Combination 68-69 69-70 70-71 71-72 76-77 85-86; UCL Res Div 2 R-up 94-95.

Goalmouth Action from Huntingdon v Cottingham. *Photo: Gordon Whittington*

BURTON PARK WANDERERS

Chairman: Bernard Lloyd **Vice Chairman:** Paul Clarke
Secretary: David Haynes, 58 Drayton Road, Lowick, Northants NN14 3BG (01832 735060 H, 01933 229777 x4706 B)
Manager: Colin Neill. **Asst Manager:** Eddie Lynch **Physio:** Nicky Mann
Ground: Latimer Park, Polwell Lane, Burton Latimer (01536 725841).
Directions: Entering Burton Latimer, turn off A6 Station Rd and right into Powell Lane; ground on the right.
Capacity: 1,000 **Seats:** 100 **Cover:** 150 **Floodlights:** No **Founded:** 1961
Colours: All blue **Change Colours:** Yellow & green/black/black
96-97 Captain: Nigel Buller **Sponsor:** Prescott Motors
Prog: 16 pages with entry **Nickname:** The Wanderers **Midweek matchday:** Tuesday
Previous Lge: Kettering Amateur **Record Attendance:** 253 v Rothwell, May 1989
Past Players to progress to Football League: Shaun Wills (Peterborough)
Honours: UCL Div 1 R-up, Benevolent Cup R-up

COTTINGHAM

Back Row (L-R); Rab Stewart, Joey Martin, Kevin McDonald, Paul Watson, James Keeney, Neil Addy, Pat Gibbons, Pat Rayment, Rob Dunion (Mgr). Front Row; Ned Burns (Asst Mgr), Neil Pask, Andy O'Neil, Ian Walker, Ian Jaffrey, Lee Addy, Steve Ewen *Photo: Gordon Whittington*

Chairman: Mike Beadsworth **Vice Chairman:** Brian Tilley
Secretary: Lindsay Brownlie, 30 Bancroft Rd, Cottingham, Market Harborough LE16 8XA (01536 771009).
Manager: Rob Dunion. **Asst Manager:** Neil Burns.
Ground: Berryfield Rd, Cottingham (01536 770051).
Directions: One and a half miles from Corby on A427 turn right to Cottingham. At junction of B670 turn left; Berryfield Road 200 yds on right.
Capacity: 1,000 **Seats:** None **Cover:** Yes **Floodlights:** No **Programme:** No
Reserves' Lge: UCL Res. Div. 2 **Clubhouse:** Bar & changing rooms
Colours: Yellow/green/yellow **Change colours:** Orange/black/black
Sponsors: B & J Decorators **96-97 Captain:** Neil Pask
Previous Leagues: Market Harborough/ Kettering Amateur/ East Midlands Alliance.
Honours: UCL Div 1 R-up 97-98; Northants Junior Cup

DAVENTRY TOWN

Chairman: Ray Humphries **Vice Chairman:** Grant Hughes **President:** Paul Webster
Secretary: Miss Joanne Place, 30 The Cherwell, Daventry, Northants NN11 4QJ (01327 311844 H, 01327 300001 B)
Manager: Barry Collinson **Physio:** Tony Jackson **Asst Manager:** Robin Humphries, Moz Elliott
Ground: Elderstubbs Farm, Leamington Way, Daventry, Northants (01327 706286).
Directions: Adjacent to A45 by-pass at top of Staverton Road Sports Complex.
Capacity: 2,000 **Seats:** 250 **Cover:** 250 **Floodlights:** Yes **Founded:** 1886.
Programme: 4 Pages. **Editor:** Nigel Foster **Sponsor:** Campbell Estate Agents
Colours: Black & white/black/black **Change colours:** All red
Midweek Matchday: Tuesday **Reserve Team's League:** Central Northants Comb.
Clubhouse: Large bar/kitchen **Record Attendance:** 350 v Ford Sports 1991.
Best FA Cup year: Prel. Rd 94-95 **Best FA Vase year:** Preliminary Rd 91-92 94-95.
Previous Leagues: Northampton Town (pre-1987)/ Central Northants Combination 87-89.
Players Progressing to Football League: Martin Aldridge (Northampton).
Hons: UCL Div 1(2) 89-91 (Lg Cup R-up 92-93, Highest Aggregate Cup), Northants Junior Cup 36-37 60-61 91-92.

HARROWBY UNITED

Harrowby United FC. *Photo: Martin Wray*

Chairman: Paul Daglish **Vice Chairman:** Robert Wilson **Secretary:** R W Wilson, 13 Dickens Road, Grantham, Lincs NG31 9QY
Manager: Barry Shaw **Asst Mgr:** Tony Cook **Coach:** Tony Cook **Physio:** Simon Shaw
Ground: Harrowby Playing Fields, Harrowby Lane, Grantham (01476 590822).
Directions: From A1 take B6403, go past A52 roundabout, past Ancaster turn and take road to Harrowby. Continue into Grantham, ground on right opposite Cherry Tree public house.
Capacity: 1,500 **Seats:** 100 **Cover:** 150 **Floodlights:** No **Founded:** 1949.
Programme: 12 pages **Clubhouse:** Large bar open normal licensing hours.
Colours: Blue & white/blue/blue **Change colours:** Red & white/white/red **Nickname:** Arrows.
Sponsor: Bailey Trailers **96-97 Captain:** Graham Drury
Reserves' League: Grantham **Best FA Vase season:** Preliminary Round 91-92.
Previous Leagues: Grantham/ Lincs/ East Mids Regional Alliance (pre-1990).
Players progressing to Football League: Richard Liburd (Middlesbrough).
Hons: Utd Co's Lg Div 1 91-92 (Benev. Cup R-up 91-92), Mids Regional All. 89-90 (Lg Cup 89-90), Lincs Snr 'B' Cup(2) 90-92.

HIGHAM TOWN

President: Vijay Patel **Chairman:** Richard Williams **Vice Chairman:** Brian Kirk
Secretary: Chris Ruff, 23 Queensway, Higham Ferrers NN10 8BU (01933 358862).
Manager: Adie Mann **Asst Mgr:** Matt Carroll **Coach:** Kevin Roberts **Physio:** Keith Bates.
Ground: Recreation Ground, Vine Hill Drive, Higham Ferrers (01933 353751).
Directions: From Kettering 1st right on A6 after A45 junction to St Neots. From Bedford, 3rd left after entering town on A6 from Rushden. Higham is served by London-Bedford-Corby United Counties Coachlines, and United Counties local services Northampton-Raunds and Bedford-Kettering.
Capacity: 1,000 **Seats:** Nil **Cover:** 100 **Floodlights:** No **Founded:** 1895.
Programme: 12 pages with admission**Editor:** Secretary **Reformed:** 1920 & 1946
Colours: Sky & navy/navy/navy **Change colours:** Black & white/black/black **Nickname:** Lankies.
Midweek home matches: Tuesday **Reserves' Lge:** UCL Reserve Div. **Sponsors:** Higham News
Previous Lges: Wellingborough 20-21/ Northants (now Utd Co's) 21-36/ Rushden 46-50.
Previous Ground: Duchy Farm Field 20-24.
Record win: 15-0 v Towcester Town (H), United Counties League Division One 3/4/93.
Record defeat: 0-12 v Kettering Town (A), United Counties League 8/2/36.
Record Attandance: 5,700 v Chesterfield, FA Cup final qualifying round replay 22-23.
Record scorer: Stuart Sinfield 136 **Record appearances:** Brian Harbour 485.
Clubhouse: Open during season 8.30-11pm Tues, Thurs & Fri, after Saturday games & 12-1.30pm Sundays. Light refreshments available after Saturday games.
Hons: UCL Div 1 97-98, R-up 70-71 71-72 92-93 94-95; Northants Lg 21-22 22-23 (R-up 23-24 26-27); Northants Snr Cup 21-22 (R-up 30-31 32-33); Maunsell Premier Cup 22-23 33-34.

IRCHESTER UNITED

Chairman: Geoff Cotter
Secretary: Glyn Cotter, 26 Denford Way, Wellingborough, Northants NN8 5UB (01933 402514)
Manager: Andy Toon **Asst. Manager:** Roy Geeves **Physio:** Mick Howarth.
Ground: Alfred Street, Irchester (01933 312877).
Directions: Off Rushden Road to Wollaston Road, next to recreation ground.
Capacity: 1,000 **Seats:** None **Cover:** Yes **Floodlights:** No **Programme:** No
Colours: Red & white/black/red **Change colours:** Red/blue/blue **Clubhouse:** Yes
Reserves' Lge: UCL Res. Div. 2 **Previous Leagues:** Rushden & District 1936-69.
Best FA Cup year: Prel. Rd 34-35 **Best FA Vase year:** Preliminary Round 77-78.
Hons: Northants Lg Div 2 30-31 31-32, Northants Snr Cup 29-30 48-49 75-76, Rushden & District Lg 28-29 29-30 36-37 46-47 50-51 51-52 56-57.

NEWPORT PAGNELL TOWN

Chairman: Gerry Ward **Vice Chairman:** **President:** Ken Inch.
Secretary: John Anderson, 59 Willen Road, Newport Pagnell, Bucks MK16 0DE (01908 610440).
Manager: Terry Ashton/D Janes
Ground: Willen Road, Newport Pagnell (01908 611993).
Directions: Adjacent to A442 Newport Pagnell by-pass.
Capacity: 2,000 **Seats:** 100 **Cover:** 100 **Floodlights:** Yes **Club Shop:**
Programme: 56 pages **Editor:** Ernie Print
Colours: White & green/green/green **Change colours:** Red/white/green
Sponsors: Brian Currie **Nickname:** Swans **Founded:** 1963.
Midweek Matchday: Tuesday **Reserve Team's League:** United Counties
Previous Leagues: Nth Bucks 63-71/ South Mids 71-73 **Best FA Vase year:** 2nd Rd 84-85
Clubhouse: Open every evening
96-97 Captain: Des Cook **P.o.Y.:** Des Cook **Top Scorer:** Darren Lynch
Honours: UCL Div 1 82-83 (R-up 91-92, Div 1 Cup 77-78), Daventry Charity Cup R-up 93-94.

NORTHAMPTON O.N. CHENECKS

Chairman: John Wilson **Vice Chairman:** Eddie Slinn **President:** Claude Hasdell
Secretary: John Goodger, 74 Beech Ave, Abington, Northampton NN3 2JG (01604 717224 H)
Manager: Neil McAllister **Asst Manager:** Claude Hasdell **Physio:** John Goodger
Ground: Billing Road, Northampton (0604 34045).
Directions: South ring road, exit A43 Kettering, left at lights, top of hill, ground 200 yds on right.
Capacity: 1,350 **Seats:** Yes **Cover:** Yes **Floodlights:** No **Founded:** 1946.
Prog.: 16 pages with entry **Editor:** Eddie Slinn **Clubhouse:** Yes
Colours: Blue & white/blue/blue **Change colours:** All red
Previous Leagues: N'pton Town (pre-1969) **Reserves' League:** UCL Res Div 1
Midweek Matchday: **96-97 Captain:** Amos Donnelly
Honours: UCL Div 1 77-78 79-80, Northants Jnr Cup R-up 93-94

NORTHAMPTON VANAID

Chairman: Rob Clarke **Vice Chairman:** Steve Tebbutt **President:** A Blundell
Secretary: Albert Gibbs, 15 Gifford Court, Lynhurst Road, Duston, NN5 6LX (01604 456944)
Manager: Nick Verity **Asst Manager:** Adam May **Physio:** Glen Botterill
Ground: Fernie Fields, Moulton, Northampton (01604 670366).
Directions: R'bout at Lumbertub pub take turn to Moulton, 1st right signposted.
Capacity: 700 **Seats:** 100 **Cover:** Yes **Floodlights:** **Founded:** 1968
Programme: Yes **Editor:** Martin Dearden **Clubhouse:** Large bar. Hot food/bar meals
Colours: Blue/blue/yellow **Change colours:** Black & white/black/black**Nickname:** Vans.
Previous League: N'pton Town (pre-1993) **Reserves' League:** UCL Res Div 2
Sponsors: Echo PLC **96-97 Captain:** Adam Sandy **Record Gate:** 78
Honours: UCL Div 1 93-94, Benevolent Cup R-up 93-94; Northants Jnr Cup 93-94 96-97 97-98; Northampton Town Lg 88-89 89-90.

Higham Town's Jon Ogden fires in a goal against Northampton Vanaid *Photo: Gordon Whittington*

Higham Town's Captain Stuart Abrahart accepts the Uhlsport UCL Division One Trophy.
Photo: Gordon Whittington

OLNEY TOWN

Chairman: Peter Shipton **President:** Andrew Soul
Secretary: Andrew Baldwin, 49 Midland Road, Olney, Bucks MK46 4BP (01234 711071)
Manager: Phil Bone **Asst Manager:** Richard Large
Coach: Mark Lancaster **Physio:** Peter Munting
Ground: East Street, Olney (0234 712227)
Directions: Enter Olney on A509 from Wellingborough, 100yds on left enter East St, ground 200 yds on left.
Capacity: 2,000 **Seats:** None **Cover:** Yes **Floodlights:** No **Founded:**
Programme: 32 pages **Editor:** Barry Simons **96-97 Captain:** Richard Large
Colours: Black & white/black/black **Change colours:** Yellow & black/black/black
Previous Leagues: Nth Bucks, Rushden & Dist. **Sponsors:** Cyclo Sports **Clubhouse:** Yes
Honours: UCL Div 1 72-73, Berks & Bucks I'mediate Cup 92-93

ROTHWELL CORINTHIANS:

Chairman: Brian Johnson **Vice Chairman:** May Clelland **President:** Terry Smith
Secretary: Bob Clelland, 5 Drake Close, Rothwell, Northants NN14 6DJ (01536 710134).
Manager: Rob Clark **Physio:** Mick Fox
Ground: Seargeant's Lawn, Desborough Road, Rothwell (01536 418688)
Directions: A6 towards Desborough, on right opposite Greening Road.
Capacity: **Seats:** 50 **Cover:** 100 **Floodlights:** No **Shop:** No
Programme: Yes **Editor:** Brian Johnson **Nickname:** Corinthians
Colours: Red & white/red/red **Change colours:** Blue & white/blue/blue
Sponsor: Springfir Estates **Founded:** 1930's **96-97 Captain:** John Cairns
Club House: Yes **Previous Lge:** East Midlands Alliance
Honours: East Midlands Alliance (2).

Harrowby United's main stand *Photo: Martin Wray*

Harrowby score their 6th goal against bottom placed Huntingdon *Photo: Martin Wray*

SHARNBROOK

Chairman: Peter Butler **President:** John Boyles
Secretary: Roy Boulton, 10 St Mary's Avenue, Rushden, Northants NN10 9EP (01933 315890)
Manager: Dai Hunt **Asst Manager:** Ali Woods **Physio:** Jim Donaldson
Ground: Lodge Rd, Sharnbrook (0234 781080). **Directions:** Second sign to Sharnbrook from Rushden on A6, under railway bridge, right at T-junction, left past church, right into Lodge Road.
Capacity: 1,000 **Seats:** None **Cover:** Yes **Floodlights:** No
Programme: 12 pages **Editor:** Ali Woods **Sponsor:** BC Cars
Colours: Yellow/black/yellow **Change colours:** White/maroon/maroon **Clubhouse:** Yes
Reserves' Lge: UCL Res Div 2 **Previous Leagues:** Bedford & Dist (pre-1968). **96-97 Captain:** Steve Denton
Hons: Beds I'mediate Cup 73-74 **Player progressing to Football Lge:** Matt Jackson (Luton, Everton)

THRAPSTON TOWN

President: Derek Barber **Chairman:** Dave Harris **Vice Chairman:** Barry Carter
Secretary: John Crawford, Smiths Farm House, Warren Lane, Bythorn, Cambs (01832 734998)
Manager: Gary Petts **Asst Manager:** Barry Carter **Physio:** Nigel Gore
Ground: Chancery Lane, Thrapston, Northants (08012 732470).
Directions: Chancery Lane off A605 in town centre.
Capacity: 1,000 **Seats:** Yes **Cover:** Yes **Floodlights:** No **Founded:** 1960.
Programme: Yes **Editor:** Dave Overend **Prev. Lge:** Kettering Amtr (pre-1978)
Colours: All blue & yellow **Change colours:** White/blue/blue **Nickname:** Venturas
Sponsor: Hobbs Direct Mail **96-97 Captain:** Mark Buckby **Clubhouse:** Yes
Honours: Northants Junior Cup 87-88, Kettering Amateur Lg 70-71 72-73 73-74 77-78.

WELLINGBOROUGH WHITWORTHS

Chairman: Bob Jarvis **Vice Chairman:** Dave Woodley **President:** Terry Faulkner
Secretary: Brian Higgins, 1 Knightlands Road, Irthlingborough NN9 5SU (01933 650031).
Manager: Phil Harvey **Asst Manager:** Mick Garrett **Physio:** Andrew King
Ground: London Road, Wellingborough, Northants (01933 227324).
Directions: Off London Road at Dog & Duck public house
Capacity: 700 **Seats:** None **Cover:** Yes **Floodlights:** No **Programme:** No
Colours: All yellow **Change colours:** Red & white/red/re**Reserves' Lge:** UCL Res Div 2
Sponsor: Whitworth Brothers **96-97 Captain:** Steve Grant
Clubhouse: Yes **Prev. Lges:** Rushden & Dist./ E. Mids All. (pre-1985).
Honours: Rushden & District Lg 76-77; Northants Jun Cup 96

WOODFORD UNITED

Chairman: Bob Justice **Vice-Chairman:** R Adams **Gen Manager:** Andy McGuire
Secretary: Andy Worrall, 30 Townsend, Woodford Halse, Daventry, Northants NN11 3QL (01327 261746)
Manager: Darren Foster, Craig Robson
Ground: Byfield Road, Woodford Halse, Daventry, Northants (01327 263734)
Directions: Off A 361 Daventry to Banbury Rd, on Woodford Road out of Byfield.
Capacity: 3,000 **Seats:** 25 **Cover:** 150 **Floodlights:** No **Club Shop:**
Programme: 16 pages **Editor:** Francis Peacock (01327 263335)
Colours: All red **Change Colours:** All blue
Sponsors: Styleglaze **Nickname:** **Founded:** 1946.
Previous Leagues: Central Northants Comb pre 70, UCL 70-78, Northants Comb
Reserve's League: Northants Comb.
97-98 - Captain: Kevin Aris **P.o.Y.:** Kevin Aris **Top Scorer:** Graham Drew
Honours: Northants Comb 66 67 90 92 95, KO Cup 66 90 93 95 98; UCL Div 2 74, KO Cup 74;

JEWSON WESSEX LEAGUE

FEEDER TO: Dr MARTENS FOOTBALL LEAGUE

President/Chairman: Alf Peckham

Vice Chairman: Norman Cook

Hon: Secretary: Tom Linden, 63 Downs Road, Winchester, Hampshire, SO21 3EW (01962 884760)

FIRST DIVISION LEAGUE TABLE 1997-98

			Home					*Away*					
		P	*W*	*D*	*L*	*F*	*A*	*W*	*D*	*L*	*F*	*A*	**Pts**
1	AFC Lymington	38	14	3	2	44	16	15	2	2	50	11	92
2	Andover	38	12	5	2	55	22	12	4	3	44	24	81
3	AFC Newbury	38	11	3	5	30	19	11	4	4	42	16	73
4	Eastleigh	38	10	7	2	38	13	10	4	5	36	18	71
5	Bemerton HH	38	10	4	5	35	19	9	7	3	34	19	68
6	Cowes Sports	38	12	1	6	40	26	8	5	6	27	25	66
7	Wimborne Tn	38	10	6	3	49	29	8	3	8	40	34	63
8	AFC Totton	38	8	5	6	29	17	7	5	7	29	24	55
9	Bournemouth	38	11	3	5	41	29	5	4	10	23	39	55
10	Thatcham Tn	38	8	4	7	34	24	8	2	9	30	30	54
11	Christchurch	38	8	3	8	25	27	7	3	9	30	42	51
12	East Cowes Vic	38	9	5	5	30	19	4	6	9	16	23	50
13	Portsmouth RN	38	9	3	7	34	30	4	4	11	30	49	46
14	BAT	38	7	5	7	34	37	5	2	12	26	45	43
15	Gosport Boro	38	6	4	9	31	32	3	6	10	17	33	37
16	Aerostructures	38	3	5	11	22	36	6	5	8	28	41	37
17	Brockenhurst	38	5	6	8	20	33	4	3	12	23	50	36
18	Downton	38	6	2	11	20	32	1	8	10	16	34	31
19	Whitchurch Utd	38	5	5	9	24	33	2	3	14	13	45	29
20	Romsey Tn	38	4	3	12	28	73	1	2	16	12	61	20

RESULTS GRID 1997-98

HOME TEAM	1	2	3	4	5	6	7	8	9	10	11	12	13	14	15	16	17	18	19	20
1. AFC Lymington	*	2-2	2-1	1-2	2-1	4-0	1-1	1-1	1-0	4-1	2-0	2-1	1-0	1-3	3-0	4-2	3-0	2-0	5-0	3-1
2. MC Newbury	0-1	*	0-6	2-0	0-0	3-2	1-1	0-1	2-0	3-1	4-0	1-0	0-0	1-2	2-0	2-0	2-1	2-0	5-0	0-4
3. MC Totton	2-1	0-1	*	6-0	0-2	0-0	0-1	2-1	1-1	3-1	1-1	2-2	1-0	1-2	3-1	4-0	1-1	0-1	2-0	0-1
4. Aerostructures	0-3	1-0	0-1	*	1-2	1-2	2-3	3-3	1-3	2-3	1-2	0-2	0-2	0-0	0-0	5-4	3-2	1-1	0-0	1-3
5. Andover	2-2	2-5	2-0	3-0	*	6-1	2-2	2-0	8-2	2-0	0-3	1-0	1-1	4-1	5-2	0-0	7-0	4-1	2-0	2-2
6. B A T	1-5	1-4	1-1	1-1	1-5	*	2-1	5-1	4-2	6-1	0-4	1-1	1-1	0-1	1-0	1-1	4-1	4-0	0-1	0-6
7. Bemerton H H	0-2	1-1	0-1	5-1	1-1	2-1	*	0-2	4-2	1-1	3-0	3-1	0-1	1-1	2-0	3-0	3-0	2-1	2-0	2-3
8. Bournemouth	0-7	2-1	0-2	2-1	1-1	3-2	1-2	*	3-2	3-1	1-1	1-1	1-0	0-4	0-1	8-1	4-0	3-1	5-0	3-1
9. Brockenhurst	1-7	1-5	1-1	2-0	1-3	2-3	0-2	0-0	*	0-2	0-0	1-1	3-0	1-3	3-1	0-3	0-0	1-0	3-2	0-0
10. Christchurch	0-2	0-2	0-0	2-4	0-2	2-1	1-0	3-2	1-2	*	3-0	0-0	2-0	0-2	1-1	5-1	3-1	0-3	2-1	0-3
11. Cowes Sports	1-3	3-2	1-0	0-3	3-2	3-0	0-4	4-0	0-2	3-0	*	4-0	1-1	2-0	3-1	2-3	3-2	0-2	3-1	4-0
12. Downton	0-1	1-2	1-0	3-3	0-4	1-2	1-3	1-2	2-1	1-3	0-1	*	1-2	1-0	0-1	2-2	2-1	0-3	1-0	2-1
13. East Cowes Vic	1-3	1-0	2-0	1-3	0-4	1-0	1-1	2-1	0-1	1-0	1-1	5-1	*	1-1	0-0	1-0	6-0	2-3	0-0	4-0
14. Eastleigh	1-2	0-0	0-0	4-0	4-1	3-0	1-1	1-0	4-0	2-2	3-1	2-0	1-1	*	0-1	4-1	4-0	0-0	1-1	3-2
15. Gosport Borough	0-2	0-3	2-4	1-2	2-3	3-0	1-3	1-1	4-2	1-2	1-1	0-0	1-1	0-3	*	3-1	5-0	2-1	3-1	1-2
16. Portsmouth RN	0-5	0-2	1-4	1-1	0-2	1-2	1-1	5-1	4-1	1-3	4-0	3-2	2-1	2-0	1-0	*	3-1	0-2	4-1	1-1
17. Romsey Town	1-2	1-7	2-1	0-4	1-2	1-5	0-7	4-2	1-1	3-1	1-7	2-2	3-1	0-10	4-4	1-4	*	1-4	1-3	1-6
18. Thatcham Town	0-0	0-0	2-4	5-1	1-2	3-3	0-1	1-2	1-1	2-3	0-1	2-0	2-1	0-1	1-0	3-1	6-0	*	2-1	3-2
19. Whitchurch Utd	0-2	0-4	2-2	1-1	3-4	3-0	0-0	1-2	1-0	1-2	0-1	1-1	2-0	2-1	1-1	0-5	0-1	2-4	*	4-2
20. Wimborne Tn	1-0	0-1	5-1	1-1	3-3	3-2	4-0	3-1	8-0	3-3	0-3	3-1	0-3	1-1	3-3	1-1	2-1	4-3	4-1	*

JEWSON WESSEX LEAGUE CUP 1997-98

First Round Aggregate Results

MC Newbury	v	Bournemouth	4-1	MC Totton	v	Christchurch	3-1
East Cowes Vics	v	B.A.T.	4-4 *	Aerostructures	v	Romsey Town	7-2
Brockenhurst	v	Whitchurch Utd	8-4				

** East Cowes Vics won on away goals rule*

Second Round Aggregate Results

Aerostuctures	v	East Cowes Vics	3-1	MC Lymington	v	Cowes Sports	1-1 *
AK Newbury	v	Downton	0-0 *	MC Totton	v	Portsmouth RN	6-3
Bemerton Heath H	v	Gosport Borough	1-1 **	Thatcham Town	v	Andover	4-3
Wimborne Town	v	Eastleigh	7-1				

** MC Lymington & AK Newbury won on away goals rule*
*** Bemerton Heath Harlequins won on penalties*

Quarter Final Aggregate Results

Bemerton Heath	v	MC Newbury	5-2	Aerostructures	v	MC Totton	3-1
Wimborne Town	v	Brockenhurst	7-0	Thatcham Town	v	AK Lymington	3-2

Semi-Final Aggregate Results

Bemerton Heath H	v	Wimborne Town	5-2	Aerostructures	v	Thatcham Town	5-3

Final at Eastleigh

Aerostructures	v	Bemerton Heath H	2-1

Officially featuring all F.A. competitions including
The F.A. Carlsberg Vase
The F.A. Umbro Trophy
The Littlewoods F.A. Cup

and all non-League football
from Conference to County League football

JEWSON WESSEX Ten Year Records

	88/9	89/0	90/1	91/2	92/3	93/4	94/5	95/6	96/7	97/8
Aerostructures Spts & Soc	10	12	16	9	12	19	17	18	12	16
AFC Lymington	5	5	9	2	1	3	8	2	1	1
AFC Newbury	-	-	-	-	-	-	-	-	-	3
AFC Totton	14	6	14	17	16	21	9	14	20	8
Andover	-	-	-	-	-	2	7	9	6	2
Bashley	1	-	-	-	-	-	-	-	-	-
BAT Sports	-	3	8	16	18	9	13	15	19	14
Bemerton Heath Harl.	-	8	18	8	3	7	5	8	5	5
Bournemouth	12	10	3	6	7	11	2	7	13	9
Brockenhurst	16	17	7	12	10	8	6	19	14	17
Christchurch	13	15	15	13	13	10	18	5	16	11
Cowes Sports	-	-	-	-	-	-	15	16	9	6
Downton	-	-	-	-	-	16	20	12	8	18
E Cowes Vict. Ath.	8	13	13	14	20	14	16	10	17	12
Eastleigh	9	14	12	10	9	15	14	4	7	4
Fleet Town	-	18	10	11	8	6	1	-	-	-
Gosport Borough	-	-	-	-	5	5	10	11	11	15
Havant Town	2	11	1	-	-	-	-	-	-	-
Horndean	11	16	20	18	11	11	22	-	-	-
Newport IOW	3	2	-	-	-	-	-	-	-	-
Petersfield Town	-	-	-	-	-	18	21	20	21	-
Portsmouth Royal Navy	17	19	17	19	17	13	11	17	10	13
Romsey Town	7	1	4	4	21	-	-	-	18	20
Ryde Sports	-	-	11	7	6	12	12	3	4	-
Sholing Sports	15	9	19	15	19	w/d				
Swanage Town & Her.	-	-	2	5	14	20	19	21	-	-
Thatcham Town	4	7	6	3	4	4	3	1	3	10
Whitchurch United	-	-	-	-	15	22	-	13	15	19
Wimborne Town	6	4	5	1	2	1	4	6	2	7
No of Clubs Competing	17	19	20	19	21	22	22	21	21	20

LEAGUE CUP WINNERS

1986-87	-	Road Sea
1987-88	-	East Cowes Victoria Athletic
1988-89	-	AFC Lymington
1989-90	-	AFC Totton
1990-91	-	Thatcham Town
1991-92	-	Thatcham Town
1992-93	-	Gosport Borough
1993-94	-	Wimborne Town
1994-95	-	Thatcham Town
1995-96	-	Downton
1996-97	-	Thatcham Town
1997-98	-	Aerostructures

CLUB DIRECTORY 1998-99

AFC NEWBURY

Chairman: Gerry Hynes **Manager:**
Secretary: Jim Goslin, The Flat, Porch Farm, Newbury Road, Kingsclere, Newbury, Berks RG20 4SX (01635 298985)
Ground: Faraday Road, Newbury, Berks (01635 523222)
Directions: A34 to Robin Hood roundabout, then A4 towards Reading. Right at lights after 100 yards into Faraday Road. Ground at end of road.
Colours: Green & white/white/green & white **Change:** Red & white/red/red & white
Midweek Matches: Tuesday

A.F.C. TOTTON

Chairman: Bob Devoy **Vice Chairman:** Mr P Maiden **President:** Mr D Maton.
Secretary: Mrs Sheila Benfield, 35 Fishers Rd, Totton, Southampton SO40 9HW (01703 865421).
Manager: Ian Robinson **Press Officer:** Mr P Chilcott (01703 860453).
Ground: Testwood Park, Testwood Place, Totton, Southampton (01703 868981).
Directions: 5 mins walk from Totton station. Turn off r'bout in Totton centre into Library Rd, then 1st left & 2nd rd.
Seats: 200 **Cover:** 250 **Capacity:** 2,500 **Floodlights:** Yes **Founded:** 1886
Colours: White & blue/blue/white & blue **Change colours:** Red & white/red/red
Sponsors: Cap'n Cod **Midweek Matches:** Tuesday **Nickname:** Stags.
Record Gate: 600 v Windsor & Eton, F.A. Cup 4th Qualifying Rd 82-83.
Club Shop: No **Programme:** 30 pages 50p **Previous League:** Hants 1886-1986
Previous Name: Totton FC (until merger with Totton Athletic in 1979).
Previous Grounds: Downs Park/ Mayfield Park.
Clubhouse: Open for matches and training sessions. Burgers, sandwiches, tea, coffee, biscuits etc available.
Honours: Hants Lg(2)

B.A.T. SPORTS

Chairman: Dixie Batt **Manager:** Eddie Harper & Paul Bishop
Secretary: Mike Geddes, 39 Pacific Close, Victoria Quay, Ocean Village, Southampton, SO14 3 TX (01703 337460 H)
Ground: BAT Sports Ground, Southern Gdns, off Ringwood Road, Totton (01703 862143).
Directions: Into centre of Totton, proceed up Ringwood Rd past small r'bout, 2nd left into Southern Gardens. Half mile from Totton (BR), bus X2 (Southampton-Bournemouth).
Seats: 150. **Cover:** 150. **Capacity:** 3,000 **Floodlights:** Yes **Founded:** 1925
Colours: Blue & yellow/blue/blue **Change:** Red & black/red/red
Programme: 20 pages, 30p **Midweek Matches:** Tuesday
Best FA Vase year: 2nd Rd 96-97
Clubhouse: Normal licensing hrs, all day for members' sports facilities. Darts, pool, CD player. Hot & cold snacks.

BEMERTON HEATH HARLEQUINS

Chairman: George Parker **President:** Peter Say. **Manager:** Steve Slade
Secretary: A.J.Hardwick, 2 Ashley Rd, Salisbury, Wilts. SP2 7BZ (01722 333015)
Ass.Manager: Kevin Franklyn. **Physio:** Andy Nash **Coach:** Gary Cross
Ground: Western Way, Bemerton Heath, Salisbury, Wilts (01722 331925).
Directions: Turn off A36 Salisbury-Bristol Rd at Skew Bridge (right turn if coming out of Salisbury), 1st left into Pembroke Rd for half mile, 2nd left along Western Way - ground quarter mile at end. 40 mins walk from Salisbury (BR) station. Bus 351 or 352 from city centre stops at junction of Pembroke Rd/ Western Way.
Seats: 155. **Cover:** 350 **Floodlights:** Yes **Founded:** May 1989 **Clubhouse:** Yes
Colours: Black & white/black/black & white **Change colours:** Yellow/white/white
Nickname: Quins **Programme:** 32 pages, 50p **Midweek Matches:** Tuesday
Record Gate:1,118 v Aldershot Town F.A.Cup Ist Qual.RD.Aug.94.
Previous Names: Bemerton Athletic, Moon FC & Bemerton Boys; all merged in 1989.
Previous Leagues: B'ton Ath.: Salis. & Wilts Comb., Moon: Salis. & Andover Sunday, B'ton Boys: Mid Wilts.
Club record appearances: Keith Richardson.
Honours: Wilts Snr Cup 92-93. *Wilts Lg(3) as Bemerton Athletic*

Bemerton Heath Harlequins Photo: Roger Turner

Bournemouth FC Photo: Roger Turner

BOURNEMOUTH

Chairman: V C Dominey **Vice Chairman:** J B Wood **President:** D Nippard
Secretary: Mrs Sandra Dominey, 26 Victoria Road, Parkstone, Poole, Dorset BH12 3BB (01202 737859 H, 01202 749584 B)
Manager: Alex Pike **Asst Manager:** Nick Jennings **Coach:** Chris Weller
Physio: Irvin Brown **Comm. Manager:** Alex Pike **Press Officer:** Mark Willis.
Ground: Victoria Park, Namu Rd., Winton, Bournemouth, Dorset (01202 515123).
Directions: Any bus to Wimborne Road, Winton. 2 miles from Bournemouth Central (BR).
Seats: 250 **Cover:** 250 **Capacity:** 3,000 **Floodlights:** Yes **Founded:** 1875.
Colours: Red & white/red/red **Change colours:** Green & yellow/green/green
Programme: 58 pages, 50p **Editor:** Mark Willis **Club Shop:** No.
Nickname: Poppies. **Sponsors:** Chapel Carpets **Midweek Matches:** Tuesday
Previous Leagues: Hants. **Reserves' League:** Jewson Wessex Comb.
Previous Ground: Dene Park 1888-90
Previous Names: Bournemouth Rovers 1875-88/ Bournemouth Dene Park 1888-90.
Clubhouse: Open daily 7-11pm. Sandwiches & hot snacks (burgers, chips etc).
Club record scorer: B Head
Record fee rec.: £1,500 for Chike Onourah (Wimborne 93-94)
Honours: Hants Lg 13-13 21-22, B'mouth Snr Cup 66-67 89-90, Texaco F'lit Cup R-up 91-92, Hant I'mediate Cup 49-50 69-70, Hants Yth Cup 54-55 57-58 67-68.

BROCKENHURST

Chairman: Brian Bidwell **Manager:** Mike Read
Secretary: Paul Christopher, 31 Brookside Road, Bransgore, Christchurch, Dorset BH23 8NA (01425 674084 H)
Ground: Grigg Lane, Brockenhurst, Hants (01590 623544).
Directions: M27 Junc 1, A337 to Lyndhurst, round one-way system, A337 to Brockenhurst, turn right at Carey's Manor Hotel into Grigg Lane, ground 200 yds on the right.
Seats: 200 **Cover:** 300 **Capacity:** 2,000 **Floodlights:** Yes **Founded:** 1898
Colours: Blue & white/blue/blue **Change colours:** Red & white/red/red
Programme: 12 pages, 20p, **Editor:** C West (01590 623714)
Midweek Matches: Wednesday. **Previous League:** Hants 24-26 47-86
Clubhouse: Every evening plus Tues, Sat & Sun lunchtimes.
Honours: F.A. Amateur Cup 2nd Rd 73-74; Hants I'mediate Cup 61-62; B'mouth Snr Cup 60-61; Hants Lg 75-76, R-up 73-74 79-80, Div 2 70-71 (R-up 60-61), Div 3 59-60;

CHRISTCHURCH

Chairman: Robin Osborne **Vice Chairman:** Jan Bridle. **President:** Dennis James.
Secretary: Mrs D Page, 87 The Albany, Manor Road, Bournemouth BH1 3EJ (01202 551977).
Manager: Ray Collins **Physio:** Brian Finch
Ground: Christchurch Sporting Club, Hurn Bridge, Avon Causeway, Christchurch (01202 473792).
Directions: A338 from Ringwood, turn off signed Hurn Airport on left. Before Airport use mini roundabout & take exit signed to Sopley and ground is immediately on the right. 3 miles from Christchurch (BR).
Seats: 215 **Cover:** 265 **Capacity:** 2,000 **Floodlights:** Yes
Programme: 16 pages, 50p **Editor:** Phil Old **Press Officer:** Dennis James.
Colours: All royal blue (white trim) **Change colours:** Yellow/black/yellow & black
Sponsors: Franklin Transport **Nickname:** Priory **Founded:** 1885
Previous League: Hampshire. **Midweek Matches:** Tuesday
Previous Ground: Barrack Rd Recreation Ground (until 1984).
Players progressing to Football Lge: Jody Craddock (Cambridge Utd/Sunderland 93), Dan West (Aston Villa 94).
Clubhouse: Normal pub hours. Cooked food at lunchtimes.
97-98 - P.o.Y.: Justin Keeler **Club record appearances:** John Haynes.
Honours: Hants Jnr Cup 1892-93 1911-12 20-21; Hants Int. Cup 86-87; Pickford Cup 91; Hants Lg Div 2 37-38 47-48 85-86 (Div 3 56-57); B'mouth Snr Cup (5) 56-57 59-60 67-70; B'mouth Page-Croft Cup 94-95.

COWES SPORTS

President: **Chairman:** Ray Sleep. **Manager:** Dale Young.
Secretary: Mr W G Murray, 53 Park Rd, Cowes, Isle of Wight PO31 7LY (01983 294445).
Ground: Westwood Park, Reynolds Close, off Park Rd, Cowes, Isle of Wight (01983 293793).
Directions: Take Park Road out of Cowes centre. Reynolds Close is a right turn half mile up hill.
Capacity: **Seats:** Yes **Cover:** Stand **Floodlights:** Yes **Founded:**
Colours: Blue & white stripes/black/blue **Change colours:** All red
Previous League: Hampshire (pre-1994) **Midweek Fixtures:** Wednesday
Best FA Cup season: Fourth Qualifying Round replay 57-58 (lost 1-4 at Trowbridge after 2-2 draw).
Honours: Hampshire Lg 93-94.

DOWNTON

Chairman: James Blake **President:** R Tanner
Secretary: Brian Trent 21 Fison Walk, Bishopdown, Salisbury, Wilts SP1 3JF (01722 323097)
Manager: M Savage **Coach:** C Huxford **Physio:** T Ship
Ground: Brian Whitehead Sports Ground, Wick Lane, Downton (01725 512162)
Directions: Travelling south from Salisbury on A338, 7 miles, turn right into Wick Lane, gr qtr mile on left.
Capacity: 1600 **Seats:** 250 **Cover:** Nil **Floodlights:** Yes **Club Shop:** No
Programme: Yes **Editor:** J Blake
Colours: Red/white/red **Change colours:** Yellow/blue/yellow
Sponsor: Lex Vauxhall Salisbury **Nickname:** The Robins **Founded:** 1905
Midweek Matchday: Wednesday **Youth League:**
Previous League: Bournemouth, Hants (pre-1993).
Clubhouse: Bar with kitchen facilities.
Honours: Wilts Sen Cup 79-80 80-81, (R-up 55-56 91-92 94-95); Wilts Jun Cup 49-50; Bournemouth Sen Lge 60 61 62 64 65 67 68, Sen Lge Cup 61-62 63-64 66-67, Cup 62-63 79-80; Wessex Lge Cup 95-96; Wessex Comb Cup (R-up 95-96); Russell Cotes Cup 95-96; Hayward Cup 64-65.

EAST COWES VICTORIA ATHLETIC

Back Row (L-R): Tony Newman (Mgr), Marvin Tyldesley, Steve Stay, Matthew Chiverton, Scott Morey, Darren Keefe, Darren Roberts, Alan Walters (Asst Mgr). Front Row: Neil Berridge, Mark Brodie, John Beard, Darren Plenty, Jamie Newnham, Simon Butler, Ian Dennis. Jamie Bray (Mascot)

Chairman: Mick Everett **Vice-Chairman:** Lee Bray **Gen Manager:** Steve Stay
Secretary: Ray Fleming, Glenmead, Chilton Lane, Brighstone, I.O.W. PO30 4DR (01983 740113)
Manager: Tony Newman **Coach:** Steve Stay **Physios:** Mike Reed & Kevin Marsay
Ground: Beatrice Avenue Ground, East Cowes, I.O.W. (01938 297165).
Directions: From the ferry: 1 mile from town centre on lower main road to Newport or Ryde, near Whippingham Church adjacent to Osborne Middle School.
Seats: 250 **Cover:** 400 **Capacity:** 4,000 **Floodlights:** Yes **Founded:** 1968.
Colours: Red & white stripes/red/red **Change colours:** Green & white/green/green
Programme: 40 pages, 50p **Editor:** Alan Green (01983 296069)
Midweek Matches: Wednesday **Sponsors:** Bishops Insurance. **Club Shop:** No.
Nickname: Vics. **Record Gate:** 2,000 v Poole Town, FA Cup 1954
Previous Leagues: (E.C. Vics): I.O.W. 1898-19 21-47/ Hants 14-21 47-87.
Midweek matchday: Wednesday **Reserve team's League:** Isle of Wight Lge.
Player progressing to Football League: Gareth Williams (Aston Villa, via Gosport Borough, 1987).
Clubhouse: Yes, open most evenings and matchdays. Crisps and confectionary available.
Club record appearances: Joe Reed.
Honours: (as East Cowes Vics pre-'68): Wessex Lg Cup 87-88, IOW Senior Gold Cup 79-80 81-82 82-83 83-84 84-85 85-86 88-89, Hants Lg 85-86 86-87 (Div 2 52-53 82-83, Div 3 63-64 71-72, Div 3 West 47-48), IOW Lg 1898-99 99-1900 30-31 34-35 78-79 82-83 86-87 87-88 94-95 (Div 2 1898-99 1904-05 06-07, Div 3 28-29 32-33, Comb Div 2 87-88 90-91,94-95 IOW Chal. Cup 1899-1900 00-01 01-02 19-20 47-48 50-51 51-52 52-53 80-81 84-85 87-88 90-91 91-92, IOW Mem. Cup 19-20 32-33 82-83 87-88 90-91, Brooklyn Cup 86-87 87-88 89-90 91-92, IOW Charity Cup 23-24 25-26, IOW Centenary Cup 89-90 91-92.

EASTLEIGH

Chairman: Roger Sherwood **President:** Phil Fernandez.
Secretary: Mr R G Kearslake, 10 Binsey Close, Millbrook, Southampton, Hants SO16 4AQ (01703 779545).
Manager: Ray Light **Asst Manager:** Dave Blandford **Physio:** Barry Wilkinson.
Ground: 'Ten Acres', Stoneham Lane, North Stoneham, Eastleigh SO50-9HT (01703 613361).
Directions: M27 to Jct 5, to r'bout - exit marked Stoneham Lane, ground on left but carry on to r'bout and come back down Stoneham Lane, turning right opposite Concord Club. Ground 400 yds on left. Three quarters of a mile from Southampton Parkway (BR). Bus 48 (Southampton-Winchester) to Stoneham Church stop.
Seats: 150 **Cover:** 210 **Capacity:** 4,300 **Floodlights:** Yes **Founded:** 1946.
Colours: All blue **Change colours:** White & blue/white/white
Programme: 32 pages with admission **Editor:** John Pothecary
Sponsors: Various **Nickname:** None. **Club Shop:** No.
Midweek matches: Wednesday **Previous Leagues:** Southampton Jnr & Snr 46-59/ Hants 50-86.
Previous Names: Swaythling Ath. 46-73/ Swaythling 73-80
Previous Grounds: Southampton Common 46-47/ Walnut Avenue, Swaythling 47-75.
Record Gate: 2,500 v Southampton, floodlight opener 30/9/75.
Club record scorer: Johnny Williams, 177 **Club record appearances:** Ian Knight, 611.
Record win: 12-1 v Hythe & Dibden, home 11/12/48
Record defeat: 0-11 v Austin Spts, away 1/1/47.
Clubhouse: Licence 11am-11pm Mon-Sat plus Sundays. Extensive facilities for weddings, parties, skittles and seminars. All catering undertaken.
Honours: FA Vase 4th Rd 90-91, Wessex Lg Cup R-up 91-92, Hants Lg Div 2 69-70 (R-up 54-55 60-61 62-63 64-65(Res), Div 3(W) 50-51 53-54 70-71(Res), Comb.(Res) 86-87)), Hants Midweek F'lit Cup 78-79, Soton Snr Lg(W) 49-50 (R-up 51-52(Res), Div 1 56-57(Res) 57-58(Res)), Russell Cotes R-up 76-77 80-81 89-90, Hants I'mediate Cup 50-51 56-57(Res) 74-75(Res)(R-up 73-74(Res)), Soton Snr Cup(Res) 74-75 78-79 87-88 (R-up(8) 55-56 57-59 60-61 66-67 71-72 80-81 87-88), Soton Jnr Lg Div 2 47-48(Res), Reg Mathieson Tphy(Res) 74-75 78-79 87-88.

FAREHAM TOWN

Chairman: Chris Solen **Director of Football:** John Green **President:** Ken Atkins
Secretary: Tony Adams, 83 Murray Road, Horndean, PO8 9JQ (0370 62874).
Manager: Mark Chamberlain **Physio:** James McKay **General Manager:** Tony Adams
Press Officer: M Willis **Commercial Manager:**
GROUND Address: Cams Alders, Highfield Avenue, Fareham, Hants PO14 1JA (01329 231151).
Directions: From junction 11 of M27, follow A27 towards Southampton. After passing Fareham station turn left at traffic lights (second left) into Redlands Avenue. Turn right at Redlands Inn then left into Highfields Avenue.
Capacity: 5,500 **Cover:** 500 **Seats:** 450 **Floodlights:** Yes
Clubhouse: Open every evening except Sundays. *Food available*
Club Shop: Sells programmes, scarves & fanzines.
Sponsors: Portsmouth Evening News
PROGRAMME DETAILS: Pages: 36 **Price:** £1 **Editor:** Ian Tewson Tel. 01329 662624
Colours: Red/black/red **Change colours:** White/white/black **Formed:** 1947
Midweek matchday: Wednesday **Reserves' League:** Hampshire Comb. **Nickname:** The Town
PREVIOUS - Name: Fareham FC. **Leagues:** Portsmouth 47-49, Hants 49-79. **Ground:** Bath Lane.
CLUB RECORDS - Attendance: 2,650 v Wimbeldon, FA Cup 1965. *(at Southampton F.C.; 6,035 v Kidderminster Harriers, FA Trophy Semi Final Second leg 86-87).* **Transfer fee paid:** £1,175 for Joe McCormack (Newport IOW).
Transfer fee received: £43,000 for David Leworthy (Spurs).
BEST SEASON - FA Cup: 1st Rd replay 88-89 (2-3 at home to Torquay after 2-2). **FA Trophy:** Semi Final 86-87.
FA Amateur Cup: Second Round 63-64 66-67 73-74
Players progressing to Football League: Ray Hiron (Portsmouth 64), John Hold (Bournemouth), David Leworthy (Spurs 84), Steve Claridge (Bournemouth 84), Darren Foreman (Barnsley), Kevin Bartlett (Cardiff City 86), Domenyk Newman (Reading 90).
HONOURS: Hants Lg(8) 59-60 62-67 72-73 74-75 (R-up 55-56 60-61 67-68 71-72 76-77 78-79, Div 2 R-up 52-53, Eastern Div 24-25, Div 3 East 49-50), Hants Snr Cup 56-57 62-63 67-68 92-93, Russell Cotes Cup(6) 64-65 72-77, Gosport War Memorial Cup, SW Co's Cup(2), Pickford Cup(2),

GOSPORT BOROUGH

Chairman: I T Hay **President:** W J Adams.
Secretary: B V Cosgrave, 2 Cavanna Close, Rowner, Gosport PO13 0PE (01329 314117).
Manager: John Hawes. **Coaches:** Dave Pitt & Barry Cook. **Physio:** Dave Topliss
Ground: Privett Park, Privett Road, Gosport, Hants (01705 583986).
Directions: M27 junct 11, then A32 Fareham to Gosport, at Brockhurst r-about (after about 3 miles) right into Military Road passing thru H.M.S. Sultan, left into Privett Road at next r-about, ground 300 yds on left signed 'Privett Park Enclosure'. 2 miles from Portsmouth Harbour (BR) or Fareham (BR).
Capacity: 4,500 **Cover:** 500 **Seats:** 450 **Floodlights:** Yes **Club Shop:** No
Clubhouse: (01705 583986). Open matchdays from 1.30pm Saturday, 6.30pm Wednesday. Refreshment hut sells hot food and drinks.
Colours: Yellow/blue/blue **Change colours:** Red/Black/Black.
Programme: 20 pages, 50p **Editor:** Ian Hay (01329 314601)
Sponsors: Cougar Marine **Founded:** 1944. **Nickname:** The Boro'
Midweek matchday: Tuesday. **Reserve Team's League:** Jewson Wessex Combination.
Club Records - Attendance: 4,770 v Pegasus, FA Amtr Cup 51. **Goalscorer:** Richie Coulbert 192 **Appearances:** Tony Mahoney 764. **Fees - Paid:** £6,000 for Sandy Baird (Basingstoke Town, 90) **Received:** £30,000+ for Gareth Williams (Aston Villa, 87). **Win:** 14-0 v Cunliffe-Owen, Hampshire Lg Div 1 45-46. **Defeat:** 0-9 twice; v Newport, Hants Lg Div 1 47-48. v Gloucester (A), Southern Lg Prem Div 89-90.
Best FA Trophy year: 1st Rd 88-89 **Best FA Amateur Cup year:** 3rd Rd 47-48 66-67
Best FA Vase year: 6th Rd rep 77-78 **Best FA Cup year:** 4th Qual. Rd 80-81 (lost to Windsor & Eton).
Previous Leagues: Portsmouth 44-45/ Hants 45-78/ Southern 78-92
Previous Name: Gosport Borough Athletic
Players progressing to Football League: P Harris (P'smouth, N'castle & Scotland), B Sherwood, D Dimmer, S Berry, R Blackman (Reading 47), R Pearson (P'smouth 49), A Mundy & M Barnard (P'smouth 51), P Smith (G'ham 54), A Grant (Brighton 56), B Gibbs (B'mouth 57), G Juryeff (P'smouth), R Carroll (Brentford 86), G Williams (A Villa 88).
Honours: Wessex Lg Cup 92-93, Southern Lg Div 1 South R-up 84-85, Hants Lg 45-46 76-77 77-78 (Div 3 (Reserves) 70-71 75-76), Portsmouth Lg R-up 44-45, Hants Senior Cup 87-88, Russell Cotes Cup R-up 94-95, Hants Intermediate Cup 70-71, Portsmouth Senior Cup 61-62 69-70 70-71 94-95, South West Counties Pratten Challenge Cup 77-78.

HAMBLE AEROSTRUCTURES SPORTS & SOCIAL CLUB

President: Al Tritten **Chairman:** Peter Mence **Gen. Mgr:** Nigel Kent
Secretary: Richard Phippard, 198 Butts Road, Sholing, Southampton SO19 1BP (01703 438413)
Manager: Sean Mallow **Reserve's Manager:**
Ground: Folland Park, Kings Avenue, Hamble (01703 452173).
Directions: M27 junction 8, then B3397 to Hamble. One and a half miles from Hamble (BR); turn right out of station, proceed for one mile then turn right into Queens Avenue. Ground 50 yards on right.
Midweek Matches: Wednesday, (Res Tuesday) **Reserve's League:** Wessex Comb.
Previous Name: Folland Sports (pre-1990).
Colours: All Maroon with sky pin stripe **Change colours:** White/white/red & white
Floodlights: Yes **Record defeat:** 1-10 v Andover (A), Wessex League 93-94.
Clubhouse: 300 capacity social club. Cricket & bowls
Honours: Hants Lg Div 3 80-81 (Div 4 79-80), Hants Intermediate Cup 79-90, Southampton Snr Cup 85 87 92

LYMINGTON & NEW MILTON

Chairman: John Mills **V-Chairmen:** Richard Millbery/Bob Philpott **President:** Jack Holliday
Secretary: John Osey, 9 Samphire Close, Lymington, Hants SO41 9LR (01590 676995).
Manager: Derek Binns **Asst Manager:** Kevin Green **Physio:** Alan Farrar
Ground: Lymington Sports Ground, Southampton Road, Lymington (01590 671305).
Directions: M27 jct 1, follow signs (A337) to Lymington via Lyndhurst and Brockenhurst, ground 250yds on left after 1st set of lights on entering town. 1 mile from Lymington Town BR station.
Seats: 200 **Cover:** 200 **Capacity:** 3,000 **Floodlights:** Yes **Club Shop:** Yes
Programme: 48 pages, 50p **Editor/Press Officer:** John Mills
Colours: Red & black/Black/Red. **Change colours:** Yellow & green/green/green.
Founded: 1988 **Nickname:** Linnets **Sponsors:**
Midweek Matches: Tuesday. **Reserve Team's League:** Jewson Wessex Combination.
Previous Name: Lymington Town (until 1988 when the club merged with Wellworthy Athletic).
Previous Ground: Ampress Ground (Wellworthy Athletic), until 1988 merger.
Record Attendance: 2,900 v Karen Mills Memorial Day 12.3.95
Club Record Scorer: Darren Pitter 197 **Club Record Appearances:** Glen Limburn 329.
Record win: 11-1 v Romsey Town (H), Wessex League 9/11/92.
Record defeat: 0-8 v Basingstoke Town (A), Hampshire Senior Cup 10/4/90.
Best FA Cup season: 3rd Qualifying Rd 92-93 (lost 0-1 at home to Cheltenham).
Players progressing to Football League: Stuart Doling (Doncaster Rovers), Russell Perrett (Portsmouth).
Clubhouse: Sat 2-7pm training and match nights. Rolls, hot pies.
Honours: Wessex Lg 92-93 96-97 (R-up 91-92 95-96), Wessex Lg Cup 88-89 (R-up 94-95), Wessex Comb. 92-93, Hants Snr Cup R-up 89-90, Texaco Cup 91-92, Bournemouth Snr Cup 92-93, (R-up 96-97), Russell Cotes Cup 93-94 94-95 (R-up 91-92 92-93), Pickford Cup R-up 92-93. *As Lymington Town: Russell Cotes Cup 35-36. Bournemouth Snr Cup 83-84 (R-up 69-71 84-85), Hants Lg Div 2 R-up 83-84, Hants Lg Div 3 67-68 (Div 2 R-up 82-83). As Wellworthy Ath: Bournemouth Snr Cup 87-88 (R-up 53-54), Hants Interm Cup 56-57 84-85, Pickford Cup 84-85, Bournemouth Lg 84-85, Hants Lg Div 3 R-up 85-86.*

MONEYFIELDS

Secretary: Peter Shires, 242 Grafton Street, Mile End, Portsmouth, (01705 645813)
Ground: Moneyfields Sports Ground, Moneyfield Avenue, Copnor Road, Portsmouth, Hampshire.
Colours: Yellow/blue/blue. **Change:** Jade & white/jade/jade

PORTSMOUTH ROYAL NAVY

Chairman: Tony Miklinski
Secretary: Paul Messitt, 9 Funtley Hill, Fareham, Hants, PO16 7UX (01705 542531 W, 01329 220580 H)
Manager: D Holland **Physio:** A Hylands
Ground: The Navy Stadium, HMS Temeraire, Burnaby Road, West Portsmouth, (01705 724235).
Directions: From Portsmouth Harbour (BR), turn right onto The Hard, pass under the rail bridge and turn left into Park Road, after approx 200yards take 1st right into Burnaby Road. Entrance to ground 100 mtrs on the right.
Seats: 500 **Cover:** 500 **Capacity:** 1,500 **Floodlights:** Yes **Club Shop:** No
Programme: 50p **Editor:** Roy Newman **Press Officer:** Jim Molloy
Colours: Royal & white/blue/blue **Change colours:** All Red
Club Sponsors: Federation Brewery **Formed:** 1962 **Nickname:** Sailors
Midweek Matches: 1st X1 Monday, Res Tuesday **Reserve Team's League:** Wessex Comb. Lge
Previous Leagues: Hampshire 62-86
Clubhouse: Open 1.5hrs before k.o. & 2hrs after game on matchdays and by arrangement only.
97-98 - Captain: Paul Barton **Top Scorer:** Jon Wallsgrove **P.o.Y.:** Paul Barton
Honours: Russell-Cotes Cup 67-68; Basingstoke Lg Div 2; Hants Lge Div 2 67-68 77-78 80-81.

AFC Newbury *Photo: Martin Wray*

AFC Lymington *Photo: Roger Turner*

Cowes Sports *Photo: Eric Marsh*

THATCHAM TOWN

Chairman: Phil Holdway **President:** **General Secretary:** John Haines
Football Secretary: Charles Heaver, 32 Baily Avenue, Thatcham, Berks RG13 3DU (01635 868179)
Manager: Jackie Stuart **Coach:** Ian Schofield
Ground: Waterside Park, Crookham Rd, Thatcham, Berks (01635 862016)
Directions: M4 junc 13, take A34 to Newbury, right onto A4 towards London. in Thatcham right towards railway station, ground on left beyond station, 2 mins walk from BR station.
Seats: 300 **Cover:** 300 **Capacity:** 3,000 **Floodlights:** Yes **Founded:** 1895
Colours: Blue & white/blue/blue **Change colours:** All red
Sponsors: Panasonic Gsm Mobile Phones **Club Shop:** Yes
Midweek Matches: Tuesday **Best FA Vase season:** 4th Qual Rd 96-97
Programme: 28 pages, 50p **Editor:** Dave Ware **Press Officer:** Dave Ware.(01635 861000)
Previous Ground: Station Road 46-52/ Lancaster Close 52-92. **Record Gate:** 1,400 v Aldershot ,F.A.Vase.
Clubhouse: Open every evening & lunchtimes.
Honours: Wessex Lg 95-96, Cup 90-91 91-92 94-95 96-97, (R-up twice)

WHITCHURCH UNITED

Chairman: Chris Rowland
Secretary: Debbie Case, 11 Falcon Close, Kempshott, Basingstoke RG22 5PP (01256 356645)
Ground: Longmeadow, Winchester Road, Whitchurch (01256 892493).
Directions: From Whitchurch (BR) station; turn left after Railway Inn, follow road to end, turn right into main road, arriving in town turn left along Winchester Road. Ground three quarters of a mile on left.
Seats: 200 **Cover:** Yes **Capacity:** **Floodlights:** Yes **Founded:**
Colours: Red & white/black/black **Change colours:** Blue/white/blue
Programme: 24 pages **Previous Leagues:** Hants (pre-1992).
Midweek Matches: Thursday
Best FA Vase season: Extra-Preliminary Rd 93-94 (lost 1-3 at home to Peppard).
Clubhouse: Hot food on matchdays. Sports hall incorporating squash courts and indoor bowling green

WIMBORNE TOWN

Chairman: Steve Churchill **Vice Chairman:** Nick O'Hara **President:** Brian Maidment
Secretary: Mark Willis, 63 Victoria Close, Corfe Mullen, Wimborne, Dorset. BH21 3TX (01202 605089)
Manager: Alex Pike. **Coach:** Mike Burton **Physio:** Irvin Brown
Ground: The Cuthbury, Cowgrove Road, Wimborne, Dorset BH21 4EL (01202 884821).
Directions: Wimborne to Blandford Road, behind Victoria Hospital.
Seats: 275 **Cover:** 50 **Capacity:** 3,250 **Floodlights:** Yes **Club Shop:** Yes
Programme: 24 pages, 50p **Editor:** Secretary **Press Officer:** Secretary.
Colours: Black & white/black/black **Change colours:** Yellow/green/yellow
Sponsors: Nicolas O'Hara **Nickname:** Magpies **Founded:** 1878
Midweek Matches: Tuesday **Reserve League:** Wessex Comb
Club Records - Attendance: 3,250 v Bamberbridge FA Vase Semi-Final 28/3/92 **Goalscorer:** Jason Lovell. **Appearances:** Nicky Bridle **Win** (in Wessex Lg): 8-0 v Eastleigh 91-92 & v Romsey Town 92-93. **Defeat** (in Wessex Lg): 2-6 v Thatcham Town 91-92. **Transfer fee paid:** £5,500 for J P Lovell (Bashley, 92). **Received:** £6,000; for J P Lovell (Bashley, 89) & for Tommy Killick (Dorchester, 93).
Best FA Vase season: Winners 91-92 **Best FA Cup season:** 1st Rd Proper 82-83.
Previous Leagues: Dorset Lge, Dorset Comb, Western 81-86.
Clubhouse: Evenings 7-11pm, Sat noon-11pm, Sun noon-3pm & 7-10.30pm. Bar. Skittle alley.
97-98 - Captain: Jamie Sturgess **Top Scorer:** Jamie Sturgess **P.o.Y.:** Mark Smith
Honours: Wessex Lg 91-92 93-94 (R-up 92-93 96-97), Lg Cup 93-94 (R-up 90-91 95-96); Dorset Lg Div 1 80-81 81-82 (R-up 38-39 72-73), Div 2 31-32 34-35 36-37 (R-up 35-36), Lg Cup R-up(4) 72-74 80-82; Dorset Snr Cup 91-92 96-97, (R-up 80-82 85-86); Mark Frowde Cup 92-93 94-95; Dorset Snr Amateur Cup 36-37 63-64; Dorset Jnr Cup 31-32 36-37 (R-up 13-14 34-35); Dorset Minor Cup 12-13; Dorset Jnr Amateur Cup(3) 34-36 38-39; Bankes Charity Cup 89-90 94-95 95-96, Texaco F/Light Cup 90-91

Bournemouth's Paul Cuglietta (Red), beats the Bemerton defence and has a shot at goal

Photo: Roger Turner

SCREWFIX DIRECT WESTERN LEAGUE

FEEDER TO: BEAZER HOMES LEAGUE

President: Stan Priddle
Chairman: R J Webber **Vice Chairman:** C D Ashton
Hon. Secretary: M E Washer, 16 Heathfield Road, Nailsea, Bristol BS19 1EB
Tel: 01275 851314

For everybody in the League and those outside with an interest, the past season was one of tremendous satisfaction, and awareness that only once in a lifetime do all things come together as they managed with this League.

Tiverton Town, of course, brought everyone's eyes upon the League with their achievements. FA Vase winners, League Championship winners, and Les Phillips Cup winners yet again. For anyone present at the latter event, the bizarre and sometimes frightening effects of electrical storms, which brought two floodlight failures during the ninety minutes, were quite unreal. For players and officials to still concentrate on the jobs in hand reflected highly on their own professionalism.

Apart from the achievements of Tiverton however, other facts must not be overlooked. In any other season Taunton Town would have had something tangible out of their performances, and Russell Musker must feel very disappointed. Also worth realising, is that despite some comments on the top two clubs, five other clubs in the top ten of the Premier Division, were not there seven years ago, and indeed Bridgwater, Brislington and Melksham were all outside our League. The same can also be said about the two promoted clubs from Division One, being Bishop Sutton and Yeovil Town. With that kind of progress, it is going to be an open League again next year, as the pressure builds up.

Our thanks once again to our Sponsors, Screwfix Direct for their very important involvement and contribution to our League and its clubs. In these days the roles and contributions made by the commercial world cannot be understated, and the necessity of it at our level of football is fundamental. When one reads about the money in the Premier League, can we really blame others for false conclusions that are made about our level? Whilst on the subject of financial pressures, the League is very sorry to see Crediton United leave us for the Westward Developments League, especially as this past season had promised so much. In their place we welcome Corsham Town from the Wiltshire League and we all hope that they will consolidate and progress in their new status. Let us all hope that this time next year we can reflect upon another season of success, but above all, one of enjoyment.

FINAL LEAGUE TABLES 1997-98

PREMIER DIVISION

	P	W	D	L	F	A	Pts
Tiverton Town	38	36	2	0	154	20	110
Taunton Town	38	31	3	4	107	28	96
Melksham Town	38	22	7	9	75	37	73
Bridgwater Town	38	22	6	10	73	43	72
Paulton Rovers	38	19	6	13	76	69	63
Mangotsfield Utd	38	18	8	12	76	50	62
Barnstaple Town	38	18	5	15	79	64	59
Brislington	38	17	8	13	62	55	59
Calne Town	38	16	9	13	68	67	57
Backwell United	38	15	7	16	70	68	52
Bridport	38	16	4	18	62	72	52
Chippenham Town	38	13	11	14	53	57	50
Bideford	38	14	6	18	68	90	48
Elmore	38	10	8	20	54	100	38
Westbury United	38	9	8	21	39	65	35
Bristol Manor Farm	38	8	10	20	37	73	34
Keynsham Town	38	10	4	24	46	94	34
Odd Down	38	9	6	23	33	80	33
Chard Town	38	8	8	22	44	77	32
Torrington	38	2	8	28	21	88	14

FIRST DIVISION

	P	W	D	L	F	A	Pts
Bishop Sutton	36	26	8	2	86	25	86
Yeovil Town	36	24	6	6	95	47	78
Devizes Town	36	22	7	7	83	38	73
Street	36	21	7	8	61	32	70
Clyst Rovers	36	20	10	6	89	39	*67
Minehead	36	16	14	6	60	39	62
Dawlish Town	36	17	10	9	78	48	*58
Crediton United	36	15	8	13	65	67	53
Exmouth Town	36	15	6	15	68	60	51
Bitton	36	14	8	14	55	53	50
Wellington	36	13	10	13	72	54	49
Ilfracombe Town	36	14	7	15	75	67	49
Larkhall Athletic	36	12	7	17	45	58	43
Welton Rovers	36	9	6	21	51	78	33
Warminster Town	36	9	5	22	40	83	32
Glastonbury	36	9	4	23	41	86	31
Frome Town	36	8	6	22	47	74	30
Heavitree United	36	3	7	26	34	135	16
Pewsey Vale	36	3	8	25	40	102	*14

* Points deducted

PREMIER DIVISION RESULTS CHART 1997-98

		1	2	3	4	5	6	7	8	9	10	11	12	13	14	15	16	17	18	19	20
1	Backwell Utd	X	0-1	0-2	4-2	4-0	0-0	4-1	3-0	2-1	2-2	1-2	3-3	3-2	1-2	5-0	1-2	3-7	0-4	2-0	2-3
2	Barnstaple Tn	2-1	X	4-1	1-2	1-3	5-0	1-1	2-1	2-1	1-1	5-1	1-2	3-4	0-0	5-2	3-2	0-3	1-2	3-0	4-2
3	Bideford	3-2	1-3	X	0-2	0-0	0-4	3-0	4-3	5-2	0-1	3-3	1-4	3-4	1-3	1-1	4-4	0-3	0-1	1-0	2-1
4	Bridgwater Tn	4-0	2-1	5-2	X	5-0	1-2	1-2	1-1	1-0	1-1	3-0	2-1	0-1	0-2	4-2	3-1	0-1	0-3	1-1	0-0
5	Bridport	3-1	1-2	5-0	2-0	X	1-2	2-0	1-2	3-4	3-2	2-0	3-5	0-5	0-1	3-1	3-2	0-5	1-2	2-0	2-1
6	Brislington	2-0	3-2	4-3	1-3	1-3	X	4-0	1-2	3-0	0-2	2-0	0-0	3-1	1-4	2-0	3-0	2-3	1-5	1-0	0-0
7	Bristol M Farm	0-0	2-0	1-2	0-4	2-2	1-1	X	2-3	2-2	1-1	2-0	1-0	0-2	0-5	0-1	0-1	1-3	0-5	3-0	2-0
8	Calne Town	3-4	3-1	4-2	0-2	4-1	0-0	1-0	X	1-0	1-1	2-1	1-3	3-1	1-4	3-0	2-2	1-3	1-4	1-0	1-1
9	Chard Town	1-2	0-0	1-1	0-1	2-2	1-0	2-2	3-2	X	1-3	2-1	1-0	0-1	1-1	0-0	1-3	1-6	0-5	4-1	0-1
10	Chippenham Tn	0-1	0-3	3-1	0-1	0-1	1-0	3-1	0-1	4-1	X	1-1	1-0	2-2	0-1	1-2	1-0	0-0	0-4	4-1	4-5
11	Elmore	2-2	1-7	1-5	0-3	4-1	1-5	3-0	1-1	3-2	2-1	X	4-1	3-1	1-1	2-0	2-4	0-6	1-6	1-2	1-1
12	Keynsham	2-3	1-4	0-2	2-3	1-3	1-3	2-2	0-3	4-2	1-1	1-3	X	0-1	2-1	1-0	1-2	0-4	0-7	1-0	0-2
13	Mangotsfield Utd	0-3	0-1	4-1	3-3	1-3	0-0	3-2	1-1	2-3	2-0	2-2	10-0	X	0-1	4-0	3-1	0-1	0-1	3-0	2-0
14	Melksham	2-1	5-1	2-2	0-2	3-0	1-1	2-1	1-1	3-1	2-3	3-0	5-0	2-2	X	1-0	2-0	0-2	0-2	2-1	2-3
15	Odd Down	0-0	2-1	5-2	0-4	0-3	1-1	2-3	1-5	1-0	1-3	3-0	1-0	0-2	0-4	X	1-2	0-2	0-3	0-0	1-0
16	Paulton Rovers	2-2	1-1	2-3	0-2	1-0	2-1	0-1	6-5	0-0	2-2	8-3	3-1	2-1	2-1	3-1	X	0-1	0-6	3-1	1-0
17	Taunton Town	3-1	3-1	0-2	4-0	2-1	4-0	4-0	5-1	2-0	4-1	6-0	2-0	0-0	1-0	4-1	2-3	X	0-4	3-1	1-1
18	Tiverton Town	3-2	6-0	7-0	2-2	3-0	6-2	3-0	5-0	4-0	5-0	4-2	8-0	2-2	3-1	5-0	4-1	2-1	X	4-0	6-1
19	Torrington	1-3	0-4	0-3	2-1	1-1	1-3	1-1	0-0	2-4	0-1	1-1	1-3	1-3	0-3	1-1	1-5	0-3	0-6	X	0-0
20	Westbury Utd	1-2	4-2	1-2	1-2	2-1	0-3	0-0	0-3	1-0	2-2	0-1	0-3	0-1	0-2	0-2	0-3	1-3	1-2	3-0	X

LES PHILLIPS CHALLENGE CUP 1997-98

First Round

Bishop Sutton	v	Devizes Town	6-7
Mangotsfield Utd	v	Backwell United	2-1
Elmore	v	Pewsey Vale	5-1
Odd Down	v	Westbury United	1-3
Bridgwater Town	v	Torrington	3-2
Minehead	v	Frome Town	0-1
Wellington	v	Street	6-4
Keynsham Town	v	Calne Town	0-3

Second Round

Barnstaple Town	v	Taunton Town	1-2
Clyst Rovers	v	Exmouth Town	3-2
Bideford	v	Bristol Manor Farm	2-0
Tiverton Town	v	Heavitree United	10-0
Chippenham Town	v	Bridport	3-0
Crediton United	v	Glastonbury	5-1
Yeovil Town	v	Paulton Rovers	1-5
Wellington	v	Dawlish Town	3-2
Bridgwater	v	Elmore	0-1
Bitton	v	Calne Town	3-4
Westbury United	v	Brislington	6-5
Welton Rovers	v	Mangotsfield	2-3
Frome Town	v	Warminster Town	5-2
Larkhall Athletic	v	Ilfracombe Town	1-2
Melksham Town	v	Chard Town	3-1
Devizes Town: bye			

Third Round

Taunton Town	v	Calne Town	3-2
Crediton United	v	Chippenham Town	5-4
Tiverton Town	v	Devizes Town	4-1
Clyst Rovers	v	Westbury United	7-5
Paulton Rovers	v	Melksham Town	3-1
Bideford	v	Frome Town	4-3
Ilfracombe Town	v	Elmore	1-2
Mangotsfield Utd	v	Wellington	2-1

Quarter-Final

Mangotsfield United	v	Bideford	3-0
Elmore	v	Clyst Rovers	2-3
Tiverton Town	v	Crediton United	9-1
Paulton Rovers	v	Taunton Town	1-2

Semi-Final

Tiverton Town	v	Mangotsfield United	2-1
Taunton Town	v	Clyst Rovers	3-0

FINAL

TIVERTON TOWN	v	TAUNTON TOWN	3-2

COMBINATION CHALLENGE CUP 1997-98

First Round

Taunton Town	v	Street	2-1
Elmore	v	Wellington	3-0
Chard Town	v	Barnstaple Town	3-1
Ottery St Mary	v	Minehead	1-7

Second Round

Minehead	v	Taunton Town	4-3
Crediton United	v	Elmore	1-4
Bideford	v	Chard Town	1-0
Exmouth Town	v	Dawlish Town	3-1

Semi-Final

Minehead	v	Exmouth Town	4-0
Elmore	v	Bideford	6-2

FINAL

MINEHEAD	v	ELMORE	0-2

REGISTRATION INFORMATION

	NUMBER OF PLAYERS REGISTERED	TRANSFERS ACTIONED
1996-97	1888	221
1995-96	1762	187
1994-95	1922	254
1993-94	1909	201
1992-93	2061	241

ATTENDANCE INFORMATION 1997-98

PREMIER DIVISION

	AGGREGATE	AVERAGE GATE	GATES OVER 200
Backwell United	2126	112	1
Barnstaple Town	2629	138	3
Bideford	2022	106	2
Bridgwater Tn	5244	276	14
Bridport	3031	160	4
Brislington	1334	70	
Bristol Manor Farm	1307	69	1
Calne Town	1707	90	1
Chard Town	1859	98	2
Chippenham Town	3241	171	5
Elmore	2213	116	1
Keynsham	2009	116	1
Mangotsfield Utd	2966	156	4
Melksham	3265	172	5
Odd Down	957	50	
Paulton Rovers	3266	172	5
Taunton Town	6175	325	18
Tiverton Town	9108	479	19
Torrington	1316	69	1
Westbury United	1924	101	
TOTAL	**57,699**	**159.8**	**89**

(361 Recorded Attendances)

DIVISION ONE

	AGGREGATE	AVERAGE GATE	GATES OVER 200
Bishop Sutton	1283	71	
Bitton	1295	72	
Clyst Rovers	864	48	
Crediton United	1035	58	
Dawlish Town	1100	61	
Devizes Town	1248	69	
Exmouth Town	1106	61	
Frome Town	1058	59	
Glastonbury	1002	56	1
Heavitree United	771	43	
Ifracombe Town	1303	72	
Larkhall Athletic	1043	58	
Minehead	944	52	
Pewsey Vale	1150	64	
Street	2740	152	2
Warminster Town	1885	105	
Wellington	857	47	
Welton Rovers	1186	66	
Yeovil Town	2550	142	3
TOTAL	**24,420**	**75.4**	**6**

(324 Recorded Attendances)

OVERALL TOTALS

	Aggregate	Average Gate	Gates Over 200
685 Recorded Attendances	82,119	119.8	95

HIGHEST LEAGUE ATTENDANCES 1997-98

Tiverton	v	Taunton	1329	23.04.98	Bridgwater	v	Tiverton	762	31.03.98
Taunton	v	Tiverton	1117	24.09.97	Elmore	v	Tiverton	709	10.04.98
Tiverton	v	Elmore	1004	27.12.97	Bridgwater	v	Taunton	620	11.04.98
Tiverton	v	Calne	859	25.04.98	Tiverton	v	Bridgwater	605	24.01.98
Taunton	v	Bridgwater	782	27.12.97	Melksham	v	Tiverton	516	15.02.98

LEADING LEAGUE GOALSCORERS 1997-98

P Everett	Tiverton Town	33	P Varley	Tiverton Town	23
A Rollason	Barnstaple Town	26	J Charlesworth	Dawlish Town	23
C Evans	Bridport	25	M Cutler	Taunton Town	22
S Daly	Tiverton Town	25	K Thaws	Paulton Rovers	22
R Wilson	Clyst Rovers	23	C Griffen	Chippenham Town	22
K Nancekivell	Tiverton Town	23			

WESTERN FOOTBALL LEAGUE CHAMPIONS

	PREMIER DIVISION		DIVISION ONE
1996-97	Tiverton Town	1996-97	Melksham Town
1995-96	Taunton Town	1995-96	Bridgwater Town
1994-95	Tiverton Town	1994-95	Brislington
1993-94	Tiverton Town	1993-94	Barnstaple Town
1992-93	Clevedon Town	1992-93	Odd Down
1991-92	Weston-Super-Mare	1991-92	Westbury United
1990-91	Mangotsfield United	1990-91	Minehead
1989-90	Taunton Town	1989-90	Ottery St Mary
1988-89	Saltash United	1988-89	Larkhall Athletic
1987-88	Liskeard Athletic	1987-88	Welton Rovers
1986-87	Saltash United	1986-87	Swanage Town & Herston
1985-86	Exmouth Town	1985-86	Portway-Bristol
1984-85	Saltash United	1984-85	Portway-Bristol
1983-84	Exmouth Town	1983-84	Bristol City Reserves
1982-83	Bideford	1982-83	Bristol Manor Farm
1981-82	Bideford	1981-82	Shepton Mallet
1980-81	Bridgwater Town	1980-81	Chippenham Town
1979-80	Barnstaple Town	1979-80	Melksham Town
1978-79	Frome Town	1978-79	AFC Bournemouth Reserves
1977-78	Falmouth Town	1977-78	Keynsham Town
1976-77	Falmouth Town	1976-77	Saltash United
1975-76	Falmouth Town	1960-76	Single Division
1974-75	Falmouth Town	1959-60	Welton Rovers
1973-74	Welton Rovers	1958-59	Bath City
1972-73	Devizes Town	1957-58	Poole Town
1971-72	Bideford	1956-57	Cinderford Town
1970-71	Bideford	1955-56	Torquay United
1969-70	Glastonbury	1954-55	Yeovil Town
1968-69	Taunton Town	1953-54	Bristol Rovers Colts
1967-68	Bridgwater Town	1952-53	Chippenham Town Reserves
1966-67	Welton Rovers	1951-52	Bideford
1965-66	Welton Rovers	1950-51	Stonehouse
1964-65	Welton Rovers	1949-50	Barnstaple Town
1963-64	Bideford	1948-49	Chippenham United
1962-63	Bristol City	1947-48	Salisbury City
1961-62	Bristol City	1946-47	Clandown
1960-61	Salisbury City	1939-46	No Competition
1959-60	Torquay United	1938-39	Trowbridge Town
1958-59	Yeovil Town	1937-38	Weymouth
1957-58	Salisbury City	1936-37	Weymouth
1956-57	Poole Town	1935-36	Swindon Town
1955-56	Trowbridge Town	1934-35	Swindon Town
1954-55	Dorchester Town	1933-34	Weymouth
1953-54	Weymouth	1932-33	Swindon Town
1952-53	Barnstaple Town	1931-32	Portland United
1951-52	Chippenham Town	1930-31	Portland United
1950-51	Glastonbury	1929-30	Trowbridge Town

PREMIER DIVISION CLUBS 1998-99

BACKWELL UNITED

Chairman: Richard Cole. **Vice-Chairman:** Peter Higgins. **President:** John Southern
Secretary: Bill Coggins, 34 Westfield Road, Backwell, Bristol BS19 3ND (01275 463424).
Manager: Alan Pridham **Asst Manager:** Martin Finn. **Physio:** Ian Pinkney
Ground: Backwell Recreation Ground, West Town Rd, Backwell, Avon (01275 462612).
Directions: Near centre of Backwell on main A370 Bristol to Weston-super-Mare road. Buses from Bristol or Weston, or 20 mins walk from Nailsea & Backwell (BR) station; turn right out of station, right at traffic lights (half mile), ground quarter mile on right just past car sales.
Seats: 60 **Cover:** 150 **Capacity:** 1,000 **Floodlights:** Yes **Club Shop:** No.
Colours: All red **Change colours:** All Gold **Nickname:** Stags
Programme: 42 pages, 50p. **Editor:** Dick Cole (01275 463627) **Press Officer:** Peter Higgins.
Midweek Matches: Tuesday **Club Sponsors:** C W Jones Carpets. **Founded:** 1983
Club Records - Attendance: 487 v Brislington, Gt Mills Lg. 2/5/94. **Goalscorer:** Steve Spalding **Appearances:** Wayne Buxton. **Win:** 8-0 v Dawlish Town (A), Western Lge Div One 4/12/93. **Defeat:** 2-6 v Tiverton Town (H), Les Phillips Cup QF 1/2/94.
Previous - Leagues: Clevedon & Dist/ Bristol Church of England/ Bristol Surburban (pre 70)/ Somerset Snr 70-83
Grounds: Two in Backwell prior to 1939. Club reformed in 1946.
Clubhouse: Open 6-11pm weekdays, 12.30-11pm Sat. Snacks available.
Honours: Somerset Snr Lg 77-78 79-80 80-81 81-82 82-83 (Lg Cup 82-83 (R-up 79-80) Div 1 72-73); Somerset Snr Cup 81-82; SW Co.'s Sutton Transformer Cup 81-82. Gt.Mills Div 1 89-90 Champions,94-95 promoted in third place.

BARNSTAPLE TOWN

President: Wilf Harris **Chairman:** John Cann
Secretary: David Cooke, 51 Walnut Way, Whiddon Valley, Barnstaple, Devon. EX32 7RF (01271-326088)
Manager: Mark Jenkins **Asst Manager:**
Ground: Mill Road, Barnstaple, North Devon (01271 743469).
Directions: A361 towards Ilfracombe (from M5 Jct 26), in Barnstaple follow A361 Ilfracombe signs, second left after crossing small bridge is Mill Road.
Seats: 250 **Cover:** 1,000 **Capacity:** 5,000 **Floodlights:** Yes **Formed:** 1948
Colours: Red/white/red **Change colours:** Yellow/black/black **Nickname:** Barum.
Sponsors: J & A Cameras. **Midweek Matches:** Tuesday **Club Shop:** Yes
Programme: 50p **Programme Editor:** David Priscott.
Previous - Leagues: Nth Devon, Devon & Exeter, S. Western **Grounds:** Town Wharf (Pre 1920's); Highfield Rd, Newport (until 1935), Pilton Pk, Rock Pk. **Name:** Pilton Yeo Vale.
Club Records - Attendance: 6,200 v Bournemouth, FA Cup 1st Rd, 54 **Appearances:** Trevor Burnell **Win:** 12-1 v Tavistock (H), FA Cup 3rd Qual Rd 54. **Defeat:** 1-10 v Mangotsfield Utd (A), Western Lge Prem Div 90-91. **Transfer fee paid:** £4,000 for Joe Scott (Hungerford Tn, 80). **Received:** £6,000 for Ian Doyle (Bristol City).
Clubhouse: Full license. Bar snacks.
Past players progressing to Football League: Len Pickard (Bristol Rovers 1951), John Neale (Exeter 1972), Barrie Vassallo (Torquay 1977), Ian Doyle (Bristol City 1978), Ryan Souter (Swindon 1994), Jason Cadie (Reading 1994).
97-98 - Captain: Paul Hutchings **P.o.Y.:** Andy Rollason **Top Scorer:** Andy Rollason
Honours: Western Lg 52-53 79-80 (R-up 80-81 81-82, Div 1 49-50 94-95, Merit Cup 74-75 83-84 84-85, Combination 92-93), FA Cup 1st Rd replay 51-52, Devon Professional Cup 62-63 64-65 67-68 69-70 71-72 72-73 74-75 76-77 77-78 78-79 79-80 80-81, Devon Lg, Devon St Lukes Cup 87-88, Devon Snr Cup 92-93, Devon Youth Cup 48-49 51-52.

BIDEFORD

President: C Prust **Chairman:** Jim McElwee
Secretary: Ron Ackland, Korna House, Shebbear, North Devon EX21 5RU (01409 281451).
Manager: Dean Edwards **Reserve Manager:** Barry Hooper
Ground: The Sports Ground, Kingsley Road, Bideford (01237 474975).
Directions: A361 for Bideford - ground on right as you enter the town.
Seats: 120 **Cover:** 1,000 **Capacity:** 6,000 **Floodlights:** Yes **Founded:** 1949
Colours: Red/white/red **Change colours:** All white **Nickname:** Robins
Programme: 32 pages, 50p **Editor:** Ian Knight.
Previous - Leagues: Devon & Exeter 47-49/ Western 49-72/ Southern 72-75 **Name:** Bideford Town **Ground:** Hansen Ground (1 season)
Midweek Matchday: Wednesday. **Club Records - Gate:** 6,000 v Gloucester C., FA Cup 4th Qual. Rd 60 **Goalscorer:** Tommy Robinson 259 **Appearances:** Derek May 527. **Win:** 16-0 v Soundwell 50-51 **Defeat:** 0-12 v Paulton 96-97
Players progressing to Football League: Shaun Taylor (Swindon Town, Bristol Rovers) Tony Dennis (Cambridge).
Clubhouse: 'Robins Nest' - on ground. Open lunchtimes and evenings, snacks and bar menu. Mgr: Mrs Sue Tyrell.
97-98 - Captain: Phil Lloyd **P.o.Y:** Mike Gilbert **Top Scorer:** Dean Edwards
Honours: FA Cup 1st Rd 64-65(replay) 73-74 77-78 81-82. Western Lg 63-64 70-71 71-72 81-82 82-83, Div 1 51-52, Div 3 49-50, Lg Cup 71-72 84-85; Alan Young Cup 64-65 69-70; Merit Cup 68-69; Subsidiary Cup 71-72; Devon Snr Cup 79-80; Devon St Lukes Cup 81-82 83-84 85-86 95-96 (R-up 86-87 91-92 94-95);

BISHOP SUTTON

Chairman: **Vice Chairman:** Roy Penney **President:** Bob Redding.
Secretary: Roy Penney, 53 Ridgway Lane, Whitchurch, Bristol BS14 9PJ (01275 541392).
Manager: Chris Mountford **Coach:** Chris Stutt **Physio:** Vernon Ashton
Ground: Lakeview Football Field, Bishop Sutton (01275 333097).
Directions: On A368 at rear of Butchers Arms pub – Ground signposted on left entering village from the West.
Seats: None **Cover:** 200 **Capacity:** 1,500 **Floodlights:** No **Club Shop:** No.
Programme: Yes **Editor:** Mr G Williams **Press Officer:**
Colours: All blue **Change colours:** All red
Sponsors: Crown Insulation. **Nickname:** Bishops. **Founded:** 1977.
Midweek Matches: Tuesday **Youth team's League:** Somerset Mid Week
Club Records - Attendance: 410 **Win:** 15-0 v Glastonbury Res.
Previous - Leagues: Weston & Dist. Yth/ Bristol & Avon/ Somerset Snr (pre 91) **Ground:** Adjacent cricket field
Players progressing to Football League: David Lee (Chelsea), S Williams (Southampton), J French (Bristol Rovers).
Clubhouse: Open matchdays. Rolls, pies and usual pub food available.
Hons: Somerset Snr Lg R-up 89-90, Div 1 83-84 (R-up 81-82), Div 2 82-83; Bristol & Avon Lg 80-81 (Div 2 79-80); Somerset Jnr Cup 80-81; Weston Yth Lg 77-78; Chew Valley KO Cup 83-84; Mid-Somerset Lg(Res) R-up 82-83 (Div 3 81-82).

BRIDGWATER TOWN '84

Chairman: Keith Setter. **President:** Tom Pearce
Secretary: Miss S A Wright, 37 Kidsbury Road, Bridgwater TA6 7AQ (01278 421189)
Manager: Alan Hooker. **Physio:** Mike Brown
Ground: Fairfax Park, College Road, Bridgwater (01278 446899 - matchdays only).
Directions: M5 jct 23, follow signs to Glastonbury (A39), turn right for Bridgwater (A39). Look for sign to Bridgwater College via College Way. One mile from Bridgwater (BR) station.
Seats: 150 **Cover:** Yes **Capacity:** 2,000 **Floodlights:** Yes **Club Shop:** Yes
Programme: Yes. **Editor:** G Nelson & R Heard **Press Officer:** G Nelson
Colours: Red/white/red **Change colours:** Blue/white/blue.
Sponsor: TMB Patterns **Founded:** 1984. **Nickname:** The Robins
Midweek Matchday: Tuesday **Youth Team's League:** U18 Floodlight
Previous League: Somerset Snr (pre-1994) **Clubhouse:** 'The Sportsman' Bath Road.
Honours: Somerset Snr Cup 93-94, Somerset Snr Lge 90-91 91-92, GMWL Div 1 95-96.

BRIDPORT

President: B Williams **Chairman:** David Fowler
Secretary: Ian Hallett, Brookside, Burstock, Beaminster DT8 3LJ (01308 868795)
Manager: Trevor Senior **Asst Manager/Physio:** Tony Diaz.
Ground: The Beehive, St Mary's Field, Bridport, Dorset (01308 423834).
Directions: Take West Bay road from town centre, turn right immediately before Palmers Brewery.
Seats: 200 **Cover:** 400 **Capacity:** 2,000 **Floodlights:** Yes **Founded:** 1887
Colours: Red & black/black/red & black **Change colours:** Blue & black/blue/blue
Programme: 36 pages, 50p **Editor:** Ian Hallett (01308 868795).
Midweek Matches: Wednesday **Reserve Team's League:** Dorset Combination.
Club Shop: No **Sponsors:** TBA **Nickname:** Bees
Previous - Leagues: Perry Street/ Western 61-84/ Dorset Comb 84-88. **Grounds:** Pymore (pre 1930s); Crown Field (pre 1953)
Club Records - Attendance: 1,150 v Exeter City, 81; 3,000 v Chelsea, at Crown, 50 **Goalscorer (in a season):** Ellis Hoole 36. **Transfer fee received:** £2,000 for Tommy Henderson. **Paid:** £1,000 for Steve Crabb.
Clubhouse: Yes, open matchdays and for functions. Hot and cold snacks available.
Honours: Western Lg Cup 70-71 72-73 77-78 (R-up 76-77, Div 1 R-up 94-95, Merit Cup 69-70 71-72 73-74); FA Vase 5th Rd 88-89; Dorset Comb.(3) 85-88 (Lg Cup 86-87 87-88); Dorset Snr Cup(8) 63-64 69-71 75-76 78-81 87-88; Dorset Snr Amtr Cup(6) 48-50 54-55 56-57 70-72; W. Dorset Chal. Bowl 07-08; Perry Str. Lg 22-23; Mark Frowde Cup 76-77 88-89

BRISLINGTON

President: C Elston **Chairman:** G Hobbs **Vice-Chairman:** M Richardson
Secretary: Philip Rex, 27 Kings Head Lane, Bishopsworth, Bristol BS13 7DB (0117 987 9146 H)
Manager: Jamie Patch **Asst Manager:** Tony Ricketts **Physio:** Dave Gould
Ground: Ironmould Lane, Brislington, Bristol (0117 977 4030)
Directions: Four miles out of Bristol on main A4 to Bath – turn left up lane opposite Garden Centre
Capacity: **Seats:** 144 **Cover:** 100 **Floodlights:** Yes **Club Shop:** No
Programme: 50p **Editor:** Laserset (0117 969 5487).
Colours: Red & black/black/black **Change colours:** Blue & yellow
Midweek matches: Tuesday **Reserve's League:** Somerset Senior
Sponsors: Trade Windows. **Nickname:** Bris.
Best FA Vase year: 3rd Rd 89-90 (lost 2-3 at Abingdon T.) **Previous League:** Somerset Senior (pre-1991).
Clubhouse: Yes - on ground, open matchdays.
Honours: Somerset Snr Cup 92-93 (R-up 93-94); Somerset Snr Lge, Les Phillips Cup SF 93-94, Prem Cup 95-96.

Barnstaple Town FC

Chippenham Town after victory in FA Cup replay at Wokingham *Photo: Eric Marsh*

First-half action at Kingsley Rd, as Bideford attack the Chard goal. *Photo: Martin Wray*

BRISTOL MANOR FARM

Chairman: F Wardle **Vice Chairman:** Brian Bartlett. **President:** Fred Wardle
Secretary: Steve Price, 19A Deans Mead, Lawrence Weston, Bristol BS11 0QX (0117 982 6952)
Manager: Geoff Bryant **Asst Mgr:** Barry Fry **Physio:** Alan Williams.
Ground: 'The Creek', Portway, Sea Mills, Bristol BS9 2HS (0117 968 3571)
Directions: M5 jct 18 (Avonmouth Bridge), follow A4 for Bristol - U-turn on dual carriageway by Bristol & West sports ground and return for half mile on A4 - ground entrance is down narrow lane on left (hidden entrance). Near to Sea Mills station (BR Temple Meads-Severn Beach line).
Seats: 84 **Cover:** 350 **Capacity:** 2,000 **Floodlights:** Yes **Club Shop:** No.
Programme: 28 pages, 50p **Editor:** Steve Price (0117 982 6952).
Colours: Red & black stripes/red/red **Change colours:** All sky blue
Club Sponsors: Wardle Fencing. **Nickname:** The Farm **Formed:** 1964
Midweek Matchday: Tuesday **Reserve League:** Somerset Senior.
Club Record - Attendance: 500 v Portway, Western Lg 1974. **Goalscorer:** Chris Rex, 222 **Appearances:** Paul Williams, 821. **Win:** 8-2, away to Frome, 2/9/84 **Defeat:** 1-8, away to Exmouth, 5/5/86. **Transfer Fee Received:** £3,000 for Nicky Dent (Yeovil Town, 89).
Previous - Leagues: Bristol Suburban 64-69/ Somerset Snr 69-77. **Name:** Manor Farm O.B. 1964-68
Players progressing to Football League: Ian Hedges (Newport) 88-89, Gary Smart (Bristol Rovers).
Clubhouse: Lounge bar, entertainments, skittle alley, bar meals. Open every night and lunchtime Sat & Sun.
Honours: Western Lg Div 1 82-83, Glos Tphy 87-88, Glos Amtr Cup 89-90, Somerset Snr Lg Div 1 (Lg Cup, Div 2).

CALNE TOWN

President: Fred Rutty **Manager:** Mal Gingel
Secretary: Laurie Drake, 22 Falcon Rd, Calne, Wilts SN11 8PL (01249 819186).
Ground: Bremhill View, Lickhill Rd., North End, Calne (01249 816716).
Directions: From Bristol to Chippenham, on entering town keep left all the way taking slip road to North End, off main Swindon Road.
Seats: 78 **Cover:** 250 **Capacity:** 2,500 **Floodlights:** Yes **Club Shop:** No.
Programme: 20 pages, 50p **Editor:** Laurie Drake (01249 819186).
Colours: White/black/black **Change colours:** Yellow/blue/yellow
Sponsors: Calne Engineering **Nickname:** Lilywhites **Founded:** 1887.
Midweek Matcheday: Tuesday **Previous - League:** Wilts Co. (pre-1986) **Names:** Calne Town (est. 1886)/ Harris Utd - clubs merged/ Calne & Harris Utd - 1921-67. **Ground:** Anchor Road Rec. 1887-1967.
Club Records - Attendance: 1,100 v Swindon, Friendly 25/7/1987. **Goalscorer:** Robbie Lardner **Appearances:** Gary Swallow, 259. **Win:** 11-1 v Heavitree (H) **Defeat:** 2-7 v Odd Down (A).
Clubhouse: Mon-Fri 7-11pm, Sat-Sun 12-11pm. Filled rolls, hot food, tea, coffee, sweets etc.
97-98 - Captain: Jamie Walters **Top Scorer:** Steve Brown **P.o.Y.:** Nick Beaverstock
Honours: Western Lg Div 1 R-up 92-93; Wilts Snr Cup 12-13 34-35 84-85 (R-up 1894-95 94-95 1911-12 49-50); Wilts Lg 33-34, ('Ghia' Cup 8) 1-81 85-86, Div 2 79-81, Div 3 85-86, Div 4 81-82.

CHIPPENHAM TOWN

Chairman: Malcolm Lyus **Vice-Chairman:** Andy Russell **President:** G W Terrell
Secretary: Chris Blake, 28 Sadlers Mead, Chippenham, Wilts SN15 3PB (01249 658212).
Manager: Vic Flippance **Physio:** John Palmer
Ground: Hardenhuish Park, Bristol Road, Chippenham (01249 650400).
Directions: M4 jct 17, A429 into Chippenham, follow signs for Trowbridge/Bath until r'bout, left onto A420 into town, ground 400yds on left. 5 mins walk from railway station on main A420 Bristol Road.
Seats: 100 **Cover:** 300 **Capacity:** 4,000 **Floodlights:** Yes **Club Shop:** Yes
Programme: 32 pages, 50p **Editor/Press Officer:** Ian Liversedge (01249 651290)
Club colours: Blue/blue/burgundy **Change colours:** All yellow
Midweek matches: Wednesday **Nickname:** The Bluebirds **Formed:** 1873
Sponsors: Cifer Ltd, Kingston Smith, Supreme Video, Shoestrings Food Services, Vanitec Computers.
Club Records - Gate: 4,800 v Chippenham Utd, Western Lg, 51. **Goalscorer:** Dave Ferris **Appearances:** Ian Monnery.
Previous - Leagues: Hellenic, Wiltshire Senior, Wiltshire Premier. **Grounds:** Westmead, Lowden, Little George Lane, Malmesbury Rd
Clubhouse: Yes, open matchdays. Food available.
Honours: FA Cup 1st Rd 51-52, Western Lg 51-52 (Div 1 80-81, Div 2 52-53(Res) 80-81), Wilts Shield, Wilts Snr Cup, Wilts Snr League.

ELMORE

Chairman: A J Cockram **Vice Chairman:** P.J.Garnsworthy.
Secretary: Mrs A Freeman, c/o Elmore FC, (01884 258215)
Manager: Peter Buckingham **Asst Manager:** R Moore. **Physio:** M Crocker.
Ground: Horsdon Park, Tiverton, Devon EX16 4DE (01884 252341).
Directions: M5 Jct 27, A373 towards Tiverton, leave at 1st sign for Tiverton & Business Park, ground 500yds on right.
Seats: 200 **Cover:** **Capacity:** 2,000 **Floodlights:** Yes **Club Shop:** Yes.
Programme: 12 pages, 30p **Editor:** Richard Tapp(01884 252341)
Club Sponsors: Ken White Signs. **Nickname:** Eagles. **Founded:** 1947
Colours: Green & white/green/green **Change colours:** Red & black/black/black
Midweek matches: Tuesday **Reserve League:** None
Previous Leagues: Devon & Exeter 47-74/ South Western 74-78.
Club Records - Attendance: 1,713 v Tiverton Town April 14th 95. **Appearances:** P Webber. **Win:** 17-0 **Defeat:** 2-7
Clubhouse: 11am-11pm Mon-Sat. Full canteen service - hot & cold meals & snacks.
Hons: East Devon Snr Cup 72-73 75-76, Western Lg Cup 90-91, Les Philips(Lg Cup)94-95 (Div 1 R-up 90-91, Prem Div Merit Cup R-up 91-92, Div 1 Merit Cup 86-87 89-90 90-91), Devon St Lukes Cup R-up 90-91, Devon Snr Cup 87-88, Devon Intermediate Cup 60-61, Football Express Cup 60-61, Devon & Exeter Lg Div 2A 73-74 86-87(res)(Div 1A 76-77(res)), Devon Yth Cup 77-78.Great Mills Western League Runners Up 94-95.

KEYNSHAM TOWN

Chairman: Steve Nicholls **President:** Lester Clements
Secretary: Iain Anderson, 195 Mount Hill Road, Hanham, Bristol BS15 9SU (0117 9616426)
Manager: Malcom Beck **Physio:** A Weaver
Ground: Crown Field, Bristol Road, Keynsham (0117 9865876).
Directions: A4 from Bristol to Bath, ground on left before entering village opposite Crown Inn. Bus service every 30 mins from Bristol passes ground. 10 mins walk from Keynsham BR station.
Seats: 120 **Cover:** 500 **Capacity:** 2,000 **Floodlights:** Yes **Club Shop:** No.
Programme: 32 pages, 50p **Editor:** Mark Brown (0117 969 5487) **Press Officer:** D Brassington
Colours: Gold/black/black **Change colours:** All white.
Sponsors: Ace Building Services Ltd. **Nickname:** K's. **Founded:** 1895
Midweek matchday: Monday **Reserve team's League:** Somerset Senior.
Record Attandance: 3,000 v Chelsea, floodlight opening 88-89. Competitive: 2,160 v Saltash, Amateur Cup, Oct 1952.
Previous - Leagues: Bristol District, Bristol Comb., Bristol Premier, Somerset **Grounds:** The Hams 1886-1910; Gaston 1910-25; Park Road 25-30; Charlton Rd 30-39.
Clubhouse: Evenings & before & after games. Sunday lunch. Snacks.
97-98 - Captain: Dave Sweeney **Top Scorer:** Gary Silverthorne **P.o.Y.:** Steve Miles
Honours: FA Cup 4th Qualifying Rd. Somerset Lg Div 1 77-78; Somerset Snr Cup 51-52 57-58; GFA Jnr Cup 25-26; Somerset & Avon (South) Premier Cup 79-80 (SF 93-94);

MANGOTSFIELD UNITED

President: A J Hill **Chairman:** R Davis **Vice Chairman:** P Selway
Secretary: R Gray, 105 Chiltern Close, Warmley, Bristol BS15 5UW (0117 9616523).
Manager: Terry Rowles. **Asst Manager:** Andy Perrett **Physio:** Ken Dodd.
Ground: Cossham Street, Mangotsfield, Bristol BS17 3EW (0117 9560119).
Directions: M4 jct 19, M32 jct 1; A4174 marked Downend, through lights, over double mini-r'bout to Mangotsfield, left by village church onto B4465 signposted Pucklechurch, ground quarter mile on right. From central Bristol take A432 thru Fishponds, Staple Hill, to Mangotsfield and turn right by village church onto B4465. From Bath/Keynsham follow A4175, right at island at Willsbridge onto A431, then rejoin A4175 at next island (Cherry Garden Hill) to Bridge Yate, straight over double mini-r'bout and take 1st left, right into Carsons Rd after 1 mile and follow to Mangotsfield village & turn right by church onto B4465.
Seats: 300 **Cover:** 800 **Capacity:** 2,500 **Floodlights:** Yes **Club Shop:** Yes
Programme: 32 pages, 50p. **Editor:** Bob Smale (0117 9401926). **Press Officer:** Secretary
Colours: Maroon/white/white **Change colours:** All white
Sponsors: Aaron Roofing Supplies **Nickname:** The Field **Founded:** 1950
Midweek matchday: Tuesday **Reserve League:** Somerset Senior.
Record Attendance: 2,386 v Bath City, FA Cup 77-78
Previous Leagues: Bristol & District 50-67/ Avon Premier Combination 67-72.
Players to progress to Football League: G.Megson, S.White, G.Penrice, P.Purnell, N.Tanner, M.Hooper.
Clubhouse: Open 11am-11pm. Snacks - hot food on matchdays. Lounge bar for official functions etc.
Honours: FA Vase Semi-fin 95-96; Western Lg 90-91 (Lg Cup 73-74 (R-up 86-87) Div 1 R-up 82-83); Somerset Prem. Cup 87-88 (R-up 88-89 95-96); Glos Snr Cup 68-69 75-76; Glos FA Trophy 84-85 86-87 90-91 94-95 96-97; Hungerford Invitation Cup 74-75; Rothmans National Cup R-up 77-78; Hanham Invitation Charity Cup 84-85 85-86; Somerset Snr Lg(Reserves) Div 2 75-76 (Div 3 74-75); Somerset Comb. Cup 74-75; Glos Yth Shield 81-82 84-85 (R-up 82-83); Somerset Floodlit Yth Lg 81-82 82-83 83-84 84-85 87-88; Somerset Yth Shield 76-77.

MELKSHAM TOWN

Melksham Town FC *Photo: Roger Turner*

President: H J Goodenough **Chairman:** Mike Perrin.
Manager: Darren Perrin
Secretary: Paul Macey, 30 Wellington Square, Bowerhill, Melksham SN12 6QX (01225 706876).
Ground: The Conigre, Melksham (01225 702843).
Directions: Just off main square ingrounds of Melksham House.
Capacity: 3,000 **Seats:** 100. **Cover:** 1,500 **Floodlights:** Yes **Founded:** 1876.
Colours: Gold/black/black **Change colours:** Blue & white/blue/blue
Previous - Leagues: Wiltshire 1894-1974 93-94/ Western 74-93. **Grounds:** Challymead/ Old Brighton Road Field.
Midweek Matchday: Tuesday **Record Gate:** 2,821 v Trowbridge Town, FA Cup 57-58.
Clubhouse: Inside ground, open every evening & weekend lunchtimes.
Honours: Wilts Lg 03-04 93-94 (R-up 24-25 29-30 59-60 67-68 68-69 71-72), Western Lg Div 1 79-80, Wilts Snr Cup 03-04 69-70 77-78 (R-up 57-58 67-68 68-69), Wilts Shield 80-81 81-82 84-85 (R-up 86-87), FA Amateur Cup 1st Rd 68-69.

ODD DOWN ATHLETIC

President: P A L Hill **Chairman:** N Fenwick **Vice Chairman:** Mike Wilkins
Secretary: Mike Mancini, 36 Caledonian Rd., East Twerton, Bath BA2 3RD (01225 423293).
Manager: Steve Langley
Ground: Coombe Hay Lane, Odd Down, Bath (01225 832491).
Directions: On main Bath/Exeter road - leaving Bath turn left into Combe Hay Lane opposite Lamplighters Pub. 40 mins walk from Bath (BR).
Seats: 160 **Cover:** 250 **Capacity:** 1,000 **Floodlights:** Yes. **Founded:** 1901
Colours: Blue/white/blue **Change colours:** White/blue/white
Programme: 12 pages with admission **Programme Editor:** Secretary **Club Shop:** No.
Sponsors: Crest Homes **Prev. Lges:** Wilts Premier, Bath & District, Somerset Senior
Midweek Matches: Tuesday **Reserve Team's League:** Somerset Senior
Clubhouse: Yes, open noon-3 & 7-11pm. Hot & cold food available.
Club Records - Goalscorer: Joe Matano 104 **Appearances:** T Mancini & T Ridewood, both 335. **Win:** 11-1 v Minehead (H), Western Lge Prem Div 19/3/94.
Honours: Western Lg Div 1 92-93, Somerset Snr Cup 91-92.

PAULTON ROVERS

President: Mr T Pow **Chairman:** David Bissex **Vice Chairman:** Mr D Carter
Secretary: John Pool, 11 Charlton Park, Midsomer Norton, Avon BA3 4BP (01761 415190).
Manager: John Goss **Physio:** John Pool.
Ground: Athletic Ground, Winterfield Road, Paulton (01761 412907).
Directions: Leave A39 at Farrington Gurney (approx 15 miles south of Bristol), follow A362 marked Radstock for two miles, left at junction B3355 to Paulton, ground on right. Bus services from Bristol and Bath.
Seats: 138 **Cover:** 200 **Capacity:** 5,000 **Floodlights:** Yes **Founded:** 1881
Colours: White/maroon/maroon **Change colours:** Green & navy/navy/navy
Midweek matches: Tuesday **Previous Leagues:** Wilts Premier/ Somerset Snr.
Previous Grounds: Chapel Field/ Cricket Ground/ Recreation Ground 1946-48.
Record Gate: 2,000 v Crewe, FA Cup, 1906-07 **Nickname:** Rovers.
Programme: 20 pages, 50p **Editor:** D Bissex (01761 412463).
Sponsors: Barons Property Centre/Bass Breweries **Reserves' League:** Somerset Snr.
Club Shop: Old programmes available - contact Chairman.
Clubhouse: 3 bars, lounge, skittle alley, dance hall. Capacity 300. Catering facilities.
Club record appearances: Steve Tovey **Club record scorer:** D Clark.
Honours: Western Lg Div 2 R-up 1900-01; Somerset Snr Cup 00-01 02-03 03-04 07-08 08-09 09-10 34-35 67-68 68-69 71-72 72-73 74-75; Somerset Snr Lg 00-01 03-04 04-05 70-71 71-72 72-73 73-74; Somerset F/Lit Youth Lge 96-97.

TAUNTON TOWN

Taunton Town line-up before the Les Phillips League Cup Final v Tiverton *Photo: Tim Lancaster*

Chairman: T F Harris **Vice Chairman:** **Treasuer:** Joan Ellis
Secretary: Tom Harris, C/O the club, (H 01823 333833)
Manager: Russell Musker. **Asst Manager:** Derek Fowler. **Physio:** David Williams
Ground: Wordsworth Drive, Taunton, Somerset TA1 2HG (01823 278191).
Directions: Leave M5 Jct 25, follow signs to town centre, at 2nd set of lights turn left into Wordsworth Drive; ground on left. 25 mins walk from Taunton (BR); turn left out of station and follow road right through town centre bearing left into East Reach. Follow road down and turn right into Wordsworth Drive shortly after Victoria pub.
Seats: 250 **Cover:** 1,000 **Capacity:** 4,000 **Floodlights:** Yes **Club Shop:** Yes
Programme: 28 pages, 50p **Editor:** Les Gill **Press Officer:** Joan Ellis
Colours: Sky & claret/claret/sky **Change colours:** Yellow/sky/yellow.
Club Sponsors: Taunton Cider Co. **Formed:** 1947 **Nickname:** Peacocks
Midweek matches: Wednesday **Reserve Team's League:** Great Mills Combination.
Best Season - FA Cup: 1st Rd Proper 81-82 (lost 1-2 at Swindon Town). **FA Trophy:** 1st Rd Proper 80-81 (lost 1-5 v Hendon at Queens Park Rangers). **FA Vase:** Finalists 93-94.
Club Records - Appearances: Tony Payne **Goalscorer** (in a season): Reg Oram 67. **Win:** 12-0 v Dawlish Tn (A), FA Cup Prel Rd, 28/8/93. **Defeat:** 0-8 v Cheltenham Tn (A), FA Cup 2nd Qual Rd, 28/9/91.
Players progressing to Football League: Charlie Rutter (Cardiff), Stuart Brace (Southend & Grimsby).
Previous - Leagues: Western 54-77/ Southern 77-83. **Grounds:** Several prior to 1953.
Clubhouse: Social club to accommodate 300, full bar facilities, separate bar & hall for private functions.
Honours: FA Vase R-up 93-94, Western Lg 68-69 89-90 (R-up 93-94, Les Phillips Cup R-up 93-94, Alan Young Cup 73-74 75-76(jt with Falmouth), Charity Challenge Cup 49-50 50-51), Somerset Snr Lg 52-53, Somerset Prem. Cup R-up 82-83 89-90 92-93.

Westbury United *Photo: Roger Turner*

TIVERTON TOWN

President: Dan McCauley **Chairman:** Dave Wright **Vice-Chairman:** Pete Buxton
Secretary: Ramsay Findlay, 35 Park Road, Tiverton, Devon EX16 6AY (01884 256341).
Manager: Martyn Rogers **Asst Manager:** Martin Grimshaw **Physio:** Alan Morgan
Ground: Ladysmead, Bolham Road, Tiverton, Devon EX16 8SG (01884 252397)
Directions: M5 Jct 27, west towards Tiverton on A373, continue to end of dual carriageway and turn left at r'about; ground entrance 300yds on right alongside BP petrol station.
Seats: 300 **Cover:** 1,200 **Capacity:** 3,500 **Floodlights:** Yes **Club Shop:** Yes
Programme: 40 pages, 60p **Editor/Press Officer:** Nigel Davis **Nickname:** Tivvy.
Colours: All Yellow **Change:** All white **Formed:** 1920
Midweek matches: Wednesday **Previous League:** Devon & Exeter
Record Attendance: 3,000 v Leyton Orient, FA Cup First Round Proper 1994-95.
Players progressing to Football League: Jason Smith (Coventry City, 1993).Mark Saunders(Plymouth Argyle,1995).
Clubhouse: Lunctimes, evenings. All day Sat during the season. 3 bars. Food (burgers, hot dogs, chips etc).
96-97 Captain: K Smith **96-97 Top Scorer:** P Everett **96-97 P.o.Y.:** S Daly
Honours: FA Vase R-up 92-93 (QF 94-95); FA Cup 1st Rnd 90-91 91-92 94-95; Western Lg 93-94 94-95 96-97 (R-up 92-93 95-96); Les Phillips Cup 92-93 94-95 95-96 96-97; Amateur Trophy 77-78 78-79, Div 1 R-up 88-89; Devon St Lukes Cup 90-91 91-92 92-93 94-95 96-97 (R-up 89-90); Devon & Exeter Lg 51-52 66-67 70-71 84-85; Devon Snr Cup 55-56 65-66; East Devon Snr Cup 35-36 37-38 52-53 55-56 60-61 62-63 66-67; North Devon Charity Cup 72-73 86-87.

WESTBURY UNITED

Chairman: Phillip Alford **Vice Chairman:** Bert Back **President:** George Nicholls.
Secretary: Mrs Joy Bown, 23 Leighton Park Road, Westbury, Wilts. BA13 3RX (01373 823987).
Manager: Nigel Tripp **Asst Manager:** Phil Back **Physio:** Lee Webb
Press Officer: Tom Lawrence. **Commercial Manager:** Paul Busby.
Ground: Meadow Lane, Westbury (01373 823409).
Directions: In town centre, A350, follow signs for BR station, Meadow Lane on right (club signposted). Ten mins walk from railway station (on main London-South West + South Coast-Bristol lines).
Seats: 150 **Cover:** 150 **Capacity:** 3,500 **Floodlights:** Yes **Formed:** 1921
Colours: Green & white/green/green **Change colours:** Sky & navy/blue/blue
Midweek Matches: Tuesday **Prev. Leagues:** Wilts Comb./ Wilts Co. (pre-1984)
Programme: 16 pages, 30p **Editor:** Mike Taylor (01373 826754).
Nickname: White Horsemen **Club Shop:** Yes **Reserve's league:** Trowbridge Lge.
Previous Ground: Redland Lane (pre-1935).
Record Gate: 4,000 v Llanelli, FA Cup 1st Rd 37; 4,000 v Walthamstow Avenue F.A.Cup 37.
Players progressing to Football League: John Atyeo (Bristol City and England).
Clubhouse: Evenings 7-11pm, Fri, Sat & Sun lunctimes 12-3pm.
Honours: Western Lg Div 1 91-92, Wilts Senior Cup 31-32 32-33 47-48 51-52, Wilts Combination, Wilts Lg 34-35 37-38 38-39 49-50 50-51 55-56, Wilts Premier Shield R-up 92-93.

YEOVIL TOWN RESERVES

Yeovil Town Reserves *Photo: Ken Gregory*

Chairman: John Fry **President:** S N Burfield
Secretary: Jean Cotton, c/o Club. (01935 428130 H)
Manager: Maurice O'Donnell/Tony Pounder **Physio:** Maurice O'Donnell
Ground: Huish Park, Lufton Way, Yeovil Somerset, BA22 8YF. (01935 23662, Fax 73956
Directions: Leave A303 at Cartgate roundabout and take A3088 signposted Yeovil. Take first exit at next roundabout and first exit at next roundabout into Lufton Way. Railway station - Yeovil Pen Mill (Bristol/Westbury to Weymouth) 2.5 miles from ground. Yeovil Junction (Waterloo to Exeter) 4 miles. Bus service from both stations on Saturday - matchdays.
Capacity: 8,720 **Seats:** 5,212 **Terracing:** 3,508 **Floodlights:** Yes **Metal Badges:** Yes.
Club Shop: Open on matchdays selling souvenirs, match programmes, scarves, hats, replica kits etc.
Colours: Green/white/green **Change colours:** All Yellow **Midweek matchday:** Wednesday
Clubhouse: Matchdays hot + cold food available. Meals can be ordered provided advance notice is given. All weather astro turf pitch available for bookings 9am-10pm.

FIRST DIVISION CLUBS 1998-99

BITTON

Chairman: David Venables **Manager:** Martyn Dyer
Secretary: Michael Hall, 14 Billingers Road, Kingswood, Bristol BS15 2DE (0117 960 3627)
Ground: The Recreation Ground, Bitton, (0117 932 3222)
Directions: M4 junc 18. Take A46 towards Bath, at first roundabout take A420 for Wick/Bridgeyate. On approach to Bridgeyate turn left at mini-roundabout onto A4175 and follow for 2.2 miles, then turn left for Bath on the A431. The ground is 100 yards on right.
Colours: Red & white/black/black **Change colours:** All yellow
Midweek Matches: Tuesday. **Previous Leagues:** Glos County

CHARD TOWN

Chairman: Brian Beer **Vice Chairman:** Roy Goodland/John Glentworth
Secretary: Daniel Glentworth, c/o Chard Town FC (01460 61132 H)
Manager: Gerry Pearson **Coach:** Peter Smith. **Physio:** Peter Smith
Ground: Town Ground, Zembard Lane, Chard (01460 61402).
Directions: 150 yards from the town centre, off Combe Street. 8 miles from Crewkerne BR station.
Seats: 60 **Cover:** 200 **Capacity:** 1,500 **Floodlights:** Yes
Programme: 24 pages with entry **Editor:** Ian Walker
Colours: Scarlet/black/black **Change colours:** White/white/red
Founded: 1920 **Nickname:** Robins. **Sponsors:** Annual Competition.
Midweek matches: Wednesday **Reserve Team's League:** Great Mills Combination.
Previous Leagues: Somerset Snr 20-24 48-75/ Perry Street 25-48.
Clubhouse: Matchdays & most evenings. Snacks served
Honours: Som. Snr Lg 49-50 53-54 59-60 67-68 69-70 (Lg Cup 61-62 71-72 76-77); Western Lg Div 1 R-up 83-84 87-88 95-96, (Merit Cup 82-83, Comb. Cup(Res) 91-92 (R-up 92-93)); Som. Snr Cup 52-53 66-67; S W Co's Cup 88-89; Western Com Lge 96-97, Cup 96-97:

CLYST ROVERS

President: Mr P W Brown **Chairman:** Bob Chamberlain **Vice Chairman:** Colin Dadson
Secretary: Bob Chamberlain, Orchard Cottage, Clyst St George, Exeter EX3 0NZ (01392 873498)
Manager: R Wilson **Physio:** Bill Wreford.
Ground: Waterslade Park, Clyst Honiton, Devon (01392 366424)
Directions: A30 following signs for Exeter Airport. Coming from Exeter take 1st right after airport turning (ground signposted) up narrow 200yds past Duke of York Pub.
Seats: 130 **Cover:** 300 **Capacity:** 3,000 **Floodlights:** Yes **Founded:** 1926.
Programme: 32 pages, 30p **Editor:** Ray Dack (01392 215075)
Colours: Yellow/blue/yellow & blue **Change colours:** Blue/black/blue
Reformed: 1951. **Nickname:** Rovers. **Sponsors:** Vantage Pharmacy, Paignton
Midweek Matches: Tuesday. **Club Shop:** Yes, Programmes, souvenirs etc.
Previous Leagues: Exeter & District 26-44 51-66/ Exeter & District Sunday 67-82/ South Western 81-92.
Record Gate: 768 v Tiverton, Devon St Lukes final 11/5/93.
Clubhouse: Open one and a half hours before kick off and after game. Excellent food available.
Honours: Devon St Lukes Cup R-up 92-93, Western Lg Cup SF 92-93.

CORSHAM TOWN

Chairman: Colin Hudd **Manager:** Peter Tripp.
Secretary: Richard Taylor, 7 Cresswells, Corsham, Wilts SN13 9NT (01249 714406)
Ground: Southbank Ground, Lacock Road, Corsham, (01249 715609)
Directions: A4 into Corsham, at Hare & Hounds roundabout, take the Melksham Road B3353 until War Memorial, then Lacock Road, ground 1/2 mile on right.
Colours: All red **Change colours:** Yellow/blue/blue
Midweek home matchday: Tuesday **Previous League:** Wiltshire Lge.

DAWLISH TOWN

President: Bob Webster **Chairman:** John Wathen
Secretary: John Wathen, 35 Lower Drive, Dawlish EX7 0AT (01626 864403)
Manager: Tony Bowker. **Assistant Manager:** Martin Tooze
Ground: Playing Fields, Sandy Lane, Exeter Road, Dawlish (01626 863110).
Directions: Approx 1 mile from centre of town, off main Exeter road (A379).
Seats: 200 **Cover:** 200 **Capacity:** 2,000 **Floodlights:** Yes **Founded:** 1889
Programme: 34 pages, 30p **Programme Editor:** Roy Bolt.
Colours: Green & white/green/white **Change colours:** Blue & white/white & blue/blue
Midweek home matchday: Tuesday **Previous League:** Devon & Exeter.
Record Gate: 1,500 v Heavitree Utd, Devon Prem. Cup Q-Final
Clubhouse: Open nightly, situated in car park opposite ground.
Honours: Western Lg Cup 80-81 83-84, Devon Premier Cup 69-70 72-73 80-81, Devon Snr Cup 57-58 67-68, Devon St Lukes Cup 82-83 (R-up 81-82), FA Vase Quarter Finals 86-87, Carlsberg Cup 96.

DEVIZES TOWN

Chairman: Philip Rossiter **Manager:** Brian Newlands
Secretary: Chris Dodd, 69 Broadleas Park, Devizes, Wilts. SN10 5JG. (01380 726205)
Ground: Nursteed Road, Devizes. (01380 722817).
Directions: Off Nursteed Road (A342 signposted Andover); leaving town ground on right opposite Eastleigh Rd.
Seats: 130. **Cover:** 400 **Capacity:** 2,500 **Floodlights:** Yes **Founded:** 1883
Colours: Red & white stripes/black/red **Change colours:** All blue
Previous Name: Southbroom (until early 1900s) **Previous Ground:** London Rd (pre 1946)
Midweek Matchday: Tuesday **Previous Leagues:** Wilts Comb./ Wilts Premier.
Honours: Wilts Snr Cup 07-08 49-50 56-57 57-58 58-59 60-61 61-62 62-63 65-66 67-68 70-71 71-72 73-74 78-79.

EXMOUTH TOWN

President: Brian Bradley **Chairman:** P Marshall **Vice Chairman:** John Dibsdall
Secretary: John Edwards, 5 Pinn Lane, Pinhoe, Exeter EX1 3QX (01392 468633)
Manager: Robert Green. **Physio:** Julian Bennett
Ground: King George V Ground, Southern Road, Exmouth (01395 263348)
Directions: On right side of main Exeter to Exmouth road (A376). Half mile from Exmouth (BR) station.
Seats: 100 **Cover:** 250 **Capacity:** 2,500 **Floodlights:** Yes **Formed:** 1933
Colours: Blue & white/blue/blue **Change colours:** Red & white/black/red & white
Nickname: 'Town' or 'Blues' **Previous Lge:** Devon & Exeter 1933-73.
Programme: 36 pages, 30p **Editor:** J.Dibsdall.
Midweek matchday: Tuesday **Reserves' League:** Gt Mills Comb. **Sponsors:** None.
Club Shop: Yes **Record Gate:** 2,395 v Liverpool XI, friendly in 1987.
Clubhouse: Open every night and weekend lunchtimes. Snacks available.
Club Record Scorer: Mel Pym, 117 **Record Appearances:** Keith Sprague, Geoff Weeks 410 (Western Lg)
Honours: FA Vase SF 84-85; Western Lg 83-84 85-86 (R-up 86-87 88-89; Lg Cup 88-89; Div 1 R-up 81-82; Sportmanship Tphy 86-87 92-93); Devon Premier Cup 70-71 79-80; Devon St Lukes Cup 84-85 88-89 89-90; Devon Snr Cup 50-51; East Devon Snr Cup 50-51 82-83; Harry Wood Mem. Cup 81-82; Exmouth Chal. Cup [7]

FROME TOWN

President: Mr C W M Norton. **Chairman:** Geoff Norton-Morris **Vice Chairman:** Steve Porter, Geoff Norris
Secretary: Mrs S J Merrill, 11 Beaconsfield Way, Frome, Somerset BA11 2UA (01373 473820).
Manager: Simon Culliford **Coach:** **Physio:** Bob Stokes
Ground: Badgers Hill, Berkeley Road, Frome (01373 453643).
Directions: On the Westbury Road, 1 mile from town centre and Frome BR station
Seats: 250 **Cover:** 800 **Capacity:** 5,000 **Floodlights:** Yes **Founded:** 1904
Colours: All red **Change colours:** Purple/navy/navy
Sponsors: Telewest Communications **Nickname:** Robins. **Club Shop:** No.
Programme: 24 pages, 50p **Editor:** Secretary
Previous League: Somerset Senior, Wilts League and Wilts Premier
Record Attendance: 8,000 v Leyton Orient, F.A.Cup 1st Rd. 58.
Midweek matchday: Wednesday **Reserve's League:** Somerset Senior.
Best Season - F.A.Cup: 1st Rd Proper v L.Orient 54-55 **F.A.Trophy:** 2nd.Rd.Proper v Boston Utd (a) 0-4, 84-85.
F.A.Vase: 2nd.Rd.Proper v Paulton R (a) 1-2.
Clubhouse: Evenings & weekends. Cold food only.
Honours: Wiltshire League 1909-10,1910-11,Western Lg 78-79 (Div 2 19-20, Div 2 R-up 54-55, Lg Cup 79-80 82-83, Merit Cup 82-83, Alan Young Cup 79-80, Subsidiary Cup 59-60), FA Cup 1st Rd 54-55, Somerset Premier Cup 66-67 68-69 82-83, Wilts Premier Lg 62-63, Western Co's F'lit Cup 83-84, Somerset Snr Cup 32-33 33-34 50-51, Somerset Snr Lg 06-07 08-09 10-11 (Div 1(res) 90-91, Div 3(res) 85-86, Lg Cup(res) 91-92).

GLASTONBURY

Chairman: Peter Watts **President:** Mr L R Reed
Secretary: Mrs S Dovey, Walnut Cottage, High Ham, Langport, TA10 9Db (01458 252477)
Life President: Les Heal **Manager:** Simon Dovey.
Ground: Abbey Moor Stadium, Godney Road, Glastonbury, Somerset (01458 831460).
Directions: From Bristol take by-pass from Tin Bridge r/about turning right at Northload Bridge r/about, then 1st right. From Taunton take by-pass at 'B&Q' turning, left at Northload Bridge r/about, then 1st right.
Seats: 80 **Cover:** 300 **Capacity:** 1,500 **Floodlights:** Yes **Founded:** 1890.
Programme: 24 pages, 30p **Editor/Press Officer:** Les Heal (01458 832037)
Colours: Yellow/black/yellow **Change colours:** All red
Midweek Matches: Wednesday **Previous Leagues:** Bristol & District, Bristol Suburban
Clubhouse: Yes, on ground. Hot snacks from tea bar on matchdays.
Club Record scorer: Jim Allaway 42 **Club Record Appearances:** Brian Mortimer 496.
Honours: Western Lg 48-49 50-51 69-70 (R-up 47-48 51-52)Great Mills Div 1 94-95 Lg Cup 65-66 (SF 83-84), Alan Young Cup 67-68 (jt with Minehead) 70-71); Somerset Professional Cup 37-38 48-49; Somerset Snr Cup 35-36; Somerset Charity Cup 32-33; Somerset Jnr Cup 12-13 13-14; Somerset Lg 49-50 50-51

HEAVITREE UNITED

President: Mr E Drew **Chairman:** Dennis Bray **Vice Chairman:** Mr K Carpenter
Secretary: Keith Gilbert, 9 Dean Street, St Leonards, Exeter EX2 4HH (01392 438637)
Manager: **Asst Manager:** Nick Bibby **Physio:**
Ground: Wingfield Park, East Wonford Hill, Exeter, Devon (01392 73020).
Directions: Leave M5 at Exeter Granada Services, follow signs for City Centre/ Heavitree for approx. 3 miles and ground is situated on left at top of East Wonford Hill.
Seats: 150 **Cover:** 150 **Capacity:** 500 **Floodlights:** No **Founded:** 1885.
Colours: All royal with yellow trim **Change colours:** All jade & black
Programme: 20 pages, 20p **Editor:** **Club Shop:** No.
Nickname: Heavies. **Sponsors:** Mortgage & Loan Centre **Midweek matchday:** Tuesday
Previous Lges: Exeter & Dist./ Devon & Exeter. **Record Gate:** 350 v Exeter City, friendly 1989.
Clubhouse: 12am-12pm daily. Wide range of matchday hot food.
Club record scorer: John Laskey **Club record appearances:** Alan Kingdom.
Honours: Exeter & Dist Lg 46-47 51-52 (Snr Div 2 56-57 59-60 60-61 67-68), Devon & Exeter Lg 70-71 76-77, Devon Snr Cup 46-47 60-61 70-71, E Devon Snr Cup 46-47 70-71 76-77, Wheaton Tphy 87-88.

ILFRACOMBE TOWN

Chairman: Mike Edmunds **Vice-Chairman:** Bob Martin. **President:** Bob Martin.
Secretary: Tony Alcock, 2 Worth Road, Ilfracombe, North Devon EX34 9JA (01271 862686).
Manager: Ian Cornish/Gary Gomez **Coach/Physio:** Eric Hayhurst
Ground: Marlborough Park, Ilfracombe, Devon (01271 865939).
Directions: A361 to Ilfracombe, 1st right in town after lights, follow Marlborough Rd to top, ground on left.
Seats: 60 **Cover:** 450 **Capacity:** 2,000 **Floodlights:** Yes **Club Shop:** No.
Programme: The Bluebird 8 pages, 40p **Editor:** Peter Bidgood (01271 864756)
Colours: All Blue **Change colours:** Yellow & black/black/yellow
Sponsors: Park View. **Nickname:** Bluebirds **Founded:** 1902
Midweek home matchday: Tuesday **Reserve team's League:** North Devon.
Record attendance: 3,000 v Bristol City, Ground opening, 2/10/24
Previous Leagues: North Devon 04-14 20-22 60-84/ East Devon Premier 22-31/ Exeter & District 32-39 46-49/ Western 49-59/ South Western League (Reserves) 53-54.
Player progressing to Football Lge: Jason Smith (Coventry via Tiverton)
Clubhouse: Every night 7-11pm and weekend lunchtimes. Hot & cold meals on matchdays.
Club Record Goalscorer: Darren Bryant **Club Record Appearances:** Paul Jenkins 410.
Honours: East Devon Premier Lg 25-26 28-29 29-30, North Devon Senior Lg, North Devon Premier Lg 66-67 70-71 81-82 82-83, Western Lg Div 2 R-up 52-53.

LARKHALL ATHLETIC

President: Tony Rhymes **Chairman:** Jim McLay **Manager:** P Rankin/M Skuse
Secretary: Mervyn Liles, 9 Eastbourne Ave., Claremont Rd., Bath BA1 6EW (01225 319427).
Ground: "Plain Ham", Charlcombe Lane, Larkhall, Bath (01225 334952).
Directions: A4 from Bath, 1 mile from city centre turn left into St Saviours Rd. In Larkhall square fork left, and right at junction, road bears into Charlcombe Lane. Ground on right as lane narrows.
Seats: None **Cover:** 50 **Capacity:** 1,000 **Floodlights:** No **Club Shop:**
Programme: Yes **Editor:** **Nickname:** Larks.
Colours: Royal & white/royal & white/royal **Change colours:** Red & white/red & white/red **Founded:** 1914
Midweek Matches: Tuesday **Previous League:** Somerset Snr
Honours: Som. Snr Cup 75-76, Som. Snr Lg, Western Lg Div 1 88-89 93-94 94-95(Div 1 Merit Cup(4) 83-86 87-88(jt with Yeovil Res).

MINEHEAD

Director of Football/Chairman/Secretary: Peter Bate, Meadow Cottage, Venniford, Minehead, Somerset. TA24 8ST. (01643 704063)
Manager: Chris Porter **Coach:** Charlie Kirk **Reserves Mgr:** Charlie Lewis
Ground: The Recreation Ground, Irnham Road, Minehead, Somerset (01643 704989).
Directions: Entering town from east on A39 turn right into King Edward Road at Police station, first left into Alexandra Rd and follow signs to car park; ground entrance within. Regular buses to Minehead from Taunton, the nearest railhead.
Seats: 350 **Cover:** 400 **Capacity:** 3,500 **Floodlights:** Yes **Founded:** 1889.
Colours: Blue & white/blue/blue **Change colours:** Yellow/Green/sky/yellow & green
Programme: 24 pages, 50p **Editor:** Dir of Football **Midweek Matches:** Tuesday.
Previous Leagues: Somerset Snr/ Southern 72-83. **Reserves League:** Combination League
Record Gate: 3,600 v Exeter City, FA Cup 2nd Rd, 77.
Honours: Southern Lg R-up 76-77 (Div 1 Sth 75-76, Merit Cup 75-76), Western Lg R-up 66-67 71-72 (Div 1 90-91, Alan Young Cup 67-68 (jt with Glastonbury), Somerset Premier Cup 60-61 73-74 76-77.

Heavitree United FC *Photo: Tim Lancaster*

Clyst Rovers FC *Photo: Martin Wray*

PEWSEY VALE

President: **Chairman:** Rob Thompson **Manager:** Graham Smith
Secretary: Mrs Barbara Flippance, 17 Slater Rd, Pewsey SN9 5EE (01672 563665).
Ground: Recreation Ground, Ball Rd, Pewsey (01672 562990).
Directions: On entering Pewsey from A345, at the Market Place proceed to end of High Street and turn right into Ball Rd, entrance to ground on right opposite pub. BR to Pewsey station.
Seats: **Cover:** Yes **Capacity:** **Floodlights:** No **Formed:**
Colours: Blue & white/blue/blue **Change colours:** All Red.
Previous League: Wiltshire County (pre-1993). **Midweek home matchday:** Wednesday
Honours: Wiltshire County League 92-93.

STREET

Chairman: Steve Bailey **Manager:** Simon White
Secretary: Mark Clarke, 1 Deerswood Gardens, Street, Somerset BA16 9PY (01458 442249)
Ground: The Tannery Ground, Middlebrooks, Street, Somerset (01458 445987)
Directions: Sign posted from both ends of A39 & B3151
Colours: All green & white **Change colours:** Red & black/black/black
Midweek home matchday: Tuesday

TORRINGTON

President: Cyril Slade **Chairman:** Winston Martin
Secretary: David Priscott, 6 Highfield Terrace, Bishops Tawton, Barnstable EX32 0AN (01271 328316)
Manager: Geoff Evans **Asst Manager:** Mike Ford **Physio:** Albert Williams
Ground: Vicarage Field, School Lane, Great Torrington (01805 622853).
Directions: (From North, Barnstaple, Exeter, South Molton) In town centre turn left by parish church, turn right at swimming pool, ground behind swimming pool. Good parking. Red Bus from Bideford and Barnstaple (nearest BR station). Bus stop 300yds from ground.
Seats: 100 **Cover:** 1,000 **Capacity:** 4,000 **Floodlights:** Yes **Formed:** 1908
Midweek Matches: Tuesday **Club Sponsors:** Bideford Tool **Club Shop:** No.
Colours: Green & white hoops/green/green & white **Change colours:** Blue & white stripes/white/white
Programme: 48 pages, 50p **Editor:** Secretary **Best F.A.Vase Season:** 5th Rd 84-85.
Nickname: Torrie or Supergreens **Previous Leagues:** N Devon/ Devon & Exeter/ S Western 77-84.
Clubhouse: Weekdays 7-11pm, Sat & Sun 12-3. Two bars. Light snacks available. New kitchen lounge, toilets and offices have been built.
Club record scorer: Trevor Watkins, 254 **Club record appearances:** Mike Gilbert 527
Honours: Western Lg R-up 90-91; Merit Cup 91-92 93-94 95-96; South Western Lg Cup 81; Devon St Lukes Cup R-up 95-96 96-97; Devon & Exeter Lg & Cup 73-74; Festival of Britain Cup 96-97; Les Phillips Cup R-up 91-92; Torridge Cup (13).

WARMINSTER TOWN

President: **Chairman:** Peter Farrell **Vice-Chairman:** Rod Kitley.
Secretary: Nigel Edwards, 26 St Johns Road, Warminster, Wilts BA12 9LY (01985 300582 (H), 0468 534695 (Mob)
General Manager: Derek Wesley **Manager:** Derek Graham
Ground: Weymouth Street, Warminster, Wilts BA12, (01985 217828).
Directions: Take A350 for Weymouth from lights at centre of town - ground on left at brow of hill.
Seats: 75 **Cover:** 150 **Capacity:** 2,000 **Floodlights:** Yes **Club Shop:** No.
Programme: 36 pages, 40p **Editor:** Chris Finch (01985 217326)
Colours: Red & black stripes/black/red **Change:** All white
Sponsors: Lyons Seafoods. **Nickname:** Red & blacks **Founded:** 1878
Midweek Matchday: Wednesday **Reserve League:** Wilthsire. **Previous League:** Wiltshire
Record Attendance: 1,500 for Ladies International, England v Wales, mid-1970s.
Clubhouse: Opened 22/7/94. Evenings/matchdays/as required
97-98 - Captain: Kevin Sparey **P.o.Y.:** Mark Jones **Top Scorer:** Peter Wakenshaw
Honours: Wilts Snr Cup 1900-01 02-03 10-11 (R-up 09-10 26-27 32-33 53-54); Wilts Prem. Lg 56-57; Wilts Jnr Cup R-up 21-22 27-28 55-56 58-59; Central Wilts Lg 08-09

WELLINGTON

Chairman: Selwyn Aspin **Vice-Chairman:** Mike Bull **President:** Alan Shire
Secretary: David Grabham, 12 Drakes Park, Wellington, Somerset TA21 8TB (01823 664946).
Manager: Iain Blake **Res. Manager:** Steve Luxon **Physio:** Ken Pearson.
Ground: Wellington Playing Field, North Street, Wellington, Somerset (01823 664810).
Directions: At town centre traffic lights turn into North St., then first left by Fire Station into the public car park that adjoins the ground.
Seats: None **Cover:** 200 **Capacity:** 3,000 **Floodlights:** Yes **Club Shop:**
Programme: Yes **Editor:** Jeff Brown
Colours: All tangerine **Change colours:** Blue & claret stripes/blue/blue
Sponsors: A J Shire & Wadham Fencing **Nickname:** **Founded:** 1892
Midweek Matches: Wednesday **Reserves League:** Combination
Previous Leagues: Taunton Saturday, Somerset Senior
Players progressing to Football League: Nick Jennings (Plymouth).
97-98 - Captain: Kevin Bryant **P.o.Y.:** Kevin Bryant **Top Scorer:** Mark McKenna
Club Record Goalscorer: Ken Jones **Club Record Appearances:**
Honours: Western Lg Div 1 R-up 80-81 (Merit Cup 91-92); Western Comb Lge 95-96; Western Comb Lge KO Cup 95-96; Somerset Snr Lg Div 1 R-up; Rowbarton & Seward Cup;

WELTON ROVERS

Chairman: Rae James **President:**
Secretary: Geoff Baker, 6 Longfellow Road, Westfield, Radstock, Bath BA3 3YZ (01761 413742).
Manager: Adrian Britton **Asst Manager:** Martin Finn **Physio:** John Carver
Ground: West Clewes, North Road, Midsomer Norton, Somerset (01761 412097).
Directions: A367 Bath to Radstock – right at lights at foot of hill onto A362, ground on right.
Seats: 300 **Cover:** 300 **Capacity:** 2,400 **Floodlights:** Yes **Club Shop:** No.
Programme: 12 pages, 25p **Editor:** M Brown
Colours: Green & white/green/green **Change colours:** All Red
Sponsors: Norad Travel **Nickname:** Rovers. **Formed:** 1887
Midweek matchday: Monday **Reserve League:** Somerset Senior.
Record Attendance: 2,000 v Bromley, FA Amateur Cup 1963 **Previous Leagues:** None
Clubhouse: 7.30-11pm daily, Sat matchdays 1.30-2.45pm, Sun noon-2pm.
Club Record Appearances: **Club Record Goalscorer:** Ian Henderson, 51
Honours: Western Lg 11-12 64-65 65-66 66-67 73-74 (Div 1 59-60 87-88; Amateur Cup 56-57 57-58 58-59 59-60; Alan Young Cup 65-66 66-67 67-68(joint)); Somerset Snr Cup 06-07 11-12 12-13 13-14 19-20 24-25 25-26 60-61 61-62 62-63, Somerset I'mediate Cup 77-78, Somerset Jnr Cup 06-07(joint) 24-25 30-31, WBC Clares City of Wells Cup 78-79.

First-half action from Irnham Road as Minehead's keeper Nicky Coles tips the ball over the bar from an effort by Clyst Rover's Russell Wilson

Photo: Martin Wray

INTERLINK EXPRESS
MIDLAND FOOTBALL ALLIANCE

FEEDER TO: BEAZER HOMES LEAGUE

President: N D Jeynes **Chairman:** P Fellows

General Secretary/Treasurer: P G Dagger, Alpine Cottage, Banbury Road, Ettington, Warwickshire CV37 7SU Tel: 01789 740597 Fax: 01789 740247

The race for the Interlink Express Midland Football Alliance title turned out to be between four clubs. Bloxwich Town set the early pace but their involvement in cup competitions allowed Boldmere to briefly take over the reins at the top during October and November. Oldbury United led from mid November to mid December before a disastrous slump in form saw them toppled again by Bloxwich. A superb mid season run by Kings Norton Town allowed them to briefly climb to second place but they then fell away before they could have any real impact on the title race. Rocester, who had promised so much with games in hand for most of the season, soon learned that these are less use than points in the bag as they dropped too many to catch Bloxwich. By April it became obvious that there was only one team in it. Bloxwich finished the season 12 points clear of runners up Rocester with Oldbury third and Boldmere fourth

In cup competitions it was not a particularly good season for Alliance clubs with one or two notable exceptions. Knypersley Victoria again led the way in the FA Cup. They reached the fourth qualifying round only to lose out 1-0 to Boston United. Bloxwich Town managed to reach the third round of the FA Vase but other results for Alliance clubs were disappointing in this competition. In county cup competitions, no Alliance clubs reached the quarter finals of the Birmingham Senior Cup but Kings Norton Town and Barwell must both feel frustrated to have reached the semi-final stages of the Birmingham County FA Vase and Leicestershire Senior Cup respectively only to lose out to opposition from lower leagues. Kings Norton Town went out on penalties to Shirley Town of the Midland Combination and Barwell lost to cup specialists Birstall United of the Leicestershire Senior League. Halesowen Harriers went one better by reaching the final of the Walsall Senior Cup before losing out 2-1 to Blakenall at Bescot Stadium. In the Midland Invitation Cup it was a disappointing season for Alliance clubs as the new Southern League entrants dominated with only one Alliance club, Kings Norton Town, reaching the quarter finals.

Final mention though must go to Knypersley Victoria who beat Bloxwich Town to lift the Industrial Rewinds League Challenge Cup 2-0. It was no more than the Vics deserved after another season of cup success, this being their 18th cup game of the season.

Congratulations also go to Chasetown's Shaun Bradbury for finishing the season as the Alliance's leading scorer with 26 goals.

Robert Shinfield

FINAL LEAGUE TABLES 1997-98

	P	*W*	*D*	*L*	*F*	*A*	*W*	*D*	*L*	*F*	*A*	*Pts*
Bloxwich Town	38	13	1	5	43	20	15	3	1	34	11	88
Rocester	38	11	4	4	31	14	12	3	4	43	22	76
Oldbury United	38	10	6	3	40	20	10	5	4	33	23	71
Boldmere St Michaels	38	10	5	4	27	17	9	6	4	27	21	68
Kings Norton Town	38	7	9	3	28	17	11	4	4	29	20	67
Barwell	38	7	7	5	29	31	9	5	5	39	25	60
Bridgnorth Town	38	8	6	5	33	21	7	7	5	31	26	58
West Midlands Police	38	8	7	4	31	21	7	5	7	27	21	57
Halesowen Harriers	38	9	2	8	26	24	8	3	8	27	39	56
Chasetown	38	7	5	7	29	20	7	6	6	28	23	53
Wednesfield	38	7	7	5	31	20	7	4	8	25	29	53
Knypersley Victoria	38	7	9	3	31	27	4	8	7	21	26	50
Willenhall Town	38	6	8	5	21	16	6	5	8	24	28	49
Pelsall Villa	38	4	6	9	30	38	6	9	4	36	28	45
Sandwell Borough	38	4	6	9	24	36	6	9	4	33	27	45
Rushall Olympic	38	5	5	9	27	32	7	3	9	24	25	44
Stapenhill	38	2	7	10	16	37	5	5	9	23	37	33
Stratford Town	38	6	2	11	24	35	2	5	12	15	35	31
Pershore Town	38	2	2	15	20	48	2	4	13	16	49	18
Shifnal Town	38	1	0	18	19	57	2	5	12	16	46	14

RESULTS CHART 1997-98

	1	2	3	4	5	6	7	8	9	10	11	12	13	14	15	16	17	18	19	20
1 Barwell	X	1-1	1-0	0-2	4-5	1-0	1-2	2-0	3-1	2-1	1-1	1-5	1-4	1-1	2-1	2-2	2-1	1-1	1-1	2-1
2 Bloxwich Town	2-1	X	0-3	1-1	1-0	4-0	0-1	2-0	0-1	3-1	4-1	1-4	1-2	3-1	4-1	3-2	2-0	5-0	3-1	4-0
3 Boldmere St Michaels	1-1	0-2	X	0-0	0-3	4-1	2-1	1-1	1-0	1-1	1-0	2-1	2-0	0-1	3-0	2-0	3-1	1-2	1-1	2-1
4 Bridgnorth Town	1-1	1-4	1-1	X	2-2	0-2	1-2	2-0	2-3	7-0	1-1	0-1	1-0	1-1	4-0	3-1	0-0	1-0	2-1	3-1
5 Chasetown	1-1	0-1	1-1	1-2	X	0-1	1-1	6-0	3-4	2-2	0-0	3-1	1-0	1-2	3-0	0-2	2-0	0-1	3-1	1-0
6 Halesowen Harriers	3-2	1-2	1-2	1-1	1-2	X	0-1	1-0	4-3	3-1	2-1	0-1	2-1	1-2	0-1	3-0	1-4	1-0	1-0	0-0
7 Kings Norton Town	0-3	0-0	1-0	2-0	2-1	6-2	X	0-0	2-4	1-1	2-2	1-1	0-0	1-1	0-0	4-0	3-0	3-1	0-0	0-1
8 Knypersley Victoria	2-2	0-4	0-2	1-1	0-0	4-1	0-1	X	3-2	4-1	1-1	0-0	2-1	3-3	1-0	2-1	3-3	2-2	1-0	2-2
9 Oldbury United	3-1	1-2	5-0	3-3	3-1	2-0	0-0	2-1	X	2-0	3-3	1-2	1-0	1-1	2-2	1-2	0-0	5-0	3-1	2-1
10 Pershore Town	0-2	1-4	1-2	2-2	0-3	2-2	0-4	0-2	2-4	X	1-2	2-4	1-3	1-3	3-0	0-2	2-0	1-4	0-3	1-2
11 Pelsall Villa	1-4	0-1	1-1	1-3	2-3	1-2	5-3	2-2	0-0	4-1	X	1-2	1-2	1-0	3-3	2-2	2-0	1-2	0-5	2-2
12 Rocester	1-1	0-1	2-0	3-0	1-0	1-2	1-0	1-1	0-2	4-0	1-1	X	2-0	4-4	3-0	0-1	3-0	2-1	1-0	1-0
13 Rushall Olympic	3-1	0-1	1-1	3-0	0-0	2-2	2-3	0-1	1-2	0-1	2-5	1-0	X	1-1	3-1	4-2	2-2	0-3	0-2	2-4
14 Sandwell Borough	1-3	1-3	1-2	2-4	2-0	2-4	1-1	1-1	0-0	3-2	1-5	1-5	1-2	X	1-0	1-1	3-0	2-2	0-1	0-0
15 Shifnal Town	1-4	0-1	0-2	0-4	1-4	1-2	3-5	0-5	1-4	1-3	3-4	1-2	1-2	0-3	X	0-1	2-1	0-3	3-4	1-3
16 Stapenhill	1-4	0-3	1-1	2-0	1-2	0-0	0-1	1-1	1-1	5-0	0-2	0-7	1-5	1-5	0-0	X	0-1	1-1	1-1	0-2
17 Stratford Town	0-2	0-2	1-1	1-5	0-0	2-3	3-1	0-3	0-1	2-0	4-2	2-3	2-0	3-1	0-3	2-1	X	0-1	0-3	2-3
18 Wednesfield	3-4	0-0	1-3	1-3	0-0	3-0	0-1	2-2	0-0	1-0	0-0	1-2	3-0	1-1	6-3	5-0	1-0	X	0-0	3-1
19 West Midlands Police	1-0	4-0	2-3	2-0	2-1	2-3	0-0	1-1	0-1	1-1	0-4	2-2	1-1	1-0	6-0	1-1	3-2	2-1	X	0-0
20 Willenhall Town	0-2	1-2	0-2	0-0	1-1	2-0	0-1	2-0	0-0	3-0	1-1	2-0	1-1	2-2	2-0	2-2	0-0	1-0	1-2	X

PROMOTION/RELEGATION

Banks's Brewery League Premier Division:	Lye Town or Stourport Swifts to be promoted
Endsleigh Combination Premier Division:	Champions Worcester Athletico to merge with Pershore Town. No other teamspromoted
Everards Senior League:	No teams promoted
Bottom of Dr Martens League Mid Division:	Corby Town (not to be relegated to Interlink Express Alliance

INTERLINK EXPRESS ALLIANCE LEADING GOALSCORERS 1997-98

26	Shaun Bradbury	Chasetown
25	Neil Hesson	Oldbury United
23	Stuart Payne	Halesowen Harriers
22	Mark Holdcroft	Bloxwich Town
	Russ Peake	Rocester
16	Martin Dean	Boldmere St Michael
15	David Crichton	Stratford Town
14	Chris Burton	West Midlands Police
	Paul Joinson	Sandwell Borough
	Jason Treharne	Bridgnorth Town
13	Jon Hanson	Pelsall Villa
12	Matt Cartwright	Bloxwich Town
	Kerry Giddings	Bridgnorth Town
	Oliver Latchford	West Midlands Police
11	Carl Dwyer	Rushall Olympic
	Tony Dixon	Pelsall Villa/Chasetown
	Mark Barnes	Stapenhill
	Andy Canning	Kings Norton Town
	Craig Skitt	Wednesfield
10	Kevin Rowlands	Kings Norton Town
	Phil Bates	Bridgnorth Town
	Mark Fisher	Rocester

INTERLINK EXPRESS MIDLAND FOOTBALL ALLIANCE RECORDS 1994-98

Biggest Wins: Sandwell Borough 9 Brierley Hill Town 0 (26.12.94), Barwell 8 Pershore Town 0 (23.4.96)

Biggest Away Win: Sandwell Borough 0 Shepshed Dynamo 7 (8.4.95), Stapenhill 0 Rocester 7 (21.3.98)

Highest Aggregate: 10 goals - Halesowen Harriers 8 Hinckley Ath 2 (8.1.95), Knypersley Victoria 7 Boldmere St Michaels 3 (5.11.94)

Most individual goals in a game: 4- John Powell for Shifnal Tn v Rushall Ol (17.12.94),
Ian Perry for Halesowen Harriers v Hinckley Athletic (7.1.95),
Martin Hallam for Pershore Town v Knypersley Victoria (2.12.95),
Lee Joinson for Sandwell Borough v Rushall Olympic (17.2.96),
Shane Riddell for Shepshed Dynamo v Oldbury United (16.4.96),
Paul James for Knypersley Victoria v Pershore Town (30.11.96),
Tony Dixon for Chasetown v Pelsall Villa (15.2.97)

Quickest Goal: 10 seconds by Neil Hitchman for Halesowen Harriers v Stratford Town (20.8.96)

Most individual goals in a season: 31 by John Burndred for Knypersley Victoria 1994-95

Highest and lowest attendances: 571 Hinckley Athletic v Barwell (8.4.96), 17 Sandwell Borough v Stratford Town (LC) (6.12.97)

SUMMARY OF LEAGUE CUP GAMES INVOLVING ALLIANCE CLUBS

INDUSTRIAL REWINDS LEAGUE CHALLENGE CUP 1997-98

First Round

Bloxwich Town	v	Stapenhill	2-0
Rocester	v	Halesowen Harriers	2-1
Pershore Town	v	Chasetown	1-2
West Midlands Police	v	Boldmere St Mich's	0-2

Second Round

Barwell	v	Pelsall Villa	1-1, 4-0
Chasetown	v	Kings Norton Town	2-3
Sandwell Borough	v	Stratford Town	1-2
Wednesfield	v	Bloxwich Town	3-3, 2-4
Boldmere St Mich's	v	Bridgnorth Town	1-4
Knypersley Victoria	v	Rushall Olympic	3-0
Shifnal Town	v	Oldbury United	0-4
Willenhall Town	v	Rocester	1-1, 1-1, 4p5

Third Round

Barwell	v	Rocester	1-0
Knypersley Victoria	v	Stratford Town	7-1
Kings Norton Town	v	Bloxwich Town	1-2
Oldbury United	v	Bridgnorth Town	0-1

Semi-Final

Bridgnorth Town	v	Knypersley Vict.	2-2 agg
Barwell	v	Bloxwich Town	1-3 agg

Final

Bloxwich Town v Knypersley Victoria 1-2 at Halesowen Harriers

INTERLINK EXPRESS MIDLAND INVITATION CUP 1997-98

First Round

Handrahan Timbers	v	Bridgnorth Town	2-3
Rocester	v	Sandwell Borough	6-0
Hinckley United	v	Knypersley Victoria	2-0
Kington	v	Halesowen Harriers	6-2
Stapenhill	v	Walsall Wood	2-1

Second Round

Barwell	v	Ludlow Town	3-1
Pelsall Villa	v	Rushall Olympic	3-0
Aylestone Park OB	v	Chasetown	2-0
Pershore Town	v	Worcester Athletico	1-4
Boldmere St Michaels	v	Shifnal Town	3-2
Wednesfield	v	Shepshed Dyn	1-1, 5p4
Solihull Borough	v	West Midlands Police	3-0
Malvern Town	v	Stratford Town	3-1
Oldbury United	v	Ibstock Welfare	1-3
Bloxwich Town	v	Bromsgrove Rovers	6-0
Stafford Rangers	v	Rocester	2-0
Bridgnorth Town	v	Studley BKL	5-2
Stapenhill	v	Willenhall Town	1-0

Kings Norton Town progressed to Round Three after Kington withdrew from the competition

Third Round

Atherstone United	v	Bloxwich Town	1-1, 5p4
Chasetown	v	Solihull Borough	0-1
Lye Town	v	Wednesfield	0-0, 4p5
Paget Rangers	v	Barwell	0-2
Stapenhill	v	Blakenall	3-4
Bilston Comm. Coll.	v	Bridgnorth Town	4-2
Cheslyn Hay	v	Kings Norton Town	0-2
Hednesford	v	Boldmere St Mich's	3-2
Pelsall Villa	v	Birstall United	1-2

Fourth Round

Barwell	v	Blakenall	0-2
Stafford Town	v	Kings Norton Town	1-2
Hinckley United	v	Atherstone United	1-1, 1p2
Meir KA	v	Ibstock Welfare	1-0
Birstall United	v	Wednesfield	2-1
Hednesford Town	v	Solihull Borough	2-1
Stourbridge	v	Bilston Com. Coll.	1-4
Stafford Rangers	v	Friar Lane OB	3-2

Fifth Round

Meir KA	v	Kings Norton Town	1-0
Blakenall	v	Bilston Com. Coll.	2-1
Atherstone United	v	Stafford Rangers	4-0
Birstall United	v	Hednesford Tn*	B W/O

* Hednesford Town withdrew

Semi-Finals

Blakenall	v	Birstall United	3-1
Meir KA	v	Atherstone Utd	2-2, 2p4

Final

BLAKENALL v ATHERSTONE UTD 0-1

KNYPERSLEY VICTORIA - celebrating their Midland Football Alliance Industrial Rewinds League Challenge Cup victory, beating league champions Bloxwich Town in the final.

ROCESTER FC - Interlink Express Alliance 1997-98 League Championship Runners-up.

CLUB DIRECTORY 1998-99

BARWELL

Chairman: David Laing. **Vice Chairman:** Ron Borman. **President:** Bob Gee
Secretary: Mrs Shirley Brown, 101 Eskdale Road, Hinckley, LE10 0NW (01455 619308)
Manager: Paul Purser **Asst Manager:** Mark Rosegreen **Physio:** Viv Coleman/Mark Moore
Ground: Kirkby Rd, Barwell, Leics (01455 843067).
Directions: M42 jct 10 (Tamworth Services), A5 towards Nuneaton. Remain on A5 for approx 11 miles, go straight on at traffic lights at the Longshoot Motel the 400 yards at r/about take 1st exit left sign A47 Earl Shilton, in 3 miles at traffic lights go straight ahead and in 1 mile at r/about take first left exit sign Barwell in village centre 1/2 mile go straight over mini r/about, 20 yards turn right into Kirkby Rd, ground 400 yards on right.
Capacity: 2,500 **Seats:** 140 **Cover:** 750 **Floodlights:** Yes **Club Shop:** No
Programme: 36 pages, 50p **Editor:** R Backhouse/R Boorman **Press Officer:** Merv Nash.
Colours: Yellow/green/yellow **Change colours:** Blue & white/blue/Blue. **Nickname:** Kirkby Roaders
Midweek matchday: Tuesday **Sponsors:** Surico **Founded:** 1992.
Previous Lges: Midland Combination 92-94. *Barwell Ath.: Leics Senior. Hinckley: Central Midlands 86-88.*
Clubhouse: Evenings & lunchtimes. Snacks available.
97-98 Captain: Steve Markham **Top Scorer:** Nick Buff **P.o.Y.:** Steve Markham
Club Record Goalscorer: Scott Kempin **Club Record Appearances:** Kevin Johnson.
Honours: Barwell Athletic: Leics Snr Lg Tebbutt Brown Cup 91-92, Leics Sen Cup 96-97.

BOLDMERE St MICHAELS

Manager: Alan Parsons
Secretary: Des Green, 4 Blandford Avenue, Castle Bromwich, Birmingham B36 9HX (0121 747 8404)
Ground: Church Road, Boldmere, Sutton Coldfield (0121 373 4435/0121 384 7531)
Directions: A38 & A5127 from City towards S. Coldfield, left at Yenton lights onto A452 (Chester Rd), Church Rd is 6th turning on the right. 400yds from Chester Road (BR).
Capacity: 2,500 **Seats:** 230 **Covered:** 400 **Floodlights:** Yes **Nickname:** Mikes.
Colours: Black & White stripes/black/black **Change Colours:** Yellow/green/yellow **Founded:** 1883
Programme: 32 pages, 75p **Editor:** Keith Fielding (0121 357 2901) **Sponsor:** Swift Forwarding
Midweek matches: Tuesday **Previous Leagues:** West Mids 49-63/ Midland Combination 63-94.
Clubhouse: Bar & lounge, every evening and four lunchtimes
Players who progressed to Football League: John Barton (Everton, Derby County), Kevin Collins (Shrewsbury), Jack Lane (Birmingham City, Notts Co.), John Lewis (Walsall), Don Moss (Cardiff, C Palace), Harry Parkes (Aston Villa), Wally Soden (Coventry).
Honours: Birmingham AFA 36-37; Birmingham AFA Snr Cup; Birmingham Jnr Cup, FA Amtr Cup SF 47-48; AFA Snr Cup 47-48; Central Amtr Lg 48-49; Midland Comb 85-86 88-89 89-90, Challenge Cup 77-78 89-90; Tony Allden Memorial Cup 78-79 88-89 91-92; Challenge Trophy 86-87; Sutton Charity Cup 96-97.

BRIDGNORTH TOWN

Chairman: Simon Bromley **Vice Chairman:** Ian Thomas **President:** Mike Williams
Secretary: Les Bristow, The Old Post Office, Eardington, Bridgnorth, WV16 5JT (01746 766187)
Manager: Ian Britton **Asst Manager:** Richus White **Physio:** Jenny Stretton
Ground: Crown Meadow, Innage Lane, Bridgnorth, Salop WV16 6PZ (01746 762747)
Directions: Follow signs for Shrewsbury (A458) over river bridge on by-pass, turn right for town centre at island, right at T junction, 1st left into Victoria Road, right at cross-road, follow road into Innage Lane, ground on left.
Capacity: 1,600 **Seats:** 250 **Cover:** 700 **Floodlights:** Yes **Club Shop:** Yes
Programme: 24 pages, 50p **Editor:** **Press Officer:**
Colours: Blue & white/white/blue **Change colours:** All red **Nickname:** The Town
Midweek matchday: Tuesday **Sponsors:** **Founded:** 1946
Clubhouse: Evenings & weekend lunchtimes. Dancehall, darts, pool, hot food on matchdays
Previous - Leagues: Kidderminster & Dist until 68; Midland Comb 68-83; Beazer Homes Midland 83-96 **Names:** St Leonards Old Boys prior to 46
Reserve's League: Midland Combination Res Div **Best FA Cup Season:** 3rd Qual Rd 64-65
Players progressing to Football League: Roger Davies (Derby County), Paul Jones (Wolves)
Club Records - Attendance: 1,600 v South Shields FA Vase 5th Rd 76 **Goalscorer:** Roger Davies 157 **Appearances:** Kevin Harris 426 **Record Fees Received:** £ 10,000 for Delwyn Humphreys (Kidderminster Harriers)
Honours: FA Vase 5th Rd 75-76 94-95, Midland Comb 79-80 82-83 (R-up 76-77 80-81); Lg Cup 78-79, Tony Allden Mem Cup R-up, Kidderminster & Dist Lge, Shropshire Snr Cup 85-86; Shropshire County Cup 70-71 75-76 76-77 78-79 79-80; Welsh Amt Cup 70-71; Shropshire Jun Cup.

CHASETOWN

Chairman: G Rollins **Vice Chairman:** B Simpson **President:** A Scorey.
Secretary: P E Dixon, c/o Club
Manager: Cliff Painter **Asst Manager:** Brian Fox **Physio:** E Highfield.
Ground: The Scholars, Church Street, Chasetown (01543 682222/684609).
Directions: Follow Motorways M5, M6 or M42 and follow signs for A5. A5 to White Horse Road/Wharf Lane, left into Highfields Rd (B5011), left into Church Street at top of hill, ground at end just beyond church. Buses 394 or 395 W Mids Travel, 94 Chase Bus,from Walsall, 860 Midland Red from Cannock.
Seats: 112 **Cover:** 250 **Capacity:** 2,000 **Floodlights:** Yes **Club Shop:** Yes
Programme: 26 pages, 50p **Editor/Press Officer:** Mike Fletcher
Colours: All blue **Change Colours:** All Red.
Sponsors: Aynsley Windows **Nickname:** Scholars **Founded:** 1954.
Midweek matchday: Tuesday **Reserves League:** West Midlands
Previous - Leagues: Cannock Yth 54-58/ Lichfield & Dist. 58-61/ Staffs Co. 61-72/ West Mids 72-94. **Name:** Chase Terrace Old Scholars 54-72. **Ground:** Burntwood Rec Cte (pre'83)
Club Records - Attendance: 659 v Tamworth, FA Cup 2nd Qual Rd 1/10/88. **Goalscorer:** T Dixon 172 **Appearances:** A Cox 469 (+15 sub). **Win:** 14-1 v Hanford (H), Walsall Snr Cup 17/10/92. **Defeat:** 1-8 v Telford United Reserves, West Mids (Regional) Lge Division One.
Clubhouse: Mon-Fri 7.30-11pm, Sat 11.30am-11pm, Sun 8-10.30pm. Basic snacks.
Honours: West Mids Lg R-up 90-91 92-93 (Lg Cup 89-90 90-91, Div 1 77-78 (R-up 73-74 74-75 75-76 80-81 82-83), Div 1 Cup R-up 80-81 82-83, Div 2 R-up 87-88, Div 2 Cup R-up 86-87); Walsall Snr Cup 90-91 92-93; Staffs Snr Cup R-up 91-92.

HALESOWEN HARRIERS

Chairman: Derek Beasley **Match Secretary:** Malcolm Pearce.
Secretary: Mrs Christine Beasley, 43 Hawne Lane, Halesowen, West Midlands B63 3RN (0121 550 3788 H).
Manager: Dave Beasley **2nd Team Mgr:** Tony Gore **Physio:** Steve Ball/Dave Bowen
Ground: Hayes Park, Park Rd, Colley Gate, Halesowen (01384 896748. Club Newsline: 0891 66 42 52).
Directions: On A458 Birmingham to Stourbridge Rd (B'ham 10 miles, Stourbridge 4 miles). M5 Jct 3 (towards Kidderminster), right at 1st island (towards Dudley), turn left at island (towards Stourbridge), straight over next island then 3m to grd left side, 200yds past Park Lane. 1 mile Lye BR
Seats: 350 **Cover:** 500 **Capacity:** 4,000 **Floodlights:** Yes **Club Shop:** Yes
Clubhouse: Open every evening. Limited range of hot snacks, but full cold snack kitchen.
Programme: 24-28 pages **Editor:** Rob Shinfield (01384 850819) **Founded:** 1961
Colours: White/black/white **Change colours:** Yellow/Blue/Yellow **Nickname:** None
Sponsors: S Griffiths & Sons Ltd **Midweek matchday:** Tuesday or Wednesday.
Club Records - Attendance: 750; friendlies v Walsall and Wolves in 85. Competitive; 450 v Lye, Lge 88. **Win:** 12-1 v Lichfield & v Malvern Town, 86. **Defeat:** 2-8 v Frickley Athletic (A), F.A. Cup 2nd Qual Rd 26/9/92. **Transfer fee paid:** £750 to Oldswinford for L Booth, 91.
Previous - Leagues: Festival (Sunday)/ West Midlands (pre-94). **Grounds:** Birmingham parks 61-70/ Halesowen Town FC 70-84 (both whilst in Sunday football).
Honours: West Mids Lg Div 1 85-86 (Div 2 84-85, Div 2 Cup 84-85), Inter City Bowl 67-68 68-69, Festival Lg(5)(R-up(9)), FA Sunday Cup SF 79-80, Midland Sunday Cup, Birmingham Sunday Cup.

KINGS NORTON TOWN.

Chairman: M Rowley **Vice-Chairman:** S Sanders.
Secretary: Mike Rowley, 61 Derwent Drive, Priorslee, Telford, Shrops TF2 9QR (01952 200020)
Manager: Pete Dunbavin **Asst Manager:** **Coach:** Morris Gittens
Ground: The Valley Stadium, Bromsgrove Road, Redditch (01527 67450).
Directions: Access 7 on town centre ring-road takes you into Bromsgrove Road (via Unicorn Hill) - ground entrance 400yds past traffic lights on right. Arriving from Bromsgrove take first exit off dual carriageway. Ground 400 yds from Redditch BR station and town centre.
Capacity: 9,500 **Cover:** 2,000 **Seats:** 400 **Floodlights:** Yes **Founded:** 1994
Colours: White & red/black/red & white **Change colours** Green/white/black **Nickname:** Nomads
Programme: Yes **Commercial Manager/Press Office:** Fred Evans
Sponsors: Swift Personalised Products/ BGR Financial Consultants. **Midweek matchdays:** Tuesday.
Previous - Names: Richmond Swifts, Swift Personalised Products (founded 1979)/ Richmond Amateurs - clubs merged in 1994. All historical entries below pertain to Swift PP except those *italicised.* **League:** Midland Comb, Birmingham Works. *Richmond Amateurs: Birmingham AFA, pre-1994.*
Club Records - Goalscorer: A Dunkley (21, 93-94). **Win:** 6-0 v Burntwood, 93-94 **Defeat:** 0-6 v Archdales, 92-93.
Honours: Midland Comb Div 1 95-96, Challenge Vase R-up 93-94, Kings Norton Lg Divs 1 + 2 & Lg Cup, J W Hunt Cup 95-96, Mercian Lg Div 1, Birmingham Works Lg, Birmingham Jnr Cup R-up, Birmingham Vase R-up 95-96.

Wednesfield *Photo: David Linney*

Sandwell Borough *Photo: David Linney*

Chasetown FC *Photo: David Linney*

KNYPERSLEY VICTORIA

Chairman: Philip Leese **Vice Chairman:** Peter Freeman **President:** G Quinn.
Secretary: J.A.Shenton, 27 Portland Drive, Biddulph, Stoke on Trent, ST8 6RY (01782 517962).
Manager: Dave Nixon **Coach:** Greg Clowes **Physio:**
Ground: Tunstall Road, Knypersley, Stoke-on-Trent, (01782 522737 club).
Directions: M6 Jct 15 join A500, 4th exit, pick up A527, follow through Tunstall, Chell, to Biddulph. Ground is situated on A527 just before Biddulph. From M6 jct 18 follow signs to Holmes Chapel then Congleton, A527 o Biddulph, continue thru lights, ground on left. Bus 61 Congleton-Tunstall passes ground.
Seats: 200 **Cover:** 200 **Capacity:** 1,200 **Floodlights:** Yes **Club Shop:** Yes
Programme: 40 pages, 50p. **Editor/Press Officer:** J A Shenton (01782 517962).
Colours: Claret & sky/claret/claret & sky. **Change Colours:** White & navy/navy/white.
Sponsors: KMF Precision Sheetmetal Ltd. **Nickname:** The Vics. **Founded:** 1969.
Midweek matchday: Tues/Thurs **Reserve League:** Staffs Senior.
Best FA Cup Season: 3rd Qual Rd 96-97 **Record Attendance:** 1,100 v Pt Vale, friendly 1989.
Previous Leagues: Leek & Moorlands 69-78/ Staffs Co. (North) 78-83/ Staffs Sen 83-90/ W Midland (Reg) 90-94.
Clubhouse: Open from 1pm on Saturdays and 7pm weekdays. Burgers, hot dogs, crisps etc at tea bar.
Club Record Goalscorer: J Burndred 128 **Club Record Appearances:** David Shallcross 508
Honours: West Mids Lg Div 1 92-93, Staffs Snr Lg 84-85 (Lg Cup 84-85 85-86), Staffs Co. Lg R-up 79-80, Staffs FA Vase 83-84 86-87, Sentinel Cup 86-87, Leek & Moorlands Lg 72-73 (Div 2 71-72).

OLDBURY UNITED

Chairman: Roy Keeling. **Vice Chairman:** Ken Harris.
Secretary: Paul Charnoch, 27 Pennyhill Lane, West Bromwich, W.Mids B71 3RP (0121 588 8369)
Manager: Kevin Hadley. **Asst Mgr:** Paul Waddington **Physio:** Tony Dandy
Ground: The Cricketts, York Road, Rowley Regis, Warley, West Midlands (0121 559 5564).
Directions: M5 jct 2, follow Blackheath & Halesowen signs, first left at lights and fourth right into York Road (turning before motorway flyover), ground 200yds on left. One and a half miles from Sandwell & Dudley and Rowley Regis BR stations. Bus 404 from West Bromwich, Oldbury and Blackheath.
Seats: 300 **Cover:** 1,000 **Capacity:** 3,000 **Floodlights:** Yes **Founded:** 1958
Colours: Navy with sky trim/blue/blue **Change colours:** All amber **Club Shop:** No
Programme: 28 pages, 50p **Editor:** Football Secretary. **Press Officer:** Martin Scott
Record Gate: 2,200 v Walsall Wood, Walsall Snr Cup Final 1982. **Nickname:** Cricketts,The Blues.
Prev. Lges: Oldbury 58-62/ Warwick & W Mids All. 62-65/ Worcs (later Midland) Comb. 65-82/ Southern 82-86.
Players progressing to F'ball Lge: C Gordon, L Conoway, J Scott, R O'Kelly, G Nardiello, Dakin, T Reece.
Midweek matchday: Tuesday **Sponsors:** Beswick Paper Group, Oldbury.
Clubhouse: Mon-Fri 7.30-11pm, Sat-Sun 12-2.30 (12-11pm Sat matchdays). Snacks available on matchdays
Honours: West Mids Lg 92-93, Staffs Snr Cup 87-88, Midland Comb. R-up 78-79 (Presidents Cup 72-73(res), Div 3 R-up 82-83(res), Chal. Vase 82-83(res)), Walsall Snr Cup 82-83, B'ham Snr Amtr Cup, Oldbury Lg Div 2 61-62, Worcs Snr Urn 86-87, Sandwell Charity Cup 86-87, Interlink Invitation Cup 96-97.

PELSALL VILLA

Chairman: V Dolphin **Vice Chairman:** J H Gough **President:** B J Hill
Secretary: Gareth J Evans, 72 St Pauls Crescent, Pelsall, Walsall WS3 4ET (01922 693114).
Manager: Reg Priest **Asst Manager:** Kevin Gough. **Physio:** J.Lancaster.
Ground: The Bush, Walsall Road, Pelsall, Walsall (01922 682018 Club, 01922 692748 Ground)
Directions: M6 jct 7 marked A34 B'gham. Take A34 towards Walsall to 1st island, turn right (marked Ring Road), cross two islands. At large island at bottom of hill take last exit marked Lichfield, up hill, cross next island to lights. Continue to next set of lights and turn left (B4154 Pelsall). Go over railway bridge to Old Bush pub on right (next to Pelsall Cricket and Sports Club).
Seats: Yes **Cover:** 624 **Capacity:** 2,000 **Floodlights:** Yes **Club Shop:** Yes
Programme: 68 pages, 60p **Editor:** Secretary **Press Officer:** B J Hill
Colours: Red & black/black/black **Change colours:** Blue & white/blue/blue
Sponsor: Metelec **Nickname:** Villians **Reformed:** 1961.
Midweek home matchday: Tuesday. **Record Gate:** 1,800 v Aston Villa 28/11/91.
Best FA Cup season: 3rd Qualifying Rd 92-93 (lost 2-4 at Gainsborough Trinity).
Best FA Vase season: 5th Rd 92-93 (lost 0-1 at Buckingham Town).
Previous League: Staffs County (South) 61-81, West Midlands 82-96
Clubhouse: Mon-Fri 7.00-11pm, Sat noon-11pm, Sun noon-3 & 7.00-10.30pm. Hot & cold meals.
Club Record Goalscorer: Dean Walters 231 **Club Record Appearances:** Kevin Gough 443.
Honours: West Mids Lg Div 1 Cup 88-89 (R-up 89-90, Div 2 Cup R-up 83-84, Walsall Snr Cup R-up 89-90 92-93, Wednesbury Charity Cup 6, (R-up 7), D Stanton Shield(2) 73-75 (R-up 75-76), Sporting Star Cup 76-77 (R-up 61-62), Prem Div Tphy(res)89-90), Rugeley Charity Cup 78-79 (R-up 69-70), Bloxwich Charity Cup(2), Edge Cup 83-84, Ike Cooper Tphy R-up 89-90. Banks's Brewery League Champions 94-95 (R-up 95-96) Div Cup 95-96, Midland Triangle Cup 95-96.

PERSHORE TOWN '88

Chairman: Anthony Broadstock **Vice Chairman:** Terry Conway, Bill Jones
Treasurer: Paul Carr **Secretary:** Don Roberts
Match Secretary: Ian Gill, 2 Sebright Close, Pershore, Worcs WR10 1QF (01386 554116 H).
Manager: Dave Boddy **Asst Mgr:** Gary Wright
Ground: King George V Playing Fields, King Georges Way, Pershore, Worcs (01386 556902).
Directions: M5 jct 7, A44 to Pershore (8 miles) cross 1st lights in Pershore, at 2nd lights turn left & fold road round into King Georges Way, ground immediately on left.
Seats: 200 **Cover:** 200 **Capacity:** 4,000 **Floodlights:** Yes **Founded:** 1988.
Colours: All blue **Change colours:** All green
Previous Names: Incorporated with Worcester Athletico 98-99
Previous League: Midland Comb 89-90 90-94.
Programme: 20 pages, 50p **Editor:** Grahan Hill **Club Shop:** No
Reserves' Lge: Banks's W.Mid Lg Div 1 (S) **Midweek matchday:** Tuesday **Nickname:** The Town
Best FA Cup season: 4th Qual Rd 94-95 (lost 1-3 to Yeading).
Best FA Vase season: 3rd Rd 95-96 (lost 2-1 to Burgess Hill Town)
Record Gate: 1,356 v Yeading, FA Cup 4th Qualifying Round 23/10/93.
Clubhouse: Bar open Mon-Thur 7.30-11pm, Fri 3-6 & 7.30-11pm, Sat noon-11pm, Sun noon-3 & 7-10.30pm. Coffee, tea, soup, hot pies and rolls available during matches.
Record scorer: Simon Judge 118 **Record appearances:** Gary Aldington, 290
97-98 - Captain: Chris Jew**P.o.Y.:** Chris Jew **Youth P.o.Y.:** M Cotton **Res P.o.Y.:** A Rogers
Hons: Midland Comb Prem 93-94, Div 2 89-90; Worcs Jnr Cup 90-91, Robert Biggart Cup 90-91 91-92 94-95 96-97, (R-up 89-90 95-96); Worcs Snr Urn 95-96, R-up 92-93, Jack Mould Cup 90-91, Alfred Terry Cup 90-91, Martley Hosp. Cup('A') 90-91, Pershore Hosp. Cup(Res) 92-93 93-94 94-95, R-up 94-95 97-98; Evesham Hosp. Minor Cup R-up('A') 94-95.

ROCESTER

Chairman: A.Hawksworth.
Secretary: Mr Gilbert Egerton, 23 Eaton Road, Rocester, Uttoxeter, Staffs ST14 5LL (01889 590101).
Manager: Mick Collins. **Asst Mgr:** P.Fernihough. **Reserves' Mgr:** Mick Collins
Ground: The Rivers Field, Mill Street, Rocester, Uttoxeter, Staffs (01889 590463).
Directions: From A50 r'bout adjoining Little Chef restaurant at Uttoxeter take B5030 towards Rocester and Alton Towers, right into Rocester village after 3 miles over narrow bridge, in village centre bear right at sharp left-hand bend into Mill Str., ground 500yds on left just past former cotton mill.
Seats: 200 **Cover:** 500 **Capacity:** 4,000 **Floodlights:** Yes **Founded:** 1876
Colours: Amber/black/black **Change colours:** All blue **Nickname:** Romans
Programme: 32 pages, 50p **Programme Editor:** Ian Cruddas (01889 564173). **Club Shop:** Yes
Players progressing to Football League: George Shepherd (Derby County), Mark Sale (Birmingham).
Record Gate: 1,026 v Halesowen Town, FA Vase 4th Rd January 1987 (at Leek Town FC).
Previous Lges: Ashbourne/ Leek & Moorland/ Cheadle & Distrist/ Uttoxeter Amateur/ Stafford 53-57/ Staffs County Nth 57-84/ Staffs Senior 84-87/ West Mids 87-94.
Reserves Lge: W Midlands **Midweek matchday:** Tuesday **Sponsors:** Stenson Bubble
Players progressing to Football League: Bert Carpenter (Manchester Utd), Joe Carpenter (Brighton), George Shepherd (Derby), Mark Sale (Birmingham, Torquay), Tony Hemmings (Wycombe (via Northwich)).
Clubhouse: On matchdays (normal licensing hours) and other special events. Hot drinks & snacks.
Club record scorer: Mick Collins **Club record appearances:** Peter Swanwick.
Hons: West Mids Lg R-up 89-90 (Div 1 87-88, Div 1 Cup 87-88), Staffs Snr Lg(2) 85-87, Staffs FA Vase 85-86 87-88.

RUSHALL OLYMPIC

Chairman: John Burks **Vice Chairman:** Trevor Westwood **President:** Brian Greenwood.
Secretary: Peter Athersmith, 46 Blakenall Lane, Leamore, Walsall, W Mids WS3 1HG (01922 712632)
Manager: John Allen **Asst Manager:** Bob Hubble **Physio:** Lee Horrocks
Ground: Dales Lane, off Daw End Lane, Rushall, Nr Walsall (01922 641021).
Directions: From Rushall centre (A461) take B4154 signed Aldridge. Approx., 1 mile on right, directly opposite Royal Oak Public House, in Daw End Lane. Grd on right. 2 miles Walsall (BR) station.
Seats: 200 **Cover:** 200 **Capacity:** 2,500 **Floodlights:** Yes **Club Shop:** No
Programme: 36 pages, 50p **Editor/Press Officer:** Darren Stockall (01922 379153).
Colours: Amber with black trim/black/black **Change colours:** White with red trim/red/red
Sponsors: WM Print **Founded:** 1951 **Nickname:** Pics.
Midweek matchday: Tuesday **Youth League:** West Mids (Reg.)
Record Attendance: 2,000 v Leeds Utd Old Boys, charity match 1982.
Previous Leagues: Walsall Amateur 52-55/ Staffs County (South) 56-78/ West Midlands (Regional) 78-94.
Players progressing to Football League: Lee Sinnott (Watford), Lee Palin (Aston Villa, Nottingham Forest, Bradford City), Stuart Watkiss (Walsall), Steve Taylor (Crystal Palace).
Clubhouse: Bar/lounge, open every night 8-11pm, Sat matchdays, Sunday noon-2.30pm.
Club Record Goalscorer: Graham Wiggin **Club Record Appearances:** Alan Dawson (400+ apps).
Honours: West Mids League Div 1 79-80; Walsall Amtr League Div 1 55-56, Div 2 52-53, Snr Cup 54-55 55-56, Jabez Cliff Cup 55-56; Staffs Co. League Div 1 60-61 61-62 62-63 64-65 (Div 2 56-57); Walsall Charity Cup 52-53; Walsall Chal. Cup 54-55 56-57; Walsall Memorial Charity Cup 55-56 56-57 57-58 58-59 59-60 60-61 61-62; W Preston Chal. Cup 56-57; Cannock & Dist. Charity Cup 56-57; Wednesbury Snr Cup 58-59 59-60 60-61; Sporting Star Cup 59-60 60-61(joint) 64-65 65-66 67-68; J W Edge 62-63 66-67; Walsall Snr Cup 64-65; Lichfield Charity 64-65 66-67; Staffs Yth Cup 81-82.

SANDWELL BOROUGH

Chairman: Joe Owen **Manager:** Paul Molesworth. **Founded:** 1918.
Secretary: Michael Stanley, 62 Lancaster House, Oldbury Road, Rowley Regis B65 0QF (0121 559 0457)
Ground: Oldbury Stadium, Newbury Lane, Oldbury (0121 544 4013).
Directions: Follow A4123 B'ham-Wolverhampton Rd, past island at jnt 2 M5, after half mile turn left into Newbury Lane and stadium is on the right. 2 miles from Sandwell & Dudley (BR).
Capacity: 3,000 **Seats:** 200 **Cover:** 200 **Floodlights:** Yes **Nickname:** Trees
Midweek matches: Wednesday **Previous Grnd:** Londonderry, Smethwick 18-81
Colours: All green **Change Colours:** Red/white/red
Record Gate: 950 v Halesowen T., FA Cup 1987
Programme: 16 pages 60p **Editor:** Trevor Hackwood
Previous Leagues: B'ham Suburban/ Central Amtr/ Worcs (Midlands Comb.) 48-88 90-94/ Southern 88-90.
Clubhouse: Licensed bar overlooking pitch. Open everyday
Players who have progressed to Football League: Andy Micklewright (Bristol Rov, Bristol City, Swindon, Exeter), Gary Bull (Southampton, Cambridge Utd)
Hons: Mids Comb Chall Cup R-up 49-50 51-53 67-68 74-75, Chall Tphy R-up 88-89, Pres. Cup 79-80 (R-up 76-77), Div 2 R-up 79-80; B'ham Jnr Cup; Industrial Rewind Lge Cup 94-95.

SHIFNAL TOWN

Chairman: Mr L Jones **Vice Chairman:** R Owen **President:** R Arnold
Secretary: Glyn Davies, 30 Drayton Road, Shifnal, Shropshire, TF11 8BT (01952 460326 H).
Manager: Mervyn Rowe **Asst Manager:** M.Humphreys. **Physio:** Danny Wedge
Ground: Phoenix Park, Coppice Green Lane, Shifnal, Shropshire.
Directions: M54 jct 3, A41 towards Newport, 1st left for Shifnal (3 miles), in Shifnal take 1st right, and sharp right again up Coppice Green Lane, ground 800yds on left past Idsall School.
Seats: 104 **Cover:** 300 **Capacity:** 3,000 **Floodlights:** Yes **Club Shop:** No
Programme: 32 pages, 60p **Editor:** J.Wilson (01952 274855). **Press Off:** G Davies (01952 460326).
Colours: Red & white/black/red & white **Change colours:** Blue & white/white/blue & white
Sponsors: Associated Cold Stores & Transport Ltd. **Nickname:** None. **Founded:** 1964
Midweek matchday: Tuesday **Reserves' League:** None at present
Club Records - Attendance: 1,002 v Bridgnorth Town, F.A. Vase 3rd Rd 83-84 (at Admirals Park). **Goalscorer:** Steve Kelly 35. **Win:** 10-1 v Malvern, 82-83 **Defeat:** 1-6
Previous - Leagues: Wellington (East Dist.) 64-69/ Shropshire County 69-77 85-93/ West Midlands 77-85/ Midland Comb 94-95. **Grounds:** Admirals Park 80-85
Clubhouse: Not on ground but in Newport Rd, Shifnal. Open Mon-Fri 7.30-11pm, noon-11pm Sat matchdays, noon-2.30 & 7.30-11pm Sat non-matchdays, Sun noon-3 & 7.30-11pm.
Honours: West Mids Lg 80-81 81-82 (Div 1 78-79), Shropshire Snr Cup 80-81 90-91 92-93.

STAPENHILL

Chairman: Tony Smith **Vice Chairman:** Ken Hulland **President:** Fred Sleigh.
Secretary: Peter Begent, 22 Grasmere Close, Stapenhill, Burton-on-Trent DE15 9DS (01283 540583)
Manager: Mick Curry **Asst Manager:** John Wayte **Physio:**
Ground: Edge Hill, Maple Grove, Stapenhill, Burton-on-Trent (01283 562471).
Directions: 3 miles from Burton on A444 Measham Rd, turn right (coming from Burton) at Copperhearth Pub Hse into Sycamore Rd, Maple Grove is 5th left. 3 miles from Burton-on-Trent (BR) buses 15, 16 from opposite station.
Capacity: 2,000 **Seats:** 200 **Covered:** 500 **Floodlights:** Yes **Club Shop:** No
Programme: 60p **Editor:** Secretary **Press Officer:** Secretary.
Colours: All red **Change Colours:** All blue
Sponsors: TAG Football Kits **Nickname:** Swans. **Founded:** 1947.
Midweek matcheday: Tuesday
Club Records - Attendance: 2,000 v Gresley, Derbys Snr Cup final 88-89. **Goalscorer:** Brian Beresford 123 **Appearances:** Ian Pearsall 172. **Win:** 11-0 v Alcester Town (H), Midland Comb Prem Div, 92-93. **Defeat:** 0-7 v Bridgnorth Town, FA Vase.
Previous - League: Leics Snr 58-89/ Midland Combination 89-94. **Name:** Stapenhill Waterside Community Centre.
Clubhouse: In ground. Pub hours. Matchday tea bar.
97-98 - Captain: David Carlin **Top Scorer:** Mark Barnes **P.o.Y.:** Martin Walton
Honours: Midland Combination R-up 92-93 (Div 1 89-90, Challenge Cup 92-93 93-94), Leics Snr Lg 59-60 86-87 88-89 (Tebbutt Brown Cup(2) 87-89), Leics Snr Cup 69-70 86-87, Derby Snr Cup R-up 88-89 91-92.

STOURPORT SWIFTS

Chairman: Chris Reynolds **Vice Chairman:** Trevor Roberts **President:** Roy Crowe.
Secretary: John McDonald, 65 Princess Way, Stourport-on-Severn (01299 822088).
Managers: Rod Brown **Coach:** Gary Whild **Physio:**
Ground: Walshes Meadow, Harold Davis Drive, Stourport-on-Severn (01299 825188).
Directions: Follow one-way system through Stourport sign posted Sports Centre. Go over River Severn Bridge, turn left into Harold Davies Drive. Ground is at rear of Sports Centre. Nearest rail station is Kidderminster.
Seats: 250 **Cover:** 150 **Capacity:** 2,000 **Floodlights:** Yes **Club Shop:** No.
Programme: 40 pages, 50p **Editor/Press Officer:** Dave Watts (01299 823349).
Colours: Yellow & black/black/black **Change colours:** All Red
Club Sponsors: M.I.P. Halesowen **Founded:** 1882. **Nickname:** Swifts.
Reserve's League: Kidderminster. **Record Attendancee:** 4,000 v Birmingham, charity match.
Club Record Goalscorer: Gary Crowther **Club Record Appearances:** Ian Johnson
Record win: 10-0 **Record defeat:** 1-7
Midweek matchday: Tuesday **Previous Leagues:** Kidderminster/ Worcester/ Midland Combination.
Previous Grounds: Bewdley Rd/ Moor Hall Park/ Feathers Farm/ Olive Grove/ Hawthorns.
Clubhouse: Clubhouse open matchdays. Hot snacks available. Licensed bar.
Honours: West Mids Prem Div R-Up 94-95 96-97, Lg Div 1 R-up 87-88, (Prem Div Cup 92-93, Div 2 Cup R-up 82-83); Worcs Snr Urn 92-93 93-94 94-95; Worcs Infirmary Cup 94-95 95-96.

STRATFORD TOWN

Chairman: G Cutler **Vice-Chairman:** T.B.A. **President:** P Chatburn
Secretary: Leslie Welsh, 10 Ivy Lane, Ettington, Warwicks. CV37 7TD. (01789 740952)
Manager: S Dixon **Physio:** N Dixon **Commercial Mgr:** J Carruthers.
Ground: Masons Road, off Alcester Road, Stratford-upon-Avon, Warks (01789 297479).
Directions: Follow Alcester/Worcester A422 signs from town centre - Masons Rd is 1st right afterrailway bridge. 400 yards from Stratford-on-Avon (BR) station. Local buses for West Green Drive.
Capacity: 1,100. **Seat/Cover:** 200 **Floodlights:** Yes **Club Shop:** No.
Programme: 20 pages, 50p **Editor:**
Colours: Tangerine/black/tangerine **Change Colours:** White/white/black
Sponsors: Porters Precision Products **Nickname:** The Town **Founded:** 1944
Midweek Matches: Tuesday **Reserves' League:** Midland Comb. Reserve Division.
Record Attendance: 1,078 v Aston Villa, Birmingham Snr Cup, Oct 1996
Previous Leagues: W Mids 57-70/ Mid Com. 70-73 75-94/ Hellenic 70-75.
Players progressing to Football League: Martin Hicks (Charlton, Reading, Birmingham), Roy Proverbs (Coventry, Bournemouth, Gillingham), Richard Landon (Stockport Co.,Plymouth Argyle (via Bedworth Utd).
Clubhouse: Open every night except Sunday
Honours: Midland Comb 56-57 86-87; Chal. Cup 86-87 88-89 (R-up 55-56); Chal. Vase 81-82; Jack Mould Tphy 81-82; Tony Allden Mem. Cup 86-87; B'ham Snr Cup 62-63.

WEDNESFIELD

Chairman: Roger Thomas **Vice Chairman:** J Massey
Secretary: Trevor Highfield, 8 Greensway, Wednesfield, Wolverhampton. WV11 1BA (01902 733086)
Manager/Coach: Ken Hall **Physio:** M Andrews
Commercial Mgr: D Clayton **Press Officer:** J Massey (01902 781819).
Ground: Cottage Ground, Amos Lane, Wednesfield, Wolverhampton (01902 735506).
Directions: From Wolverhampton on the A4124 Wednesfield Rd. Stay on road right through Wednesfield until island. Leave island at 1st exit (Wood End Rd), left after 200yds into Amos Lane. Ground on right, approx. 400yds along. 3 miles Wolverhampton BR station. Bus 559 to Wood End or 560 to Red Lion.
Seats: 148 **Cover:** 250 **Capacity:** 1,000 **Floodlights:** Yes **Founded:** 1961.
Colours: Red & white/black/red & white **Change colours:** Yellow & blue/blue/blue & yellow
Programme: 50p **Editor:** TBA **Club Shop:** No. **Nickname:** Cottagers.
Sponsors: Ansells **Record Gate:** 480 v Burton Albion, FA Cup 1981.
Midweek matchday: Tuesday
Previous League: Wolverhampton & District Amateur 61-76/West Midlands 77-97.
Previous Ground: St Georges PF 61-76 **Previous Name:** Wednesfield Social 61-89.
Clubhouse: Evenings 7-11pm. Food (burgers, chips etc) on 1st team matchdays.
Honours: West Mids Lg Div 1 76-77 (R-up 77-78).

WEST MIDLANDS POLICE

President: Chief Constable R Hadfield OBE
Chairman: Asst Chief Constable Anne Summers **Vice Chairman:** Jim Swingeford
Secretary: John Black, 57 Grosvenor Close, Sutton Coldfield, W.Mids. B75 6RP.(0121 308 7673)
Manager: Colin Brookes/Mark Fogarty
Commercial Manager: John Black. **Press Officer:** Tony Pearson.
Ground: Police Spts Ground, 'Tally Ho', Pershore Road, Edgbaston, Birmingham B5 7RN (0121 472 2944).
Directions: 2 miles south west of city on A441 Pershore Road. Ground is on the left 50yds past Priory Road lights (Warks County Cricket Ground). 3 miles from Birmingham New Street (BR) - buses 41, 45 & 47 from city.
Capacity: 2,500 **Seats:** 224 **Covered:** 224 **Floodlights:** Yes **Founded:** 1974
Midweek matches: Tues/Thurs. **Reserve's League:** Midland Combination.
Programme: 16 pages, 50p **Editor:** K Horrigan (0121 626 4020x6100) **Club Shop:** No.
Colours: Red & black stripes/black/black & red **Change Colours:** Yellow with blue trim/yellow/yellow
Record Gate: 1,072 v Sudbury Town, FA Vase QF 29/2/92.
Previous Leagues: B'ham Wednesday 28-38/ Mercian 46-53/ B'ham Works 53-69/ Mid Comb 74-94.
Clubhouse: Complex of 3 bars including snooker room, ballroom, kitchen. Hot & cold food. Open all day.
Honours: FA Vase QF 91-92, Mids Comb 90-91 (R-up 94-95, Chal. Cup 74-75 (R-up 85-86)), Tony Allden Mem. Cup 75-76 (R-up 91-92), B'ham Jnr Cup, Worcs Snr Urn 84-85 90-91 91-92 (R-up 81-82 85-86), National Police Cup(12) 61-65 66-67 69-70 73-76 80-81 87-88 91-92 (R-up(7) 67-68 70-72 76-78 88-89 94-95), Aston Villa Cup 60-61 64-65 65-66.

WILLENHALL TOWN

President: Jack Williams **Chairman:** Don Crutchley **Vice Chairman:** David Homer.
Secretary: Malcolm Skitt, 52 Longwood Rise, Willenhall, West Midlands WV12 4AX (01902 632557).
Manager: Kenny Drakeford. **Asst Manager:** Phil Embury. **Physios:** Mike Andrews & Steve Hooper.
Ground: Noose Lane, Willenhall, West Midlands (01902 605132-club, 636586-office).
Directions: M6 Jnc 10 follow 'new' Black Country route and then 'Keyway'. On leaving 'Keyway' follow signs to Wolverhampton(A454). At 'Neachells' P H house right into Neachells Lane, and first right again into Watery Lane. At island turn left onto Noose Lane, ground is 200yds on left.
Seats: 324 **Cover:** 500 **Capacity:** 5,000 **Floodlights:** Yes **Club Shop:** Yes
Programme: 40 pages, 70p **Editor:** Bill Taylor (01902 843435). **Nickname:** Reds
Colours: Red & white/red/red **Change colours:** Blue & red **Founded:** 1953
Sponsors: Aspray Transport. **Midweek matchday:** Tuesday. **Reserves League:** Midland Comb.
Record Attendanc: 3,454 v Crewe Alexandra, FA Cup 1st Rd 1981.
Previous Leagues: Wolverhampton Amateur/ Staffs County/ West Mids 75-82 91-94/ Southern 82-91.
Players progressing to Football League: Sean O'Driscoll (Fulham & Bournemouth), Joe Jackson (Wolves), Stuart Watkiss (Wolves & Walsall), Tony Moore (Sheff Utd), Andy Reece (Bristol Rovers), Wayne O'Sullivan (Swindon).
Clubhouse: Open Mon-Thurs 12-3 & 7-11pm, Fri-Sat 11am-11pm, Sun 12-2 & 7-10.30pm. Snacks available.
Club Record Goalscorer: Gary Matthews **Club Record Appearances:** Gary Matthews.
Honours: FA Vase R-up 80-81; West Mids Lg 78-79, Div 1 75-76, Prem. Div Cup 79-80, Div 2 Cup 78-79(res); Southern Midland 83-84; Birmingham Snr Cup R-up 82-83; J W Hunt Cup 73-74.

ENDSLEIGH INSURANCE MIDLAND COMBINATION

FEEDER TO: MIDLAND ALLIANCE

Chairman: Ian Johnson
Hon. Secretary: Norman Harvey
115 Millfield Road, Handsworth Wood, Birmingham B20 1ED
Tel: 01213 574172

ATHLETICO GO OUT ON A HIGH

Worcester Athletico, in their last season in the current form scooped the Endsleigh Combination premier Division title. Just two league defeats all season saw manager Dave Boddy scoop the Manager of the Year award for the League and saw them well clear of Southam United who pipped Bolehall Swifts for runners up with an impressive end of season winning run. Southam also lifted the Birmingham County Vase for the first time. Worcester Athletic will be merging with Pershore Town in the summer and playing under the Pershore Town banner. We wish all the Athletico personnel the best in this venture.

The Challenge Cup provided consolation for Bolehall Swifts in the shape of a penalty shoot out win over a Meir KA side that faded badly at the end of the season after promising much. They did however reach the Semi Final of the Midland Invitation Cup which was an excellent achievement. Next season sees the advent of all Floodlit Premier Division so expect some new faces in the Premier next season.

Alveston were the clear winners of Division One, 14 points clear. Steve Sykes' men also lifted the Smedley Crooke Cup, beating Fairfield Villa. The chasing pack all faltered at the end of the season, Feckenham, Fairfield Villa and Colletts Green all had chances of runners up but it was Northfield Town who stormed through at the end of the season with another superb run.

Shirley Town provided the best result of the season for a Division One club as they beat Kings Norton Town, a top Midland Alliance side in the Semi Final of the Birmingham Vase before losing to Southam in the Final. The President's Cup was won by Chelmsley Town. In a tight game they beat Newhall United 2-1. There were outside cup wins for Colletts Green in the Worcester Junior Cup and Polesworth NW in the Ernie Brown Cup.

In Division Two we saw the only double of the season as Blackheath Electrodrives, having clinched a Challenge Vase win over Brownhills Town on penalties then proceeded to draw 2-2 in a league game against the same opposition to take the league title on goal difference. Stourbridge CC had looked like Champions for much of the season but fell away, while runs from Swan Sports and Alvis came too late, leaving Kings Norton Town Reserves to come through for runners up.

Old Hill Town were crowned as Champions of a very tight Division Three with 5 or 6 teams fighting for the top spots. Handsaker finished runners up, followed by Wyre Forest. The Challenge Urn saw the latter edge out Handsaker on penalties after a 3-3 draw.

As always the Reserve Division was of a high standard and Burton Albion were the outstanding side winning by 14 points. Gresley Rovers fought hard in a tough season to finish runners up.

Rushden & Diamonds lifted the Challenge Trophy beating Oldbury United 4-0. There were excellent outside cup wins for Atherstone Reserves in the Coventry Evening Telegraph Cup, Boldmere Reserves in the Fazeley Charity Cup and Tamworth in the JW Hunt Cup.

Ten clubs are leaving the Combination this season. We wish them well and welcome 16 new clubs, a healthy surplus again. The new clubs are in no particular order: BCS Kenmore, Sutton Coldfield Town Reserves, Mile Oak Rovers & Youth, Wilmcote F&E, Loughborough Athletic, Lichfield Enots, Northfield Town Reserves, Wisbech Town Reserves, Ilkeston Town Reserves, MCL Claines, Bedworth United Reserves, Bustleholme Reserves, County Sports, Burman Hi-Ton, Leamington Hibernians and Massey Ferguson Reserves.

Finally, the Combination Management Committee would like to congratulate our old friend and old boys Bloxwich Town on winning the Midland Alliance after just two seasons and wish them well in the Dr Martens League

Steve Davies, Vice President.

MIDLAND FOOTBALL COMBINATION
PREMIER DIVISION

LEAGUE TABLE 1997-98

		P	W	D	L	F	A	Pts
1	Worcester Atletico	40	26	12	2	111	41	90
2	Southam United	40	24	11	5	84	38	83
3	Bolehall Swifts	40	25	8	7	78	43	83
4	Studley B.K.L.	40	24	4	12	79	36	76
5	Coleshill Town	40	21	9	10	78	38	72
6	G.P.T. Coventry	40	20	8	12	71	46	66
7	Meir K.A.	40	20	7	13	81	58	67
8	David Lloyd	40	19	7	14	80	66	64
9	Kings Heath	40	17	12	11	62	45	63
10	Continental Star	40	18	7	15	78	69	61
11	Knowle	40	14	12	14	81	72	54
12	Bilston Community C.	40	15	9	16	69	76	54
13	Coventry Sphinx (-3 pts)	40	15	9	16	72	78	51
14	Cheslyn Hay	40	14	9	17	66	86	51
15	Highgate United	40	12	14	14	59	54	50
16	Handrahan Timbers	40	11	10	19	52	53	43
17	Alvechurch	40	12	6	22	67	88	42
18	Massey-Ferguson	40	12	5	23	49	73	41
19	Kenilworth Town	40	6	8	26	43	98	26
20	Dudley Sports	40	4	7	29	54	137	19
21	Wellesbourne	40	1	6	33	38	155	9

RESULTS GRID 1997-98

HOME TEAM	1	2	3	4	5	6	7	8	9	10	11	12	13	14	15	16	17	18	19	20	21
1. Alvechurch	*	0-2	2-4	4-1	1-3	1-2	2-0	2-0	5-1	0-1	0-0	1-0	0-1	2-1	1-4	1-2	4-2	1-3	1-2	7-0	0-4
2. Bilston C. C.	4-1	*	1-4	2-2	1-0	2-0	1-2	3-1	3-2	2-2	1-1	0-0	3-1	0-1	3-2	2-2	3-2	3-4	0-3	4-1	0-2
3. Bolehall S.	3-2	1-0	*	3-1	0-1	3-2	2-0	2-1	5-0	2-1	1-0	1-0	3-0	1-2	2-2	2-0	3-1	1-0	2-1	5-0	0-0
4. Cheslyn Hay	1-0	0-3	1-1	*	3-3	2-3	2-4	2-2	3-4	1-2	2-1	1-0	2-0	0-0	2-1	3-2	0-3	0-1	0-1	7-4	0-4
5. Coleshill T.	2-2	4-1	2-0	5-1	*	2-1	4-3	1-2	5-0	2-0	0-2	0-4	3-0	0-1	3-0	2-1	3-0	1-0	1-2	3-0	0-1
6. Continental Star	3-4	5-2	1-2	0-1	1-0	*	3-1	3-0	7-1	1-1	3-0	2-0	2-4	0-1	5-2	4-2	2-0	3-3	0-5	2-1	1-1
7. Coventry Sphinx	0-0	3-3	0-3	4-0	0-0	1-2	*	3-2	4-1	1-2	2-1	1-1	2-0	3-2	1-4	0-2	1-3	0-2	2-5	1-0	0-3
8. David Lloyd	4-1	2-4	0-0	2-1	1-1	0-0	2-1	*	6-0	1-4	4-3	2-0	1-0	2-2	4-1	7-0	0-1	2-2	1-2	7-1	1-1
9. Dudley Sports	4-4	1-4	1-2	3-3	0-4	2-3	0-0	0-4	*	1-3	1-4	2-1	2-2	1-2	1-1	0-1	1-5	1-4	0-6	5-2	1-3
10. GPT Coventry	4-0	1-2	2-0	2-2	1-1	1-3	1-2	4-0	1-0	*	3-0	2-2	2-0	3-1	3-2	1-0	3-2	0-0	0-2	5-0	0-4
11. Handrahan Timb.	4-1	4-0	0-1	0-1	1-4	0-0	1-1	1-2	3-1	0-1	*	0-1	1-0	0-1	1-1	0-0	0-4	0-2	0-1	1-1	1-2
12. Highgate Utd.	6-0	2-0	2-2	4-1	2-2	4-1	2-2	2-3	3-3	2-1	2-3	*	1-1	0-1	1-1	2-1	0-1	1-1	2-0	3-1	1-2
13. Kenilworth T.	0-3	0-3	0-0	2-3	1-3	2-4	1-3	2-4	2-0	0-2	0-6	0-0	*	4-3	1-3	3-1	2-4	0-3	1-3	4-0	1-8
14. Kings Heath	1-1	4-1	1-2	4-2	1-0	0-0	2-2	0-1	1-1	1-1	1-3	1-1	4-0	*	1-1	3-0	2-1	2-2	0-0	3-0	0-1
15. Knowle	4-4	1-1	5-3	3-3	0-3	4-0	1-2	1-3	8-1	1-0	1-1	2-0	1-0	0-3	*	0-1	0-2	1-3	3-2	6-1	3-1
16. Massey-Ferguson	1-2	0-0	2-5	2-3	0-1	4-0	2-5	2-0	4-1	2-1	0-1	0-2	2-2	2-0	0-2	*	0-1	1-0	0-3	4-1	0-0
17. Meir K.A.	2-1	3-1	3-1	0-1	1-1	2-0	7-2	3-1	5-0	0-2	2-2	0-0	1-1	1-2	1-1	3-1	*	1-2	0-4	5-2	2-1
18. Southam Utd.	2-0	5-1	1-1	4-3	2-0	1-0	3-0	4-0	4-2	2-0	0-0	3-0	1-1	2-0	2-2	2-1	4-1	*	0-0	1-1	0-1
19. Studley BKL	4-1	2-0	0-1	0-1	0-0	2-0	3-0	0-2	2-1	1-0	0-3	1-2	2-0	1-1	4-1	3-0	0-2	1-3	*	5-0	1-2
20. Wellesbourne	1-4	2-2	0-2	1-2	0-5	1-5	1-6	1-3	0-6	1-6	3-2	2-2	3-3	1-5	1-4	1-3	1-1	1-4	0-3	*	1-4
21. Worcester Athletico	5-1	3-1	0-0	2-2	1-1	4-4	2-2	5-0	7-2	2-2	2-1	6-1	6-1	2-1	1-1	4-1	3-3	4-2	3-2	4-0	*

DIVISION ONE LEAGUE TABLE & RESULTS GRID 1997-98

		P	W	D	L	F	A	Pts
1	Alveston	30	23	5	2	82	24	74
2	Northfield Town	30	18	6	6	70	40	60
3	Feckenham	30	18	5	7	60	36	59
4	Fairfield Villa (-3 pts)	30	17	6	7	85	38	54
5	Colletts Green	30	17	3	10	67	45	54
6	Polesworth N.Warwick	30	15	4	11	86	62	49
7	Monica Star	30	12	8	10	70	53	44
8	Shirley Town	30	10	11	9	54	48	41
9	Leicester YMCA	30	11	7	12	52	60	40
10	Newhall United	30	11	5	14	52	51	38
11	Thimblemill R.E.C.	30	12	2	16	55	62	38
12	Chelmsley Town	30	11	3	16	50	68	36
13	Holly Lane	30	8	5	17	33	59	29
14	Barlestone St. Giles	30	7	5	18	45	74	26
15	Hams Hall	30	7	3	20	26	73	24
16	W. Midlands Fire Service	30	3	2	25	26	120	11

HOME TEAM	1	2	3	4	5	6	7	8	9	10	11	12	13	14	15	16
1. Alveston	*	3-1	4-0	3-0	2-2	0-1	3-0	2-0	4-1	2-0	2-1	4-1	1-0	3-2	3-2	10-0
2. Barlaston St.G.	1-4	*	0-1	0-4	3-3	1-4	2-3	4-2	2-4	1-1	1-3	1-3	0-2	2-3	1-0	3-1
3. Chelmsley Town	0-2	5-3		1-3	0-5	0-6	1-2	2-0	2-2	3-2	2-0	2-0	3-5	1-2	5-2	2-0
4. Colletts Green	1-1	0-1	6-1	*	0-1	3-2	1-2	2-1	2-0	0-1	1-0	0-3	2-1	0-1	2-1	4-0
5. Fairfield Villa	0-1	2-1	4-1	0-3	*	4-1	8-1	3-0	3-3	0-1	5-1	2-1	3-0	3-36	3-0	8-0
6. Feckenham	1-1	1-1	2-1	0-3	1-0	*	3-0	1-1	1-0	2-2	1-3	0-1	1-1	2-1	3-1	3-0
7. Hams Hall	0-4	1-1	3-0	0-4	0-4	0-3	*	0-2	0-2	0-3	0-5	0-1	0-1	0-1	0-1	4-0
8. Holly Lane	0-3	3-1	2-0	1-5	0-4	1-3	2-0	*	1-2	2-0	3-1	0-3	2-4	1-1	1-3	0-0
9. Leicester YMCA	1-4	2-1	4-2	3-2	5-1	1-3	1-1	2-0	*	2-4	3-1	2-2	0-4	4-2	2-5	2-3
10. Monica Star	1-1	5-0	0-2	1-3	1-7	1-2	10-2	1-0	0-0	*	0-2	2-2	6-1	3-3	2-2	4-0
11. Newhall Utd.	0-0	0-2	1-1	4-1	3-0	0-2	0-2	2-2	1-1	0-1	*	1-4	5-0	4-6	3-1	3-2
12. Northfield Town	2-4	8-0	2-0	5-4	2-2	3-0	1-1	2-1	1-0	3-2	3-1	*	1-0	1-1	0-1	2-0
13. Polesworth NW	1-4	1-2	4-1	2-2	2-2	5-2	2-3	6-0	5-0	7-4	1-1	7-2	*	4-3	1-0	6-2
14. Shirley Town	1-2	1-0	2-2	0-1	2-1	0-1	4-0	0-0	0-0	3-3	2-0	0-0	4-1	*	1-2	3-3
15. Thimblemill REC	4-2	3-3	0-3	6-2	0-2	0-3	4-1	1-3	2-1	0-4	0-1	1-5	4-2	1-2	*	5-1
16. WM Fire Service	0-3	1-6	0-6	0-6	0-5	1-5	1-0	1-2	1-2	1-5	2-5	1-2	2-10	3-1	0-3	*

DIVISION TWO	P	W	D	L	F	A	Pts
Blackheath Elect.	32	18	8	6	66	28	62
K. Norton Res.	32	18	8	6	79	45	62
Alvis SGL	32	16	11	5	70	35	59
Stourbridge CC	32	18	5	9	70	50	59
Swan Sports	32	16	9	7	67	53	57
Burntwood	32	15	8	9	83	45	53
Studley BKL Res	32	16	4	12	52	37	52
Mitchells	32	13	6	13	59	56	45
Cadbury Ath.	32	13	5	14	45	50	44
Brownhills T.	32	12	5	15	65	66	41
Ledbury T.	32	11	6	15	53	61	39
Albright & W.	32	9	6	17	52	64	33
Tipton S & S	32	9	9	14	56	74	*33
Birmingham V.	32	9	6	17	46	72	33
Earlswood T.	32	7	11	14	46	69	32
Enville Ath.	32	8	2	22	29	96	26
WM Police Res.	32	6	7	19	32	69	25

DIVISION THREE	P	W	D	L	F	A	Pts
Old Hill T.	28	20	4	4	88	40	64
Handsaker	28	19	2	7	81	27	59
Wyre Forest	28	18	5	5	84	35	59
GNP Sports	28	16	4	8	44	31	52
Kenilworth Wands.	28	15	4	9	61	49	49
Cont. Star Res.	28	15	1	12	52	49	46
Barnt Green S.	28	12	7	9	71	70	43
Birchfield Oaklands	28	12	6	10	60	69	39
Knowle Res.	28	9	10	9	64	50	37
Erdington Alb.	28	9	6	13	62	71	33
Archdales	28	9	3	16	50	69	30
Tipton T. Res.	28	7	7	14	65	78	28
Dudley Sp. Res.	28	7	3	18	41	75	24
Alvechurch Res.	28	5	5	18	54	95	20
Kenilworth T. Res.	28	1	5	22	21	100	8

DIVISION TWO RESULTS GRID 1997-98

HOME TEAM	1	2	3	4	5	6	7	8	9	10	11	12	13	14	15	16	17
1. Albright & Wilson	*	1-2	3-4	0-0	4-1	2-2	1-2	2-0	5-1	1-2	1-2	3-1	1-2	2-3	2-2	0-2	0-2
2. Alvis SGL	0-1	*	2-0	3-2	6-0	2-0	0-2	1-1	3-3	1-2	2-0	1-1	4-2	1-0	1-4	8-1	3-1
3. Birmingham Vaults	1-3	0-0	*	0-4	1-1	1-3	3-2	5-2	0-1	1-5	3-2	0-0	1-2	1-0	2-2	2-3	2-5
4. Blackheath E.	2-0	0-2	2-1	*	2-2	3-2	1-0	3-0	4-0	2-2	0-0	2-1	1-3	3-0	4-1	6-0	2-1
5. Brownhills Town	1-2	1-1	0-0	0-1	*	0-3	4-2	3-4	5-0	0-2	4-0	5-1	4-3	0-1	3-5	2-4	2-0
6. Burntwood	3-0	2-2	5-0	1-0	6-2	*	1-1	3-1	10-1	2-5	1-2	10-1	1-1	1-0	1-1	3-1	5-0
7. Cadbury Ath.	4-0	1-1	2-1	1-0	1-4	1-3	*	0-1	2-1	1-0	0-5	2-3	2-1	2-0	0-2	1-4	0-0
8 Earlswood Town	2-2	2-2	1-2	1-5	0-3	1-1	1-0	*	1-2	0-3	1-0	0-3	2-2	1-0	3-3	2-2	1-1
9. Enville Ath.	1-0	1-0	0-0	0-0	1-3	0-4	0-3	1-7	*	0-3	2-1	0-3	0-1	0-1	1-3	2-6	5-1
10. K. Norton T. Res.	4-1	2-2	3-1	0-4	3-0	4-2	3-2	2-2	7-1	*	3-0	2-2	1-1	1-1	1-1	2-1	4-0
11. Ledbury Town	6-1	1-1	1-2	1-5	2-2	2-1	1-4	1-1	1-3	4-3	*	2-0	5-1	4-1	2-3	3-2	0-0
12. Mitchells	4-0	2-2	4-2	0-1	0-4	0-1	2-0	4-2	4-1	1-0	2-1	*	1-2	2-1	1-2	9-0	1-2
13. Stourbridge C&C	2-1	0-4	4-1	1-1	2-1	3-2	3-0	6-0	3-0	2-4	2-0	3-1	*	2-1	4-0	2-2	5-0
14. Studley BKL Res.	1-2	0-1	6-0	2-1	3-2	3-1	0-0	3-1	2-0	4-1	3-0	0-0	4-0	*	3-1	1-1	3-1
15. Swan Sports	2-2	1-6	2-1	1-3	3-2	1-1	1-1	0-3	3-0	1-1	5-0	2-1	2-0	5-0	*	4-1	1-0
16. Tipton S&S	2-2	1-4	1-1	1-1	4-0	2-2	3-4	3-1	0-1	2-3	2-2	2-3	2-1	0-1	2-1	*	0-0
17. WM Police Res.	1-7	0-2	1-2	1-1	2-4	2-0	0-2	1-1	5-0	2-1	0-2	1-1	1-4	0-4	1-2	0-2	*

DIVISION THREE RESULTS GRID 1997-98

HOME TEAM	1	2	3	4	5	6	7	8	9	10	11	12	13	14	15
1. Alvechurch Res.	*	2-1	8-1	3-3	1-4	2-3	2-2	1-1	0-3	5-2	3-5	0-1	2-7	0-2	2-4
2. Archdales	5-2	*	0-1	1-3	3-0	5-4	2-1	0-1	0-8	2-0	1-4	1-4	2-3	1-0	1-2
3. Barnt Green S.	5-4	2-2	*	2-2	3-1	1-0	4-3	1-2	1-3	3-3	6-1	2-2	3-3	4-1	1-1
4. Birchfield O.	2-0	1-0	0-0	*	2-2	3-3	5-3	1-3	1-4	1-0	0-1	1-5	2-1	2-2	2-1
5. Cont. Star Res.	1-0	5-3	3-1	1-2	*	4-1	3-2	0-2	2-1	4-2	1-3	2-1	1-2	4-1	3-0
6. Dudley Sp. Res.	1-2	1-2	1-5	2-3	0-1	*	0-2	2-0	0-5	3-1	1-3	3-3	0-3	3-2	1-4
7. Erdington Alb.	6-1	1-7	2-3	4-3	6-2	2-3	*	0-0	0-3	4-1	0-2	0-0	1-8	4-4	1-0
8. GNP Sports	1-1	5-1	3-1	3-2	1-0	1-0	2-1	*	1-0	3-0	1-2	2-2	0-2	1-2	0-3
9. Handsaker	4-1	5-1	7-2	2-3	2-1	3-0	3-1	1-2	*	4-0	3-0	2-2	0-1	3-1	1-3
10. Kenilworth T. Res.	5-5	1-2	3-2	2-2	0-2	1-2	1-2	0-2	0-5	*	1-8	0-6	0-2	2-2	1-3
11. Kenilworth Wardens	3-2	4-0	2-3	2-3	0-1	0-2	1-3	3-1	2-1	1-1	*	3-2	1-0	1-1	2-2
12. Knowle Res.	2-3	1-1	2-4	3-4	1-0	3-0	0-2	1-3	0-0	4-1	1-1	*	1-2	4-1	2-2
13. Old Hill Town	7-2	4-4	6-0	3-1	1-3	5-0	4-2	3-1	1-2	2-1	3-1	3-3	*	3-1	3-2
14. Tipton T. Res.	4-2	5-2	3-3	2-4	6-1	3-3	5-5	0-2	0-6	6-2	3-4	4-1	2-4	*	1-3
15. Wyre Forest	10-0	1-0	4-2	3-2	2-0	8-2	2-2	1-0	1-2	12-0	3-0	3-1	2-2	4-1	*

CHALLENGE CUP

ROUND ONE

Feckenham 4 v 1 Shirley Tn.
Kenilworth Tn. 4 v 1 Barlestone St G.
Alvechurch 3 v 2 David Lloyd
W.M. Fire Serv. 0 v 4 Kings Heath

ROUND TWO

Bolehall Swifts 3 v 2 Cheslyn Hay
Dudley Sports 0 v 2 GPT Coventry
Meir KA 4 v Handrahan Timb.
Hams Hall 0 v 4 Chelmsley Town
Leicester YMCA 2 v 1 Coleshill Tn.
Massey-Ferguson 2 v 1 Monica Star
Northfield Tn. 2 v 3 Coventry Sphinx
Polesworth N.W. 5 v 1 Alveston
Highgate Utd. 2 v 3 Bilston C.C.
Knowle 4 v 2 Fairfield Villa
Southam Utd. 3 v 0 Colletts Green
Studley BKL 4 v 1 Kenilworth Tn.
Wellesbourne 3 v 2 Feckenham
Holly Lane 0 v 3 Worcester Ath.
Kings Heath 2 v 1 Newhall Utd.
Alvechurch 2 v 1 Continental Star

ROUND THREE

Alvechurch 3 v 4 GPT Coventry
Bilston C.C. 7 v 5 Polesworth N.W.
Chelmsley Tn. 0 v 1 Bolehall Swifts
Coventry Sphinx 1 v 2 Meir K.A.
Knowle w/o Wellesbourne
Leicester YMCA 0 v 1 Kings Heath
Worcester Ath. 2 v 0 Southam Utd.
Massey-Ferguson 3 v 0 Studley B.K.L.

QUARTER-FINALS

GPT Coventry 0 v 1 Bolehall Swifts
Kings Heath 0 v 1 Bilston C.C.
Meir K.A. 3 v 1 Massey-Ferguson
Worcester Ath. 3 v 0 Knowle

SEMI-FINALS

Bolehall Swifts 4 v 0 Bilston C.C.
Worcester Ath. 0 v 4 Meir K.A.

FINAL

Meir K.A. 2 v 2 Bolehall Swifts
Bolehall Swifts win 5-4 on pens.

PREMIER DIVISION CLUBS 1998-99

ALVECHURCH VILLA

Manager: Keith Westwood/Stewart Anderson **Chairman:** Gordon Wilkie **Patron:** Roy Yardley
Secretary: Alan Deakin, 58 Chesterfield Close, Northfield, Birmingham, B31 3TR (0121 411 1745)
Ground: Lye Meadow, Redditch Rd, Alvechurch, Worcs (0121 445 2929).
Directions: M42 jct 2, follow signs to Redditch, taking dual carriageway. At island turn right (signed Alvechurch) ground approx one mile on right. Ground is actually on Redditch Road, just south of Alvechurch village.
Seats: 100 **Cover:** Yes **Capacity:** 3,000 **Floodlights:** Yes **Founded:** 1994
Colours: Gold/black/black **Change colours:** TBA
Sponsors: Centreprint **Nickname:** The Church. **Midweek matchday:** Wednesday
Previous Leagues: None **Best FA Cup year:** Not entered to date
Club record scorer: Dean Meyrick **Club record appearances:** Dean Meyrick/ Matthew Pugh
Hons: Mid Comb Chall Cup R-up 95-96, Smedley Crooke Cup R-up 94-95.

ALVESTON

Secretary: P Beese, 36 Bishops Close, Stratford-upon-Avon, Warks CV37 9ED (01789 267966).
Ground: Home Guard Club, Main Street, Tiddington, Stratford-upon-Avon.(01789 297718)
Colours: All Maroon and Sky Blue.

BILSTON COMMUNITY COLLEGE

Chairman: I K Wymer
Secretary: J Calloway, 4 Mervyn Rd, Bradley, Bilston, West Midlands WV14 8DF (01902 681660).
Manager: Gary Smith **Coach:** Ty Jones **Physio:** Andrew Kiddle
Ground: Queen Street, Bilston, West Midlands. (01902 491498)
Colours: Orange/white/white **Change:** White/black/orange. **Programme:** Yes
Previous League: Staffs County (South) (pre-1993)
Sponsors: Stowlawn Ltd **Nickname:** The College **Founded:** 1981
Honours: Midland Comb. Chall. Urn 93-94, Presidents Cup 94-95, Staffs Co. (Sth) Lg(5) 88-93, J W Hunt Charity Cup 90-91.

BOLEHALL SWIFTS

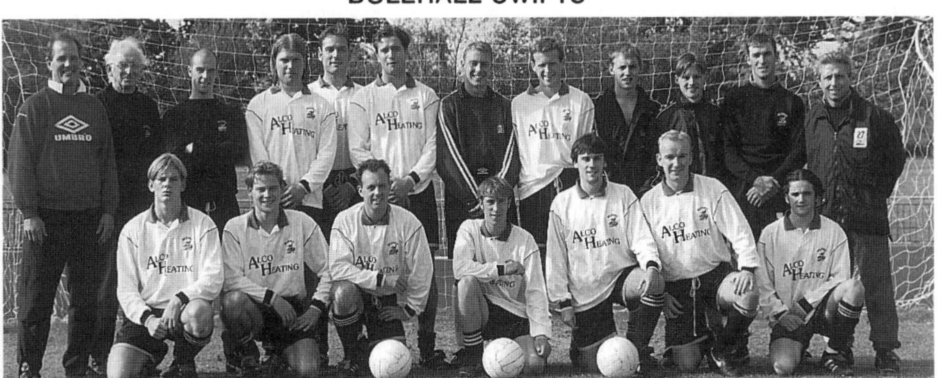

President: Mr Dennis Baker **Chairman:** Mr G Mulvey **Vice-Chairman:** Mr W Gould.
Secretary: Mal Tooley, 7 Ninefoot Lane, Belgrave, Tamworth, Staffs B77 2NA (01827 251973).
Manager: Ron Tranter **Player/Coach:** Mick Thurman. **Physio:** Barry Davis.
Commercial Mgr: Mike Fletcher. **Press Officer:** Mr L Bretherton/ Mr W Gould (01827 64530).
Ground: Rene Road, Bolehall, Tamworth (01827 62637).
Directions: A51 signs south to Bolebridge island, left under railway arches into Amington Rd, 4th left into Leedham Ave, fork right into Rene Rd, ground on right by school. From Tamworth BR station walk up Victoria Road for three quarters of a mile and catch No.3 or No.6 mini-bus to Bolehall. Alight at Leedham Avenue or Rene Road and follow as above.
Capacity: 2,000 **Seats:** 500 **Cover:** 600 **Floodlights:** Yes **Founded:** 1953
Midweek matches: Wednesday **Youth Team :** Play Sunday afternoons. **Nickname:** Swifts
Colours: Yellow/Black/Green. **Change Colours:** All green **Sponsors:** Walton Homes.
Programme: 32 pages, 70p **Editor:** W Gould (01827 64530).
Previous Leagues: Sutton Lge/ Staffs County 74-80/ Midland Combination 80-94. **Club Shop:** No.
Clubhouse: Large Social Club - 2 rooms. Open every evening (7-11) and lunchtimes. Entertainment Saturday nights. Cobs and crisps etc available.
Hons: Midland Combination Div 2 84-85, F/Lit Cup R-up 96-97, Challenge Vase 84-85, Presidents Cup R-up 85-86; Fazeley Charity Cup 84-85 (R-up 85-86); Ernie Brown Memorial Cup R-up 89-90 90-91 91-92 92-93 94-95; Jack Mould Cup R-up 85-86.

CHESLYN HAY

Secretary: Daryl Oulton, 12 Brunslow Close, Willenhall, W Midlands WV13 2HN (01902 630336)
Ground: Wednesfield FC, Cottage Ground, Amos Lane, Wednesfield, Wolverhampton (01902 735506).
Directions: From Wolverhampton on the A4124 Wednesfield Rd. Stay on road right through Wednesfield until island. Leave island at 1st exit (Wood End Rd), left after 200yds into Amos Lane. Ground on right, approx. 400yds along. 3 miles Wolverhampton BR station. Bus 559 to Wood End or 560 to Red Lion.
Seats: 148 **Cover:** 250 **Capacity:** 1,000 **Floodlights:** Yes
Clubhouse: Evenings 7-11pm. Food (burgers, chips etc) on 1st team matchdays.
Colours: Orange/white/orange

COLESHILL TOWN

Manager: Martin Sockett
Secretary: Neil Hamilton, 31 Fourfields Way, New Arley, N Warwicks, CV7 8PX (01676 54088)
Ground: Pack Meadow, Packington Lane, Coleshill, Birmingham B46 3JQ (01675 63259).
Directions: A446 to A4117 towards Coleshill, Packington Lane forks from A4117, south of village and ground is 150 yds on right. M6 jct 4, 1 mile away.
Capacity: 3,000 **Seats:** 50 **Cover:** 50 **Floodlights:** Yes **Founded:** 1894.
Colours: All green. **Change Colours:** Green/white/green **Record Gate:** 1,000.
Programme: 30p, **Editor:** Mavis Gordon **Nickname:** Coalmen. **Midweek matches:** Tues/Thurs
Clubhouse: Bar open 7 nights a week. Bar manager resident.
Players who have progressed to Football League: Gary Shaw (Aston Villa, Walsall)
Honours: Mercian Lg 75-76, Walsall Snr Cup 82-83 (R-up 83-84), Midland Comb. R-up 83-84 (Div 2 69-70 (R-up 74-75), Invitation Cup 1970, Presidents Cup R-up(2) 67-69).

CONTINENTAL STAR

Secretary: Derek Stevens, Bungalow, Burbury Street South, Newtown, Birmingham B19 2JP (0121 523 3776)
Manager: Derek Stevens/ Lincoln Moses.
Ground: Colehill Town FC, Pack Meadow, Packington Lane, Coleshill, Birmingham B46 3JQ (01675 63259).
Directions: A446 to A4117 towards Coleshill, Packington Lane forks from A4117, south of village and ground is 150 yds on right. M6 jct 4, 1 mile away.
Capacity: 3,000 **Seats:** 50 **Cover:** 50 **Floodlights:** Yes
Colours: Yellow/Blue/Yellow **Clubhouse:** Bar open 7 nights a week. Bar manager resident.
Honours: Midland Comb Div One R-up 96-97; Birmingham Vase.

COVENTRY SPHINX

Manager: Willie Knibbs
Secretary: K Whitehall, 34 Engleton Road, Radford, Coventry CV6 1JE (01203 598148).
Ground: Sphinx Drive, off Siddeley Avenue, Stoke Aldermoor, Coventry (01203 451361).
Colours: Sky blue & navy/Navy & sky blue/navy & sky blue.

DAVID LLOYD AFC

Ground: Rushall Olympic, Dales Lane, off Daw End Lane, Rushall, Nr Walsall (01922 641021).
Directions: From Rushall centre (A461) take B4154 signed Aldridge. Approx., 1 mile on right, directly opposite Royal Oak Public House, in Daw End Lane. Grd on right. 2 miles Walsall (BR) station.
Seats: 200 **Cover:** 200 **Capacity:** 2,500 **Floodlights:** Yes
Clubhouse: Bar/lounge, open every night 8-11pm, Sat matchdays, Sunday noon-2.30pm.

DUDLEY SPORTS

Secretary: John Lewis, 6 Hern Road, Brieley Hill, West Mids DY5 2PW (01384 895782)
Ground: High Ercal Avenue, Brierley Hill, West Mids (01384 826420).
Colours: Red+Blue/Blue/Red. **Change colours:** All blue

FECKENHAM

Secretary: M G Hawkes 23 High Street, Astwood Bank, Redditch, Worcs (01527 893341)
Ground: Feckenham Playing Fields, Mill Lane, Feckenham **Colours:** All green

G.P.T. (COVENTRY)

Secretary: P Scanlon, 61 Norton Hill, Wyken, Coventry, West Mids CV2 3AX (01203 616576).
Ground: Coventry Sphinx FC, Sphinx Drive, off Siddeley Avenue, Stoke Aldermoor, Coventry (01203 451361).
Colours: White with blue trim/blue/blue. **Change colours:** All red
Honours: Midland Comb Div 1 96-97, Presidents Cup 96-97.

HANDRAHAN TIMBERS

Chairman: E J Smith **President:** W J Handrahan
Secretary: Robert Hopkins, Junction Road, Audham, Stourbridge, W Mids DY8 4JY (01384 838270)
Manager: Glen Taylor/Nigel Kirkham **Asst Manager:** Phillip McNally
Ground: The Mile Flat Sports Ground, Mile Flat, Wallheath, Kingswinford, West Mids (01381 484755).
Cover: 200 **Seats:** 40 **Floodlights:** No **Nickname:** Timbers **Founded:** 1982.
Colours: Red/black/black. **Change colours:** Sky/navy/navy **Club Shop:** No.
Programme: All games except outside cups). **Press Officer:** E J Smith (01384 295394).
Sponsors: W J Handrahan & Son **Previous Leagues:** Staffs County Lg (South) 82-86.
Clubhouse: Teas and refreshments. **Midweek matchday:** Wednesday
Club record scorer: Paul Baker **Club record appearances:** Jonathan Pole.
Honours: Midland Comb Div 1 R-up 93-94, Birmingham Challenge Vase R-up 93-94, Wednesbury Charity Cup 91-92, J W Hunt Cup 92-93 (R-up 93-94). Invitation Cup (Mid Comb Champs v Cup Winners) 94-95.

HIGHGATE UNITED

Chairman: T G Bishop **Treasurer:** G Read **Founded:** 1947.
Secretary: G Read, 23 Southam Rd, Hall Green, Birmingham B28 8DQ (0121-777-1786)
Manager: Jim Simms **Assistant Manager:** **Physio:** Richard Flynn
Ground: The Coppice, Tythe Barn Lane, Shirley, Solihull B90 1PH (0121 7444194).
Directions: A34 from City through Shirley, fork right B4102 (Tanworth Lane), half mile then right into Dickens Heath Rd, then first right and the ground is on the left. 100yds from Whitlocks End (BR).
Capacity: 5,000 **Seats:** 250 **Covered:** 750 **Floodlights:** Due 1996
Colours: All red **Change Colours:** All white **Nickname:** The Gate.
Midweek matches: Tuesday **Record Gate:** 4,000 v Enfield, FA Amateur Cup QF 1967.
Programme: 28 pages, 50p **Editor:** Terry Bishop (0676 22788). **Press Officer:** N C Sawyer.
Players progressing to Football League: John Gayle (W'ledon), Keith Leonard (A Villa, P Vale), Geoff Scott (Leic.)
Clubhouse: Members Club open Tues, Wed, Thurs, Sat & Sun. Light refreshments available at weekends.
97-98 - Captain: T Gormley **P.o.Y.:** K Chechetts **Top Scorer:** N Kitching
Honours: Midland Comb (3) 72-75 (Div 2 66-67 68-69 71-72), Lg Cup (5) 72-74 75-77 84-85 (R-up 78-79 92-93); Presidents Cup 70-71 85-86); Tony Allden Mem. Cup 74-75; Invit. Cup 68-69 71-72 85-86; West Mids All. 63-64; Birmingham Snr Cup 73-74.

KENILWORTH TOWN

Secretary: R Butler, 52 Farmer Wardroad, Kenilworth, Warwicks (01926 857097)
Ground: Gypsey Lane (off Rouncil Lane), Kenilworth, Warks (01926 50851).
Colours: All Red with white trim.

KINGS HEATH

Manager: Clive Seeley
Secretary: Richard Johnson, 156 Station Road, Kings Norton, Birmingham B30 (0121 459 1386)
Ground: Highgate United FC, The Coppice, Tythe Barn Lane, Shirley, Solihull B90 1PH (0121 744 4194).
Directions: A34 from City through Shirley, fork right B4102 (Tanworth Lane), half mile then right into Dickens Heath Rd, then first right and the ground is on the left. 100yds from Whitlocks End (BR).
Capacity: 5,000 **Seats:** 250 **Covered:** 750 **Floodlights:** Due 1996
Colours: Gold stripes/black/gold **Change Colours:** All red **Nickname:** The Kings
Programme: 12 pages **Editor:** M Kite **Founded:** 1964.
Players progressing to Football League: Geoff Scott (Stoke, Leicester, Birmingham).
Honours: Midland Combination Div 1 R-up 92-93, Div 2 R-up 82-83, Presidents Cup R-up 79-80 81-82 92-93; Birmingham Challenge Vase R-up 86-87; Worcester Sen Urn 96-97, Challenge Cup R-up 96-97.

MASSEY-FERGUSON

Chairman: Dave Malintel **Manager:** John Halford, Geoff Brassington
Secretary: Lee Thomas, 730 Broad Lane, Coventry, West Midlands CV5 7BB (01203 465476).
Coach: Carl Lascelles **Physio:** Joe Doolan
Ground: Massey-Ferguson Sports Ground, Banner Lane, Tile Hill, Coventry.(01203 694400)
Directions: A45 to Meridan turn (B4104). Over two traffic islands, turn right at 3rd island into Pickford Grange Lane, continue to Pickford Green Lane, & Hockley Lane, left into Broad Lane, right into Banner Lane, 3rd entrance right.
Seats: 70 **Cover:** 200 **Programme:** Yes
Previous League: Coventry Alliance (pre-1993). **Colours:** Red & Black,Black,Red.
Clubhouse: Not on ground
Honours: Midland Comb. Div 1 94-95, Div 2 93-94, Chall. Vase 93-94, Chall Cup 94-95, Presidents Cup 94-95; Coventry Evening Telegraph Cup 95-96.

MEIR K.A.

President: Peter Bott **Chairman:** Des Reaney **Vice Chairman:** Graham Lovatt.
Secretary: Graham Birks, 35 Greenacres Avenue, Blythe Bridge, Stoke on Trent ST11 9HU (01782 395647)
Manager: Des Reaney **Coach:** Neil Eltringham/Neil Moston **Commercial Mgr:** Paul Robinson
Ground: Stanley Park, Hilderstone Road, Meir Heath, Stoke-on-Trent (01782 388465)
Directions: M6 jct 14, A34 to Stone, A520 to Rough Close then Meir Heath, turn right (B5066) ground approx 1 mile on right. 3m Blythe Bridge (BR)
Capacity: 5,000 **Seats:** 200 **Cover:** 250 **Floodlights:** Yes **Founded:** 1972.
Colours: Old gold/black/black **Change colours:** Claret & blue/blue/blue **Nickname:** Kings.
Programme: 32 pages 50p **Editor:** Kelly Reaney (01782 325624) **Press Officer:** Phil Bott (01782 317309)
Midweek matchday: Wednesday **Sponsors:**
Previous Leagues: Staffs Alliance/ Staffs Snr 84-92.
Clubhouse: open matchdays. Hot food.
Club Record Scorer: W J Anderson 219 **Club Record Appearances:** David Preston, 547
97-98 - Captain: Darren Reaney **P.o.Y.:** Neil Eltringham **Top Scorer:** Alan Hope (21)
Honours: Staffs Snr Lg 88-89, 90-91; Staffs FA Vase 93-94; Walsall & Dist Sen Cup 89-90; Mid Comb Prem Lge R-up 96-97; Mid Comb Lge Chall Cup 97-98.

SOUTHAM UNITED

Secretary: R J Hancocks, 18 Warwick Road, Southam, Leamington Spa CV33 0HN (01926 813483).
Ground: Banbury Road Ground, Southam, Leamington Spa (01926 812091).
Colours: White & black/black/black

STUDLEY B.K.L.

Chairman: D Robinson **Vice-Chairman:** Alec James
Secretary: Phil Summers, c/o club.
Manager: John Adams **Asst Manager:** Alan Scarfe. **Physio:** Derrick Mutton
Ground: 'Beehive', BKL Spts Ground, Abbeyfields, Birmingham Rd, Studley, Warks (01527 853817)
Capacity: **Seats:** None **Cover:** Yes **Floodlights:** No **Founded:** 1971.
Colours: Sky/navy/navy **Change colours:** White/red **Nickname:** Bees.
Sponsors: BKL Fittings **Clubhouse:** Yes, on ground **Reserve's League:** Skol Midland Comb Div 2
Programme: 30p **Editor:** Alec James **Press Officer:** Dave Chiswell.
Previous League: Redditch & South Warwickshire Sunday Combination 71-87.
Club record appearances: Lee Adams. **Club Record Scorer:** Kevin Rowlands.
Hons: Midland Comb. Div 1 91-92, Chall Cup R-up 91-92, Presidents Cup R-up 91-92, Div 2 Cup 87-88; Smedley Crooke Charity Cup 90-91 91-92; Birmingham Vase R-up 96-97.

DIVISION ONE CLUBS 1998-99

ALVIS S.G.L.

Secretary: D A Leslie, 9 Stephenson Close, Milverton, Leamington Spa CV32 6BS (01926 336700).
Ground: Alvis Spts & Social Club, Green Lane, Finham, Coventry.(01203 692576)
Colours: Blue and White/White/Blue.

BLACKHEATH ELECTRODRIVES

Secretary/Press Officer: G.Ellison, 12 Meadowhill Drive,Wordsley, West Midlands.DY8 5AF.(01384 836112)
Ground: Electrodrives Sports Ground, Cakemore Road, Rowley Regis, Warley (01215 599105 Social Club)
Colours: All red

BURNTWOOD

Secretary: Mervyn Ellis, 11 Green Meadows, Heath Hayes, Cannock, Staffs WS12 5YA (01543 271770)
Ground: Memorial Institute, Rugeley Road, Burntwood. (01543 675578)
Colours: Red and Blue /Blue/Red.

COLLETTS GREEN

Secretary: Marg Coldicott, 3 Blagdon Close, St Peters, Worcester, (01905 767386)
Ground: Victoria Park, Pickersleigh, Malvern Link (01905 830442)
Colours: All green with white trim.

HAMS HALL

General Mgr/Press Officer: Bob Ringrose, 6 Holly Drive, Hurley, Atherstone, Warks CV9 2JY (0827 872747).
Ground: Hams Hall Generating Station, Lea Marston, Sutton Coldfield B76 0BG (0370 936219).
Colours: White/black/black

HOLLY LANE '92

Secretary: R G Ashton, 19 Grange Road, Erdington, Birmingham B24 0DG (0121 350 2352).
Ground: Holly Sports & Social Centre, Holly Lane, Erdington, Birmingham B24 9LH.(01213 730979)
Colours: Yellow/green/green.

KINGSNORTON TOWN RESERVES

Secretary: Mike Rowley, 61 Derwent Drive, Priorslee, Telford, Shrops TF2 9QR
Ground: The Valley Stadium, Bromsgrove Rd, Redditch
Colours:

KNOWLE

Secretary: George Phillips, 49 Circus Avenue, Chelmsley Wood, Birmingham B37 7NG (0121 770 9513).
Ground: Hampton Rd, Knowle, Solihull (01564 779807).
Colours: Red/white/red

LOUGHBOROUGH ATHLETIC

NORTHFIELD TOWN

Secretary: Monty Patrick, 38 Pensford Rd, Northfield, Birmingham B31 3AG (0121 475 2057).
Ground: Shenley Lane, Selly Oak, Birmingham B29 (0121 478 3900).
Colours: Yellow/blue/yellow

POLESWORTH NORTH WARWICK

Secretary: Phillip Dempster, 17 Stonehill Walk, Wilnecote, Tamworth, Staffs (01827 262543)
Ground: North Warwick Sports Ground, Hermitage Hill, Tamworth Road, Polesworth (01827 892482).
Colours: All Green.

SHIRLEY TOWN

Secretary: B Fox, 26 Claines Road, Northfield, Birmingham B31 2EE (0121 475 4465)
Ground: Shirley Stadium, Tile House Lane, Shirley, Solihull (0121 744 1560).
Colours: All maroon.

STUDLEY B.K.L. RESERVES

Secretary: Phil Summers, c/o club.
Ground: 'Beehive', BKL Spts Ground, Abbeyfields, Birmingham Rd, Studley, Warks (01527 853817)

SWAN SPORTS

Secretary: Tony Howell, 156 Westwood Road, Streetley, Sutton Coldfield B73 6UG (0121 605 2062)

THIMBLEMILL R.E.C.

Secretary: Karl Young, 30 Moorpool Close, Harborne, Birmimgham (0121 427 2807)
Ground: Thimblemill Recreation, Thimblemill Road, Smethwick, Warley (0121 4292459).
Colours: White (blue trim)/white/navy blue

WELLESBOURNE

Secretary: Ted Forster (01926 494507)
Ground: The Sports Field, Loxley Close, Wellesbourne (01789 841878).
Colours: Blue & white halves/blue/blue

WEST MIDLANDS FIRE SERVICE

Secretary: Mr J Clarke, 51 Stonebury Ave., Eastern Green, Coventry CV5 7FW (01203 467997).
Ground: 'The Glades', Lugtrout Lane, Solihull (0121 705 8602).
Colours: Red with black pin stripe/Black/Black.

DIVISION TWO CLUBS 1998-99

BARLESTONE St GILES

Secretary: John Farrington, c/o club.
Ground: Barton Road, Barlestone, Leics. (01455 291392)

BIRMINGHAM VAULTS

Secretary: Kamaljit Rai, 89 Coopers Road, Handsworth Wood, Birmingham B20 (0956 833 990)
Ground: Bloxwich Town AFC, Abbey Park, Glastonbury Crescent, Bloxwich, Walsall

BROWNHILLS TOWN

Secretary: Bernard Parr, 53 Poole Crescent, Brownhills, West Midlands (01543 370140)
Ground: Walsall Wood FC, Oak Park, Lichfield Road, Walsall (01543 361084)

CADBURY ATHLETIC

Secretary: G.Boyle, 1 Greenway Gardens, Kings Norton, Birmingham B38 9RY (0121 628 6533)
Ground: Bournville Recreation Ground, Bournville Lane, Bournville, Birmingham. (0121 458 2000 Ext 3316)

CHELMSLEY TOWN '94

Secretary: Martin Smallwood, 244 Coleshill Heath Road, Marston Green, Birmingham B37 7HH (01926 493098)
Ground: The Pavilion, Coleshill Road, Marston Green, West Midlands (0121 779 5400).

COUNTY SPORTS

EARLSWOOD TOWN

Secretary: Jim Jones, 22 Antony Road Shirley, Solihull, B90 2NX (0121 603 4436)
Ground: Malthouse Lane, Earlswood, near Solihull (015646 703989).

ENVILLE ATHLETIC

Secretary: Gary Cooney, 16 The Dell, Wollaston, Stourbridge.
Ground: Hall Drive Ground, Hall Drive, Enville, Stourbridge (01384 872368).

FAIRFIELD VILLA

Secretary/Press Officer: C W Harris, 7 Churchill Road, Catshill, Bromsgrove B61 0PE (01527 831049).
Ground: Recreation Ground, Stourbridge Road (B4091), Fairfield, Bromsgrove (01527 77049).

G N P SPORTS

HANSAKER

KENILWORTH WARDENS

LEDBURY TOWN '84

Secretary: M.Cluett, 55 Lawnside Rd, Ledbury, Herefordshire. HR8 2AE (01531 633182)
Ground: New Street, Ledbury (01531 6314630

MILE OAK ROVERS

OLD TOWN HILL

TIPTON SPORTS & SOCIAL

Secretary: Bill Andrews, 42 Ambleside, Bradley, Bilston, West Midlands WV14 0SN (01902 497404)
Ground: Coneygre Leisure Centre.

WEST MIDLANDS POLICE RESERVES

Secretary: Steve Tonks, 28 Charlotte Close, Tividale, W.Mids. (0121 557 4574)
Ground: Police Spts Ground, 'Tally Ho', Pershore Road, Edgbaston, Birmingham B5 7RN (0121 472 2944).

WYRE FOREST

Old Hill Town FC; Division Three Champions

BANKS'S BREWERY
WEST MIDLANDS (REGIONAL) LEAGUE

FEEDER TO: MIDLAND ALLIANCE

Hon. Secretary: Neil Juggins
14 Badgers Lane, Blackwell, Bromsgrove

Congratulations are in order for Lye Town who won the WMRL Championship for the first time after 51 years of trying!

Newly promoted Kington Town were the early pacesetters in the Premier Division, apart from a brief spell of leadership by Bloxwich Strollers, whilst Lye Town and Stourport Swifts were the other contenders. Kington still led the way in the new year before Lye finally overtook them at the end of January, followed by Stourport a week later, but Lye never relinquished their lead and were finally confirmed as champions with a 5-2 victory over Wolverhampton Casuals on Easter Monday, with three games still remaining. Despite recording a century of goals again Stourport had to settle for the Keys Cup, as they had done a year ago, whilst Brierley Hill Town came with a late run to finish third, their highest placing since joining the WMRL back in 1975.

There was a major consolation for Kington when they denied Lye a League and Cup double, beating them 2-1 at Malvern to win the Premier Division Cup at the first attempt, a feat last performed by Alvechurch in 1974.

Wolverhampton United started in reasonable fashion with five points from the opening four games of the campaign, but they managed only six more in the thirty remaining games and finished bottom with a century of goals against them and a record only marginally better than that of Hill Top Rangers a year earlier. Hill Top had resigned from the league shortly before the start of the season.

Blakenall Reserves were the early pacesetters in Division One (North) after winning the first five games, whilst the Bridgnorth-based pair of Bandon and newcomers Lawson Mardon Star were the main challengers. By February Blakenall and Bandon were clear of the other clubs but it was not until March that Bandon finally took over top spot, which they held for the rest of the campaign. Lawson Mardon Star finished strongly, overtaking Blakenall to claim the runners-up spot and then adding the Division One Cup for good measure. Their final tally of 100 goals in just 28 games (at 3.57 per game) was the best ever recorded at this level.

Division One (South) was the closest fought of the three sections. At the top Smethwick Rangers were early leaders with Tipton Town and Leominster Town having games in hand, whilst Halesowen Harriers Reserves and Mahal also challenged briefly. By the turn of the year the first three named had pulled away from the pack but with Leominster's challenge faltering towards the end the championship was decided in dramatic fashion as Smethwick and Tipton met head-to-head on the last Saturday of the season. A goalless draw for the hosts meant Smethwick were champions.

The bottom places were also closely contested as Hinton and the reserve sides of Gornal Athletic and Pershore Town struggled all season. Gornal did not reach last place until January but there they remained and their second victory did not come until the very last game. Their final tally of 18 goals was a record low for this section.

FINAL LEAGUE TABLES 1997-98

PREMIER DIVISION

	P	W	D	L	F	A	Pts
Lye Town	34	26	6	2	91	35	84
Stourport Swifts	34	23	6	5	101	34	75
Brierley Hill Town	34	21	5	8	64	34	68
Kington Town	34	21	3	10	97	67	66
Bloxwich Strollers	34	18	4	12	81	49	58
Malvern Town	34	17	4	13	73	59	55
W'ton Casuals	34	15	6	13	64	52	51
Gornal Athletic	34	15	5	14	56	50	50
Darlaston Town	34	15	3	16	78	70	48
Tividale	34	15	6	13	64	57	*48
Ludlow Town	34	14	3	17	58	71	45
Stafford Town	34	12	7	15	49	57	43
Walsall Wood	34	11	7	16	49	64	40
Westfields	34	11	5	18	57	69	38
Bustleholme	34	11	3	20	48	76	36
Cradley Town	34	9	5	20	54	80	32
Ettingshall HT	34	5	7	22	37	100	22
W'ton United	34	2	5	27	19	116	11

DIVISION ONE (NORTH)

	P	W	D	L	F	A	Pts
Bandon	28	20	6	2	86	31	66
Lawson Mardon S	28	19	3	6	100	48	60
Blakenall Res	28	17	4	7	78	33	55
Brereton Social	28	14	7	7	60	43	49
Heath Hayes	28	15	2	11	62	55	47
Great Wyrley	28	14	5	9	55	37	*44
Morda United	28	13	5	10	47	47	44
Brereton Town	28	13	4	11	63	61	*42
Newport	28	11	8	9	64	45	41
Sikh Hunters	28	10	4	14	46	53	34
Lucas Flight Cont.	28	8	7	13	60	72	31
W'ton Casuals Rs	28	9	4	15	51	79	31
Corestone Serv.	28	6	2	20	37	78	20
Cannock Chase	28	6	2	20	40	102	20
Walsall Wood Rs	28	3	1	24	33	98	10

DIVISION ONE (SOUTH)

	P	W	D	L	F	A	Pts
Smethwick Rngrs	26	18	5	3	75	32	59
Tipton Town	26	18	4	4	71	26	58
Leominster Town	26	15	4	7	68	44	49
Halesowen H Rs	26	12	7	7	54	35	43
Bromyard Town	26	11	6	9	62	47	39
Tividale Reserves	26	11	7	8	38	36	*37
Wellington	26	11	4	11	45	53	37
Cradley Tn Res	26	10	6	10	52	40	36
B'ham Coll. Food	26	11	3	12	55	48	36
Malvern Tn Res	26	9	8	9	38	52	35
Mahal	26	10	2	14	54	62	32
Pershore Tn Res	26	3	7	16	28	94	16
Hinton	26	4	3	19	33	67	15
Gornal Ath Res	26	2	8	16	18	55	14

* Points deducted

PREMIER DIVISION LEAGUE CUP 1997-98

First Round (Over 2 legs)

W'ton Casuals	v	Stourport Swifts	5-6 Agg
Bloxwich Strollers	v	Walsall Wood	6-3 Agg

Second Round (Over 2 legs)

Lye Town	v	Westfields	8-3 Agg
Stafford Town	v	Stourport Swifts	1-6 Agg
Bustleholme	v	Kington Town	4-6 Agg
Darlaston Town	v	Brieerley Hill Tn	7-5 Agg
Malvern Town	v	Bloxwich Strllrs	0-13 Agg
Cradley Town	v	W'ton United	2-3 Agg
Ettingshall HT	v	Tividale	4-6 Agg
Ludlow Town	v	Gornal Athletic	3-1 Agg

Third Round (Over 2 legs)

Ludlow Town	v	Lye Town	5-7 Agg
W'ton United	v	Kington Town	4-7 Agg
Darlaston Town	v	Bloxwich Strllrs	5-4 Agg
Tividale	v	Stourport Swifts	3-6 Agg

Semi-Final (Over 2 legs)

Darlaston Town	v	Lye Town	2-4 Agg
Stourport Swifts	v	Kington Town	3-6 Agg

FINAL

KINGTON TOWN v LYE TOWN 2-1

PREMIER DIVISION RESULTS CHART 1997-98

		1	2	3	4	5	6	7	8	9	10	11	12	13	14	15	16	17	18
1	Bloxwich Str	X	1-2	0-3	2-1	2-1	6-1	1-0	5-2	0-2	1-2	2-1	1-2	1-1	2-0	1-2	3-1	7-0	7-0
2	Brierley H Tn	1-0	X	2-1	5-2	4-1	3-0	1-0	4-2	3-1	0-0	0-0	1-1	2-1	3-2	4-0	3-0	0-2	2-0
3	Bustleholme	1-5	0-2	X	2-1	1-2	1-2	0-2	1-2	5-3	2-4	2-0	0-4	2-7	1-2	0-0	3-0	2-0	0-1
4	Cradley Town	0-5	2-1	4-2	X	1-0	1-1	1-2	4-1	0-1	2-2	2-5	3-4	2-1	2-2	0-2	3-0	5-1	2-2
5	Darlaston Tn	0-1	0-4	1-2	4-0	X	7-1	8-0	4-2	4-0	2-3	2-3	5-2	0-4	2-1	2-1	5-1	3-2	4-0
6	Ettingshall HT	1-1	1-4	1-3	3-2	1-4	X	3-3	1-3	0-3	0-5	0-5	0-0	0-2	0-1	3-0	5-4	1-3	4-0
7	Gornal Ath	1-1	0-0	2-0	2-3	3-0	4-0	X	0-1	3-1	1-2	5-0	2-0	0-1	1-4	1-1	3-1	2-1	4-0
8	Kington Tn	5-1	3-0	3-1	3-3	7-2	3-1	3-0	X	3-1	0-4	3-2	3-1	4-3	3-0	4-1	2-2	4-2	*-0
9	Ludlow Tn	1-3	2-1	2-2	3-1	3-1	3-1	1-0	3-3	X	0-1	2-5	3-1	0-4	0-1	2-2	2-3	2-1	2-1
10	Lye Town	2-1	1-0	7-1	2-0	4-1	5-0	2-1	4-1	4-0	X	0-1	3-2	3-3	2-0	3-1	2-1	5-2	2-1
11	Malvern Tn	1-4	1-3	4-2	4-0	3-3	4-0	1-4	1-3	4-2	0-1	X	5-1	0-4	4-2	2-1	2-0	0-0	2-1
12	Stafford Tn	1-4	1-3	0-0	1-0	2-0	1-1	1-0	0-3	1-2	1-2	1-3	X	2-2	0-2	2-1	2-0	0-3	7-0
13	Stourport S	1-1	2-1	5-0	2-1	2-2	4-0	2-0	3-0	5-2	1-1	3-2	2-0	X	5-0	3-0	3-0	2-0	4-0
14	Tividale	6-1	2-0	0-1	3-2	0-2	4-2	1-2	4-1	0-2	2-2	0-0	0-3	3-2	X	0-0	3-1	0-0	6-0
15	Walsall W	0-5	0-2	0-3	4-1	4-3	3-2	4-0	3-2	3-2	0-2	3-1	1-1	0-2	2-2	X	2-0	0-1	5-0
16	Westfields	3-2	4-0	3-0	3-1	2-3	0-0	1-2	1-2	4-2	4-1	2-4	0-0	1-7	8-2	3-0	X	0-0	3-0
17	Wolv'ton Cas	4-0	1-1	1-2	5-1	4-0	7-0	1-3	4-2	1-0	2-2	1-0	2-3	3-1	0-2	4-2	0-0	X	3-0
18	Wolv'ton Utd	0-4	0-2	4-2	0-1	0-0	1-1	3-3	1-4	0-3	1-6	0-3	0-1	1-7	1-7	1-1	0-1	0-3	X

DIVISION ONE LEAGUE CUP 1997-98

First Round (Aggregte Scores)

Brereton Town	v	Blakenall Reserves	4-0	Walsall Wood Rs	v	Blakenall Res	4-0
Cradley Town Res	v	Lucas F. Control	4-4, 3p5	Mahal	v	Bromyard Town	2-3
Bandon	v	Smethwick Rangers	1-2	Hinton	v	Pershore Town Res	2-3
B'ham Coll. of Foods	v	Cannock Chase	1-2	Lawson Mardon Star	v	Tipton Town	4-3
Great Wyrley	v	Brierley Hill Town Rs	Void	Wellington	v	Tividale Reserves	4-3
Malvern Town Res	v	Heath Hayes	3-5	Leominster Town	v	Sikh Hunters	9-5
Corestone Services	v	W'ton Casuals Res	4-3	Brereton Social	v	Morda United	1-2

Gornal Athletic and Halesowen Harriers Reserves have Byes to Round Two

Second Round (Aggregte Scores)

Lawson Mardon Star	v	Great Wyrley	4-3	Wellington	v	Cannock Chase	6-2
Heath Hayes	v	Pershore Town Res	3-1	Leominster Town	v	Smethwick Rngrs	2-3
Corestone Services	v	Bromyard Town	P-P	Morda United	v	Lucas F Controls	4-2
Gornal Athletic Res	v	Newport	2-4	Halesowen H Res	v	Brereton Town	4-0

Third Round (Aggregte Scores)

Halesown H Res	v	Bromyard Town	1-3	Lawson Mardon Star	v	Morda United	9-3
Wellington	v	Newport	3-7	Smethwick Rngrs	v	Heath Hayes	1-2

Semi-Final (Aggregte Scores)

Bromyard Town	v	Lawson Mardon Star	3-4	Newport	v	Heath Hayes	3-4

Final

HEATH HAYES	v	LAWSON M STAR	1-3

PREMIER DIVISION CLUBS 1998-99

BANDON

Chairman: Michael Smith **Founded:** 1988
Secretary: Timothy Hebbard, Old Hall Cottage, 4 Wapping Alley, Claverley, Bridgnorth, Shrops WV5 7DS (01746 710633)
Ground: Crown Meadow, Innage Lane, Bridgnorth (01746 762747)
Directions: Follow signs for Shrewsbury A458, over river bridge on by-pass, At next island turn right (Town Centre). At 'T' junc turn right, 1st left into Victoria Rd, right at crossroads and follow road into Innage Lane.
Colours: Blue & white/blue/blue **Change colours:** White/blue/white

BUSTLEHOLME

Chairman: Geoff Fellows
Secretary: Suzanne Glover, 15 Swann Hill, Hurst Hill, Coseley, Wolverhampton WV14 9UP (01902 659380)
Ground: Darlaston Town FC, Waverley Rd, Darlaston, W Midlands (0121 526 4423)
Directions: M6 jct 10, A454 Walsall/Willenhall. Take the A454 towards Willenhall. Turn left at traffic lights, outside the Lane Arms Public House into Bentley Road North. Follow road down hill, over railway & canal bridges to lights. Cross over lights into Richard Street & along Victoria Road. Take the first right into Slater Street, ground on left.
Seats: Yes **Cover:** Yes **Capacity:** **Floodlights:** Yes. **Club Shop:**
Colours: Yellow/green/green **Change colours:** White/green/green **Founded:** 1975.

CRADLEY TOWN

Chairman: Graham Taylor **Vice Chairman:** T Hetheridge **President:** W Forrest
Secretary: David Attwood, 4 Birch Coppice, Quarry Bank, Brierley Hill, W Midlands DY5 1AP. (01384 637430)
Manager: Trevor Thomas **Asst Manager:** John Gilbert **Physio:** Martin Bennett
Ground: Beeches View, Beeches View Avenue, Cradley, Halesowen, B63 2HB. (01384 569658)
Directions: M5 jct 3, take A456, right at 2nd island, left into Rosemary Rd after Fox Hunt pub, Lansdown Rd, Dunstall Rd, left at T-junction, left again at next T-junction (Beecher Rd East), 1st left (Abbey Rd), right at end, ground 50yds on left. Nearest BR station is Cradley Heath.
Seats: 200 **Cover:** 1,500 **Capacity:** 3,000 **Floodlights:** Yes **Club Shop:** No.
Programme: Yes **Editor:** **Press Officer:** Trevor Thomas (01384 569658)
Colours: Red & black/black/black **Change colours:** Yellow/blue/blue
Sponsors: Allen Homes/Garian Roofing & Cladding **Founded:** 1948 **Nickname:** Lukes
Midweek matchday: Tuesday **Reserve's League:** West Mids Lge Div One
Record Gate: 1,000 v Aston Villa, friendly.
Previous Leagues: Metropolitan/ Brierley Hill/ Kidderminster/ West Mids Amtr/ Midland Comb. 71-82.
Players progressing to Football Lge: Alan Nicholls (Plymouth (via Cheltenham)), John Williams, Jon Ford, Andy McFarlane (all Swansea), Duane Darby (Torquay).
Clubhouse: Open all day every day. Food available.
97-98 - Captain: Jason Thomas **Top Scorer:** Arron Roberts **P.o.Y.:** Paul Smith
Club Record Goalscorer: Jim Nugent **Club Record Apearances:** R J Haywood.
Hons: West Mids Lg Div 1 90-91, Midland Comb. Div 2 72-73 (R-up 75-76 77-78, Presidents Cup 74-75 75-76, Invitation 72-73), Metropolitan Lg 70-71, Wednesbury Charity Cup 90-91, Dudley Guest Hosp. Cup 71-72 72-73 75-76 90-91.

DARLASTON TOWN

Chairman: Gilbert Preece **Match Sec:** Neil Arrowsmith (01902 450612)
Secretary: Mrs Kath Abley, 42 Addenbrooke Street, Darlaston (0121 531 0487)
Manager: David Downing. **Assistant Manager:** Martin Seal. **Physio:**
Ground: City Ground, Waverley Rd, Darlaston (0121 526 4423).
Directions: M6 Jct 10, onto A454 towards Willenhall, left at lights outside 'Lane Arms' into Bentley Rd North, follow this down hill and over the railway and canal bridges to traffic lights. Cross over the lights into Richards St and along into Victoria Rd, 1st right into Slater St and ground on left but entrance is next left in Waverley Rd.
Seats: Yes **Cover:** Yes **Capacity:** **Floodlights:** Yes. **Club Shop:** Yes
Programme: Yes **Editor:** Dave Stevenson (0121 526 2465). **Press Officer:** Neil Chambers
Colours: Blue & white stripes/blue/blue **Change colours:** All yellow
Sponsors: Metafin Holdings **Nickname:** Blues. **Founded:** 1874
Midweek matcheday: Tuesday **Reserves League:**
Previous Leagues: Jun lges (inc Wednesbury League) pre-1908/ B'gham Comb. 08-11 28-54/ W Mids 11-28.
Players progressing to Football League: Jack Burkett (Nottingham Forest), Andy McFarlane (Swansea City).
Clubhouse: Open matchdays. Tues/Wed/Thur evenings & Sunday Lunch. Hot/cold drinks/snacks.
Honours: West Mids Lg Div 1 89-90 (R-up 91-92 92-93, Div 1 Cup Cup 89-90), Birmingham Snr Cup 72-73, Birmingham Vase 90-91 91-92, Birmingham Jnr Lg 07-08, Birmingham Comb. 10-11 37-38 45-46 (Tillotson Cup 36-37 37-38 38-39 45-46), Keys Cup 11-12), Wednesbury Lg(5) 1896-1901.

DUDLEY TOWN

Chairman: Trevor Lester **Vice Chairman:** Philip Edwards **President:** N D Jeynes.
Secretary: Tony Turpin, 24 Andrew Drive, Short Heath, Willenhall WV12 5PP (01922 475541).
Manager: John Chambers. **Asst Manager/Coach:** Alan Moore.
GROUND Address: The Grove, Old Hawne Lane, Halesowen, West Midlands B63 3TB 0121 550 2179. **Directions:** Leave M5 Motorway at Junc 3, follow A456 Kidderminster Rd to t island, turn right signposted A459 Dudley. Turn left at next island singposted Stourbridge. At next island take 3rd turn on left into Grammar School Lane/old Hanne Lane, ground 500 yds on left.
Capacity: 5,000 **Cover:** 1000 **Seats:** 380 **Floodlights:** Yes **Formed:** 1893
Clubhouse: Dudley Town Sports & Social Club, John Street, Brierley Hill. Open nightly, all day Saturday and Sunday lunchtimes. Bar, lounge bar, ballroom, bowling green etc. Bar snacks available.
Club Shop: Progs & badges etc. Frank Whitehouse 01902-674068
Sponsors: Crest Homes & Thornleigh Freight Ltd **Nickname:** The Robins
Colours: Red/black/black **Change colours:** All yellow
Midweek matchday: Tuesday 7.45pm **Reserves' League:** No reserve team
PROGRAMME DETAILS: Pages: 36 **Price:** 80p **Editor:** David Lawrence
PREVIOUS - Leagues: West Mids (previously Birmingham) 1898-1915 35-38 53-82/ Midland (Worcs) Comb 29-32/ Birmingham Comb 32-35 45-53.
CLUB RECORDS - Attendance: 3,000 v West Bromwich Albion, pre-season friendly 91. *(At old grd; 16,500 the official opening (a representative game) 36).* **Win:** 8-0 v Banbury, 65. **Career Goalscorer:** Frank Treagust, 56 (47-48). **Career Appearances:** Brendon Hackett & John Muir, 55.
BEST SEASON - FA Trophy: 2nd Rd 84-85 **FA Cup:** 1st Rd replay 76-77 (v York)
HONOURS: Southern Lg Midland Div 84-85, Birmingham Comb 33-34 (R-up 34-35 47-48), Midland (Worcs) Comb 31-32 (R-up 29-30 30-31), West Mids Lg Cp R-up 75-76 (Div 2 Cp R-up 80-81), Birmingham Senior Cp 85-86 (R-up 64-65 83-84), Worcs Senior Cp 45-46(joint)(R-up 84-85), Camkin Cp 64-65, Worcs Junior Cp 83-84.

ETTINGSHALL HOLY TRINITY

Chairman: John O'Dell. **President:** David Gadd.
Secretary: Graham Mills, 27 Ashen Close, Sedgley, Dudley, West Mids DY3 3UZ (01902 66222)
Manager: Graham Mills. **Asst Manager:** **Physio:** Tony Kiddle.
Ground: Aldersley Stadium, Aldersley Road, Tettenhal, Wolverhampton (01902 751171)
Directions: From Wolverhampton take A41 Tettenhall Road, 1.5 miles turn right into Lower Street, then right into Aldersley Road, ground on right
Colours: All Green/white **Change colours:** Red & white/red/red **Nickname:** Trins.
Previous League: Wednesbury Church & Chapel (early 1900s), Bilston Youth (1950s), Wolverhampton & District Amateur (1960s), Staffs County (South)
Programme: Yes **Editor:** John Edwards (01785 713458) **Founded:** 1920.
Midweek matchday: Wednesday **Club Sponsors:** DKB Electric/ John O'Dell
Honours: West Mids Lg Div 1 Cup R-up 85-86 (Div 2 R-up 84-85), Sporting Award 85-86, Staffs Co. Lg R-up 82-83 (Lg Shield 82-83 83-84), Ike Cooper Cup 82-84 83-84, Sporting Club Award 81-82, Wolverhampton & District Amateur Lg 80-81 (Div 1 65-66, Div 2 64-65), Div 1/2 Cup 64-65 65-66, A H Oakley Cup 80-81, J W Hunt Cup 82-83 83-84 (R-up 79-80), Wolverhampton Cup 83-84 (R-up 82-83).

GORNAL ATHLETIC

Chairman: Colin Worth
Secretary: Keith Birch, 24 Dursley Close, Willenhall, West Midlands WV12 4DE (01902 410784)
Manager: John Gwinnell **Coach:** Ian Clark/ Ross Hill. **Reserves' Manager:** Ian Davies
Ground: Garden Walk Stadium, Lower Gornal, Dudley, West Midlands (01384 252285).
Directions: From Dudley take A459 to Sedgley past the Burton Rd Hospital. 1st on left at the Green Dragon public house on the B4175 (Jews Lane). Follow the road until you come to the Old Bull's Head, turn left into Rednall Road, 2nd left to Garden Walk.
Seats: 100 **Cover:** 500 **Capacity:** 3,000 **Floodlights:** Yes **Founded:** 1945.
Colours: Yellow/green/green **Change colours:** Blue & black/blue/black **Club Shop:** No.
Previous League: Midland Comb. 51-63 **Nickname:** Peacocks
Sponsors: Jasper Steels **Reserve's League:** West Mids (Regional) Lge Res. Div.
Honours: West Mids Lg Div 1 R-up 83-84 (Div 1 Cup 92-93), Birmingham Vase 91-92.

KINGTON TOWN

Chairman: William Mayglothing
Secretary: Karen Mayglothing, Wells Cottage, Stanner Road, Kington, Hereford HR5 3NL (01544 231151 H)
Ground: Park Road Ground, Mill Street, Kington, Hereford (01544 231007)
Directions: Follow signs for kington Town Centre, look for left turn between the Town Clock and the Burton Hotel. Carry on this road for 500 metres, ground on left as road bends.
Colours: Yellow & black/black/black **Change colours:** Maroon & white/maroon/maroon

LUDLOW TOWN

Chairman: P.Gwilliam.
Secretary: Mr J Nash, 58 Hucklemarsh Road, Ludlow, Shropshire (01584 874337)
Manager: Martin MacKenzie **Asst Manager:** Jeremy Mulliner. **Coach:**
Ground: Riddings Park, Riddings Road, Ludlow, Shropshire (01584 875103).
Directions: From Kidderminster A4117; straight over r'bout into Henley Rd, 2nd left into Sandpits Rd, follow road for 1/4 mile until road bears round to the left into Ridding Rd - grd on right.
Seats: No **Cover:** 150 **Floodlights:** Yes **Clubhouse:** Yes **Programme:** No
Colours: Red & white/black/black **Change colours:** Blue & white/white/blue
Previous League: Kidderminster.
Honours: West Mids. Prem Lg.Cup, Finalists 94-95. Div 1 Cup 90-91; Shropshire County Challenge Cup 93-94,94-95 96-97; Presteigne-Otway Cup 90-91.94-95:

LYE TOWN

Chairman: Roy Pearson **President:** Ian Cole.
Secretary: Peter Timmins, Sports Ground, Stourbridge Rd, Lye, Stourbridge, West Midlands (01384 827471 H)
Manager: David Beasley. **Coach:** Alan Moore **Physio:** Harry Hill.
Ground: Sports Ground, Stourbridge Road, Lye (01384 422672).
Directions: On A458 Birmingham-Stourbridge road about 400yds after lights/crossroads at Lye. From M5 jct 3 take road marked Kidderminster as far as lights at bottom of Hagley Hill, right at island, 3rd turn off at next island,turn off left at crossroads/lights, ground about 400yds on left. Quarter mile from Lye (BR).
Seats: 200 **Cover:** 600 **Capacity:** 5,000 **Floodlights:** Yes **Founded:** 1930.
Colours: Blue & white/white/blue **Change Colours:** Red/black/red **Nickname:** Flyers.
Programme: 24 pages, 40p **Editor:** J.Galloway. **Clubhouse:** Yes (01384 822672).
Previous Leagues: Midland Combination 31-39. **Record Gate:** 6,000 v Brierley Alliance.
Honours: West Mids Lg R-up 76-77 78-79 79-80 80-81 (Prem. Div Cup 75-76), Midland Comb. 35-36 (R-up 32-33 34-35 37-38), B'ham Snr Cup R-up 80-81.

MALVERN TOWN

Chairman: Paul Carter **President:** R H Mann **Manager:** Martyn Day
Secretary: Glynne Knapper, 27 Alexandra Lane, Malvern, Worcs WR14 1JF (01684 574861).
Ground: Langland Stadium, Langland Avenue, Malvern, Worcs (01684 574068).
Directions: From Worcester take main road to Malvern. When reaching Malvern turn left at 1st lights into Pickersleigh Ave., follow to Langland Arms Pub on left, left into Madresfield Rd, 2nd left into Langland Ave., ground 100yds on right. 1 mile from Malvern (BR).
Seats: 140 **Cover:** 310 **Capacity:** 4,000 **Floodlights:** Yes **Founded:** 1947.
Colours: Claret/white/sky **Change colours:** White/black/maroon
Programme: 12 pages 20p (special matches) **Editor:** Dave Liley **Previous League:** Midland Comb. 55-79.
Clubhouse: 2 bars, large dance area **Record Gate:** 1,221 v Worcester, FA Cup
Honours: Worcester/ Midland Comb. 55-56.

SMETHWICK RANGERS

Chairman: Sukbinder Binning **Founded:** 1972
Secretary: Mohan S Gill, 11 Middlesmoor, Wilnecote, Tamworth, Staffs B77 4PL (01827 330702)
Ground: Bilston United FC Parkfield Stadium, Rooker Ave, Parkfields, Wolverhampton
Directions: From Wolverhampton Centre, proceed along A459 to junc Parkfields Rd & Sedgley Rd. Turn left at the main Parkfield traffic lights A4039, sign Ettingshall, travel 500yds ,left into Myatt Ave, 1st right into Lawn Rd. Ground on right
Colours: Blue & white/blue/blue **Change colours:** Red & black/black/black

STAFFORD TOWN

Chairman: Graham Hollingshead **President:** T Logan
Secretary: Dave Rowley, 32 Lodge Road, Brereton, Rugely, Staffs WS15 1HG (01889 583000)
Manager: Chris Curtiss **Press Officer:** David Howard (01785 222686).
Ground: Stafford Rangers FC, Aston Fields Rd, Stafford
Directions: From M6 junction 14, Take 3rd left to Red Hill Roundabout and follow signs for Aston Fields Ind Est along Beaconside. Aston Fields is sign posted 3rd right along Common Road, over railway bridge, ground on right
Capacity: 6,000 **Cover:** 3,000 **Seats:** 426 **Floodlights:** Yes **Founded:** 1974
Programme: 28 pages, 50p **Editor:** David Howard (01785 222686)
Colours: All red **Change colours:** Blue/navy/navy
Nickname: Reds or Town **Midweek matches:** Mon/Wed **Club Shop:** No
Previous Leagues: Staffs County (North) 74-77 82-84/ Midland Combination 77-82/ Staffs Senior 84-93.
Honours: WMRL Div 1 93-94, Staffs Snr Lg R-up 91-92, Midland Comb. Div 2 78-79, Staffs Vase 84-85 92-93 (R-up 87-88), Bourne Sports Trophy 84-85, Walsall Senior Cup SF 91-92.

Westfield FC *Photo: Eric Marsh*

TIPTON TOWN

Chairman: Harold Charles Hackett **Founded:** 1948
Secretary: John Cross, 1 Moreton Close, Tipton, West Midlands Dy4 0DG (0121 530 2524)
Ground: Oldbury Leisure Centre, Newbury Lane, Oldbury, Warley (0121 552 1818)
Directions: M5 Junc 2, take A4123 Wolverhampton New Road towards Dudley, at 1st lights turn left into Newbury Lane. Ground 50 yds on right
Colours: Black & white/black/red **Change colours:** All red

TIVIDALE

Chairman: Donald Ashton **President:** Lord Peter Archer.
Secretary: Paul Boswell, 34 Princes Rd, Tividale, Oldbury, W Mids. B69 2LR (0121 532 4023)
Manager: Paul Madders **Asst Manager:** Ron Blackwood **Physio:** John Cotton
Ground: The Beeches, Packwood Rd, Tividale, Warley, West Midlands B69 1UL (01384 211743).
Directions: Dudley Port Station to Burnt tree, left towards Birmingham, ground 1 mile on right. Or, M5 jct 2, follow Dudley signs A4123, after approx 2 miles turn left into Regent Rd and left again into Elm Terraces, first left into Birch Crescent. Packwood Rd is second left - ground at end of cul-de-sac.
Seats: 200 **Cover:** 1,000 **Capacity:** 3,500 **Floodlights:** Yes **Club Shop:** No.
Programme: 40 pages, 60p **Editor:** c/o Club **Press Officer:** T Clark.
Colours: Yellow/yellow/blue **Change colours:** All Red.
Sponsors: Midland & North Security Consultants **Nickname:** Dales **Founded:** 1954
Midweek matchday: Tuesday **Reserves League:** Div. One.
Record Attendance: 2,400 v Telford United, FA Cup.
Previous Leagues: Handsworth & District 56-60/ inactive 60-62/ West Mids Alliance 62-66.
Players progressing to Football League: G Hughes, L May.
Clubhouse: Mon-Fri 8-11pm, Sat 12-11pm, Sun 12-3 & 8-10.30. Cobs, rolls, sandwiches available.
Honours: W Mids Lg Div 1 72-73 (Prem. Div Cup 76-77, Div 1 Cup 72-73), Wednesbury Charity Cup 76-77.

WALSALL WOOD

Chairman: Robert Thomas **Manager:** Michael Speake
Secretary: John Rousell, 19 Kinver Avenue, Short Heath, Willenhall, West Midlands, WV12 4LS (01902 637711)
Ground: Oak Park, Lichfield Rd, Walsall (01543 361084).
Directions: Off A461 Walsall-Lichfield Rd, 4 miles from Walsall town centre and 100yds south of junction with A4152 Aldridge-Brownhills. If travelling via M6/M5 exit motorway at jct 7 (Post House) and continue on A34 towards Walsall before joining A4148 which connects with the A461. 4 miles from Walsall (BR) station - regular buses pass ground.
Capacity: 3,000 **Seats:** 400 **Cover:** 400 **Floodlights:** Yes **Founded:** 1926
Colours: Red/black/red **Change colours:** All blue **Programme:** Yes
Previous Leagues: Mids Comb. 51-92/ Staffs Snr 92-93. **Record Gate:** 800 v Aston Villa, 1980.
Clubhouse: Evenings, matchdays and Sunday lunchtimes. Darts, pool. Hot snacks on matchdays.
Honours: Midland Comb. 51-52 (R-up 53-54 54-55 57-58 58-59 60-61, Lg Cup 54-55 60-61 (R-up 56-57 58-59)), B'ham Jnr Cup 76-77. *Walsall Sportsco: Mids Comb. Lg Cup 79-80.*

WESTFIELDS

Chairman: Alan Dunsford **Vice Chairman:** Neil Preece **President:** Graham Preece.
Secretary: Andrew Morris, 17 Fayre Oaks Green, Kings Acre, Hereford HR4 0QT (01432 264711)
Manager: Gary Stevens **Coach:** Sean Edwards/Phil Dean **Physio:** Peter Boulton
Ground: Thorn Lighting, Holme Lacy Rd, Rotherwas, Hereford (01432 268131)
Directions: Proceed 1.5 mile south from Hereford on A49, left in Home Lacy Rd at Broadleys Inn, proceed 1 mile to Thorn Lighting Rotherwas, ground on the right on Rotherwas Ind. Estate. 2 miles from Hereford (BR).
Seats: 100 **Cover:** 150 **Capacity:** 2,000 **Floodlights:** Yes **Club Shop:** Yes
Programme: Yes **Editor:** Andy Morris **Press Officer:** Secretary
Colours: Maroon & sky/sky/sky **Change colours:** Sky/white/sky & maroon
Sponsors: Hereford Times **Founded:** 1966 **Nickname:** The Fields.
Midweek matchday: Tuesday **Youth team's League:** W Midlands Youth Lge Floodlite
Record Attendance: 518 v Rushden & Diamonds FA Cup 96
Previous Leagues: Herefordshire Sunday 66-74/ Herefordshire 72-74/ Worcester & Dist. 74-77.
Players progressing to Football League: Alex Sykes (Mansfield Town 92), Gary Bowyer (Nottingham Forest 89), John Layton (Hereford Utd 74).
Clubhouse: 'Gamecock Inn' Holme Lacey Rd. Hereford (1/2 mile from ground).
Club Record Goalscorer: Paul Burton. **Club Record Appearances:** Phil Powell/ Mark Tabb.
Honours: West Mids Lg Div 1 86-87, Div 2 R-up 83-84 (Div 2 Cup 79-80 83-84), Herefordshire Snr Cup 85-86 88-89 91-92 95-96 (Yth Cup 92-93 95-96), Kington Chall. Cup 83-84 85-86 86-87 89-90 91-92, Kington Invitation Cup 84-85 85-86 86-87 95-96, Presteigne Ottway Cup 78-79 81-82 84-85 93-94, Worcs Jnr Cup 79-80, Wye Guild Cup 74-75 77-78, Hereford Sunday Lg Prem 75-76 76-77 (Div 1 71-72, Div 2 76-77, Div 3 75-76, Prem Div Cup 75-76 76-77, Div 1 Cup 73-74 74-75, Div 3 Cup 72-73), Smart Brown Cup 67-68, Fair Play Cup 67-68. Dennis Hartland Mem Trophy 95-96, Robert Biggart Trophy 95-96.

WOLVERHAMPTON CASUALS

Chairman: Barry Austin **President:** Clive Hammond **Manager:** Gary Walters
Secretary: Michael Green, 63 St Phillips Avenue, Pennfields Wolverhampton WV6 7ED (01902 333677)
Ground: Brinsford Lane, Coven Heath, Wolverhampton (01902 783214)
Directions: Onto M54 from M6 North, at Junc 2 turn right (A449 to Stafford). Ground half a mile, turn right into Brinsford Lane. Billbrooke (BR) 2 miles.
Seats: 50 **Cover:** 50 **Capacity:** 2,000 **Floodlights:** No. **Founded:** 1896.
Colours: White & green/green/green **Change colours:** Gold/black/gold
Programme: 28pages 30p **Editor:** G Smith
Previous Name: Staffs Casuals (pre 81) **Previous Ground:** Aldersley Stadium
Players progressing to Football League: David Heywood (Wolves), Chris Lewis (Leicester C), Des Lyttle (Nott F)
Clubhouse: Bar & snacks, open Tues/Wed/Thurs/Sat/Sun & alternate Mondays
Honours: WMRL Div 1 94-95, R-up (3) 85-88, Div 1 Cup 85-86.

WOLVERHAMPTON UNITED

Chairman: Brian Vaughan **President:** Geoff Parker **Vice Chairman:** Ken Boothe
Match Secretary: Cliff Dulstone, 34 Broadway, Finchfield, Wolverhampton (01902 753644).
Manager: Dave Downing **Club Sec:** John Lee **Commercial Manager:** Graham Jones
Match Secretary: Cliff Dulstone, 34 Broadway, Finchfield, Wolverhampton (01902 753644).
Ground: Cannock Sports Stadium, Pye Green Road, Cannock.
Directions: M6 Junc 11, follow signs to Cannock. At island turn left (down the ringway), at next island follow sign for A34, then take first turn on right. ground 9th turn on right.
Seats: 300 **Cover:** Yes **Capacity:** 5,000 **Floodlights:** Yes **Founded:** 1976
Colours: Gold with black trim/black/gold **Change colours:** All blue
Programme: 28 pages, 50p **Editor:** Graham Jones
Clubhouse: Wolverhampton, open every evening, Sat, Sun
Honours: W Mids Lg Div 1 B Champ 76-77, R-up 81-82 95-96, Cup 76-77 93-94 R-up 79-80 81-82; Walsall Sen Cup R-up 81-82 84-85; Wednesbury Sen Charity Cup 84-85 94-95.

EVERARDS BREWERY
LEICESTERSHIRE SENIOR FOOTBALL LEAGUE

Founded 1896

President: John M Elsom F.C.A. **Chairman:** David Jamieson
Hon. Secretary: Robert J Holmes, 8 Huntsman Close, Markfield, Leics LE67 9XE
Tel: 01530 243093

The 1997-98 season marked a new era, the first time that the league could boast an all lit Premier division, with the last four clubs lighting up in the Autumn.

On the field of play the Premier division was a close ran affair with Holwell Sports, Friar Lane Old Boys, Kirby Muxloe and defending champions Oadby Town all in the hunt until the death. However, Oadby Town came from behind, to win a real thriller away at Friar Lane Old Boys, on a foul night in front of 300 spectators, a win that kept them just out in front until they clinched their third title in the last four season, during the final week. Second place went to the final day when victory for Kirby Muxloe was enough to edge out Friar Lane Old Boys into third spot. Consolation for Friar Lane Old Boys and Holwell Sports was the contest of the Leagues' Beacon Bitter Cup Final, at Anstey Nomads, which eventually went to Friar Lane Old Boys, after a magnificent second half fight back, to win 4-2 after being 2 down.

Division One was also tight for much of the time until Thurnby Rangers, in their last season with the league, went away over the last few weeks. Stoney Stanton eventually emerged from the pack, and a victory over promotion rivals Fosse Imps, in Stoney Stanton's final match, secured the runners-up spot from Saffron Dynamo and Blaby & Whetstone Athletic.

In other competitions, pride of place went to Oadby Town, who reached the last 16 of the FA Vase before losing 2-1 at eventual winners Tiverton Town. Friar Lane Old Boys also enjoyed a good Vase run whilst Birstall United had a tremendous season in cup competitions. They had a marvellous run in the Vase, reached the semi-final of the Midland Interlink Express Invitation Cup and then capped it all with victory over Ibstock Welfare in the Leics & Rutland County FA Jelson Homes Senior Cup.

The league has continued to play its part in the National League system, and look to promote football throughout the Midland region by being able to offer a club for promotion to the Midland Football Alliance. For this purpose the ground requirements of the Premier Division have been raised. Thus, with the Division One championship clubs, Thurnby Rangers and Stoney Stanton unable to meet the ground requirements for the Premier Division, in the main floodlights, and the highest placed club with the required ground standard, Leicester Constabulary, in 6th place, no promotion or relegation has taken place between the two divisions. Barrow Town, who finished 17th, and United Collieries who finished bottom gained a relegation reprieve.

FINAL LEAGUE TABLES 1997-98

PREMIER DIVISION

	P	W	D	L	F	A	Pts
Oadby Town	34	27	2	5	101	34	83
Kirby Muxloe	34	24	5	5	83	38	77
Friar Lane OB	34	24	2	8	88	33	74
Holwell Sports	34	22	7	5	86	41	73
St Andrews	34	19	6	9	81	39	63
Ibstock Welfare	34	19	3	12	76	52	60
Downes	34	18	4	12	67	57	58
Birstall	34	16	6	12	52	41	54
Cottesmore	34	15	4	15	63	61	49
Highfield Rgs	34	15	3	16	46	62	48
Quorn	34	10	7	17	61	73	37
Thringstone	34	9	10	15	34	47	37
Anstey Nomads	34	10	5	19	49	69	35
Coalville	34	9	5	20	42	72	32
Aylestone	34	8	6	20	49	81	30
Lutterworth	34	8	6	20	51	89	30
Barrow	34	5	7	22	41	87	22
Unitd Collieries	34	4	0	30	30	124	9

DIVISION ONE

	P	W	D	L	F	A	Pts
Thurnby Rangers	30	24	2	4	89	33	74
Stoney Stanton	30	18	7	5	67	40	61
Saffron Dynamo	30	18	4	8	65	36	58
Blaby Whetstone	30	17	6	7	52	38	57
Fosse Imps	30	17	5	8	71	36	56
Constabulary	30	15	10	5	80	35	55
Huncote Sports	30	13	7	10	75	55	46
Anstey Town	30	12	6	12	60	53	42
Bardon Hill	30	11	7	12	56	52	40
Loughborough Dyn	30	11	7	12	52	63	40
Sileby Town	30	9	7	14	43	54	34
Earl Shilton Alb	30	9	5	16	38	39	32
Narborough	30	9	4	17	42	61	31
Asfordby Amateurs	30	6	5	19	29	74	23
Harborough Town	30	3	4	23	26	112	13
North Kilworth	30	2	6	22	32	96	12
Newfoundpool	30	0 Resigned at start of season					
Syston	30	0 Resigned - record expunged					

PREMIER DIVISION RESULTS CHART 1997-98

		1	2	3	4	5	6	7	8	9	10	11	12	13	14	15	16	17	18
1	Anstey Nomads	X	2-0	3-1	1-0	1-2	0-5	1-4	1-4	4-2	0-1	1-3	2-5	0-0	0-1	5-1	1-3	3-0	0-1
2	Aylestone	0-1	X	1-2	2-0	0-2	1-0	2-3	0-5	1-2	0-2	2-2	1-2	6-1	1-6	5-5	0-3	0-0	3-0
3	Barrow	0-0	2-2	X	1-2	0-3	1-2	1-1	1-4	2-1	0-4	2-2	0-3	2-1	3-5	0-4	2-2	4-1	2-1
4	Birstall	1-1	5-1	3-1	X	5-1	1-0	1-0	0-4	0-1	0-2	1-4	0-4	7-0	0-1	0-0	1-0	2-0	3-0
5	Coalville	0-4	1-3	1-0	0-2	X	2-2	1-1	1-2	2-0	1-3	0-1	0-1	2-3	1-2	2-2	1-3	0-0	0-6
6	Cottesmore	2-2	3-2	3-0	0-2	3-1	X	4-0	0-2	1-2	2-6	2-1	1-0	3-1	3-3	0-1	0-4	1-3	3-0
7	Downes	3-1	4-0	3-1	0-2	1-2	3-2	X	2-1	1-0	2-2	0-3	4-0	2-2	1-2	2-1	0-7	5-0	5-1
8	Friar Lane OB	5-1	2-1	3-2	5-2	1-0	2-2	2-0	X	2-0	1-2	4-0	0-0	2-0	2-3	2-1	2-3	1-0	3-1
9	Highfield	1-0	4-0	3-1	1-0	2-2	2-0	1-2	1-3	X	0-1	0-1	1-2	6-1	0-6	2-1	1-0	0-0	2-1
10	Holwell	3-2	2-2	2-1	2-0	8-1	2-3	2-1	1-3	5-0	X	6-1	1-1	3-0	2-0	1-1	0-6	2-2	4-0
11	Ibstock Welfare	4-1	5-1	1-0	0-2	2-0	1-2	1-2	2-1	6-1	3-4	X	3-4	5-2	0-4	3-0	1-1	2-1	5-1
12	Kirby Muxloe	3-0	5-1	3-1	1-1	0-2	5-3	2-0	3-1	5-2	1-1	1-0	X	4-3	3-0	5-1	1-0	2-0	2-1
13	Lutterworth	2-3	2-2	5-1	1-1	2-4	1-0	3-4	2-1	0-2	1-4	2-1	1-3	X	1-0	0-4	1-2	0-0	-
14	Oadby Town	1-0	2-0	4-0	4-2	2-0	6-2	2-3	1-0	1-1	2-0	3-0	3-2	6-0	X	4-2	3-2	0-1	5-0
15	Quorn	2-2	2-3	2-2	0-1	3-2	0-3	3-2	0-2	5-2	1-2	0-3	4-1	3-4	0-5	X	1-1	0-1	5-1
16	St Andrews	6-1	2-0	3-3	2-2	6-1	2-1	2-0	0-2	5-0	3-2	0-2	0-2	1-3	0-4	2-1	X	1-1	4-1
17	Thringstone	3-0	1-2	4-91	1-1	1-0	0-2	1-2	0-2	0-1	0-0	1-3	1-1	1-1	2-4	2-3	1-2	X	3-0
18	United Collieries	0-5	1-4	5-1	0-2	0-4	2-3	1-4	0-12	1-2	0-4	0-5	0-6	3-1	0-6	1-2	0-5	0-2	X

SENIOR LEAGUE AND SPORTSWORLD CUP SCORERS

PREMIER DIVISION

26	Culpin D	Oadby
25	Hunter	Oadby
24	Hennigan	Quorn
23	Marsden	Friar Lane
22	Roberts D	Friar Lane
22	Warner	St Andrews
22	Warren	Kirby
21	Keast	Holwell
21	Seal	Coalville
19	Pywell	Lutterworth
18	Knight M	St Andrews
17	Houghton	Holwell
17	Johnson	Birstall
17	Pitman	Nomads
17	Smith D	Ibstock
16	Walker R	Oadby
15	Budge	Ibstock
13	Mogg L	Holwell
13	Rowe M	Nomads
12	Christmas	Cottesmore
11	Horner	Kirby
11	Maisey	Friar Lane
11	Turner	Quorn
11	Postlethwaite	Friar Lane
10	Boyles	Oadby
10	Foster	Kirby
10	Jackson	Birstall United
10	Mitchell	Thringstone
10	Tanner	Lutterworth

DIVISION ONE

23	Tallis	Huncote
22	Wingfield	Fosse
21	Collier	Bardon
21	Smith S	Fosse
19	Cross	Constabulary
17	Thomas C	Constabulary
17	Pritchard Lee	Huncote
17	McManus	Saffron
16	Kee	Thurnby
13	Cuttiford	Stanton
12	Kidger	Thurnby
12	Murning	Thurnby
11	Fitzpatrick	Narborough
11	Gurney	Blaby/Whet
11	Johnstone	Narborough
10	Griffin	Loughborough
10	Devlin	Saffron
10	Preston A	Sileby
10	Hyde	N Kilworth
10	Phillips Tim	Loughborough
10	Nelson	Thurnby
10	Brown	Harborough

CLUB DIRECTORY 1998-99

ANSTEY NOMADS **Colours:** Red & white stripes/black/white
Secretary: John Sutherington, 43 George St, A0stey, Leicester LE7 7DT (0116 236 5153)
Ground: Llimah International Park, Cropston Road, Anstey (0116 236 4868)

ANSTEY TOWN **Colours:** All blue
Secretary: Marten Almen, 86 Rockhill Drive, Mountsorrel, Leics. (0116 237 4062)
Ground: Leicester Road, Thurcaston (0116 236 8231)

ASFORDBY AMATEURS **Colours:** Green/black/black
Secretary: Graham Hunt, 8 Winster Drive, Thurmaston, Leics LE4 8GH (0116 269 3598)
Ground: Hoby Road Sports Ground, Asfordby, Melton Mowbray (01664 434545).

AYLESTONE PARK **Colours:** Red & white/red/red
Secretary: Brendon Tyrrell, 7 Magnolia Close, Leicester Forest East, Leicester (0116 224 7186)
Ground: Dorset Avenue, Fairfield Estate, Wigston, Leics (0116 277 5307)

BARDON HILL **Colours:** Blue & white/blue/blue & white
Secretary: Adrian Bishop, 138 Bradgate Drive, Coalville, Leics LE67 4HG (01530 815560).
Ground: Bardon Close, Coalville, Leicester (01530 815569).

BARROW TOWN **Colours:** Red & black/black/red
Secretary: Alan Dawkins, 72 Beaumont Road, Barrow-on-Soar, Loughborough, Leics LE12 8PJ (01509 413288).
Ground: Riverside Park, Barrow Road, Quorn, Leics (01509 620650).

BIRSTALL UNITED **Colours:** White/navy/red
Secretary: Bob Garrard, 58 Halstead Rd, Mountsorrel, Leicester LE12 7HF (0116 237 6886)
Ground: Meadow Lane, Birstall (0116 267 1230)

BLABY & WHETSTONE ATHLETIC **Colours:** Navy/navy red & white trim
Secretary: Mrs S C Morris, 10 Winchester Road, Blaby, Leics LE8 3HJ (0116 277 3208)
Ground: Blaby & Whetstone Boys Club, Warwick Road, Whetstone (0116 286 4852)

COALVILLE **Colours:** White/black/black.
Secretary: Robert Brooks, 17 Ashland Drive, Coalville, Leics LE67 3NH (01530 833269).
Ground: Owen Street Sports Ground, Owen Street, Coalville (01530 833365)

COTTESMORE AMATEURS **Colours:** Green/navy/green.
Secretary: K Nimmons, 17 Redwing Close, Oakham, Rutland LE15 6DA (01572 724582).
Ground: Rogues Park, Main Street, Cottesmore, Rutland (01572 813486).

DOWNES SPORTS **Colours:** Tangerine/black/tangerine
Secretary: Andy Wells, c/o 4 Mortiboys Way, Stoney Stanton LE9 4WP (01455 274834).
Ground: Leicester Rd, Hinckley (01455 615062)

EARL SHILTON ALBION **Colours:** Green & gold/green/green
Secretary: Carolyn Knight, 141 Rugby Rd, Burbage, Leics LE10 2NB (01455 230193)
Ground: Stoneycroft Park, New Street, Earl Shilton, Leics (01455 844277).

FOSSE IMPS **Colours:** Red & blue/blue/blue
Secretary: Ivan V Colbourne, 55 Harrowgate Drive, Birstall, Leics LE4 3GQ (0116 267 1424)
Ground: Co-op Ground, Birstall Rd, Leicester (0116 267 4059)

FRIAR LANE OLD BOYS **Colours:** Black & white stripes/black/black
Secretary: Kevin Brooks, 299 Milligan Rd, Leicester LE4 2RJ (0116 224 3854)
Ground: Knighton Lane East, Leicester (0116 283 3629)

HARBOROUGH TOWN **Colours:** Red & black stripes/black/black
Secretary: John Chambers, 9 Meltham Close, Weston Favell, Northampton NN3 9QY (01604 785707)
Ground: Imperial Park, Northampton Road Sports Ground, Market Harborough, Leics.

HIGHFIELD RANGERS **Colours:** Yellow/navy/yellow
Secretary: Maurice Christian, 18 Blanklyn Avenue, Leicester LE5 5FA (0116 273 4002)
Ground: 443 Gleneagles Ave., Rushey Mead, Leicester (0116 266 0009)

HOLWELL SPORTS **Colours:** Green & gold/green/green
Secretary: Mrs Anne Marriott, 24 Church Lane, Croxton Kerrial, Grantham, Lincs NG32 1PZ (01476 870658)
Ground: Welby Road, Asfordby Hill, Melton Mowbray, Leics (01664 812663)

HUNCOTE SPORTS & SOCIAL **Colours:** Blue & yellow/yellow/blue
Secretary: D Russell, 72 Sycamore Way, Littlethorpe, Leics LE9 5HU (0116 284 1952)
Ground: Enderby Lane, Thurlaston, Leics (01455 888430).

IBSTOCK WELFARE **Colours:** Red/black/red
Secretary: R A Wilkinson, 6 Valley Rd, Ibstock, Leicester LE67 6NY (01530 260744).
Ground: The Welfare, Leicester Road, Ibstock (01530 260656).

KIRBY MUXLOE S.C. **Colours:** Navy & sky/navy/navy
Secretary: Philip Moloney, 16 Church Lane, Ratby, Leics LE6 0JE (0116 239 2916)
Ground: Ratby Lane, Kirby Muxloe (0116 239 3201)

LEICESTER YMCA **Colours:** Red & black/black/red & black
Secretary: Colin Chappell, 132 South Knighton Rd, Leicester, LE2 3LE (0116 247 8989)
Ground: YMCA Sports Ground, Belvoir Drive, Leicester

LEICESTERSHIRE CONSTABULARY **Colours:** Green & yellow/green/green & yellow
Secretary: Ian Leacy, 6 Lena Drive, Groby, Leicester LE6 0FJ (01530 243110).
Ground: Police HQ, St Johns, Enderby (0116 248 2198)

LOUGHBOROUGH DYNAMO **Colours:** Gold/black/black
Secretary: Max Hutchinson, 3 Wythburn Close, Loughborough, Leics LE11 3SZ (01509 266092).
Ground: Nanpanton Sport Ground, Loughborough (01509 612144).

LUTTERWORTH TOWN **Colours:** White/navy/navy
Secretary: Tony Martin, 5 Toms Close, Theddingworth, Leics LE17 6QH (0402 353492)
Ground: Hall Lane, Bitteswell, Lutterworth, Leics (01455 554046)

NARBOROUGH & LITTLETHORPE **Colours:** Yellow/green/green
Secretary: Mick Dodds, 24 Princess Street, Narborough, Leics LE9 5DH (0116 286 7042)
Ground: Ray Hurd Pavilion, Leicester Road, Narborough (Near M1 bridge) (0116 275 1855)

NORTH KILWORTH **Colours:** Red & black/black/red & black
Secretary: Mrs H Cheney, 109 Queens Drive, Enderby, Leics LE9 5LL (0116 275 1460)
Ground: Rugby Road, North Kilworth, Lutterworth, Leics (01858 880890).

OADBY TOWN **Colours:** Red/white/black
Secretary: Kevin Zupp, 14 Swiftway, Lutterworth, Leics LE17 4PB (01455 550358)
Ground: Invicta Park, Wigston Road, Oadby, Leics (0116 271 5728)

QUORN **Colours:** Red/white/red
Secretary: W L Caunt, 64 Wood Lane, Quorn, Leics LE12 8DB (01509 414213).
Ground: Farley Way, Quorn, Leics (01509 620232)

SAFFRON DYNAMO **Colours:** Red/black/black
Secretary: Bob King, 14 Bramley Close, Broughton Astley, Leicester LE9 6QU (01455 284270).
Ground: Cambridge Road, Whetstone, (0116 284 9695)

SILEBY TOWN **Colours:** Red & white/black/black
Secretary: Ann Bettles, 6 Jubilee Avenue, Sileby, Leics LE12 7TH (01509 813864)
Ground: Memorial Park, Seagrave Road, Sileby, Leics (01509 816104)

St ANDREWS SOCIAL CLUB **Colours:** Black & white/white/red
Secretary: L Botting, 2 Neston Road, Saffron Lane, Leicester LE2 6RD
Ground: Canal Street, Old Aylestone, Leicester (0116 283 9872)

STONEY STANTON **Colours:**
Secretary: Brian Chapman, 54 John Bold Avenue, Stoney Stanton, Leics (01455 274295)
Ground:

THRINGSTONE MINERS WELFARE **Colours:** Blue & orange/blue/blue
Secretary: Paul Harley, 62 Henson Lane, Coalville, Leics LE67 8LH (01530 222810)
Ground: Homestead Road, Thringstone (01530 223367).

THURMASTON TOWN **Colours:**
Secretary: Kevin Sadler, 81 Woodgreen Road, Leicester LE4 9UD (0116 246 0093)
Ground:

THURNBY RANGERS **Colours:** Green & white/green/green
Secretary: Pat Darby, 83 Kinsdale Drive, Thurnby, Leics LE5 2PU
Ground: Dakyn Road, Thurnby Lodge, Leics

UNITED COLLIERIES **Colours:** Sky/navy/navy.
Secretary: John Meason, 29 Standard Hill, Coalville, Leics LE67 3HN (01530 810941)
Ground: 1 Terrace Rd, Ellistown, Coalville. (01530 230159)

WEST MIDLANDS FINAL LEAGUE TABLES 1997-98

SPRINGBANK VENDING MIDLAND LEAGUE

DIVISION ONE	*P*	*W*	*D*	*L*	*F*	*A*	*Pts*
Audley	36	26	5	5	82	28	83
Norton United	36	24	5	7	89	51	77
Eccleshall	36	23	6	7	93	38	75
Redgate Clayton	36	17	11	8	79	46	62
Brocton	36	18	6	12	87	72	60
Baddeley Green R	36	17	8	11	74	56	59
Kidsgrove Ath	36	15	8	13	58	58	53
Stone Dominoes	36	15	7	14	54	57	52
Foley	36	14	8	14	75	79	50
Stallington	36	13	10	13	75	77	49
Milton United	36	14	6	16	52	55	48
Rists United	36	13	7	16	56	58	46
Hanford	36	11	11	14	56	51	44
Adderley Green	36	11	8	17	58	75	41
Ball Haye Green	36	9	11	16	53	63	38
Cheadle Old Boys	36	10	5	21	51	89	35
Knypersley Vics	36	9	3	24	53	94	30
Nantwich Town	36	8	5	23	61	111	29
Goldenhill Wdrs	36	6	8	22	45	93	26

MIDLAND FLOODLIT YOUTH LEAGUE
CENTRAL DIVISION

	P	*W*	*D*	*L*	*F*	*A*	*Pts*
Bedworth United	18	12	6	0	52	16	42
West Bromwich A.	18	11	4	3	51	22	37
Halesowen Town	18	10	5	3	45	21	35
Boldmere St Mich's	18	10	5	3	40	21	35
Atherstone United	18	7	5	6	34	30	26
Nuneaton Borough	18	7	2	9	37	30	23
Stourbidge	18	4	4	10	29	45	16
Tamworth	18	5	1	12	27	51	16
Lutterworth Town	18	4	2	12	21	49	14
Coleshill Town	18	1	4	13	14	65	7

MIDLAND FLOODLIT YOUTH LEAGUE
SOUTHERN DIVISION

	P	*W*	*D*	*L*	*F*	*A*	*Pts*
Bromsgrove Rovers	18	15	0	3	49	19	48
Solihull Borough	17	11	2	4	48	21	35
Kidderminster Har-	18	10	3	5	39	24	33
Gloucester City	18	10	2	6	34	27	32
Stratford Town	18	8	7	3	41	26	*28
Racing Club Warwick	18	8	5	5	43	31	*23
Malvern Town	17	6	2	9	22	25	20
Pegasus Juniors	18	4	2	12	15	50	14
Pershore Town	18	3	1	14	22	48	10
Evesham United	18	0	4	14	15	57	*1

R T HARRIS
OXFORD CITY FA

PREMIER DIV	*P*	*W*	*D*	*L*	*F*	*A*	*Pts*
Great Milton	10	7	2	1	36	15	16
Risinghurst	10	5	3	2	21	15	13
Beckley Sports	10	5	1	4	24	21	11
East Oxford	10	3	1	6	26	30	7
Barton	10	3	1	6	18	28	7
North Oxford	10	3	0	7	14	30	6

SKIMTEX PLASTERING
SHROPSHIRE COUNTY LEAGUE

PREMIER DIV	*P*	*W*	*D*	*L*	*F*	*A*	*Pts*
Shawbury United	22	17	2	3	75	27	53
Lt Drayton Rgrs	22	11	6	5	55	37	39
Hanwood Utd	22	12	3	7	50	36	39
Wem Town	22	11	4	7	39	44	37
Meole Brace	22	9	5	8	48	36	32
Broseley	22	10	2	10	42	40	32
Belvidere	22	9	4	9	47	44	31
Belle Vue O B	22	8	4	10	56	52	28
Oakengates	22	7	2	13	43	57	23
Wellington Amt	22	6	5	11	22	55	23
St Martins	22	7	1	14	38	51	22
Snailbeach W Star	22	5	2	15	33	69	17

STAFFORDSHIRE COUNTY
LEAGUE NORTH

	P	*W*	*D*	*L*	*F*	*A*	*Pts*
Abbey Hulton U	34	24	7	3	105	34	55
Vale Juniors	34	22	9	3	116	45	53
Alsager MMU	34	23	6	5	98	47	52
Redgate Clayton	34	16	13	5	81	40	45
Eccleshill	34	18	7	9	81	42	43
Wolstanton Utd	34	17	9	8	81	50	43
Audley	34	15	11	8	61	51	41
Congleton Vale	34	15	8	11	86	57	38
Middlewich Ath	34	13	7	14	58	76	33
Goldenhill Wdrs	34	14	5	15	60	85	33
Meir Park	34	11	7	16	64	65	29
Alsegers Bank	34	8	9	17	50	71	25
Stone Dominoes	34	9	7	18	51	79	25
Oakamoor	34	10	5	19	41	86	25
Alsager	34	9	4	21	50	92	22
Stone Old Alley	34	10	1	23	55	92	21
Rocester	34	6	5	23	46	103	17
Meir K A	34	4	4	26	34	103	12

WITNEY & DISTRICT FA

PREMIER DIV	*P*	*W*	*D*	*L*	*F*	*A*	*Pts*
Enstone	20	18	1	1	67	24	55
Brize Norton	20	13	4	3	57	19	43
Ducklington	20	13	4	6	40	32	34
Stonesfield	20	9	3	8	40	32	30
Spartan Rangers	20	9	2	9	40	39	29
Hanborough	20	7	5	8	35	34	26
North Leigh 'A'	20	7	4	9	32	42	25
Henley	20	6	4	10	34	49	22
Minster Lovell	20	5	4	11	27	42	19
Chadlington	20	5	4	11	19	42	19
West Witney	20	3	1	16	21	58	10

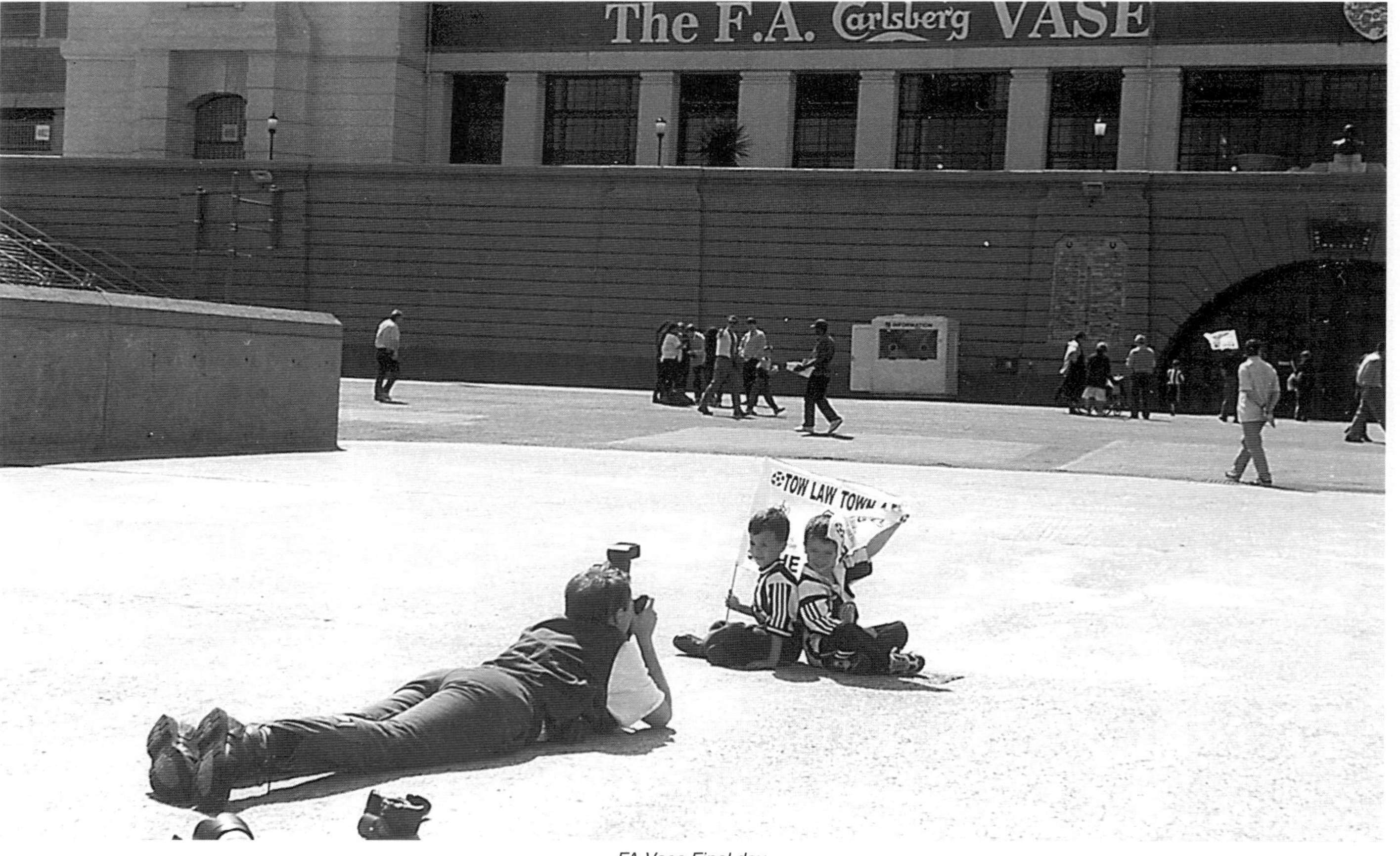

FA Vase Final day
Memories are made of this - getting the low down!
Photo: Gordon Whittington

KEYLINE DORSET COMBINATION LEAGUE

Founded: 1957

President: A P Humphries **Chairman:** R E Maidment
Secretary: G A Theobold
41 South Road, Corfe Mullen, Wimborne, Dorset BH21 3HZ
Tel: 01202 697994

FINAL LEAGUE TABLE 1997-98

	P	W	D	L	F	A	Pts
Sturminster M	36	32	2	2	140	24	98
Portland Utd	36	24	2	10	90	45	74
Hamworthy Eng.	36	21	5	10	99	55	68
Parley Sports	36	20	6	10	86	64	66
Sturminster New.	36	19	8	9	71	61	65
Hamworthy Utd	36	18	7	11	60	48	*60
Bournemouth Sp	36	18	4	14	90	66	58
Gillingham Town	36	17	4	15	70	77	55
Blandford United	36	14	10	12	56	50	52
Swanage T & H	36	14	5	17	50	67	47
Shaftesbury	36	13	6	17	62	64	45
Dorchester Tn	36	12	8	16	60	73	44
Flight Refuelling	36	10	13	13	45	52	43
Allendale	36	11	9	16	68	71	42
Weymouth Spts	36	12	3	21	67	88	39
Westland Sports	36	8	8	20	56	104	32
Wareham Rngrs	36	8	6	22	43	96	30
Sherborne Town	36	6	9	21	58	104	27
Lytchett Red Tri	36	4	7	25	40	102	19

* Point deducted

KEYLINE COMBINATION CUP 1997-98

FIRST ROUND

Blandford United	v	Allendale	0-1
Wareham Rangers	v	Sturminster Newton	0-2
Flight Refuelling	v	Sturminster Marshall	1-4

SECOND ROUND

Allendale	v	Hamworthy Eng.	3-2
Dorcester Tn Res	v	Sturminster Marshall	4-3
Lytchett Red Triangle	v	Sturminster Newton	3-4
Sherborne Town	v	Westland Sports	0-2
Bournemouth Sp	v	Shaftesbury	9-2
Gillingham Town	v	Swanage Tn & Hers.	2-1
Parley Sports	v	Portland United	2-2, 0-4
Weymouth Spts	v	Hamworthy United	1-2

THIRD ROUND

Dorchester Tn Res	v	Allendale	2-3
Hamworthy United	v	Portland United	1-1, 0-2
Gillingham Town	v	Westland Sports	1-2
Sturminster New.	v	Bournemouth Sports	1-2

SEMI-FINALS

Bournemouth Spts	v	Westland Sports	2-3
Portland United	v	Allendale	1-0

FINAL

PORTLAND UTD v WESTLAND SPTS 3-0 after extra time

INTER-LEAGUE REPRESENTATIVE MATCHES 1997-98

Bournemouth FA	v	Combination Lge (Int)	1-0
Bournemouth FA	v	Combination Lge (U21)	0-5
Combination League	v	Wiltshire League	1-0

CLUB DIRECTORY 1998-99

ALLENDALE F.C.

Chairman: E Case (01202 887920 H, 01258 857191 B)
Secretary: Rod Pope, 51 Dalkeith Road, Corfe Mullen Wimborne, BH21 3PQ (01202 602922 H, 01929 424601 B)
Ground: Redcotts Recreation Ground, School Lane, Wimborne
Colours: White/blue/blue
Change Colours: All red

BLANDFORD UNITED

Chairman: M Bellman **Secretary:** Martin Holdaway, 13 Damory Court, Blandford Forum, Dorset DT11 7RN (01258 454733).
Ground: Recreation Ground, Park Lane, Blandford Forum, Dorset. (HQ Tel: 01258 456374).
Colours: All Royal Blue
Change colours: Green & white/white & green/green
Cover: No
Programme: Yes
Clubhouse: No

BRIDPORT RESERVES

Chairman: David Fowler
Secretary: Ian Hallett, Brookside, Burstock, Beaminster DT8 3LJ (01308 868795)
Ground: The Beehive, St Mary's Field, Bridport, Dorset (01308 423834).
Colours: Red & black/black/red & black
Change colours: Blue & black/blue/blue

BOURNEMOUTH SPORTS CLUB

Chairman: T Bloor.
Secretary: John Field, 33 Stanton Road, Ensbury Park, Bournemouth, BH10 5DS (01202 388486)
Ground: Chapel Gate, East Parley, Christchurch, Dorset BH23 6BD (01202 581933).
Colours: Gold/black/gold
Change colours: All red
Cover: No
Programme: Yes
Clubhouse: Yes

DORCHESTER TOWN RESERVES

Chairman: C E Clarke
Secretary: Albert Miller, 29 Shaston Crescent, Dorchester DT1 2EB (01305 264843)
Ground: The Avenue Stadium, Dorchester. (01305 262451)
Colours: Black & white/black/black
Change: Sky/white/sky
Cover: Yes
Floodlights: Yes
Programme: Yes
Clubhouse: Yes

FLIGHT REFUELLING

Chairman: A Miles
Secretary: Harry W Doyle, 39 Towers Way, Corfe Mullen, Wimborne, BH21 3UA (01202 604640).
Ground: Merley Park, Merley, Wimborne, Dorset (01202 885773).
Colours: Blue & black stripes/black/blue
Change colours: All yellow
Cover: No **Programme:** Yes
Clubhouse: Yes

GILLINGHAM TOWN

Chairman: E Murphy.
Secretary: David J Ayles, 37 Sylvan Way, Bay Road, Gillingham SP8 4EQ (01747 822065).
Ground: Hardings Lane, Gillingham (01747 823673).
Colours: Tangerine/black/black
Change colours: Yellow & green/green/green
Cover: Yes
Programme: Yes
Clubhouse: Yes

HAMWORTHY ENGINEERING

Chairman: M Robson.
Secretary: Ray Willis, 52 Heckford Rd, Poole BH15 2LY (01202 773290).
Ground: Hamworthy Rec. Club, Magna Rd, Canford Magna, Wimborne, Dorset BH21 3AE (01202 881922).
Colours: Green & white/green/green
Change colours: Blue & white/navy/navy
Cover: No **Programme:** No
Clubhouse: Yes

HAMWORTHY UNITED

Chairman: D.Manmuel
Secretary: Peter Gallop, 51A Symes Road, Hamworthy, Poole, Dorset BH15 4PR (01202 670792).
Ground: The County Ground, Blandford Close, Hamworthy, Poole, Dorset (01202 674974).
Colours: Maroon & sky/maroon/maroon
Change colours: Green & black stripes/black/black
Cover: Yes **Floodlights:** Yes
Programme: Yes
Clubhouse: Yes

PARLEY SPORTS

Chairman: P Vass
Secretary: Mrs Shirley Jones, 10 Heath Farm Way, Ferndown. BH22 8JR (01202 872924)
Ground: Parley Sports Club, Christchurch, West Parley, Bournemouth, Dorset (01202 573345).
Colours: Yellow/blue/yellow
Change colours: Blue/burgundy/burgundy
Cover: No
Clubhouse: Yes

PORTLAND UNITED

Chairman: P.Laming
Secretary: David M Camp, 23 Four Acres, Weston, Portland DT5 2LG (01305 821816).
Ground: New Grove Corner, Grove Road, Portland (01305 861489)
Colours: All blue.
Change colours: White/black/red.
Cover: Yes
Programme: Yes
Clubhouse: Yes

SHAFTESBURY

Chairman: A P Humphries.
Secretary: Mrs S White, 5 The Venn, Shaftsbury (01747 853376)
Ground: Cockrams, Coppice Street, Shaftesbury (01747 853990).
Colours: Red & white/red/red
Change colours: Yellow/black/black
Cover: Yes
Floodlights: Yes
Clubhouse: Yes

SHERBORNE TOWN

Chairman: F Henderson.
Secretary: Malcolm Bartlett, 5 Wessex Road, Stallbridge DT10 2PF (01963 362880)
Ground: Raleigh Grove, The Terrace Playing Fields, Sherborne (01935 816110).
Colours: White & black/white/white
Change colours: Tangerine/black/black
Cover: Yes
Programme: Yes
Clubhouse: Yes

STURMINSTER MARSHALL

Chairman: R Copeland
Secretary: David Miller, 8 Blaney Way, Corfe Mullen, Wimborne BH21 3HG (01202 602366)
Ground: Churchill Close, Sturminster Marshall, Wimborne
Colours: Jade/black/jade
Change: Yellow/navy/yellow

STURMINSTER NEWTON UNITED

Chairman: D Walters
Secretary: Richard Frear, 44 Green Close, Sturminster Newton DT10 1BL (01258 473036)
Ground: Barnetts Field, Honeymead Lane, Sturminster Newton, Dorset. (01258 471406)
Colours: All red
Change colours: All green
Cover: Yes
Programme: Yes
Clubhouse: No

SWANAGE TOWN & HERSTON

Chairman: Leonard Marsh
President: Mayor of Swanage
Fixture Secretary: Eric Webster, 24 James Day Mead, Ulwell Road, Swanage BH19 1NQ (01929 423522)
Ground: Days Park, off De Moulham Road, Swanage, Dorset (01929 424633).
Colours: White/black/black.
Change colours: Red/white/red
Cover: Yes
Floodlights: Yes
Programme: Yes
Clubhouse: Yes

WAREHAM RANGERS

Chairman: A.White
Secretary: Mrs Carol White, 18 Folly Lane, Wareham, Dorset BH20 4HH (01929 551765).
Ground: Wareham Recreation Ground, Worgret Rd, Wareham, Dorset.
Colours: Amber & black/black/black
Change colours: All sky blue
Cover: No
Programme: Yes
Clubhouse: No

WESTLAND SPORTS

Chairman: M Murley.
Secretary: Mike Mock, 67 Yew Tree Close, Yeovil BA20 2PB (01935 426219)
Ground: Westland Sports Ground, Westbourne Close, Yeovil (01935 703810).
Colours: Blue & Black stripes/Black/Black.
Change colours: Red/white/red.
Cover: No
Programme: Yes
Clubhouse: No

WEYMOUTH SPORTS

Chairman: A Burt
Secretary: Steve Walker, 48 Jestrys Avenue, Weymouth DT3 5NN (01305 813566)
Ground: Weymouth College, Cranford Ave., Weymouth, Dorset (01305 208859/208860).
Colours: Yellow & black stripes/black/black
Change: Blue & white/blue/blue
Prev. Lge: Dorset (champs 1993)

GLOUCESTERSHIRE COUNTY LEAGUE

Founded 1968

Chairman: A C Barrett **Vice Chairman:** J D Hart

Hon. Secretary: D J Herbert
8 Fernhurst Road, St. George, Bristol, BSS 7TQ
Tel. No. 0117 951 7696

Hon. Treasurer: P T McPherson
36 St. Andrews Road, Avonmouth, Bristol BS11 9EU
Tel. No. 0117 982 7035

	P	W	D	L	F	A	Pts
Cadbury Heath	34	24	5	5	81	27	77
Henbury Old Boys	37	19	8	7	55	31	65
Pucklechurch Sports	34	18	9	7	52	31	63
Dursley Town	34	16	12	6	40	23	60
Patchway Town	34	15	11	8	51	36	56
D.R.G.	34	15	10	9	78	56	55
Wotton Rovers	34	14	8	12	53	58	50
Broadwell Amateurs	34	13	9	12	54	48	48
Viney St. Swithins	34	13	8	13	56	47	47
Frampton Athletic	34	12	11	11	43	46	47
Winterbourne United	34	11	12	11	68	59	45
Totterdown P.O.B.	34	12	6	16	41	55	42
Old Georgians	34	11	6	17	46	60	39
Brockworth	34	9	10	15	36	58	37
Ellwood	34	9	7	18	38	54	34
Broad Plain House	34	8	7	19	39	58	31
Oldland	34	5	8	21	46	82	23
Stapleton	34	6	5	23	31	77	23

CLUBS DIRECTORY 1998-99

BROAD PLAIN HOUSE

Secretary: Larry Hartrey, 11 Smythe Croft, Whitchurch, Bristol BS14 0UB (01275 835247)
Ground: Filwood Playing Fields, Creswicke Road Knowle, Bristol.
Colours: Red & black/black/black **Change colours:** Yellow/blue/blue

BROADWELL AMATEURS

Secretary: Glyn Barnes, Orchard Cottage, Maze Walk, Christchurch, Coleford, Glos. GL16 7AN (01594 832523)
Ground: The Hawthorns, Poolway Road, Broadwell, near Coleford (01594 837347).
Directions: B4228 to Coleford then B4028 out of Coleford, B4226 into Broadwell ground on right.
Colours: Claret & blue/blue/blue **Change colours:** Yellow/blue/yellow
Prev. Lge: Glos Northern Snr (pre-1994) **Honours:** Glos Northern Snr Lg 93-94 (R-up 92-93).

BROCKWORTH (1958)

Secretary: Geoffrey Bick, 18 The Wend, Longhope, Gloucester GL17 0QR (01452 830889)
Ground: Brockworth Rugby & Assc. Football Club, Mill Lane, Brockworth Glos.
Colours: Black & white/black/black. **Change colours:** Red & blue/blue/blue

CADBURY HEATH

Secretary: C Thomas, 73 Ridgeway Rd, Fishponds, Bristol BS16 3ED (01179 518097).
Ground: 'Springfield', Cadbury Heath Rd, Warmley, Bristol (01179 675730).
Directions: A420 from Bristol through Kingswood, across new r'bout, right into Tower Rd North, past school, right into Cadbury Heath Rd, ground immediately on right down alley.
Colours: Red/red & black/red & white **Change Colours:** Yellow/black/black.
Hons: Glos Co. Lg 70-71 71-72 72-73 73-74 93-94 (R-up 74-75 90-91 91-92), Glos Amtr Cup Sth(3), FA Vase QF.

D.R.G.

Secretary: Robert Wakefield, 101 Wellsway, Keynsham, Bristol. BS18 1HZ (0117 9865516)
Ground: DRG Sports Ground, Carson Road, Mangotsfield, Bristol (01179 560390).
Directions: M4 jct 19 onto M32, off at jct 1 onto A4174 follow signs for Downend then Mangotsfield. Continue through town, road becomes Carsons Road, ground on right after factory.
Colours: Maroon & sky/maroon/sky **Change Colours:** Yellow/black/black
Previous Name: R.W.P. (pre-1986) **Previous Ground:** St Johns Lane 62-66. **Clubhouse:** Yes.

DURSLEY TOWN

Secretary: Phil James, 8 Meadow Vale, Tilsdown, Dursley, Glos. GL11 6HJ (01453 547413).
Ground: Memorial Ground, Kingshill Road, Dursley, Glos. (01453 546122) **Founded:** 1893.
Colours: Red & black/black/black **Change Colours:** Blue & black/black/black

ELLWOOD

Secretary: Ian Edwards, 24 Forest Road, Milkwall, Coleford, Glos Gl16 7LB (01594 833585)
Ground: Bromley Rd, Ellwood, Coleford, Glos (01594 832927).
Directions: B4234 to Parkend then B4431 up hill to next crossroads, turn left - ground half mile on left.
Colours: Blue/black/black **Change Colours:** Red/black/black

FRAMPTON ATHLETIC

Secretary: Keith Potter, 117 Goldcrest Road, Chipping Sodbury, Bristol BS17 6XN
Ground: Beesmoor Road, Frampton Cotterill, Bristol
Colours: Red/black/red **Change colours:** Black & white/black/black

HENBURY OLD BOYS

Secretary: C B Barron, 126 Charlton Rd, Westbury-on-Trym, Bristol BS10 6NL (01179 504002).
Ground: Arnall Drive Playing Fields, Henbury, Bristol (01179 590475). **Founded:** 1962
Directions: M5 jct 17, down Cribbs Causeway, into Station Road, left into Henbury Rd, ground on left.
Colours: Amber & black/black/amber & black **Change Colours:** Red & black/black/red & black.
Hons: Avon Combination 82-83 (Lg Cup 83-84), Glos Snr Amtr Cup South, Fry Club Cup 92-93.

HIGHRIDGE UNITED

OLD GEORGIANS

Secretary: B M Latchem, 87 Vicarage Rd, Whitehall, Bristol BS5 9AQ (01179 556292).
Ground: St George's School PF, Johnsons Lane, Whitehall, Bristol (01179 516888).
Directions: M32 jct 2, left, left, right at lights, right behind Kings Head. Buses 6 or 7 from central Bristol. One mile from Stapleton Road (BR).
Colours: Azure & navy/navy/navy **Change Colours:** Red/red/white
Hons: Glos Co. Lg 82-83 84-85 (R-up 83-84 92-93), Glos Chal. Tphy, Glos Snr Amtr Cup Sth, FA Vase QF 83-84.

PATCHWAY TOWN

Secretary: R Stewart, 22 Arlingham Way, Patchway, Bristol, BS12 5NQ (01179 792983).
Ground: 'Scott Park', Coniston Rd, Patchway, Bristol (01179 691203)
Directions: M5 jct 16, A38 towards Bristol, right into Coniston Road, ground signposted Scott Park.
Colours: Black & white stripes/black/black **Change Colours:** Red/white/black
Hons: Glos County Lg 91-92

PUCKLECHURCH SPORTS

Secretary: R B Savage, 54 Shortwood Rd, Pucklechurch, Bristol BS17 3RN (01179 373972).
Ground: Recreation Ground, Pucklechurch, Bristol (01275 822102).
Directions: M32 jct 1 follow A4174 through Downend to Mangotsfield, left signposted Pucklechurch, continue to village, turn right, ground on left.
Seats: No **Cover:** None **Clubhouse:** Yes **Prog:** 32 pages,40p **Editor:** M Dowse.
Colours: All green **Change Colours:** White/white/green.
Hons: Avon Comb. 77-78 78-79 87-88 (Div 2 66-67, Lg Cup 77-78 78-79 87-88), Glos Jnr Cup 65-66 82-83, Bristol & District Lg 72-73.

TOTTERDOWN P.O.B.

Secretary: Brian Truman, 10 Elmore Road, Patchway, Bristol BS12 5LL (0117 976 0386)
Ground: City & Port of Bristol Sports Ground, Nibley Rd, Shirehampton, Bristol.
Directions: 5 mins walk from Shirehampton (BR) station (Temple Meads-Severn Beach line).
Colours: Red/navy/navy. **Change Colours:** Yellow/blue/blue.
Prevous Names: Totterdown Ath., Port of Bristol - clubs merged 1994. *Notes below apply to Totterdown.*
Prev. Lge: Bristol & Suburban (pre'93) **Hons:** Bristol & Suburban Lg R-up 92-93.
Previous Ground: Bristol & West Indian Cricket Ground, Gordon PF, Gordon Rd, Whitehall, Bristol (pre-1994).

TYRINGTON ROCKS

VINEY ST SWITHINS

Secretary: Alex Thomas, 28 Allaston Road, Lydney, Glos GL15 5ST (01594 843634)
Ground: Viney Sports & Social Club, Viney Hill, Lydney, Glos.
Colours: Red & black/black/red **Change colours:** Blue & white/blue/blue

WINTERBOURNE UNITED

Secretary: John Lloyd, 9 Stanford Close, Frampton Cotterill, Bristol BS17 2DG (01454 775841)
Ground: The Rec, Parkside Road, Winterbourne, Bristol
Colours: White with blue trim/black/black **Change colours:** Blue & black/black/blue

WOTTON ROVERS

Secretary: M P Excell, 94 Bearlands, Wotton-under-Edge, Glos. GL12 7SB (01453 845178).
Ground: Synwell Playing Field, Synwell Lane, Wotton-under-Edge (01453 842929).
Directions: From Wotton war memorial down hill and follow Synwell Lane. Ground on left.
Seats: None **Cover:** No **Capacity:** 2,000 **Clubhouse:** Yes **Founded:** 1959.
Colours: All royal **Change Colours:** White/black/red
Record Gate: 2,000 **Programme:** 20 pages, 50p
Previous Names: Synwell Rovers (pre-1959)/ Wotton-under-Edge FC.

Some players are just all arms and legs!
Photo: (top) Roger Turner (bottom) Graham Cotterill

JEWSON SOUTH WESTERN FOOTBALL LEAGUE

Chairman: T Scott **Vice-Chairman:** Bob Bell
Hon. Secretary: Mrs Wendy Donohue
115 Longfield, Falmouth TR11 4SL
Tel/Fax: 01326 316642

The season climaxed on the last two matches in May, Falmouth Town won at Kiskeard Athletic but Truro City grabbed a late winner at home to Porthleven to take the league title from Falmouth, who had taken from Truro, on goal difference, last season!

Truro City also won the Cornwall Senior Cup Final, the game on Easter Monday against Porthleven was drawn but Truro won the replay. Both games were played at Falmouth.

The JSWL Challenge Cup Final also featured Truro City but this time Bodmin Town took the silverware. This final was staged at Blaise Park, St Blazey.

Truro took the league title, Falmouth were second, Porthleven third and St Blazey fourth. Tavistock and Launceston will have to apply for re-election.

There will be one new team in the league for next season, Plymouth Parkway having been successful in their application to transfer from the Devon League to the JSWL.

FINAL LEAGUE TABLE 1997-98

	P	*W*	*D*	*L*	*F*	*A*	*Pts*
Truro City	30	23	3	4	76	15	72
Falmouth Town	30	22	5	3	76	33	71
Porthleven	30	20	6	4	88	25	66
St Blazey	30	16	3	11	60	39	51
Torpoint Athletic	30	15	4	11	72	56	49
Millbrook	30	14	7	9	52	42	49
Bodmin Town	30	15	4	11	51	48	49
Penzance	30	13	8	9	54	47	47
Saltash United	30	14	3	13	64	60	45
Holsworthy	30	13	5	12	61	68	44
Wadebridge	30	11	2	17	40	53	35
Liskeard Athletic	30	7	6	17	45	63	27
Newquay	30	8	3	19	37	73	27
St Austell	30	5	8	17	33	82	23
Tavistock	30	3	6	21	38	87	15
Launceston	30	3	3	24	27	84	12

* Denotes points adjustment

CLUB DIRECTORY 1998-99

BODMIN TOWN

Chairman: C.Hooper. **Vice-Chairman:** P.Lee. **President:** A.Gynn.
Secretary: David Sandry, 21 Rock Lane, Bodmin PL31 1NR (01208 75248).
Manager: Ricky Cardew. **Asst Manager:** Phil Brown. **Physio:** Jim Brewer
Ground: Priory Park (01208 78165) - Just off town centre in large park complex, at rear of town car park.
Capacity: **Cover:** Grandstand **Seats:** Yes **Floodlights:** Yes **Founded:** 1889
Colours: Yellow & black/black/yellow **Change colours:** All white
Programme: 20 pages, 30p **Programme Editor:** Secretary **Club Shop:** No.
Sponsors: Gynn Construction **Nickname:** Black & Ambers
Midweek home matchday: Wednesday **Reserve team's League:** East Cornwall Premier.
Clubhouse: Mon-Fri 6.30-11pm (matchdays 6-11), Fri-Sat noon-11pm, Sun noon-3 & 7-10.30pm (except when Sky matches are on then 12 noon-10.30 p.m.). Bar snacks available most times.
Honours: South Western Lg 90-91 93-94 (R-up 76-77,92-93,94-95,Lg Cup 93-94 (R-up 77-78 88-89 94-95), Cornwall Snr Cup R-up 93-94, Cornwall Charity Cup 86-87 89-90.Cornish Guardian E.C.P.L.Supplimentary Cup 91-92 (R-Up. 93-94),Gordon Sweet Cup 90-91,92-93.

FALMOUTH TOWN

Chairman: Malcolm Newland **Vice Chairman:** Paul Ashburn **President:** Seb Coe.
Secretary: David Woon,Llamedos,Mount Stephens Lane,Falmouth,Cornwall TR11 2LJ (01326 315151(H)
Manager: Ray Nicholls **Asst Manager:** Dave Ball. **Coach:** Keith Barker
Ground: Bickland Park, Bickland Vale, Falmouth, Cornwall (01326 375156).
Directions: Follow A39 to Tregoniggie Industrial Estate - will pass ground on left. One and a half miles from Penmere Halt (BR) on Falmouth-Truro branch line. Bus service from town centre.
Seats: 300 **Cover:** 1,200 **Capacity:** 6,000 **Floodlights:** Yes **Club Shop:** TBA
Programme: 16 pages, 30p **Editor/Press Officer:** Mike Odgers (01209 715766).
Colours: Amber/black **Change colours:** Red/white.
Nickname: Town **Club Sponsors:** Stralfors/ Diadora. **Founded:** 1949.
Midweek home matchday: Tues/Wed **Reserve team's League:** Jollys Cornwall Comb.
Record Gate: 6,300 v Oxford United, FA Cup 1st Round 3/11/62.
Best FA Cup season: 1st Round 62-63 (lost 1-2 v Oxford United) 67-68 (lost 2-5 at Peterborough Utd).
Best FA Vase season: Quarter-Final replay 86-87 (lost 0-1 after 1-1 draw at St Helens Town).
Best FA Trophy season: 2nd Round proper 77-78.
Previous Leagues: Cornish Snr 50-51/ South Western 51-74/ Western 74-83.
Players progressing to Football League: Roy Carter (Hereford 1975), Joe Scott (Bournemouth 1978), Tony Kellow (Exeter 1976), John Hodge (Exeter 1991).
Clubhouse: Mon-Fri 7-11pm, Sat 12-11pm, Sun 12-3 & 7-10.30pm. Meals available.
Club Record Scorer: Joe Scott 198, 72-78 **Club Record Appearances:** Keith Manley 580 (appr) 70-83.
Honours: Cornish Snr Cup(10) 61-62 64-66 67-68 70-71 73-74 75-79 (R-up(7) 66-67 72-73 81-83 89-92), Western Lg(4) 74-78 (Lg Cup 74-75, Alan Young Cup 74-75 75-76 77-78(joint)), South Western Lg(12) 61-62 65-66 67-68 70-74 85-87 88-90 91-92 (R-up 58-59 64-65 69-70 87-88, Lg Cup(10) 57-59 61-63 67-68 70-71 85-86 90-92 (R-up(5) 59-60 71-72 86-88 92-93)), Pratten Cup 73-74, Cornwall Charity Cup 59-60 94-95, Cornwall Comb.(res) 83-84 (Supplementary Cup 93-94 (R-up 90-91)).

HOLSWORTHY

Manager: Peter England. **Assistant Manager:** Alan Mayes.
Secretary: Rob Moores, Rydon View, Central Avenue, Holsworthy, EX22 6DB (01409 253982).
Ground: Upcott Field (01409 254295) **Nickname:** The Magpies. **Cover:** Yes **Floodlights:** No.
Programme:28 pages, £2 with entry **Editor:** Terry Trewin.& Bob Thomson.
Colours: Black & White/Black/black & white **Change colours:** Gold/white/gold. **Nickname:** Magpies
Hons: Devon Snr Cup 53-54 (Prem. Cup 71-72 78-79),Devon Junior Cup 38-39.

LAUNCESTON

Joint Chairman: Keith Ellacott, Alan Bradley **President:**
Secretary: Chris Martin, 3 Tavistock Road, Launceston, Cornwall PL15 9HA (01566 776175).
Manager: M Hocking **General Manager:** Keith Ellacott.
Physio: J Hayward **Ground:** Pennygillam, Launceston (0566 773279)
Directions: Follow signs to Pennygillam Industrial Est., just off main A30 - ground 400yds on left.
Programme: Yes **Seats:** 150 **Cover:** 150 **Floodlights:** Yes **Nickname:** Clarets
Cols: Claret & blue/blue/claret **Change:** Sky/Sky/claret
Midweek matchday: Tues/Wed **Club Shop:** No.
Sponsors: **Reserve team's League:** Plymouth & Dist.
Clubhouse: Open after every game. Bar meals.
Hons: S. Western Lg R-up 84-85, Cornish Snr Cup 1899-1900 00-01 82-83 (R-up 92-93, Charity Cup R-up 88-89).

LISKEARD ATHLETIC

Chairman: David Hick **Vice Chairman:** Dave Rawlings **President:** R.D.Burt.
Secretary: Adrian Wilton, Martina, Dawes Close, Dobwalls, Liskeard, Cornwall PL14 6JD (01579 20980).
Manager: Phil Sullivan. **Asst Manager:** Geof Battams. **Physio:**
Ground: Lux Park, Liskeard, Cornwall (01579 42665).
Directions: Take Tavistock Road (A390) from town centre, after 1/2 mile turn left on St Cleer Road (following signs to Lux Park Sports Complex) and the ground is 200 yards on left. Half mile from Liskeard BR station.
Seats: 100 **Cover:** 300 **Capacity:** 2,000 **Floodlights:** Yes **Club Shop:** No.
Programme: 40 pages, 50p **Editor:** D.J.Rawlings.
Colours: Blue & White/blue/blue & white **Change colours:** All white.
Sponsors: Aviation C.B.International/ Gilbert Outfitters. **Nickname:** Blues. **Formed:** 1889
Midweek matchday: Tuesday
Previous Leagues: East Cornwall Premier, Plymouth & District, South Western 66-79, Great Mills 79-95.
Players progressing to Football League: Bradley Swiggs.
Clubhouse: (01579 342665) Normal licensing hours. Hot & cold food available.
96-97 Captain: **96-97 Top Scorer:** **96-97 P.o.Y.:**
Club Record Goalscorer: Not known **Club Record Appearances:** Brian Bunney, 500+.
Hons: South Western Lg 76-77 78-79 (R-up 75-76 77-78; Lg Cup 76-77 78-79) Western Lg 87-88 (R-up 85-86 89-90, Merit Cup 80-81); Cornwall Snr Cup 04-05 83-84 84-85 85-86 88-89 89-90 93-94 (R-up 70-71 75-76 76-77 78-79 94-95); Cornwall Charity Cup 21-22 79-80, Cornwall Jnr Cup 05-06 13-14 26-27; SW Pratten Cup 78-79; E Cornwall Prem RAOB Cup 67-68, Plymouth & Dist. Lg 60-61 (Div 1 59-60 (R-up 54-55 73-74), Div 2 76-77(Res)), Victory Cup 60-61, Charity Cup 59-60), E Cornwall Prem. Lg (Reserves) 84-85 92-93 93-94(Lg.Cup 88-89 93-94).

MILLBROOK

President: Mrs E Weekes **Chairman:** Mr J Weekes **Vice Chairman:** Mr K Townsend.
Secretary: Bob Bell, 15 Carew Close, Crafthole, Cornwall PL11 3EB (01503 230953)
Manager: Mr J Bennett **Asst Manager:** Mr S Matthews **Press Officer:** Mr W Linney.
Ground: Mill Park, Millbrook, Cornwall (0752 822113)
Directions: From Torpoint Ferry - 3 miles to Antony on A374, fork left, after 1 mile turn left again and follow B3247 to Millbrook (3 miles), take road marked 'Town Centre Southdown', right at mini-r'bout after quarter mile, ground clearly visible. From Tamar Bridge - follow signs for Torpoint, 2 miles after Polbathic take right turning marked Millbrook, 5 miles to Millbrook then proceed as above.
Capacity: **Seats:** None **Cover:** 200 **Floodlights:** Yes **Founded:** 1973.
Colours: White & Black/black/red **Change colours:** Sky/white/white **Nickname:** The Brook
Previous Leagues: Plymouth Comb.(8yrs)/ Plymouth & Dist.(6yrs).
Programme: 20 pages, 10p **Editor:** Mr J Weekes (0752 822637) **Club Shop:** No.
Sponsors: Plymouth Boat Cruises Ltd.
Midweek matchday: Tuesday **Reserve's League:** Plymouth & District.
Clubhouse: Weekdays 7-11pm, Sat 11am-11pm, Sun noon-3 & 7.30-10.30. Hot food (chips, burgers etc) available during and after matchdays.
Club record scorer: Unknown **Club record appearances:** John Horne 215.
Hons: South Western Lg R-up 81-82, Cornwall Snr Cup R-up 83-84 (Charity Cup 84-85, Jnr Cup 75-76), Plymouth & District Lg 80-81 (Div 1 R-up 76-77).

NEWQUAY

Chairman: A Kendall **Vice-Chairman:** J.Lugg. **President:** J L Parker
Secretary: John Hawkey, 16 Higher Tower Rd, Newquay, Cornwall.TR7 1QL (01637 871884)
Mgr/Coach: Graham Nicholls **Asst Manager:** Andy Mattock **Physio:** Ross McOpie
Ground: Mount Wise, Newquay (01637 872935)
Directions: 1/2 mile from Newquay BR, follow 1-way system for 1/2 miles - grd signed on left before Windsor Hotel.
Seats: 250 **Cover:** 500 **Capacity:** 4,000 **Floodlights:** Yes **Club Shop:** No
Programme: 16 pages, 30p **Editor:** M Lowry **Press Officer:**
Colours: Red & white stripes **Change colours:** Sky & navy
Sponsors: Studs Sports **Nickname:** Peppermints **Founded:** 1890.
Midweek Matchday: **Reserve League:** Cornwall Combination.
Previous Leagues: West Cornwall/ Plymouth & District 21-27/ Cornish Senior 31-51.
Players progressing to Football League: Chris Morris (Sheffield Wednesday, Celtic & Eire), David Philp (Plymouth Argyle), Kevin Miller (Exeter City,Birmingham C,Watford), John Hodge (exeter City,Swansea).
Clubhouse: 7-11pm w/days, 12-11pm Sat, 12-3 & 7-10.30pm Sun. Hot & cold snacks after matchs.
96-97 Captain: **96-97 P.o.Y.:** **96-97 Top Scorer:**
Hons: FA Vase 3rd Rd 90-91, Cornish Snr Cup 34-35 52-53 54-55 56-57 91-92 (R-up(9) 05-07 08-09 25-26 33-34 35-36 57-58 69-70 84-85), S. Western Lg(7) 58-60 77-78 79-80 81-82 83-84 87-88 (R-up 57-58 85-86 94-95, Lg Cup 55-56 88-89 (R-up(4) 56-58 79-81), Cornish Charity Cup(13) 06-07 08-09 53-56 57-59 62-63 69-70 74-75 76-78 88-89 (R-up(9) 07-08 20-21 56-57 60-61 73-74 75-76 81-82 84-86), W. Cornwall Lg 06-07 (R-up(2) 07-09), Cornish Snr Lg Herald Cup 34-35 (R-up(7) 33-34 35-36 49-51 55-57 58-59).

PENZANCE

President: Len Stanbury **Chairman:** Jim Dann
Secretary: Jim Dann, Carthew Farm, Newbridge, Penzance, Cornwall, TR20 8QL (01736 62749)
Manager: Martin Smith **Coach:** T.B.A. **Trainer:** Ken Prowse.
Ground: Penlee Park (0736 61964) **Floodlights:** Yes **Seats:** Yes **Founded:** 1888.
Directions: Seafront road past harbour, after amusement arcade turn right at r'bout (Alexander Rd), ground second right. Fifteen minutes walk from Penzance (BR); directions as above.
Colours: Black & white/black/black **Change colours:** All yellow **Nickname:** Magpies.
Clubhouse: Yes **Reserve team's league:** Cornwall Comb.
Players progressing to Football League: Gerry Gazzard (Brentford), Tony Kellow (Exeter).
Hons: Cornish Snr Cup 1892-93 95-96 97-98 98-99 1903-04 07-08 47-48 60-61 72-73 80-81 (R-up 1896-97 99-1900 00-01 04-05 48-49 49-50 54-55 56-57 74-75), South Western Lg 55-56 56-57 74-75 (Lg Cup R-up 60-61), Cornwall Charity Cup 47-48 48-49 (R-up 21-22 63-64), Cornwall Snr Lg Div 2 57-58 (Div 2 Cup 53-54 54-55), Cornwall Comb. R-up 65-66 (Lg Cup 69-70 (R-up 81-82)), Cornwall Jnr Cup (West) 03-04 04-05 05-06 07-08 09-10.

PLYMOUTH PARKWAY FC

Chairman: M Rowles **Manager:** G Baggott
Secretary: Stuart Cadmore, 25 Dudley Gardens, Eggbuckland, Plymouth PL6 5PE (01752 782661)
Ground: The Parkway, Ernesettle Lane, Plymouth, (01752 363080 Clubhouse)
Directions: From Tamar Bridge, 1st exit signed St Budeaux/Ernesettle, 1st exit at roundabout, followung Ernesettle Ind Est. Ground at bottom of hill on right.
Colours: Yellow/royal/white **Change colours:** Azure/black

PORTHLEVEN

President: Mr W O Allen **Chairman:** Mr W Tearney **Vice Chairman:** Mr L Williams
Secretary: Vidal James, 11 Primrose Close, Weeth Park, Camborne, TR14 7HS (01209 710618) 561160).
Manager: Trevor Mewton **Coach:** Paul Christie **Comm. Mgr:** Mr V James.
Ground: Gala Parc, Mill Lane, Porthleven (0208 574754).
Directions: From Penzance on A394, B3304 into Porthleven, ground on left immediately before town. From Helston on B3304 ground on right as you exit town. Buses from Helston and Penzance.
Capacity: **Seats:** None **Cover:** Yes **Floodlights:** No. **Programme:** 20p
Colours: Amber/black **Change colours:** All blue **Nickname:** Fishermen
Previous Leagues: West Penwith/ Cornwall Snr/ South Western 66-77/ Cornwall Combination 77-89.
Reserves' Lge: Cornwall Comb. **Previous Grounds:** Treza Downs/ Sunset Farm.
Clubhouse: Mon-Fri 7-11pm, Sat 11am-8pm, Sun 11am-3 & 7-10.30pm. Full food menu.
Hons: Sth Western Lg R-up 72-73, Cornwall Comb.(6),(Lg Cup(6), Cornwall Charity Cup 70-71, Cornwall Snr Cup R-up 68-69, George Evely Cup 64-65 65-66 83-84 86-87, West Penwith Lg, Penzance Hosp. Cup, Penzance Charity Cup.

SALTASH UNITED

President: P Skinnard **Chairman:** M Howard **Manager:** Leigh Cooper
Secretary: P J Gammage, 23 Spire Hill Park, Saltash, Cornwall, PL12 4SR (01752 844046).
Ground: Kimberley Stadium, Callington Road, Saltash, Cornwall (01752 845746).
Directions: First left after crossing Tamar Bridge, through town centre, at top of town fork right at mimi r'bout, ground 400 yds ahead on left.
Seats: 250 **Cover:** 250 **Capacity:** 3,000 **Floodlights:** Yes **Formed:** 1945.
Programme: 40 pages, 40p **Editor:** Marian Gammage.
Colours: Red/Black/Black **Change:** Blue & gold/blue/gold
Nickname: The Ashes **Midweek Matcheday:** Wednesday
Previous Leagues: Cornwall Snr/Sth Western 51-59 62-76/E Cornwall Prem 59-62/Gt Mills West 76-95.
Clubhouse: Club attached to stand and caters for dancing and club activities.Saphire Lounge caters for wedding receptions,quiz nights and private functions etc.
Hons: Cornwall Snr Lg 49-50 50-51, Western Lg 84-85 86-87 88-89 (R-up 83-84 87-88, Lg Cup 86-87 87-88 (R-up 88-89), Div 1 76-77, Merit Cup 79-80 87-88), Sth Western Lg 53-54 75-76 (R-up 3), Lg Cup 3, Cornwall Snr Cup 6.

St AUSTELL

Chairman: Colin Marshall **Asst Chairman:** Derek Silk
Secretary: Peter Beard, 24 Alexandra Rd, St Austell, Cornwall PL25 4QP (01726 64138).
Manager: John Peters **Asst Manager:** Colin Bunney **Physio:** N McKenna
Ground: Poltair Park (0726 77099). **Directions:** 5 mins walk north of St Austell (BR).
Seats: 200 **Cover:** 300 **Capacity:** 8,000 **Floodlights:** No **Founded:** 1890.
Colours: White/black/black **Change colours:** Blue/black/blue.
Previous Leagues: Rocky Park (1890s) **Record Gate:** 15,000 v Penzance, Senior Cup 49.
Hons: S West Lg 68-69 (R-up 4), Lg Cup 64-65 71-73 87-88 (R-up 4), Cornish Snr Cup(11)

St BLAZEY

Vice Chairman: Mr P Clemow. **President:** K.Cocks. **Chairman:** Mr H Cooke
Secretary: Ken Cocks, 20 North St Tywardreath, Par, Cornwall PL24 2PN (01726 815187)
Manager: Trevor Mewton **Coach:** Gareth Lobb. **Physio:** T.B.A.
Ground: St Blaise Park, Station Road, St Blazey (01726 814110).
Directions: A390 Liskeard-St Austell road, turn into Station Road at lights in St Blazey village; ground 100 yards on left. One and a half miles from Par (BR).
Seats: 200 **Cover:** 700 **Capacity:** 3,500 **Floodlights:** Yes **Founded:** 1896.
Colours: All Green & black **Change colours:** Blue & white/blue/blue **Nickname:** Saints
Programme: 24 pages, 30p **Editor:** M.Newcombe(011726 815964) **Club Shop:** No.
Sponsors: Express Joinery **Record Gate:** 6,500 v St Austell, Cornwall Snr Cup 48-49.
Midweek matchday: Wednesday **Reserve's League:** East Cornwall Premier.
Clubhouse: Mon-Thurs 11am-3pm & 7-11pm, Fri-Sat 11-11.45pm, Sun noon-3pm & 7-11pm. Bar snacks.
Club record scorer: B Tallamy **Club record appearances:** W Isbell.
Hons: South Western Lg 6, (R-up 9), Lg Cup 5, (R-up 5), Cornish Snr Cup 8, Cornish Charity Cup 35-36 56-57 83-84, Cornwall Snr Lg Cup (Herald Cup) 35-36 48-49.

TAVISTOCK

President: **Chairman:** R A Fenner **Vice Chairman:** D R D Pethick
Secretary: Philip Lowe, 1 Bainbridge Court, Colebrook, Plympton, PL7 4HH (01752 335273).
Manager: Steve Metters **Asst Manager:** Jerry Collins. **Coach:** Les Mewton.
Physio: Les Mewton **Press Officer:** Chairman.
Ground: Langsford Park, Crowndale Rd, Tavistock (01822 614447)
Directions: A386 from Plymouth, left after Ford garage into Crowndale Rd, ground half mile on left.
Capacity: 2,000 **Seats:** 200 **Cover:** 200 **Floodlights:** Yes **Founded:** 1888.
Colours: Red & Black/black/black. **Change colours:** All Blue
Programme: 32 pages, with entry **Editor:** Secretary **Club Shop:** No.
Sponsors: Dave Carter Spts, Plymouth **Record Gate:** 5,000 v Calstock, Bedford Cup final 1952.
Midweek matchday: Wednesday. **Reserve's League:** Plymouth & Dist **Nickname:** 'Tavy' or 'Lambs'
Players progressing to Football League: Peter, Neil Langman (Plymouth, 51 53).
Clubhouse: Open all day Saturday and evenings 6.30-10.30 or 11pm. Hot & cold food
Club record appearances: A Pethick 1,000+.
Hons: Devon Premier Cup 90-91 (R-up 94-95), Devon Snr Cup 1889-90 1968-69 77-78 81-82, South Western Lg Cup 68-69 (R-up 76-77 83-84), Bedford Cup on numerous occasions.

TORPOINT ATHLETIC

Manager: Phil Cardew
Secretary: Vic Grimwood, 43 Henerdon Heights, Plympton PL7 3EY (01752 81344).
Ground: Mill Field (01752 812889)
Directions: Bear left from Torpoint ferry, ground down hill on left after half a mile.
Clubhouse: Yes **Programme:** Yes **Seats:** Yes **Cover:** Yes **Floodlights:** No
Colours: Gold & black stripes/black/gold **Change colours:** White & Black/White/White.
Previous League: Plymouth & District League.(Premier)
Best FA Vase season: 4th Round 93-94 (lost 0-3 at home to Diss Town, eventual winners).
Hons: South Western Lg 64-65 66-67 (Lg Cup R-up 65-66), Cornish Snr Cup 8.

TRURO CITY

Manager: Graeme Kirkup
Secretary: Ray Rowe, 5 Alverton Gardens, Truro, Cornwall TR1 1JA (01872 270684)
Ground: Treyew Road, Truro, Cornwall (01872 278853) **Seats:** Yes **Floodlights:** Yes.
Directions: On A39 by-pass south of city. 10 mins walk from BR station; up hill and left at junction.
Colours: Red & black/black/black **Change colours:** All white
Reserve Team's League: Jolly's Cornwall Combination.
Hons: South Western Lg 60-61 69-70 92-93 95-96 97-98, (R-up 54-55 62-63 66-67 67-68 70-71 96-97), Lg Cup 59-60 66-67(jt) 92-93 (R-up 54-55 58-59 67-68 93-94 95-96 97-98); Cornish Snr Cup 13; Cornish Charity Cup 7; Cornish Snr Lg 31-32 32-33; Cornwall Comb.

WADEBRIDGE TOWN

Manager: Robbie Black.
Secretary: Barry Cudmore, 3 Marine Terrace, Wadebridge, Cornwall PL27 7AJ (0208 813826).
Ground: Bodieve Park (0208 812537) **Seats:** Yes **Cover:** Ample **Floodlights:** No
Directions: At junction of A39 and B3314 to east of Wadebridge. **Nickname:** Bridgers.
Colours: Red & White/red/red **Change colours:** All blue.
Reserve Team's League: East Cornwall Premier.
Hons: South Western Lg R-up 68-69 78-79 79-80 (Lg Cup 5), (R-up 3), Cornish Snr Cup 79-80, Cornish Charity Cup 8,

WESTWARD DEVELOPMENTS DEVON COUNTY LEAGUE

Chairman: David Moore **Vice Chairman:** Stephen Ware

Secretary: Phillip Hiscox
18 Ivy Close, Wonford, Exeter EX2 5LX Tel/Fax: 01392 493995

FINAL LEAGUE TABLE 1997-98

	P	W	D	L	F	A	Pts
Topsham Town	38	27	4	7	97	30	85
Cullompton Rgrs	38	25	7	6	95	35	82
Newton Abbot	38	25	6	7	84	40	81
Willand Roves	38	22	9	7	88	32	75
Stoke Gabriel	38	20	9	9	85	41	69
Appledore BAAC	38	20	6	12	94	71	66
Plymouth Comm.	38	19	9	10	97	77	66
Budleigh Salt.	38	19	7	12	84	66	64
Dartmouth Utd	38	18	9	11	82	54	63
Plymouth Pkway	38	17	11	10	87	57	62
Ottery St Mary	38	18	6	14	72	61	60
Newton St Cyres	38	13	7	18	63	79	46
Alphington	38	10	11	17	56	79	41
Buckfastleigh R	38	11	7	20	56	85	40
Newton Abbot Sp	38	10	7	21	63	81	37
Teignmouth	38	11	1	26	59	122	*31
Elburton Villa	38	8	6	24	45	86	30
Weston Mill O V	38	9	3	26	51	98	30
Plymstock Utd	38	7	4	27	57	114	25
Ivybridge Town	38	6	1	31	50	157	*16

* Points deducted

WESTWARD DEVELOPMENTS DEVON COUNTY LEAGUE HONOURS

	Champions	*Runners-up*
1992-93	Buckfastleigh	Newton Abbot
1993-94	Newton Abbot	Stoke Gabriel
1994-95	Stoke Gabriel	Alphington
1995-96	Budleigh Salterton	Stoke Gabriel
1996-97	Stoke Gabriel	Dartmouth United
1997-98	Topsham Town	Cullompton Rangers

DEVON COUNTY LEAGUE CUP COMPETITION HONOURS

	Winners	*Runners-up*
1992-93	Newton Abbot	Willand Rovers
1993-94	Alphington	Willand Rovers
1994-95	Elburton Villa	Weston Mill Oak Villa
1995-96	Topsham Town	Newton Abbot
1996-97	Topsham Town	Dartmouth United
1997-98	Stoke Gabriel	Budleigh Salterton

DEVON COUNTY LEAGUE OTHER HONOURS

CHARITY SHIELD

1994	Alphington and Newton Abbot (shared)
1995	Stoke Gabriel
1996	Budleigh Salterton and Topsham Town (shared)
1997	Topsham Town

SPORTSMANSHIP CUP

1993	Newton St Cyres
1994	Stoke Gabriel
1995	Stoke Gabriel
1996	Plymouth Command
1997	Plymouth Command
1998	Plymouth Command

HOSPITALITY SHIELD

1995	Willand Rovers
1996	Budleigh Salterton
1997	Ottery St Mary
1998	Stoke Gabriel

PROGRAMME AWARD

1993	Plymstock United
1994	No Contest
1995	No Contest
1996	Stoke Gabriel
1997	Newton Abbot Spurs
1998	Budleigh Salterton/ Newton Abbot Spurs

GROUND HOP '99

"End of a Millennium"

Friday 2nd April

12.00	Dartmouth Utd	v	Newton Abbot Spurs
4.00	Vospers Oak Villa	v	Buckfastleigh Rangers
6.45	Plymouth Command	v	Plymstock United

Saturday 3rd April

12.00	Stoke Gabriel	v	Alphington
3.30	Newton Abbot	v	Cullompton Rangers
7.00	Crediton United	v	Topsham Town

Sunday 4th April

11.00		TBA	
2.00	Appledore	v	Newton Abbot Spurs

These fixtures have been nationally advertised and cannot be changed under any circumstances

ALPHINGTON

Secretary: Nick Cain, 49 Fairfield Rd Alphington, Exeter EX2 8UF (01392 491652)

Ground: The Chronicles, Church Road, Alphington (01392 279556)

Directions: From M5/A30/A38 follow signs for Marsh Barton

Colours: Amber/black/black

Change colours: Blue/white/orange

Previous League: Devon & Exeter.

Hons: Devon County Lg Cup 93-94.

APPLEDORE & BIDEFORD AAC

Secretary: Eddie Nichols, 14 Alexandra Terrace, Bideford, EX39 2PL (01237 475493)

Ground: Marshford, (01237 477099). **Directions:** From Bideford the ground is on the A386

Colours: Amber/black/amber

Change: All Blue

BUCKFASTLEIGH RANGERS

Secretary: Linda Tope, 27 Villiers Close, Plymstock, Plymouth PL9 7QP (01752 493105)

Ground: Duckspond Playing Fields, Buckfastleigh, Devon

Directions: On east side of A3380, just off main A38, to south of Buckfastleigh village centre.

Colours: Green/black/black

Change colours: Yellow/blue/blue

Hons: Devon County Lg 92-93.

BUDLEIGH SALTERTON A.F.C.

Secretary: Nick Pannell, 33 Armytage Road, Budleigh Salterton, Devon, EX9 6SD, (01395 445877).

Ground: Greenway Lane, Budleigh Salterton (01395 443850). **Directions:** Immediately before Budleigh turn left to Knowle Village, 2nd right (Bedlands Lane), left at school then right into Greenway Lane.

Colours: All Red & white

Change colours: All blue

CREDITON UNITED

Secretary: Tony Sheriff

Ground: Lords Meadow (01363 774671)

Directions: From Exeter A377, turn right at Crown Pub, follow road, right sign Sports Centre ground on left by phone box

Colours: Yellow & green/green/yellow

Change Colours: All blue

CULLOMPTON RANGERS

Secretary: Marcus Scott, 13 Chestnut Ave, Cullompton, EX15 1ES (01884 432662)

Ground: Speeds Meadow, Duke Street, Cullompton, Devon.

Directions: M5 jct 28, head for town centre, turn left, through thru town centre for 1 mile, left into Meadow Lane, past sports centre, right at T-junction, left after 100yds and follow signs.

Colours: Red/black/red

Change colours: Yellow/blue/blue

Nickname: Rangers

Hons: Devon & Exeter Lg 61-62 63-64, Snr Div 59-60 78-79; East Devon Snr Cup 83-84; Devon Premier Cup R-up 84-85; Axminster Hosp. Cup 92-93.

DARTMOUTH UNITED F.C.

Secretary: Kath Greeno, 79 Victoria Rd, Dartmouth, Devon, TQ6 9RX, (01803 834421)

Ground: Longcross, (01803 832902). **Directions:** From Totnes ground is on road into Dartmouth, after Mobil garage take next right (Milton Lane), the 1st right.

Colours: Black & white/black/white

Change colours: Blue/white/black

ELBURTON VILLA

Secretary: Yvonne Westcott, 4 Gara Close, Elburton, Plymouth PL9 8UN, (01752 405474).

Ground: Haye Road, Elburton, Plymouth. (01752 480025). **Directions:** From Plymouth take dual-carriageway to Elburton. Left at 2nd r/about, ground 50 yards left.

Colours: Red/white/black

Change colours: Yellow/blue/white.

IVYBRIDGE TOWN

Secretary: Garfield Goodwin, 36 Longwood Close, Plympton, Plymouth PL7 2HD (01752 344364)

Ground: Erme Playing Fields, Ivybridge (01752 892584).

Directions: Coming from Plymouth on A38 take Ivybridge turn, double back over A38 and take 1st left - ground entrance quarter mile on right after Industrial Estate.

Colours: Green & white/white/green

Change colours: Yellow/green/yellow

NEWTON ABBOT

Secretary: Roy Perkins, 21 Prospect Terrace, Newton Abbot, Devon, TQ12 2LN (01626 61596).

Ground: The Playing Fields, Coach Rd, Newton Abbot (01626 335011).

Directions: Half mile off the Torquay Road leading to Newton Abbot centre, past Ford Park tennis courts.

Colours: Red & black/black/black

Change colours: Black & white/white/white

Hons: Devon Co. Lg 93-94 (R-up 92-93, Lg Cup 92-93), Devon Prem. Cup R-up 82-83 87-88 (Snr Cup R-up 90-91.

NEWTON ABBOTT SPURS

Secretary: Mark Hayman, 9 Shapley Way, Liverton, Newton Abbott TQ12 6PN (01626 821839)
Ground: Recreation Ground, Newton Abbott (01626 65343)
Directions: After racecourse take 1st exit at next roundabout, 200 yards turn right at signpost Rec Trust.
Colours: All blue
Change Colours: Red/black/red

NEWTON St CYRES

Secretary: Roger Dymond, 12 New Estate, Newton St Cyres, Devon (01392 851719).
Ground: The Recreation Ground, Station Rd, Newton St Cyres, (01392 851546). **Directions:** A377 from Exeter towards Crediton, on reaching Newton Cyres proceed to village centre, turn right (signposted station) - grd 1/2 mile on right.
Colours: Blue & white/blue/blue
Change: Yellow & red/black/black **Nickname:** Saints
Hons: Devon Prem Cup 88-89, Snr Cup 74-75, I'med Cup 72-73; Devon & Exeter Lg 88-89 (Cup 88-89), E Devon Snr Cup (4).

OTTERY St MARY

Secretary: Derek Priest, The Granary, Ware Farm, Ottery St Mary EX11 1PJ (01404 815939)
Ground: Washbrook Meadows, Butts Road, Ottery St Mary, Devon EX11 1EL (01404 813539).
Directions: From main town square, turn left following road around church, 2nd right into Butts Rd. Or, B3177 to Ottery from A30 Honiton by-pass - ground on left past Otter workshops.
Colours: Blue & white/blue/blue
Change colours: All red
Nickname: The Otters
Hons: East Devon Snr Cup, Devon & Exeter Lg, Western Lg Div 1 89-90

PLYMOUTH COMMAND FC

Secretary: M.A.Launce, 57 Chaucer Way, Brake Farm, Plymouth, PL5 3EQ, (01752 700168)
Ground: HMS Drake (01752 555257). **Directions:** Follow signs for Naval Base (Weston Mill Entrance), report to gate.
Colours: Red/black/red
Change colours: Yellow & green/green/yellow

PLYMSTOCK UNITED

Secretary: Dave Baskwill, 334 Fort Austin Avenue, Crownhill, Plymouth PL6 5TG (01752 706284)
Ground: Deans Cross, Plymstock, Plymouth, Devon (01752 406776).
Directions: A38 Ernesettle junc, follow signs for Ind Est. ground half way down hill on right
Colours: Red & black/black/black
Change colours: White/red/red
Nickname: Reds.
Hons: Plymouth & Dist Lg (3), R-up (3); Devon Snr Cup R-up 87-88, Victory Cup (4), R-up (6)

STOKE GABRIEL

Secretary: John Webber, 47 Kingsway Ave, Paignton, TQ4 7AA (01803 843281)
Ground: G J Churchward Mem. Grnd, Broadley Lane, Stoke Gabriel, (01803 78223)
Directions: Turn right into Broadley Lane just before Four Crosses crossroads approaching from Paington.
Colours: Navy & red/blue/blue
Change colours: All Sky
Hons: Devon Premier Cup 93-94 (R-up 91-92), Devon County Lg R-up 93-94, Torbay Herald Cup 83-84 88-89, South Devon Lg 87-88 88-89 (Belli Cip 90-91),

TEIGNMOUTH

Secretary: Bob Haskell, 63 Oakland Road, Newton Abbott, TQ12 4EE (01626 363983)
Ground: Coombe Valley, Lower Combe Lane, Teignmouth, Devon (01626 776688).
Directions: From Newton Abbot: Turn left into Mill Lane 100yds past lights at Shaldon Bridge, right after 100yds into Fourth Ave., 2nd right, car park down hill on left.
Colours: White/black/black
Change colours: Red/white/red
Nickname: Teigns
Hons: Torbay Herald Cup 58-59 79-80 80-81, Sth Western Lg Cup R-up 85-86, Sth Devon Lg Div 1 85-86(res) 89-90, Devon County Lg Cup SF 93-94.

TOPSHAM TOWN

Secretary: Andrew James, Windfall, Station Rd, Broadclyst, Exeter EX5 3AZ (01392 468455)
Ground: Coronation Field, Exeter Road, Topsham (01392 873678). **Directions:** B3182 Exeter Topsham Rd, Ground is 3/4 mile after Countess Wear r/about.
Colours: All Blue
Change colours: Red/black/black

VOPERS OAK VILLA

Secretary: John Davey, 74 Molesworth Road, Plympton, Plymouth, PL7 4NU (01752 348301)
Ground: WMOV Sports Ground, Ferndale Rd, Weston Mill, Plymouth (01752 363352). **Direction:** A38 Devenport junc, at 1st lights turn left, ground 100 yards left.
Colours: Green & white/black/green
Change colours: Blue & yellow/blue/yellow
Hons: Devon County Lg Cup SF 93-94

WILLAND ROVERS

Secretary/Press Officer: Andrew Jarrett, 2 College Court, Uffculme, Cullompton Devon, EX15 3EQ (01884 841210).
Ground: Silver Street, Willand, nr Cullompton, Devon (01884 33885).
Directions: Ground situated on east side of B3181, halfway between M5 jcts 27 & 28.
Colours: White/black/black
Change colours: All blue
Nickname: Rovers
Hons: Devon Snr Cup 85-86, I'med Cup 66-67; Devon Co. Lg Cup R-up 92-93 93-94, Exeter & Dist. Lg Snr Div 1 70-71, Jnr Div 1 67-68, Div 2 64-65, Div 3 65-66, Prem Lg Cup 79-80; East Devon Snr Cup 72-73 91-92 93-94.

CLUBSAVER

HAMPSHIRE LEAGUE

FOUNDED 1896

Chairman: **N White**

Hon. Secretary: **J Moody**

13 Tadfield Crescent, Romsey, Hampshire. SO51 5AN. Tel: 01749 514073

	DIVISION ONE	P	W	D	L	F	A	**Pts**
1	Blackfield & Langley	38	31	5	2	146	47	98
2	Moneyfields	38	31	2	5	123	40	95
3	Poole Town	37	28	4	5	137	39	88
4	New Street	38	20	7	11	103	80	67
5	Brading Town	38	16	10	12	76	69	58
6	Horndean	37	16	7	14	83	99	55
7	Liss Athletic	38	16	6	16	69	67	54
8	Pirelli General	38	14	11	13	63	74	53
9	Colden Common	38	13	11	14	59	61	50
10	(Bass) Alton Town	38	13	10	15	67	69	49
11	Locksheath	38	13	7	18	64	81	46
12	Fleetlands	38	12	9	17	79	77	45
13	Stockbridge	38	14	3	21	77	90	45
14	Winchester City	38	12	7	19	63	78	43
15	Bishopstoke Social	38	12	6	20	66	102	42
16	Mayflower	38	10	10	18	72	94	40
17	Hayling United	38	10	8	20	51	100	38
18	AC Delco	38	9	8	21	52	88	35
19	Petersfield Town	38	9	7	22	63	118	34
20	Netley Central Sports	38	7	8	23	51	91	29

DIVISION TWO	P	W	D	L	F	A	Pts
Fleet Spurs	30	20	8	2	76	27	68
Vosper Thorneycroft	30	19	6	5	79	31	63
Otterbourne	30	17	5	8	63	42	56
Hilsea Club	30	15	7	8	69	46	52
Esso (Fawley)	30	13	7	10	52	47	46
Overton United	30	14	3	13	69	64	45
Hamble Club (-3 pts)	30	14	5	11	66	57	44
Yateley Green	30	13	3	14	55	66	42
Paulsgrove	30	12	4	14	52	55	40
Verwood Town	30	9	9	12	53	59	36
Winchester Castle	30	8	10	12	53	63	34
Tadley	30	9	7	14	48	73	34
Co-op Sports	30	8	8	14	48	62	32
Hythe & Dibden	30	8	4	18	45	84	28
New Milton Tn. (-3 pts)	30	7	6	17	48	59	24
Broughton	30	5	6	19	31	72	21

Malshanger & Ludgershall Sports records expunged.

DIVISION THREE	P	W	D	L	F	A	Pts
AFC Basingstoke	30	20	6	4	82	22	66
Queens Keep	30	19	4	7	84	45	61
Ordnance Survey	30	18	5	7	67	28	59
Ringwood Town	30	17	6	7	77	31	57
Clanfield	30	16	7	7	99	61	55
Awbridge	30	14	8	8	49	42	50
Bishops Waltham	30	13	10	7	58	47	49
Compton (-1 pt)	30	15	3	12	55	51	47
Hedge End	30	12	8	10	65	50	44
Covies	30	12	5	13	75	59	41
AFC Aldermaston	30	12	5	13	67	71	41
Four Marks	30	11	3	16	60	72	36
Laverstock Ford	30	8	7	15	58	74	31
Braishfield	30	5	5	20	45	117	20
Swanmere (-3 pts)	30	4	1	25	35	119	10
Basing Rovers (-3 pts)	30	2	1	27	42	131	4

DIVISION ONE CLUBS 1998-99

ALTON TOWN

Secretary: A J M Hillman, 19a Beechwood Rd, Alton, Hants GU34 1RL (01420 87103).
Ground: Bass Spts Ground, Anstey Rd, Alton (01420 82465).
Colours: Black & red/black/black **Change:** Blue & Yellow/Blue/Blue.
Programme: No **Midweek home matchday:** Any.

BISHOPSTOKE SOCIAL

Secretary: Tony Boland, 34 Fryern Close, Chandlers Ford, Hants SO50 2LF (01703 262763).
Ground: Chicken Hall Lane, Bishopstoke, Eastleigh, Hants (01860 612038).
Colours: Green & Black/Black/Black. **Change:** All Blue.

BLACKFIELD & LANGLEY

Secretary: Ian Hore, 5 Foxhayes Lane, Blackfield, Southampton, Hants SO45 2QD (01703 893325).
Ground: Gang Warily Rec., Newlands Rd, Blackfield, Southampton, Hants (01703 893603).
Colours: All Green. **Change:** Yellow/blue/blue
Programme: Yes **Midweek home matchday:** Wednesday.

BRADING TOWN

Secretary: Mick Edmondston, Seawinds, Nunwell St., Sandown.I.O.W. PO36 9DE (01983 404770)
Ground: Vicarage Lane, Brading, Isle of Wight (01983 405217).
Cols: All red. **Change:** All blue **Programme:** Yes

COLDEN COMMON

Secretary: M.Budden, 44 Orchard Close, Colden Common, Winchester, Hampshire.SO21 1ST (01962 713813)
Ground: Colden Common Recreation Ground, Main Road, Colden Common (01962 712365).
Colours: Red & white/black/red **Change:** All yellow
Programme: Yes **Midweek home matchday:** Wednesday.

FLEETLANDS

Secretary: David Bell, 72 White Hart Lane, Portchester, Hants. PO16 9BQ.(01705 321781)
Ground: Lederle Lane, Gosport, Hants (01329 239723).
Colours: Red & black/white/white **Change:** All white.
Programme: Yes **Midweek home matchday:** Any.

FLEET SPURS

Secretary: C R Filkins, 5 Byron Close, Fleet, Hants GU13 9QD (01252 627385).
Ground: Ancells Farm, Fleet, Hants.
Colours: Red & black/black/red **Change:** Blue or green or purple/turqu/white.

HAYLING UNITED

Secretary: Mrs S Westfield, 14 Harold Road, Hayling Island, Hants PO11 9LT.(01705 463305).
Ground: Hayling Park, Hayling Island, Hants.
Colours: Red & navy/navy/navy **Change:** Blue & white/blue/blue
Programme: No **Midweek home matchday:** Tuesday.

HORNDEAN

Secretary: Mrs Gladys Berry, 74 Five Heads Road, Horndean PO8 9NZ (01705 591698).
Ground: Five Heads Park, Five Heads Road, Horndean (01705 591363).
Colours: Black & Red/black/black **Change colours:** Navy & white/white/navy.

LISS ATHLETIC

Secretary: W.E.Moseley, 3 Yew Tree Place, Liss, Hants. GU33 7ET (01730 894631)
Ground: Newman Collard PF, Hill Brow Rd, Liss, Hants (01730 894022).
Colours: All Blue & White. **Change:** All yellow
Programme: No **Midweek home matchday:** Thursday.

LOCKSHEATH

Secretary: Michael Harrison, 30 Whitebeam Road, Hedge End, Southampton, Hants. SO30 OPZ (01489 784470)
Ground: Locksheath Rec, Warsash Rd, Titchfield Common, Eastleigh (01489 600932).
Colours: Red/black/black. **Change:** All white

MAYFLOWER

Secretary: Mr C J Papadatos, 5 Albion Close, Porchester, Fareham, Hants PO16 9EW (01329 510623)
Ground: Clarence Gardens, Southsea (01705 824246 - FAX 01705 727273)
Colours: Blue & black stripes/black/black **Change:** Yellow & green/green/yellow

NEW STREET

Secretary: Mrs F J Waterman, 'Jorin Bay' 2 Pine Walk, Andover, Hants SP10 3PW (01264 362751)
Ground: Foxcotte Park, Charlton Down, Andover.(01264 358358)
Colours: Green & black/black/green **Change colours:** Red/white/red.
Programme: Yes **Midweek home matchday:** Tuesday or Wednesday.

PIRELLI GENERAL

Secretary: Miss Bernice Fox 31 Spring Close, Fair Oak, Eastleigh, Hants SO50 7BB (01703 693537).
Ground: Jubilee Spts Ground, Chestnut Ave., Eastleigh (01703 612721).
Colours: Blue & white/white/white **Change:** Yellow/black/yellow
Programme: Yes **Midweek home matchday:** Tuesday.

POOLE TOWN

Secretary: Bill Read, 15 Addison Close, Romsey, Hants SO51 7TL (01794 517991)
Ground: Petersham Lane, Gants Common, Holt, Wimborne, Dorset (01258 840379)
Colours: Red & white/red/white **Change Colours:** Yellow & black/blue/yellow

ROMSEY TOWN

Secretary: Andy Spreadbury, 13 Tanners Road, North Baddesley Southampton S)52 9FD (01703 739034)
Ground: The By-Pass Ground, South Front, Romsey (01794 512003)
Colours: Yellow & black/black/black **Change colours:** Red & black/red/red
Programme: Yes **Midweek Matchday:** Wednesday

STOCKBRIDGE

Secretary: Graham Howard, 1 Moat Cottages, Longstock,Stockbridge, Hants.SO20 6EP (01264 810753)
Ground: The Recreation Ground, High Street, Stockbridge, Hants.
Colours: All red **Change:** All blue

VOSPER THORNYCROFT

Secretary: Peter Prin, 454 Bursledon Road, Sholing, Southampton, Hants. SO19 8QQ (01703 403829)
Ground: Vosper Thornycroft Spts Ground, Portsmouth Rd, Sholing, Southampton (01489 403829).
Colours: All royal **Change:** Red & black/black/black

WINCHESTER CITY

Secretary: Geoffrey Cox, 9 Burnetts Gdns, Horton Heath, Eastleigh, Hants SO5 7BY (01703 693021).
Ground: Hillier Way, Abbotts Barton, Winchester (01962 863553).
Colours: Red & white/black/red **Change:** White/green/green

DIVISION TWO CLUBS 1998-99

A.C. DELCO

Secretary: Brian Cook, 17 Hickory Gardens, West End, Southampton.SO30 3RN (01703 613334)
Ground: AC Delco Spts Ground, Stoneham Lane, Eastleigh (01703 613334).
Colours: Royal Blue & white stripes/black/blue. **Change:** Red & Black stripes/White/Black.
Programme: No **Midweek home matchday:** Wednesday.

AFC BASINGSTOKE

Secretary: T Purnell, 1 Byfleet Avenue, OLd Basing, Basingstoke, Hants RG24 7HD (01256 23239)
Ground: War Memorial Park, Crossborough Hill, Basingstoke, Hants.
Colours: Blue & black/black/black **Change Colours:** Green & white/green/white

COOP SPORTS

ESSO (FAWLEY)

Secretary: Mr A Haws, 40 Hollybank Rd, Hythe, Southampton, Hants SO45 5FQ (01703 843402).
Ground: Esso Recreation Club, Long Lane, Holbury, Southampton, Hant (01705 893750).
Colours: White/blue/red **Change:** Red/white/white

HAMBLE CLUB

Secretary: H.J.Noice, 55 The Oaks, Bitterne,Southampton, Hants. SO19 7RP(01703 398370)
Ground: Mount Pleasant Rec, Hamble Lane, Hanble, Southampton, Hants (01703 452327).
Colours: All Red **Change:** All Blue.

HILSEA CLUB

Secretary: Mr Terry Harwood, 147 Manners Rd, Southsea, Hants PO4 0BD (01705 785140).
Ground: Portsmouth Sailing Centre, Eastern Rd, Portsmouth PO3 5LY (01705 670119).
Colours: Yellow/blue/white **Change:** Blue/blue/white

HYTHE & DIBDEN

Secretary: Mr A Moyst, 105 Hobart Drive, Hythe, Southampton, Hants SO40 6FD (01703 847335).
Ground: Ewart Rec Ground, Jones Lane, Hythe, Southampton (01703 845264 - matchdays only).
Colours: Green/green/yellow **Change:** Blue & white stripes/blue/black.

NETLEY CENTRAL SPORTS

Secretary: Mr R W Crompton, 47 Station Rd, Netley Abbey, Southampton SO31 5AE (01703 452049).
Ground: Netley Rec, Station Rd, Netley Abbey, Southampton (01703 452267).
Colours: Royal & white/royal/royal **Change:** All red
Programme: Yes **Midweek home matchday:** Wednesday.

OTTERBOURNE

Secretary: R J Broom, 249 Passfield Rd, Eastleigh, Hants SO5 5DE (01703 328992).
Ground: Oakwood Park, off Oakwood Ave., Otterbourne (01962 714681).
Colours: Red/white/red & white
Change: Blue & white/blue/blue.

OVERTON UNITED

Secretary: Mrs A Wheeler, 3 Lordsfield Gardens, Overton, Hants RG25 2EW (01256 771241).
Ground: Recreation Centre, Bridge Street, Overton (01256 770561).
Colours: Blue & white stripes/white/blue **Change:** Green & purple/purple/purple
Programme: No **Midweek home matchday:** Tuesday or Thursday

PAULSGROVE

Secretary: S J Cox, 22 Alameda Road, Purbrook, Waterlooville, Hants. PO7 5HD (01705 785110)
Ground: The Grove Club, Marsden Rd (off Allaway Avenue), Paulsgrove, Portsmouth (01705 324102).
Colours: Red & black stripes/black/red **Change:** Blue & white/blue/black
Programme: **Midweek home matchday:** Wednesday.

PETERSFIELD TOWN

Secretary: M Nicholl, 49 Durford Rd, Petersfield, Hants GU31 4ER (01730 300518).
Ground: Love Lane, Petersfield, Hants (01730 233416).
Colours: Red & Black/Black/Black. **Change cols:** White/blue/white
Programme: Yes **Midweek Matches:** Wednesday.

QUEENS KEEP

Secretary: Donald Campbell, 81 Lumsden Avenue, Shirley, Southampton, Hants SO15 5EJ (01703 781362)
Ground: Civil Service Club, off Malmesbury Road, Shirley, Southampton, (01703 771950)
Colours: Yellow & green/emerald/emerald **Change Colours:** Royal & maroon/royal/royal

TADLEY

Secretary: Mike Miller, Meadow View, West Heath, Baughurst, Hants RG26 5LE (01256 850700).
Ground: The Green, Tadley, Hants.
Cols: Blue & maroon stripes/maroon/maroon **Change:** Yellow/blue/blue

VERWOOD TOWN

Secretary: Mrs J A Fry, 19a Noon Hill Rd, Verwood, Dorset BH31 7DB (01202 822826).
Ground: Pottern Park, Pottern Way, Verwood, Dorset.
Colours: All red **Change:** All blue
Programme: Yes **Midweek home matchday:** Tuesday.

WINCHESTER CASTLE

Secretary: A J Rutter, 79 South Ham Road, Basingstoke, Hants RG22 6AA (01256 842689)
Ground: Hants County Council Spts Ground, Petersfield Rd, Chilcomb, Winchester (01962 866989).
Colours: Red & black/black/red **Change:** Blue & white/white/blue.

YATELEY GREEN

Secretary: Alan Baynes, 7 Borderside, Yateley, Camberley Surrey GU17 7LJ
Ground: Yateley Recreation Ground, Reading Road, Yateley, Camberley, Surrey
Colours: Green/black/black **Change:** Red/black/black

BRITISH ENERGY
KENT COUNTY FOOTBALL ASSOCIATION LEAGUE

President: Bill Manklow **Chairman:** C T C Winiate
Press Officer: J C Mugridge, 14 Cherry Tree Rd, Tunbridge Wells, TN2 5QA (01892 521578)

Premier Division League Table 1997-98

	P	W	D	L	F	A	Pts
Milton Athletic	26	18	5	3	69	26	59
Rye United	26	16	4	6	64	41	52
Greenways	26	15	6	5	60	36	51
Sevenoaks Town	26	13	7	6	75	49	46
Bearsted	26	13	7	6	45	45	46
Knatchbull	26	12	5	9	42	43	41
Ex Blues	26	12	4	10	51	44	40
Lydd Town	26	10	8	8	49	44	38
Stansted O & B Club	26	8	4	14	34	50	28
Aylesford Paper Mill	26	6	8	12	42	46	26
A C Egerton	26	8	2	16	47	60	26
Thames Polytechnic	26	6	7	13	41	53	25
Tenterden St Michaels Utd	26	4	4	18	38	77	16
Teynsham & Lynsted	26	4	3	19	25	68	15

Division One East 97-98

	P	W	D	L	F	A	Pts
New Romney	22	17	3	2	67	15	54
Kennington	22	16	4	2	60	23	52
Bishopsbourne	22	16	3	3	59	20	51
University of Kent	22	12	5	5	65	22	41
Bromley Green	22	10	5	7	59	46	35
Woodnesborough	22	9	5	8	39	47	32
St Margarets	22	9	1	12	55	59	28
Snowdon Colliery Wel	22	7	3	12	35	39	24
Iden	22	5	4	13	52	71	19
Broomfield United	22	5	3	14	36	77	18
Walmer Rovers	22	4	2	16	28	86	14
Lydd Town Res	22	2	2	18	21	71	8

Division One West 97-98

	P	W	D	L	F	A	Pts
Snodland	24	19	3	2	71	25	60
Ten Em Bee/Elms	24	18	3	3	72	25	57
AFC Blackheath	24	13	5	6	70	36	44
Beauwater	24	14	2	8	53	45	44
Otford United	24	13	4	7	50	29	43
Eynsford	24	12	3	9	56	49	39
Phoenix Sports	23	7	8	8	50	49	32
Maidstone United	24	7	7	10	36	48	28
Westerham	24	6	5	13	39	53	23
Rusthall	24	6	4	14	37	38	22
Sutton Athletic	24	6	2	16	44	72	20
Hawkenbury	23	3	7	13	37	88	16
Oakwood	24	4	1	19	33	91	13

Division Two East 97-98

	P	W	D	L	F	A	Pts
Rye Utd Res	26	21	1	4	87	28	64
Sheerness East	26	19	3	4	62	21	60
Wittersham	26	17	4	5	70	27	55
Smarden	26	15	5	6	69	39	50
Knatchbull Res	26	15	4	7	65	36	49
Broomfield Utd Res	26	14	6	6	58	41	48
AFC Ocean	25	11	3	12	70	81	36
University Kent Res	26	11	2	13	68	61	35
Teynsham & Lyn Res	26	9	4	13	50	64	31
Tenterden Res	26	8	3	15	62	81	27
Kennington Res	26	5	8	13	35	67	23
New Romney Res	26	5	3	18	35	72	18

Division Two West 97-98

	P	W	D	L	F	A	Pts
Wickham Park	24	18	3	3	62	22	57
Moonshot Athletic	24	18	0	6	62	33	54
Edenbridge Utd	24	15	2	7	49	50	47
Tonbridge Rangers	24	14	3	7	62	42	45
Chipstead	24	11	2	11	46	40	35
Platt United	24	9	6	9	40	45	33
Borough United	24	10	2	12	46	50	32
Fleetdown United	24	10	1	13	43	44	31
Eltham Palace	24	8	4	12	47	45	28
Chislehurst	24	6	5	13	43	67	23
Old Bexleians	24	6	4	14	43	55	22
Farnborough O B	24	6	3	15	30	48	21
Leaves Green	24	5	5	14	41	73	20

CLUB DIRECTORY 1998-99

Premier & Division One East & West

A.C. EGERTON

Secretary: Mr D Pask, 1 Lewis Cottages, Leydenhatch Lane, Swanley, Kent BR8 7PU (01322 669539)
Ground: St Marys Cray Rec Grd, Park Rd, St Marys Cray **Founded:** 1971
Colours: Royal/royal/white **Change Colours:** Green & white/white/green & white

A.F.C. BLACKHEATH

Secretary: Derv Dervish, 79 Brownhill Road, Catford, London SE6 2HF (0181 697 3483)
Ground: Huntsman Sports, Manor Way, Blackheath, London SE3 (0181 852 3602) **Founded:** 1983
Colours: All red **Change Colours:** Green & navy/navy/navy

A.F.C. LEWISHAM

Secretary: Brian Roberts, 5 Sunnyhill Road, Lewisham, SE13 7SS (0181 691 5289)
Ground: Old Bromley Road Playing Fields, Old Bromley Road, Downham BR1 4JY **Founded:** 1998
Colours: All blue & gold **Change Colours:** Yellow/blue/blue

AYLESFORD PAPER MILL

Secretary: Mrs L Casey, 41 Cobdown Close, Ditton, Aylesford, Kent ME20 6SZ (01732 849476)
Ground: Cobdown, Station Road, Ditton, Nr Maidstone (01622 717771) **Founded:** 1979
Colours: Black & white/black/black **Change Colours:** Red & black/white/white

BEARSTED

Secretary: Mrs Liz Owen, 21 Copsewood Way, Bearsted, Maidstone, Kent ME15 8PL (01622 737709)
Ground: Honey Lane, Otham, Maidstone. (0860 302086) **Founded:** 1895
Colours: White/blue/blue **Change Colours:** Blue & yellow/blue/blue

BEAUWATER

Secretary: Mr R Taylor, 24 Sun Lane, Gravesend, Kent DA12 5HG (01474 332208)
Ground: Beauwater Leisure Club, Nelson Road, Northfleet (01474 336456) **Founded:** 1927
Colours: Blue & yellow/navy/navy **Change Colours:** All red

BISHOPSBOURNE

Secretary: Colin Smith, 39 Bridge Down, Bridge, Canterbury, Kent CT4 5AZ (01227 830537)
Ground: Canteen Meadow, The Street, Bishopsbourne, Nr Canterbury, Kent **Founded:** 1963
Colours: Royal/white/royal & white **Change Colours:** Red & white/black/black

BROMLEY GREEN

Secretary: Miss Samantha Bartholomew, 31 Upper Denmark Rd, Ashford, Kent tn23 7TZ (01233 336904)
Ground: The Swan Centre, South Willesborough, Ashford, Kent **Founded:** 1930
Colours: All green **Change Colours:** White/green/green

BROOMFIELD UNITED

Secretary: Mr R Cork, Flat 17, Francis Court, 117 High Street, Herne Bay, Kent CT6 5LA (01227 742480)
Ground: Bridge Rec Ground, Patrixbourne Road, Bridge, Nr Canterbury **Founded:** 1925
Colours: All Tangerine & black **Change Colours:** Black & azure/black/black & azure

Ex BLUES

Secretary: Mr M Harvey, 29 Crown Lane, Bromley, Kent, BR2 9PG (0181 464 4815)
Ground: Coney Hall, Recreation Ground, Church Drive, Coney Hall, Hayes, Kent **Founded:** 1945
Colours: Blue & yellow/navy/navy **Change Colours:** Red/black/black

EYNESFORD

Secretary: Mr E Walking, 76 Pollyhaugh, Eynesford, Nr Dartford, Kent DA4 0HF (01322 863673)
Ground: Harrow Meadow, Rear of Castle Hotel, Bower Lane, off Eynesford High Street. **Founded:** 1894
Colours: White/black/black **Change Colours:** Red/black/black

GREENWAYS

Secretary: Mr W Miller, 14 Cygnet Gardens, Northfleet, Kent DA11 7DN (01474 560913)
Ground: Beauwater Leisure Centre, Nelson Road, Northfleet, (01474 359222) **Founded:** 1965
Colours: All green **Change Colours:** Red/black/red

IDEN

Secretary: Mr G Say, 18 Parkwood, Iden, Rye, East Sussex TN31 7XE (01797 280495)
Ground: Iden Playing Field, Iden, Rye, East Sussex **Founded:** 1965
Colours: Tangerine/white/tangerine **Change Colours:** Green & white/white/green

KENNINGTON

Secretary:. Kevin Hayden, 33 Grosvenor Road, Kennington, Ashford, Kent TN24 9PA (01233 627826)
Ground: Kennington Cricket Club Pav. Ulley Road, Kennington, Ashford, Kent **Founded:** 1888
Colours: Yellow & sky/yellow/yellow **Change Colours:** Red/black/black

KNATCHBULL

Secretary: Mr D Howie, 13 Charminster, Washford Farm, Ashford, Kent TN23 2UH (01233 611207)
Ground: Hatch Park, Off A20, Mersham, Nr Ashford, (01585 663171) **Founded:** 1981
Colours: Claret & blue/white/white **Change Colours:** All white

LYDD TOWN & Reserves

Secretary: Mr P Sisley, The Lobster Pot, Warren Road, Littlestone, Romney Marsh, Kent TN28 8PW, (01797 366101)
Ground: The Rype, Manor Road, Lydd. **Founded:** 1885
Colours: All green **Change Colours:** Red & green/green/green

MAIDSTONE UNITED

Secretary: Mr G Gray, 6 Morella Walk, Lenham, Maidstone, Kent ME17 2JX (01622 859964)
Ground: The Athletic Ground, London Road, Maidstone. **Founded:** 1992
Colours: Gold/black/black **Change Colours:** All blue

MILTON ATHLETIC

Secretary: Mr P Duffin, 18 Hales Road, Tunstall, Sittingbourne, Kent ME10 1SR (01795 471260)
Ground: UK Paper Sports Ground, Gore Court Road, Sittingbourne, Kent **Founded:** 1926
Colours: White & navy/navy/navy **Change Colours:** Red & white/black/black

MMONSHOT ATHLETIC

Secretary: Joseph Collymore, 37 Vaughan Williams Close, Deptford SE8 4AW (0181 691 2543)
Ground: Old Bromley Rd Playing Fields, Old Bromley Rd. **Founded:** 1970
Colours: Blue & white/blue/blue **Change Colours:** Green & yellow/green/green

NEW ROMNEY

Secretary: Mr D Masters, 44 Fernbank Cres, Folkstone, Kent CT19 5SF (01303 253961)
Ground: Station Road, New Romney **Founded:** 1895
Colours: Yellow & navy/navy/yellow **Change Colours:** White/blue/white

NORTON SPORTS

Secretary: Colin Page, 2 Foxgrove, Milton Regis, Sittingbourne, Kent ME10 2DW (01795 426675)
Ground: Norton Park, Norton. **Founded:** 1927
Colours: Blue & yellow/blue/yellow **Change Colours:** White/black/black

OTFORD UNITED

Secretary: Roger Gulliver, 22 Berwick Way, Sevenoaks, Kent TN14 5EY (01732 459064)
Ground: Otford Recreation Ground, High Street, Otford, Kent **Founded:** 1900
Colours: Amber/black/black **Change Colours:** Blue/black/black

PHOENIX SPORTS

Secretary: Mr M Cole, 91 Hurst Road, Northumberland Heath, Erith, Kent DA8 3EW (01322 350750)
Ground: Phoenix Sports Club, Mayplace Road East, Bexleyheath, Kent DA7 6JT **Founded:** 1935
Colours: Red & white/black/red **Change Colours:** Yellow/black/black

RUSTHALL

Secretary: Mr M Mace, 28 Allan Close, Rusthall, Tunbridge Wells, Kent TN4 8PL (01892 540634)
Ground: Jockey Farm, Nellington Road, Rusthall, Tunbridge Wells **Founded:** 1899
Colours: All green **Change Colours:** Blue/black/black

WICKHAM PARK

Secretary: Len Simmons, 77 Darenth Road, Welling, Kent DA16 3EG (0181 855 3871)
Ground: Wickham Spts & Soc. Club, Pickhurst Rise. **Founded:** 1934
Colours: Red & black/black/red **Change Colours:** All navy

RYE UNITED

Secretary: Bob Dixon, 32 The Maltings, Peasmarsh, Nr Rye, East Sussex TN31 6ST (01797 234430)
Ground: Sydney Allnut Pav. Rye Cricket & Football Salts, Rye, East Sussex **Founded:** 1938
Colours: White & red & black/black/white **Change Colours:** Black & blue/black/black

SEVENOAKS TOWN

Secretary: Mr E Diplock, 23 Hollybush Lane, Sevenoaks, Kent TN13 3TH (01732 454280)
Ground: Greatness Park, Seal Road, Sevenoaks, (01732 741987) **Founded:** 1883
Colours: Azure & black/azure & black/black **Change Colours:** Navy & scarlet/navy/navy

SHEERNESS EAST

Secretary: Jonathan Longhurst, 16 Hilda Rd, Halfway, Sheerness ME12 3BN (01795 667758)
Ground: Sheerness East Working Mens Club, Queenborough Rd, Halfway **Founded:** 1932
Colours: Yellow/royal/royal **Change Colours:** White & blue/royal/royal

SNODLAND

Secretary: Mr T Reeves, 136 Townsend Road, Snodland, Kent ME6 5RN (01634 240076)
Ground: Potyn's Field, Paddlesworth Road, Snodland **Founded:** 1940
Colours: Sky & navy/navy/navy **Change Colours:** White/navy/navy

SNOWDOWN COLLIERY WELFARE

Secretary: Ernest Travers, 21 Bell Grove, Aylesham, Kent CT3 3AT (01304 842680)
Ground: Spinney Lane, Aylesham, Canterbury CT3 3AF **Founded:** 1907
Colours: Black & white/black/black **Change Colours:** All green

St MARGARETS

Secretary: Mr W Hay, 28 The Freedown, St Margarets at Cliffe, Nr Dover, Kent CT15 6BD (01304 852386)
Ground: The Alexander Field, Kingsdown Road, St Margarets at Cliffe, Nr Dover **Founded:** 1993
Colours: All White & red & blue **Change Colours:** Yellow & black/black/black

STANSFELD OXFORD & BERMONDSEY CLUB

Secretary: Mr E Ellis, 40 Tilbrook Road, Kidbrooke, London SE3 9QE (0181 319 0903)
Ground: St James Squash & Leisure Club, 35 Marvels Lane, Grove Park, SE12. **Founded:** 1897
Colours: Yellow/blue/yellow **Change Colours:** All red

SUTTON ATHLETIC

Secretary: Mr J Willis, 6 Somerset Road, Dartford, Kent DA1 3DP (01322 222540)
Ground: The Roaches, Parsonage Lane, Sutton at Hone, Nr Dartford. **Founded:** 1904
Colours: Green & yellow/green/green & yellow **Change Colours:** Red/red & black/red

TENTERDEN ST MICHAELS UNITED

Secretary: Mr S Stevens, Kent House, Ashford Road, St Michaels, Tenterden, Kent TN30 6PY (01580 762703)
Ground: Recreation Ground, Tenterden High Street, Tenterden **Founded:** 1890
Colours: Blue & white/blue/blue **Change Colours:** All red

THAMES POLYTECHNIC

Secretary: Mrs S Jarvis, 31 Monkton Road, Welling, Kent DA16 3JU (0181 854 5509)
Ground: Thames Polytechnic, Kidbrooke Lane, Eltham, London SE9 **Founded:** 1888
Colours: Green & yellow/green/yellow & green **Change Colours:** All blue

UNIVERSITY OF KENT

Secretary: Mrs I Simmonds, Sports Federation, Sports Centre, University of Kent Canterbury, Kent CT2 7NL
Ground: The Playing Fields, University of Kent, Canterbury **Founded:** 1967
Colours: Black & white/black/black **Change Colours:** Red & black/black/black

WESTERHAM

Secretary: Mr D Sayers, 16A The Green, Westerham, Kent TN16 1AX (01959 563163)
Ground: King George V Playing Fields, Costells Meadow, Westerham **Founded:** 1888
Colours: Red/black/black **Change Colours:** Green/white/green

WOONESBOROUGH

Secretary: Mr G Hunt, Hillcross Farm, Eastry, Sandwich, Kent CT13 0NY (01304 611311)
Ground: Hillborough, Woodnesborough Road, Eastry **Founded:** 1962
Colours: Red/black/black **Change Colours:** Green/black/black

SOUTH WESTERN FINAL LEAGUE TABLES 1997-98

JOLLYS
CORNWALL COMBINATION

	P	W	D	L	F	A	Pts
Perranwell	38	29	5	4	118	25	92
Penryn Ath 3	38	31	2	5	105	29	92
Falmouth Tn Res	38	28	5	5	105	40	89
Helston Ath	38	23	8	7	116	50	77
St Lves Town	38	22	8	8	78	36	74
Truro City Res	38	21	6	11	91	60	69
RNAS Culdrose 1	38	21	5	12	86	46	67
Illogan RBL	38	17	7	13	77	62	*58
Goonhavern	38	16	5	17	97	84	53
Porthleven Rs	38	15	7	16	83	90	52
St Agnes	38	13	9	16	46	55	48
Newquay Res	38	12	4	22	62	90	40
St Just	38	11	11	16	58	81	44
Penzance Res-1	38	10	9	19	77	92	38
Troon	38	11	5	22	61	93	38
Mousehole	38	10	7	21	59	91	37
Mullion Res	38	8	8	21	57	79	*32
Ludgvan	38	8	7	23	45	97	31
Marazion Blues	38	6	8	24	44	129	26
Pendeen Rovers	38	2	4	32	33	146	10

CORNISH GUARDIAN
EAST CORNWALL LEAGUE

PREMIER DIV	*P*	*W*	*D*	*L*	*F*	*A*	*Pts*
Callington Town	36	29	4	3	121	47	91
Liskeard Ath Res	36	24	8	4	116	40	80
Bodmin Town Res	36	23	7	6	109	40	76
Camelford	36	23	7	6	84	39	76
Padstow United	36	19	9	8	88	55	66
Saltash United Res	36	19	7	10	76	59	64
Nanpean Rovers	36	18	6	12	68	46	60
St Blazey	36	17	8	11	73	47	59
Wadebridge Tn Rs	36	15	7	14	75	63	52
St Breward	36	15	7	14	77	68	52
Torpoint Ath Res	36	15	7	14	73	75	52
St Cleer	36	13	3	20	51	71	42
Roche	36	10	9	17	52	56	39
St Dennis	36	11	6	19	59	77	39
Bude Town	36	10	5	21	42	77	35
St Austell Res	36	7	12	17	41	69	33
Sticker	36	8	4	24	42	85	28
Foxhole Stars	36	5	3	28	37	119	18
Bugle	36	1	4	31	28	179	7

DEVON & EXETER LEAGUE

PREMIER DIV	*P*	*W*	*D*	*L*	*F*	*A*	*Pts*
Exeter University	28	24	2	2	108	27	74
Exeter Civ Serv	28	23	2	3	103	28	71
Buckland Ath	28	20	2	6	89	35	62
St Martins	28	17	5	6	66	33	56
Witheridge	28	15	4	9	71	60	49
Budleigh S Res	28	13	4	11	64	56	43
Exeter St Thomas	28	11	9	8	56	41	42
Exmouth Amat	28	13	2	13	50	54	41
Feniton	28	10	5	13	66	67	35
Dawlish Villa	28	9	6	13	54	60	33
Okehampton Arg	28	9	4	15	54	72	31
Sidmouth Town	28	6	6	16	41	70	24
Morchard Bishop	28	6	4	18	32	71	22
Culm United	28	3	2	23	28	113	11
Clyst Valley	28	2	1	25	24	119	7

Honiton Town - Record expunged

BIDEFORD TOOLS
NORTH DEVON LEAGUE

PREMIER DIV	*P*	*W*	*D*	*L*	*F*	*A*	*Pts*
Shamwickshire	34	28	1	5	169	50	85
Fremington FoxH	34	26	3	5	163	54	81
Ilfracombe Town	34	25	5	4	147	39	80
Braunton	34	22	6	6	104	41	72
Morwenstow	34	22	2	10	101	46	68
Appledore BAAC	34	18	6	10	93	53	60
Bradworthy	34	17	8	9	116	54	59
Barnstaple	34	18	4	12	88	88	58
Putford	34	14	3	17	60	54	45
Braunton FP	34	14	3	17	75	118	45
Georgeham 6	34	14	6	14	92	59	42
Holsworthy	34	12	5	17	61	61	41
South Molton	34	12	3	19	82	99	39
Combe Martin	34	10	4	20	84	86	34
Torrington Admiral	34	7	6	21	58	112	27
Kilkhampton 6	34	7	3	24	49	105	18
Chittlehampton	34	5	0	29	46	168	15
Torrington Res 9	34	1	0	33	14	318	-6

HAYWARTH BOURNEMOUTH LEAGUE

DIVISION ONE	*P*	*W*	*D*	*L*	*F*	*A*	*Pts*
Bournemouth CS	24	20	3	1	75	17	63
B'mouth Electric	24	18	1	5	71	35	53
Lansdowne	24	15	5	4	85	30	50
Westover B'mouth	24	15	5	4	61	32	50
Kinson	24	14	3	7	56	30	45
Sway	24	11	3	10	68	47	36
Bisterne United	24	11	3	10	55	52	36
Hamworthy E Rs	24	8	1	15	41	48	25
Stourvale	24	7	0	17	44	80	21
B'mouth Spts Rs	24	6	4	14	39	69	20
Queens Pk Ath	24	6	1	17	26	85	19
Christchurch 'A'	24	5	2	17	25	70	17
Burton	24	3	3	18	29	80	12

SOMERSET SENIOR LEAGUE

PREMIER DIV	*P*	*W*	*D*	*L*	*F*	*A*	*Pts*
Portishead	34	24	6	4	78	39	78
Clevedon United	34	18	7	9	82	43	63
Nailsea United	34	19	5	10	81	52	62
Peasedown Ath	34	17	9	8	79	63	60
Radstock Town	34	17	8	9	64	42	59
Shepton Mallet T	34	15	12	7	64	37	57
Bridgwater Tn Rs	34	15	5	14	65	54	50
Frys Club	34	14	8	12	70	72	50
Bumham United	34	12	12	10	66	54	48
Brislington	34	11	11	12	50	59	44
Shirehampton	34	12	6	16	58	61	42
Hengrove Ath	34	12	4	18	41	57	40
Westland United	34	11	6	17	53	71	39
Imperial FC	34	11	6	17	48	73	39
Longwell Green A	34	10	8	16	46	64	38
Weston St John	34	11	3	20	52	94	36
Wells City	34	6	9	19	58	79	27
Winscombe	34	5	5	24	49	90	20

YEOVIL & DISTRICT LEAGUE

PREMIER DIV	*P*	*W*	*D*	*L*	*F*	*A*	*Pts*
Henstridge Utd	19	17	0	2	76	23	51
Stoke sub Ham.	20	16	3	1	60	17	51
Ash Rovers	20	13	1	6	47	22	40
Milborne Port	20	8	4	8	43	32	28
Bradford Sports	20	8	4	8	42	35	28
Baltonsborough	20	9	0	11	36	55	27
Tintinhull	19	7	1	11	39	57	22
Camel	20	7	1	12	33	56	22
Ilchester United	20	5	3	12	24	62	18
Martock United	20	3	7	10	30	42	16
Masons Arms	20	2	4	14	22	54	10

RB SERVICES MID SOMERSET LEAGUE

PREMIER DIV	*P*	*W*	*D*	*L*	*F*	*A*	*Pts*
Mells/Vobster Utd	18	13	2	3	48	25	41
Coleford Ath	18	11	2	5	52	28	34
Frome SH	18	10	4	4	47	24	34
Stoke Rovers	18	9	5	4	35	28	32
Timsbury A Res	18	9	3	6	35	22	30
Littleton Spts	18	8	2	8	35	33	26
Farmborough	18	5	2	11	37	48	17
Evercreech	18	4	4	10	33	66	16
Chew Magna	18	2	6	10	31	43	12
Belrose	18	3	2	13	23	59	11

PERRY STREET LEAGUE

PREMIER DIV	*P*	*W*	*D*	*L*	*F*	*A*	*Pts*
Combe St Nich	22	19	3	0	82	16	60
Axminster Town	22	16	4	2	58	18	52
Merriott Rovers	22	16	1	5	104	34	42
Crewkerne	22	12	5	5	63	24	41
Lyme Regis	22	13	3	6	70	33	36
Halstock	22	10	5	7	63	52	35
Forton	22	9	2	11	39	71	29
South Petherton	22	7	4	11	39	49	25
Beaminster Res	22	3	3	14	23	62	12
Chard Athletic	22	3	3	16	23	65	12
Hinton St George	22	2	3	17	28	89	9
Shepton B'champ	22	1	6	15	27	113	9

MAGNOX NUCLEAR ELECTRIC TAUNTON LEAGUE

DIVISION ONE	*P*	*W*	*D*	*L*	*F*	*A*	*Pts*
Sydenham Rgrs	22	17	4	1	85	26	55
Foresters	22	15	5	2	75	26	50
Bishops Lydeard	22	14	2	6	70	40	44
Porlock	22	12	4	6	68	45	40
Wyvern	22	12	4	6	55	42	40
British Cellophane	22	10	3	9	67	57	33
Redgate	22	9	4	9	53	50	31
Creech	22	9	4	9	46	44	31
Dulverton Town	22	7	4	11	39	57	25
Middlezoy Rovers	22	4	2	16	31	77	14
Watchet Town Rs	22	3	1	18	20	63	10
Nether Stowey	22	1	1	20	20	102	4

WESTON SUPER MARE & DISTRICT LEAGUE

DIVISION ONE	*P*	*W*	*D*	*L*	*F*	*A*	*Pts*
Draycott	22	19	2	1	105	20	40
East Worle	22	15	3	4	62	31	33
Worle Res	22	13	5	4	74	35	31
Bournville Rvrs	22	12	3	7	51	43	27
Hutton	22	11	3	8	69	50	25
Selkirk United	22	8	3	11	37	46	19
Portishead 'A'	22	10	1	11	45	58	19
Smurfit United	22	8	3	11	45	60	19
Nailsea Utd 'A'	22	6	5	11	45	37	17
Winscombe Res	22	6	1	15	26	73	13
Langford Rovers	22	4	3	15	26	76	11
Clevedon Utd 'A'	22	3	2	17	35	91	8

BRISTOL PREMIER COMBINATION

PREMIER DIV	*P*	*W*	*D*	*L*	*F*	*A*	*Pts*
Highbridge Utd	26	20	3	3	75	21	63
RG St George	26	18	4	4	80	25	58
Bristol 5 OB	26	13	6	7	44	50	45
Hartcliffe	26	13	5	8	53	39	44
Hallen Res	26	10	11	5	56	43	41
Nicholas Wdrs	26	12	5	9	61	49	41
Sun Life	26	11	3	12	57	47	36
Hanham Athletic	26	11	3	12	47	51	36
Thornbury Town	26	9	6	11	42	44	33
Olveston United	26	9	4	13	48	56	31
Long. Grn Sports	26	9	4	13	42	52	31
St Philips MAS	26	7	3	16	52	76	24
Sea Mills Park	26	6	5	15	34	68	23
Hambrook	26	3	0	23	24	94	9

BRISTOL SUBURBAN LEAGUE

PREMIER DIV	*P*	*W*	*D*	*L*	*F*	*A*	*Pts*
Tyth'gton Rocks	29	22	5	2	75	18	49
Cadbury Hth Rs	30	20	5	5	62	39	43
Ridings High	30	16	7	7	62	31	39
Avonside Court	30	16	6	8	54	47	38
P & W United	30	13	9	8	64	50	35
Avonmouth	30	13	8	9	71	57	34
Glenside HSC	30	15	2	13	75	59	32
St Aldheims	30	14	4	12	51	54	32
Yate Town Res	30	13	4	13	61	68	30
Stoke Gifford	30	13	5	12	66	42	29
Old Cothamians	30	11	4	15	59	63	26
Raysfield	30	11	4	15	64	77	26
Almondsbury	30	7	7	16	51	71	21
Broad PHOB Rs	30	5	7	18	30	62	17
Alm'bury T Res	30	4	4	22	39	90	12
Imperial Saints	29	4	3	22	37	93	11

SKURRAYS WILTSHIRE LEAGUE

DIVISION ONE	*P*	*W*	*D*	*L*	*F*	*A*	*Pts*
Corsham Town	22	13	6	3	55	25	45
Devizes Town Res	22	14	3	5	49	29	45
Biddestone	22	13	4	5	58	24	43
Shrewton United	22	12	5	5	54	33	41
Raychem	22	9	7	6	42	39	34
Bradford Town 1	22	9	6	7	29	29	32
Malmesbury Vics	22	8	7	7	31	30	31
Wroughton	22	9	2	11	47	49	29
Southbrook Walcot	22	8	4	10	37	46	28
Aldbourne	22	4	5	13	36	60	17
Tisbury United	22	3	4	15	27	58	13
Marlborough Tn	22	2	3	17	20	63	9

TROWBRIDGE & DISTRICT LEAGUE

DIVISION ONE	*P*	*W*	*D*	*L*	*F*	*A*	*Pts*
Broughton Gifford	24	21	2	1	91	22	44
The Deverills	24	16	5	3	73	26	37
West Lavington	24	16	3	5	64	28	35
Westbury Utd Rs	24	15	2	7	56	32	32
Bradford United	24	13	2	9	76	50	28
Bratton	24	11	4	9	77	44	26
Calne Town SC	24	12	1	11	50	58	25
Heytesbury	24	11	2	11	54	58	24
Avon Bradford	24	9	2	13	57	54	20
Hilperton Utd	24	8	2	14	37	52	18
Seend United	24	7	1	16	39	64	15
Steeple Ashton	24	4	0	20	20	86	8
Rowde Sports	24	0	0	24	20	140	0

BLACKMORE VALE SUNDAY FOOTBALL LEAGUE

DIVISION ONE	*P*	*W*	*D*	*L*	*F*	*A*	*Pts*
Milborne Port	14	13	1	0	62	17	40
Stour Provost	14	12	0	2	65	23	36
White Horse	14	6	2	6	34	38	20
Shaft Cor	14	6	2	6	31	40	20
Thornford	14	5	0	9	32	61	15
Iwerne Minster	14	4	0	10	33	45	12
South Cheriton	14	3	2	9	40	50	11
Fountain	14	3	1	10	31	54	10

TAUNTON SATURDAY LEAGUE

DIVISION ONE	*P*	*W*	*D*	*L*	*F*	*A*	*Pts*
Foresters	22	15	5	2	75	25	50
Sydenham	20	15	4	1	75	20	49
Bishops Lydeard	22	14	2	6	70	40	44
Porlock	22	12	4	6	64	45	40
Wyvern	22	12	4	6	85	42	40
BCL	22	10	3	3	67	57	33
Redgate	21	9	4	8	43	45	31
Creech 93	22	9	4	9	46	44	31
Dulverton	22	7	4	11	39	57	25
Middlezoy	22	4	2	16	31	77	14
Watchet Res	22	3	1	18	20	83	10
Nether Stowey	21	1	1	19	18	97	4

DIV TWO (cont.)	*P*	*W*	*D*	*L*	*F*	*A*	*Pts*
Alcombe	22	19	1	2	92	34	58
Highbridge	22	17	2	3	56	27	53
Galmington	22	13	5	4	66	32	44
Civil Service	22	12	4	6	50	35	40
Bish. Lyd. Res	22	9	4	9	62	52	31
Westonzoyland	22	9	4	9	65	58	31
T'ton GWR	22	9	2	11	51	63	29
Spaxton	22	9	1	12	54	50	28
Norton	22	9	1	12	62	54	28
Crown Oyns	22	7	3	12	50	69	24
BCL Res	22	2	2	18	25	120	5
Blackbrook	22	1	4	17	29	87	1

DIV THREE	*P*	*W*	*D*	*L*	*F*	*A*	*Pts*
Haygrove	20	18	0	2	117	25	54
Marketers	20	18	0	2	103	21	51
N Petherton	20	16	0	4	71	48	44
Wyvern Res	20	10	3	7	46	42	33
White Rgrs	20	10	1	9	77	48	31
Knight Rgrs	20	10	0	10	63	48	24
Norton Res	20	7	1	12	35	82	22
Tavaners	20	7	0	13	87	64	21
W/Som Spts	20	5	2	13	28	54	17
BCL Cats	20	3	0	17	27	110	9
Williton	20	1	3	16	29	87	6

TAUNTON SUNDAY LEAGUE

PREMIER DIV	*P*	*W*	*D*	*L*	*F*	*A*	*Pts*
Staplegrove	20	17	1	2	107	35	52
YYCC	20	17	1	2	85	38	52
Britannia Inn	20	10	3	7	73	54	33
Clavel	20	8	4	8	46	45	28
Bathpool	20	8	3	9	57	53	27
Rail Rock	20	8	2	10	40	40	26
Kings United	20	7	5	8	35	42	26
Kings Arms	20	7	3	10	51	47	24
Bishops Lydeard	19	7	2	10	54	74	23
Lindon City	20	3	5	12	33	34	14
Westgate	19	1	3	15	27	83	6

DIVISION ONE	*P*	*W*	*D*	*L*	*F*	*A*	*Pts*
Curry Rivel	22	18	1	3	114	31	55
Ash Rangers	22	18	1	3	87	31	55
Spartans	22	16	2	4	105	44	50
Milverton	22	12	2	8	83	43	35
Priorswood	22	10	2	10	62	76	72
Norton	21	10	1	10	48	60	31
Blackbrook	21	10	0	11	68	71	30
Wiveliscombe	22	6	2	14	56	90	20
West Som W	22	6	1	15	44	87	19
Kings Pk Rgs	22	3	2	17	38	103	10
Williton Rocks	22	1	4	17	25	104	7

DIVISION TWO	*P*	*W*	*D*	*L*	*F*	*A*	*Pts*
Wyvern Ferr.	19	17	1	1	74	25	52
Inter Royal	20	14	0	6	92	42	42
Vicery Rovers	18	10	5	3	69	45	36
North Curry	20	11	1	9	74	45	34
Galmington	20	8	4	8	38	43	28
Cottage Crus.	20	8	3	9	58	55	27
Dolphin Inn	20	6	6	8	38	40	24
Blue Waves	20	7	3	11	40	65	24
Trull Rovers	20	6	5	9	59	56	23
Blues Bros	20	4	1	15	37	80	13
Dunster	20	2	2	16	23	107	8

DIV THREE	*P*	*W*	*D*	*L*	*F*	*A*	*Pts*
Perfecto	22	20	0	2	153	20	60
Gardners Arms	22	16	3	3	136	38	51
Cherry Grove	22	16	2	4	111	48	51

PYRAMID
FOOTBALL

RESERVE TEAM FOOTBALL 1997-98

OPTIMUM INTERIORS CAPITAL FOOTBALL LEAGUE FINAL LEAGUE TABLE 1997-98

	P	W	D	L	F	A	Pts
Northampton Town	26	17	5	4	59	31	56
Fulham	26	16	5	5	45	25	53
Rushden & Dia.	26	13	6	7	45	30	45
Brentford	26	13	6	7	48	35	45
Colchester Utd	26	12	6	8	49	32	42
Peterborough Utd	26	12	6	8	47	36	42
Reading	26	9	10	7	45	33	37
Gillingham	26	11	4	11	41	36	37
Cambridge Utd	26	10	6	10	40	37	36
Wycombe Wndrs	26	10	4	12	49	52	34
Barnet	26	6	7	13	27	48	25
Leyton Orient	26	6	5	15	35	60	23
Stevenage Boro	26	6	1	19	26	58	19
Welling United	26	3	5	18	33	76	14

CAPITAL FOOTBALL LEAGUE DOXHILL PRESIDENT'S CHALLENGE CUP 1997-98

SEMI-FINALS

Brentford	v	Northampton Town	3-2
Cambridge United	v	Reading	4-1

FINAL

CAMBRIDGE UTD	v	BRENTFORD	2-1

OPTIMUM INTERIORS CENTRAL CONFERENCE FINAL LEAGUE TABLE 1997-98

	P	W	D	L	F	A	Pts
Hereford United	18	10	6	2	34	15	36
Stoke City	18	9	5	4	40	19	32
Hednesford Town	18	9	3	6	27	29	30
Gloucester City	18	7	5	6	27	24	26
Kidderminster H	18	7	3	8	31	42	24
Cheltenham Town	18	5	5	8	18	23	20
Worcester City	18	1	3	14	19	44	6

CENTRAL CONFERENCE DOXHILL CHALLENGE CUP 1997-98

SEMI-FINALS

Worcester City	v	Cheltenham Town	0-2
Hednesford Town	v	Stoke City	2-3

FINAL

STOKE CITY	v	CHELTENHAM TOWN	5-0

OPTIMUM INTERIORS CAPITAL FOOTBALL LEAGUE 1997-98 RESULTS

		Bar	Bre	Cam	Col	Ful	Gil	Ley	Nor	Pet	Rea	Rus	Ste	Wel	Wyc	
1	Barnet	X	0-1	0-2	2-3	0-1	3-1	2-1	1-2	2-2	2-1	1-3	1-0	0-1	2-2	1
2	Brentford	2-2	X	3-1	1-1	2-1	1-2	0-1	1-1	1-2	1-1	1-2	4-0	3-1	4-1	2
3	Cambridge United	0-0	3-0	X	1-2	0-0	1-3	3-2	2-5	1-2	1-2	2-2	2-1	1-0	3-1	3
4	Colchester United	1-2	3-3	2-3	X	0-0	4-2	3-0	1-2	3-1	2-1	1-0	1-0	9-0	1-0	4
5	Fulham	2-0	3-0	3-0	2-1	X	0-0	3-2	0-2	0-0	1-2	2-1	4-1	2-1	3-0	5
6	Gillingham	1-1	1-2	2-1	2-0	0-2	X	4-1	0-1	0-2	3-0	1-3	3-1	7-0	3-7	6
7	Leyton Orient	5-2	0-1	0-1	2-2	1-4	1-0	X	1-1	4-2	0-3	2-2	0-1	3-2	2-5	7
8	Northampton Towm	4-2	1-3	1-0	2-1	3-0	0-1	2-0	X	2-3	2-2	1-3	6-0	3-2	4-0	8
9	Peterborough United	0-1	2-2	2-2	2-1	1-2	1-0	6-0	1-3	X	1-1	0-3	2-0	6-0	2-0	9
10	Reading	6-0	1-3	0-0	1-1	1-2	0-1	1-1	1-1	3-1	X	1-2	3-0	3-2	0-0	10
11	Rushden & Diamonds	0-0	0-2	1-0	1-1	1-1	0-1	5-2	1-2	1-3	2-2	X	4-0	4-0	0-3	11
12	Stevenage Borough	3-0	1-2	0-5	1-3	1-2	3-2	0-1	1-2	3-0	2-2	0-1	X	2-0	0-2	12
13	Welling United	1-1	2-4	2-2	1-0	4-2	0-0	1-1	4-4	0-2	2-3	0-1	2-3	X	3-7	13
14	Wycombe Wanderers	3-0	2-1	1-3	0-2	1-3	1-1	4-2	0-2	1-1	0-4	1-2	4-2	3-2	X	14

OPTIMUM INTERIORS CENTRAL CONFERENCE 1998-99 RESULTS

		Chelt	Glouc	Hednes	Heref	Kidd	Stoke	Worc	
1	Cheltenham Town	X	0-0/2-1	0-1/0-1	0-1/--	3-1/0-1	0-0/--	1-1/--	1
2	Gloucester City	1-0/--	X	2-3/1-1	0-1/1-1	2-4/4-3	2-1/--	2-0/--	2
3	Hednesford Town	2-1/--	1-1/--	X	1-3/--	4-2/1-0	1-2/0-5	2-0/2-1	3
4	Hereford Town	0-1/1-1	1-0/--	5-0/1-0	X	1-1/--	1-1/--	3-4/3-0	4
5	Kidderminster Harriers	1-3/--	0-0/--	2-1/--	5-5/0-4	X	2-6/0-6	3-0/1-0	5
6	Stoke City	2-0/4-0	1-2/3-2	2-2/--	0-2/0-0	0-2/--	X	4-1/--	6
7	Worcester City	3-4/2-2	1-2/1-4	1-4/--	0-1/--	2-3/--	1-1/1-2	X	7
		1	2	3	4	5	6	7	

ESSEX & HERTS BORDER COMBINATION
FINAL LEAGUE TABLES 1997-98

EASTERN DIVISION

	P	W	D	L	F	A	Pts
Dagenham & Red	32	26	4	2	110	22	82
Braintree Town	32	20	7	5	85	39	67
Canvey Island	32	20	5	7	80	37	65
Grays Athletic	32	17	11	4	87	48	62
Billericay Town	32	17	8	7	93	56	59
Tilbury	32	16	5	11	64	56	53
Witham Town	32	12	9	11	50	46	45
Heybridge Swifts	32	10	11	11	63	62	41
East Thurrock Utd	32	11	5	16	72	79	38
Aveley	32	10	6	16	54	75	36
Gt Wakering Rvrs	32	7	12	13	55	84	33
Concord Rangers	32	8	7	17	54	96	31
Bowers United	32	8	6	18	54	87	30
Burnham Ramblers	32	6	11	15	52	73	29
Tiptree United	32	6	9	17	33	68	27
Southend Manor	32	6	9	17	33	71	27
Hornchurch	32	6	7	19	41	81	25

WESTERN DIVISION

	P	W	D	L	F	A	Pts
Enfield	32	22	7	3	98	27	73
Romford	32	22	6	4	83	31	72
Bishop's Stortford	32	21	6	5	69	25	69
Leyton Pennant	32	15	7	10	63	39	52
Stevenage Borough	32	15	6	11	66	41	51
Hertford Town	32	14	9	9	53	50	51
Harlow Town	32	14	10	8	61	41	*49
Hoddesdon Town	32	14	5	13	67	68	47
Ford United	32	13	6	13	42	45	*44
Norwich City	32	10	9	13	35	45	39
Ware	32	9	10	13	46	63	37
Clapton	32	8	9	15	56	80	33
Waltham Abbey	32	9	8	15	43	60	*32
Cheshunt	32	7	10	15	53	72	31
Barkingside	32	7	4	21	39	94	25
Sawbridgeworth T	32	6	4	22	32	74	22
St Margaretsbury	32	5	6	21	38	89	21

CHAMPIONSHIP PLAY-OFF
Enfield v Dagenham & Redgridge 2-2 aet, 5p4

COMBINATION CUP FINAL
Enfield v Braintree Town 2-1

FRED BUDDEN TROPHY FINAL
Grays Athletic v Romford 2-1

SUBURBAN LEAGUE
FINAL LEAGUE TABLES 1997-98

PREMIER DIVISION

	P	W	D	L	F	A	Pts
Slough Town	26	19	3	4	79	29	60
Farnborough Town	26	15	7	4	71	32	52
Hayes	26	12	7	7	67	43	43
Sutton United	26	13	4	9	60	47	43
Dulwich Hamlet	26	12	5	9	56	45	41
Basingstoke Town	26	10	9	7	53	47	39
Met. Police	26	11	5	10	48	41	38
Bromley	26	10	5	11	39	48	35
Whyteleafe	26	10	4	12	42	61	34
Woking	26	7	11	8	40	35	32
Oxford City	26	9	5	12	45	57	32
Marlow	26	7	7	12	32	63	28
Thame United	26	4	4	18	39	82	16
Aldershot Town	26	3	4	19	25	66	13

NORTH DIVISION

	P	W	D	L	F	A	Pts
Uxbridge	26	17	4	5	65	27	55
Hendon	26	16	6	4	80	38	54
Wembley	26	12	7	7	40	33	43
Northwood	26	11	9	6	68	51	42
Edgware Town	26	11	5	10	47	44	38
Ruislip Manor	26	10	7	9	61	65	37
Yeading	26	10	6	10	57	42	36
Egham Town	26	10	4	12	42	55	34
Leighton Town	26	7	11	8	43	52	32
Feltham	26	8	5	13	45	57	29
Kingsbury Town	26	7	7	12	48	70	28
Chesham United	25	7	6	12	53	57	27
Hillingdon Borough	26	5	7	14	36	61	22
Wingate & Finchley	25	6	4	15	41	74	*19

* Wingate & Finchley deducted 3 points

SOUTH DIVISION

	P	W	D	L	F	A	Pts
Fisher Athletic	28	21	3	4	75	27	66
Leatherhead	28	19	3	6	65	33	60
Corinthian Casuals	28	15	8	5	59	35	53
Banstead Athletic	28	16	4	8	67	44	52
Walton & Hersham	28	16	3	9	69	52	51
Crawley Town	28	14	6	8	57	36	48
Hampton	28	14	4	10	50	39	46
Tooting & Mitcham	28	14	2	12	56	52	44
Raynes Park Vale	28	12	1	15	46	70	37
Carshalton Athletic	28	9	3	16	43	55	30
Epsom & Ewell	28	7	5	16	37	56	26
Croydon Athletic	28	4	10	14	47	78	22
Chipstead	28	6	4	18	33	65	22
Croydon	28	4	9	15	44	69	21
Molesey	28	6	1	21	47	84	19

WEST DIVISION

	P	W	D	L	F	A	Pts
Maidenhead United	26	19	5	2	102	26	62
Fleet Town	26	19	4	3	70	31	61
Bracknell Town	26	18	2	6	68	25	56
Hungerford Town	26	14	5	7	63	42	47
Camberley Town	26	13	4	9	45	46	43
Staines Town	26	13	2	11	62	48	41
Thatcham Town	26	11	6	9	49	39	39
AFC Newbury	26	12	2	12	41	51	38
Wokingham Town	26	10	3	13	52	54	33
Abingdon Town	26	7	5	14	44	74	26
Flackwell Heath	26	7	3	16	33	75	24
Burnham	26	4	8	14	32	62	20
Whitchurch United	26	4	3	19	31	77	15
Windsor & Eton	26	4	2	20	43	85	14

RYMAN LEAGUE

PYRAMID SECTION

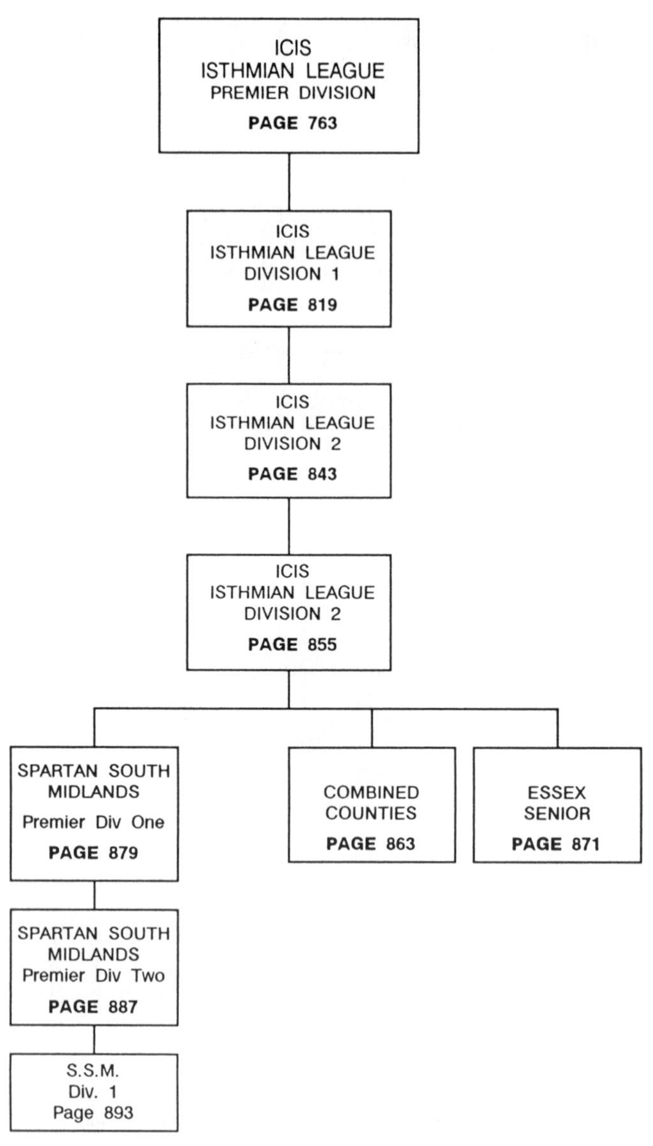
ICIS
ISTHMIAN LEAGUE
PREMIER DIVISION
PAGE 763
ICIS
ISTHMIAN LEAGUE
DIVISION 1
PAGE 819
ICIS
ISTHMIAN LEAGUE
DIVISION 2
PAGE 843
ICIS
ISTHMIAN LEAGUE
DIVISION 2
PAGE 855
SPARTAN SOUTH
MIDLANDS
Premier Div One
PAGE 879
COMBINED
COUNTIES
PAGE 863
ESSEX
SENIOR
PAGE 871
SPARTAN SOUTH
MIDLANDS
Premier Div Two
PAGE 887
S.S.M.
Div. 1
Page 893

FEEDER AND OTHER FEATURED LEAGUES

RYMAN LEAGUE

Chairman: A C F Turvey, MCIM. 18 Apple Way, Old Basing, Basingstoke, Hants RG24 7HA
Tel: 01256 461789 (H), 0836 251368 (M)

Secretary & Treasurer: N R Robinson, FCIArb 226 Rye Lane, Peckham, London SE15 4NL
Tel: 0181 409 1978 (H), 0171 639 5726 (B), 0836 241666 (M)

Kingstonian signalled their championship aspirations prior to the start of the season when they signed up Geoff Chapple as manager and he proved himself once again to be one of the best managers outside the Football League by winning Kingstonian's first League championship since 1937.

The lead at the top chopped throughout the season but in the last couple of weeks it came down to a two horse race between Boreham Wood and Kingstonian who won with two games to spare.

In Division One Aldershot Town were another club who had signalled their intentions early on when they appointed George Borg as Manager and he did not let them down, the Shots always looked as though they were going to win the Division and the local support received in the latter stages of the season will have a number of Premier Division clubs this season opening up turnstiles not used for a long time. Billericay Town and Hampton were also promoted, Hampton's promotion being decided with ten days to go when they beat Maidenhead United at home to strike a fatal blow to United's own championship hopes.

In Division Two the championship went to the wire when, on the last day, leaders at 3.00p.m. Braintree Town lost at home to bottom club Cheshunt while Canvey Island beat Tilbury away to not only give themselves a second championship in three years but also to condemn Tilbury to Division Three. The presentation of the trophy was delayed for an hour while the League Secretary travelled rather quickly from Braintree to Tilbury! Third placed club was Wealdstone who rejoined the Isthmian League in 1995 after a 24 year gap and no doubt they will now have their sights set on the Premier Division.

Division Three began the season with two clubs short but the 'H' clubs will not mind that because Hemel Hempstead, Harlow Town and Hertford Town will simply say that it was four games less to lose. They were the promoted clubs in that order with Hemel Hempstead going up as champions and celebrating the fact by seeking to change their name by adding 'Town' to be like the other two. Fortunes have certainly turned around at Hemel who were not assured of survival until new chairman Dave Boggins took over at the start of the season. Runners-up Harlow Town had narrowly missed out on promotion in season 1996/97 but showed consistency over two seasons to obtain promotion.

In the Cup Competitions the final seasons sponsorship by Guardian Insurance of the League Cup saw a record win for Sutton United against Oxford City. The full Members Cup and the Associate Members Trophy both had new associate sponsors and no doubt Puma and Vandanel will be happy with the respective competitions which resulted in Hendon winning the Full Members Cup for a second time but there is a new name, that of Bedford Town, on the Associate Members Trophy when they beat Epsom & Ewell at Hendon. Hendon's success came against Basingstoke Town at Chesham while Sutton performed their feat at Harrow Borough.

All in all a good inaugural season for main sponsors Ryman with whom it has been a pleasure to work as they have been supportive of the League and we look forward to a long and mutually beneficial relationship with them.

THE GUARDIAN INSURANCE LEAGUE CUP 1997-98

PRELIMINARY ROUND

Hungerford Town	2 v 1	Northwood*
Hemel Hempstead	4 v 2	Kingsbury Town*
Southall	1 v 2	Hornchurch*
Tooting & Mitcham	5 v 2	Dorking
Camberley Town	1 v 0	Witham Town
Egham Town	2 v 4	Braintree Town
Tilbury	2 v 1	Chalfont St Peter
Croydon Athletic	3 v 3	Ware*
(r) Ware	0 v 1	Croydon Athletic
East Thurrock Utd	2 v 4	Ford United*
Leatherhead	0 v 1	Canvey Island
Wembley	2 v 1	Leighton Town
Wealdstone	2 v 1	Edgware Town
Corinthian Casuals	2 v 2	Wingate & Finchley*
(r) Wingate & Finchley	2 v 0	Corinthian Casuals
Cheshunt	0 v 5	Marlow
Horsham	2 v 4	Harlow Town
Tring Town	0 v 2	Bracknell Town*
Aveley	3 v 0	Epsom & Ewell
Flackwell Heath	1 v 2	Lewes*
Hertford Town	1 v 1	Clapton*
(r) Clapton	2 v 0	Hertford Town
Metropolitan Police	2 v 1	Barking
Bedford Town	1 v	Windsor & Eton

ROUND ONE

Carshalton Athletic	3 v 2	Hungerford Town
Yeading	3 v 2	Hemel Hempstead
Billericay Town	5 v 2	Hornchurch*
Wivenhoe Town	0 v 2	Purfleet
Worthing	0 v 1	Tooting & Mitcham U
Camberley Town	2 v 1	Kingstonian
Thame United	1 v 2	Heybridge Swifts
Oxford City	4 v 1	Braintree Town
Chesham United	1 v 4	Boreham Wood
Tilbury	0 v 2	Bognor Regis Town*
Aldershot Town	4 v 0	Croydon Athletic
Ford United	1 v 3	Dagenham & Red.
Staines Town	1 v 8	Hendon
Harrow Borough	0 v 3	Canvey Island
Hitchin Town	2 v 0	Wembley
Wealdstone	4 v 1	Barton Rovers
Maidenhead United	1 v 2	Romford
Wingate & Finchley	1 v 2	Chertsey Town*
Marlow	1 v 4	Harlow Town
Bromley	3 v 1	Bishop's Stortford
Bracknell Town	0 v 2	Sutton United
Leyton Pennant	2 v 2	Uxbridge*
(r) Uxbridge	3 v 0	Leyton Pennant
Basingstoke Town	3 v 1	Dulwich Hamlet
Aveley	4 v 2	Abingdon Town
Gravesend & Northflt	1 v 0	Aylesbury
Wokingham Town	1 v 0	Grays Athletic
Molesley	0 v 4	Hampton
Berkhamsted Town	1 v 2	Walton & Hersham
Lewes	0 v 4	Clapton
Enfield	1 v 2	St Albans City*
Croydon	4 v 0	Metropolitan Police
Bedford Town	1 v 0	Whyteleafe

ROUND TWO

Carshalton Athletic	1 v 0	Yeading
Billericay Town	0 v 0	Purfleet*
(r) Purfleet	1 v 2	Billericay Town*
Tooting & Mitcham U	0 v 2	Camberley Town
Heybridge Swifts	0 v 1	Oxford City
Boreham Wood	4 v 3	Bognor Regis Town*
Aldershot Town	0 v 1	Dagenham & Red.
Hendon	2 v 4	Canvey Island
Hitchin Town	4 v 4	Wealdstone*
(r) Wealdstone	2 v 6	Hitchin Town
Romford	4 v 1	Chertsey Town
Harlow Town	2 v 3	Bromley
Sutton United	3 v 0	Uxbridge
Basingstoke Town	1 v 1	Aveley*
(r) Aveley	1 v 3	Basingstoke Town
≠Gravesend & North	3 v 2	Wokingham Town*
Hampton	2 v 3	Walton & Hersham
Clapton	1 v 2	St Albans City
Croydon	1 v 2	Bedford Town

ROUND THREE

Carshalton Athletic	1 v 0	Billericay Town
Camberley Town	0 v 3	Oxford City
Boreham Wood	1 v 0	Dagenham & Red.
Canvey Island	2 v 0	Hitchin Town
Romford	3 v 1	Bromley
Sutton United	2 v 2	Basingstoke Town*
(r) Basingstoke Town	1 v 3	Sutton United
Wokingham Town	1 v 0	Walton & Hersham
St Albans City	1 v 1	Bedford Town*
(r) Bedford Town	3 v 3	St Albans City*

St Albans City won 4-2 on penalties

ROUND FOUR

Carshalton Athletic	0 v 1	Oxford City
Boreham Wood	2 v 0	Canvey Island
Romford	2 v 2	Sutton United*
(r) Sutton United	5 v 3	Romford*
Wokingham Town	0 v 3	St Albans City

SEMI FINALS

Oxford City	2 v 1	Boreham Wood
Boreham Wood	0 v 3	Oxford City
Sutton United	0 v 0	St Albans City
St Albans City	0 v 3	Sutton United

FINAL

Oxford City	1 v 6	Sutton United

at Harrow Borough FC

* after extra time ≠ Removed from competition

PUMA FULL MEMBERS CUP 1997-98

ROUND ONE

Hendon	3 v 0	Purfleet
St Albans City	5 v 1	Enfield
Gravesend & North.	4 v 3	Berkhamsted Town*
Molesley	0 v 1	Worthing
Chertsey Town	3 v 3	Wokingham Town*
Bromley	2 v 3	Maidenhead Utd*
Hitchin Town	1 v 2	Boreham Wood
Bishop's Stortford	0 v 2	Leyton Pennant
Wembley	2 v 0	Billericay Town
Walton & Hersham	3 v 4	Staines Town
Abingdon Town	0 v 1	Basingstoke Town
Dulwich Hamlet	0 v 3	Kingstonian

ROUND TWO

Hendon	6 v 1	St Albans City
Chesham United	0 v 3	Gravesend & North.
Dagenham & Red.	3 v 0	Romford
Barton Rovers	0 v 2	Harrow Borough
Carshalton Athletic	1 v 0	Aldershot Town
Bognor Regis Town	3 v 1	Worthing
Leatherhead	2 v 1	Chertsey Town
Hampton	0 v 4	Maidenhead United
Boreham Wood	6 v 1	Aylesbury United
Uxbridge	1 v 1	Heybridge Swifts*
Leyton Pennant	3 v 0	Grays Athletic
Yeading	3 v 2	Wembley*
Croydon	0 v 2	Whyteleafe
Staines Town	3 v 0	Sutton United
Oxford City	3 v 1	Thame United
Basingstoke Town	3 v 2	Kingstonian

ROUND THREE

Hendon	1 v 0	Gravesend & North.
Dagenham & Red.	3 v 1	Harrow Borough
Carshalton Athletic	3 v 2	Bognor Regis Town
≠Leatherhead	1 v 0	Maidenhead United
Boreham Wood	2 v 1	Uxbridge
Leyton Pennant	1 v 2	Yeading
Whyteleafe	1 v 3	Staines Town
Oxford Cty	1 v 2	Basingstoke Town

ROUND FOUR

Hendon	3 v 1	Dagenham & Red.
Carshalton Athletic	1 v 2	Maidenhead United
Boreham Wood	2 v 2	Yeading*
Staines Town	1 v 4	Basingstoke Town

SEMI FINALS

Hendon	2 v 1	Maidenhead United
Yeading	2 v 4	Basingstoke Town

FINAL

Hendon 4 v 1 Basingstoke T
at Harrow Borough FC

* after extra time ≠ Removed from competition

VANDANEL TROPHY 1997-98

ROUND ONE

Egham Town	1 v 0	Chalfont St Peter*
Flackwell Heath	3 v 1	Tring Town
Croydon Athletic	0 v 2	Corinthian Casuals
Kingsbury Town	0 v 4	Braintree Town
Hertford Town	0 v 3	Canvey Island
Ware	2 v 2	Aveley*
East Thurrock United	4 v 3	Witham Town
Clapton	1 v 4	Ford United
Banstead Athletic	2 v 1	Camberley Town
Wingate & Finchley	1 v 8	Marlow

ROUND TWO

Egham	4 v 0	Hungerford Town
Flackwell Heath	2 v 0	Dorking
Tooting & Mitcham	0 v 1	Corinthian Casuals
Southall	1 v 1	Hornchurch*
Barking	5 v 4	Braintree Town
Leighton Town	1 v 2	Bedford Town*
Northwood	4 v 0	Wivenhoe Town
Canvey Island	4 v 1	Harlow Town
Aveley	1 v 0	Cheshunt
Hemel Hempstead	0 v 2	East Thurrock United
Ford United	1 v 4	Edgware Town
Tilbury	1 v 2	Wealdstone
Bracknell Town	1 v 2	Epsom & Ewell*
Metropolitan Police	1 v 4	Windsor & Eton
Banstead Athletic	2 v 4	Marlow*
Lewes	0 v 2	Horsham

ROUND THREE

Egham	6 v 1	Flackwell Heath
Corinthian Casuals	4 v 1	Southall
Barking	0 v 3	Bedford Town*
Northwood	3 v 1	Canvey Island
Aveley	2 v 3	East Thurrock United
Edgware Town	1 v 2	Wealdstone
Epsom & Ewell	4 v 1	Windsor & Eton
Marlow	3 v 2	Horsham

ROUND FOUR

Egham Town	3 v 0	Corinthian Casuals
Bedford Town	2 v 1	Northwood
East Thurrock United	1 v 2	Wealdstone
Epsom & Ewell	2 v 1	Marlow

SEMI FINALS

Egham Town	0 v 1	Bedford Town
Wealdstone	0 v 1	Epsom & Ewell

FINAL

Bedford Town 2 v 0 Epsom & Ewell
at Hendon FC

* after extra time ≠ Removed from competition

RYMAN FOOTBALL LEAGUE ROLL OF HONOUR 1997-98

Premier Division	Kingstonian
Division One	Aldershot Town
Division Two	Canvey Island
Division Three	Hemel Hempstead
Guardian Insurance Cup	Sutton United
Puma Full Members Cup	Hendon
Vandanel Trophy	Bedford Town

UMBRO FAIR PLAY AWARDS

Premier Division	Basingstoke Town
Division One	Maidenhead United
Division Two	Bracknell Town
Division Three	Croydon Athletic

LEADING GOALSCORERS

PREMIER DIVISION

			Lge	GIC	PFMC
37	Shaun Marshall	Boreham W	30	6	1
33	Joff Vansittart	Sutton Utd	22	11	
30	Steve Portway	Grave. & N	27	2	1
28	Paul Cobb	Dag & Red	24	2	2
25	David Leworthy	Kingstonian	22	1	2

DIVISION ONE

			Lge	GIC	PFMC
36	Leon Guzmore	Billericay T	34	2	
300	Adie Miles	Bognor Regis	24	4	2
29	Wade Falana	Romford	25	4	
27	Vinny John	Romford	27		
24	Steve Lunn	Leatherhead	22		2

DIVISION TWO

			Lge	GIC	VT
39	Gary Bennett	Braintree T	36	3	
29	Andy Jones	Canvey Island	26	1	2
25	Simon Liddle	Canvey Island	19	3	3
24	Jason Prins	Met Police	24		

DIVISION THREE

			Lge	GIC	PFMC
33	Jeff Wood	Ford Utd	30	1	2
26	Josh Price	Hemel Hemp.	24	2	
23	Ian Jopling	Camberley T	22	1	
23	Tim Sills	Camberley T	21	2	

HONOURS WON BY:

PREMIER DIVISION CLUBS

Basingstoke Town	Puma Cup Finalists
Boreham Wood	Premier Division Runners Up
	Herts Senior Cup Finalists
	London Challenge Cup Winners
Enfield	Middlesex Senior Cup Winners
Gravesend & North.	Kent Senior Cup Finalists
Hendon	Puma Cup Winners
Kingstonian	Premier Division Champions
	Surrey Senior Cup Winners
Oxford City	Guardian Insurance Cup Finalists
	Oxfordshire Senior Cup Finalists
Sutton United	Guardian Insurance Cup Winners

DIVISION ONE CLUBS

Aldershot Town	Division One Champions
Barton Rovers	Bedfordshire Senior Cup Winners
Billericay Town	Division One Runners Up
Maidenhead Utd	Berks/Bucks Senior Cup Winners
Hampton	Promotion from Division One
Uxbridge	Middlesex Senior Cup Finalists
	London Challenge Cup Finalists

DIVISION TWO CLUBS

Bedford Town	Vandanel Trophy Winners
Braintree Town	Division Two Runners Up
Canvey Island	Division Two Champions
Wealdstone	Promotion from Division Two

DIVISION THREE CLUBS

Epsom & Ewell	Vandanel Trophy Finalists
Ford United	London Senior Cup Winners
Harlow Town	Promotion from Division Three
Hemel Hempstead	Division Three Champions
Hertford Town	Division Three Runners Up
Southall	London Senior Cup Finalists

RYMAN (Isthmian) LEAGUE Premier Division Ten Year Records

	88/9	89/0	90/1	91/2	92/3	93/4	94/5	95/6	96/7	97/8
Aylesbury United	-	3	3	7	10	12	4	11	7	18
Barking	10	20	21	-	-	-	-	-	-	-
Basingstoke Town	-	8	18	14	11	21	-	-	-	8
Bishop's Stortford	7	9	13	22	-	-	19	12	19	19
Bognor Regis Town	9	19	17	21	22	-	-	-	-	-
Boreham Wood	-	-	-	-	-	-	-	3	10	2
Bromley	14	21	-	12	17	15	6	19	18	15
Carshalton Athletic	4	10	9	8	4	6	12	6	13	17
Chertsey Town	-	-	-	-	-	-	-	15	22	-
Chesham United	-	-	-	4	1	4	20	-	-	14
Croydon	22	-	-	-	-	-	-	-	-	-
Dagenham	18	6	14	9		(see Dagenham & Redbridge)				
Dagenham & Redbridge	-	-	-	-	-	-	-	-	4	4
Dorking	-	-	-	-	-	20	-	-	-	-
Dulwich Hamlet	16	22	-	-	14	16	11	5	12	16
Enfield	-	-	2	2	3	2	1	2	2	7
Farnborough Town	8	2	-	-	-	-	-	-	-	-
Gravesend & Northfleet	-	-	-	-	-	-	-	-	-	13
Grays Athletic	5	5	6	15	6	14	18	17	21	-
Harrow Borough	19	18	20	18	8	9	10	9	17	12
Hayes	8	14	8	19	9	13	3	1	-	-
Hendon	12	12	15	17	11	11	17	14	16	5
Heybridge Swifts	-	-	-	-	-	-	-	-	9	6
Hitchin Town	-	-	-	-	-	8	5	18	14	21
Kingstonian	6	4	5	10	13	10	13	8	11	1
Leytonstone-Ilford	1						(see Redbridge Forest)			
Leyton-Wingate	15	7	22	-	-	-	-	-	-	-
Marlow	20	17	7	6	15	3	21	-	-	-
Molesey	-	-	-	-	-	18	8	20	-	-
Oxford City	-	-	-	-	-	-	-	-	15	22
Purfleet	-	-	-	-	-	-	16	16	8	10
Redbridge Forest	-	11	1			(see Dagenham & Redbridge)				
St Albans City	17	15	16	13	2	7	7	7	6	11
Slough Town	3	1	-	-	-	-	2	-	-	-
Staines Town	-	16	19	20	20	-	-	-	20	-
Stevenage Borough	-	-	-	-	7	1	-	-	-	-
Sutton United	-	-	-	3	5	5	15	10	3	3
Tooting & Mitcham United	21	-	-	-	-	-	-	-	-	-
Walton & Hersham	-	-	-	-	-	-	14	21	-	9
Windsor & Eton	13	13	12	11	21	-	-	-	-	-
Wivenhoe Town	-	-	10	16	18	22	-	-	-	-
Woking	-	-	4	1	-	-	-	-	-	-
Wokingham Town	11	2	11	5	16	19	22	-	-	-
Worthing	-	-	-	-	-	-	-	22	-	-
Yeading	-	-	-	-	19	17	9	13	5	20
Yeovil Town	-	-	-	-	-	-	-	4	1	-
No of clubs competing	22	22	22	22	22	22	22	22	22	22

RYMAN PREMIER DIVISION

Final League Table	P	HOME W	HOME D	HOME L	HOME F	HOME A	AWAY W	AWAY D	AWAY L	AWAY F	AWAY A	PTS	GD	Leading Goalscorers (these include all goals as reported in the league bulletin)		
Kingstonian	42	14	4	3	51	18	11	8	2	33	17	87	49	22 Leworthy	10 Pitcher, 9 Akuamoah & Luckett	
Boreham Wood	42	11	6	4	44	22	12	5	4	37	20	80	39	33 Marshall	17 Samuels	6 Brown
Sutton United	42	14	3	4	43	30	8	9	4	40	26	78	27	23 Vansittart	18 Hanlon	12 Salako
Dagenham & Redbridge	42	11	6	4	43	25	10	4	7	30	25	73	23	25 Cobb	10 Shipp	9 Pratt
Hendon	42	15	2	4	44	18	6	8	7	25	32	73	19	21 Lewis	14 Whitmarsh, 8 Hyatt & Kelly T	
Heybridge Swifts	42	9	6	6	39	30	9	5	7	35	32	65	12	17 Springett	12 Caldon	10 Greene
Enfield	42	9	4	8	33	28	9	4	8	33	30	62	8	13 Darlington	10 May	7 West
Basingstoke town	42	9	6	6	32	26	8	5	8	24	34	62	-4	24 Coumbs	16 Carey	13 Manley
Walton & Hersham	42	9	6	6	30	28	9	0	12	20	42	60	-20	23 Sayer	6 Blackman	5 Johnson
Purfleet	42	10	4	7	32	28	5	9	7	25	30	58	-1	11 Gentle	8 Carthy, 7 Lawrence & Perkins	
St Albans City	42	9	3	9	29	30	8	4	9	25	29	58	-5	20 Clark	9 Hawoprth	7 Gentle
Harrow Borough	42	10	3	8	27	29	5	7	9	33	38	55	-7	18 Xavier	13 Gavin	7 Webster
Gravesend & Northfleet	42	10	5	6	41	25	5	3	13	24	42	53	-2	27 Portway	6 Arter, Jackson & Powell	
Chesham United	42	8	7	6	46	33	6	3	12	25	37	52	1	21 Lawford	14 Argrave	12 Maguire
Bromley	42	7	6	8	28	25	6	7	8	25	28	52	0	18 Tompkins	7 Kyte	6 Sharman
Dulwich Hamlet	42	10	3	8	33	29	3	8	10	23	38	50	-11	13 Holness	9 Restarick	4 by 4 players
Carshalton Athletic	42	7	4	10	26	30	6	5	10	28	47	48	-23	18 Thompson	11 Newberry	6 Fowler
Aylesbury United	42	8	6	7	31	22	5	2	14	24	48	47	-15	19 Swaysland	8 Davies, 4 Hayward & Liburd	
Bishop's Stortford	42	9	4	8	30	26	5	1	15	23	43	47	-16	11 Adekola	8 Comerford	7 Cooper
Yeading	42	4	7	10	22	35	8	4	9	27	30	47	-16	13 Pickett	10 Kellman	8 Carter
Hitchin Town	42	3	9	9	24	31	5	6	10	21	31	39	-17	11 Parker	9 Williams G, 6 Abbey & Hall	
Oxford City	42	4	6	11	18	29	3	3	15	17	47	30	-41	12 Concannon	6 Smith, 5 Carlisle & Herbert.	

Results 1997-98

		1	2	3	4	5	6	7	8	9	10	11	12	13	14	15	16	17	18	19	20	21	22	
1	Aylesbury United	X	1-2 (318)	2-0 (593)	2-2 (423)	1-2 (471)	4-1 (422)	0-0 (801)	1-2 (325)	0-0 (356)	1-1 (556)	0-2 (803)	1-0 (524)	3-0 (508)	1-3 (414)	1-0 (468)	2-0 (374)	4-1 (267)	0-2 (657)	1-2 (1104)	1-1 (568)	4-0 (427)	1-1 (567)	1
2	Basingstoke Town	1-0 (623)	X	3-1 (483)	2-2 (528)	0-3 (525)	1-2 (489)	2-0 (538)	1-2 (502)	4-3 (451)	0-0 (413)	2-1 (536)	2-2 (621)	1-1 (489)	2-0 (456)	3-0 (383)	0-0 (765)	2-1 (567)	0-2 (536)	3-1 (378)	1-1 (723)	1-2 (523)	1-2 (489)	2
3	Bishops Stortford	1-0 (290)	1-1 (221)	X	3-1 (383)	2-0 (264)	4-3 (90)	4-2 (454)	1-1 (437)	1-1 (202)	0-2 (694)	1-2 (516)	1-2 (315)	1-2 (190)	2-2 (191)	0-2 (242)	0-1 (319)	0-1 (424)	2-0 (378)	1-0 (302)	0-1 (445)	3-1 (331)	2-1 (519)	3
4	Boreham Wood	2-1 (404)	5-0 (178)	1-0 (278)	X	0-0 (229)	2-2 (235)	3-1 (348)	0-0 (629)	4-0 (224)	2-1 (502)	4-1 (223)	2-2 (237)	1-2 (515)	2-3 (313)	0-0 (339)	0-1 (1029)	3-1 (283)	3-1 (229)	2-3 (461)	2-2 (474)	3-0 (138)	3-1 (232)	4
5	Bromley	3-0 (429)	0-2 (365)	3-2 (313)	1-2 (383)	X	3-0 (376)	1-2 (275)	2-0 (529)	1-1 (370)	3-1 (447)	2-0 (542)	2-1 (149)	0-0 (303)	2-2 (197)	0-0 (250)	0-2 (460)	1-2 (281)	2-3 (302)	1-1 (404)	1-1 (405)	0-1 (374)	0-2 (331)	5
6	Carshalton Athletic	2-3 (245)	1-2 (282)	1-2 (251)	0-2 (245)	1-0 (224)	X	0-1 (248)	0-2 (511)	3-3 (340)	2-0 (265)	1-1 (348)	3-0 (328)	3-1 (287)	1-1 (286)	1-2 (249)	1-1 (642)	2-0 (403)	1-0 (308)	0-2 (208)	1-5 (812)	1-2 (357)	1-0 (245)	6
7	Chesham United	4-2 (1034)	0-1 (505)	1-1 (552)	1-1 (381)	2-3 (364)	3-0 (575)	X	0-0 (419)	5-1 (541)	1-2 (602)	4-2 (549)	1-5 (362)	4-1 (406)	0-3 (411)	3-3 (448)	1-1 (434)	6-0 (565)	1-1 (523)	1-2 (349)	3-3 (362)	2-0 (441)	3-1 (341)	7
8	Dagenham & Redbridge	2-3 (793)	2-1 (663)	2-1 (739)	1-1 (539)	2-1 (704)	2-0 (765)	2-0 (778)	X	2-1 (677)	0-2 (1161)	2-0 (1006)	1-2 (689)	1-1 (743)	6-2 (836)	1-0 (851)	2-2 (1076)	7-0 (808)	2-2 (661)	1-1 (847)	0-2 (1214)	4-2 (624)	1-1 (726)	8
9	Dulwich Hamlet	2-1 (306)	0-1 (284)	5-0 (255)	0-1 (335)	3-3 (417)	0-3 (314)	3-1 (211)	0-2 (511)	X	2-0 (423)	1-1 (429)	1-0 (160)	1-2 (314)	1-2 (370)	2-2 (319)	2-1 (603)	3-2 (237)	2-1 (235)	1-2 (302)	1-0 (511)	1-3 (421)	2-1 (237)	9
10	Enfield	2-1 (666)	2-1 (550)	4-1 (688)	0-3 (847)	1-1 (484)	3-0 (659)	0-1 (773)	1-2 (957)	0-0 (656)	X	1-2 (572)	3-5 (683)	3-3 (742)	4-2 (653)	2-1 (601)	0-1 (1142)	2-0 (862)	0-0 (906)	0-2 (772)	0-2 (823)	3-0 (608)	2-0 (444)	10
11	Gravesend & Northfleet	6-0 (454)	3-0 (408)	1-2 (614)	1-1 (537)	1-0 (859)	3-3 (654)	3-2 (630)	2-2 (487)	0-1 (603)	1-3 (723)	X	3-0 (466)	4-0 (678)	1-0 (478)	2-0 (517)	1-2 (753)	3-2 (456)	0-0 (602)	2-1 (405)	2-2 (691)	1-2 (512)	1-2 (526)	11
12	Harrow Borough	1-1 (320)	2-0 (171)	2-1 (184)	1-0 (162)	2-3 (245)	1-3 (188)	1-0 (352)	0-5 (172)	1-2 (205)	5-2 (328)	2-1 (355)	X	0-0 (312)	0-2 (559)	1-1 (205)	0-2 (430)	0-3 (252)	3-0 (202)	1-0 (343)	0-2 (315)	2-0 (207)	2-1 (210)	12
13	Hendon	3-0 (339)	2-1 (287)	3-0 (341)	2-1 (343)	1-0 (208)	4-0 (447)	3-0 (247)	3-0 (295)	2-1 (266)	0-3 (534)	1-2 (357)	2-1 (551)	X	0-2 (221)	0-2 (251)	1-1 (458)	1-0 (211)	1-1 (201)	2-1 (501)	4-2 (370)	4-0 (237)	5-0 (228)	13
14	Heybridge Swifts	5-1 (269)	5-1 (301)	1-0 (390)	2-1 (229)	2-2 (302)	0-0 (295)	0-3 (370)	2-5 (402)	3-1 (304)	4-1 (507)	2-2 (274)	1-0 (238)	1-1 (268)	X	1-2 (251)	1-3 (428)	3-0 (213)	0-1 (226)	3-2 (258)	1-1 (574)	0-1 (219)	2-2 (218)	14
15	Hitchin Town	2-3 (354)	1-2 (275)	2-4 (326)	0-2 (248)	1-1 (350)	1-2 (246)	1-2 (369)	0-1 (351)	2-0 (245)	1-1 (559)	4-0 (349)	2-2 (286)	1-1 (141)	1-1 (269)	X	0-0 (514)	0-0 (178)	3-3 (258)	1-1 (411)	0-3 (471)	1-0 (253)	0-2 (243)	15
16	Kingstonian	3-0 (1247)	2-0 (704)	1-0 (1034)	2-5 (640)	4-1 (958)	5-1 (675)	3-1 (701)	0-2 (141)	2-1 (1203)	0-0 (1002)	3-1 (783)	5-2 (805)	2-1 (911)	3-0 (1595)	2-0 (754)	X	0-0 (669)	2-2 (581)	5-0 (894)	0-0 (2019)	7-0 (1011)	0-1 (1294)	16
17	Oxford City	2-2 (267)	0-1 (426)	1-0 (171)	0-1 (178)	1-1 (171)	1-1 (191)	2-1 (359)	2-0 (272)	1-2 (217)	1-2 (412)	2-1 (269)	2-4 (231)	0-2 (196)	0-2 (221)	2-2 (162)	0-1 (361)	X	0-0 (161)	0-0 (279)	1-2 (273)	0-1 (126)	0-3 (151)	17
18	Purfleet	0-2 (181)	1-2 (85)	3-1 (203)	0-2 (194)	2-0 (214)	1-2 (189)	3-2 (172)	4-0 (841)	2-2 (185)	4-0 (431)	2-0 (412)	2-2 (102)	1-0 (203)	1-1 (149)	1-0 (132)	1-1 (603)	2-1 (129)	X	0-1 (185)	0-6 (279)	1-0 (179)	1-3 (102)	18
19	St. Albans City	1-3 (510)	2-2 (647)	2-1 (298)	0-2 (634)	0-1 (298)	3-0 (486)	1-1 (502)	2-0 (756)	1-0 (506)	0-4 (939)	1-0 (644)	0-0 (467)	1-2 (515)	0-3 (356)	4-1 (652)	0-3 (612)	4-1 (376)	3-2 (232)	X	4-2 (607)	0-1 (513)	0-1 (416)	19
20	Sutton United	2-1 (575)	1-1 (671)	2-4 (485)	1-2 (714)	1-0 (707)	3-1 (1833)	2-4 (690)	2-1 (678)	1-1 (841)	0-5 (1122)	3-1 (583)	2-1 (586)	2-1 (592)	4-1 (524)	2-0 (579)	3-3 (1901)	2-1 (635)	3-0 (515)	3-1 (963)	X	2-0 (747)	2-1 (652)	20
21	Walton & Hersham	3-0 (301)	1-1 (269)	3-0 (219)	1-4 (269)	0-2 (301)	3-4 (218)	1-1 (298)	2-1 (296)	1-0 (160)	3-1 (318)	0-1 (285)	0-0 (247)	2-2 (270)	1-0 (182)	2-1 (207)	1-4 (687)	1-0 (170)	2-4 (186)	1-0 (244)	1-1 (596)	X	1-1 (187)	21
22	Yeading	1-0 (187)	2-2 (158)	0-2 (162)	0-1 (152)	1-1 (155)	0-0 (103)	2-0 (219)	0-2 (161)	2-2 (118)	0-2 (402)	4-3 (238)	2-2 (325)	0-2 (156)	0-3 (152)	1-2 (153)	1-3 (331)	1-1 (155)	0-0 (112)	0-2 (178)	3-1 (256)	2-4 (243)	X	22

PROGRAMME DETAILS:
Pages: 40 **Price:** £1.20
Editor: Karl Prentice/ Graham Brookland
Tel: 01256 471630

ALDERSHOT TOWN

Colours: Red & blue/white & red/red **Sponsors:** TB
Change colours: Black & white/black & red/white **Formed:** 199
Midweek matchday: Tuesday **Nickname:** The Shot
Reserve Team's League: None. **Club Newsline:** 0930 555 855
Local Press: Aldershot News, Farnham Herald
Local Radio: County Sound (203m m/w, 1476 khz), BBC Radio Surrey (104. fm), Radio 210 (210m m/w).
Chairman: Karl Prentice **Vice Chairman:** TBA
Company Secretary: Graham Brookland, c/o Aldershot Town FC, (097 172073)
Manager: George Borg. **Asst Man.:** Stuart Cash **Physio:** Phil Sheddon
Press Officer: Nick Fryer Tel: 01483 563570
GROUND Address: Recreation Ground, High Street, Aldershot, Hants GU1 1TW (01252 20211. Fax: 24347).
Directions: Ground situated on eastern end of High Street next to large mult storey B.T. building. From M3 (jct 4) take A325 to Aldershot. After five miles a r'bout take 1st exit marked town centre (A323) into Wellington Ave. At Burge King r'bout take 2nd exit into High Street - ground on left, large car par adjacent. 5 mins walk from Aldershot (BR).
Capacity: 7,500 **Cover:** 6,850 **Seats:** 1,800 **Floodlights:** Yes
Clubhouse: 7-11pm every evening and matchdays except Wednesday. Pool, darts, satellite TV & skittles alle Steward: Wally Clarke 01252 338426. **Club Shop:** Range of souvenirs, programmes, replica kits. Open matchday or contact Janet Guess (01252-20211) for mail order.

PREVIOUS - **Leagues:** None. **Names:** None. **Grounds:** None.

CLUB RECORDS - **Attendance:** 5,961 v Farnborough Town, Hants Senior Cup SF 16/3/93. 4,289 v Berkhamste 2/5/98 League. *Ground record: 19,138 Aldershot FC v Carlisle United, FA Cup 4th Rd repla 28/1/70.* **Win:** 8-1 v Leyton Pennant League 7/2/98. **Defeat:** 1-5 v Gloucester City, FA Troph Nov 1995. **Career Goalscorer:** Mark Butler 155. (92-date). **Career Appearances:** Mark Butle 303. (92-date). **Transfer Fee Paid:** £8,000 to Slough Town for Gary Abbott. **Transfer Fe Received:** £5,000 for Jason Tucker from Enfield 96

BEST SEASON - **FA Cup:** Fourth Qual Rd 95-96. **FA Trophy:** Third Qual Rd 94-95 95-96 96-97 97-98. **FA Vase** Quarter Final 93-94.

HONOURS - Isthmian League Div 3 92-93; Simpsonair Trophy 92-93; Skol Invitation Trophy 92-93; Han Senior Cup SF 92-93; Suburban Lge Western Div champions 94-95; Allied Counties Youth Lg Champions 1994-95; Guradian Insurance Lge Cup R-up 95-96.

97-98 - Captain: Mark Harper **Top scorer:** Roy Young (27) **P.o.Y.:** Otis Hutchings

(L-R); Phil Sheddon (Physio), George Borg (Mgr), Jon Denton, Mark Harper, Stuart Cash (Asst Mgr), Lee Rogers, Rc Young, Tony Cleeve, Terry Howard, Simon Bassey, Neil Champion, John Humphrey, Otis Hutchings, Mark Butle Michael Bullen, Joe Nartey, Jason Tucker, Johnson Hippolyte, Paul Priddy (Coach), Jimmy Sugrue, Gary Phillips, Le Endersley, Jason Chewins.

ALDERSHOT TOWN - Match Facts 97-98

HSC - Hampshire Sen. Cup

Match No.	Date	Venue H / A	Comp.	Opponents	Result & Score		Att.	Goalscorers	League Position
1	16.08	H	IL-1	Chertsey Town	L	0-1	1,748		18
2	19.08	A	IL-1	Worthing	D	2-2	*1,264*	Cleeve, Beeks.	13
3	23.08	A	IL-1	Abingdon Town	W	2-0	*595*	Beeks,Young.	10
4	26.08	H	IL-1	Hampton	W	2-0	1,544	Cleeve, Beeks.	5
5	30.08	H	IL-1	Bognor Regis Town	D	1-1	1,777	Keown.	6
6	07.09	A	IL-1	Grays Athletic	L	1-2	*606*	Young.	7
7	13.09	A	**FAC 1Q**	Newport	L	1-2	*848*	Burton.	-
8	16.09	H	IL-1	Wembley	W	3-1	1,122	Wooler, Butler, Brown.	7
9	20.09	H	IL-1	Croydon Athletic	D	1-1	1,618	Butler.	5
10	24.09	A	IL-1	Leyton Pennant	D	3-3	*380*	Cleeve, Young 2.	6
11	27.09	A	IL-1	Uxbridge	W	2-1	*670*	Beeks, Young.	4
12	04.10	H	IL-1	Leatherhead	W	1-0	1,888	Beeks.	4
13	11.10	A	IL-1	Whyteleafe	W	4-0	*702*	Brodrick, Young, Butler, Sugrue.	4
14	14.10	A	IL-1	Billericay Town	W	2-1	*655*	Cash, Sugrue.	2
15	18.10	H	**FAT1Q**	Croydon	W	5-1	1,705	Brodrick, Beeks, Young, Butler, Keown.	-
16	21.10	H	**GIC**	Croydon	W	4-0	1,003	**Young 3,** Butler.	-
17	25.10	H	IL-1	Barton Rovers	W	1-0	1,905	Keown.	3
18	28.10	H	**HSC**	Whitchurch	W	7-1	1,006	Butler 2, Sugrue 2, Brodrick, Beeks, OG.	-
19	01.11	A	IL-1	Maidenhead United	W	2-0	*991*	Beeks, Hippolyte.	2
20	04.11	H	**GIC**	Dagenham & Redbridge	L	0-1	1,398		-
21	08.11	A	**FAT 2Q**	Carshalton Athletic	D	0-0	*853*		-
22	11.11	H	**FAT 2Q R**	Carshalton Athletic	W	3-0	1,652	Harper, Young, OG.	-
23	15.11	A	IL-1	Staines Town	W	5-2	*1,060*	Cleeve, Hutchings, Young 2, Mernagh.	3
24	18.11	H	**HSC**	Bournemouth	W	4-1	926	Mernagh, Butler.	-
25	22.11	H	RL-1 1	Thame United	D	1-1	1,948	Hutchings.	3
26	25.11	H	RL-1	Molesey	W	3-1	1,487	Harper, Sugrue, Young.	2
27	29.11	A	**FAT 3Q**	Billericay Town	L	1-2	*982*	Mernagh.	-
28	06.12	H	RL-1	Worthing	W	3-1	1,885	Cleeve, Young, Butler.	2
29	09.12	A	RL-1	Berkhamsted Town	**L**	**2-4**	*426*	Cleeve, Hippolyte.	2
30	13.12	H	RL-1	Maidenhead Unitedd	L	0-2	2,125		3
31	20.12	A	RL-1	Romford	W	2-1	*600*	Brodrick, Butler.	3
32	22.12	A	**FMC**	Carshalton Athletic	L	0-1	*220*		-
33	27.12	H	RL-1	Wokingham Town	W	4-0	2,496	Cash, Hutchings, Hippolyte 2.	1
34	10.01	H	RL-1	Grays Athletic	W	2-1	2,565	Sugrue, Young.	1
35	17.01	A	RL-1	Chertsey Town	L	0-2	*1,445*		1
36	21.01	A	**HSC QF**	Eastleigh	W	2-1	*435*	Brodrick, Young.	-
37	24.01	H	RL-1	Abingdon Town	W	3-1	2,194	Young 2, Sugrue.	1
38	31.01	A	RL-1	Hampton	D	1-1	*1,566*	Hippolyte.	1
39	07.02	H	RL-1	Leyton Pennant	**W**	**8-1**	2,163	Tucker 2, Young 2, Hippolyte 2, Sugrue 2.	1
40	14.02	A	RL-1	Bognor Regis Town	W	2-1	*1,459*	Chewins, Hippolyte.	1
41	21.02	H	RL-1	Whyteleafe	W	3-0	2,302	Young, Sugrue 2.	1
42	28.02	A	RL-1	Leatherhead	D	0-0	*1,540*		1
43	07.03	H	RL-1	Uxbridge	W	4-0	2,394	Butler, Hippolyte 2, Endersby.	1
44	11.03	N	**HSC SF**	Newport I.o.W.	L	1-2	*742*	Hutchings. at Eastleigh FC	-
45	14.03	A	RL-1	Croydon	L	1-2	*800*	Sugrue.	1
46	21.03	A	RL-1	Barton Rovers	D	1-1	*620*	Howard.	1
47	28.03	H	RL-1	Billericay Town	W	1-0	3,543	Endersby.	1
48	31.03	A	RL-1	Wembley	W	1-0	*650*	Hippolyte.	1
49	04.04	A	RL-1	Molesey	W	1-0	*1,016*	Tucker.	1
50	11.04	H	RL-1	Romford	W	2-0	2,870	Hippolyte, Endersby.	1
51	13.04	A	RL-1	Wokingham Town	W	3-0	*1,661*	Harper, Nartey.	1
52	18.04	H	RL-1	Staines Town	W	2-0	3,410	Sugrue, Young.	1
53	25.04	A	RL-1	Thame United	W	4-1	*812*	Howard, **Young 3.**	1
54	02.05	H	RL-1	Berkhamsted Town	W	3-0	4,289	Hutchings, Bassey, Endersby.	1

PLAYING SQUAD 1998 - **Goalkeepers:** Gary Phillips (Aylesbury U, Barnet, Reading, Brentford, Barnet,WBA, Brighton). **Defenders:** Mark Harper (Kingstonian, Chertsey T, Egham T, Hampton, Bedfont,Wolves), Darren Brodrick (Hendon, Walton & Hersham, Kingstonian, CarshaltonAth, Kingstonian, Fulham), Lee Rogers (Youth), Jon Denton (Hayes,Chertsey T, Hayes, Chertsey T, Yeading, Hounslow, Harefield U, Hillingdon), Jason Chewins (Wealdstone, Basingstoke T, Alton T), Tony Cleeve (BasingstokeT, Aldershot T, Cove, Southampton), Stuart Cash (Enfield, Kingstonian,Halesowen T, Chesham U, Slough T, Chertsey T, Stevenage B, Wycombe W,Chesterfield, Nottingham F, Halesowen T, Stourbridge, Bilston T), Terry Howard (Yeovil T, Woking, Wycombe W, Leyton Orient, Chelsea), Gary Smart * (Slough T,Hayes, Stevenage B, Oxford U, Wokingham T). **Midfielders:** Jason Tucker (Enfield, Aldershot T, Chertsey T, Yeading,Aldershot), Otis Hutchings (Dulwich Hamlet, Molesey, Tooting & Mitcham U,Walton & Hersham, Chelsea), Simon Bassey (Carshalton Ath, Charlton Ath), Neil Champion (Fareham T, Petersfield U, AFC Bournemouth), John Humphrey (Millwall, Leatherhead), Simon Stapleton *(Stevenage B., Rushden & D., Slough T., Wycombe W., Bristol R., Portsmouth). **Forwards:** Mark Butler (Egham T, Chesham U, Wycombe W, Egham T, Farnborough T,Ash U, Tongham), Roy Young (Poole T, Portsmouth), Lee Endersby (Enfield,Harrow B, Wembley, Brimsdown R), Johnson Hippolyte (Dulwich Hamlet, Chesham U,Chertsey T, Yeading, Wealdstone, Chalfont St.Peter, Uxbridge, Hounslow), Jimmy Sugrue (Hayes, Aldershot T, Kingstonian, Fulham), Joe Nartey (Chertsey T,Hayes, Hillingdon B), Gary Abbott * (Slough T, Enfield, Welling U, Enfield,Barnet, Welling U).

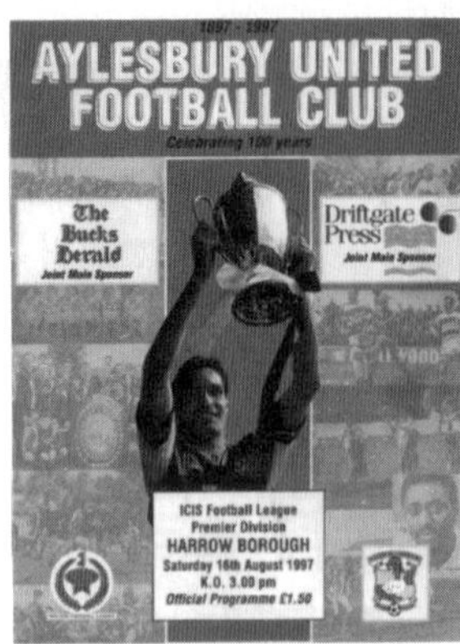

PROGRAMME DETAILS:
Pages: 36 **Price:** £1
Editor: Dave Gamage
(01844 342308)

AYLESBURY UNITED

Colours: Green & white qtrs/green/green
Change colours: Amber & black
Newsline: 0891 446 824
Midweek home matchday: Tuesday
Reserve Team's League: None
Local Press: Bucks Herald, Bucks Advertiser.
Local Radio: Three Counties Radio, Chiltern Radio, Mix 96.

Formed: 1897
Nickname: The Ducks
Sponsors:

Chairman: Bill Carroll **Vice Chairman:** Roger Payne
Secretary / Press Officer: Tony Graham c/o the club. 01296 - 88178 (H) 436350
Manager: Bob Dowie **Coach:** Peter Lawrence
Assistant Manager: Dave Anderson **Physio:** Paul Thawley

GROUND Address: The Stadium, Buckingham Road, Aylesbury HP20 2AQ (01296 436350/436891). **Directions:** On A413 to Buckingham, just off ring road opposite Horse & Jockey PH. Arriving from Buckingham ground is on left - from all other directions follow Buckingham signs and ground on right. Half hour walk from Aylesbury rail and bus stations.
Floodlights: Yes **Capacity:** 4,500 **Cover:** 1000 **Seats:** 400
Clubhouse: Pub hours, but shut during matches. Function room available for hire (01296 436891). Bar snacks available.
Club Shop: Sells programmes, magazines, leisurewear, badges etc. Contact Debbie Gamage c/o The Club.

PREVIOUS - **Leagues:** Bucks Contiguous 1897-1903, South Eastern 03-07, Spartan 07-51, Delphian 51-63, Athenian 63-76, Southern 76-88, GMV Conference 88-89
Grounds: Printing Works Ground 1897-1935, Sports Stadium, Wendover Rd (ground name changed to The Stadium, Turnfurlong Lane) 35-85, shared grounds 85-86.
Name: Night School, Printing Works (merged in 1897).

CLUB RECORDS - **Attendance:** 6,000 v England 1988 *(at old ground: 7,500 v Watford, FA Cup 1st Rd 1951).* **Career goalscorer:** Cliff Hercules. **Career appearances:** Cliff Hercules. **Transfer fee paid:** £15,000 for Glenville Donegal (Northampton, 1990). **Transfer fee received:** £35,000 for Glenville Donegal (Maidstone Utd, 1991)

BEST SEASON - **FA Trophy:** Quarter-Final replay 80-81. **FA Cup:** 3rd Rd 95. **League clubs defeated:** Southend Utd 89-90.

HONOURS - Southern Lg 87-88 (Mids Div R-up 84-85, Sth Div R-up 79-80); Athenian Lg Div 2 R-up 67-68; Delphian Lg 53-54 (R-up 52-53, Lg Cup 59-60); Spartan Lg 08-09 (R-up 52-53), West Div 28-29 (R-up 45-46), Div 1 38-39 (R-up 34-35); Berks & Bucks Snr Cup 13-14 85-86 96-97; Isthmian League Cup 94-95, Isthmian Charity Shield 95-96.

Players progressing to Football League: Ray Mabbutt (Bristol Rovers), Phil Barber (Crystal Palace 1986)

97-98 - Captain: Lee Harvey **P.o.Y.:** Matt Hayward **Top scorer:** Mick Swaysland

Photo taken at a 10 year reunion match at the end of 97-98 season, between the current team and the team that won the Southern League in 1988.

AYLESBURY UNITED - Match Facts 97-98

B&BSC - Berks & Bucks Senior Cup

Match No.	Date	Venue H / A	Comp.	Opponents	Result & Score		Att.	Goalscorers	League Position
1	16.08	H	IL	Harrow Borough	W	1-0	524	Gallagher.	7
2	19.08	A	IL	Basingstoke Town	L	0-1	*623*		9
3	23.08	A	IL	Carshalton Athletic	W	3-2	*402*	Swaysland 2, Gallagher.	5
4	25.08	H	IL	Purfleet	L	0-2	657		8
5	30.08	H	IL	Bishop's Stortford	W	2-0	593	Swaysland, Gallen.	8
6	05.09	A	IL	Heybridge Swifts	L	1-5	*269*	Liburd.	9
7	09.09	A	**GIC 1**	Gravesend & Northfleet	L	0-1	*306*		-
8	13.09	A	**FAC 1Q**	Edgware Town	W	5-2	*274*	**Swaysland 4,** Davies.	-
9	20.09	A	IL	Bromley	L	0-3	*429*		16
10	23.09	H	IL	Hitchin Town	W	1-0	468	Hayward	14
11	27.09	H	**FAC 2Q**	Carshalton Athletic	L	0-3	516		-
12	30.09	H	IL	Dagenham & Redbridge	L	1-2	325	Swaysland.	16
13	04.10	A	IL	Yeading	L	0-1	*187*		16
14	07.10	A	IL	Gravesend & Northfleet	**L**	**0-6**	*454*		19
15	11.10	H	IL	Boreham Wood	D	2-2	423	Hayward, Brady.	19
16	14.10	H	IL	Kingstonian	W	2-0	374	Sullivan, Swaysland.	15
17	25.10	A	IL	Walton & Hersham	L	0-3	*301*		16
18	01.11	H	IL	Sutton United	D	1-1	568	Swaysland.	17
19	08.11	A	IL	Dulwich Hamlet	L	1-2	*306*	Hayward.	17
20	15.11	H	IL	Oxford City	W	4-1	267	Liburd 47, 56 (pen), Davies 64, Scott 87.	13
21	22.11	A	II	St. Albans City	W	3-1	*510*	Meara, Swaysland 2.	11
22	25.11	H	IL	Enfield	D	1-1	556	Meara (pen).	11
23	29.11	H	**FAT 3Q**	Dulwich Hamlet	L	0-3	406		-
24	06.12	A	RL	Purfleet	W	2-0	*181*	Davies 20, Gallagher 56 (pen).	8
25	13.12	A	RL	Sutton United	L	1-2	*575*	Swaysland.	9
26	20.12	H	RL	Hendon	W	3-0	508	Williams, Clarry, Gallagher.	
27	23.12	A	**FMC 2**	Boreham Wood	L	1-6	*111*		-
28	27.12	A	RL	Chesham United	L	2-4	*1,034*	Hayward, Swaysland.	10
29	03.01	H	RL	Gravesend & Northfleet	L	0-2	803		11
30	17.01	A	RL	Harrow Borough	D	1-1	*320*	Williams 84.	13
31	24.01	H	RL	Carshalton Athletic	W	4-1	422	Swaysland, Liburd, Davies, Jones.	11
32	27.01	H	**B&BSC 1**	Burnham	W	4-0	234	Gallagher, Swaysland, Williams 2.	-
33	31.01	A	RL	Bishop's Stortford	L	0-1	*290*		11
34	07.02	H	RL	Bromley	L	1-2	471	Davies.	12
35	14.02	A	RL	Hitchin Town	W	3-2	*354*	Swaysland 2, Roudette.	13
36	24.02	H	**B&BSC 2**	Chesham United	W	2-0	403	Gallagher, Williams.	-
37	28.02	H	RL	Yeading	D	1-1	567	Williams	14
38	07.03	A	RL	Dagenham & Redbridge	W	3-2	*793*	Court, Ndeke, Davies.	11
39	14.03	H	RL	Heybridge Swifts	L	1-3	414	Ndeke.	14
40	21.03	H	RL	Walton & Hersham	**W**	**4-0**	427	Swaysland 2, Davies, James.	13
41	28.03	A	RL	Kingstonian	L	0-3	*1,247*		14
42	01.04	H	**B&BSC S-F**	Reading	L	0-4	464		-
43	03.04	H	RL	Dulwich Hamlet	D	0-0	356		15
44	11.04	A	RL	Hendon	L	0-3	*339*		16
45	13.04	H	RL	Chesham United	D	0-0	801		16
46	17.04	A	RL	Oxford City	D	2-2	*267*	Roudette, Darlington.	15
47	21.04	H	RL	Basingstoke Town	L	1-2	318	Davies.	
48	25.04	H	RL	St Albans City	L	1-2	1,104	Court.	18
49	28.04	A	RL	Boreham Wood	L	1-2	*404*	James.	18
50	02.05	A	RL	Enfield	L	1-2	*666*	Howell.	18

PLAYING SQUAD 1998 - **Goalkeepers:** Andy Lomas (Yeading, Hendon, Boreham Wood, Rushden & D, StevenageB, Chesham U, Barnet, Baldock T, Arlesey T, Eaton Bray U). **Defenders:** Matt Hayward (Thame U, Pitstone & Ivinghoe, Aylesbury U), Lee Harvey (Yeovil T, Slough T, Aylesbury U, Hemel Hempstead, Chertsey T,Berkhamsted T, Edgware T, Watford), Justin Skinner (Wimbledon), Aidan O'Brien (Abingdon T, Morpeth T, South Shields), Jason Court (Harrow B, LeverstockGreen, Harrow B, Hayes, Leverstock Green, Hayes, Boreham Wood, ChalfontSt.Peter, St.Albans C), Paul Benning (Harrow B, Chesham U, Sutton U, AylesburyU, Chesham U, Hungerford T, Hayes, Peterborough U, Gosnells C (Aust), Hayes), Warren Kelly * (Rushden & D, Stevenage B, Hayes, St.Albans C, Hemel Hempstead). **Midfielders:** Greg Howell (Hemel Hempstead, St.Albans C, Enfield, Wellington U(NZ), Barnet, Notts Co, Aston Villa, Tottenham H), Keiran Gallagher (Barnet,Chelsea), Mark Jones (Rushden & D, Watford), Ricky Sullivan (Hertford Heath), Adam Clarry (London Colney, Sutton U, St.Albans C), Jim Meara (Doncaster R,Watford), Steve Butler (Harrow B, Lincoln Brigade (USA), Harrow B, BerkhamstedT, Wycombe W), Phil Mason * (Oxford C, Brackley T, Worcester C, Spennymoor U,Worcester C, Kettering T, Blyth Spartans, Newcastle U). **Forwards:** Marc Liburd (Boreham Wood, Peterborough U, Watford), Kevin Davies (Chesham U, Harow B, Chalfont St.Peter, Leighton T, Marlow, Aylesbury U,Marlow, Chesham U, Tring T, Kingstonian, Aylesbury U, Luton T), Dean Williams (Berkhamsted T, Staines T, Chesham U, Hayes, Aylesbury U, Stevenage B,Brentford, St.Albans C, Wokingham T, Hemel Hempstead, Chesham U, HemelHempstead, St.Albans C, Cambridge U), Chris James (Dulwich Hamlet, Hendon,Leyton Pennant, Molesey, Hendon, Walton & Hersham), Jermaine Darlington (Heybridge S, Dulwich Hamlet, Hendon, Dover Ath, Charlton Ath, Watford,Chelsea, Tottenham H), Gary Crawshaw * (Stevenage B, Hendon, Staines T, WycombeW, Luton T).

PROGRAMME DETAILS:
Pages: 40 **Price:** £1
Editor: Michael Edwards
Tel: 01256 410103

BASINGSTOKE TOWN

Colours: Blue & gold stripes/blue/blue **Formed:** 1896
Change colours: Red & black stripes/black/black **Nickname:** Stoke
Midweek home matchday: Tuesday
Reserve Team's League: Suburban (Prem Div)
Local Press: Basingstoke Gazette (461131).
Local Radio: Radio 210 (01189 413131), Kestrel Radio (01256 694000)

Chairman: David Knight **President:** Rafi Pazzak
Secretary: Richard Trodd, 5 Lehad Close, Brighton Hill, Basingstoke RG22 4HT (01256 413076)
Manager: Ernie Howe **Asst Manager:** Pete Peters
Coach: Steve Richardson **Physio:** Paul Bell
Press Officer: John Gray
Commercial Manager: Chris Richardson.

GROUND Address: Camrose Road, Western Way, Basingstoke RG24 6HW (01256 325063).
Directions: Exit 6 off M3 and follow A30 west, ground off Winchester Road. Two miles from bus and rail stations.
Capacity: 6,000 **Cover:** 1,500 **Seats:** 651 **Floodlights:** Yes
Sponsors: Centerprise International & New Way Nissan
Clubhouse: Open every day (incl. lunchtime) **Steward:** Cheryl Fox (01256 464353).
Club Shop: Selling programmes, books, scarves, shirts etc. Contact Neil Tysoe. **Metal Badges:** Yes

PREVIOUS - **Leagues:** Hants 1900-40 45-71; Southern 71-87. **Ground:** Castle Field 1896-1947.

CLUB RECORDS - **Attendance:** 5,085 v Wycombe Wanderers, FA Cup 1st Rd replay 97-98. **Win:** 10-0 v Chichester City (H), FA Cup 1st Qualifying Round, September 1976. **Defeat:** 0-8 v Aylesbury United, Southern League, April 1979. **Goalscorer:** Paul Coombs 159 (Oct 91 -). **Appearances:** Billy Coombs. **Fees - Paid:** £4,750 for Steve Ingham (Gosport Borough). **Received:** £6,750 for Steve Ingham (Bashley)

BEST SEASON - **FA Trophy:** 1st Rd 88-89 lost 3-5 at Kettering. **FA Cup:** 2nd Rd 89-90 (lost 2-3 at home to Torquay), 2nd Rd 97-98 (lost 4-3pen aet v Northampton H). **League clubs defeated in FA Cup:** Wycombe Wanderers 97-98.

HONOURS - Southern Lge Southern Div 85-86; Isthmian League Div 1 R-up 88-89 96-97; Hants League 67-68 69-70 70-71 (R-up 65-66 66-67 68-69, North Div 11-12 19-20); Hants Senior Cup 70-71 89-90 95-96 96-97.

Players progressing to Football League: Tony Godfrey (Southampton 58), John Neale (Exeter 72), Mike Doherty (Reading 82), Micky Cheetham (Ipswich 88), Matt Carmichael (Lincoln), Tony Franklin (Exeter), Steve Welsh (Peterborough 90).

97-98 Captain: Steve Richardson **P.o.Y.:** Danny Barker **Top scorer:** Paul Coombs

Basingstoke Town celebrating after their 1-1 draw against Northampton Town in the FA Cup Second Round.
Photo: Eric Marsh

BASINGSTOKE TOWN - Match Facts 97-98

Match No.	Date	Venue H / A	Comp.	Opponents	Result & Score	Att.	Goalscorers	League Position
1	16.08	A	IL	Walton & Hersham	D 1-1	269	Coombs.	
2	19.08	H	IL	Aylesbury United	W 1-0	623	Coombs.	
3	23.08	H	IL	Kingstonian	D 0-0	765		7
4	26.08	A	IL	Boreham Wood	**L 0-5**	178		
5	30.08	A	IL	Hendon	L 1-2	287	Medford.	15
6	02.09	H	IL	Chesham United	W 2-0	538	Manley, Barker.	
7	07.09	H	IL	Bromley	L 0-3	525		14
8	13.09	A	**FAC 1Q**	Havant Town	D 1-1	236	Carroll.	-
9	16.09	H	**FAC 1Q R**	Havant Town	W 2-0	211	Medford, Ferrett.	-
10	20.09	H	IL	Dagenham & Redbridge	L 1-2	502	Medford.	18
11	23.09	A	IL	Yeading	D 2-2	158	Manley, Harris.	18
12	27.09	H	**FAC 2Q**	Bath City	D 1-1	488	Manley	-
13	30.09	A	**FAC 2Q R**	Bath City	W 3-1	388	Wilkinson 13, Coombs 41, 47.	-
14	04.10	A	IL	Heybridge Swifts	L 1-5	301	Barker.	20
15	07.10	A	IL	Carshalton Athletic	W 2-1	282	Coombs, Coney.	19
16	11.10	H	**FAC 3Q**	Calne Town	D 0-0	411		-
17	14.10	A	**FAC 3Q R**	Calne Town	W 2-1	287	OG (Pike), Coombs	-
18	18.10	H	**FAT 1Q**	Leatherhead	W 2-0	402	Coombs 2.	-
19	25.10	H	**FAC 4Q**	Braintree Town	W 5-1	867	**Coombs 3,** Wilkinson, Tydeman.	-
20	28.10	A	**FMC 1**	Abingdon Town	W 1-0			-
21	01.11	H	IL	Dulwich Hamlet	W 4-3	451	Harris, Tydeman, Coombs, Manley.	19
22	08.11	H	**FAT 2Q**	Witney Town	W 2-0	320	Harris, Wilkinson.	-
23	15.11	A	**FAC 1**	Wycombe Wanderers	D 2-2	3,932	Coombs, Wilkinson.	-
24	22.11	A	RL	Sutton United	D 1-1	671	Coombs.	21
25	26.11	H	**FAC 1 R**	Wycombe Wanderers	D *2-2	5,085	Coombs 2 (1 pen). A.E.T. Won 5-4 after penalties.	
26	-29.11	H	**FAT 3Q**	Romford	W 4-0		Coombs, Harris, Carey, Manley.	-
27	06.12	A	**FAC 2**	Northampton Town	D 1-1	5,881	Carey 75.	-
28	13.12	A	RL	Dulwich Hamlet	W 1-0	284	Wilkinson.	21
29	16.12	H	**FAC 2 R**	Northampton Town	D *0-0	4,933	A.E.T. Lost 3-4 after penalties.	
30	-20.12	H	RL	Purfleet	L 0-2	536		21
31	23.12	H	**FMC 2**	Kingstonian	W 3-2		Medford 2, OG.	-
32	27.12	A	RL	Oxford City	W 1-0	426	Harris.	21
33	03.01	H	RL	Yeading	L 1-2		Coombs	21
34	10.01	H	**FAT 1**	Gloucester City	L 0-1	715		-
35	17.01	H	RL	Walton & Hersham	L 1-2	523	Coombs.	21
36	20.01	A	**FMC 3**	Oxford City	W 2-1		Coombs, Wilkinson.	-
37	24.01	A	RL	Kingstonian	L 0-2	704		21
38	31.01	H	RL	Hendon	D 1-1	489	Mancey	21
39	07.02	A	RL	Dagenham & Redbridge	L 1-2	663	Coombs.	21
40	10.02	H	RL	St Albans City	**W 3-1**	378	Beeks, Wilkinson, Tydeman.	
41	14.02	H	RL	Boreham Wood	D 2-2	528	Beeks, Line.	21
42	17.02	A	**FMC 4**	Staines Town	W 4-1		Line, Wilkinson, Asker, Manley.	-
43	21.02	A	RL	Hitchin Town	W 2-1	275	Carey, Mancey.	19
44	24.02	A	RL	Gravesend & Northfleet	L 0-3	408		
45	28.02	H	RL	Heybridge Swifts	W 2-0	456	Carey, Wilkinson.	18
46	03.03	H	RL	Enfield	D 0-0	413		18
47	07.03	H	RL	Carshalton Athletic	L 1-2	489	Coombs.	19
48	10.03	A	RL	Harrow Borough	L 0-2	171		
49	14.03	A	RL	Bromley	W 2-0	365	Carey 2.	17
50	17.03	A	**FMC SF**	Yeading	W 4-2	122	Emsden, Tydeman, Asker, Mancey.	-
51	21.03	A	RL	Bishop's Stortford	D 1-1	221	Carey.	17
52	24.03	H	RL	Hitchin Town	**W 3-1**	383	**Carey 3.**	
53	28.03	H	RL	Harrow Borough	D 2-2	621	Becks, Carey.	16
54	31.03	A	RL	Chesham United	W 1-0	505	Carey.	
55	04.04	H	RL	Gravesend & Northfleet	W 2-1	536	Carey 2.	13
56	07.04	H	RL	Bishop's Stortford	**W 3-1**	483	Carey 2, Mancey.	
57	13.04	H	RL	Oxford City	W 2-1	567	Wilkinson, Manley.	9
58	18.04	A	RL	Enfield	L 1-2	550	Tydeman.	11
59	21.04	A	RL	Aylesbury United	W 2-1	318	Emsden, Coombs.	9
60	23.04	A	RL	Purfleet	W 2-1	85	Mancey 2.	8
61	25.04	H	RL	Sutton United	D 1-1	723	Asker.	7
62	29.04	N	**FMC Final**	Hendon	L 1-4	550	Mancey.	-
63	02.05	A	RL	St Albans City	D 2-2	647	Emsden 2.	8

OTHER MATCHES - **GIC** - **Rd.1** 09.09 v Dulwich Hamlet (H), W 3-1; **Rd. 2** 04.11v Aveley (H), D *1-1; **Replay** 18.11 v Aveley (A), W 3-1; **Rd.3** 30.12 v Sutton United (A), D *2-2; **Replay** 06.01v Sutton United (H), L 1-3.

PLAYING SQUAD 1998 - **Goalkeepers:** Graham Benstead (Brentford, Kingstonian, Rushden & D, KetteringT, Brentford, Sheffield U, Norwich C, QPR), Dean Beale (Worthing, Poole T,Newport IOW, Basingstoke T, Andover, Pirelli General, Sunderland, Southampton). **Defenders:** Steve Harris (Aldershot T, Farnham T, Aldershot), Simon Line(Wokingham T, Chertsey T, Kingstonian, Brentford, Crystal Palace), Andy Morley (Poole T), Steve Richardson (Newbury T, Reading, Southampton), Danny Barker (Portsmouth), Richard Skelly (King's Lynn, Northampton T, Cambridge U,Newmarket T), Rob Marshall (Stevenage B, Kettering T, St.Leonards Stamcroft,Stevenage B, Watford). **Midfielders:** Robbie Carroll (Salisbury C, Bashley, Crawley T, Worthing,Woking, Yeovil T, Fareham T, Brentford, Gosport B, Southampton), Scott O'Neill (Royal Navy, Dundee U, Motherwell), Paul Wilkinson (Dorchester T, Bashley,Wokingham T, Reading), Steve Beeks (Aldershot T, Staines T, Sutton U, Woking,Aldershot, Egham T), Nigel Emsden (Oxford U), Adam Galvin (Wokingham T,Basingstoke T), Alan Carey (Bromley, Reading), Jamie Medford (Wokingham T), Bruce Tydeman (Whitchurch U). **Forwards:** Paul Coombs (Farnborough T, Aldershot), Chris Ferrett (Fleet T, AFCBournemouth, Portsmouth), Ian Mancey (Basing R).

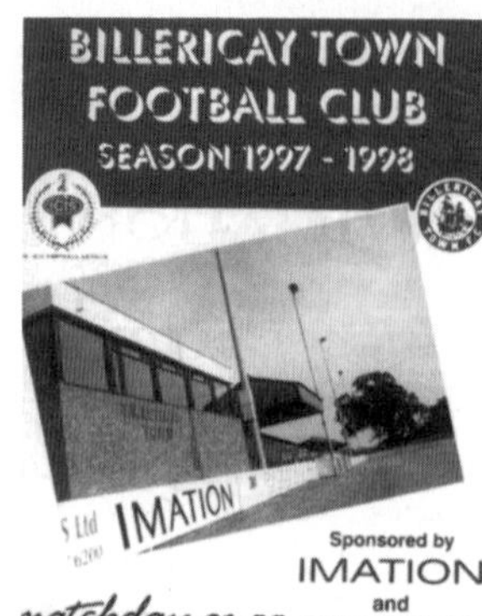

BILLERICAY TOWN
FOOTBALL CLUB
SEASON 1997 - 1998
IMATION
Sponsored by
IMATION
and
SPALL SPORTS
matchday magazine £1.00

PROGRAMME DETAILS:
Pages: 60 **Price:** £1
Editor: Mark Kettlety
(01277 636149)

BILLERICAY TOWN

Colours: All Blue. **Sponsors:** Tony Thake Distribution
Change colours: All yellow. **Formed:** 1880
Midweek Matches: Tuesday. **Nickname:** The Town
Reserves' Lge: Essex & Herts Border Comb.
Local Press: Evening Echo, Billericay Gazette.
Local Radio: BBC Radio Essex, Essex Radio, Essex FM

Chairman: Rod Moore **Vice Chairman:** John Bennewith, Tony Thake
President: Barry Spall **Secretary:** Len Dewson, 14 Graham Close, Billericay, Essex CM12 0QW (01277 622375).
Manager: John Kendall **Press Officer:** TBA
Coach: Ken Varney **Physio:** Colin Masterson

GROUND Address: New Lodge, Blunts Wall Road, Billericay CM12 9SA (01277 652188). **Directions:** From Shenfield (A129) right at 1st lights then 2nd right. From Basildon (A129) over 1st lights in town, then left at next lights and 2nd right. Half mile from Billericay (GER) station (London Liverpool St. - Southend line). Ground 5 mins walk from buses 222, 251, 357, 255, 551.
Capacity: 3,500 **Seats:** 424 **Cover:** 600 **Floodlights:** Yes
Clubhouse: Open every evening 8-11pm (except Monday)(1pm-11pm Sat) and weekend lunchtimes noon-2.30pm. Discos, live entertainment.
Club Shop: Open matchdays for souvenirs, metal badges, old progs, programme swaps. Nigel Harris (01268 558114).

PREVIOUS - **Grounds:** Laindon Road (pre-1971). **Leagues:** Romford & Dist. 1890-1914; Mid Essex 18-47; South Essex Comb. 47-66; Essex Olympian 66-71; Essex Snr 71-77; Athenian 77-79.

CLUB RECORDS - **Attendance:** 3,841 v West Ham Utd, Floodlight opener 77. Comp match: 3,193 v Farnborough Tn, FA Vase SF 1st leg 76. **Win:** 11-0 v Stansted (A), Essex Senior League 5/5/76. **Defeat:** 3-10 v Chelmsford City (A), Essex Senior Cup 4/1/93. **Goalscorer:** (career) F Clayden 273, (season) Leon Gutmore 51 (97-98) **Appearances:** J Pullen 418. **Fees - Paid:** Undisclosed. **Received:** £22,500+ increments for Steve Jones (West Ham, Nov. 1992).

BEST SEASON - **FA Cup:** 1st Rd Proper 97-98. **FA Vase:** Winners - 75-76, 76-77 & 78-79. **FA Trophy:** 1st Rd Prop 93-94. **FA Amateur Cup:** 3rd Qual Rd 73-74

HONOURS - Essex Snr Lg 72-73 74-75 75-76, R-up 71-2 73-4, Lg Cup 71-74 76-77 (R-up 74-5), Challenge Cup 72-73; Isthmian Lge - Div 2 79-80, Div 1 R-up 80-81, 97-98; Athenian Lg 77-79 (Lg Cup 77-78); East Anglian Cup R-up 79-80 84-5; Essex Snr Cup 75-76 (R-up 85-6 93-4 94-5 95-6); Essex Snr Tphy 77-78 79-80; Essex Thameside Tphy 86-87 91-92 (R-up 90-1); Essex F'lit Tphy 77-78; Phillips F'lit Tphy 76-77; Rothmans Merit Award 1978.

Players progressing to Football League: D Westwood (QPR) 75, A Hull, D Carter (Peterborough, Orient), D Cass (Orient) 88, D Ludden (Orient) 92, S Jones (West Ham Utd) 92.
97-98 - Captain: John Ridout **P.o.Y.:** Leon Gutzmore **Top scorer:** Leon Gutzmore (51 Record)

Back Row (L-R); Craig Davidson, Peter Carey (Coach), John Kendall (Mgr), Paul Battram, Billy Goldstone, Gary Waters, Marc Sinfield, Simon Livett, John Ridout, Martin St Hilaire, Dave Root. Front Row; Colin Sowerby, Chris Payne, Jon Hooker, Chris Moore, Andy Theodosiou, Leon Gutzmore, Ken Varney (Asst Mgr).

Photo: Eric Marsh

BILLERICAY TOWN - Match Facts 97-98

ESC - Essex Senior Cup

Match No.	Date	Venue H / A	Comp.	Opponents	Result & Score		Att.	Goalscorers	League Position
1	16.08	H	IL-1	Worthing	W	4-0	368	Hooker 2, Theodosiou, Gutzmore.	2
2	19.08	A	IL-1	Berkhamsted Town	**W**	**5-1**	*151*	Theodosiou, Barry, Kelly 2, Payne.	1
3	23.08	A	IL-1	Bognor Regis Town	L	2-4	*292*	Moore, Ridout.	5
4	26.08	H	IL-1	Leyton Pennant	L	1-2	400	Gutzmore.	7
5	30.08	A	IL-1	Staines Town	W	2-0	*174*	Gutzmore 2.	3
6	02.09	H	IL-1	Romford	W	2-1	628	Goldstone, Hooker.	2
7	10.09	A	IL-1	Chertsey Town	W	3-1	*164*	Goldstone, Moore.	2
8	13.09	A	**FAC 1Q**	Tooting & Mitcham United	W	2-1	*214*	Gutzmore, Payne.	-
9	20.09	H	IL-1	Barton Rovers	W	4-0	372	Goldstone, Barry, Gutzmore 2.	2
10	23.09	A	IL-1	Hampton	W	2-0	*150*	Goldstone, Francis.	2
11	27.09	H	**FAC 2Q**	Dulwich Hamlet	W	2-1	369	Goldstone, Gutzmore.	-
12	04.10	H	IL-1	Wokingham Town	W	3-0	397	Moore, Theodosiou, Gutzmore.	2
13	07.10	H	**GIC 1**	Hornchurch	W	*5-2	207	Battram, Barnett, Payne, Gutzmore.	-
14	11.10	H	**FAC 3Q**	Erith & Belvedere	W	4-1	368	Gutzmore 2, Payne, Battram.	-
15	14.10	H	IL-1	Aldershot Town	L	1-2	655	Battram.	4
16	18.10	H	**FAT** 1Q	Grays Athletic	W	3-2	438	OG, Gutzmore 2.	-
17	25.10	H	**FAC 4Q**	Camberley Town	D	1-1	790	Gutzmore.	-
18	28.10	A	**FAC 4Q R**	Camberley Town	W	1-0	*599*	Gutzmore.	-
19	01.11	A	IL-1	Leatherhead	D	1-1	*285*	Gutzmore.	6
20	04.11	H	**GIC 2**	Purfleet	D	*0-0	188		-
21	08.11	H	**FAT** 2Q	Forest Green Rovers	W	4-0	426	Moore, Hooker 2 (1 pen), Payne.	-
22	15.11	H	**FAC 1**	Wisbech Town	L	2-3	2,200	Battram, Moore.	-
23	17.11	A	**GIC 2 R**	Purfleet	W	2-1		Gutzmore, Battram	-
24	22.11	H	RL-1	Wembley	W	4-0		Gutzmore, Barry, Davidson, Battram.	
25	25.11	A	**FMC 1**	Wembley	L	0-2			-
26	29.11	H	**FAT 3Q**	Aldershot	W	2-1		Battram 2.	-
27	06.12	H	RL-1	Berkhamsted Town	D	1-1		Theodosiou	
28	08.12	H	**ESC 2**	Witham Town	W	4-2		Gutzmore 2, Barry, Kelly.	-
29	13.12	H	RL-1	Leatherhead	W	1-0		Gutzmore	6
30	16.12	A	**GIC 3**	Carshalton Athletic	L	0-1			-
31	20.12	H	RL-1	Chertsey Town	**L**	**1-5**		Goldstone	7
32	27.12	H	RL-1	Grays Athletic	W	2-1		Gutzmore 2.	7
33	30.12	A	**ESC 3**	Heybridge Swifts	W	5-3		**Gutzmore 3**, Moore 2.	-
34	10.01	A	**FAT 1**	Dagenham & Redbridge	L	0-1			-
35	17.01	A	RL-1	Worthing	D	1-1		Gutzmore	8
36	24.01	H	RL-1	Bognor Regis Town	L	0-2			11
37	26.01	A	**ESC 4**	Dagenham & Redbridge	L	2-4		Gutzmore 2.	-
38	31.01	A	RL-1	Leyton Pennant	W	3-2		Gutzmore 2, Theodosiou.	9
39	03.02	A	RL-1	Thame United	W	2-0		Gutzmore, Kelly.	
40	07.02	H	RL-1	Hampton	D	1-1		Gutzmore.	7
41	11.02	A	RL-1	Molesey	W	3-2		Gutzmore 2, Hooker.	
42	14.02	A	RL-1	Abingdon Town	W	1-0		Battram.	6
43	17.02	H	RL-1	Maidenhead United	L	0-2			
44	21.02	H	RL-1	Uxbridge	D	1-1		Battram.	6
45	24.02	A	RL-1	Whyteleafe	W	3-1		Battram, Gutzmore, Goldstone.	
46	28.02	A	RL-1	Wokingham Town	W	1-0		Battram.	3
47	07.03	H	RL-1	Croydon	W	2-1		Gutzmore, OG.	3
48	10.03	H	RL-1	Abingdon Town	W	3-1		Gutzmore, Battram, Ridout.	
49	14.03	A	RL-1	Barton Rovers	L	0-2			3
50	17.03	A	RL-1	Uxbridge	D	0-0			
51	31.03	H	RL-1	Whyteleafe	W	4-1		Gutzmore 2, Goldstone, Ridout.	2
52	24.03	A	RL-1	Romford	W	2-1		Gutzmore, Moore.	2
53	28.03	A	RL-1	Aldershot Town	L	0-1	3,543		2
54	01.04	A	RL-1	Croydon	W	3-1		Gutzmore 2, Battram.	2
55	04.04	A	RL-1	Maidenhead United	L	0-1			2
56	11.04	H	RL-1	Staines Town	W	2-0		Gutzmore 2.	2
57	13.04	A	RL-1	Grays Athletic	L	1-2		Gutzmore.	2
58	18.04	H	RL-1	Molesey	W	2-1		Gutzmore, Payne.	2
59	25.04	A	RL-1	Wembley	L	0-1			2
60	02.05	H	RL-1	Thame United	W	4-0		**Gutzmore 3,** Barry.	2

PLAYING SQUAD 1998 **Goalkeepers:** David Root (Kingstonian,Hendon,Eton Manor,Hendon,Walthamstow Ave,Barking,Launceston T). **Defenders:** Billy Goldstone (Grays Ath,Purfleet,Hendon,Enfield,Grays Ath,Chesham U,Chelmsford C,Barking,East Ham U,Woodford T,Barking), Chris Moore (B Stortford,Dag & Red,Heybridge Swifts,Braintree T,Chelmsford C), Lee Francis (Grays Ath,Hendon,Yeovil T,Grays Ath,Boreham Wood,Enfield,Chesterfield,Arsenal), Gary Waters (Barking,Grays Ath,Aveley,West Ham U), Andy Theodosiou (Dover Ath,Brighton,Hereford U,Norwich C,Tottenham H), Craig Davidson (Dag & Red,Chelmsford C,Southend U,Aldershot), Barry Fox (Boreham Wood,B Stortford,Boreham Wood,Grays Ath,Millwall), Marc Sinfield (Enfield,WBA). **Midfielders:** Jon Hooker (B Stortford,Brentford,Hertford T,Hertford Heath), Mark Barry (Cambridge U,Norwich C), John Ridout (B Stortford,Enfield,Purfleet,Enfield,Harrow B,Parmitarians,Leyton O), Simon Livett (Grays Ath,C.Row & Romford,Dag & Red,West Ham U), Mark Brewer (Braintree T,Enfield,Margate,Maidstone U), Tony Constantinou (Barnet,Charlton Ath,Tottenham H). **Forwards:** Leon Gutzmore (Cambridge U), Martin St.Hilaire (Enfield,Yeovil T,Enfield,Harrow B,Harlow T,Chesham U,Aveley), Greg Vallely (Erith &Belvedere,Billericay T), Paul Battram (Erith & Belvedere,Harlow T,Gravesend,Welling U,Gravesend,Hornchurch,Aveley,Barking), Chris Payne (Heybridge Swifts,Dag & Red,Billericay T,Harlow T,Brentwood), Colin Sowerby (Dover Ath,Purfleet,Erith & Belvedere,Hendon,Redbridge F,Dartford,LeytonO,Southend U,Hendon,Aveley,Tilbury).

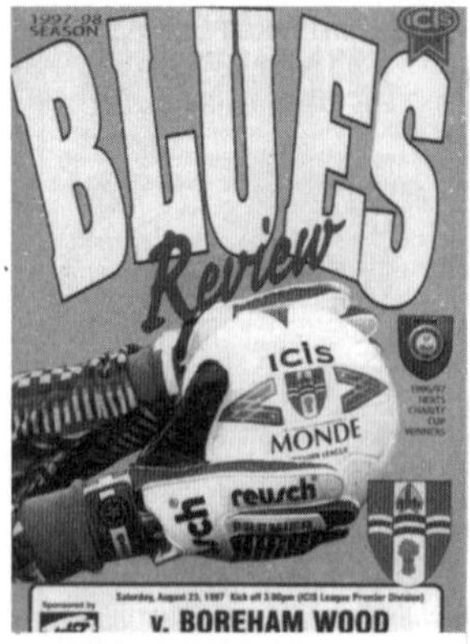

PROGRAMME DETAILS
Pages: 48 **Price:** £1.20
Editor: Mick Hooker
(01279 817097)

BISHOP'S STORTFORD

Colours: White & blue stripes/blue/blue **Formed:** 1874
Change colours: Yellow/white/yellow. **Nickname:** Blues
Midweek matchday: Tuesday
Reserve League: Essex & Herts Border Comb.
Local Press: B.Stortford Gazette, Herts & Essex Observer, Herald & Post.
Local Radio: BBC Essex, Essex Radio, Breeze AM, 1017.

Chairman: Gordon Lawrence **President:** B W A Bayford
Vice-Chairman: Mick Hancock **Secretary:** Graeme Auger, 58 Braziers Quay, South Street, Bishop's Stortford, Herts. CM23 3YW. (01279 465998)
Gen Manager: John Radford **Team Manager:** Dave Edwards
Coach: Ray Wickenden. **Physio:** Micky Stevens
Press Officer: Martin Stone (01376 510162).

GROUND Address: George Wilson Stadium, Rhodes Ave., Bishop's Stortford CM23 3JN (01279 654140) **Directions:** M11 jct 8, A1250 towards town centre, left at crossroads into London Rd (A1184), right at mini-r'bout and cross railway bridge, right at next island (by garage), Rhodes Ave is 2nd left (5-10 mins from M11). By rail: BR W Anglia Line (London Liverpool Str.-Cambridge)
Capacity: 6,000 **Cover:** 1,770 **Seats:** 270 **Floodlights:** Yes
Clubhouse: Open matchdays & Mondays (bingo). Available for hire.
Club Shop: Full stock inc. scarves, badges and other souvenirs. Massive stock of programmes and books etc. Contact Gareth Stephens (01279 501046)

PREVIOUS - **Leagues:** East Herts 1896-97, 02-06, 19-21; Stansted & Dist. Lg 06-19; Herts County 21-25 27-29; Herts & Essex Border 25-27; Spartan 29-51; Delphian 51-63; Athenian 63-73.

CLUB RECORDS - **Attendance:** 6,000 v Peterborough Utd, FA Cup 2nd Rd 1972 & v Middlesbrough FA Cup 3rd Rd replay, 1983 **Win:** 11-0: Nettleswell & Butntmill, Herts Jun Cup 2nd Rd 1911 **Defeat:** 0-13 v Cheshunt (H), Herts Sen. Cup 1st Rd 9/1/26. **Fee Paid:** £1,500 for Phil Hopkins (Walthamstow Ave., 84). **Fee Received:** £10,000 for Carl Hoddle (Leyton O., 89) **Scorer:** (Since 29) Jimmy Badcock 123 **Appearances:** Phil Hopkins 543.

BEST SEASON - **FA Amateur Cup:** Winners 73-74. **FA Trophy:** Winners 80-81. **FA Cup:** 3rd Rd rep. 82-83 (above) - **League clubs beaten:** Reading 82-83.

HONOURS - Isthmian Lg Div 1 80-1 94-5 (Lg Cup 88-9, Full Mem. Cup 90-1), Prem. Inter Lg Cup 89-90; Athenian Lg 69-70 (R-up 66-7, Div 1 65-6, Div 2 R-up 64-5); Delphian Lg 54-5; London Snr Cup 73-4; Herts Snr Cup 58-9 59-0 63-4 70-1 72-3 73-4 75-6 86-7; E Anglian Cup 81-2; Herts Charity Cup 62-3 65-6 73-4 81-2 82-3 84-5 87-8 96-7; Herts Charity Shield 54-5; Herts I'mediate Cup(res) 94-95; Eastern F'lit Cup 84-5; Essex F'lit Cup 67-8; Essex & Herts Border Comb(W) 81-2 88-9 (R-up(2) 92-4); Fred Budden Tphy R-up 78-9 90-1 92-3.

Players progressing to Football Lge: P Phelan (Southend) 61, M Hollow (Orient 62), P Phillips (Luton 69), T Baker (Colchester) 86, T Sorrell (Maidstone, Colchester, Barnet) 88, C Hoddle (Leyton O., Barnet) 89, T English (Colchester) 89.L Fortune-West (Gillingham) 95, L Braithwaite (Exeter City) 96.

Bishop Stortford's goalkeeper Gavin King punchs clear from Dulwich Hamlet's Steve Restartick.
Photo: Alan Coomes

BISHOP'S STORTFORD - Match Facts 97-98

Match No.	Date	Venue H / A	Comp.	Opponents	Result & Score		Att.	Goalscorers	League Position
1	16.08	A	IL	Kingstonian	L	0-1	*1,034*		18
2	19.08	H	IL	Dagenham & Redbridge	D	1-1	437	Forbes.	
3	23.08	H	IL	Boreham Wood	W	3-1	383	Comerford, Forbes, Waller (pen).	11
4	26.08	A	IL	Sutton United	**W**	**4-2**	*485*	Cooper, Forbes, Thomas, Comerford.	
5	30.08	A	IL	Aylesbury United	L	0-2	*593*		10
6	02.09	H	IL	Oxford City	L	0-1	424		15
7	09.09	A	**GIC 1**	Bromley	L	1-3			-
8	13.09	A	**FAC 1Q**	St Leonards Stamcroft	L	0-1	*408*		-
9	16.09	H	IL	Hitchin Town	L	0-2	242		-
10	20.09	H	IL	Walton & Hersham	W	3-1	331	Walker, Adekola, Comerford.	13
11	23.09	A	IL	Dulwich Hamlet	**L**	**0-5**	*255*		15
12	30.09	H	IL	Bromley	W	2-0	264	Greaves, Adekola.	9
13	04.10	A	IL	Enfield	L	1-4	*688*	Adekola.	13
14	06.10	A	IL	Dagenham & Redbridge	L	1-2	*739*		13
15	11.10	H	IL	Harrow Borough	L	1-2	315	Cooper.	17
16	18.10	H	IL	Chesham United	**W**	**4-2**	454	Adekola 15, 67, Cooper 48, 76.	13
17	25.10	H	IL	Purfleet	W	2-0	378	Adekola (pen), Thomas.	12
18	28.10	H	**FMC 1**	Leyton Pennant	L	1-2			-
19	01.11	H	IL	Gravesend & Northfleet	L	1-2	516	Cooper.	12
20	08.11	A	**FAC 2Q**	Crawley Town	W	2-1	*1,255*	Shufflewood, Thomas.	-
21	12.11	A	IL	St Albans City	L	1-2	*298*	Cove (pen).	
22	15.11	H	IL	Enfield	L	0-2	694		14
23	22.11	A	RL	Purfleet	L	1-3	*203*	Swdgwick.	16
24	29.11	A	**FAT 3Q**	St Albans City	L	2-5	*333*	Deluca 2.	-
25	06.12	A	RL	Oxford City	L	0-1	*171*		19
26	13.12	A	RL	Gravesend & Northfleet	W	2-1	*614*	Cooper 2.	15
27	16.12	H	RL	Hendon	L	1-2	190	Thomas.	
28	20.12	H	RL	Yeading	W	2-1	519	Graves (pen), Greene.	14
29	27.12	A	RL	Heybridge Swifts	L	0-1	*390*		16
30	03.01	H	RL	Sutton United	L	0-1	445		17
31	17.01	H	RL	Kingstonian	L	0-1	319		17
32	24.01	A	RL	Boreham Wood	L	0-1	*278*		18
33	31.01	H	RL	Aylesbury United	W	1-0	290	De Luca.	17
34	07.02	A	RL	Walton & Hersham	L	0-3	*219*		17
35	14.02	H	RL	Dulwich hamlet	D	1-1	202	Greaves 14 (pen).	19
36	21.02	A	RL	Bromley	L	2-3	*313*	Comerford 25, Conroy 71.	20
37	03.03	H	RL	Carshalton Athletic	W	4-3	90	Comerford 7, 26, Forbes 51, Adekola 54.	19
38	07.03	A	RL	Hitchin Town	**W**	**4-2**	*326*	Conway, Edwards, Adekola, Comerford.	18
39	14.03	A	RL	Harrow Borough	L	1-2	*184*	Adekola.	19
40	21.03	H	RL	Basingstoke Town	D	1-1	221	Ahmet.	18
41	28.03	H	RL	Bishop's Stortford	W	2-1	251	Antoine, Campbell.	17
42	04.04	H	RL	St Albans City	W	1-0	302	Jordan.	18
43	07.04	A	RL	Basingstoke Town	L	1-3	*483*	Adekola 65.	
44	11.04	A	RL	Yeading	W	2-0	*162*	Comerford 84, Conroy 89.	17
45	13.04	H	RL	Heybridge Swifts	D	2-2	191	Campbell 4, Adekola 90.	17
46	18.04	A	RL	Hendon	L	0-3	*341*		17
47	02.05	A	RL	Chesham United	D	1-1	*552*	De Velde.	19

PLAYING SQUAD 1998

Goalkeepers: Gavin King (Cheshunt).

Defenders: Ricky Antoine (Leyton Pennant, Harrow B, Dulwich H, Bromley,Charlton Ath), Kevin Jordan (Southend U, Tottenham H), Stuart Wardley (Saffron Walden T), Paul Campbell (Bromley, Charlton Ath), Roy Edwards (Leyton Pennant, St.Albans C, Aveley, Dulwich H, Stevenage B, St.Albans C,Dagenham, Leyton-Wingate).

Midfielders: Scott Forbes (Youth), Steve Greaves (Sudbury T, Dag & Red,Scunthorpe U, Ipswich T, Preston NE, Fulham), Will Cooper (Dag & Red), Robbie Gammons (Leyton Pennant, Boreham Wood, Heybridge Swifts, Dag & Red, Barking,Purfleet, Aveley, Barking, Chesham U, Chelmsford C, Barking, Arsenal), Tony Comerford (Harlow T, B Stortford, Sawbridgworth T, B Stortford, West Ham U), Richard Thomas (Worthing, Leyton O, West Ham U).

Forwards: David Adekola (Brighton, Pruessain Koln (Ger), B Stortford,Cambridge U, Bath C, Halifax T, Bury), Paul De Luca (Guiseley, Farsley Celtic,Cambridge U, Leyton O), Ian Hollamby (Clavering, B Stortford), Steve Conroy (Berkhamsted T, Grays Ath, Enfield, Bedford T, B Stortford, Hitchin T,Aylesbury U, Stevenage B, Hitchin T, Harrow B, Kingstonian, Hitchin T, CheshamU, St.Albans C, Hemel Hempstead, Colchester U).

PROGRAMME DETAILS:
Pages: 32 **Price:** £1.
Editor: John Gill
(0181 723 6407)

BOREHAM WOOD

Colours: White/black/red **Formed:** 1948
Change colours: Amber & black **Nickname:** The Wood
Midweek matchday: Tuesday **Sponsors:** L & M Foods / Wansons
Local Radio: Chiltern Radio.
Local Press: Boreham Wood Times, Watford Observer, Herts Advertiser.

Chairman: Phil Wallace **President:** W F O'Neill.
Secretary: Bob Nicholson, 56 Newcombe Road, Shenley, Radlett, Herts WD7 9EJ (01923 856077).
Manager: Bobby Makin **Asst Manager:** Alan Carrington
Coach: Billy Harrigan **Physio:** Dave Dickens
Press Officer: John D Gill (0181 723 6407)

GROUND Address: Meadow Park, Broughinge Road, Boreham Wood, Herts WD6 5AL (0181 953 5097). **Directions:** A1 towards London from M25, 1st turn off for Boreham Wood, head for town centre, into Brook Rd at r'bout before town centre, Broughinge Rd is 1st left. 1 mile from Elstree & Boreham Wood station (Thameslink), then bus 292 or 107 to Red Lion (5 minutes walk).
Capacity: 4,502 **Cover:** 1,568 **Seats:** 500 **Floodlights:** Yes
Clubhouse: (0181 953 5097). Open during normal licensing hours. Snacks available. Function room (250) available for hire.
Club Shop: Sells good selection of souvenirs & programmes. Contact: Dell Ward 0181 363 7345.

PREVIOUS - **Ground:** Eldon Avenue 1948-63. **Leagues:** Mid Herts 48-52, Parthenon 52-57, Spartan 56-66, Athenian 66-74. **Names:** Boreham Wood Rovers and Royal Retournez, amalgamated in 1948

CLUB RECORDS - **Attendance:** 2,500 v St Albans, F.A. Amateur Cup 70-71. **Goalscorer:** Micky Jackson, 208. **Appearances:** Dave Hatchett, 617. **Transfer Fee Received:** £10,000 from Barnet for Dean Samuels 1996

BEST SEASON - **FA Amateur Cup:** 3rd Rd. replay 70-71. **FA Trophy:** Quarter Finals 1995-96. Replay at Chorley 3-4. **FA Cup:** 2nd Round v Luton Town 1996-97. 1st Rd 77-78, 73-74.

HONOURS - Isthmian Lg. Div I 94-95, Isthmian Lg Div 2 76-77 (Yth Cup R-up 80-81), Isthmian Lge. Cup 96-97; Athenian Lg 73-74 (Div 2 68-69, Div 1 R-up 69-70), Spartan Lg R-up 65-66, Herts Senior Cup 71-72 (R-up 66-67 74-75 79-80 87-88), Herts Junior Cup 51-52, Parthenon Lg 55-56 (R-up(2) 53-55 56-57, Herts Charity Shield 64-65, Herts Intermediate Cup 69-70, Herts Charity Cup(5) 80-81 83-84 85-86 88-90 (R-up 71-72 84-85 86-87 90-91 91-92 92-93), London Senior Cup R-up 89-90, London Intermediate Cup 70-71, Neale Trophy 69-70, Essex & Herts Border Comb 72-73 (Lg Cup 72-73, Western Div R-up 82-83 89-90), Mithras Cup 76-77, Middx Border Lg 81-82 (Lg Cup 79-80), Wallspan Floodlit 86-87.

Players progressing to Football League: Colin Franks (Watford & Sheff Utd), Charles Ntamark (Walsall), Dean Samuels (Barnet 96)

Boreham Wood FC. Photo: Clive Butchins

BOREHAM WOOD - Match Facts 97-98

Match No.	Date	Venue H / A	Comp.	Opponents	Result & Score		Att.	Goalscorers	League Position
1	16.08	H	IL	Bromley	D	0-0	229		11
2	19.08	A	**IL ChS**	Yeovil Town	L	0-1	*873*		-
3	23.08	A	II	Bishop's Stortford	**L**	**1-3**	*383*	Marshall	20
4	26.08	H	II	Basingstoke Town	**W**	**5-0**	178	Heffer, Brown, Daly, Samuels, Hunter.	
5	30.08	H	IL	Carshalton Athletic	D	2-2	235	Brown 47, Nisbet 86.	14
6	02.09	A	II	Heybridge Swifts	L	1-2	*229*	Hollingdale.	
7	07.09	A	IL	Dagenham & Redbridge	D	1-1	*539*	OG (Parrett).	18
8	09.09	A	**GIC 1**	Chesham United	W	4-1	165	**Marshall 3** (1 pen), Heffer.	-
9	13.09	H	IL	St Albans City	L	2-3	461	Marshall 47 (pen), Brown 52.	18
10	16.09	H	IL	Walton & Hersham	W	3-0	138	Marshall, Daly, Samuels.	-
11	20.09	A	IL	Hitchin Town	W	2-0	*248*	Robbins, Brown.	7
12	30.09	A	IL	Harrow Borough	L	0-1	*162*		10
13	04.10	H	IL	Oxford City	W	3-1	283	Samuels, Marshall 2.	6
14	07.10	A	IL	Kingstonian	W	5-2	*640*	**Samuels 3**, Marshall 2.	
15	11.10	A	IL	Aylesbury United	D	2-2	*423*	Marshall 2 (1 pen).	4
16	18.10	H	IL	Purfleet	W	3-1	229	Samuels 4, Grime 16, Marshall 45.	3
17	25.10	A	**FAC 4Q**	Rushden & Diamonds	D	1-1	*2,107*	Samuels 54.	-
18	28.10	H	**FAC 4Q R**	Rushden & Diamonds	W	*1-0	704	Shaw.	-
19	01.11	H	IL	Yeading	W	3-1	232	Dixon, Samuels, Nisbet.	
20	04.11	H	**GIC 2**	Bognor Regis Town	W	*4-3			-
21	08.11	A	IL	Sutton United	W	2-1	*714*	Marshall 55, 87.	3
22	15.11	A	**FAC 1**	Hayes	W	1-0	*1,343*	Marshall 31.	-
23	18.11	A	**FMC 1**	Hitchin Town	W	2-1			-
24	22.11	A	RL	Hendon	L	1-2	*343*	Samuels.	4
25	29.11	A	**FAT 3Q**	Hitchin Town	W	2-0	*321*	Daly, Samuels.	-
26	06.12	A	**FAC 2**	Cheltenham Town	D	1-1	*3,528*	Marshall 13.	-
27	13.12	A	RL	Yeading	W	1-0	*152*	Samuels.	4
28	16.12	H	**FAC 2 R**	Cheltenham Town	L	0-2	1,615		-
29	20.12	H	RL	Chesham United	W	3-1	348	**Marshall 3.**	4
30	23.12	H	**FMC 2**	Aylesbury United	W	6-1			-
31	27.12	A	RL	Enfield	W	3-0	*847*	Samuels, Robbins, Marshall.	4
32	30.12	H	**GIC 3**	Dagenham & Redbridge	W	1-0			-
33	10.01	H	**FAT 1**	Chelmsford City	W	2-1	407	Hollingdale 19, Samuels 24.	-
34	17.01	A	RL	Bromley	W	2-1	*383*	Prutton 40, Samuels 41.	4
35	24.01	H	RL	Bishop's Stortford	W	1-0	278	Marshall.	4
36	27.01	H	**GIC 4**	Canvey Island	W	2-0			-
37	31.01	A	**FAT 2**	Bishop Auckland	W	4-1	*369*	Marshall 2, Samuels, Hollingdale.	-
38	07.02	H	RL	Hitchin Town	D	0-0	339		5
39	10.02	H	RL	Gravesend & Northfleet	W	4-1	223	Marshall 2, Brown, Robbins.	
40	14.02	A	RL	Basingstoke Town	D	2-2	*528*	Shaw 2.	4
41	17.02	H	**FMC 3**	Uxbridge	W	2-1			
42	21.02	A	**FAT 3**	Slough Town	D	1-1	*1,221*	Marshall 16.	-
43	24.02	H	**FAT 3 R**	Slough Town	L	*1-2	544	Robbins (pen). A.E.T.	-
44	28.02	A	RL	Oxford City	W	1-0	*178*	Marshall.	4
45	03.03	H	RL	Dulwich hamlet	W	4-0	224	Daly 4, P Shaw 62, Marshall 72, 84.	4
46	05.03	A	**GIC S-F 1**	Oxford City	L	1-2			-
47	07.03	A	RL	Walton & Hersham	W	4-1	*269*	Heffer, Marshall, Joyce, Grime.	4
48	10.03	H	**GIC S-F 2**	Oxford City	L	0-3	126		-
49	12.03	H	**FMC 4**	Yeading	D	*2-2		A.E.T. Lost 0-3 after penalties.	-
50	14.03	H	RL	Dagenham & Redbridge	D	0-0	629		4
51	17.03	A	RL	Carshalton Athletic	W	2-0	*245*	Heffer, Marshall.	4
52	21.03	H	RL	Kingstonian	L	0-1	1,029		4
53	24.03	H	RL	Harrow Borough	D	2-2	237	OG (James), Samuels.	4
54	28.03	A	RL	Purfleet	W	2-0	*194*	Samuels, Marshall.	3
55	31.03	H	RL	Enfield	W	2-1	502	Marshall, Heffer.	2
56	04.04	H	RL	Sutton United	D	2-2	472	Hollingdale, Samuels.	2
57	18.04	A	RL	Dulwich Hamlet	W	1-0	*335*	Nisbett.	3
58	21.04	A	RL	St Albans City	W	2-0	*634*	Marshall, Shaw.	2
59	23.04	H	RL	Heybridge Swifts	L	2-3	313	Sewell 31, Dixon 35.	2
60	25.04	H	RL	Hendon	L	1-2	515	Marshall.	2
61	28.04	H	RL	Aylesbury United	W	2-1	404	Sewell 43, Marshall 56.	2
62	30.04	A	RL	Chesham United	D	1-1	*381*	Marshall 65.	2
63	02.05	A	RL	Gravesend & Northfleet	D	1-1	*537*	Sewell 87.	2

PLAYING SQUAD 1998 - **Goalkeepers:** Martin Taylor (B Stortford, Epping T, Woodford T, Hendon, Jyderup(Den), Charlton Ath, Arsenal). **Defenders:** Steve Daly (Wembley, Chalfont St.Peter, Ruislip Manor), Dave Hatchett (Enfield), Gary Nisbet (Collier Row, Walthamstow Pennant, CollierRow, Eton Manor, Barkingside), Billy Harrigan (B Stortford, Chesham U,Leytonstone & Ilf, Walthamstow Ave, B Stortford, Cambridge U), Alan McCarthy (Leyton O, QPR), Dominic Grime (Stevenage B, Watford). **Midfielders:** Rob Hollingdale (Wembley), Mark Brown (Luton T, Exeter C), Jason Shaw (Harrow B, Dartford, Redbridge F, West Ham U), Andy Prutton (Harrow B,Dartford, Cheshunt, Wormley R), Steve Heffer (Hendon, Grays Ath, Swindon T,Southend U, West Ham U), Matt Corbould (Potters Bar T, Cheshunt, BorehamWood), Simon Ireland (Doncaster R, Mansfield T, Blackburn R, Huddersfield T), Bruce Sewell (Yeading, Purfleet, Collier Row, E Thurrock U, Ford U, BillericayT, Collier Row, Basildon U), Paul Moran * (Enfield, Peterborough U, TottenhamH). **Forwards:** Kerry Dixon (Basildon U, Doncaster R, Watford, Millwall, Luton T,Southampton, Chelsea, Reading, Dunstable), Shaun Marshall (Enfield, StevenageB, Hitchin T, Stevenage B), Tony Samuels (Leyton, Collier Row, Bromley,Leyton-Wingate, Leytonstone & Ilf), Paul Shaw (Barkingside), Mark Xavier * (Harrow B, Hendon, Ruislip Manor, Hendon), Kenrick Roudette (Barkingside).

BROMLEY

Colours: White/black/black. **Formed:** 1892
Change colours: All red **Nickname:** The Lilywhites
Midweek home matchday: Tuesday
Reserve's League: Suburban **Youth League:** Southern Youth
Newsline: 0930 555 838
Local Press: Bromley Times
Local Radio: Radio Kent, Bromley Local Radio.

Chairman: Glyn Beverly **Managing Director:** Eddy Davies
Secretary: Kerry Phillips, 15 Watling Street, Bexleyheath, Kent. DA6 7QJ. (01322 554108/529682, Fax 550543)
Manager: George Wakeling **Coach:** John Kane
Physio: John De Palma

GROUND Address: Hayes Lane, Bromley, Kent BR2 9EF (0181 460 5291 or 0181-313-3992).
Directions: One mile from Bromley South (BR). Buses 316, 146 and 119 pass ground. Junction 4 off M25, then A21 towards London.
Capacity: 5,000 **Cover:** 2,500 **Seats:** 1,300 **Floodlights:** Yes
Clubhouse: Open matchdays. Food available.
Club Shop: Yes. contact Jim Brown

PROGRAMME DETAILS:
Pages: 32 **Price:** £1.20
Editor: John Self.
Tel: (0181 402 2391)

PREVIOUS - **Leagues:** South London - 1894; Southern 94-96; London 96-98 99-1901; West Kent 01-04; Southern Suburban 04-07; Kent 1898-99, 11-14; Spartan 07-08; Isthmian 08-11; Athenian 19-52. **Grounds:** White Hart Field Cricket Ground, Widmore Rd (pre-1904); Plaistow Cricket Field 1904-37; Hayes Lane 06-37; Present Hayes Lane 38 to date

CLUB RECORDS - **Attendance:** 12,000 v Nigeria, 1950. **Goalscorer:** George Brown 570 (1938-61) **Appearances:** George Brown **Win:** 12-1 v Chertsey FA Cup 75. **Defeat:** 1-11 v Cray Wands 33. **Fees - Paid:** Unknown **Received:** £50,000 for Jon Goodman (from Millwall 90)

BEST SEASON - **FA Amateur Cup:** Winners 10-11, 37-38, 48-49. **FA Trophy:** Second Round 91-92. **FA Cup:** 2nd Rd replay v Scarborough 37-38, Lincoln 38-39, Watford 45-46.

HONOURS - Isthmian League(4) 08-10 53-54 60-61 (R-up 52-53 55-56 87-88), Div 1 R-up 79-80 85-86 90-91, Prince Phillip 5-a-side Cup 1979; Athenian League 22-23 48-49 50-51 (R-up 35-36); London League Div 2 1896-97; Spartan League 07-08; London Snr Cup 09-10 45-46 50-51; Kent Senior Cup 49-50 76-77 91-92 96-97; Kent Amateur Cup(12) 07-08 31-32 35-37 38-39 46-47 48-49 50-51 52-53 53-55 59-60; London Challenge Cup 1995-96.

Players progressing to Football League: Roy Merryfield (Chelsea), Stan Charlton (Arsenal 52), Ron Heckman (Orient 55), John Gregory (West Ham 51), Bill Lloyd (Millwall 56), Brian Kinsey (Charlton 56), Harold Hobbs (Charlton & England), Matt Carmichael (Lincoln 90), Leslie Locke (QPR 56), Jon Goodman (Millwall 90), Dean Wordsworth (Crystal Palace 97).

97-98 - Captain: Frank Coles **P.o.Y.:** Keith Sharman **Top Scorer:** Mark Tompkins

Back Row (L-R); Glyn Beverly (Chr), George Wakeling (Mgr), David Gray, Bobby Dennington, Lionel Best, Keith Sharman, Ian Rawlings, Danny Carroll, Dave Wietecha, Dean Francis, Mark Tompkins, John Kane (Coach), Martin Coates (Asst Mgr). Front Row; John De Palma (Physio), Mark Loveday, Ollie Adadeji, Simon Miller, Frank Coles (Capt), Matthew Dorrity (Mascot), David May, Tim Griggs, Kevin Allen.

Photo: Courtesy Kentish Times Newspapers Ltd.

BROMLEY - Match Facts 97-98

Match No.	Date	Venue H / A	Comp.	Opponents	Result & Score		Att.	Goalscorers	League Position
1	16.08	A	IL	Boreham Wood	D	0-0	*229*		12
2	19.08	H	IL	Walton & Hersham	L	0-1	374		
3	23.08	H	IL	Oxford City	L	1-2	281	Tompkins.	21
4	26.08	A	IL	Dulwich Hamlet	D	3-3	*417*	Best, Tompkins (pen), Terry.	
5	30.08	A	IL	Kingstonian	**L**	**1-4**	*958*	White.	22
6	02.09	H	IL	Hendon	D	0-0	303		
7	07.09	A	IL	Basingstoke Town	**W**	**3-0**	*525*	Francis, Sharman, Tompkins.	19
8	09.09	H	**GIC 1**	Bishop's Stortford	W	3-1			-
9	12.09	A	**FAC 1Q**	Staines Town	L	1-3	*180*	Allon.	-
10	16.09	H	IL	Harrow Borough	W	2-1	149	Sharman 2.	
11	20.09	H	IL	Aylesbury United	**W**	**3-0**	429	Allon, Tompkins, White.	8
12	22.09	A	IL	Dagenham & Redbridge	L	1-2	*704*	Best.	
13	30.09	A	IL	Bishop's Stortford	L	0-2	*264*		11
14	04.10	H	IL	Purfleet	L	2-3	302	Wordsworth, Best.	15
15	11.10	H	IL	Chesham United	W	3-2	364	Wordsworth 2, Minurs.	12
16	14.10	H	IL	Sutton United	D	1-1	405	Wordsworth.	12
17	21.10	H	IL	Hitchin Town	D	0-0	250		
18	25.10	H	IL	Gravesend & Northfleet	W	2-0	542	Sharman, Wordsworth.	9
19	28.10	H	**FMC 1**	Maidenhead United	L	2-3			-
20	01.11	H	IL	St Albans City	D	1-1	404	Kyte.	10
21	05.11	A	**GIC 2**	Harlow Town	W	3-2			-
22	08.11	H	**FAT 2Q**	Hendon	W	2-1	303	Kyte 2.	-
23	22.11	A	RL	Yeading	D	1-1	*155*	Tompkins.	12
24	29.11	H	**FAT 3Q**	Purfleet	L	1-4		Tompkins.	-
25	13.12	A	RL	St. Albans City	W	1-0	*298*	Griggs.	13
26	16.12	A	**GIC 3**	Romford	L	1-3			-
27	20.12	H	RL	Enfield	W	3-1	447	Griggs, Sharman, Tompkins.	13
28	27.12	A	RL	Gravesend & Northfleet	L	0-1	*859*		12
29	10.01	A	RL	Walton & Hersham	W	2-0	*301*	Dennington, Allon.	11
30	17.01	H	RL	Boreham Wood	L	1-2	383	Dennington (pen).	12
31	24.01	A	RL	Oxford City	D	1-1	*171*	Sharman.	12
32	31.01	H	RL	Kingstonian	L	0-2	460		13
33	07.02	A	RL	Aylesbury United	W	2-1	*471*	Griggs (p[en), Kite.	11
34	14.02	H	RL	Dagenham & Redbridge	W	2-0	529	White 2.	10
35	21.02	H	RL	Bishop's Stortford	W	3-2	313	Allen 74, Gray 82, White 90.	10
36	28.02	A	RL	Purfleet	L	0-2	*214*		10
37	07.03	A	RL	Harrow Borough	W	3-2	*245*	Tompkins, Loveday, Kyte.	8
38	10.03	A	RL	Carshalton Athletic	L	0-1	*224*		
39	14.03	H	RL	Basingstoke Town	L	0-2	365		9
40	17.03	H	RL	Heybridge Swifts	D	2-2	197	Tompkins 2.	
41	21.03	H	RL	Carshalton Athletic	**W**	**3-0**	376	Kyte, Allen, Franks.	9
42	28.03	A	RL	Hitchin Town	D	1-1	*350*	Adedeji.	11
43	07.04	A	RL	Hendon	L	0-1	*208*		
44	18.04	A	RL	Heybridge Swifts	D	2-2	*302*	Tompkins (pen), Coles.	13
45	21.04	H	RL	Dulwich Hamlet	D	1-1	370	Miller.	13
46	23.04	H	RL	Chesham United	L	1-2	275	Tompkins.	
47	25.04	H	RL	Yeading	L	0-2	331		14
48	28.04	A	RL	Enfield	D	1-1	*484*	Francis.	
49	02.05	A	RL	Sutton United	L	0-1	*707*		15

PLAYING SQUAD 1998

Goalkeepers: David Wietecha (Millwall)

Defenders: David May (Enfield, Barking), Mark Loveday (Youth team), Ollie Adedeji (Boreham Wood, Bromley, Finchley), Ian Rawlings (Leyton-Wingate,Leyton O), Keith Sharman (Barking, Leyton O, Clapton), Tim Griggs (Arsenal), Steve Oakey (Youth team)

Midfielders: Dean Francis (Millwall), Jamie Kyte (Charlton Ath), Frank Coles (Enfield, Leyton-Wingate, Leytonstone & Ilf, Dagenham, Leytonstone & Ilf,Charlton Ath), David Gray (Youth team), Danny Carroll (Whyteleafe, Chipstead,Whyteleafe), Bobby Dennington (Crawley T, Bromley, Tooting & M, Bromley,Tooting & M, Bromley, Leyton-Wingate)

Forwards: Lionel Best (Tooting & M, Kingstonian, Croydon, Dulwich H, Elms,Fisher Ath), Mark Tompkins (Tooting & M, Fisher Ath, Corinthian, Dulwich H,Darenth Heathside, AFC Eltham), Kevin Allen (Potters Bar T), Simon Miller (Aveley, Boreham Wood, Barkingside, Wycombe W, West Ham U).

PROGRAMME DETAILS:
Pages: 14 **Price:** 80p
Editor: Andy Hill.
(0181 647 6288)

CARSHALTON ATHLETIC

Colours: White, maroon trim/maroon/white. **Formed:** 1903
Change colours: Maroon/white. **Nickname:** Robins
Midweek matchday: Tuesday **Sponsors:** Mile Train
Reserve League: Suburban. **Newsline:** 0891 446849.
Local Radio: Capital.
Local Press: Wallington & Carshalton Advertiser, Carshalton Herald.

Chairman: Mike Dawes. **Jt-Presidents:** W Stephenson & B Plumbridge
Vice Chairman: Keith Dawes. **Secretary:** Vic Thompson, 11 Poulton Avenue, Sutton, Surrey. SM1 3PZ. 0181 644 6402 (H)
General Manager: Fred Callaghan. **Manager:** Chris Kilby
Coach: Tommy Mason **Physio:** Alan McCreeney
Press Officer: Roger Fear **Comm. Man.:** John Carpentiere.

GROUND Address: War Memorial Sports Ground, Colston Av, Carshalton SM5 2PW (0181 642 8658). **Directions:** Turn right out of Carshalton BR Station, and Colston Avenue is first left. Entrance 150 yards on right. London Transport bus 151 from Morden to Wrythe Green Lane.
Capacity: 8,000 **Cover:** 4,500 **Seats:** 240 **Floodlights:** Yes
Clubhouse: Open every evening and lunchtime. Licenced bar, pool, darts, machines, discos on Saturday. Separate function hall (bookings taken). Food: sandwiches, rolls, burgers, hot dogs, teas, coffees and soft drinks. (0181 642 8658).
Club Shop: Sells hats, scarves, T-shirts, badges, programmes etc.

PREVIOUS - **Leagues:** Southern Sub (pre-1911); Surrey Snr 22-23; London 23-46; Corinthian 46-56; Athenian 56-73. **Grounds:** Wrythe Recreation Ground 1907-14; Culvers Park 19-20.

CLUB RECORDS - **Attendance:** 7,800 v Wimbledon, London Senior Cup. **Career goalscorer:** Jimmy Bolton. **Career appearances:** Jon Raffington and Jon Warden. **Transfer fee paid:** £2,000 for Jimmy Bolton, 1990. **Transfer fee received:** £15,000 for Curtis Warmington (Enfield). **Win:** 13-0 v Worthing, Loctite Cup Third Round 28/2/91.

BEST SEASON - **FA Trophy:** 3rd Rd 80-81 (lost 0-3 at home to Mossley, eventual Runners-up).
FA Cup: 2nd Rd 82-83, lost 1-4 at Torquay. **- League clubs defeated:** None.

HONOURS - Isthmian League Div 2 Runners-up 76-77, Corinthian League 52-53 53-54, Surrey Senior League Runners-up 22-23, Surrey Senior Cup(3) 88-90 91-92, Surrey Senior Shield (Runners-up(2)), London Challenge Cup 91-92.

Players progressing to Football League: Roy Lunnes (Crystal Pal. 1960), Les Burns (Charlton 1967), Ron Walker (Watford), Nobby Warren (Exeter), Gus Caesar (Arsenal), Darren Annon (Brentford) 1994, Ian Cox (Crystal Pal.) 1994.

Back Row (L-R); Chris Kilby (Mgr), Lea Barkus, Richard Verseci, Tony Nartey, Adrian Blake, Martin Beard, Steve Shaw, Martin Ford, Nail Thompson, Tommy Mason (Coach). Front Row; Richard Thompson, Neil Robson, Simon Bassey, Dean Coney (Capt), Barry Kingsford, Kevin Smith, Viv Jeffrey.

CARSHALTON ATHLETIC - Match Facts 97-98

Match No.	Date	Venue H / A	Comp.	Opponents	Result & Score	Att.	Goalscorers	League Position
1	16.08	A	IL	Dagenham & Redbridge	L 0-2	765		21
2	19.08	H	IL	Yeading	W 1-0	245	Thompson.	
3	23.08	H	IL	Aylesbury Unitrd	L 2-3	245	Barker 2.	16
4	26.08	A	IL	Chesham United	L 0-3	575		
5	30.08	A	IL	Boreham Wood	D 2-2	235	Thompson 25, Kingsford 38.	20
6	02.09	H	IL	Dulwich Hamlet	D 3-3	340	Thompson, Smith, Adam.	
7	07.09	A	IL	Hitchin Town	W 2-1	246	Saunders, Harper.	12
8	09.09	H	**GIC 1**	Hungerford Town	W 3-2			-
9	13.09	A	**FAC 1Q**	Harwich & Parkeston	D 1-1	232		-
10	16.09	H	**FAC 1Q R**	Harwich & Parkeston	W 4-0	192	Bartley, Saunders, Barker, Thompson.	-
11	20.09	H	IL	Kingstonian	D 1-1	642	Saunders.	15
12	23.09	A	IL	Walton & Hersham	W 4-3	218	Bartley 2, Thompson, Saunders.	12
13	27.09	A	**FAC 2Q**	Aylesbury United	W 3-0	516	Thompson 2, Coney.	-
14	04.10	A	IL	Gravesend & Northfleet	D 3-3	654	Coney, Saunders, Thompson.	11
15	07.10	H	IL	Basingstoke Town	L 1-2	282	Newbury.	-
16	11.10	H	**FAC 3Q**	Fisher Athletic	W 1-0	201	Alexander.	-
17	18.10	H	**FAT 1Q**	R. C.Warwick	W 2-0	223	Allon, Jeffrey.	-
18	25.10	A	**FAC 4Q**	Enfield	W 2-1	717	Thompson 2.	-
19	01.11	H	IL	Purfleet	W 1-0	308	Thompson.	18
20	04.11	H	**GIC 2**	Yeading	W 1-0			-
21	08.11	H	**FAT 2Q**	Aldershot Town	D 0-0	890		-
22	12.11	A	**FAT 2Q R**	Aldershot Town	L 0-3	1,602		-
23	15.11	H	**FAC 1**	Stevenage Borough	D 0-0	1,405		-
24	22.11	A	RL	Oxford City	D 1-1	191	Newbury.	18
25	24.11	A	**FAC 1 R**	Stevenage Borough	L 0-5	2,377		-
26	29.11	H	RL	Hendon	W 3-1	287	Ford, Newbury, Robson.	16
27	06.12	A	RL	Dulwich Hamlet	**W 3-0**	314	Thompson 2, Reid.	12
28	13.12	A	RL	Purfleet	W 2-1	189	Alexander 2.	11
29	16.12	H	**GIC 3**	Billericay Town	W 1-0			-
30	20.12	H	RL	Heybridge Swifts	D 1-1	286	Thompson.	13
31	22.12	H	**FMC 2**	Aldershot Town	W 1-0			-
32	27.12	A	RL	Sutton United	L 1-3	1,833	Thompson (pen).	13
33	10.01	H	RL	Harrow Borough	**W 3-0**	328	Beard 37, Newbury 56, Thompson 83(pen).	12
34	17.01	H	RL	Dagenham & Redbridge	L 0-2	511		14
35	24.01	A	RL	Aylesbury United	L 1-4	422	Thompson.	15
36	27.01	H	**GIC 4**	Oxford City	L 0-1			-
37	31.01	A	RL	Enfield	L 0-3	659		15
38	07.02	A	RL	Kingstonian	**L 1-5**	675	Thompson.	16
39	10.02	A	RL	Yeading	D 0-0	103		16
40	14.02	H	RL	Walton & Hersham	L 1-2	337	Newbury.	16
41	17.02	H	**FMC 3**	Leatherhead	L 1-2			-
42	21.02	A	RL	Harrow Borough	W 3-1	188	Fowler, Smith.	15
43	24.02	H	RL	St Albans City	L 0-2	208		16
44	28.02	H	RL	Gravesend & Northfleet	D 1-1	348	Fowler.	16
45	03.03	A	RL	Bishop's Stortford	L 3-4	90	Newberry 2, Wise.	16
46	07.03	A	RL	Basingstoke Town	W 2-1	489	Fowler, Newberry.	15
47	10.03	H	RL	Bromley	W 1-0	224	Fowler.	
48	14.03	H	RL	Hitchin Town	L 1-2	249	Robson.	13
49	17.03	H	RL	Boreham Wood	L 0-2	197		
50	19.03	H	**FMC 4**	Maidenhead United	L 1-2			-
51	21.03	A	RL	Bromley	L 0-3	376		16
52	24.03	H	RL	Chesham United	L 0-1	248		
53	28.03	H	RL	Bishop's Stortford	L 1-2	251	Fowler (pen).	17
54	07.04	H	RL	Enfield	W 2-0	265	Newberry, Kirby.	
55	11.04	A	RL	Heybridge Swifts	D 0-0	295		18
56	13.04	H	RL	Sutton United	**L 1-5**	812	Fowler.	18
57	18.04	A	RL	St Albanns City	L 0-3	486		18
58	25.04	H	RL	Oxford City	W 2-0	403	Newberry 2.	16
59	02.05	A	RL	Hendon	L 0-4	447		17

PLAYING SQUAD 1998 - **Goalkeepers:** Adrian Blake (Chertsey T, Kingstonian, Walton & H, Yeading,Feltham & H, Walton & H). **Defenders:** Kevin Smith (Croydon, Dulwich H, Auckland (NZ), Dulwich H,Leatherhead, Millwall, Ipswich T), Stuart May (Crystal Palace, Wimbledon), Tim Alexander (Walton & H, Bromley, Dag & Red, Woking, Brentford), Steve Firminger (Croydon Ath), Neil Robson (Molesey, Carshalton Ath, Dorking, Sutton U, Epsom& Ewell, Sutton U), Mark Ford (Crawley T, Sutton U), Ian Dawes (Whyteleafe,Fisher Ath, Bromley, Millwall, QPR). **Midfielders:** Paul Adam (Crawley T, Molesey, Sutton U), Jamie Buckley (Hayes,Fulham), Martin Beard (Harrow B, Carshalton Ath, Croydon, Crystal Palace,Carshalton Ath), Barry Kingsford (Youth team), Simon Underwood (Grays Ath,Buckingham T, Hendon, Kettering T, Northampton T), Mark Biggins (Hampton,Kingstonian, Hampton, Hendon, St.Albans C, Harrow B, Wealdstone, Aldershot T,Woking, Windsor & Eton, St.Albans C, Maidenhead U, Feltham, Hanwell T, Hampton). **Forwards:** Richard Newbery (Gravesend, Wokingham T, Woking, Wokingham T,Hampton, Staines T, Farnborough T), Matt Fowler (Youth team), Matt Edwards (Enfield, Walton & H, Kettering T, Brighton, Tottenham H), Lee Cormack (Wokingham T, Worthing, Bognor Regis T, Fareham T, Newport IOW, Waterlooville,Basingstoke T, Bognor Regis T, Fisher Ath, Brighton, Southampton), Steve White (Bromley), Jon Fowler (Chipstead).

CHESHAM UNITED
FOOTBALL CLUB

ICIS LEAGUE DIVISION ONE

CHESHAM UNITED

Colours: Blue & orange
Change colours: All Yellow & green
Midweek home matchday: Tuesday
Reserve Team's League: Suburban North
Local Radio: Three Counties
Local Press: Bucks Examiner, Bucks Advertiser, Bucks Free Press.

Formed: 1886
Nickname: The Generals
Sponsors: MFI

PROGRAMME DETAILS:
Pages: 52 **Price:** £1
Editors: J & S Chambers
(01494 775490 [H])

President: Bill Wells **Chairman:** David Pembroke
Secretary: Ronald Campion c/o Chesham United FC. Tel: 01494 837494 (H) 01494 783964 (B).
Manager: Graham Roberts **Assistant Manager:** Tony O'Driscoll
Physio: Michael Burgess **Commercial Manager:** Peter Wright
Press Officer: Jim Chambers
GROUND - Address: The Meadow, Amy Lane, Amersham Road, Chesham, Bucks. HP5 1NE (01494 783964 - ground clubhouse. 01494 791608 - fax. 0891 884580 - match information service). **Directions:** M25 junction 18, A404 to Amersham, A416 to Chesham - go down to r-about at foot of Amersham Hill, then sharp left. 10 mins walk from Chesham station (Metropolitan Line).
Capacity: 5,000 **Cover:** 2,500 **Seats:** 284 **Floodlights:** Yes
Clubhouse: Open every evening & matchdays. Bar snacks. Available for hire (business training meetings, weddings etc).
Club Shop: Open matchdays **Metal Badges:** Yes

PREVIOUS - **Leagues:** Spartan 17-47; Corinthian 47-63; Athenian 63-73.

CLUB RECORDS - **Attendance:** 5,000 v Cambridge Utd, FA 3rd Rd 5/12/79. **Goalscorer:** John Willis. **Appearances:** Martin Baguley (600+). **Record Fees - Paid & Received:** Undisclosed (club policy).

BEST SEASON - **FA Cup:** 3rd Rd 79-80. 1st Rd 66-67 68-69 76-77 82-83. **FA Amtr Cup:** R-up 67-68. **FA Trophy:** 3rd Rd 92-93 (1-3 v Sutton United [H])

HONOURS - FA Amtr Cup R-up 67-68, Isthmian Lg 92-93 (Div 1 90-91 96-97), Div 2 Nth 86-87, Associate Members Cup R-up 90-91, Charity Shield 94-95; Athenian Lg Div 1 Cup 63-64 68-69; Corinthian Lg R-up(2) 60-62 (Lg Cup 60-61); Spartan Lg(4) 21-23 24-25 32-33 (R-up 26-27 29-30 33-34); Berks & Bucks Snr Cup 21-22 25-26 28-29 33-34 47-48 50-51 64-65 66-67 75-76 92-93 (R-up 94-95).

Players progressing to Football League: Bill Shipwright & Jimmy Strain (Watford 53 & 55), Stewart Scullion (Charlton 65), John Pyatt (L'pool 67), Brian Carter (Brentford 68), Kerry Dixon (Spurs 78), Tony Currie (Torquay 84).

Chesham's Graham Roberts is out jumped by Sutton's Joff Vansittant. Photo: Garry Letts

CHESHAM UNITED - Match Facts 97-98

B&BSC - Berks. & Bucks Sen. Cup

Match No.	Date	Venue H / A	Comp.	Opponents	Result & Score		Att.	Goalscorers	League Position
1	16.08	H	IL	Gravesend & Northfleet	W	4-2	549	McGuire, Nabil, Hazel, Lawford.	1
2	19.08	A	IL	St Albans City	D	1-1	*502*	Nabil	
3	23.08	A	IL	Heybridge Swifts	W	3-0	*370*	Lawford, Nabil, McGuire.	2
4	26.08	H	IL	Carshalton Athletic	W	3-0	575	McGuire 2, Lawford.	1
5	30.08	H	IL	Purfleet	D	1-1	523	Purdie (og).	1
6	02.09	A	IL	Basingstoke Town	L	0-2	*538*		
7	07.09	H	IL	Oxford City	W	6-0	565	S Fontaine 2, Lawford, Morrisey, Hazel, C Fontaine.	3
8	09.09	H	**GIS**	Boreham Wood	L	1-4			-
9	13.09	A	**FAC 1Q**	Bedfont	W	4-2	200	Morrisey 2, Argrave, Gurney.	-
10	16.09	A	IL	Hendon	L	0-3	*247*		
11	20.09	A	IL	Harrow Borough	L	0-1	*352*		4
12	23.09	H	IL	Enfield	L	1-2	602	Lawford.	7
13	27.09	A	**FAC 2Q**	Braintree Town	L	0-3	*452*		-
14	30.09	A	IL	Dulwich Hamlet	L	1-3	*211*	McGuire.	7
15	04.10	A	IL	Dagenham & Redbridge	L	0-2	*778*		10
16	11.10	A	IL	Bromley	L	2-3	*364*	Argrave, Dawber.	14
17	18.10	A	IL	Bishop's Stortford	L	2-4	*454*	Richardson 6, Argrave 87.	16
18	01.11	A	IL	Kingstonian	L	1-3	*701*	Pierson.	20
19	08.11	A	**FAT 2Q**	Bognor Regis Town	W	3-2		Argrave, Lawford, McGuire.	-
20	12.11	H	IL	Yeading	W	3-1	341	Lawford 2, Greaves.	
21	15.11	A	IL	Walton & Hersham	D	1-1	*298*	Argrave.	15
22	22.11	H	RL	Hitchin Town	D	3-3	448	Argrave, Lawford, Pluckrose (pen).	15
23	25.11	H	RL	Sutton United	D	3-3	362	**Lawford 3.**	15
24	29.11	H	**FAT 3Q**	Sutton United	W	2-1		Murphy, McGuire.	-
25	02.12	H	**FMC 2**	Gravesend & Northfleet	L	0-3			-
26	13.12	A	RL	Kingstonian	D	1-1	*434*	Lawford.	16
27	20.12	A	RL	Boreham Wood	L	1-3	*348*		18
28	27.12	H	RL	Aylesbury United	W	4-2	1,034	McGuire, Pearson, C Fontaine, Argrave.	17
29	06.01	H	**B&B SC 1**	Chalfont St Peter	W	2-1			
30	10.01	A	**FAT 1**	Stevenage Borough	D	2-2	*2,685*	Fontaine 35, Lawford 80 (pen).	-
31	13.01	H	**FAT 1 R**	Stevenage Borough	L	0-3	986		-
32	17.01	A	RL	Gravesend & Northfleet	L	2-3	*630*	Pluckrose 28, Lawford 67.	18
33	24.01	H	RL	Heybridge Swifts	L	0-3	411		19
34	31.01	A	RL	Purfleet	L	2-3	*172*	McGuire, Argrave.	20
35	07.02	H	RL	Harrow Borough	**L**	**1-5**	362	Argrave.	21
36	14.02	A	RL	Enfield	W	1-0	*773*	Lawford.	20
37	21.02	A	RL	Yeading	L	0-2	*219*		21
38	24.02	H	**B&B SC2**	Aylesbury United	L	0-2			-
39	28.02	H	RL	Dagenham & Redbridge	D	0-0	419		21
40	07.03	H	RL	Hendon	W	4-1	406	Argrave, Lawford, Engwell, Thompson.	20
41	13.03	A	RL	Oxford City	L	1-2	*359*	Argrave.	21
42	17.03	H	RL	St Albans City	L	1-2	349	Argrave	21
43	21.03	A	RL	Sutton United	W	4-2	*690*	**Engwell 3,** Argrave.	21
44	24.03	A	RL	Carshalton Athletic	W	1-0	*248*	Bushay	
45	28.03	H	RL	Dulwich Hamlet	**W**	**5-1**	541	McGuire, Thompson, Engwell, Bushay, Lawford.	18
46	31.03	H	RL	Basingstoke Town	L	0-1	505		
47	13.04	A	RL	Aylesbury United	D	0-0	*801*		20
48	18.04	H	RL	Walton & Hersham	W	2-0	441	McGuire 2.	19
49	23.04	A	RL	Bromley	W	2-1	*275*	Lawford, Nabil.	
50	25.04	A	RL	Hitchin Town	W	2-1	*369*	Nabil, Lawford.	15
51	30.04	H	RL	Boreham Wood	D	1-1	381	Lawford.	
52	02.05	H	RL	Bishop's Stortford	D	1-1	552	Argrave.	14

PLAYING SQUAD 1998 - **Goalkeepers:** Kenny Addai (St.Albans C, Grays Ath, Leyton Pennant, Boreham Wood,Fisher Ath, Walton & H, Sutton U). **Defenders:** Graham Roberts (Wealdstone, Yeovil T, Stevenage B, Slough T,Enfield, WBA, Chelsea, Glasgow Rangers, Tottenham H, Weymouth, Dorchester T,Portsmouth, AFC Bournemouth, Sholing Sports), David Thompson (Yeovil T,Cambridge U, Blackpool, Brentford, Bristol C, Millwall), Micky Engwell (YeovilT, Grays Ath, Enfield, Harrow B, Chesham U, Crewe Alexandra, Barking,Chelmsford C, Southend U), Richard Pierson (Oxford C), Allan Pluckrose (Aylesbury U, St.Albans C, Slough T, Aylesbury U, SV Viktoria Goch (Ger),Torquay U, Falmouth T). **Midfielders:** Steve Browne (Yeovil T, Hendon, Yeovil T, Walton & H, Wealdstone,Yeading, Sutton U, Kingstonian, Sutton U, Wealdstone, Newmont Travel, GraysAth, Dartford, Maidstone U, Fulham, Charlton Ath), Graham Kemp (Yeovil T,Newbury T, Reading, Shrewsbury T), Richard Gell * (Yeading, Wycombe W,Chelsea), Trevor Argrave (Sutton U, Chertsey T, Burnham, Chertsey T), Ian Hazel (Carshalton Ath, Aylesbury U, Slough T, Maidstone U, Bristol R,Wimbledon), John Hurlock (Harrow B, Droylsden, Altrincham, Nuneaton B,Bedworth U, Stockport Co), Clive Gartell * (Sutton U, Molesey, Sutton U,Dulwich Hamlet, Molesey, Dulwich Hamlet, Molesey, Leatherhead, Epsom & Ewell). **Forwards:** Mick Swaysland * (Aylesbury U, London Colney, Evergreen), Kris Huckstepp (Wivenhoe T), Ansil Bushay (Walton & H, Slough T, St.Albans C,Woking, Marlow, Chalfont St.Peter, Beaconsfield U), Chris Maguire (Havant T,Witney T, Lossiemouth, RAF), Youness Nabil (Chertsey T, F.A.S. (Morocco).

DAGENHAM & REDBRIDGE

Club colours: Red/blue/red **Formed:** 1992
Change colours: All yellow **Nickname:** Daggers
Midweek home matchday: Monday
Reserve's League: Essex & Herts Border Comb.
Match Reports: 0930 555840
Local Press: Dagenham Post, Waltham Forest Gazette,, Ilford Recorder
Local Radio: Breeze AM, BBC Radio Essex, Capital Radio, Active FM.

Chairman: Dave Andrews **President:** Harry Hammond
Secretary: Derek Almond, 149 Kings Head Hill, Chingford, London E4 7JG (0181 524 2689)
Manager: Ted Hardy **Asst Manager:** Dennis Moore
Safety Officer: David Simpson **Physio:** John Stannard
Press Officer: Paul Mullender (0181 553 1653)

PROGRAMME DETAILS:
Pages: 48 **Price:** £1.40
Editor: Dave Simpson
Tel: 0181 521 9554

GROUND - Address: Victoria Road, Dagenham RM10 7XL. (0181 592 1549. Fax: 0181 593 7227).
Directions: On A112 between A12 & A13. Buses 103 & 174 or, exit Dagenham East tube station, turn left and after approximately 500 yards take 5th turning left into Victoria Road.
Capacity: 6,000 **Seated:** 700 **Covered:** 3,000 **Floodlights:** Yes
Clubhouse: Open 7 days 11am-11pm. Hot & cold food available. Functions contact: Tony Manhood (0181 592 7194)
Club Shop: Yes, open matchdays, contact Steve Thompson 0181 592 1549

Sponsors - **Main:** Compass Plumbing Supplies **Programme:** Recorder Group Newspapers **Kit:** Vandenell

PREVIOUS - **Names:** Ilford FC (1881-1979) & Leytonstone (1886-1979) *merged becoming* Leytonstone-Ilford (1979-88). *The new club merged with* Walthamstow Avenue (1900-88) *to become* Redbridge Forest (1988-92) *who merged with* Dagenham (1949-92) *becoming* Dagenham & Redbridge. All details refer to the club since the amalgamation in 1992
Grounds: None **Leagues:** GMV Conference 92-96.

CLUB RECORDS - **Attendance:** 5,500 v Leyton Orient - FA Cup 1st Rnd - 14.11.92. **Career goalscorer:** (League only) Paul Cavell - 47; Ian Richardson - 31; Jason Broom - 32. **Career appearances:** Paul Watts - 174; Steve Corner - 245; Jason Broom - 186. **Win:** 8-1 v Woking (A), GMV Conference 19/4/94, 7-0 v Oxford (H) Rymans Lge 1/11/97. **Defeat:** 0-5 v Stalybridge Celtic (A), GMV Conference 31/4/94; 0-5 v Northwich Victoria, GMV Conference 3/9/94; 0-5 v Hyde Utd (H) FA Trophy 2nd Rd. **Transfer fee paid** £30,000 to Boston United for Paul Cavell & Paul Richardson - 1991. **Transfer fee received:** £85,000 from Watford for Andy Hessenthaler - 1991.

BEST SEASON - **FA Cup:** 2nd Rd Proper v Peterborough lost 2-3, 97-98. **FA Trophy:** R-up 96-97

HONOURS - F.A. Trophy Runners-up 96-97; Essex Senior 97-98.

Past players progressed to the Football League: Juan Mequel DeSouza/Ian Richardson (Birmingham City 94,95), Terry Hurlock (Southampton 97), A Hessenthaler (Watford 91), Trevor Morton (Bournemouth 78)

97-98 - Captain: Steve Connor **Top scorer:** Paul Cobb (30) **P.o.Y.:** Tim Cole

Back Row (L-R); John Stimson, David Culverhouse, Steve Connor, Courtney Naylor, Danny Shipp, Paul Gothard, Lee Matthews, Tim Cole, Danny Hazle, Jason Broom, Matty Bird, John Stannard (Physio), Gary Seymour (Coach). Front Row; Bill Edmans (Kit), David Pratt, Mark Janney, John Nicholson, Dean Parratt, Ted Hardy (Mgr), Gary Howard, Paul Cobb, Tolo Mas, Lee Double, Sam Bass.

DAGENHAM & REDBRIDGE - Match Facts 97-98

ESC - Essex Sen. Cup

Match No.	Date	Venue H / A	Comp.	Opponents	Result & Score		Att.	Goalscorers	League Position
1	16.08	H	IL	Carshalton Athletic	W	2-0	765	Bird, John.	2
2	19.08	A	IL	Bishop's Stortford	D	1-1	*437*	Hazle.	
3	23.08	A	IL	Hitchin Town	W	1-0	*351*	Hazle	1
4	25.08	H	IL	Gravesend & Northfleet	W	2-0	1,006	Cobb 2.	1
5	30.08	H	IL	Harrow Borough	L	1-2	689	Broom.	2
6	07.09	H	IL	Boreham Wood	D	1-1	539	Cobb (pen).	6
7	09.09	A	**GIC 1**	Ford United	W	3-1	*266*	Cobb 2, OG.	-
8	13.09	A	IL	Enfield	W	2-1	*957*	OG (Cash), Cobb.	4
9	20.09	A	IL	Basingstoke Town	W	2-1	*502*	Bird, Cobb.	2
10	22.09	H	IL	Bromley	W	2-1	704	Pratt, Conner.	2
11	27.09	H	IL	Hendon	D	1-1	743	Cobb (pen).	2
12	30.09	A	IL	Aylesbury United	W	2-1	*325*	Wallace, Cobb.	1
13	04.10	H	IL	Chesham United	W	2-0	778	Cobb 2 (1 pen).	1
14	06.10	H	IL	Bishop's Stortford	W	2-1	739	Wallace, Cobb.	1
15	14.10	H	IL	Walton & Hersham	W	4-2	624	Cobb, Mas, Pratt, OG (Rushay).	1
16	18.10	A	IL	St Albans City	L	0-2	*756*		1
17	25.10	H	IL	Yeading	D	1-1	726	Cobb.	1
18	01.11	H	IL	Oxford City	**W**	**7-0**	808	Wallace 2, O.G., Cobb, Platt, Howard, Conner.	1
19	04.11	A	**GIC 2**	Aldershot Town	W	1-0	*1,398*	Conner.	-
20	15.11	A	**FAC 1**	Farnborough Town	W	1-0	*1,236*	Stimson.	-
21	18.11	A	**ESC 2**	Hornchurch	W	*2-0	*146*	Flanagan, Schneider. A.E.T.	-
22	22.11	A	RL	Dulwich Hamlet	W	2-0	*511*	Cobb 2.	1
23	24.11	H	RL	Heybrdige Swifts	W	6-2	836	**Pratt 4,** Cobb, Cow.	1
24	29.11	A	RL	Kingstonian	W	2-0	*1,411*	Pratt, Bird.	1
25	06.12	A	**FAC 2**	Peterborough United	L	2-3	*5,572*	Cobb, Shipp.	-
26	13.12	A	RL	Oxford City	L	0-2	*272*		1
27	20.12	H	RL	Sutton United	L	0-2	1,214		1
28	22.12	H	**FMC 2**	Romford	W	3-0	391	Cobb 2, Shipp.	-
29	27.12	A	RL	Purfleet	**L**	**0-4**	*841*		2
30	30.12	A	**GIC 3**	Boreham Wood	L	0-1	*201*		
31	03.01	H	RL	Enfield	L	0-2	1,161		2
32	10.01	H	**FAT 1**	Billericay Town	W	1-0	1,056	OG (Sinfield).	-
33	12.01	H	**ESC 3**	Leyton Pennant	W	*3-1	303	Shipp, Schneider, OG. A.E.T.	-
34	17.01	A	RL	Carshalton Athletic	W	2-0	*511*	Mas, Oakley.	2
35	19.01	H	**FMC 3**	Harrow Borough	W	3-1	258	Howard, Double, Bird.	-
36	24.01	H	RL	Hitchin Town	W	1-0	851	Cobb.	2
37	26.01	H	**ESC 4**	Billericay Town	W	4-2	373	Janney, Bird, Shipp, Naylor.	-
38	31.01	H	**FAT 2**	Hyde United	L	0-5	989		-
39	07.02	H	RL	Basingstoke Town	W	2-1	663	Shipp, Pratt.	3
40	14.02	A	RL	Bromley	L	0-2	*529*		3
41	17.02	A	**FMC 4**	Hendon	L	1-3	175	Shipp.	-
42	21.02	H	RL	Kingstonian	D	2-2	1,076	Shipp 2.	3
43	28.02	A	RL	Chesham United	D	0-0	*419*		3
44	03.03	A	RL	Gravesend & Northfleet	D	2-2	*487*	Cobb (pen), Bird.	3
45	07.03	H	RL	Aylesbury United	L	2-3	793	Cobb 2.	3
46	09.03	H	**ESC S-F**	Southend United	W	6-2	511	**Shipp 4,** Bird 2.	-
47	14.03	A	RL	Boreham Wood	D	0-0	*629*		3
48	17.03	A	RL	Harrow Borough	W	5-0	*172*	OG (Graham), Partratt, Cobb, Janney 2.	3
49	21.03	H	RL	St Albans City	D	1-1	847	Cobb.	3
50	28.03	A	RL	Walton & Hersham	L	1-2	*296*	Shipp.	4
51	04.04	A	RL	Hendon	L	0-2	*295*		4
52	11.04	A	RL	Sutton United	L	1-2	*678*	Shipp.	4
53	13.04	H	RL	Purfleet	D	2-2	661	Cobb, Cole.	4
54	18.04	A	RL	Yeading	W	2-0	*161*	Shipp 2.	4
55	25.04	H	RL	Dulwich Hamlet	W	2-1	677	Double, Janney.	4
56	27.04	N	**ESC Final**	Purfleet	W	2-1	779	Cobb, Naylor.	-
57	02.05	A	RL	Heybridge Swifts	W	5-2	*402*	Cobb, Shipp 2, Janney 2.	4

PLAYING SQUAD -

Goalkeepers: Paul Gothard (Grays Ath, Chelmsford C, Colchester U)

Defenders: Dave Culverhouse (Spurs), Mark Janney (Spurs), Steve Connor (Dartford, Tilbury, East Thurrock U), Tim Cole (Leyton Pen.,Walthamstow Pen.), Bartolome Mas (Billericay T, Barking, Dag & Red,Maidstone U), Lee Matthews (Purfleet, Southend U), Steve Davies (Chelsea)

Midfielders: Jason Broom (Billericay T, Eton Manor), David Pratt (SK Vard(Nor), Leyton Pennant, Leyton Orient, West Ham U), Lee Double (Beckton U), Dean Parratt (B Stortford, Purfleet, Dag & Red, Wimbledon, Arsenal), Danny Shipp (Coleraine, West Ham U), Ian Bass (Youth team), Greg Allen (Purfleet,Billericay T, Dag & Red, Barking, Billericay T, Dag & Red, Arsenal), John Nicholson (Romford, Met.Police, Boreham Wood, Met.Police, Wisbech T, March T,Huntingdon)

Forwards: Paul Cobb (Purfleet, Enfield, Purfleet, Leyton Orient, Purfleet), Courtney Naylor (Local football), Matthew Bird (Leyton Orient), Danny Hazle (Billericay T, Collier Row, Witham T, Billericay T, Gillingham, Charlton Ath,Crystal Palace), Paul Terry (Bromley, Charlton Ath).

DULWICH HAMLET FC
SEASON
1997
98
official programme
£1
SPONSORED BY
South London Press

DULWICH HAMLET

Colours: Navy blue & pink stripes/navy/navy **Nickname:** The Hamlet
Change colours: Green & white stripes/white/white **Formed:** 1893
Midweek matchday: Tuesday **Sponsors:** South London Press
Reserve League: Suburban
Local Press: South London Press, Southwark News

Chairman: Martin Eede. **President:** Tommy Jover
Vice Chairman: Brian Shears **Secretary:** Martyn Cole, c/o Ground. Tel. 0181 398 1751.
Manager: Dave Garland **Commercial Manager:**
Physio: Danny Keenan. **Press Officer:** John Lawrence (0171 733 6385)

GROUND Address: Champion Hill Stadium, Edgar Kail Way, East Dulwich, London SE22 8BD (0171 274 8707). **Directions:** East Dulwich station, 200yds. Denmark Hill station, 10 mins walk. Herne Hill station then bus 37 stops near ground. Also buses 40 & 176 from Elephant & Castle, 185 from Victoria.
Capacity: 3,000 **Cover:** 1,000 **Seats:** 500 **Floodlights:** Yes
Clubhouse: Open 7 days a week, 3 bars. Function rooms and meeting room available for hire. Gymnasium, squash courts (0171 274 8707).
Club Shop: Sells programmes, pennants, badges, scarves, baseball caps, replica shirts (by order only). Contact Mishi D Morath at club.

PROGRAMME DETAILS:
Pages: 36 **Price:** £1
Editor: John Lawrence

PREVIOUS - **Grounds:** Woodwarde Road 1893-95; College Farm 95-96; Sunray Avenue 96-1902; Freeman's Ground, Champion Hill 02-12; Champion Hill (old ground) 1912-92; Sandy Lane (groundshare with Tooting & Mitcham F.C.) 91-92. **Leagues:** Camberwell 1894-97; S/thern Sub 1897-1900 01-07; Dulwich 00-01; Spartan 07-08.

CLUB RECORDS - **Attendance:** 20,744, Kingstonian v Stockton, FA Amateur Cup Final 1933 *(at refurbished ground: 1,604 v Enfield 95/96).* **Career Goalscorer:** Edgar Kail 427 (1919-33) **Career Appearances:** Reg Merritt 571 (50-66). **Fee Paid:** T Eames (Wimbledon), G Allen (Carshalton Ath 80). **Fee Received:** E Nwajiobi (Luton 83). **Win:** 13-0 v Walton-on-Thames, 37-38. **Defeat:** 1-10 v Hendon, 63-64.

BEST SEASON - **FA Amateur Cup:** Winners 19-20 31-2 33-4 36-7. **FA Trophy:** Quarter Final 79-80. **FA Cup:** 1st Rd replay 30-31 33-34. 1st Rd on 13 occasions; 25-31 32-38 48-49.

HONOURS - Isthmian League 19-20 25-26 32-33 48-49, (R-up(7) 21-22 23-24 29-31 33-34 46-47 58-59, Div 1 77-78); London Senior Cup 24-25 38-39 49-50 83-84 (R-up 05-06 07-08 20-21 27-28); Surrey Senior Cup(16) 04-06 08-10 19-20 22-23 24-25 27-28 33-34 36-37 46-47 49-50 57-59 73-75, (R-up(6) 11-12 31-33 37-38 50-51 67-68); London Chal. Cup R-up 91-92; London Charity Cup(12) 10-11(jt) 19-21 22-23 23-24(jt) 25-26 27-29 30-31(jt) 47-48 56-58; Surrey Senior Shield 72-73; Surrey Centen. Shld 77-78; Sth of the Thames Cup(4) 56-60; Southern Comb Cup 73-74.

Players progressing to Football League: W Bellamy (Spurs), A Solly (Arsenal), L Fishlock/A Gray/A Pardew (C Palace), J Moseley & E Toser (Millwall), R Dicks (Middlesborough), G Jago/J Ryan (Charlton Ath 51/63), G Pearce (Plymouth), R Crisp (Watford 61), E Nwajiobi (Luton 83), C Richards & J Glass (Bournemouth), P Coleman (Millwall 86), A Perry (Portsmouth 86), N Kelly (Stoke City), C Emberson (Rotherham), C Asaba (Brentford).

97-98 - Captain: Russell Edwards **P.o.Y.:** Darren Williams **Top scorer:** Dean Holness (15)

Dulwich Hamlet's Steve McKimm in action against Hitchin Town Photo: Vanida Pansroi

DULWICH HAMLET - Match Facts 97-98

LCC - London Challenge Cup
SSC - Surrey Senior Cup

Match No.	Date	Venue H / A	Comp.	Opponents	Result & Score		Att.	Goalscorers	League Position
1	16.08	H	IL	Heybridge Swifts	L	1-2	370	Hippolyte.	
2	19.08	A	IL	Enfield	D	0-0	*656*		
3	23.08	A	IL	Purfleet	D	2-2	*185*	Whitmarsh, Hutchings.	19
4	26.08	H	IL	Bromley	D	3-3	417	Hippolyte, Johnson, OG (Gray).	
5	30.08	H	IL	Gravesend & Northfleet	D	1-1	429	Rootes (pen).	17
6	02.09	A	IL	Carshalton Athletic	D	3-3	*340*	Holness 2, Anderson.	20
7	09.09	A	**GIC**	Basingstoke Town	L	1-3	*261*	Hutchings.	-
8	13.09	A	**FAC 1Q**	Bedford Town	D	1-1	*497*	Edwards.	-
9	16.09	H	**FAC 1Q R**	Bedford Town	W	2-0	226	Holness, Hutchings.	-
10	20.09	A	IL	St Albans City	L	0-1	*506*		22
11	23.09	H	IL	Bishop's Stortford	**W**	**5-0**	255	Restarick 2, Holness, Edwards, OG (Shuttleworth).	19
12	27.09	A	**FAC 2Q**	Billericay Town	L	2-1		Holness.	-
13	30.09	H	IL	Chesham United	W	3-1	211	Whitmarch, Roots (pen), Hutchings.	15
14	04.10	A	IL	Hitchin Town	L	0-2	*245*		17
15	07.10	H	IL	Enfield	W	2-0	423	Whitmarsh, Holness.	
16	11.10	H	IL	Hendon	L	1-2	314	Anderson.	13
17	14.10	A	IL	Yeading	D	2-2	*118*	Holness, Hutchings.	
18	25.10	A	IL	Oxford City	W	2-1	*217*	Holness, McKimm.	11
19	28.10	H	LCC 1	Metropolitan Police	W	1-0			
20	01.11	A	IL	Basingstoke Town	L	3-4	*451*	Whitman, Holness, Gallagher.	13
21	04.11	H	**FMC**	Kingstonian	L	0-3			
22	08.11	H	IL	Aylesbury United	W	2-1	306	Holness, Gallagher.	
23	22.11	H	IL	Dagenham & Redbridge	L	0-2	511		13
24	25.11	A	IL	Walton & Hersham	L	0-1	*160*		13
25	29.11	A	**FAT 3Q**	Aylesbury United	W	3-0	*406*	McKimm, Anderson, Sullivan (og).	-
26	06.12	H	RL	Carshalton Athletic	L	0-3	314		15
27	13.12	H	RL	Basingstoke Town	L	0-1	284		15
28	16.12	H	SSC 1	Redhill	W	2-1	90		-
29	20.12	A	RI	Harrow Borough	W	2-1	*205*	Jones, Anderson.	15
30	27.12	H	RI	Kingstonian	W	2-1	603	Restarick, Holness.	15
31	10.01	A	**FAT 1**	Hereford United	L	0-3	*2,101*		-
32	13.01	A	SSC 2	Walton & Hersham	L	1-2			
33	17.01	A	RL	Heybridge Swifts	L	1-3	*304*	Restarick.	15
34	24.01	H	RL	Purfleet	W	2-1	235	James, Edwards.	14
35	27.01	H	LCC 2	Leyton Pennant	W	2-1			
36	31.01	A	RL	Gravesend & Northfleet	W	1-0	*603*	Garland.	12
37	07.02	H	RL	St Albans City	L	1-2	302	Tivey.	13
38	10.02	H	RL	Sutton United	W	1-0	511	Restarick.	
39	14.02	A	RL	Bishop's Stortford	D	1-1	*202*	Tivvey.	11
40	21.02	A	RL	Hendon	L	1-2	*266*	Garland.	11
41	28.02	H	RL	Hitchin Town	D	2-2	319	Thompson 2.	12
42	03.03	A	RL	Boreham Wood	L	0-4	*224*		12
43	07.03	A	RL	Sutton United	D	1-1	*841*	Ndah.	13
44	14.03	H	RL	Yeading	W	2-1	237	Thompson 2.	12
45	21.02	H	RL	Oxford City	W	3-2	237	Holness, Restarick, McKimm.	11
46	28.03	A	RL	Chesham United	**L**	**1-5**	*541*	Restarick.	13
47	04.04	A	RL	Aylesbury United	D	0-0	*356*		14
48	13.04	A	RL	Kingstonian	L	1-2	*1,203*	Holness.	15
49	16.04	A	LCC S-F	Boreham Wood	L	1-5			
50	18.04	H	RL	Boreham Wood	L	0-1	335		16
51	21.04	A	RL	Bromley	D	1-1	*370*	Holness.	17
52	25.04	A	RL	Dagenham & Redbridge	L	1-2	*677*	Restarick.	17
53	29.04	H	RL	Harrow Borough	W	1-0	160	Tivey.	16
54	02.05	H	RL	Walton & Hersham	L	1-3	421	Restarick.	16

PLAYING SQUAD 1998

Goalkeepers: Darren Williams (Chelmsford C, Dag & Red, Dover Ath, Welling U,Chelmsford C, Sorrento (Aust), Wealdstone, Barnet, Dagenham). **Defenders:** Mark Garland (Crawley T, Kingstonian, Crystal Palace), MickeyRootes (Molesey, Tooting & M, Woking, Wimbledon), Dave Stephenson (Chesham U,Hendon, Malden Vale, Croydon, Tooting & M, Dorking, Croydon), Russell Edwards (Barnet, Crystal Palace), Simon Connell (Molesey), Tony Chin (Youth team), John Humphrey (Chesham U, Charlton Ath, Crystal Palace, Charlton Ath, Wolves), Nick Andrews (Molesey, Fulham), Gary Hewitt (Erith & B, Bromley, Margate,Bromley, Gravesend, Hendon, Dulwich Hamlet, Erith & B, Gateway). **Midfielders:** Lee Akers (Tonbridge, Croydon, Erith & B, Croydon, DulwichHamlet, Malden Vale, Dulwich Hamlet, Bromley, Greenwich B, Bromley, DulwichHamlet, Arsenal), Martin Ferney (Dover Ath, Fulham), Tyrone Myton (Youthteam), Steve McKimm (Molesey, Hendon, Malden Vale), Mark Tivey (Youth team), Dean Holness (Bromley). **Forwards:** Steve Restarick (Crawley T, Dover Ath, Chelmsford C, Colchester U,West Ham U), Jamie Ndah (Kingstonian, Rushden & D, Barnet, Torquay U,Kingstonian, Dulwich Hamlet), Peter Garland (Crawley T, Leyton Orient,Charlton Ath, Newcastle U, Tottenham H), Richard Thompson (Carshalton Ath,Kingstonian, Dulwich Hamlet, Fulham, Reading).

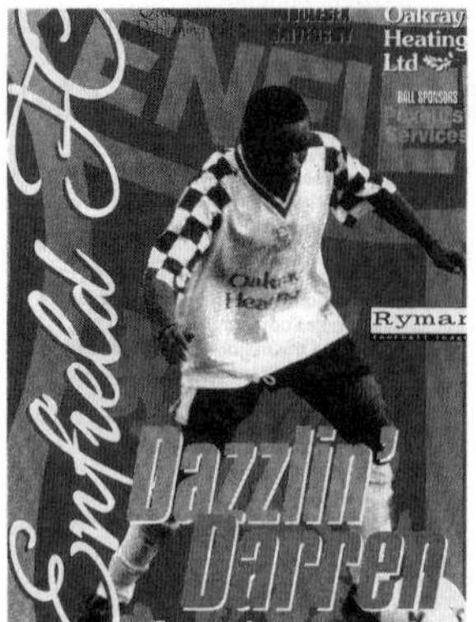

PROGRAMME DETAILS:
Pages: 48 **Price:** £1.50.
Editor: Scott Reed

ENFIELD

Colours: All White with blue trim **Sponsors:** Oakray Heating
Change colours: Yellow & Sky **Formed:** 1893
Midweek matchday: Tuesday **Nickname:** The E's
Reserve's League: Essex & Herts Border Comb. **Newsline:** 0930 555845
Local Press: Enfield Gazette, Enfield Advertiser, Enfield Independent, Enfield Town Express.

Chairman: A Lazarou **President:** T F Unwin
Secretary: Roger Reed, 16 College Gardens, Enfield, Middx EN2 0QF (0181 350 4064).
Manager: Gary Calder **Physio:** Dave Wilson
Coaches: Joe Dunwell/Chris King
Press Officer: John Jefferson Tel. 0181 3636273.

GROUND Address: The Stadium, Southbury Road, Enfield EN1 1YQ (0181 292 0665). **Directions:** At junction of A10 & A110. 800 yards from Southbury Road station. Buses from town centre.
Floodlights: Yes **Capacity:** 6,919 **Cover:** 2,800 **Seats:** 665
Clubhouse: Sportsmans Lounge, open every lunch & evening. Snacks. Starlight nightclub, cabaret, dinner & dance.
Club Shop: Yes, contact Dave Hicks 01992 769156 or Alan Farmer 0181 366 0166

PREVIOUS - **Leagues:** Tottenham & Dist 1894-95; Nth Middx 96-1903; London 03-13 20-21; Middx 08-12, 19-20; Athenian 12-14 21-39 45-63; Herts & Middx Comb 39-42; Isthmian 63-81; GMV Conference 81-90. **Name:** Enfield Spartans 1893-1900. **Grounds:** Baileys Field 1893-96; Tuckers Field 96-1900; Cherry Orchard Lane 1900-36.

CLUB RECORDS - **Attendance:** 10,000 (10/10/62) v Spurs, floodlight opener. **Victory:** 18-0 v Stevenage FA Cup 2nd Qual 22/10/27 (H). **Defeat:** 0-12 v Woolwich Polytechnic, London Lge Div 2 27/4/04. **Fee Paid:** for Gary Abbott (Barnet) **Fee Received:** for Paul Furlong (Coventry City) **Scorer:** Tommy Lawrence, 191 1959-1964. **Appearances:** Steve King 617 (77-89)

BEST SEASON - **FA Amateur Cup** Winners 66-7 69-70 R-up 63-4 71-2. **FA Trophy:** Winners 81-2 87-8. **FA Cup:** 4th Rd replay 80-81 (0-3 to Barnsley at Spurs (Att 35,244) after 1-1 draw). **- League clubs beaten:** Wimbledon, Northampton 77-78, Hereford, Port Vale 80-81, Wimbledon 81-82, Exeter 84-85, Orient 88-89, Aldershot 91-92, Cardiff City 94-95, Torquay Utd 94-95.

HONOURS - Alliance Premier Lge 82-83 85-86 (R-up 81-82), Lg Cup R-up 81-82; Isthmian Lg(8) 67-70 75-78 79-80 94-95 (R-up 64-65 71-72 74-75 80-81 90-92 95-96), Lg Cup(2) 78-80 (R-up 91-92 94-95); Athenian Lg(2) 61-63 (R-up 34-35); London Lg Div 1 11-12 (R-up 04-05 06-07); Middx Snr Cup 13-14 46-47 61-62 65-66 68-71 77-81 88-89 90-91 97-98, (R-up 10-11 20-21 47-48 51-52 57-60 62-63 66-67 72-73 75-76 84-85); London Snr Cup 34-35 60-61 66-67 71-73 75-76 (R-up 63-64 67-68 70-71); Middx Lg (West) 09-10 (R-up 10-11); European Amtr Cup Winners Cup 69-70.

Players progressing to Football League: Terry McQuade (Millwall 61), Roger Day (Watford 61), Jeff Harris (Orient 64), Peter Feely (Chelsea 70), Carl Richards & Jon Bailey (B'mouth 80 & 95), Paul Furlong (Coventry 91), Andy Pape (Barnet 91), Greg Heald (Peterborough 94), Lee Marshall (Norwich City 97).

97-98 Captain: **P.o.Y.:** Darrel Annon **Top Scorer:** Steve Darlington (15)

Back Row (L-R); Dave Lawson (Physio), Gary Calder (Mgr), Jimmy Carstairs, Andy Pape, Steve McGrath, Gary Fitzgerald, Grant Cooper, Steve Terry, Terry Smith (Kit), Joe Dunwell (Coach). Front Row; Paul Moran, John Deadman, Darren Annon, Lee Williams, Danny Adams, Leroy May, Steve Darlington, Danny Jones.

ENFIELD - Match Facts 97-98

MSC - Middlesex Senior Cup

Match No.	Date	Venue H / A	Comp.	Opponents	Result & Score		Att.	Goalscorers	League Position
1	16.08	A	IL	Oxford City	W	2-1	*412*	West, Gentle.	4
2	19.08	H	IL	Dulwich Hamlet	D	0-0	656		
3	23.08	H	IL	Hendon	D	3-3	742	West 2, Moran.	6
4	26.08	A	IL	Kingstonian	D	0-0	*1,002*		
5	30.08	A	IL	Yeading	W	2-0	*402*	May 2.	7
6	05.09	A	IL	Gravesend & Northfleet	W	3-1	*723*	West 2, Moran.	4
7	09.09	H	**GIC**	St Albans City	L	*1-2			
8	13.09	H	IL	Dagenham & Redbridge	L	1-2	957	West.	5
9	20.09	H	IL	Sutton United	L	0-2	823		9
10	23.09	A	IL	Chesham United	W	2-1	*602*	West, Pearson (og).	6
11	27.09	H	IL	St Albans City	L	0-2	772		6
12	30.09	A	**FMC**	St Albans City	L	1-5			-
13	04.10	H	IL	Bishop's Stortford	W	4-1	688	Endersby, St Hilaire, Venables, May.	5
14	07.10	A	IL	Dulwich Hamlet	L	0-2	*423*		
15	11.10	A	IL	Walton & Hersham	L	1-3	*318*	Mernagh.	8
16	18.10	H	IL	Heybridge Swifts	W	4-2	653	Deadmasn 26, May 57, 84, Hunter 88.	6
17	20.10	A	IL	Purfleet	**L**	**0-4**	*431*		
18	25.10	H	**FAC 4Q**	Carshalton Athletic	L	1-2	717	St Hilaire.	-
19	01.11	A	IL	Hitchin Town	D	1-1	*559*	McGrath.	8
20	15.11	A	IL	Bishop's Stortford	W	2-0	*694*	Tucker, McGrath.	7
21	22.11	H	RL	Harrow Borough	L	3-5	683	May, McGrath, Darlington.	8
22	25.11	A	RL	Aylesbury United	D	1-1	*556*	Moran.	8
23	29.11	H	RL	Gravesend & Northfleet	L	1-2	572	Moran.	7
24	06.12	H	RL	Kingstonian	L	0-1	1,142		9
25	13.12	H	RL	Hitchin Town	W	2-1	601	May, Tucker.	6
26	20.12	A	RL	Bromley	L	1-3	*447*	Moran (pen).	11
27	27.12	H	RL	Boreham Wood	L	0-3	847		11
28	03.01	A	Rl	Dagenham & Redbridge	W	2-0	*1,161*	Venables, McGrath.	10
29	10.01	H	**FAT 1**	Cheltenham Town	D	1-1	966	Terry (pen).	-
30	13.01	H	**MSC** 2	Hendon	W	3-0	170	Venables, Darlington, May.	-
31	17.01	H	RL	Oxford City	W	2-0	862	Venables, McGrath.	8
32	22.01	A	**FAT 1 R**	Cheltenham Town	L	1-5	*1,650*	Endersby.	-
33	24.01	A	RL	Hendon	W	3-0	*534*	Darlington, May, Williams.	6
34	31.01	H	RL	Carshalton Athletic	W	3-0	659	Terry, Williams, Darlington.	6
35	04.02	H	**MSC** 3	Hayes	D	*1-1	116	Fitzgerald. A.E.T.	-
36	07.02	A	RL	Sutton United	**W**	**5-0**	*1,122*	**Darlington 3,** May, Fitzgerald.	6
37	10.02	A	**MSC** 3 R	Hayes	W	1-0		Darlington.	-
38	14.02	H	RL	Chesham United	L	0-1	773		6
39	21.02	H	RL	Walton & Hersham	W	3-0	608	Darlington 2, McGrath.	7
40	03.03	A	RL	Basingstoke Town	D	0-0	*413*		6
41	07.03	A	RL	St Albans City	W	4-0	*939*	**Darlington 3,** Moran.	5
42	10.03	A	**MSC** S-F	Hampton	W	1-0	197		-
43	21.03	H	RL	Purfleet	D	0-0	906		7
44	27.02	A	RL	Heybridge Swifts	L	1-4	*507*	Williams.	7
45	31.03	A	RL	Boreham Wood	L	1-2	*502*	Deadman.	
46	07.04	A	RL	Carshalton Athletic	L	0-2	*265*		10
47	13.04	N	**MSC** Final	Uxbridge	W	3-2		May, Moran, McGrath. at Hendon F.C.	-
48	18.04	H	RL	Basingstoke Town	W	2-1	550	Venables, Terry.	9
49	21.04	H	RL	Yeading	W	2-0	444	May, Venables.	6
50	25.04	A	RL	Harrow Borough	L	2-5	*328*	Venables, Darlington.	8
51	28.04	H	RL	Bromley	D	1-1	484	Hammett.	8
52	02.05	H	RL	Aylesbury United	W	2-1	666	OG (Roudette), Darlington.	7

PLAYING SQUAD 1998

Goalkeepers: Andy Pape (Barnet, Enfield, Harrow B, Feltham, Charlton Ath,Crystal Palace, Ikast (Den), QPR), Richard Wilmot * (Stevenage B, Halifax T,Scunthorpe U, Stevenage B, Hitchin T, Pirton)

Defenders: Steve McGrath (Yeading, Shamrock FC), Jim Carstairs (Stockport Co,Cambridge U, Arsenal), Gary Cooper (Kingstonian, Welling U, Birmingham C,Peterborough U, Maidstone U, Barnet, Fisher Ath, QPR), Steve Terry (Walton &H, Aylesbury U, Northampton T, Hull C, Watford)

Midfielders: Gary Fitzgerald (Yeading, Watford), John Deadman (Kingstonian,Purfleet, Hendon, Grays Ath), Danny Adams (Yeovil T, Hendon, Enfield, Walton &H, St.Albans C, Enfield, St.Albans C, Watford), Dave Venables (Kettering T,Stevenage B, Wealdstone, Crawley T, Eastbourne U), Darron Annon (Kingstonian,Brentford, Carshalton Ath), Robbie Bourne (Aylesbury U, Grays Ath, Purfleet,Boreham Wood, Brimsdown R, Finchley, Brimsdown R)

Forwards: Leroy May (Kettering T, Kidderminster H, Stafford R, Walsall,Altrincham, Tividale, Hereford U, Tividale), Steve Darlington (Kingstonian,Wokingham T, Staines T, Windsor & Eton, Chalfont St.Peter, Hounslow), Lee Williams (Grays Ath, Purfleet, BK-IFK (Fin), Leyton Orient, Purfleet), Busby Finch (Edgware T, Enfield).

PROGRAMME DETAILS:
Pages: 32 **Price:** £1.50
Editor: R Edwards

GRAVESEND & NORTHFLEET

Colours: Red/white/red
Sponsors: Mister Ham Man.
Change colours: All blue
Formed: 1946
Midweek home matchday: Monday
Nickname: The Fleet
Reserves' League: London Suburban Lge
Local Press: Gravesend Reporter, Kent Evening Post, Gravesend Extra, Leader
Local Radio: Invicta Radio, Radio Kent, RTM, Medway FM

Chairman: Peter Dean
Vice Chairman / Secretary: Michael Alan Sears, c/o club address
Press Officer: D J Conley (01474 533796)
Manager: Andy Ford **Physio:** Micky Ward
GROUND Address: Stonebridge Road, Northfleet, Kent DA11 9BA (01474 533796). **Directions:** From A2 take Northfleet/Southfleet exit (B262), follow to Northfleet then B2175 (Springhead Rd) to junc A226, turn left (The Hill, Northfleet), rd becomes Stonebridge Rd, grd on right at bottom of steep hill after 1 mile - car parking for 400-500. 2 mins from Northfleet BR station.
Capacity: 3,300 **Cover:** 2,200 **Seats:** 600 **Floodlights:** Yes
Clubhouse: Fleet Social Centre. Hot and cold food available at tea bars on matchdays.
Club Shop: Sells progs, hats, scarves, badges etc, & other memorabilia. Contact John Still or Angela Still.

PREVIOUS - **Leagues:** Kent (Gravesend Utd), Southern 46-79, Alliance Prem. 79-80. **Names:** Gravesend Utd, Northfleet Utd (merged 1946). **Ground:** Central Avenue (Gravesend Utd) *(Northfleet always played at Stonebridge Rd).*

CLUB RECORDS - **Attendance:** 12,036 v Sunderland, FA Cup 4th Rd 12.2.63. *26.081 v Aston Villa FA Cup 3rd Rd 95-96 at Villa Park.* **Goalscorer (career):** Bert Hawkins. **Goalscorer :** Steve Portway 130+ (92-94, 97-present). **Appearances:** Ken Burrett 537. **Win:** 8-1 v Clacton Tn, Sth Lge 62-63, 7-0 Godalming 95-96 FAC. **Defeat:** 0-9 v Trowbridge Tn, Southern Lge Prem Div 91-92. **Fee Paid:** £8,000 for Richard Newbery (Wokingham 96), £8,000 for Craig Williams (Tonbridge 97). **Fee Received:** £17,500 for Steve Portway (Gloucester C 94).

BEST SEASON - **FA Cup:** 4th Rd Replay 1963, 2-5 v Sunderland (A), 1-1 (H). **FA Trophy:** 3rd Rd 88-89.

HONOURS - Southern Lg 57-58, Southern Div 94-95, Div 1 Sth 74-75 (R-up 70-71 88-89), Lg Cup 77-78 (R-up 57-58), Champ Cup 77-78; Kent Sen Cup 48-49 52-53 80-81 (R-up 47-48 76-77 90-91 97-98); Kent Floodlit Cup 69-70 (R-up 72-73); Kent Sen Shield R-up 47-48 51-52; Kent Interm Cup R-up 87-88; Kent Midweek Lg 95-96, R-up 92-93 93-94 94-95; Kent Youth Lg Cup 82-83 86-87 96-97; Kent Youth Lg 95-96 96-97; John Ullman Cup 82-83.

Players progressing to Football League: Several incl. most recently:
K Baron (Aldershot 60), R Dwight (Coventry 62), R Cameron (Southend 63), R McNichol (Carlisle 65), A Humphreys (Mansfield 64), B Thornley (Brentford 65), P Jeavons (Lincoln 66), B Fry (Orient 66), B Gordine (Sheffield Utd 68), T Baldwin (Brentford 77), L Smelt (Nottm Forest 80), T Warrilow (Torquay 87)

97-98 Captain: Mark Newsom **P.o.Y.:** Jimmy Jackson **Top scorer:** Steve Portway

Back Row (L-R); Glen Billiness, Anthony Brown, Corey Campbell, Andy Adebovale, Darron Broderick, Darren Smith, Richard Dimmock, Craig Wilkins, Steve Portway, Mick Ward (Physio). Front Row; Ian Docker, Peter Mortley, Jimmy Jackson, Mark Newsome, Dave Powell.
Photo: Eric Rons

GRAVESEND & NORTHFLEET - Match Facts 97-98

KSC - Kent Sen. Cup

Match No.	Date	Venue H / A	Comp.	Opponents	Result & Score	Att.	Goalscorers	League Position
1	16.08	A	IL	Chesham United	L 2-4	549	Newbery, Kearns.	20
2	19.08	H	IL	Hendon	W 4-0	678	Robinson 2, Lovell, Newbery.	
3	23.08	H	IL	Yeading	L 1-2	526	Jackson.	14
4	25.08	A	IL	Dagenham & Redbridge	L 0-2	1,006		16
5	30.08	A	IL	Dulwich Hamlet	D 1-1	429	Lovell.	16
6	05.09	H	IL	Enfield	L 1-3	723	Newbery.	21
7	09.09	H	**GIC 1**	Aylesbury United	W 1-0			-
8	13.09	H	**FAC 1Q**	Braintree Town	D 3-3	547	Murtley, Lovell, Docker.	-
9	16.09	A	**FAC 1Q R**	Braintree Town	L 1-3	334		-
10	20.09	H	IL	Oxford City	W 3-2	456	Murtley, Arter 2.	19
11	23.09	A	IL	Sutton United	L 1-3	583	Lovell	
12	04.10	H	IL	Carshalton Athletic	D 3-3	654	Arter, Portway, Powell.	21
13	07.10	H	IL	Aylesbury United	**W 6-0**	454	**Portway 3**, Jackson, Arter, O.G.	
14	11.01	A	IL	Purfleet	L 0-2	412		
15	18.10	A	**FAT 1Q**	Walton & Hersham	W 6-2	150	Docker, Newsome, Arter 2, Portway 2.	-
16	21.10	H	IL	St Albans City	W 2-1	405	Portway 2.	17
17	25.10	A	IL	Bromley	L 0-2	542		18
18	28.10	H	**FMC 1**	Berkhamsted Town	W 4-3			-
19	01.11	A	IL	Bishop's Stortford	W 2-1	516	Portway (pen), Mortley.	14
20	04.11	H	**GIC 2**	Wokingham Town	W *3-2	258	Watts, Portway, Arter.	-
21	08.11	A	**FAT 2Q**	Cirencester Town	L 0-1	186		-
22	11.11	H	**KSC 1**	Sittingbourne	W 5-0	393	Jackson, Portway 2, Powell, Dimmock.	-
23	15.11	A	Il	Harrow Borough	L 1-2	355	Newson 90.	17
24	18.11	A	IL	Kingstonian	L 1-3	783	Powell	
25	22.11	H	RL	Walton & Hersham	L 1-2	512	Portway.	19
26	29.11	A	RL	Enfield	W 2-1	577	Portway 2.	17
27	02.12	A	**FMC 2**	Chesham United	W 3-0	153	Powell G Smith, Portway.	-
28	13.12	H	RL	Bishop's Stortford	L 1-2	614	Wilkins	18
29	20.12	A	Rl	Hitchin Town	**L 0-4**	349		19
30	27.12	H	RL	Bromley	W 1-0	859	Powell.	17
31	03.01	A	RL	Aylesbury United	W 2-0	803	Portway 2 (2 pens).	16
32	10.01	A	RL	Hendoon	W 2-1	357	Jackson, S Smith.	14
33	13.01	A	**KSC 2**	Erith & Belvedere	W 2-1	292	Honeyball, Powell.	-
34	17.01	H	RL	Chesham United	W 3-2	630	Portway, Savage, Powell.	11
35	20.01	A	**FMC 3**	Hendon	L 0-1			-
36	24.01	A	RL	Yeading	L 3-4	238	Portway,, Adebowale 2.	13
37	27.01	H	RL	Dulwich Hamlet	L 0-1	603		-
38	07.02	A	RL	Oxford City	L 1-2	269	Portway.	15
39	10.02	A	RL	Boreham Wood	L 1-4	223	Portway.	
40	14.02	H	RL	Sutton United	D 2-2	691	Portway 2 (1 pen).	15
41	17.02	A	RL	Heybridge Swifts	D 2-2	274	Newson, Dimmock.	
42	21.02	H	RL	Purfleet	D 0-0	602		14
43	24.02	H	RL	Basingstoke Town	W 3-0	408	Portway 2 (1 pen), Dimmock.	
44	28.02	A	RL	Carshalton AThletic	D 1-1	348	Smith.	11
45	03.03	H	RL	Dagenham & Redbridge	D 2-2	487	Dimmock, Abdowale.	11
46	07.03	H	RL	Kingstonian	L 1-2	753	Portway (pen).	12
47	21.03	H	RL	Heybridge Swifts	W 1-0	478	Jackson.	
48	24.03	H	**KSC S-F**	Dover Athletic	W 3-1	584	Jackson 2, Portway.	-
49	28.02	A	RL	St Albans City	L 0-1	644		15
50	04.04	A	RL	Basingstoke Town	L 1-2	536	Portway.	16
51	11.04	H	RL	Hitchin Town	W 2-0	517	Portway, Jackson.	14
52	18.04	A	RL	Harrow Borough	W 3-0	466	Powell 2, Portway.	14
53	25.04	A	RL	Walton & Hersham	W 1-0	285	Jackson.	13
54	02.05	H	RL	Boreham Wood	D 1-1	537	Portway.	13
55	04.05	H	**KSC Final**	Margate	L 0-1	1,618		-

PLAYING SQUAD 1998 - **Goalkeepers:** Paul Sansome (Southend U, Millwall, Crystal Palace), Darren Smith (Youth). **Defenders:** Mark Newson (Aylesbury U, Oster (Swe), Barnet, Fulham, AFCBournemouth, Maidstone U, Charlton Ath), Peter Mortley (Sittingbourne, Erith &B, Ipswich T), Jay Saunders (Gillingham), Corey Campbell (Yeading, Dover Ath,Brentford), Ben Bray (Sittingbourne), Scott Honeyball (Leyton Orient), Anthony Browne (Whitstable T, West Ham U), Ian Black (Youth). **Midfielders:** Jimmy Jackson (Charlton Ath), Ian Docker (Sittingbourne, InstantDict (HK), Bromley, Kettering T, Redbridge F, Gillingham), Gary Smith (Aylesbury U, Barnet, Welling U, Wycombe W, Enfield, Colchester U, Fulham), Ady Adebowale (Gloucester C, Merthyr Tl, Chesham U, B Stortford, Hertford T,Balls Park), Richard Savage (Youth), Clint Gooding (Ashford T), Glen Billiness (Youth). **Forwards:** Steve Portway (Purfleet, Erith & B, Purfleet, Romford, Gloucester C,Gravesend, Barking, Boreham Wood, Witham T, Brentwood, B Stortford, Walthamstow Ave, Dagenham), Richard Dimmock (Welling U), Craig Wilkins (Tonbridge,Maidstone Invicta, Maidstone U), Kirk Watts (Slade Green, Corinthian), Dave Powell (Sheppey U), Stacey Joseph (Purfleet, Aylesbury U, Leyton Orient,Wimbledon), Lennie Dennis * (Kingstonian, Welling U, Sutton U, Woking, SuttonU, Dulwich Hamlet, Bromley, Crystal Palace).

HAMPTON

Colours: Red & blue/white/blue **Sponsors:** TBA
Change Colours: White/tangerine/white. **Formed:** 1920
Midweek Matchday: Tuesday **Nickname:** Beavers
Reserve Team's League: Suburban
Local Press: Middx Chronicle, Surrey Comet, Richmond & Twickemham Times, The Informer.

PROGRAMME DETAILS:
Pages: 28 **Price:** £1
Editor: Lee Rance

Chairman: Robert Hayes **President:** Alan Simpson
Vice Chairman: Ken Gazzard **Press Officer:** Les Rance
Secretary: Adrian Mann, 30 Burniston Court, Manor Rd, Wallington, Surrey SM6 0AD (0181 773 0858).
Manager: Chick Botley **Assistant Manager:** Tony Coombe
Coach: Paul Shrubb **Physio:** TBA

GROUND Address: Beveree Stadium, Beaver Close, off Station Rd, Hampton TW12 2BX (0181 979 2456 Club; 0181 941 4936 Boardroom; 0181 941 2838 Office matchdays only). **Directions:** A3 out of London, fork left (signed Staines/Esher/Sandown Pk) onto A243, A309 Staines exit to Hampton Ct at 'Scilly Isles' r'bout, left at r'bout after Hampton Court Bridge onto A308, after 1 mile right into Church St (A311), left after White Hart after 200yds into High St, Station Rd on right just before junction with A308.
Capacity: 3,000 **Seats:** 300 **Cover:** 800 **Floodlights:** Yes
Clubhouse: (0181 979 2456). Lounge bar and hall, open on matchdays and training nights. Hall available for hire.
Steward: Steve Penny. **Club Shop:** Sells various souvenirs & prog. Contact Stefan Rance (0181 287 4682)

PREVIOUS - **Leagues:** Kingston & District 21-33; South West Middx 33-59; Surrey Snr 59-64; Spartan 64-71; Athenian 71-73. **Grounds:** Hatherop Rec (until 1959).

CLUB RECORDS - **Win:** 11-1 v Eastbourne Utd, Isthmian Lge Div 2 (S), 90-91. **Defeat:** 0-13 v Hounslow Town, Middlesex Senior Cup 62-63. **Goalscorer:** Peter Allen (176) 1964-73. **Appearances:** Tim Hollands (700) 1977-95. **Fees - Paid:** £850 for Andy Gray (Wokingham Town) November 97. **Received:** £10,000 for Derek Bryan (Brentford) August 97.

BEST SEASON - **FA Cup:** 4th Qual Rd 77-78 (1-2 v Barnet). **FA Vase:** 3rd Rd 91-92 (0-1 v Newport IOW), 95-96 (0-1 v Colllier Row). **FA Trophy:** 1st Rd Prop 83-84 (0-2 v Maidstone Utd). **FA Amateur Cup:** 1st Rd Prop 73-74 (2-4 v Leytonstone)

HONOURS - London Snr Cup(2) 86-88; Spartan Lg(4) 64-67 69-70, (R-up 67-68), Lg Cup(4) 64-68 (R-up 2); Surrey Snr Lg 63-64 (Lg Cup R-up 60-61); Middx Charity Cup 69-70 95-96 97-98, (R-up 68-69 71-72 89-90 94-95); Middx Snr Cup R-up 71-72 76-77 95-96; Athenian Lg Div 2 R-up 72-73; Southern Comb. Cup 68-69 71-72 76-77 81-82 83-84 85-86 96-97 (R-up 77-78 79-80 97-98); Isthmian Lge Div 1 97-98, Div 2 95-96, Div 3 91-92.

Players progressing to Football League: Andy Rogers (Southampton, Plymouth, Reading), Dwight Marshall (Plymouth, Luton Town), Paul Rogers (Sheffield Utd), Derek Bryan (Brentford 97)

97-98 - Captain: Steve Cheshire **P.o.Y.:** Darren Powell **Top scorer:** Francis Vines

Back Row (L-R); Paul Shrubb (Coach), Steve Cheshire, Darren Powell, Mark Russell, Phil Gallagher, Francis Vines, Nick Burton, Andy Gray, Tony Coombe (Asst Mgr), Malcom Taylor (Asst Physio). Front Row; Warren Drew, Nigel Thompson, Barry Moore, Ian Savage, Robin Lewis, John Crouch, Craig Reilly, Peter Wood.

HAMPTON - Match Facts 97-98

LCC - London Challenge Cup; MSC Middx. Senior Cup; MCC - Middx. Charity Cup; SCC - Southern Comb. Cup.

Match No.	Date	Venue H / A	Comp.	Opponents	Result & Score		Att.	Goalscorers	League Position
1	16.08	A	IL-1	Uxbridge	W	2-1		Pearce 2.	8
2	19.08	H	IL-1	Staines Town	W	3-1	230	Pratt, Reilly, Buckwell.	4
3	23.08	H	IL-1	Barton Rovers	L	1-2	177	Pearce.	7
4	26.08	A	IL-1	Aldershot Town	**L**	**0-2**	*1,544*		9
5	30.08	A	IL-1	Molesey	D	1-1		Pearce	7
6	05.09	H	IL-1	Croydon	D	2-2	153	Reilly, Lewis.	8
7	10.09	A	**GIC** 1	Molesey	W	4-0		Mitchell, Jellow 2, Vines.	-
8	13.09	A	**FAC** 1Q	Walton & Hersham	L	0-2			-
9	16.09	H	**SCC** 1	Fleet Town	W	4-0	81	Moore, Tutt, Vines 2.	-
10	20.09	A	IL-1	Abingdon Town	W	2-0		Reilly, Pearce.	7
11	23.09	H	IL-1	Billericay Town	**L**	**0-2**	225		9
12	27.09	H	IL-1	Leatherhead	W	2-0	215	Pearce, Wood.	6
13	30.09	A	IL-1	Whyteleafe	D	1-1		Reilly.	7
14	04.10	H	IL-1	Romford	W	1-0	267	Moore.	6
15	11.10	A	IL-1	Wokingham Town	W	4-3		Moore, Vines, Jolly, Reilly.	7
16	14.10	H	IL-1	Leyton Pennant	W	3-1	127	Moore, Pearce 2.	7
17	18.10	H	**FAT** 1Q	Wokingham Town	L	0-1	217		-
18	25.10	A	IL-1	Chertsey Town	D	1-1		Vines.	6
19	28.10	A	**LCC** 1	Uxbridge	L	1-2		Lewis.	-
20	01.11	A	IL-1	Worthing	D	2-2		Moore, Lewis.	5
21	04.11	H	**GIC** 2	Walton & Hersham	L	2-3	112	Wood, Vines.	-
22	08.11	H	IL-1	Grays Athletic	D	2-2	200	OG, Moore.	5
23	15.11	A	IL-1	Wembley	W	3-1		OG, Wood, Nassim.	5
24	18.11	H	**MCC** 2	Wealdstone	W	3-1	122	Lewis, Vines, Wilson.	-
25	22.11	H	IL-1	Berkhamsted Town	W	3-2	224	Powell, Moore, Vines.	4
26	29.11	A	IL-1	Leatherhead	D	0-0			4
27	06.12	H	RL-1	Molesey	W	1-0	191	Reilly.	4
28	13.12	H	RL-1	Worthing	W	2-0	229	Moore, Vines.	4
29	16.12	H	RL-1	Bognor Regis Town	W	2-1	153	Gray, Vines.	2
30	20.12	A	RL-1	Thame United	**W**	**5-0**		OG, Cheshire, Gray, Savage, Powell.	1
31	23.12	H	**FMC** 2	Maidenhead United	L	0-4			-
32	06.01	A	**MSC** 2	Wembley	W	3-0		Wood, Vines, Moore.	-
33	10.01	A	RL-1	Croydon	L	1-2		Vines.	3
34	17.01	H	RL-1	Uxbridge	W	1-0	196	Burton.	2
35	24.01	A	RL-1	Barton Rovers	D	1-1		Vines	2
36	31.01	H	RL-1	Aldershot Town	D	1-1	1,566	Feltham.	2
37	03.02	H	**MSC** QF	Ashford Town	D	*1-1	116	Vines. A.E.T.	-
38	07.02	A	RL-1	Billericay Town.	D	1-1		Harvey.	2
39	10.02	A	**MSC** QF R	Ashford Town	W	*2-1		Vines, Moore. A.E.T.	-
40	14.02	H	RL-1	Whyteleafe	W	2-1	233	Moore, Vines.	2
41	17.02	H	**SCC** QF	Epsom & Ewell	W	2-1	184	Jellow 2.	-
42	21.02	H	RL-1	Wokingham Town	D	3-3	223	Vines, Gray 2.	2
43	24.02	A	**MCC** QF	Uxbridge	D	*0-0		A.E.T. Won 7-6 after penalties.	-
44	28.02	A	RL-1	Romford	W	1-0		Moore.	2
45	07.03	A	RL-1	Bognor Regis Town	W	2-1		Lewis, Savage.	2
46	10.03	H	**MSC** QF	Enfield	L	*0-1	197		-
47	14.03	H	RL-1	Abingdon Town	W	4-2	176	Moore, Gallagher, Vines 2.	2
48	17.03	A	**MCC** SF	Wembley	W	2-0		Vines, Moore.	-
49	21.03	H	RL-1	Chertsey Town	D	2-2	222	Gallagher, Gray.	3
50	24.03	A	**SCC** SF	Chipstead	W	*4-1		**Vines 3,** Moore.	-
51	28.03	A	RL-1	Leyton Pennant	L	0-1			3
52	31.03	A	RL-1	Staines Town	D	2-2		Gallagher, Savage.	3
53	11.04	H	RL-1	Thame United	W	4-1	211	Harvey, Cheshire, Gallagher 2.	3
54	13.04	A	RL-1	Maidenhead United	D	1-1		Vines.	3
55	16.04	A	RL-1	Grays Athletic	W	2-1		Vines, Thompson.	3
56	18.04	H	RL-1	Wembley	D	1-1	209	Lewis.	3
57	21.04	H	**SCC** Final	Godalming & Guildford	L	0-3			-
58	28.04	H	RL-1	Maidenhead United	W	1-0		Vines.	3
59	30.04	A	RL-1	Berkhamsted Town	W	2-1		Lewis, Moore.	3
60	15.05	N	**MCC** Final	Waltham Abbey	W	2-1		Moore, Gallgher. At Uxbridge FC.	-

PLAYING SQUAD 1998

Goalkeepers: Mark Russell (Windsor & Eton)

Defenders: John Crouch (Wokingham T, Staines T, Godalming T), Nick Burton(Aldershot T, Yeovil T, Torquay U, Portsmouth), Andy Russell (Wokingham T,Aldershot T, Kingstonian, Woking, Wycombe W, Bracknell T), Darren Powell (Egham T, Hampton), Warren Drew (Malden Vale), Peter Wood (Malden Vale), Kevin Duffell (Molesey, Dorking, Tooting & M, Epsom & E, Leatherhead, Epsom &E)

Midfielders: Barry Moore (Local football), Andy Gray (Wokingham T, Slough T,Leyton Orient, Reading), Ian Savage (Wokingham T, Chertsey T, Farnborough T,Southampton), Craig Reilly (Staines T, Fulham), Steve Cheshire (Molesey,Hampton)

Forwards: Francis Vines (Carshalton Ath, Dulwich H., Kingstonian,Molesey), Roy Jellow (Tooting & M, Redhill, Croydon Ath, Fisher Ath), Danny Collyer (Egham T), Chris Nassim (Croydon, Carshalton Ath, Kingstonian), Phil Gallagher (Dulwich H., Molesey, Hendon, Malden Vale).

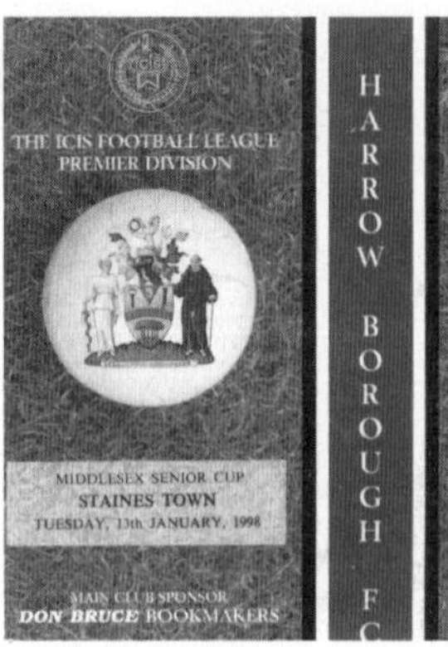

PROGRAMME DETAILS:
Pages: 32 **Price:** £1
Editor: Jim Rogers
(0181 248 8003)

HARROW BOROUGH

Colours: Red with white trim/white/red with white hoops **Formed:** 1933
Change colours: Black & white stripes/black/black **Nickname:** The Boro
Midweek matchday: Tuesday **Sponsors:** TBA.
Local Press: Harrow Observer, Harrow Times

Chairman: Jim Ripley **President:** Jim Rogers
Secretary/Press Officer: Peter Rogers, 21 Ludlow Close, South Harrow, Middx HA2 8SR (0181 248 8003)
Manager: Alan Paris **Asst Manager:** Robyn Jones
Physio: Eddie Cole.
Commercial Manager: Jim Hayes c/o the club.

GROUND Address: Earlsmead, Carlyon Avenue, South Harrow, Middx HA2 8SS (0181 422 5989/5221).
Directions: Underground to Northolt (Central Line) then 140 or 282 bus, or to South Harrow (Piccadilly Line) then 114 or H10. By road leave A40 at Macdonalds roundabout towards Northolt station (A312 north), left at lights, right at next island, ground 5th turning on right.
Floodlights: Yes **Capacity:** 3,070 **Cover:** 1,000 **Seats:** 350
Clubhouse: Open every day with normal licensing hours. Four bars, games room, varied entertainment venue for major sporting and social events. Hot and cold food available, buffets by prior request.
Club Shop: Sells programmes, scarves, badges, T-shirts, etc. Contact Tony Trowbridge c/o club.

PREVIOUS - **Leagues:** Harrow & Dist 33-4; Spartan 34-40, 45-58; W Middx Comb 40-1; Middx Sen 41-45; Delphian 58-63; Athenian 63-75; Isthmian 75-to date. **Names:** Roxonian 1933-8; Harrow Town 38-66. **Ground:** Northolt Road 33-4.

CLUB RECORDS - **Attendance:** 3,000 v Wealdstone, F.A. Cup 1st Qualifying Round 1946. **Scorer:** Dave Pearce, 153. **Appearances:** Steve Emmanuel 522 (1st team only), Les Currell 582, Colin Payne 557. **Fee Paid:** Unspecified to Dagenham for George Duck & Steve Jones, Summer 81. **Fee Received:** £16,000 for Lee Endersby (Enfield 97) **Win:** 13-0 v Handley Page (A), Middlesex Snr Lg 18/10/41. **Defeat:** 0-8 5 times: Wood Green T. (A) Middx Lge 40, Met Police (A) Spartan Lg 52, Briggs Spts (A) Spartan Lg 53, Hertford T. (A) Spartan Lge 53, Hendon (A) Middx Snr Cup 65.

BEST SEASON - **FA Trophy:** Semi final 82-83. **FA Cup:** 2nd Rd 83-84 (1-3 at home to Newport Co).

HONOURS - Isthmian Lg 83-84 (Div 1 R-up 78-79); Athenian Lg Div 2 R-up 63-64; Spartan Lg R-up 57-58 (Div 2 West 38-39 (R-up 37-38); Middx Senior Cup 82-83 92-93; Harrow & Dist. Lg Div 1 R-up 33-34; Middx Charity Cup 79-80 92-93 (R-up 78-79); Middx Intermediate Cup 55-56; Middx Premier Cup 81-82; Harrow Sen Cup 95 97.

Players progressing to Football League: M Bottoms (QPR 60), C Hutchings (Chelsea 80), R Holland (Crewe 85), J Kerr (Portsmouth 87), D Howell, A Pape & E Stein (Barnet), D Byrne (Gillingham), R Rosario (Norwich), D Kemp (Crystal Palace), M Doherty (Reading), D Bassett (Wimbledon), G Borthwick (Bournemouth), B Laryea (Torquay).

97-98 Captain: Kenny Webster **P.o.Y.:** Kenny Webster **Top scorer:** Mark Xavier (26)

Back Row (L-R); Eddie Cole (Physio), Sean James, Pat Gavin, Nko Ekoku, David Hook, Alan Paris (Player/Mgr), John Mutch, Steve Brown, Darren Coleman, Robyn Jones (Coach). Front Row; Micky Tomlinson, Mark Xavier, Paul Adolphe, Kenny Webster, Jeremy Lord, Jon-Barrie Bates, Danny Nwaokolo. Photo: Paul Carter

HARROW BOROUGH - Match Facts 97-98

MSC - Middlesex Senior Cup

Match No.	Date	Venue H / A	Comp.	Opponents	Result & Score		Att.	Goalscorers	League Position
1	16.08	A	IL	Aylesbury United	L	0-1	524		19
2	23.08	H	IL	Walton & Hersham	W	2-0	207	Gavin, Webster (pen).	15
3	26.08	A	IL	Oxford City	W	4-2	231	OG (Smith), Clarke, Xavier 2.	
4	30.08	A	IL	Dagenham & Redbridge	W	2-1	689	Gavin, Webster (pen).	5
5	02.09	H	IL	Sutton United	L	0-2	315		8
6	09.09	H	**GIC 1**	Canvey Island	L	0-3			-
7	13.09	A	**FAC 1Q**	Burgess Hill	W	3-1	307	Xavier 2, Gavin.	-
8	16.09	A	IL	Bromley	L	1-2	149	Gavin.	
9	20.09	H	IL	Chesham United	W	1-0	352	Hooper.	10
10	23.09	A	IL	Kingstonian	L	2-5	805	Paris, Rutherford.	11
11	27.09	A	**FAC 2Q**	Margate	L	0-4	302		-
12	30.09	H	IL	Boreham Wood	W	1-0	162	Xavier.	7
13	04.10	H	IL	St Albans City	W	1-0	343	Alexander	6
14	11.01	A	IL	Bishop's Stortford	W	2-1	315	Gavin 2.	7
15	25.10	A	IL	Hitchin Town	D	2-2	286	Rutherford, Metcalfe.	4
16	28.10	A	**FAT 1Q**	Weston-super-Mare	W	2-0	225	Butler, Gavin.	-
17	01.11	H	IL	Heybridge Swifts	L	0-2	559		6
18	08.11	H	**FAT 2Q**	Molesey	W	5-0	206	Ekoku, Court, Gavin, Xavier, Bates.	-
19	15.11	H	IL	Gravesend & Northfleet	W	2-1	355	James, Xavier.	6
20	22.11	A	RL	Enfield	W	5-3	683	OG (McGrath), Gavin, Webster (pen), Xavier, Hurlock.	5
21	25.11	H	RL	Yeading	W	2-1	210	Xavier, Webster (pen).	4
22	29.11	H	**FAT 3Q**	Bath City	L	1-3	320	Butler	-
23	02.12	A	**FMC 2**	Barton Rovers	W	2-0			-
24	06.12	A	RL	Sutton United	L	1-2	566	Xavier.	4
25	13.12	A	RL	Heybridge Swifts	L	0-1	238		5
26	15.12	A	RL	Purfleet	D	2-2	102	Rutherford, Butler.	
27	20.12	H	RL	Dulwich Hamlet	L	1-2	205	Denny	5
28	27.12	A	RL	Hendon	L	1-2	551	Rutherford	8
29	03.01	H	RL	Oxford City	L	0-3	252		9
30	10.01	A	RL	Carshalton Athletic	L	0-3	328		10
31	13.01	H	**MSC 2**	Staines Town	W	2-1			
32	17.01	H	RL	Aylesbury United	D	1-1	320	Webster (pen).	10
33	19.01	A	**FMC 3**	Dagenham & Redbridge	L	1-3			-
34	24.01	A	RL	Walton & Hersham	D	0-0	247		10
35	07.02	A	RL	Chesham United	**W**	**5-1**	362	Xavier, Webster, **Ekoku 3.**	11
36	10.02	H	**MSC 3**	Brimsdown Rovers	W	8-1			
37	14.02	H	RL	Kingstonian	L	0-2	430		12
38	21.02	H	RL	Carshalton Athletic	L	1-3	188	Rutherford.	12
39	28.02	A	RL	St Albans City	D	0-0	467		13
40	03.03	H	**MSC S-F**	Uxbridge	L	1-2		Webster.	
41	07.03	H	RL	Bromley	L	2-3	245	Xavier 2.	14
42	10.03	H	RL	Basingstoke Town	W	2-0	171	Gavin, Xavier.	
43	14.03	H	RL	Bishop's Stortford	W	2-1	184	Gavin 2.	10
44	17.03	H	RL	Dagenham & Redbridge	**L**	**0-5**	172		
45	21.03	H	RL	Hitchin Town	D	1-1	205	Xavier.	12
46	24.03	A	RL	Boreham Wood	D	2-2	237	Tomlinson, Bates.	
47	28.03	A	RL	Basingstoke Town	D	2-2	621	Gavin, Xavier.	12
48	04.04	H	RL	Purfleet	W	3-0	202	**Brown 3.**	10
49	13.04	H	RL	Hendon	D	0-0	312		11
50	18.04	A	RL	Gravesend & Northfleet	L	0-3	466		12
51	25.04	H	RL	Enfield	W	5-2	328	Gavin, Webster (pen), Xavier 2, Tomlinson.	12
52	29.04	A	RL	Dulwich Hamlet	L	0-1	160		12
53	02.05	A	RL	Yeading	D	2-2	325	McCormack, Tomlinson.	12

PLAYING SQUAD 1998

Goalkeepers: David Hook (Hampton, Feltham, Reading, Southampton), Lee Pearce (Staines T, Hitchin T, Barnet, QPR)

Defenders: Alan Paris (Stevenage B, Slough T, Notts Co, Leicester C,Peterborough U, Watford, Slough T), Darren Coleman (St.Albans C, Chesham U,Edgware T, Kingsbury T, Finchley, Forest U), Kenny Webster (Stevenage B,Peterborough U, Arsenal), John Mutch (Uxbridge, Buckie Thistle, Elgin C), Daniel Nwaokolo (Wokingham T, Slough T, Watford), Sean James (Bedfont), PaulAdolphe (St.Albans C, Grays Ath, Leyton Pennant, Enfield)

Midfielders: Jon-Barri Bates (Wembley, Southall), Jeremy Lord (HaywardsHeath, Egham T, Haywards Heath), Nko Ekoku (Hampton, Malden Vale, Sutton U), John Kumah (Kingsbury T), Micky Tomlinson (Barnet, Leyton Orient)

Forwards: Pat Gavin (Farnborough T, Harrow B, Aylesbury U, Hayes, Wigan Ath,Northampton T, Barnet, Peterborough U, Leicester C, Gillingham, Hanwell T), Richard Denny (Aldershot T, Farnborough T, Hanwell T, Brook House, MaidenheadU).

HENDON

Colours: Blue & black/blue/black **Sponsors:** UK Packaging.
Change: Green & white/green/green & white **Formed:** 1908
Midweek matchday: Tuesday **Nickname:** Dons or Greens
Reserve League: Suburban (North) **Club Line:** 0930 555 836
Local Press: Hendon Times, Willesden & Brent Chronicle.
Local Radio: Capital, GLR, LBC.

Chairman: Ivor Arbiter. **President:**
Secretary: Graham Etchell, c/o Hendon FC. 0181 201 9494(Club)
Manager: Frank Murphy **Asst Manager:** Barry Simmonds
Coach: John Johnson **Press Officer:** Club Secretary
Physio: Caroline Brouwer **Commercial Manager:** Joanne Landsberg

GROUND Address: Claremont Road, Cricklewood, London NW2 1AE. 0181 201 9494 Fax: 0181 9055966. **Directions:** From Brent Cross station (Northern Line) to the east take first left after flyover on North Circular - Claremont Rd is then left at 3rd mini-r'bout. Buses 102, 210, 226 and C11 pass ground.
Capacity: 3,029 **Cover:** 601 **Seats:** 329 **Floodlights:** Yes
Clubhouse: (contact Sue Damary 0181 455 9185). Two banqueting suites, conference centre, room hire, restaurant & bars open licensing hours 7 days a week. Hot & cold food, pool, darts, bingo, members club, satelite TV, entertainments.
Club Shop: (Contact Derek Furmedge, 01814 592042(H) Sells kit, bags, badges, pens, mugs, scarves, ties, programmes and other football souvenirs.

PROGRAMME DETAILS:
Pages: 64 **Price:** £1.20p
Editor: Secretary

PREVIOUS - **Leagues:** Finchley & Dist. 08-11, Middx 10-11, London 11-14, Athenian 14-63. **Names:** Christ Church Hampstead to 08, Hampstead Town to 26, Hampstead to 33, Golders Green to 46. **Grounds:** Kensal Rise 08-12; Avenue Ground, Cricklewood Lane 12-26.

CLUB RECORDS - **Attendance:** 9,000 v Northampton, FA Cup 1st Rd 1952. **Goalscorer:** Freddie Evans 176 (1929-35). **Appearances:** Bill Fisher 787 (1940- **Defeat:** 2-11 v Walthamstow Ave. (A), Athenian Lge 9/11/35. **Win:** 13-1 v Wingate (H), Middx Senior Cup 2/2/57. **Fee Paid:** £5,000 paul Whitmarsh. **Fee Received:** £30,000 for Iain Dowie (Luton).

BEST SEASON - **F.A. Cup:** First Rd 17 times, Second Rd 5 times. **FA Amateur Cup:** Winners 59-60 64-65 71-72. R-up 54-55 65-66. **FA Trophy:** 3rd Rd replay 76-77, 77-78.

HONOURS - European Amtr Champions 72-3; Isthmian Lg 64-5 72-3 (R-up 63-4 65-6 73-4), Lg Cup 76-7 (R-up 86-7), Full Members Cup 94-5 97-8, Premier Inter-Lge Cup R-up 86-7; Middx Lge 12-3 13-4; Athenian Lg 52-3 55-6 60-1 (R-up 28-9 32-3 47-8 48-9 51-2); London Lg Div 1 R-up 12-13 (Amtr Div 13-4); Finchley & Dist. Lg 10-1; London Snr Cup 63-4 68-9 (R-up 35-6 50-1 54-5 58-9 71-2); Middx Snr Cup (11) (R-up 83-4), Middx Interm 64-5 66-7 72-3, Middx Charity Cup(14); London Interm Cup 64-5 72-3 75-6 79-80 (R-up 63-4 68-9); Suburban Lg 92-3 (R-up 84-5 97-8).
Players progressing to Football League: Peter Shearing (West Ham 60), Iain Dowie (Luton 88), Peter Anderson (Luton), Jeff Harris (Orient), Phil Gridelet (Barnsley 90), Gerry Soloman (Leyton Orient 91), Junior Hunter & Micah Hyde (both Cambridge 94-95), Simon Clark (Peterborough 94-95).
97-98 Captain: Steve Bateman **P.o.Y.:** Steve Bateman **Top scorer:** Junior Lewis

Hendon celebrating after winning the Full Members Cup. Photo: Hannah Vilensky

HENDON - Match Facts 97-98

Match No.	Date	Venue H / A	Comp.	Opponents	Result & Score		Att.	Goalscorers	League Position
1	16.08	H	IL	St Albans City	W	2-1	501	Dawber, Lewis.	5
2	19.08	A	IL	Gravesend & Northfleet	**L**	**0-4**	*678*		
3	23.08	A	IL	Enfield	D	3-3	*742*	Nugent, Bateman, Richardson.	13
4	26.08	H	IL	Hitchin Town	L	0-2	251		
5	30.08	H	IL	Basingstoke Town	W	2-1	287	Hyatt, Bashir .	11
6	02.09	A	IL	Bromley	D	0-0	*303*		
7	07.09	A	IL	Sutton United	L	1-2	*592*	Hyatt.	13
8	09.09	A	**GIC 1**	Staines Town	W	8-1			-
9	16.09	H	IL	Chesham United	W	3-0	247	Hynes, Hurd, Nugent.	
10	20.09	A	IL	Purfleet	L	0-1	*203*		12
11	23.09	H	IL	Heybridge Swifts	L	0-2	221		
12	27.09	A	IL	Dagenham & Redbridge	D	1-1	*743*	OG (Creaser).	13
13	04.10	H	IL	Kingstonian	D	1-1	458	Kelly.	12
14	11.10	A	IL	Dulwich Hamlet	W	2-1	*314*	OG (Stephenson), Kelly.	10
15	14.10	H	IL	Oxford City	W	1-0	211	Lewis	7
16	18.10	A	**FAT 1Q**	Havant Town	D	2-2	*222*	Nugent 2.	-
17	21.10	H	**FAT 1Q R**	Havant Town	W	2-1	139		-
18	25.10	A	**FAC 4Q**	St Albans City	W	2-1	*768*	Simpson 2.	-
19	28.10	H	**FMC 1**	Purfleet	W	3-0			-
20	01.11	A	IL	Walton & Hersham	D	2-2	*270*	Heard, Lewis.	12
21	08.11	A	**FAT 2Q**	Bromley	L	1-2	*303*	Lewis.	-
22	15.11	H	**FAC 1**	Leyton Orient	D	2-2	2,241	Simpson 2.	-
23	18.11	H	**GIC 2**	Canvey Island	L	2-4			-
24	22.11	H	RL	Boreham Wood	W	2-1	343	Simpson (pen), Hyatt.	10
25	25.11	A	**FAC 1 R**	Leyton Orient	W	1-0	*3,355*	Lewis	-
26	29.11	A	RL	Carshalton Athletic	L	1-3	*287*	Howard.	
27	06.12	A	**FAC 2**	Cardiff City	L	1-3	*2,578*	Bashir.	-
28	13.12	H	RL	Walton & Hersham	W	4-0	237	**Lewis 3,** Banton.	12
29	16.12	A	RL	Bishop's Stortford	W	2-1	*190*	Lewis, Whitmarsh.	
30	20.12	A	RL	Aylesbury United	L	0-3	*508*		10
31	23.12	H	**FMC 2**	St Albans City	W	6-1			-
32	27.12	H	RL	Harrow Borough	W	2-1	551	Heard 2.	9
33	10.01	H	RL	Gravesend & Northfleet	L	1-2	357	Lewis.	8
34	17.01	A	RL	St Albans City	W	2-1	*515*	Howard, Kelly.	7
35	20.01	H	**FMC 3**	Gravesend & Northfleet	W	1-0			-
36	24.01	H	RL	Enfield	L	0-3	534		8
37	27.01	A	RL	Yeading	W	2-0	*156*	Nugent, Whitmarsh.	
38	31.01	A	RL	Basingstoke Town	D	1-1	*489*	Lewis.	7
39	07.02	H	RL	Purfleet	D	1-1	201	Banton.	7
40	14.02	A	RL	Heybridge Swifts	D	1-1	*268*	Lynch.	9
41	17.02	H	**FMC 4**	Dagenham & Redbridge	W	3-1		Banton 2, Bashir.	-
42	21.02	H	RL	Dulwich Hamlet	W	2-1	266	Whitmarsh 2.	8
43	28.02	A	RL	Kingstonian	L	1-2	*911*	Whitmarsh.	8
44	07.03	A	RL	Chesham United	L	1-4	*406*	T Kelly.	9
45	14.03	H	RL	Sutton United	W	4-2	370	Whitmarsh 2, Hyatt, Bateman.	8
46	21.03	H	RL	Yeading	**W**	**5-0**	228	Hyatt, Lynch, P Kelly, Whitmarsh 2 (1 pen).	8
47	24.03	H	**FMC S-F**	Maidenhead United	W	2-1		Lewis, Hyatt.	-
48	28.03	A	RL	Oxford City	W	2-0	*196*	Lewis, Whitmarsh.	6
49	04.04	H	RL	Dagenham & Redbridge	W	3-0	295	Lewis. Hyatt, Kelly.	6
50	07.04	H	RL	Bromley	W	1-0	208	Lewis.	
51	11.04	H	RL	Aylesbury United	W	3-0	339	Whitmarsh 2, Kelly.	5
52	13.04	A	RL	Harrow Borough	D	0-0	*312*		5
53	18.04	H	RL	Bishop's Stortford	W	3-0	341	Whitmarsh 2, Lewis.	5
54	21.04	A	RL	Hitchin Town	D	1-1	*141*	Kelly.	5
55	25.04	A	RL	Boreham Wood	W	2-1	*515*	Lewis 2.	5
56	29.04	N	**FMC Final**	Basingstoke Town	W	4-1	550	T Kelly, Lewis, Warmington, Banton.	-
57	02.05	H	RL	Carshalton Athletic	W	4-0	447	Whitmarsh, Heard, Kelly, Lewis.	5

PLAYING SQUAD 1998

Goalkeepers: Gary McCann (Dulwich H. , Sutton U, Chesham U, Walton & H,Enfield, Sutton U, Fulham). **Defenders:** Steve Bateman (Slough T, Harrow B, Chesham U, Everton), Richard Nugent (Kettering T, Yeovil T, Stevenage B, Woking, Barnet, St.Albans C,Barnet, Hitchin T, Stevenage B, Royston T), John-Simon White (Watford), MattHoward (Chesham U, Boreham Wood, St.Albans C, Hayes, Aylesbury U, St.Albans C,Brentford, Boreham Wood), Mark Burgess (Wembley, Kingsbury T), Andy Cox * (Hayes, St.Albans C, Berkhamsted T, Tring T, Chipperfield Corinth). **Midfielders:** Simon Clarke (Kettering T, West Ham U), Paul Kelly (Chertsey T,Chesham U, Fulham), Steve Heard (Aylesbury U, Eynesbury R, Rushden & D,Silkeborge (Nor), Cambridge U), Freddie Hyatt (Hayes, Wokingham T, Burnham,Ruislip), Greg Tello (Chelmsford C, Arsenal), Warren Ryan (Purfleet, Yeading), Hakan Altinok (Wembley, Yeading, Hendon, Istanbul Sports (Turk). **Forwards:** Paul Whitmarsh (Dulwich H. , Stevenage B, Doncaster R, West HamU), Nassem Bashir (St.Albans C, Aylesbury U, Chesham U, Chalfont St.Peter,Slough T, Reading), Junior Lewis (Hayes, Dover Ath, Fulham, Brentford), Tony Kelly (Hayes, Wealdstone, Hayes, Harefield U, Hillingdon, Wealdstone), Micky Banton (Walton & H, Chesham U, Barnet, Windsor & Eton, Hellenic (SA), Aggreyobonyo Obiero (Bromley, Millwall).

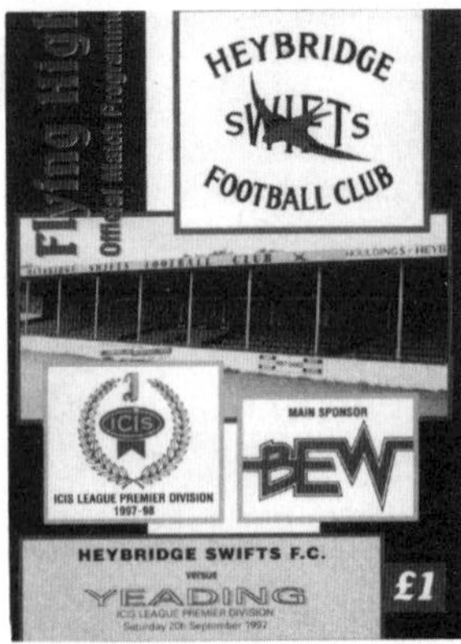

PROGRAMME DETAILS:
Pages: 40 **Price:** £1
Editor: Peter Fenn
(01621 740878)

HEYBRIDGE SWIFTS

Colours: Black & white stripes/black/black **Formed:** 1880
Change colours: All Red **Sponsors:** Balham Electrical Wholesalers
Midweek home matchday: Tuesday **Nickname:** Swifts
Reserve Team's League: Essex & Herts Border Comb.
Local Press: Maldon & Burnham Standard (01621 852233).
Local Radio: BBC Essex, Essex FM.

Chairman: Michael Gibson **President:** Ronnie Locker.
Vice Chairman: Paul Wilkinson **Secretary:** Dennis Fenn, 31 Saxon Way, Maldon, Essex CM9 7JN (01621 854798).
Manager: Garry Hill **Asst Man.:** Mick Loughton **Physio:** Barry Anthony
Press Officer: Tim Huxtable **Treasurer:** Chris Deines

GROUND Address: Scraley Road, Heybridge, Maldon, Essex (01621 852978).
Directions: Leave Maldon on the main road to Colchester, pass through Heybridge then turn right at the sign to Tolleshunt Major (Scraley Road). The ground is on the right. Six miles from nearest station (Witham). By bus via Chelmsford and Maldon.
Capacity: 3,000 **Cover:** 1,200 **Seats:** 550 **Floodlights:** Yes
Clubhouse: Two bars open every night. Games room, boardroom, kitchen (on matchdays).
Club Shop: Open matchdays, selling club sweaters, shirts, scarves, baseball hats, enamel badges, old programmes etc. Contact Chris Fenn, 40 Drake Avenue, Mayland CM3 6TY (01621 740878).

PREVIOUS - **Leagues:** Essex & Suffolk Border, North Essex, South Essex, Essex Senior 1971-84.

CLUB RECORDS - **Attendance:** 2,477 v Woking FA Trophy 97. **Goalscorer:** Julian Lamb 115 (post war), Dave Matthews 112 (Isthmian). **Appearances:** Hec Askew 500+, Robbie Sach 358 (Isthmian). **Fee Paid:** None. **Fee Received:** £35,000, Simon Royce (Southend Utd)

BEST SEASON - **FA Trophy:** Qtr finals v Woking 22/3/97 (lost 0-1). **FA Cup:** First round 0-2 v Gillingham 11/11/94. **League clubs defeated:** None

HONOURS - Isthmian Lg Div 1 R-up 95-96, Div 2 North 89-90; Essex Senior Lg 81-82 82-83 83-84, Lg Cup 82-83, Trophy 81-82; JT Clarke Cup 82-83; Thorn EMI National Floodlit Competition R-up 82-83; Eastern Floodlit Cup 93-94; East Anglian Cup 93-94 94-95; Essex & Suffolk Border Lge 31-32; Essex Jun Cup 31-32; North Essex Lge 46-47.

Players progressing to Football League: Simon Royce (Southend United), Peter Cawley & Ben Lewis (Colchester Utd), Alan Hull (Leyton Orient), Jonathan Hunt (Birmingham City), Dominic Naylor (Leyton Orient), Haken Hayrettin (Doncaster Rovers), Derek Payne & Tom Meredith (Peterborough Utd), Ben Barnett, Eddie Stein & Tim Alexander (Barnet).

Heybridge Swifts FC

HEYBRIDGE SWIFTS - Match Facts 97-98

Match No.	Date	Venue H / A	Comp.	Opponents	Result & Score		Att.	Goalscorers	League Position
1	16.08	A	IL	Dulwich Hamlet	W	2-1	*370*	Caldon, Springett (pen).	6
2	19.08	H	IL	Oxford City	W	3-0	213	Springett (pen), Caldon 2.	
3	23.08	H	IL	Chesham United	L	0-3	370		4
4	26.08	A	IL	Walton & Hersham	L	0-1	*182*		
5	30.08	A	IL	Sutton United	L	1-4	*524*	Jones.	12
6	02.09	H	IL	Boreham Wood	W	2-1	229	Pollard, Springett.	
7	05.09	H	IL	Aylesbury United	**W**	**5-1**	269	**Gentle 3,** Greene, Game.	5
8	09.09	A	**GIC 1**	Thame United	W	2-1			-
9	13.09	A	**FAC 1Q**	Chertsey Town	D	1-1	*217*	Springett.	-
10	16.09	H	**FAC 1Q R**	Chertsey Town	W	*2-1	208	Caldon, Keen.	-
11	20.09	H	IL	Yeading	D	2-2	218	Keen, Adcock.	6
12	23.09	A	IL	Hendon	W	2-0	*221*	Raynor, Gentle.	5
13	27.09	A	**FAC 2Q**	Whyteleafe	W	2-1		Springett, Game.	-
14	04.10	H	IL	Basingstoke Town	**W**	**5-1**	301	Caldon 2, Game, Springett 2.	4
15	11.01	H	**FAC 3Q**	Flackwell Heath	W	4-0		Raynor, Springett (pen), Game, Greene.	-
16	18.10	A	IL	Enfield	L	2-4	*653*	Keen, Game.	8
17	25.10	H	**FAC 4Q**	Ashford Town	W	5-2	575	Greene 2, Caldon 2, Raynor.	-
18	01.11	A	Il	Harrow Borough	W	2-0	*559*	Kane, Greene.	5
19	04.11	H	**GIC 2**	Oxford City	L	0-1			-
20	08.11	A	IL	St Albans City	W	3-0	*356*	Adcock 2, Pollard.	5
21	15.11	A	**FAC 1**	AFC Bournemouth	L	0-3	*3,385*		-
22	22.11	H	RL	Kingstonian	L	1-3	428	OG (Wye).	7
23	24.11	A	RL	Dagenham & Redbridge	**L**	**2-6**	*836*	Caldon, Game.	8
24	29.11	A	**FAT 3Q**	Hastings Town	L	2-3		Springett, Rayner.	-
25	02.12	A	**FMC 2**	Uxbridge	D	*1-1		A.E.T. Lost 4-5 after penalties.	-
26	06.12	H	RL	Walton & Hersham	L	0-1	219		10
27	13.12	H	RL	Harrow Borough	W	1-0	238	Caldon.	7
28	20.12	A	RL	Carshalton Athletic	D	1-1	*286*	Holden	9
29	27.12	H	RL	Bishop's Stortford	W	1-0	390	Jones.	7
30	10.01	A	RL	Oxford City	W	2-0	*221*	Caldon, Rayner.	5
31	17.01	H	RL	Dulwich Hamlet	W	3-1	304	Keen, Jones, Docking.	5
32	24.01	A	RL	Chesham United	W	3-0	*411*	Game, Springett, Caldon.	5
33	31.01	H	RL	Sutton United	D	1-1	574	Harding.	5
34	07.02	A	RL	Yeading	W	3-0	*152*	Springett 2, Docking.	4
35	10.02	H	RL	Hitchin Town	L	1-2	251	Springett.	
36	14.02	H	RL	Hendon	D	1-1	268	Adcock.	5
37	17.02	H	RL	Gravesend & Northfleet	D	2-2	274	Docking, Keen.	5
38	21.02	H	RL	St Albans City	W	3-2	258	Springett (pen), Jones, Keen.	4
39	28.02	A	RL	Basingstoke Town	L	0-2	*456*		5
40	07.03	H	RL	Purfleet	L	0-1	226		7
41	14.03	A	RL	Aylesbury United	W	3-1	*414*	Pollard, Jones, Greene.	5
42	17.03	A	RL	Bromley	D	2-2	*197*	OG (Gray), Greene.	
43	21.03	A	RL	Gravesend & Northfleet	L	0-1	*478*		5
44	27.03	H	RL	Enfield	W	4-1	507	Springett (pen), Cranfield, Game, Adcock.	5
45	30.03	A	RL	Purfleet	D	1-1	*149*	Game.	5
46	04.004	A	RL	Hitchin Town	D	1-1	*269*	Harding.	5
47	11.04	H	RL	Carshalton Athletic	D	0-0	295		6
48	13.04	A	RL	Bishop's Stortford	D	2-2	*191*	Harding, Greene.	6
49	18.04	H	RL	Bromley	D	2-2	302	Harding, Pollard.	6
50	23.04	A	RL	Boreham Wood	W	3-2	*313*	Springett, Harding, Greene.	
51	25.04	A	RL	Kingstonian	L	0-3	*1,595*		6
52	02.05	H	RL	Dagenham & Redbridge	L	2-5	402	Greene, Springett (pen).	6

PLAYING SQUAD 1998

Goalkeepers: Kingsley Banks (Witham T, Barking, Enfield, Basildon U, Dartford,Gillingham, Tottenham Hotspur)

Defenders: Mark Cranfield (Braintree T, Brightlingsea U, Colchester U), John Pollard (Bury T, Colchester U), Mark Keen (Chelmsford C, Enfield, Dartford,Witham T), Kirk Game (Maldon T, Gt.Wakering R, Stambridge, Chelmsford C,Homburg (Ger), Colchester U, Southend U, Chelsea)

Midfielders: Mitchell Springett (Wivenhoe T, Bury T, Chelmsford C, BraintreeT, Wivenhoe T, Braintree T, Halstead T, Cambridge U), Mark Kane (Chelmsford C,Hendon, Enfield, Chelmsford C, Barking, Tampa Bay Rowdies (USA), Barking,Woodford T, Walthamstow Ave, Woodford T, Leyton Orient), Ashley Bond (Youth team), Terry Raynor (Harwich & P, Halstead T), Graham Mansfield (Dage & Red,Dover Ath, Chelmsford C, Ipswich T), Adam Gillespie (Youth team)

Forwards: Wayne Adcock (Witham T, Braintree T, Chelmsford C, Eton Manor), Steve Harding (Burnham Ramblers, Maldon T, Heybridge S), Dean Caldon (MaldonT), Neal Docking (Chelmsford C, Saffron Walden T).

PURFLEET

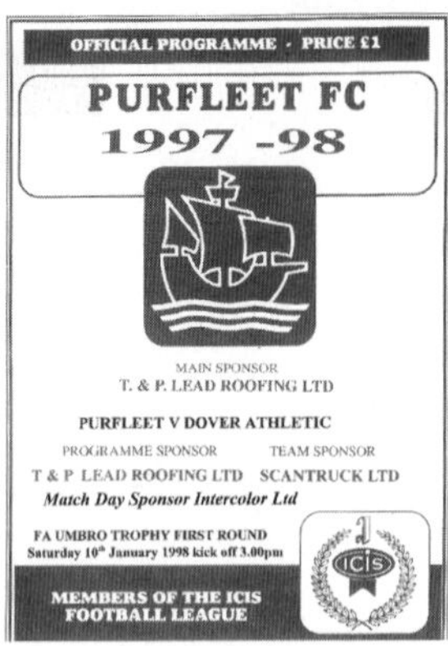

PROGRAMME DETAILS:
Pages: 44 **Price:** £1
Editor: Norman Posner
Tel: 01708 458301 H

Colours: Green & yellow/green/green & yellow **Founded:** 1985
Change colours: All white. **Nickname:** Fleet
Midweek home matchday: Monday
Reserve's League: None.
Local Press: Romford, Thurrock Recorder, Thurrock Gazette.
Local Radio: Essex Radio, BBC Radio Essex.

Chairman: Grant Beglan **President:**
Vice Chairman/Chief Executive: Tommy Smith
Secretary: Tony Perkins 48 Saltash Road, Hainault, Essex IG6 2NL (0181 500 3092) **Match Secretary/Press Officer:** Norman Posner
Commercial Manager: Tony Joy (01375 392906).
Manager: Colin McBride **Asst Manager:** David Crown
Coach: George Cook **Physio:** Bob Johnson.

GROUND Address: Thurrock Hotel, Ship Lane, Grays, Essex (01708 868901) (Fax 01708 866703)
Directions: M25 or A13 to Dartford tunnel r'bout. Ground is fifty yards on right down Ship Lane. Nearest station is Purfleet, two miles from ground.
Capacity: 4,500 **Cover:** 1,000 **Seats:** 300 **Floodlights:** Yes
Clubhouse: 10am-11pm every day. Snooker, squash, weights room, aerobics, a-la carte restaurant, steam room. Three Bars. 56 Bedroom Hotel. **Steward:** Tommy South.
Club Shop: Yes, selling programmes and magazines. Contact Tommy South (01708 868901).
SPONSORS: Main: Aspect Contracts Ltd. **Team:** Lakeside Shopping Centre. **Prog:** T & P Lead Roofing Ltd

PREVIOUS - **League:** Essex Senior 85-89. **Grounds:** None.

CLUB RECORDS - **Attendance:** 1,578 v West Ham United, friendly 1997. **Goalscorer:** Paul Cobb, 101. **Appearances:** John Rees, 286. **Win:** 10-0 v Stansted (H) 86-87, v East Ham Utd (A) 87-88 (both Essex Senior League). **Defeat:** 0-6 v St Leonards Stamco (A), FA Trophy 96-97. 0-6 v Sutton United (H) Isthmian Lge 97-98.

BEST SEASON - **FA Cup:** Fourth Qual Rd 95-96 (lost 1-3 away to Rushden & D) **FA Trophy:** Second Rd Prop 95-96 (lost 1-2 away to Macclesfield Tn)

HONOURS - Isthmian Lg Div 2 91-92 (Div 1 R-up 93-94), Div 2 Nth R-up 88-89, Associate Members Tphy 91-92; Essex Snr Lg 87-88 (Lg Cup(2) 86-88, R-up 97-98), Stanford Charity Cup 87-88 (R-up 85-86); Essex Thames-Side Trophy 94-95; Loctite Trophy 91-92; Essex Bus Houses Sen L/Cup 93-94; F Budden Trophy 94-95; Essex & Herts Border Comb R-up 94-95.

Players progressing to Football League: Paul Cobb & Lee Williams (Leyton O.)

97-98 - Captain: Jimmy McFarlane **P.o.Y.:** Jimmy McFarlane **Top scorer:** Martin Carthy/Dominic Gentle (13)

Back Row (L-R); Robert Garvey, Colin McBride (Mgr), Martin Carthy, Dave Carter, Steve Perkins, Jimmy McFarlane, Kevin Gray, Steve Mead, Darren Pitcher, David Crown (Asst Mgr), John Purdie, Tony Jones, Danny Cowley, Jamie Southon. Front Row; Declan Perkins, Martin Lawrence, Dominic Gentle, Paul Pizzey, John Keeling, Bob Johnson, Gary Ansell.

PURFLEET - Match Facts 97-98

Match No.	Date	Venue H / A	Comp.	Opponents	Result & Score		Att.	Goalscorers	League Position
1	16.08	A	IL	Yeading	D	0-0	*112*		14
2	18.08	H	IL	Sutton United	**L**	**0-6**	279		
3	23.08	H	IL	Dulwich Hamlet	D	2-2	185	Lawrence, McFarlane.	19
4	25.08	A	IL	Aylesbury United	W	2-0	*657*	Taylor, Portway.	9
5	30.08	A	IL	Chesham United	D	1-1	*523*	Southon.	13
6	01.09	H	IL	Walton & Hersham	W	1-0	179	Carthy.	10
7	09.09	A	**GIC 1**	Wivenhoe Town	W	2-0			-
8	13.09	A	**FAC 1Q**	Concorde Rangers	W	1-0	*150*	Portway.	-
9	20.09	H	IL	Hendon	W	1-0	203	Portway (pen).	11
10	23.09	A	IL	Oxford City	D	0-0	*161*		8
11	27.09	A	**FAC 2Q**	Sittingbourne	L	1-2	*420*	Portway.	-
12	04.10	A	IL	Bromley	W	3-2	*302*	Southon, Perkins, Gentle.	8
13	11.01	H	IL	Gravesend & Northfleet	W	2-0	412	Gentle (pen), Crown.	6
14	18.10	A	IL	Boreham Wood	L	1-3	*229*	Gentle (pen).	9
15	20.10	H	IL	Enfield	**W**	**4-0**	431	Carthy, Lawrence, Ware, Perkins.	4
16	25.10	A	IL	Bishop's Stortford	L	0-2	*378*		
17	28.10	A	**FMC 1**	Hendon	L	0-3			-
18	01.11	A	IL	Carshalton Athletic	L	0-1	*308*		7
19	04.11	A	**GIC 2**	Billericay Town	D	*0-0			-
20	15.11	A	IL	Hitchin Town	D	3-3	*258*	Perkins, Berry, McFarlane.	9
21	17.11	H	**GIC 2 R**	Billericay Town	L	*1-2			-
22	22.11	H	RL	Bishop's Stortford	W	3-1	203	Carthy, Lawrence 2.	6
23	25.11	A	RL	Kingstonian	D	2-2	*581*	Perkins 2.	
24	29.11	A	**FAT 3Q**	Bromley	W	4-1	*270*	Perkins 2, Gentle, Rawlings (og).	-
25	06.12	H	RL	Aylesbury United	L	0-2	181		7
26	13.12	H	RL	Carshalton Athletic	L	1-2	189	Gentle.	8
27	15.12	H	RL	Harrow Borough	D	2-2	102	Gewntle, McFarlane.	
28	20.12	A	RL	Basingstoke Town	W	2-0	*536*	Richardson (og), Malklin.	6
29	27.12	H	RL	Dagenham & Redbridge	**W**	**4-0**	841	Gentle, Berry, Malklin, Lawrence.	5
30	10.01	H	**FAT 1**	Dover Athletic	L	0-1	333		-
31	17.01	H	RL	Yeading	L	1-3	102	Southon 90.	9
32	20.01	A	RL	Sutton United	L	0-3	*515*		9
33	24.01	A	RL	Dulwich Hamlet	L	1-2	*235*	Perkins 21.	9
34	27.01	A	RL	St Albans City	L	2-3	*232*	Gentle 2.	
35	31.01	H	RL	Chesham United	W	3-2	172	Gentle 2, D Perkins.	8
36	14.02	H	RL	Oxford City	W	2-1	129	Carthy. Southon.	8
37	17.02	A	RL	Walton & Hersham	W	4-2	*186*	Perkins, Carthey 2, McFarlane.	7
38	21.02	A	RL	Gravesend & Northfleet	D	0-0	*602*		7
39	28.02	H	RL	Bromley	W	2-0	214	Carthy, Lawrence.	6
40	07.03	A	RL	Heybridge Swifts	W	1-0	*226*	Carthy.	6
41	14.03	H	RL	St Albans City	L	0-1	185		7
42	21.03	A	RL	Enfield	D	0-0	*906*		7
43	28.03	H	RL	Boreham Wood	L	0-2	194		8
44	30.03	H	RL	Heybridge Swifts	D	1-1	149	McFarlane.	
45	04.04	A	RL	Harrow Borough	L	0-3	*303*		7
46	13.04	A	RL	Dagenham & Redbridge	D	2-2	*661*	Lawrence, McFarlane.	8
47	18.04	H	RL	Hitchin Town	W	1-0	132	Ansell.	7
48	23.04	H	RL	Basingstoke Town	L	1-2	81	Pizzey.	
49	02.05	H	RL	Kingstonian	D	1-1	603	Keeling.	10

PLAYING SQUAD 1998

Goalkeepers: Steve Mead (Concord R)

Defenders: Jim McFarlane (Concord R, Purfleet, Clapton, Millwall W), Steve Perkins (Welling U, Dartford, Aveley, Barking, Romford, Millwall), John Purdie (Billericay T, Wycombe W, Southend U, West Ham U), Tony Jones (Concord R,Hornchurch, Billericay T, Colchester U, Southend U), Gary Ansell (Canvey Is), Jamie Southon (Chelmsford C, Grays Ath, Sing Tao (HK), Purfleet, Dag & Red,Southend U)

Midfielders: Martin Carthy (Erith & B, Fisher Ath, Erith & B, Welling U), Robbie Garvey (Enfield, Chelmsford C, Hendon, Redbridge F, Dartford, Grays Ath,Billericay T, Purfleet), Paul Taylor (Southend U), Jon Keeling (Tilbury,Concord R), Scott Williams (Eton Manor), Paul Pizzey (Concord R, Tilbury,East Thurrock U, Canvey Is, Purfleet, Aveley, Purfleet, East Thurrock U,Purfleet)

Forwards: Martyn Lawrence (Concord R, Maldon T, Billericay T, Southend Manor,Barking, Southend U), David Carter (Concord R, East Thurrock U, Basildon U), Declan Perkins (Dag & Red, Sing Tao (HK), Peterborough U, Southend U), Greg Berry (Millwall, Wimbledon, Leyton Orient, East Thurrock U), Tony Macklin (Concord R, Tilbury, Aveley, Tilbury, Purfleet, Grays Ath, Tilbury, West Ham U).

ST ALBANS CITY

Colours: Yellow with blue trim/blue/white **Formed:** 1908
Change colours: All white red trim **Nickname:** The Saints
Midweek home matchday: Monday **Newsline:** 0930 555822
Local Press: St Albans & District Observer, Herts Advertiser.
Local Radio: BBC Three Counties, Chiltern Radio.
Internet: http://www.andyzad.demon.co.uk
E-Mail: andy@andyzad.demon.co.uk

Chairman: Lee Harding **President:** Cllr Malcolm MacMillan
Vice Chairman: Gary Elliott
Secretary: Janice Hutchings c/o Club
Manager: Garry Hill **Physio:** Richard Harper
Team Asst: Steve Eames **Safety Officer:** Rex Winn
Press Off.: David Tavener (01582 401487, Mob 0966 175124)
Managing Director: Roberta Rolland (01727 864296).

PROGRAMME DETAILS:
Pages: 32 **Price:** £1.50
Editor: David Tavener
(01582 401487)

GROUND - Address: Clarence Park, York Rd, St Albans, Herts AL1 4PL (01727 866819). **Directions:** Left out of St Albans station - Clarence Pk 200yds ahead across Hatfield Rd. M25, jct 21 to Noke Hotel island, straight on thru Chiswell Green towards St Albans, straight over 2 mini-r'bouts and one larger island, thru 2 sets of lights and right at island at far end of city centre (St Peters St.) into Hatfield Rd, over mini-r'bout, left at 2nd lights into Clarence Rd, ground on left.
Capacity: 6,000 **Cover:** 1,900 **Seats:** 904 **Floodlights:** Yes
Clubhouse: Open matchdays and available for functions. Manager: Ray McCord (01727 837956). Tea bar within ground serves hot food.
Club Shop: Large selection of club merchandise & League & non-League progs, magazines, videos & badges etc. Managers: Terry Edwards 01727 833685 & Ray Stanton. New brick built shop fo 98-9 includes disabled toilet

PREVIOUS - **Leagues:** Herts County 08-10; Spartan 08-20; Athenian 20-23.

CLUB RECORDS - **Attendance:** 9,757 v Ferryhill Ath., FA Amtr Cup QF 27/2/26. **Appearances:** Phil Wood 900 (62-85) **Goalscorer:** W H (Billy) Minter 356 (top scorer for 12 consecutive seasons 1920-32). **Win:** 14-0 v Aylesbury United (H) Spartan Lge 19/10/12. **Defeat:** 0-11 v Wimbledon (H), Isthmian Lge 9/11/46. **Fee Paid:** £6,000 for Paul Turner (Yeovil Town Aug 97) **Fee Received:** £92,750 for Dean Austin (Southend 90/Spurs 92).

BEST SEASON - **FA Amateur Cup:** Semi final 22-23 24-25 25-26 69-70. **FA Trophy:** 2nd Rd 81-82 92-93 96-97 98-98. **FA Cup:** 2nd Rd replay 68-69 (1-3 at Walsall after 1-1 draw), 80-81 (1-4 at Torquay after 1-1 draw), 96-97 (9-2 at Bristol City).

HONOURS - Isthmian Lg 23-24 26-27 27-28 (R-up 54-55 92-93), Div 1 85-86, Div 2 R-up 83-84, Lg Cup R-up 89-90, Res. Sect. R-up 48-49 60-61 61-62; Athenian Lg 20-21 21-22 (R-up 22-23); Spartan Lg 11-12 (R-up 12-13, East Div 09-10); Herts Co. Lg 09-10 (West Div 08-09, Aubrey Cup(res) 61-62); London Snr Cup 70-71 (R-up 69-70); AFA Snr Cup 33-34 (R-up 30-31 32-33 34-35); E Anglian Cup 92-93; Herts Snr Cup(12) (R-up 10), Herts Snr Tphy 86-87, Herts Charity Cup(25) (R-up(18); Mithras Cup 64-65 71-72 (R-up 76-77); Wycombe F'lit Cup(2) 68-70; St Albans Hosp Cup 45-46; Hitchin Centenary Cup 70-71 (R-up 71-72); Victory Cup 25-26 27-28, Liege Cup 26-27; Billy Minter Invit. Cup (3) 90-93.

Players progressing to Football League: A Grimsdell (Spurs 11), G Edmonds (Watford 14), R Burke (Man Utd 46), J Meadows (W'ford 51), M Rose (Charlton 63), J Kinnear (Spurs 65), J Mitchell (Fulham 72), A Cockram (Brentford 88), D Austin (Southend 90), T Kelly (Stoke 90), M Danzey (Cambridge 92), D Williams (Brentford 93),

97-98 - Captain: Kevin Mudd **P.o.Y.:** Kevin Mudd **Top scorer:** Steve Clark (19 Lge, 9 Cup)

Back Row (L-R); Westley Foley, Gary Caldon, Paul Turner, Ashley Vickers, Jon Daly, Richard Evans, Steve Clark, Barry Blackman, Kevin Mudd, John Cheesewright. Front Row; Gareth Howells, Tom Meredith, Justin Gentle, Matt Jones, Rob Haworth.

ST. ALBANS CITY - Match Facts 97-98

Match No.	Date	Venue H / A	Comp.	Opponents	Result & Score		Att.	Goalscorers	League Position
1	16.08	A	IL	Hendon	L	1-2	*501*	Daly.	17
2	19.08	H	IL	Chesham United	D	1-1	502	Moors	
3	23.08	H	IL	Sutton United	W	4-2	607	**Clark 3,** Ristey.	
4	26.08	A	IL	Yeading	W	2-0	*178*	Clark 2.	
5	30.08	A	IL	Oxford City	D	0-0	*279*		9
6	02.09	H	IL	Kingstonian	L	0-3	612		11
7	09.09	A	**GIC 1**	Enfield	W	*2-1	*371*	Haworth, OG.	-
8	13.09	A	IL	Boreham Wood	W	3-2	*461*	Mudd, Turner (pen), Daly.	7
9	20.09	H	IL	Dulwich Hamlet	W	1-0	506	Haworthy.	5
10	27.09	A	IL	Enfield	W	2-0	*772*	Haworth, Daly.	4
11	30.09	H	**FMC 1**	Enfield	W	5-1	327	Deleon, Cobb, **Foley 3.**	-
12	04.10	A	IL	Harrow Borough	L	0-1	*343*		7
13	18.10	H	IL	Dagenham & Redbridge	W	2-0	756	Haworth, Adolphe.	7
14	21.10	A	IL	Gravesend & Northfleet	L	1-2	*405*	Clark.	
15	25.10	H	**FAC 4Q**	Hendon	L	1-2	768	Clark.	-
16	01.11	A	IL	Bromley	D	1-1	*404*	Cobb.	9
17	04.11	A	**GIC 2**	Clapton	W	2-1	*84*	Clark, Blackman.	-
18	08.11	H	IL	Heybridge Swifts	L	0-3	356		11
19	12.11	H	IL	Bishop's Stortford	W	2-1	298	Clark, Cobb.	8
20	22.11	H	RL	Aylesbury United	L	1-3	510	Haworth.	9
21	29.11	H	**FAT 3Q**	Bishop's Stortford	W	5-2	330	Gentle 2, Turner 2, Daly.	-
22	13.12	H	RL	Bromley	L	0-1	298		14
23	16.12	H	**GIC 3**	Bedford Town	D	*1-1	167	Turner.	-
24	20.12	A	RL	Walton & Hersham	L	0-1	*244*		16
25	23.12	A	**FMC 2**	Hendon	L	1-6	*130*	Haworth.	-
26	27.12	H	RL	Hitchin Town	**W**	**4-1**	652	Clark 2, Gentle, Haworth.	14
27	30.12	A	**GIC 3 R**	Bedford Town	D	*3-3	*510*	Mudd, Haworth, Clark. A.E.T. Won 4-2 after penalties.	-
28	03.01	A	RL	Kingstonian	**L**	**0-5**	*894*		15
29	10.01	H	**FAT 1**	Sittingbourne	D	0-0	475		-
30	14.01	A	**FAT 1 R**	Sittingbourne	W	1-0	*450*	Gentle.	-
31	17.01	H	RL	Hendon	L	1-2	515	Clark.	17
32	20.01	A	**GIC 4**	Wokingham	W	3-0	*120*	Blackman, Akinbolu, OG.	-
33	24.01	A	RL	Sutton United	L	1-3	*967*	Turner.	17
34	27.01	H	RL	Purfleet	W	3-2	232	Turner, Clark, Mudd.	
35	07.02	A	RL	Dulwich Hamlet	W	2-1	*302*	Haworth, Clark.	14
36	10.02	A	RL	Basingstoke Town	L	1-3	*578*	Mudd.	
37	14.02	H	RL	Yeading	L	0-1	416		14
38	21.02	A	RL	Heybridge Swifts	L	2-3	*258*	Mudd, Daley.	17
39	24.02	A	RL	Carshalton Athletic	W	2-0	*208*	Turner, Gentle.	
40	28.02	H	RL	Harrow Borough	D	0-0	467		15
41	03.03	A	**GIC S-F 1**	Sutton United	D	0-0	*272*		
42	07.03	H	RL	Enfield	L	0-4	939		16
43	10.03	H	**GIC S-F 2**	Sutton United	L	0-3	247		
44	14.03	A	RL	Purfleet	W	1-0	*185*	Haworth.	16
45	17.03	A	RL	Chesham United	W	2-1	*349*	Clark 2.	
46	21.03	A	RL	Dagenham & Redbridge	D	1-1	*847*	Clark.	14
47	24.03	H	RL	Oxford City	**W**	**4-1**	376	Daly, Haworth, Meredith, Gentle.	
48	28.03	H	RL	Gravesend & Northfleet	W	1-0	644	Clark.	9
49	04.04	A	RL	Bishop's Stortford	L	0-1	*302*		11
50	11.04	H	RL	Walton & Hersham	L	0-1	513		12
51	13.04	A	RL	Hitchin Town	D	1-1	*411*	Gentle.	12
52	18.04	H	RL	Carshalton Athletic	W	3-0	486	Meredith, Clark, Caldon.	10
53	21.04	H	RL	Boreham Wood	L	0-2	634		
54	25.04	A	RL	Aylesbury United	W	2-1	*1,104*	Haworth, Clark (pen).	10
55	02.05	H	RL	Basingstoke Town	D	2-2	647	Blackman, Clark.	11

PLAYING SQUAD 1998 - **Goalkeepers:** Paul Newell * (Leyton Orient, Heybridge S, Gravesend, Darlington,Barnet, Leyton Orient, Southend U), John Cheesewright (Heybridge S, AldershotT, Romford, Wycombe W, Wimbledon, Colchester U, Braintree T, Birmingham C,Southend U, Tottenham Hotspur). **Defenders:** Andy Polston (Hendon, Brighton, Tottenham Hotspur), Kevin Mudd (Sittingbourne, St.Albans C, Harrow B, Finchley, Enfield, St.Albans C, MountGrace), Richard Evans (Barnet), Peter Risley (Dagenham, B Stortford, Ware,Hoddesdon T), Scott Darton * (Heybridge S, Cambridge C, Ipswich W, King's Lynn,Blackpool, WBA), Andy Alexander (Chesham U, Harrow B, Grays Ath, Chesham U,Grays Ath, Brimsdown R, Haringey B, Fulham), Darren Lonergan (Stalybridge C,Oldham Ath, Waterford). **Midfielders:** Jon Daly (Kingstonian, Hendon, Dulwich Hamlet, Whyteleafe,Croydon, Tooting & M, Croydon, Crystal Palace), Paul Turner (Yeovil T,Enfield, Farnborough T, Cambridge U, Arsenal), Gary Cobb (Aylesbury U, CheshamU, Fulham, Luton T), Scott Witney * (Maldon T, Bowers U, Heybridge S), Matt Jones (Heybridge S, Chelmsford C, Southend U, Arsenal), Tom Meredith (Bury T, Peterborough U). **Forwards:** Steve Clark (Wivenhoe T, Saffron Walden T, Stansted), Neil Trebble * (Stevenage B, Scarborough, Preston NE, Scunthorpe U, Stevenage B), Rob Haworth (Aylesbury U, Kettering T, Millwall, Fulham), Gary Caldon (Heybridge S, MaldonT, Basildon U, Billericay T), Dion Osbourne * (Barnet), Chris Moors (Yeovil T,West Ham U), Dominic Gentle * (Purfleet, Heybridge S, Enfield, Grays Ath,Boreham Wood, Cockfosters, ICL Letchworth), Justin Gentle (Enfield, Chesham U,Colchester U, Luton T, Boreham Wood, Cockfosters, Swindon T, Wimbledon).

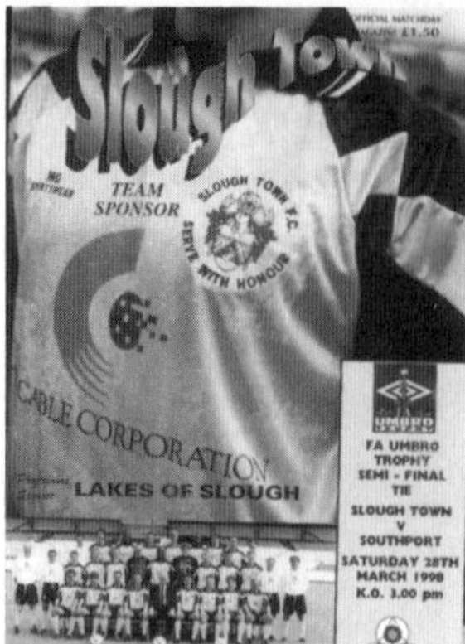

PROGRAMME DETAILS:
Pages: 36 **Price:** £1.50
Editor: Committee

SLOUGH TOWN

Colours: Amber shirts, navy blue shorts, amber socks
Change colours: All white **Nickname:** The Rebels
Midweek home matchday: Tuesdays **Sponsor:** The Cable Corporation
Local Newspapers: Slough Observer Slough Express
Local Radio Stations: Thames Valley FM, Star FM

Chief Executive: Bob Breen **Chairman:** A A Thorne
Vice-Chairman: B A Thorne
Secretary / Press Officer: Trevor Gorman
Tel: 01753 523358 (B) Address - c/o the club.
Manager: Brian McDermott **Physio:** Kevin McGoldrick
Asst Manager: David Brown
Commercial Manager: Bob Breen (Chief Exec.)

Ground: Wexham Park Stadium, Wexham Road, Slough, Berkshire. SL2 5QR. 01753 523358 Fax: 01753 516956. **Directions:** Fron North: M25 J16 East London M40 J1 - South A412 through Iver Heath to George Green. 2nd set lights turn right by George PH, George Green. Church Lane 1 mile to end, then small roundabout, turn left, ground 1/4 mile on right.
Capacity: 5,000 **Cover:** 1,890 **Seats:** 450 **Floodlights:** Yes
Clubhouse: Rebels bar & Lounge bar open weekdays 7pm-11pm, weekends lunchtime/evenings. Banqueting hall for all types of functions.
Club Shop: Contact John Linlow (0753 571710).

PREVIOUS - **Leagues:** Southern Alliance 1892-93; Berks & Bucks 1901-05; Gt Western Suburban 1906-19; Spartan 1920-39; Herts & Middx 1940-45; Corinthian 1946-63; Athenian 1963-73; Isthmian 1973-90, 94-95; Alliance Prem. (GMVC) 90-94. **Grounds:** Dolphin Playing Fields & Stadium, Chalvey Road Sports Ground, York Road Maidenhead 1920, Centre Sports Ground 1936-42.

CLUB RECORDS - **Attendance:** 8,000 - Schoolboys u15 Final Slough v Liverpool - 1976 **Win:** 17-0 v Railway Clearing House - 1921-22. **Defeat:** 1-11 v Chesham Town 1909/10. **Transfer fee paid:** £18,000 for Colin Fielder from Farnborough - 1991 **Received:** £22,000 from Wycombe Wanderers for Steve Thompson **Career goalscorer:** Terry Norris 84 - 1925/26 **Career appearances:** Terry Reardon 458 - 1964/81

BEST SEASON - **FA Cup:** 2nd Round Proper, 79-80 (Yeovil T), 82-83 (Bishop's Stortford), 85-86 (Leyton O.), 86-87 (Swansea C.). **League clubs defeated:** Millwall, 1-0 (H) Jan. 1983
FA Trophy: Semi-Final 1976-77, 2-6(agg) v Dagenham; 97-98, 1-2(agg) v Southport.

HONOURS - FA Amateur Cup R-up 72-73; Great Western Suburban League R-up 19-20: Spartan League R-up 20-21 21-22 31-32 32-33 38-39; Herts & Middx League R-up 43-44; Corinthian League 50-51 (R-up 45-46 46-47 57-58); Athenian League 67-68 71-72 72-73 (R-up 68-69, Div 1 64-65, Memorial Shield 64-65 71-72 72-73); Isthmian League 80-81 89-90 R-up 94-95, (Div 2 R-up 73-74), League Shield 80-81 89-90 (R-up 94-95); Berks & Bucks Senior Cup(9) 02-03 19-20 23-24 35-36 54-55 70-72 76-77 80-81.

Past players who progressed to the Football League: Bill McConnell, Peter Angell, Dennis Edwards, Ralph Miller, John Delaney, Paul Barron, Dave Kemp, Roy Davies, Mickey Droy, Eric Young, Alan Paris, Tony Dennis.

Slough Town

SLOUGH TOWN - Match Facts 1997-98

Match No.	Date	Venue H / A	Comp.	Opponents	Result	& Score	Att.	Goalscorers	League Position
1	16.08	A	VC	Kettering Town	D	3-3	*1,349*	Abbott 46, 58, Randall 49.	10
2	19.08	H	VC	Dover Athletic	L	2-4	868	Brazil 61, Owusu 64.	
3	23.08	H	VC	Halifax Town	D	1-1	790	Browne 41.	20
4	25.08	A	VC	Woking	L	1-2	*2,829*	Brazil 8.	20
5	30.08	A	VC	Stalybridge Celtic	W	1-0	*809*	Abbott 57.	16
6	02.09	H	VC	Rushden & Diamonds	L	1-2	872	Randall 3.	19
7	07.09	A	VC	Southport	W	2-1	*1,460*	Owusu 46, 90.	14
8	10.09	H	VC	Welling United	L	1-2	385	Abbott 76.	14
9	20.09	H	VC	Northwich Victoria	W	3-0	637	Hercules 57, Bolt 63, Browne 66 (pen).	13
10	23.09	A	VC	Cheltenham Town	D	1-1	*1,539*	Bolt 70.	13
11	04.10	A	VC	Leek Town	W	2-0	*565*	Abbott 16, Owusu 83.	10
12	18.10	H	VC	Morecambe	D	3-3	792	Owusu 53, Fiore 79, Brazil 90.	12
13	01.11	A	VC	Rushden & Diamonds	W	1-0	*2,193*	Hardyman 45.	10
14	08.11	H	VC	Cheltenham Town	L	1-2	1,037	Bolt 47.	11
15	22.11	A	VC	Hednesford Town	L	1-2	*1,685*	Bolt 4.	
16	29.11	H	VC	Southport	W	1-0	589	Owusu 74.	12
17	06.12	A	VC	Welling United	D	1-1	*604*	Owusu 52.	12
18	13.12	H	VC	Kidderminster Harriers	W	2-0	746	Owusu 42, 52	11
19	20.12	A	VC	Yeovil Town	L	1-2	*2,509*	Hercules 81	12
20	26.12	H	VC	Hayes	D	0-0	1,219		12
21	29.12	H	VC	Farnborough Town	W	1-0	786	Bolt 75	10
22	01.01	A	VC	Hayes	W	1-0	*1,224*	Bolt 87	9
23	17.01	A	VC	Telford United	W	1-0	*668*	Bolt 27.	9
24	24.01	A	VC	Halifax Town	L	0-1	*2,098*		10
25	07.02	H	VC	Hereford United	W	3-0	1,056	Abbott 13, 39, Browne 50.	9
26	14.02	A	VC	Northwich Victoria	W	1-0	*878*	Brazil 12.	8
27	18.02	A	VC	Farnborough Town	L	0-1	*642*		9
28	28.02	A	VC	Morecambe	L	1-2	*1,092*	West 19.	9
29	03.03	H	VC	Telford United	W	1-0	547	Hardyman 40.	8
30	07.03	H	VC	Hednesford Town	W	2-0	770	Hercules 38, Fiore 663.	8
31	10.03	H	VC	Woking	L	1-3	1,288	OG (Sutton) 85.	8
32	16.03	A	VC	Stevenage Borouugh	L	2-4	*1,413*	Browne 4, Bolt 59 (pen).	8
33	21.03	A	VC	Hereford United	D	1-1	*2,013*	Bolt 40 (pen).	8
34	31.03	H	VC	Gateshead	W	1-0	559	West 87.	8
35	07.04	H	VC	Stevenage Borough	W	3-1	828	Angus 66, Bolt 73, Abbott 78.	8
36	13.04	H	VC	Yeovil Town	D	1-1	912	Abbott 38.	8
37	18.04	A	VC	Gateshead	**L**	**1-5**	*415*	West 21.	8
38	21.04	A	VC	Dover Athletic	L	1-2	*803*	Smart 49.	8
39	23.04	H	VC	Kettering Town	D	1-1	515	Hercules 73.	8
40	28.04	H	VC	Leek Town	D	1-1	510	Hercules 87.	8
41	30.04	H	VC	Stalybridge Celtic	**W**	**4-0**	435	Hercules 6, 23, West 41, Bolt 83.	8
42	02.05	A	VC	Kidderminster Harriers	W	1-0	*1,709*	Stowell 12.	8

CUP COMPETITIONS

Date	Venue H / A	Comp.	Opponents	Result	& Score	Att.	Goalscorers	
13.09	A	**FAC** 1Q	Baldock Town	D	0-0	290		
16.09	H	1Q R	Baldock Town	W	5-0	259	Hardyman 28, Browne 43, 80, Brazil 16, Abbott 86.	
27.09	A	2Q	Walton & Hersham	D	0-0	519		
30.09	H	2Q R	Walton & Hersham	D	0-0	377	A.E.T.	Won 4-3 on penalties
11.10	H	3Q	Tilbury	W	6-1	484	**Browne 3** (27, 38, 44), Abbott 35 (pen), 45, Owusu 81.	
25.10	H	4Q	Kingstonian	W	2-1	1,271	Abbott 29 (pen), OG (Luckett) 31.	
15.11	H	1	Cardiff City	D	1-1	2,262	Bolt 68.	
25.11	A	1 R	Cardiff City	L	2-3	2,343	Owusu 5, Angus 74.	
10.01	A	**FAT** 1	Welling United	D	1-1	663	Owusu 2.	
13.01	H	1 R	Welling United	W	2-1	560	Owusu 47, Browne 55.	
31.01	A	2	Hailfax Town	D	1-1	1,633	West 84.	
03.02	H	2 R	Halifax Town	W	2-0	876	Brazil 17, Abbott 64.	
21.02	H	3	Boreham Wood	D	1-1	1,221	Stowell 11.	
24.02	A	3 R	Boreham Wood	W	*2-1	544	West 37, Abbott 102.	A.E.T.
16.03	A	4	Stevenage Borough	W	1-0	3,482	Bolt 32.	
28.03	H	SF - 1	Southport	L	0-1	2,106		
05.04	A	SF - 2	Southport	D	1-1	4,895	Bailey 30.	
07.10	H	**SCC** 1	Welling United	W	1-0	293	Abbott 61.	
18.11	A	2	Hayes	L	0-2	374		
27.01	A	**B&BC** 1	Reading	L	2-6	224	West (2).	

SCC - Spalding Challenge Cup
B&BC - Berks & Bucks Cup

SUTTON UNITED

Colours: Amber & chocolate/chocolate/amber & chocolate **Formed:** 1898
Change colours: Green & white/black/black **Nickname:** The U's
Midweek matchday: Tuesday **Sponsors:** Securicor.
Reserve League: Suburban.
Local Newspapers: Sutton Herald, Sutton Guardian.

Chairman: Bruce Elliott **President:** Andrew W Letts.
Secretary: Brian Williams, 49 Panmure Rd, Sydenham, London SE26 6NB (0181 699 2721).
Manager: John Rains **Asst Manager:** Tony Rains
Coach: Bobby Mapleson
Press Officer: Tony Dolbear (0171 782 8644 daytime, even & weekends mob 0966 507023)
GROUND - Address: Borough Sports Ground, Gander Green Lane, Sutton, SM1 2EY (0181 644 4440 Fax: 5120). **Directions:** Gander Green Lane runs between A232 (Cheam Road - turn by Sutton Cricket Club) and A217 (Oldfields Road - turn at 'Gander' PH lights). Ground opposite 'The Plough' 50 yards from West Sutton BR station. Bus 413 passes ground.
Capacity: 7,032 **Cover:** 1,900 **Seats:** 765 **Floodlights:** Yes
Clubhouse: Open every day, food. Available for hire.
Club Shop: Open matchdays selling full range of souvenirs, etc, contact Tony Cove via club.

PROGRAMME DETAILS:
Pages: 48 **Price:** £1.20
Editor: Tony Dolbear
Press Officer

PREVIOUS - **Leagues:** Sutton Jun, Southern Sub 10-21, Athenian 21-63, Isthmian 63-86, GMVC 86-91. **Names:** Sutton Association, Sutton Guild Rovers.

CLUB RECORDS - **Attendance:** 14,000 v Leeds United, FA Cup 4th Rd 24/1/70. **Victory:** 11-1 v Clapton 66, & leatherhead 82-83. **Defeat:** 13-0 v Barking 25-26. **Scorer:** Paul McKinnon (279). **Appearances:** Larry Pritchard 781 (65-84) **Fee Paid:** to Malmo FF for Paul McKinnon 83. **Fee Received:** £100,000 for Efan Ekoku (Bournemouth 90)

BEST SEASON - **FA Amateur Cup:** R-up 62-63 68-69 SF 28-29 36-37 67-68. **FA Trophy:** R-up 80-81. SF 92-93. **FA Cup:** 4th Rd 69-70 88-89.

HONOURS - Bob Lord Trophy 90-91; Isthmian Lg(3) 66-67 84-86 (R-up 67-68 70-71 81-82), Lg Cup(3) 82-84 85-86 (R-up 79-80); Loctite Cup 91-92; Athenian Lg 27-28 45-46 57-58 (R-up 46-47), Lg Cup 45-46 55-56 61-62 62-63, Res Sec 61-62 (R-up 32-33); Anglo Italian Semi-Pro Cup 79 (R-up 80 82); London Snr Cup 57-58 82-83; London Charity Cup 69-70 (R-up(3) 67-69 72-73); Surrey Snr Cup(13) (R-up(9); Surrey Intermediate Cup (4) (R-up (6); Surrey Jnr Cup R-up 09-10; Surrey Snr Charity Shield(3) (R-up (6); Surrey Interm Charity Cup 31-32 (R-up 34-35 38-39); Dylon Charity Shield 84 (R-up 80 82 83 85); Groningen Yth tournament 83 85 (R-up 79 81 89 91); John Ullman Invit. Cup 88-89; Carlton Cup 95-96

Players Progressing to Football Lge: Numerous incl the following since 1980 - M Robinson (C Palace 84), P McKinnon (Blackburn 86), R Fearon (I'wich 87), P Harding (Notts Co), E Ekoku (Bournemouth 91), M Golley (Maidstone), A Barnes (C Palace 91), P Rogers (Sheff U 92), S Massey (C Palace 92), A & R Scott (Sheff U 93), O Morah (Cambridge 94), M Watson (West Ham 95).

97-98 - Captain: G Berry **P.o.Y.:** D Brooker **Top scorer:** J Vansittart

Back Row (L-R); Andy Salako, Matt Hanlan, Gwynne Berry, Azeez Akinbolu, Barry Laker, Mark Watson, Steve Watson, Jeff Vansittart, Nassim Akrour, Paul Clark, John Ugbah. Front Row; Junior Haynes, David Everitt, Danny Brooker, Les Cleevely, Jimmy Dack, Dominic Feltham Photo: Garry Letts

SUTTON UNITED - Match Facts 97-98

Match No.	Date	Venue H / A	Comp.	Opponents	Result & Score		Att.	Goalscorers	League Position
1	16.08	H	IL	Hitchin Town	W	2-0	579	Hanlan, Virgo.	3
2	18.08	A	IL	Purfleet	**W**	**6-0**	*279*	**Vansittart 3,** Hanlan, Brooker, Salako.	1
3	23.08	A	IL	St Albans City	L	2-4	*607*	Dack, Brooker.	3
4	26.08	H	IL	Bishop's Stortford	L	2-4	485	Vansittart 2.	
5	30.08	H	IL	Heybridge Swifts	W	4-1	524	Hanlan 2 (1 pen), Vansittart, Salako.	4
6	02.09	A	IL	Harrow Borough	W	2-0	*315*	Vansittart, Salako.	
7	07.09	H	IL	Hendon	W	2-1	592	Hanlan, Vansittart.	1
8	09.09	A	**GIC 1**	Bracknell Town	W	2-0	*110*	Dack, Feltham.	-
9	13.09	A	**FAC 1Q**	Cheshunt	W	4-0	*200*	Hanlan 2, Vansittart, Salako.	-
10	20.09	A	IL	Enfield	W	2-0	*823*	Vansittart, Clark.	1
11	23.09	H	IL	Gravesend & Northfleet	W	3-1	583	Hanlan, Dack, Vansittart.	1
12	27.09	A	**FAC 2Q**	Welling United	D	2-2	*704*	Vansittart, Clark.	-
13	30.09	H	**FAC 2Q R**	Welling United	W	2-1	502	Dack, Feltham.	-
14	04.10	H	IL	Walton & Hersham	W	2-0	747	Vansittart, Feltham.	2
15	11.10	H	**FAC 3Q**	Tonbridge Angels	W	5-1	716	Hanlan 2 (1 pen), Vansittart, Dack, OG (Broadway).	-
16	14.10	A	IL	Bromley	D	1-1	*405*	Clark.	2
17	18.11	H	IL	Yeading	W	2-1	652	Hanlan, Clark.	2
18	25.10	A	**FAC 4Q**	Cheltenham Town	L	0-1	*1,505*		-
19	28.10	A	IL	Oxford City	W	2-1	*273*	Vansittart, Ugbah.	2
20	01.11	A	IL	Aylesbury United	D	1-1	*568*	Hanlan.	2
21	04.11	H	**GIC 2**	Uxbridge	W	3-0	186	Vansittart 2, Ugbah.	-
22	08.11	H	IL	Boreham Wood	L	1-2	714	Ugbah.	2
23	15.11	A	IL	Kingstonian	D	0-0	*2,019*		2
24	22.11	H	RL	Basingstoke Town	D	1-1	671	Salako.	2
25	25.11	A	RL	Chesham United	D	3-3	*362*	Ugbah 2, Dack.	2
26	29.11	A	**FAT 3Q**	Chesham United	L	1-2	*380*	Hanlan.	-
27	02.12	A	**FMC 2**	Staines Town	L	0-3	*108*		-
28	06.12	H	RL	Harrow Borough	W	2-1	586	Virgo, Dack.	2
29	13.12	H	RL	Aylesbury United	W	2-1	575	Vansittart, Ugbah.	2
30	20.12	A	RL	Dagenham & Redbridge	W	2-0	*1,214*	Akrour 2.	2
31	27.12	H	RL	Carshalton Athletic	W	3-1	1,833	Dack 2, Ugbah.	1
32	30.12	H	**GIC 3**	Basingstoke Town	D	*2-2	361	Vansittart, Hanlan.	-
33	03.01	A	RL	Bishop's Stortford	W	1-0	*445*	Feltham.	1
34	06.01	A	**GIC 3 R**	Basingstoke Town	W	3-1	*243*	Vansittart, Hanlan, S Watson.	-
35	17.01	A	RL	Hitchin Town	W	3-0	*471*	Ugbah, Vansittart 2.	1
36	20.01	H	RL	Purfleet	W	3-0	515	Hanlan, Ugbah, Everitt.	1
37	24.01	H	RL	St Albans City	W	3-1	967	Hanlan, Ugbah, Vansittart.	1
38	27.01	A	**GIC 4**	Romford	D	*2-2	*257*	Vansittart, Hanlan. A.E.T.	-
39	31.01	A	RL	Heybridge Swifts	D	1-1	*574*	Hanlan.	1
40	07.02	H	RL	Enfield	**L**	**0-5**	1,122		1
41	10.02	A	RL	Dulwich Hamlet	L	0-1	*511*		1
42	14.02	A	RL	Gravesend & Northfleet	D	2-2	*691*	Vansittart, S Watson.	1
43	21.02	H	RL	Oxford City	W	2-1	635	Hanlan, Vansittart.	1
44	24.02	H	**GIC 4 R**	Romford	W	*5-3	293	Vansittart, Hanlan, Salako, Akrour 2. A.E.T. (2-2 at F.T.)	-
45	28.02	A	RL	Walton & Hersham	D	1-1	*596*	Akrour.	1
46	03.03	H	**GIC S-F 1**	St Albans City	D	0-0	272		-
47	07.03	H	RL	Dulwich Hamlet	D	1-1	841	Salako.	2
48	10.03	A	**GIC S-F 2**	St Albans City	W	3-0	*247*	Hanlan, M Watson, Clark.	-
49	14.03	A	RL	Hendon	L	2-4	*370*	M Watson 2 (1 pen).	2
50	21.03	H	RL	Chesham United	L	2-4	690	M Watson, Everitt.	2
51	28.03	A	RL	Yeading	L	1-3	*256*	Haynes.	2
52	04.04	A	RL	Boreham Wood	D	2-2	*474*	Vansittart, OG (Daly).	3
53	11.04	H	RL	Dagenham & Redbridge	W	2-1	678	Salako, Akrour.	2
54	13.04	A	RL	Carshalton Athletic	W	5-1	*812*	Vansittart, Akrour, **Salako 3.**	2
55	18.04	H	RL	Kingstonian	D	3-3	1,901	Akrour 2, M Watson.	2
56	25.04	A	RL	Basingstoke Town	D	1-1	*723*	Salako.	3
57	02.05	H	RL	Bromley	W	1-0	707	Salako.	3
58	05.05	N	**GIC Final**	Oxford City	W	6-1	433	**Vansittart 5,** Akrour.	

PLAYING SQUAD - **Goalkeepers:** Les Cleevely (Carshalton Ath, Yeovil T, Welling U, CarshaltonAth, Epsom & E, Farnborough T, Wealdstone, Kungsbaka (Swe), Crystal Palace,Southampton). **Defenders:** David Everitt (Leyton Orient, Walton & H), David Pattullo (DulwichHamlet, Molesey, Sutton U, Molesey, Sheen Ath), Gwynne Berry (Welling U,Sutton U, Woking, Sutton U, Whyteleafe), John Ugbah (Hendon, Carshalton Ath,Stevenage B, Carshalton Ath, Fisher Ath, Faweh), Azeez Akinbolu (St.Albans C,Woodford T, Barnet), Barry Laker (Banstead Ath, Wimbledon), Mark Wood (Torquay U), Paul Clark (Carshalton Ath, Kingstonian, St.Albans C, CarshaltonAth, Molesey, Walton & H, St.Albans C, Cambridge U).

Midfielders: Mark Pye* (Hayes, Slough T, Enfield, Harrow B, Nth.Greenford U,West Ham U), James Virgo (Brighton), Sean Daly (Carshalton Ath, Sutton U,Croydon), Danny Brooker (Kingstonian, Sutton U, Dorking, Wimbledon), Steve Watson (Croydon, Whyteleafe).

Forwards: Andy Salako (Carshalton Ath, Bromley, Tonbridge, St.Albans C,Croydon, Welling U, Charlton Ath), Mark Watson (Welling U, AFC Bournemouth,West Ham U, Sutton U), Junior Haynes (Hayes, Hendon, Barnet, Luton T,Tottenham H.), Nassem Akrour (Olympic Nosiy-Lesee (Fr), Matt Hanlan (Carshalton Ath, Molesey, Dorking, Farnborough T, Dorking, Wycombe W, Sutton U).

PROGRAMME DETAILS:
Pages: 36 **Price:** £1.20
Editor: Mark Massingham
Tel: 01932 885814

WALTON & HERSHAM

Colours: White with red band/white/red.
Change colours: Yellow/Blue/White.
Midweek home matchday: Tuesday
Reserve Team's League: Suburban.
Local Newspapers: Surrey Herald, Surrey Comet.
Local Radio Stations: County Sound, BBC Southern Counties.

Sponsors: T.B.A.
Formed: 1896
Nickname: Swans

Chairman: TBA **President:** Mick Brown
Secretary: Mark Massingham, 7b Sidney Rd., Walton-on-Thames, Surrey. KT12 2NP (01932 885814).
Manager: Laurie Craker **Asst Manager:** Mark Hill
Physio: Stuart Smith **Press Officer:** Mervyn Rees (01932 245756)
GROUND Address: Sports Ground, Stompond Lane, Walton-on-Thames (01932 245263-club).
Directions: From North: Over Walton Bridge & along New Zealand Ave., down 1-way street and up A244 Hersham Road - ground 2nd right. From Esher: Down Lammas Lane then Esher Rd, straight over 1st r'bout, 4th exit at next r'bout (West Grove) 2nd left at end of Hersham Rd and Stompond Lane is half mile on left. Ten minutes walk fron Walton-on-Thames (BR). Bus 218 passes ground.
Capacity: 6,500 **Cover:** 2,500 **Seats:** 500 **Floodlights:** Yes
Clubhouse: (01932 244967). Open most nights. Bar, TV, darts, pool, refreshments on matchdays.
Club Shop: Open matchdays. Contact Richard Old, c/o the club.

PREVIOUS - **Leagues:** Surrey Senior; Corinthian 45-50; Athenian 50-71.
CLUB RECORDS - **Attendance:** 6,500 v Brighton, FA Cup First Round 73-74. **Scorer:** Reg Sentance 220 in 11 seasons. **Appearances:** Terry Keen 449 in 11 seasons. **Win:** 10-0 v Clevedon, FA Amateur Cup 1960. **Defeat:** 11-3 v Kingstonian Surrey Sen Shield 58. **Transfer fee paid:** £6,000. **Transfer fee received:** £5,000.
BEST SEASON - **FA Trophy:** 1st Round 91-92, 94-95. **FA Amateur Cup:** Winners 72-73, (SF 51-52, 52-53). **FA Cup:** 2nd Rd 72-73 (v Margate), 73-74 (v Hereford). **League clubs defeated:** Exeter 72-73, Brighton 73-74.
HONOURS - Isthmian Lg R-up 72-73, Barassi Cup 73-74; Athenian Lg 68-69 (R-up 50-51 69-70 70-71, Lg Cup 69-70); Corinthian Lg 46-49 (R-up 49-50), Premier Midweek F'lit Lg 67-69 70-71 (R-up 71-72); Surrey Snr Cup 47-48 50-51 60-61 61-62 70-71 72-73 (R-up 46-47 51-52 59-60 69-70 71-72 73-74); London Snr Cup R-up 73-74; Southern Comb. Cup 82-83 88-89 91-92; Surrey Comb. Cup 49-50 91-92; John Livey Memorial Trophy 91-92.
Players progressing to Football League: Andy McCulloch (QPR 1970), Mick Heath (Brentford 1971), Paul Priddy (Brentford 1972), Richard Teale (Queens Park Rangers 1973), Steve Parsons (Wimbledon 1977), Stuart Massey (Crystal Palace), Ross Davidson (Sheffield Utd).
97-98 - Captain: Trevor Baron **P.o.Y.** Delroy Preddie **Top Scorer:** Andy Sayer

Back Row (L-R); Hutchinson, Bushay, Blackman, Holdsworth, Preddie, Smith, Pearson, Smart, Johnson. Middle Row; Golding, Sayer, L Holloway, Bourne, H Holloway, Powell, Smart, Dowson, Chandler. Front Row; Hill, Pearson, Rake, Craker, Smith, Baron, Ray, Ellis.

WALTON & HERSHAM - Match Facts 97-98

Match No.	Date	Venue H / A	Comp.	Opponents	Result & Score		Att.	Goalscorers	League Position
1	16.08	H	IL	Basingstoke Town	D	1-1	269	Sayer.	10
2	19.08	A	II	Bromley	W	1-0	*374*	Sayer.	
3	23.08	A	IL	Harrow Borough	L	0-2	*207*		12
4	26.08	H	IL	Heybridge Swifts	W	1-0	182	Sayer.	
5	30.08	H	IL	Hitchin Town	W	2-1	207	Ray, Sayer.	3
6	01.09	A	IL	Purfleet	L	0-1	*179*		
7	05.09	H	IL	Kingstonian	L	1-4	687	Johnson.	7
8	09.09	A	**GIC 1**	Berkhamsted Town	W	2-1			-
9	13.09	H	**FAC 1Q**	Hampton	W	2-0	233	Sayer, Holloway.	-
10	16.09	A	IL	Boreham Wood	L	0-3	*138*		
11	20.09	A	IL	Bishop's Stortford	L	1-3	*331*	Bushay.	14
12	23.09	H	IL	Carshalton Athletic	L	3-4	218	Blackman 2, Rake.	
13	27.09	H	**FAC 2Q**	Slough Town	D	0-0	519		-
14	30.09	A	**FAC 2Q R**	Slough Town	D	*0-0	*377*	A.E.T. Lost 2-3 on penaties.	-
15	04.10	A	IL	Sutton United	L	0-2	*747*		19
16	11.10	H	IL	Enfield	W	3-1	318	**Sayer 3.**	18
17	14.10	A	IL	Dagenham & Redbridge	L	2-4	*624*	Blackman, Pearson.	-
18	18.10	H	**FAT 1Q**	Staines Town	W	3-1	270	Sayer 2, Hutchinson.	-
19	25.10	H	IL	Aylesbury United	**W**	**3-0**	301	Sayer 2, Bushay.	15
20	28.10	H	**FMC 1**	Staines Town	L	3-4			-
21	01.11	H	IL	Hendon	D	2-2	270	Blackman, Baron.	16
22	04.11	A	**GIC 2**	Hampton	W	3-2			-
23	08.11	H	**FAT 2Q**	Bashley	D	0-0	257		-
24	12.11	A	**FAT 2Q R**	Bashley	L	0-2	*225*		-
25	15.11	H	IL	Chesham United	D	1-1	298	Baron.	16
26	22.11	A	RL	Gravesend & Northfleet	W	2-1	*512*	Sayer, Rake.	10
27	25.11	H	RL	Dulwich Hamlet	W	1-0	160	Balckman.	7
28	06.12	A	RL	Heybridge Swifts	W	1-0	*219*	Bushay.	7
29	13.12	A	RL	Hendon	L	0-4	*237*		10
30	16.12	A	**GIC 3**	Wokingham Town	L	0-1			-
31	20.12	H	RL	St Albans City	W	1-0	244	Blackman.	8
32	27.12	A	RL	Yeading	W	4-2	*243*	Sayer 2, Rake, Johnson.	6
33	10.01	H	RL	Bromley	L	0-2	301		7
34	17.01	A	RL	Basingstoke Town	W	2-1	*523*	Johnson, Pearson.	6
35	24.01	H	RL	Harrow Borough	D	0-0	247		7
36	31.01	A	RL	Hitchin Town	L	0-1	*253*		9
37	07.02	H	RL	Bishop's Stortford	**W**	**3-0**	219	Sayer 2, Holloway.	8
38	14.02	A	RL	Carshalton Athletic	W	2-1	*337*	Johnson, Pearson (pen).	7
39	17.02	H	RL	Purfleet	L	2-4	186	Holloway, Blackman.	
40	21.02	A	RL	Enfield	L	0-3	*608*		9
41	28.02	H	RL	Sutton United	D	1-1	596	Sayer.	9
42	07.03	H	RL	Boreham Wood	L	1-4	269	Sayer.	10
43	14.03	A	RL	Kingstonian	**L**	**0-7**	*1,011*		11
44	18.03	A	RL	Oxford City	W	1-0	*126*	Sayer.	
45	21.03	A	RL	Aylesbury United	L	0-4	*427*		10
46	28.03	H	RL	Dagenham & Redbridge	W	2-1	296	Sayer, Baron.	10
47	04.04	H	RL	Oxford City	W	1-0	170	Sayer.	8
48	11.04	A	RL	St Albans City	W	1-0	*513*	Holloway.	7
49	13.04	H	RL	Yeading	D	1-1	187	Pearson.	7
50	18.04	A	RL	Chesham United	L	0-2	*441*		8
51	25.04	H	RL	Gravesend & Northfleet	L	0-1	285		11
52	02.05	A	RL	Dulwich Hamlet	W	3-1	*421*	Johnson, Sayer 2.	9

PLAYING SQUAD 1998

Goalkeepers: Delroy Preddie (Slough T, Northampton T), John Gregory (Northwood, Yeovil T, Kingstonian, Woking, Fulham)

Defenders: Trevor Baron (Woking, Slough T, Woking, Slough T, Marlow, Woking,Windsor & Eton, Slough T, Windsor & Eton, Chertsey T, Burnham, Marlow), Matthew Pearson (Aldershot T, Bracknell T, Egham T, Crawley T, Carshalton Ath,Kingstonian, Wimbledon), Erskine Smart (Kingstonian, St.Albans C, DulwichHamlet, St.Albans C, Enfield, Hendon, Kingsbury T, Watford), Gary Powell (Staines T), Alan Dowson (Gateshead, Slough T, Darlington, Bradford C,Millwall), Matt Elverson (Kingstonian, Walton & H)

Midfielders: Garfield Blackman (Slough T, Marlow, Northwood, Welwyn GC), Gary Holloway (Youth), Barry Rake (Slough T, Chesham U, Slough T, Millwall), Jamie Pearson (Youth team), Jeremy Jones (Molesey, Whyteleafe, Tooting & M,Dulwich Hamlet, Chelsea)

Forwards: Andy Sayer (Enfield, Slough T, Leyton Orient, Fulham, Wimbledon),Simon Ray (Whyteleafe, Sutton U, Walton & H), Curtis Johnson (Worthing,Chesham U, Worthing, Kingstonian), Clive Zammit (Youth).

HITCHIN TOWN - Match Facts 97-98

Match No.	Date	Venue H / A	Comp.	Opponents	Result & Score		Att.	Goalscorers	League Position
1	16.08	A	IL P	Sutton United	L	0-2	*579*		22
2	19.08	H	IL P	Kingstonian	D	0-0	514		
3	23.08	H	IL P	Dagenham & Redbridge	L	0-1	351		22
4	26.08	A	IL P	Hendon	W	2-0	*251*	Dellar, Parker.	
5	30.08	A	IL P	Walton & Hersham	L	1-2	*207*	Dellar.	18
6	02.09	H	IL P	Yeading	L	0-2	243		
7	07.09	H	IL P	Carshalton Athletic	L	1-2	246	Clark	22
8	16.09	A	IL P	Bishop's Stortford	W	2-0	*242*	Burke, Parker.	
9	20.09	H	IL P	Boreham Wood	L	0-2	248		20
10	23.09	A	IL P	Aylesbury United	L	0-1	*468*		22
11	04.10	H	IL P	Dulwich Hamlet	W	2-0	245	Hall, Parker.	18
12	11.10	A	IL P	Oxford City	D	2-2	*162*	Williams, Scott.	15
13	21.10	A	IL P	Bromley	D	0-0	*250*		
14	25.10	H	IL P	Harrow Borough	D	2-2	286	Bone, Parker.	20
15	01.11	H	IL P	Enfield	D	1-1	559	Hall.	21
16	15.11	H	IL P	Purfleet	D	3-3	258	Parker, Barr, Williams.	20
17	22.11	A	RL P	Chesham United	D	3-3	*448*	Parker, Williams G.	20
18	06.12	A	RL P	Yeading	W	2-1	*153*	Parker, Debnam.	18
19	13.12	A	RL P	Enfield	L	1-2	*601*	Barr.	19
20	20.12	H	RL P	Gravesend & Northfleet	**W**	**4-0**	349	Hall 2, Clark, Honeyball (og).	17
21	27..12	A	RL P	St Albans City	**L**	**1-4**	*652*	Williams.	19
22	06.01	H	RL P	Oxford City	D	0-0	178		
23	10.01	A	RL P	Kingstonian	L	0-2	*754*		19
24	17.01	H	RL P	Sutton United	L	0-3	471		20
25	24.01	A	RL P	Dagenham & Redbridge	L	0-1	*851*		20
26	31.01	H	RL P	Walton & Hersham	W	1-0	253	Parker.	19
27	07.02	A	RL P	Boreham Wood	D	0-0	*339*		18
28	10.02	A	RL P	Heybridge Swifts	W	2-1	*251*	Elad, Williams G.	16
29	14.02	H	RL P	Aylesbury United	L	2-3	354	Parker, Williams.	18
30	21.02	H	RL P	Basingstoke Town	L	1-2	275	Parker.	18
31	28.02	A	RL P	Dulwich Hamlet	D	2-2	*319*	Hall, Abbey.	19
32	07.03	H	RL P	Bishop's Stortford	L	2-4	326	Abbey, Clark.	21
33	14.03	A	RL P	Carshalton Athletic	W	2-1	*249*	Abbey 2.	20
34	21.03	A	RL P	Harrow Borough	D	1-1	*205*	Wiliams C.	20
35	24.03	A	RL P	Basingstoke Town	L	0-3	*383*		
36	28.03	H	RL P	Bromley	D	1-1	350	Abbey.	21
37	04.04	H	RL P	Heybridge Swifts	D	1-1	269	Bone.	21
38	11.04	A	RL P	Gravesend & Northfleet	L	0-2	*517*		21
39	13.04	H	RL P	St. Albans City	D	1-1	411	Williams.	21
40	18.04	A	RL P	Purfleet	L	0-1	*132*		21
41	21.04	H	RL P	Hendon	D	1-1	141	Abbey	21
42	25.04	H	RL P	Chesham United	L	1-2	369	Abbey	21

CUP COMPETITIONS

F.A. CUP

Date	Venue	Comp.	Opponents	Result	Score	Att.	Goalscorers	Position
13.09	H	**FAC 1Q**	Bognor Regis Town	L	0-2	309		-

F.A. TROPHY

Date	Venue	Comp.	Opponents	Result	Score	Att.	Goalscorers	Position
18.10	H	**FAT 1Q**	Erith & Belvedere	W	7-1	367	G Williams 2, Hall 2, C Williams, Bone, Clark.	-
08.11	H	**FAT 2Q**	Barton Rovers	W	3-0	349	Dellar 2, Williams.	-
29.11	H	**FAT 3Q**	Boreham Wood	L	0-2			-

GUARDIAN INSURANCE CUP

Date	Venue	Comp.	Opponents	Result	Score	Att.	Goalscorers	Position
09.09	H	**GIC**	Wembley	W	2-0			-
11.11	H	**GIC**	Wealdstone					-
16.12	A	**GIC**	Canvey Island	L	0-2			-

FULL MEMBERS CUP

Date	Venue	Comp.	Opponents	Result	Score	Att.	Goalscorers	Position
18.11	H	**FMC**	Boreham Wood	L	1-2			-

OXFORD CITY - Match Facts 97-98

Match No.	Date	Venue H / A	Comp.	Opponents	Result & Score		Att.	Goalscorers	League Position
1	16.08	H	IL P	Enfield	L	1-2	412	Jenkins.	16
2	19.08	A	IL P	Heybridge Swifts	L	0-3	*213*		
3	23.08	A	IL P	Bromley	W	2-1	*281*	Smith, Herbert (pen).	18
4	26.08	H	IL P	Harrow Borough	L	2-4	231	Smith, Carlisle.	
5	30.08	H	IL P	St Albans City	D	0-0	279		21
6	02.09	A	IL P	Bishop's Stortford	Q	1-0	*474*	Concannon.	
7	07.09	A	IL P	Chesham United	L	0-6	*565*		17
8	20.09	A	IL P	Gravesend & Northfleet	L	2-3	*456*	Sharkes, Smith.	21
9	23.08	H	IL P	Purfleet	D	0-0	161		
10	04.10	A	IL P	Bromley	L	1-3	*283*	Concannon.	22
11	07.10	H	IL P	Yeading	L	0-3	151		
12	11.10	H	IL P	Hitchin Town	D	2-2	162	Caffel, McCleary.	22
13	14.10	A	IL P	Hendon	L	0-1	*211*		22
14	25.10	H	IL P	Dulwich Hamlet	L	1-2	217	Charles.	22
15	28.10	H	IL P	Sutton United	L	1-2	273	Concannon.	22
16	01.11	A	IL P	Dagenham & Redbridge	**L**	**0-7**	*808*		22
17	15.11	A	IL P	Aylesbury United	L	1-4	*465*	Wallbridge.	22
18	22.11	H	RL P	Carshalton Athletic	D	1-1	191	Carlisle.	22
19	06.12	H	RL P	Bishop's Stortford	W	1-0	171	McSporran.	22
20	13.12	H	RL P	Dagenham & Redbridge	W	2-0	272	Carlisle, Concannon.	22
21	20.12	A	RL P	Kingstonian	D	0-0	*669*		22
22	27.12	H	RL P	Basingstoke Town	L	0-1	426		22
23	03.01	A	RL P	Harrow Borough	**W**	**3-0**	*252*	Wallbridge, Concannon, Carlisle.	22
24	06.01	A	RL P	Hitchin Town	D	0-0	*178*		22
25	10.01	H	RL P	Heybridge Swifts	L	0-2	221		22
26	17.01	A	RL P	Enfield	L	0-2	*862*		22
27	24.01	H	RL P	Bromley	D	1-1	171	Jenkins.	22
28	07.02	H	RL P	Gravesend & Northfleet	W	2-1	269	Concannon 2.	20
29	14.02	A	RL P	Purfleet	L	1-2	*129*	Concannon.	22
30	21.02	A	RL P	Sutton United	L	1-2	*635*	McSporran.	22
31	28.02	H	RL P	Boreham Wood	L	0-1	178		22
32	07.03	A	RL P	Yeading	D	1-1	*155*	McSporran.	22
33	13.03	H	RL P	Chesham United	W	2-1	359	Jenkins (pen), Lee.	22
34	18.03	H	RL P	Walton & Hersham	L	0-1	126		22
35	21.03	A	RL P	Dulwich Hamlet	L	2-3	*237*	Concannon, Smith.	22
36	24.03	A	RL P	St Albans City	L	1-4	*376*	Lee.	22
37	28.03	H	RL P	Hendon	L	0-2	196		22
38	04.04	A	RL P	Walton & Hersham	L	0-1	*170*		22
39	13.04	A	RL P	Basingstoke Town	L	1-2	*567*	Herbert.	22
40	17.04	H	RL P	Aylesbury United	D	2-2	267	Herbert, Smith.	22
41	25.04	A	RL P	Carshalton Athletic	L	0-2	*403*		22
42	30.04	H	RL P	Kingstonian	L	0-1	361		22

F.A. CUP

Date	Venue	Comp.	Opponents	Result	Score	Att.	Goalscorers
13.09	H	1Q	Dorchester Town	D	1-1	274	Lee.
16.09	A	1Q **R**	Dorchester Town	L	0-1	353	

F.A. TROPHY

Date	Venue	Comp.	Opponents	Result	Score	Att.	Goalscorers
18.10	H	1Q	Cinderford Town	W	6-0	162	Herbert 2, Carlisle, Charles, McLeary, Concannon.
08.11	H	2Q	Wisbech Town	L	0-2	367	

FULL MEMBERS CUP

Date	Venue	Comp.	Opponents	Result	Score
25.11	H	1	Thame United	W	3-1
20.01	H	2	Basingstoke Town	L	1-2

GUARDIAN INSURANCE CUP

Date	Venue	Comp.	Opponents	Result	Score	Att.	Goalscorers	
04.11	A	1	Heybridge Swifts	W	1-0			
30.09	H	2	Braintree Town	W	4-1			
30.12	A	3	Camberley Town	W	3-0			
27.01	A	4	Carshalton Athletic	W	1-0			
05.03	H	S-F 1	Boreham Wood	W	2-1			
10.03	A	S-F 2	Boreham Wood	W	3-0	126	Smith, Concannon 2.	
05.03	N	Final	Sutton United	L	1-6	433	Concannon.	Played at Harrow Borough FC.

YEADING - Match Facts 97-98

Match No.	Date	Venue H / A	Comp.	Opponents	Result & Score		Att.	Goalscorers	League Position
1	16.08	H	IL P	Purfleet	D	0-0	112		14
2	19.08	A	IL P	Carshalton Athletic	L	0-1	*245*		
3	23.08	A	IL P	Gravesend & Northfleet	W	2-1	*526*	Kellman, Pickett.	11
4	26.08	H	IL P	St Albans City	L	0-2	178		
5	30.09	H	IL P	Enfield	L	0-2	402		19
6	02.09	A	IL P	Hitchin Town	W	2-0	*243*	Kellman, Carter.	16
7	20.09	A	IL P	Heybridge Swifts	D	2-2	*218*	Kellman, Houghton.	17
8	23.09	H	IL P	Basingstoke Town	D	2-2	158	Delisser, Pickering.	17
9	04.10	H	IL P	Aylesbury UNited	W	1-0	187	Kellman.	14
10	07.10	A	IL P	Oxford City	**W**	**3-0**	*151*	Kellman, Carter, Delisser.	
11	14.10	H	IL P	Dulwich Hamlet	D	2-2	118	Gell, Kellman.	14
12	18.10	A	IL P	Sutton United	L	1-2	*652*	Houghton.	
13	25.10	A	IL P	Dagenham & Redbridge	D	1-1	*726*	Houghton.	14
14	01.11	A	IL P	Boreham Wood	L	1-3	*232*	Sewell.	
15	08.11	H	IL P	KIngstonian	L	1-3	331	Pickett (pen).	
16	12.11	A	IL P	Chesham United	L	1-3	*341*	Protheroe.	18
17	22.11	H	RL P	Bromley	D	1-1	155	Flitter.	17
18	25.11	A	RL P	Harrow Borough	L	1-2	*210*	Allen.	
19	06.12	H	RL P	Hitchin Town	L	1-2	153	Sewell.	21
20	13.12	H	RL P	Borehham Wood	L	0-1	152		21
21	20.12	A	RL P	Bishop's Stortford	L	1-2	*519*		21
22	27.12	H	RL P	Walton & Hersham	L	2-4	243	Pickett 2.	21
23	03.01	A	RL P	Basingstoke Town	W	2-1	*489*	Pickett, Gell.	21
24	17.01	A	RL P	Purfleet	W	3-1	*102*	Pickett, Carter, Allen.	19
25	24.01	H	RL P	Gravesend & Northfleet	W	4-3	238	Flitter, Carter, Pickett 2 (1 pen).	16
26	27.01	H	RL P	Hendon	L	0-2	156		
27	07.02	H	RL P	Heybridge Swifts	L	0-3	152		19
28	10.02	H	RL P	Carshalton Athletic	D	0-0	103		
29	14.02	A	RL P	St Albans City	W	1-0	*416*	Harrak.	17
30	21.02	H	RL P	Chesham United	W	2-0	219	Dicker, Pickett (pen).	16
31	28.02	A	RL P	Aylesbury United	D	1-1	*567*	Pickett (pen).	17
32	07.03	H	RL P	Oxford City	D	1-1	155	Gell.	17
33	14.03	A	RL P	Dulwich Hamlet	L	1-2	*237*	Kellman.	18
34	21.03	A	RL P	Hendon	**L**	**0-5**	*228*		19
35	28.03	H	RL P	Sutton United	W	3-1	256	Delisser, Carter 2.	19
36	04.04	A	RL P	Kingstonian	W	1-0	*1,297*	Carter.	17
37	11.04	H	RL P	Bishop's Stortford	L	0-2	162		19
38	13.04	A	RL P	Walton & Hersham	D	1-1	*197*	Abercrumbie.	19
39	18.04	H	RL P	Dagenham & Redbridge	L	0-2	161		20
40	21.04	A	RL P	Enfield	L	0-2	*444*		
41	25.04	A	RL P	Bromley	W	2-0	*331*	Pickett (pen), Protheroe.	20
42	02.05	H	RL P	Harrow Borough	D	2-2	325	Kellman, Pickett (pen).	20

F.A. CUP

Date	Venue	Round	Opponents	Result	Score	Att.	Goalscorers
13.09	H	1Q	Chelmsford City	W	4-2	261	Houghton 2, Carter, Kellman.
27.09	H	2Q	Stansted	W	3-0	180	Kellman, Gell, Pickett.
11.10	H	3Q	Romford	L	0-2	210	

F.A. TROPHY

Date	Venue	Round	Opponents	Result	Score	Att.	Goalscorers
29.11	H	3Q	St Leonards Stamcroft	W	2-1	120	Allen, Gell.
10.01	A	1	Yeovil Town	D	0-0	2,016	
13.01	H	1 R	Yeovil Town	W	1-0	286	Gell 87.
31.01	H	2	Southport	L	0-6	342	

GUARDIAN INSURANCE CUP

Date	Venue	Round	Opponents	Result	Score	Att.	Goalscorers
09.09	H	1	Hemel Hempstead	W	3-2		
04.11	A	2	Carshalton Athletic	L	0-1		

FULL MEMBERS CUP

Date	Venue	Round	Opponents	Result	Score	Att.	Goalscorers
02.12	H	2	Wembley	W	*3-2		A.E.T.
18.02	A	3	Leyton Pennant	W	2-1		
12.03	A	4	Boreham Wood	D	*2-2		A.E.T. Won 3-0 after penalties.
17.03	H	S-F	Basingstoke Town	L	2-4	122	Delisser, Kellman.

FIRST DIVISION

LEAGUE TABLE 1997-98

	P	Home W	Home D	Home L	Away W	Away D	Away L	F	A	Pts
Aldershot Town	42	16	3	2	12	5	4	89	36	92
Billericay Town	42	13	3	5	12	3	6	78	44	81
Hampton	42	13	6	2	9	9	3	75	47	81
Maidenhead United	42	14	3	4	11	2	8	76	37	80
Uxbridge	42	13	5	3	10	1	10	66	59	75
Grays Athletic	42	11	6	4	10	4	7	79	49	73
Romford	42	11	4	6	10	4	7	92	59	71
Bognor Regis Town	42	12	2	7	8	7	6	77	45	69
Leatherhead	42	11	6	4	7	5	9	70	51	65
Leyton Pennant	42	9	5	7	8	6	7	66	58	62
Chertsey Town	42	8	6	7	8	7	6	83	70	61
Worthing	42	10	4	7	7	2	12	64	71	57
Berkhamsted Town	42	9	5	7	6	3	12	59	69	53
Staines Town	42	8	4	9	5	6	10	54	71	49
Croydon	42	10	4	7	3	6	12	47	64	49
Barton Rovers	42	6	9	6	5	4	12	53	72	46
Wembley	42	5	7	9	5	8	8	38	61	45
Molesey	42	8	4	9	2	7	12	47	65	41
Whyteleafe	42	5	6	10	5	4	12	48	83	40
Wokingham Town	42	5	4	12	2	6	13	41	74	31
Abingdon Town	42	5	2	14	4	2	15	47	101	31
Thame United	42	4	6	11	3	3	15	33	96	30

RESULTS GRID 1997-98

HOME TEAM	1	2	3	4	5	6	7	8	9	10	11	12	13	14	15	16	17	18	19	20	21	22
1. Abingdon T.	*	0-2	3-3	0-2	0-1	1-3	0-2	1-2	0-2	0-2	1-2	0-4	1-4	0-3	1-6	2-0	1-0	1-2	2-0	1-0	2-2	3-0
2. Aldershot T.	3-1	*	1-0	3-0	1-0	1-1	0-1	1-1	2-1	2-0	1-0	8-1	0-2	3-1	2-0	2-0	1-1	4-0	3-1	3-0	4-0	3-1
3. Barton Rovers	1-2	1-1	*	2-2	2-0	1-1	0-0	1-0	1-2	1-1	4-4	0-0	1-0	3-0	2-4	0-0	3-0	0-1	0-0	3-0	0-3	1-4
4. Berkhamsted T.	0-1	4-2	1-0	*	1-5	3-2	3-1	1-0	1-0	1-2	2-1	3-3	5-0	2-2	2-4	4-2	3-3	0-2	1-2	1-3	1-1	0-0
5. Billericay T.	3-1	1-2	4-0	1-1	*	0-2	1-5	2-1	2-1	1-1	1-0	1-2	0-2	2-1	2-1	2-0	4-0	1-1	4-0	4-1	3-0	4-0
6. Bognor Regis T.	7-0	1-2	4-0	0-0	4-2	*	2-3	0-1	2-0	1-2	2-0	0-2	2-1	4-1	3-0	1-1	4-0	2-1	1-2	2-0	3-0	1-2
7. Chertsey Town	1-1	2-0	3-2	4-2	1-3	1-1	*	5-1	3-3	1-1	3-4	1-1	0-2	1-1	2-4	4-0	3-0	1-3	4-1	1-3	4-1	1-4
8. Croydon	3-0	2-1	3-5	1-0	1-3	0-0	0-0	*	1-2	3-1	3-2	2-1	2-1	0-0	1-2	1-2	1-1	0-1	0-1	1-0	2-0	1-0
9. Grays Athletic	7-1	2-1	2-2	2-0	2-1	2-2	3-0	1-1	*	1-2	3-1	1-2	1-0	2-0	2-2	0-1	2-0	2-3	2-0	1-1	1-1	1-0
10. Hampton	4-2	1-1	1-2	3-2	0-2	2-1	2-2	2-2	2-2	*	2-0	3-1	1-0	1-0	1-0	3-1	4-1	1-0	1-1	2-2	3-3	2-0
11. Leatherhead	3-4	0-0	2-1	3-0	1-1	0-1	2-1	1-1	1-1	0-0	*	1-2	2-1	1-0	3-1	1-0	1-2	5-2	0-0	2-0	2-1	5-1
12. Leyton Pennant	2-1	3-3	2-0	0-1	2-3	0-0	1-1	2-0	1-2	1-0	1-3	*	1-2	3-1	3-1	1-2	4-1	4-0	2-1	1-1	2-2	1-3
13. Maidenhead U.	2-1	0-2	3-0	2-1	1-0	1-0	4-1	6-1	0-1	1-1	2-1	0-0	*	1-1	1-3	3-0	5-0	2-1	4-0	5-0	2-1	1-2
14. Molesey	1-0	0-1	2-1	0-1	2-3	5-0	2-4	3-2	1-0	1-1	0-2	0-1	0-3	*	1-1	3-2	2-3	2-3	0-0	0-0	1-0	1-0
15. Romford	3-2	1-2	6-1	2-1	1-2	1-2	2-2	3-1	3-3	0-1	1-0	0-0	0-1	0-0	*	2-1	3-1	3-1	1-2	1-0	3-0	4-0
16. Staines T.	2-1	2-5	2-3	3-2	0-2	3-0	0-1	3-1	1-4	2-2	1-1	1-0	0-4	2-3	1-4	*	4-1	0-1	1-1	3-1	3-0	1-1
17. Thame Utd.	3-0	1-4	1-1	0-1	0-2	0-3	1-6	1-2	2-0	0-5	0-3	0-0	0-0	2-1	0-1	1-1	*	0-1	1-1	0-2	0-0	3-2
18. Uxbridge	5-2	1-2	2-1	3-1	0-0	2-1	1-1	2-1	3-2	1-2	1-1	1-0	1-1	1-0	3-2	0-0	3-1	*	3-0	1-3	1-0	2-1
19. Wembley	1-0	0-1	0-1	1-0	1-0	0-5	2-2	0-0	0-1	1-3	1-1	2-3	0-2	1-1	3-3	0-0	5-0	1-3	*	0-0	2-1	1-3
20. Whyteleafe	0-3	0-4	1-1	0-1	1-3	2-2	4-1	2-1	0-3	1-1	0-3	3-5	1-2	2-2	2-8	2-2	4-0	3-2	0-0	*	2-1	0-1
21. Wokingham T.	1-1	0-3	4-0	0-1	0-1	0-2	0-2	1-1	1-2	3-4	2-2	2-1	0-1	2-1	1-1	1-0	0-1	2-1	0-2	1-2	*	2-1
22. Worthing	7-2	2-2	0-2	3-1	1-1	0-2	2-1	2-0	1-7	2-2	0-3	1-0	2-1	4-1	0-4	0-1	3-1	3-0	1-1	4-0	0-1	*

RYMAN (Isthmian) LEAGUE Division One Ten Year Records

	88/9	89/0	90/1	91/2	92/3	93/4	94/5	95/6	96/7	97/8
Abingdon Town	-	-	-	6	6	7	10	16	11	21
Aldershot Town	-	-	-	-	-	-	4	5	7	1
Aveley	-	-	4	21	21	-	-	-	-	-
Barking	-	-	-	12	19	14	15	22	-	-
Barton Rovers	-	-	-	-	-	-	-	18	17	16
Basildon United	21	-	-	-	-	-	-	-	-	-
Basingstoke Town	2	-	-	-	-	-	7	9	2	-
Berkhamsted Town	-	-	-	-	-	18	19	17	19	13
Billericay Town	-	-	-	-	8	6	5	6	5	2
Bishop's Stortford	-	-	-	-	5	1	-	-	-	-
Bognor Regis Town	-	-	-	-	-	12	18	7	6	8
Boreham Wood	11	7	14	4	11	10	1	-	-	-
Bracknell Town	20	-	-	-	-	-	-	-	-	-
Bromley	-	2	-	-	-	-	-	-	-	-
Canvey Island	-	-	-	-	-	-	-	-	20	-
Chalfont St Peter	16	11	11	13	18	20	-	-	-	-
Chertsey Town	-	-	-	-	-	-	3	-	-	11
Chesham United	14	10	1	-	-	-	-	12	1	-
Collier Row	19	-	-	-	-	-	-	-	-	-
Croydon	-	17	17	18	17	22	-	-	18	15
Dorking	-	6	10	11	3	-	22	-	-	-
Dulwich Hamlet	-	-	12	3	-	-	-	-	-	-
Grays Athletic	-	-	-	-	-	-	-	-	-	6
Hampton	17	19	-	-	-	-	-	-	4	3
Harlow Town	-	8	13	17	-	-	-	-	-	-
Heybridge Swifts	-	-	18	19	16	5	16	2	-	-
Hitchin Town	4	4	5	8	1	-	-	-	-	-
Kingsbury Town	8	22	-	-	-	-	-	-	-	-
Leatherhead	12	20	-	-	-	-	-	-	-	9
Lewes	6	15	20	-	20	-	-	-	-	-
Leyton Pennant	-	-	-	14	13	9	14	4	12	10
Maidenhead United	-	-	16	-	12	17	12	14	13	4
Marlow	-	-	-	-	-	-	-	8	21	-
Metropolitan Police	13	9	21	-	-	-	-	-	-	-
Molesey	-	-	8	10	2	-	-	-	10	18
Newbury Town	-	-	-	-	-	-	20	-	-	-
Oxford City	-	-	-	-	-	-	-	1	-	-
Purfleet	-	21	-	-	4	2	-	-	-	-
Romford	-	-	-	-	-	-	-	-	-	7
Ruislip Manor	-	-	-	-	-	19	17	21	-	-
Southwick	15	3	19	-	-	-	-	-	-	-
Staines Town	1	-	-	-	-	11	6	3	-	14
Stevenage Borough	-	-	1	-	-	-	-	-	-	-
Thame United	-	-	-	-	-	-	-	13	14	22
Tooting & Mitcham United	-	12	6	7	7	4	8	19	22	-
Uxbridge	9	18	16	15	15	15	13	10	8	5
Walton & Hersham	7	5	7	9	10	3	-	-	3	-
Wembley	10	16	15	5	9	13	9	20	-	17
Whyteleafe	-	14	9	20	14	16	11	15	9	19
Windsor & Eton	-	-	-	-	-	21	-	-	-	-
Wivenhoe Town	5	1	-	-	-	-	21	-	-	-
Woking	3	2	-	-	-	-	-	-	-	-
Wokingham Town	-	-	-	-	-	-	-	11	-	20
Worthing	18	13	22	-	-	8	2	-	16	12
Yeading	-	-	3	2	-	-	-	-	-	-
No of clubs competing	21	22	21	22	21	22	22	22	22	22

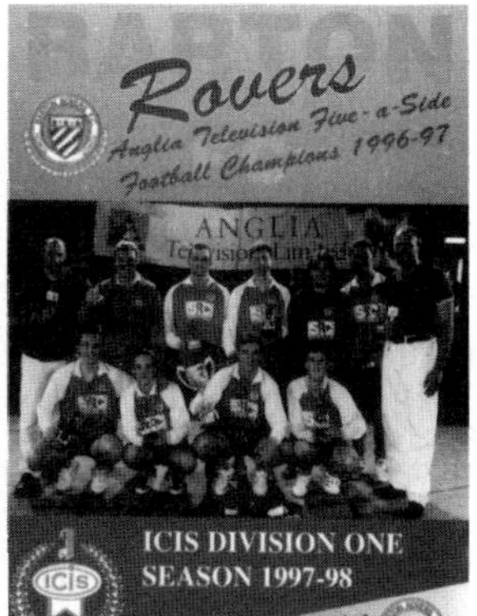

PROGRAMME DETAILS:
Pages: 64 **Price:** £1
Editor: Nick Rhodes
(01582 881865)

BARTON ROVERS

Colours: All royal blue
Change colours: All yellow
Midweek Matchday: Tuesday
Reserves' League: None
Local Press: Luton News, Herald, Beds on Sunday.
Local Radio: Radio Chiltern, Radio Beds, Three Counties Radio.

Sponsors: SRC Contractors
Formed: 1898
Nickname: Rovers

Chairman: Stephen J Harris **President:** P Howarth
Vice Chairman: T Capon **Secretary:** Owen Clark, 108 Manor Road, Barton-le-Clay, Bedford MK45 4NS (01582 882398).
Press Officer: Nick Rhodes (01582 881865)
Manager: Ian Allinson **Asst Manager:** Ken Davidson
Coach: **Physio:** Mick Clark
GROUND Address: Sharpenhoe Road, Barton-le-Clay, Bedford MK45 4SD (01582 882607). **Directions:** M1 Jct 12, from London exit turn right, take 2nd right through Harlington and Sharpenhoe. Ground on right entering village. Four and a half miles from Harlington (BR), 6 miles from Luton (BR), good bus service from Luton.
Capacity: 4,000 **Seats:** 160 **Cover:** 1,120 **Floodlights:** Yes
Clubhouse: Noon-3pm weekends (no football), noon-11pm (matchdays), 7-11pm weekdays. Real ale, hot & cold snacks, pool, darts, gaming machines. **Club Shop:** Yes

PREVIOUS - **Grounds:** Church Pitch 1898-1912; Barton Cutting 1912; Sharpenhoe Rd 12-33; Faldo Rd 33-38; Barton Rec. 46-75. **Leagues:** Luton & Dist. 47-54; Sth Midlands 54-79.

CLUB RECORDS - **Attendance:** 1,900 v Nuneaton, FA Cup 4th Qual. Rd 1976. **Win:** 17-1 v Flitwick Athletic (H), S Midlands Lge Div 1 55-56. **Defeat:** 1-11 v Leighton United (H), S Midlands Lge Prem Div 62-63. **Scorer:** Richard Camp 152, 1989-98. **Appearances:** Bill Goodyear 478, 1982-98. **Fees - Paid:** £1,000 for B Baldry (Hitchin Town, 1980). **Received:** £1,000 for B Baldry (Bishop's Stortford, 1981).

BEST SEASON - **FA Cup:** 1st Round 1980-81, 0-2 v Torquay United (A). **FA Vase:** Runners-up 77-78 (SF 76-77 81-82, QF 75-76 78-79), **FA Trophy:** 1st Qual Rd 96-97, 97-98

HONOURS - Sth Mids Lg(8) 70-73 74-79 (R-up 67-68), Div 1 64-65 (R-up 55-56), Div 2 54-55, Lg Shield 57-58 60-61 68-69, Chal. Tphy 71-72 74-75 77-78 78-79; Beds Snr Cup (5) 71-73 80-82 89-90, R-up (5); Beds Premier Cup 95-96, R-up 81-82 83-84 88-89, Beds Intermediate Cup 53-54; Luton & Dist. Lg Div 3 47-48; North Beds Charity Cup 72-73 74-75 76-77 77-78 79-80 80-81 (R-up 70-71); Isthmian Lg Associate Members Tphy R-up 92-93; Isthmian Div 2 R-Up 94-95.

Players progressing to Football Lge: Kevin Blackwell (Huddersfield, Torquay, Notts Co., Scarborough, Plymouth).

97-98 - Captain: Danny Turner **P.o.Y.:** Gary Turner **Top scorer:** Jamie Pace (22)

Back Row (L-R); Gordon Brown (Mgr), Jamie Pace, Adrian Headley, Frank Thompson, Tony McNally, Gary Turner, Kevin Wheeler, Steve Hunt, Stuart Endacott, Paul Seaman, Mick Clark (Physio), Owen Clark (Sec). Front Row; John Coley, Colin McGill, Richard Wilcox, Danny Turner (Capt), Richard Camp (Asst Mgr), Danny Howell, Scott Turner.

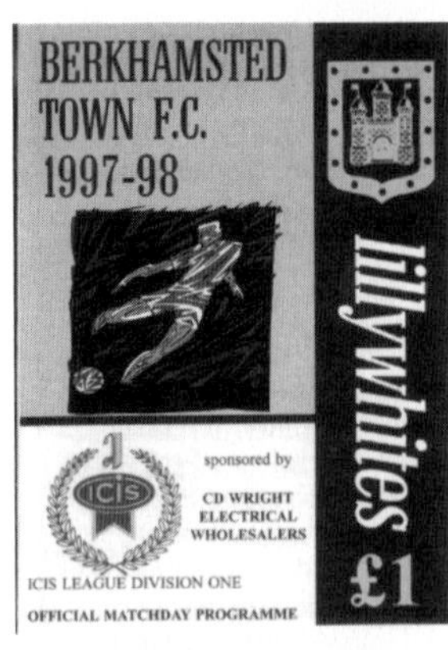

PROGRAMME DETAILS:
Pages: 64 **Price:** £1
Editor: Adrian Marson
(01442 243053)

BERKHAMSTED TOWN

Colours: White/black/black **Sponsors:** C D Wright Elect Wholesalers.
Change Colours: Red/blue **Formed:** 1895
Midweek Matchday: Tuesday **Nickname:** Lilywhites
Reserve Team's League: Essex & Herts Border Combination.
Local Press: Berkhamsted Herald, Berkhamsted Gazette, Dacorum Independent
Local Radio Stations: Chiltern Radio, Mix '96', Three Counties Radio

Chairman: Brian McCarthy. **President:** Dennis Wright
Secretary: Keith Hicks, 24 Holly Drive, Berkhamsted, Herts HP4 2JR (01442 863216 H & B), (04674 30087 Mobile)
Press Officer: Bob Sear (01442 864547 H & B)
Manager: Neil Bartlett **Match Sec:** Lee Whybrow
Coach: Mark Pearson **Physio:** Chris Hewitt

GROUND Address: Broadwater, Lower Kings Road, Berkhamsted, Herts HP4 2AA (01442 862815).
Directions: Adjacent to Berkhamsted station (Euston-Birmingham line). A41 to Berkhamsted town centre traffic lights, left into Lower Kings Road.
Capacity: 2,500 **Seats:** 170 **Cover:** 350 **Floodlights:** Yes
Clubhouse: Open 7 days a week. Pool & darts.
Club Shop: Old programmes and club scarves, ties, boot bags, and baseball hats available. Contact Grant Hastie.

PREVIOUS - **Grounds:** Sunnyside Enclosure 1895-1919, Sports Ground 1919-83. **Leagues:** W Herts & Herts Co. 1895-1922; Spartan 22-51, 66-75; Delphian 51-63; Athenian 63-66, 83-84; London Spartan 75-83.

CLUB RECORDS - **Attendance:** 1,163 v Barnet, FA Cup 3rd Qual. Rd 1987. **Career appearances:** Ray Jeffrey (612)

BEST SEASON - **FA Cup:** 3rd Qual Rd v Barnet 87-88, v Slough 91-92, v Chesham Utd 92-93. **FA Vase:** 4th Rd v Collier Row 84-85. **FA Trophy:** 1st Rd v Kidderminster Harriers 97-98.

HONOURS - Herts Senior Cup 52-53; London Spartan Lge 79-80 (Div 2 26-27); Herts Charity Shield 50-51 (jt) 73-74 79-80 84-85 90-91; Herts Senior County Lge Aubrey Cup 52-53; St Marys Cup(13); Apsley Senior Charity Cup(9); Southern Comb 84-85 (F/lit Cup 84-85).

Players progressing to Football League: Frank Broome, Maurice Cook, Keith Ryan (Wycombe).

97-98 - Captain: Mark Barnard **Top scorer:** Dean Williams (15) **P.o.Y.:** Peter Clifford

Berkhamsted Town FC Photo: Bob Sear

PROGRAMME DETAILS:
Pages: 36 **Price:** £1
Editor: Maurice Warner
Tel: 01243 822325

BOGNOR REGIS TOWN

Colours: White (green trim)/green/white **Founded:** 1883
Change colours: Blue/white/red **Sponsors:** Butlins South Coast World
Midweek home matchday: Tuesday **Nickname:** The Rocks
Reserve's League: None.
Local Press: Bognor Regis Journal & Guardian, Bognor Observer, Brighton Argus, Portsmouth News. **Local Radio:** Radio Sussex, Ocean Sound, Radio Solent, Southern Sound, Spirit FM.

Chairman: Jack Pearce **President:** S Rowlands
Secretary: Brian Pitchford, c/o The Club. 01243 587421 (H)
Comm. Manager: Maurice Warner **Gen. Manager:** Jack Pearce
Manager: Jack Pearce **Press Officer:** Paul Edwards
Asst Manager: Neil Hider **Physio:** Steve Robinson/Clair Eastland
GROUND Address: Nyewood Lane, Bognor Regis PO21 2TY (01243 822325).
Directions: West along seafront from pier, past Aldwick shopping centre, and right into Nyewood Lane.
Capacity: 6,000 **Cover:** 3,800 **Seats:** 243 **Floodlights:** Yes
Clubhouse: Open every night, matchdays and Sunday lunchtimes. Hot food available.
Club Shop: Selling programmes and normal club items.

PREVIOUS - **Leagues:** W Sussex Lge 1896-1926; Brighton, Hove & District Lge 26-27; Sussex County Lge 27-72; Southern Lge 72-81

CLUB RECORDS - **Attendance:** 3,642 v Swansea FA Cup 1st Rd replay, '84. **Goalscorer:** Kevin Clements (206) **Appearances:** Mick Pullen, 967 (20 seasons) **Transfer Fee Paid:** £2,200 Guy Rutherford 95-96 **Transfer Fee Received:** £10,500 for John Crumplin & Geoff Cooper (Brighton & Hove Alb, 87) & Simon Rodger (Crystal Palace 89).

BEST SEASON - **FA Amateur Cup:** 1st Round 71-72 **FA Trophy:** 3rd Round 95-96 **FA Cup:** 2nd Rd 84-85 2-6 v Reading (A), 85-86 1-6 v Gillingham (A), 88-89 0-1 v Cambridge (H), 95-96 0-4 v Peterborough (A). **League clubs beaten:** Swansea 84-85, Exeter 88-89.

HONOURS - Isthmian Lg Div 1 R-up 81-82, (Lg Cup 86-87); Southern Lg R-up 80-81 (Lg Cup R-up 80-81), Merit Cup 80-81; Sussex Lg 48-49 71-72 (R-up 38-39 51-52), Div 2 70-71, Invitation Cup 40-41 49-50 62-63 71-72; Brighton Lg R-up 26-27; W Sussex Lg(5) 20-25 (R-up 1896-97, 25-26), Jnr Lg 10-11 13-14; Southern Co's Comb 78-79; Sussex Snr Cup(9) 54-56 79-84 86-87 94-95 (R-up 51-52 58-59 84-85); Sussex Prof. Cup 73-74, Sussex RUR Cup 71-72; Sussex I'mediate Cup 52-53, Littlehampton Hosp. Cup 29-30 33-34; Bognor Charity Cup(8) 28-29 30-31 32-33 37-38 47-48 58-59 71-73; Gosport War Mem. Cup(2) 81-83 (R-up 86-87); Snr Midweek F'lit Cup R-up 74-75.

Players progressing to Football League: E Randall (Chelsea 50), J Standing (Brighton 61), A Woon (Brentford 72), J Crumplin & G Cooper (Brighton 87), Simon Rodger (C Palace 89).
97-98 - Captain: M Birmingham **P.o.Y.:** Gary Young **Top Scorer:** Adie Miles

Bognor's Micky Birmingham about to fire a shot at Leatherhead's goal Photo: Graham Cotterill

BRAINTREE TOWN

Colours: Yellow & blue stripes/blue/yellow **Sponsors:** Asset Paper
Change colours: White/navy **Founded:** 1898
Midweek matches: Tuesday **Nickname:** The Iron
Reserves' Lg: Essex/Herts Border Comb.
Local Radio: BBC Essex (103.5 fm), Essex Radio (102.6 fm).

PROGRAMME DETAILS:
Pages: 40 **Price:** £1
Editor: David Gore
01376 330976

Chairman: George Rosling **Vice Chairman:** Ivan Kibble
President: Ron Webb **Secretary:** T A Woodley, 19a Bailey Bridge Rd., Braintree, Essex CM7 5TT (01376 326234).
Press Officer: Ron Webb (01376 325338)
Manager: Tony Hall **Ass.Mans.:** Phil Boyland **Physio:** Tony Last

GROUND Address: Cressing Road Stadium, Clockhouse Way, Braintree, Essex (01376 345617). **Directions:** From Braintree by-pass, turn into Braintree at the McDonalds r'bout, follow signs for East Braintree Ind. Est. - floodlights on left 1/2 mile into town opp. Orange Tree Pub. Entrance next left in Clockhouse Way, then left again. 1 mile from Braintree & Bocking (BR). Bus 353 from Witham or town centre stops near ground. Town centre 20 mins walk.
Capacity: 4,000 **Cover:** 1,500 **Seats:** 248 **Floodlights:** Yes
Clubhouse: Open evenings 7.30-11, Sunday 12-3, Saturday matchday 12.00-11.00. Full bar facilites.
Club Shop: Yes, contact Jon Weaver 01376 347920

PREVIOUS - Leagues: North Essex 1898-1925; Essex & Suffolk Border 25-28 55-64; Spartan 28-35; Eastern Co's 35-37 38-39 52-55 70-91; Essex Co. 37-38; London 45-52; Gtr London 64-66; Metropolitan 66-70; Southern 91-96. **Names:** Manor Works 1898-1921; Crittall Ath. 21-68; Braintree & Crittall Ath. 68-81; Braintree FC 81-82. **Grounds:** The Fair Field 1898-1903; Spaldings Meadow, Panfield Lane 03-23.

CLUB RECORDS - Attendance: 4,000 v Spurs, charity challenge match, May 1952. **Career Goalscorer:** Chris Guy 211, 63-90. **Seasonal Record Scorer:** Gary Bennett 57, 97-98. **Career Appearances:** Paul Young 524, 66-77 **Fee Paid:** £2,000 for Shane Bailey (Sudbury Town) **Fee Received:** £10,000 Matt Metcalf (Brentford 93) & John Cheesewright (Colchester 93) **Win** 15-3 v Hopes (Birmingham Friendly 39), 12-0 v Thetford Tn (Eastern Lge 35-36) **Defeat** 0-14 v Chelmsford City A (Nth Essex Lge 23)

BEST SEASON - FA Cup: 4th Qual. Rd 69-70 85-86 94-95 97-98

HONOURS - Isthmian Lge Div 2 R-up 97-98, Div 3 R-up 96-97; Guardian Insurance Cup R-up 96-97; Eastern Counties Lg 36-37 83-84 84-85 (R-up 86-87 87-88 88-89 90-91), Lg Cup 87-88 (R-up 35-36 74-75); Essex County Lg R-up 37-38; London Lg (East) R-up 45-46, Lg Cup 47-48(joint) 48-49 51-52 (R-up 49-50); Metropolitan Lg Cup 69-70; Essex Elizabethan Tphy R-up 68-69; E. Anglian Cup 46-47 68-69 95-96; Essex Sen. Tphy 86-87 (R-up 90-91); Essex & Suffolk Border Lg 59-60 84-85 (Lg Cup 59-60); Nth Essex Lg 05-06 10-11 11-12; Essex Sen Cup 95-96 R-up 96-97; Essex Jnr Cup R-up 04-05 05-06 22-23; RAFA Cup 56-57; Gtr Lon. Ben. Cup 65-66; Worthington Evans Cup (3) R-up (4); Eastern F'lit Cup 85-86 96-97 (R-up 94-95 97-98); Anglian F'lit Lg 69-70; Jan Havanaar Inter. Tour. 94-95 (R-up 92-93).

Players progressing to Football League: J Dick (West Ham 53), S Wright (Wrexham 83), J Cheesewright (Birmingham C. 91, Colchester 94), G Bennett, M Metcalf (Brentford 93), R Reinhelt (Gillingham 93), M de Souza (Birmingham C, Wycombe W), G Culling (Colchester U 94).

97-98 - Captain : Gary Collins **Top scorer:** Gary Bennett (57) **P.o.Y.:** Gary Bennett

Back Row (L-R); George Rosling (Chr), Phil Boyland (Asst Mgr), Trevor Gunn, Shane Bailey, Russell Tanner, Tony Cherry, Neil Orice, Lee Hunter, Paul Knights, Tony Hall (Mgr), Paul Catley. Front Row; Bobby Mayes, Gary Bennett, Mark Farthing, John Bishop, Nicky Simpson, Nicky Smith, Gary Collins. Photo: Jon Weaver

CANVEY ISLAND

Colours: Yellow/white/white **Formed:** 1926
Change colours: White/yellow/yellow **Nickname:** Gulls
Midweek matchday: Tuesday **Sponsors:** Kings The Nightclub
Reserves' League: Essex & Herts Border Comb.
Local Press: Evening Echo
Local Radio: Essex FM, BBC Essex

PROGRAMME DETAILS:
Pages: 32 **Price:** £1
Editor: Rod Hall
(01268 697348)

Chairman: Ray Cross, 95 Lakeside Path, Canvey Island, Essex SS8 5PD. 01268 684357 (H)
Secretary: Mrs Frances Roche, 56 Harvest Road, Canvey Island SS8 9RP. 01268 698586 (H/Fax)
Manager: Jeff King. 01268 511555 (B) 0850 654321 (Mobile)
Press Officer: Tony Roche (01268 698586)
Asst Manager: Glenn Pennyfather **Physio:** Harry Johnson

GROUND Address: Park Lane, Canvey Island, Essex SS8 7PX (01268 682991).
Directions: A130 from A13 or A127 at Sadlers Farm roundabout, 1 mile right through town centre, first on right past old bus garage. Bus 3 or 151 from Benfleet (BR) to stop after Admiral Jellicoe (PH).
Seats: 165 **Cover:** 250 **Capacity:** 2,500**Floodlights:** Yes
Clubhouse: Open Tues, Thurs & Sats. Full licence. Food avaiable
Club Shop: Yes, open matchdays. Sellind programmes, badges, shirts etc. Contact Mrs J Edwards.

PREVIOUS - **Leagues:** Southend & Dist.; Thurrock & Thameside Comb.; Parthenon; Metropolitan; Gtr London 64-71; Essex Senior. **Grounds:** None. **Names:** None

CLUB RECORDS - **Attendance:** 3,250 v Tiverton, FA Vase SF 27/3/93. **Win:** 7-1 v Bedford. **Defeat:** 7-0 v Halstead. **Career Appearances:** Steve Price (407). **Career Goalscorer:** Andy Jones (200). **Transfer fee received:** £3,000 for Ian Durrant from Grays Athletic. **Transfer fee paid:** £ 3,500 for Steve Ward to Grays Athletic 96.

BEST SEASON - **FA Cup:** 1st Rd v Brighton (2-2) (replay 1-4) 95-96. **FA Vase:** Semi-final v Tiverton 27/3/93. **FA Trophy:** Prelimm Round v Heybridge S. .gap 2

HONOURS - ICIS Lge - Div 2 95-96, 97-98, Div 3 R-up 94-95; Carlton Trophy 95-96; Essex Sen Lg 86-87 92-93 (Lg Cup 79-80 92-93), Trophy R-up 93-94; Harry Fisher Mem. Tphy 93-94; Essex Thameside Trophy 93-94; Parthenon Lge Cup 58-59; Metropolian Lge 67-68 68-69, Cup 67-68 68-69; Thameside 95-96 97-98; Res. Lge 95-96, Cup 95-96

Players progressing to Football League: Peter Taylor (Spurs, Crystal Palace & England), Gary Heale (Luton Reading)

97-98 - Captain: Alan Brett **P.o.Y.:** Steve Porter **Top scorer:** Andy Jones

Canvey Island's Simon Liddle in a tussle with Paul Boxhall of Burgess Hill in the FA Vase 2nd Rd.

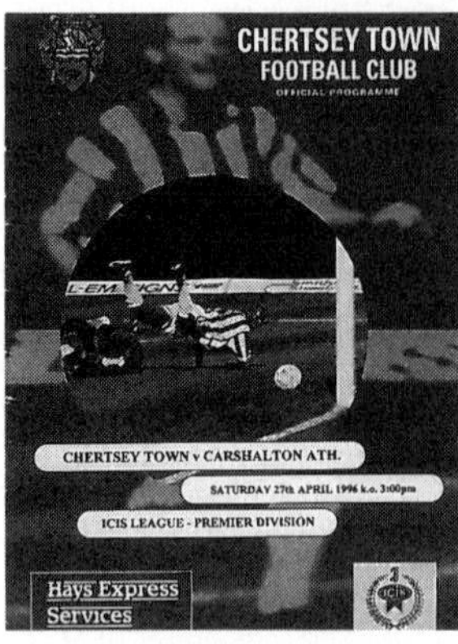

PROGRAMME DETAILS:
Pages: 36 **Price:** £1
Editor: Chris Gay
(01276 20745)

CHERTSEY TOWN

Colours: Blue & white stripes/white/white
Change colours: All red.
Midweek Matchday: Tuesday
Local Press: Surrey Herald.
Local Radio: BBC Southern Counties, County Sound.

Formed: 1890
Sponsors: TBA.
Nickname: Curfews

Chairman: Alan McKane
President: Cllr Chris Norman
Vice Chairman: Nick Keel
Press Officer/Secretary: Chris Gay, 23 Richmond Close, Frimley, Camberley, Surrey GU16 5NR (01276 20745).
Manager: Colin Payne.
Physio: Julia Richards
Asst Manager: Roger Goodhind
Coach: Steve Stairs
Commercial Manager:

GROUND Address: Alwyns Lane, Chertsey, Surrey KT16 9DW (01932 561774).
Directions: Alwyns Lane is off Windsor Street at north end of shopping centre. 10 mins walk from Chertsey (BR). London Country bus.
Capacity: 3,000 **Seats:** 250 **Cover:**1000 **Floodlights:** Yes
Clubhouse: Open weekday evenings and weekend lunchtimes.
Club Shop: Open matchdays, selling club & football souvenirs. Contact Steve Maughan.

PREVIOUS - **Leagues:** West Surrey (pre-1899); Surrey Jnr 1899-1920; Surrey Intermediate 20-46; Surrey Snr 46-63; Metropolitan 63-66; Gtr London 66-67; Spartan 67-75; London Spartan 75-76; Athenian 76-84; Isthmian 84-85; Combined Counties 85-86. **Grounds:** The Grange (pre-World War 1), The Hollows (pre-1929).

CLUB RECORDS - **Attendance:** 2,150 v Aldershot, Isthmian Lge Division Two 4/12/93. **Goalscorer:** Alan Brown 54, 1962-63. **Win:** 10-1 v Clapton (H), Isthmian Lge Division Three, 91-92. **Defeat:** 1-12 v Bromley (H), FA Cup Preliminary Rd, 82-83. **Transfer fee received:** £56,500. **Paid:** Nil

BEST SEASON - **FA Vase:** Quarter Final 87-88 91-92. **FA Cup:** 3rd Qualifying Rd 92-93 (lost 1-3 at home to Kingstonian). **FA Trophy:** 2nd Qual Rd 95-96. **FA Amateur Cup:** 3rd Qual Rd 61-62.

HONOURS - Isthmian Lge Cup 94-95 (Associate Members Trophy 94-95), Div 2 R-up 94-95, Div 3 R-up 91-92; Surrey Snr Lge 59-60 61-62 62-63 (Lge Cup 59-60 61-62); Combined Co's Lge R-up 85-86 (Concours Tphy 85-86); Surrey Snr Cup R-up 85-86; Spartan Lge & Lge Cup R-up 74-75.

Players progressing to Football League: Rachid Harkouk (Crystal Palace, Queens Park Rangers & Notts County), Peter Cawley (Wimbledon 1987), Lee Charles (Queens Park Rangers 1995).

97-98 - Captain: Steve Stairs **Top scorer:** Joe Nartey **P.o.Y.:** Alan Hamlet/Craig Ravencroft

Chertsey Town

PROGRAMME DETAILS:
Pages: 28 **Price:** 70p
Editor: Russell Chandler
(0181 406 4573 H)

CROYDON

Colours: Sky & navy quarters/navy & sky/navy & sky **Sponsors:** Philips.
Change colours: All red **Formed:** 1953
Midweek home matchday: Monday **Nickname:**
Reserve Team's League: Suburban.
Local Press: Croydon - Advertiser, Midweek Post, Times, Guardian.

Chairman: Ken Jarvie
Secretary: Mrs Jacqueline Jarvie, 2 Spa Close, London SE25 6DS. 0181 653 7250 (H), 0181 654 8555 (B).
Press Officer: Russell Chandler, 26 Dartnell Road, Croydon, Surrey. CR0 6JA. 0181 406 4573 (H) 0181 654 8555 (B).
Manager: Ken Jarvie **Match Sec:** Gordon Tennant
Coach: Dave Ndjie **Physio:** Stewart Wilbey/Bobby Childs

GROUND Address: Croydon Sports Arena, Albert Road, South Norwood, London. SE25 4QL 0181 654 3462/8555. **Directions:** Train to East Croydon or Norwood Junction, then bus 12 to either Belmont or Dundee Road. Walk down either - ground at bottom. 5 mins walk from Woodside (BR).
Capacity: 8,000 **Cover:** 450 **Seats:** 450 **Floodlights:** Yes
Clubhouse: Open every evening and lunchtime, holds 250, snacks available. Dancing, discos, bingo. Lounge bar available for private hire.
Club Shop: Yes

PREVIOUS - Leagues: Surrey Senior 53-63; Spartan 63-64; Athenian 64-74. **Name:** Croydon Amateurs 1953-74.

CLUB RECORDS **Attendance:** 1,450 v Wycombe, FA Cup 4th Qualifying Rd 1975.
Career appearances: Alec Jackson (400+).
Transfer fee paid: Steve Brown
Transfer fee received: Peter Evans (to Sutton Utd)

BEST SEASON - **FA Cup:** 2nd Round replay 79-80 (2-3 v Millwall after 1-1)
FA Trophy: 2nd Round 81-82, 82-83 **FA Amateur Cup:** 3rd round 71-72

HONOURS: Isthmian Lg Div 2 R-up 75-76 95-96, Surrey Snr Cup 81-82 (R-up 76-77), Surrey Prem Cup 86-87, Spartan Lg 63-64, Athenian Lg R-up 71-72 (Div 2 65-66 (R-up 70-71)), Surrey Snr Lg R-up 56-57 60-61 62-63 (Lg Cup 60-61, Charity Cup 53-54 62-63, Res Section 57-58), London Senior Cup R-up 78-79, Suburban Lg South 86-87 (Lg Cup(2)), Southern Yth Lg 85-86 (Lg Cup 85-86 87-88), Berger Yth Cup 78-79.

Players progressing to Football League: Alan Barnett (Plymouth 1955), Peter Bonetti (Chelsea), Leroy Ambrose (Charlton 1979), Steve Milton (Fulham - via Whyteleafe), Murray Jones (Crystal & Exeter - via Carshalton).

Croydon

PROGRAMME DETAILS:
Pages: 48 **Price:** £1
Editor: Jeremy Mason
(01375 376428)

GRAYS ATHLETIC

Colours: Royal & white **Formed:** 1890
Change colours: Red/white **Nickname:** The Blues
Midweek matchday: Tuesday
Local Press: Thurrock Gazette
Local Radio: BBC Essex, Radio Essex.

Chairman: Frank Harris **Secretary:** Jeff Saxton, 216 Thundersley Park Road, South Benfleet, Essex SS7 1HP (01268 756964).
Manager: Chris Snowsill **Asst Man.:** Mark Shelton
Physio: David Guthrie **Press Officer:** Gordon Norman (014024 51733)

GROUND Address: Recreation Ground, Bridge Road, Grays RM17 6BZ (01375 391649). **Directions:** Seven minutes walk from Grays station - turn right round one way system, right into Clarence Road, and at end into Bridge Road. Bus No. 370. By road - A13 towards Southend from London, take Grays exit and follow signs to town centre, keep left on one-way system, continue up hill for about half a mile, turn right into Bridge Road, ground half mile on right.
Capacity: 4,500 **Cover:** 1,200 **Seats:** 300 **Floodlights:** Yes
Clubhouse: Bar, pool, darts, bar snacks available. Indoor sports hall, **Stewardess:** Sue Riley (01375 377753)
Club Shop: Selling 'The First Hundred Years', sweaters, T-shirts, replica shirts, scarves, ties, etc. Contact Bill Grove & Dave Smith, 01375 391649
Sponsors: Roehlig & Co (UK) Ltd; Harris Commercials.

PREVIOUS - Leagues: Athenian 12-14, 58-83; London 14-24, 26-39; Kent 24-26; Corinthian 45-58.
CLUB RECORDS - Attendance: 9,500 v Chelmsford City, FA Cup Fourth Qualifying Round 1959. **Win:** 12-0 v Tooting (H) London Lge 24/2/23. **Defeat:** 0-12 v Enfield (A) Athenian Lge 20/4/63. **Goalscorer:** Harry Brand 269 (1944-52) **Appearances:** Phil Sammons, 673. 1982-97. **Fee Paid:** For Ian Durant (Canvey Island 85) **Fee Received:** Undisclosed for Tony Witter (C. Palace) and Dwight Marshall (Plymouth 1991).
BEST SEASON - FA Cup: 1st Rd 51-52 88-89. **FA Trophy:** 3rd Rd 92-93. **FA Amateur Cup:** 3rd Rd 63-64.
HONOURS - Isthmian Div 1 R-up 87-88 (Div 2 Sth 84-85, Lg Cup 91-92); Athenian Lg R-up 82-83, Reserve Section R-up 58-59 (Cup R-up 59-60); Corinthian Lg 45-46 (R-up 51-52 54-55 56-57), Lg Cup(2) 45-47, Mem. Shield(4) 45-47 77-78 79-80; Essex Snr Cup 4 (R-up 6); East Anglian Cup 44-45 (R-up 43-44 54-55); Essex Thameside Tphy 6 (R-up 7); Essex Elizabeth Trophy 76-77 (R-up 65-66); Claridge Tphy 87-88 88-89; Mithras Cup 79-80; Essex Int Cup(3) 56-57 58-60 (Jun Cup 19-20 (R-up 58-59); Essex & Herts Border Comb. East 87-88 (Ancillary Cup 78-79, Comb Cup 82-83); Fred Budden Tphy 86-87; Hornchurch Charity Cup 78-79 86-87; Neale Tphy 50-51; Ford Rate Tphy 83-84 85-86 87-88 (R-up 84-85 86-87); Stan Veness Memorial Trophy (8) 87-96.
Players progressing to Football League: J Jordan (Spurs 47), R Kemp (Reading 49), B Silkman & T Banfield (Orient), G O'Reilly (Spurs), W Entwhistle (Bury 83), M Welch (Wimbledon 84), T Witter (C Palace 90), D Marshall (Plymouth 91), M Lawrence (Wycombe Wand 96-97)
97-98 - Captain: Steve Mosley **P.o.Y.:** Jason Walker **Top scorer:** Joe Odegbami

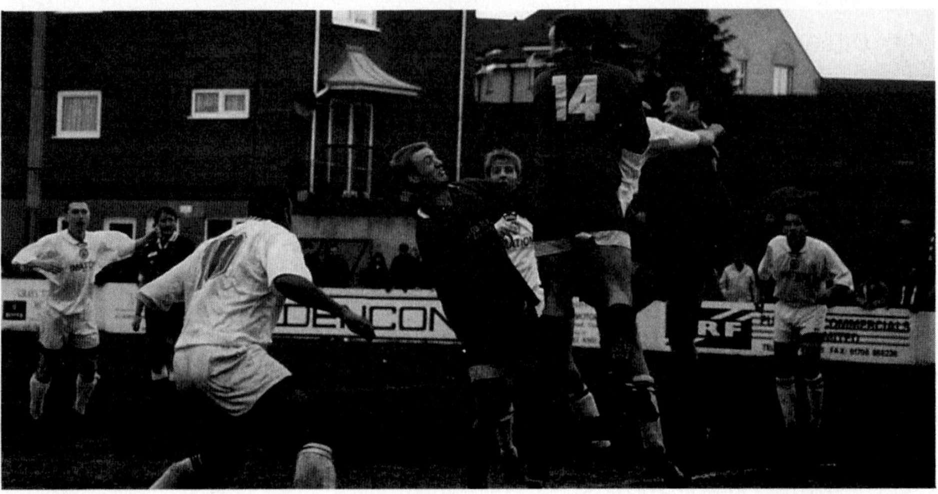

Gray's Paul Green heads clear a corner from Billericay Photo: Alan Coomes

PROGRAMME DETAILS:
Pages: 48 **Price:** £1
Editor: Barry Swain
Tel: 01462 455096

HITCHIN TOWN

Colours: Yellow/green/green
Sponsors:
Change colours: Black & white/black/black
Formed: 1865
Midweek matchday: Tuesday
Nickname: The Canaries
Reserves League: Suburban
Clubcall Line: 0930 555 817
Local Press: Hitchin Gazette/Hitchin Comet, Herts on Sunday
Local Radio: Chiltern, Three Counties

Chairman: Terry Barratt
Secretary: Roger Austin, 4 Beech Hill, Letchworth, Herts SG6 4ED (01462 625043)
Fixture Sec:
Press Officer: Bary Swain (01462 455096).
Manager: Andy Melvin **Physio:** Peter Prince.
Asst Mgr: Robbie O'Keefe **Coach:** Tony Martin
GROUND Address: Top Field, Fishponds Road, Hitchin SG5 1NU (01462 459028-matchdays only).
Directions: On A505 near town centre opposite large green. 1 mile from Hitchin (BR).
Capacity: 3,800 **Cover:** 1,250 **Seats:** 400 **Floodlights:** Yes
Clubhouse: (01462 434483). Members bar, Function Hall (hireable). Open every day. Steward: Eamonn Watson/ Nigel Collins
Club Shop: Yes, contact Medwyn Williams

PREVIOUS - **Leagues:** Spartan 28-39; Hert & Middx 39-45; Athenian 39,45-63.

CLUB RECORDS - **Attendance:** 7,878 v Wycombe Wanderers, FA Amateur Cup 3rd Rd 18/2/56. **Win:** Spartan Lge 29-30 13-0 v Cowley, 13-0 v RAF. **Defeat** (Isthmian Lge): 0-10 v Kingstonian (A) 65-66, v Slough T. (A) 79-80. **Career** (Isthmian Lge) **appearances:** Paul Giggle 950+ 67-88. **Career** (Isthmian Lge) **goals:** Paul Giggle, 129. **Transfer fee paid:** £2,000 for Ray Seeking (Potton United, July 1989). **Transfer fee received:** Undisclosed

BEST SEASON - **FA Trophy:** 3rd Round (rep) 76-77. **FA Amateur Cup:** Semi Final 60-61, 62-63
FA Cup: 2nd Rd - v Swindon 1-3 (A) 76-77, v Boston Utd, 0-1 (A) 73-74, v Wycombe Wand. 0-5 (H) 94-95, v Gillingham lost 0-3 (A) 95-96

HONOURS - Isthmian Lge R-up 68-69 (Div 1 92-93); Spartan Lge 34-35; AFA Sen Cup 30-31; Herts Snr Cup (19-record); London Sen Cup 69-70 (R-up 72-73); E Anglian Cup 72-73; Herts Charity Cup(16), Herts I'mediate Cup(8); Woolwich Trophy 82-83; Televised Sport International Cup 88-89 90-91; Southern Comb. Senior Floodlit Cup 90-91.

Players progressing to Football League: R Smith (Millwall & England), L Garwood (Spurs 46), C J Walker, W Odell, S Foss, R Stevens, T Clarke, G Goodyear, L Harwood, P Burridge, R Kitchener (Chelsea 54), D Bumstead, M Dixon, D Pacey (Luton 56), M Dixon & B Whitby (Luton 57), K Abiss (Brighton 57), D Hille, G Ley, R Morton, L Payne (Newcastle & Reading), M Small (Brighton), R Nugent (Barnet), Chris McMenamin (Coventry 96).

97-98 Captain: **P.o.Y.:** **Top scorer:**

Back Row (L-R); A Melvin (Mgr), S Turner, D Mosley (Asst Mgr), T Allpress, A Parker, G Williams, A Palfreyman, S Atkinson, A Barr, I Scott, N Sopowski (Asst Physio), B Dellar, J Woodsford, D Swaile, P Prince (Physio). Front Row; I Jones, C Williams, A Clark, R Hall, N Grime, M Burke, J Bone. Photo: Garry Letts

LEATHERHEAD FOOTBALL CLUB

MATCHDAY PROGRAMME

1997-98

ICIS FOOTBALL LEAGUE DIVISION 1

PROGRAMME DETAILS:
Pages: 24 **Price:** £1
Editor: Keith Wenham
(01689 870316)

LEATHERHEAD

Colours: Green and White. **Sponsors:** TBA
Change colours: Blue & white **Founded:** 1946
Midweek Matchday: Tuesday **Nickname:** Tanners
Reserves' League: Suburban (South)
Local Press: Leatherhead Advertiser, Surrey Advertiser
Local Radio: County Sound.

Chairman: David Zackheim **President:** Gerald Darby
Chief Executive: Bob Davies **General Manager:** Roland Head
Secretary: Gerald Darby, Ranmore, Harriots Lane, Ashtead, Surrey, KT21 2QG
Press Officer/Comm. Director: Keith Wenham
Manager: Gary Richards **Asst. Manager:** Terry Quick
Coach: Bob Davies **Physio:** Steve Young

GROUND Address: Fetcham Grove, Guildford Rd, Leatherhead, Surrey KT22 9AS (01372 360151, Fax 01372 362705)
Directions: M25 jct 9 to Leatherhead; follow signs to Leisure Centre, ground adjacent. Half mile from Leatherhead (BR).
London Country Buses 479 and 408 - ground opposite bus garage.
Capacity: 3,400 **Seats:** 200 **Cover:** 445 **Floodlights:** Yes
Clubhouse: (01372 360151) Licensed bar open noon - 11pm matchdays. Full catering for 98-99 season. **Club Shop:** Yes. 01372 362705

PREVIOUS - **Leagues:** Surrey Snr 46-50; Metropolitan 50-51; Delphian 51-58; Corinthian 58-63; Athenian 63-72. **Names:** None **Grounds:** None.

CLUB RECORDS - **Attendance::** 5,500 v Wimbledon, 1976. **Win:** 13-1 v Leyland Motors 46-47 Surrey Sen Lge. **Defeat:** 1-11 v Sutton United.
Career goalscorer: Steve Lunn 96-97 (46). **Career appearances:** P Caswell.
Fee paid: £1,500 to Croydon (B Salkeld). **Fee received:** £1,500 from Croydon (B Salkeld)

BEST SEASON - **FA Amateur Cup:** Semi finalists 70-71 73-74. **FA Trophy:** R-up 77-78 **FA Cup:** 4th Round 74-75, 2-3 v Leicester C.(A). (2nd Rd 75-76 76-77 78-79, 1st Rd 77-78 80-81). **League clubs defeated:** Colchester, Brighton 74-75, Cambridge Utd 75-76, Northampton 76-77.

HONOURS: Isthmian Lg Cup 77-78; Corinthian Lg 62-63; Athenian Ld Div 1 63-64; Surrey Snr Cup 68-69 (R-up 64-65 66-67 74-75 78-79); Surrey Snr Lg 46-47 47-48 48-49 49-50 (Lg Cup 49-50), Snr Shield 68-69, Charity Cup 46-47 49-50); East Surrey Charity Cup 68-69 (R-up 67-68); London Snr Cup R-up 74-75 77-78; Surrey Inter Cup 89-90; Southern Comb. Cup 89-90.

Players progressing to Football League: Chris Kelly (Millwall), B Friend (Fulham), L Harwood (Port Vale), John Humphrey (Millwall).

97-98 - Captain: **Top Scorer:** Steve Lunn **P.o.Y.:** Scott Tarr

Players: Back Row (L-R); Scott Tarr, David Smith, Alex O'Brien, Tony Webb, Ray Arnett, Elliott Davidson, Ben Papa, Ross Edwards. FRont Row; Laurence Head, Alan Whiter, Steve Lunn, Gani Ahmet, Toby South, Nigel Webb, Noel Frankum.

Leyton Pennant
FOOTBALL CLUB
1997 - 1998
SEASON
THE ICIS FOOTBALL LEAGUE
£1
Official Match Day Programme

PROGRAMME DETAILS:
Pages: 32 **Price:** £1
Editor: John Stacey
(0181 527 8116)

LEYTON PENNANT

Colours: White/navy/navy **Sponsors:** Maplin Electronics
Change colours: All navy **Formed:** 1868
Midweek home matchday: Tuesday **Nickname:** Lilywhites
Reserves' League: Essex & Herts Border Comb.
Local Press: Waltham Forest Guardian, Hackney Gazette
Local Radio: LBC.

Chairman: Dave Crabb **Vice-Chairman:** Tom Kelly
President: George Cross **Secretary:** Andy Perkins, 4 Chestnut Drive, Wanstead, London E11 2TA, (0181 530 4551, Webb site: http://www.btinternet.com/~andy.perkins)
Gen. Manager: Kevin Moran **Press Officer:** Andy Perkins
Team Manager/Coach: Trevor Harvey **Physio:** Christie Keene

GROUND Address: Wadham Lodge Sports Ground, Kitchener Road, Walthamstow, London. E17 4JP (0181 527 2444)
Directions: North Circular Road to Crooked Billet,turn into Chingford Road,then into Brookscroft Road,first on left.Walthamstow Central (Victoria Line tube) one mile away,then buses W21 or 256.
Capacity: 2,000 **Cover:** 600 **Seats:** 200 **Floodlights:** Yes
Clubhouse: (0181 527 2444). Open 11am-11pm Mon-Sat, 12-3 & 7-10.30pm Sun. No hot food. Hot snacks from tea bar on matchdays.
Club Shop: Sells programmes, pennants, scarves, badges etc. Contact Ian Ansell c/o the club.

PREVIOUS - **Leagues:** Leyton & District Alliance, South Essex, Southern 05-11, London 20-26, Athenian 27-82, Spartan Lge as Walthamstow Pennant. **Name:** Leyton FC, Leyton Wingate (75-92), Walthamstow Pennant (64-92). **Grounds:** Brisbane Rd (Home of Leyton Orient), Hare & Hounds Leabridge Road.

CLUB RECORDS - **Attendance:** 676 v Aldershot Icis Lge 10/2/96, *(100,000 saw Leyton v Walthamstow Avenue, FA Amateur Cup final at Wembley, April 26th 1952).* **Win:** 10-2 v Horsham 82. **Transfer fee paid:** £200 for Dwight Marshall (Hampton). **Defeat:** 1-11 v Barnet 46. **Transfer fee received:** £6,000 for T Williams (Redbridge Forest). **Career goalscorer:** Steve Lane 118. **Career appearances:** Steve Hamberger 387.

BEST SEASON - **FA Amateur Cup:** Winners 26-27 27-28, R-up x6. **FA Vase:** Sixth Rd 83-84. **FA Trophy:** 3rd Rd 86-87. **FA Cup:** 3rd Rd 09-10. **League clubs defeated:** None

HONOURS - Isthmian Lg Div 1 R-up 86-87 (Div 2 North 84-85); Essex Snr Tphy R-up 84-85; Thorn EMI National Floodlight Cup 84-85; London Senior Cup 03-04 (R-up 33-34 37-38 45-46); London Charity Cup 34-35 36-37 (R-up 32-33 46-47 66-67 70-71); London Lg 23-24 24-25 25-26 (R-up 26-27), Lg Cup 56-57; Athenian Lg 28-29 65-66 66-67 76-77 81-82 (R-up 45-46 64-65 77-78), Div 2 Cup R-up 69-70; London Challenge Cup R-up 09-10 27-28 95-96; East Anglian Cup R-up 45-46 72-73; Essex Thameside Trophy 64-65 66-67 81-82 (R-up 63-64); Leyton & Dist. All 1892-93 94-95; Eastern Floodlight Comp 97-98.

Players progressing to Football League: C Buchan (Sunderland) 10, Casey (Chelsea) 52, K Facey (Orient 52), M Costello (Aldershot 56), D Clark (Orient 61).

97-98 - Captain: Paul Salmon **P.o.Y.:** Andy Silk **Top scorer:** Che Stadhart/Billy Cove

Back Row (L-R); Kevin Moran (Co Mgr), Colin Halpin, Jason Geraghty, Stuart McLean, Kevin Riley, Tom Kelly (Vice Chr), Paul Salmon, Ian Brooks, Phil Lovell, Trevor Harvey (Co Mgr). Front Row; Billy Cove, Cyril Baffour, Andy Silk, John Lowe, Billy Read, Che Stadhart, Sid Nelson, Mark Salmon.

PROGRAMME DETAILS:
Pages: 36 **Price:** £1
Editor: J Swan/R Jackson
Tel: 01344 723750

MAIDENHEAD UNITED

Colours: Black & white stripes/black/black **Formed:** 1870
Change colours: Red/white/white **Nickname:** Magpies
Midweek matchday: Tuesday **Sponsors:** Trademark Windows
Reserve League: Suburban
Local Press: Maidenhead Advertiser, Reading Evening Post, Slough Observer
Local Radio: 2-Ten FM, Star FM, Thames Valley FM

Chairman: Roger Coombs **Vice Chairman:** Jon Swan
Secretary: Ken Chandler, c/o Maidenhead United
Manager: Alan Devonshire **Asst. Mgr./Coach:** Carl Taylor
Physio: Jon Urry **Press Off.:** Jon Swan (01628 473411)

GROUND Address: York Road, Maidenhead, Berks SL6 1SQ (01628 624739/636314)
Directions: From Maidenhead BR station proceed eastwards down Bell St - grd 300yds. Ground in Town Centre five minutes from M4
Capacity: 3,500 **Cover:** 1,200 **Seats:** 400 **Floodlights:** Yes
Clubhouse: Open evenings & matchdays. Some hot food.
Club Shop: Yes, wide range of programmes and club souvenirs. Contact Mark Smith (01753 854674).

PREVIOUS - **Leagues:** Southern 1894-1902; West Berks 02-04; Grt West Sub 04-22; Spartan 22-39; Grt West Comb 39-45; Corinthian 45-63; Athenian 63-73. **Names:** Maidenhead FC, Maidenhead Norfolkians. **Grounds:** None

CLUB RECORDS - **Attendance:** 7,920 v Southall, FA Amat Cup Q/F 7/3/36. **Career goalscorer:** George Copas 270, 1924-35. **Season's goalscorer:** Jack Palethorpe 66, 1929-30. **Career appearances:** Bert Randall 532, 1950-64. **Win:** 14-1 v Buckingham Town (H), FA Amat. Cup 6/9/52. **Defeat:** 0-14 v Chesham United (A), Spartan Lge 31/3/23. **Transfer fee paid:** Undisclosed. **Transfer fee received:** £5,000 from Norwich for Alan Cordice, 79.

BEST SEASON - **FA Cup:** Qtr Finals 1873-74 74-75 75-76 **FA Trophy:** 3rd Qual Rd **FA Amateur Cup:** Semi Final 35-36

HONOURS - Isthmian Lg Div 2 Sth R-up 90-91, Full Members Cup 96-97; Spartan Lg(3) (R-up [2]); Corinthian Lg 57-58 60-61 61-62 (R-up 58-59 59-60), Mem. Shield 56-57 61-62, R-up (4), Neale Cup 48-49 57-58 60-61; Gt Western Suburban Lg 19-20 (R-up 20-21); Berks & Bucks Snr Cup(17), Berks & Bucks Benev. Cup(6) (R-up [2]); Mithras Cup R-up (4); Southern Comb. Cup R-up 81-82; Sub Lge West 97-98; Allied Counties Champ 97-98.

Players progressing to Football League: A Cordice (Norwich 79), P Priddy (Brentford 72), D Kemp (Plymouth/Portsmouth/C Palace), L Sanchez (Reading, Wimbledon), E Kelsey, J Palethorpe (Reading 30), B Laryea (Torquay), R Davies (Torquay/Reading).

97-98 - Captain: Trevor Roffey **P.o.Y.:** Tim Cook **Top scorer:** Mickey Creighton

Celebrations after winning Berks & Bucks senior cup. Back Row (L-R): Tyrone Houston, Brian Connor, Obinna Ulasi, Garry Attrell, Dave Harrison, Vernon Pratt, Luke Evans, Michael Beaton, Ben Freeman, Richie Goddard (Res Mgr). Front Row; Mickey Creighton, Chuk Agudosi, Trevor Roffey, Andy Robertson, Andy Eaton. Photo: Courtesy Maidenhead Advertiser

MOLESEY

PROGRAMME DETAILS:
Pages: 44 **Price:** £1
Editor: Simon Carthew
c/o the club

Colours: White/black/black
Formed: 1950
Change colours: All Red
Nickname: The Moles
Midweek home matchday: Wednesday
Reserve Team's League: Suburban.
Youth Team: Southern Yth Lge
Local Press: Surrey Comet, Surrey Herald, Molesey News.
Local Radio: Thames 107.8 FM.

Chairman: Norman Clark **President:** Fred Maynard
Secretary/Press Officer: Ben O'Connor (c/o the club)
Manager: Ray Best **Coach:** Dave Swindlehurst
Reserve Manager:

GROUND - Address: 412 Walton Road, West Molesey, Surrey KT8 0JG (0181 941 7989 Boardroom, 0181 979 4823 Clubhouse). **Directions:** A3 from London to Hook, then A309 to Marquis of Granby pub, right to Hampton Court station, turn left for West Molesey, ground one mile on left.
Capacity: 4,000 **Cover:** 600 **Seats:** 400 **Floodlights:** Yes
Clubhouse: Open every evening and weekend lunchtimes. 2 bars, discos, live artists, darts, bingo, pool. **Steward:** Carol White
Club Shop: Contact John Chambers.

PREVIOUS - **Leagues:** Surrey Intermediate 53-56; Surrey Snr 56-59; Spartan 59-72; Athenian 72-77. **Name:** Molesey St Pauls 1950-53. **Grounds:** None.

CLUB RECORDS - **Attendance:** 1,255 v Sutton United, Surrey Senior Cup Semi-Final 1966. **Career Goalscorer:** Michael Rose, 139. **Career Appearances:** Frank Hanley, 453. **Transfer fee paid:** £500 for Chris Vidal (Leatherhead 88). **Transfer fee received:** £5,000 for Chris Vidal (Hythe Town 89).

BEST SEASON - **FA Vase:** 6th Rd 81-82. **FA Trophy:** 1st Rd replay 90-91. **FA Cup:** First Round Proper 94-95 (0-4 at home to Bath City).

HONOURS - Isthmian Lg Div 1 R-up 92-93 (Div 2 South R-up 89-90, Lg Cup R-up 92-93), Surrey Senior Lg 57-58, (Lg Charity Cup 56-57), Spartan Lg R-up 59-60 (Lg Cup 61-62 (R-up 63-64)), Surrey Senior Shield R-up 74-75, Southern Combination Cup 90-91 94-95.

Players progressing to Football League: John Finch (Fulham), Cyrille Regis (WBA, Coventry & England).

97-98 - Captain: Geoff Taylor **P.o.Y.:** James Wastell **Top Scorer:** Jon Richards

Molesey FC Photo: Clive Butchins

Last season's trophies including the Oxfordshire Senior, Intermediate and Youth Cups

OFFICIAL PROGRAMME

Club Sponsors

PROGRAMME DETAILS:
Pages: 60 **Price:** £1
Editor: Laurie Simmons

OXFORD CITY

Colours: Blue & white hoops/blue/blue
Change colours: All yellow
Midweek Matchday: Tuesday
Reserve's League: Suburban Lge Prem Div
Local Press: Oxford Mail, Oxford Journal
Local Radio: Thames Valley FM, Fox FM.

Sponsors: Unipart D.C.M.
Formed: 1882
Nickname: City

Chairman: M Woodley **President:**
Vice Chairman: R Holt **Press Officer/Secretary:** John Shepperd, 20 Howe Close, Wheatley, Oxford OX33 1SS (01865 872181 & Fax).
Manager: Paul Lee
Asst Manager: **Physio:** G Bowerman.

GROUND Address: Court Place Farm, Marsh Lane, Marston, Oxford. OX3 0NQ. Tel: 01865 744493. 01865 742394 (Clubhouse).
Directions: From London M40/A40, ring-road to North, take 1st slip road, follow signs to John Radcliffe hospital, ground on left after leaving flyover. From the north same ring-road.
Capacity: 3,000 **Seats:** 300 **Cover:** 400 **Floodlights:** Yes
Clubhouse: Open matchdays, most refreshments available.
Club Shop: Yes, open matchdays, selling souvenirs. Contact Paul Cotterell.

PREVIOUS - **Grounds:** The White House 1882-1988; Cuttleslowe Pk 90-91; Pressed Steel, Romanway 91-93. **Leagues:** Isthmian 07-88; South Midlands 90-93.

CLUB RECORDS - **Attendance:** 9,500 v Leytonstone, FA Amateur Cup 50. **Win:** 9-0 v Harlow Town, Isthmian League 9/10/76. **Defeat:** 0-8 v Wycombe Wanderers, Isthmian League - date unknown. **Scorer:** John Woodley. **Appearances:** John Woodley. **Fee Paid:** £3,000 for S Adams (Woking). **Fee Received:** £17,500 for H Forinton (Yeovil T. 1.97)

BEST SEASON - **FA Amateur Cup:** Winners 05-06 R-up 02-03 12-13. **FA Vase:** R-up 94-95. **FA Cup:** Second Round 69-70 (lost 1-5 at home to Swansea Town). **FA Trophy:** 1st Rd Prop 96 v Merthyr Tydfil

HONOURS - FA Amateur Cup 05-06 (R-up 02-03 12-13); F.A.Vase R-Up 94-95; Isthmian Lg R-up 34-35 45-46 (Div 1 R-up 77-78), Icis Lg Div 1 Champions 95-96; South Midlands Lg 92-93; Oxon Senior Cup - 27 times.

Players progressing to Football League: A Blakeman (Brentford 46), C Holton (Arsenal 50), K Savin (Derby 50), R Adams (Blackpool 48), A Jeffries (Brentford 49), P James (Luton 49), D Gordon/E Wilcox (WBA 47/48), V Mobley (Sheffield Wed 63), J Varney (Hull 50), P Lee (Hereford 73), H Poole (Port Vale 55), G Parker (Luton 81), M Keown (Arsenal 84), D Meeson (Wolves 52).

97-98 - Captain: Andy Wallbridge **Top scorer:** Jan Concannon **P.o.Y.:** Andy Wallbridge

Back Row (L-R); Jess Cormier, Darren Watts, Phil Mason, Andy Smith, Andy Wallbridge, Mick Torres, Robert Carlisle, Martin Brown, Justin Lee, Graham Bowerman (Physio), Paul Lee (Football Dir). Front Row; Ian Concannon, Julian Dark, Jason Caffel, Steve Jenkins, Kevin Brock (Player/Mgr), Liam Herbert, Keith Knight.

ROMFORD

Carlsberg

ROMFORD F C

Ryman

WEMBLEY

RYMAN LEAGUE DIVISION ONE

Saturday 21st March 1998

Kick-off 3.00 pm

PROGRAMME DETAILS:
Pages: 36 **Price:** £1.20
Editor: David Fletcher
Tel: 01708 726893

Colours: Blue & old gold/blue/blue
Change colours: Blue & black/black/black
Att change colours: Red & black/white/white
Midweek home matchday: Tuesday (7.45)
Reserves' League: Essex & Herts Border West
Local Press: Romford Recorder, Barking & Dagenham Post.
Local Radio: Essex Radio.

Sponsors: TBA
Reformed: 1992
Nickname: The Boro
Club Call: 0930 555 841

Life President: Ron Walker **Chairman:** John Goodwin
Vice-Chairman: Steve Gardener
Secretary: Sue Quantrill, Tel: 01708 705755
Team Manager: Steve Wheeler **Physio:** Don Calder
Press Officer: Steve Gardener
Commercial Manager: John Barrington

GROUND - Address: 'Sungate', Collier Row Road, Collier Row, Romford, Essex. Tel: 01708 722766. **Directions:** Take the A12 from London as far as the Moby Dick junction. Turn left and then right at the 1st roundabout into Collier Row Road. The ground entrance is signposted 200 yards on the right. Nearest station is Romford (BR). From directly outside the station the London bus 247 passes within 50 yards of the ground.
Capacity: 2,000 **Cover:** 550 **Seats:** 150 **Floodlights:** Yes
Clubhouse: Open seven days a week 11am - 11pm.
Club Shop: Open matchdays, selling replica shirts, programmes etc. Contact Barry Quantrill 01708 705755.

PREVIOUS - **Names:** Romford FC was formed in 1876 but folded in the Great War. The club reformed in 1929 and continued until 78. In 92 the club restarted and in 96 they merged with Collier Row - both names being used for that season only. They changed their name in 1997 to Romford. **Leagues:** Essex Senior 92-96 **Grounds:** Hornchurch 92-95, Ford United 95-96.

CLUB RECORDS - **Attendance:** 820 v Leatherhead (IL2) 15/4/97. **Career Goalscorer:** Micky Ross 57. **Season goalscorer:** Vinny John 45 (97-98). **Appearances:** Danny Benstock 164. **Win:** 9-0 v Hullbridge (H) ESL 21/10/95. **Defeat:** 1-7 v St Albans (A) EAC 29/10/96. **Transfer fee paid:** Four figure fee for Wade Falana (Braintree) June 97. **Transfer fee received:** None

BEST SEASON - **FA Cup:** 4th Qual Rd 97-98 v Bromsgrove Rovers (A). **FA Vase:** 5th Rd 96-97 v Bedlington Terriers 2-1. **FA Trophy:** 3rd Qual Rd v Basingstoke Town (A) 97-98.

HONOURS - Essex Senior Lge Champ 95-96, Lge Cup 95-96; Isthmian Div 2 Champ 96-97; East Anglian Cup 97-98.

97-98 - Captain: Danny Benstock **P.o.Y.:** Mark Reed **Top scorer:** Vinny John (45)

Back Row (L-R); John Barrington (Comm Mgr), Don Calder (Physio), Vic Coals (Match Sec), Kevin Marsden, Wade Falana, Hurracia Willock, Stuart Horne, Vinny John, Steve Stott, Francis Duku, Danny Foot, Brad Brotherton, Mick Wetherall (Kit & Groundsman), Steve Wheeler (Res Mgr), Darren George. Front Row; Alan Hyde (Physio), Martin Hayes, Mark Reed, Troy Braham, Les Whitton (Mgr), Danny Benstock, Lee Fulling, John Doyle, Billy Hudson.

PROGRAMME DETAILS:
Pages: 44 **Price:** £1
Editor: Sec. & Stuart Moore (01784 421118)

STAINES TOWN

Colours: Old gold (blue trim)/royal/royal **Sponsors:** Barratt Homes.
Change colours: All white. **Formed:** 1892
Midweek matchday: Tuesday **Nickname:** The Swans
Reserve league: Suburban (since 72).
Local Press: Staines & Ashford News, Middx Chronicle, Informer.
Local Radio: County Sound, GLR, Capital, Star FM, Radio Wey

Chairman: Alan Boon **President:** Nigel Iggulden
Vice Chairman: Ken Williams **Secretary:** Steve Parsons, 3 Birch Green, Staines, Middx TW18 4HA (01784 450420).
Manager: Chris Wainwright **Asst Manager:** Keith Bristow
Physio: Mick Minter/Jug Stephen **Commercial Mgr:** Ken Williams
Press Officer: Stuart Moore (01784 421118)

GROUND - Address: Chertsey Town FC. Alwyns Lane, Chertsey, Surrey KT16 9DW (01932 561774). **Directions:** Alwyns Lane is off Windsor St N end of shopping centre. 10 mins Chertsey (BR).
Capacity: 3,000 **Cover:** 1000 **Seats:** 250 **Floodlights:** Yes
Club HQ & Clubhouse: Staines Town FC, Wheatsheaf Lane, Staines (01784 450420). Fully furnished clubhouse & function hall, open 7-11 matchdays and every evening. Rolls and other snacks available.
Club Shop: Souvenirs available from Harry Trim, 23 Grosvenor Rd, Staines, Middx TW18 2RN.

PREVIOUS - Leagues: W London All (pre-1900), W London, W Middx (pre-1905), Gt Western Suburban 05-13 20-24, Gt Western Comb, Munitions Lg (World War 1), London Works (World War 1), Hounslow & Dist 19-20, Spartan 24-35 58-71, Middx Sen 43-52/ Parthenon 52-53, Hellenic 53-58, Athenian 71-73. **Names:** Staines Albany and St Peters Institute (merged) in 1895, Staines 05-18, Staines Lagonda 18-25, Staines Vale (2nd World War). **Grounds:** Edgell Rd (St Peters Inst); The Lammas, Shortwood Common, Mill Mead (Hammonds/Wicks/Pursers Farm); Shepperton Road (to 51); Wheatsheaf Lane (51-96) still open for non-sen fixtures.

CLUB RECORDS - Attendance: 2,750 v Banco di Roma (Barassi Cup) 1975 *(70,000 saw 1st leg in Rome).* **Goalscorer:** Alan Gregory 122 **Appearances:** Dickie Watmore 840 **Win:** 14-0 v Croydon (A), Isthmian League Div. 1 19/3/94. **Defeat:** 1-18 v Wycombe Wanderers (A), G West Sub Lge 1909. **Fee Paid:** For R Teale (Slough 81) **Fee Received:** For Scott Taylor (Millwall 95-96).

BEST SEASON - FA Amateur Cup: 3rd Rd 23-24. **FA Trophy:** 2nd Rd 2nd Replay 76-77. **FA Cup:** 1st Rd 84-85 (0-2 at Burton Alb) & 1879-80 & 80-81 (as St Peters Institute).

HONOURS - Isthmian Lg Div 1 74-75 88-89 (Div 2 74-75); Athenian Lg Div 2 71-72 (Div 1 R-up 72-73); Spartan Lg 59-60 (R-up 70-71), Lg Cup 68-69 (R-up 60-61 70-71); Hellenic Lg R-up 55-56 (Lg Cup R-up 53-54 55-56); Gt Western Suburban Lg Div 1 R-up 11-12 22-24 (Div 2 (Middx) 20-21); W London All Div 1 1899-1900; W London Lg Div 1 00-01; W Middx Lg 04-05 (R-up 03-04); London Snr Cup R-up 76-77 80-81; Middx Snr Cup(7), (R-up 09-10 32-33 79-80), Snr Charity Cup 94-95; Barassi Cup 76; Southern Comb. Chall. Cup 64-65 66-67 68-69 94-95 96-97,(R-up 67-68 94-95); W Middx Cup 23-24; Staines Cottage Hosp Cup 24-25; Merthyr Middx Charity Shield 90-91,(R-up 94-95); El Canuelo Trophy 92-93 94-95 94-95; Carlsberg Cup 94-95; Melksham Middx Charity Shield 96-97.

Players progressing to Football League: R Bennett (Southend 72), J Love (C Palace 75), P Shaw (Charlton 77), E Young (Wolves), G Hill (Millwall), W Stemp (Brighton), M Ferney (Fulham), S Taylor (Millwall & Bolton W).

Back Row (L-R); Keith Bristow (Asst Mgr), Frank Dotson (Physio), Lee Passmore, Tommy Williams, Phil Grainger, Matthew Lovett, Steve Battams, Wayne Noad, Charlie Carter, Kelly Phillips, Chris Wainwright (Mgr). Front Row; Andy Driscoll, Mark Fleming, Andy Clement, Mark Costello, Justin Mitchell, Lloyd Wye, Zak Newman

PROGRAMME DETAILS:
Pages: 48-56 **Price:** £1.00
Editor: A Peart (01895 443094)
& Roy Green (01895 254784)

UXBRIDGE

Colours: Red/white/red **Sponsor:** Dagenham Motors
Change colours: Sky & navy blue **OR** White and black **Formed:** 1871
Midweek matchday: Tuesday **Nickname:** The Reds
Reserves' League: Suburban Lge (Prem Div).
Local Press: Uxbridge Gazette & Leader, Uxbridge Recorder.
Local Radio: Capital, G L R, Star FM.

Chairman: Alan Holloway **Vice-Chairman:** Tom Barnard
Joint President: Tom Barnard & Alan Odell.
Secretary: Roger Stevens, 9 Bourne Ave, Hillingdon, Middlesex UB8 3AR (01895 236879). **Res & Youth Sec:** Bob Clayton (01895 857001)
Press Officer: Andy Peart (01895 443094)
Commercial Manager: Trevor Birch (0181 561 1789)
Manager: George Talbot **Coach:** Mike Nicks **Res Mgr:** Andy Everley
Physio: Ernie Kempster/Stuart Everley **Youth Mgr:** Derek Marshall

GROUND - Address: Honeycroft, Horton Road, West Drayton, Middx UB7 8HX (01895 443557). **Directions:** From West Drayton (BR) turn right then 1st right (Horton Road). Ground 1 mile on left. From Uxbridge (LT) take 222 or U3 bus to West Drayton station, then follow as above. By road, ground 1 mile north of M4 jct 4 taking road to Uxbridge and leaving by first junction and turning left into Horton Rd - ground 500yds on right.
Capacity: 3,770 **Cover:** 760 **Seats:** 339 **Floodlights:** Yes
Club Shop: Good selection of souvenirs & programmes. Contact Averill Hinde
Clubhouse: (01895 443557). Large clubhouse with bar and function room available for hire. Open every evening and weekend/bank holiday lunchtimes. Hot & cold snacks available on matchdays.

PREVIOUS - Leagues: Southern 1894-99; Gt Western Suburban 1906-19, 20-23; Athenian 1919-20, 24-37, 63-82; Spartan 37-38; London 38-46; Gt Western Comb. 39-45; Corinthian 46-63. **Name:** Uxbridge Town 23-45. **Grounds:** RAF Stadium 23-48, Cleveland Rd 48-78.

CLUB RECORDS - Attendance: 1,000 v Arsenal, floodlight opening 1981. **Career Scorer:** Phil Duff, 153. **Career Appearances:** Roger Nicholls, 1054.

BEST SEASON - FA Trophy: 1st Rd replay 88-89. **FA Vase:** 4th Rd 83-84. **FA Cup:** 2nd Rd 1873-74. 1st Rd on three other occasions 1883-84 84-85 85-86. **FA Amateur Cup:** Runners-up 1897-98

HONOURS - FA Amateur Cup R-up 1897-98; London Challenge Cup 93-94 96-97, R-up 97-98; Isthmian Lge Div 2 S. R-up 84-85; Athenian Lge Cup R-up 81-82, Res. Section 69-70, Res. Cup R-up 68-69; Corinthian League 59-60 (R-up 48-49), Lge Memorial Shield 50-51 52-53; Middx Senior Cup 1893-94 95-96 1950-51, R-up 97-98; Middx Senior Charity Cup 07-08 12-13 35-36 81-82 (R-up 69-70 82-83 85-86); Middx Prem Cup 95-96; Allied Counties Yth Lge [East] 92-93 (Lge Cup R-up 86-87), Lge Shield 88-89 92-93, R-up 97-98; AC Delco Cup R-up 85-86; Suburban Lge North Div Champions 95-96 97-98, R-up 96-97; Middx Sen Yth Cup 96-97.

Players progressing to Football League: William Hill (QPR 51), Lee Stapleton (Fulham 52), Gary Churchouse (Charlton A.), Tony Witter (QPR & Millwall), Guy Butters (Spurs & Portsmouth), Michael Meaker (QPR & Reading).

97-98 - Captain: Jamie Jarvis **P.o.Y.:** Gavin Bamford **Players P.o.Y.:** Gavin Bamford
Top Scorer: Mark Gill/Jamie Jarvis/Nicky Ryder (17) **Supporters P.o.Y.:** Kevin Cleary

Back Row (L-R); Ernie Kempster (Physio), Mike Nicks (Coach), Andy Campbell, Jamie Jarvis, Mark Gill, Kevin Cleary, Phil Granville, Sean Dawson, George Talbot (Mgr). Gavin Bamford, Michael Fredriksen, Nicky Ryder, Paul Mills, Micky Perry, Jamie Cleary, Danny Hawksworth, Stuart Bamford

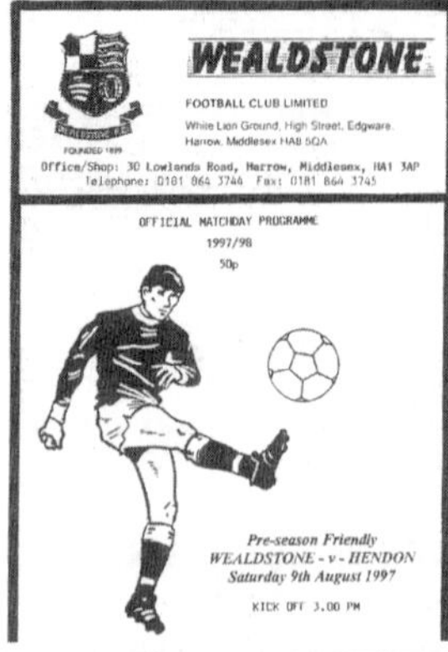

PROGRAMME DETAILS:
Pages: 30 **Price:** £1
Editor: Roy Couch
(0181 907 4421)

WEALDSTONE

Colours: Blue & white quarters
Change colours: Yellow & blue
Midweek matches: Tuesday
Reserves' League: None
Local Newspapers: Harrow Observer, Harrow Times
Local Radio: Capital, Greater London Radio, Radio Northwick Park

Sponsors: Albro Windows
Formed: 1899
Nickname: The Stones

Chairman: Paul Rumens **Vice Chairman:** Nick Dugard
Secretary: Steve Hibberd, 17 Brancaster Rd, Newbury Park, Ilford, Essex IG2 7ER (0181 597 7534).
Administrative & Commercial Manager: Layne Patterson.
Press Officer: Graham Sharpe **Manager:** Gordon Bartlett
Asst Mgr: Leo Morris **Physio:** Alan Wharton

GROUND: (Sharing with Edgware Town FC) - **Address:** White Lion Ground, High Street, Edgware HA8 5AQ. **Tel:** 0181 952 6799.
Directions: Turn left out of Edgware tube station (Northern Line), turn left again at crossroads and ground 300yds on right in Edgware High Street behind White Lion pub. Buses 32, 288 and 142.
Clubhouse: Yes, normal licensing hours. **Club Shop:** Yes

PREVIOUS - **Leagues:** Willesden & Dist. 1899-1906 08-13; London 1911-22; Middx 13-22; Spartan 22-28; Athenian 28-64; Isthmian 64-71; Southern 71-79 81-82,88-95; GMV Conference 79-81 82-88. **Grounds:** College Farm 03-10; Belmont Rd 10-22; Lower Mead Stadium 22-91; Vicarage Rd (Watford FC) 91-93; The Warren (Yeading F.C.) 93-95.

CLUB RECORDS - **Attendance:** 13,504 v Leytonstone FA Amateur Cup Fourth Round replay 5/3/49. **Goalscorer:** George Duck, 251 **Appearances:** Charlie Townsend, 514 **Win:** 22-0 v The 12th London Regiment (The Rangers)(H), FA Amateur Cup 13/10/23. **Defeat:** 0-14 v Edgware Town (A), London Senior Cup 9/12/44. **Fees Paid:** £15,000 for David Gipp (Barnet, 1990). **Received:** £25,000; for Stuart Pearce (Coventry City 1983); for Sean Norman (Chesham, 1989).

BEST SEASON - **FA Amateur Cup:** Winners 1965-66 **FA Trophy:** Winners 1984-85 **FA Cup:** Third Round 77-78, 0-4 v Q.P.R. (A). 1st Rd on 13 occasions. **League clubs defeated:** Hereford Utd and Reading, 77-78.

HONOURS - FA Trophy 84-85; FA Amateur Cup 65-66; GMV Conference 84-85; Isthmian Lge - Div 3 96-97; Southern Lg Southern Div 81-82, Div 1 South 73-74, Lg Cup 81-82; Athenian Lg 51-52 (R-up 52-53 58-59 60-61); Spartan Lg R-up 22-23; London Lg Div 2 12-13 (R-up 11-12); London Snr Cup 61-62(joint) (R-up 39-40 51-52 60-61); Middx Snr Cup (11); Middx Senior Charity Cup (11); Capital League 84-85 86-87.

Players progressing to Football League: include Stuart Pearce (Coventry City 83), Vinnie Jones (Wimbledon 86), Danny Bailey (Exeter 89).

97-98 - Captain: Fergus Moore **P.o.Y.:** Brian Jones **Top scorer:** Keith Boreham (29)

Wealdstone FC Photo: James Smith

WEMBLEY

FOOTBALL CLUB
OFFICIAL MATCH PROGRAMME

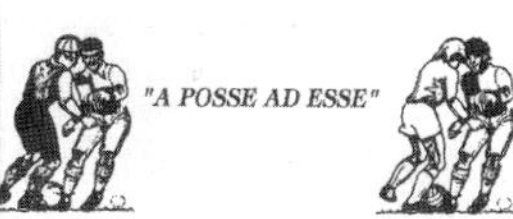

WEMBLEY V ALDERSHOT
SAT. 3RD JAN. 1998
KICK OFF 3.00 P.M.
PROGRAMME £1

PROGRAMME DETAILS:
Pages: 28 **Price:** £1
Editor: Richard Markiewicz
(0181 902 0541 - before 9pm)

WEMBLEY

Colours: Red & white/red/red
Change colours: Yellow & navy/navy/navy
Midweek matchday: Tuesday
Reserves' League: Suburban
Local Press: Wembley & Harrow Observer.
Local Radio: Capital, G.L.R.

Sponsors: G & B Builders.
Formed: 1946.
Nickname: The Lions

Chairman: Brian Gumm **President:** Jim Bryan, BEM
Vice Chairman: Eric Stringer **General Manager:** Glen Charles.
Press Officer: Richard Markiewicz (0181 902 0541 before 9pm)
Commercial Manager:
Secretary: Mrs Jean Gumm, 14 Woodfield Avenue, North Wembley, Middx HA0 3NR (0181 908 3353).
Manager: John Walsh **Asst. Manager:** Paul Shields.

GROUND Address: Vale Farm, Watford Road, Sudbury, Wembley HA0 4UR (0181 908 8169).
Directions: Sudbury Town station (Underground) 400 yds, or 10 mins walk from North Wembley (BR) station. Buses 18, 92, 245 & 182.
Capacity: 2,000 **Cover:** 350 **Seats:** 350 **Floodlights:** Yes
Clubhouse: (0181 904 8169). Open every night & weekend lunchtimes. Hot food on matchdays. **Club Shop:** No

PREVIOUS - **Leagues:** Middx 46-49; Spartan 49-51; Delphian 51-56; Corinthian 56-63; Athenian 63-75.

CLUB RECORDS - **Attendance:** 2,654 v Wealdstone, FA Amateur Cup 52-53. **Career goalscorer:** Bill Handrahan 105 (1946-52) **Career appearances:** Spud Murphy 505 (78-88). **Win:** 11-1 v Hermes, London Senior Cup 1963. **Defeat:** 0-16 v Chelsea, London Challenge Cup 59-60. **Transfer fee paid:** Nil **Transfer fee received:** £10,000 for Gary Roberts (Brentford, 1981).

BEST SEASON - **FA Trophy:** 1st Round proper 91-92 **FA Amateur Cup:** 2nd Round 66-67, 68-69 **FA Cup:** 1st Round Proper 1980-81 (lost 0-3 at Enfield).

HONOURS - Middx Sen Cup 83-84 86-87 (R-up 55-56 68-69 78-79 87-88 91-92 92-93); Middx Lge 47-48 (Lge Cup 46-47), Middx Charity Cup 67-68(jnt) 80-81(jnt) 82-83 86-87 94-95,(R-up 83-84 87-88 96-97); Middx Invitation Cup 56-57; Athenian Lge R-up 74-75 (Div 1 R-up 67-68); Corinthian Lge Mem Shield R-up 58-59; Delphian Lge R-up 55-56; Spartan Lge Div 1 West 50-51 (Dunkel Trophy 50-51 jnt); London Sen Cup R-up 55-56; Hitachi Cup SF 83-84; Suburban Lge North 85-86, Lge Cup 84-85 (R-up 83-84).

Players progressing to Football League: Keith Cassells (Watford 1977), Mike O'Donague (Southampton 1979), A McGonigle (Olympiakos), Gary Roberts (Brentford 1980), Richard Cadette (Orient 1984).

Wembley under aerial threat from Grays Athletic Photo: Gordon Whittington

WHYTELEAFE F.C.
Season 1997-1998

MOLESEY
RYMAN LEAGUE DIVISION 1
SATURDAY 13TH DECEMBER 1997
KICK OFF 3.00 PM
WELCOME TO CHURCH ROAD
£1

WHYTELEAFE

Colours: Green & white/white/white
Change colours: Yellow & black/black/black
Midweek matchday: Tuesday
Reserve Team's League: Suburban.
Local Press: Croydon Advertiser.
Local Radio: Mercury

Sponsors: Sunday Sport.
Formed: 1946
Nickname: Leafe

Chairman: Paul Owens **President:** A F Lidbury
Secretary: Ian Robertson, 253 Godstone Road, Whyteleafe, Surrey. CR3 0BD. 01883 622096 (H&B)
Press Officer: Peter Stimpson 01883 348310 (H)
Commercial Manager: T Dounce (01883 343450)
Manager: Lee Richardson **Assistant Man.:** B Donnelly
Coach: Mark Coote **Physio:** John Knapton

PROGRAMME DETAILS:
Pages: 36 **Price:** 70p
Editor: Warren Filmer
(0181 660 3255)

GROUND Address: 15 Church Road, Whyteleafe, Surrey CR3 0AR. Tel: 0181 660 5491 *(Ground)* 0181 645 0422 *(Boardroom).*
Directions: Five minutes walk from Whyteleafe (BR) - turn right from station, and left into Church Road.
Capacity: 5,000 **Cover:** 600 **Seats:** 200 **Floodlights:** Yes
Clubhouse: Open every lunchtime and evening. Hot and cold food, pool, darts, gaming machines. **Clubshop:** No.

PREVIOUS - **Leagues:** Caterham & Edenbridge, Croydon, Thornton Heath & Dist., Surrey Intermediate (East) 54-58, Surrey Senior 58-75, Spartan 75-81, Athenian 81-84.
Names: None. **Grounds:** None.

CLUB RECORDS - **Attendance:** 780 **Transfer fee paid:** £1,000 for Gary Bowyer (Carshalton) **Transfer fee received:** £25,000 for Steve Milton.

BEST SEASON - **FA Vase:** 5th Rd 80-81 85-86. **FA Trophy:** 3rd Qualifying Rd 89-90. **FA Cup:** Third Qualifying Round replay (lost 1-2 after 1-1 draw at Wokingham Town).

HONOURS - Isthmian Lge Div 2 South R-up 88-89; Surrey Senior Lge 68-69 (Lge Cup R-up 68-69, Lge Charity Cup 71-72, Res Sect 62-63 (Challenge Cup 62-63 (R-up 59-60); Surrey Senior Cup 68-69 (R-up 87-88); Surrey Premier Cup R-up 84-85; East Surrey Charity Cup 79-80 (R-up 76-77 77-78); Thornton Heath & Dist Lge 51-52 (Lge Cup 51-52) Div 4 R-up 51-52; Edenbridge Charity Cup 51-52; Caterham & Purley Hospital Cup 51-52; Surrey County Interm Lge East Sect 1 55-56; Surrey Junior Cup R-up 51-52; Caterham & Edenbridge Lge Div 3 51-52; Borough of Croydon Charity Cup 56-57; Southern Yth Lge 89-90 (R-up 88-89), Lge Cup 88-89 89-90; Southern Count Midweek Floodlit cup 95-96.

Players progressing to Football League: Steve Milton (Fulham).

Action between Whyteleafe & Aldershot Photo: Ian Morsman

ICIS FOOTBALL LEAGUE DIVISION ONE
OFFICIAL MATCHDAY PROGRAMME 1997/98
Match Details
Saturday 30th August 1997
Eastbourne Town
F.A. Cup Preliminary Round

PROGRAMME DETAILS:
Pages: 48 **Price:** £1
Editor: Neil Wycherley

WORTHING

Colours: Red, blue & white trim/red/red **Sponsors:** Wessex Cleaning
Change colours: All yellow **Formed:** 1886
Midweek matches: Tuesday. **Nickname:** The Rebels
Local Press: Evening Argus, Worthing Herald.
Local Radio: Southern FM, Southern Counties Radio.

Chairman: Beau Reynolds **President:** Morty Hollis
Vice Chairman: Ray Smith **Press Officer:** Paul Damper Tel: 01903 210290
Secretary: Paul Damper, 19 Fletcher Road, Worthing, West Sussex BN14 8EX.
Manager: Brian Donnelly
Physio: Alan Robertson **Asst Manager:** Glen Geard

GROUND Address: Woodside Road, Worthing, West Sussex BN14 7HQ (01903 239575).
Directions: Follow A24 to town, at end of Broadwater Rd having gone over railway bridge, take 1st right into Teville Rd, take right into South Farm RD, 2nd left into Pavilion Rd, Woodside Rd is first right. Half a mile from Worthing (BR).
Capacity: 4,500 **Seats:** 450 **Cover:** 1,000 **Floodlights:** Yes
Clubhouse: Open 2 hrs before kick-off & closes 11pm. Hot & cold food available.
Shop: Sells a good range of souvenirs & programmes. Open matchdays.

PREVIOUS - **Leagues:** West Sussex Sen 1896-04, 05-14, 19-20; Brighton, Hove & Dist 19-20; Sussex County 20-40, 45-48; Corinthian 48-63; Athenian 63-77. **Names:** None **Grounds:** Homefield Park, Beach House Park

CLUB RECORDS - **Attendance:** 4,500 v Depot Battalion Royal Engineers, FA Amtr Cup 07-08. **Transfer fee paid:** £1,000 for Steve Guille (Bognor Regis Tn 89). **Transfer fee received:** £7,500 for Tim Read (Woking, 1990). **Win:** 25-0 v Littlehampton (H) West Sussex Lge 1911-12. **Defeat:** 0-14 v Southwick (A), Sussex County Lge 1946-47. **Career Goalscorer:** Mick Edmonds 275. **Career Appearances:** Geoff Raynsford

BEST SEASON - **FA Vase:** 5th Rd 78-79. **FA Trophy:** 3rd Rd Replay 85-86. **FA Amateur Cup:** Quarter-Final replay 07-08. **FA Cup:** 2nd Rd 82-83, (0-4 to Oxford Utd), 1st Rd 36-37, 94-95, (1-3 v AFC Bournemouth).

HONOURS - Isthmian Lg R-up(2) 83-85 (Div 1 82-83, Div 2 81-82 92-93); Athenian Lg Div 1 R-up 63-64, Div 2 R-up 71-72, Lg Cup R-up 72-73, Mem. Shield R-up 63-64; Sussex Snr Cup (20); Sussex RUR Char. Cup (13); Sussex Co. Lg(8) 20-22 26-27 28-29 30-31 33-34 38-40; W Sussex Lg (7); Brighton Char. Cup(9) 29-31 34-35 62-63 69-71 73-74(jt) 80-82; Worthing Char. Cup (10); AFA Invit. Cup 63-64 68-69 73-74 75-76 (Snr Cup R-up 36-37 46-47 48-49); Corinth. Lg Mem. Shield R-up 49-50 (Neale Tphy 58-59); Roy Hayden Mem. Tphy 75(jt), 77 78; Don Morecraft Tphy 72 73 76 81 82; Sussex F'lit Cup(3) 88-90 97-98; Sussex I'mediate Cup 34-35 64-65; Brighton Chal. Shield 29-30 31-32.

Players progressing to Football League: Ken Suttle (Chelsea 48), Alan Arnell & Fred Perry (Liverpool 54), Craig Whitington (Scarborough, via Crawley Town) 93, Darren Freeman (Gillingham), Paul Musselwhite (Scunthorpe,Port Vale), Trevor Wood (Port Vale,Walsall), Richard Tiltman (Brighton).

97-98 - Captain: Graham Waller **P.o.Y.:** John Keeley **Top scorer:** Jason Reed

Back Row (L-R); Alan Robertson (Physio), Jamie Bryant, Daren Pearce, Paul O'Sullivan, Simon Robinson, Paul Kennett, Mark Burt, Simon Funnell, Lee Watson, Tony Holden, Mark Knee, Jay Pickering, John Keeley, Don Read (Match Sec). Front Row; Jason Reed, Mick Russell, Mathew Major (Comm Dir), Sammy Donnelly (Mgr), Graham Waller (Capt), Glen Geard (Asst Mgr), Beau Reynolds (Chr), Lee Cox, Danny Smith. Photo: Courtesy Worthing Herald

PROGRAMME DETAILS:
Pages: 32 **Price:** £1
Editor: David Low.

YEADING

Colours: Red & black stripes/black/black
Change colours: All white.
Midweek matchday: Tuesday
Reserve League: Suburban Lge
Local Newspapers: Hayes Gazette.

Sponsors: Heineken.
Formed: 1965
Nickname: The Dinc

Chairman: Philip Spurden **President:** Mr R Carter
Vice Chairman: Steve Perryman **Secretary:** Peter Bickers, 140 Hercies Rd, Hillingdon, Middlesex (01895 203562).
Manager: Steve Cordery. **Asst Manager:** Leo Morris
Coach: T Choules. **Physio:** Edward Cole.
Commercial Manager:
Press Officer: Peter Bickers (as above)

GROUND Address: The Warren, Beaconsfield Road, Hayes, Middx (0181 848 7362/7369. Fax: 0181 561 2222).
Directions: Two miles from Hayes (BR) - take Uxbridge Road and turn right towards Southall, right into Springfield Road and then left into Beaconsfield Road. Bus 207 stops half mile from ground.
Capacity: 3,500 **Cover:** 1,500 **Seats:** 250 **Floodlights:** Yes
Clubhouse: Open normal pub hours. Social Secretary: William Gritt.
Club Shop: Planned **Metal Badges:** Yes

PREVIOUS - **Leagues:** Hayes & District Yth; Uxbridge; S W Middx 1967-74; Middx 74-84; Spartan 1984-87.

CLUB RECORDS - **Attendance:** 3,000; v Hythe Town, FA Vase SF 1990; v Tottenham Hotspur, friendly. **Goalscorer:** Dave Burt 327 **Appearances:** Norman Frape **Fee Paid:** Unknown **Fee Received:** £45,000 for Andrew Impey (QPR).

BEST SEASON - **FA Cup:** Third Qualifying Round 90-91. **FA Vase:** Winners 89-90.

HONOURS - Isthmian League Div 2 Sth 89-90 (Div 1 R-up 91-92); Spartan League 86-87 (R-up 85-86, Senior Div R-up 84-85, League Cup 85-86 86-87); Middlesex Snr League(6) 71-73 74-76 81-82 83-84 (R-up 73-74 74-75 78-79, League Cup(6) 72-73 75-76 79-83); South West Middlesex League(2) 69-71; Middlesex Snr Cup 89-90 91-92, Middlesex Prem. Cup 80-81, Middlesex I'mediate Cup(5) 70-72 74-76 77-78, Middlesex Jnr Cup(4) 68-69 70-72 74-75; Uxbridge League 66-67; Middlesex Border League Cup 86-87 (AJA Cup 86-87); Suburban League Nth 87-88; Allied Counties Yth League 89-90 (League Cup 89-90).

Players progressing to Football League: Andrew Impey (QPR & England u-21).

Yeading FC Photo: Andrew Chitty

SECOND DIVISION LEAGUE TABLE 1997-98

	P	Home W	Home D	Home L	Away W	Away D	Away L	F	A	Pts
Canvey Island	42	17	3	1	13	5	3	116	41	98
Braintree Town	42	16	3	2	13	8	0	117	45	98
Wealdstone	42	13	6	3	11	5	5	81	46	83
Bedford Town	42	13	5	3	9	7	5	55	25	78
Metropolitan Police	42	12	2	7	9	6	6	80	65	71
Wivenhoe Town	42	9	6	6	9	6	6	84	66	66
Edgware Town	42	11	4	6	7	6	8	81	65	64
Chalfont St Peter	42	9	7	5	8	6	7	63	60	64
Northwood	42	8	7	6	9	4	8	65	69	62
Windsor & Eton	42	10	4	7	7	3	11	74	72	58
Tooting & Mitcham	42	9	5	7	7	4	10	58	56	57
Barking	42	7	6	8	8	6	7	62	75	57
Banstead Athletic	42	7	6	8	8	3	10	60	63	54
Marlow	42	11	2	8	5	3	13	64	78	53
Horsham	42	8	3	10	5	6	10	67	75	48
Bracknell Town	42	8	4	9	5	4	12	69	93	47
Leighton Town	42	8	3	10	5	3	13	45	78	45
Hungerford Town	42	7	5	9	4	6	11	66	77	44
Witham Town	42	5	7	9	4	6	11	55	68	40
Tilbury	42	4	9	8	5	3	13	57	88	39
Egham Town	42	8	4	9	1	1	19	47	101	32
Cheshunt	42	1	5	15	3	5	13	31	90	22

RESULTS GRID 1997-98

HOME TEAM	1	2	3	4	5	6	7	8	9	10	11	12	13	14	15	16	17	18	19	20	21	22
1. Banstead Ath.	*	1-2	0-2	3-1	0-0	2-2	1-2	3-2	2-2	1-0	1-2	0-4	1-3	1-2	3-1	1-1	5-2	1-1	4-1	2-1	0-0	1-3
2. Barking	3-1	*	1-2	3-3	1-3	0-4	1-1	0-0	0-0	2-1	0-1	4-2	0-1	1-0	0-2	1-1	0-3	1-2	2-1	3-0	2-2	4-3
3. Bedford Town	2-0	2-0	*	1-1	0-1	2-3	0-0	3-1	3-2	2-0	0-0	2-0	1-0	0-1	1-0	4-0	3-0	2-0	0-0	3-0	1-0	1-1
4. Bracknell T.	1-0	1-2	2-0	*	1-4	1-1	1-2	1-1	0-*03-1		3-2	4-1	1-2	3-2	2-0	2-4	1-2	1-2	3-4	5-3	1-1	1-8
5. Braintree Town	4-0	1-1	3-0	4-2	*	2-1	4-1	0-1	1-1	4-1	5-1	3-1	4-0	5-3	7-0	4-0	4-1	3-0	0-1	3-0	1-0	4-4
6. Canvey Is.	1-2	6-0	1-0	5-1	1-1	*	4-0	3-0	3-2	6-1	2-0	7-2	2-0	3-1	11	4-0	5-1	3-0	2-0	5-1	3-0	3-3
7. Chalfont St. P.	2-1	2-2	0-0	5-5	1-4	0-5	*	0-0	0-3	4-2	1-0	1-2	2-0	2-0	1-1	3-1	1-1	2-0	1-1	4-0	0-1	2-0
8. Cheshunt	0-1	1-2	0-1	1-0	1-2	1-2	0-2	*	2-2	0-3	0-0	2-3	1-1	3-5	0-3	0-0	0-2	0-3	0-2	0-3	0-0	0-2
9. Edgware T.	2-0	2-2	0-0	0-1	2-2	3-0	2-1	8-0	*	3-1	5-2	2-1	1-2	3-2	3-4	3-1	2-1	2-2	0-2	0-4	0-2	2-1
10. Egham T.	0-4	1-0	1-2	2-0	0-2	4-3	0-2	2-2	1-0	*	3-2	2-0	0-0	2-0	0-3	2-0	2-2	1-4	3-5	0-1	1-2	2-2
11. Horsham	0-4	31-21-0		0-1	1-1	0-3	2-2	2-3	1-3	2-0	*	1-1	4-0	3-0	0-2	0-1	5-2	2-1	0-2	3-0	3-1	0-1
12. Hungerford T.	4-1	0-2	1-1	1-2	2-3	1-1	1-1	1-0	1-0	7-1	2-4	*	4-0	1-2	1-3	1-3	2-0	1-3	1-1	1-2	3-1	2-2
13. Leighton T.	0-2	2-2	0-0	1-0	0-4	2-4	2-0	3-2	0-3	2-0	2-1	2-1	*	2-1	1-3	1-3	2-3	1-3	0-1	1-1	2-0	1-3
14. Marlow	0-3	5-2	2-0	2-1	1-3	1-3	1-3	3-1	1-3	2-1	2-2	1-1	2-0	*	2-1	1-2	1-0	4-3	0-2	4-1	4-2	0-1
15. Met. Police	3-1	5-1	0-1	5-0	4-4	1-2	1-4	3-1	2-2	1-0	1-7	4-2	3-0	3-2	*	2-1	2-0	0-1	1-0	0-2	2-1	1-2
16. Northwood	3-1	1-1	0-3	2-1	1-2	1-2	3-1	6-0	1-0	2-1	2-2	1-1	2-1	1-1	3-3	*	4-2	1-1	0-0	1-4	1-2	0-3
17. Tilbury	0-0	2-1	1-1	3-4	1-4	1-2	1-2	2-1	3-4	1-1	1-1	1-0	3-2	1-1	2-2	1-2	*	1-1	1-2	0-0	2-2	1-3
18. Tooting & Mit.	2-0	1-1	0-0	2-3	1-1	0-1	0-3	1-2	3-0	4-0	1-2	1-1	3-0	2-0	1-0	0-1	1-2	*	2-2	2-1	1-0	1-0
19. Wealdstone	1-1	4-2	0-1	2-0	1-1	1-1	2-0	5-1	3-1	4-2	4-2	3-1	2-1	5-0	0-2	1-1	3-1	2-0	*	2-0	1-1	1-1
20. Windsor & Eton	0-2	2-3	0-4	4-2	3-3	0-3	3-0	3-0	2-3	7-1	1-0	0-0	2-2	2-1	1-1	2-4	5-0	1-0	1-2	*	3-1	5-1
21. Witham Town	1-1	1-2	1-1	3-0	2-3	1-2	1-1	1-1	2-4	3-1	3-3	1-2	0-2	0-1	2-2	1-2	2-1	5-1	3-4	0-0	*	2-1
22. Wivenhoe T.	0-2	1-3	1-3	2-2	2-3	1-1	1-1	1-0	3-1	5-0	6-2	2-2	3-1	0-0	0-2	3-1	2-2	2-1	2-1	0-3	2-1	*

RYMAN DIVISION TWO 1998-99

ABINGDON TOWN

Colours: Yellow & green/green/green **Formed:** 1870
Change colours: Black & white **Nickname:** Over The Bridge
Midweek home matchday: Wednesday **Sponsors:** Morlands.
Reserve Team's League: Suburban (West).
Local Press: Oxford Mail, Oxford Times, Abingdon Herald, South Oxon Guardian.

Chairman: Phil Evans **President:** Dr Tim Reynolds
Vice Chairman: Craig Norcliffe **Secretary:** Ted Quail, 107 Park Lane, Thatcham, Newbury, Berks RG18 3BZ (01635 868967).
Press Officer: Nick Quail (01235 832499)
Manager: Paul Lee **Asst Manager:** Roger Nicholls.
Physio: Ian Maskell. **Coach:** Kelvin Alexis.

GROUND Address: Culham Road, Abingdon OX14 3BT (01235 521684).
Directions: On A415 road to Dorchester-on-Thames half a mile south of town centre. Nearest rail station is Culham. Main line: Didcot Parkway or Oxford. Bus service from Didcot and London.
Capacity: 3,000 **Cover:** 1,771 **Seats:** 271 **Floodlights:** Yes
Clubhouse: (01235 521684). 7.30-11pm. 6pm matchdays. 12.30-2.30, 4-11 on Saturdays. Hot food on matchdays. Pool, darts, jukebox, canteen.
Club Shop: Yes, selling programmes, magazines, scarves, badges. **Metal Badges:** £2
PROGRAMME DETAILS: Pages: 40 **Price:** 80p **Editor:** Simon Element (01235 520605)

PREVIOUS - **Name:** Abingdon FC (merged with St Michaels in 1899). **Leagues:** Oxford & District, West Berks, Reading Temperance, North Berks, Reading & Dist. 1927-50, Spartan 50-53, Hellenic 53-88, London Spartan 88-89.

CLUB RECORDS - **Attendance:** 1,400 v Oxford City, FA Cup September 1960. **Career appearances:** John Harvey-Lynch.

BEST SEASON - **FA Cup:** 4th Qual. Rd 60-61 0-2 v Hitchin, 89-90 1-3 v Slough(H), 92-93 1-2 v Merthyr T.(A) after 0-0. **FA Vase:** 5th Round replay 89-90.

HONOURS - Berks & Bucks Senior Cup 58-59 (R-up 88-89 92-93); Isthmian Lge Div 2 (Sth) 90-91 (Associate Members Tphy R-up 90-91); London Spartan Lge 88-89 (Lge Cup SF 88-89); Hellenic Lge(4) 56-57 58-60 86-87, R-up(3) 70-72 87-88, Lge Cup 57-58 70-71 81-82 (R-up 83-84 86-87), Div 1 75-76, Div 1 Cup 75-76, Res. Div(3) 69-71 86-87, Res. Div Cup 70-71 85-86, Res. Div Suppl. Cup 74-75; Oxford & Dist Lge(3) 1898-1901; Reading & Dist Lge 47-48; Berks & Bucks Jnr Cup 06-07; Abingdon Centenary Cup 58-59; Joan Lee Memorial Cup 69-70 70-71 86-87; Oxford I'mediate Lge (Res) 47-48; Newbury Graystoke Cup (Res) 92-93 94-95 (R-up 90-91).

Players progressing to Football League: Maurice Owen (Swindon Town), George Buck (Stockport County & Reading), Sammy Chung (Reading, Norwich City, Watford & Wolverhampton Wanderers).

BANSTEAD ATHLETIC

Founded: 1944 **Nickname:** A's. **Colours:** Amber/black/black
Midweek Matchday: Tuesday **Reserves' League:** Suburban **Change colours:** Red & white

Chairman: Terry Molloy **President:** **Press Officer:** Colin Darby
Secretary: Gordon Taylor, 116 Kingston Avenue, North Cheam, Surrey SM3 9UF (0181 641 2957).
Manager: Bob Langford. **Asst. Manager/Coach:** Micky Stephens **Physio:** Kevin Taylor
GROUND Address: Merland Rise, Tadworth, Surrey KT20 5JG (01737 350982).
Directions: Follow signs to Tattenham Corner (Epsom racecourse), then to Banstead Sports Centre. Ground adjacent to swimming pool. Half a mile from Tattenham Corner (BR). Bus 420 from Sutton stops outside ground. Also buses 406 & 727 from Epsom.
Capacity: 3,500 **Seats:** 250 **Cover:** 800 **Floodlights:** Yes
Clubhouse: All week 11am-11pm. 2 bars, real ale, bar snacks.
Club Shop: Yes **Sponsors:** PDM Marketing
PROGRAMME DETAILS: Pages: 38 **Price:** 80p **Editor:** Colin Darby (0181 643 5437)

PREVIOUS - Leagues: Surrey Int., Surrey Snr 49-65, Spartan 65-75, London Spartan 75-79, Athenian 79-84.

CLUB RECORDS - **Attendance:** 1,400 v Leytonstone, FA Amateur 53. **Win:** 11-0 **Defeat:** 0-11 **Career goalscorer:** Harry Clark **Career appearances:** Dennis Wall. **Transfer fee received:** None **Transfer fee paid:** None

BEST SEASON - **FA Cup:** 3rd Qual.Rd. 86-87. **FA Vase:** Semi - finals 96-97
Players progressing to Football League: W Chesney & B Robinson (Crystal Palace).
97-98 - Captain: Richard Langley **P.O.Y.:** Richard Langley **Top scorer:** Warren Burton

HONOURS: Surrey Snr Lg(6) 50-54 56-57 64-65, R-up(5) 49-50 54-56 57-59, Lg Cup 57-58, Charity Cup 52-53 58-59; London Spartan Lg R-up 77-78 (Lg Cup(2) 65-67); Surrey Prem. Cup R-up 91-92, 95-96; Surrey Snr Shield 55-56; Gilbert Rice F'lit Cup 81-82 86-87 (R-up(4) 82-86); Athenian Lg Cup(2) 80-82 (R-up 82-83 (SF 79-80); Surrey Int. Lg(2) 47-49, Cup 46-47 54-55; E. Surrey Charity Cup(4) 59-60 66-67 76-78, R-up 79-80, I'mediate Sect. 75-76 (R-up 76-77), Jnr Sect. 81-82; Southern Comb. Cup R-up 69-70; Suburban Lg R-up 86-87; Carlton T.V. Trophy R-Up 95-96.

BARKING

Founded: 1880 **Nickname:** The Blues **Colours:** Blue & white
Midweek matchday: Tuesday **Reserves' League:** None **Change colours:** Red & white

Chairman: John Edgeworth **Vice-Chairman:** Paul Lovell **President:** Terry Lovell
Secretary: Roger Chilvers, 50 Harrow Rd, Barking, Essex IG11 7RA (0181 591 5313).
Press Officer: Derek Pedder (0181 529 2483)
Manager: Arthur Wenborn **Asst Manager**. TBA **Physio:** TBA
GROUND Address: Mayesbrook Park, Lodge Avenue, Dagenham RM8 2JR (0181 595 6900).
Directions: Off A13 on A1153 (Lodge Ave), and grd 1 mile on left. Bus 162 from Barking station. Nearest tube Becontree.
Capacity: 2,500 **Cover:** 600 **Seats:** 200 **Floodlights:** Yes
Clubhouse: 2 large bars, open daily 11am-11pm (Sundays Noon-11pm). Hot & cold food and drinks.
Club Shop: No **Sponsors:** Capital Coin Ltd
PROGRAMME DETAILS: **Pages:** 16 **Price:** 80p **Editor:** Roger Chilvers

PREVIOUS - **Leagues:** London 1896-98 09-23, South Essex 1898-21, Leyton & Dist 1899-1900, Athenian 23-52. **Names:** Barking Rovers, Barking Institute, Barking Woodville, Barking Town. **Grounds:** Eastbury Field, Vicage Field (until 1973).

CLUB RECORDS - **Attendance:** (At Mayesbrook) 1,972 v Aldershot FA Cup 2nd Rd 78. **Win:** 14-0 v Sheppey Utd Mithras Cup 69-70 **Defeat:** 0-8 v Marlow. **Transfer fee received:** £6,000 for Alan Hull (Orient). **Transfer fee paid:** None over £1,000 **Career goalscorer:** Neville Fox 241 (65-73) **Career appearances:** Bob Makin 566

BEST SEASON - **FA Vase:** 96-97 **FA Amateur Cup:** Runners-up 26-27 **FA Cup:** 2nd Rd rep. 81-82 1-3 v Gillingham (A) after 1-1. Also 2nd Rd 78-79 79-80 83-84, and 1st Rd 26-27 28-29 78-80. - **League clubs defeated:** Oxford Utd 79-80.

Players progressing to Football League: 21 players since 1908 - 1956; Peter Carey (Orient 57), Lawrie Abrahams (Charlton 77), Kevin Hitchcock (Nottm Forest 83), Dennis Bailey (Fulham 86), Alan Hull (Orient 87).
97-98 Captain: **P.O.Y.:** Marc Baker **Top Scorer:** Micky Waite
HONOURS: FA Amateur Cup R-up 26-27; Isthmian Lg 78-79 (Lg Cup R-up 76-77); Athenian Lg 34-35 (R-up 24-25); London Lg 20-21 (Div 1 (A) 09-10); South Essex Lg Div 1 1898-99,R-up (2), Div 2 (4); London Senior Cup (4), R-up (3); Essex Senior Cup (7), R-up (8); Dylon Shield 79-80; Eastern Floodlit R-up (3); Essex Elizabethean 66-67, R-up (2); Essex Thameside (4), R-up (4); London Charity Cup 61-62 R-up 21-22; London Intermediate Cup 85-86; East Anglian Cup 37-38 53-54; Mithras Cup (3), R-up (2); Premier Midweek (2).

BEDFORD TOWN

Founded: 1908 **Reformed:** 1989 **Nickname:** Eagles **Colours:** Blue & white
Midweek Matchday: Tuesday **Change Colours:** Yellow & black

Chairman: David Donnelly. **Vice Chairman:** John Laing. **President:** Allen J Sturgess
Secretary: Barry Stephenson, 9 Aspen Ave., Bedford, Beds MK41 8BX (01234 342276).
Manager: Mick Foster **Asst Manager:** **Physio:** Mick Dilley
GROUND Address: Meadow Lane, Cardington, Beds.
Directions: On A603 Bedford to Sandy rd. Come off A1 at Sandy following signs to Bedford - grd on right. From Bedford take Cardington Rd out of town signed Biggleswade and Sandy.
Capacity: 3,000 **Seats:** 150 **Cover:** 500 **Floodlights:** Yes
Clubhouse: Open matchdays. Bar meals and snacks.
Club Shop: Good range of merchandise incl. programmes. Contact Les Usher (01234 303595).
PROGRAMME DETAILS: **Pages:** 40 **Price:** £1 **Editor:** Ray Horner (01234 359855)
Press Officer: **Sponsors:** Allen Sturges Travel

CLUB RECORDS - **Attendance:** 3,000 v Peterborough Utd, ground opening 6/8/93. At Allen Park: 1,227 v Bedford Utd, South Midlands League Division One, 26/12/91.
(predecessors: 18,407 v Everton, FA Cup 4th Round 12/2/66).
Career scorer: Jason Reed **Career appearances:** Jason Reed.

PREVIOUS - **Leagues:** South Midlands 91-94 *(predecessors: Utd Co's 08-39/ Southern 46-82).*
Grounds: Allen Park, Queens Park, Bedford (park pitch) 1991-93
(predecessors: London Rd; Gasworks; Queens Pk; The Eyrie, Raleigh Street).

Players progressing to Football League: Bill Garner (Southend 69), Nicky Platnaeur (Bedford Town, Bristol Rovers 77). Ray Bailey/Derek Bellotti/Billy Brown/Bert Carberry/Peter Hall/Dave Quirke/Bobby Fold (Gillingham 56-67), Phil Driver (Wimbledon 78), Joe Dubois (Grimsby T 53), Ted Duggan (Luton T 56), Harry Duke (Noprwich C 46), John Fahy (Oxford U 64), Ken Flint (Spurs 47), Joe Hooley (Accrington 61), Joe Kirkup (Reading 55), Graham Moxon (Exeter C 75), Bela Olah (Northampton 58), Gary Sergeant (Peterborough U 77), Neil Townsend (Southend U 73).
97-98 - Captain: **Top Scorer:** **P.O.Y.:**
HONOURS: South Midlands Lg 94-95 (Div 1 92-93, Floodlit Cup 94-95); Hinchingbrook Cup 94-95 94-95; Beds Sen Cup 94-95. *(predecessors: Southern Lg 58-59 (Div 1 69-70), Utd Co's Lg 30-31 32-33 33-34 (R-up 11-12 12-13 13-14 29-30 31-32 34-35 36-37), FA Cup 4th Rd 63-64 65-66, FA Tphy SF 74-75)*

BRACKNELL TOWN

Bracknell Town FC *Photo: Ian Morsman*

Founded: 1896 **Nickname:** Robins **Reserve's League:** Suburban (west)
Colours: Red & white/red/red **Change colours:** All blue **Midweek Matchday:** Tuesday
Chairman: Dave Mihell **Vice Chairman:** **President:**Jack Quinton.
Secretary: Cliff McFaden, 15 Goodways Drive, Bracknell, Berks RG12 9AU (01344 640349)
Manager: Bob Pritchard **Asst Manager:** **Physio:** Karen Cook

GROUND **Address:** Larges Lane, Bracknell RG12 9AN. Tel: 01344 412305 (club), 01344 300933 (office).
Directions: Off A329 just before Met Office r'bout by Bracknell College, ground 200 yards. From Bracknell (BR)/bus station - right out of station, follow path over bridge, left down steps and follow cycle path ahead, after 300yds follow curve over footbridge, right and follow lane to end, left and ground on left after bend.
Capacity: 2,500 **Seats:** 190 **Cover:** 400 **Floodlights:** Yes
Clubhouse: Members' bar open 11am-11pm Mon-Sat, 12-3 & 7-10.30pm Sun. Function hall bookable.
Club Shop: Yes, selling metal badges, programmes, scarves, club sweaters, club ties.

PROGRAMME DETAILS: Pages: 32 **Price:** 80p **Editor/Press Officer:** Robert Scully (01344 640721).

PREVIOUS - **Leagues:** Great Western Comb./ Surrey Snr 63-70/ London Spartan 70-75.
Grounds: None **Names:** None

CLUB RECORDS - **Attendance:** 2,500 v Newquay, FA Amateur Cup 1971. **Career Goalscorer:** Richard Whitty **Career Appearances:** James Woodcock. **Best FA Cup season:** 4th Qual Rd 88 (lost 1-2 v Cheltenham Tn), 4th Qual Rd 96 (lost 3-1 v Burton Albion)

Players progressing to Football League: Willie Graham (Brentford).
97-98 - Captain: Alan Williams **P.o.Y:** Tony Wood **Top Scorer:** Mark Anderson

HONOURS: Isthmian Lg Div 3 94-95 (Div 2 Sth R-up); Berks & Bucks Snr Cup R-up; Spartan Lg 82-83, R-up (2); Surrey Snr Lg 69-70 (Lg Cup 68-69 69-70).

CHALFONT St PETER

Founded: 1926 **Nickname:** Saints **Colours:** Red with green trim/green/green & red
Midweek home matchday: Tuesday **Change colours:** Yellow/blue/blue
Chairman: Peter Manson **Manager:** Kevin Stone **Physio:**
Secretary: Mal Keenan, 41 Cedar Avenue, Hazlemere, Nr High Wycombe, Bucks HP15 7EA (01494 718332)

GROUND Address: The Playing Fields, Amersham Road, Chalfont St Peter SL9 7BQ Tel: 01753 885797.
Directions: A413 from Uxbridge (London) to Chalfont. Turn left 100 yds after 2nd major roundabout (between Ambulance station and Community Centre. Two miles from Gerrards Cross (BR), regular buses from Slough.
Capacity: 4,500 **Cover:** 120 **Seats:** 220 **Floodlights:** Yes **Club Shop:** Yes
Clubhouse: Open every evening, Saturday afternoons and Sunday lunchtimes.

PROGRAMME DETAILS - Pages: 30 **Price:** 50p **Editor:** Secretary **Press Officer:** Secretary.

PREVIOUS - **Leagues:** Great Western Combination 1948-58; Parthenon 58-59; London 60-62; Spartan 62-75; London Spartan 75-76; Athenian 76-84.

CLUB RECORDS - **Attendance:** 2,550 v Watford, benefit match 85. **Career Goalscorer:** Unknown **Career Appearances:** Colin Davies **Transfer Fee Paid:** £750 to Chertsey (Steve Church, March 1989)

BEST SEASON - **FA Trophy:** 3rd Qual Rd 89-90 91-92. **FA Vase:** 4th Rd 87-88. **FA Cup:** 3rd Qual Rd 85-86 (wins over Banbury, King's Lynn and Barking).

Players progressing to Football League: Paul Barrowcliff (Brentford), Dean Hooper (Swindon).
97-98 - Captain: Rob Lee **P.o.Y.:** Matt Ward **Top scorer:** Jamie Cochrane

HONOURS: Isthmian Lg Div 2 87-88; Athenian Lg R-up 83-84 (Lg Cup 76-77 82-83); London Spartan Lg Div 2 75-76; Berks & Bucks Intermediate Cup 52-53; Berks & Bucks Benevolent Cup 64-65.

EDGWARE TOWN

Founded: 1939 **Nickname:** Wares. **Colours:** Green & white Qtrs
Midweek Matchday: Tuesday **Reserve League:** Suburban **Change colours:** All yellow

Chairman: Michael Flynn. **President:** Mr V Deritis **Patron:** Russell Grant.
Secretary: Barry Boreham, 28 St Brides Ave., Edgware, Middx HA8 6BS (0181 952 1685).
Manager: Jim McGleish. **Asst Manager:** **Physio:** Sarah Gow

GROUND Address: White Lion Ground, High Street, Edgware HA8 5AQ. **Tel:** 0181 952 6799.
Directions: Turn left out of Edgware tube station (Northern Line), turn left again at crossroads and ground 300yds on right in Edgware High Street behind White Lion pub. Buses 32, 288 and 142.
Capacity: 5,000 **Seats:** 220 **Cover:** 1,500 **Floodlights:** Yes **Club Shop:** No
Clubhouse: Open nightly and Fri, Sat, Sun lunchtimes. Hot & cold food matchdays, cold food lunchtimes.

PROGRAMME DETAILS - Pages: 16 **Price:** 50p **Editor:** Paul Gregory (0181 959 2535).
Press Officer: Tom Hooks **Sponsor:** Philiam Construction

PREVIOUS - **Leagues:** Corinthian 46-63; Athenian 64-84; London Spartan 84-90.
Names: Edgware F.C. **Grounds:** None.

CLUB RECORDS - **Attendance:** 8,500 v Wealdstone, FA Cup 1948. **Career Appearances:** John Mangan
Career Goalscorer: Steve Newing **Best season - FA Vase:** 5th Round, 1991-92

Players progressing to Football League:
Brian Stein (Luton), Dave Beasant (Wimbledon), Scott McGleish (Charlton 1994).

HONOURS - Isthmian Lg Div 3 91-92; London Spartan Lg 87-88 89-90 (Lg Cup 87-88); Corinthian Lg R-up 53-54, Memorial Shield 52-53 61-62; Athenian Lg R-up 81-82; Middx Snr Lg 40-41 41-42 42-43 43-44 44-45, Cup 47-48 (R-up 73-74 94-95); London Snr Cup R-up 47-48; Middx Border Lg Cup 79-80; Suburban Lg Div R-up 89-90.

HARLOW TOWN

Chairman: Jeff Bothwell **Press Officer:** Gavin McWilliams (01279 441894) **Founded:** 1879
Secretary: Jim Aldridge, 1 Brockles Mead, Harlow CM19 4PS (01279 860561)
Manager: Eddie McCluskey **Asst. Manager:** Fred Donnelly **Physio:** Malcolm Roddy
Ground: Harlow Sports Centre, Hammarskjold Rd, Harlow CM20 2JF (01279 445319).
Directions: Near town centre, 10 mins walk from Harlow (BR) station.
Capacity: 10,000 **Cover:** 500 **Seats:** 400 **Floodlights:** Yes **Nickname:** Hawks **Club Shop:** Yes
Clubhouse: Open daily 11-11 (10.30 Sundays). Hot & cold food available. **Sponsors:** BritSec Int. Ltd
Colours: Red & white/white/white **Change:** White & yellow/yellow/yellow
Midweek matches: Wednesday **Reserve's League:** Essex & Herts Border Comb.
Programme: 32 pages, 70p **Editor:** Phil Tuson (01279 416743)

Previous - **Leagues:** East Herts (pre-1932); Spartan 32-39 46-54; London 54-61; Delphian 61-63; Athenian 63-73; Isthmian 73-92; inactive 92-93. **Grounds:** Marigolds 1919-22; Green Man Field 22-60.

Honours - Isthmian Lg Div 1 78-79 (R-up 82-83, Div 2 Nth 88-89, Yth Cup 77-78), Ath'n Lg Div 1 71-72, E Angl. Cup 89-90, Knight F'lit Cup R-up 87-88, Essex Snr Cup 78-79, Essex F'lit Competition R-up 71-72, London Lg Chal. Cup 59-60, Spartan Lg Cup 52-53, Epping Hosp. Cup(3) 46-49, Essex & Herts Border Comb Cup 75-76, Fred Budden Tphy 88-89 89-90, Chelmsford Yth Lg 86-87 (Lg Cup 86-87 87-88).

CLUB RECORDS - **Attendance:** 9,723 v Leicester, FA Cup 3rd Rd replay 8/1/80. **Goalscorer:** Jeff Wood (45 in 88-89). **Appearances:** Norman Gladwin 646 (1949-70). **Win:** 12-0 v Hertford Ath. (H), E. Herts Lge 5/10/29. **Defeat:** 0-11 v Ware (A), Spartan Lge Div. One (East) 6/3/48.

BEST SEASON - **FA Amtr Cup** 2nd Rd 72-73, **FA Tphy** 2nd Rd(2) 80-82, **FA Vase** 3rd Rd 88-89. **FA Cup:** 4th Rd 79-80 (lost 3-4 at Watford). Also 1st Rd 80-81 81-82.
League clubs defeated in FA Cup: Southend, Leicester 79-80.

Players progressing to Football League: Jeff Wood (Charlton 75), Neil Prosser (B'mouth 80)

HEMEL HEMPSTEAD

Chairman: Ted Garnham **President:** Tom Abbott. **Vice President:** Dave Lloyd.
Secretary: Adrian Marson, 1 Pelham Court, Hemel Hempstead HP2 4UN. (01442 243053)

Manager: Mike Vipond. **Asst Manager:** Mark Pearson. **Physio:** Chris Hewitt

Ground: Vauxhall Ground, Adeyfield Rd, Hemel Hempstead HP2 4HW (01442 259777) **Nickname:** Hemel
Directions: Euston to Hemel Hempstead Station. H2 or H3 bus to Windmill Rd, Longlands.
Capacity: 3,000 **Seats:** 100 **Cover:** Yes **Floodlights:** Yes **Founded:** 1885 **Club Shop:** Yes
Clubhouse: (01442 259777). 7-11pm weekdays, 12-11pm w/ends & Bank Hols. Tea bar open matchdays

Colours: All red with white trim **Change colours:** All blue **Reserves' League:** Essex & Herts Border Comb.
Programme: 36 pages, 50p **Editor/Press Off.:** Brian Jackson **Sponsors:** Dexion **Midweek Matches:** Tuesday

Previous - **Leagues:** Spartan 22-52; Delphian 52-63; Athenian 63-77. **Names:** Apsley 1885-1947; Hemel H'stead Town (merged with Hemel H'stead Utd in 1947). **Grounds:** Crabtree Lane (til '71).

HONOURS - Herts Snr Cup 05-06 07-08 08-09 25-26 61-62 65-66 91-92, Herts Charity Cup/Shield 25-26 34-35 51-52 63-64 76-77 83-84 (R-up 90-91), Spartan Lg 33-34, Herts Intermediate Cup 54-55 65-66 83-84, West Herts St Mary Cup 70-71 75-76 82-83 85-86 90-91 91-92 93-94, Athenian Lg Div 1 R-up 64-65 (Reserves Cup 65-66), Delphian Lg(reserves) 54-55 (Reserves Cup 54-55 61-62).

CLUB RECORDS - **Goalscorer:** Dai Price. **Appearances:** John Wallace, 1012. **Attendance:** 2,000 v Watford 1985 (at Crabtree Lane: 3,500 v Tooting, FA Amtr Cup 1st Rd 1962).

BEST SEASON - **FA Cup:** Never past Qualifying Rounds.
Players progressing to Football League: Colin and Ernie Bateman (Watford).
Local Press: Hemel Gazette, Herald. **Local Radio:** Beds Radio.

HERTFORD TOWN

President: Bernard Molloy **Chairman:** John Hedley **Vice Chairman:** Graham Wood.

Secretary: Stephen Hedley, 28 Cherry Tree Green, Hertford SG14 2HP (0992 587011).
Press Off.: Graham Showell **Comm. Mgr:** Peter Slade **Manager:** David Whitehead **Physio:** Ray Price

Ground: Hertingfordbury Park, West Street, Hertford (0992 5837011). **Nickname:** The Blues
Directions: Rail to Hertford Nth (from Moorgate) or Hertford East (Liverpool Str.); both 15 mins walk. Green Line bus to town centre then 10 mins walk. By road; off bypass heading east, turn off at Ford garage.
Capacity: 6,500 **Seats:** 200 **Cover:** 1,500 **Floodlights:** Yes **Founded:** 1908
Club Shop: Souvenirs from Graham Showell, 5 Beehive Lane, Welwyn Garden City AL7 4BB. **Clubhouse:** Yes

Colours: Blue & yellow/blue/blue **Change colours:** All red **Midweek Matches:** Tuesday **Sponsors:** None
Programme: 28 pages, 40p **Editor:** Martin Climpson:(01992 589972)
Reserves' Lge: Essex & Herts Border Comb.

PREVIOUS - **Leagues:** Herts Co./ Spartan 21-47 48-59/ Delphian 59-63/ Athenian 63-72/ Eastern Co's 72-73. **Names:** None **Grounds:** None.

HONOURS - Herts Char. Cup 72-73, Herts Snr Cup 66-67, Hertford Char. Shd 19-20 20-21 35-36 49-50 55-56 59-60, Eastern Co's Lg Cup 72-73, East Anglian Cup 62-63 69-70, Southern Co's Comb. F-lit Cup 94-95, Mithras Cup SF 85-86.

BEST SEASON - **FA Cup:** 4th Qual. Rd. 73-74 (lost 1-2 at Hillingdon Borough).

CLUB RECORDS - **Attendance:** 5,000 v Kingstonian, F.A. Amateur Cup 2nd Rd 55-56.
Appearances: Robbie Burns.
Players progressing to Football League: G Mazzon (Aldershot)

HORSHAM

Founded: 1885 **Nickname:** Hornets **Colours:** Yellow & green halves/green/yellow
Midweek Matches: Tuesday **Reserves' League:** Suburban **Change colours:** Sky & navy/navy/sky
Chairman: Frank King **Vice Chairman:** Jeff Barratt **President:** Geoff Holtom
Secretary: Eric Mallard, 6 Morrell Avenue, Horsham, West Sussex RH12 4DD (01403 267687 H; 0181 643 6406 B)
Manager: Russell Mason **Asst Mgr/Coach:** Peter Shaw **Physio:** Geoff Brittain.
GROUND: Queen Street, Horsham RH13 5AD (01403 252310). **Directions:** From the station turn left into North Street. Pass the Arts Centre to the traffic lights and turn left. At the next set of lights (200 yards) turn left again into East Street. East Street becomes Queen Street after the Iron Bridge and the ground lies opposite Queens Head public house.
Capacity: 4,500 **Seats:** 300 **Cover:** 3,000 **Floodlights:** Yes **Club Shop:** Yes
Clubhouse: Normal licensing hours. Hot and cold snacks. Dancehall.
PROGRAMME: 40 pages, £1 **Editor:** A Hammond (01403 217316). **Press Officer:** J Barratt (01403 267627)
Club Sponsors: Sunley Homes.
Record Attendance: 8,000 v Swindon, FA Cup 1st Rd, November 1966.
Best FA Cup year: 1st Rd 47-48 (lost 1-9 at Notts County), 66-67 (lost 0-3 v Swindon).

PREVIOUS - **Leagues:** W Sussex Sen; Sussex County 26-51; Metropolitan 51-57; Corinthian 57-63; Athenian 63-73. **Grounds:** Horsham Park, Hurst Park, Springfield Park

HONOURS - Sussex Snr Cup 33-34 38-39 49-50 53-54 71-72 73-74 75-76; Sussex RUR Cup (13); Sussex Floodlight Cup 77-78; Sussex County Lg (7), R-up (4), Lg Cup 45-46 46-47; Metropolitan Lg 51-52; Athenian Lg Div 1 72-73, Div 2 69-70 72-73; West Sussex Sen Lge (4); ICIS Div 3 95-96.

Players progressing to Football League: Jamie Ndah (Barnet), Darren Freeman (Fulham).
97-98 - Captain: R Knight **P.o.Y.:** D Green **Top scorer:** M Smart

HUNGERFORD TOWN

Founded: 1886 **Nickname:** Crusaders **Colours:** White/blue/white
Midweek Matchday: Tuesday **Reserves' League:** Suburban (West) **Change colours:** All red
Chairman: Alan Holland **Vice Chairman:** Ron Tarry **President:** Sir Seton Wills
Secretary: Ken Holmes, 10 Bulpit Lane, Hungerford, Berks RG17 0AU (01488 682277)
Manager: Don Rogers **Asst Manager:** Colin Moyle **Physio:** Gerald Smith
GROUND Address: Town Ground, Bulpit Lane, Hungerford RG17 0AY. (01488 682939 -club, 684597 - boardroom, 684597 Fax). **Directions:** M4 jct 14 to A4, right and left at Bear Hotel, through town centre on A338, left into Priory Rd, second left into Bulpit Lane, over crossroads, ground on left. 3/4 mile from Hungerford BR station.
Capacity: 3,000 **Seats:** 172 **Cover:** 200 **Floodlights:** Yes **Club Shop:** Yes
Clubhouse: Open every evening and lunchtimes including Sunday. 2 bars, dancehall, boardroom/committee room, darts, pool, fruit machines. Hot & cold snacks. Stewards: Richard Crook & Chris Barrett (01488 682939).
PROGRAMME: 24 pages, 50p **Editor:** M Wiltshire (01488 682818).
Press Officer: Ron Tarry (01488 682539) **Club Sponsors:** Kerridge Insurance
Best FA Cup year: 1st Rd 79-80, 1-3 v Slough T. (A)

PREVIOUS - **Leagues:** Newbury & D.; Swindon & D.; Hellenic 58-78. **Names:** None **Grounds:** None

CLUB RECORDS - **Attendance:** 1,684 v Sudbury Town, FA Vase SF 1st leg 88-89 (20,000 v Modena in Italy 1981). **Scorer:** Ian Farr (268) **Appearances:** Dean Bailey (approx 400) **Record Transfer Fee Paid:** £4,000 for Joe Scott (Yeovil Town) **Received:** £3,800 for Joe Scott (Barnstaple Town).

HONOURS - FA Vase SF 77-78 79-80 88-89; Berks & Bucks Snr Cup 81-82 (R-up 75-76 76-77); Hellenic Lg Div 1 70-71, Prem Div Cup 77-78, Div 1 Cup 70-71, Benevolent Cup 60-61; Hungerford Cup 96-97.

Players progressing to Football League: Steve Hetzke (Reading, Blackpool, Sunderland), Bruce Walker (Swindon, Blackpool), Des McMahon (Reading), Brian Mundee (Bournemouth, Northampton), Darren Anderson.
97-98 - Captain: Keith Pennicott-Brown **P.o.Y.:** Daniel Gay **Top scorer:** Barry Flippance (17)

LEIGHTON TOWN

Founded: 1885 **Nickname:** Reds **Colours:** Red & white
Midweek Matchday: Tuesday **Reserve's League:** Suburban **Change colours:** All blue
Chairman: Iain S McGregor **President:** Mike Hide
Secretary: Alec Irvine, 12 Rowley Furrows, Linslade, Leighton Buzzard, Beds LU7 7SH (01525 376475).
Press Officer: Iain S McGregor (01525 370142) **Manager:** Peter Lawrence **Physio:** George Lathwell
GROUND: Bell Close, Lake Street, Leighton Buzzard, Beds (01525 373311).
Directions: From bypass (A505) take A4146 (Billington Rd) towards Leighton Buzzard, straight over mini-r'bout & 1st left into car park - ground behind Camden Motors just before town centre. Half mile from Leighton Buzzard (BR) station. Buses from Luton, Aylesbury and Milton Keynes.
Capacity: 2,800 **Seats:** 155 **Cover:** 300 **Floodlights:** Yes **Club Shop:** Yes
Clubhouse: Normal licensing hours. Snack/refreshment bar on matchdays - full rang of hot snacks & drinks.
PROGRAMME: 50p **Editor:** Andrew Massey (01908 613404) **Sponsors:** Camden Motors

PREVIOUS - **Leagues:** Leighton & District; South Midlands 22-24 26-29 46-54 55-56 76-92; Spartan 22-53 67-74; United Counties 74-76. **Name:** Leighton United **Ground:** None

CLUB RECORDS - **Attendance:** 1,522 v Aldershot T., Isthmian Lg Div 3, 30/1/93 **Record win:** 7-2. **Record defeat:** 1-6.
Best Season - FA Cup: Third Qual. Round 70-71, 1-2 v St Albans City (A)

HONOURS: Isthmian Lge Div 3 R-up 95-96; Sth Midlands Lg 66-67 91-92, Lg Cup 90-91, O'Brien Tphy 90-91, Reserve Div 1 87-88 91-92 94-95, Res Div 2 76-77, Res Challenge Cup 93-94 94-95; Beds Snr Cup 26-27 67-68 68-69 69-70 92-93; Bucks Charity Cup 94-95; Spartan Lg Div 2 23-24 27-28; Leighton & District Lg, Beds Intermediate Cup(res) 90-91; Beds Yth Cup 91-92 92-93 94-95; Chiltern Youth Lg 94-95, Lg Cup 93-94; East Anglian Yth.Cup 94-95; Assoc Mem Cup 96-97;

MARLOW

Formed: 1870 **Nickname:** The Blues **Colours:** Royal, white trim/royal/royal
Midweek matchday: Tuesday **Reserves' League:** Suburban Premier. **Change colours:** Orange & black

Chairman: Terry Staines **President:** **Vice-Chairman:**
Secretary: Paul Burdell, 69 Wycombe Rd., Marlow. (01628 483722)
Press Off./Comm. Man.: Terry Staines. **Information Line** (local call rates): 01628 477032).
Manager: Graham Pritchard **Coach:** Derek Sweetman **Physio:** TBA

GROUND Address: Alfred Davis Memorial Ground, Oak Tree Road, Marlow SL7 3ED (01628 483970).
Directions: A404 to Marlow (from M4 or M40), then A4155 towards town centre. Turn right into Maple Rise (by ESSO garage), ground in road opposite (Oak Tree Rd). 1/2 mile from Marlow (BR). 1/4 mile from Chapel Street bus stops.
Capacity: 3,000 **Cover:** 600 **Seats:** 250 **Floodlights:** Yes
Clubhouse: Open matchdays & most evenings. Snack bar open matchdays.
Club Shop: Sells programmes, badges, ties, pens, videos etc. **Sponsors:** The Marlow Building Company

PROGRAMME DETAILS: Pages: 40 **Price:** £1 **Editor:** Terry Staines

PREVIOUS - **Leagues:** Reading & Dist.; Spartan 1908-10 28-65; Great Western Suburban; Athenian 65-84. **Name:** Great Marlow. **Grounds:** Crown Ground 1870-1919); Star Meadow 19-24.

CLUB RECORDS - **Attendance:** 3,000 v Oxford United, FA Cup 1st Rd 1994. (Ground - 8,000 Slough T. v Wycombe W., Berks & Bucks Snr Cup Final, 1972). **Goalscorer:** Kevin Stone 31. **Appearances:** Mick McKeown 500+. **Fees - Paid:** £5,000 for Richard Evans (Sutton Utd. 94). **Received:** £8,000 for David Lay from Slought Town 94.

BEST SEASON - **FA Cup:** Semi-Finals 1882; 3rd Rd 92-93 (1-5 v Tottenham); 1st Rd on 19 times - 1871-85 86-88 92-93 1991-92 94-95. **FA Trophy:** 1st Rd 1987-88, 91-92. **FA Vase:** 5th Rd replay 74-75.

HONOURS - Isthmian Lg Div 1 87-88, Div 2 South R-up 86-87, Lg Cup 92-93; Spartan Lg Div 1 37-38 (Div 2 West 29-30); Berks & Bucks Sen Cup (11) + 90-91 94-95.

Players progressing to Football League: Leo Markham (Watford 1972), Naseem Bashir (Reading).
96-97 - Captain: Colin Ferguson **P.o.Y.:** Grant Goodall **Top scorer:** J Caesar

Local Press: Bucks Free Press, Maidenhead Advertiser, Evening Post.
Local Radio: Eleven 70, Radio 210, Thames Valley Radio

METROPOLITAN POLICE

Founded: 1919 **Nickname:** Blues **Colours:** All blue
Midweek Matches: Tuesday **Reserves' League:** Suburban **Change colours:** Black & White stripes

Chairman: Des Flanders QPM. **Vice Chairman:** Dick Hebberd **President:** Sir Paul Condon QPM
Secretary: Tony Brooking, 15 Westmoreland Avenue, Hornchurch, Essex. RM11 2EJ.(01708 450715)
Manager: Mel Thomas **Physio:** Dick Pierce **Club Sponsors:** McDonalds

GROUND: Metropolitan Police Sports Ground, Imber Court, East Molesey (0181 398 7358). **Directions:** From London: A3 then A309 to Scilly Isles r'bout, right into Hampton Court Way, left at 1st r'bout into Imber Court Rd - ground faces in 300yds. From M25 jct 10: A3 towards London for 1 mile, A307 through Cobham, left immediately after Sandown Park into Station Rd - ground 1 mile on left. Half mile from either Thames Ditton or Esher BR stations.
Capacity: 3,000 **Seats:** 297 **Cover:** 1,800 **Floodlights:** Yes **Club Shop:** No
Clubhouse: (0181 398 1267). Four bars, dancehall, cafeteria open 9am-11pm. Hot & cold food.

PROGRAMME DETAILS: 10 pages, 50p **Editor/Press Officer:** Cliff Travis (01932 782215).

PREVIOUS - **Leagues:** Spartan 28-60; Metropolitan 60-71; Southern 71-78 **Grounds:** None **Name:** None

CLUB RECORDS - **Attendance:** 4,500 v Kingstonian, FA Cup 1934. **Goal Scorer:** Mario Russo **Appearances:** Pat Robert **Win:** 10-1 v Tilbury 1995 **Defeat:** 1-11 v Wimbledon, 1956

BEST SEASON - **FA Cup:** 1st Rd - 32-33, 0-9 v Northampton T. (A); 84-85, 0-3 v Dartford (H); 94-95, 0-3 v Crawley T. (H)

HONOURS - Isthmian Lg Div 2 R-up 77-78 87-88; Spartan Lg 28-29 29-30 36-37 38-39 45-46 53-54 54-55, (R-up 47-48), Lg Cup 59-60 (R-up 57-58); Middx Snr Cup 27-28; Surrey Snr Cup 32-33, Charity Shield 38-39; Metropolitan Lg Cup 68-69 (Amtr Cup 68-69 69-70); London Snr Cup R-up 34-35 40-41; Herts & Middx Comb. 39-40; Diadora Lg Carlsberg Trophy Winners 94-95.

97-98 - Captain: Paul Towler **P.o.Y:** Adam Wickens **Top Scorer:** Jason Prins
Local Press: Surrey Comet, Surrey Herald.
Local Radio: County Sounds.

Metropolitan Police

NORTHWOOD

Back Row (L-R): Bob Webster (Asst Mgr), Terry Hibbert, mark Keadell, Tony Sibanda, Tony Choules (Mgr), Dave Sargent, Gary Williams, Dave Walters, Gary Boreham. Front Row: John Toogood (Coach), Lee Carroll, Chris Gell, Keith Welsh, Andy Sherry, Andy Reeder, Paul Halbert, Lawrence Holmes

Founded: 1902 **Nickname:** Woods **Colours:** All red
Midweek Matches: Tuesday **Reserve League:** Suburban **Change colours:** All white
Chairman: Andy Johnson **Vice Chairman:** Geoff Foster **President:** Lothar Hahn
Secretary: Steve Williams, 35 Evelyn Drive, Hatch End, Pinner, Middx HA5 4RL (0181 428 1533 - H & fax).
Manager: Tony Choules **Physio:** George Price **Sponsors:** IFS Freight Forwarding
GROUND: Northwood Park, Chestnut Avenue, Northwood (01923 827148).
Directions: A404 (Pinner-Rickmansworth) - Chestnut Ave. on left by large grey iron railway bridge. Third of a mile from Northwood Hills station (Metropolitan Line) - turn right out of station to r'bout, left into Pinner Rd, left into Chestnut Ave. after 300yds. Buses 282 and H11 to Northwood Hills.
Capacity: 2,250 **Seats:** 150 **Cover:** 400 **Floodlights:** Yes **Club Shop:** No
Clubhouse: Weekends and most evenings from 6pm. Bar. Hot and cold food. Pool, juke-box.
PROGRAMME: 52 pgs 80p **Editor:** A Evans (0181 566 2880) **Press Off:** M Russell (01923 827690)
PREVIOUS - Leagues: Harrow & Wembley 32-69; Middx 69-78; Hellenic 79-84; London Spartan 84-92.
Names: Northwood Town **Grounds:** None
CLUB RECORDS - Attendance: 1,642 v Chelsea Friendly July 97 **Goal Scorer:** Martin Ellis **Appearances:** Norman Heslop **Best Season - FA Cup:** 2nd Qual Rd 94-95 **FA Vase:** Qtr finals 96-97
Players progressing to Football League: Gavin Maguire, Derek Payne (Barnet), Warren Patmore (Cambridge).
97-98 - Captain: Chris Gell **P.o.Y:** Chris Gell/Dave Walters **Top Scorer:** Paul Halbert
HONOURS: Isthmian Lg Associate Members Cup 92-93; London Spartan Lg 91-92 (R-up 89-90), Lg Cup 89-90 91-92; Hellenic Lg Div 1 78-79 (Prem Div Cup R-up 81-82); Middx Lg 77-78 (R-up 72-73 76-77), Div 1 R-up 71-72, Challenge Cup 74-75 76-77 77-78; Middx Snr Charity Cup R-up 93-94; Middx Snr Cup SF 91-92 92-93, Jnr Cup 46-47 47-48 48-49; Harrow & Wembley Lg (9); Middlesex Premier Cup 94-95.

THAME UNITED

Colours: Red & black hoops/black/red & black hoops. **Founded:** 1883
Change colours: Green & white **Sponsors:**
Midweek Matchday: Tuesday **Nickname:** United
Reserves' League: Suburban (Prem)
Chairman: Jim Tite **Vice Chairman:**
Secretary: Neil Crocker, 8 Lincoln Place, Thame, Oxford OX9 2ER (01844 213568)
Press Officer: Neil Crocker **Manager:** Andy Sinnott **Asst Man:** Alan Thorn
GROUND Address: Windmill Road, Thame, Oxon OX9 2DR (01844 213017).
Directions: Into Nelson Street from Market Square. 3 miles from Haddenham & Thame Parkway (BR). Nearest bus stop at Town Hall (half mile away).
Capacity: 2,500 **Seats:** 230 **Cover:** 400 **Floodlights:** Yes **Club Shop:** No
Clubhouse: Open every evening and weekend lunchtimes. Banquetting facilities for 200 (weddings, dinners, etc).
PROGRAMME DETAILS: Pages: 24 **Price:** £1 **Editor:** Sally Turner

PREVIOUS - **Leagues:** Oxon Senior; Hellenic 1959-87; South Midlands 1987-91. **Name:** Thame FC. **Ground:** None.

CLUB RECORDS - **Attendance:** 1,035 v Aldershot, Isthmian Div 2 4/4/94. **Win:** 9-0 v Bracknell, 31/10/92 **Defeat:** 2-11 v Hungerford, FA Cup Prelim. Rd 1984. **Career Goalscorer:** Not known **Career Appearances:** Steve Mayhew.

BEST SEASON - **FA Cup:** Third Qualifying Round 91-92 (lost 0-4 to Salisbury).

HONOURS - Isthmian Lg Div 2 94-95, Div 3 R-up 92-93; Hellenic Lg 61-62 69-70, Premier Div Cup(4); Sth Mids Lg 90-91; Oxon Snr Cup 1894-95 05-06 08-09 09-10 75-76 80-81 92-93; Oxon Intermediate Cup 76-77 78-79 91-92; Oxon Charity Cup.

TOOTING & MITCHAM UTD

Formed: 1932 **Nickname:** Terrors **Colours:** Black & white stripes/black/white
Midweek matchday: Tuesday **Reserve League:** Suburban. **Change colours:** All red.

Chairman: John Buffoni **President:** Cliff Bilham **Vice Chairman:** Alan Simpson
Secretary: Les Roberts, 91 Fernlea Road, Mitcham, Surrey CR4 2HG (01816 465275)
Commercial Manager: John Pollard. **Press Officer:** Jim Silvey 0181 640 5678 (H)
Manager: James Bolton **Coach:** Peter Shaw **Physio:** Danny Keenan
GROUND Address: Sandy Lane, Mitcham, Surrey CR4 2HD (0181 648 3248).
Directions: Tooting (BR) quarter mile. Sandy Lane is off Streatham Road near Swan Hotel.
Capacity: 8,000 **Cover:** 1,990 **Seats:** 1,990 **Floodlights:** Yes
Clubhouse: Open every evening and weekend lunchtimes. Wide variety of food available.
Club Shop: Sells souvenirs & confectionary. **Sponsors:** Claremont Coaches.
PROGRAMME DETAILS: Pages: 24 **Price:** 80p **Editor:** Jim Silvey.

PREVIOUS - Leagues: London 32-37, Athenian 37-56. **Ground:** None **Name:** None

CLUB RECORDS - **Goalscorer:** Alan Ives 92 (1972-78). **Appearances:** Danny Godwin 470. **Attendance:** 17,500 v QPR, FA Cup 2nd Rd 56-57. **Win:** 11-0 v Welton Rovers, FA Amateur Cup 62-63. **Defeat:** 1-8 v Kingstonian, Surrey Snr Cup 66-67 & v Redbridge F. (H), Loctite Cup 3rd Rd 19/2/91. **Fee Paid:** £9,000 for Dave Flint (Enfield). **Fee Received:** £10,000 for Herbie Smith (Luton).

BEST SEASON - **FA Trophy:** 2nd Qualifying Rd Replay 71-72 81-82. **FA Amateur Cup:** 1st Rd replay 22-23. **FA Cup:** 4th Rd 75-76, 1-3 v Bradford C. (A); 3rd Rd 58-59; 2nd Rd 56-57 76-77; 1st Rd 5 other occasions. - **League clubs defeated:** Bournemouth & Boscombe Ath, Northampton 58-59, Swindon 75-76.

HONOURS - Isthmian League 57-58 59-60 (Full Members Cup 92-93), Athenian League 49-50 54-55, London Challenge Cup R-up 59-60, Surrey Senior Cup 37-38 43-44 44-45 52-53 59-60 75-76 76-77 77-78, London Senior Cup 42-43 48-49 58-59 59-60 (R-up 43-44 44-45), South Thames Cup 69-70, Surrey Senior Shield 51-52 60-61 61-62 65-66.

Players progressing to Football League: Trevor Owen (Orient 1958), Dave Bumpstead (Millwall 1958), Paddy Hasty (Aldersot 1958), Walter Pearson (Aldershot 1961), Richie Ward & Alex Stepney (Millwall 1962 & 63), Vic Akers (Watford 1975), Paul Priddy (Wimbledon 1978), Carlton Fairweather & Brian Gayle (Wimbledon 1984).
Local Press: Mitcham News, South London Press, South London Guardian. **Local Radio:** Capital.

Thame United FC: Back Row (L-R); James Saulsbury, Richard Carr, Darren Cross, Chris Johnson, Keith Appleton. Middle Row; Shaun Liptrot, Andy Williams, Richard Gregory, Luke Beauchamp, Simon Anderson, Dave Tregurtha, Greg Williams, Chris Perkins (Physio). Front Row; Pete Lamont (Asst Mgr), Jon Gardner, Adrian Roberts, Dennis Gascoyne, Jim Tite (Chr), Anthony Burden, Jason Maciak, Darren McNamara, Andy Sinnott (Mgr).

WINDSOR & ETON

Founded: 1892 **Nickname:** Royalists **Colours:** All red with green trim
Midweek matches: Tuesday **Reserves' League:** Suburban (North) **Change colours:** White/black/black
Chairman: Peter Simpson/Kevin Stott **President:** Sir David Hill-Wood, Bt
Secretary: Steve Rowland, 91 Duke Street, Windsor, Berks SL4 1SJ (01753 774528 H, emergency only)
Press Officer: Secretary **Manager:** Allan Davies **Asst Manager:** Alan Rowe **Physio:** Des Hunt
GROUND: Stag Meadow, St Leonards Road, Windsor, Berkshire SL4 3DR (01753 860656).
Directions: A332 from M4 junct 6. Left at r'bout (B3173), left into St Leonards Rd at lights on T-junction, ground 500 yards on right on B3022 opposite Stag & Hounds PH. 1 mile from town centre - pass available to St Leonards Rd. BR to Windsor Central station (from) Slough or Windsor Riverside (change at Staines from Waterloo).
Capacity: 4,500 **Cover:** 650 **Seats:** 400 **Floodlights:** Yes **Club Shop:** Yes
PROGRAMME: 28 pages **Editor:** Eric Richford **Sponsors:** Murex Welding Products **Clubhouse:** Yes
PREVIOUS - Leagues: Southern 1895-96; West Berks; Great Western Suburban 1907-22; Athenian 22-29 63-81; Spartan 29-32; Great Western Comb; Corinthian 45-50; Metropolitan 50-60; Delphian 60-63.
CLUB RECORDS - Attendance: 8,500 (Charity match) **Appearances:** Kevin Mitchell **Fee Paid:** £9,000 for Keith White (Slough Town) **Fee Received:** £45,000 for Michael Banton & Michael Barnes (Barnet) **Best Season - FA Amateur Cup:** 4th Rd 21-22 **FA Vase:** Semi-Final 80-81 (QF 79-80) **FA Trophy:** 3rd Rd 88-89 **FA Cup:** 2nd Rd replay 83-84. 1st Rd on seven occasions; 25-26 80-81 82-86 91-92. **League clubs defeated:** None
Players progressing to Football League: Steve Adams (Charlton 1979), Dave Barnett (Colchester 1988), Vic Woodley (Chelsea & England), Billy Coward (QPR, Walsall), Ken Groves (Preston), Dave Regis (Notts County).
HONOURS: Isthmian Lg Div 1 83-84 (Div 2 R-up 82-83), Athenian Lg 79-80 80-81 (Lg Cup 79-80 (R-up 78-79 80-81), Div 2 Cup 63-64 (R-up 68-69)), Spartan Lg R-up 36-37 37-38 (Div 1 30-31), Metropolitan Lg R-up 53-54 (Lg Amtr Cup 51-52 52-53, Lg Cup 52-53 (R-up 53-54 54-55)), Gt Western Suburban Lg R-up 21-22, Berks & Bucks Snr Cup(11) 10-11 36-38 40-45 61-62 87-89 (R-up 07-08 24-25 26-27 38-39 46-47 62-63), Berks & Bucks Benev. Cup 35-36 37-38 46-47 62-63 (R-up 38-39 47-48 49-50).

WITHAM TOWN

Founded: 1947 **Nickname:** Town **Colours:** Red & black stripes/white/white
Midweek Matchday: Tuesday **Res's Lge:** Essex & Herts Border Comb. **Change colours:** Blue & white
Chairman: Mr A Marshall **Vice Chairman:** Reg Wright **President:** B Olley.
Secretary: J Claydon, 58 Silver St, Silver End, Witham, Essex CM8 3QG (01376 584086 H, 01376 583241 x426 B)
Manager: Spencer Pratten **Asst Mgr:** George Young **Physio:** John Barwick
GROUND: Spa Road, Witham, Essex CM8 1UN (01376 511198-lounge, 500146-reception, 520996-boardroom).
Directions: From Witham BR (network S.E.) station; through pub car park and follow road to Faulkbourne, at main r'bout turn left and ground is on the right. By road; Off A12 at Witham sign, left at 1st lights (Spinks Lane), right at end of road, follow road under railway bridge - ground 100yds on left.
Capacity: 2,500 **Seats:** 150 **Cover:** 300 **Floodlights:** Yes **Club Shop:** No.
Clubhouse: Open every night and weekend lunctimes. Hot bar snacks. Steward: Richard Green.
PROGRAMME: 24 pages, 60p **Editor:** Alison Gray **Press Officer:** G Vale (01376 513861)
PREVIOUS - Leagues: Mid Essex; Essex & Suffolk Border; Essex Senior 71-87. **Ground:** The Park
CLUB RECORDS - Attendance: 800 v Billericay Town, Essex Senior League, May 76. **Win:** 7-0 v Banstead 27/9/94 **Defeat:** 0-9 v Collier Row 21/10/95. **Goalscorer:** Colin Mitchell **Appearances:** Keith Dent (16 years)
Best Season - FA Vase: 5th Round, 85-86 **FA Cup:** 2nd Qual. Rd 87-88 (v Gravesend), 88-89 (v B. Stortford), 89-90 (v Dartford).
Players progressing to Football League: Steve Tilson (Southend).
HONOURS: Essex Snr Lg 70-71 85-86 (R-up 84-85 86-87), Tphy 85-86 (R-up 88-89); Essex Thameside Trophy R-up 95-96; Loctite Tphy SF 90-91.

WIVENHOE TOWN

Formed: 1925 **Nickname:** The Dragons **Colours:** Royal blue/yellow
Reserves' League: Essex & Suffolk Border Lge **Midweek matchday:** Tuesday **Change colours:** Red/black
Chairman: T.B.A. **Vice Chairman:** Dave Whymark **President:** Harry Welsh
Secretary/Press Officer: Mike Boyle, 15 Daniell Drive, Colchester, Essex (01206 573223).
Manager: Steve Dowman **Asst Manager:** Steve Pitt **Physio:** Barry Wreford
Ground: Broad Lane Ground, Elmstead Road, Wivenhoe CO7 7HA (01206 823416).
Directions: Coming out of Colchester towards Clacton take first turning (right) towards Wivenhoe, first left and ground clearly visible on right at cross-roads. 1 mile from Wivenhoe (BR).
Capacity: 3,000 **Cover:** 1,300 **Seats:** 250 **Floodlights:** Yes
Clubhouse: (01206 825380). Open normal pub hours. **Club Shop:** Sells a full range of souvenirs etc.
PROGRAMME: 36 pages 80p **Editor:** P Reeve

PREVIOUS - **Leagues:** Brighlingsea & District 1927-50; Colchester & East Essex 50-71; Essex & Suffolk Border 71-79; Essex Senior 79-86. **Grounds:** Spion Kop; Broomfield; Claude Watcham's Meadow; Vine Farm; Spion Kop; Broomfield; King George V Playing Fields; Essex University. **Name:** Wivenhoe Rangers.

CLUB RECORDS - **Attendance:** 1,912 v Runcorn, FA Trophy 1st Rd, Feb 1990. **Transfer fee received:** £5,875 for Bobby Mayes (Redbridge Forest). **Win:** 18-0 v Nayland. **Defeat:** 0-8 v Carshalton A. (H), Isthmian Lg 28/8/93. **Career goalscorer:** Paul Harrison, 258 in 350 games. **Career appearances:** Keith Bain, 536. **Best season - FA Cup:** 4th Qual Rd 89-90 2-3 v Halesowen Town (A), 94-95 1-2 v Enfield (H) **FA Trophy:** 2nd Rd replay 89-90 **FA Vase:** 5th Rd 82-83;
Players progressing to Football League: Robert Reinelt (Gillingham) 1993.

HONOURS: Isthmian Lg Div 1 89-90 (Div 2 Nth 87-88); Essex Snr Lg R-up 79-80 81-82 85-86 (Harry Fisher Tphy 83-84 85-86); Essex & Suffolk Border Lg 78-79, Div 1 72-73, Div 2 71-72, Lg Cup R-up(2); Colchester & East Essex Lg 52-53 55-56 (R-up 70-71), Div 1 59-60 69-70, Div 2 R-up 68-69, Lg KO Cup 51-52 52-53 54-55 55-56 (R-up 59-60), Challenge Cup 52-53); Brighlingsea & Dist Lg Div 1 35-36 36-37 47-48 (R-up 37-38), Lg KO Cup 36-37 37-38 47-48, Challenge Cup 36-37; Essex Snr Tphy 87-88. Essex Jnr Cup R-up 55-56 78-79; Amos Charity Cup(7) (R-up 72-73); Stokes Cup(3); Wivenhoe Charity Cup (4), (R-up [4]); Cristal Monopole Cup (5), (R-up 2); Sidney James Mem. Tphy 69-70 (R-up 72-73), Tolleshunt D'Arcy Mem. Cup(3) (R-up 2); Walton & District Charity Cup 73-74 78-79; Coggeshall Brotherhood Cup 80-81; Brantham Charity Cup R-up 82-83; Worthington Evans Cup 81-82 (R-up 80-81 85-86); Harwich Snr Cup R-up 84-85; Woodbridge Chal. Cup 91-92; Mat Fowler Shield 92-93 94-95.
Local Press: East Anglian Daily Times, Colchester Evening Gazette.
Local Radio: BBC Radio Essex, Radio Orwell.

WOKINGHAM TOWN

Sponsors: Swan Hill Homes. **Formed:** 1875 **Nickname:** The Town
Colours: Yellow & black/black/black **Change colours:** Red/white/red.
Midweek matchday: Tuesday **Reserves' League:** Suburban
Local Press: Wokingham Times, Wokingham News, Reading Evening Post. **Local Radio:** 210 FM
Chairman: P Walsh **President:** G Gale **Vice Chairman:** R Harrison
Secretary: John Aulsberry, 8 Paice Green, Wokingham RG40 1YN (0118 9790441).
Manager: Simon Pentland. **Physio:** Jon Croyden **Commercial Mgr:** Roy Merryweather (0118 9780253).
GROUND Address: Town Ground, Finchampstead Road, Wokingham, Berks RG40 2NR (0118 9780253/9780377).
Directions: Half mile from town centre on A321 (signed Camberley & Sandhurst) Finchampstead Rd - walk down Denmark Street to swimming pool and straight on onto Finchampstead Rd. Half mile from Wokingham (BR) - turn right out of station, walk along Wellington Rd to swimming pool, right into Finchampstead Rd - ground entrance on right immediately after railway bridge.
Capacity: 3,500 **Cover:** 1,500 **Seats:** 300 **Floodlights:** Yes
Clubhouse: Mon-Sat 12-3 & 7-11pm (12-3 & 4.30-11pm Sat matchdays), Sun 12-2.30pm. Hot & cold food & snacks.
Club Shop: Range of souvenirs. Football League & Non League programmes.

PROGRAMME DETAILS: **Pages:** 32 **Price:** £1 **Editor:** Mrs Anne Gale (c/o the club)
PREVIOUS - **Leagues:** Reading & Dist.; Great Western Comb 07-54; Metropolitan 54-57; Delphian 57-59; Corinthian 59-63; Athenian 63-73. **Grounds:** Oxford Road 1875-1883; Wellington Road 83-96; Langborough Rd 96-1906.

CLUB RECORDS - **Attendance:** 3,473 v Norton Woodseats, FA Amateur Cup 57-58. **Career Goalscorer:** Dave Pearce, 79. **Career Appearances:** Dave Cox, 533. **Transfer fee paid:** £5,000 for Fred Hyatt (Burnham, 1990). **Transfer fee received:** £25,000 for Mark Harris (C Palace 88).

BEST SEASON - **FA Cup:** 1st Rd replay 82-83, 0-3 v Cardiff (A) after 1-1. - **League clubs defeated:** None.
FA Trophy: Semi finals 87-88 **FA Amateur Cup:** 4th Rd 57-58

HONOURS - Isthmian Lg R-up 89-90 (Div 1 81-82, Full Members Cup R-up 94-95), Berks & Bucks Snr Cup 68-69 82-83 84-85 95-96, Berks & Bucks Intermediate Cup 52-53.
Players progressing to Football League: Ian Kirkwood (Reading 53), John Harley (Hartlepool 76), Kirk Corbin (Cambridge 78), Phil Alexander (Norwich 81), Doug Hatcher (Aldershot 83), Steven Butler & George Torrance (Brentford 84), Mark Harris (C Palace 88), Gary Smart (Oxford 88), Darren Barnard (Chelsea 90), Paul Holsgrove (Luton Town 91), Darron Wilkinson (Brighton) 92.

97-98 - Captain: Steve Croxford **P.o.Y.:** Neil Selby **Top scorer:** Neil Selby (20)

Corinthian Casuals Photo: Eric Marsh

Croydon Athletic

Ware FC Photo: Roger Turner

THIRD DIVISION

LEAGUE TABLE 1997-98

	P	Home W	Home D	Home L	Away W	Away D	Away L	F	A	Pts
Hemel Hempstead	38	15	3	1	12	3	4	86	28	87
Hertford Town	38	13	4	2	13	1	5	77	31	83
Harlow Town	38	10	6	3	14	5	0	81	43	83
Camberley Town	38	13	1	5	11	6	2	93	43	79
Ford United	38	11	5	3	12	4	3	90	34	78
East Thurrock United	38	11	3	5	12	4	3	70	40	76
Epsom & Ewell	38	10	2	7	7	4	8	69	57	57
Ware	38	9	2	8	8	4	7	69	57	57
Aveley	38	10	3	6	6	4	9	65	57	55
Corinthian Casulas	38	7	3	9	9	3	7	59	57	54
Hornchurch	38	6	7	6	6	2	11	55	68	45
Clapton	38	8	4	7	5	2	12	46	61	45
Flackwell Heath	38	7	4	8	5	5	9	50	76	45
Croydon Athletic	38	8	3	8	4	4	11	58	63	43
Tring Town	38	5	5	9	7	2	10	51	69	43
Southall	38	7	3	9	3	3	13	41	85	36
Dorking	38	7	4	8	2	2	15	49	94	33
Wingate & Finchley	38	4	3	12	3	5	11	46	80	29
Lewes	38	7	1	11	0	4	15	34	88	26
Kingsbury Town	38	3	2	14	2	1	16	35	93	18

RESULTS GRID 1997-98

HOME TEAM	1	2	3	4	5	6	7	8	9	10	11	12	13	14	15	16	17	18	19	20
1. Aveley	*	1-3	2-1	3-0	2-1	2-0	0-1	1-2	1-3	2-2	3-4	2-0	3-0	2-0	2-1	1-1	1-0	1-1	0-1	2-0
2. Camberley T.	1-3	*	3-0	1-0	0-1	7-2	0-2	1-1	4-0	1-2	2-3	2-1	1-0	4-0	2-1	5-0	2-1	6-0	1-0	2-0
3. Clapton	0-3	0-3	*	3-3	1-1	1-0	0-1	4-2	2-2	1-3	4-5	0-3	1-0	1-0	2-1	3-0	1-0	2-2	0-2	3-0
4. Corinthian C.	3-1	4-2	1-3	*	3-2	3-0	0-0	0-1	1-1	0-2	1-3	0-1	2-4	0-2	3-0	1-1	1-2	2-1	3-2	2-0
5. Croydon Ath.	3-2	1-4	0-1	1-3	*	7-1	1-2	5-2	2-1	0-1	1-1	1-1	0-3	2-1	2-1	3-1	1-2	1-4	2-2	5-1
6. Dorking	3-2	1-4	2-0	3-2	1-0	*	1-4	4-3	0-3	3-3	0-2	0-0	0-3	0-5	2-2	3-1	2-1	2-3	2-2	1-2
7. E Thurrock U.	1-1	0-1	1-0	3-0	3-0	3-0	*	3-1	3-1	1-0	1-2	0-2	0-0	2-1	1-2	3-0	1-1	3-0	3-1	0-2
8. Epsom & Ewell	4-2	1-1	0-1	0-1	3-1	2-1	7-2	*	1-0	0-1	2-3	2-1	1-2	2-2	2-0	4-0	6-0	1-2	1-2	2-0
9. Flackwell H.	1-1	1-3	1-1	3-1	0-0	4-1	0-3	0-3	*	2-3	1-3	1-3	3-2	2-3	3-0	2-1	2-1	2-1	0-2	1-1
10. Ford United	1-1	0-1	6-0	1-1	1-0	3-1	1-1	6-1	8-0	*	1-1	0-6	0-1	3-1	8-0	5-0	1-1	3-2	3-0	6-0
11. Harlow Town	1-1	2-2	2-0	2-0	1-1	3-0	2-0	1-1	0-0	1-3	*	0-1	2-4	1-0	2-0	2-1	4-1	1-0	2-0	2-2
12. Hemel Hemps.	1-0	1-1	2-1	3-0	3-0	2-1	6-0	1-0	7-0	3-1	2-2	*	1-2	2-1	3-2	2-0	2-1	1-0	1-1	3-0
13. Hertford T.	3-1	0-1	1-0	0-1	2-1	2-0	2-2	2-1	2-0	0-0	1-1	1-1	*	6-1	4-2	3-0	2-0	5-0	4-2	1-0
14. Hornchurch	4-2	3-3	1-1	0-3	3-1	0-0	1-2	1-1	0-0	1-0	0-3	2-4	0-4	*	0-2	2-0	2-1	4-2	1-1	4-4
15. Kingsbury T.	1-2	2-3	2-1	0-2	1-2	4-4	0-3	0-1	0-1	0-2	1-5	3-2	0-1	0-2	*	1-1	2-0	0-3	0-4	0-2
16. Lewes	0-3	1-4	2-0	1-3	2-1	3-1	0-5	1-2	1-4	0-3	0-1	0-1	3-0	1-2	4-1	*	2-2	2-1	1-6	1-0
17. Southall	3-2	1-7	2-1	1-1	1-4	2-0	1-2	1-0	2-2	1-3	0-4	0-7	0-1	1-0	1-0	2-0	*	2-3	1-7	2-2
18. Tring T.	0-2	1-1	0-1	0-4	1-1	2-0	0-2	1-1	3-1	0-2	2-2	0-1	0-3	2-1	4-1	3-1	1-2	*	1-3	1-1
19. Ware	2-0	4-2	2-1	0-1	1-0	0-4	3-3	2-3	5-0	0-2	1-2	0-2	0-5	1-2	3-1	1-1	4-1	1-0	*	1-0
20. Wingate & F.	4-5	2-2	0-4	1-3	0-3	2-3	0-3	1-2	1-2	0-0	3-6	1-3	0-1	2-2	4-1	2-0	5-0	0-1	1-0	*

RYMANS DIVISION THREE CLUBS 1998-99

AVELEY

Chairman: David Patient **President:** Ken Clay **Press Officer:** Terry King
Secretary: Alan Suttling, 50 Harvey, Grays, Essex RM16 2TX (01375 400741).
Manager: Craig Johnson **Asst Mgr/Coach:** Paul Armstrong **Physio:** Phil Hunter
GROUND: 'Mill Field', Mill Road, Aveley, Essex RM15 4TR (01708 865940). **Directions:** London - Southend A13, turn into Sandy Lane at Aveley. Rainham or Purfleet BR stations then bus No. 723 to the ground.
Capacity: 4,000 **Cover:** 400 **Seats:** 400 **Floodlights:** Yes **Founded:** 1927
Clubhouse: Normal pub hours. Bar snacks and hot food available **Club Shop:** No
Colours: Royal blue/white/royal blue **Change:** Red & white/red/red **Sponsors:** Dagenham Motors
Previous Leagues: Thurrock Combination 46-49/ London 49-57/ Delphian 57-63/ Athenian 63-73.
Midweek matches: Tuesday **Reserves' League:** Essex & Herts Border Comb.
CLUB RECORDS - Attendance: 3,741 v Slough T., FA Amateur Cup 27.2.71 **Goalscorer:** Jotty Wilks, 214
Appearances: Ken Riley, 422 **Win:** 11-1 v Histon, 24/8/63 **Defeat:** against Orient, Essex Thameside Trophy, 11/4/85.
Best FA Cup season: 1st Rd 70-71, 0-1 v Yeovil
League clubs defeated in F.A. Cup: None.
Honours: Isthmian Lg Div 2 (North) R-up 89-90, Lg (AC Delco) Cup 89-90; London Lg 51-52 54-55 (R-up 55-56, Lg Cup 53-54); Delphian Lg R-up 57-58 (Lg Cup 61-62); Athenian Lg 70-71 (Div 2 R-up 68-69); Essex Junior Cup 47-48 48-49; Essex Thameside Trophy 79-80; Hornchurch Charity Cup 81-82 (R-up 83-84); East Anglian Cup 88-89; FA Amateur Cup QF 70-71; FA Tphy 3rd Qualifying Rd replay 74-75; FA Vase 3rd Rd 89-90.

CAMBERLEY TOWN

Chairman: Ian Waldren **Vice Chairman:** **President:**
Secretary: Dave Slater, 33 Blythwood Drive, Frimley, Camberley, Surrey. GU15 1SD (01276 23096).
Manager: Paul Holden **Asst Manager:** Eric Howard **Coach:** Paul Holden
Press Officer: Andy Vaughan **Comm. Manager:** **Physio:** Ken Weaver
Ground: Krooner Park, Krooner Road, off Frimley Rd, Camberley, Surrey GU15 2QP (01276 65392).
Directions: M3 Jct 4, follow signs to Frimley, then B3411 towards Camberley, ground on left opp. 'The Standard' pub.
Capacity: 3,000 **Seats:** 195 **Cover:** 280 **Floodlights:** Yes **Founded:** 1896
Clubhouse: Open matchdays & 2 evenings. Food available from burger bar on matchdays. **Club Shop:** Yes
Colours: Red & white/red/red & white **Change colours:** Blue & yellow **Nickname:** Krooners, Reds or Town
Programme: 24 pages, 50p **Sponsors:** Zip Print **Midweek Matches:** Tuesday **Reserve's League:** Suburban
PREVIOUS - Leagues: Ascot & District; West Surrey; Aldershot Snr; Surrey Snr 22-73; Spartan 73-75; Athenian 75-77 82-84; Isthmian 77-82.
Club Records - Attendance: 3,500 v Crystal Pal. friendly 14.10.74. *Competitive: 2,066 v Aldershot T., Isthmian Lge Div. 3, 10.11.92.* **Appearances:** Brian Ives. **Win:** 15-0 v Royal Engineers, friendly, 20/9/19. **Defeat:** 0-11 v Abingdon Town (A), Isthmian League Division Two (South) 25/8/90.
Best F.A. Cup year: 4th Qual. 32-33 33-34 97-98.
HONOURS: FA Vase QF 85-86; Isthmian Lg Div 2 R-up 78-79; Surrey Snr Lg 30-31 31-32 32-33 (R-up 46-47 61-62), Lg Charity Cup 37-38 51-52 (R-up 31-32 36-37 54-55 72-73); Surrey Snr Cup 78-79 (R-up 35-36).

CHESHUNT

Founded: 1946. **Nickname:** Ambers **Colours:** Gold & black
Midweek matchday: Tuesday **Reserves' Lge:** Essex & Herts Border Comb **Change colours:** All blue

Chairman: Georgius Savva **Vice Chairman:** Paul Cully **President:** Paul Philips
Secretary: Mr Keith Hughes, 28 Peace Close, Rosedale, Cheshunt, Herts EN7 5EQ.
Manager: Tom Loizou **Asst Manager:** Kevin O'Dell **Physio:** Lou Dedman.

GROUND Address: The Stadium, Theobalds Lane, Cheshunt, Herts. **Tel:** 01992 626752
Directions: M25 to junction 25, A10 north towards Hertford, next roundabout third exit to next roundabout, turn left proceed under railway bridge, turn left, ground approx 400 yards on right. 400yds from Theobalds Grove BR station, Buses 310, 242, 311 & 363 to Theobalds Grove station.
Seats: 285 **Cover:** 600 **Capacity:** 2,500 **Floodlights:** Yes **Club Shop:** No
Clubhouse: Yes **Press Officer:** Neil Harrison **Sponsors:** None
PROGRAMME DETAILS - Pages: 28 **Price:** £1 **Editor:** Keith Hughes (01992 627195)
PREVIOUS - Leagues: Athenian 19-20 21-31 64-77; London 20-21 24-25 46-51 55-59; Delphian 51-55; Aetolian 59-62; Spartan 62-64; Isthmian 77-87.
Name: None **Ground:** None

CLUB RECORDS - Attendance: 7,000 v Bromley, London Senior Cup 1947. **Best FA Vase season:** Qtr Final 81-82 **Best FA Cup season:** 4th Qual. Rd(4)

Players progressing to Football League: Ian Dowie, Ruben Abgula, Steve Sedgeley, Lee Hodges, Paul Marquis, Steve Terry, Neil Prosser, Mario Walsh.

97-98 - Captain: Glen Wilkie **P.o.Y.:** Noel Lenihan **Top Scorer:** Glen Wilkie

HONOURS: Athenian Lg 75-76 (R-up 73-74), Div 1 67-68, Div 2 R-up 65-66, Lg Cup 74-75 75-76; Spartan Lg 62-63, Lg Cup 63-64 92-93, (R-up 89-90); London Lg 49-50 (R-up 56-57), Div 1 47-48 48-49 (R-up 46-47), Div 1 Cup 46-47, Lg Cup R-up 58-59, Park Royal Cup 46-47; Isthmian Lg Div 2 R-up 81-82 (Div 3 R-up 94-95); Herts Snr Cup 23-24 (R-up 48-49 49-50 68-69 69-70 71-72 73-74).

CLAPTON

Chairman: Ken Harris **President:** **Founded:** 1878
Secretary: Steven Walters,10 Buttfield Close,Dagenham Village,Essex.RM10 8TJ. (0181 596 0424).
Press Officer: Secretary **Manager:** Lyndon Lynch **Coach:** Jeff Davis **Physio:** Tony Blackwell
Ground: The Old Spotted Dog, Upton Lane, Forest Gate, London E7 9NP (0181 472 0822).
Directions: BR to Forest Gate, tube to Plaistow (District Line). Official entrance in Upton Lane. Docklands Light Railway to Prince Regent then 325 bus to ground.
Capacity: 2,000 **Seats:** 100 **Cover:** 180. **Floodlights:** Yes **Nickname:** Tons **Club Shop:** Yes
Clubhouse: Open most evenings & match day. Light snacks available. To hire please contact club.
Colours: Red & white stripes/black/black **Change colours:** All blue. **Midweek Matchday:** Tuesday
Programme: 12-16 pages 60p **Editor:** Secretary **Reserves' Lge:** Essex/Herts Border Com.
Previous Leagues: Southern 1894-96 (founder members); London 1896-97. **Sponsors:** Mullalley Const.
Club Records - Attendance: 12,000 v Tottenham Hotspur, FA Cup 1898-99. **Appearances:** Dave Fahy. **Defeat:** 0-14 v Nottingham Forest (H), FA Cup 1st Rd 1890-91.
League clubs defeated in FA Cup: Norwich City 1925-26.
Best FA Cup year: 3rd Rd Proper 25-26 (lost 2-3 to Swindon at Upton Park).
Players progressing to Football Lge: Numerous over past 116 years. Currently: Paul Williams (Crystal Palace), Gary Charles (Derby), Miguel de Souza (Birmingham).
97-98 - Captain: Dwayne Lewis **P.o.Y.:** Tony Marsh **Top scorer:** Robert Thorne
Hons: FA Amtr Cup 06-07 08-09 14-15 23-24 24-25 (R-up 04-05); Isthmian Lg 10-11 22-23 (R-up 05-06 07-08 09-10 24-25), Div 2 82-83; Essex Thames-side Tphy(2); A.F.A. Invitation Cup(2); London Snr Cup(2); London Charity Cup; Essex Snr Cup(4); Middlx Snr Cup; Essex Sen Trophy; First English team to play on the continent, beating a Belgian Select XI over Easter 1890.

CORINTHIAN-CASUALS

Chairman: D G Harrison **President:** Jimmy Hill **Gen Manager:** Steve Bangs.
Secretary: Brian Wakefield, 5 Martingales Close, Richmond, Surrey (0181 940 9208).
Match Secretary: G.Young, (0181 330 6643 H) **Team Manager:** Trevor Walker
Ground: King George's Field, Hook Rise South, Tolworth, Surrey KT6 7NA (0181 397 3368).
Directions: A3 to Tolworth r'bout (The Toby Jug). Hook Rise is slip road immediately after the Toby Jug pub. Turn left under railway bridge after a 1/4 mile - grd on right. Half mile from Tolworth (BR); turn left, continue to Toby Jug, then as above. K2 Hoppa bus from Kingston passes ground.
Seats: 126 **Cover:** 500 **Capacity:** 1,700 **Floodlights:** Yes **Founded:** 1939.
Clubhouse: Evenings, matchdays, Sunday lunchtimes. Darts, pool, hot & cold snacks on matchdays.
Programme: 24-48 pages, £1 **Editor:** Team Manager **Press Officer:** Secretary
Colours: White/navy/white **Change colours:** Chocolate & pink/sky/sky **Reserves' League:** Suburban
Previous Leagues: Isthmian 39-84, Spartan 84-97 **Best FA Cup season:** 1st Rd replay 85-86.
Players progressing to Football League: Peter Phillips (Luton Town), Andy Gray, Tony Finnegan, Alan Pardew to Crystal Palace.
Honours: FA Amat Cup R-up 55-56 (SF 56-57), London Spartan Lg R-up 92-93 (Lg Cup R-up 91-92).

CROYDON ATHLETIC

Chairman: Keith Tuckey **Vice Chairman / Press Officer:** Clive Thompson
Secretary: Dean Fisher, Flat 4, 316 Whitehorse Road, Croydon, Surrey CR0 2LE, (0181 405 4300 H, 0171 221 7292 B)
Manager: Micky Taylor **Asst Man.:** Des McCarthy **Physio:** M Reed **Coach:** Leon Maxwell
Ground: Mayfields, off Mayfield Road, Thornton Heath, Surrey CR7 6DN (0181-664-8343)
Directions: Follow A23 from London & continue on A23 into Thornton Road. After roundabout take 2nd on right into Silverleigh Road, left fork into Trafford Road which continues into Mayfield Road. To end and turn left and follow narrow road to ground. 1 mile from Norbury (BR). Buses 109, 154.
Seats: 163 **Cover:** 300 **Capacity:** 3,000 **Floodlights:** Yes **Founded:** 1990
Clubhouse: Open every evening & Sunday lunch. **Club Shop:** Yes **Sponsors:** T.C.S. Media
Programme: 52 pages, £1 **Editor:** Secretary **Midweek matches:** Tuesday **Reserve League:** Suburban (S)
Colours: Maroon & white/maroon/maroon **Change colours:** Yellow/royal
Club Records - Attendance: 550 **Record scorer:** Graham Edginton **Appearances:** Graham Edginton/ Paul Gall/Leon Maxwell.
Best season - FA Vase: 3rd Rd 94-95 **FA Cup:** 2nd Qual. Rd 94-95
97-98 - Captain: Steve Packer **P.o.Y.:** John Kennedy **Top Scorer:** John Kennedy
Players progressing to Football League: Jamie Ndah (Torquay Utd)
Honours: London Spartan Lg winners 94-95, R-up 88-89 93-94, (Reserve Div 88-89, R-up 88-89); London Snr Cup R-up 91-92; Southern Youth Lg 92-93; Bearman Harber Mem Trophy 87-88; Wirral Prog 86-87 96-97.

DORKING

Chairman: Jack Collins **President:** Ingram Whittingham **Vice-Chairman:** Ray Collins **Co. Sec.:** Martin Collins
Secretary: David Short, 29 Bennett Close, Cobham, Surrey KT11 1AH (01932 866496)
Manager: Steve Osgood **Asst Manager:** Bryan Stannard **Physio:** Bennie Fishlock
Ground: Meadowbank, Mill Lane, Dorking, Surrey RH4 1DX (01306 884112).
Directions: Mill Lane is off Dorking High St. next to Woolworths and Marks & Spencers opposite the White Horse pub. Fork right in Mill Lane past the Malthouse pub. 1/2 mile from both Dorking and Deepdene (BR) stations.
Capacity: 3,600 **Cover:** 800 **Seats:** 200 **Floodlights:** Yes **Formed:** 1880 **Nickname:** The Chicks
Clubhouse: Open matchdays, w/ends & training nights. Hot & cold food on matchdays. **Club Shop:** Yes
Programme: 48 pages £1 **Editor:** Paul Mason **Press Officer:** Bryan Bletso **Reserve League:** Suburban
Colours: Green & white hoops/green/yellow **Change colours:** All blue **Midweek matches:** Tuesday
Best FA Cup season: 1st Round Proper 92-93, 2-3 v Plymouth A. (H)
Previous Leagues: Surrey Senior 22-56 77-78; Corinthian 56-63; Athenian 63-74 78-80; Southern 74-77.
Honours: Isthmian Lge Div 2 Sth 88-89, (Full Members Cup R-up 92-93); Surrey Sen Cup R-up 1885-86 1989-90; Surrey Senior Shield (2), R-up (3); Surrey Sen Lge (4), R-up (2), Lge Cup (3); Lge Charity Cup (4), R-up (5); Gilbert Rice F'lit Cup 87-88 (R-up 89-90); Surrey I'mediate Cup 56-57 (R-up 54-55); Southern Comb. Challenge Cup 92-93; FA Trophy 2nd Rd 91-92; FA Vase 3rd Rd(3) 83-84 86-88.
PREVIOUS - Ground: Prixham Lane (until 1953). **Names:** Guildford & Dorking United (when club merged with Guildford in 1974)/Dorking Town 77-82.
CLUB RECORDS -
Attendance: 4,500 v Folkestone Town, FA Cup 1st Qual. Rd 1955. **Win:** 7-0 v Barking, Isthmian Lge Div. One, 31/10/92. **Goalscorer:** Andy Bushnell. **Appearances:** Steve Lunn.
Players progressing to Football League: Steve Scrivens & John Finch (Fulham), Andy Ansah (Brentford 1989).

EAST THURROCK UNITED

Chairman: Brian Grover **Vice Chairman:** Harry Caine. **President:** Alan Gower
Secretary: Malcolm Harris, 14 Colne Valley, Upminster, Essex RM14 1QA (017082 28818).
Press Officer: Secretary **Manager:** Tommy Lee **Physio:** Dave Sage
Ground: Rookery Hill, Corringham, Essex (01375 644166-club).
Directions: A13 London-Southend, take 1014 at Stanford-le-Hope for two and a half miles - ground on left. Two miles from Stanford-le-Hope and Basildon BR stations.
Seats: 160 **Cover:** 360 **Capacity:** 3,000 **Floodlights:** Yes **Founded:** 1969 **Nickname:** Rocks
Clubhouse: Open all day seven days a week. Hot and cold snacks. **Club Shop:** Yes
Programme: 24 pages, 50p **Editor:** Tony Smith (01375 892888)
Colours: Amber/black/black **Change:** Blue/white/white **Reserves' Lge:** Essex/Herts Border Com.
Previous Leagues: Sth Essex Comb.; Gtr London; Metropolitan 72-75; London Spartan 75-79; Essex Snr 79-92.
Players progressing to Football League: Greg Berry (Leyton Orient).
Honours: Metropolitan Lg Div 2 72-73, Essex Snr Lg R-up 88-89 (Lg Cup 88-89 91-92, Harry Fisher Mem. Tphy 83-84 90-91, Sportsmanship Award 81-82 86-87 89-89), Essex Snr Tphy R-up 91-92 95-96, Fred Budden Tphy R-up 89-90, Essex & Herts Border Comb. 89-90 (Lg Cup 89-90).
PREVIOUS - Name: Corringham Social (pre-1969 Sunday side). **Grounds:** Billet, Stanford-le-Hope 70-73 74-76/ Grays Athletic FC 73-74/ Tilbury FC 77-82/ New Thames Club 82-84.
CLUB RECORDS - Attendance: 947 v Trevor Brooking XI, May 1987. Competitive: 845 v Bashley, FA Vase 1989. **Goalscorer:** Graham Stewart 102. **Appearances:** Glen Case 600+. **Win:** 7-0 v Coggeshall (H) 1984. **Defeat:** 0-9 v Eton Manor (A) 1982, both Essex Snr League. **Transfer Fee Paid:** £2,000 + 10% of future fee for Greg Berry (Orient, 1989).

EGHAM TOWN

Founded: 1877 **Nickname:** Sarnies/Town **Colours:** All old gold with royal piping
Midweek Matches: Tuesday **Reserves' League:** Suburban **Change colours:** All royal or all white
Chairman: Patrick Bennett **Vice Chairman:** Peter Barnes **President:** Peter Barnes.
Club Administrator: Alison Thompson, 138A Thorpe Lea Rd, Egham, Surrey. TW20 8BL (01784 463562)
Managers: Steve Roberts & Derek Sweetman **Physio:** Alan Maynard.
GROUND: Runnymeade Stadium, Tempest Road, Egham, Surrey TW20 8HX (01784 435226).
Directions: M25 jct 13, follow signs to Egham, under M25 at r'bout, left to end, left at mini-r'bout, over railway crossing, left to end (Pooley Green Rd), right, Tempest Rd 2nd right. Bus 41 43 441 from Staines to Pooley Green Rd. Thirty mins walk from Egham or Staines (BR) station.
Capacity: 5,635 **Seats:** 335 **Cover:** 1,120 **Floodlights:** Yes **Club Shop:** No
Clubhouse: (01784 435226) 7-11pm daily & weekend lunchtimes. Members bar and function hall
PROGRAMME: 40 pages, £1 **Editor:** Mark Ferguson (01784 238606 W), Chris Thompson (01784 463562 H)
Press Officer: Mark Ferguson (01784 238606 W)
Record Gate: 2,000 - Egham XI v Select XI, Billy King Memorial match 1981. Competitive: 1,400 v Wycombe Wanderers, FA Cup 2nd Qualifying Rd 1972.
PREVIOUS - Leagues: Hounslow & District 1896-1914; Surrey Intermediate 19-22; Surrey Senior 22-28 65-67; Spartan 29-33 67-74; Parthenon 64-65; Athenian 74-77. **Names:** Runnymede Rovers 1877-1905; Egham FC 05-63
Record Scorer: Mark Butler 50 (91-92). Career record scorer too. **Record Appearances:** Dave Jones 850+
Best FA Cup year: 4th Qual Rd 90-91, 0-2 v Telford Utd (A)
HONOURS: Isthmian Lg Assoc Members Tphy R-up 91-92; Spartan Lg 71-72 (Lg Cup R-up 67-68); Athenian Lg R-up 75-76 (Div 2 74-75); Surrey Snr Cup R-up 91-92, Surrey Snr Lg 22-23, Lg Charity Cup 22-23 (R-up 26-27 34-35); Surrey Intermediate Lg 20-21, Charity Cup 19-20 20-21 (R-up 26-27); North West Surrey Charity Cup 20-21; Egham Twinning Tournament 67-68 71-72 74-75 75-76 76-77 80-81; Southern Comb. Floodlit Cup 77-78 (R-up 83-84).

EPSOM & EWELL

Chairman: Peter Atkins **Vice Chairman:** Stella Lamont **Nickname:** E's **Founded:** 1917
Secretary: David Wilson, 33 Delaporte Close, Epsom, Surrey KT17 4AF (01372 729817).
Press Officer: Sec. **Manager:** Adrian Hill **Coach:** John Wood **Physio:** John Wood
Ground: (Share with Banstead Ath. FC) Merland Rise, Tadworth, Surrey KT20 5JG (01737 350982).
Clubhouse: Normal licensing hours, food available. **Club Shop:** No
Programme: 28/32 pages, 50p **Editor:** Stella Lamont (01737 356245).
Colours: Royal & white **Change:** All yellow **Midweek Matches:** Tuesday **Reserves' League:** Suburban
Best Season - FA Cup: 1st Rd Proper 33-34, lost 2-4 at Clapton Orient.
FA Vase: R-up 74-75 **FA Trophy:** 2nd Rd Proper 81-82.
Previous Leagues: Surrey Snr 24-27 73-75; London 27-49; Corinthian 49-63; Athenian 63-73 75-77.
97-98 - Captain: Tony Boorman **Top Scorer:** Andy Boxall (23) **P.o.Y.:** Andy Nimmo
Hons: FA Vase R-up 74-75; London Lg 27-28, R-up (5); Corinthian Lg Memorial Shield 59-60 (R-up 51-52 56-57); Athenian Lg Div 2 R-up 75-76 (Lg Cup R-up 76-77, Div 2 Cup R-up 67-68); Isthmian Lg Div 2 77-78 (Div 1 R-up 83-84), Vanranel Ass Members Trophy R-up 97-98; Surrey Snr Lg 25-26 26-27 74-75 (R-up 73-74), Lg Cup 73-74 74-75, Charity Cup 26-27 (R-up 73-74), Surrey Snr Cup 80-81 (R-up 28-29 53-54 83-84); Surrey Snr Shield 32-33 54-55; Surrey Intermediate Cup 29-30, Charity Cup 57-58; Southern Comb. Cup 79-80 (R-up 82-83 92-93).

FLACKWELL HEATH

Chairman: T Glynn **Vice Chairman:** M Baker **President:** Ken Crook
Secretary: Mrs Christine Hobbs, 23 Southfield Rd., Flackwell Heath, Bucks. HP10 9BT (01628-521051)
Ground: Wilks Park, Heath End Rd, Flackwell Heath, High Wycombe, Bucks HP10 9EA (01628 523892).
Directions: M40 jct 4, follow A404 towards High Wycombe, 1st turning into Daws Hill Lane, continue for 2 miles until you see signs for the club, left into Magpie Lane, ground at rear of Magpie (PH). Bus 301 either from bus station or High Street near bottom of Crendon Street which comes from BR station. Ask for Oakland Way.
Capacity: 2,000 **Seats:** 150 **Cover:** Yes **Floodlights:** Yes **Club Shop:** No
Clubhouse: Open every night 6.30-11pm and before and after matches. Hot food in tea bar.
Programme: 18 pages 50p **Reserves' League:** Suburban **Founded:** 1907
Colours: Red/white/red **Change colours:** Yellow/black/yellow**Midweek Matches:** Tuesday
Best F.A. Cup season: 2nd Qualifying Round replay 1990-91 (lost 0-3 at Grays after 2-2 draw).
Previous Leagues: Wycombe & District; Gt Western Comb.; Hellenic 76-82; Athenian 82-84.
Hons: Gt Western Combination 57-58 62-63; Hellenic Lg Div 1 R-up 76-77; Berks & Bucks Snr Cup SF 85-86.

FORD UNITED

Chairman: Jim Chapman **Vice-Chairman:** George Adams **President:** Paddy Byrne **Manager:** Denis Elliott
Secretary: Colin Mynott, 11 Rantree Fold, Basildon, Essex SS16 5TG (01268 452965 H, 01268 404624 B).
Ground: Ford Spts & Soc. Club, Rush Green Rd., Romford (01708 745678). **Directions:** On the A124 (Rush Green road) on left going towards Hornchurch. 2 miles from Romford (BR). Buses 173, 175 87, 106, 23.
Seats: 354 **Cover:** Yes **Capacity:** 3,000 **Floodlights:** Yes **Founded:** 1958 **Club Shop:** No
Clubhouse: 4 bars, 2 dance halls, tea bar. **Programme:** Yes **Editor:** Michael Ewen (01708 724178 H)
Colours: All blue **Change:** All red
Sponsor: Sky Sports **Nickname:** Motormen **Reserves' League:** Essex & Herts Border Comb.
Record Attendance: 58,000 Briggs Sports v Bishop Auckland, at St James Park, Newcastle, FA Amateur Cup.
Previous Leagues: Spartan, Aetolian, Metropolitan, Essex Senior
97-98 - Captain: Jeff Wood **Top Scorer:** Jeff Wood **P.o.Y.:** Jeff Wood
Honours: FA Amateur Cup SF 53-54; London Snr Cup 55-56 56-57 94-95 97-98; Essex Snr Lge 91-92 96-97,(R-up 94-95), Trophy 90-91 91-92, Cup 39-40 49-50 50-51 51-52 85-86, R-up 96-97; Spartan Lg 49-50 50-51 55-56 56-57 57-58; London Lg 36-37 38-39; Essex Elizabethan 59-60 60-61 70-71; Gtr London Lg 70-71; Sportsmanship Award 77-78 79-80 80-81); Essex & Herts Border Comb.(res) 94-95 (Lg Cup 94-95).

HORNCHURCH

Chairman: Brian Davie **Vice Chairman:** K Nicholls **Manager:** Dave Cox **Physio:** D Edkins
Secretary: Ted Harris, 13 Claremont Gdns, Upminster, Essex RM14 1DW (01708 227891).
Ground: The Stadium, Bridge Avenue, Upminster, Essex RM14 2LX (01708 220080).
Directions: Fenchurch Street to Upminster (BR) then 10 mins walk. Or tube to Upminster Bridge (LT), right outside station, 2nd right into Bridge Ave., ground 150yds on right. By road Bridge Avenue is off A124 between Hornchurch and Upminster. Buses 248, 348, 370, 373 from Romford or Upminster BR stations.
Capacity: 3,000 **Seats:** 300 **Cover:** 350 **Floodlights:** Yes **Founded:** 1923 **Nickname:** Urchins
Clubhouse: Mon-Fri 7.30-11, Sat 12-11, Sun 12-3. Cafeteria open matchdays on ground. **Club Shop:** Yes
Colours: Red & white/red/red **Change colours:** Purple & yellow **Sponsors:** Premier Snacks
Programme: 16-20 pages with admission **Editor/Press Off.:** Rob Monger(01268 490847)
Midweek Matches: Tuesday **Reserves' League:** Essex & Herts Border Comb.
Previous Leagues: Romford 1925-38/ Spartan 38-52/ Delphian 52-59/ Athenian 59-75.
Honours: Athenian Lg 66-67, Romford Lg(2), Essex Snr Trophy R-up 86-87, Essex Jnr Cup, Essex Thameside Tphy 84-85, F.A. Vase 5th Rd 74-75, Isthmian Yth Cup, Carlsberg Trophy R-up 93-94.

KINGSBURY TOWN

Chairman: Allan J Davies **Secretary:** David Thomas, 9 Hillview Gardens, Kingsbury, NW9 0DE
Press Officer: Allan Davies (01895 443761) **Manager:** Peter Blain **Physio:** Margaret Romer
Ground: Silver Jubilee Park, Townsend Lane, Kingsbury, London NW9 7NE (0181 205 1645).
Directions: Underground to Kingsbury, cross road and take bus 183 to Townsend Lane (2 miles) - ground in far left-hand corner of Silver Jubilee Park.
Capacity: 2,500 **Seats:** 165 **Cover:** 400 **Floodlights:** Yes **Nickname:** Kings **Founded:** 1927
Clubhouse: Mon-Fri 7-11, Sat 12-11, Sun 12-2.30 & 7-10.30. Food on matchdays. **Club Shop:** Yes
Colours: Royal/white/royal **Change colours:** Yellow/navy/yellow **Sponsors:** VPA Entertainment Technology.
Programme: 16-20 pages, 50p **Editor:** Allan Davies **Reserves' League:** Suburban **Midweek Matches:** Tuesday
Previous Leagues: Hellenic 27-30 (as Davis Sports)/ Willesden & District 30-43/ Middx Snr 44-47/ Parthenon 47-59/ / Spartan 59-76 78-81/ Athenian 76-78 81-84.
Hons: FA Vase 4th Rd 74-75; Isthmian Lg Div 2 Nth R-up 85-86; Spartan Lg Cup R-up 59-60 64-65; Parthenon Lg 51-52 (Prem Charity Cup 52-53 53-54; Snr Charity Cup 53-54); Middx Snr Cup R-up 88-89; Middx Charity Cup 85-86 (R-up 88-89); Middx Lg Charity Cup(3) 44-47; Willesden & Dist. Lg R-up 30-31 (Div 2 34-35).

LEWES

Chairman: S White **President:** W D Carr **Manager:** Jimmy Quinn **Asst Man.:**
Secretary: John Lewis, 16 The Haven Brighton Road, Lancing, BN15 8EU (01903 537641)
Ground: The Dripping Pan, Mountfield Road, Lewes BN7 1XN (01273 472100). **Directions:** Two minute walk from Lewes (BR) - turn left out of station and left into Mountfield Road. Ground 100 yards on right.
Capacity: 2,600 **Cover:** 400 **Seats:** 400 **Floodlights:** Yes **Nickname:** Rooks **Founded:** 1885
Clubhouse: (01273 472100). Bar, tea bar, pool, table tennis. **Steward:** P Brook. **Club Shop:** Yes
Colours: Red & Black stripes/black/red **Change colours:** Yellow/green **Midweek matches:** Tuesday
Programme: 32 pages, £1 **Editor:** Martin Burke **Reserves' League:** Sussex Co. Res. Sect.
Previous Leagues: Mid Sussex 1886-1920; Sussex County 20-65; Athenian 65-77.
Honours: Isth. Lg Div 2 R-up 79-80 91-92; Ath'n Lg Div 1 69-70 (Div 2 67-68); Sussex Co. Lg 64-65 (R-up 24-25 33-34 58-59 63-64, Lg Cup 39-40); Mid Sussex Lg 10-11 13-14; Sussex Snr Cup 64-65 70-71 84-85 (R-up 79-80 82-83 87-88); Sussex Royal Ulster Rifles Charity Cup(3) 61-63 64-65; Gilbert Rice F'lit Cup 82-83 88-89; Neale Tphy 68-69; Sussex F'lit Cup 76-77 (SF 83-84); Southern Counties Comb Div 1 80-81.

SOUTHALL

Chairman: J Gurney **President:** R E Fowler **Founded:** 1871
Secretary: Keith Chamberlin, 4 Shelley Avenue, Greenford, Middx UB68 8RU (0181 575 6023)
Manager: Keith Chamberlin **Assistant Manager:** Steve Hawkins **Physio:** Keith Chamberlin
Ground: Pendley Sports Centre, Cow Lane, Tring, Herts. HP23 5NS (014428 23075). Sharing with Tring Town for another season. **Ground directions & details:** As Tring Town
Clubhouse: Normal pub hours. Hot snacks available on matchdays. **Club Shop:** No **Nickname:** Fowlers
Colours: Red & white stripes/white/red **Change:** Blue & black **Sponsors:**
Programme: 6 pages, 50p **Editor:** Keith Lavender **Midweek Matchday:** Tuesday **Res' Lge:** Middx County
Previous Leagues: Southern 1896-1905; Gt Western Suburban; Herts & Middx; Athenian 19-73.
97-98 - Captain: Steve Whitehead **P.o.Y.:** Danny Yeoman **Top Scorer:** Alan Hughes
Hons: FA Amtr Cup R-up 24-25 (SF 25-26 52-53), FA Vase R-up 85-86, Isthmian Lg Div 2 R-up 74-75, Gt Western Suburban Lg 12-13, Athenian Lg 26-27 (R-up 54-55), Middx Snr Cup(12) 07-08 10-11 11-12 12-13 22-23 23-24 24-25 26-27 36-37 44-45 53-54 54-55, Middx Charity Cup 10-11 11-12 13-14 22-23(jt with Botwell Mission) 23-24(jt with Botwell Mission) 27-28 36-37 51-52 68-69 83-84, London Snr Cup SF 35-36 84-85.

Dorking FC *Photo: Eric Marsh*

TILBURY

Founded: 1900 **Nickname:** Dockers **Colours:** Black & white qtrs/black/red
Midweek Matches: Tuesday **Reserves' League:** Essex & Herts Border Comb. **Change colours:** All red
Chairman: R Nash **Vice Chairman:** T.Harvey **President:** J B Wilson
Secretary: L Brown, 52 Lionel Oxley House, Grays, Essex (01375 409938)
Press Officer: Chairman **Manager:** Shaun McCann **Physio:** Roger Hutton

GROUND: Chadfields, St Chad's Rd, Tilbury, Essex RM18 8NL (01375 23093). **Directions:** BR from Fenchurch Street to Tilbury Town then bus 377 or 20 mins walk - right out of station, walk along Left Hand Road fork to town centre traffic lights, left into St Chads Rd, Chadfields 1 mile on left. By road: M25 (jct 30 or 31) - A13 Southend bound, Tilbury Docks turn off after 4 miles, Chadwell St Mary turn off (left) after another one and a half miles, left again after 400 metres, right at r'bout (signed Tilbury), right into St Chad's Rd after half mile, 1st right into Chadfields for ground.
Capacity: 4,000 **Seats:** 350 **Cover:** 1,000 **Floodlights:** Yes **Club Shop:** No.
Clubhouse: Open every evening, all day Fri. & Sat. and Sun. lunchtimes. Hot & cold food available.
PROGRAMME: 32 pages, 50p **Editor:** Lloyd Brown **Club Sponsors:** None

CLUB RECORDS - Attendance: 5,500 v Gorleston, FA Cup 4th Qual. Rd 19/11/49.
Best Season - FA Cup: 3rd Rd 77-78, 0-4 v Stoke City (A). 1st Rd 49-50, 0-4 v Notts Co. (A)
HONOURS: FA Amtr Cup QF; Isthmian Lg Div 1 75-76, (Div 1 Cup 74-75); Athenian Lg 68-69 (Div 2 62-63); London Lg 58-59 59-60 60-61 61-62, Lg Cup 58-59 60-61 61-62, R-up (3); Delphian Lg 67-68 (Div 2 62-63); Essex Snr Cup 60-61 63-64 72-73 74-75 (R-up 46-47 47-48 69-70 71-72 78-79).

TRING TOWN

Chairman: Harry Bowden **Secretary:** Tony Huhn, 6 Sovereign Court, Willow Road, Aylesbury, Bucks HP19 3NL (01296 432496 H, 0956 281797 Mob)
Manager: Paul Burgess **Asst Manager:** Micky Connolly **Physio:** Stuart McCorkindale
Ground: Pendley Sports Centre, Cow Lane, Tring, Herts HP23 5NS (01442 823075).
Directions: One mile from Tring centre on A41 - direct connection to M25 (jct 20) via new A41 bypass. One and a half miles from Tring (BR). Numerous buses from station and Watford-Aylesbury routes serve ground.
Capacity: 2,500 **Seats:** 150 **Cover:** 250 **Floodlights:** Yes **Nickname:** T's. **Founded:** 1904
Clubhouse: All licensing hours. Dancehall, pool, darts, kitchen. **Club Shop:** No
Programme: 24 pages 50p **Editor/Press Officer:** Alan Lee (01702 216063) **Midweek Matchday:** Monday
Colours: Red & white stripes/white/white **Change:** Yellow & blue stripes/blue/blue **Reserves' Lge:** None
Previous Leagues: Gt Western Combination; Spartan 53-75; Athenian 75-77.
Honours: Spartan Lg 66-67, R-up 68-69. Herts Charity Shield winners twice, R-up 4. Athenian Lg Div 2 R-up 76-77, Herts Snr Cup R-up 77-78.
CLUB RECORDS - Attendance: 2,500 v West Ham, friendly.
Best FA Cup year: 3rd Qual. Rd replay 84-85, 0-5 v Fisher(A) after 1-1.

WARE

Chairman: W J Luck **Secretary:** I Bush, 42 Burnett Squ, Hertford, Herts SG14 2HD (01992 587334).
Manager: Steve Ringrose **Coach:** Dermot Drummy **Physio:** Frank Roberts
Ground: Wodson Park, Wadesmill Road, Ware Herts SG12 0HZ (01920 463247).
Directions: A10 off at junction A602 & B1001 (Ware North), turn right at roundabout 300yds, and follow Ware sign, past Rank factory, turn left at main roundabout onto A1170 (Wadesmill Rd). After 3/4 mile stadium on right.
Capacity: 3,300 **Seats:** 312 **Cover:** 500 **Floodlights:** Yes **Nickname:** Blues **Founded:** 1892
Clubhouse: Licensed bar open matchdays. Light snacks at refreshment bar. **Club Shop:** Yes
Programme: 24 pages, 50p **Editor/Press Officer:** Tony Raisborough (01707 656568)
Colours: Blue & white stripes/blue/red **Change colours:** Amber/black **Midweek Matchday:** Tuesday
Reserves' Lge: Essex & Herts Border Comb. **Sponsors:** Charvill Bros Ltd.
Previous Leagues: East Herts; North Middx 07-08; Herts County 08-25; Spartan 25-55; Delphian 55-63; Athenian 63-75.
Honours: Herts Snr Cup 1898-99 03-04 06-07 21-22 53-54, Herts Char. Shield 26-27 56-57 58-59 62-63 85-86, Herts Char. Cup R-up 64-65 65-66 78-79 89-90, Spartan Lg 52-53 (Div 1 Sect.B 51-52, Div 2 Sect.A 26-27), Athenian Lg Div 2 Cup 65-66 72-73, East Anglian Cup 73-74, Herts Co. Lg 08-09 21-22, East Herts Lg 04-05 06-07 (Lg Cup 06-07).
RECORD Attendance: 3,800 v Hendon Amt Cup 56-57.
Best FA Cup year: First Round Proper 68-69 (lost 6-1 to Luton Town).

WINGATE & FINCHLEY

Chairman: Peter Rebak **Vice Chairman:** **President:** H Whidden.
Secretary: Richard Cooper, c/o Club Tel,0181 446 2217 Fax 0181 343 8194
Press Off.: Harvey Ackerman **Manager:** Bobby Fisher **Coach:** Jeff Bookman **Physio:** Amos Shanaan
Ground: The Abrahams Stadium, Summers Lane, Finchley, London N12 0PD.(0181 446 2217)
Directions: North Circular (A406) to jct with High Road Finchley (A1000), go north and Summers Lane is 200 yds on rt - parking 80 cars. Tube to East Finchley (Northern Line) and then 263 bus to Summers Lane towards North Finchley
Capacity: 8,500 **Seats:** 500 **Cover:** 500 **Floodlights:** Yes **Founded:** 1991 **Nickname:** Blues
Clubhouse: Open during matches. Also tea-bar selling most refreshments. **Club Shop:** No.
Colours: Blue/white/blue **Change Colours:** All red **Midweek matches:** Tuesday
Programme: 24 pages, 50p **Editor:** Marc Morris (0181 371 6008) **Reserve's Lge:** Sub Lge U18
Previous Leagues: (as Wingate & Finchley) South Mids 89-95
Honours: None since Wingate (1946) and Finchley (late 18800s) merged in 1991
Record Attendance: 9,555 - Finchley v Bishop Auckland, F.A. Amateur Cup QF 49-50.

COURAGE COMBINED COUNTIES FOOTBALL LEAGUE

Chairman: Bill Lale
20 Beverley Gardens, Rustington, Sussex BN16 3LT Tel: 01903 770551

Hon. Secretary: Clive Tidey
22 Silo Road, Farncombe, Godalming, Surrey GU7 3PA Tel: 01483 428453

A highly successful season for the Courage Combined Counties League saw Ashford Town (Middlesex) win the Premier Division Championship for the fourth season in succession, an unprecedented achievement and surely unequalled at this level of football.

Just as they had in the previous season, Ashford came from behind in the last few matches, when title favourites Reading Town, who had been at the top for virtually the whole of the season, slipped up over the Easter period. In the end the margin was four points and the championship was clinched on the penultimate Saturday of the season when to be certain Ashford needed a win at fourth placed Raynes Park Vale. Against one of the best teams in the division, Ashford were supreme on the day, a 3-0 victory ensuring that they could not be caught.

Reading then had to take a point from their last match at Netherne to ensure the runners-up spot, following a magnificent run by Ash United, who after a poor start did not lose a single league match after 28th October 1997. Reading made no mistake with a 5-0 victory on Cup Final morning but Ash, under player-manager Jamie Horton, will surely pose a significant threat in season 1998-99.

On their way to the championship Ashford equalled the league goal scoring record, held by themselves, when they beat Cranleigh at home by 12 goals to nil. Just for good measure, they scored ten the following Saturday at Hartley Wintney.

At the other end of the table it was extremely disappointing for Cove, in their centenary season, to finish at the bottom, ten points behind Cranleigh, who after winning their first four games in August, only managed four more victories over the remainder of the season.

In the Premier Challenge Cup many of the top sides were knocked out early and it was newcomers Chessington & Hook who fought their way to the final, after narrowly overcoming the existing cup-holders, Feltham, in extra time in the semi-final. Their opponents were Ash United who had scored six goals in each of the previous three rounds, including a 6-3 victory in the semi-final over Raynes Park Vale. On a pleasant evening at Woking's magnificent ground, Chessington froze on the night and were unable to contain a rampant Ash United, superbly marshalled by Tony Calvert who was named "man of the match". The final scoreline was 5-0 to Ash which clinched some well deserved silverware but Chessington had much to be pleased about, consolidating well in their first season back in senior football after several years. They had set an excellent example to all new clubs with the exceptional level of hospitality they showed to visitors and, with floodlights now due at Chalky Lane, they should have a bright future in more ways than one.

In national competitions, although only one side, Viking Sports, managed a victory in the FA Cup, both Ashford and Chipstead reached the Third Round Proper of the Carlsberg FA Vase, eventually sustaining narrow defeats at Stotfold and Folkestone Invicta respectively. In County competitions, success was fairly hard to find but Godalming & Guildford put up a splendid show at Woking in the Surrey Senior Cup, losing only by the odd goal.

In other competitions, Godalming & Guildford pulled off an excellent win at hosts Hampton FC to win the Southern Combination Challenge Cup by three goals to nil in their first season of entry, whilst in an all Combined Counties affair, Chipstead beat Farnham Town 3-2 in the final of the Southern Counties Floodlight Competition. Farnham also battled their way through to the final of the Aldershot Senior Cup but were narrowly beaten by Camberley Town.

With neither Ashford nor Reading able to meet the ground improvement deadline for promotion to the Ryman League, it is anticipated that all of last season's clubs will again be competing in the League with the addition of AFC Wallingford, Chiltonian League champions, who have complied with all of the grading requirements for the Combined Counties. This will give a constitution of 21 clubs.

Several clubs are in the process of upgrading their facilities and season 1998-99 will be the crunch for some as all member clubs are required to have lights for the start of season 1999-2000. At the time of writing there are six clubs still to light up (plus Wallingford). Several now have the necessary planning permission but finances may still be a problem for some.

In the Reserve competition, known as Division One, a close race ensued between existing champions Godalming & Guildford, Chessington & Hook, Merstham and Bedfont. In the end the title went to Chessington by a single point from Godalming, with Merstham a point behind Godalming.

In the Division One Challenge Cup, some high powered administration was required when the final due to be at Woking was called off at the last moment due to the unseasonable weather at the end of April. With no other date available, some frantic phone calls found Sandhurst Town willing and able to stage the final at short notice and the match went ahead, with Godalming a& Guildford beating Reading Town by two goals to nil. the League's grateful thanks go to Sandhurst, where the playing surface at their new ground is a credit to all concerned.

In the Division One Challenge Shield, where the opening matches are played on a league basis, Cobham and Ash United reached the final, at Farnham Town, which was deadlocked at one apiece after extra time. The dreaded penalty shoot out saw the Shield go to Cobham with a 3-2 margin, to clinch only the club's third trophy in 100 years of football. In County Cup matches, Cove Reserves did well to reach the Fifth Round of the Hampshire Intermediate Cup.

The League, thanks to the ongoing sponsorship from Courage, was able to resume representative matches for the first time in several seasons. Although only one match was eventually played for various reasons, it was an excellent evening, with the League team, managed by Derek Parsons, losing 2-3 to a strong Hellenic League side at Ashford Town FC. With new friendships being made it is very much hoped that this fixture will become an annual event in the future.

The annual sportsmanship awards, presented in honour of the late John Whitefoot, were won by Ash United and Ashford Town respectively, whilst the Programme of the Year award went to Walton Casuals, with Ash the runners-up.

Two of the League's referees achieved well-merited promotion. Paul Kelly, who refereed the Premier Challenge Cup Fina,l has been elevated to the Ryman League, while Steve Chreighton will be going to the Doc Martens League. The League's very best wishes go with them.

In conclusion the League would like to offer their grateful thanks to sponsors, Courage PLC, who have renewed the agreement

FINAL LEAGUE TABLES 1997-98

Premier Division

	P	W	D	L	F	A	Pts
Ashford Town (Middx)	38	30	3	5	123	31	93
Reading Town	38	28	5	5	102	26	89
Ash United	38	28	3	7	107	52	87
Raynes Park Vale	38	24	5	9	86	61	77
Chipstead	38	23	5	10	79	43	74
Farnham Town	38	22	4	12	94	60	70
Bedfont	38	18	5	15	75	70	59
Godalming & Guildford	38	15	10	13	77	69	55
Sandhurst Town	38	16	7	15	67	64	55
Chessington & Hook	38	16	6	16	63	65	54
Feltham	38	15	7	16	70	71	52
Netherne	38	13	8	17	61	88	47
Westfield	38	12	7	19	54	63	43
Viking Sports	38	11	7	20	52	82	40
Merrstham	38	12	4	22	58	91	40
Hartley Wintney	38	10	6	22	47	91	36
Cobham	38	9	7	22	55	73	34
Walton Casuals	38	8	10	20	45	84	34
Cranleigh	38	8	3	27	53	110	27
Cove	38	5	2	31	33	107	17

Division One

	P	W	D	L	F	A	Pts
Chessington & Hook	30	20	7	3	74	29	67
Godalming & Guildford	30	20	6	4	64	26	66
Merstham	30	19	8	3	80	41	65
Bedfont	30	19	4	7	57	31	61
Cobham	30	13	10	7	56	31	49
Walton Casuals	30	14	6	10	46	44	48
Sandhurst Town	30	15	5	10	66	51	*47
Ashford Town (Middx)	30	13	2	15	70	59	*44
Reading Town	30	11	2	17	58	69	35
Farnham Town	30	10	5	15	74	78	*34
Cranleigh	30	10	3	17	51	79	33
Viking Sports	30	9	5	16	53	86	32
Ash United	30	9	3	18	57	75	30
Westfield	30	8	4	18	40	64	*30
Cove	30	8	1	21	35	82	25
Netherne	30	3	7	10	41	77	16

* Indicates points adjustment

RESULTS CHART 1997-98

		1	2	3	4	5	6	7	8	9	10	11	12	13	14	15	16	17	18	19	20
1	Ashford	X	2-3	5-0	3-0	2-0	4-3	2-0	12-0	4-2	2-0	1-1	5-0	5-1	0-1	1-2	1-2	8-2	3-0	3-0	4-1
2	Ash United	0-2	X	3-1	4-0	1-3	1-0	7-0	3-2	2-2	3-1	3-2	6-0	4-2	9-3	1-0	1-0	1-2	2-0	5-3	2-0
3	Bedfont	2-1	5-1	X	1-1	1-2	1-1	1-2	1-0	1-2	5-4	6-2	3-2	2-1	4-2	0-1	1-3	2-0	5-4	2-2	1-2
4	Chessington	0-1	2-6	0-1	X	1-0	1-4	2-1	1-2	0-2	4-2	4-1	2-0	1-0	5-0	3-4	0-0	3-0	1-1	3-2	0-1
5	Chipstead	0-0	1-2	4-1	1-1	X	5-0	5-1	1-2	3-2	3-0	2-3	2-1	4-0	2-2	4-1	0-4	1-0	4-0	2-0	1-0
6	Cobham	2-4	3-6	1-0	1-2	0-3	X	6-0	4-1	0-1	0-1	0-2	2-0	2-1	1-1	0-1	0-2	0-1	0-1	0-0	1-1
7	Cove	1-3	0-3	1-3	0-3	2-4	2-2	X	1-2	2-5	0-1	1-4	1-2	1-2	1-2	0-1	1-5	0-5	2-1	0-2	1-0
8	Cranleigh	0-3	0-8	0-4	3-2	1-2	6-2	2-3	X	4-6	1-2	0-2	1-3	1-3	1-3	2-2	0-3	1-1	1-4	0-2	2-2
9	Farnham	0-2	0-2	0-0	2-1	1-1	4-1	3-0	3-2	X	4-0	3-2	2-1	5-1	3-0	3-4	2-1	3-1	1-2	6-2	1-3
10	Feltham	1-6	5-1	0-1	1-2	1-2	1-0	2-0	3-0	2-6	X	2-2	1-0	5-1	5-2	3-2	1-2	0-0	0-0	6-0	4-2
11	Godalming	1-3	0-0	4-2	1-2	2-0	4-3	5-0	1-3	0-1	2-2	X	0-2	5-3	1-0	3-1	2-1	1-1	2-2	2-2	0-0
12	Hartley W	0-10	3-2	1-2	4-0	1-1	0-3	3-3	1-0	0-6	3-2	1-8	X	3-3	1-2	0-0	0-2	1-2	1-2	1-1	4-1
13	Merstham	2-3	1-2	5-4	2-0	1-5	3-2	1-0	2-1	1-4	0-2	1-1	2-1	X	1-3	1-2	0-3	1-1	4-3	2-0	2-0
14	Netherne	0-3	0-0	0-4	3-3	2-1	1-1	3-0	3-1	3-2	2-3	2-0	1-1	1-1	X	3-3	0-5	2-4	0-2	3-2	0-2
15	RP Vale	0-3	4-2	4-2	3-0	1-2	4-3	5-0	3-2	0-2	2-1	3-2	3-0	4-1	6-4	X	0-5	3-2	3-1	1-2	6-0
16	Reading	2-2	0-2	4-0	3-2	1-3	1-1	2-0	7-0	3-0	2-1	3-0	3-0	3-1	2-0	0-0	X	2-1	7-0	6-0	2-1
17	Sandhurst	0-1	3-4	1-1	2-2	2-0	2-0	1-0	5-1	3-2	1-1	5-2	1-2	2-0	4-2	0-1	1-5	X	0-1	1-0	3-0
18	Viking	0-4	0-2	1-2	1-3	3-1	0-1	1-4	0-1	4-2	3-3	1-3	1-4	1-0	3-0	1-3	1-1	2-6	X	0-0	1-1
19	Walton Casuals	2-3	0-2	1-0	1-6	0-3	1-2	3-1	1-7	2-1	0-0	2-2	1-0	3-4	0-2	1-1	1-2	3-1	2-3	X	1-1
20	Westfield	0-2	0-2	2-3	1-2	0-1	4-3	3-1	2-0	0-0	5-1	1-2	4-0	2-1	1-3	1-2	2-3	5-0	3-1	0-0	X

Asfhord Town: Premier Challenge Cup Winners 1997-98, First Division Fair Play Trophy Winners 1997-98. Behind the cup is Ian Squires from Courage Thames Valley. *Photo: SGA Photography*

PREMIER CHALLENGE CUP 1997-98

FIRST ROUND

Cove	v	Ashford Town (Middx)	1-2
Sandhurst Town	v	Netherne	1-3
Cranleigh	v	Hartley Wintney	3-0
Walton Casuals	v	Reading Town	4-0

SECOND ROUND

Ashford Town (Middx)	v	Westfield	1-3
Chessington & Hook	v	Netherne	3-1
Feltham	v	Chipstead	3-3 aet, 5-3 aet
Raynes Park Vale	v	Cranleigh	6-2
Ash United	v	Viking Sports	6-0
Cobham	v	Bedfont	2-1
Merstham	v	Godalming & Guildford	4-2
Walton Casuals	v	Farnham Town	4-3

THIRD ROUND

Ash United	v	Cobham	6-1
Walton Casuals	v	Chessington & Hook	0-6
Merstham	v	Feltham	1-2
Westfield	v	Raynes Park Vale	2-3

SEMI-FINAL

Ash United	v	Raynes Park Vale	6-3
Chessington & Hk	v	Feltham	2-1 aet

FINAL

Ash United v Chessington & Hook 5-0 at Woking FC

DIVISION ONE CHALLENGE CUP 1997-98

SEMI-FINAL

Reading Town Res	v	Bedfont Reserves	2-1
Sandhurst Town Rs	v	Godalming & G Res	1-2 aet

FINAL

Godalming & G Res v Reading Town Res 2-0

DIVISION ONE CHALLENGE SHIELD 1997-98

SEMI-FINAL

Bedfont Reserves	v	Cobham Reserves	1-2
Cove Reserves	v	Ash United Reserves	0-2

FINAL

Cobham Reserves v Ash Utd Res 1-1 aet, 3p2 at Farnham Town FC

FAIR PLAY TABLE 1997-98

Premier Division

Ash United	38
Ashford Town (Middx)	38
Farnham Town	41
Godalming & Guildford	41
Bedfont	47
Viking Sports	49
Westfield	53
Chipstead	54
Feltham	54
Raynes Park Vale	54
Chessington & Hook	56
Hartley Wintney	56
Cove	58
Sandhurst Town	59
Merstham	59
Cranleigh	61
Netherne	64
Walton Casuals	64
Reading Town	68
Cobham	70

Division One

Ashford Town (Middx)	20
Chessington & Hook	36
Westfield	36
Walton Casuals	37
Sandhurst Town	38
Ash United	39
Cobham	39
Farnham Town	40
Netherne	43
Cranleigh	45
Reading Town	46
Godalming & Guildford	50
Cove	51
Viking Sports	52
Merstham	53
Bedfont	62

LEADING GOALSCORERS 1997-98

PREMIER DIVISION

35	S Joyce	Ash United
31	S Gorman	Godalming & Guildford
31	E Barr-James	Raynes Park Vale
28	R McDonald	Ashford Town (Middx)
27	J Fowler	Chipstead

DIVISION ONE

25	I Pennells	Merstham
22	S Monagahan	Reading Town
19	L Callan	Ash United
18	S Ellis	Sandhurst Town
17	C Swift	Cobham

CLUB DIRECTORY 1998-99

AFC WALLINGFORD

Secretary: Mr E Gniadek, 17 Offas Close, Benson, Wallingford, Oxon OX10 6NR (01491 838540).
Ground: Hithercroft, Wallingford, Oxon.
Colours: Red & black/black **Change colours:** Green & yellow/green

ASH UNITED

President: Mrs B Wallman
Chairman: Robert J Atkins, 3 Vale Road, Ash Vale, Aldershot, Hants. Tel: 01252 311259 (H)
Secretary: Alex Smith-Gander, 41 Ast Street, Ash, Aldershot, Hants. Tel/Fax: 01252 345221 (H)
Ground: Youngs Drive, off Shawfield Rd, Ash, Nr Aldershot (01252 20385).
Directions: A323 towards Ash, left into Shawfield Rd, right into Ash Church Rd, right at crossroads into Shawfield Rd. 1 mile from both Ash and Ash Vale BR stations.Bus - Stagecoach 20A, 550.
Capacity: 1,500 **Seats:** None **Cover:** Yes **Floodlights:** Yes **Founded:** 1911
Colours: Green/black/black. **Change colours:** All blue or all red. **Midweek Matchday:** Tuesday
Admission: £2 **Programme:** 36 pages, 50p. **Editor:** Gareth Watmore.
Previous Ground: Ash Common Rec. 70-71 **Previous Leagues:** Surrey Snr, Aldershot Snr

ASHFORD TOWN (MIDDX)

Chairman: Robert Parker **Vice Chairman:** Peter Hefferman **President:** E Britzman **Formed:** 1964
Secretary: Alan B J Constable, 30 Marlborough Rd, Ashford, Middx TW15 3QA 01784 885092 (H)
Manager: Dave Kent **Physio:** D Hanks **Press Secretary:** D Baker
Ground: Short Lane, Stanwell, Staines, Middx (01784 245908). **Directions:** M25 jct 13, A30 towards London, 3rd left at footbridge after Ashford Hospital crossroads - ground signposted after quarter of a mile on right down Short Lane. Two miles from Ashford (BR) and Hatton Cross (tube) stations. Bus route - Westlink 116.
Seats: None **Cover:** 75 **Capacity:** 2,000 **Floodlights:** Yes **Nickname:** Ash Trees
Clubhouse: Open 7 days a week. Refreshments always available - hot food on matchdays. **Club Shop:** No
Colours: Tangerine & white/white/tangerine. **Change colours:** All blue **Midweek matchday:** Tuesday
Programme: 24 pages, 75p **Editor:** Secretary **Sponsors:** A. C. Frost Ltd.
PREVIOUS - Ground: Clockhouse Lane Rec. **Leagues:** Hounslow & Dist. 64-68; Surrey Intermediate 68-82; Surrey Premier 82-90.
CLUB RECORD - Goalscorer: Andy Smith **Appearances:** Alan Contable 650. **Attendances:** 750 v Brentford, friendly 29/7/86.
97-98 - Captain: Gary Cambridge **Top Scorer:** Richard McDonald (38)**P.o.Y.:** Dannie Bulman
Honours: Combined Co's Lg Champions 94-95, 95-96, 96-97, Chall Cup R-up 92-93 94-95, Lg Vase Cup R-up 91-92 94-95; Surrey I'mediate Lg, Surrey Prem. Cup 89-90; Middx Prem. Cup R-up 89-90; Southern Comb Cup 95-96.

BEDFONT

President: Roger Cooper **Chairman:** John Dollimore **Vice Chairman:** K Stone. **Founded:** 1968.
Secretary: Geoff Knock, 187 Northumberland Cres., Bedfont, Middlesex TW14 9SR Tel: 0181 890 6233 (H)
Manager: Alan Humphries **Coach:** Cliff Williamson. **Ass. Man.:** Bob Barnes
Ground: The Orchard, Hatton Rd, Bedfont, Middx. Tel: 0181 890 7264.
Directions: Turn down Faggs Rd opposite Hatton Cross (Picadilly Line) station on Great South Western Rd (A30), then sharp right into Hatton Rd. Ground opposite Duke of Wellington pub.
Seats: None **Cover:** 50 **Capacity:** **Floodlights:** Yes **Clubhouse:** Yes **Midweek matches:** Tuesday
Programme: 28 pages, 50p. Editors: Alan Humphries (01932 563548) and Colin McNeill (0181 384 8410).
Colours: Yellow & blue stripes/blue/blue **Change colours:** Blue/yellow/yellow.
Previous - Names: Bedfont Inst. (est. 1900), Bedfont Rangers (est. 1950) & Fairholme Utd (est. 1953) merged 1968. Club later merged with Interharvester (1973) & Bedfont Eagles (1988). **Ground:** Bedfont Recreation
Honours: Comb. Co's Lg Chal. Vase 92-93 (Res. Div R-up 88-89, Res. Cup R-up 89-90, Grant McClennan Yth Cup 91-92), Middx Lg 73-74 76-77 (Div 1 (Res) 71-72 78-79 79-80, Div 1 Cup 71-72 78-79 79-80), Surrey Prem. Lg 84-85 86-87, Middx I'mediate Cup 69-70 76-77, Inter. Contois Tour. 1992, Liege Euromann Tour. 89, Harold Clayton Cup 90-91, Hounslow & Dist. Lg Div 1 (Res) 86-87.

CHESSINGTON & HOOK UNITED

Chairman: Mr G Ellis, 63 Stormont Way, Chessington, Surrey. KT9 2QW. Tel: 0181 241 2832 (H)
Secretary: Mr A Warwick, 38 Hartfield Road, Chessington, Surrey. KT9 2PW. Tel: 0181 397 1843
Ground: Chalky Lane, Chessington, Surrey. Tel: 013727 29892
Directions:
Railway station - Chessington South. Bus - London Transport 71.
Manager:
Colours: All blue **Change colours:** All purple

CHIPSTEAD

Chairman: D Parsons, 32 Cannons Hill, Old Coulsdon, Surrey. Tel.: 01737 552682 **President:** Keith Rivers
Secretary: Geoff Corner, 20 Sunnymede Avenue, Carshalton Beeches, Surrey SM5 4JF. Tel: 0181 642 0827
Manager: John Sears **Coach:** Paul Duffield **Midweek matchday:** Tuesday.
Ground: High Road, Chipstead, Surrey. Tel: 01737 553250.
Directions: Brighton Road northbound, left into Church Lane, left into Hogcross Lane, right into High Road. One and a half miles from Chipstead (BR). Bus - London County 405, 407.
Seats: 30 **Cover:** 100 **Capacity:** 2,000 **Floodlights:** Yes **Founded:** 1906
Colours: Green/green/black. **Change colours:** Red or Purple/black/black **Programme:** 44 pages
Previous Leagues: Surrey Intermediate 62-82/ Surrey Premier 82-86 **Nickname:** Chips
Hons: Surrey Premier Lg R-up 82-83 83-84 85-86 (Lg Cup 82-83 84-85 85-86), Combined Co's Lg 89-90 (R-up 90-91 92-93, Lg Cup 86-87 90-91 92-93, Elite Class Cup R-up 89-90, Reserve Section Cup 92-93).

COVE

Chairman: Bob Clark, 3 Linstead Rd., Farnborough, Hants. Tel: 01276 33435 **President:** Ron Brown
Secretary: Graham Brown, 126 Prospect Road, Cove, Farnborough, Hants. GU14 8LB. Tel: 01252 650920
Ground: 7 Squirrels Lane, Farnborough, Hants GU14 8PB. Tel.: 01252 543615.
Directions: Farnborough (BR) 2 miles; right into Union Street, right at lights into Prospect Rd, left into West Heath Rd, right into Romayne close and follow signs to Cove FC. Or, M3 jct 4, follow A325 signed Aldershot & Farnham, right into Prospect Avenue (signposted Cove FC and Farnborough Town FC), then as above.
Capacity: 3,500 **Seats:** 75 **Cover:** 475 **Floodlights:** Yes **Founded:** 1897 **Midweek Matches:** Tuesday
Clubhouse: Mon-Fri 7-11, Sat 12-11, Sunday 12-3 & 7-11. Hot food on matchdays.
Club Shop: No, but souvenirs available in clubhouse. **Reserves' League:** Comb. Cos. 1st Div.
Programme: 30 pages, 50p **Editor:** Graham Brown (01252 650920) **Sponsors:** Sunnyside Removals
Colours: Black & amber/black/black **Change colours:** Red & white stripes/red/red
Honours: Surrey I'mediate Lg; Surrey Prem. Lg x5, R-up x3, Lg Cup x3, Res. Section x4, R-up x4, Res. Cup x2; Combined Co's Lg Cup 81-82; Hants Lg Div 3 x1, Div 4 x1, Div 2 R-up x1; Aldershot - Snr Cup x5, R-up x1, Snr Shield x4, Snr Lg x1, Div 2 x3, Div 2 Cup x1, Div 4 Cup x1.

CRANLEIGH

Chairman: Vic Simmonds **Vice Chairman:** Roy Kelsey **President:** Alan Pavia
Secretary: Roy Kelsey, 2 Wayside Cottages, High St., Bramley, Surrey. Tel: 01483 898117
Manager: Roy Kelsey **Asst Manager:** Paul Jones. **Coach:** Andy Clements.
Ground: Snoxall Playing Fields, Knowle Lane, Cranleigh (01483 275295). **Directions:** A281 from Guildford towards Horsham, at Shalford take B2128 to Cranleigh High Street, right opposite Onslow Arms into Knowle Lane, ground half mile on left. Public transport: Guildford (BR) then bus (Alder Valley) 273 or 283.
Seats: None **Cover:** 50 **Capacity:** 450 **Floodlights:** No **Club Shop:** No.
Clubhouse: Licensed bar. Hot food on matchdays. **Midweek matchday:** Tuesday **Founded:** 1893.
Programme: £1.50 **Editor:** Peter Slater (01483 894245) **Sponsors:** Roger Coupe, Est. Agents
Colours: Blue/black/blue **Change colours:** Yellow/green/yellow **Nickname:** Cranes.
Honours: W Sussex County Times Cup 92-93; F.A. Vase 3rd Rd 92-93.

FARNHAM TOWN

Chairman: Nigel Harrington 01252 716647 (H). **Nickname:** The Town **Founded:** 1921
Secretary: Mrs Barbara Fripp, 70 Lower Farnham Rd., Aldershot, Hampshire. GU12 4EA 01252 657184 (H)
Manager: Peter Browning **Asst Manager:** Roy Atkin **Coach:** A Wyciechowski/A Metcalfe
Ground: Memorial Ground, Babbs Mead, West Street, Farnham, Surrey (01252 715305).
Directions: Take A31, direction Winchester. Take second turning into town at Coxbridge roundabout. Follow West Street until you come to new mini roundabout - The Memorial Ground is on the right.
Capacity: 2,000 **Seats:** None **Cover:** 150 **Floodlights:** Yes **Club Shop:** No
Clubhouse: Open every evening and match days.
Programme: 32 pages 50p **Editor:** Ann Butters **Press Officer:** Charlie White **Sponsors:** Frazer Freight.
Colours: All claret & blue. **Change colours:** Gold, black trim/black/black **Midweek Matchday:** Tuesday
Reserve League: Comb Counties Res Div
Honours: Combined Counties Lg 90-91 91-92, Challenge Cup Prem Div 95-96, Challenge Tphy 91-92 (R-up 89-90).

FELTHAM

Chairman: Willi F P Seuke 0181 386 9630 (H) **Manager:** Carl Taylor. **Asst. Man:** Gary Jenkins
Secretary: John Cronk, 37 Ruskin Ave, Feltham, Middlesex. TW14 9HY. (01817 513663)
Ground: Feltham Arena, Shakespeare Ave., Feltham, Middx TW14 9HY. 0181 384 5048 (club) 0181 890 6905 (ground) **Directions:** BR to Feltham & 5 mins walk thro' Glebelands Park. Buses 90, 285, 117, 237, H24 or H25 to Feltham station, or 116 to top of Shakespeare Ave. By car: M3, M4, A312 Staines road towards Bedfont, 2nd left is Shakespeare Ave.
Capacity: 10,000 **Seats:** 650. **Cover:** 1,500 **Floodlights:** Yes **Club Shop:** No
Clubhouse: Open 7 days a week. 2 bars, dancehall available for hire. **Founded:** 1946.
Programme: 20 pages, 50p. **Editor/Press Off.:** Richard Sevice 01932 - 761544 (Tel) 761744 (Fax)
Colours: Royal blue & white halves/blue/blue. **Change colours:** Red & blue strips.
Reserves' League: Suburban. **Sponsors:** Cowley Security Locksmiths/Damar Glass
Midweek Matches: Wednesday
Honours: Surrey Snr Lg R-up 65-66 (Lg Cup 65-66, Charity Cup 63-64 65-66), Southern Comb. Cup(2)(R-up(2)), Middx Summer Cup, Isthmian Div 2 80-81, Comb. Cos. Lge Co. 96-97

GODALMING & GUILDFORD

Back Row (L-R): Mick Wollen (Mgr), Darren Burge, Nigel Kay, Liam Keane, Sean Gorman, JezJukes, Neil Munro, Dave Thompson, Adam Gregory, Tim Daly (Coach). Front Row: Justin Horner, Terry Vick, Dale Homersham John Ferrucci, Jamie Collin, Terry Worsfold, Len Brown (Train). *Photo: Garry Letts*

Chairman: Dave Allen **President:** W F Kyte **Nickname:** The Gees **Founded:** 1950
Secretary / Press Officer: Eddie Russell, 31 Harts Gardens, Guildford, Surrey GU2 6QB. 01483 535287 (H & B)
Manager: Mick Wollen **Asst Manager:** Mel Coombs **Physio:** Steve Snelling
Ground: Wey Court, Meadrow, Godalming, Surrey (01483 417520). **Midweek matchday:** Tuesday.
Directions: A3100 from Guildford - past Beefeater Hotel on left, then 'Save' petrol station on right, then 1st right 50 yards on. From Godalming on A3100, grd on left by Leather Bottle pub. Three quarters of a mile from Farncombe BR station.
Capacity: 3,000 **Seats:** 200 **Cover:** 200 **Floodlights:** Yes **Club Shop:** No
Clubhouse: Open Tues, Wed, Thurs eves, matchdays. Hot & cold snacks available.
Programme: Yes **Colours:** Green & yellow/green/yellow **Change colours:** Red & blue/blue/blue
Honours: Combined Co's Lg 83-84, Lge Challenge Trophy 82-83, Res Lge 95-96 96-97, Res Chall Cup 92-93 97-98, Chall Shield 96-97: Southern Comb Chall Cup 97-98.

HARTLEY WINTNEY

Chairman: Fred Humphreys Tel: 01252 843098 **President:** W A Mitchell **Founded:** 1897
Secretary: Ross Hillair, 17 Rye Close, Farnborough, Hants. GU14 9LU. Tel: 01252 516174 (H)
Ground: Memorial Playing Fields, Green Lane, Hartley Wintney, Hants 01252 843586
Directions: A30 west through Camberley, left at parade of shops at beginning of village then sharp right - ground on right. Two miles from Winchfield (BR). **Midweek matchday:** Tuesday.
Capacity: 2,000 **Seats:** None **Cover:** No **Floodlights:** No **Programme:** Yes **Nickname:** The Row
Colours: Orange/black/orange **Change colours:** White/sky blue/sky blue or All green.
Previous Leagues: Basingstoke/ Aldershot

MERSTHAM

Chairman: Stan Baker **President:** Bill Lawton **Founded:** 1892.
Secretary: Matthew Boardman, 49 Orpin Road, Merstham,Surrey. RH1 3EX Tel: 01737 212543 (H) 0181 770 4818 (B)
Press Officer: Roger Peerless. **Manager:** Joe McElligott **Asst Manager:** Colin Humphries
Ground: Merstham Rec., Weldon Way, Merstham, Redhill, Surrey (01737 644046). **Directions:** Leave Merstham village (A23) by School Hill, take 5th right (Weldon Way), clubhouse and car park 100m on right. 10 mins walk from Merstham (BR); down School Hill, under railway bridge, then 5th turning on right into Weldon Way.
Capacity: 2,000 **Seats:** 100 **Cover:** 100 **Floodlights:** Yes **Club Shop:** No
Clubhouse: Across adjacent footpath. Open daily (am & pm). Snacks available.
Programme: Yes **Editor:** Matthew Boardman. **Midweek matches:** Tuesday/Thursday
Colours: Amber/black/amber. **Change colours:** Purple/white/purple **Club Sponsors:** LDC Plant
Previous Leagues: Redhill & Dist./ Surrey Co. S.E. I'mediate/ Surrey Snr 64-78/ London Spartan 78-85.
Honours: Combined Co's Lg R-up 87-88 89-90 (Elite Class Cup 89-90 (R-up 90-91), Res. Sect. 90-91), Spartan Lg 79-89 (Lg Cup 79-80), Surrey Snr Lg 71-72, Surrey Snr Char. Cup 79-80, E. Surrey Char. Cup 80-81, Surrey I'mediate Lg 52-53.

NETHERNE

Chairman / President: Noel Duffy Tel: 01737 552453. **Secretary:** John Duffy, c/o Netherne FC.
Ground: Netherne Sports Club, Woodplace Lane, Hooley, Coulsdon, Surrey CR5 1YE (01737 553580).
Ground: One mile from end of M23. Turn right off Brighton Rd into Woodplace Lane, follow up hill for about half a mile, ground on left. Approx 20 mins walk from Coulsdon South (BR) station.
Capacity: 2,000 **Seats:** None **Cover:** 50 **Floodlights:** No **Club Shop:** No
Clubhouse: Open matchdays with hot food available over bar. Outside tea also available with hot food.
Programme: 20 pages, 50p **Reserves' League:** Combined Co's Res Div. **Founded:** 1968
Change Colours: Green/white/black **Colours:** Blue & black stripes/black/black
Previous Leagues: Croydon Saturday 68-76; Surrey Eastern Interm 76-79; Surrey S E Interm 79-89; Surrey County Prem 89-94.
Honours: Surrey Co. Prem. Lg 93-94 (Lg Cup 92-93), Surrey South Eastern Intermediate Comb. 88-89.

RAYNES PARK VALE

President: R Hallett
Chairman: Dave Brenen, 22 The Crescent, Belmont, Surrey. SM2 0BJ. Tel: 0181 296 8626.
Secretary: Paul Armour, 68 Oaks Avenue, Worcester Park, Surrey. KT4 8XD. Tel: 0181 337 4989 (H)
Ground: Grand Drive, Raynes Park. SW20 (0181 542 2193)
Directions: Bus - London Transport 131 & 152. Nearest railway station - Raynes Park.
Colours: Blue & red stripes/blue/red **Change colours:** Green & white stripes/green/green.

READING TOWN

Chairman: Roland Ford, 103 Little Heath Road, Tilehurst, Berkshire RG31 5TG. Tel: 0118 941 2270.
Secretary: Richard Grey, 37 Orchard Grove, Caversham, Reading. RG4 6NF. Tel: 0118 948 2006 (H).
Fixture Sec.: Mrs Pauline Semple, 278 Hemdean Rd., Caversham, Reading RG4 7QT. Tel: 0118 947 9394.
Ground: Reading Town Spts Ground, Scours Lane, Tilehurst, Reading, Berks (0118 945 3555).
Directions: Out of Reading on Oxford road (A329), past Battle Hosp. Scours Lane 1st right after r'bout. Nearest station - Tilehurst or Reading (General). Bus - Reading Bus 17. **Manager:** Paul Evans
Capacity: 2,000**Seats:** No **Cover:** Yes **Floodlights:** Yes **Founded:** 1968.
Programme: 16pages 50p **Editor:** Richard Grey **Sponsors:** Constant Intruder Security
Clubhouse: Yes **Colours:** Red & black stripes/black/black **Change colours:** All Sky blue.
Previous - Leagues: Chiltonian 89-95, Reading 66-89 **Grounds:** Adwest Spts Grd, Kings Meadow **Names:** Lower Burghfield, XL United, Vincents United, Reading Garage, ITS Reading Town
Club Records - Attendance: 253 v Banstead Ath FA Vase 96-97 **Win:** 7-0 v Cranleigh/Viking Spts/AFC Wallingford all Home 97-98. **Defeat:** 0-10 v Feltham (A) 96-97
Best Season - FA Cup: Prelim Rd 97-98. **FA Vase:** 4th Rd 96-97
97-98 - Captain: Gary Stevens **P.o.Y.:** Tony Mukabaa **Top Scorer:** Paul Lockyer
Honours: Comb Counties Lge R-up 97-98; Chiltonian Lge Champ 94-95; Berks & Bucks Sen. Trophy 95-96, R-up 96-97.

SANDHURST TOWN

Chairman: Brian Levey. Tel: 01276 32788 **President:** M Watts
Secretary: John Parker, 24 Florence Rd, College Town, Sandhurst, Berkshire. GU47 0QD Tel: 01276 32308 (H), 01276 61203 B.
Match Sec.: Tony Ford (01483 567284) **Manager:** Phil Long **Coach:** Ray Clack
Ground: Bottom Meadow, Memorial Ground, Yorktown Rd, Sandhurst (01252 873767).
Directions: A30 westwards through Camberley, right at r-bout with traffic lights onto A321, past superstore turning left the 3rd set of traffic lights on A321 towards Wokingham. Ground situated near to Town & Council offices and Community Centre. Nearest station - Sandhurst. Bus - Bee Line 193, 194.
Capacity: 2,000 **Seats:** None **Cover:** Yes **Floodlights:** Yes **Nickname:** Fizzers
Programme: Yes **Editor:** Tony Fold **Founded:** 1910
Colours: Red/black/black **Change colours:** All blue **Midweek matchday:** Wednesday
Previous Leagues: Reading & Dist.; East Berks; Aldershot Snr 79-84; Chiltonian 84-90.
Club Records - Attendance: 353 v Aldershot Town (Friendly) **Career goalscorer:** Glenn Price **Appeaances:** John Parker **Win:** 6-2 v Viking Sports **Defeat:** 8-2 v Ashford Town (Middx).
Best Season - FA Vase: 1st Rd 93-94
97-98 - Captain: Lee Goddard **Top Scorer:** Graham Huddison **P.o.Y.:** Lee Goddard
Hons: Combined Co's Lge Chal. Vase R-up 92-93 (Reserve Chal. Cup R-up 91-92), Chiltonian Lge R-up 86-87, Aldershot Snr Lge R-up 83-84; Berks & Bucks Sen. Trophy R-up 92-93.

Cove FC (100 years old). *Photo: Eric Marsh*

VIKING SPORTS

Chairman: Jim Sargeant Tel: 01895 810748 **President:** Roy Bartlett **Founded:** 1945
Secretary: John Bennett, 6 Bridge House, Boston Manor Rd, Brentford TW8 9LH (0181 568 9047).
Press Officer: Jamie Cuttica **Manager:** Terry Cross. **Asst Man.:** Brian Callaghan **Physio:** Ernie Stockwell
Ground: Avenue Park, Western Avenue, Greenford, Middx (0181 578 2706).
Directions: On London-bound carriageway of A40, 300 yds before Greenford flyover and slip road to A4127. 12 mins walk from Greenford (Central Line) station - turn right out of station to A40, turn right - grd 1/4 mile on rght.
Capacity: 450 **Seats:** 50 **Cover:** 100 **Floodlights:** Yes **Midweek matchday:** Tuesday
Clubhouse: Open every evening except Sunday. Hot & cold snacks on matchdays. **Club Shop:** No.
Programme: 12 pages, 50p **Editor:** Secretary **Nickname:** Vikings. **Sponsors:** Measham Self-Drive
Colours: All tangerine, black trim **Change colours:** Sky blue & maroon/sky blue/sky blue
97-98 - Captain: Jamie Cuttica **P.o.Y.:** Gary King **Top Scorer:** Jamie Cuttica
Honours: Hellenic Lg Div 1 85-86 (Div 1 Cup R-up 90-91).Co.Counties Lg.(R-Up. 94-95).

WALTON CASUALS

Chairman: Graham James **General Manager:** David Symonds **President:** John Russell
Secretary: Stuart Roberts, 47 Foxholes, Weybridge, Surrey. KT13 0BN. Tel: 01932 845923
Manager: Mick Byrne **Midweek Matchday:** Tuesday. **Nickname:** The Stags **Founded:** 1948.
Ground: Franklin Road Sports Ground, Waterside Drive, Walton-on-Thames, Surrey. KT12 2JG. Tel: 01932 787749 (24hrs ansaphone). **Directions:** Next to Elmbridge Leisure Centre, left off Terrace Road at first roundabout out of Walton centre. Hersham (BR), then bus 564 to Elmbridge Leisure Centre.
Capacity: 1,500 **Seats:** None **Cover:** 80 **Floodlights:** Applied for. **Club Shop:** No
Clubhouse: Matchdays only. Hot food available from Tea Bar.
Programme: 26 pages 50p **Editor/Press Officer:** Stuart Roberts **Sponsors:** John Russell (Allied Dunbar)
Colours: Orange & white/white/white **Change colours:** Red & black/black/black
Previous Leagues: Surrey Premier, Surrey Senior, Surrey Intermediate, Suburban League.
Record Attendance: 178 v Pagham FA Vase 96/97
Honours: Suburban Lge (South) 82-83, (R-up 83-84); Surrey Prem Lge R-up 94-95, S.P.L. Chall Cup 93-94, (R-up 94-95); Surrey Premier Cup R-up 86-87.

WESTFIELDS

Chairman: Alan Dunsford **Vice Chairman:** **President:** Graham Preece.
Secretary: Andrew Morris, 17 Fayre Oaks Green, Kings Acre, Hereford HR4 0QT (01432 264711 H)
Manager: Gary Stevens **Coach:** Sean Edwards/Phil Dean **Physio:** Peter Boulton
Ground: Thorn Lighting, Holme Lacy Rd, Rotherwas, Hereford (01432 268131)
Directions: Proceed 1.5 mile south from Hereford on A49, left in Home Lacy Rd at Broadleys Inn, proceed 1 mile to Thorn Lighting Rotherwas, ground on the right on Rotherwas Ind. Estate. 2 miles from Hereford (BR).
Seats: 100 **Cover:** 150 **Capacity:** 2,000 **Floodlights:** Yes **Club Shop:** Yes
Programme: Yes **Editor:** Andy Morris **Press Officer:** Secretary
Colours: Maroon & sky **Change colours:** Sky & white
Sponsors: Hereford Times **Founded:** 1966 **Nickname:** The Fields.
Midweek matchday: Tuesday **Youth team's League:** W Midlands Youth Lge Floodlite
Clubhouse: 'Gamecock Inn' Holme Lacey Rd. Hereford (1/2 mile from ground).
Hons: West Mids Lg Div 1 86-87, Div 2 R-up 83-84 (Div 2 Cup 79-80 83-84), Herefordshire Snr Cup 85-86 88-89 91-92 95-96 (Yth Cup 92-93 95-96).

Ashford Town (Middx). Back Row (L-R): A Eggington, J Heggarty, S Kent, L Holman, D Smith, N Hutchinson, G Cambridge. Front Row: A Sherwood, R McDonald, I Kierman, I Miles, B Jolly, D Bulman, G Hill

SCHWEPPES ESSEX SENIOR LEAGUE

Chairman & Publicity: Robert Errington
Tel/Fax: 01702 613713

Secretary: David Walls
77 Thorpedene Gardens, Shoeburyness, Southend on Sea, Essex SS3 9JE

CONCORD RANGERS WIN THEIR FIRST CHAMPIONSHIP

Concord Rangers, for so long, the "other" team from Canvey Island, took honours themselves with a brilliant Championship win from Basildon United who themselves had created all-time records in their quest for the title. Concord's triumph was master-minded by Lee Patterson in his first season as a Manager but, as so often happens, Lee has moved over to Basildon to try his luck with the new town side. There was no promotion to the Ryman League as neither side could, at this stage, fulfil the ground criteria for entry, so they will try again, with Great Wakering Rovers also attempting a promotion place as they, slowly but surely, build their ground up to Ryman standard.

Basildon United won their first fifteen games of the season, and actually went seventeen games without dropping a point from April 1997, both all time league records, but a draw at Gardiners Close and a defeat at Thames Road by the potential champions saw Dave Cusack's lads having to take second place. Consolation came in the form of a League Cup success by 1-0 over Burnham Ramblers at Great Wakering FC on a windy April day - this game being sponsored by Schweppes who as a company were so pleased with the outcome and have now added their most famous name to the title of the League which will be known this season as the Schweppes Essex Senior League.

The Harry Fisher Memorial Trophy went, at last, to its mother club, East Ham United, winning their first Senior League trophy after years of battling against lack of funds, fans and a guaranteed future but with a spirit that emanates from the undying enthusiasm of Reuben Gane - his year being made even happier by winning the League Sportsmanship Trophy. Sadly, the losing finalists were Burnham Ramblers, the final being held at Park Lane, Canvey Island.

Great Wakering Rovers had a thoroughly enjoyable run in the FA Vase to round five and made many new friends in the process, but the "journey" of the season fell to Bowers United who found themselves paired with Bodmin Town in Cornwall and were proud ambassadors of the League in the process, the League Chairman joining in the weekend away. Bowers United were also recipients of the Secretary of the Year Award in the shape of Ernie Brown and the Don Douglas (Leading Goalscorer) Award went to David Hope. Stansted quite deservedly won the Wirral Programme Award for the second year running with Alan Russell producing a "masterpiece" of reading material every home game.

So with the same fourteen clubs in our constitution (Eton Manor sharing at Barkingside), Len Llewellyn taking over the Fixture Secretary's job and Schweppes injecting sponsorship that will be enjoyed by the clubs and the most welcome injection of Football Association funds to help administration, the Senior County League of Essex looks forward with extreme optimism to the new season and the forthcoming Millennium - even Hullbridge Sports and Brentwood will be lit up as 98-99 progresses.

Robert Errington, Chairman

Southend Manor see the 'glamorous' side of soccer . . . *Photo: Robert Errington*

FINAL LEAGUE TABLES 1997-98

	P	W	D	L	F	A	W	D	L	F	A	Pts
Concord Rangers	26	12	0	1	40	11	11	2	0	34	9	71
Basildon United	26	11	2	0	36	10	11	1	1	39	5	69
Bowers United	26	10	1	2	39	11	9	1	3	26	14	59
Stansted	26	8	1	4	38	24	7	2	4	33	19	48
Burnham Ramblers	26	6	3	4	24	16	7	2	4	28	17	44
Hullbridge Sports	26	8	2	3	27	16	3	3	7	17	21	38
Great Wakering Rovers	26	8	2	3	22	12	2	3	8	17	30	35
Brentwood	26	2	2	9	13	27	7	2	4	21	17	31
East Ham United	26	6	1	6	23	26	3	2	8	18	35	30
Sawbridgeworth Town	26	5	1	7	19	28	3	2	8	13	29	27
Ilford	26	4	2	7	18	19	3	3	7	20	29	26
Southend Manor	26	1	4	8	9	35	3	2	8	18	31	18
Eton Manor	26	2	3	8	19	23	1	1	11	15	36	13
Saffron Walden Town	26	3	2	8	16	49	0	0	13	8	51	11

DIVISION ONE RESULTS CHART 1997-98

		1	2	3	4	5	6	7	8	9	10	11	12	13	14
1	Basildon United	X	3-1	4-1	1-1	2-2	4-3	3-2	3-0	1-0	6-0	3-0	4-0	1-0	1-0
2	Bowers United	0-2	X	1-1	2-0	2-3	5-0	4-1	7-1	4-2	1-0	6-0	3-1	3-0	1-0
3	Brentwood	1-2	1-2	X	0-1	0-1	0-4	0-2	0-5	1-3	2-2	2-1	2-2	3-0	1-2
4	Burnham Ramblers	0-5	0-1	0-0	X	0-0	1-2	3-0	2-1	2-1	4-1	5-0	0-1	5-2	2-2
5	Concord Rangers	0-2	2-0	2-1	4-1	X	5-1	3-0	2-0	4-1	3-1	5-1	4-1	3-1	3-1
6	East Ham Utd	0-3	0-2	0-5	1-2	1-2	X	3-2	3-2	0-0	4-1	5-2	2-1	3-1	1-3
7	Eton Manor	1-2	1-4	0-1	0-1	0-3	4-0	X	1-1	0-3	1-1	7-0	1-1	1-2	2-4
8	Great Wakering Rovers	1-1	1-0	2-3	1-0	2-3	2-0	2-0	X	1-3	1-0	3-0	3-0	2-1	1-1
9	Hullbridge Sports	1-0	0-1	2-0	4-2	0-2	3-1	3-2	0-0	X	1-4	3-0	3-1	2-2	5-1
10	Ilford	0-1	2-2	1-2	1-2	0-3	4-0	3-1	2-1	1-1	X	4-1	0-1	0-2	0-2
11	Saffron Walden Town	0-7	1-5	0-1	1-7	1-8	0-1	2-1	3-3	3-2	1-5	X	4-1	0-0	0-8
12	Sawbridgeworth Town	0-1	1-4	1-2	2-2	1-3	4-3	4-1	1-0	1-0	0-2	2-0	X	1-6	1-4
13	Southend Manor	0-9	1-2	1-3	0-6	0-3	1-1	1-1	1-2	0-0	1-1	2-1	0-1	X	1-5
14	Stansted	1-4	1-2	3-1	0-3	0-1	2-2	5-2	5-1	3-1	4-2	4-2	3-2	7-1	X

LEADING GOALSCORERS 1997-98

25	David Hope	Bowers United
23	Mark Cox	Concord Rangers
21	Paul Flack	Burnham Ramblers
18	Gary Hart	Stansted
17	Micky Hall	Basildon United
	Steve Warner	Bowers United
16	Danny Wallace	Concord Rangers
15	Graham Dorrell	Burnham Ramblers
14	Adam French	Basildon United
12	Alan Hull	Great Wakering Rovers
11	Simon Deakin	Bowers United
	Phil Donnelly	Hullbridge Sports
	Michael Gore	Brentwood
	Scott Nixon	Stansted
10	Dean Duncan	East Ham United
	Dean Francis	Burnham Ramblers
	Mark Saggers	Stansted
9	Tommy Dalgarno	Basildon United
	Khan Stevens	Basildon United
8	Ricky Finning	Concord Rangers
	Gaby Nguidjol	Saffron Walden Town

Other leading goalscorers (of clubs not mentioned above)

7	Sonuc Saldiray	Sawbridgeworth Town
	Scott Williams	Eton Manor
6	Casey Grylls	Ilford
5	Mark Holton	Southend Manor

ESSEX SENIOR LEAGUE CHALLENGE CUP 1997-98

FIRST ROUND

Hullbridge Sports	v	Stansted	1-1 aet, 3-5 aet
Southend Manor	v	Ilford	2-0
Gt Wakering Rovers	v	Eton Manor	1-0
Basildon United	v	Sawbridgeworth T	3-0 aet
Brentwood	v	East Ham United	1-3
Bowers United	v	Concord Rangers	2-0 aet

Saffron Walden Town and Burnham Ramblers byes

SECOND ROUND

Stansted	v	Basildon United	1-2
Gt Wakering Rovers	v	Saffron Walden Tn	4-1
Southend Manor	v	East Ham United	0-1
Bowers United	v	Burnham Ramblers	1-2

SEMI-FINAL

Basildon United	v	East Ham Utd	1-0, 2-2 aet
Gt Wakering Rvrs	v	Burnham R	2-3, 2-1, 2p3

FINAL

Basildon United v Burnham Ramblers 1-0 at Great Wakering Rovers FC

Teams:

Basildon United: Craig Tucker, Wes Faulkner, Mark Keune, Mick Munro, Micky Hall, Liam Cutbush, Adam French, Bobby Kellard, Khan Stevens, Wayne Mitchell, Tommy Dalgarno

Subs: Craig Huttley Subs not used: Nigel Hewes, Ian Renshaw

Burnham Ramblers: John Reeve, Gary Ewers, Paul Wheeler, Shaun Tracey, Ian Cousins, Graeme Brown, Nicky Wright, Paul Flack, Billy Herbert, Dean Francis, Graham Dorrell, Neil Sutton, Jamie Tolhurst, Chris Evans

All subs used

THE HARRY FISHER MEMORIAL TROPHY 1997-98

FIRST ROUND

Basildon United	v	Southend Manor	7-1
Stansted	v	Bowers United	2-3
East Ham United	v	Hullbridge Sports	1-1, 2-1
Ilford	v	Gt Wakering Rvrs	1-2
Sawbridgeworth T	v	Brentwood	3-0
Concord Rangers	v	Saffron Walden Tn	7-0

Burnham Ramblers and Eton Manor Byes

SECOND ROUND

Burnham Ramblers	v	Basildon United	3-1
Sawbridgeworth Tn	v	East Ham United	0-2
Gt Wakering Rvrs	v	Bowers United	0-1
Concord Rangers	v	Eton Manor	0-0, 0-0, 3p5

SEMI-FINAL

Burnham Ramblers	v	Bowers United	2-1, 1-2
East Ham United	v	Eton Manor	1-1, 1-0

FINAL

Burnham Ramblers v East Ham Utd 0-0 aet, 3p4 at Canvey Island FC

Teams:

Burnham Ramblers: John Reeve, Neil Sutton, Paul Wheeler, Shaun Tracey, Ian Cousins, Graeme Brown, Chris Evans, Paul Flack, Billy Herbert, Nick Wright, Graham Dorrell

Subs: Dean Francis, Jamie Tolhurst, Gary Ewers

East Ham United: Derek Burnett, Alan Maskell, Andy Steele, Leigh Colman, Eddie Nwachukwu, Simon Ayaoge, Omer Mussie, David Coleman, Dean Duncan, Tony Manning, Ivan Thomas

Subs: John Charlton, Leslie Ayaoge, Danny Singleton

HONOURS LIST

League Champions	Concord Rangers
Runners Up	Basildon United
Challenge Cup Winners	Basildon United
Runners Up	Burnham Ramblers
Harry Fisher Memorial Trophy	East Ham United
Runners Up	Burnham Ramblers
The Don Douglas Memorial Trophy	David Hope (Bowers U)
Sportsmanship Award	East Ham United
Wirral Programme Award	Stansted
Club Secretary of the Year	Ernie Brown (Bowers U)

CLUBS 1998-99

BASILDON UNITED

President: J Oakes **Chairman:** J Moran **Secretary:** Dave Cusack, c/o the club. **Founded:** 1963.
Manager: Lee Patterson **Press Officer:** Frank Ford (01268 552994
Ground: Gardiners Close, Gardiners Lane, Basildon, Essex SS14 3AW (01268 520268).
Directions: A176 off Southend arterial (A127), left at r'bout into Cranes Farm Road, proceed to end of duel carriageway, left at lights, Gardiners Close is 1st left (Football Club signed). Two and a half miles from Basildon BR station.
Seats: 400 **Cover:** 1,000 **Capacity:** 2,000 **Floodlights:** Yes
Clubhouse: Open lunchtimes, evenings, weekends. Hot food sold.
Programme: 16 pages, 50p. **Editor:** F Ford **Midweek Matches:** Wednesday **Club Shop:** No.
Colours: Amber & black stripes **Change:** Green & white squares/white/white **Sponsors:** Orsett Cock
Previous - Name: Armada Sports. **Ground:** Grosvenor Park 63-69. **Leagues:** Grays & Thurrock; Gtr London 68-70; Essex Snr 70-80; Athenian 80-81; Isthmian 81-91. **Record Gate:** 4,000 v West Ham, ground opening 11/8/70
Players progressing to Football League: Jeff Hull (Colchester), Alan Hull (Orient), David Matthews & Steve Tilson (Southend), Jonathan Gould (Coventry City), Ken Charlery (Watford), Steve Jones (West Ham (via Billericay)).
97-98 - Captain: **Top Scorer:** Micky Hall **P.o.Y.:**
Honours: Isthmian Lge Div 2 83-83; Essex Senior Lge (5) 76-80 94-95, Lg Cup 77-78 94-95 97-98, Reserve Cup 92-93; Essex Senior Trophy 78-79; Reserve League & Shield 94-95.

BOWERS UNITED

Chairman: Denis Taylor **Manager:** Tony Cross
Secretary: Stephen Bond, 42 Brandish, Pitsea, Basildon, Essex SS13 3EV. 01268 478035 (H)
Ground: Crown Avenue, off Kenneth Rd, Pitsea, Basildon (01268 452068).
Directions: Turn into Rectory Rd from Old London Rd (B1464) at Pitsea Broadway into Kenneth Rd, right at top Crown Ave. 1.25 miles Pitsea (BR). Bus 523 to Rectory Rd, Bowers Gifford
Seats: 200 **Stand:** Yes **Capacity:** 2,000 **Floodlights:** Yes **Founded:** 1946
Clubhouse: Open every night. **Midweek Matches:** Wednesday.
Colours: Red & white/red/red **Change colours:** Green & black/black/black
Previous Leagues: Thurrock & Thameside Comb.;Olympian **Previous Ground:** Gun Meadow, Pitsea.
Players progressing to Football League: Steve Tilson (Southend Utd).
97-98 - Captain: **Top Scorer:** David Hope **P.o.Y.:** John Warner
Honours: Thurrock & Thameside Comb. 58-59; Essex Snr Lg 80-81 (Div 1 Cup 90-91, Harry Fisher Mem. Tphy 91-92, Res. Div R-up 92-93).

BRENTWOOD

Chairman: K J O'Neale **Manager:** Derek Stittle 01708 440486 (H)
Secretary: Colin Harris, 56 Viking Way, Pilgrims Hatch, Brentwood, Essex CM15 9HY. 01277 219564 (H)
Ground: Brentwood Centre, Doddinghurst Rd, Brentwood, Essex. 01277 215151 Ext. 713. **Directions:** Junc. 28 M25, take A12 signposted Brentwood. At Town Centre, turn right and ground is in Doddinghurst Lane at the Leisure Centre.
Cover: Yes **Seats:** **Capacity:** **Floodlights:** Yes **Founded:** 1955.
Colours: All sky blue. **Change colours:** Mauve & purple strips
Programme: Free with admission **Midweek Matches:** Tuesday **Nickname:** Blues
PREVIOUS - Names: Manor Ath. 55-70, Brentwood Ath. 70-72. **Grounds:** King George, Hartswood, 'Larkins', Ongar (pre-1992), East Thurrock. **Leagues:** Romford & District, Sth Essex Combination, London & Essex Border, Olympian.
Hons: Olympian Lg Cup 67-68, Essex Inter. Cup 76-77, Essex Lg Cup 75-76 78-79 90-91; Harry Fisher Mem. Trophy 95-96.

BURNHAM RAMBLERS

Chairman: Gordon Brasted **Vice-Chairman:** Ron Hatcher **President:** R J Cole, Esq.
Secretary: Gordon Brasted, 6 Ramblers Way, Burnham on Crouch, Essex. CM0 8LR Tel. 01621 782785
Fixture Secretary: Chris Dobson, 13 Chapel Rd, Burnham on Crouch Essex CM10 8JB (01621 786334)
Manager: Colin Wallington **Asst Manager:** **Physio:** Cyril Tennant
Ground: Leslie Field, Springfield Rd, Burnham-on-Crouch CM0 8QL (01621 784383).
Directions: On B1010 from South Woodham Ferrers, turn right half mile before town. 15 mins from Burnham (BR).
Seats: 300 **Stand:** Yes **Capacity:** 2,000 **Floodlights:** Yes **Founded:** 1900
Clubhouse: Open Mon-Fri 7-11pm, Sat noon-3 & 5-11pm, Sun noon-3 & 7-9.30pm. Hot meals & snacks available.
Programme: 36 pages, 50p **Editor:** Chairman **Press Officer:** Nigel Radcliffe, 01621 783774.
Colours: All Royal blue **Change colours:** Yellow/black/yellow **Nickname:** Ramblers
Midweek matches: Tuesday. **Reserves' Lge:** Essex & Herts **Record Gate:** 1,500.
Previous - Leagues: N Essex, Mid-Essex, Olympian, S.E. Essex. **Grounds:** Wick Rd, Millfields, Saltcourts (orig.)
Players moving to Football League: I Woolf, West Ham 11, Gordon Brasted, Arsenal 53, John Warner, Colchester 90.
97-98 - Captain: Shaun Tracey **P.o.Y:** John Reeves **Top Scorer:** Paul Flack
Honours: Olympian Lg 65-66; Essex I'mediate Cup R-up 81-82; Essex Snr Lg Cup R-up 86-87 89-90 97-98, (Reserve Cup 89-90 (R-up 92-93), Reserve Shield R-up 90-91; Harry Fisher Mem. Trophy 96-97, R-up 97-98; Sportsmanship Award 96-97.

CONCORD RANGERS

President: Albert Lant **Chairman:** Rob Fletcher **Manager:** Terry Bravey **Founded:** 1967.
Secretary: Mrs Carol McKenna, 1A Letzen, Canvey Island, Essex SS8 9AW. 01268 515048 (H)
Ground: Thames Road, .Canvey Island, Essex. SS8 0HP (01268 691780/515750) **Directions:**
Capacity: 1,500 **Cover:** Yes **Seats:** No **Floodlights:** Yes **Midweek Matches:** Tuesday.
Clubhouse: Evenings & weekends **Programme:** 10 pages, 50p **Editor:** Mike Stephenson (01268 684638)
Colours: Yellow & blue/blue/blue **Change colours:** Red & black/black/black
Previous - Leagues: Southend & D. All., Essex I'mediate (pre-1991). **Ground:** Waterside
Record - Gate: 1,500 v Lee Chapel North, FA Sunday Cup 89-90. **Win:** 9-0 v Eton Manor, Essex Snr Lge 96-97.
97-98 - Top Scorer: Mark Cox **Captain:** **P.o.Y.:**
Hons: Southend & Dist. Lge - Lge & Cup 84-85; Southend Alliance - Lge & Cup 87-88; Essex Intermediate Lg Div 2 90-91; Essex Sen Lge 97-98, Cup 96-97; Wirral Programme Award 93-94.

EAST HAM UNITED

Chairman: Ted Whatmough, 85 Mill lane, Chadwell Heath, Romford. RM6 6YH. 0181 599 4542 (H)
Secretary: Reuben Gane, 108 Beccles Drive, Barking, Essex IG11 9HZ. 0181 594 7861 (H)
Manager: Reuben Gane **Head of Coaching:** Cornel Dobbs **Trainer:** Roy Smith
Press Officer: Roland Clooge **Physio:** Regan Cavanagh.
Ground: Ferndale Sports Ground, Pennyroyal Ave., off East Ham Manorway, Cyprus Place, Beckton E6 4NG Tel: 0171 476 5514, Fax: 0181 507 1099. **Directions:** East Ham Manorway - Cyprus Place - Beckton off A13 Newham Way from east or west. Nearest tube - East Ham, then bus 101 to ground, or Cyprus Station (Docklands Light Railway).
Seats: 150 **Cover:** 300 **Capacity:** 2,500 **Floodlights:** Yes **Founded:** 1933.
Clubhouse: Evenings & weekends. **Midweek Matchday:** Tuesday **Nickname:** Hammers.
Colours: Green/black/gold **Change colours:** Gold/green/gold **Programme:** Yes.
Previous Ground: Whitebarn Lane (previous East Ham Utd, formed 1880 and played in Sth Essex Lge) 1892-1914; Tilletss Farm 1933-46. **Previous Lges:** Spartan, Metropolitan **Previous Name:** Storey Ath. 1933-55
Record Gate: 4,250 - East Ham XI v West Ham, friendly 15/2/76 at Terrance McMillan Stadium. 2,400 v Sutton United, FA Amateur Cup 14/11/53. **Record scorer:** David Norris **Record appearances:** Ken Bowhill, 1964-84.
Players progressing to Football League: Lee Holmes (Brentford 1972), Miguel de Souza (Peterborough U. via Birmingham C. & Charlton Ath.), Buck Ryan (Charlton), Ian Richardson (Notts Co.).
97-98 - Captain: Cornel Dobbs **Top Scorer:** Dean Duncan **P.o.Y.:** Tony Manning
Hons: Metropolitan Lg; FA Vase QF; Essex Snr Tphy 76-77, Sportsmanship Trophy 97-98; Gtr London Lg Cup 69-70; London Jnr Cup 46-47; Bob Murrant Memorial Trophy 94-95; Carpathian Charity Cup 94-95; Harry Fisher Memorial Trophy 97-98, (R-u 94-95).

ETON MANOR

Secretary: Reg Curtis, 13 Kingsdale Court, Lamplighters Close, The Shires, Waltham Abbey, Essex EN9 3AZ
Chairman: **Manager:** Tony Jones **Coach:** **Physio:** C Drane
Ground: (Sharing with Barkingside), Oakside, Station Road, Barkingside, Ilford, Essex (0181 550 3611).
Directions: From London A12 Eastern Avenue to Green Gate, left into Hurns Rd to Barkingside, right into Craven Gardens, right again Carlton Drive leading to Station Road, under bridge and ground entrance on right. Adjacent to Barkingside station (Central Line). From Ilford station (BR) take 169 Bus to Craven Gardens.
Capacity: 1,000 **Seats:** 60 **Cover:** 60 **Floodlights:** Yes
Clubhouse: Yes **Programme:** 12 pages with entry **Editor:** Secretary **Midweek Matches:** Monday
Colours: Sky/navy/navy **Change colours:** Maroon & green/maroon/maroon**Nickname:** The Manor
Founded: 1901 **Previous - Grounds:** Wildness, Hackney; GUS Sports Ground, Clapton; Walthamstow Avenue FC; Norwegian Ground, Barking; Roding Lane, Buckhurst Hill, Thurrock Hotel **Name:** Wilderness Leyton. **Leagues:** London 33-59; Aetolian 59-64; Greater London 64-69; Metropolitan 69-75.
Record Gate: 600 v Leyton Orient, opening of floodlights at Roding Lane. **Club record scorer:** Dave Sams
97-98 - Captain: **Top scorer:** Scott Williams **P.o.Y.:**
Hons: Essex Snr Cup R-up 37-38, London Lg 33-34 37-38 52-53 53-54 (R-up 48-49 57-58, Lg Cup 55-56 (R-up 46-47 54-55)), Greater London Lg 64-65, Essex Intermediate Cup 64-65, London Intermediate Cup R-up 33-34 66-67, Essex Snr Lg Sportsmanship Award 75-76 (Div 1 Cup 90-91, Reserve Div 76-77, Reserve Div Cup 91-92).

GREAT WAKERING ROVERS

Chairman: Fred Smith **Vice-Chairman:** Barry Beadle **President:** Eddie Ellis **Founded:** 1919
Secretary: Roger Sampson, 37 Lee Lotts, Gt Wakering, Southend-on-Sea, Essex SS3 0HA. 01702 218794 (H)
Manager: Kevin Maddocks **Assistant Manager:** Eddie Nash. **Physio:** Cleave Taylor.
Ground: Burroughs Park, Little Wakering Hall Lane, Gt Wakering, Southend-on-Sea SS3 0HQ (01702 217812).
Directions: 4a bus from Shoeburyness (BR), 4a or 4b from Southend - alight at British Legion in Gt Wakering alongside which runs Little Wakering Hall Lane. A127 past Southend signposted Gt Wakering. In Gt Wakering, half mile past large Esso garage is along High Street is Little Wakering Hall Lane, ground 250 yds along on left.
Capacity: 1,500 **Cover:** 300 **Seats:** 150 **Floodlights:** Yes **Club Shop:** No **Nickname:** Rovers
Clubhouse: Weekday evenings, Sat 11-11pm, Sun 12-3 & 7.30-10.30pm. Hot meals, snacks etc available matchdays.
Programme: 24-32 pages, 50p **Editor:** Nobby Johnson (01702 611964). **Sponsors:** Fox Surveillance
Colours: Green & white stripes/white/green **Change colours:** Yellow & blue stripes/blue/blue
Midweek Matchday: Tuesday **Reserves' League:** Essex & Herts Border Comb
Record Attendance: 659 v Potters Bar FA Vase 5th Rd 7-2-98
Record win (in Senior Football): 9-0 v Stansted . 27/12/93.
Record defeat (in Senior Football): 1-7 v Bowers Utd, Essex Snr Lge 1-4-98.
Previous - Ground: Gt Wakering Rec. **Leagues:** Southend & District 19-81, Southend Alliance 81-89, Essex Intermediate 89-92.
97-98 Captain: John Heffer **P.o.Y.:** Jimmy Ablitt **Top Scorer:** Alan Hull
Players progressing to Football League: Les Stubbs (Southend, Chelsea) 1947, Jackie Bridge (Southend Utd) 1948, Kevin Maddocks (Maidstone Utd).
Honours: Essex I'mediate Cup 91-92, Essex I'mediate Lg Div 2 91-92 (Div 3 90-91, Lg Cup 91-92), Southend Charity Shield 90-91 91-92, Essex Snr Lg. 94-95, Lg Res. Section 94-95 (Wirral Programme Essex Sen. Lg. Award 92-93 94-95).

HULLBRIDGE SPORTS

Chairman: Martyn Hardy **Joint Managers:** David Hughes & Howard Mackler **Founded:** 1945
Secretary: Mrs Beryl Petre, 58 Grasmere Ave, Hullbridge, Essex SS5 6LF, 01702 230630 (H), 01702 552211 (B)
Ground: Lower Road, Hullbridge, Hockley, Essex SS5 6BJ (01702 230420).
Directions: Turn into Rawreth Lane from A130 (left if arriving from Chelmsford), down to mini-r'bout, left, across next mini-r'bout, up hill, ground signed on right just past garage. **Prog. Editor:** Bryan Heggety
Capacity: **Seats:** No **Cover:** Yes **Floodlights:** Yes **Midweek matches:** Tues/Thursday.
Clubhouse details: Lounge bar, function hall with bar & changing rooms - set in 16 acre.
Colours: Royal Blue & white/white/blue **Change colours:** Maroon/navy/maroon **Sponsor:** Thermo Shield
Previous Grounds: Pooles Lane Rec. **Previous Leagues:** Southend & Dist., Alliance, Essex I'mediate.
97-98 - Captain: **Top Scorer:** Phil Donnelly **P.o.Y.:**
Honours: Essex Intermediate Snr Div Cup 87-88, Southend & District Lg Div 1 65-66 (Div 2 51-52, Div 3 56-57), French Cup 51-52, Essex Snr Lg Sportsmanship Award 91-92 92-93 94-95.

ILFORD

Chairman: George Hogarth **Manager:** Ray Lee
Secretary: Kevin Wilmot, 83 Mandeville Court, Lower Hall Lane, Chingford, London E4 8SD (0181 529 9475 H, 0956 902456 Club Mob)
Fixture Secretary: D Quinlan, 25 Burwood Gardens, Rainham, Essex. RM13 8JS. 01708 526323
Ground: Cricklefield Stadium, High Road, Ilford, Essex. IG1 1UB (0181 514 0019)
Directions: Within 5 minutes walk of Seven Kings Station. Opposite 'The Cauliflower' public house.
Colours: Royal blue & white hoops/navy/navy **Change colours:** Red & white qtrs/red/red
Midweek matches: Monday **Programme Editor:** L Llewellyn
Previous League: Spartan 87-95 **Sponsor:** Kelvin Hughes, Intersport.

SAFFRON WALDEN TOWN

Chairman: Steve Cox **Vice Chairman:** **Founded:** 1872 **Nickname:** Bloods
Secretary: Peter Rule, 48 Church Street, Saffron Walden, Essex, CB10 1VQ
Manager: Tim Moylette **Asst. Man.:** **Physio:** **Press Officer:**
Ground: Catons Lane, Saffron Walden, Essex CB10 2DU (01799 522789).
Directions: In Saffron Walden High Street turn into Castle Street, left at T-junction, 1st left by Victory pub.
Club Sponsors: Tolly Cobbold.
Capacity: 5,000 **Seats:** 500 **Cover:** 2,000 **Floodlights:** Yes **Clubhouse:** Yes **Club Shop:** Yes
Programme: 24 pages, 40p **Editor:** R Smith (01799 500061) **Midweek Matchday:** Tuesday
Colours: Red & black/black/black **Change cols:** Blue & yellow/yellow/yellow
Reserves' League: Essex & Herts Comb.
Previous Leagues: Haverhill & Dist., Stansted & Dist., Cambridgeshire, Nth Essex/ Herts Co., Spartan 33-49 50-54, Parthenon 49-50, Essex Snr 71-74, Eastern Co's 74-84. **Prev. Grounds:** None **Prev. Names:** None.
Best F.A. Cup year: Second Qualifying Round replay 84-85 (lost 1-2 at King's Lynn).
Record Attendance: 6,000 v Rainham Ath., Essex Junior Cup Final 1926 (played at Crittals, Braintree).
Club Record Scorer: John Tipputt **Club Record Appearances:** Les Page, 700+.
Hons: Essex Snr Lg 73-74, Eastern Co's Lg 82-83, Spartan Lg Eastern Div 2 36-37, Essex Snr Tphy 82-83 83-84 84-85, Eastern F'lit Competition 91-92 (R-up 88-89, Nth Thames Group B 82-83), Essex Jnr Cup 1896-97 (R-up 25-26), Cambs Lg R-up 22-23, Essex & Herts Border Lg R-up 25-26(joint), Stansted & Dist. Lg 07-08 08-09 09-10 11-12 20-21 22-23 23-24, Haverhill & Dist. Lg 08-09 22-23 23-24 29-30 33-34.

SAWBRIDGEWORTH TOWN

Chairman: Barry Mutimer **President:** Ron Alder **Founded:** 1890 **Nickname:** Robins
Secretary: Gary Bennett, 21 Sayesbury Road, Sawbridgeworth, Herts, CM21 0EB. 01279 830306 (H)
Manager: Graham Norcott **Coach:** TBA **Physio:** Brian Latchford
Ground: Crofters End, West Road, Sawbridgeworth, Herts. CM21 0DE (01279 722039)
Directions: Three quarters of a mile from the station; up Station Road then into West Road.
Capacity: 1,500 **Seats:** None **Cover:** 250 **Floodlights:** Yes **Club Shop:** **Clubhouse:**
Programme Editor: R Alder (01279 722360) **Press Officer:** Micky Phillips **Sponsor:**
Colours: Red & black stripes/black/white **Change colours:** Green/white/green
Previous - Grounds: Hyde Hall, Pishiobury, Hand & Crown. **Leagues:** Essex Olympian, Spartan 36-53.
97-98 - Captain: **Top Scorer:** Sonvc Saldiray **P.o.Y.:**
Record Attendance: 610 v Bishop's Stortford.
Honours: Essex Olympian Lg 71-72; Essex Snr Lg R-up 92-93 94-95; Harry Fisher Mem. Cup 87-88; Lg Cup 94-95 R-up 92-93 93-94, Reserve Div 91-92 92-93 (R-up 93-94), Reserve Shield R-up 92-93); Herts Snr Tphy 90-91 93-94 (R-up 92-93); Herts Charity Shield 92-93 94-95 95-96; Uttlesford Charity Cup 92-93; Herts Intermediate Cup R-up 93-93(res); South Midlands Floodlit Cup R.Up.94-95; Reserve Sect S.M Lge & Lg.Cup R-Up 94-95:

SOUTHEND MANOR

Chairman: Robert Westley **Vice-Chairman:** John Hughes **Nickname:** The Manor
Secretary: Dave Kittle, 15 Seymour Rd, Hadleigh, Benfleet, Essex SS7 2HB. 01702 559581 (H)
Manager: Mark Jenkins **Coach:** Peter Heathcote **Physio:**
Ground: Southchurch Park Arena, Lifstan Way, Southend-on-Sea. (01702 615577). **Directions:** A127 then A1159 for 1 mile turn right at second roundabout by Invisible Man PH, due south for 1 mile, ground on right near sea front.
Seats: 500 **Cover:** Yes **Capacity:** 2,000 **Floodlights:** Yes **Founded:** 1955
Clubhouse: Open every evening **Programme:** 10 pages, 50p **Editor/Press Officer:** Paul Docherty.
Colours: Yellow/black/black **Change colours:** White/red/red
Sponsors: Hi-Tech. **Midweek Matchday:** Tuesday. **Reserves Lge:** Essex & Herts Border Comb.
Previous Leagues: Southend Borough Combination, Southend Alliance
Previous Grounds: Victory Spts/ Oakwood Rec.
Record Attendance: 1,521 v Southend Utd, 22/7/91, floodlight opener.
97-98 - Captain: M Jackson **Top Scorer:** M Holton **P.o.Y.:** D Ames
Honours: Essex Snr Trophy 92-93; Essex Intermediate Cup 78-79; Essex Snr Lg 90-91, Cup 87-88; ESL Challenge Cup 89-90; Harry Fisher Mem. Tphy 90-91 92-93 (R-up 91-92).

STANSTED

Chairman: Terry Shoebridge **General Manager:** Alan Russell **President:** Percy Heal
Secretary: Mrs Denise Murnane, Appletree House, Fullers End, Elsenham, Bishops Stortford. CM22 6DU. 01279 815404 (H&B)
Manager: Don Watters
Ground: Hargrave Park, Cambridge Road, Stansted, Essex. (01279 812897)
Directions: B1383 north of Bishops Stortford on west side of Cambridge Rd. Stansted (BR) - 1/2 mile
Capacity: 2,000 **Seats:** 200 **Cover:** Yes **Floodlights:** Yes **Founded:** 1902 **Nickname:** The blues
Clubhouse: Matchdays till 11pm. Sandwiches available. **Club Shop:** No
Colours: Blue & white/blue/blue **Change:** Yellow & blue/blue/yellow **Sponsor:** Desavoury Foods
Programme Editor: Alan Russell **Midweek matches:** Tuesday. **Reserves League:** Cambridgeshire League
Previous - Leagues: Spartan; London; Herts Co. **Grounds:** Greens Meadow; Chapel Hill
97-98 - Captain: **Top Scorer:** G Hart **P.o.Y.:**
Record Attendance: 828 v Whickham (FA Vase 83-84). **Honours:** FA Vase Winners 83-84; Essex Snr Lg R-up 82-83; Essex Snr Lg Cup 83-84, (R-up 72-73 94-95); Harry Fisher Mem Cup 82-83 84-85 (R-up 92-93 93-94); East Anglian Cup 83-84; Courage East F/lit Cup 83-84; Uttlesford Char. Cup 93-84 86-87 88-89 94-95 97-98.

FINAL LEAGUE TABLES 1997-98

PREMIER DIVISION NORTH

	P	W	D	L	F	A	Pts
Brache Sparta	28	23	2	3	75	17	71
Potters Bar Tn	28	20	7	1	62	21	67
London Colney	28	16	4	8	67	46	52
Royston Town	28	14	5	9	52	34	47
Hoddesdon Tn	28	15	2	11	50	36	47
Welwyn Gdn C	28	12	10	6	47	42	46
Arlesey Town	28	13	5	10	51	41	44
Harpenden Rvrs	28	12	5	11	46	45	41
Toddington Rvrs	28	10	5	13	39	52	35
Buckingham Ath	28	9	6	13	46	55	33
Letchworth	28	8	5	15	50	63	29
Biggleswade T	28	7	7	14	41	53	28
Milton Keynes	28	8	5	15	40	52	*28
Bedford United	28	3	8	17	25	67	*14
Langford	28	1	2	25	23	90	5

* Denotes points deducted

PREMIER DIVISION SOUTH

	P	W	D	L	F	A	Pts
Brook House	28	18	6	4	66	27	60
Beaconsfield SY	28	16	8	4	59	27	56
Ruislip Manor	28	17	4	7	61	29	55
Hillingdon Boro	28	15	7	6	73	35	52
Barkingside	28	12	7	9	44	34	43
Waltham Abbey	28	12	6	10	54	42	42
Haringey Boro	28	12	4	12	42	44	40
Brimsdown Rvrs	28	11	4	13	46	58	37
St Margaretsbury	28	11	4	13	46	58	*36
Islington St Marys	28	10	4	14	42	52	*33
Woodford Town	28	7	9	12	48	59	30
Hanwell Town	28	8	4	16	45	76	28
Harefield Utd	28	7	6	15	27	67	27
Amersham Tn	28	8	2	18	26	45	26
Cockfosters	28	5	7	16	35	61	22

Note: For season 1998-99 the top two divisions of the League will not be titled Premier Division One and Premier Division Two, as previously advised, but Premier Division and Senior Division respectively.

PREMIER DIVISION NORTH RESULTS CHART 1997-98

		1	2	3	4	5	6	7	8	9	10	11	12	13	14	15
1	Arlesey Town	X	2-0	2-1	0-2	3-0	0-0	1-1	4-1	3-0	5-1	0-4	2-44	1-1	1-1	0-1
2	Bedford United	2-4	X	1-1	0-3	0-1	2-2	0-1	1-2	1-1	3-1	0-3	0-1	0-7	0-2	1-1
3	Biggleswade Town	1-1	0-1	X	1-3	2-2	3-1	2-0	3-2	3-1	0-2	3-0	3-3	1-3	2-0	3-4
4	Brache Sparta	2-1	5-0	0-0	X	2-1	4-2	3-1	6-0	6-0	1-2	6-0	2-0	2-0	3-1	2-0
5	Buckingham Athletic	3-4	1-0	2-2	2-4	X	1-2	1-3	2-2	4-3	2-3	2-1	1-2	2-0	1-1	1-1
6	Harpenden Town	1-0	5-1	3-2	0-1	3-7	X	0-4	5-1	1-2	3-4	2-0	1-1	0-2	1-0	1-0
7	Hoddesdon Town	1-0	2-1	2-1	0-1	1-0	1-3	X	4-1	2-6	0-2	4-0	0-0	4-2	4-0	3-0
8	Langford	1-2	1-1	2-3	1-8	1-4	0-3	1-5	X	0-3	1-5	0-1	0-4	0-2	1-2	0-1
9	Letchworth	3-2	3-0	1-0	0-4	1-3	0-1	1-3	3-1	X	2-4	1-1	2-2	2-2	1-2	2-2
10	London Colney	1-0	9-1	5-0	1-2	5-0	1-0	0-3	3-1	2-1	X	2-2	0-1	0-0	2-2	2-3
11	Milton Keynes	2-5	1-1	1-1	0-1	1-2	2-1	1-0	5-1	2-4	1-2	X	2-3	1-0	3-1	1-2
12	Potters Bar Town	4-0	3-1	3-0	2-0	2-0	0-0	3-0	5-1	2-0	4-1	1-1	X	1-0	3-0	3-2
13	Royston Town	0-1	1-3	2-1	1-0	3-1	3-3	2-1	2-1	2-1	3-1	2-1	0-2	X	6-1	1-2
14	Toddington Rovers	2-3	3-3	2-0	0-1	3-0	2-0	2-0	1-0	5-4	2-3	2-1	0-1	0-4	X	0-2
15	Welwyn Garden City	1-4	1-1	4-2	1-1	0-0	1-2	2-0	2-0	3-2	3-3	3-2	2-2	1-1	2-2	X

PREMIER DIVISION SOUTH RESULTS CHART 1997-98

		1	2	3	4	5	6	7	8	9	10	11	12	13	14	15
1	Amersham Town	X	2-1	1-1	1-2	0-1	0-3	1-1	1-3	1-4	0-4	0-2	2-0	1-1	0-1	1-2
2	Barkingside	1-0	X	0-0	1-1	0-1	3-0	0-1	3-2	0-1	2-0	5-2	1-0	2-0	2-1	2-1
3	Beaconsfield SYCOB	2-0	3-0	X	3-1	1-1	2-1	9-1	3-0	5-1	3-3	2-1	0-1	1-0	1-1	1-1
4	Brismdown Rovers	1-0	0-2	0-2	X	0-6	1-2	1-2	2-0	0-1	2-2	4-3	1-0	4-1	2-7	3-3
5	Brook House	2-1	1-1	1-1	4-2	X	0-1	1-2	5-0	5-2	2-2	3-1	1-1	1-1	3-1	5-1
6	Cockfosters	0-3	2-2	1-6	1-3	1-3	X	2-3	0-1	0-1	1-4	1-1	1-3	3-3	2-2	2-0
7	Hanwell Town	1-2	2-2	0-1	0-2	2-3	6-5	X	2-0	0-1	2-2	3-4	1-1	1-4	0-3	4-6
8	Harefield United	4-2	1-1	3-0	1-1	0-5	1-2	1-0	X	0-3	2-2	0-3	0-6	0-2	1-3	2-2
9	Haringey Borough	2-1	4-2	0-1	3-2	0-1	0-0	3-3	0-1	X	0-1	2-3	0-3	4-1	1-2	1-1
10	Hillingdon Borough	1-2	2-0	0-2	5-0	2-1	5-1	12-0	0-0	3-0	X	3-1	1-0	2-1	2-3	2-0
11	Islington St Marys	1-2	0-5	1-2	3-1	0-1	0-0	2-0	1-2	2-4	2-1	X	1-4	3-0	1-0	2-0
12	Ruislip Manor	2-0	3-1	2-1	0-2	2-1	3-0	2-1	5-1	3-2	2-2	1-1	X	3-0	1-2	1-2
13	St Margaretsbury	2-1	0-2	3-1	3-1	1-4	2-1	4-1	4-0	0-1	1-5	1-0	1-6	X	1-3	2-2
14	Waltham Abbey	1-0	1-1	0-2	1-4	1-2	2-2	1-2	9-1	2-0	3-2	1-1	1-3	0-1	X	1-3
15	Woodford Town	0-1	3-2	3-3	1-3	0-2	1-0	1-5	0-0	1-1	2-3	4-0	2-3	5-6	1-1	X

LEADING GOALSCORERS 1997-98

Premier Division North

John Tipper	Brache Sparta	26
David Russell	Hoddesdon Tn	26

Premier Division South

Steven Hale	Ruislip Manor	35
Nathan Thomas	Woodford Town	25

Senior Division

Darren Lynch	New Brad. St P	40
Shaun Martin	Holmer Green	34

Division One North

Roy Henney	Pitstone & Iv.	39
Clive Batchelor	Luton Old Boys	28

Division One South

Justin Georgiou	Crown & Manor	35
Paul Jaggard	Old Roan	27

Reserve Division One

Leon Archer	Potters Bar Tn	26
Carl Dean	Stony Stratford T	24

Reserve Division Two

Paul Monahan	Houghton Town	39
Danny Glass	Tring Athletic	19

Reserve Division Three

Kevin Souster	Luton OB	18
Steven Brown	Risboro Rngrs	16

SPARTAN SOUTH MIDLANDS FOOTBALL LEAGUE

President: B F Smith **Chairman:** Pat Burns

Hon. Press Secretary: Jim Bean
224 The Hide, Netherfield, Milton Keynes MK6 4JE
Tel/Fax: 01908 696059

The first season of the newly-combined League provided a close finish in each of the five divisions. With the two regional Premier Divisions combining to form Premier Division One for season 1998-99, this effectively meant relegation for the five bottom clubs from each division and the final positions were not settled until the last few weeks of the season.

In Premier Division North (ex-SML), Harpenden Town were eight points clear on 1st January, having lost just one of their fifteen games, but with only two victories in the second half of the season they finished mid-table. The battle for the championship was once again between last season's winners and runners-up, Potters Bar Town and Brache Sparta respectively. However, this time the roles were reversed. Though Potters Bar lost only one of their 28 League games, Brache's finishing run of six successive wins finally gave them the title by a four point margin. For Brache, who also won the O'Brien Butchers Premier Division Cup, these were the first trophies in their 23-season tenure of the (South Midlands) League. Potters Bar finished fifteen points clear of third-placed London Colney. The five Clubs relegated to Premier Division Two (formerly the Senior Division) were Letchworth, Biggleswade Town, Milton Keynes, Bedford United and 1988-89 champions, Langford.

In Premier Division South (ex-Spartan), the tenancy of the top position alternated between Beaconsfield SYCOB and Ruislip Manor for much of the season, but Brook House turned their games-in-hand into points and, with only one defeat in their last 10 games, lifted the title by a margin of four points. For Brook House, who finished thirteenth last season, this was their first League trophy since joining the (Spartan) League's top division and manager, Mick Harvey, who was appointed at the start of the season following spells at Uxbridge and Dagenham, was certainly pleased with his first season in charge. On the last day of the season, Ruislip Manor appeared to have secured runners-up spot with the draw they required against Waltham Abbey but a last-minute goal by Abbey left Ruislip in third place, one point behind Beaconsfield SYCOB. Relegated clubs were Woodford Town (who have since joined the newly-formed London Intermediate League), Hanwell Town, Harefield United, Amersham Town and Cockfosters.

The Senior Division, composed entirely of ex-SML Clubs, provided a breathtaking finish. Tring Athletic, who dropped just nine points out of 48 in a late run, required a 6-0 win in their last match at Holmer Green (who were themselves competing for third place) to pip long-time leaders, New Bradwell St Peter, for the championship on goal difference. In a dramatic early second half spell, Tring led 4-0 but a Holmer recovery produced a 4-1 final score and runners-up spot for Tring. New Bradwell (whose floodlights were erected during the season) and third-placed Mercedes Benz (now re-named Milton Keynes City) have been promoted to Premier Division One. Three Clubs were relegated to Division One - Ampthill Town, Kent Athletic and former (SML) Premier Division stalwarts, The 61 FC. With Biggleswade United, Holmer Green and Leverstock Green obtaining planning permission during the season, fifteen of the 22 Premier Division Two Clubs will have floodlights.

In Division One North (all ex-SML Clubs), Luton Old Boys were crowned champions when a 75th minute goal in the last game of the season gave them victory and top spot for the first time. At one stage Old Boys trailed long-time leaders, Greenacres, by twelve points but a late run of successes gave them the title by a point. Greenacres, in their first season in the League and who ground-shared with Isthmian League Club, Berkhampsted Town, finished a point ahead of third-placed Pitstone & Invinghoe. Both Luton Old Boys and Greenacres are promoted to Premier Division Two for next season.

Division One South (all ex-Spartan Division One and Two Clubs) was won by Old Roan, another club who converted games-in-hand to points. They topped the table for the first time at the end of April and finally finished four point s ahead of Cray Valley. Crown & Manor were third, a further point behind. As all of the Clubs have resigned from the League, most of them to join the London Intermediate League, the division will cease to exist.

Potters Bar Town won the two-legged O'Brien Butchers Challenge Trophy final against Brache Sparta, 4-2 on aggregate. Brache gained some consolation by lifting the Premier Division Cup, defeating Haringey Borough 2-1. Holmer Green retained the Senior Division Cup with a 5-0 replay win against Totternhoe, following a 2-2 draw, and Scot won their first trophy since joining the league, defeating Bridon Ropes 4-2 in the Division One Cup final.

Some of the finest performances by SSMFL Clubs were in the FA Vase. In the early rounds, Brache Sparta defeated Isthmian League Division Two Club, Chalfont St Peter, 3-0, and Hoddesdon Town knocked out Cheshunt, from the same division. Against Isthmian League Division Three Clubs, Hanwell Town beat Harlow, Amersham Town beat Wingate & Finchley and Hillingdon Borough won a replay, 4-2 at Ware. Four clubs reached the Third Round, including Brache Sparta, whose 8-1 defeat of Jewson Eastern League Ely City was the top score of the round. However, Brache went out in the next round, losing a replay 0-3 at North West Counties Club, Kidsgrove Athletic, following a 2-2 draw at home, where they missed a penalty in the closing minutes. Potters Bar Town reached the last eight before they, too, lost to Kidsgrove, 0-2 after extra time. Their victories included a 3-0 win at home to United Counties League Club Potton United, a 2-1 win at Jewson Eastern League Fakenham Town, a 4-2 win at home to Kent League Whitstable Town, a 4-0 win at Bridport, a 1-0 extra time win at eventual United Counties League champions, Stamford, and a 1-0 win at Great Wakering Rovers.

Both Clubs and Management Committee view this transitional season as a success and look forward to the new season.

Stan Eaton

O'BRIEN BUTCHERS PREMIER DIVISION CUP 1997-98

SECOND ROUND

Barkingside	v	Welwyn Garden C	0-4, 0-0	Haringey Borough	v	Toddington R	1-0, 1-2, 4p2
London Colney	v	Brook House	4-1, 0-2	Brache Sparta	v	Hillingdon Boro	1-1, 1-0

SEMI-FINAL

Haringey Borough	v	London Colney	1-1, 3-1	Brach Sparta	v	Welwyn Gdn C	3-0, 1-3

FINAL

Haringey Borough	v	Brache Sparta	1-2

PLATE COMPETITION 1997-98

FINAL

Hoddesdon Town	v	Beaconsfield SYCOB	2-0

SENIOR DIVISION CUP 1997-98

FINAL

Totternhoe	v	Holmer Green	2-2 aet, 5-0

DIVISION ONE CUP 1997-98

FINAL

Scot	v	Bridon Ropes	4-2

SPORTSMANSHIP LEAGUE WINNERS 1997-98

	Games	*Total*	*Average*
Premier Division North			
Langford	37	298	8.00
Premier Division South			
Hillingdon Borough	39	309	7.92
Senior Division			
Shillington	32	282	8.19
Division One North			
Emberton	33	251	7.61
Division One South			
Old Roan	33	252	7.64

Top:
Premier Division North Champions at last, Brache Sparta celebrate after clinching the title at Harpenden
Photo: Gordon Whittington

Bottom:
Brook House FC, Premier Division South Champions 1997-98

PREMIER DIVISION ONE CLUBS 1998-99

ARLESEY TOWN

Chairman: John Milton **Vice-Chairman:** Scott Geekie **President:** Maurice Crouch
Secretary: John Albon, 13 St Johns Rd, Arlesey, Beds SG15 6ST. Tel: 01462 731318 (H & B), Mob 0411 566044.
Manager: Gary Pilsworth **Asst Manager:** Phil Cavener **Physio:** Eric Turner
Ground: Lamb Meadow, Hitchin Rd, Arlesey. Tel: 01462 731448. **Directions:** The ground is situated on the main road thru village. From Hitchin direction the ground is 200 yds past Biggs Wall on left.
Capacity: 8,000 **Seats:** 120 **Cover:** 1,000 **Floodlights:** Yes **Club Shop:** Yes
Clubhouse: Members bar & function room. Open daily 6-11.30, Sat 12-11.30, Sun 12-2.30 & 6-11.30
Programme: 50p **Editor:** Pete Brennan (01462 834455) **Nickname:** Blues **Founded:** 1891
Colours: Sky & navy/navy/navy **Change Colours:** All white.
Sponsors: Milcutt Goldstar **Midweek matchday:** Tuesday **Reserves' League:** South Midlands Lge Res Div
Prev. Lges: Biggleswade & Dist.; Beds. Co. (S. Mids) 22-26,27-28; Parthenon; London 58-60; Utd Co's 33-36 82-92.
Record Attendance: 2,000 v Luton Res, Beds Snr Cup 1906 **Club Record Appearance:** Gary Marshall
Players to progress to Football League: Roland Legate (Luton), Pat Kruse (Brentford, Leicester)
Honours: FA Vase Winners 1994-5; Beds Sen Cup 65-66 78-79 96-97, Prem Cup 83-84, Interm Cup 57-58; South Mids Lge Prem Div 51-52 52-53 94-95 95-96, Div 2 29-30 31-32 35-36, Chall Trophy 79-80, Prem Shield 64-65, O'Brien Prem Cup 93-94, Flood-Lit Cup 90-91; Utd Co Lge Prem Div 84-85, KO Cup 87-88; Hinchingbrooke Cup 77-78 79-80 81-82 96-97; Biggleswade KO Cup 77-78 80-81.

BARKINGSIDE

President: A Smith **Chairman:** Greg Hall **Founded:** 1898.
Secretary/Press Officer: Norman A Ingram, 45 Cheneys Rd, Leytonstone, London E11 3LL. 0181 555 1447 (H)
Manager: C Edwards **Asst Manager:** A Marsden **Physio:** M Stevens
Ground: Oakside, Station Road, Barkingside, Ilford, Essex (0181 550 3611).
Directions: From London A12 Eastern Avenue to Green Gate, left into Hurns Rd to Barkingside, right into Craven Gardens, right again Carlton Drive leading to Station Road, under bridge and ground entrance on right. Adjacent to Barkingside station (Central Line). From Ilford station (BR) take 169 Bus to Craven Gardens.
Capacity: 1,000 **Seats:** 60 **Cover:** 60 **Floodlights:** Yes **Reserves' League:** Essex & Herts Border Comb.
Clubhouse: Saturdays 1pm-12. midweek matchnights 6.30-11pm. Rolls, hotdogs, hamburgers. **Club Shop:** No.
Colours: All white **Change colours:** All yellow **Midweek matchday:** Tuesday **Sponsors:** Directa
Programme: 12 pages with admission **Editor:** J Brown (0181 500 5125)
Previous - Leagues: Ilford & Dist. 1898-1925 44-47/ Ilford Minor 25-44/ Sth Essex 47-48/ Walthamstow 48-50/ London 50-64/ Gtr London 64-71/ Metropolitan-London 71-75. **Grounds:** Fulwell Cross PF 1898-1921/ Clayhall Rec 21-29/ Hainault PF 29-33/ Barkingside Rec 33-57.
Record Gate: 957 v Arsenal Res., London Lg 1957.
Hons: Spartan Lge. Prem. Div. 96-97, R-up 90-91 (Harry Sunderland Shld 83-84 (R-up 84-85); London Sen. Cup 96-97; S. Essex Lge R-up 46-47, L'don Lg R-up 49-50 (Lg Cup 55-56 (R-up 52-53 62-63)), Ilford Fest. Cup 51-52, Romford Char. Cup 51-52, Gtr L'don Lg 64-65.

BEACONSFIELD S.Y.C.O.B.

President: D Piercy **Chairman:** Fred Deanus **Manager:** Simon Delahunty
Secretary: Ken Barrett, 31 Stockley End, Abingdon, Oxon OX14 2NF. Tel: 01235 202058 (H), 01235 537080 (B).
Ground: Holloway Park, Slough Road, Beaconsfield, Bucks (01494 676868). **Directions:** M40 (Jct 2), 1st exit to A355. Club 100yds on right. One and a miles from Beaconsfield (BR). Bus 441 Slough/ High Wycombe.
Seats: 250 **Cover:** 250 **Capacity:** 3,000 **Floodlights:** Yes **Founded:** 1994.
Clubhouse: Open eves & matchdays. Bar, Committee Room, Hall, Kitchen, Changing Room **Club Shop:** No
Programme: Yes, £1. **Editor:** Andy Jackson, 17 Boundary Cottages, Chipperfield Rd., Bovingdon, Herts. HP3 0JT.
Midweek Matches: Tuesday **Reserves' League:** Middlesex **Nickname:** SYCOB
Colours: Red & white quarters/black/red & black **Change colours:** All yellow
PREVIOUS - Names: Beaconsfield Utd (1921); Slough Youth Club Old Boys (1941). Clubs merged 1994. **Leagues:** Beaconsfield Utd: Wycombe & District; Maidenhead. *Slough YCOB: Windsor, Slough & District; East Berks; Chiltonian (pre-1994).* **Grounds:** *Slough YCOB: Hatmill Community Centre, Burnham Lane, Slough (pre-1994).*
Best FA Vase season: Beaconsfield: 1st Rd 83-84 85-86 87-88.
Record Gate: 300 Beaconsfield Utd v Chesham Utd, Berks & Bucks Sen Cup 1985.
Honours: *Slough YCOB: Chiltonian Lg Rup 93-94 (Lg Cup 92-93), Slough Town Cup R-up 91-92.*

BRACHE SPARTA

Chairman: Roy Standring **President:** Doug Smith **Nickname:** The Foxes **Founded:** 1960
Secretary: Roy Standring, 37 Taunton Avenue, Luton, Beds. LU2 0Ln. Tel: 01582 736574
Manager: Steve Brinkman **Physio:** Ben Smith **Colours:** White/navy/white **Change Colours:** All royal
Ground: Foxdell Sports Ground, Dallow Rd, Luton LU1 1UP (01582 20751). **Directions:** Left off A505 to Dunstable into Chaul Lane at r'bout. Proceed across new relief road - ground entrance adjacent to Foxdell Junior School.
Capacity: 400 **Cover:** 100 **Seats:** 25 **Floodlights:** Yes **Midweek matches:** Wednesday
Clubhouse: Open daily 12-3 & 7.30-11. Light snacks & refreshments etc available. **Club Shop:** No
Programme: 30 pages, £2 (incl. admission) **Club Sponsors:** A & E Engineering.
Previous - League: Luton & Dist. **Grounds:** Crawley Green Rd, Luton (public park); Hitchin Town FC (share 93-94).
Club Record Scorer: Keith Denness
Honours: South Mids Lg R-up 92-93, 96-97 (Div 1 R-up 83-84 87-88), Lg Cup R-up 75-76 80-81 92-93 97-98, Premier Div Cup R-up 91-92, Reserve Div 2 R-up 75-76, Reserve Cup R-up 87-88; Luton & Dist. Lg 67-68 69-70 70-71 71-72; William Pease Trophy 66-67 67-68 70-71 71-72; Beds Intermediate Cup 71-72 (R-up 68-69 70-71), Beds Jnr Cup 82-83; Leighton Challenge Cup R-up 69-70.

BRIMSDOWN ROVERS

Chairman/Secretary: Graham Dodd, 57 Roundmoor Drive, Cheshunt, Herts EN8 9HU. 01992 626820 (H&B), 01992 637111 (Fax).
Match Secretary: Tony Beasley, 80 Cobham Road, Fetcham, Leatherhead, Surrey. KT22 9JS. 01372 376820 (H)
Ground Brimsdown Sports & Social Club, Goldsdown Road, Enfield, Middlesex (0181 804 5491).
Directions: BR from Liverpool Street to Brimsdown (half mile away) or Southbury Road. By road off Green Street, itself off Hertford Road (A1010). Buses 191 or 307.
Seats: 25 **Cover:** 50 **Capacity:** 1,000 **Floodlights:** Yes **Founded:** 1947
Clubhouse: Large lounge & clubroom, games room & stage. 3 bars (300 capacity)
Manager: Nigel McGrath **Programme:** With admission **Editor:** Peter Wade
Colours: Black & white stripes/black/black **Change colours:** All yellow & blue
Best season - FA Vase: 3rd Rd 93-94 **FA Cup:** 3rd Qual. replay 91-92. **Previous - Leagues:** Northern Suburban
Names: Durham Rovers; Brimsdown FC. **Record Gate:** 412 v Chesham Utd, FA Cup 3rd Qual. Rd 12/10/91.
Honours: Spartan Lg 92-93. Spartan Lg Cup 95-96.

BROOK HOUSE

President: T Dean **Chairman:** Mick Ralph **Vice-Chairman:** M Powell
Secretary: Barry Crump, 19 Bradenham Road, Hayes, Middlesex UB4 8LP. Tel: 0181 841 3959 (H), 0850 253924 (B).
Manager: Mickey Harvey **Asst. Manager:** Bobby Strutton **Coach:** Reggie Leather
Ground: Farm Park, Kingshill Avenue, Hayes, Middlesex (0181 845 0110).
Directions: From North Circular road: A40 Western Ave. to Target r'about, left towards Hayes (A312), over White Hart r'about towards Yeading/Hayes, right at traffic lights in to Kingshill Ave, ground 1 mile on right. Nearest BR station is Hayes & Harlington, then bus 90 or 195 to Brook House pub. Nearest tube is Northolt (central line), then bus to ground.
Seats: 90 **Cover:** 100 **Capacity:** 1,800 **Floodlights:** Yes **Founded:** 1974 **Club Shop:** No
Clubhouse: Open weekdays 7-11pm, Sat noon-11pm, Sun noon-11.00pm **Midweek matchday:** Wednesday
Programme: 28 pages, £2 with entry **Editor:** John Handell/Dave Ball **Press Officer:** Lawrie Watts
Colours: Blue & white/blue/blue **Change colours:** Black & red stripes/black
Best season - FA Vase: 3rd Prop 97-98. **FA Cup:** 1st Qual Rd 93-94. **Reserve League:** Middlesex County
Players progressing to Football League: Neil Shipperley (Crystal Palace), Mark Hyde (Orient), Mark Perry (QPR).
Honours: SSM Prem South 97-98.

BUCKINGHAM ATHLETIC

Chairman: Alex Miller **President:** J Burgess **Manager:** Malcolm East
Secretary: Chris Forman, 10 Elm Drive, Deanshanger, Milton Keynes. MK19 6JF. Tel: 01908 563526 (H).
Ground: Stratford Fields, Stratford Rd, Buckingham (01280 816945).
Directions: From Milton Keynes take the A422 Stony Stratford-Buckingham road - ground on left just before town centre. From Oxford, Aylesbury or Bletchley, take the ring road to the A422 Stony Stratford roundabout, turn left, the ground is situated at the bottom of the hill on the left.
Capacity: 1,500 **Seats:** No **Cover:** 200 **Floodlights:** Yes **Founded:** 1933
Programme: 10 pages, 50p **Editor:** Tony Checkley, 01280 817826 (H) **Midweek matches:** Wednesday
Colours: All sky & navy blue **Change Colours:** Red & white/white/red **Nickname:** Swans
Previous Leagues: North Bucks; Hellenic. **Players progressing to Football League:** None.
Hons: Sth Mids Lg Div 1 85-86 90-91 (R-up 88-89, Div 1 Cup 90-91), Nth Bucks Lg 84-85 (Lg Cup 83-84, Lg Shield 60-61), Berks & Bucks Jnr Cup 65-66, Buckingham Charity Cup 69-70 71-72.

HARINGEY BOROUGH

Chairman: Peter Lawlor **Secretary:** George Kilikita, Unit 12A, 16-22 Seven Sisters Rd, London N7 6AE.
Vice-Chairman: T O'Connell Tel: 0171 607 7419 (H), 0181 368 2783 (B)
Ground: Coles Park, White Hart Lane, Tottenham N17 (081 889 1415)
Directions: From M1 take North Circular Road (A406). Leave A406 turning right into Bounds Green Rpad (A109), proceed to end then turn left into Wood Gren High Rd (A105) and then first right into White Hart Lane. Ground is on right 300 yds past New River Sports Centre. Wood Green (Picadilly Line). BR (Eastern Region) to White Hart Lane, W3 bus passes ground A105 or A10 from Nth. Circular to Wood Green.
Seats: 280 **Cover:** Yes **Capacity:** 2,500 **Floodlights:** Yes **Clubhouse:** Open 7 days a week
Colours: Green & white/white/green **Change colours:** Yellow & black/black/yellow
Previous Leagues: London 07-14; Isthmian 19-52 84-88; Spartan 52-54; Delphian 54-63; Athenian 63-84.
Previous Names: Edmonton; Tufnell Park; Tufnell Park Edmonton; Edmonton & Haringey.
Senior Honours: None

HARPENDEN TOWN

Chairman: **Managers:** Mark Nicholls, Paul Woolfrey **Nickname:** The Town **Founded:** 1891
Secretary: Stephen Whiting, 169 Grove Rd, Harpenden, Herts AL5 1SY (01582 761606).
Ground: Rothamsted Park, Amenbury Lane, Harpenden (01582 715724).
Directions: A1081 to Harpenden. Turn left/right at George Hotel into Leyton Rd. Turn left into Amenbury Rd, then left again (50yds) into 'Pay and Display' car park - entrance is signposted thru car park to opposite corner.
Capacity: 1,500 **Seats:** 25 **Cover:** 100 **Floodlights:** Yes **Programme:** 50p **Editor:** Secretary
Midweek matches: Tuesday **Colours:** Yellow/blue/blue **Change Colours:** Blue/yellow/red
Previous Name: Harpenden FC 1891-1908. **Previous Leagues:** Mid-Herts; Herts County.
Honours: Sth Mids Lg 61-62 64-65, Championship Shield 67-68, Lg Cup 70-71, Div 1 89-90, Prem Div Tphy 89-90, Res Div 89-90; Herts Co. Lg 11-12 49-50 51-52 53-54 (Aubrey Cup 20-21 28-29 50-51 51-52); Mid-Herts Lg 09-10 20-21; Pratt Cup 06-07 08-09 10-11; Herts Jnr Cup 01-02 09-10 11-12 20-21 25-26; Herts I'mediate Cup 52-53; Herts Charity Shield 07-08; Bingham Cox Cup 1896-97 1902-03 09-10 20-21.

HILLINGDON BOROUGH

Chairman: John Mason
Secretary: Bob Bevis, Beech Cottage, Uxbridge Road, Hillingdon, Middx. UB10 0LF.
Commercial Mgr: Gamdoor Dhaliwal
Manager: Stuart Leavy **Asst Man.:** Ian Lancaster **Physio:** Dave Pook
Ground: Middlesex Stadium, Breakspear Road, Ruislip, Middx HA4 7SB (01895 639544).
Directions: From A40 take B467 (signed Ickenham), left at 2nd r'bout into Breakspear Rd South, right after 1 mile by Breakspear pub - ground half mile on left. Nearest station is Ruislip. Bus U1 passes ground.
Seats: 150 **Cover:** 150 **Capacity:** 1,500 **Floodlights:** Yes **Founded:** 1990
Clubhouse: Mon-Fri 7.30-11pm, Sat & Sun lunchtime & 7.30-10.30pm. **Club Shop:** No.
Midweek Matches: Tuesday **Sponsors:** Airport Motor Radiator Co. **Nickname:** Boro.
Colours: White/blue/blue **Change colours:** Red/white/red
Programme: 20 pages **Editor/Press Off:** Alan Taylor (0181 581 0981) **Reserves' League:** Suburban
Club Records - Win: 12-0 v Hanwell Town (H), Spartan South Midlands Prem 97/98. **Defeat:** 1-11 v St. Albans City (A), FA Cup 2nd Qual. Rd. 24.9.94 **Transfer Fee Received:** £1,000 for Craig Johnson (Wealdstone).

HODDESDON TOWN

Back Row (L-R); Ian Barnes, Lee Browne, Spencer Knight, Joel Miller, Chris Chaplin, Danny Nicholls, Richard Evans, Rocco Tona, Stuart Dorward, Leon Hughton, John Clowes. Front Row; Steve Cokell, Paul Toms, Paul Mann, Jeff Cross, Alan Moore (Mgr), Paul Surridge (Asst Mgr), Simon Riddle, Tony Dalli, Alex Barnes.

President: Peter Haynes **Chairman:** Roger Merton **Deputy Chairman:** Stewart Edwards
Secretary: Brenda Timpson, 82 Tolmers Road, Cuffley, Potters Bar, Herts EN6 4JY (01707 874028)
Manager: Alan Moore **Asst Manager:** Paul Surridge **Nickname:** Lilywhites/ Lowfielders **Founded:** 1879
Ground: 'Lowfield', Park View, Hoddesdon, Herts (0992 463133).
Directions: A10, A1170 into Hoddesdon, over 1st r'about, right at 2nd r'about and follow signs to Broxbourne, keeping to the left. Turn right at 1st mini r-about into Cock Lane and 1st right is Park View. Ground 200yds on the left, entrance opposite Park Rd. Nearest BR station is Broxbourne.
Capacity: 3,000 **Seats:** 100 **Cover:** 250 **Floodlights:** Yes **Club Shop:** No.
Clubhouse: Bar and well-stocked Tea Bar with hot food. Open at every home game.
Colours: White/black/black **Change Colours:** All red **Reserves' Lge:** Essex/Herts Border Com
Programme: 88-100 pages 80p **Editor:** Mrs Jane Sinden (01767 631297) **Midweek matchday:** Tuesday
Honours: FA Vase 74-75 (1st winners); Spartan Sth Mids Lg Prem Div Plate 97-98 (R-up 96-97, Sth Mids League Lg Cup 85-86 86-87 91-92 (Premier Div Tphy R-up 92-93); Spartan Lg 70-71 (R-up(3) 71-74), Div 1 35-36, Div 2 'B' 27-28, Lg Cup(2) 70-72; Herts Snr Cup(3) 1886-88 89-90; Herts Charity Shield (4) 47-48 70-72 78-79; Herts Snr Centenary Tphy 86-87; Sth Mids Floodlit Cup 89-90 (R-up 92-93); Waltham Hospital Cup 27-28; Perry Charity Cup (7), East Anglian Cup Group finalists 92-93.

ISLINGTON St MARYS

Chairman: Ian Myclam
Tel: 0171 359 6112
Secretary: Nick Adams, 5 Hambledon Chase, 58 Crouch Hill London N4 4AH. Tel: 0171 263 1530 (H), 0171 226 3400 (B), 0370 625235 (M).
Match Secretary: Eddie Webb, 34 Bidwell Gardens, Bounds Green, London, N11 2AU. Tel: 0181 881 0538 (H)
Ground: Coles Park, White Hart Lane, Tottenham N17 (0181 889 1495)
Directions: From M1 take North Circular Road (A406). Leave A406 turning right into Bounds Green Rpad (A109), proceed to end then turn left into Wood Gren High Rd (A105) and then first right into White Hart Lane. Ground is on right 300 yds past New River Sports Centre. Wood Green (Picadilly Line). BR (Eastern Region) to White Hart Lane, W3 bus passes ground A105 or A10 from Nth. Circular to Wood Green.
Capacity: 2,500 **Cover:** Yes **Seating:** 280 **Floodlights:** Yes **Founded:**
Colours: Blue/white/blue **Change Colours:** Black & white/black/white

LONDON COLNEY

London Colney *Photo: Clive Butchins*

Chairman: Bill Gash **Vice Chairman:** P Light **President:** I Holt.
Secretary: Dave Brock, 50 Seymour Rd., St Albans, Herts. AL3 5HW. Tel: 01727 761644 (H)
Ground: Cotslandswick, London Colney (01727 822132). **Manager:** S Seabrook, M Wright **Physio:** J Burt
Directions: From London Colney r'bout (junction of A414/A1081) take A414 towards Watford, after layby (300yds) turn left (hidden turning marked 'Sports Ground') and follow around to gates. Three miles from St Albans (BR).
Capacity: 1,000 **Cover:** 100 **Seats:** 30 **Floodlights:** Yes **Club Shop:**
Clubhouse: Open after games. Hot food available. **Founded:** 1907
Programme: £1 with entry **Editor:** Matt Kelly Tel: 01727 761644 (H) **Nickname:** Blueboys
Colours: All royal blue with white trim **Change Colours:** All Red **Sponsors:** Harris Mortgage & Finance
Previous - Leagues: Mid Herts 1907-54; Herts Co. 07-92. **Ground:** Whitehorse Lane 07-75.
Hons: Sth Mids Lg Snr 94-95 Div R-up 93-94 (Challenge Trophy 93-94, Div 1 R-up 92-93, Res. Div 1 92-93), Herts Co. Lg 56-57 59-60 86-87 88-89 (R-up 57-58 58-59, Aubrey Cup 21-22 22-23 56-57 58-59 81-82; Herts Centenary Tphy 89-90 (R-up 90-91), Herts I'mediate Cup 58-59 74-75 82-83, Herts Charity Shield 61-62 (R-up 59-60), Herts Jnr Cup 54-55; Mid Herts Benevolent Cup (3), Bene Shield (4), Charity Cup 48-49; St Albans Playing Fields Cup (4); Frank Major Tphy 74-75 75-76.

MILTON KEYNES CITY

Chairman: Bob Flight. Tel: 01604 764433 (H), 01980 245375 (B) **President:** Nigel Wells
Secretary: Peter Baldwin, c/o Mercedes-Benz (UK) Ltd, Tongwell, Milton Keynes MK15 8BA.
01604 870457 (H) 01908 245408 (B) 01908 245088 (Fax).
Manager: Cliff Peters **Asst Man.:** Mark Collender **Coach:** Kevin England **Physio:** Nick Booth
Ground: The Barn, Pannier Place, Downs Barn, Milton Keynes, Bucks (01908 245158).
Directions: M1 jct 14, A509 for Milton Keynes, right onto H5 Portway at 1st island, right onto V9 Overstreet at 3rd island, 1st left into Downs Barn Boulevard, 2nd left into Pannier Place, ground at top of hill.
Capacity: 300 **Cover:** No **Seats:** None **Floodlights:** No **Founded:** 1967.
Clubhouse: The Mercedes-Benz Sports & Social Club, 1 mile from ground, open normal licensing hours.
Programme: 16 pages, 50p **Editor:** Stuart Collard, 01908 660796 (H), 01908 600394 (B) **Club Shop:** No
Colours: Royal/navy/navy **Change Colours:** All white **Nickname:** Blues
Midweek matches: Wednesday **Sponsors:** Mercedes-Benz (UK) Ltd **Reserves' league:** S.S.M. Reserve Div.
Record scorer: Stuart Collard 132. **Record appearances:** Stuart Collard 206.
Hons: North Bucks Lge - Div 1 90-91, Prem. Div Cup 92-93, I'mediate Tphy 91-92; Daimler-Benz Austrian International Tournament R-up 1990.

NEW BRADWELL ST PETER

Chairman: John Haynes **Vice-Chairman:** K Felce **President:** J P Booden
Secretary: Les Smith, 47 Rowle Close, Stantonbury, Milton Keynes MK14 6BJ. Tel.: 01908 319522 (H)
Manager: S Spooner **Press Officer:** P Smith
Ground: Recreation Ground, Bradwell Road, New Bradwell, Milton Keynes MK13 7AT (01908 313835)
Directions: From M1 Jnt 14 go towards Newport Pagnell, left at 1st r-about into H3 (A422 Monks Way). Over 5 r-abouts, right at 6th island into V6 (Grafton St.), go right the way round (back on yourself) 1st island, 1st left, left at mini-roundabout, ground half mile on left (before bridge).
Nickname: Peters **Seats:** 30 **Cover:** 100 **Floodlights:** No **Founded:** 1902
Clubhouse: Members only (member can sign in 2 guests). Open every evening and w/e lunchtimes. No food.
Colours: Maroon & blue stripes/blue/blue **Change:** Green & yellow halves/green/yellow
Programme: 32 pages, £1 with entry **Editor:** Paul Smith 01908 315766 (H)
Midweek matches: Wednesday **Sponsors:** New Bradwell St Peter V-Presidents.
Hons: South Midlands Lge - Div 1 76-77,83-84, Reserve Div 2 R-up 76-77

POTTERS BAR TOWN

Chairman: Peter Waller. **Vice Chairman:** Alan Bolt. **President:** Bert Wright
Secretary: Carole Waller, 26 Queen Annes Grove, Bush Hill Park, Enfield, Middx EN1 2JR (0181 360 7859).
Manager: Ray Kierstenson & Micky Darling
General Manager: Les Eason **Physio:** Brian Goymer
Ground: Parkfield, The Walk, Potters Bar, Herts EN6 1QN, 01707 654833
Directions: M25 jct 24, enter Potters Bar along Southgate Rd (A111), at 1st lights right into the High St (A1000), half mile left into The Walk, ground 200 yds on right (opp. Potters Bar Cricket Club). BR to Potters Bar - The Walk is directly opposite station - ground half mile up hill on left.
Capacity: 2,000 **Seats:** 25 **Cover:** 100 **Floodlights:** Yes **Club Shop:** No
Clubhouse: Sat 12.30-11pm, Sun noon-5pm, Tues & Thurs 7.30-11pm, midweek matchnights 6-11pm.
Programme: 24 pages, £1 **Editor/Press Officer:** Robert Brassett, 0181 364 4058
Colours: Red & royal stripes/royal/royal **Change colours:** White/red/red
Sponsors: Century 21 Estates **Nickname:** The Grace or The Scholars. **Founded:** 1960
Midweek matchday: Tuesday or Wednesday **Best FA Vase season:** Third Round, 90-91.
Previous Leagues: Barnet & Dist. 60-65/ Nth London Comb. 65-68/ Herts Snr Co. 68-91.
Record Attendance: 4000 v Eastenders XI, 20.4.97. 387 v Barnet, floodlight opener 8/12/93.
Players progressing to Football League: Keith Bertschin (Birmingham, Ipswich, Stoke, Barnet etc).
Honours: South Midlands Lge. - Prem. Div. 96-97, Plate 96-97; Herts. Sen. Co. Lge. - Prem. Div. 90-91, Div. 1 73-74, 81-82, Div. 2 68-69; North London Comb. - Prem. Div. 67-68, Div. 1 67-68, Div. 2 R-up 65-66; Barnet & Dist. Lge - Prem. Div. R-up 64-65, Div. 1 61-62; Herts Charity Shd. R-up 95-96, Potters Bar Charity Cup 76-77, 95-96, R-up x8; Mid Herts FA - Bingham Cox Cup R-up 94-95.

ROYSTON TOWN

Chairman: Tony Moulding **Vice-Chairman:** Bernard Brown **President:** Alan Barlow
Secretary/Press Officer: Trevor Glasscock, 39 Poplar Drive, Royston, Herts. SG8 (01763 230783)
Manager: Kevin Pugh **Asst Mgr:** Sam Salomone **Physio:** Colin Mardell
Ground: Garden Walk, Royston, Herts SG8 7HP (01763 241204). **Directions:** From Baldock, A505 to Royston bypass, right at 2nd island onto A10 towards London, 2nd left is Garden Walk; ground 100 yds on left. From A11, exit 10 turning left onto A505, left at 1st island, 2nd left is Garden Walk. Ten mins walk from Royston (BR).
Capacity: 4,000 **Seats:** 300 **Cover:** 300 **Floodlights:** Yes **Club Shop:** Yes
Clubhouse: Mon-Thurs 7-11, Fri 11-3 & 7-11, Sat 11-3 & 4-11, Sun 12-3. Steward: Mr & Mrs P Nesbitt.
Programme: 16 pages, 30p **Editor:** Steve Langridge (01438 356661) **Nickname:** Crows.
Colours: White/black/black **Change colours:** Red/white/white **Founded:** 1875
Midweek Matches: Tuesday **Reserve League:** Essex & Herts Border Comb. **Sponsors:** ABA Consultants.
Previous - Names: None **Grounds:** Newmarket Rd, Baldock Rd, Mackeral Hall. **Leagues:** Buntingford & Dist. 18-28; Cambs 28-50; Herts Co. 50-59 62-77; Sth Mids 59-62 77-84; Isthmian 84-94.
Club Records - Attendance: 876 v Aldershot, 13/2/93 **Scorer:** Trevor Glasscock 289 (1968-82) **Appearances:** Fred Bradley 713. **Best FA Cup year:** Second Qual. Round - 59-60, 0-9 v Barnet (A), 89-90, 0-3 V Bromley (A)
Players progressing to Football League: John Smith (Spurs).
Hons: Herts Co. Lg 76-77 (Div 1 69-70 76-77); Sth Mids Lg R-up 79-80 (Div 1 78-79, Chall. Cup R-up 78-79; Herts Charity Shield 81-82 89-90 (R-up 78-79 88-89), Creake Shield 20-21; Cambs Lg Div 2 29-30; Herts Intermediate Cup 88-89 (R-up 89-90), Nth Herts Lg 4 Cup 78-79 79-80 (Div R-up 82-83, Div 3 R-up 81-82, Div 4 R-up 79-80).

RUISLIP MANOR

Chairman: Mick Connors **Vice Chairman:** Jim Evans **President:** TBA
Secretary: Andy Torrance, 55 Ryefield Avenue, Hillingdon, Middlesex. 01895 257631.
Manager: Andy Waddock **Asst Manager:** Gary Farrant **Physio:** Gary Strudwick
Ground: Grosvenor Vale, off West End Road, Ruislip, Middx (01895 637487-office, 676168-boardroom)
Directions: A40 to Ruislip, turn off on A4180, right at r'bout into West End Rd, right into Grosvenor Vale after a 1 1/2 miles - ground at end. From Ruislip Manor station (Metropolitan Line) turn left out of station, then 1st right into Shenley Ave, 3rd left into Cranley Dr - ground 150 yds on left.
Capacity: 3,000 **Seats:** 250 **Cover:** 600 **Floodlights:** Yes **Founded:** 1938 **Nickname:** The Manor
Clubhouse: Mon-Fri 12-3.30 & 5.30-11pm, Sat & Sun 12-3 & 7.30-10.30. **Club Shop:** Yes
Programme: 24 **Price:** 50p **Editor / Press Officer:** Steve Szymanski, 01895 637933
Colours: Black & White/black/black **Change colours:** Yellow & blue/yellow/yellow
Midweek Matches: Monday **Reserve League:** Suburban Lge (North) **Sponsors:** Eastcote Birds & Pets
Record Attendance: 2,000 v Tooting & Mitcham United, F.A. Amateur Cup 1962.
Previous Lges: Uxbridge 38-39; Middx Snr 39-46; London 46-58; Spartan 58-65; Athenian 65-84; Isthmian 84-96.
Best F.A. Cup year: Fourth Qual. Round 90-91, 2-5 v Halesowen Town (A)
Players progressing to Football League: Dave Carroll, Paul Barrowcliffe, Michael Meaker, Warren Goodhind, Ray Knowles, Barry & Roy Davies.
Club Record Appearances: Chris Balls, 350 **Club Record Goalscorer:** Kevin Quinn, 76
Honours: London Lg R-up 51-52 (Div 1 R-up 47-48), Isthmian Lg Div 2 R-up 92-93 (Associate Members Tphy 90-91), Athenian Lg Div 2 72-73, Middx Snr Cup SF(6), Middx Charity Cup R-up 90-91 95-96.

St MARGARETSBURY

Chairman: T I Blacktin **President:** R L Groucott
Secretary: K Myall, 30 Crib St, Ware, Herts. SG12 9EX 01920 485067 (H), 01920 830356 (W)
Manager: Kelvin Hart **Asst Manager:** Colin Richards **Coach:** Ian Priest
Physio: Derek Ridgewell.
Ground: Station Road, Stanstead St Margarets, Nr Ware, Herts (01920 870473).
Directions: Harlow/Chelmsford exit from A10 to A414, take B181 at Amwell after 300yds towards Stanstead Abotts - ground quarter mile on right. 300yds from St Margaretsbury BR station (Liverpool Str.-Hertford East line).
Seats: 60 **Cover:** 60 **Capacity:** 1,000 **Floodlights:** No **Founded:** 1894
Colours: Red & black/Black/Black & Red. **Change colours:** All white **Nickname:** The Bury.
Previous Grounds: Mill Field, Stanstead Abbotts pre-1962.
Previous Leagues: East Herts/ Hertford & Dist./ Waltham & District 47-48/ Herts Co. 48-92.
Programme: 16 pages, £1.50 with entry **Editor:** Jane Free (0920 870431)
Club Shop: No, but Centenary Brochure available from J Smith, 97 Lampits, Hoddesdon, Herts (cheques for £6 (inc p&p) payable to St Margaretsbury FC).
Sponsors: Universal Office Automation, Hertford.
Record Gate: 327 v Wisbech Town, FA Vse 3rd Round 14/12/85.
Midweek home matchday: Tuesday **Reserve team's League:** Hertford & District.
Clubhouse: Bar open 7-11pm + Sat noon-2, Sun noon-3pm. Bar snacks available.
Hons: Herts Snr Centenary Tphy 92-93, Herts County Lg Div 2 48-49 (Div 3 78-79, Aubrey Cup 48-49 71-72, Reserve Div 1 82-83 86-87, Reserve Cup 84-85 86-87 87-88), Waltham & Dist Lg 46-47.

SOMERSET AMBURY V & E

TODDINGTON ROVERS

Chairman: Alan Fieldhouse **Vice Chairman:** Brian Horne **President:** Hugh Geddes
Secretary: Barry Hill, 9 Fairfield Rd, Dunstable,Beds. LU5 4JT. Tel: 01582 471150 (H), 01582 723122 (B).
Manager: John Alder **Asst Man.:** Martin Everet **Coach:** Roger King **Physio:** John Cullen
Ground: Sharing with Barton Rovers, Sharpenhoe Road, Barton-le-Clay, Bedford MK45 4SD (01582 882607).
Directions: M1 Jct 12, from London exit turn right, take 2nd right through Harlington and Sharpenhoe. Ground on right entering village. 4.5 miles from Harlington (BR), 6 miles from Luton (BR), good bus service from Luton.
Capacity: 4,000 **Seats:** 160 **Cover:** 1,120 **Floodlights:** Yes
Nickname: Rovers **Founded:** 1894 **Club Shop:** No.
Clubhouse: Club use Toddington Social & Services Club. **Midweek matches:** Wednesday
Colours: All black & white stripes **Change Colours:** All Blue. **Press Officer:** Colin Bryson
Programme: 50p **Editor:** T Simmonds & Andrew Parker, 01582 599158 (H) **Sponsors:** TBA
Club Records - Scorer: David Ashby **Appearances:** George Stewart, 1050. **Attendance:** 160 v Silsoe, Luton & Dist. Lge 26/1/23.
Honours: South Midlands Lg Snr Div 94-95 (Snr Div Cup 94-95), Luton & District South Beds Lge R-up x3 (Div 1 x3, Div 2 x2, Div 3 x2, Div 4 x1).

WALTHAM ABBEY

Chairman: Greg Brooker **President:** Dennis Cordell
Secretary: Alex Myers, 88 The Weymarks, Weir Hall Road, Tottenham N17 8LD. Tel/Fax: 0181 808 2706 (H)
Ground: 'Capershotts', Sewardstone Road, Waltham Abbey, Essex (01992 711287).
Directions: Just off M25 jct 26. Waltham Cross (BR Eastern Region) station three miles distant. 242 Bus.
Seats: None **Cover:** 400 **Capacity:** 2,000 **Floodlights:** Yes **Nickname:** The Abbey **Founded:** 1948
Clubhouse: 7-11pm Mon-Fri, 11am-11pm Sat, noon-3pm Sun. Cold snacks, pool, darts. **Club Shop:** No
Programme: 8 pages 50p **Editor:** Alex Myers (Sec.) **Reserves' League:** Essex & Herts Border Comb.
Colours: All green and white **Change colours:** Red & black hoops/red/red **Midweek matches:** Tuesday
Previous Leagues: Northen Suburban
Club Records - Attendance: 1,800 v Spurs, charity game **Scorer:** Paul Holloway **Appearances:** Colin Winter
Best Season - FA Cup: Prel. Rd 90-91 **FA Vase:** Prel. Rd 87-88 88-89 89-90

WELWYN GARDEN CITY

Chairman: John Newman **Manager:** Ian Priest. **Physio:** Arthur Wood
Secretary: James Bruce, 6 Autumn Grove, Welwyn G.C., Herts AL7 4DB. Tel: 01707 331048 (H).
Ground: Herns Lane, Welwyn Garden City (01707 328470).
Directions: From A1 follow signs for industrial area. Take one-way system opposite Avdel Ltd (signed Hertford B195), take 2nd exit off one-way system. Ground 400 yards on left. One and a half miles from Welwyn GC (BR).
Capacity: 1,500 **Seats:** 40 **Cover:** 120 **Floodlights:** Yes **Founded:** 1921 **Club Shop:** Yes
Clubhouse: Open every night and weekend lunchtimes. Members Bar, Hall. Steward: Dave Parham.
Colours: Maroon & blue/blue/maroon **Change Colours:** Yellow/blue/yellow **Nickname:** Citzens
Programme: 24 pages, 50p **Editor:** Keith Browne (01707 251854) **Midweek Matches:** Tuesday
Best Season - FA Vase: 1st Rd 86-87. **FA Cup:** First Qual.Rd. 94-95. **Record Gate:** 600 v Welwyn Garden United.
Previous - Leagues: Spartan; Metropolitan; Gtr London. **Ground:** Springfields
Honours: Herts Snr Centenary Tphy 84-85 (R-up 88-89), Herts Charity Shield 27-28 86-87 87-88 94-95 (R-up 48-49), Sth Mids Lg 73-74 (R-up 85-86, Div 1 69-70 81-82, Lg Cup R-up 74-75 81-82 88-89, Reserve Cup 85-86).

Brache Sparta FC. with the Premier Division North Champions Cup and the Premier Division Knockout Cup. Back Row (L-R): Isaac Fevrier, Paul Mulling, Craig Linney, Daren Walker, Archie Devlin (Vice Chr). Middle Row: Brendan Healy, Fason Campbell, Ben Smith (Physio), Johnson Baptiste, Pat Walsh, Steve Georgiou, Steve Brinkman (Mgr), Stuart Strange, Kevin Wright. Front Row: Dave Seaton, Colin Massie, Mark Smith (Capt & Asst Mgr), Dean Walker, John Tipper, Jason Huntly.

Greenacres (Hemel) FC

PREMIER DIVISION TWO CLUBS 1998-99

AMERSHAM TOWN

Chairman: Howard Lambert **Vice Chairman:** David Holdcroft **President:** Graham Taylor
Secretary: Ian Wright, 80 Somervell Road, Harrow, Middlesex. HA2 8TT
Manager: Paul Pitfield **Coach:** Oscar Ringsell
Ground: Spratley's Meadow, School Lane, Old Amersham, Bucks. (01494 727428).
Directions: From London A413 to Amersham Old town, infront of market hall, right into Church St., first left into School Lane, ground on left past Mill Lane. 1 mile from Amersham Station - BR & underground Metropolitan Line.
Seats: None **Cover:** 100 **Capacity:** 1,500 **Floodlights:** Yes **Founded:** 1890
Clubhouse: Open matchdays. Bar facilities. Teas, coffees and light snacks **Club Shop:** No.
Programme: With admission **Editor/Press Officer:** David Holdcroft 01494 725201 **Sponsors:** Llumarlite Ltd.
Colours: Black & white stripes/black/black **Change colours:** Red/black/black
Midweek matches: Tuesday **Reserve's League:** Middx Co. **Nickname:** Magpies.
Hons: Hellenic Lg 63-64 (R-up 64-65 65-66, Div 1 62-63, Cup 53-54), Ldn Spartan Lg R-up 79-80, St Marys Cup 89-90 96-97 (R-up 90-91), Berks & Bucks Jnr Cup 22-23 (Snr Cup SF 79-80 80-81), Wycombe Chal. Cup 23-24.

BEDFORD UNITED

Chairman: John Cleverley **Vice Chairman:** Jim McMullen **President:** D Rostron
Secretary: Geoff Seagrave, 16 Riverview Way, Kempston, Bedford MK42 7BB. 01234 402369 (H)
Manager: Simon Ackroyd **Asst. Man.:** Mark Ackroyd **Coach/Physio:** Dave Petrie
Ground: McMullen Park, Meadow Lane, Cardington, Bedford MK45 3SB (01234 831024)
Directions: M1 jct 13, A421 to Bedford by-pass. Take third exit, A603 sandy, ground 500 yards on left hand side.
Capacity: 5,000 **Seats:** 25 **Cover:** 100 **Floodlights:** Yes **Founded:** 1957
Clubhouse: Open matchdays. Hot & cold snacks and drinks available.
Colours: Blue & White/blue/blue **Change colours:** All red **Nickname:** United
Programme: 24 pages, £1 **Editor:** Robin King (01234 364654) **Press Officer:** Jim McMullem
Midweek matches: Wednesday **Reserves' League:** S. Mids Lge Res. sect. **Club Sponsors:** JDP Finance
Honours: Bedford & Dist Lg Premier Division & Division One, County Junior Cup, Biggleswade KO Cup, Butchers Cup(2), Britania Cup, Bedford Charity Cup.

BIGGLESWADE TOWN

Chairman: Maurice Dorrington **Vice Chairman:** M Jarvis **President:** R Dorrington
Secretary: Graham Arkwright, 21 Willsheres Road, Biggleswade, Beds SG18 0BU (01767 221574).
Manager: D Northfield **Physio:** J Maher **Nickname:** Waders **Founded:** 1874
Ground: 'Fairfield', Fairfield Road, Biggleswade, Beds (01767 312374).
Directions: A1 North r'bout, left immediately after metal bridge into car park. 10 mins walk from Biggleswade (BR).
Capacity: 2,400 **Seats:** 250 **Cover:** 400 **Floodlights:** Yes **Club Shop:** No.
Clubhouse: Open all matchdays. Filled rolls available. Refreshment hut sells hotdogs, teas, coffees, snacks.
Programme: 32 pages, with entry. **Editor:** Brian Doggett (01767 318307 (H).
Colours: All green **Change:** Tangerine/black/black **Club Sponsors:** Mantles Ford
Previous Leagues: Biggleswade & Dist. 02-20/ Bedford & Dist. 09-12/ Utd Co's (prev. Northants Lg) 20-39 51-55 63-80/ Spartan 46-51/ Eastern Co's 55-63.
Honours: South Mids Lge: Res Div 2 87-88, Res Chall Trophy 88-89, S.M. Floodlit Cup 95-96; Beds Snr Cup 02-03 07-08 46-47 51-52 61-62 62-63 66-67 73-74; Beds Premier Cup 22-23 27-28; Nth Beds Charity Cup 07-08 09-10 26-27 33-34(joint) 49-50 52-53 54-55 57-58 62-65 67-69 73-74 91-92 94-95; Utd Co's Lg Cup 73-74; Hunts Premier Cup 92-93 93-94(joint) 94-95 97-98; Hinchingbrooke Cup 03-04 12-13 92-93; Jess Piggott Trophy 87-88 89-90 91-92 92-93; Key Consul. Res F/Light Cup 89-90.

BIGGLESWADE UNITED

Chairman: David McCormick. Tel: 01767 316018
Secretary: Tracey James, 17 Havelock Road, Biggleswade, Beds SG18 0DB. Tel: 01767 316270 (H), 0171 962 8551 (B), 0467 372176 (M).
Match Secretary: Mick Brown, 46 Glebe Road, Biggleswade, Beds. Tel: 01767 312412 (H).
Ground: Second Meadow, Fairfield Road, Biggleswade, Beds. (01767 600408)
Directions: From A1 Sainsbury's roundabout, cross over iron bridge and take first left into Sun Street. Take next turn left into Fairfield Road ground at bottom of road in lane
Colours: Blue & black/black/black **Programme Editor:** Tracey James (Sec.).

CADDINGTON

Chairman: David Mark. Tel: 01582 421404 (H). **Manager:** Leigh Glenister
Secretary: Leigh Glenister, 14 Elaine Gardens, Woodside, Luton, LU1 4DI. Tel: 01582 730502 (H), 01582 477557 (B).
Match Secretary: Fred Rook, 44 Clifford Crescent, Luton. LU4 9HR. Tel: 01582 580453 (H).
Ground: Caddington Recreation Club, Manor Road, Caddington (01582 450151).
Directions: On entering village turn into Manor Road (adjacent to shops and village green), proceed 500 metres: Clubhouse and ground on left side next to Catholic Church.
Capacity: Unknown **Seats:** None **Cover:** None **Floodlights:** No **Clubhouse:** Yes
Colours: Red & black/black/black **Programme:** Yes **Editor:** John Fowler, 01582 732041 (H)
Founded: 1971 **Nickname:** The Oaks **Midweek matchday:** Tuesday or Thursday.
Hons: Beds Intermediate Cup 85-86 92-93 **Record Gate:** 150 v Barton Rvrs, Beds Snr Cup.

COCKFOSTERS

Chairman/Press Officer: Frank Brownlie (0181 500 5930) **President:** Vic Bates
Secretary: Graham Bint, 15 Chigwell Park, Chigwell, Essex IG7 5BE (0181 500 7369).
Manager: Derek Townsend **Physio:** Derek Carlisle **Nickname:** Fosters
Ground: Cockfosters Sports Ground, Chalk Lane, Cockfosters, Barnet (0181 449 5833).
Directions: Ground on A111. M25 Jct 24 (Potters Bar), take A111 signed Cockfosters - ground 2 miles on right. Adjacent to Cockfosters underground station (Picadilly Line). Bus 298 to Cockfosters station.
Seats: None **Cover:** 50 **Capacity:** 1,000 **Floodlights:** No **Founded:** 1921.
Clubhouse: 7-11pm Tues & Thurs, 4-11pm Sat, 12-3pm Sun. Hot & cold food on matchdays. **Club Shop:** No.
Programme: 12 pages with entry **Editor:** A Simmons (0181 440 7998) **Midweek matches:** Tuesday
Colours: All Red **Change colours:** All White **Reserve League:** Middx County **Sponsors:** T.S.I. Design
Honours: London Intermediate Cup 70-71 89-90, Herts Snr Co. Lg 78-79 80-81 83-84 (R-up 82-83 84-85, Aubrey Cup 78-79 84-85 (R-up 70-71 77-78)), Herts Intermediate Cup 78-79 (R-up 71-72 73-74 74-75), Northern Suburban Lg 61-62 (R-up 50-51 65-66, Div 1 49-50 60-61 (R-up 46-47 48-49)), F.A. Vase 2nd Rd 91-92.

GREENACRES (HEMEL)

Secretary: Adrian Marson, 1 Pelham Court, Leverstock Green, Hemel Hempstead, Herts. HP2 4Un. Tel: 01442 243053 (H), 0976 447128 (B)
Ground: Berkhamsted Town FC, Broadwater, Lower Kings Road, Berkhamsted, Herts. HP4 2AA. (01442 862815)
Directions: Bypass to the Chesham/Berkhamsted turn off. Turn left at r'about & left at next r'about into Kingshill Way. Take Kings Road to traffic lights, into Lower Kings Rd & left into Broadwater Rd. Ground on the rt.

HANWELL TOWN

Chairman/Press Officer: Bob Fisher Tel: 0181 952 4142 (H) 0181 519 7511 (B) **President:** Dave Iddiols
Secretary: John A Wake, 38 Warwick Ave., South Harrow, Middx. HA2 8RD. Tel/Fax: 0181 422 1048 (H)
Manager: Roy Nairn **Asst Manager:** Arthur Rowlands **Physio:** Catherine Horne
Ground: Reynolds Field, Perivale Lane, Perivale, Greenford, Middx (0181 998 1701).
Directions: A40(M) west from London, leave opposite Hoover building (B456 for Ealing), turn left into Argyle Road and left into Perivale Lane. Ground is on the left. 500 yards from Perivale tube station (Central line).
Seats: None **Cover:** 200 **Capacity:** 2,000 **Floodlights:** Yes **Founded:** 1948
Clubhouse: Saturday matchdays 2-11pm, Tuesdays 6-11pm, Non-matchdays 7.30-11pm. **Club Shop:** No.
Programme: 16 pages, with entry **Editor:** Julie Soutar, c/o The club. **Midweek matchday:** Tuesday
Colours: Black & white stripes/black/black & white **Change colours:** All red **Nickname:** The Town
Reserves' League: Middx County **Record Att.:** 600 v Spurs, Floodlight opening October 1989.
Hons: Spartan Lg 83-84 (Lg Cup R-up 93-94, London Snr Cup 91-92 92-93 (R-up 93-94), Middx Charity Cup R-up 92-93.

HAREFIELD UNITED

Chairman: Keith Ronald. Tel: 01895 824287 **President:** Mr Ivor Mitchell
Secretary: Terry Devereux, 72 Williamson Way, Rickmansworth, Herts WD3 2GL. Tel: 01923 711451 (H/B)
Ground: Preston Park, Breakespeare Road North, Harefield, Middx UB9 6DG (01895 823474).
Directions: M25 junction 16 to M40 East, left at first roundabout, then second left into Harvill Road. Follow this road up the Church Hill into village, right at small roundabout & the ground is on the right. Denham (BR).
Capacity: 2,000 **Seats:** 150 **Cover:** Yes **Floodlights:** Yes **Founded:** 1868 **Nickname:** Hares.
Clubhouse: (01895 823474) Lunchtimes and evenings. Cold snacks (hot on matchdays) **Club Shop:** No
Colours: Red & white/black/black & red **Change colours:** White/black/black **Reserves' League:** Suburban
Programme: 12-40 pages, 30p **Editor:** Terry Deveraux (Sec.) **Midweek Matches:** Tuesday
Previous Leagues: Uxbridge & Dist.; Gt Western Comb. 46-64; Parthenon 64-68; Middx 68-75; Athenian 75-84.
Best FA Cup year: 2nd Qual. Rd replay 80-81, 86-87 **Record Gate:** 430 v Bashley, FA Vase.
Honours: Middx Premier Cup 85-86, Athenian Lg R-up 83-84, Parthenon Lg 64-65 (Div 1 Cup 65-66), Middx Lg 66-67 68-71 (Lg Cup 66-67 68-69).

HOLMER GREEN

Chairman: Bill Scholes, The Brambles, Penfold Lane, Holmer Green Bucks HP15 6XS. 01494 713867 (H).
Secretary: John Anderson, 1 Jason House, Cressex Rd., High Wycombe, Bucks. HP12 4TT.
Tel: 01494 446128 (H), 01494 465454 (B).
Match Secretary: Ray Ansell, 76 Buckingham Drive, High Wycombe. HP13 7XP. Tel: 01494 535175 (H).
Ground: Watchet Lane, Holmer Green, High Wycombe (01494 711485)
Directions: From Amersham on A404 High Wycombe Road, after approx 2 miles turn right into Sheepcote Dell Road. Continue until end of road by Bat & Ball PH. Turn right then immediate left, continue approx 1/2 mile until 2 mini roundabouts, turn left in front of the Mandarin Duck into Watchet Lane. The ground is 150 yards on the right.
Colours: All Green **Programme:** Yes **Editor:** Bill Scholes (Chairman)

HOUGHTON TOWN

Chairman: David Pigg. Tel: 01582 867058 (H) **Manager:** P Rowe
Secretary: Ken Dye, 9 Luxembourg Close, Luton, Beds LU3 3TD. Tel.: 01582 563378 (H)
Ground: Houghton Town Association Club, Park Road North, Houghton Regis. (01582 864862)
Directions: M1 jct 11, head towards Dunstable, right at island into Poynters Rd, straight over next island keeping left at small r'bout onto Park Rd North - ground on left 10yds before pelican crossing.
Capacity: 200 **Seats:** None **Cover:** Yes **Floodlights:** No **Founded:** 1993
Colours: Green & white/green/white **Change Colours:** All red
Programme: 50p **Editor:** Sally Whitlock, 01582 861181 (H) **Midweek matches:** Tuesday
Hons: South Midlands Lge - Chall Trophy R-up 93-94, Div 1 94-95, Div 1 Cup 94-95, R-up 93-94.

LANGFORD

Chairman: Mick Quinlan **President:** Ted Rutt **Commercial Manager:** Diane Woodward
Secretary: Frank Woodward, 4 West View, Langford, Biggleswade. Beds. SG18 9RT. 01462 701015 (H).
Manager: Gerald Rogers **Asst Mgr:** Andy Wellings **Coach:** Phil Elcock
Ground: Forde Park, Langford Road, Henlow SG16 6AF (0426 816106). **Press Officer:** Secretary
Directions: Halfway between Langford and Henlow on A6001 Hitchin to Biggleswade road. Bus 177 on main Hitchin-Biggleswade route stops right outside ground.
Capacity: 4,000 **Seats:** 50 **Cover:** 250 **Floodlights:** Yes **Founded:** 1910 **Club Shop:** Yes
Clubhouse: Weekday evenings, matchdays 11am-11pm, Sun 12-3pm. Hot food on matchdays only.
Colours: All red with white trim **Change Colours:** Blue & white
Programme: With admission. **Editors:** Lesley Deveraux 01462 701443 (H); Candy Elcock 01462 700472 (H)
Sponsors: B.B & E.A.; The Boot, Pub & Rest. **Midweek matches:** Tuesday **Nickname:** Reds.
Hons: S Mids Lg 88-89 (Lg Cup 73-74 75-76, Prem. Div Tphy 88-89,94-95.O'Brien Div 1 Tphy 84-85), N Beds Charity Cup 27-28 30-31 69-70 75-76 86-87 92-93 94-95, Bedford & Dist. Lg 30-31 31-32 32-33, Bedford I'mediate Cup 68-69, Hinchingbrooke Cup 72-73.

LETCHWORTH

Chairman: Adrian Earl **President:** None **Manager:** Grahaem Hopkins
Secretary: June Earl, 92 Bilberry Road, Clifton, Shefford, Beds SG17 5HD. Tel: 01462 816683 (H)
Ground: Baldock Road, Letchworth, Herts SG6 2GN (01462 684691).
Directions: Jct 9 (A6141) off A1M straight over large r-about, right at next r-about, ground on right. From Luton (A505) thru Hitchin, ground 3 miles after Hitchin. 2 miles from Letchworth (BR).
Capacity: 3,200 **Cover:** 400 **Seats:** 200 **Floodlights:** Yes **Founded:** 1906
Colours: All Blue **Change Colours:** Red & white stripes/red/red **Nickname:** Bluebirds.
Programme: 24 pages, 50p **Editor:** Keith Brown 0385 338584 **Midweek matchday:** Tuesday
Hons: Herts Charity Shield 22-23 47-48 87-88 91-92:

LEVERSTOCK GREEN

Chairman: Bill Dawes, 01442 395748 (H) **Press Officer:** M Connors
Secretary: Steve D Robinson, 11 Connaught Close, Hemel Hempstead, Herts HP2 7AB. Tel: 01442 65734 (H)
Manager: M Goodson **Asst Manager:** H Boycott-Brown
Ground: Pancake Lane, Leverstock Green, Hemel Hempstead. Tel: 01442 246280. **Directions:** From M1 leave at A4147 to 2nd r-about. 1st exit to Leverstock Green, Pancake Lane is on left 300 yrds past the 'Leather Bottle' pub.
Capacity: **Seats:** 25 **Cover:** 100 **Floodlights:** No **Club Shop:** No **Clubhouse:** Yes
Programme: 24 pages, 50p **Editor:** Bill Dawes (Chairman) **Nickname:** The Green **Founded:** 1907
Colours: All white and green **Change Colours:** Green & black/white/black **Sponsor:** Sunshine Cabs
Previous Leagues: West Herts (pre-1950); Herts County 50-91.
Honours: South Midlands Lge - Sen. Div 96-97, Sen Div Cup R-up 93-94, Herts Centenary Tphy R-up 91-92, Herts Charity Shield R-up 91-92, Frank Major Tphy 91.

LUTON OLD BOYS

Secretary: Terry Owen, 29 Elm Park Close, Houghton Regis, Dunstable, Beds. LU5 5PN. Tel: 01582 863273 (H).
Ground: Luton Old Boys, Dunstable Road, Luton, Beds. (01582 582060)
Directions: On the A505 Luton to Dunstable Road between junction 11 of the M1 and Lex Vauxhall Luton. **Please Note:** There is NO right turn when approaching the ground from the Dunstable direction.

MILTON KEYNES

Chairman: Jacqui Higgins **Managing Director:** A Denman **Founded:** 1993 **Nickname:** None
Secretary: Mr Neasham Galloway, 22 Bascote, Tinkers Bridge, Milton Keynes, MK6 3DW. Tel: 0956 948829
Manager: W Marr **Asst Manager:** A Milne **Physio:** John Butcher
Ground: Manor Fields, Bletchley, Milton Keynes (01908 375256). **Directions:** Old A5 to Fenny Stratford, about 500yds on left go over bridge opposite Belvedere Nursuries into Manor Fields - ground on right.
Capacity: 3,000 **Seats:** 160 **Cover:** 1,000 **Floodlights:** Yes **Club Shop:** No.
Clubhouse: Two bars. Upstairs bar open every evening. Snacks available.
Programme: 16 pages, 40p **Editor:** Drew Dias
Colours: Red and black/black/black **Change Colours:** Blue/white/blue
Midweek matches: Tuesday **Record Gate:** 250 v Bedford Town, S. Mids Lge 30/4/94
Record scorer: Andy McCabe **Record appearances:** Andy McCabe
Hons: Leighton Challenge Cup 94-95, 95-96

RISBOROUGH RANGERS

Chairman: Terry Taylor Tel: 01844 343309 (H)
Secretary: Derrick J Wallace, 42 Ash Road, Princes Risborough, Bucks, HP27 0BQ Tel.: 01844 345179 (H), 01844 345435 (B).
Manager: Dave Dunsworth **Asst Manager:** Mark Avery **Physio:** Ken Sheppard
Ground: 'Windsor', Horsenden Lane, Princes Risborough. (01844 274176)
Directions: Rear of Princes Risborough BR Station (Chiltern Line). A4010 from Aylesbury thru Princes Risborough, fork right onto A4009, left by thatched cottage, over railway bridge, immediate right ground 150 yds on right.
Capacity: 2,000 **Seats:** 25 **Cover:** 100 **Floodlights:** No **Founded:** 1971
Clubhouse: Yes. Snacks available matchdays. **Club Sponsors:** Systems 3R
Colours: Red & white/black/black **Change Colours:** Blue & white stripes/white/white
Programme: 20+ pages, £1 with entry **Midweek matches:** Tuesday **Club Shop:** No.
Previous League: Wycombe & Dist. **Record Gate:** 1,200 v Showbiz XI **Record scorer:** Craig Smith
Hons: Berks & Bucks Jnr Cup 85-86, Wycombe & District Lg Div 2 85-86 (Div 3 84-85).

SHILLINGTON

Chairman: Jack Farmer.
Tel: 01462 711757 (H)
Secretary: Aubrey Cole, 32 Greenfields, Shillington, Hitchin, Herts, SG5 3NX. Tel: 01462 711322 (H).
Ground: Playing Field, Greenfields, Shillington, Hitchin, Herts. (01462 711757).
Directions:
From Luton on A6, after bypassing Barton, turn right at large r'about. Through Higham Gobian to Shillington. From Bedford or Hitchin, A600 to RAF Henlow Camp. At 'Bird in Hand' r'about take exit to Upper Stondon.
Colours: Black & white stripes/black/black. **Programme:** Yes **Editor:** Douglas Riggs, 01462 712695 (H).

TOTTERNHOE

Totternhoe FC *Photo: Gordon Whittington*

Chairman: Jim Basterfield **Vice Chairman:** John Power **President:** Alf Joyce
Secretary: Jim Basterfield, 41 Park Avenue, Totternhoe, Dunstable, Beds LU6 1QF. Tel: 01582 667941 (H)
Manager: Alex Butler **Asst. Man.:** Paul Simmonds **Physio:** Roy Mackerness
Ground: Totternhoe Recreation Ground, Dunstable (01582 606738).
Directions: Turn off the main Dunstable to Tring Road B489. Ground on right as you enter the Totternhoe. Five miles from Leighton Buzzard (BR), 7 miles from Luton. Bus 61 Luton-Aylesbury.
Capacity: 1,000 **Seats:** 30 **Cover:** 200 **Floodlights:** No **Founded:** 1906 **Nickname:** Totts.
Clubhouse: Open evenings 8pm, Saturday after games, Sunday lunchtime. Tea, coffee, soups at matches.
Colours: All red **Change Colours:** White/blue/black **Club Shop:** No **Sponsors:** Building Conservations
Programme: 16 pages with entry **Editor:** Andrew Massey 01908 613404 (H) **Midweek matchday:** Tuesday
Club Records - Gate: 300 v Luton Town, clubhouse opening 13/10/82. **Scorer:** John Waites, 48
Hons: Sth Mids Lg Div 1 61-62 (R-up 68-69 85-86). **Appearances:** John Binding, 631.

TRING ATHLETIC

President: Paul Nichols
Chairman: Steve Thomas Tel: 01442 381633 (H)
Secretary: Ralph Griffiths, 42 Bedgrove, Aylesbury, Bucks HP21 7BD. Tel: 01296 26425 (H), 01296 393363 x 278 (B).
Manager: Mick Eldridge **Asst Manager:** Ray Brimson **Physio:** Jean Adams
Ground: Miswell Lane, Tring, Herts. (01442 828331) **Directions:** Through Tring on main road towards Aylesbury, right just after Anchor PH into Miswell Lane, pitch approximately 500yds on right opposite Beaconsfield Road. Tring railway station is several miles outside town, but ground can be reached by bus or taxi.
Seats: 25+ **Cover:** 100+ **Floodlights:** No **Founded:** 1958 **Nickname:** Athletic
Clubhouse: Bar, open matchdays, training nights & Sunday lunchtimes. **Club Shop:** No
Colours: Red & black/black/black **Change colours:** Blue & yellow/blue/blue **Sponsors:** Heygates
Programme: 36 pages, 50p **Editor:** Secretary **Midweek matchday:** Wednesday
Previous League: West Herts 58-88. **Record scorer:** Ian Butler **Record appearances:** Alan Sheppard
Honours: West Herts Lg R-up 72-73 (Lg Cup 65-66, Div 1 61-62 64-65 65-66 (R-up 71-72 85-86), Div 2(res) 71-72 (R-up 62-63), Div 3 R-up 83-84, Reserve Cup 72-73), Apsley Snr Cup R-up 71-72 87-88, Marsworth Cup(res) 72-73, Apsley Jnr Cup(res) R-up 94-95.

WINSLOW UNITED

Chairman: Jeff B Robins.
Tel: 01296 714206 (H)
Secretary: David F Ward, 28 Park Road, Winslow, Buckingham MK18 3DL. Tel: 01296 713202 (H), 01865 781210 (B).
Ground: Recreation Ground, Elmfields Gate, Winslow, Bucks. (01296 713057)
Directions: A413 from Aylesbury to Winslow, in High Street turn right into Emerald Gate, ground 100yds on left opposite car park. From Milton Keynes take A421 to Buckingham, turn left thru Gt Horwood to Winslow, turn left off High Street into Emerald Gate.
Capacity: 2,000 **Seats:** 25 **Cover:** 100 **Floodlights:** Yes **Founded:** 1891 **Club Shop:** No
Clubhouse: Open every evening except Wed & full weekend. **Programme:** 16 pages with entry
Colours: Yellow/blue/yellow **Change Colours:** Red/white/white **Midweek matches:** Tuesday
Honours: Sth Mids Lg R-up 75-76 (Div 1 74-75), Leighton Challenge Cup 92-93.

Ampthill Town FC

Bridger Packaging FC: Back Row (L-R); John Furness (Physio), Paul Howard (Trainer), Paul Martin, Stephen Anthony, Kevin Higlett, Jason Kitchener, James Cranston, Paul Starling (Mgr). Front Row; Peter Jarvis, Michael Everitt, Kevin Minnis, Stuart Potasnick, Joseph McGown, Peter Holloway, Michael Page.
Photo: Gordon Whittington

DIVISION ONE

ABBEY NATIONAL (M.K.)

Secretary: Steve White, 5 Hambleton Grove, Emerson Valley, Milton Keynes, Bucks. MK4 2JS. Tel: 01908 505910 (H), 01908 345513 (B).
Ground: Loughton Sports & Social Club, Linceslade Grove, Loughton, Milton Keynes (01908 690668)
Directions: From M1 Jct 14 follow H6, Childs Way for 5 miles until V4 Watling Way (Knowlhill r-about), right to Loughton r-about, right along H5 Portway - 1st right Linceslade Grove.

AMPTHILL TOWN

Secretary: Eric Turner, 34 Dunstable Street, Ampthill, Beds MK45 2JT. Tel: 01525 403128 (H & B).
Ground: Woburn Road, Ampthill, Beds. (01525 404440)
Directions: From Ampthill Town Centre follow signs to Woburn then 1st right into Ampthill Park.

BRIDGER PACKAGING

Secretary: Laurence Jack, 17 Curlew Close, Letchworth, Herts. SG6 4TG. Tel: 01462 625936 (H), 0181 905 1992 (B).
Ground: Letchworth Corner Sports Club, Muddy Lane, Letchworth, Herts. SG6 3TB. (01462 486459)
Directions: A1(M) junc 9 towards Letchworth, over large roundabout, turn left at next roundabout A505 Hitchin, thr lights, turn left at pelican crossing into Muddy Lane.

DE HAVILLAND

Secretary: Roy Ridgway, 85 Garden Ave., Hatfield, Herts AL10 8LH. Tel: 01707 267327 (H).
Ground: De Havilland (Hatfield) Sports & Social Club, Comet Way, Hatfield (01707 263204).
Directions: From south leave A1(M) at Hatfield turn, A1001 to Birchwood r'bout, 1st exit into car park. From north leave A1(M) at Welwyn G.C., A1001 to Birchwood r'bout and 4th exit into car park.

DUNSTABLE TOWN 98

Secretary: Colin Howes, 3 Rotherwood Close, Dunstable, Beds LU6 1UA (01582 478395)
Ground: Creasey Park, Brewers Hill Rd, Dunstable
Directions: Travel north on A5, Through centre Dunstable, left at 1st r/about into Brewers Hill Rd, str over mini r/about, grd on right.

FLAMSTEAD

Secretary: Yvonne Rutherford, 51 Parkfield, Markyate, St Albans, Herts. AL3 8RB. Tel: 01582 841671 (H)
Ground: Flamstead Sports Assoc., Friendless Lane, Flamstead, St Albans, Herts (0582 841307).
Ground Directions: From Dunstable Town Centre travel south on A5 Trunk Road towards the M1. Follow for approximately 3 miles then turn right opposite Hertfordshire Moat House Hotel. Ground and parking approximately half a mile on the corner of the first right turn.

KENT ATHLETIC

Secretary: Michael Bayliss, 57 Brickley Road, Leagrave, Luton, Beds. LU4 9EF. Tel: 01582 597894 (H).
Ground: Kent Social Club, Tenby Drive, Leagrave, Luton (01582 582723)
Directions: M1 jct 11 take A505 towards Luton. Take the first turning on the left (Stoneygate Road), straight over at the roundabout and turn right at traffic lights into Beechwood Road. Take the first road on the left and then the first right into Tenby Drive. Ground and car park 100 yards on left.

LEIGHTON ATHLETIC

Secretary: Salvatore Leotta, 28 Ashburnham Crescent, Linslade, Leighton Buzzard, Beds. LU7 7PB. Tel: 01525 382396 (H).
Ground: Memorial Playing Fields, Mentmore Road, Linslade, Leighton Buzzard, Beds (01525 370469)
Directions: On A5 north of Dunstable travelling towards Hockliffe turn left on to A505 Leighton Buzzard bypass. At end of bypass turn right towartds Leighton Buzzard and take the first right immediately after the railway bridge into Cedars Way. At 'T' Junction turn left into Mentmore Road, ground 300 yards on right

MARKYATE

Secretary: John Dephley, 15 Long Meadow, Markyate, Herts AL3 8JW (01582 840855)
Ground: Cavendish Rd, Markyate (01582 841731)
Directions: M1 Junc 9, take A5 north towards Dunstable. After 2 miles left into village after footbridge. Right into High Street, 5th left Cavendish Rd, grd on right before school

MURSLEY UNITED

Secretary: Roger Gurnett, 20 Tweedale Close, Mursley, Milton Keynes MK17 0SB. Tel: 01296 720505 (H).
Ground: Station Road, Mursley, Milton Keynes.
Directions: A421 Bletchley to Buckingham Road, first right in village

NEWPORT ATHLETIC

Secretary: Charles Stanley, 1 Hemingway Close, Newport Pagnell, Bucks MK16 8QP (01908 615216 H)
Ground: Willen Rd Sports Ground, Willen Rd, Newport Pagnell.
Directions: M1 Junc 14, A509 to Newport Pagnell. 1st r/about turn left A422. 1st r/about right into Willen Rd. 1st right Sports Ground 100 yds right

OLD BRADWELL UNITED

Secretary: David Bird, 24 Loughton Road, Bradwell, Milton Keynes MK13 9AA. Tel: 01908 315947 (H).
Ground: Abbey Road, Bradwell, Milton Keynes (01908 312355)
Directions: M1 junction 14 go towards Newport Pagnell. Turn left at first roundabout into H3 Honks Way. Go six r'abouts then left onto V6 Grafton Street. Take 1st right at mini-r'about into Rawlins Road and then 2nd left into Loughton Road. Take 1st right into Primrose Road and at the 'T' junction turn right into Abbey Road

OLD DUNSTABLIANS

Secretary: Craig Renfrew, 75B Princes Street. Dunstable. LU6 3AS. Tel: 01582 471794 (H), 01234 265444 (B).
Ground: Lancot Park. Dunstable Road, Totternhoe (01582 663735)
Directions: From Dunstable Town Centre take the B489 Tring Road. At the 4th roundabout turn right, signposted Totternhoe. The pitch is located withion Dunstable Town Cricket Club which is on the right just before entering the village of Totternhoe.

PITSTONE & IVINGHOE

Secretary: Jay Adlem, 22 Maud Janes Close, Ivinghoe, Leighton Buzzard. LU7 9ED. Tel: 01296 668663 (H).
Ground: Pitstone Recreation Ground, Vicarage Road, Pitstone, Bucks (01296 661271)
Directions: Tring Rd (B489) from Dunstable, turn right for Ivinghoe, and continue through to Pitstone r-about; ground left then right. From Aylesbury - left at 'Rising Sun' in Aston Clinton, keep on that road to Pitstone r'bout; ground right then right. Bus 61 from Luton or Aylesbury. Nearest BR stations are Tring or Cheddington.

SCOT

Secretary: Mrs Ann Land, 18 Coleridge Close, Bletchley, Milton Keynes. MK3 5AF. Tel: 01908 372228 (H).
Ground: Selbourne Avenue, Bletchley, Milton Keynes (01908 368881).
Directions: Main roads to Bletchley then A421 Buckingham road, at Glen Garage right into Newton Rd, 2nd left into Selbourne Ave., through railway bridge to bottom of road.

THE 61 FC (LUTON)

Secretary/Manager: Richard Everitt, 44 Somersby Close, Luton LU1 3XB. 01582 485095 (H)
Ground: Kingsway, Beverley Road, Luton, Beds. (01582 582965).
Directions: M1 jct 11, A505 to Luton centre, right at 1st island, 1st left, Beverley Rd is 3rd left, entrance in Beverley Rd, exactly 1 mile junction 11. All Luton to Dunstable buses pass ground - alight at Beech Hill Bowling Club. 1 mile from both Leagrave & Luton BR stations.

WALDEN RANGERS

Secretary: Irene Oodian, 9 Garfield Court, Handcross Rd, Luton, Beds LU2 8JZ. Tel: 01582 483090 (H), 01582 405060 Ext 2354 (B).
Ground: Breachwood Green Recreation Ground, Chapel Road, Breachwood Green, Nr Kings Walden, Herts (01438 833332). **Directions:** From Luton Airport roundabout (Eaton Green Rd)(away from Vauxhall/ IBC direction) take country road to Breachwood Green (2 miles). From Hitchin on A602, take country road to Preston (6 miles to Breachwood Green).

HERTS SENIOR COUNTY LEAGUE

President: W J R Veneear **Chairman:** C T Hudson
Secretary: E H Dear, 48 Wilshere Road, Welwyn, Herts

Centenary Match

The Herts Senior County League celebrated its centenary on Wednesday 5th August with a rep match against Watford at St. Albans City's Clarance Park ground.

With guest of honour Keith Wiseman, F.A. Chairman and Watford supremo Graham Taylor watching, the County League amateurs gave a good account of themselves, writes Kevin Folds.

Watford fielded first team pairing Keith Millen and Nigel Gibbs at the back, and when one adds to that new acquisition Dean Yates, a player with Premiership experience at Derby County, it's no wonder the 'home' side's chances were limited.

Watford made the earlier running, and this afforded Cuffley Keeper Jason Henderson the opportunity to shine. He followed up a stunning save with a penalty stop from Wayne Andrews, another visitor with first team experience.

Nonetheless it was no surprise when Watford took the lead midway through the opening half, David Perpetuini's shot looked speculative but Wayne Andrews, diving to head the ball, did enough to distract the keeper without making contact. Five minutes later reserve striker Tommy Smith made it 2-0, and it looked as if the floodgates were about to open.

However, the County Leaguers redoubled their efforts and were rewarded on the stroke of half-time. Benington striker Paul Morris struck perhaps the sweetest shot of his life, a dipping volley which gave England Under 21 keeper Chris Day no chance.

Luther Blissett's half-time team talk was clearly effective as Watford added two goals to their tally quickly after the break. Youth team forward Grant Cornock scored the third with Icelandic International Johann Gudmundsson getting the fourth from the spot. Another rapid brace midway through the half - via an own-goal and Perpetuini's second - completed the scoring. The County League side were in no way disgraced and continued to battle gamely until the end.

Considering the Watford line-up also included former Villa winger Tony Daley, and that his performance was good enough to earn the offer of a contract after the game, the Herts boys could feel well pleased with their night.

Premier Division League Table 1997-98

	P	W	D	L	F	A	Pts
Cuffley	30	20	6	4	77	32	66
Somerset Ambury	30	20	4	6	76	37	64
Metropolitan Police	30	10	4	10	70	50	52
Colney Heath	30	15	6	9	61	39	51
Bennington	30	14	6	10	45	44	48
Wormley Rovers	30	13	8	9	54	50	47
Elliott Star	30	13	5	12	85	70	44
Oxhey Jets	30	13	4	13	164	67	43
Sun Postal Sports	30	13	4	13	55	58	43
Chipperfield Corinthians	30	12	6	12	53	43	42
Bedmond Sports & Soc	30	11	8	11	158	45	41
Agrevo Sports	30	9	8	13	50	51	35
Kingslangley	30	8	8	14	51	67	32
Sandridge Rovers	30	9	4	17	51	72	31
St Peters	30	7	2	21	45	100	23
Bragbury Athletic	30	4	3	23	36	285	15

AGREVO SPORTS

Secretary: Mrs Marion Howlett, 7 Beckets Square, Berkhamsted, Herts. HP4 1BZ. 01442 872497 (H).
Ground: Kitcheners Field, Castle Hill, Berkhamsted. 01442 864937 **Directions:** A4251 into Berkhamsted. At main traffic lights (from Hemel Hempstead) turn right into Lower Kings Rd. At railway station turn left under bridge then 2nd left. Ground entrance is on next corner.

BEDMOND S & S

Secretary: Peter Johnson, 101 Spring Lane, Hemel Hempstead, Herts. HP1 3RB. 01442 397869 (H)
Ground: Toms Lane Recreation Ground, Toms Lane, Bedmond. 01932 267991 **Directions:** MI to jnt 8, A414 to 2nd r'about, left on St. Albans route A4147, bear rt. to Bedmond at church (Bedmond Rd), right in village into Toms Lane at mini r'about, grd 300 yds left. Bus 344 from Hemel or Watford.

BENINGTON

Secretary: John W Batchelor, 16 Cedar Close, Shefford, Beds. SG17 5RT. 01462 628426 (H), 01438 752146 (B).
Ground: Benington Recreation Ground, Town Lane, Benington. **Directions:** Leave A1(M) at Stevenage South, over 1st r'about (A602) left at 2nd r'about (Burger King), over next r'about, rt at next one by Swimming Pool, follow signs to Walkern (B1037), turn rt at junction in Walkern, past Walkern FC for approx 800 yds turn left where signed Benington. Thro' Benington, past Bell PH & ground is 800 yds on left.

BRAGBURY ATHLETIC

Secretary: Raymond C Poulter, 292 Jessop Rd., Stevenage, Herts. SG1 5NA. 01438 358078 (H).
Ground: British Aerospace Sports & Social Club, Bragbury End, Stevenage, Herts. 01438 812985.
Directions: A1(M) to Steveange, take Stevenage South exit (Junct. 7), follow A602 Hertford/Ware signs to Bragbury End, ground on left just past golf course.

CHIPPERFIELD CORINTHIANS

Secretary: Rowland Marshall, 45 Blackwell Drive, Watford, Herts. WD1 4HP. 01923 461457(H), 254646(B).
Ground: Moatfield, Bournehall Lane, Bushey, Herts. 0181 386 1875. **Directions:** A41 to Hartspring Lane, into Aldenham Rd., left at r'about into the Avenue, rt at top into Herkomer Rd., then 4th on left. Bus - from Watford 142, 258, 306, 706, 719 to Red Lion, Bushey.

COLNEY HEATH

Secretary: Michael Wright, 5 Grove Lea, Hatfield, Herts. AL10 8LA. 01707 880825 (H).
Ground: The Pavilion Rec. Ground, High St., Colney Heath, Herts. 01727 826188. **Directions:** Turn off A414 (was A405) into Colney Heath village, ground is behind school on left.

CUFFLEY

Secretary: Dave Chapman, 51 Woodlands Rd., Hertford. SG13 7JF. 01992 582358 (H), 0171 480 6410 (B).
Ground: King George's Playing Fields, Northaw Road East, Cuffley, Herts. 01707 875395. **Directions:** A121 from Potters bar or Cheshunt, 5 miles from junction 25 or 26 on M25. Bus - 242 from Potters Bar or Cheshunt to Playing Fields, Cuffley.

ELLIOTT STAR

Secretary: Raymond Capper, 28 Alban Crescent, Boreham Wood, Herts. WD6 5JF. 0181 207 3940 (H).
Ground: GEC Sports Ground, Rowley Lane, Borehamwood. 0181 953 5087. **Directions:** A1 from Hatfield to Elstree Moat House, left turn (flyover) into town and turn into Elstree Way. Ground on right behind Clarendon Garage.

KINGS LANGLEY

Secretary: Brian Aldersley, 49 Diamond Rd., Watford. WD2 5EN. 01923 493462 (H), 01468 906089 (M).
Ground: Kings Langley FC, Hempstead Rd., Kings Langley. **Directions:** M25, junct. 20 (Aylesbury) then A4251 to Kings Langley. Ground is approx. 1 mile on right.

METROPOLITAN POLICE BUSHEY

Secretary: J R (Jim) Howard, Met. Police Sports Club, Aldenham Road, Bushey, Herts. WD2 3TR. 01923 674373 (H), 0171 321 7903 (B).
Ground: Met. Police Sports Club, Aldenham Road, Bushey. 01923 243947 **Directions:** M1, Junct. 5 take A41 for Harrow/South watford to 1st r'about, rt into Hartspring Lane, leading into Aldenham Road (A4008), ground 1/4 mile on left opposite Caledonian school. Bus - 312 from watford stops outside club.

OXHEY JETS

Secretary: John R Elliott, 7 Brampton Road, South Oxhey, Watford, Herts. WD1 6PF. 0181 428 6382 (H), 0181 424 5891 (B).
Ground: Chigwell Gardens, South Oxhey, Watford. 0181 421 4965. **Directions:** From Watford follow Bushey signs. at Bushey Arches turn rt. into Eastbury Rd., left into Brookdene Ave., cont along Prestwick Rd. past station. Right into Northwick Rd., then left into Chilwell Gdns. Bus - 348 from Watford, alight at Northwick Rd.

ST. PETERS

Secretary: John E W Lister, 32 Thirlestane, Lemsford Road, St. Albans. AL1 3PE. 01727 850246 (H), 01707 651115 (B).
Ground: William Bird Playing Fields, Toulmin Drive, St. Albans. 01727 852401. **Directions:** Join St. Albans ring road. Into Batchwood Drive from either A1081 or A5183. Turn right into Green Lane from the former or left from the latter, then 1st left into Toulmin Drive. Ground at the end.

SANDRIDGE ROVERS

Graham Hardwick, 21 Woodcock Hill, Sandridge, St. Albans, AL4 9EF. 01727 855334 (H), 01483 742200 (B).
Ground: Spencer Recreation Ground. 01727 855159 or 835506 clubhouse. **Directions:** Buses 304, 357 & 358 from St. Albans. By road B651 from St Albans or Wheathampstead to High Street. Ground at the rear of the public car park.

SOMERSETT AMBURY V & E

Secretary: John Venables, 156 Crossbrook Street, Cheshunt, Herts. EN8 8JY. 01992 636991 (H).
Ground: The V & E Club, Goffs Lane, Cheshunt. 01992 624281. **Directions:** M25 junct. 25, take A10 north towards Cheshunt. Left at 1st r'about onto B198 (Flamstead End relief road). At 1st r'about right into Goffs Lane. Clubhouse immediately on right.

SUN POSTAL SPORTS

Secretary: Alan Cowland, 132 Bushey Mill Lane, Watford. WD2 4PB. 01923 233045 (H), 01442 229509 (B).
Ground: Bellmount Wood Ave, Watford. 01923 227453.
Directions: By road from Kings Langley to Watford on Hempstead Rd, right at Langley Rd lights, right at r'about, then 1st left. Ground entrance 50 yds on right.

WORMLEY ROVERS

Secretary: David Smith, 19 Nursery Gardens, Enfield, Middx. EN3 5NG. 0181 804 3608 (H), 01992 445577 (B)
Ground: Wormley Sports Ground, Church Lane, Wormley. 01992 460650. **Directions:** Buses 310, 316 from Hertford and London. By road from A10 take A1170, turn off for Broxbourne and Turnford. Left at the 'New River Arms', left again into Church Lane. Ground 1/4 mile on right.

Cherry Red Records
CHILTONIAN FOOTBALL LEAGUE

Secretary: A R Ford, Pennings Cottage, Aldershot Road, Guildford Surrey Tel: (01483 567284)

Premier Division League Table 1997-98

	P	W	D	L	F	A	Pts
AFC Wallingford	34	26	7	1	148	42	85
Henley Town	34	25	3	6	104	32	78
RS Basingstoke	34	21	5	8	122	37	68
Stocklake	34	21	5	8	103	53	68
Finchampstead	34	20	5	9	91	49	65
Peppard	34	20	5	9	74	42	65
Wraysbury	34	10	7	8	72	59	64
Eton Wick	34	15	10	9	97	74	55
Penn & Tylers	34	14	11	9	87	63	53
Quarry Nomads	34	12	6	16	49	64	42
Denham United	34	10	10	14	56	68	40
Wooburn Athletic	34	11	7	16	77	100	40
Prestwood (-3)	34	13	2	19	84	101	38
Broadmoor Sports	34	7	8	19	57	97	29
Binfield	34	8	4	22	60	103	28
Iver	34	3	8	23	53	123	17
Martin Baker Sports	34	4	3	27	54	155	15
Old Paludians	34	2	4	28	35	161	10

Division One 1997-98

	P	W	D	L	F	A	Pts
Cippenham Village	26	20	2	4	89	40	62
Aston Clinton	26	19	4	3	90	27	61
Finchampstead Res	26	17	5	4	82	30	53
Wraysbury Res	26	15	4	7	65	42	49
Englefield G Rvrs	26	13	1	12	58	62	40
Peppard Res	26	11	5	10	67	58	38
Drayton Wanderers	26	12	1	13	46	52	37
Wallingford Res	26	10	2	14	60	81	32
Eton Wick Res	26	8	7	11	49	57	31
Penn & Tyler Res	26	8	6	12	43	56	30
Binfield Res	26	6	7	13	44	66	25
Denham Utd Res	26	7	4	15	40	66	25
Chalfont Wasps	26	6	3	17	49	71	21
Iver Res	26	4	1	21	43	117	13
Beaconsfield Res.	W/D Record Expunged						

Division Two 1997-98

	P	W	D	L	F	A	Pts
Henley Town Res	24	18	3	3	102	19	57
Chalfont SP Res	24	18	3	3	73	21	57
RS Basingstoke Res	24	16	3	5	68	36	51
Aston Clinton Res	24	13	4	7	58	38	43
Wooburn Ath Res	24	11	6	7	68	55	39
Drayton Wand Res	24	11	2	11	54	47	35
Cippenham V Res	24	10	5	9	45	39	35
Broadmoor Res	24	7	5	12	45	72	26
Stocklake	24	6	6	12	39	59	24
Chalfont W Res	24	6	5	13	43	72	23
Englefield Res	24	7	1	16	29	72	22
Quarry Nomads Res	24	4	7	13	35	81	19
Martin Baker Res	24	3	2	19	28	76	11
Prestwood Res withdrawn							

PREMIER DIVISION CLUBS 1998-99

ASTON CLINTON

BINFIELD

Secretary: Paul Hammerstone, 3 Knox Green, Binfield, Berks RG12 5HZ (01344 427179).
Ground: Stubbs Hill, Binfield, Berks.
Colours: All red **Change colours:** Blue/black

DENHAM UNITED

Secretary: Colin Stevens, 18 The Dene, West Molesey, Surrey KT8 2HL (0181 783 0433).
Ground: Oxford Road, Denham, Bucks (01895 238717).
Colours: Blue & white/blue **Change colours:** Red & Black/black

ETON WICK

Secretary: Mr Joe Bussey, 50 Tilestone Close, Eton Wick, Windsor, Berks SL4 6NG (01753 859493).
Ground: Haywards Mead, Eton Wick, Windsor (01753 852749).
Colours: Amber/black **Change colours:** All white

FINCHAMPSTEAD

Secretary: Mr R Bradley, 37 Alpha Rd, Chobham, Surrey GU24 8NE (01276 855367).
Ground: Memorial Ground, Finchampstead (01734 732890).
Colours: Blue & white stripes/blue **Change colours:** All red.

HENLEY TOWN

Secretary: Mr A Kingston, 50 Birdhill Ave., Reading, Berks RG2 7JU.
Ground: The Triangle Ground, Mill Lane, Henley-on-Thames, Oxon (0491 576463).
Colours: White/black/black **Change colours:** Claret & blue/black.

PENN & TYLERS GREEN

Secretary: Mr R Dalling, 28 Baring Rd, Beaconsfield, Bucks HP9 2NE (01494 671424).
Ground: French School Meadow, Elm Road, Penn, Bucks (01494 815346).
Colours: Blue & white stripes/blue. **Change colours:** Yellow/blue.

PEPPARD

Secretary: Chris Boyles, 14 Redwood Ave, Woodley, Reading, Berks RG5 4DR (0118 969 9488)
Ground: Bishopswood Sports Centre, Horsepond Rd, Sonning Common, nr Reading (01734 712265).
Colours: All red **Change colours:** Sky/navy/navy

PRESTWOOD

Secretary: Mr G Stansbury, 31 Colne Rd, High Wycombe, Bucks (01494 521792).
Ground: Prestwood Sports Centre, Honor End Lane, Prestwood, Great Missenden, Bucks (01240 65946).
Colours: Claret & sky/white **Change colours:** Sky/white.

QUARRY NOMADS

Secretary: K Dalton, 58 Pitts Rd, Headington, Oxon (01865 65332).
Ground: St Margarets Road, Headington, Oxford.
Colours: Black & white stripes/black **Change colours:** Red & white stripes/white.

R.S. BASINGSTOKE

Secretary: D J Brand, 128 Stratfield Rd, Oakridge, Basingstoke, Hants RG21 2SA (01256 57309).
Ground: Whiteditch Playing Field, Sherbourne Rd, Basingstoke, Hants (01256 844866).
Colours: Maroon/Navy/Navy

RAYNERS LANE

STOCKLAKE

Secretary: Mr Tom Exton, 116 Narbeth Drive, Aylesbury, Bucks HP20 1PZ (01296 415780).
Ground: Stocklake Sports & Social Club, Hayward Way, Aylesbury, Bucks (01296 23324).
Colours: Yellow/blue **Change colours:** Coral/purple

TALOW UNITED

Secretary: D Aslett, 14 Cornwall Close, Eton Wick, Windsor, Berks SL4 6NB (01628 31176).
Ground: Stanley Jones Field, Berry Hill, Taplow, near Maidenhead (01628 21745).
Colours: Sky/navy **Change colours:** Maroon/white.

A QUOTE INSURANCE READING LEAGUE

President: Leon Summers
Chairman: John Dell, 55 Victoria Road, Mortimer, Reading RG7 3SL (01734 332156)
Secretary: David Jeanes, 6 Hawkesbury Drive, Fords Farm, Calcot, Reading RG31 5ZP (01734 413926 H)

Senior Division

	P	W	D	L	F	A	Pts
Forest Old Boys	20	15	1	4	51	23	46
Cookham Dean	20	13	4	3	36	17	43
Mortimer	20	12	3	5	47	22	39
Checkenham Spts	20	11	3	6	44	29	36
Emmbrook Sports	20	9	5	6	28	30	32
West Reading	20	9	3	8	44	35	30
Reading Exiles	20	9	2	9	34	38	29
South Reading	20	8	2	10	39	46	26
Sutton Exiles	20	5	4	11	36	44	19
Sonning Common	20	2	2	16	16	51	8
AFC Maidenhead	20	1	3	16	15	55	6

Premier Division

	P	W	D	L	F	A	Pts
Westwood United	20	15	3	2	61	20	48
Unity	20	11	6	3	52	23	39
REME Arborfield	20	13	0	7	62	37	39
Marlow United	20	12	2	6	50	42	38
Rdg Exiles Res	20	12	1	7	58	37	37
Highmoor	20	10	3	7	60	48	33
ARM Athletic	20	8	4	8	47	46	28
Roundhead	20	7	3	10	26	46	24
Earlbourne United	20	3	3	14	30	70	12
SEB Reading	20	3	1	16	37	74	10
Ibis	20	2	2	16	22	62	8

Premier Division Clubs

ARM Athletic
Earlbourne
Frilsham
Goring United
Highmoor
IBIS
Marlow
Reading Exiles Res
REME Arborfield
Roundhead
Southend
Whitley Rovers

SENIOR DIV.

A.F.C. MAIDENHEAD
Secretary: Mrs D Saunders, 63 Furze Road, Maidenhead, SL6 7NF (01628 35994)
Ground: Cox Green School, Highfield Lane, Maidenhead
Colours: Green/white/green

CHECKENDON SPORTS
Secretary: Ernie Smith, 10 Emmens Close, Checkendon, Reading RG8 0TU (01491 681575).
Ground: Checkendon PF
Colours: Blue & white/black/white

COOKHAM DEAN
Secretary: Rory Gavin, 14 Northfield Rd, Maidenhead SL6 7JP (01628 832997)
Ground: Alfred Major Rec., Hillcrest Ave., Cookham Rise, Maidenhead.
Colours: Red & black/black/red.

EMMBROOK SPORTS CLUB
Secretary: Steve Haynes, 15 Tilney Way,Lower Earley RG6 4AD (01734 670459).
Ground: Emmbrook Sports Ground, Lowther Road, Emmbrook, Wokingham (01734 780209).

FOREST OLD BOYS
Secretary: Bob Hulett, 10 Ramsbury Drive, Earley, Reading RG6 2RT (01734 663514).
Ground: Holme Park, Sonning (01734 690356)
Colours: Yellow & blue/blue/blue.

MORTIMER
Secretary: Steve Dell, 30 Croft Rd, Mortimer, nr Reading RG7 3TS (01734 333821).
Ground: Alfred Palmer Mem. P.F., West End Rd, Mortimer.
Colours: Amber/black/black

READING EXILES
Secretary: M J Aust, 24 Aylsham Close, Tilehurst, Reading RG3 4XG (01734 421453).
Ground: Palmer Park Sports Stadium, Wokingham Road Reading
Colours: Royal & white stripes/royal/royal

SONNING COMMON
Secretary: Steve Hill, 52 Loxwood, Lower Earley, Reading RG6 5QZ (01734 752753)
Ground: The Pavilion, King George VI Memorial Playing Fields, Pound Lane Sonning

SUTTON EXILES
Secretary: Michael Charles, 32 Eastwood Rd, Woodley, Reading RG5 3PY (01734 448130).
Ground: Cantley Park, Milton Road, Wokingham (01734 793188)
Colours: All blue

UNITY
Secretary: Trevor Lowe, 161 Cotswold Way, Tilehurst, Reading RG31 6ST (01734 455133)
Ground: Cintra Park
Colours: Amber/black/black

WEST READING
Secretary: Mrs Susan Porton, 6 Hampstead Court, Grovelands Rd, Reading RG3 2QQ (01734 504034).
Ground: Victoria Recreation Ground.
Colours: Amber/black/black & amber

WESTWOOD UNITED
Secretary: Penny Brodie, 58 Devonshire Gardens, Tilehurst, Reading RG31 6FP (01734 624572)
Ground: Cotswold Sports Centre, Downsway, Tilehurst, Reading
Colours: Green & white/black/black

PREMIER DIVISION

A.R.M. Athletic
Secretary: David Wyeth, 101 Park Lane, Tilehurst, Reading RG31 4DR (01734 678006)
Ground: Lower Whitley Rec, Basingstoke Rd, Reading
Colours: Red & black/black/black & red

EARLBOURNE
Secretary: Andrew Beach, 24 Quentin Road, Woodley, Reading RG5 3NE (01734 697162).
Ground: Woodford Park, Haddon Drive, Woodley, Reading RG5 4LY (01734 690356).
Colours: Black & blue/black/black

FRILSHAM
Secretary: Nigel Wyatt, 2 Laurel Bank, Frilsham, Nr Hermitage RG18 9XQ (01635 201352)
Ground: Frilsham Playing Field, Frilsham Common, Frilsham, Nr Hermitage
Colours: Blue/black/black

GORING UNITED
Secretary: Peter Jones, Bywater, Icknield Rd, Goring-on-Thames RG80DE (01491 872809)
Ground: Gardiners Rec Ground, Upper Red Cross Rd, Goring
Colours: Blue & white/blue/blue

HIGHMOOR
Secretary: Chris Gallimore, 10 Patrick Rd, Caversham, Reading RG4 8DD (01734 478964)
Ground: Highmoor Ath Grd, Highmoor, Henley, Oxon
Colours: Yellow/blue/white

IBIS
Secretary: Tony McGrath, 25 Luscombe Close, Caversham, Reading RG4 0LG (01734 478161).
Ground: IBIS Sports Club, Scours Lane, Reading RG3 6AY (01734 424130).
Colours: Blue & black/black/black

MARLOW UNITED
Secretary: Rae Flint, 30 Dean Street, Marlow, Bucks SL7 3AE (01628 476611).
Ground: Gossmore Park, Gossmore Lane, Marlow.
Colours: Blue & white/white/white

R.E.M.E. ARBORFIELD
Secretary: Peter Davies, 73 Chestnut Cres., Shinfield, Reading RG2 9HA (01734 884107).
Ground: Sports Pavilion, Biggs Lane, Princess Marina College, Arborfield
Colours: Blue & yellow/blue/blue

READING EXILES RESERVES
Colours: Navy & white/navy/navy

ROUNDHEAD
Secretary: Eric Wise, 63 St Saviours Rd, Reading RG1 6EJ (01734 588426).
Ground: Prospect Park, St Saviours Rd, Coley, Reading.
Colours: Green & yellow/black/black

SOUTHEND
Secretary: Mrs S Dawson, 1 Bushnells Cottages, Westrop Green, Coldash, Thatcham RG18 9WW (01635 200789)
Ground: Bradfield Cricket Club, Heath Rd, Bradfield, Berks
Colours: All emerald gold & white

WHITLEY ROVERS
Secretary: Mrs T Slade, 126 Whitley Wood Road, Reading RG2 8JG (01734 620708)
Ground: Rabson Recreation Ground, South Reading Leisure Centre, Northumberland Ave, Reading
Colours: Red & black/black/red

SOUTHERN FINAL LEAGUE TABLES 1997-98

SURREY COUNTY PREMIER LEAGUE

	P	W	D	L	F	A	Pts
Vandyke Co Utd	28	20	5	3	97	21	65
Ottershaw	28	20	5	3	89	23	65
Kingston Town	28	19	4	5	84	45	61
Virginia Water	28	17	7	4	57	21	58
Farleigh Rovers	28	13	1	14	54	55	40
Chess'ton WH	28	12	9	7	71	38	39
Bookham	28	11	6	11	56	43	39
Bisley Sports	28	12	3	13	60	62	39
Holmesdale	28	11	5	12	49	65	38
Shottermill	28	9	3	16	57	82	30
Chobham	28	7	5	16	38	57	26
Sheerwater	28	8	1	19	32	68	25
Croydon Mun Off	28	8	0	20	43	120	24
AFC Guildford	28	6	5	17	45	73	23
Coney Hall	28	5	5	18	35	94	20

GUILDFORD & WOKING ALLIANCE

DIVISION ONE	P	W	D	L	F	A	Pts
Guildford Rail OB	18	14	1	3	72	32	43
Surrey Univ 'A'	18	13	2	3	70	20	41
Hale	18	13	2	3	67	18	41
Anglo Sports	18	13	0	5	52	28	39
Surrey Athletic	18	8	3	7	52	35	27
Hambledon	18	5	3	10	34	57	18
Horsley 'A'	18	5	2	11	36	58	17
Shalford	18	4	3	11	32	67	15
Ribero	18	3	3	12	37	74	12
Millmead	18	2	1	15	24	87	7

SURREY SOUTH EAST COMBINATION

DIVISION ONE	P	W	D	L	F	A	Pts
Crescent Rovers	22	14	3	5	85	32	45
Worcester Park	22	14	2	6	64	37	44
Woodmansterne	22	14	2	6	64	41	44
Ashtead	22	12	6	4	74	36	42
Osterley	22	11	5	6	50	38	38
Battersea Iron.	22	11	4	7	50	34	37
Racal Decca	22	7	7	8	40	55	28
Hersham RBL	22	6	8	8	32	42	25
Greenside	22	5	9	8	42	43	24
Halliford	22	6	6	10	44	58	24
Chipstead 'A'	22	3	4	15	28	77	15
Reigate Priory	22	1	0	21	11	93	3

REDHILL & DISTRICT LEAGUE

PREMIER DIV	P	W	D	L	F	A	Pts
Nutfield	18	14	3	1	46	18	31
Walton Heath	18	9	6	3	45	25	24
Monotype Sports	18	9	5	4	35	28	23
Westcott	18	8	4	6	27	25	20
Caterham OB	18	7	5	6	41	43	19
South Park	18	6	5	7	42	41	17
Limpsfield Blues	18	5	3	10	46	56	13
Smallfield	18	4	6	8	36	19	10
Edwards Spts Rs	18	4	2	12	38	50	10
Tatsfield Rovers	18	2	5	11	36	65	9

ESSEX INTERMEDIATE LEAGUE

DIVISION ONE	P	W	D	L	F	A	Pts
Danbury Trafford	24	16	3	5	66	28	35
Frenford Senior	24	15	4	5	51	28	34
Kelvedon Hatch	24	12	10	2	46	32	34
Metpol Chigwell	24	14	5	5	43	31	33
Takeley	24	13	5	6	60	29	31
Herongate Ath	24	9	4	11	30	33	22
Runwell Hospital	24	9	4	11	43	64	22
Ekco First Data	24	9	3	12	44	51	21
Essex Police	24	7	7	10	34	41	21
Rayleigh Town	24	7	6	11	36	37	20
Writtle	24	6	6	12	26	42	18
Broomfield	24	5	2	17	31	63	12
Stambridge	24	3	3	18	31	62	9

MID-ESSEX FOOTBALL LEAGUE

PREMIER DIV	P	W	F	A	Pts
Shenfield AFC	20	16	69	21	50
Milan	20	12	43	20	43
Tillingham	20	13	50	28	41
Rainsford	20	11	50	28	38
Marconi Ath	20	9	44	34	32
Braintree & B	20	5	44	45	22
Shelley R'ls	20	5	39	64	20
Estric	20	5	36	62	19
Weir House	20	4	27	33	16
St Margarets	20	2	16	37	12
Heybridge Sports	20	3	15	57	12

ESSEX & SUFFOLK BORDER LEAGUE

PREMIER DIV	P	W	D	L	F	A	Pts
Gas Recreation	30	20	4	6	85	41	64
St Johns (Clac)	30	17	9	4	61	31	60
Stowmarket Res	30	18	3	9	71	42	57
Mistley Utd	30	16	3	11	61	52	51
Harwich & P Rs	30	15	6	9	47	42	51
Haverhill Res	30	14	7	9	59	42	49
West Bergholt	30	12	12	6	61	29	48
Alresford CR	30	12	6	12	41	50	42
Little Oakley	30	11	5	14	52	59	38
Sudbury Wd Res	30	10	5	15	51	56	35
Ipswich Wdrs Res	30	9	8	13	43	59	35
Royal London	30	11	2	17	37	66	35
Long Melford	30	9	5	16	47	69	32
Halstead Tn Res	30	8	5	17	40	67	29
Rowhedge	30	5	9	16	39	58	24
Clacton Res	30	7	3	20	42	74	24

EAST SUSSEX LEAGUE

PREMIER DIV	P	W	D	L	F	A	Pts
Wadhurst Utd	18	14	2	2	73	23	44
Rock a Nore	18	12	5	1	49	22	41
Hollington Utd	18	12	2	4	50	24	38
Polegate	18	11	2	5	55	32	35
Seaford	18	10	2	6	65	34	32
Northiam 75	18	6	6	6	35	38	24
Willingdon Ath	18	5	3	10	37	42	18
Icklesham Casuals	18	2	4	12	20	71	10
Punnetts Town	18	2	1	15	24	73	7
Eastbourne Fisher	18	2	1	15	21	70	7

WEST SUSSEX LEAGUE

PREMIER DIV	P	W	D	L	F	A	Pts
North Holmwood	18	12	2	3	55	25	*38
AFC Swan	18	11	4	3	52	36	37
Henfield	18	9	4	5	38	26	31
Upper Beeding	18	9	2	7	45	28	29
South Bersted	18	7	5	6	39	36	26
Cowfold	18	7	3	8	34	33	24
Lancing United	18	6	2	10	25	40	20
Alford	18	5	4	9	23	32	19
Ferring	18	4	4	9	29	58	*16
Roffey	18	3	2	13	17	43	11

MID SUSSEX FOOTBALL LEAGUE

PREMIER DIV	P	W	D	L	F	A	Pts
Pease Pottage V	24	20	3	1	88	31	63
Wealden	24	18	2	4	77	19	56
Lindfield	24	15	2	7	58	39	47
Cuckfield	24	9	7	8	46	41	34
Maresfield Village	24	9	6	9	31	39	33
Clayton	24	8	6	10	53	62	30
Hurstpierpoint Rs	24	8	5	11	49	55	29
Wisdom Sports	24	8	4	12	44	57	28
Nutley	24	7	4	13	56	69	25
East Grinstead U	24	7	4	13	34	47	25
Plumpton Athletic	24	7	4	13	45	71	25
St Francis Hosp Rs	24	6	5	13	33	53	23
Handcross Village	24	7	2	15	47	78	23

SOUTH LONDON FOOTBALL ALLIANCE

PREMIER DIV	P	W	D	L	F	A	Pts
Metrogas	20	15	1	4	63	17	46
R.A.C.S.	20	13	3	4	47	27	42
Samuel Montagu	20	13	3	4	38	24	42
Avery Hill College	20	12	4	4	45	20	40
Johnson & Phillips	20	11	4	5	33	23	37
Segas (Sydenham)	20	6	3	11	37	39	21
Cambridge U. Miss.	20	4	7	9	20	43	19
Drummond Ath	20	4	5	11	24	42	17
R A S R A	20	5	2	13	27	50	17
AFC Blackheath Rs	20	4	4	12	28	49	16
Bickley Town	20	3	4	13	26	54	13
Keyworth	withdrawn - record expunged						

SOUTH LONDON FOOTBALL FEDERATION

PREMIER DIV	P	W	D	L	F	A	Pts
Eltham & Ladywell U	14	11	2	1	56	25	35
TC Sports	14	9	1	4	37	19	31
Balham Puzzle	14	7	1	6	44	38	22
AFC Albert	14	6	1	7	29	32	19
Marshall	14	5	2	7	25	25	17
Catford Wanderers	14	5	1	8	23	38	16
Lewisham Borough	14	2	5	7	17	33	11
Sceptre	14	2	5	7	26	47	8

CRAWLEY & DISTRICT FOOTBALL LEAGUE

PREMIER DIV	P	W	D	L	F	A	Pts
Thomas Bennett	20	13	7	0	62	25	46
Longley	20	10	7	3	51	25	37
T D Sports	20	9	8	3	50	26	35
Ifield Res	20	8	5	7	48	55	29
Holland Sports	20	7	6	7	49	50	27
Edward Sports	20	7	6	7	41	42	27
B O C	20	8	3	9	42	46	27
Bluebird Rangers	20	7	3	10	44	50	24
Phoenix	20	4	7	9	31	47	19
Three Bridges A	20	6	0	14	42	68	18
Worth PK Rangers	20	3	4	13	40	66	13

BRIGHTON, HOVE & DISTRICT FOOTBALL LEAGUE

PREMIER DIV	P	W	D	L	F	A	Pts
AFC Falcons	20	16	3	1	59	10	51
Old Varndeanians	20	16	2	2	74	25	50
Midway	20	12	4	4	59	27	40
Sussex University	20	10	4	6	48	33	34
Rottingdean Vill	20	10	3	7	36	44	33
Downs	20	7	3	10	34	47	24
Montpelier Villa	20	6	5	9	28	34	23
Portslade Ath	20	5	3	12	26	45	18
Patcham	20	5	3	12	20	49	18
Preston Village	20	5	1	14	23	55	16
Rutland	20	1	3	16	17	55	6

TONBRIDGE LEAGUE

PREMIER DIV	P	W	D	L	F	A	Pts
Pembury	18	16	0	2	69	23	32
Woodlands	18	12	3	3	38	27	27
Atcost	18	11	4	3	44	25	26
Penshurst Park	18	9	2	7	50	54	20
High Brooms Cas	18	7	2	9	44	44	16
Town Malling Utd	18	7	1	10	41	43	15
Dowgate	18	6	2	10	43	57	14
Southborough	18	7	0	11	29	48	14
Horsmonden	18	5	3	10	40	54	13
Goulhurst Utd	18	1	1	16	29	52	3

DAVID FOLK MAIDSTONE & DISTRICT LEAGUE

PREMIER DIV	P	W	D	L	F	A	Pts
MPE	18	15	2	1	60	18	47
Cherry Tree Rgrs	18	14	2	2	65	33	44
Eccles	18	11	4	3	43	23	37
Ditton United	17	8	3	6	37	33	27
Loose Rangers	18	8	3	7	43	51	27
Knoxbridge Mon.	17	8	1	8	42	45	25
Staplehurst	18	5	2	11	31	44	17
Snodland Res	18	3	4	11	36	47	13
West Farleigh	18	1	5	12	26	56	8
Larkfield/NHW Rs	18	2	2	14	22	57	8

NORTH HAMPSHIRE SENIOR LEAGUE

	P	W	D	L	F	A	Pts
Hadleigh	20	14	4	2	49	19	46
Micheldever	20	14	1	5	50	23	43
Oakley Athletic	20	11	3	6	48	33	36
ABC United	20	11	2	7	53	36	34
Alresford Town	20	10	2	8	40	27	32
King Alfred YC	20	8	3	9	56	41	27
Winch. Castle Rs	20	8	2	10	38	30	26
New Street 'A'	20	8	1	11	39	68	25
AFC B'stoke Rs	20	6	4	10	40	44	22
Sherborne St J	20	4	4	12	30	56	16
Broughton Rs	20	2	2	16	20	86	8

READING FOOTBALL LEAGUE

SENIOR DIVISION	*P*	*W*	*D*	*L*	*F*	*A*	*Pts*
Forest Old Boys	20	15	1	4	51	23	46
Cookham Dean	20	13	4	3	36	17	43
Mortimer	20	12	3	5	47	22	39
Checkendon Sp	20	11	3	6	44	29	36
Emmbrook Sports	20	9	5	6	28	30	32
West Reading	20	9	3	8	44	35	30
Reading Exiles	20	9	2	9	34	38	29
South Reading	20	8	2	10	35	47	26
Sutton Exiles	20	5	4	11	36	44	19
Sonning Common	20	2	2	16	16	51	8
Round Head	20						

BASINGSTOKE & DISTRICT LEAGUE

PREMIER DIV	*P*	*W*	*D*	*L*	*F*	*A*	*Pts*
Hook	20	18	2	0	61	25	56
Royal Mail Rgrs	20	18	1	1	81	20	55
Oakridge	20	12	3	5	79	41	39
Hart Rovers	20	8	3	9	39	45	27
Tadley Youth	20	8	2	10	36	46	26
Basing. Rvrs Rs	20	6	5	9	23	40	23
Basing. Labour	20	6	3	11	51	54	21
Aldermaston Rs	20	6	3	11	31	57	21
Barbican	20	4	5	11	32	56	17
Hillborne	20	4	3	13	26	44	15
J Davy	20	5	0	15	30	61	15

SPORTEX SOUTHAMPTON LEAGUE

PREMIER DIV	*P*	*W*	*D*	*L*	*F*	*A*	*Pts*
Brendon	26	24	2	0	111	13	74
North Baddesley	26	19	5	2	70	17	62
BTC Southampton	26	19	3	4	93	42	60
Fair Oak A'vine	26	16	3	7	76	46	51
AC Delco Res	26	13	6	7	44	44	45
Durley	26	10	5	11	49	53	35
Locksheath Res	26	8	4	14	41	59	28
Esso Fawley Res	26	9	0	17	37	58	27
Otterbourne Res	26	7	5	14	40	48	26
O Tauntonians	26	8	5	13	40	59	26
Ford Sports	26	6	7	13	51	61	24
Bishopstoke Res	26	6	6	14	43	59	24
Sholing Select	26	5	6	15	39	69	21
East Boldre	26	3	1	22	25	131	10

NORTH BERKSHIRE LEAGUE

DIVISION ONE	*P*	*W*	*D*	*L*	*F*	*A*	*Pts*
Shrivenham	20	16	1	3	52	19	49
Saxton Rovers	20	15	2	3	44	17	47
Drayton	20	13	3	4	60	26	43
Long Wittenham	20	13	3	4	60	26	42
Faringdon Town	20	10	3	7	39	27	33
Blewbury	20	10	2	8	42	42	32
Sutton Courtenay	20	6	3	11	27	50	21
Didcot Casuals	20	5	4	11	25	39	19
Marcham	20	5	2	13	29	48	17
Radley	20	3	4	13	30	46	13
Harwell Village	20	1	2	17	17	67	5

FOX & SONS ISLE OF WIGHT LEAGUE

DIVISION ONE	*P*	*W*	*D*	*L*	*F*	*A*	*Pts*
Binstead COB	24	17	2	5	68	34	53
Oakfield	24	16	3	5	74	36	51
Seaview	24	15	2	7	66	30	47
East CVics Res	24	14	5	5	54	38	47
Newport Res	24	13	5	6	68	38	44
Shanklin	24	12	4	6	39	30	40
West Wight	24	9	6	9	48	40	33
GKN Weastland	24	10	2	12	50	46	32
Newhaven	24	9	5	10	61	70	32
W and B	24	9	2	13	44	59	29
Ventnor	24	6	2	12	37	67	20
Cowes Res	24	4	1	19	29	81	13
Northwood	24	1	3	20	17	86	6

No wonder Newcastle United were worried about Stevenage Borough!
Photo: Peter Barnes

BEDFORDSHIRE F.A.

Secretary: Peter D Brown

Century House, Skimpot Road, Dunstable LU5 4JU

Tel: (H) 01582 476163 (B) 01582 565111 (F) 01582 565222

BEDFORDSHIRE SENIOR CUP
(FOUNDED 1894-95)

RECENT FINALS

1992-93	Leighton Town	v	Kempston Rovers	2-1
1993-94	Potton United	v	Stotfold	2-1
1994-95	Bedford Town	v	Toddington Rovers	5-3 (AET)
1995-96	Bedford Town	v	Barton Rovers	1-0
1996-97	Luton Town	v	Leighton Town	2-1

MOST WINS Waterlows 10 Dunstable 9 Luton Clarence 8

1997-98
BEDFORDSHIRE PREMIER CUP

HOLDERS: LUTON TOWN

FIRST ROUND

Stotfold	v	Potton United	5-3*	Bedford United	v	Langford	3-2
Barton Rovers	v	Shillington	3-0	Leighton Town	v	Arlesey Town	1A1 2-3
Brache Sparta	v	Biggleswade Town	5-1				

SECOND ROUND

Brache Sparta	v	Bedford United	5-0	Barton Rovers	v	Luton Town	3-5
Bedford Town	v	Wootton Blue Cross	3-5	Stotfold	v	Arlesey Town	2-1

SEMI-FINALS

Brache Sparta	v	Luton Town	1-0	Bedford Town	v	Stotfold	3-1

FINAL

BRACHE SPARTA v BEDFORD TOWN 1-0 at Brache Sparta

BEDFORDSHIRE SENIOR CUP

HOLDERS: ARLESEY TOWN

PRELIMINARY ROUND

Kempston Rovers	v	Potton United	1-3	Bedford Town	v	Houghton Town	2-0
Kent Athletic	v	Shillington	0-2	Totternhoe	v	Langford	3-6
Stotfold	v	Biggleswade Utd	3-3*, 3-3*, 1-4p				

FIRST ROUND

Arlesey Town	v	Bedford Town	1-3	Bedford United	v	Caddington	5-1
Brache Sparta	v	Barton Rovers	1-2	Biggleswade Utd	v	Langford	4-1
61 FC Luton	v	Potton United	0-6	Toddington Rovers	v	Ampthill Town	2-1
Leighton Town	v	Shillington	5-0	Wootton Blue Cross	v	Biggleswade Town	2-3

SECOND ROUND

Bedford United	v	Potton United	0-3	Biggleswade Town	v	Bedford Town	1-2
Leighton Town	v	Barton Rovers	1-4	Toddington Rovers	v	Biggleswade Utd	2-2, 0-3

SEMI-FINALS

Barton Rovers	v	Biggleswade United	4-1*	Bedford Town	v	Potton United	0-1

FINAL

BARTON ROVERS v POTTON UNITED 4-1 at Leighton Town

BERKS & BUCKS F.A.

Secretary: Brian Moore,
15a London Street, Faringdon, Oxon SN7 8AG
Tel: (B) 01367 242099 (F) 01367 242158

BERKS & BUCKS SENIOR CUP (FOUNDED 1878-79)

RECENT FINALS

1992-93	Chesham United	v	Abingdon Town	1-0
1993-94	Marlow	v	Chesham United	1-0
1994-95	Reading	v	Slough Town	1-0
1995-96	Wokingham Town	v	Aylesbury United	1-0
1996-97	Aylesbury Utd	v	Reading	2-1

MOST WINS Wycombe 24 Maidenhead United 15 Marlow 13

1997-98 BERKS & BUCKS SENIOR CUP

HOLDERS: AYLESBURY UNITED

SECOND QUALIFYING ROUND

Beaconsfield SYCOB	v	Windsor & Eton	0-1	Wycombe Wndrs	v	Milton Keynes	2-0
Newport Pagnell Tn	v	Abingdon Town	1-2	Maidenhead Utd	v	Kintbury Rangers	4-0
Hungerford Town	v	Wokingham Town	1-3				

FIRST ROUND PROPER

Aylesbury United	v	Burnham	4-0	Windsor & Eton	v	Buckingham Town	1-0
Reading	v	Slough Town	6-2	Bracknell	v	Wycombe Wanderers	1-4
Maidenhead United	v	Wokingham Town	1-1*, 3-0	Flaxkwell Heath	v	Marlow	0-3
Chesham United	v	Chalfont St Peter	2-1	Thatcham Town	v	Abingdon United	1-0

SECOND ROUND

Thatcham Town	v	Marlow	0-0*, 0-1	Reading	v	Wycombe Wanderers	1-0
Windsor & Eton	v	Maidenhead Utd	2-2*, 1-4	Aylesbury United	v	Reading	0-4

SEMI-FINALS

Aylesbury United	v	Reading	0-4	Maidenhead Utd	v	Marlow	2-1

FINAL

MAIDENHEAD UTD v READING 2-1 at Wycombe Wanderers

BERKS & BUCKS SENIOR TROPHY

HOLDERS: ABINGDON UNITED

FIRST QUALIFYING ROUND

Wantage Town	v	Stony Stratford Town	4-3
Wallingford	v	Sandhurst Town	4-3*
Denham United	v	Forest Old Boys	0-2

SECOND QUALIFYING ROUND

AFC Wallingford	v	Forest Old Boys	5-0
Risborough Rangers	v	Prestwood	3-1
Didcot Town	v	Amersham Town	3-1
Winslow United	v	Olney Town	2-2, 3-1
Penn & Tylers Green	v	Holmer Green	0-3
Finchampstead	v	Buckingham Athletic	2-1
Stockdale Sports	v	New Bradwell Star	2-5
Milton United	v	Binfield	3-1
Broadmoor Social	v	Wantage Town	2-5
Eton Wick	v	Old Paludians	8-0
Wooburn Athletic	v	Iver	1-2
AFC Newbury	v	Martin Baher Sports	9-0
Mortimer	v	Mercedes Benz	4-1
Reading Exiles	v	Wraysbury	1-4

FIRST ROUND PROPER

Wantage Town	v	Abingdon United	0-1
Reading Town	v	Wallingford	7-0
Mortimer	v	Finchampstead	0-3
Risborough Rangers	v	Winslow United	1-1*, 0-1
Eton Wick	v	Milton United	5-1
Wraysbury	v	Didcot Town	0-3
New Bradwell St P	v	Holmer Green	1-1*, 4-1
Iver	v	AFC Newbury	0-12

SECOND ROUND

Abingdon United	v	Reading Town	2-1
Finchampstead	v	Eton Wick	3-1
Didcot Town	v	New Bradwell St Peters	3-0
Winslow United	v	AFC Newbury	1-3

SEMI-FINALS

Finchampstead	v	Didcot Town	3-1
AFC Newbury	v	Abingdon United	2-2, 0-3

FINAL

ABINGDON UNITED	v	FINCHAMPSTEAD	1-0	at Chesham United

Berks & Bucks Trophy, first round: Iver (Chiltonian League) 0 v AFC Newbury (Jewson Wessex League) 12
First-half action from Lee Barber as AFC Newbury assault the Iver goal

Photo: Martin Wray

BIRMINGHAM F.A.

Secretary: M Pennick FFA,
Ray Hall Lane, Great Barr, Birmingham B43 6JF
Tel: 0121 357 4278 (County Office)

BIRMINGHAM SENIOR CUP
(FOUNDED 1875-76)

RECENT FINALS

1992-93	Nuneaton Borough	v	VS Rugby	2-0
1993-94	Walsall	v	Hednesford Town	3-0
1994-95	Solihull Borough	v	Aston Villa	2-0
1995-96	Birmingham City	v	Aston Villa	2-0
1996-97	Burton Albion	v	Tamworth	3-1

MOST WINS Aston Villa 19 Birmingham City 7 Kidderminster Harriers 7 Wolverhampton Wanderers 7

1997-98
BIRMINGHAM SENIOR CUP

HOLDERS: BURTON ALBION

FIRST ROUND

Coleshill Town	v	Boldmere St Michaels	0-5	Gornal Athletic	v	Bolehill Swifts	2-0
Stourbridge	v	Tividale	2-2, 2-1	Sutton Coldfield Tn	v	Paget Rangers	1-2
Oldbury United	v	Worcester City	1-3	Darlaston Town	v	VS Rugby	2-3
Cradley Town	v	Highgate United	2-5	Sandwell Borough	v	Moor Green	0-4
Evesham United	v	Banbury Town	2-0	Athestone United	v	Halesowen Harriers	4-1

SECOND ROUND

VS Rugby	v	Kings Heath	2-0*	Redditch United	v	Stourbridge	2-2, 3-1
Evesham United	v	Paget Rangers	2-2, (5-3p)	West Mids Police	v	West Bromwich Albion	1-3
Racing Warwick	v	Highgate United	3-0	Moor Green	v	Wolverhampton Wndrs	2-4
Halesowen Town	v	Aston Villa	0-0, 7-4	Coventry City	v	Stratford Tn (at S.T.)	2-0
Brierley Hill Town	v	Bedworth United	3-3, 2-0	Wednesfield	v	Tamworth	0-3
Atherstone United	v	Worcester City	2-0	Walsall	v	Burton Albion	1-1, 2-0
Birmingham City	v	Boldmere St Michaels	2-0	Gornal Athletic	v	Hednesford Town	2-2, 0-1
Solihull Borough	v	Nuneaton Borough	3-0	Lye Town	v	Willenhall Town	**??**

NB: Evesham United were removed from the competition for fielding an ineligible player; Paget Rangers were reinstated

THIRD ROUND

Walsall	v	Paget Rangers	1-3	Hednesford Town	v	Racing Warwick	7-1
Halesowen Town	v	Tamworth 2-2*, 2-2*, (3-2p)		Brierley Hill Town	v	Birmingham City	1-2
Solihull Borough	v	Wolverhampton Wndrs	1-0	Atherstone United	v	Redditch United	1-2
Lye Town	v	Coventry City	0-1	West Bromwich A.	v	VS Rugby (at VSR)	4-1

FOURTH ROUND

Paget Rangers	v	Halesowen Tn	1-1, 0-1	Redditch United	v	West Bromwich Albion	3-2
Hednesford Town	v	Coventry City	1-2*	Solihull Borough	v	Birmingham City	1-3

SEMI-FINALS

Halesowen Town	v	Birmingham City	3-2*	Redditch United	v	Coventry City	4-0

FINAL

HALESOWEN TOWN v REDDITCH UNITED 3-1 at Halesowen Town

CAMBRIDGESHIRE F.A.

Secretary: Roger Pawley,
3 Signet Court, Swanns Road, Cambridge CB5 8LA
Tel: (01223) 576770 (County Office) Fax: (01223) 576780

CAMBRIDGESHIRE INVITATION CUP
(FOUNDED 1950-51)

RECENT FINALS

1992-93	Cambridge City	v	Wisbech Town	3-1
1993-94	Chatteris Town	v	Wisbech Town	3-1
1994-95	Wisbech Town	v	Cambridge City	4-2
1995-96	Mildenhall Town	v	Foxton	3-0
1996-97	Histon	v	Newmarket Town	2-2, 5-1p

MOST WINS Wisbech Town 9 Cambridge City 8 Chatteris Town 7

1997-98
CAMBRIDGESHIRE INVITATION CUP

HOLDERS: HISTON

FIRST ROUND

Histon	v	Over Sports	6-0	March Town Utd	v	Whittlesey Town	2-0
Chatteris Town	v	Warboys Town	3-1	Soham Tn Rngrs	v	Great Shelford	4-0

SECOND ROUND

Ely City	v	Mildenhall Town	3-0	March Town Utd	v	Wisbech Town (at WT)	1-2
Newmarket Town	v	Histon	3-1	Soham Tn Rngrs	v	Chatteris Town	3-1

SEMI-FINALS

Newmarket Town	v	Wisbech Town	2-4	Soham Tn Rngrs	v	Ely City	3-1

FINAL

SOHAM TN RNGRS v WISBECH TOWN 3-0 at Cambridge United FC, Att: 532

CHESHIRE F.A.

Secretary: Alan Collins,
The Cottage, Hartford Moss Rec Centre, Winnington, Northwich, Cheshire CW8 4BG
Tel: 01619 804706 (H) 01606 871166 (B) Fax: 01606 871292

CHESHIRE SENIOR CUP
(FOUNDED 1879-80)

RECENT FINALS

1992-93	Winsford United	v	Witton Albion	3-0
1993-94	Northwich Victoria	v	Runcorn	1-0
1994-95	Witton Albion	v	Altrincham	2-1
1995-96	Witton Albion	v	Hyde United	3-1
1996-97	Hyde United	v	Macclesfield Town	3-0

MOST WINS Macclesfield Town 18 Northwich Victoria 16 Crewe Alexandra 12 Runcorn 12

1997-98
CHESHIRE SENIOR CUP

HOLDERS: HYDE UNITED

FIRST ROUND

Stalybridge Celtic	v	Altrincham	2-0
Winsford United	v	Runcorn	1-1, 1-2
Cheadle Town	v	Warrington Town	6-4
Vauxhall GM	v	Congleton Town	4-1
Witton Albion	v	Nantwich Town	0-1

SECOND ROUND

Cheadle Town	v	Macclesfield Town	0-2
Hyde United	v	Northwich Victoria	1-2
Runcorn	v	Stalybridge Celtic	3-0
Nantwich Town	v	Vauxhall GM	0-5

SEMI-FINALS

Runcorn	v	Vauxhall GM	2-2, 3-1
Northwich Victoria	v	Macclesfield Tn	1-1, 0-0*

(Macclesfield Town win on away goal rule)

FINAL

MACCLESFIELD TN v RUNCORN 1-0 at The Drill Field, Northwich Victoria FC, Att: 995

1997-98
KELLY FOOTBALL KITS CHESHIRE AMATEUR CUP
(100th Competition)

ASHVILLE v POULTON VICTORIA 3-2 at Vauxhall GM FC

1997-98
NORTHERN COUNTIES AMATEUR CHAMPIONSHIP

(CHESHIRE FA v CUMBERLAND FA) POULTON VICTORIA v CARLISLE CITY 1-0

1997-98
CHESTER SENIOR CUP

CHRISTLETON v KYDDS ATHLETIC 5-0 at Christleton

Ashville FC (Winners Kelly Football Kits Cheshire Amateur Cup 1997-98)

Poulton Victoria FC (Finalists Kelly Football Kits Cheshire Amateur Cup 1997-98)

CORNWALL F.A.

Secretary: Barry Cudmore,
1 High Cross Street, St Austell, Cornwall PL25 4AB
Tel: (H) 01208 813826 (B) 01726 74080

CORNWALL SENIOR CUP
(FOUNDED 1892-93)

RECENT FINALS

1992-93	Saltash United	v	Launceston	3-2
1993-94	Liskeard Athletic	v	Bodmin Town	2-1
1994-95	Truro City	v	Liskeard Athletic	2-1
1995-96	Torpoint Athletic	v	Porthleven	2-0
1996-97	Falmouth Town	v	Nanpean Rovers	1-1, 2-1

MOST WINS Truro City 12 St Austell 11 Penzance 10 St Blazey 10 Torpoint Athletic 10

1997-98
CORNWALL SENIOR CUP

HOLDERS: FALMOUTH TOWN

FIRST ROUND

Bugle	v	St Cleer	0V4	Goonhavern	v	Perranwell	3-0
Helston Athletic	v	St Ives Town	0-3	Ludgvan	v	RNAS Culdrose	0-4
Mousehole	v	Nanpean Rovers	2-3	Mullion	v	Penryn Athletic	0-3
Padstow United	v	Callington	0-1	St Breward	v	Sticker	2-2, 2-1
St Just	v	Marazion Blues	4-2				

V: St Cleer eliminated owing to the fielding of an ineligible player

SECOND ROUND

Bude	v	Camelford	1-0	Bugle	v	Millbrook	0-8
Goonhavern Athletic	v	Launceston	2-3	Liskeard Athletic	v	Penzance	4-2
Nanpean Rovers	v	Bodmin Town	1-4	Pendeen Rovers	v	Penryn Athletic	1-8
Porthleven	v	St Breward	8-2	RNAS Culdrose	v	Foxhole	3-0
Roche	v	Torpoint Athletic	2-3	St Agnes	v	Illosan RBL	2-1
St Austell	v	St Ives Town	4-2	St Blazey	v	Falmouth Town	5-1
Saltash United	v	Newquay	2-0	Troon	v	St Just	2-0
Truro City	v	St Dennis	2-0	Wadebridge Town	v	Callington	2-3

THIRD ROUND

Millbrook	v	Porthleven	1-2	Launceston	v	Torpoint Athletic	0-3
Bodmin Town	v	St Blazey	2-2, 4-2*	RNAS Culdrose	v	Liskeard Athletic	0-2
St Agnes	v	Callington Town	1-2	St Austell	v	Bude Town	4-0
Troon	v	Penryn Athletic	1-3	Truro City	v	Saltash United	4-1

FOURTH ROUND

Callington	v	Truro City	0-1	Penryn Athletic	v	Torpoint Athletic	1-1, 0-2
Porthleven	v	Liskeard Athletic	2-2, 4-0	St Austell	v	Bodmin Town	2-1

NB: St Austell expelled for rule infringement. Bodmin Town reinstated.

SEMI-FINALS

Bodmin Town at Newquay	v	Truro City	1-3	Torpoint Athletic at St Blazey	v	Porthleven	2-5

FINALS

PORTHLEVEN	v	TRURO CITY	2-2, 2-3	both matches at Falmouth Town

CUMBERLAND FA

Secretary: Albert Murphy,
17 Oxford Street, Workington, Cumbria CA14 2AL
Tel: (H) 01900 605758 (County Office) 01900 872310

CUMBERLAND SENIOR CUP (FOUNDED 1960-61)

RECENT FINALS

1992-93	Carlisle United Res	v	Gretna	0-0 (Rep 3-1)
1993-94	Gretna	v	Carlisle United Res	3-0
1994-95	Gretna	v	Penrith	2-0
1995-96	Workington	v	Cleator Moor Celtic	4-1
1996-97	Gretna	v	Gillford Park	??

MOST WINS Penrith 10 Gretna 9 Haig Colliery 3

1997-98 CUMBERLAND SENIOR CUP

HOLDERS: GRETNA

FIRST ROUND

Northbank	v	Whitehave Amateurs	8-2
Whitehaven Mw	v	Whitehaven Raiders	2-1
Alston Town	v	Braithwaite	1-0
Gillford Pk Reserves	v	Workington	2-1
Silloth	v	Langwathby	4-0
Inglewood Forest	v	Longtown	0-12
Keswick	v	St Bees	2-1
Cockermouth	v	Carlisle United	C-WO
Windscale Res	v	Penrith	1-13

SECOND ROUND

Wigston Harriers	v	Northbank Reserves	0-3
Gretna	v	Silloth	5-0
Sporting Museum	v	Carlisle City Reserves	5-0
Silloth Cotts	v	Cockermouth	1-4
Kirkoswald	v	Wetheriggs	2-3
Windscale	v	Whitehaven Am. Res	5-0
Gillford Pk Reserves	v	Northbank	1-3
British Steel	v	Frizington WMC	2-5
Parton United	v	Abbeytown	0-3
Greystoke	v	Dalston Athletic	11-1
Alston Town	v	Whitehaven MW	3-0
Keswick	v	Longtown	6-4
Carlisle City	v	Cleaton Moor Celtic	4-0
Gillford Park	v	Penrith	3-1
Egremount St Mary	v	Whitehaven Mw Res	1-2
Carleton Rovers	v	Hearts of Liddlesdale	4-2

THIRD ROUND

Abbey Town	v	Windscale	1-2*
Keswick	v	Gillford Park	1-3
Wetheriggs United	v	Sporting Museum	0-2
Whitehaven Mw	v	Carlisle City	1-2
Northbank Res.	v	Cockermouth	0-1
Carleton Rovers	v	Frizington WMC	0-2
Gretna	v	Greystoke	5-1
Northbank	v	Alston Town	5-1

FOURTH ROUND

Gillford Park	v	Cockermouth	5-0
Sporting Museum	v	Northbank	0-3
Frizington WMC	v	Carlisle City	0-7
Gretna	v	Windscale	3-4

SEMI-FINALS

Gillford Park	v	Windscale	3-5
Carlisle City	v	Northbank	2-1

FINAL

CARLISLE CITY	v	WINDSCALE	1-2	at Gretna

Cumberland Senior Cup Final at Raydale Park, Gretna. City's Mark Wilson is tackled by Windscale's Clive Heaney (4). Windscale knocked out holders Gretna 4-3 on the way to the Final

Photo: Alan Watson

DERBYSHIRE F.A.

Secretary: K Compton,
The Grandstand, Moorways Stadium, Moor Lane
Derby DE2 8FB Tel: (01332) 361422

DERBYSHIRE SENIOR CUP
(FOUNDED 1883-84)

RECENT FINALS

1992-93	Ilkeston Town	v	Alfreton Town	1-1 (Agg) 7-6 (Pens)
1993-94	Gresley Rovers	v	Matlock Town	4-1 (Agg)
1994-95	Alfreton Town	v	Ilkeston Town	8-1 (Agg)
1995-96	Gresley Rovers	v	Belper Town	2-1
1996-97	Gresley Rovers	v	Ilkeston Town	3-2 (Agg)

MOST WINS Derby County 15 Ilkeston Town 11 Buxton 8 Chesterfield 8 Heanor Town 8

1997-98
DERBYSHIRE SENIOR CUP

HOLDERS: GRESLEY ROVERS

FIRST ROUND

Stanton Ilkeston	v	Shirebrook Town	1-3
Holbrook	v	Long Eaton United	1-3
Shardlow St James	v	Newhall United	1-2
South Normanton Ath	v	Heanor Town	3-4
Blackwell MW	v	Graham Street Prims	1-6
Mickleover Sports	v	Sandiacre Town	3-2
Sheepbridge	v	Mickleover RBL	0-1

SECOND ROUND

Shirebrook Town	v	Graham St Prims	2-2, 1-3
Newhall United	v	Long Eaton United	0-6
Heanor Town	v	Mickleover Sports	3-2

Mickleover Royal British Legion FC bye

THIRD ROUND

Stapenhill	v	Ilkeston Town	0-7
Gresley Rovers	v	Belper Town	1-3
Borrowash Victoria	v	Glapwell	0-1
Glossop North End	v	Buxton	1-0
Graham St Prims	v	Heanor Town	1-1, 2-1
Matlock Town	v	Long Eaton Utd	5-1
Alfreton Town	v	Mickleover RBL	1-0

Staveley Miners Welfare bye

FOURTH ROUND

Staveley MW	v	Ilkeston Town	1-4
Glapwell	v	Belper Town	1-0
Matlock Town	v	Graham St Prims	1-0
Glossop Nth End	v	Alfreton Town	3-0

SEMI-FINALS

Glapwell	v	Ilkeston Town	2-0
Glossop Nth End	v	Matlock Town	0-0, 1-3

FINAL (First Leg)

GLAPWELL v MATLOCK TOWN 1-2

FINAL (Second Leg)

MATLOCK TOWN v GLAPWELL 1-2 = 3-3 aggregate. Glapwell win 3-2 on penalties

DEVON F.A.

Secretary: Chris Davidson,
Tel: (01626) 332077 (County Office) Fax: (01626) 336814

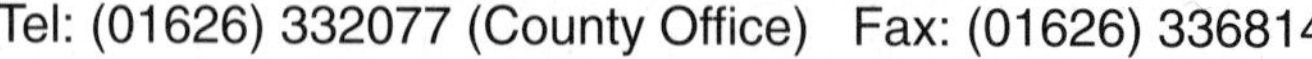

DEVON ST LUKES COLLEGE CUP (FOUNDED 1981-82)

RECENT FINALS

1992-93	Tiverton Town	v	Clyst Rovers	3-0
1993-94	Tiverton Town	v	Bideford	1-0
1994-95	Tiverton Town	v	Bideford	5-1
1995-96	Bideford	v	Torrington	2-1
1996-97	Tiverton Town	v	Torrington	6-0

MOST WINS Tiverton Town 7 Bideford 3 Exmouth Town 3

1997-98 DEVON ST LUKES BOWL

HOLDERS: TIVERTON TOWN

FIRST ROUND

Barnstaple Town	v	Dawlish Town	2-0	Bideford	v	Ilkeston Town	3-1
Crediton Town	v	Clyst Rovers	4-3	Exeter City	v	Elmore	5-0
Exmouth Town	v	Plymouth Argyle	2-4	Torrington	v	Heavitree United	6-0

QUARTER-FINALS

Bideford	v	Plymouth Argyle	1-0	Crediton United	v	Exeter City	0-5
Torquay United	v	Barnstaple Town	3-2	Torrington	v	Tiverton Town	1-7

SEMI-FINALS

Exeter City	v	Bideford Town	5-1	Tiverton Town	v	Torquay United	0-1

FINAL

TORQUAY UNITED	v	EXETER CITY	1-0	at Torquay, att: 858

DORSET F.A.

Secretary: P S Hough,
County Ground, Blandford Close, Hamworthy, Poole BH15 4BF
Tel: (01202) 682375 (County Office) Fax: (01202) 666577

DORSET SENIOR CUP (FOUNDED 1887-88)

RECENT FINALS

1992-93	Weymouth	v	Poole Town	4-0
1993-94	Dorchester Town	v	Poole Town	1-0
1994-95	Hamworthy Eng	v	Poole Town	4-1
1995-96	Dorchester Town	v	St Pauls	3-1
1996-97	Wimborne Town	v	Wareham Rangers	2-0

MOST WINS Weymouth 24 Portland United 10 Poole Town 10 Bridport 9

1997-98 DORSET SENIOR CUP

HOLDERS: WIMBORNE TOWN

FIRST ROUND

Blandford United	v	Parley Sports	6-2
Portland United	v	Allendale	2-2, 1-4
Wareham Rangers	v	Lytchett Red Triangle	1-2
Flight Refuelling	v	Sherborne Town	1-1, 7-0
Sturminster N. Utd	v	Shaftesbury	0-3

SECOND ROUND

Wimborne Town	v	Weymouth Sports	3-1
Allendale	v	Swanage & Herston	4-3
Flight Refuelling	v	Bournemouth Sports	1-5
Lytchett Red Triangle	v	Hamworthy United	1-1, 2-5
Bridport	v	Poole Town	1-1, 1-1*, 1-2*
Blandford United	v	Gillingham Town	2-7
Hamworthy EFC	v	Northerners Athletic	6-0
Sturminster Marsh.	v	Shaftesbury	0-6

THIRD ROUND

Shaftesbury	v	Wimborne Town	2-8
Poole Town	v	Hamworthy EFC	2-2, 2-0
Gillingham Town	v	Allendale	1-3
Hamworthy Utd	v	Bournemouth Sports	3-0

SEMI-FINALS

Poole Town	v	Wimborne Town	0-0, 3-2
Allendale	v	Hamworthy United	0-4

FINAL

POOLE TOWN v HAMWORTHY UTD 2-1 at Weymouth

DURHAM F.A.

Secretary: John Topping,
'Codeslaw', Ferens Park, Durham DH1 1JZ
Tel: 0191 384 8653 Fax: (01367) 242158

DURHAM CHALLENGE CUP (FOUNDED 1883-84)

RECENT FINALS

1992-93	Murton	v	Bishop Auckland	2-1
1993-94	Spennymoor United	v	Bishop Auckland	2-2 (Rep 3-2)
1994-95	Spennymoor United	v	South Shields	1-1 (Rep 3-0)
1995-96	Spennymoor United	v	Durham City	1*0
1996-97	Bishop Auckland	v	Spennymoor United	2-0

MOST WINS Sunderland 21 Spennymoor United 15 Bishop Auckland 13

1997-98 DURHAM CHALLENGE CUP

HOLDERS: BISHOP AUCKLAND

PRELIMINARY ROUND

S Kennek Roker	v	Crook Town	3-0
Shildon	v	S Ryhope CW	1-1, 0-2
Chester-le-Street Tn	v	Seaham Red Star	4-2
Eppleton CW	v	South Tyneside United	1-3
South Shields	v	Annfield Plain	2-1
Hartlepool United 'A'	v	Ryehope CA	4-0
Washington	v	Hartlepool BWOB	0-1
Dunston FB	v	Horden CW	5-0
Whickham	v	Wolviston	1-2
Wash'ton Nyssan	v	Shotton Comrades	2-1
Evenwood Town	v	Billingham Sinthonia	5-0
Birtley Town	v	Willington	5-1
Sth Sh'ld Cleadon	v	Hebburn	1-0
Esh Winning	v	Norton & Stockton	2-2, 5-2

Horden Colliery Wefare and South Shields Harton & Westoe byes

FIRST ROUND

Horden CW	v	Easington Colliery	0-6
Evenwood Town	v	SS Norton & Westoe	5-1
West Auckland Town	v	Bishop Auckland	0-1
Durham City	v	Washington Nissan	4-0
Spennymoor United	v	South Shields	2-1
Murton	v	Birtley Town	0-1
Dunston FB	v	Consett	2-1
S Kennek Roker	v	Stanley United	3-1
Cockfield	v	Jarrow	1-0
Jarrow R & BCA	v	Tow Law Town	1-2
Billingham Town	v	Sunderland Ryhope CW	0-1
Peterlee Newtown	v	South Shields Cleadon	2-0
Brandon United	v	Hartlepool Utd 'A'	3-4
Boldon CA	v	Chester-le-Street Tn	1-0
Hartlepool BWOB	v	Esh Winning	3-0
Woolviston	v	South Tyneside Utd	1-2

SECOND ROUND

Easington Colliery	v	Tow Law Town	1-3
Bishop Auckland	v	Cockfield	3-1
Ryehope CW	v	Durham City	2-1
Birtley Town	v	South Tyneside Utd	3-1
Spennymoor Utd	v	S Kennek Roker	5-0
Hartlepool Utd 'A'	v	Dunston Federation	2-1
Evenwood Town	v	Hartlepool BWOB	3-1
Boldon CA	v	Peterlee Newtown	3-6*

THIRD ROUND

Birtley Town	v	Hartlepool Utd 'A'	2-2, 2-4
Bishop Auckland	v	Peterlee Newtown	9-1
Tow Law Town	v	Ryehope CW	5-1
Spennymoor Utd	v	Evenwood Town	8-0

SEMI-FINALS

Tow Law Town	v	Hartlepool Utd 'A'	0-0*, 1-3
Spennymoor Utd	v	Bishop Auckland	2-2*, 3-1

FINAL

HARTLEPOOL U. 'A' v SPENNYMOOR UTD 2-1 at Durham CIty, Att: 443

EAST RIDING F.A.

Secretary: D R Johnson,
50 Boulevard, Hull HU3 2TB
Tel: (01482) 641458 Fax: 01482 647512

EAST RIDING SENIOR CUP
(FOUNDED 1903-04)

RECENT FINALS

1992-93	Bridlington Town	v	North Ferriby United	3-1
1993-94	Hall Road Rangers	v	Sculcoates Amateurs	1-0
1994-95	Sculcoates Amateurs	v	Hall Road Rangers	2-1
1995-96	Sculcoates Amateurs	v	Reckitts	2-1
1996-97	North Ferriby United	v	Filey Town	3-0

MOST WINS Hull City 25 Bridlington Town 12 North Ferriby United 6 Bridlington Trinity 5

1997-98
EAST RIDING SENIOR CUP

HOLDERS: NORTH FERRIBY UNITED

FIRST ROUND

Savoy Wanderers	v	Ideal Standard	3-4	Hall Rd Rgrs Rs	v	Fiveways A	F-WO
Cottingham Sports	v	Chisholms	2-1	Sculcoates Amat.	v	Westella & Willerby	2-1
Maler Lambert YC	v	Hider Foods	2-1				

SECOND ROUND

East Hull Amateurs	v	Rechitts	2-1	Bulmans	v	Cottingham Sports	3-4
Bridlington Town	v	Hull City	0-6	Filey Town	v	Maler Lambert YC	4-3
Sculcoate Amateurs	v	Dairycoates	6-1	Smith & Nephew	v	Kingburn	6-0
Ideal Standard	v	North Ferriby United	1-3	Hall Rd Rangers	v	Fiveways A	8-0

THIRD ROUND

Cottingham Sports	v	Smith & Nephew	2-0	Filey Town	v	North Ferriby United	3-6
Sculcoates Amateurs	v	Hall Road Rangers	0-3	East Hull Amat.	v	Hull City	1-2

SEMI-FINALS

Hall Road Rangers	v	North Ferriby United	1-3	Cottingham Sports	v	Hull City	0-5
at Church Road, North Ferriby United FC				at Church Road, North Ferriby United FC			

FINAL

HULL CITY v NORTH FERRIBY UTD 1-2 at Boothferry Park, Hull City AFC

EAST RIDING COUNTRY CUP

HOLDERS: BRIDLINGTON TOWN

FIRST ROUND

Ward FC	v	Full Measure	2-1
Rillington Athletic	v	Crown FC	1-2
Hilderthrope AFC	v	Driffield Tn Panthers	H W/O
Pack Horse	v	Flamborough	3-1
Holme Rovers	v	Walkington Wanderers	7-3
Middleton Rovers	v	Holmpton Utd	MR W/O
Pocklington Town	v	Withernsea	4-0
Beverley O Gramm	v	AFC Bridlington George	6-0
South Cave United bye			
Globe FC	v	Bridlington Rovers	1-7
Hornsea Town	v	Bridlington LC	3-2
Market Weighton	v	North Cave	1-2
Nafferton	v	Bridlington LC 2nd	7-1
Rudston United	v	North Ferriby URs	NF W/O
Bridlington Tn Res	v	Shiptonthorpe Utd	2-1
Driffield EI	v	Filey Town 2nd	2-7

SECOND ROUND

Filey Town 2nd	v	Nafferton	2-2, 1-3
Hornsea Town	v	Bridlington Rovers	0-2
South Cave United	v	Holme Rovers	3-4
North Cave	v	Hilderthorpe	3-1
Pocklington Town	v	Ward	2-2, 1-3
Bridlington Tn Res	v	Crown	2-1
North Ferriby U Rs	v	Beverley OG	1-0
Pack Horse	v	Middleton Rovers	5-0

THIRD ROUND

Ward	v	Bridlington Rovers	3-2
Pack Horse	v	Bridlington Town Res	2-4
Filey Town 2nd	v	North Cave	3-2
Nth Ferriby Utd Rs	v	Holme Rovers	2-3

SEMI-FINALS

Ward	v	Filey Town 2nd	1-3
Bridlington Tn Res	v	Holme Rovers	1-5

FINAL

FILEY TOWN 2nd	v	HOLME ROVERS	3-2	at Queensgate, Bridlington Town FC

FOUNDED 1882

ESSEX F.A.

FOUNDED 1882

Secretary: Philip Sammons,
31 Mildmay Road, Chelmsford CM2 0DN
Tel: (01245) 357727

ESSEX SENIOR CUP
(FOUNDED 1883-84)

RECENT FINALS

1992-93	Chelmsford City	v	Wivenhoe Town	1-0
1993-94	Grays Athletic	v	Billericay Town	1-0
1994-95	Grays Athletic	v	Billericay Town	1-0
1995-96	Braintree Town	v	Billericay Town	2-1
1996-97	Southend United	v	Braintree Town	2-1

MOST WINS Ilford 13 Walthamstow Avenue 12 Grays Athletic 8 Leyton 8

1997-98
ESSEX SENIOR CUP

HOLDERS: SOUTHEND UNITED

PRELIMINARY ROUND

Ilford	v	Waltham Avenue	1V3 TA	Eton Manor	v	Gt Wakering Rovers*	1-4
Bowers United	v	Brightlingsea United	3-1	Southend Manor	v	Concord Rangers	1-4
Stanway Rovers	v	Clacton Town	4-1	Burnham Ramblers	v	Brentwood	4-1

* at Purfleet

FIRST ROUND

Concord Rangers	v	Burnham Ramblers	0-3	Maldon Town	v	Hullbridge Sports	2-1
Stanway Rovers	v	East Ham United	2-1	Basildon United	v	Barkingside	2-1
Harwich & Parkeston	v	Stansted	4-1	Gt Wakering Rvrs	v	Bowers United	2-1
Saffron Walden Tn	v	Ilford	0-3				

SECOND ROUND

Barking	v	Ford United	0-4	Gt Wakering Rvrs	v	Heybridge Swifts	0-4
Ilford	v	Colchester United	1-3	Purfleet	v	Aveley	3-1
Grays Athletic	v	Tilbury	3-0	Leyton Orient	v	Romford (at Romf'd)	1-4
Clapton	v	Southend United	1-2	Billericay Town	v	Witham Town	4-2 aet
Canvey Island	v	East Thurrock United	4-1	Maldon Town	v	Harlow Town	0-5
Hornchurch	v	Dagenham & R'bridge	0-2	Halstead Town	v	Basildon Utd	1-2
Braintree Town	v	Stanway Rvrs	4-4 aet, 0-1	Wivenhoe Town	v	Chelmsford City	3-1
Leyton Pennant	v	Harwich & Parkeston	4-1	Tiptree United	v	Burnham Ramblers	4-6 aet

THIRD ROUND

Heybridge Swifts	v	Billericay Town	3-5	Colchester Utd	v	Canvey Island	0-1
Southend United	v	Stanway Rovers	2-0	Wivenhoe Town	v	Harlow Town	2-1
Dag. & Redbridge	v	Leyton Pennant	3-1 aet	Grays Athletic	v	Basildon United	6-1
Romford	v	Ford United	6-2	Burnham Rmblrs	v	Purfleet	2-5

FOURTH ROUND

Dag. & Redbridge	v	Billericay Town	4-2	Grays Athletic	v	Purfleet	2-3 aet
Canvey Island	v	Romford	3-2	Southend United	v	Wivenhoe Town	8-0

SEMI-FINALS

Dag. & Redbridge	v	Southend United	6-2	Canvey Island	v	Purfleet	1-2 aet

FINAL

PURFLEET	v	DAG. & REDBRIDGE	1-2	at Purfleet FC

ESSEX THAMES-SIDE TROPHY
(FOUNDED 1945-46)

RECENT FINALS

1992-93	Leyton	v	Rainham Town	5-4
1993-94	Canvey Island	v	Grays Athletic	2-2 (4-3 Pns)
1994-95	Purfleet	v	Chelmsford City	2-0
1995-96	Canvey Island	v	Witham Town	5-0
1996-97	Canvey Island	v	Barking	1-1 (7-8Pns)

MOST WINS Ilford 13 Walthamstow Avenue 12 Grays Athletic 8 Leyton 8

1997-98
ESSEX THAMES-SIDE TROPHY

HOLDERS: BARKING

FIRST ROUND

Hornchurch	v	Concord Rangers	3-1	Waltham Abbey	v	Maldon Town	
Harlow Town	v	Gt Wakering Rvrs	0-0, 2-4p	Southend Manor	v	Romford	0-5
East Thurrock United	v	Tiptree United	2-0 aet	Bowers United	v	Burnham Ramblers	1-2
Aveley	v	Tilbury	3-0	Clapton	v	Ford United	0-2

SECOND ROUND

Hornchurch	v	Purfleet	0-1	Basildon United	v	Ford United	1-1, 2-4p
Southend United	v	Grays Athletic	2-0	Barkingside	v	Witham Town	3-2
Romford	v	Aveley	2-4	Burnham Rmblrs	v	Gt Wakering Rvrs	0-2
Canvey Island	v	Waltham Ab./Maldon Tn	3-1	E. Thurrock Utd	v	Barking	1-2

THIRD ROUND

Canvey Island	v	Barking	2-0	Aveley	v	Basildon United	4-1
Purfleet	v	Southend United	0-2 aet	Gt Wakering Rvrs	v	Barkingside	0-1

SEMI-FINALS

Aveley	v	Barkingside	2-0	Southend United	v	Canvey Island	1-3

FINAL

AVELEY v CANVEY ISLAND 0-1 at Aveley FC

GLOUCESTERSHIRE F.A.

Secretary: Paul Britton,
Oaklands Park, Almondsbury, Bristol BS12 4AG
Tel: 01454 615888 (County Office)

GLOUCESTERSHIRE SENIOR CUP
(FOUNDED 1936-37)

RECENT FINALS

1992-93	Gloucester City	v	Yate Town	3-2 (AET)
1993-94	Newport AFC	v	Gloucester City	1-0
1994-95	Cheltenham Town	v	Yate Town	1-1 (5-4 Pns)
1995-96	Cheltenham Town	v	Gloucester City	0-0 (3-1 Pns)
1996-97	Cheltenham Town	v	Gloucester City	2-1

MOST WINS Cheltenham Town 31 Gloucester City 18 Forest Green Rovers 3

1997-98
GLOUCESTERSHIRE SENIOR CUP

HOLDERS: CHELTENHAM TOWN

FIRST ROUND

Forest Grn Rovers	v	Cirencester Town	2-1 aet				

SECOND ROUND

Cinderford Town	v	Gloucester City	0-1	Cheltenham Town	v	Bristol City	1-1, 2-4p
Forest Green Rovers	v	Yate Town	5-0	Bristol Rovers	v	Mangotsfield Utd	2-1

SEMI-FINALS

Forest Green Rovers	v	Gloucester City	2-1	Bristol City	v	Bristol Rovers	6-0

FINAL

BRISTOL CITY v FOREST GREEN RVRS 2-1 at Ashton Gate, Bristol, Att: 590

GLOUCESTERSHIRE SENIOR TROPHY
(FOUNDED 1978-79)

RECENT FINALS

1992-93	Hallen	v	Cinderford Town	4-1
1993-94	Mangotsfield United	v	Moreton Town	3-1 (AET)
1994-95	Shortwood United	v	Fairford Town	2-1
1995-96	Cirencester Town	v	Endsleigh	2*1
1996-97	Bitton	v	Mangotsfield United	2-3

MOST WINS Mangotsfield United 5 Moreton Town 3 Shortwood United 2

1997-98
GLOUCESTERSHIRE SENIOR TROPHY

HOLDERS: MANGOTSFIELD UNITED

FIRST ROUND

Fairford Town	v	Harrow Hill	5-0	Cadbury Heath	v	Brockworth	7-2
Bishops Cleve	v	Cheltenham Saracens	1-3	Bitton	v	Wotton Rovers	3-0
DRG	v	Old Georgians	2-0	Viney St Swithins	v	Broad Plain House	0-3
Ellwood	v	Henbury Old Boys	0-1	Winterbourne Utd	v	Hallen	3-1
Cirencester United	v	Tuffley Rovers	2-3	Frampton Athletic	v	Almondsbury Town	3-1
Stapleton	v	Patchway Tn	3-3 aet, 1-2	Bristol Manor Farm	v	Shirehampton	3-1
Pucklechurch Sports	v	Endsleigh	1-5	Totterdown POB	v	Shortwood United	0-2
Longwell Green Abb.	v	Dursley Town	2-1	Broadwell Am	v	Oldland	7-0

SECOND ROUND

Bitton	v	Endsleigh	2-1	Winterbourne Utd	v	Patchway Town	2-1
DRG	v	Cheltenham Saracens	3-2	Tuffley Rovers	v	Fairford Town	4-1
Henbury Old Boys	v	Cadbury Heath	1-5	Longwell Grn Abb.	v	Broadwell Amateurs	0-1
Shortwood United	v	Frampton Athletic	1-3	Bristol Manor Fm	v	Broad Plain House	0-2

THIRD ROUND

Frampton Athletic	v	Broad Plain House	3-0	DRG	v	Cadbury Heath	4-2
Broadwell Am.	v	Tuffley Rovers	1-0	Winterbourne Utd	v	Bitton	3-0

SEMI-FINALS

Frampton Athletic	v	DRG	0-2	Broadwell Am.	v	Winterbourne Utd	3-2 aet

FINAL

DRG v BROADWELL AM. 1-0 at Oaklands Park, Almondsbury Town FC

GLOUCESTERSHIRE FOOTBALL ASSOCIATION

ADDITIONAL COUNTY CUP FINALS 1997-98

SENIOR PROFESSIONAL
Not played

SENIOR AMATEUR SOUTH
Ridings High v Sun Life 3-3 aet, 3-0
2-0

JUNIOR SOUTH
RMC Wick v Glenside Hosp SC Rs 3-1

INTERMEDIATE SOUTH
Sandringham Sports v Frys SR 3-0

MINOR SOUTH
Marshfield v Frampton Athletic 2-1

PRIMARY SOUTH
Old Georgians A v Brimsham Grn R 1-1*, 1-1*
(Old Georgians won 7-6 on penalties - 26 taken!)

SUNDAY PREMIER SOUTH
Lebeq Tavern Cour. v Hanham Sunday 2-0

SUNDAY INTERMEDIATE SOUTH
AFC Downend v Langton Court 2-1

SUNDAY MINOR SOUTH
CR Windows v Rangeworthy Sunday 2-1

YOUTH SHIELD (UNDER 18)
Yate Town v St Valier 3-1 aet

OSBORNE (UNDER 14)
St Valier v Shirehampton 5-1

WOMENS CUP
Cheltenham v Cam Bulldogs 5-0

SENIOR AMATEUR NORTH
Cirencester Academy v Hardwicke

JUNIOR NORTH
Slimbridge v Kingswood 1-0

INTERMEDIATE NORTH
Winchcombe Tn Rsv Coaley Rovers 2-2 aet, 3-0

MINOR NORTH
Lydbrook Athletic Av Adlestrop, D & O 1-0

PRIMARY NORTH
Blakeney Reservesv Dursley Town B 1-0

SUNDAY PREMIER NORTH
Lokomotiv Bass v Porky's 3-1

SUNDAY INTERMEDIATE NORTH
NCN Express v Guiting Rangers 5-1

SUNDAY MINOR NORTH
Kempsford v Renegades 4-1

KENNEDY (UNDER 16)
Brislington v Pershore 1-0

BUCKLAND (UNDER 12)
Windsor Drive v Badsey Rangers 2-1

COUNTY MATCHES 1997-98

SENIOR

v	Gwent (Fr)	a	Won	1-0
v	Somerset (SWC)	h	Lost	2-4
v	Royal Navy (SWC)	a	Lost	2-3
v	County League		Won	3-1
v	Dorset (SWC)	h	Drawn	1-1
v	Army (SWC)	a	Lost	1-5
v	Wiltshire (SWC)	a	Lost	0-1

YOUTH

v	Hertfordshire (FACC)	a	Won	2-1
v	Cambridgeshire (FACC)	a	Won	2-0
v	Dorset (SWC)	h	Won	3-0
v	Wiltshire (SWC)	a	Drawn	1-1
v	Hampshire (SWC)	a	Won	2-1
v	Birmingham (FACC)	a	Won	3-1
v	Northumberland (FACC)	a	Lost	2-4
v	Army (SWC)	h	Won	6-0
v	Somerset (SWC)	a	Drawn	2-2
v	Herefordshire (Fr)	a	Won	4-0

WOMEN

v	Wiltshire (SWC)	h	Lost	1-7
v	Dorset (SWC)	h	Won	2-1
v	Somerset (SWC)	a	Lost	2-3

FACC = FA County Championship SWC = South West Counties Championship Fr = Friendly

HAMPSHIRE F.A.

Secretary: R G Barnes,
8 Ashwood Gardens, off Winchester Road
Southampton SO16 7PW Tel: 01703 79110

HAMPSHIRE SENIOR CUP
(FOUNDED 1887-88)

RECENT FINALS

1992-93	Fareham Town	v	Farnborough Town	4-1
1993-94	Havant Town	v	Farnborough Town	1-0
1994-95	Havant Town	v	Farnborough Town	1-0
1995-96	Basingstoke Town	v	Waterlooville	2-0
1996-97	Basingstoke Town	v	Waterlooville	2-0

MOST WINS Southampton 13 Newport 7 Cowes 6

1997-98
HAMPSHIRE SENIOR CUP

HOLDERS: BASINGSTOKE TOWN

FIRST ROUND

Aerostructures SS	v	Netley Central Spts	4-0	AFC Totton	v	New Street	2-1
Bass Alton Town	v	Blackfield & Langley	3-5	BAT Sports	v	AC Delco	1-3
Bournemouth	v	Colden Common	7-2	Brockenhurst	v	Fleetlands	1-0
Cove	v	Moneyfields	3-1	Cowes	v	Petersfield Town	4-3 aet
East Cowes Vics Ath	v	Christchurch	2-0	Eastleigh	v	RS Basingstoke	3-2 aet
Hartley Wintney	v	Winchester City	2-2, 1-0	Horndean	v	Gosport Borough	2-2, 1-2
Liss Athletic	v	Mayflower	2-1	Portsmouth RN	v	Pirelli General	5-0
Romsey Town	v	Stockbridge	1-4	Whitchurch United	v	Brading Town	2-0

SECOND ROUND

Aldershot Town	v	Whitchurch United	7-1	Andover	v	Blackfield & Langley	3-1 aet
Basingstoke Town	v	Newport IoW	1-2	Bishopstoke	v	Hayling Island	1-2
Bournemouth	v	Gosport Borough	2-1	Brockenhurst	v	Liss Athletic	2-1
Cowes Sports	v	AC Delco	0-4	East Cowes V. A.	v	Cove	1-0
Eastleigh	v	Fleet Town	3-1	Fareham Town	v	Locksheath	8-0
Farnborough Town	v	Totton AFC	3-2	Havant Town	v	Lymington AFC	3-2
Portsmouth RN	v	Hartley Wintney	4-3 aet	Ryde Sports	v	Bashley (at Bashley)	1-7
Sylvans Guernsey	v	Aerostructures	2-2 aet, 3-1	Waterlooville	v	Stockbridge	1-0

THIRD ROUND

Aldershot Town	v	Bournemouth	4-1	Andover	v	Portsmouth RN	1-3
Bashley	v	Brockenhurst	3-4	East Cowes V.A.	v	AC Delco	0-2
Fareham Town	v	Sylvans Guernsey	6-3 aet	Havant Town	v	Eastleigh	0-2
Newport IoW	v	Hayling Island	4-0	Waterlooville	v	Farnborough Town	3-0

FOURTH ROUND

Eastleigh	v	Aldeshot Town	1-2	Fareham Town	v	AC Delco	6-0
Newport IoW	v	Brockenhurst	3-0	Portsmouth RN	v	Waterlooville	0-0, 1-0

SEMI-FINALS

Fareham Town	v	Waterlooville	1-0 aet	Newport IoW	v	Aldershot Town	2-1

FINAL

FAREHAM TOWN v NEWPORT IoW 0-1 at The Dell, Southampton FC, Att: 897

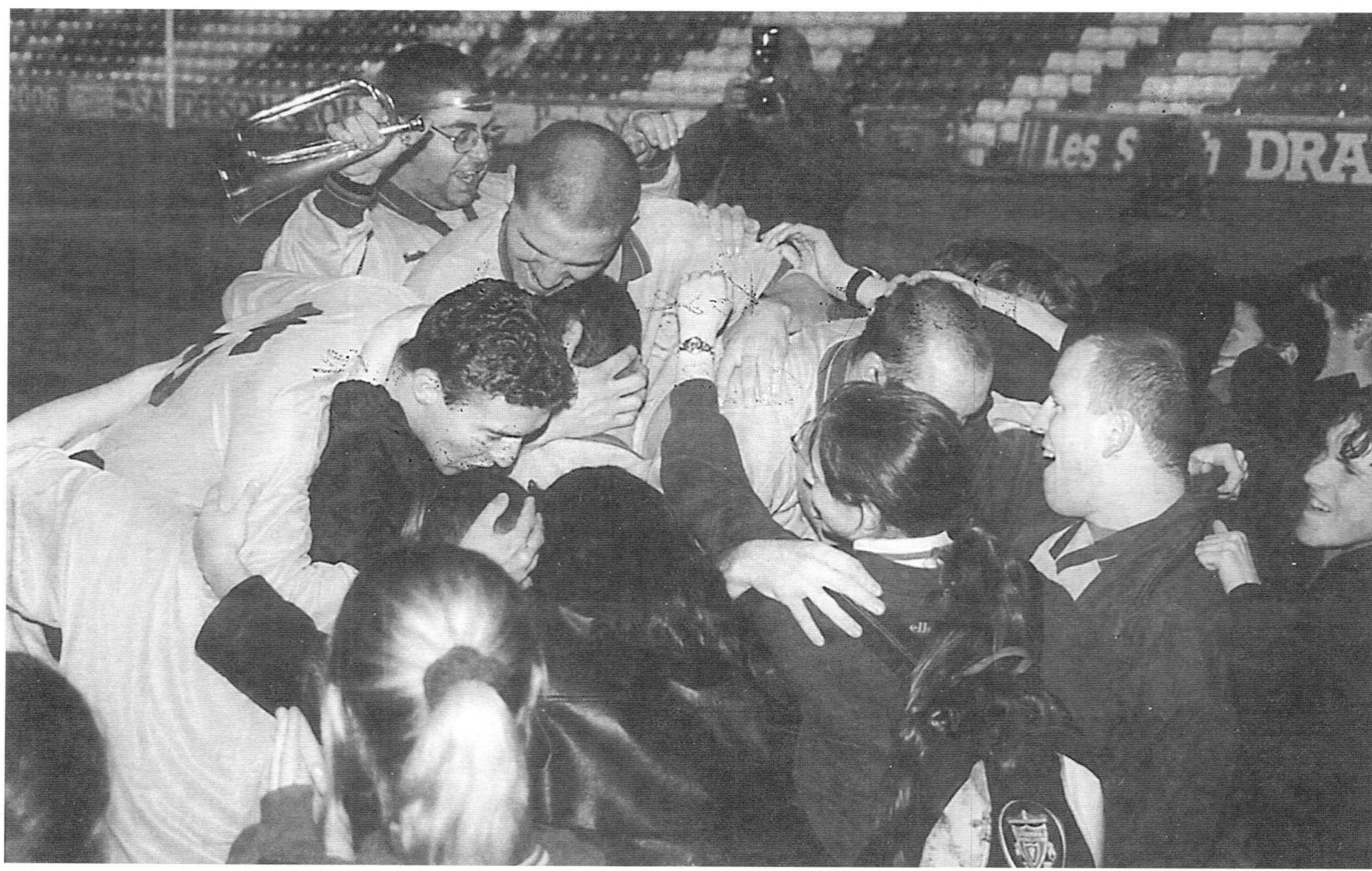

Newport IoW fans and players celebrate their win in the Hampshire Senior Cup at the final whistle. Approximately 400 locals travelled to the mainland to see Newport triumph - their first success in this competition since 1981.

HEREFORDSHIRE F.A.

Secretary: Jim Lambert,
1 Muirfield Close, Holmer, Hereford HR1 1QB
Tel: (H) 01432 270308 (B) 01432 355157

HEREFORDSHIRE SENIOR CUP
(FOUNDED 1973-74)

RECENT FINALS

1992-93	Hinton	v	Westfields	3-1
1993-94	Hinton	v	Pegasus Juniors	1-1 (Rep 3-2)
1994-95	Hinton	v	Pegasus Juniors	4-1
1995-96	Ross Town	v	Westfields	2-2 (2-4 Pns)
1996-97	Bromyard Town	v	Ledbury Town	3-0

1997-98
HEREFORDSHIRE SENIOR CUP

HOLDERS: BROMYARD TOWN

FIRST ROUND

Weston	v	Pegasus Junior	2-5	Bromyard Town	v	Ledbury Town	3-1
Westfields	v	Ross United Services	6-1				

SECOND ROUND

Golden Valley	v	Kington Town	1-3	Hereford Lads Cb	v	Pegasus Juniors	1-4
Civil Service	v	Bromyard Town	2-1	Ross Town	v	Leominster Town	1-0
Hinton	v	Ewyes Harold	2-1	Fownhope	v	Wellington	3-1
Westfields	v	Pencomby	5-1	Sutton United	v	Woofferton	3-1

THIRD ROUND

Kington Town	v	Pegasus Juniors	3-2	Hinton	v	Westfields	2-4
Ross Town	v	Fownhope	1-0	Civil Service	v	Sutton United	1-3

SEMI-FINALS

Ross Town	v	Sutton United	2-0	Westfields	v	Kington Town	1-3

FINAL

KINGTON TOWN	v	ROSS TOWN	2-3	at Edgar Street, Hereford United FC

HERTFORDSHIRE F.A.

Secretary: R G Kibble,

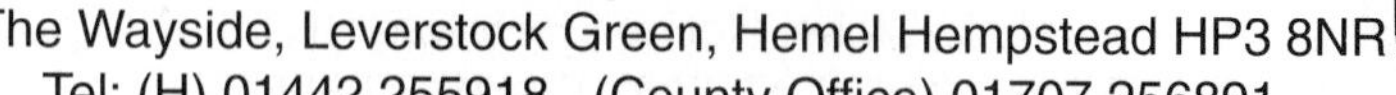

4 The Wayside, Leverstock Green, Hemel Hempstead HP3 8NR

Tel: (H) 01442 255918 (County Office) 01707 256891

HERTFORDSHIRE SENIOR CUP
(FOUNDED 1886-87)

RECENT FINALS

1992-93	Barnet	v	Watford	4-2
1993-94	Watford	v	Stevenage Borough	3-1
1994-95	Watford	v	St Albans City	4-0
1995-96	Barnet	v	Watford	2-1
1996-97	Hitchin Town	v	Boreham Wood	4-1

MOST WINS Hitchin Town 21 Barnet 16 Watford 14

1997-98 HERTFORDSHIRE SENIOR CUP

HOLDERS: HITCHIN TOWN

FIRST ROUND

Hitchin Town	v	Potters Bar Town	4-1	Berkhamsted Town	v	Bishop's Stortford	2-1
Harpenden Town	v	Royston Town	2-1	Cheshunt	v	Barnet	2-4
Welwyn Garden City	v	Hertford Town	1-2	Hemel Hempstead	v	Stevenage Borough	2-4

SECOND ROUND

Sawbridgeworth Tn	v	Hoddesdon Town	0-1	Watford	v	Ware (at Ware)	3-1
Berkhamsted Town	v	Boreham Wood	2-4 aet	Harpenden Town	v	Stevenage Borough	2-1
London Colney	v	Hitchin Town	0-4	Barnet	v	Hertford Town (at HT)	1-0
Letchworth	v	Baldock Town	1-2	St Albans City	v	Tring Town	4-0

THIRD ROUND

Boreham Wood	v	Harpenden Town	5-2	Hoddesdon Town	v	Baldock Town	2-5
Barnet	v	St Albans City	3-0	Watford	v	Hitchin Town	5-2 aet

SEMI-FINALS

Boreham Wood	v	Baldock Town	4-0	Barnet	v	Watford	1-2 aet

FINAL

BOREHAM WOOD v WATFORD 0-1 at Clarence Park, St Albans City FC

1997-98 HERTFORDSHIRE CENTENARY TROPHY

HOLDERS: COLNEY HEATH

FIRST ROUND

Somerset A V&E	v	St Margaretsbury	4-3
Sandbridge Rovers	v	Elliott Star	0-5
Chipperfield Corries	v	Tring Athletic	0-0 aet, 2-1

SECOND ROUND

Kings Langley	v	Wormley R.	2-2 aet, 3-1 aet
Met Police Bushey	v	Sun Postal Sports	1-2
Agrevo Sports	v	Leverstock Green	3-1
Cuffley	v	St Peters	7-1
Benington	v	Elliott Star	4-1
Oxhey Jets	v	Bedmond S & S	0-7
Somerset A V&E	v	Colney Heath	1-2
Bragbury Athletic	v	Ch'field Corinth.	3-3 aet, 0-6

THIRD ROUND

Bedmond S & S	v	Agrevo Sports	1-2
Benington	v	Sun Postal Sports	1-0
Colney Heath	v	Ch'field Corinthians	1-2
Kings Langley	v	Cuffley	1-4

SEMI-FINALS

Agrevo Sports	v	Cuffley	0-3
Chipperfield Cor.	v	Benington	1-2 aet

FINAL

BENINGTON	v	CUFFLEY	2-1	at Wave FC

ADDITIONAL 1997-98 CUP RESULTS

CHARITY CUP

St Albans City	v	Berkhamsted Town	6-0

CHARITY SHIELD

St Margaretsbury	v	London Colney	0-0 aet

(St Margaretsbury won on penalties)

INTERMEDIATE CUP

Greenacres	v	Hatfield Town	3-0

JUNIOR CUP

Bragbury Ath. 'A'	v	Watton-at-Stone	1-0

INTER-LEAGUE CUP

Astral West Herts FL	v	Herts Senior Co FL	5-0

SUNDAY (SENIOR) CUP

St Josephs (S Ox)	v	Tring Park	4-2

SUNDAY (INTERMEDIATE) CUP

Ashwell	v	Hemel Hemp'd Soc	3-2 aet

SUNDAY (JUNIOR) CUP

The Cross '94	v	Michaelians	3-2

SUNDAY (INTER-LEAGUE) CUP

Berkhamsted SFL	v	Stevenage & Dist SFL	2-1

HUNTINGDONSHIRE F.A.

Secretary: Maurice Armstrong,
1 Chapel End, Gt Gidding, Huntingdon
Cambs PE17 5NP Tel: 01832 293262 (County Office)

HUNTINGDONSHIRE SENIOR CUP
(FOUNDED 1888-89)

RECENT FINALS

1992-93	Eynesbury Rovers	v	Warboys Town	4-2
1993-94	Somersham Town	v	Ortonians	1-0
1994-95	Warboys Town	v	Godmanchester Rovers	2-1
1995-96	Eynesbury Rovers	v	Warboys Town	3*2
1996-97	Ortonians	v	Huntingdon United	2-1

MOST WINS St Neots 33 Eynesbury Rovers 12 Huntingdon Town 12

1997-98
HUNTINGDONSHIRE SENIOR CUP

HOLDERS: ORTONIANS

FIRST ROUND

Somersham Town	v	Eynesbury Rovers	2-1
Skilton United	v	Alconbury	1-2
St Neots Town	v	Yaxley	4-1 aet
Buckden	v	Ortonians	1-8
Warboys Town	v	Huntingdon United	4-1 aet
Hotpoint	v	Bluntisham Rangers	1-0
Brampton	v	Godmanchester Rvrs	0-3

SECOND ROUND

Warboys Town	v	Somersham Town	4-2
St Neots Town	v	Alconbury	3-1
Ortonians	v	St Ives Town	2-1
Godmanchester R.	v	Hotpoint	6-2

SEMI-FINALS

St Neots Town	v	Godmanchester Rvrs	2-0
Ortonians	v	Warboys Town	3-1

FINAL

ORTONIANS v ST NEOTS TOWN 0-1 at Somersham FC

KENT F.A.

Secretary: K T Masters,
69 Maidstone Road, Chatham, Kent ME4 6DT
Tel: 01634 843824

KENT SENIOR CUP (FOUNDED 1888-89)

RECENT FINALS

1992-93	Ashford Town	v	Bromley	3-2
1993-94	Margate	v	Dover Athletic	3-2
1994-95	Charlton Athletic	v	Gillingham	4-2
1995-96	Ashford Town	v	Charlton Athletic	3-0
1996-97	Bromley	v	Dover Athletic	4-1

MOST WINS Maidstone United 15 Dartford 9 Northfleet United 9

1997-98 KENT FACIT SENIOR CUP

HOLDERS: BROMLEY

FIRST ROUND

Tonbridge Angels	v	Herne Bay	0-1	Gravesend & N.	v	Sittingbourne	5-0
Margate	v	Fisher Athletic	1-0 aet	Ashford Town	v	Dartford	0-1
Welling United	v	Erith & Belvedere	1-2				

SECOND ROUND

Erith & Belvedere	v	Gravesend & Northfleet	1-2	Margate	v	Dartford	3-0
Bromley	v	Dover Athletic	0-1	Herne Bay	v	Gillingham	1-2

SEMI-FINALS

Gravesend & North.	v	Dover Athletic	3-1	Margate	v	Gillingham	1-0

FINAL

GRAVESEND & N	v	MARGATE	0-1	at Gravesend & Northfleet FC

KENT SENIOR TROPHY (FOUNDED 1874-75)

RECENT FINALS

1992-93	Cray Wanderers	v	Whitstable Town	1-0
1993-94	Alma Swanley	v	Folkestone Invicta	3-1
1994-95	Deal Town	v	Folkestone Invicta	2-2 (5-4 Pns)
1995-96	Dartford	v	Chatham Town	3-0
1996-97	Greenwich Borough	v	Herne Bay	0-2

MOST WINS Alma Swanley 2 Corinthian 2 Faversham Town 2 Fisher Athletic 2 Ramsgate 2

1997-98 KENT PLAAYA SENIOR TROPHY

HOLDERS: HERNE BAY

FIRST ROUND

VCD Athletic	v	Corinthian	3-1	Sheppey United	v	Canterbury City	4-1 aet
Faversham Town	v	Crockenhill	8-1	Knatchbull	v	Thamesmead Town	1-2
Slade Green	v	Lordswood	1-1, 0-2	Tunbridge Wells	v	Chatham Town	0-4
Ramsgate	v	West Wickham	2-0	Whitstable Town	v	Thames Polytechnic	3-2

SECOND ROUND

Cray Wanderers	v	Erith Town	2-1	Greenwich Boro	v	Ramsgate	3-1 aet
Lordswood	v	Whitstable Town	3-4	Folkestone Invicta	v	Chatham Town	1-0
Deal Town	v	Sheppey United	3-1	Hythe United	v	Swanley Furness	0-2
Thamesmead Town	v	VCD Athletic	TT W/O	Faversham Town	v	Beckenham Town	1-3

THIRD ROUND

Faversham Town	v	Whitstable Town	2-3 aet	Deal Town	v	Thamesmead Town	0-4
Folkestone Invicta	v	Swanley Furness	3-1	Greenwich Boro	v	Cray Wanderers	2-2, 3-0

SEMI-FINALS

Folkestone Invicta	v	Thamesmead Town	2-1	Greenwich Boro	v	Whitstable Town	4-0

FINAL

FOLKESTONE INV. v GREENWICH BORO 0-1 at Ashford Town FC

LANCASHIRE F.A.

Founded: 28th September 1878

Hon. Secretary: J Kenyon, ACIS,
Northbank, 31a Wellington Street (St Johns), Blackburn BB1 8AU
Tel: 01254 24433 (County Office) Fax: 01254 260095

LANCASHIRE ATS CHALLENGE TROPHY (FOUNDED 1885-86)

RECENT FINALS

1992-93	Southport	v	Chorley	5-2 (AET)
1993-94	Morecambe	v	Southport	4-3 (AET)
1994-95	Bamber Bridge	v	Morecambe	2-1
1995-96	Morecambe	v	Bamber Bridge	1-0
1996-97	Southport	v	Accrington Stanley	3-0

1997-98 LANCASHIRE ATS TROPHY

HOLDERS: SOUTHPORT

FIRST ROUND

Blackpool Rovers	v	Atherton LR	3-0
Clitheroe	v	Haslingden	3-0
Leigh RMI	v	Marine	1-4
Radcliffe Borough	v	Darwen	2-0
Ramsbottom United	v	Atherton Collieries	2-0
Chorley	v	Holker OB	3-0
Lancaster City	v	Skelmersdale United	2-0
Nelson	v	Castleton Gabriels	0-3
Rossendale Utd	v	Bacup Borough	0-1 aet

SECOND ROUND

Accrington Stanley	v	Great Harwood Town	1-0
Castleton Gabriels	v	Ramsbottom United	0-1
Lancaster City	v	Bacup Borough	3-0
Morecambe	v	Burscough	2-1
Bamber Bridge	v	Blackpool Rovers	5-1
Clitheroe	v	Chorley	0-2 aet
Radcliffe Borough	v	Barrow	0-1
Southport	v	Marine	4-0

THIRD ROUND

Accrington Stanley	v	Ramsbottom United	1-0
Morecambe	v	Bamber Bridge	3-1
Lancaster City	v	Chorley	1-1 aet, 2-1
Southport	v	Barrow	1-0

SEMI-FINALS

Accrington Stanley	v	Southport	0-1
Morecambe	v	Lancaster City	2-0

FINAL

MORECAMBE v SOUTHPORT 0-2 at Deepdale, Preston North End FC

1997-98 LANCASHIRE AMATEUR COUNTY CUP

Merseyside Police v Crawfords UB 2-1 aet

LEICESTERSHIRE & RUTLAND F.A.

Hon. Secretary: Ron Barston,
Holmes Park, Dog & Gun Lane, Whetstone LE8 3LJ
Tel: 0116 288 0312 (Home) 0116 286 7828 (County Office) Fax: 0116 286 7828

LEICESTERSHIRE SENIOR CUP (FOUNDED 1887-88)

RECENT FINALS

1992-93	Friar Lane Old Boys	v	Birstall United	2-1 aet
1993-94	Ibstock Welfare	v	St Andrews SC	2-1
1994-95	Anstey Nomads	v	Holwell Sports	2-0
1995-96	Leicester City	v	St Andrews	2-1
1996-97	Barwell	v	Friar Lane OB	1-0 aet

MOST WINS Leicester City 27 Enderby Town 6 Shepshed Dynamo 6

1997-98 LEICESTERSHIRE 'JELSON HOMES' SENIOR CUP

HOLDERS: BARWELL

FIRST ROUND

Asfordby Amateur	v	Bardon Hill Sports	0-3	Barlestone St Giles	v	United Collieries	1-3
Fosse Imps	v	North Kilworth	3-2	Hemington	v	Anstey Nomads	AN W/O
Huncote S & S	v	Slack & Parr	6-0	Narborough & L'pe	v	Friar Lane OB	0-5
Oadby Town	v	Cottesmore Amateurs	4-2	Stoney Stanton	v	Downes Sprts	3-3 aet, 1-3
Syston St Peters	v	Earl Shitlon Albion	E W/O	Thurnby Rangers	v	St Andrews	2-1

SECOND ROUND

Anstey Nomads	v	Sileby Town	3-1	Aylestone Pk OB	v	Birstall United	1-4
Bardon HIll Sports	v	Highfield Rangers	2-3	Barwell	v	Thringstone MW	4-1
Blaby & Whetstone	v	Leics Constabulary	4-2	Castle Donington T	v	Huncote S & S	1-8
Coalville	v	Ibstock Welf.	0-0 aet, 0-1	Downes Sports	v	Leicester YMCA	3-2
Earl Shilton Albion	v	Friar Lane OB	1-6	Harborough T Imp	v	Fosse Imps	0-3
Kirby Muxloe	v	Anstey town	4-1	Loughborough D.	v	Oadby Town	0-6
Lutterworth Town	v	Barrow Town	0-3	Saffron Dynamo	v	Thurnby Rangers	1-0
United Collieries	v	Quorn	1-3	Holwell Sports	v	Newfoundpool	HS W/O

THIRD ROUND

Barrow Town	v	Oadby Town	1-6	Highfield Rangers	v	Fosse Imps	4-1*
Barwell	v	Holwell Sports	4-2	Kirby Muxloe	v	Friar Lane OB	2-4 aet
Blaby & Whetstone	v	Downes Sports	2-0	Birstall United	v	Huncote S & S	6-1
Saffron Dynamo	v	Ibstock Welfare	1-2	Anstey Nomads	v	Quorn	4-4 aet, 0-1

*Highfield Rangers disqualified, Fosse Imps re-instated

FOURTH ROUND

Friar Lane OB	v	Oadby Town	0-0 aet, rep	Blaby & Whet.	v	Ibstock Welfare	0-2
Barwell	v	Fosse Imps	5-2	Quorn	v	Birstall United	0-3

SEMI-FINALS

Friar Lane/Oadby T	v	Ibstock Welfare	0-1	Barwell	v	Birstall United	1-2 aet

FINAL

BIRSTALL UTD v IBSTOCK W. 4p3, 1-1 aet at Holmes Park, Whetstone, Leics FA

1997-98 LEICESTERSHIRE WESTERBY CHALLENGE CUP

HOLDERS: ST ANDREWS

FIRST ROUND

Hinckley United	v	Oadby Town	5-2	Anstey Nomads	v	Cottesmore Amateurs	0-4
Ibstock Welfare	v	Downes Sports	0-0, 2-0	Friar Lane OB	v	Birstall United	1-2

SECOND ROUND

Birstall United	v	Barwell	5-3	Leicester City	v	Cottesmore Amateurs	2-1
St Andrews	v	Shepshed Dynamo	1-2	Hinckley United	v	Ibstock Welfare	1-3

SEMI-FINALS

Leicester City	v	Birstall United	3-1	Shepshed D'mo	v	Ibstock Welfare	3-2

FINAL

LEICESTER CITY v SHEPSHED D'MO 6-1 at Filbert Street, Leicester City FC

LINCOLNSHIRE F.A.

Hon. Secretary: Mr John Griffin,
PO Box 26, 12 Dean Road, Lincoln LN2 4DP
Tel: 01522 524917 (County Office) Fax: 01522 528859

LINCOLNSHIRE SENIOR CUP
(FOUNDED 1935-36)

RECENT WINNERS

1992-93	Grimsby Town
1993-94	Grimsby Town
1994-95	Grimsby Town
1995-96	Grimsby Town
1996-97	Scunthorpe United

MOST WINS Grimsby Town 13 Lincoln City 12 Boston United 5

1997-98
LINCOLNSHIRE SENIOR CUP

HOLDERS: SCUNTHORPE UNITED

FIRST ROUND

Gainsborough Trinity	v	Grantham Town	0-1
Lincoln United	v	Boston United	5-1
Scunthorpe United	v	Lincoln City	1-2

SEMI-FINALS

Lincoln City	v	Grimsby Town	3-1
Lincoln United	v	Grantham Town	3-0

FINAL

LINCOLN CITY v LINCOLN UNITED 2-0 at Sincil Bank, Lincoln City FC

LINCOLNSHIRE SENIOR 'A' CUP
(FOUNDED 1968-69)

RECENT FINALS

1992-93	Mirrlees Blackstone	v	Bourne Town	1-1 aet
1993-94	Brigg Town	v	Lincoln United	5-2
1994-95	Holbeach United	v	Boston Town	1-0
1995-96	Lincoln United	v	Boston Town	2*1
1996-97	Louth United	v	Nettleham	0-2

MOST WINS Boston Town 6 Holbeach United 4 Skegness Town 4

1997-98
LINCOLNSHIRE SENIOR 'A' CUP

HOLDERS: NETTLEHAM

PRELIMINARY ROUND

Winterton Rangers	v	Holbeach United	3-0
Brigg Town	v	Boston Town	1-2

FIRST ROUND

Boston Town	v	Nettleham	2-2 aet, 5-2
Mirrlees Blackstone	v	Stamford AFC	3-4 aet
Spalding United	v	Bourne Town	4-1 aet
Louth United	v	Winterton Rangers	0-1

SEMI-FINALS

Stamford AFC	v	Boston Town	3-1
Winterton Rangers	v	Spalding United	0-3

FINAL

SPALDNG UNITED v STAMFORD AFC 3p4, 1-1aet at Stamford AFC

LINCOLNSHIRE SENIOR 'B' CUP
(FOUNDED 1949-50)

RECENT FINALS

1992-93	Appleby Frod Ath	v	Humberside United	1-1 (11-10 P)
1993-94	Wyberton	v	Hykeham Town	2-2 (4-1 Pns)
1994-95	Immingham Blos Way	v	Limestone Rangers	3-0
1995-96	Appleby Frod Ath	v	Barton Old Boys	0-2
1996-97	Lincoln Moorlands	v	Lymstone Rangers	4-0

MOST WINS Brigg Town 5 Appleby Frodingham Athletic 4

1997-98
LINCOLNSHIRE SENIOR 'B' CUP

HOLDERS: LINCOLN MOORLANDS

FIRST ROUND

Lincoln Moorlands	v	Epworth Town	4-0	Appleby Frod. Ath	v	Barton Town OB	1-4
Grimsby-I Amateurs	v	Hykeham Town	6-1	Lymestone Rngrs	v	Wyberton	0-2
Ruston Sports	v	Sleaford Town	1-3	Deeping Rangers	v	Skegness Town	2-0
Harrowby Town	v	Horncastle Town	2-1	Bottesford Town	v	Louth Old Boys	BT W/O

SECOND ROUND

Bottesford Town	v	Sleaford Town	1-1, 0-1	Harrowby United	v	G-Imminham Amat.	2-1
Wyberton	v	Barton Town OB	5-2	Lincoln Moorlands	v	Deeping Rangers	3-0

SEMI-FINALS

Sleaford Town	v	Wyberton	2-0	Lincoln Moorlands	v	Harrowby United	2-0

FINAL

SLEAFORD TOWN v LINCOLN M'LANDS 2-1 at Sincil Bank, Lincoln City FC

LIVERPOOL F.A.

Secretary: Fred Hunter

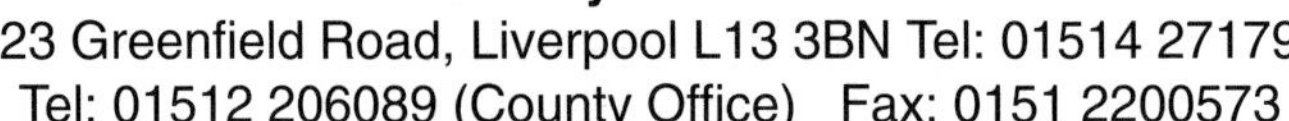

23 Greenfield Road, Liverpool L13 3BN Tel: 01514 27179
Tel: 01512 206089 (County Office) Fax: 0151 2200573

LIVERPOOL SENIOR CUP
(FOUNDED 1977-78)

RECENT FINALS

1992-93	Southport	v	Burscough	2-1
1993-94	Marine	v	Southport	2-1
1994-95	Tranmere Rovers	v	Marine	2-0 aet
1995-96	Everton	v	Tranmere Rovers	
1996-97	Tranmere Rovers	v	Everton	

MOST WINS Marine 5 Liverpool 3 South Liverpool 3

1997-98
LIVERPOOL SENIOR CUP

HOLDERS: EVERTON

FIRST ROUND

Marine	v	Bootle	2-1	St Helens Town	v	Warrington Town	3-1
Skelmersdale Utd	v	Prescot Cables	0-3				

SECOND ROUND

Burscough	v	Tranmere Rovers	3-2	Everton	v	Prestoct Cables (at P)	1-4
Marine	v	Liverpool	0-4	Southport	v	St Helens Town	4-2

SEMI-FINALS

Burscough	v	Prescot Cables	2-1 aet	Southport	v	Liverpool	2-3 aet

FINAL

BURSCOUGH V LIVERPOOL Awaiting details

ADDITIONAL 1997-98 CUP RESULTS

LIVERPOOL CHALLENGE CUP
Manweb v Plessey GPT 1-0 aet
at Maghull FC

LIVERPOOL INTERMEDIATE CUP
The Anchor v Clifton
at Liverpool Nalgo FC

WIRRAL AMATEUR CUP
New Brighton v Heswall Reserves 2-1
at Ashville FC

LIVERPOOL JUNIOR CUP
Child v Beeches 3-1
at Prescot Cables FC

WIRRAL SENIOR CUP
Heswall v Poulton Victoria 4-2
at Cammell Laird FC

RUNCORN SENIOR CUP
Bridge Athletic v Mond Rangers 1-0
at Runcorn FC

LONDON F.A.

Secretary: David Fowkes,
Aldworth Grove, Lewisham, London SE13 6HY
Tel: 0181 690 9626 (County Office) Fax: 0181 690 9471

LONDON CHALLENGE CUP
(ORIGINAL COMPETITION FOUNDED 1908)

RECENT FINALS

1992-93	Leyton Orient	v	Barnet	3-2
1993-94	Uxbridge	v	Welling United	3-0
1994-95	St Albans City	v	Fisher Athletic	6-0
1995-96	Bromley	v	Leyton Pennant	3-2 aet
1996-97	Uxbridge	v	Leyton Pennant	3-3, 1-0

1997-98
LONDON CHALLENGE CUP

16 CLUBS **HOLDERS: UXBRIDGE**

FIRST ROUND

Bromley	v	Boreham Wood	0-2 aet	Hendon	v	Croydon	5-1
Fisher Athletic	v	Tooting & Mitcham	5-0	St Albans City	v	Welling United	1-2
Erith & Belvedere	v	Romford	1-2	Uxbridge	v	Hampton	2-1
Dulwich Hamlet	v	Metropolitan Police	1-0	Barking	v	Leyton Pennant	1-3

SECOND ROUND

Fisher Athletic	v	Boreham Wood	1-4	Dulwich Hamlet	v	Leyton Pennant	2-1
Welling United	v	Romford	2-1	Uxbridge	v	Hendon	3-1

SEMI-FINALS

Uxbridge	v	Welling United	2-1 aet	Boreham Wood	v	Dulwich Hamlet	5-1

FINAL

BOREHAM WOOD v UXBRIDGE 3-1 at Dulwich Hamlet FC

LONDON SENIOR CUP
(FOUNDED 1882)

RECENT FINALS

1992-93	Hanwell Town	v	Croydon Athletic	4-3
1993-94	Ford United	v	Hanwell Town	2-1
1994-95	Wingate & Finchley	v	Tower Hamlets	4-3
1995-96	Tottenham Omada	v	Kingsbury Town	2-1
1996-97	Barkingside	v	Hillingdon Borough	2-0

1997-98
LONDON SENIOR CUP

25 CLUBS **HOLDERS: BARKINGSIDE**

FIRST ROUND

Hillingdon Boro	v	Brimsdown Rovers	2-3
Ford United	v	Ilford	3-1
Croydon Athletic	v	Wingate & Finchley	3-4 aet
Islington St Marys	v	Thames Polytechnic	3-0
Cray Wanderers	v	Cockfosters	2-0
East Ham United	v	Erith Town	1-0
Haringey Boro	v	Clapton	3-4
Thamesmead Tn	v	Bedfont	1-0
Corinthian Casuals	v	Kingsbury Town	2-1

SECOND ROUND

Ford United	v	Brimsdown Rovers	1-0
East Ham United	v	Waltham Abbey	0-3
Barkingside	v	Corinthian Cas.	0-0 aet, 4p5
Clapton	v	Hanwell Town	0-1
Civil Service	v	Islington St Marys	2-1
Hoddesdon Town	v	Thamesmead Town	7-1
Wingate & Finch.	v	Cray Wanderers	1-2
Southall	v	Woodford Tn	2-2 aet, 5p4

THIRD ROUND

Ford United	v	Corinthian Casuals	3-1
Waltham Abbey	v	Hoddesdon Town	5-3
Southall	v	Cray Wanderers	2-1
Hanwell Town	v	Civil Service	4-3

SEMI-FINALS

Southall	v	Hanwell Town	6-1
Waltham Abbey	v	Ford United	0-3

FINAL

FORD UNITED v SOUTHALL 2-0 at Hendon FC

ADDITIONAL 1997-98 CUP RESULTS

LFA INTERMEDIATE CUP
Little Heath Athletic v Ten-Em-Bee & Elms (L) 2-1
at Ford United FC

LFA JUNIOR CUP
CMB (Metal Box) v Victoria 1-0
at Dulwich Hamlet FC

LFA SUNDAY JUNIOR CUP
AC Italia v Notre Dame 0-2
at Wingate & Finchley FC

LFA WOMEN'S CUP
Arsenal Ladies v Millwall Lionesses 1-2 aet
at Croydon Athletic FC

LFA MIDWEEK CUP
Crown & Manor v St George's PHG 9-1
at Metropolitan Police FC

LFA SUNDAY INTERMEDIATE CUP
AFC Saxon v Binatli Yilmaz Spor 2-4 aet
at Dulwich Hamlet FC

LFA SUNDAY CHALLENGE CUP
Continental v Omonia 0-1
at Wingate & Finchley FC

MANCHESTER F.A.

Secretary: Philip Smith,
Sports Complex, Branthingham Road, Chorlton, Manchester M21 1TG
Tel: 01618 810299 (County Office) Fax: 01618 816833

MANCHESTER PREMIER CUP (FOUNDED 1979-80)

RECENT FINALS

1992-93	Droylsden	v	Curzon Ashton	2-0 aet
1993-94	Hyde United	v	Droylsden	4-1
1994-95	Hyde United	v	Trafford	2-1
1995-96	Hyde United	v	Curzon Ashton	2*2 4p3
1996-97	Glossop North End	v	Trafford	1*1 5p3

MOST WINS Curzon Ashton 5 Ashton United 3 Droylsden 2 Hyde United 2 Mossley 2

1997-98 MANCHESTER PREMIER CUP

HOLDERS: GLOSSOP NORTH END

FIRST ROUND

Hyde United	v	Salford City	1-2
Droylsdon	v	Mossley	0-1
Glossop North End	v	Maine Road	3-0
Trafford	v	Buxton	0-0 aet, 0-2
Curzon Ashton	v	Chadderton	2-0
Castleton Gabriels	v	Flixton	1-2
Ashton United	v	Radcliffe Borough	1-2
Oldham Town bye			

SECOND ROUND

Oldham Town	v	Radcliffe Borough	0-1
Flixton	v	Buxton	1-0
Glossop Nth End	v	Salford City	8-0
Curzon Ashton	v	Mossley	3-1

SEMI-FINALS

Curzon Ashton	v	Radcliffe Borough	1-2 aet
Glossop Nth End	v	Flixton	2-1

FINAL

GLOSSOP NTH END v RADCLIFFE BORO 1-0 at Maine Road, Manchester City FC

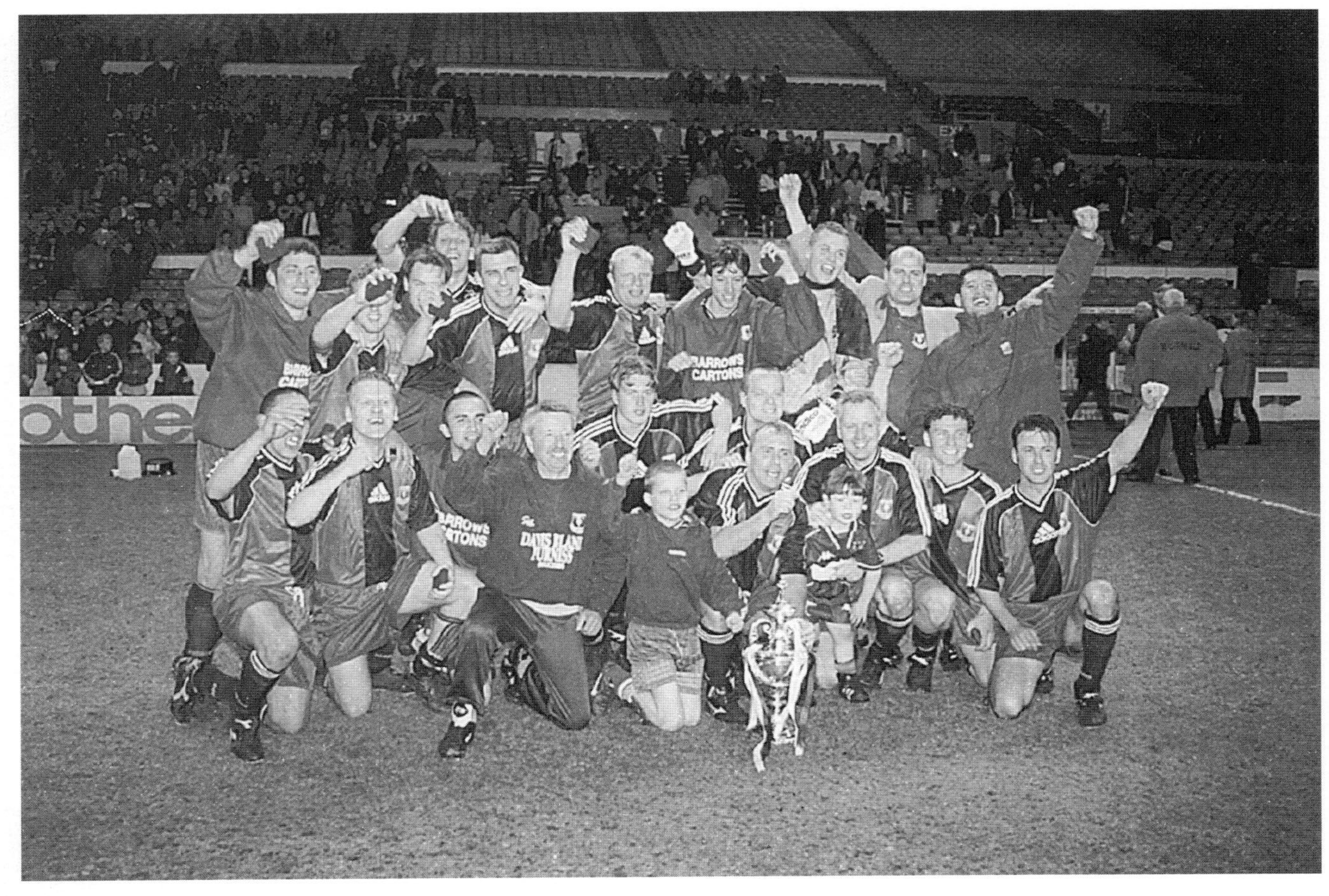

Glossop North End with the Manchester Premier Cup at Maine Road

Photo: John L Newton

MIDDLESEX F.A.

Secretary: Peter Clayton,
39 Roxborough Road, Harrow, Middlesex HA1 1NS
Tel: 01814 248524 Fax: 0181 862062 (County Office)

MIDDLESEX SENIOR CHARITY CUP (FOUNDED 1901-02)

RECENT FINALS

1992-93	Harrow Borough	v	Hanwell Town	3-1 aet
1993-94	Staines Town	v	Northwood	4-0
1994-95	Wembley	v	Hampton	2-0
1995-96	Hampton	v	Ruislip Manor	3-2
1996-97	Edgware Town	v	Wembley	1-0 aet

MOST WINS Wealdstone 11 Hayes 10 Southall 10

1997-98 MIDDLESEX SENIOR CHARITY CUP

HOLDERS: EDGWARE TOWN

FIRST ROUND

Potters Bar Town	v	Hanwell Town	2-0	Kingsbury Town	v	Beaconsfield SYCOB	3-1
Waltham Abbey	v	Cockfosters	2-1	Harefield United	v	Hillingdon Borough	1-3
Hayes	v	Feltham	3-1	Amersham Town	v	Southall	0-2
Ruislip Manor	v	Brook House	0-2 aet	Bedfont	v	Brimsdown Rovers	4-3

SECOND ROUND

Ashford Town	v	Kingsbury Town	10-0	Hillingdon Boro	v	Waltham Abbey	1-5
Potters Bar Town	v	Brook House	1-0	Wembley	v	Southall	5-2
Edgware Town	v	Bedfont	3-2	Uxbridge	v	Northwood	3-0
Hayes	v	Staines Town	4-0 aet	Hampton	v	Wealdstone	3-1

QUARTER-FINALS

Edgware Town	v	Waltham Abbey	1-3	Ashford Town	v	Hayes	2-7
Wembley	v	Potters Bar Town	1-0	Uxbridge	v	Hampton	0-0 aet, 6p7

SEMI-FINALS

Hayes	v	Waltham Abbey	1-3	Wembley	v	Hampton	0-2

FINAL

WALTHAM ABBEY	v	HAMPTON	1-2	at Uxbridge FC

MIDDLESEX SENIOR CUP
(FOUNDED 1888-89)

RECENT FINALS

1992-93	Harrow Borough	v	Wembley	1-0
1993-94	Staines Town	v	Edgware Town	2-1
1994-95	Yeading	v	Staines Town	2-0
1995-96	Hayes	v	Hampton	3-2
1996-97	Staines Town	v	Yeading	0-0, 6p5

MOST WINS Enfield 13 Southall 12 Wealdstone 11

1997-98
MIDDLESEX SENIOR CUP

HOLDERS: STAINES TOWN

PRELIMINARY ROUND

Waltham Abbey	v	Potters Bar Town	2-1
Cockfosters	v	Ruislip Manor (at RM)	1-2
Harefield United	v	Viking Sports	2-1
Brimsdown Rovers	v	Kingsbury Tn (at KT)	3-1

FIRST ROUND

Feltham	v	Wembley	0-4
Ruislip Manor	v	Harefield United	1-2
Brook House	v	Bedfont	5-0
Hillingdon Borough	v	Hanwell Town	6-0
Southall	v	Waltham Abbey	1-2
Brimsdown Rvrs	v	Wingate & Finchley	4-0
Wealdstone	v	Ashford Town	1-4 aet
Hendon	v	Northwood	3-1

SECOND ROUND

Hayes	v	Edgware Town	5-3
Staines Town	v	Harrow Boro	2-2 aet, 1-2
Yeading	v	Uxbridge	1-3
Enfield	v	Hendon	3-0
Brook House	v	Ashford Town	1-2
Brimsdown Rvrs	v	Harefield United	BR W/O
Waltham Abbey	v	Hillingdon Boro	3-1
Wembley	v	Hampton	0-3

QUARTER-FINALS

Enfield	v	Hayes	1-1 aet, 1-0
Uxbridge	v	Waltham Abbey	4-1
Harrow Borough	v	Brimsdown Rvrs (2A0)	8-1
Hampton	v	Ashford Tn	1-1 aet, 2-1 aet

SEMI-FINALS

Hampton	v	Enfield	0-1
Harrow Borough	v	Uxbridge	1-2

FINAL

ENFIELD	v	UXBRIDGE	3-2	at Claremont Road, Hendon FC

MIDLAND INVITATION CUP

RECENT FINALS

1994-95	Blakenall	v	Shifnal Town	1-1, 4-3 p
1995-96	Pelsall Villa	v	Oldbury United	1-0
1996-97	Oldbury United	v	Bridgnorth Town	2-1

1997-98
INTERLINK EXPRESS MIDLAND INVITATION CUP

HOLDERS: OLDBURY UNITED

FIRST ROUND

Evesham United	v	Gornal Ath.	2-2 aet, 7p6
Hinckley United	v	Knypersley Victoria	2-0
Rocester	v	Sandwell Borough	6-0
Stourbridge	v	Moor Green	S W/O
Handrahan T'bers	v	Bridgnorth Town	2-3
Kington Town	v	Halesowen Harriers	6-2
Stapenhill	v	Walsall Wood	2-1
Worcester City	v	Bolehall Swifts	5-1

SECOND ROUND

Anstey Nomads	v	Kirby Muxloe	2-4
Aylestone Park OB	v	Chasetown	0-2
Barwell	v	Ludlow Town	3-1
Birstall	v	Alvechurch	6-1
Bloxwich Strollers	v	Stafford Town	0-2
Boldmere St Micheal	v	Shifnal Town	3-2
Coleshill Town	v	Stourbridge	1-2
Dudley Sports	v	Friar Lane OB	1-3
HInckley United	v	Bustleholme	5-1
Lye Town	v	Ettingshall HT	1-1 aet, 5-3p
Oadly Town	v	Hednesford Town	1-3
Paget Rangers	v	Cradley Town	9-0
Pershore Town	v	Worcester Athletico	1-4
Stafford Rangers	v	Rocester	2-0
Tividale	v	Evesham United	1-2
Wolverhampton Cas	v	St Andrews	0-2
Atherstone Utd	v	Kings Heath	4-0
Barrow Town	v	Meir KA	1-3
Bilston CC	v	Holwell Sports	1-0
Blakenall	v	Lutterworth Town	3-2
Bloxwich Town	v	Bromsgrove Rovers	6-0
Bridgnorth Town	v	Studley BKL	5-2
Continental Star	v	Cheslyn Hay	3-5
Highgate United	v	Massey Ferguson	1-2
Kings Norton Tn	v	Kington	KNT W/O
Malvern Town	v	Stratford Town	3-1
Oldbury United	v	Ibstock Welfare	1-3
Pelsall Villa	v	Rushall Olympic	1-0
Solihull Borough	v	West Midlands Police	3-0
Stapenhill	v	Willenhall	1-0
Wednesfield	v	Shepshed D.	1-1 aet, 5-4p
Worcester City	v	Stouport Swifts	5-1

THIRD ROUND

Cheslyn Hay	v	Kings Norton	0-2
Stapenhill	v	Blakenall	3-4 aet
Meir KA	v	Malvern Town	MKA W/O
Kirby Muxloe	v	Ibstock Welfare	1-2
Paget Rangers	v	Barwell	0-2
Worcester Athletico	v	Stafford Rangers	1-2
Hednesford	v	Boldmere St Michael	3-2
Lye Town	v	Wednesfield	0-0 aet, 4-5p
Pelsall Villa	v	Birstall	1-2 aet
Bilston CC	v	Bridgnorth Town	4-2
Stratford Town	v	Massey Ferguson	3-1
St Andrews	v	Friar Lane OB	1-2
Atherstone Utd	v	Bloxwich Tn	1-1 aet, 5-4p
Chasetown	v	Solihull Borough	0-1
Evesham United	v	Hinckley United	0-3
Worcester City	v	Stourbridge	1-2

FOURTH ROUND

Birstall United	v	Wednesfield	2-1
Meir KA	v	Ibstock Welfare	1-0
Stourbridge	v	Bilston CC	1-4
Hednesford Town	v	Solihull Borough	2-1
Hinckley United	v	Atherstone U	1-1 aet, 1-2p
Barwell	v	Blakenall	0-2
Stafford Rangers	v	Friar Lane OB	3-2
Stafford Town	v	Kings Norton Town	1-2 aet

FIFTH ROUND

Atherstone United	v	Stafford Rangers	4-0
Birstall United	v	Hednesford Town	BU W/O
Blakenall	v	Bilston CC	2-1
Meir KA	v	Kings Norton Town	1-0

SEMI-FINALS

Blakenall	v	Birstall United	3-1 aet
Meir KA	v	Atherstone U	2-2 aet, 2-4p

FINAL

BLAKENALL v ATHERSTONE UTD 0-1 at Oldbury United FC, Att: 190

NORFOLK F.A.

Secretary: Roger Howlett,
153 Middletons Lane, Hellesdon, Norwich NR6 5SF
Tel: 01603 717177

NORFOLK SENIOR CUP
(FOUNDED 1881-82)

RECENT FINALS

1992-93	Wroxham	v	Watton United	3-0
1993-94	Fakenham Town	v	King's Lynn	4-0
1994-95	Fakenham Town	v	Gorleston	2-1
1995-96	Diss Town	v	Wroxham	4-0
1996-97	Wroxham	v	Diss Town	4-1

MOST WINS King's Lynn 19 Great Yarmouth Town 14 Gorleston 13

1997-98
NORFOLK SENIOR CUP

HOLDERS: WROXHAM

FIRST ROUND

Wortwell	v	Scole United	0-2	North Walsham Tn	v	Coltishall HV	3-1
Loddon United	v	Poringland Wanderers	1-3	Mulbarton United	v	Newton Flotman	7-0
Mattishall	v	Town Hall Scripts	0-3	Anglian Windows	v	Lakeford Rangers	6-2

SECOND ROUND

Anglian Windows	v	Town Hall Scripts	0-2	Stalham Town	v	Attleborough Town	1-5
Thorpe Village	v	Mulbarton United	1-2	St Andrews	v	Acle United	4-2
Thelford Town	v	Swaffham Tn	2-2 aet, 2-4	Downham Town	v	Dereham Town	0-2
Scole United	v	P'land W.	0-0aet 2-2aet 1-3p	Norwich United	v	North Walsham	4-3
Cromer United	v	Wymondham Town	6-0	Blofield United	v	Horsfield United	8-0

THIRD ROUND

Great Yarmouth Tn	v	Gorleston	2-0	Cromer United	v	Dereham Town	3-1
Fakenham Town	v	Poringland Wndrs	7-0	Mulbarton United	v	Attleborough Town	1-3
Town Hall Scripts	v	Watton United	1-4	Norwich United	v	Swaffham Town	1-2
Wroxham	v	Diss Town	2-1	Blofield United	v	St Andrews	3-2

QUARTER-FINALS

Wroxham	v	Watton United	0-0 aet, 7-0	Gt Yarmouth Tn	v	Fakenham Town	1-2 aet
Cromer United	v	Swaffham Town	1-3	Attleborough Tn	v	Blofield Ut	1-1 aet, 0-1 aet

SEMI-FINALS

Swaffham Town	v	Blofield U	2-2aet 0-0aet 4-3p	Fakenham Town	v	Wroxham	0-2

FINAL

SWAFFHAM TOWN v WROXHAM 1-3 at Carrow Road, Norwich City FC

Above: Swaffham Town's Robbie Back (black and white stripes with ball) in Norfolk Senior Cup semi-final action against Blofield United. The Pedlars needed a penalty shoot-out victory in a replay against their Lovewell Blake Anglian Combination opponents to earn their first Senior Cup final appearance.

Photo: Lynn News/Citizen Newspapers

Below left: Fakenham Town's Mark Howard (centre) burst through the Wroxham defence at Clipbush Park. But it proved to be in vain for the former Manchester City and Stockport County player whose side lost their Norfolk Senior Cup semi-final.

Photo: Lynn News/Citizen Newspapers

Below right: Norfolk Senior Cup fourth round - Cromer United 1 Swaffham Town 3. First-half action from Cabbets Park as Cromer defend their goal.

Photo: Martin Wray

NORTHAMPTONSHIRE F.A.

Secretary: Brian Walden,
2 Duncan Close, Red House Road, Moulton Park, Northampton NN3 6WL
Tel: 01604 670741 (County Office) Fax: 01604 670742

NORTHAMPTONSHIRE SENIOR CUP
(FOUNDED 1883-84)

RECENT FINALS

1992-93	Kettering Town	v	Rushden & Diamonds	2-1
1993-94	Rushden & Diamonds	v	Northampton Spencer	5-0
1994-95	Kettering Town	v	Rushden & Diamonds	2-2
			(Rep 2-2, 3-1 Pens)	
1995-96	Rothwell Town	v	Rushden & Diamonds	1-0
1996-97	Kettering Town	v	Ford Sports	3-1 aet

MOST WINS Kettering Town 29 Northampton Town 11 Peterborough United 11

1997-98
NORTHAMPTONSHIRE 'HILLIER' SENIOR CUP

HOLDERS: KETTERING TOWN

FIRST ROUND

Ford Sports	v	Corby Town	1-0	Desborough Tn	v	Brackley Tn	1-1 aet, 0-2
Raunds Town	v	Cogenhoe	6-2	Stewart & Lloyds	v	Long Buckby	1-2
Wellingborough Tn	v	Northampton S.	2-2 aet, 1-0				

SECOND ROUND

Brackley Town	v	Rushden & Diamonds	1-3	Raunds Town	v	Daventry Ford Sports	4-1
Kettering Town	v	Wellingborough Town	1-0	Rothwell Town	v	Long Buckby	2-3

SEMI-FINALS

Rushden & Dia.	v	Raunds Town	0-1	Kettering Town	v	Long Buckby	0-0 aet, 7-1

FINAL

KETTERING TOWN v RAUNDS TOWN 1-0 at Rockingham Road, Kettering Town FC

NORTHUMBERLAND F.A.

Secretary: Roland Maughan,
Seymour House, 10 Brenkley Way, Blezard Business Pk, Seaton Burn, Newcastle NE13 6DT
Tel: 0191 236 8020

NORTHUMBERLAND SENIOR CUP
(FOUNDED 1883-84)

RECENT FINALS

1992-93	Newcastle Blue Star	v	Newcastle Utd Reserves	2-1
1993-94	Blyth Spartans	v	Newcastle Blue Star	1-0
1994-95	Blyth Spartans	v	Newcastle Utd Reserves	6-2
1995-96	Newcastle United	v	Blyth Spartans	3-0
1996-97	Bedlington Terriers	v	Morpeth Town	2-0

MOST WINS Blyth Spartans 21 Newcastle United 19 North Shields 12

1997-98
NORTHUMBERLAND SENIOR CUP

HOLDERS: BEDLINGTON TERRIERS

FIRST ROUND

Newcastle Utd Res.	v	Lemington Social Utd	7-1	Alnwick town	v	RTM Newcastle	4-0
Blyth Spartans	v	Ashington	3-2	West Allot. Celtic	v	Ponteland United	1-4

SECOND ROUND

Whitley Bay	v	Newcastle U Rs 2-2 aet,	2-0	Morpeth Town	v	Bedlington Terriers	0-3
Prudhoe Town	v	Ponteland United	0-2	Blyth Spartans	v	Alnwick Town	2-0

SEMI-FINALS

Whitley Bay	v	Blyth Spartans 0-2 (V),	0-2	Bedlington Terriers	v	Ponteland United	2-0

FINAL

BEDLINGTON TER. v BLYTH SPARTANS 2-0 at St James' Park, Newcastle United FC

NORTHUMBERLAND BENEVOLENT BOWL
(FOUNDED 1975-76)

RECENT FINALS

1992-93	West Allot Celtic	v	Walker	4-3
1993-94	Spittal Rovers	v	Longbenton	1-1 (Rep 2-1)
1994-95	Westerhope	v	North Shields St Columbas	2-0
1995-96	Haltwhistle	v	Ponteland United	1-2
1996-97	Leamington United	v	Ponteland United	1-1 (Rep1-0)

MOST WINS Morpeth Town 2 Stobswood Welfare 2

1997-98
NORTHUMBERLAND BENEVOLENT BOWL

HOLDERS: LEAMINGTON UNITED

FIRST ROUND

North Shields Ath	v	Amble Town	3-4	Shankhouse	v	Haltwhistle C-P	S W/O
Newbiggin Central	v	Walker Central	3-1	Gosforth Bohem.	v	N/C Benfield Park	1-2

SECOND ROUND

Newbiggin Central	v	Seaton Delaval Am	0-2	NS St Columbas	v	Walker Ledwood Fosse	2-1
Shankhouse	v	Amble Town	1-2	N/C Benfield Park	v	Spittal Rovers	2-1

SEMI-FINALS

Seaton Delaval Ams	v	NS St Columbas	3-0	N/C Benfield Park	v	Amble Town	0-3

FINAL

N/C BENFIELD PK	v	SEATON DEL. AM.	1-3 aet	at Craik Park, Morpeth Town FC
N/C BENFIELD PK	v	SEATON DEL. AM.	2-4 aet	Replayed (due to ineligible player)

NORTH RIDING F.A.

Secretary: Mark Jarvis,
284 Linthorpe Road, Middlesborough TS1 3QU
Tel: 01642 224585

NORTH RIDING SENIOR CUP
(FOUNDED 1881-82)

RECENT FINALS

1991-92	Scarborough	v	Guisborough Town	3-2 (AET)
1992-93	Guisborough Town	v	Rowntrees	2-0
1993-94	Guisborough Town	v	Pickering Town	2-0
1994-95	Marske United	v	Pickering Town	5-2
1996-97	Middlesbrough	v	York City	3-1

MOST WINS Middlesbrough 46 Scarborough 17 South Bank 8 Stockton 8

1997-98
NORTH RIDING SENIOR CUP

HOLDERS: MIDDLESBROUGH

FIRST PRELIMINARY ROUND

York RI	v	South Bank	5-3
Richmond Town	v	Fishburn Park	2-0
Stokesley SC	v	Tees Components	1-5
Grangetown BC	v	New Marske SC	5-0

SECOND PRELIMINARY ROUND

Tees Components	v	York RI	1-2
Grangetown BC	v	Richmond Town	2-0

FIRST QUALIFYING ROUND

Grangetown BC	v	Pickering Town	1-2
Northallerton Town	v	Marske United	3-2
Guisborough Tn	v	Whitby Town	1-0
Yorkshire Rwy Ins	v	Stockton	0-2

SECOND QUALIFYING ROUND

Northallerton Town	v	Whitby Town	0-6
Stockton	v	Pickering Town	3-2

THIRD QUALIFYING ROUND

Stockton	v	Whitby Town (at WT)	0-3

SEMI-FINALS

Middlesbrough, Scarborough, Whitby Town, Stckton (pre 1998-99 season)

NOTTINGHAMSHIRE F.A.

Secretary: M P Kilbee,
7 Clarendon Street, Nottingham NG1 5HS
Tel: 0115 941 8954 (County Office) Fax: 01705 724923

NOTTINGHAMSHIRE SENIOR CUP
(FOUNDED 1883-84)

RECENT FINALS

1992-93	Arnold Town	v	Rainworth Miners Welfare	3-1
1993-94	Clipstone Welfare	v	Boots Athletic	3-2
1994-95	Oakham United	v	Clipstone Welfare	3-0
1995-96	Arnold Town	v	Boots Athletic	2-0
1996-97	Arnold Town	v	Boots Athletic	1-0

MOST WINS Nottingham Forest 17 Sutton Town 17 Notts County 11

1997-98
NOTTINGHAMSHIRE SENIOR CUP

HOLDERS: ARNOLD TOWN

FIRST ROUND

Collingham	v	Eastwood Town	3-1
Worthington Simp	v	Cotgrove CW	6-2
City & Sherwood	v	Southwell City	0-3
Arnold Town	v	Ruddington United	2-1
Gedling Town	v	Keyworth United	3-1
Wollaton	v	Hucknall Town	0-4
Rainworth MW	v	Siemens	4-1
Pelican	v	Notts Police	2-1 aet
Basford United	v	Blidworth Welfare	4-1
Dunkirk	v	Greenwood Meadows	5-0
Kimberley Town	v	Linby CW	0-3
Ollerton Town	v	Clipstone Welfare	2-0
Awsworth Villa	v	Thoresby CW	1-1 aet, 5p4
Hucknall RR	v	Retford United	4-0
Boots Athletic	v	Sneinton	3-0
Welbeck Colliery	v	Radford	6-1

SECOND ROUND

Basford United	v	Dunkirk	0-2
Hucknall Town	v	Rainworth MW	6-0
Linby CW	v	Worthington Simpsons	4-2
Hucknall Rolls Royce	v	Pelican	2-3
Awsworth Villa	v	Southwell City	2-1
Collingham	v	Ollerton Town	3-2
Boots Athletic	v	Welbeck Colliery	0-2
Arnold Town	v	Gedling Town	0-2

THIRD ROUND

Hucknall Town	v	Dunkirk	2-0
Pelican	v	Linby CW	1-0
Collingham	v	Welbeck Colliery	0-3
Awsworth Villa	v	Gedling Town	1-4

SEMI-FINALS

Gedling Town	v	Hucknall Town	3-4
Pelican	v	Welbeck Coll.	1-1 aet, 7p6

FINAL

HUCKNALL TN	v	PELICAN	2-0	at Coronation Park, Eastwoof Town FC

OXFORDSHIRE F.A.

Secretary: Peter J Ladbrook,
3 Wilkins Road, Cowley, Oxford OX4 2HY
Tel: 01865 775432

OXFORDSHIRE SENIOR CUP
(FOUNDED 1884-85)

RECENT FINALS

1992-93	Thame United	v	Banbury United	2-1
1993-94	Witney Town	v	Peppard	1-0
1994-95	Witney Town	v	North Leigh	1-0
1995-96	Oxford City	v	Thame United	2-1
1996-97	Oxford City	v	Carterton Town	1-1, 5p4

MOST WINS Oxford City 30 Witney Town 9 Oxford United 8

1997-98
OXFORDSHIRE SENIOR CUP

HOLDERS: OXFORD CITY

FIRST ROUND

Adderbury Park	v	Bennsfield CA	3-4
Henley Town	v	Worcester College OB	1-0
Woodstock Town	v	Headington Amateurs	0-2
Chinnor	v	Yarnton	3-1
Eynsham	v	Chechendon	0-4
Fritwell	v	Old Woodstock	0-4
Middle Barton	v	Launton Sports	3-2 aet
Chipping Norton T	v	Easington Sports	3-5
Sonning Common	v	Charlton	1-3

SECOND ROUND

Easington Sports	v	Kidlington	3-1
Bennsfield CA	v	Chechendon	3-1
Quarry Nomads	v	Charlton	0-2
Middle Barton	v	Ardley United	2-4
Chinnor	v	Watlington Town	1-1, 3-0
North Leigh	v	Bicester Town	1-0
Garsington	v	Clanfield	2-0
Carterton Town	v	Peppard	5-0
Banbury United	v	Headington Amateurs	4-1
Henley Town	v	Old Woodstock	4-1

THIRD ROUND

North Leigh	v	Chinnor	3-0
Carterton Town	v	Bennsfield CA	8-0
Banbury United	v	Ardley United	4-1
Garsington	v	Easington Sports	1-0
Henley Town	v	Charlton	3-0 aet

FOURTH ROUND

Oxford City	v	Henley Town	5-1
Banbury United	v	Witney Town	0-5
Carterton Town	v	North Leigh	1-0
Garsington	v	Thame United	1-4

SEMI-FINALS

Witney Town	v	Thames United	3-1
Oxford City	v	Carterton Town	2-0

FINAL

OXFORD CITY v WITNEY TOWN 1-1 aet at Oxford United FC, Att: 1,227
(Witney won after penalties)

SHEFFIELD & HALLAMSHIRE F.A.

Secretary: G Thompson JP,
Clegg House, 5 Onslow Road, Sheffield S11 7AF
Tel: 0114 267 0068

SHEFFIELD & HALLAMSHIRE CUP
(FOUNDED 1876-77)

RECENT FINALS

1992-93	Stocksbridge Pk Steels	v	Worksop Town	5-3 (Agg)
1993-94	Sheffield	v	Worksop Town	1-1 (6-5 Pns)
1994-95	Worksop Town	v	Emley	1-0
1995-96	Stocksbridge Pk Steels	v	Grimethorpe	1-0
1996-97	Worksop Town	v	Harworth Colliery Institute	6-0

MOST WINS Sheffield 10 Frickley Athletic 9 Sheffield Wednesday 9

1997-98
SHEFFIELD & HALLAMSHIRE CUP

HOLDERS: WORKSOP TOWN

FIRST QUALIFYING ROUND

Wickersley	v	Yorkshire Main	4-0	Old Edwardians	v	Hare & Hounds	1-5

SECOND QUALIFYING ROUND

Wath Saracens Ath	v	Oughtibridge WMSC	1-5	Penistone Church	v	Sheffield Lane Top	1-5
Throstles Ridgeway	v	Thorpe Hesley	TH W/O	Davy	v	Wickersley	1-3
Caribbean Sports	v	Athersley Recreation	1-2	Rossington	v	Woodhouse West End	1-0
Wombwell Main	v	Mexborough Athletic	4-1	Elsecar Mkt Hotel	v	Phoenix	2-6
Swinton Athletic	v	Ecclesfield Red Rose	1-2	S. Hallam Univ.	v	Treeton Welfare	0-2
The Wetherby	v	H&H Holyland Com'n	2-1	ABM	v	High Green Villa	0-1
NCB Maltby MW	v	Frechevelle CA	1-3	Hemsworth Town	v	Parramore Sports	4-3
Clifton Rovers	v	Grimethorpe MW	G W/O	Mexboro Main St	v	Grapes Roy Hancock	3-0
Norton Woodseats	v	Wombwell Town	3-1	Sheffield Bankers	v	Sheffield Centralians	2-1
Brinsworth Athletic	v	Queens Hotel	3-0	Harworth Colliery	v	Avesta Sheff. Sports	6-3

FIRST ROUND PROPER

Emley	v	Brodsworth W	4-1	Rossington	v	Phoenix	8-5
Denaby United	v	Treeton Welfare	5-1	Frecheville CA	v	Norton Woodseats	4-1
Worksop Town	v	Sheffield Bankers	5-1	Athersley Rec	v	Sheffield	0-1
Harworth Coll. Inst	v	Thorpe Hesley	0-3	Stocksbridge PS	v	The Wetherby	3-1
Frickley Athletic	v	Ecclesfield Red Rose	3-1	Maltby Main	v	Wombwell Main WMC	6-1
Wickersley	v	High Green Villa	2-3	Sheffield Lane Top	v	Hallam	2-0
Brinsworth Athletic	v	Rossington Main	1-6 aet	Parkgate	v	Mexborough Main St	2-0
Grimethorpe MW	v	Ou'bridge MW	0-0 aet, 3-0	Hemsworth Town	v	Worsboro Bridge M	1-2

SECOND ROUND PROPER

Denaby United	v	Stocksbridge Pk Steels	0-2	Rossington Main	v	Worsboro Bridge	1-0
Sheffield Lane Top	v	Frecheville CA	3-1	Emley	v	Grimethorpe MW	1-0
Worksop Town	v	Rossington Main	5-0	Thorpe Hesley	v	Parkgate	0-5
Maltby Main	v	Sheffield	5-0	Frickley Athletic	v	High Green Villa	3-0

THIRD ROUND

Stocksbridge PS	v	Sheffield Lane Top	5-1	Emley	v	Frickley Athletic	2-1
Parkgate	v	Rossington Main	2-1	Maltby Main	v	Worksop Town	2-3

SEMI-FINALS

Stocksbridge Pk St	v	Parkgate	0-1 aet	Emley	v	Worksop Town	3-1

FINAL

EMLEY v PARKGATE 3-0 at Hillsborough, Sheffield Wednesday FC

SHROPSHIRE F.A.

Secretary: A W Brett
Gay Meadow, Abbey Foregate, Shrewsbury, SY2 6AB
Tel: 01743 362769

SHROPSHIRE SENIOR CUP (FOUNDED 1877-78)

RECENT FINALS

1991-92	Telford United	v	Shrewsbury Town	1-0
1992-93	Telford United	v	Shrewsbury Town	2-0
1993-94	Telford United	v	Shrewsbury Town	2-1
1994-95	Shrewsbury Town	v	Telford United	5-1
1995-96	Shrewsbury Town	v	Telford United	2-0
1996-97	Shrewsbury Town	v	Telford United	1-0

MOST WINS Shrewsbury Town 52 Telford United 34 Oswestry Town 11

1997-98 SHROPSHIRE SENIOR CUP

HOLDERS: SHREWSBURY TOWN

SEMI-FINALS

Bridgnorth Town	v	Shrewsbury Town	0-4	Shifnal Town	v	Telford United	1-3

FINAL

SHREWSBURY T v TELFORD UTD 1-0 at Gay Meadow, Shrewsbury

1997-98 SHROPSHIRE COUNTY CHALLENGE CUP

FIRST ROUND

Broseley	v	Newport	2-1	Oakengates Tn	v	Shawbury Utd	2-2, 3-1
Belvidere	v	Bandon	2-4	Meole Brace	v	Little Drayton Rgrs	2-3

SECOND ROUND

Snailbeach WS	v	Wem Town	1-3	St Martins	v	Ludlow Town	0-2
Broseley	v	Morda United	1-1, 0-1	Little Drayton R	v	Bandon	0-1
Oakengates Town	v	Lawson Mardon Star	2-4	Clee Hill United	v	Hanwood United	1-3
Whitchurch Alport	v	Belle Vue OB	4-0				

THIRD ROUND

Wem Town	v	Whitchurch Alport	3-4	Morda United	v	Wellington Amateurs	1-0
Bandon	v	Ludlow Town	1-2	Hanwood United	v	Lawson Mardon Star	0-2

SEMI-FINALS

Ludlow Town	v	Whitchurch Alport	1-2	Morda United	v	Lawson Mardon Star	2-0

FINAL

MORDA UNITED v WHITCHURCH AL. 2-3 at Gay Meadow, Shrewsbury

SOMERSET F.A.

Secretary: Mrs Helen Marchment,
30 North Road, Midsomer Norton, Bath, Somerset BA3 2QQ
Tel: 01761 410280

SOMERSET SENIOR CUP
(FOUNDED 1895-96)

RECENT FINALS

1992-93	Brislington	v	Saltford	1-0
1993-94	Bridgwater Town	v	Brislington	1-0
1994-95	Brislington	v	Bridgwater Town	0-0 (5-4 Pns)
1995-96	Bridgwater Town	v	Peasedown Athletic	2-0
1996-97	Portishead	v	Bridgwater Town	2-0

MOST WINS Paulton Rovers 12 Radstock Town 12 Welton Rovers 9

1997-98
SOMERSET SENIOR CUP

HOLDERS: PORTISHEAD

FIRST ROUND

Watchet Town	v	Bristol Manor Farm Rs	2-0
Temple Cloud	v	Burnham United	2-7
Paulton Rovers Rs	v	Street	4-2 aet
Nailsea United	v	Shield & Dagger	NU W/O
Saltford	v	Kewstoke	3-3 aet, 4p2
St George E in G	v	Hartcliffe OB	3-2
Larkhall Athletic	v	Frome Town Res	4-2
Westland United	v	Bishop Sutton Res	6-0
Teyfont Athletic	v	Peasedown Athletic	2-8
Backwell Utd Res	v	Keynsham Town Res	1-2
Bridgwater Tn Res	v	Stockwood Green	1-2 aet
Fry's	v	Clevedon Town Rs	F W/O
Cleeve West Town	v	Odd Down Rs	0-0 aet, 4p2
EP Somerdale U	v	Keynsham Cricketers	2-4
Brislington Res	v	Clutton	5-1
Frome Collegians	v	Winscombe	3-5 aet
Ilminster	v	Long Ashton	1-1 aet, 2p4
Wells City	v	Congresbury	3-0
Shepton Mallet	v	Wrington-Redhill	3-2
Castle Cary	v	Timsbury Athletic	1-3
Westland Sports	v	Tunley Athletic	6-3
Wellington Res	v	Clevedon United	0-2
Dundry Athletic	v	Welton Rovers Res	1-2
Long Sutton	v	Hengrove Athletic	2-1
Imperial	v	Cutters Friday	0-0 aet, 4p3

SECOND ROUND

Westland United	v	Long Sutton	2-3
Peasedown Athletic	v	Weston St Johns	3-0
Saltford	v	Clevedon Town	2-0
Shepton Mallet	v	Welton Rovers Res	1-0
Wells City	v	Keynsham Town Res	3-0
Brislington Res	v	Keynsham Cricketers	6-1
Nailsea United	v	Fry's	2-3
Cheddar	v	Burnham United	1-5
St George E in G	v	Portishead	1-4
Stockwood Green	v	Winscombe	0-1
Watchet Town	v	Worle	1-2
Timsbury Athletic	v	Cleeve West Town	1-2
Imperial	v	Clandwn	4-0
Radstock	v	Paulton Rovers Res	4-1
Westland Sports	v	Long Ashton	5-1
Glastonbury Res	v	Larkhall Athletic	1-5

THIRD ROUND

Radstock Town	v	Brislington Res	1-0
Saltford	v	Westland Sports	4-2
Winscombe	v	Long Sutton	?
Imperial	v	Fry's	?
Cleeve West Tn	v	Burnham United	0-2
Larkhall Athletic	v	Worle	3-2
Portishead	v	Wells City	2-0
Peasedown Ath	v	Shepton Mallet	2-6

FOURTH ROUND

Shepton Mallet	v	Saltford	2-0
Burnham Athletic	v	Radstock Town	0-1
Larkhall Athletic	v	Portishead	1-2 aet
Winscombe	v	Imperial	0-1

SEMI-FINALS

Radstock Town	v	Imperial	2-0
Portishead	v	Shepton Mallet	0-1

FINAL

RADSTOCK TOWN v SHEPTON MALLET 1-3 at Paulton Rovers FC

SOMERSET PREMIER CUP
(FOUNDED 1948-49)

RECENT FINALS

1992-93	Bristol Rovers Res	v	Taunton Town	5-1 (Agg)
1993-94	Bath City	v	Bristol Rovers Res	5-4 (Agg)
1994-95	Bath City	v	Taunton Town	2-0 (Agg)
1995-96	Brislington	v	Mangotsfield United	1*1 (6-5 Pns)
1996-97	Bristol City	v	Yeovil Town	1-2

MOST WINS Bath City 17 Yeovil Town 15 Bristol City 5

1997-98
SOMERSET PREMIER CUP

HOLDERS: YEOVIL TOWN

FIRST ROUND

Keynsham Town	v	Taunton Town	0-1	Bishop Sutton	v	Bath City	1-2
Bristol Manor Farm	v	Yeovil Town	0-6				

SECOND ROUND

Welton Rovers	v	Brislington	0-3	Bath City	v	Wellington	7-0
Paulton Rovers	v	Yeovil Town	1-4	Backwell United	v	Taunton Town	1-2
Odd Down	v	Mangotsfield Utd	0-3	Chard Town	v	Weston super Mare	1-4
Frome Town	v	Bridgwater Town	0-6	Glastonbury	v	Clevedon Tn (at CT)	0-7

THIRD ROUND

Weston super Mare	v	Bridgwater Town	2-1	Brislington	v	Yeovil Town	0-2
Taunton Town	v	Mangotsfield United	4-0	Clevedon Town	v	Bath City	3-2 aet

SEMI-FINALS

Weston super Mare	v	Yeovil Town	1-2	Taunton Town	v	Clevedon Town	0-0 aet

FINAL

CLEVEDON TOWN v YEOVIL TOWN 0-1 at Twerton Park, Bath City FC

Yeovil Town Football Club with the Somerset Premier Cup after a 1-0 success against Clevedon Town at Bath City FC
Photo: Tim Lancaster

STAFFORDSHIRE F.A.

Secretary: Brian Adshead,
County Showground, Weston Road, Stafford ST18 0DB
Tel: 01785 256994 (County Office) Fax: 01785 224334

STAFFORDSHIRE SENIOR CUP
(FOUNDED 1877-78)

RECENT FINALS

1992-93	Stoke City Res	v	Hednesford Town	6-1 (Agg)
1993-94	Macclesfield Town	v	Wednesfield	10-3 (Agg)
1994-95	Stoke City Res	v	Paget Rangers	4-2 (Agg)
1995-96	Leek Town	v	Newcastle Town	4-3 (Agg)
1996-97	Macclesfield Town	v	Bilston Town	2-1

MOST WINS Stoke City 17 Aston Villa 16 West Bromwich Albion 13

1997-98
STAFFORDSHIRE SENIOR CUP

HOLDERS: MACCLESFIELD TOWN

FIRST ROUND

Blakenall	v	Oldbury United	1-0
Kidsgrove Athletic	v	Boldmere St Michaels	4-1
Rusall Olympic	v	Bridgnorth Town	0-2
Chasetown	v	Bloxwich Town	2-3
Port Vale	v	Stourbridge	2-0
Shifnal Town	v	Hednesford Town	1-4

SECOND ROUND

Bloxwich Town	v	Blakenall	2-2 aet, 0-1
Leek Town	v	Rocester Town	2-0
Hednesford Town	v	Stoke City	1-3
Port Vale	v	Bilston Town	1-2
Kidsgrove Athletic	v	Pelsall Villa	6-1
Bridgnorth Town	v	Newcastle Town	0-2
Knypersley Vict.	v	Halesowen Harriers	3-1
Stafford Rangers	v	Tamworth	2-7 aet

THIRD ROUND

Knypersley Victoria	v	Blakenall	2-2 aet, 1-2
Newcastle Town	v	Tamworth	0-1
Leek Town	v	Kidsgrove Athletic	3-0
Bilston Town	v	Stoke City	3-2

SEMI-FINALS

Bilston Town	v	Blakenall	3-1
Leek Town	v	Tamworth	3-3 aet, 3-1

FINAL (First Leg)

TAMWORTH	v	BILSTON TOWN	0-1

FINAL (Second Leg)

BILSTON TOWN	v	TAMWORTH	1-1	aggregate 2-1 to Bilston

SUFFOLK F.A.

Secretary: William Steward,
2 Millfields, Haughley, Stowmarket IP14 3PU
Tel: 01449 673481

SUFFOLK SENIOR CUP (FOUNDED 1885-86)

RECENT FINALS

1992-93	Woodbridge Town	v	Stonham Aspal	5-2 (AET)
1993-94	Woodbridge Town	v	Saxmundham Sports	4-0
1994-95	Grundisburgh	v	Whitton United	2-0
1995-96	Grundisburgh	v	Framlingham Town	3-0
1996-97	Ipswich Wanderers	v	Haverhill Rovers	2-1

MOST WINS Ipswich Town 16 Lowestoft Town 10 Stowmarket Town 8

1997-98 SUFFOLK SENIOR CUP

HOLDERS: HAVERHILL ROVERS

FIRST ROUND

Walsham le Willows	v	Kesgrave	3-1
Oulton Broad & LR	v	Hadleigh Utd (at HU)	0-3
Sudbury Wndrs Res	v	Whitton United	1-3
Grundisburgh	v	Ipswich Athletic	1-0
Stonham Aspal	v	Westerfield United	3-1
Achilles	v	BT Research	5-0
Ipswich Wanderers	v	Leigton	1-0
Framlingham Town	v	Brantham & Sutton U.	3-1
Kirkley	v	Haverhill R.	1-1aet 2-2aet 4p1
Lowestoft Tn Rs	v	East Bergholt Utd	1-0
Bramford United	v	Long Merford	0-1
Needham Market	v	BS Fonnercau Ath	1-1, 0-1
Mildenhall Town	v	Brandon Town	5-1
Stowmarket Tn Rs	v	Beccles Town	2-2, 0-4
Ashlea	v	Walton United	2-2, 1-5
Haughley United	bye		

SECOND ROUND

Whitton United	v	Walsham le Willows	0-1
Needham Market	v	Ipswich Wanderers	0-3
Haughley United	v	Lowestoft Town Res	4-2
Beccles Town	v	Kirkley	0-1
Framlingham Tn	v	Long Melford	4-1
Achilles	v	Hadleigh United	0-1
Stonham Aspal	v	Mildenhall Town	0-0, 4-3
Walton United	v	Grundisburgh	0-1

THIRD ROUND

Haughley United	v	Kirkley	4-2
Stonham Aspal	v	Ipswich Wanderers	4-0
Framlingham Tn	v	Hadleigh United	0-1
Walsham le Will's	v	Grundisburgh	1-1, 0-2

SEMI-FINALS

Hadleigh United	v	Grundisburgh	0-1
Haughley United	v	Stonham Aspal	1-3

FINAL

GRUNDISBURGH v STONHAM ASPAL 2-1 at Portman Road, Ipswich Town FC

SUFFOLK PREMIER CUP (FOUNDED 1958-59)

RECENT FINALS

1992-93	Sudbury Town	v	Brantham Athletic	2-1
1993-94	Newmarket Town	v	Sudbury Town	2-1
1994-95	Newmarket Town	v	Felixstowe Town	1-1 (Rep 1-0)
1995-96	Bury Town	v	Woodbridge Town	0*0 (5-4 Pns)
1996-97	Newmarket Town	v	Stowmarket Town	0*0 (Rep 1-0)

MOST WINS Sudbury Town 12 Bury Town 10 Lowestoft Town 5

1997-98 SUFFOLK PREMIER CUP

HOLDERS: NEWMARKET TOWN

PRELIMINARY ROUND

Sudbury Town v Stowmarket Town 1-1, 2-1

FIRST ROUND

Lowestoft Town	v	Felixstowe Port & Tn	3-0
Bury Town	v	Newmarket Town	2-1
Woodbridge Town	v	Sudbury Wndrs	2-3
Sudbury Town	v	Conard United	5-0

SEMI-FINALS

Bury Town	v	Lowestoft Town	0-1
Sudbury Town	v	Sudbury Wanderers	0-1

FINAL

LOWESTOFT TOWN v SUDBURY W. 0-0 aet, 2-5 aet at Woodbridge Town FC, Att: 427 & 402

SURREY F.A.

(Est. 1877)

Secretary: Ray Ward,

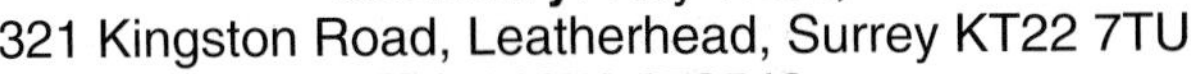

321 Kingston Road, Leatherhead, Surrey KT22 7TU

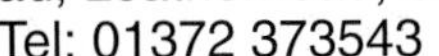

Tel: 01372 373543

SURREY SENIOR CUP
(FOUNDED 1882-83)

RECENT FINALS

1992-93	Sutton United	v	Carshalton Athletic	2-1
1993-94	Woking	v	Sutton United	3-1
1994-95	Sutton United	v	Carshalton Athletic	3-1
1995-96	Woking	v	Tooting & Mitcham Utd	2-0
1996-97	Crystal Palace	v	Carshalton Athletic	1-0

MOST WINS Dulwich Hamlet 16 Sutton United 13 Kingstonian 9

1997-98
SURREY SENIOR CUP

HOLDERS: CRYSTAL PALACE

PRELIMINARY ROUND

Epsom & Ewell	v	Egham Town	1-3
Walton Casuals	v	Raynes Park Vale	2-4 aet
Farnham Town	v	Camberley T.	3-3,3-3aet, 3p4

FIRST ROUND

Godalming & G'ford	v	Molesey	2-1
Cobham	v	Crystal Palace	1-2
Sutton United	v	Ash United	6-1
Kingstonian	v	Chessington & Hook	5-1
Whyteleafe	v	Netherne	4-0
Banstead Athletic	v	Egham Town	3-4
Merstham	v	Metropolitan Police	1-3
Westfield	v	Toot./Mitch. U.	1-1 0-0aet 0-2
Walton & Hersham	v	Dorking	2-1
Leatherhead	v	Croydon	3-0
Ashford Town	v	Camberley Town	2-0
Cranleigh	v	Raynes Park Vale	2-2, 3-6
Dulwich Hamlet	v	Redhill	2-1
Croydon Athletic	v	Woking	0-7
Carshalton Athletic	v	Corinthian Casuals	1-0
Chipstead	v	Chertsey Town	0-4

SECOND ROUND

Sutton United	v	Ashford Town	2-0
Walton & Hersham	v	Dulwich Hamlet	2-1
Tooting & Mitcham U	v	Raynes Park Vale	2-1
Chertsey Town	v	Carshalton Athletic	3-1
Met Police	v	Kingstonian	1-3
Whyteleafe	v	Crystal Palace Res	1-0
Woking	v	God'ming & Guidlford	1-0
Leatherhead	v	Egham Town	3-0

THIRD ROUND

Whyteleafe	v	Walton & Hersham	1-0
Leatherhead	v	Woking	2-0
Kingstonian	v	Sutton United	4-0
Chertsey Town	v	Tooting/Mitcham Utd	2-0

SEMI-FINALS

Kingstonian	v	Whyteleafe	0-0, 2-0
Woking	v	Chertsey Town	2-1

FINAL

KINGSTONIAN v WOKING 1-1 aet, 2-1 at Gander Green Lane, Sutton United FC

SUSSEX F.A.

Secretary: David Worsfold,
Culver Road, Lancing, West Sussex BN15 9AX
Tel: 01903 753547

SUSSEX SENIOR CUP (FOUNDED 1882-83)

RECENT FINALS

1992-93	Wick	v	Oakwood	3-1
1993-94	Brighton & Hove Alb Res	v	Peacehaven & Telscombe	1-0
1994-95	Brighton & Hove Alb Res	v	Bognor Regis Town	2-0
1995-96	Hastings Town	v	Crawley Town	1-0
1996-97	St Leonards Stamcroft	v	Saltdean United	2-1

MOST WINS Worthing 19 Eastbourne Town 12 Southwick 10

1997-98
SUSSEX SENIOR CUP

HOLDERS: ST LEONARDS STAMCROFT

FIRST ROUND

Hailsham Town	v	Eastbourne United	1-2
Portfield	v	Whitehawk	4-3
Lancing	v	Southwick	0-0 aet, 5-3 aet
Crawley Down Vlge	v	Worthing United	5-1
East Preston	v	Oakwood	5-1
Shinewater Assoc	v	Withdean	5-0
Littlehampton Town	v	Bexhill Town	4-1
Lewes	v	Sidley United	2-1
Three Bridges	v	Midhurst & Easebourne	8-1
Chichester City	v	Mile Oak	5-4
Crowborough Ath	v	Sidlesham	0-4
Newhaven	v	Broadbridge Heath	2-3
East Grinstead Tn	v	Selsey	1-2

SECOND ROUND

Worthing	v	Sidlesham	8-0
Bognor Regis Tn	v	Crawley Town	1-0
Selsey	v	Broadbridge Heath	1-0 aet
Hastings Town	v	Horsham	2-1
Burgess Hill Town	v	Brighton & Hove Alb.	5-1
East Preston	v	Hassocks	5-1
St Leonards Stam.	v	Saltdean United	2-1
Pagham	v	Ringmer	1-2
Lancing	v	Peacehaven & Tels	2-3
Shoreham	v	Eastbourne Town	5-3
Langney Sports	v	Three Bridges	5-2
Horsham YMCA	v	Chichester City	4-2
Crawley Tn Vlge	v	Arundel	1-3
Lewes	v	Eastbourne United	2-1
Shinewater	v	Littlehampton Town	0-1
Wick	v	Portfield	3-2 aet

THIRD ROUND

Bognor Regis Tn	v	Wick	0-1
Selsey	v	St Leonards Stamcroft	1-3
Littlehampton Town	v	Lewes	4-1
Arundel	v	Shoreham	1-3
Hastings Town	v	Horsham YMCA	9-1
Peacehaven & T	v	Worthing	0-4
East Preston	v	Burgess Hill Town	0-4
Langney Sports	v	Ringmer	1-4

QUARTER-FINALS

Burgess Hill Town	v	Ringmer	3-1
Shoreham	v	Hastings Town	0-2
Littlehampton	v	Worthing	0-2
Wick	v	St Leonards Stam	2-1

SEMI-FINALS

Worthing	v	Hastings Town	0-1
at Langney Sports			
Wick	v	Burgess Hill T	1-1 aet, 0-1
at Worthing			

FINAL

BURGESS HILL T	v	HASTINGS TOWN	1-2	at Broadfield Stadium, Crawley Town FC, Att: 1,256

SUSSEX ROYAL ULSTER RIFLES CHARITY CUP
(FOUNDED 1896-97)

RECENT FINALS

1992-93	Peacehaven & Tels	v	Lancing	2-1
1993-94	Newhaven	v	Pagham	4-0
1994-95	Peacehaven & Tels	v	Stamco	1-0
1995-96	Peacehaven & Tels	v	Saltdean United	1-0
1996-97	Peacehaven & Tels	v	Shoreham	3*3, 4-0

MOST WINS Horsham 13 Worthing 12 Southwick 10

1997-98
SUSSEX ROYAL ULSTER RIFLES CHARITY CUP

HOLDERS: PEACEHAVEN & TELSCOMBE

PRELIMINARY ROUND

Horsham YMCA	v	Mile Oak	3-2
Arundel	v	Chichester City	0-3
Bexhill Town	v	Crawley Down Village	1-2
Eastbourne Town	v	Newhaven	2-3
Sidlesham	v	Worthing United	2-1

FIRST ROUND

Horsham YMCA	v	Broadbridge H.	1-1 aet, 3-1
Crawley Down Vlge	v	East Grinstead	3-1
East Preston	v	Shoreham	3-4
Langney Sports	v	Three Bridges	3-1
Midhurst & Easeb'ne	v	Sidlesham	2-0
Portfield	v	Oakwood	3-1
Southwick	v	Selsey	Southwick W/O
Wick	v	Pagham	5-1
Chichester City	v	Hassocks	0-1
Crowborough Ath	v	Sidley United	2-0
Hailsham Town	v	Eastbourne Utd	4-1
Littlehampton Tn	v	Lancing	2-0
Newhaven	v	Burgess Hill Town	1-2
Saltdean United	v	Peacehaven & Tels	2-0
Whitehawk	v	Shinewater A	0-0 aet, 3-2
Withdean	v	Ringmer	3-1

SECOND ROUND

Hailsham Town	v	Langney Sports	3-1
Saltdean United	v	Burgess Hill Town	3-4
Littlehampton Town	v	Midhurst & Easebourne	4-1
Portfield	v	Horsham YMCA	0-4
Crowborough Ath	v	Crawley Down Vlge	0-3
Withdean	v	Whitehawk	2-1
Shoreham	v	Hassocks	1-0
Wick	v	Southwick	5-0

THIRD ROUND

Burgess Hill Town	v	Crawley Down Village	2-0
Hailsham Town	v	Wick	0-5
Horsham YMCA	v	Littlehampton T	2-2 aet, 2-1
Shoreham	v	Withdean	2-0

SEMI-FINALS

Wick	v	Horsham YMCA	4-0
Burgess Hill Town	v	Shoreham	1-3

FINAL

SHOREHAM	v	WICK	2-3	at Lancing FC, Att: 303

WESTMORLAND F.A.

Founded: 1897

Secretary: Peter Ducksbury,

Westmorland County FA, Dalton Close, Kendal, Cumbria LA9 6AG

WESTMORLAND SENIOR CUP
(FOUNDED 1896-97)

RECENT FINALS

1992-93	Coniston	v	Ambleside	4-2
1993-94	Kendal United	v	Keswick	2-0
1994-95	Kendal United	v	Staveley United	2-1
1995-96	Milnthorpe Corinthians	v	Netherfield Reserves	2-1
1996-97	Kirkby Lonsdale	v	Milnthorpe Corinthians	1-2

MOST WINS Corinthians 11 Netherfield 8 Burneside 7 Windermere 7

1997-98
"WESTMORLAND GAZETTE" SENIOR CHALLENGE CUP

HOLDERS: MILNTHORPE CORINTHIANS

FIRST ROUND

Burton Thistle	v	Endmoor KGR	4-3		Coniston	v	Staveley United	1-3
Ambleside	v	Keswick	3-4		Kendal County	v	Sedburgh Wndrs	8-2
Milnthorpe Corinth	v	Burneside	3-2		Windermere SC	v	Kirkby Stephen	1-2
Kendal United	v	Wetheriggs United	0-5					

SECOND ROUND

Dent	v	Kirkoswald	2-0	Victoria SC	v	Lunesdale United	2-0
Appleby	v	Burton Thistle	1-3	Staveley United	v	Kendal County	2-4
Netherfield Reserves	v	Kirkstephen	K W/O	Kirkby Lonsdale	v	Wetheriggs United	3-1
Milnthorpe Corinth	v	Keswick	3-1	Grange Amateurs	v	Shap	2-7

THIRD ROUND

Milnthorpe Corinth	v	Kendal County	2-1	Burton Thistle	v	Kirkby Lonsdale	1-4
Kirkby Stephen	v	Dent	2-2 aet, 4-2	Victoria Sporting	v	Shap	3-1

SEMI-FINALS

Kirkby Lonsdale	v	Milnthorpe Corinthians	3-1	Victoria Sporting	v	Kirkby Stephen	3-3 aet, 1-5

FINAL

KIRKBY LONSDALE v K'BY STEPHEN 1-1 aet, 1-0 at Parkside, Kendal, Netherfield FC

WEST RIDING F.A.

Secretary: Roy Carter JP
Fleet Lane, Woodlesford, Leeds LS26 8NX
Tel: 0113 231 0101 (County Office)

WEST RIDING COUNTY CUP (FOUNDED 1924-25)

RECENT FINALS

1992-93	Glasshoughton Welfare	v	Selby Town	4-2
1993-94	Guiseley	v	Goole Town	1-0
1994-95	Farsley Celtic	v	Thackley	2-1
1995-96	Guiseley	v	Farsley Celtic	3-2
1996-97	Farsley Celtic	v	Armthorpe Welfare	3-0

MOST WINS Goole Town 11 Farsley Celtic 9 Guiseley 5

1997-98 WEST RIDING COUNTY CUP

HOLDERS: FARSLEY CELTIC

FIRST ROUND

Harrogate Railway	v	Hatfield Main	5-3	Glassh'ton MW	v	Harrogate Town	2-0
Guiseley	v	Halifax Town	1-0				

SECOND ROUND

Tadcaster Albion	v	Selby Town	2-1	Harrogate Railway	v	Osset Albion	0-2
Eccleshill Utd SC	v	Yorkshire Amateurs	3-2	Thackley	v	Armthorpe Welfare	2-0
Farsley Celtic	v	Liversedge	1-3	Glasshoughton W	v	Garforth Town	1-2
Ossett Town	v	Pontefract Collieries	2-4	Bradford Park Ave	v	Guiseley	2-2 aet, 0-1

THIRD ROUND

Garforth Town	v	Pontefract Collieries	4-2	Thackley	v	Tadcaster Albion	2-1
Guiseley	v	Ossett Albion	0-2	Eccleshall United	v	Liversedge	0-2

SEMI-FINALS

Ossett Albion	v	Liversedge	1-2	Garforth Town	v	Thackley	2-1

FINAL

GARFORTH TOWN v LIVERSEDGE 2-0 at Fleet Lane, Woodlesford, Leeds, County FA HQ

Garforth Town FC - 1997-98 Northern Counties (East) League Division One Champions and West Riding Senior Cup Winners
Back Row: Norman Hebbron (President), Paul Bracewell (Secretary), Dave Harrison (Asst. Manager), Jack Coop (Physio), Richard Ramsden, Elliott Beddard, Aiden Lobey, Dave Bramhill, Dave Woodhead, Patrick Flaherty, Chris Sullivan, Dave Parker (Manager), Stephen Hayle (Chairman)
Front Row: Andy Sibson, Scott Stirk, Darren Abrams, Brendan Ormsby (Club Captain), Darren Falk, Richard Smith, Damien Holmes

Photo: Neil Thaler

WILTSHIRE F.A.

Secretary: Mr E M Parry
44 Kennet Avenue, Swindon, Wiltshire SN2 3LG

WILTSHIRE SENIOR CUP (FOUNDED 1886-87)

RECENT FINALS

1992-93	Bemerton Heath Harl	v	Wollen Sports	3-1
1993-94	Amesbury Town	v	Swindon Supermarine	2-1
1994-95	Purton	v	Downton	1-0
1995-96	Highworth Town	v	Amesbury Town	3-0
1996-97	Corsham Town	v	Marlborough Town	4-1 aet

MOST WINS Devizes Town 14 Swindon Town 10 Chippenham Town 8

1997-98 WILTSHIRE SENIOR CUP

HOLDERS: CORSHAM TOWN

FIRST ROUND

Corsham Town	v	Bradford Town	1-1 aet, 1-2	Highworth Town	v	Marlborough Town	5-1
Dunbar Athletic	v	Wroughton	1-4	Burmah Castrol	v	Malmesbury Victoria	3-4

SECOND ROUND

Wroughton	v	Pewsey Vale	1-3	Southbrook	v	Bromham	6-2
GPS Plessey	v	Shrewton Town	1-3	Wootton Bassett T	v	Purton	0-2
Aldbourne Park	v	Raychem SS	0-2	Bradford Town	v	Biddestone	2-0
Malmesbury Victoira	v	Cricklade Town	0-3	Tisbury United	v	Highworth Town	1-8

THIRD ROUND

Purton	v	Pewsey Vale	2-1	Shrewton United	v	Highworth Town	0-5
Southbrook	v	Raychem	2-1	Cricklade Town	v	Bradford Town	3-6 aet

SEMI-FINALS

Bradford Town	v	Purton	1-2	Southbrook	v	Highworth Town	2-3 aet

FINAL

HIGHWORTH TN	v	PURTON	2-1 aet	at Swindon Town FC

WILTSHIRE PREMIER SHIELD (FOUNDED 1926-27)

RECENT FINALS

1992-93	Trowbridge Town	v	Westbury United	1-0
1993-94	Trowbridge Town	v	Chippenham Town	3-0
1994-95	Trowbridge Town	v	Swindon Supermarine	1-0
1995-96	Chippenham Town	v	Salisbury City	0-2
1996-97	Devizes Town	v	Swindon Supermarine	0-2

MOST WINS Swindon Town 26 Salisbury City 10 Trowbridge Town 9

1997-98 WILTSHIRE PREMIER SHIELD

HOLDERS: SWINDON SUPERMARINE

FIRST ROUND

Calne Town	v	Devizes Town	2-3	Downton	v	Swindon Supermarine	0-3
Chippenham Town	v	Melksham Town	1-3				

SECOND ROUND

Trowbridge Town	v	Swindon Super.	6-3 aet	Westbury United	v	Bemerton HH	1-1 aet, 2-1
Melksham Town	v	Devizes Town	1-0	Warminster Town	v	Salisbury City	0-6

SEMI-FINALS

Salisbury City	v	Trowbridge Town	2-1	Melksham Town	v	Westbury United	1-0

FINAL

MELKSHAM TOWN	v	SALISBURY C	0-0 aet, 5p3	at Swindon Town FC

WORCESTERSHIRE F.A.

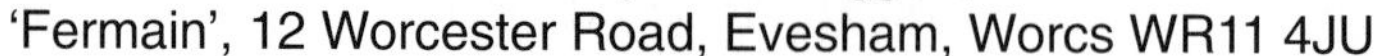
Secretary: M R Leggatt,
'Fermain', 12 Worcester Road, Evesham, Worcs WR11 4JU

Tel: 01905 612336

WORCESTERSHIRE SENIOR CUP (FOUNDED 1893-94)

RECENT FINALS

1992-93	Kidderminster Harriers	v	Solihull Borough	3-1 (Agg)
1993-94	Bromsgrove Rovers	v	Kidderminster Harriers	5-1 (Agg)
1994-95	Bromsgrove Rovers	v	Moor Green	4-1 (Agg)
1995-96	Bromsgrove Rovers	v	Stourbridge	4-3 (Agg)
1996-97	Worcester City	v	Solihull Borough	4-1 (Agg)

1997-98 WORCESTERSHIRE SENIOR CUP

HOLDERS: WORCESTER CITY

FIRST ROUND

Sutton Coldfield Tn	v	Stourbridge	2-3	Solihull Borough	v	Evesham United	3-1
Moor Green	v	Paget Rangers	0-0, 5-2				

SECOND ROUND

Solihull Borough	v	Redditch United	3-1	Stourbridge	v	Kidd. Harr.	0-0, 1-1 aet, 0p3
Worcester City	v	Moor Green	0-0, 3-1	Bromsgrove Rvrs	v	Halesowen Town	1-2

SEMI-FINALS

Worcester City	v	Solihull Borough	1-3	Kidderminster H.	v	Halesowen Town	1-0

FINAL

KIDDERMINSTER H v SOLIHULL BORO 2-1 at Aggborough, Kidderminster Harriers FC
(This match was scheduled for two legs but eventually by agreement settled in one tie)

1997-98 WORCESTERSHIRE SENIOR URN

HOLDERS: KINGS HEATH

FIRST ROUND

Studley BKL	v	Cradley Town	4-1	Bromsgrove R Rs	v	Kidderminster H Rs	2-3
Pegasus Juniors	v	Highgate United	3-1	Stourport Swifts	v	Worcester Athletico	2-1
Pershore Town	v	Malvern T 1-1, 1-1 aet, 1p3		Worcester C. Res	v	Kings Norton Town	1-3
Alvechurch	v	Dudley Sports	5-2	Bye: Kings Heath			

SECOND ROUND

Stourport Swifts	v	Studley BKL	Worcester City Rs	v	Malvern Town
Pegasus Juniors	v	Alvechurch	Kidderminster H R	v	Kings Heath

SEMI-FINALS

FINAL

STOURPORT S. v WORCESTER C R 2-1 aet at Stourport Swifts FC

WELSH FOOTBALL

The League of Wales was formed in 1992 and although recent years have seen it become noted for the many successes of Barry Town, it has not always been so. Its formation was clouded by a controversial decision of the Football Association of Wales who tried to enforce clubs into playing within the Principality rather than in the English semi-professional pyramid. Clubs exempted from this ruling were the three teams in the Nationwide League - Cardiff, Swansea and Wrexham - along with Merthyr Tydfil, who were at that time in the Conference. All other clubs were required to compete in Welsh football.

Most clubs agreed, perhaps identifying the newly formed League of Wales as the best way to progress. Newtown, for example, describe the league as "a positive venture" and the opportunity to be successful and thus compete in Europe as "a challenge that cannot be underestimated".

As a national league recognised by UEFA, entry into their club competitions was to be the carrot. However three clubs - Newport AFC, Colwyn Bay and Caernarfon - held out for the right to carry on competing in English leagues.

The case was eventually settled in the High Court when it was found in the clubs' favour due to potential restraint of trade. All this came after the FA of Wales had exiled them into playing their home games on the grounds of English clubs; Newport groundshared with Gloucester City, for example.

Caernarfon subsequently joined the League of Wales in 1995 but Newport, the by now relegated Merthyr Tydfil and Colwyn Bay still compete to this day in the English Pyramid; the first two in the Dr Martens League and the latter in the Unibond.

Despite these anxieties before and after its inception the League of Wales was introduced for the 1992/93 season with 20 clubs and was won in its inaugural year by Cwmbran Town. A league cup also sponsored by the league's sponsors Konica was introduced at the same time. Clubs competed in four groups of five on a geographical basis, with the group winners progressing to the semi-finals. Afan Lido won the first competition, beating Caersws in a single leg final.

Seasons 1993-94 and 1994-95 saw the League championship won on both occasions by Bangor City. Their first championship year also saw City reach the final of the League Cup, now played on a regionalised two leg format where they were beaten by the holders, just four days after winning the league title. This was very much against the odds, as Afan had only just avoided relegation.

These two championships were important trophies for the North Wales club but they are remembered in Welsh football circles for having won the Welsh Cup in 1961-62 and losing narrowly to the mighty Napoli of Italy in the European Cup Winners Cup.

Bangor's second championship season had heralded the arrival of Barry Town into the League of Wales. Barry had competed in the English Southern League for over 70 years in two spells, interspersed with a period in the 1980's in the Welsh League. this interlude back in Welsh football had seen Town win the eague title on six occasions in seven seasons (including five in a row) and finish runners-up in the remaining year! The Jenner Park club finished in seventh place in their debut season in the League of Wales. However they also competed that year in the European Cup Winners Cup after sensationally beating hot favourites Cardiff City 2-0 in the previous season's Welsh Cup final. Town were eventually beaten 7-0 on aggregate by Zalgiris Vilnius of Lithuania.

A new name was added to the role of honour in the League of Wales League Cup for 1994-95 - Llansantffraid beating Ton Pentre 2-1 in the final.

The 1995-96 season was an historic one for the League of Wales, as Barry became the first club to play in it as full-time professionals, backed by the finances of chairman Neil O'Halloran's family steel business. Town won the league that year after a long battle with Newtown. Connah's Quay Nomads beat Ebbw Vale by the only goal to take the League Cup, which had reverted to a group format to accommodate the return of Caernarfon.

Barry retained their league title in the 1996-97 season, this time emphasising the advantages of a full-time squad. The championship was won by a margin of 21 points over runners-up Inter Cable Tel with a superior goal difference of 103 from 40 matches!

Town completed a clean sweep of Welsh domestic football by beating Bangor on penalties in the now sponsored Gilbert League Cup final (once again a two legged competition) and Cwmbran 2-1 in the final of the Welsh Cup. The season was also notable for a magnificent UEFA Cup run, beating Dinaburg of Latvia 2-1 on aggregate, overcoming the Hungarians of Vasutas Budapest on penalties at Jenner Park after a 4-4 aggregate tie and only losing 6-4 over two legs to Aberdeen, despite being beaten 3-1 at Pittodrie in the first leg.

Last year's League of Wales season, the sixth in the competition's brief history, was won again by Barry to complete a hat trick of league titles. The Jenner Park men won 33 out of their 38 league games, equalling their own league record set the previous year, while drawing the remaining fixtures to become the first club to complete a season undefeated. A winning margin of 26 points over second placed Newtown re-emphasised the gulf, as did a goals record of 134 scored and only 31 conceded.

Barry retained the League Cup after a penalty shoot-out following a 1-1 draw against unlucky Bangor City, third time losers in this competition. The North Wales club gained due reward for an excellent season under manager Graeme Sharp by lifting the Welsh Cup for the first time since 1962 by overcoming Connah's Quay Nomads 4-2 on penalties in the final.

The League of Wales has now firmly established itself as the premier competition in Wales. Its recognition as a national league by UEFA means that four member clubs can compete each year in the UEFA club competitions including the Inter Toto Cup.

Since the League's formation 10 of its member clubs have participated in one or other of the UEFA competitions. The current 1998-99 campaign was Barry's fourth in Europe and a wealth of experience is being accrued within the league.

This year's first entrants to European competition came in the Inter Toto competition when Ebbw Vale took part for the second consecutive year. However they were well beaten by a 6-1 scoreline at Eugene Cross Park against the Norwegians of Kinigsvinger, although they performed better in the second leg only to lose 3-0.

Welsh clubs in the three major European competitions fared a little better. The European Cup paired Barry with Dinamo Kiev, the strongest team at that stage of the competition. Kiev reached the Champions League quarter-finals last season and were the club who ended Town's hoped in the competition last year with 2-0 and 4-0 defeats. This year it was worse as Barry were on the wrong end of an 8-0 hammering in Kiev. They deserved at least a draw in the return when a goal by last year's top scorer Eifion Williams was the Barry reply to two goals from the Ukraine club in front of 1,500 people at Jenner Park.

The highlight of this year's European ties was Newton's backs-to-the-wall 0-0 draw at home against the Polish club Wisla Krakow. A crowd of 1,500 gave them a standing ovation at Latham Park but once agin the might of full time Eastern European professional football was seen at its best as the Welsh club was swept away by 7 goals to nil in the return leg. In the European Cup Winners Cup Bangor City were drawn against the Finnish side Haka Valkeakoski.

The League of Wales is slowly but surely establishing itself as a major force in Welsh football. Perhaps those still on the outside may come to regret their absence.

Steve Corbett

Recent aerial photo of Jenner Park, Barry Town FC

Inter Cable-Tel v Celtic: Celtic's T McKinlay challenges J Murray
Photo: Huw Evans Picture Agency Cardiff

Inter Cable-Tel v Celtic: Celtic's A Thom jumps through Inter Cable-Tel defence
Photo: Huw Evans Picture Agency Cardiff

WELSH FINAL LEAGUE TABLES 1997-98

LEAGUE OF WALES

	P	W	D	L	F	A	Pts
Barry Town	38	33	5	0	134	31	104
Newtown	38	23	9	6	101	47	78
Ebbw Vale	38	22	11	5	94	55	77
Inter Cable-Tel	38	23	5	10	58	27	74
Cwmbran	38	22	7	9	78	47	73
Bangor	38	20	8	10	72	54	68
Connah's Quay	38	18	12	8	75	54	66
Rhyl	38	17	10	11	61	49	61
Conwy	38	15	8	15	66	59	53
Aberystwyth	38	13	12	13	64	63	51
Caersws	38	14	4	20	64	71	46
Carmarthen Town	38	11	11	16	57	72	44
Caernarfon	38	12	7	19	57	66	43
TNS	38	9	15	14	54	67	42
Rhayader Town	38	11	6	21	55	78	39
Hyrfrdwst	38	10	8	20	54	87	38
Porthmadog	38	10	5	23	55	77	35
Flint Town	38	9	7	22	50	77	34
Welshpool	38	6	7	25	55	97	25
Cemaes Bay	38	2	3	33	30	155	9

CC SPORTS WELSH LEAGUE

DIVISION ONE	P	W	D	L	F	A	Pts
Ton Pentre	36	28	4	4	122	39	88
Afan Lido	36	27	4	5	86	26	85
Llanelli	36	26	4	6	88	30	82
Treowen	36	24	2	10	76	43	74
Port Talbot	36	22	5	9	70	51	71
Goytre	36	20	3	13	89	42	63
UWIC	36	18	7	11	59	35	61
AFC Rhondda	36	15	3	8	73	51	58
Bridgend Town	36	14	7	15	80	65	48
Maesteg Park	36	13	8	15	82	73	47
Grange Harlequins	36	13	6	17	54	66	45
Porthcawl	36	13	3	20	63	78	42
Cardiff Corries	36	9	12	15	63	66	39
Cardiff Civil Service	36	12	3	21	63	94	39
Briton Ferry	36	11	5	20	50	83	27
Aberaman	36	9	4	23	43	77	31
Taffs Well	36	6	9	21	46	83	27
Llanwern	36	6	10	20	53	79	25
Abergavenny Thurs	36	0	3	33	31	210	3

FITLOCK WELSH ALLIANCE

	P	W	D	L	F	A	Pts
Holyhcad Hotspurs	26	23	1	2	102	32	70
Colwyn Bay YMCA	26	17	3	6	71	41	54
Loco Llanberis	26	15	5	6	71	50	50
Halkyn United	26	15	2	9	60	40	47
Llangefni Town	26	12	6	8	73	46	42
Prestatyn Town	26	13	3	10	50	34	42
Bangor City Res	26	12	4	10	72	53	40
Nantlle Vale	26	11	5	10	41	49	38
Llanfairpwll	26	8	5	13	38	51	29
Caenarfon T Rs	26	9	1	16	46	61	28
Saltney Comm C	26	7	7	12	40	60	28
Rhyl Res	26	6	5	15	33	63	23
Conwy Utd Res	26	5	2	19	48	108	17
Llandymor Utd	26	2	5	19	29	86	11

THE WELSH NATIONAL LEAGUE WREXHAM

PREMIER DIV	P	W	D	L	F	A	Pts
Penley	24	17	3	4	65	38	54
Corwen	24	16	2	6	72	46	50
Llangollen Town	24	15	3	6	66	52	48
Castell Alun Colts	24	14	5	5	74	35	47
Gresford Athletic	24	11	4	9	54	36	37
British Aerospace	24	10	5	9	68	53	35
Cefn Druids Rs	24	8	6	10	46	41	30
Llay Welfare	24	8	4	12	37	61	28
Brymbo Bton Res-3	24	8	4	12	47	61	25
Rhos Aelwyd	24	7	4	13	38	64	25
Glyn Ceiriog	24	7	3	14	58	73	24
Ruthin Town Res	24	5	7	12	30	51	22
Lex XI Res	24	4	2	18	28	72	14
Rhostyllen Villa	Suspended-Record expunged						

SPAR
MID WALES LEAGUE

	P	W	D	L	F	A	Pts
Kerry	28	22	4	2	94	30	70
Pendarm United	28	22	2	4	91	23	68
Camo	28	17	7	4	81	28	58
Caersws Res	28	16	7	5	88	47	55
TNSLlan fraid Rs	28	15	8	5	61	30	53
Newtown Res	28	16	4	8	89	38	52
Guilsfield	28	13	5	10	75	54	44
Aberystwyth T Rs	28	12	7	9	66	43	43
Builth Wells	28	12	4	12	65	61	40
UCW Abstwyth	28	11	5	12	60	66	38
Presteigne St A	28	5	3	20	69	97	18
Penparcau	28	6	0	22	37	87	18
Berriew	28	5	2	21	32	92	17
Rhayader Tn Res	28	5	1	22	32	107	16
Montgomery Tn	28	3	1	24	22	159	10

TREMONT FORD AND ROVER
MID WALES LEAGUE (SOUTH)

	P	W	D	L	F	A	Pts
Newcastle	24	17	4	3	68	22	55
Llandrindod Res	24	17	2	5	62	34	53
Vale of Arrow	24	13	5	6	70	37	44
Presteigne Res	24	12	5	7	54	46	41
Hay St Mary's	24	10	8	6	47	44	38
Newbridge	24	10	8	6	38	36	38
Penybont	24	10	6	8	39	34	36
Radnor Valley	24	8	7	9	39	40	31
Knighton Res	24	7	4	13	51	61	24
Rhosgoch	24	7	4	13	43	66	25
Llandiloes Res	24	7	3	14	40	64	24
Buith Wells Res	24	5	6	13	39	55	21
Bucknell	24	0	4	20	21	82	4

CAMBRIA HOUSING
ANGLESEY LEAGUE

	P	W	D	L	F	A	Pts
Gwalchmai	20	15	5	0	68	22	50
Holyhead Hr Res	20	14	5	1	81	24	47
Beaumaris Town	20	13	3	4	56	27	42
Bodedern	20	11	2	7	55	30	35
Llanerchymedd Bulls	20	9	2	9	48	43	29
Pentraeth	20	9	2	9	57	57	29
Llangoed	20	8	2	10	42	53	26
Treaddur Bay	20	7	2	11	45	62	23
Valley Jnrs	20	4	4	12	42	59	16
Llanfairpwll	20	4	1	15	29	58	13
Bryngwran Bulls	20	2	0	18	21	109	6

WELSH BREWERS CAFL

PREMIER DIV	*P*	*W*	*D*	*L*	*F*	*A*	*Pts*
Tostre Sports	22	16	4	2	73	21	52
Garden Village	22	14	6	2	56	24	48
Felinfoel	22	13	4	5	62	37	43
Gorseinon Ath	22	11	4	7	48	39	37
Pengelli United	22	10	6	6	43	33	36
Penyfan United	22	9	6	7	49	47	33
Bwich Rangers	22	8	7	7	45	39	31
Pontardulais Town	22	7	6	9	49	40	27
Camford Sports	22	5	7	10	36	50	22
Pwll Athletic	22	6	3	13	39	61	21
Llanelli Steel	22	2	5	15	23	70	11
Ammanford	22	1	2	19	29	91	5

TALCRE BEACH CARAVAN PARK CLWYD FOOTBALL LEAGUE

PREMIER DIV	*P*	*W*	*D*	*L*	*F*	*A*	*Pts*
Rhyl Delta	24	21	2	1	84	31	65
Trefnant Village FC	24	15	4	5	70	38	49
Caerwys FC	24	14	2	8	79	45	44
Pilkingtons FC	24	12	7	5	59	36	43
Penmaenmawr PH	24	12	4	8	78	55	40
Llansannan FC	24	11	4	9	48	44	37
Denbigh Town Res	24	11	3	10	59	57	36
Flint Town Res	24	11	2	11	51	52	*32
Hawarden Rngrs FC	24	7	5	12	56	52	26
Holywell Town Rs	24	7	5	12	48	48	25
Prestatyn Town Rs	24	7	3	14	46	70	*21
CPD Y Glannau	24	3	7	14	41	80	16
Llandyrnog Utd Rs	24	1	0	23	23	134	3

VALE OF CONWY LEAGUE

	P	*W*	*D*	*L*	*F*	*A*	*Pts*
Glan Conwy	26	20	4	2	141	38	64
Llanfairfechan Tn	26	20	3	3	65	23	63
Blaenau Amateurs	26	19	4	3	125	33	61
Llandudno Reserves	26	15	4	7	80	49	49
Penrhyn United	26	13	5	8	90	42	44
Dynamo Dolgarrog	26	12	5	9	72	46	41
Mochdre Sports	26	13	2	11	70	62	41
Machno United	26	12	3	11	80	73	39
Bro Cernyw	26	11	5	10	69	56	38
Hotpoint	26	8	7	11	69	71	31
Llanrwst Utd Res	26	7	2	17	48	96	23
Llandudno Cricketers	26	5	1	20	43	130	16
Betws-Y-Coed	26	3	1	22	23	127	10
Llansannan Res	26	1	0	25	19	148	3

EVANS CARS CYMRU ALLIANCE

	P	*W*	*D*	*L*	*F*	*A*	*Pts*
Rhydymwyn	36	25	6	5	86	34	81
Holywell Town	36	24	5	7	72	29	77
Cefn Druids	36	21	12	3	100	30	75
Knighton Town	36	21	8	7	74	41	71
Glantraeth	36	18	6	12	88	63	60
CPD Penrhyncoch	36	16	8	12	72	67	56
Denbigh Town	36	15	8	12	82	79	53
Oswestry Tn-12	36	17	11	8	72	49	50
Llandudno	36	14	7	15	60	66	49
Llandrindod Wells	36	12	11	13	54	55	47
Lex XI	36	12	11	13	64	66	47
Ruthin Town	36	12	9	15	57	54	45
Brymbo Broughton	36	12	9	15	39	41	45
Mostyn	36	11	8	17	42	65	41
Buckley Town	36	11	8	17	62	88	41
Penycae	36	10	6	20	52	95	36
CHirk AAA	36	10	4	22	46	74	34
Lianidloes Town	36	4	7	25	54	110	19
Mold Alexandra	36	2	6	28	32	102	12

FFIGAR LEAGUE

DIVISION ONE	*P*	*W*	*D*	*L*	*Pts*
Penrhyn R	26	23	0	3	69
Bow Street	26	22	1	3	67
Padarn R	26	15	5	6	50
Tywyn/Bryn	26	13	6	7	45
Aberdyfi	26	13	2	11	41
Llanilar	26	12	6	8	40
Dolgellau	26	11	6	9	39
Bont	26	12	3	11	39
Talybont	26	10	6	10	36
Tregaron	26	9	3	14	30
Trawsgoed	26	8	4	14	28
Llanrhystud	26	6	2	18	18
Llanon	26	5	1	20	14
Borth	26	0	1	25	0

GEORGE FORD GWENT COUNTY LEAGUE

DIVISION ONE	*P*	*W*	*D*	*L*	*F*	*A*	*Pts*
Tredegar Town	26	22	2	2	95	41	68
Cwm Welfare	26	17	6	3	71	33	57
Spencer Youth	26	16	4	6	67	33	52
Civil Service	26	12	8	6	59	44	44
Cwmtillery	26	13	3	10	51	48	42
Girling Ponty	26	12	8	9	65	56	41
Pill FC	26	9	11	6	44	42	38
Lilswerry	26	9	4	13	44	52	31
RTB Ebbw Vale	26	6	8	12	54	68	26
Aberbargoed	26	6	4	16	35	61	22
Monmouth Town	26	4	9	13	46	61	21
Croesyceilog	26	4	9	13	38	61	21
Fleur-de-Lys	26	5	6	15	42	81	21
Rogerstone AFC	26	5	5	16	42	72	20

OWENS CORNING GWENT CENTRAL LEAGUE

DIVISION ONE	*P*	*W*	*D*	*L*	*F*	*A*	*Pts*
Goytre	26	24	1	1	119	29	73
Pontypool Town	26	22	2	2	107	34	65
Crickhowell	25	21	0	4	125	36	57
Fairfield Utd	26	15	3	8	77	49	48
Usk Town	26	12	4	10	77	67	40
Owens Corning	26	12	2	12	90	72	38
Mardy	26	12	1	13	64	69	37
Aber Rangers	25	11	1	13	62	80	31
Sebastopol	26	8	4	14	79	89	28
Gilwern & District	26	7	6	13	44	64	27
Tranch United	26	7	3	16	62	117	18
Little Mill	26	5	3	18	75	134	15
Race United	24	3	4	17	39	104	7
New Inn	26	3	4	19	35	111	7

NESTLE EAST GWENT LEAGUE

DIVISION ONE	*P*	*W*	*D*	*L*	*F*	*A*	*Pts*
Red & White A	22	19	0	3	98	34	57
Broadstone	22	19	0	3	82	24	57
Tintern A	22	18	2	2	103	21	56
Castle A	22	15	3	4	72	30	48
Sudbrook A	22	13	1	8	74	41	40
Bulwark	22	8	4	10	40	44	28
Undy A	22	8	4	10	45	49	28
Chepstow Town A	22	7	0	15	44	78	21
Monmouth Town	22	6	2	14	43	104	11
Club Santos	22	1	3	18	43	132	3

GWYNEDD LEAGUE

	P	W	D	L	F	A	Pts
Amlwch Town	2423	1	0	107	21	70	
Llanrwst	24	18	2	4	94	35	56
Penrhyndeudraeth	24	15	2	7	93	46	47
Deiniolen	24	14	4	6	70	44	46
Llandegfan	24	15	0	9	57	47	45
Pwllheli	24	10	4	10	52	55	34
Llanfairfechan Ath.	24	9	5	10	56	60	32
Llanrug United	24	9	2	13	52	67	29
Llangefni Athletic	24	8	3	13	59	69	27
Y Felinheli	24	6	4	14	34	65	19
Barmouth & Dyffryn	24	4	6	14	39	87	18
Bangor University	24	5	2	17	43	96	17
Talysarn Celts	24	2	1	21	30	94	7

HIGHADMIT PROJECTS AMATEUR LEAGUE

DIVISION ONE	P	W	D	L	Pts
Dinas Powys	30	23	4	3	73
British Steel	30	22	2	6	68
Trefelin B & GC	30	21	2	7	65
Bryntirion Ath	30	19	2	9	59
Barry Athletic	30	17	4	9	55
Llantwit Fardre	30	14	5	11	47
Red Dragon (Pt)	30	12	6	12	42
Cambrian	30	12	5	13	41
Ton/Gelli BC	30	11	8	11	41
FC Cwmaman	30	14	11	5	38
Cardiff	30	8	8	14	32
Treforest FC	30	8	6	16	30
AFC Bargoed	30	8	2	20	26
Cardiff Corries	30	7	2	21	23
Llanharry	30	6	4	20	22
Trelewis Welfare	30	1	3	26	6

L'HIRONDELLE LEAGUE

DIVISION ONE	P	W	D	L	Pts
Dewi Stars	21	17	3	1	54
Felinfach	21	13	6	2	45
Saron	20	13	3	4	42
St Dogs	21	10	5	6	35
NC Emlyn	21	9	5	7	32
Lampeter	22	9	4	9	30
Cardigan	21	8	3	10	27
Crannog	19	7	5	7	26
Llandysul	21	6	8	7	26
Bargod R	22	7	4	11	25
Llanboidy	22	3	0	19	9
SDUC	19	0	1	18	0

MONMOUTHSHIRE BUILDING SOCIETY NEWPORT FOOTBALL LEAGUE

	P	W	D	L	F	A	Pts
Bettws Social	28	22	4	2	103	28	70
Greenmeadow	28	20	4	4	138	48	64
Whiteheads	28	17	6	5	81	47	57
Marshfield	28	15	7	6	78	56	49
Rhiwderin FC	28	15	4	9	62	52	49
Crosskeys	28	11	10	7	70	66	43
Hamdden FC	28	14	3	10	56	50	42
Maesglas Utd	28	10	3	15	70	104	33
St Julians	28	9	3	15	64	78	30
Merry Miller	28	8	5	15	49	71	29
Barrett	28	8	4	16	61	71	28
Pontnewydd WMC	28	7	5	16	62	70	26
Burtons Sports	28	8	2	18	61	110	26
Dynamo	28	5	6	17	53	95	21
Shaftesbury	28	6	2	20	51	113	20

J T HUGHES MONTGOMERYSHIRE AMATEUR LEAGUE

HONDA DIVISION ONE

	P	W	D	L	F	A	Pts
Meifod	18	12	3	3	49	36	39
Llanhaeadr	18	11	5	2	62	32	38
Waterloo Rovers	18	9	5	4	49	26	32
Dyffryn Banw	18	10	2	6	45	39	32
Llangedwyn	18	8	5	5	34	28	29
Llanfyllin Town	18	7	5	6	47	40	26
Bishops Castle	18	5	3	10	36	50	18
Welshpool Town Rs	18	3	6	9	28	50	15
Abermule	18	1	7	10	30	43	10
Llanfair Caereinion	18	2	3	13	25	59	9

JAMES WILLIAMS PEMBROKESHIRE LEAGUE

DIVISION ONE	P	W	D	L	F	A	Pts
Hakin United	26	26	0	0	140	16	78
Narberth	26	20	2	4	86	35	62
Goodwick	26	20	0	6	91	41	60
St Ishmaels	26	15	2	9	77	39	47
Camrose	26	12	5	9	53	35	41
P Robins	26	13	2	11	58	63	41
M Bridge	26	12	4	9	70	42	40
Saundersfoot	26	12	3	11	82	60	39
Carew	26	12	3	11	39	45	39
Fishguard	26	11	2	13	59	72	35
Herbrandston	26	7	0	19	63	106	21
Johnston	26	6	3	17	43	87	21
Kilgetty	26	2	1	23	33	117	7
Lamphey	26	0	1	25	31	165	1

HAPPY HOME FURN. NEATH & DISTRICT LEAGUE

PREMIER DIV	P	W	D	L	Pts
Seven Sisters	21	18	2	1	56
Giants Grave	21	17	1	3	52
Cwm Wdrs	19	13	3	3	42
Cwmtawe	20	12	2	6	38
Cwmamman Utd	22	9	5	8	32
Ynysgerwn CC	22	9	4	9	31
Cilfrew Rovers	19	9	3	7	30
Clydach Sports	20	7	3	10	24
CMB	18	4	6	8	18
AFC Cimla	21	6	1	14	19
Travellers Well	21	2	2	16	8
Sunnybank WMC	22	1	0	21	3

PIC UP SPARES SWANSEA SENIOR LEAGUE

DIVISION ONE	P	W	D	L	Pts
West End	22	15	4	3	49
PT Colts	22	10	5	7	35
Ragged School	22	10	4	5	34
North End	22	8	10	4	34
Dunvant & 3X's	22	10	3	7	33
Star Athletic	22	10	3	8	33
Brunswick United	22	8	3	10	27
Naval & Military	22	7	6	9	27
Maltster Sports	22	7	3	12	24
Mumbles Rangers	22	6	5	11	23
Manselton Utd	22	6	3	12	21
Treboeth Utd	22	5	3	14	18

TAFF-ELY SENIOR LEAGUE

PREMIER DIV	P	W	D	L	F	A	Pts
Cwm Welfare	20	17	1	2	81	24	52
Pontypridd Town	20	13	4	3	59	24	43
Llantwit Fardre	20	11	2	7	58	48	35
Taffs Well	20	11	2	7	56	41	*32
Treforest	20	10	2	8	55	40	32
Craig United 'A'	20	8	2	10	48	47	26
Ynysbwl A	20	7	3	10	42	48	24
Caerphilly Athletic	20	8	2	10	44	67	*23
Craig Metals	20	5	1	14	46	67	16
Pontypridd Athletic	20	4	4	12	32	67	*13
Talbot Green	20	2	5	13	46	93	11
Univ of Glamorgan	Record deleted						

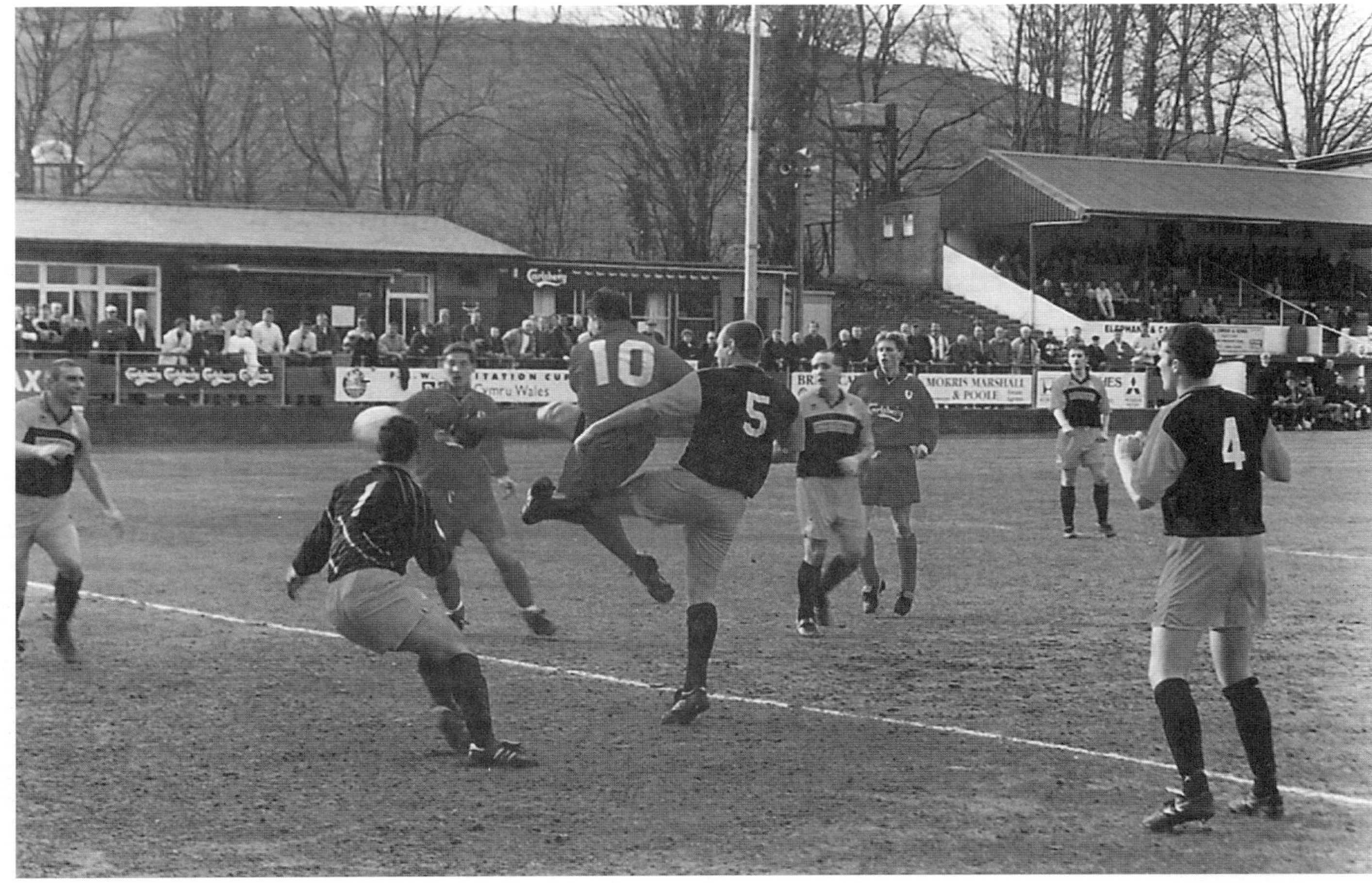

Welsh Cup action - Quarter final Newtown v Ebbw Vale 1997-98 season

DIRECTORY OF CLUBS 1998-99

ABERYSTWYTH TOWN

Chairman: Derek Dawson. **President:** Mr D Jones **Vice-Chairman:**
Secretary: Mr D Dawson, Underwood, Lorweth Avenue, Aberystwyth, SY23 1EW (1970 624548)
Manager: Meirion Appleton **Asst Manager:** **Physio:**
Ground: Park Avenue, Aberystwyth, Dyfed (01970 612122).
Directions: From south: A487, 1st right at Trefachan Bridge to r'bout, 1st right with Park Avenue being 3rd right. From north: A487 and follow one-way system to railway station, at r'bout 1st left with Park Avenue being 3rd right. 5 mins walk from Aberystwyth (BR) - follow as above.
Seats: 300 **Cover:** 1,200 **Capacity:** 4,500 **Floodlights:** Yes **Shop:** Yes
Programme: 24 pages, 60p. **Editor:** Steve Moore (01970 617705). **Press Officer:** David Thomas
Colours: Black & green/black/black. **Change colours:** Yellow/white/white
Sponsors: Continental Cambria Tyres. **Nickname:** Seasiders **Founded:** 1884.
Midweek Matchеday: Wednesday **Reserves League:** Mid-Wales
Record Attendance: 4,500 v Hereford, Welsh Cup 1971.
Previous League: Welsh 1896-97/ Nth Wales Comb. 99-1900/ Montgomeryshire & Dist. 04-20/ Central Wales 21-25 81-87/ Mid-Wales 26-32 51-81/ Cambrian Coast 32-51/ Welsh Lg South 51-63/ Abacus 87-92.
Clubhouse: Open daily noon-3 & 7-12pm. Snacks available.
Club Record Scorer: David Williams 476, 66-83. **Club Record Appearances:** David P Whitney 572, 62-81.
Hons: Welsh Cup 1899-1900; Welsh I'mediate Cup 85-86 87-88; Mid Wales Lg(11) (Lg Cup(7); Welsh Amtr Cup (3); Welsh Lg Div 2 Sth 51-52; Cambrian Coast Lg(8) Central Wales Chal. Cup(6)

BANGOR CITY

President: Lady Pennant **Chairman:** Gwyn Pierce Owen **Vice Chairman:** David Gareth Jones.
Secretary: Alun Griffiths, 12 Lon-Y-Bryn, Menai Bridge, Anglesey, Gwynedd LL57 5NM (01248 712820).
Manager: Graeme Sharp **Asst Manager:** John Hulse **Physio:** Arwel Jones
Ground: The Stadium, Farrar Road, Bangor, Gwynedd (01248 355852)
Directions: Old A5 into Bangor, 1st left before railway station, ground on left by garage.
Seats: 700 **Cover:** 1,200 **Capacity:** 5,000 **Floodlights:** Yes **Shop:** Yes
Programme: 32 pages, 70p **Editor:** Anthony Evans **Press Officer:** Alun Griffiths
Colours: All navy blue **Change colours:** All white
Sponsors: Pentraeth Mazda **Nickname:** Citizens **Founded:** 1876
Midweek Matchedays: Tuesday **Reserve League:** Welsh Alliance.
Record Attendance: 10,000 v Wrexham, Welsh Cup final 78-79.
Previous Leagues:: N Wales Coast 1893-98 1911-12/The Comb 1898-1910/N Wales Comb 30-33/W Mids 32-38/Lancs Comb 38-39 46-50/Ches Co 50-68/NPL 68-79 81-82 84-92/Alliance Prem 79-81 82-84.
Clubhouse: Not on ground
Honours: FA Tphy R-up 83-84; Northern Prem. Lg 81-82 (R-up 86-87, Lg Cup 68-69, Presidents Cup 88-89, Chal. Shield 87-88), Cheshire Co. Lg R-up 53-54 58-59, Lancs Comb. R-up 30-31, League of Wales 94-95 (Lg Cup R-up 94-95), Welsh National Lg 27-28 (R-up 26-27), Nth Wales Coast Lg 1895-96, Welsh Cup 1888-89 95-96 1961-62 (R-up 27-28 60-61 63-64 72-73 77-78 84-85), Nth Wales Chal. Cup 26-27 35-36 36-37 37-38 46-47 51-52 57-58 64-65 67-68, Welsh Amtr Cup 1894-95 96-96 97-98 98-99 1900-01 02-03 04-05 05-06 11-12, Welsh Jnr Cup 1995-96 97-98 1919-20, Welsh All. Alves Cup 49-50 59-60 (Cookson Cup 61-62 68-69 84-85 86-87).

BARRY TOWN

Chairman: Paula O'Halloran **Player Manager:** Gary Barnett
Secretary: Alan Whelan, 132 Westward Rise, Barry, South Glam. CF62 6NQ (01446 737188).
Ground: Jenner Park, Barry (01446 735858)
Directions: M4 jct 33 via Wenvoe (A4050) to Barry. Left at 1st 2 r'bouts to Jenner Park. Nearest rail station is Cadoxton.
Capacity: 3,000 **Floodlights:** Yes **Cover:** Yes **Seats:** 3,000 **Programme:** Yes
Colours: Yellow/yellow/blue. **Change:** All white
Sponsors: Vale of Glamorgan Council **Nickname:** Dragons **Founded:** 1923.
Midweek Matchedays: Tuesday.
Record Attendance: 7,400 v Queens Park Rangers, FA Cup 1st Rd 1961.
Previous Leagues: Western 08-13/ Southern 13-82 89-93/ Welsh 82-89 94-95.
Best FA Cup season: 2nd Rd 29-30.
Best FA Trophy season: 3rd Qualifying Rd replay 90-91.
Players progressing to Football League: Chris Simmonds (Millwall) 47, Derek Tapscott/Dai Ward (Arsenal) 53/54, Laurie Sheffield/Gordon Fazer/Phil Green (Newport) 62/66/84, Chris Pike (Fulham) 85, Ian Love (Swansea) 86, Tony Bird/Dave O'Gorman (Swansea City) 97, Mark Ovendaze (Bournemouth) 98
Clubhouse: Open normal licensing hours, 11.00-11.00 daily
97-98 - Captain: Andrew York **Top Scorer:** Eifon Williams **P.o.Y.:** Danny Carter
Club Record Goalscorer: Clive Ayres **Club Record Appearances:** Basil Bright.
Honours: Welsh Cup (3); Welsh Trophy 94-95; Southern Lg R-up 20-21; Western Lg R-up 11-12, Welsh Lg (7), Lg Cup (4); South Wales Senior Cup (13); SA Brain Cup (3); League of Wales 95-96 96-97 97-98; UEFA Cup 2 Qual Rds 96-97, Prel Rd 97-98.

CAERNARFON TOWN

President: Jack F Thomas. **Chairman:** G.Lloyd Owen. **Vice-Chairmen:** Eilian Angel
Secretary: Irfon Roberts, Ceris, Ffrwd Cae Du, Bontnewydd, Caernarfon (01286 830417)
Manager: Paul Rowlands **Coach:** Alan McDonald **Physio:** Ian Humphreys
Ground: The Oval, Marcus Street, Caernarfon, Gwynedd (01286 675002).
Directions: A55 coast road to A487 bypass to Caernarfon. At inner relief road r'bout follow Beddlegert sign, then 2nd right - ground opposite. Nearest BR station is 9 miles distant at Bangor. Local buses to Hendre estate.
Capacity: 3,678 **Seats:** 178 **Cover:** 1,500 **Floodlights:** Yes **Club Shop:** Yes
Programme: 48pgs 70p **Editor:** Marc Roberts **Press Officer:** Geraint Lloyd Owen (01286 830307).
Colours: Yellow/green/yellow **Change colours:** Sky & claret/claret/claret
Sponsors: T.J. Fixit **Nickname:** Canaries
Midweek Matchday: Wednesday. **Founded:** 1876 **Reserve Team:** Yes.
Record Attendance: 6,002 v Bournemouth, FA Cup 2nd Rd 1929.
Best FA Trophy season: 1st Round replay 87-88.
Best FA Cup season: 3rd Rd replay 86-87 (lost 0-1 at Barnsley). Also 2nd Rd 29-30.
Previous Leagues: North Wales Coast 06-21/ Welsh National 26-30/ North Wales Combination 32-33/ Welsh Lg (North) 37-76 77-80/ Lancs Combination 80-82/ North West Counties 82-85/ Northern Prem Lge, Prem & Div 1
Players progressing to Football League: Ernie Walley (Spurs), Gwyn Jones (Wolves 1955), Wyn Davies & Haydn Jones (Wrexham 1960 & 64), Tom Walley (Arsenal 1964), Paul Crooks (Stoke 1986), David Martindale & Steve Craven & David Higgins (Tranmere 1987), Gary Jones (Swansea City)
Clubhouse: Yes. 2 snooker tables, darts, pool, fruit machines and live entertainment.
97-98 - Captain: Paul McAndrew **P.o.Y.:** Stuart Heeps **Top scorer:** Mark Aitken
Club Record Goalscorer: W Jones 255 (1906-26) **Club Record Appearances:** Walter Jones 306.
Honours: N West Co's Lg R-up 84-85 (Div 2 R-up 82-83); Lancs Comb 81-82 (Lg Cup 80-81); Welsh Lg (North)(4) 46-47 65-66 77-79, R-up(4) 56-58 72-73 79-80; Alves Cup(4) 38-39 74-75 77-79; Cookson 56-57 77-78; N Wales Combination 32-33; Welsh National Lg 26-27 29-30 (R-up 28-29); N Wales Coast Lg 11-12.

CAERSWS

Chairman: Garth Williams **Vice Chairman:** Hadyn Jones **President:** Dilwyn Lewis
Secretary: T M B Jones, 3 Hafren Terrace, Caersws, Powys SY17 5ES (01686 688103).
Manager: Mickey Evans **Asst Manager:** Barry Harding **Physio:** Wynne Jones
Ground: The Recreation Ground, Caersws, Powys.(01686 688753)
Directions: Entering Caersws (between Newtown & Llanidloes on A470) grd entrance on left by bridge.
Seats: 150 **Cover:** 300 **Capacity:** 3,250 **Floodlights:** Yes **Shop:** No.
Programme: 44 pages, 50p **Editor:** Graham Burrows. **Press Officer:** Ivor Williams
Colours: Blue/white/blue **Change colours:** Orange/black/black
Sponsor: Dave Smith **Nickname:** Bluebirds **Founded:** 1887.
Midweek Matchday: Tuesday **Reserve League:** Mid-Wales.
Record Attendance: 2,795 v Swansea City, Welsh Cup 1990.
Previous Leagues: Mid-Wales (pre-1989)/Cymru Alliance 90-92.
Players progressing to Football League: P Woosnam (Leyton Orient, West Ham United, Aston Villa, Atlanta), M Evans (Wolverhampton Wanderers, Wrexham), K.Lloyd (Hereford U, Cardiff City).
Clubhouse: Not on ground, but in village centre. Normal licensing hours. Food served.
97-98 - Captain: Anthony Griffiths **Top Scorer:** D Russell
Supporters P.o.Y.: A Thomas **Players P.o.Y.:** M Hughes
Club Record Scorer: Gareth Davies. **Club Record Appearances:**
Hons: Welsh Amtr Cup 60-61, I'mediate Cup 88-89 (R-up 91-92); Mid-Wales Lg (9) 59-61 62-63 77-78 82-83 85-86 88-90 96-97 (Lg Cup 79-80 82-83 87-88 89-90); Cent. Wales Challenge Cup 77-78 82-83 87-88 89-90 (Yth Cup 69-70 72-73); Montgomeryshire Challenge Cup(18) 52-53 59-60 62-63 69-72 74-75 76-78 83-89 90-91 94-95 94-95 96-97; Montgomeryshire Lg 77-78.

CARMARTHEN TOWN

Chairman: Jeff Thomas **President:** Anthony Jenkins
Secretary: Alan Latham, 3 Maesdolau, Idole, Carmarthen SA32 8DQ (01267 232432 H), Fax (01267 222851).
Manager: John Mahoney **Asst Manager:** Ievan John **Physio:** T Poynton/A Underwood
Ground: Richmond Park, Priory Street, Carmarthen Dyfed (01267 232101)
Directions: Proceed into Carmarthen on A48, pick up 440 to Llandilo at the 1st rounabout and follow signs for 800 meters. The ground is on left in Priory Street.
Seats: 120 **Cover:** 750 **Capacity:** 3,000 **Floodlights:** Yes **Club Shop:** Yes
Programme: Yes **Editor:** Alun Charles
Colours: Gold/black/black **Change colours:** Red/blue/blue
Sponsors: Jewson Carmarthen **Nickname:** The Town **Founded:** 1948
Midweek Matchday: Wednesday **Reserve League:** C C Sports Welsh Lge
Record Attendance: 3,000 **Previous Leagues:** Welsh League **Clubhouse:** Yes
97-98 - Captain: Mark Delaney **P.o.Y.:** **Top Scorer:** Simon Jones
Honours: Welsh Lge Div 2 59-60, Div 1 95-96, Cup Winners 95-96.

CEMAES YNYS MON

Chairman: R Madoc-Jones
Secretary: Mrs N Hughes, 12 Maes Garnedd, Tregele, Cemaes Bay, Anglsey LL67 0DR (01407 710297)
Manager: Paul Wheelan **Asst Manager:** Brian Roberts **Physio:** G Humphries
Ground: School Lane Stadium, Cemaes Bay, Anglesey (01407 710600)
Directions: A5025 from Brittania Bridge into Anglsey
Seats: 300 **Cover:** 1000 **Capacity:** 3,000 **Floodlights:** Yes **Club Shop:** Yes
Programme: 50p **Editor:**
Colours: Black/yellow **Change colours:** All red
Sponsors: Various **Nickname:** **Founded:** 1976
Midweek Matchday: Wednesday **Reserve League:** Anglesey Lge
Record Attendance: 721 v Bangor City 95-96
Previous Leagues: Anglesey Lge, Welsh Alliance, Cymru Alliance
Clubhouse: No
97-98 - Captain: Simon Flower **P.o.Y.:** Mark Turner **Top Scorer:** Matk Turner
Honours: Cookson Cup 91-92 92-93; Welsh Alliance 92-93; Cymru Alliance 94-95; League of Wales 95-96 96-97 97-98.

CONNAH'S QUAY NOMADS

Chairman: Mr R Morris **President:** Mr R Jones.
Secretary/Press Officer: Mr Robert Hunter, 40 Brookdale Avenue, Connah's Quay, Deeside, Clywd CH5 4LU (01244 831212(h)/ 520299(b)).
Managers: Neville Powell **Asst Manager:** Gary Wynne **Physio:** Mr M Latter.
Ground: Halfway Ground, Connah's Quay, Deeside, Clwyd.
Directions: On main coast road (A548) from Chester to Rhyl west end of Connah's Quay behind Halfway Hotal.
Seats: 105 **Cover:** 500 **Capacity:** 1,500 **Floodlights:** Yes **Club Shop:** No
Programme: 26 pages, 50p **Editor:** Rachel Morgan
Colours: White/navy/White. **Change colours:** Yellow/blue/yellow
Sponsors: Hallows Associatres Solicitors **Nickname:** Westenders **Founded:** 1946
Midweek Matchday: Tuesday. **Reserve League:** Sealink Welsh Alliance.
Record Attendance: 1,500 v Rhyl, Welsh Cup SF 29/3/93.
Previous Leagues: Clywd/ Welsh Alliance/ Cymru Alliance 90-92.
Clubhouse: No, but Halfway Hotel is adjacent
96-97 Captain: Barry Thukas **96-97 P.o.Y.:** Carl Smyth **96-97 Top Scorer:** Chris Davies
Honours: Welsh Amtr Cup 52-53 54-55, Nth Wales FA Amtr Cup 52-53 54-55, North Wales Coast Challenge Cup, Welsh Intermediate Cup 80-81, Welsh Alliance Cookson Cup 87-88, Welsh Youth Cup 47-48.

CONWY UNITED

Chairman: J C Davis. **Vice Chairman:** G Rees **President:** K Davies
Secretary: Mr G Rees, 1 Tan y Maes, Glan Conwy LL28 5LQ (01492 573243)
Manager: Stan Allan **Coach:** Jim Coffey **Youth Dev:** Mike Roberts
Ground: Morfa Stadium, Penmaen Rd, Conwy, Gwynedd (01492 573080).
Directions: Leave A55 on 1st slip road after river tunnel and turn left towards Conwy. Sharp left immediately after overhead railway bridge - ground 400yds on left of Penmaen Rd.
Seats: 650 **Cover:** 800 **Capacity:** 4,000 **Floodlights:** Yes **Shop:** Yes
Programme: 32 pages, 75p **Editor:** Chris Lingwood **Press Officer:** G Rees
Colours: Tangerine/black/tangerine **Change colours:** All white
Sponsors: **Nickname:** Musselmen **Founded:** 1977.
Midweek Matches: Wednesday **Reserves League:** Welsh Alliance
Record Attendance: 853 v Swansea City, FAW Invitation Cup 97
Previous Leagues: Vale of Conwy/ Gwynedd/ Welsh Alliance/ Cymru Alliance.
Players progressing to Football League: Neville Southall (via Winsford to Bury, Everton), Carl Dale (via Rhyl and Bangor to Chester City, Cardiff City).
Clubhouse: Yes,at Ground.
Club Record Goalscorer: Carl Dale **Club Record Appearances:** Gwyn Williams.
Honours: UEFA Inter Toto Cup Qual 96; Welsh Alliance 84-85 85-86; Barritt Cup 84-85 96-97; Welsh Intermediate Cup 81-82; Gwynedd Lge 95-96; Jack Owen Cup 81-82 82-83; Ron Jones Cup 87-88.

CWMBRAN TOWN

Chairman: J C Colley **Vice Chairman:** K M McCarthy **President:** John Colley
Secretary: Mr K M McCarthy, 30 Llanover Road Estate, Blaenavon, NP4 9HP (01495 792557 H)
Manager: Tony Willcox **Coach:** Mark Aizelwood **Physio:** Terry Cutlan
Ground: Cwmbran Stadium, Henllys Way, Cwmbran, Gwent (01633 866192 Fax 863324).
Directions: M4 jct 26, follow signs for Cwmbran. At 1st r/about (approx 1.5 miles) take 1st exit & proceed along Cwmbran Drive umtil passing Stadium on right. At r/about take 1st exit, then immediately at next r/about take 3rd exit. Ground entrance 150 yardson right. One and a half miles from Cwmbran (BR).
Seats: 2,201 **Cover:** 1,857 **Capacity:** 8,201 **Floodlights:** Yes **Shop:** Yes
Programme: 28 pages, 50p. **Programme Editor/Press Officer:** Andrew Havelot
Colours: White/blue/white. **Change colours:** All red
Sponsors: Exide Batteries Ltd **Nickname:** The Town **Founded:** 1951.
Midweek Matches: Wednesday. **Reserves League:** Welsh Lge Res Div East
Record Attendance: 8,148 v Manchester Utd Aug 1994
Previous Leagues: Monmouthshire Snr 51-59/ Welsh 60-92.
Players progressing to Football League: Simon King (Newport 1984), Mark Waite (Bristol Rovers 1984), Nathan Wigg (Cardiff 1993), Chris Watkins (Swansea 1993).
Clubhouse: Pub hours, on ground. Catering facilities.
Club Record Scorer: Graham Reynolds **Club Record Appearances:** Mostyn Lewis.
Honours: Lg of W. 92-93; Welsh Lg Div 1 66-67, Welsh Lg Cup 85-86 90-91.

EBBW VALE

President: J S Harrison **Chairman:** D Coughlin **V-Chairmanm** M.Carini.
Secretary: V Reed, Troed yr Afon, Alexander Place, Abercanaid, Merthyr Tydfil CF48 1SJ (01443 692631)
Manager: John Lewis **Asst Manager:** Mick Martin. **Physio:**
Ground: Eugene Cross Park, Ebbw Vale, Gwent (01495 302995).
Directions: From A465 follow signs to Ebbw Vale, 1st left at next two r'bouts - ground on left.
Seats: 1,200 **Cover:** 1,200 **Capacity:** 10,000 **Floodlights:** Yes **Shop:** No
Programme: 26 pages, 50p **Editor:**
Change colours: White & black/white/white **Colours:** Yellow & black/yellow/black
Sponsor: **Nickname:** Cowboys **Founded:** 1950
Midweek matches: Wednesday
Record Attendance: 1,762 v Wrexham, Welsh Cup 1989.
Previous League: Abacus
Clubhouse: Yes open daily share with Rugby Club
96-97 Captain: **96-97 Top Scorer:** **96-97 P.o.Y.:**
Honours: Abacus Lg 87-88 (Div 1 64-65, Southern Div 52-53, Div 2 East 60-61), Sth Wales Lg 03-04, Welsh Cup 25-26, South Wales Snr Cup 04-05, Gwent Snr Cup 24-25 26-27 28-29 32-33 45-46 50-51.

FLINT TOWN UNITED

Chairman: A Baines **Vice Chairman:** J Simon **President:**
Secretary: Keith Biggs, 10 Powell Road, Buckley, Flintshire, CH7 2BZX (01244 541789 H)
Manager: Steve Myers **Asst Manager:** S Buxton **Physio:** T Jennings
Ground: Cae-Y-Castell, Marsh Lane, Flint, Clywd CH6 5JP (01352 730982).
Directions: Approaching Flint on A548 from Chester, turn right at signpost for Flint Castle. Ground to right of car park. Flint BR station and bus stops are adjacent to ground.
Seats: 300 **Cover:** 500 **Capacity:** 6,000 **Floodlights:** Yes **Shop:** Yes
Programme: 36 pages, £1 **Editor:** Graham George (01352 735148) **Press Officer:** N Sheen
Colours: All black & white **Change colours:** Blue & white/white/white
Sponsors: **Nickname:** Silkmen **Founded:** 1886
Midweek matchday: Tuesday **Reserves League:** Clywd
Previous Leagues: Clwyd/ Welsh Alliance/ Cymru Alliance 90-92.
Clubhouse: Yes open every evening and matchdays.
97-98 - Captain: S Buxton **Top Scorer:** R McNeil **P.o.Y.:** S Jones
Honours: Cymru Alliance 90-91, Welsh Cup 53-54, Welsh Amtr Cup 47-48, Welsh All.(4) 54-57 89-90 (Alves Cup 53-54 89-90, Cookson Cup 52-53 88-89), Welsh Championship Cup 90-91, N. Wales Coast Chal. Cup 90-91, Nth Wales Coast Amtr Cup(8) 09-10 30-36 68-69.

HAVERFORDWEST COUNTY

Chairman: Roger Cottrell **Manager:** Eddie May
Secretary: Barry Vaughan, Tremy Gorsal, Chapel Road, Keston, Haverfordwest, Pembs SA62 6HL
Ground: Bridge Meadow Stadium, Haverfordwest Pembs.
Directions: Off the Safeway roundabout near town centre
Capacity: 4,000 **Covered Seats:** 500 **Floodlights:** Yes **Shop:** Yes
Colours: All Blue **Change colours:** Yellow/black
Midweek Matchday: Wednesday **Sponsor:** Calder Computers **Nickname:** Bluebirds
Programme: 20 pages 60p **Editor:** George Blythe **Press Officer:** Secretary
Honours: West Wales Sen Cup 81-82 88-89 91-92 92-93 97-98, R-up 37-38 49-50 56-57 60-61 80-81; Welsh Lge 56-57, R-up 67-70 70-71, Prem Div 80-81, National Div 89-90, Div 1 96-97, R-up 94-95 95-96; SA Brains Cup 88-89 R-up 84-85.

INTER-CABLE TEL

Chairman: Max James **Commercial Mgr:**
Secretary: John McTavish, 17 Coed Bach, Highlight Park, Barry CF62 8AE (01446 741144)
Manager: George Wood **Asst Manager:** Phil Holme **Physio:** Roy Langley
Ground: Cardiff Athletic Stadium, Leckwith Road, Cardiff (01222 225345)
Directions: M4 Junc 33 towards Penarth, A4232 past Culverhouse Cross turn off onto Leckwith Road, grd on right.
Capacity: 5,000 **Covered:** 2,500 **Seats:** 2,500 **Floodlights:** Yes **Shop:** Yes
Programme: 24 pages, £1 **Editor:** Colin Hicks. **Press Officer:** Clive Harry
Colours: White/black/red **Change colours:** All Yellow
Sponsors: Cabletel **Nickname:** Seagulls **Founded:** 1990.
Midweek Matchdays: Tuesday. **Record Attendance:** 1,500 v Everton August 1996.
Previous Leagues: Barry & District/ South Wales Amateur/ Abacus
97-98 - Captain: Sean Wharton **Top Scorer:** **P.o.Y.:**
Honours: League of Wales R-up 92-93 93-94 96-97, Abacus Lg Div 1 86-87, Sth Wales Amtr Lg 84-85 85-86. *As Sully: Sth Wales Amtr Lg Coronation Cup 69-70, Corinthian Cup 78-79, Abacus Lg Div 1 83-84 85-86 89-90 (Div 2 80-81), Sth Wales Snr Cup 80-81 81-82.*

NEWTOWN

President: Richard Edwards **Chairman:** Keith Harding **Manager:** Brian Coyne
Secretary: Mrs S Reynolds, 19 Brynwood Drive, Milford Rd, Newtown, Powys (01686 628089 H), (01686 626965 B), Fax (01681 623813)
Manager: Brian Coyne **Asst Manager:** Richard Pike **Physio:** Elwyn Morgan
Team Secretary: Howard Ellis **Match Sec/Press Officer:** John Anneran
Ground: Latham Park, Newtown, Powys (01686 622644/623120, Fax 623813)
Directions: A43 to Newtown, right at 1st lights into Back Lane & town centre - 400yds left into Park St., 500yds right (at Library) into Park Lane - ground at end.
Seats: 700 **Cover:** 500 **Capacity:** 5,000 **Floodlights:** Yes **Shop:** Yes.
Programme: 36 pages, £1 **Editor:** Keith Harding/ Nigel Bevan.
Colours: All red **Change colours:** Blue & yellow/blue/blue & yellow
Sponsors: Carlsberg **Nickname:** Robins **Founded:** 1875.
Midweek Matchdays: Tuesday. **Reserves League:** Mid Wales
Record Attendance: 5,002 v Swansea City, Welsh Cup 1954.
Previous Leagues: The Combination/ Central Wales/ Northern Premier.
Best FA Trophy year: 3rd Qual. 89-90 **Best FA Cup year:** 2nd Rd 1884-85. Also 1st Rd 1885-86.
Players progressing to Football League: C Lloyd (Orient), J Smout (C Palace & Exeter), M Bloor (Stoke & Lincoln), I Woan (Nottm Forest), J Hill (Rochdale), R Newlands (Plymouth), M Williams (Shrewsbury), Andy Cooke (Burnley), G Hanner (WBA), Peter Wilding/M Williams (Shrewsbury)
Clubhouse: Open every evening & matchday afternoons. Hot/cold snacks, pool, darts.
Honours: League of Wales R-up 95-96 97-98; Welsh Cup 1878-79 94-95 (R-up 85-65 87-88 96-97), Welsh Amtr Cup 1954-55, Central Wales Lg 75-76 78-79 81-82 86-87 87-88 (R-up 51-52 52-53 55-56 56-57 74-75 82-83, Lg Cup 54-55 56-57 74-75 75-76 81-82 83-84), Arthur Barritt Cup 86-87, Central Wales Cup 74-75 80-81 92-93, Emrys Morgan Cup 80-81.

PORTHMADOG

Chairman: R.J.Havelock **President:** William Pike
Secretary: Mr R I Griffiths, Llyn-yr-Eryr, Ynys, Cricieth, Gwynedd LL52 0PH (01766 810349).
Manager: Colin Hawkins **Physio:** Ifor Roberts
Ground: Y Traeth, Porthmadog, Gwynedd,(01766 514687). **Directions:** At town centre crossroads (by Woolworths) into Snowdon Str., pass RBL/Craft Centre onto unmade track, over railway line - ground on right.
Seats: 100 **Cover:** 400 **Capacity:** 4,000 **Floodlights:** Yes **Club Shop:** No.
Programme: 28 pages, 50p **Editor:** Dylan Ellis. **Founded:** 1884.
Colours: Red & black/black/black **Change:** Yellow/red/red **Nickname:** Porth.
Midweek Matchday: Wednesday. **Reserve League:** Gwynedd.
Record Attendance: 3,500 v Swansea, Welsh Cup 64-65.
Previous Leagues: N Wales/Gwynedd/Bangor & Dist/Lleyn & Dist/Cambrian Coast/Welsh All/Cymru All
Clubhouse: Not on ground (use Midland Hotel), but matchday refreshments available.
Honours: Welsh Amtr Cup(3) 55-58, N. Wales Amtr Cup 37-38 56-57 58-59 62-63, Lge of Wales Cup R-up 92-93, N. Wales Coast Chal. Cup(5) 55-56 73-75 76-78, Welsh All.(8) 02-03 37-38 66-69 74-76 89-90 (Cookson Cup 75-76 89-90, Barritt Cup 77-78, Alves Cup 65-66 73-74 76-77).

RHAYDER TOWN

Chairman: M A Pugh **Manager:** R Cross
Secretary: P Woosnam, Bwthyn Lon, Hazelmere, Rhayader, Powys LD6 5LG (01597 810067)
Ground: The Weirglodd, Bridge Street, Rhayader, Powys (01597 810067)
Colours: White & red/white & red/red **Change Colours:** Jade & white/jade & white/jade
Midweek Matchday: Wednesday

RHYL

Chairman: J B Williams **President:** R B G Webster
Secretary: Dennis McNamee, 3 Maes Rhosyn, Rhuddlan, (01745 591287 H)
Ground: Belle Vue, Grange Road, Rhyl, Clwyd (01745 338327).
Directions: A55 Expressway to Rhyl turn-off and follow signs thru Rhuddlan. Follow signs for Sun Centre along Pendyffryn Rd and turn left at junction - ground 200 yards on left.
Capacity: 4,000 **Floodlights:** Yes **Cover:** 1,200 **Seats:** 200 **Shop:** Yes
Programme: 40 pages £1 **Editor:** Ian Johnson (01745 353976) **Press Officer:** Graham Cartlidge
Colours: White/black/black **Change:** Blue/white/white
Sponsors: **Nickname:** Lilywhites **Founded:** 1883.
Midweek matches: Tuesday.
Record Attendance: 10,000 v Cardiff City, Welsh Cup 1953.
Previous Leagues: Cheshire County/ North West Counties/ Northern Premier/ Cymru Alliance 92-94.
Best FA Cup season: 4th Rd Proper 56-57 (lost 0-3 at Bristol City).
Players progressing to Football League: Ian Edwards, Grenville Millington, Brian Lloyd, Andy Holden, Barry Horne, Andy Jones.
Clubhouse:
Club record scorer: Don Spendlove. **Club record appearances:** Not known.
Honours: Welsh Cup 51-52 52-53 (R-up 29-30 36-37 92-93), Welsh Amateur Cup 72-73, Northern Premier Lg Presidents Cup 84-85, North West Counties Lg R-up 82-83, North Wales Coast Challenge Cup, Cheshire County Lg 47-48 50-51 71-72 (R-up 48-49 49-50 51-52 55-56, Div 2 R-up 81-82, Lg Cup 48-49 51-52 70-71, Div 2 Shield 81-82), Cyrmu Alliance 93-94 (R-up 92-93, Lg Cup 92-93).

TOTAL NETWORK SOLUTIONS

President: Mike Hughes. **Chairman:** Edgar Jones **Vice-Chairman:** Tony Williams
Secretary: Gwynfor Hughes, Birch Lea, Porthywaen, Oswestry, Shrops SY10 8LY (01691 828645 H), (01691 828862 Fax)
Manager: Dr Andy Cale **Asst Manager:** Peter Hepper **Physio:** Gordon Evans.
Ground: Recreation Park, Treflan, Llansantffraid (01691 828112).
Directions: A470 between Oswestry and Welshpool, right for Llansantffraid at Llynclys, follow signs to village. Turn opposite Mill silos towards Community Centre. Ground is behind housing estate.
Seats: 120 **Cover:** 250 **Capacity:** 1,500 **Floodlights:** Yes **Shop:** Yes
Programme: 36 pages, £1 **Editor:** Norman Langley
Colours: All Green **Change:** Red/black/black.
Sponsors: Total Network Solutions. **Nickname:** The Saints. **Founded:** 1959
Midweek Matchedays: Wednesday **Reserves League:** Montgomeryshire Lge
Record Attendance: 2,100 v KS Ruch Chorzow Euro Cup Winners 96
Previous League: Mid-Wales/ Cymru Alliance (pre-1993)
Clubhouse: Open weekends & evenings during week
97-98 - Captain: Garry Evans **P.o.Y.:** Arwell Jones **Top Scorer:** Adrian Jones
Club Record Goalscorer: Adrian Jones **Club Record Appearances:** Andy Mulliner
Honours: Welsh Cup 95-96; Welsh Intermediate Cup 92-93; League of Wales Cup 94-95; Cymru Alliance Lge 92-93, R-up 91-92; Central Wales Sen Cup R-up 92-93 97-98; Central Wales Lg R-up 90-91 94-95 95-96, Lge Cup 95-96; Montgomeryshire Amtr Lg (7), Village Cup (17); Montgomeryshire Cup R-up 82-83 96-97, Euro Cup Winners Cup Prem Rd 96-97.

WELSHPOOL

Chairman: M G Edwards. **Manager:** Gareth Cadwallader
Secretary: Mr J A Bartley, 24 Bryn Glas, Welshpool, Powys SY21 7TL (01938 552131 H), (01686 626246 B).
Ground: Maesydre Recreation Ground, Welshpool, Powys.
Directions:
Seats: **Cover:** 100 **Capacity:** **Floodlights:** **Club Shop:**
Colours: White/black/white **Change colours:** Red/black/black
Sponsors: **Nickname:** Seasiders **Founded:** 1878
Midweek Matchday: Wednesday

Away supporters are sometimes shy
Photo: Kevin Black

SCOTTISH FOOTBALL

OVD SCOTTISH JUNIOR CUP

FINAL (Sunday, 17th May 1998. At Fir Park, Motherwell)

ARTHURLIE v POLLOK 4-0

McLaughlin,
Millar,
Convery,
Nugent

H.T. 2-0 Attendance: 4,751

ARTHURLIE: D Cormack; G Duncan, M McLaughlin, S Allison, G Gardner, M McGarvey, J Millar, S Archer, S Quigg, D Fulton (captin), S Convery. Substitutes: S Nugent for McLaughlin 75 minutes, S McLean for Cormack 81 minutes, S Watson for Quigg 84 minutes; R Brown, B Phillips not used. Yellow cards: Millar, McGarvey.

POLLOK: R Lowrie; K O'Neil, C Cranmer, I Spittal (captain), I Ashcroft, D Elliot, D Fontana, P McLean, J Paisley, D Diver, J Morrison. Substitutes: D Walker for Spittal 27 minutes, M Thompson for Paisley 62 minutes; S Bonnar, I McLaughlan, G Smith not used. Yellow cards: Elliot, Ashcroft, O'Neil. Red card: Elliot.

Referee: C Hardie.

SCOTTISH JUNIOR CUP LAST TEN FINALS

1996-97	Pollok	v	Tayport	3-1	at Motherwell FC	Att: 3523
1995-96	Tayport	v	Camelon	2-0	at Motherwell FC	Att: 4652
1994-95	Camelon	v	Whitburn	2-0	at Motherwell FC	Att: 8019
1993-94	Largs Thistle	v	Glenafton Ath	1-0	at Motherwell FC	Att: 8668
1992-93	Glenafton Ath	v	Tayport	1-0	at Partick Th FC	Att: 6250
1991-92	Auchinleck T	v	Glenafton Ath	4-0	at Partick Th FC	Att: 8000
1990-91	Auchinleck T	v	Newtongrange	1-0	at Falkirk FC	Att: 8000
1989-90	Hill of B Hawth	v	Lesmahagow	1-0	at Kilmarnock FC	Att: 5800
1988-89	Cumnock	v	Ormiston P	1-0	at Kilmarnock FC	
1987-88	Auchinleck T	v	Petershill	1-0	at Kilmarnock FC	Att: 9260

HIGHLAND LEAGUE

HIGHLAND LEAGUE TABLE

	P	W	D	L	F	A	Pts
Huntly	30	22	5	3	92	32	71
Fraserburgh	30	21	4	5	69	31	67
Peterhead	30	20	5	5	88	34	65
Cove Rangers	30	19	4	7	101	39	61
Elgin City	30	16	7	7	59	33	55
Keith	30	15	6	9	65	54	51
Forres Mechanics	30	13	6	11	64	58	45
Clachnacuddin	30	14	3	13	59	57	45
Deveronvale	30	11	6	13	59	61	39
Buckie Thistle	30	11	6	13	42	47	39
Brora Rangers	30	10	4	16	54	66	34
Lossiemouth	30	9	6	15	39	66	33
Rothes	30	7	8	15	41	56	29
Wick Academy	30	5	5	20	40	74	20
Fort William	30	3	4	23	31	130	13
Nairn County	30	3	3	24	30	94	12

Huntly are champions for a fifth consecutive season.

NORTH CALEDONIAN LEAGUE

	P	W	D	L	F	A	Pts
Inverness CT 'A'	20	16	2	2	84	23	34
Balintore	20	15	2	3	70	27	32
Golspie Sutherland	20	13	4	3	72	25	30
Alness United	20	10	3	7	45	20	23
Ross County 'A'	20	10	2	8	76	37	22
Halkirk	20	8	5	7	55	38	21
Invergordon	20	10	0	10	44	46	20
Tain	20	7	3	10	43	34	17
Bunillidh Bridge	20	4	2	14	30	66	10
Bonar Bridge	20	4	2	14	30	87	10
Dornoch	20	0	1	19	15	141	1

NB: This is the most senior league in the North of Scotland after the Highland League. In the new season Ross County 'A' have been withdrawn and replaced by Thurso FC.

Huntly - Highland League champions for the fifth consecutive season

HIGHLAND LEAGUE CUP

QUALIFYING TABLES

Group 1

	P	W	D	L	F	A	Pts
FRASERBURGH	3	3	0	0	10	1	9
Peterhead	3	1	0	2	5	4	3
Deveronvale	3	1	1	1	3	7	3
Rothes	3	0	1	2	1	7	1

Group 2

	P	W	D	L	F	A	Pts
COVE RANGERS	3	3	0	0	8	2	9
Buckie Thistle	3	1	1	1	3	5	4
Keith	3	0	2	1	3	4	2
Huntly	3	0	1	2	3	6	1

Group 3

	P	W	D	L	F	A	Pts
ELGIN CITY	3	2	1	0	10	5	7
FORRES MECHS	3	2	1	0	10	5	7
Lossiemouth	3	1	0	2	6	8	3
Nairn County	3	0	0	3	7	15	0

Elgin City (h) beat Forres Mechanics (3-0 after extra-time) in the play-off for a semi-final place.

Group 4

	P	W	D	L	F	A	Pts
BRORA RNGRS	3	2	1	0	6	3	7
Clachnacuddin	3	2	0	1	8	3	6
Fort William	3	1	0	2	2	8	3
Wick Academy	3	0	1	2	4	6	1

Semi-finals: (Saturday, 23rd August 1997)

Cove Rangers	v	Fraserburgh	4-1	Elgin City	v	Brora Rangers	2-0

FINAL (Saturday, 13th September 1997. At Christie Park, Huntly)

COVE RANGERS v ELGIN CITY 0-1 H.T. 0-1
Polworth 21

COVE RANGERS: Charles; Megginson, Whyte, Smart, Gerrad, Nicol, Park, Wilson, Coull, Presslie, Pilichos. Substitutes: Johnston for Gerrad 46 minutes, Ritchie for Coull 61 minutes, Morrison for Whyte 72 minutes.
ELGIN CITY: Pirie; Dunsire, McVicar, O'Brien, McHardy, Cameron, Whyte, Greem Polworth, Scott, Ord. Substitutes: Morrison, McLennan, McDonald (none used).
Referee: G Simpson, Aberdeen.

SCOTTISH QUALIFYING CUP

NORTH

First Round (Saturday, 30th August 1997)

Golspie Sutherland v Forres Mechanics 1-1

Replay (Saturday, 13th September 1997)

Forres Mechanics v Golspie Sutherland 2-2 (aet; Golspie Sutherland win 3-2 on penalties)

Second Round	(Saturday, 20th September 1997)						
Clachnaccuddin	v	Elgin City	1-2	Cove Rangers	v	Deveronvale	0-0
Fort William	v	Brora Rangers	1-1	Fraserburgh	v	Golspie Sutherland	6-0
Huntly	v	Wick Academy	3-2	Keith	v	Peterhead	1-3
Nairn County	v	Buckie Thistle	1-1	Rothes	v	Lossiemouth	0-1
Replays	(Saturday, 27th September 1997)Deveronvale			v		Cove Rangers	2-1
Brora Rangers	v	Fort William	2-3	Buckie Thistle	v	Nairn County	2-1
Quarter-finals	(Saturday, 4th October 1997)						
Deveronvale	v	Buckie Thistle	5-0	Elgin City	v	Lossiemouth	0-0
Fraserburgh	v	Fort William	9-0	Peterhead	v	Huntly	0-0
Replays	(Saturday, 11th October 1997)						
Huntly	v	Peterhead	5-6	Lossiemouth	v	Elgin City	2-1
Semi-finals	(Saturday, 18th October 1997)						
Deveronvale	v	Fraserburgh	1-2	Peterhead	v	Lossiemouth	2-2
Replay	(Saturday, 25th October 1997)						
Lossiemouth	v	Peterhead	1-4				

FINAL (Saturday, 8th November 1997, at Christie Park, Huntly)

FRASERBURGH v PETERHEAD 0-8 H.T. 0-5

Milne (2), Smith (2), Yule (1), Clark (1), Paterson (1), Cormack (1)

FRASERBURGH: Gordon; Milne Michie, A Stephen, Geddes, McBride, Keith, Hunter, M Stephen, Murray, Norris. Substitutes: McCafferty, Killoh, Wemyss. Yellow cards: McBride, Hunter.
PETERHEAD: Pirie; Clark, Cheyne, King, Simpson, Yule, Smith, Paterson, Milne, Brown, Livingstone.
Substitutes: McKenzie, Cormack, Baxter. Yellow card: Milne.
Referee: W Young, Clarkston.

In an astonishing final played on a quagmire in Huntly the Blue Tooners took charge from the kick-off and were already three up in ten minutes with goals by Yule (an unchallenged header from 10 yards out) and a pair from Milne - one after a twisting run and neat chip and the other after a deflection past Gordon. In 23 minutes Smith tapped in a rebound from the bar after another Yule effort and then headed home goal No 5 just on half-time.

There would be no way back for Broch but they held out until 63 minutes before Clark picked his spot after a Yule cutback. and in another two minutes Paterson made it seven as he headed home from a Livingstone left-wing centre. It remained for Cormack, on as a substitute, to complete the rout.

What more can be said? The Fraserburgh fans in a crowd of 1,427 were on their way home long before the final whistle and who can blame them? It was hard to believe that Broch were leading the league table at the time.

Peterhead with the Qualifying Cup they won in such style last November

SOUTH

First Round	(Saturday, 30th August 1997)						
Burntisland Shipyard	v	Glasgow University	0-0	Dalbeattie Star	v	Tarff Rovers	1-5
Preston Athletic	v	Whitehill Welfare	2-2	St Cuthbert W	v	Vale of Leithen	0-2
Spartans	v	Gala Fairydean	3-3				
Replays	(Saturday, 6th September 1997)						
Gala Fairydean	v	Spartans	1-4	Glasgow Univ	v	Burntisland Shipyard	1-4
Whitehill Welfare	v	Preston Athletic	3-2				

Second Round	(Saturday, 20th September 1997)						
Annan Athletic	v	Edinburgh University	3-1	Burntisland S	v	Coldstream	1-2
Civil S. Strollers	v	Hawick Royal Albert	2-1	Girvan	v	Wigtown & Bladnoch	2-1
Newton Stewart	v	Whitehill Welfare	0-8	Spartans	v	Selkirk	0-2
Tarff Rovers	v	Edinburgh City	1-4	Vale of Leithen	v	Threave Rovers	0-0
Replay	(Saturday, 27th September 1997)						
Threave Rovers	v	Vale of Leithen	2-3				

Quarter-finals	(Saturday, 4th October 1997)						
Annan Athletic	v	Coldstream	4-2	Girvan	v	Edinburgh City	1-2
Vale of Leithen	v	Civil Service Strollers	1-0	Whitehill Welfare	v	Selkirk	3-0

Semi-finals	(Saturday, 18th October 1997)						
Annan Athletic	v	Edinburgh City	2-0	Whitehill Welfare	v	Vale of Leithen	3-0

FINAL Saturday, 8th November 1997. At Livingston FC)

WHITEHILL WELF.	v	ANNAN ATHLETIC	3-2
McGovern (2),		Montgomery (1)	
Bennett (1)		Cochrane (1)	

INVERNESS CUP

1996-97 Final

INVERNESS C. T. v ROSS COUNTY 2-0 (played in October 1997)

1997-98

First Round							
Brora Rangers	v	Ross County 'A'	3-2	Forres Mech's	v	Fort William	4-3 aet
Inverness C. T. 'A'	v	Lossiemouth	7-2	Nairn County	v	Clachnacuddin	0-4

Semi-finals							
Brora Rangers	v	Clachnacuddin	0-3	Forres Mech's	v	Inverness C. T. 'A'	1-6

FINAL (at Caledonian Stadium, Inverness)

INVERNESS C. T. 'A' v CLACHNACUDDIN 2-1

ABERDEENSHIRE SHIELD

First Round							
Cove Rangers	v	Keith	1-2	Deveronvale	v	Huntly	2-1
Fraserburgh	v	Keith	2-2				
Replay							
Keith	v	Fraserburgh	3-2				

Semi-finals							
Keith	v	Buckie Thistle	4-1	Peterhead	v	Deveronvale	3-1 aet

FINAL (Wednesday, 3rd December 1997. In Banff)

KEITH v PETERHEAD 3-2

Northern Cup Finals:

PCT North Caledonian Cup
(final at Tain)
Balintore v Invergordon 3-2

Chic Allan Cup
(final at Caledonian Stadium Inverness)
Balintore v Ross County 'A' 3-2

Morris Newton Cup
(final at Victoria Park, Dingwall)
Invergordon v Inverness C. T. 'A' 2-2
(Invergordon won 5-4 on penalties)

Football Times Cup
(final at Tain)
Balintore v Alness United 2-1

NON-LEAGUE CLUBS IN THE SCOTTISH CUP PROPER

First Round

Saturday, 6th December 1997

Inverness C. T.	v	Whitehill Welfare	3-1

Saturday, 13th December 1997

Fraserburgh	v	Clyde	1-0

Second Round

Saturday, 3rd January 1998

Annan Athletic	v	Vale of Leithen	3-1
Lossiemouth	v	Dumbarton	0-1
Peterhead	v	Alloa	0-2

Saturday, 10th January 1998

East Stirlingshire	v	Edinburgh C.	1-1, 0-0, 3p4
Stenhousemuir	v	Deveronvale	4-0
Stranraer	v	Fraserburgh	2-1

Third Round Saturday, 24th January 1997

Dunfermline Athletic	v	Edinburgh City	7-2
Inverness C. T.	v	Annan Athletic	8-1

JARLAW ABERDEENSHIRE CUP CENTENNIAL 1997-98

First Round

(Tuedsay, Wednesday, 10th/11th March 1998)

Deveronvale	v	Huntly	2-1
Fraserburgh	v	Keith	2-2, 2-3
Peterhead	v	Buckie Thistle	3-0

(Monday, 16th March 1998)

Cove Rangers	v	Aberdeen 'A'	2-4

Semi-finals (Saturday, 28th March 1998)

Deveronvale	v	Peterhead	1-0
Keith	v	Aberdeen	1-5

FINAL (Sunday, 12th April 1998. At Kynoch Park, Keith)

ABERDEEN v DEVERONVALE 5-1 H.T. 3-1

Wyness 3 — Douglas

Duncan

Derek Young

ABERDEEN: Watt; Hart, Good, Darren Young, Newlands, Brown, Duncan, Bett, Wyness, Derek Young, Milne. Substitutes: Clark for Good, Craig for Bett. Red card: Newlands.
DEVERONVALE: Grant; Gray, Simmers, Montgomery, Hendesron, Souden, Milne, Douglas, Rowley, Yeats, Dolan. Substitute: Ellis for Rowley.
Referee: A Roy, Westhill.

McEWAN'S LAGER NORTH OF SCOTLAND CUP 1997-98

First Round (Saturday, 14th March 1998)

Brora Rangers	v	Lossiemouth	2-1
Nairn County	v	Elgin City	0-2
Inverness C. T.	v	Forres Mechanics	1-1
Rothes	v	Ross County	2-1

First Round Replay (Saturday, 21st March 1998)

Forres Mechanics	v	Inverness C. Thistle	1-2

Quarter-finals

(Saturday, 21st March 1998)

Brora Rangers	v	Elgin City	0-3
Fort William	v	Golspie Sutherland	3-0
Rothes	v	Wick Acad.	2-2, 1-1, 2p4

(Saturday, 28th March 1998)

Inverness C. T.	v	Clachnacuddin	2-1

Semi-finals (Saturday, 4th April 1998)

Fort William	v	Elgin City	0-2
Wick Academy	v	Inverness C. T.	0- 0, 1-2

FINAL (Saturday, 25th April 1998. At Caledonian Stadium, Inverness)

ELGIN CITY v INVERNESS C.T. 'A' 3-1 H.T. 1-1

Maguire — Tokely

Polworth

Cameron

ELGIN CITY: Pirie; Dunsire, McVittie, McLenanan, McHardy, O'Brien, Whyte, Green, Polworth, Maguire, Cameron. Substitutes: Ord, Moir, McDonald.
INVERNESS CALEDONIAN THISTLE 'A': Fridge; McCuish, Munro, Noble, Allan, Tokely, McLeod, Hind, Huband, Calderwood, Craig. Substitutes: K MacDonald, P MacDonald, Sanderson.
Referee: M Ritchie, Macduff.

EAST OF SCOTLAND LEAGUE

FINAL LEAGUE TABLES 1997-98

PREMIER DIVISION

	P	W	D	L	F	A	Pts
Whitehill Welfare	18	13	3	2	48	19	42
Spartans	18	8	5	5	37	26	29
Craigroyston	18	8	5	5	27	28	29
Annan Athletic	18	8	4	6	44	28	28
Edinburgh City	18	8	4	6	31	23	38
Civil Service Str	18	8	3	7	30	31	27
Lothian Thistle	18	5	7	6	25	36	22
Pencaitland	18	5	6	7	27	28	21
Gala Fairydean	18	8	3	9	24	39	21
Edinburgh Athletic	18	0	2	16	19	54	2

FIRST DIVISION

	P	W	D	L	F	A	Pts
Peebles Rovers	22	14	4	4	44	22	46
Tollcross United	22	13	7	2	40	20	46
Coldstream	22	12	5	5	46	25	41
Preston Athletic	22	12	4	6	43	25	40
Edinburgh Univ	22	9	8	5	31	25	35
Kelso United	22	8	6	8	44	41	30
Vale of Leithen	22	8	5	9	46	37	29
Easthouses Lily	22	7	6	9	27	29	27
Hawick Royal Alb.	22	6	7	9	38	42	25
Selkirk	22	5	8	9	33	49	23
Heriot Watt Univ	22	4	2	16	25	56	14
Eyemouth United	22	2	2	18	18	64	8

EAST LEAGUE CUP

Quarter-finals

Craigroyston V Annan Athletic 1-1aet, 4p3
Spartans v Lothian Thistle 1-1 aet, 3p5
Eyemouth United v Tollcross 2-4 aet
Whitehill Welfare v Preston Athletic 2-1

Semi-finals

Craigroyston v Lothian Thistle 2-1
Whitehill Welfare v Tollcross United 4-0

FINAL (Sunday, 3rd May 1998. At Pennypit Stadium, Preston)

WHITEHILL WELF. v CRAIGROYSTON 3-0

IMAGE PRINTERS EAST OF SCOTLAND QUALIFYING CUP

Quarter-finals

Gala Fairydean v Pencaitland 4-1
Tollcross United v Kelso United 2-2, 7-3
Spartans v Lothian Thistle 2- 0
Whitehill Welfare v Craigroyston 2-1

Semi-finals

Gala Fairydean v Tollcross United 1-0
Whitehill Welfare v Spartans 1-2

FINAL (Sunday, 22nd March 1998. In Innerleithen)

SPARTANS v GALA FAIRYDEAN 2-0

ALEX JACK CUP

First Round

Heriot Watt Univ v Pencaitland 0-6
Kelso United v Craigroyston 3-2

Quarter-finals

Edinburgh Athletic v Lothian Thistle 0-6
Peebles Rovers v Pencaitland 1-2
Kelso United v Easthouses Lily 2-7
Tollcross United v Eyemouth United 1-0

Semi-finals

Easthouses Lily v Tollcross United 0-3
Pencaitland v Lothian Thistle 0-2

FINAL (Sunday, 25th January 1998. At Whitehill Welfare FC)

TOLLCROSS UTD v LOTHIAN THISTLE 2-1 (After extra-time - score 1-1 at 90 minutes)

CITY CUP

Semi-finals

Berwick Rangers v Spartans 2-3
Livingston v Gala Fairydean 3-1

FINAL (Monday, 11th May 1998. At Livingston)

LIVINGSTON v SPARTANS 1-2

'CLUB SERVICES' KING CUP

Third Round

Heriot Watt University v Craigroyston 0-1
Lothian Thistle v Gala Fairydean 5-1
Edinburgh Ath v Whitehill Welfare 1-9
Tollcross United v Civil Service Strollers 1-1

Replay
Civil Service Strollers v Tollcross United 3-0

Semi-finals

Civil Service Strollers v Lothian Thistle 1-0
Whitehill Welfare v Craigroyston 1-0

FINAL (Tuesday, 12th May 1998. At Whitehill Welfare FC)
WHITEHILL WELF. v CIVIL SERVICE STR. 3-2

NB: Whitehill Welfare won three of the four East of Scotland competitions they entered plus the South Qualifying Cup. Threave Rovers have transferred to the East of Scotland League from the South of Scotland League.

SOUTH OF SCOTLAND LEAGUE

FINAL LEAGUE TABLE 1997-98

	P	W	D	L	F	A	Pts
Tarff Rovers	24	21	2	1	75	19	65
Threave Rovers	24	21	0	3	113	25	63
Dumfries HS FP	24	14	2	8	71	48	44
Creetown	24	14	2	8	72	52	44
St Cuthbert Wands	24	13	3	8	56	48	42
Dalbeattie Star	24	11	5	8	55	48	38
Girvan	24	9	4	11	65	86	31
Annan Athletic	24	8	6	10	55	56	30
Stranraer Athletic	24	7	3	14	46	70	24
Maxwelltown HSFP	24	6	2	16	43	82	20
Wigtown/Bladnoch	24	4	7	13	35	49	19
Newton Stewart	24	3	5	16	26	77	14
Blackwood D'mos	24	3	3	18	31	85	12

LEAGUE CUP

Semi-finals (first legs)

Creetown v Tarff Rovers 2-2
Threave Rovers v Annan Athletic 3-1

Semi-finals (second legs)

Tarff Rovers v Creetown 8-1
(Tarff Rovers win by 10-3 aggregate)
Annan Athletic v Threave Rovers 0-4
(Threave Rovers win by 7-1 aggregate)

FINAL

(first leg - Saturday, 23rd August 1998)
Threave Rovers v Tarff Rovers 1-1
A McGinlay — Milligan

(second leg - Saturday, 13th September 1998)
Tarff Rovers v Threave Rovers 4-1
Simpson (3), McSkimming (1) — P McGinlay

AGGREGATE: TARFF ROVERS v THREAVE ROVERS 5-2

SOUTHERN COUNTIES CHALLENGE CUP

First Round

Creetwon v Queen of the South 'A' 1-3
St Cuthbert Wndrs v Annan Athletic 2-4
Tarff Rovers v Blackwood Dynamos 5-1
Dumfries HS FP v Maxwelltown HS FP 3-1
Stranraer Athletic v Stranraer 'A' 1-6
Threave Rovers v Dalbeattie Star 5-1 aet

Second Round

Newtown Stewart v Wigtown & Bladnoch 3-2
Stranraer 'A' v Annan Athletic 4-2
Queen of Sth 'A' v Dumfries HS FP 5-2
Tarff Rovers v Threave Rovers 0-2

Semi-finals

Newton Stewart v Queen of the South 'A' 3-2
Stranraer 'A' v Threave Rovers 0-2

FINAL (Wednesday, 13th May 1998. At Blairmont Park, Newton Stewart)
BEWTON STEWART v THREAVE ROVERS 1-5
McDonald — Docherty (2), Adams (2), Fraser (1)

POTTS CUP

Second Round

Blackwood Dynamos	v	Newton Stewart	2-3	Creetown	v	Stranraer Athletic	7-2
Dalbeattie Star	v	Wigtown & Bladnoch	4-1	Threave Rovers	v	Tarff Rovers	1-4

Semi-finals

Dalbeattie Star	v	Newton Stewart 5-5 aet, 4p3	Tarff Rovers	v	Creetown 3-3 aet, 8p7

FINAL (Saturday, 18th April 1998. At Blairmont Park, Newton Stewart)

NEWTON STEWART v TARFF ROVERS 0-3

Simpson (1), G True (1), Hunter (1)

HAIG GORDON MEMORIAL TROPHY

Second Round

Dumfries HS FP	v	Threave Rovers	3-4	Newton Stewart	v	Maxwelltown HS FP	4-3
St Cuthbert Wndrs	v	Annan Athletic	5-0	Tarff Rovers	v	Creetown	1-0

Semi-finals

Newton Stewart	v	Tarff Rovers	3-1	Threave Rovers	v	St Cuthbert Wndrs	1-2

FINAL (Saturday, 9th May 1998. At Blairmont Park, Newton Stewart)

NEWTON STEWART v ST CUTHBERT W 1-4

Own goal — Blount (2), Simpson (1), Bennieworth (1)

TWEEDIE CUP

Second Round

Dalbeattie Star	v	Creetown	2-4	St Cuthbert W	v	Threave Rovers	2-0
Stranraer Athletic	v	Tarff Rovers	1-5	Wigtown/Blad.	v	Annan Ath. 0-0 aet, 3p4	

Semi-finals

Creetown	v	Annan Athletic	1-4	Tarff Rovers	v	St Cuthbert Wndrs	5-1

FINAL (Saturday, 25th April 1998)

TARFF ROVERS v ANNAN ATHLETIC 2-0

Robinson (1),
Hunter (1)

CREE LODGE CUP

Second Round

Annan Athletic	v	St Cuthbert Wanderers	7-2	Blackwood D'mos	v	Tarff Rovers	3-8
Newton Stewart	v	Threave Rovers	1-3	Wigtown & Blad.	v	Girvan	6-2

Semi-finals

Tarff Rovers	v	Annan Athletic	2-0	Wigtown & Blad.	v	Threave Rovers	0-4

FINAL (Saturday, 11th April 1998. At Meadow Park, Castle Douglas)

THREAVE ROVERS v TARFF ROVERS 0-1

Hunter

NB: In the Second Round Paul Stewart (Tarff Rvrs) scored 7 goals and Norman Montgomery (Annan Ath.) 6 goals.

DETROIT TROPHY

(Overall Champions - First four places

Tarff Rovers	91 points
Threave Rovers	79 points
Creetwon	50 points
St Cuthbert Wands	47 points (- three points)

JUNIORS

(With thanks to Stewart Davidson, editor of the Scottish Non-League Review of 1996-97)

On a beautiful afternoon at Motherwell's neat Fir Park Stadium Arthurlie confunded all pre-match forecasts from the experts to thrash holders Pollok by four clear goals, and there was nothing flattering about the final scoreline so total was their skilful domination of a one-sided match. Even the lunacy of David Elliot, which led to his dismissal before half-time, made no difference to the ultimate result.

The Barrhead club's only previous success in the competition had been in 1937, and they had been runners-up in 1945-46 and 1980-81, when they lost unfortunately to the same club whom they faced in the hot sun this year, so they had some lost time to make up and this they did with a vengeance scoring two goals in the first 28 minutes plus a couple of missed chances in between.

The scoring started in the seventh minute when a concerted attack saw Quigg cleverly head the ball across the rear of the area in the direction of left-back Mark McLaughlin, whose left foot drove a powerful shot against the inside of Lowrie's left-hand post and from there into the net.

'Lok's cause was then further damaged by an injury to skipper and 1997 hero Ian Spittal and, while the team was adjusting to his departure with Walker taking his place, a bouncing ball to veteran John Millar was gathered first time and lobbed past the hestitant Ronnie Lowrie, who was not enjoying one of his better days in any case. Millar was shortly to become the game's first booking for failing to retreat at a free kick, but that was the only blight on his afternoon.

The Glasgow club had everything to do and their chances virtually vanished when midfielder David Elliot, who had scored a decisive third goal a year earlier, found himself entering the referee's notebook after yet another aggressive challenge brought about probably by frustration - this time on David Fulton. Instead of accepting the decision with dignity Elliot then sarcastically appauded referee Colin Hardie's action and the latter with a dexterity, which would have done justice to a Dodge City poker player, swiftly flashed a second yellow card followed by the inevitable red, which meant a free afternoon for the rest of the action for the errant midfielder. It was an irony that only a few minutes before the event The Sun's Scott Campbell had suggested that Elliot might not see out the game, little realising that he was soon to be proved right.

The second half became a formality and The Lea coasted through it with only occasional Pollok thrusts and a last minute shot from Diver to shake them. A marvellous run and square pass by Millar set up Convery for a third goal on the hour - he only had Lowrie to beat - and when the 35-year-old veteran Steve Nugent was sent on in place of the brilliant McLaughlin with fifteen minutes left he duly said his thanks with a superb shot through a crowded defence after he had been on the field for six minutes. Man of the match John Millar was the provider yet again.

Arthurlie could have scored more, but their shooting since there was no pressure on them was off target, although their approach play was excellent to watch and the leadership of David Fulton, the second player of that name to pick up a cup in 24 hours, was faultless, an adjective that can particularly be applied to the whole defence, which picked off puny 'Lok attacks with ease and apart from the hard working John Morrison few of the losers' men earned any credit marks. Referee Hardie had no choice with the Elliot dismissal and had a sound match.

It was no fault of the winners that they were able to stroll through the second half, but their display in general would have done justice to an even bigger occasion, which deserved a larger attendance. Skilled football with cool work in both defence and attack justifies any long journey.

BILL MITCHELL

Fifth Round

Arthurlie	v	Petershill	5-1	Johnstone Boro	v	Maryhill	2-4
Kilbirnie Ladeside	v	Hill of Beath Hawthorn	1-1	Larkhall Thistle	v	Beith	1-2
Neilston	v	Auchenleck Talbot	1-0	St Josephs	v	Pollok	1-2
Shettleston	v	Kilwinning Rangers	0-1	Tayport	v	Linlithgow Rose	2-0

Replay

Hill of Beath Hawthorn	v	Kilbirnie Ladeside	3-0

Quarter-finals

Arthurlie	v	Beith	2-2	Kilwinning Rngrs	v	Hill of Beath Hawth.	2-2
Neilston	v	Maryhill	1-4	Tayport	v	Pollok	3-3.

Replays

Beith	v	Arthurlie	2-3 aet	Pollok	v	Tayport	0-0 aet, 5p3

Semi-final

(Friday, 1st May 1998. At Love Street, Paisley):

Arthurie	v	Kilwinning R	2-2 aet, 4p2

(Sat, 2nd May 1998. At Firhill Park, Glasgow):

Maryhill	v	Pollok	0-3

FINAL

Arthurlie	v	Pollok	4-0

'WHYTE & MacKAY' WEST OF SCOTLAND CUP

Fourth Round

Auchinleck Talbot	v	Pollok	1-1 aet, 2p4	Cumnock	v	Glenafton Athletic	2-1
Neilston	v	Blantyre Victoria	4-2	Petershill	v	Johnstone B	1-1 aet, 4p3

Semi-finals

Cumnock v Petershill 1-1 (aet - Petershill won 3-1 on penalties)

FINAL (Saturday, 23rd May 1998. At Somervell Park, Cambuslang)

PETERSHILL v POLLOK 1-3 (after extra-time - score at 90 minutes 1-1)

Dunne — Elliot (2), Paisley (1)

1997-98 Whyte & MacKay West of Scotland Cup quarter final action. Auchinleck Talbot v Pollok (black & white). Pollok went on to win the cup.
Photo: John B Vass

AYRSHIRE DISTRICT LEAGUE

FINAL LEAGUE TABLES 1997-98

DIVISION ONE

	P	W	D	L	F	A	Pts
Cumnock Rovers	20	14	3	3	44	20	45
Auchinleck Talbot	20	13	4	3	38	17	43
Kilwinning Rangers	20	10	7	3	56	32	37
Glenafton Athletic	20	8	5	7	32	27	29
Beith Juniors	20	7	6	7	34	33	27
Troon	20	7	5	8	31	33	26
Kilbirnie Ladeside	20	6	5	9	22	37	23
Dalry Thistle	20	6	5	9	30	33	23
Largs Thistle	20	6	5	9	22	37	23
Irvine Meadow XI	20	6	3	11	32	47	21
Muirkirk Juniors	20	2	2	16	19	50	8

DIVISION TWO

(first five positions)

	P	W	D	L	F	A	Pts
Ardrossan W'ton R	22	14	3	5	56	28	45
Annbank United	22	12	6	4	59	35	42
Craigmark Burnt	22	12	4	6	48	27	40
Ardeer Thistle	22	10	7	5	53	40	37
Maybole Juniors	22	9	5	8	42	32	32

Other teams and points:
Irvine Victoria (32), Lugar Boswell Thistle (30), Darvel Juniors (30), Kello Rovers (29), Saltcoats Victoria (26), Whitletts Victoria (13), Hurlford United (10).

AYRSHIRE LEAGUE (JACKIE SCARLETT CUP)

Quarter-finals:

Glenafton Athletic	v	Craigmark Burntonians	7-1
Kilbirnie Ladeside	v	Troon	3-2
Irvine Meadow	v	Beith	1-4
Maybole	v	Auchinleck Talbot	0-4

Semi-finals

Beith	v	Kilbirnie Ladeside	2-1
Auchinleck Talbot	v	Glenafton Athletic	2-1

FINAL (Monday, 29th September 1997. At Somerset Park, Ayr)

AUCHINLECK T'BOT v BEITH 2-1

Auchinleck Talbot - Winners of the Jackie Scarlett Cup 1997-98
Photo: John B Vass

1997-98 Ayrshire Region Jackie Scarlett Cup action
Auchinleck Talbot (who went on to win the cup) v Glenafton Athletic
Photo: John B Vass

ARDROSSAN & SALTCOATS HERALD AYRSHIRE JUNIOR CUP

THIRD ROUND

Ardrossan W Rovers	v	Kilbirnie Ladeside	0-2	Hurlford United	v	Troon	1-3
Irvine Meadow	v	Cumnock	0-0, 2-1	Kilwinning Rngrs	v	Auchinleck Talbot	2-1

SEMI-FINALS

Irvine Meadow	v	Troon	2-4	Kilbirnie Ladeside	v	Kilwinning Rangers	1-4

FINAL (Friday 12th June 1998. At Meadow Park, Irvine)

KILWINNING RGRS v TROON 3-2
Sloan (2) — Hume (2)
McCaffrey (1)

'IRVINE TIMES' AYRSHIRE DISTRICT CUP

THIRD ROUND

Auchinleck Talbot	v	Troon	3-1	Craigmark Br.	v	Ardrossan W Rvrs	0-1
Dairy Thistle	v	Irvine Meadow	1-1, 2p3	Kilbirne Ladeside	v	Glenafton Ath.	1-1, 2p3

SEMI-FINALS

Ardrossan W Rovers	v	Glenafton Athletic	0-5	Irvine Meadow	v	Auchinleck T	1-1, 4p3

FINAL (Saturday 4th April 1998. At Townhead Park Cumnock)

GLENAFTON A v IRVINE MEADOW 4-1
McLaren (2) — McCrindle (1)
Gibson (1)
Raeburn (1)

NORTH AYRSHIRE CUP

SEMI-FINALS

Dairy Thistle	v	Beith	2-0	Kilwinning Rngrs	v	Ardeer Thistle	2-0

FINAL (Sunday 24th April 1998. At Ardeer Stadium, Ardeer)

KILWINNING RGRS v DAIRY THISTLE 2-1
Cameron (1) — Bradford (1)
Harkness (1)

EAST AYRSHIRE CUP

SEMI-FINALS

Cumnock	v	Glenafton Athletic	1-2	Kello Rovers	v	Darvel	4-4, 5p4

FINAL (Wednesday 27th May 1998. At Beechwood Park, Auchinleck)

GLENAFTON ATH v KELLO ROVERS 3-1
McLaren (2) — Nohar (1)
Kennedy (1 pen)

SOUTH AYRSHIRE CUP

SEMI-FINALS

Annbank United	v	Troon	4-3	Maybole	v	Whitletts Victoria	3-2

FINAL (Wednesday 20th April 1998. At Dam Park, Ayr)

ANNBANK UNITED v MAYBOLE 3-0
McCaffery (1)
Stewart (1)
Gilluley (1)

AYRSHIRE SUPER CUP

SEMI-FINALS

Glenafton Athletic	v	Cumnock	1-1, 4p2	Kilwinning Rangers	v	Annbank United	7-0

FINAL (Wednesday 9th June 1998. At Meadow Park, Irvine)

GLENAFTON ATH. v KILWINNING RGRS 1-1, 4p2

JUNIOR INTERNATIONALS

Tournament in Republic of Ireland

SEMI-FINALS	(Friday 17th April 1998)	Republic of Ireland	v	Scotland	2-1
3rd/4th PLACE	(Saturday 18th April 1998)	Scotland	v	Northern Ireland	3-0

OTHER REPRESENTATIVE MATCHES BY SJFA

SJFA	v	Dundee	4-0	(4th February 1998. At Linlithgow)
Arniston Rangers	v	SJFA	0-3	(15th March 1998. At Arniston)
Maryhill	v	SJFA	2-5	(24th March 1998. At Maryhill)

CENTRAL REGION

FINAL LEAGUE TABLES 1997-98

PREMIER DIVISION

	P	W	D	L	F	A	Pts
Maryhill	22	12	7	3	53	28	43
Pollok	22	13	3	6	46	27	42
Arthurlie	22	10	6	6	42	29	36
Benburb	22	10	5	7	35	28	35
Lanark United	22	8	7	7	31	30	31
Petershill	22	8	7	7	22	25	31
Lesmahagow	22	6	10	6	33	34	28
Neilston	22	6	9	7	30	28	27
Baillieston	22	6	8	8	29	40	26
Blantyre Victoria	22	5	8	9	32	38	23
Larkhall Thistle	22	4	6	12	23	44	18
Shettleston	22	4	4	14	23	48	16

DIVISION ONE

(first five posiitons)	P	W	D	L	F	A	Pts
Shotts Bon Accord	26	17	4	5	69	22	55
Rutherglen Glenc'n	26	18	4	4	52	20	55*
Cambuslang Rngrs	26	16	6	4	54	30	54
Johnstone Borough	26	15	7	4	56	28	52
Kirk'illoch Rob Roy	26	13	9	4	51	35	48

* Denotes 3 points deducted

Other teams and points:
Renfrew (44), Vale of Clyde (36), Forth Wanderers (34), Vale of Leven (34), Cumbernauld United (27), Kilsyth Rangers (26), Bellshill Athletic (24), Ashfield (12), Yoker Athletic (11).

CENTRAL LEAGUE CUP

Quarter-finals

Baillieston	v	Johnstone Borough	1-1
Maryhill	v	Arthurlie	1-4
Kilsyth Rangers	v	Shotts Bon Accord	0-0
Vale of Clyde	v	Blantyre Victoria	2-2

Replays

Johnstone Borough	v	Baillieston	3-1
Blantyre Victoria	v	Vale of Clyde	2-1

Semi-finals

Arthurlie	v	Blantyre Victporia	3-2
Shotts Bon Acc.	v	Blantyre Victoria	1-o

FINAL (Monday, 20th October 1997. At Fir Park, Motherwell)

ARTHURLIE v SHOTTS BON ACC. 0-0 (Shotts Bon Accord won 4-1 on penalties)

'ABERCORN BUILDERS' LEAGUE CUP

Semi-finals

East Kilbride Thistle	v	Shettleston	2-3
Petershill	v	Arthurlie	0-0, 2p3

FINAL (Saturday, 30th May 1998. At Pollok FC)

ARTHURLIE v SHETTLESTON 4-0

EVENING TIMES CUP WINNERS CUP

Semi-finals

Arthurlie	v	Greenock	0-1
Naryhill	v	Shotts Bon Accord	1- 0

FINAL (Saturday, 13th June 1998. At Maryhill FC)

MARYHILL v GREENOCK 5-1

EAST REGION

FINAL LEAGUE TABLES 1997-98

DIVISION ONE

	P	W	D	L	F	A	Pts
Whitburn	22	14	6	2	46	25	48
Linlithgow Rose	22	13	3	6	36	20	42
Bonnybridge	22	12	5	5	38	36	41
Bo'ness United	22	12	3	7	38	26	39
Newtongrange Star	22	11	6	5	25	24	39
Arniston Rangers	22	11	5	6	29	24	38
Camelon	22	10	5	7	32	30	35
Bonnyrigg Rose	22	7	5	10	26	36	26
Musselburgh Ath	22	6	6	10	26	35	24
Fauldhouse United	22	5	6	11	24	39	21
Armadale Thistle	22	3	3	16	26	56	12
Tranent	22	1	1	20	23	97	4

DIVISION TWO

(first five positions)	P	W	D	L	F	A	Pts
Dunbar United	26	18	4	4	53	31	58
Bathgate Thistle	26	16	6	4	48	25	54
Haddington Athletic	26	15	6	5	50	29	51
Pumpherston	26	13	7	6	37	29	46
Broxburn Athletic	26	12	9	5	41	31	45

Other teams and points:
Stoneyburn (44), Ormiston Primrose (38), Harthill Royal (37), West Calder United (36), Sauchie (31), Blackburn United (30), Edinburgh United (24), Livingston United (9), Dalkeith Thistle (6).

EAST LEAGUE (CARLSBERG) CUP

Quarter-finals

Bo'ness United v Harthill Royal 5-1
Newtongrange Star v Camelon 0-1
Broxburn Athletic v Musselburgh A. 0-0, 1-6
Whitburn v Dunbar United 3-0

Semi-finals

Camelon v Bo'ness United 4-2
Whitburn v Musselburgh Athletic 4-0

FINAL WHITBURN v CAMELON 5-1
Ramage (2), Prior (1), Hume (1), Black (1). — Ross

'CALDERS' EAST REGIONAL CUP

Third Round

Camelon v Bathgate Thistle 2-3
Linlithgow Rose v Bonnybridge 1-2
Dunbar United v Pumphesrton 1-3
Sauchie v Whitburn 0-2

Semi-finals

Bathgate Thistle v Whitburn 0-1
Pumpherston v Bonnybridge 0-0, 0-3

FINAL WHITBURN v BONNYBRIDGE 2-0
Campbell (1), Ramage (1)

DAVID MOFFAT CUP

Third Round

Camelon v Bo'Ness United 0-0, 4p5
Tranent v Arniston Rangers 2-2, 5p4
Newtongrange S. v Linlithgow Rose 1-4
Whitburn v Faudhouse United 5-2

Semi-finals

Linlithgow Rose v Tranent 4-0
Whitburn v Bo'Ness United 1-2

FINAL BO'NESS UNITED v LINLITHGOW ROSE 1-0
McKinlay pen

DALKEITH GLAZING CUP

Third Round

Camelon v Haddington Athletic 3-1
Linlithgow Rose v Arniston Rangers 2-1
Harthill Royal v Armadale Thistle 1-2
Whitburn v Bonnybridge 3-3, 4p3

Semi-finals

Camelon v Armadale Thistle 2-1
Linlithgow Rose v Whitburn 1-1, 4p5

FINAL CAMELON v WHITBURN 2-2, 5p6
Wood (1), Ramage (1) — Ross (1), Newbiggins (1 pen)

FIFE & LOTHIANS CUP

Fourth Round

Arniston Rangers	v	Kelty Hearts	0-0, 2-1	Bathgate Thistle	v	Dunbar United	5-1
Camelon	v	Hill of Beath Hawthorn	1-0	Linlithgow Rose	v	Haddington United	2-3

Semi-finals

Bathgate Thistle	v	Haddington Athletic	1-2	Camelon	v	Arniston Rangers	2-3

FINAL ARNISTON RNGRS v HADDINGTON ATH 1-0
Locke

FIFE REGION

FINAL LEAGUE TABLE 1997-98

	P	W	D	L	F	A	Pts
Hill of Beath Haw	28	24	3	1	110	28	75
Kelty Hearts	28	21	6	1	86	26	69
Oakley United	28	20	2	6	76	40	62
Newburgh	28	19	4	5	57	27	61
Glenrothes	28	13	10	5	49	26	49
St Andrews United	28	13	9	6	63	48	48
Thornton Hibs	28	12	8	8	48	41	44
Rosyth Rec	28	9	7	12	57	52	34
Lochore Welfare	28	9	6	13	40	50	33
Dundonald Bluebell	28	7	3	18	52	75	24
Crossgates P'rose	28	7	3	18	46	72	24
Kirkcaldy YMCA	28	7	2	19	35	81	23
Loghgelly Albert	28	6	4	18	37	68	22
Tulliallan Thistle	28	4	2	22	30	84	14
Steelend Victoria	28	4	1	23	32	100	13

PEDDIE SMITH MALOCCO CUP

Second Round

Bathgate Thistle	v	Haddington Athletic	1-2	Camelon	v	Arniston Rangers	2-3
Glenrothes	v	St Andrews United	2-0	Hill of Beath H.	v	Newburgh	2-1
Kelty Hearts	v	Thornton Hibs	6-0	Tulliallan Thistle	v	Oakley United	0-3

Semi-finals

Kelty Hearts	v	Hill of Beath H.	2-2, 3p4	Oakley United	v	Glenrothes	0-1

FINAL GLENROTHES v HILL OF BEATH H. 4-3

'BARTON AGGREGATES' FIFE CUP

Second Round

Kelty Hearts	v	Crossgates Primrose	6-3	Oakley United	v	Dundonals Bluebell	1-2
St Andrews United	v	Newbburgh	2-0	Thornton Hibs	v	Hill of Beath Hawth.	1-3

Semi-finals

Dundonald Bluebell	v	Hill of Beath Hawthorn	1-2	Kelty Hearts	v	St Andrews United	2-0

FINAL HILL OF BEATH H. v KELTY HEARTS 1-0

WHITBREAD TROPHY

Second Round

Dundonald Bluebell	v	Oakley United	0-1	Glenrothes	v	Rosyth Rec	1-0
Hill of Beath Hawth.	v	Kelty Hearts	2-1	Lochgelly Albert	v	St Andrews United	0-3

Semi-finals

Glenrothes	v	Oakley United	1-3	St Andrews Utd	v	Hill of Beath Hawth.	0-3

FINAL HILL OF BEATH H. v OAKLEY UTD 3-2

TAYSIDE REGION

FINAL LEAGUE TABLES 1997-98

DIVISION ONE

	P	W	D	L	F	A	Pts
North End	26	22	1	3	66	21	67
Tayport	26	21	2	3	81	19	65
St Josephs	26	20	3	3	75	26	63
Carnoustie Pan.	26	12	5	9	63	45	41
Forfar West End	26	12	3	11	51	50	39
Lochee United	26	11	6	9	35	36	37
Dundee Violet	26	11	5	10	45	42	38
Arbroath SC	26	9	8	9	42	41	35
Downfield	26	10	5	11	48	48	35
Kirrie Thistle	26	9	5	12	35	49	32
Elmwood	26	6	6	14	30	52	24
Jeanfield Swifts	26	5	6	15	46	82	21
East Craigie	26	4	2	20	29	85	14
Kinnoull	26	0	3	23	20	73	3

DIVISION TWO

(first five positions)	P	W	D	L	F	A	Pts
Lochee Harp	20	14	3	3	50	23	45
Coupar Angus	20	12	5	3	40	24	41
Scone Thistle	20	12	4	4	41	21	40
Bankfoot Athletic	20	11	5	4	54	29	38
Broughty Athletic	20	10	5	5	51	36	35

Other teams and points:
Montrose Roselea (29), Forfar Albion (27), Arbroath Victoria (18), Brechin Victoria (14), Blairgowrie (13), Luncarty (8).

NORTH END CENTENARY CUP

(for North and Tayside Region clubs)

Fourth Round

Inverurie Loco Works	v	Islavale	2-1
St Josephs	v	Arbroath SC	2-1
North End	v	Downfield	2-1
Tayport	v	Lewis United	4-0

Semi-finals

North End	v	Inverurie Loco Works	3-1
Tayport	v	St Josephs	0-1

FINAL ST JOSEPHS v NORTH END 0-0, 5p4

TAYCARS TROPHY

(for Tayside and Fife Region clubs)

Fourth Round

Kelty Hearts	v	Glenrothes	4-1
St Josephs	v	Oakley United	3-0
Lochee United	v	Downfield	2-3
Tayport	v	Hill of Beath Hawth.	1-3

Semi-finals

Downfield	v	Hill of Beath Hawthorn	0-3
Kelty Hearts	v	St Josephs	1-1, 5p4

FINAL KELTY HEARTS v HILL OF BEATH H. 4-0

DOWNFIELD SC LEAGUE CUP

Semi-finals

Brechin Victoria	v	Lochee Harp	1-3
Coupar Angus	v	Scone Thistle	1-0

FINAL LOCHE HARP v COUPAR ANGUS 6-1

D J LAING HOMES TROPHY

Third Round

Bankfoot Athletic	v	Elmwood	1-1, 5p6
St Josephs	v	Carnoustie Panmure	2-1
Forfar Albion	v	Tayport	0-2
Dundee Violet	v	Forfar West End	4-1

Semi-finals

St Josephs	v	Elmwood	6-0
Dundee Violet	v	Tayport	0-1

FINAL TAYPORT v ST JOSEPHS 2-1

WHYTE & MacKAY CUP

Third Round

Arbroath SC	v	Downfield	0-1	Kirrie Thistle	v	Elmwood	5-3
St Josephs	v	Forfar West End	2-0	Dundee Violet	v	Tayport	0-3

Semi-finals

Downfield	v	Kirrie Thistle	2-0	St Josephs	v	Tayport	2-1 aet

FINAL ST JOSEPHS v DOWNFIELD 3-1

ROSEBANK C.C. CUP

Second Round

Bankfoot Athletic	v	Lochee Harp	1-2 aet	Blairgowrie	v	Arbroath Victoria	3-1
Coupar Angus	v	Scone Thistle	3-5	Forfar Albion	v	Broughty Athletic	2-3

Semi-finals

Blairgowrie v Scone Thistle 1-1 aet, 1p3

FINAL BROUGHTY ATH v SCONE TH'TLE 2-2, 4p2

NORTH REGION

EAST SECTION

EAST PREMIER LEAGUE

	P	W	D	L	F	A	Pts
Inverurie Loco Wks	22	16	2	4	60	36	50
Sunnybank	22	15	3	4	43	19	48
Longside	22	14	3	5	49	32	45
Lewis United	22	9	5	8	40	38	32
Turriff United	22	9	5	8	34	38	32
Hermes	22	9	4	9	39	34	31
Formartine United	22	8	4	10	31	31	28
FC Stonehaven	22	7	5	10	31	36	27
Culter	22	5	6	11	27	44	21
Banks o' Dee	22	4	5	13	21	38	17
Hall Russell United	22	2	6	14	23	48	12

EAST DIVISION TWO

(first five places)	P	W	D	L	F	A	Pts
Cruden Bay	20	16	1	3	65	29	49
East End	20	12	5	3	59	24	41
Lads Club	20	12	3	5	61	24	39
Buchanhaven Hrts	20	10	5	5	54	32	35
Fraserburgh United	20	9	5	6	37	27	32

Other teams and points:
Parkvale (30), Banchory St Ternan (29), Ellon United (28), Dyce (20), Maud (12), Inverurie Juniors (0).

CABLE TV LEAGUE CUP

Third Round

Dyce	v	Lads Club	2-4	Formartine Utd	v	Cruden Bay	2-1
Inverurie Loco Works	v	Stoneywood	1-2	Stonehaven	v	Sunnybank	0-1

Semi-finals

Formartine United	v	Lads Club	0-0, 3p5	Stoneywood	v	Sunnybank	5-2

FINAL STONEYWOOD v LADS CLUB 2-0

ACORN HEATING CUP

Third Round

Banks o' Dee	v	Lewis united	1-2	Ellon United	v	Sunnybank	0-3
Inverurie Loco Works	v	Bacnchory St Ternan	5-2	Stoneywood	v	Stonehaven	5-1

Semi-finals

Stoneywood	v	Lewis United	4-3	Sunnybank	v	Inverurie Loco Works	4-3

FINAL STONEYWOOD v SUNNYBANK 2-2

'ROLLSTUD' ARCHIBALD CUP

Third Round

Dyce	v	Hall Russell United	1-3	Inverurie Loco Works	v	FC Stoneywood	1-0
Lads Club	v	Culter	2-1	Sunnybank	v	Lewis United	5-0

Semi-finals

Lads Club	v	Inverurie Loco Works	0- 6	Sunnybank	v	Hall Russell United	2-1

FINAL SUNNYBANK v INVERURIE L. W. 1-0

GORDON CAMPBELL CONSTRUCTION TROPHY

Third Round

Foemartine United	v	Fraserburgh United	6-0	Hermes	v	Stoneywood	4-0
Lewis United	v	Culter	4-3	Sunnybank	v	Ellon United	2-1

Semi-finals

Formartine United	v	Lewis United	2-0	Hermes	v	Sunnybank	1-4

FINAL SUNNYBANK v FORMARTINE UTD 4-2

MORRISON TROPHY

Second round

Cruden Bay	v	Dyce	5-2	East End	v	Inverurie Juniors	11-0
Fraserburgh United	v	Ellon United	1-0	Lads Club	v	Banchory St T.	1-2 aet

Semi-finals

Banchory st Ternan	v	East End	1-3	Fraserburgh Utd	v	Cruden Bay	0-2

FINAL EAST END v CRUDEN BAY 1-1, 3p4

JIMMY GIBB TROPHY

INVERURIE L. W. v CRUDEN BAY 3-1

NORTH REGIONAL PLAY OFF

INVERURIE L. W. v ISLAVALE
2-0

HAROLD PETRIES MEMORIAL TROPHY

NORTH REGION v TAYSIDE REGION 3-1

	P	W	D	L	F	A	Pts
Islavale	26	22	1	3	115	19	57
Nairn St Ninians	26	19	3	4	64	29	60
Buckie Rovers	26	17	2	7	53	36	53
Strathspey Thistle	26	16	1	9	65	38	49
Deveronside	26	13	4	9	60	34	43
Lossiemouth Utd	26	12	4	10	73	55	40
Bishopmill United	26	12	4	10	39	33	40
New Elgin	26	11	3	12	34	41	36
RAF Lossiemouth	26	8	4	14	39	70	28
Burghead Thistle	26	8	2	16	24	65	26
Portgordon United	26	7	4	15	38	56	25
Forres Thistle	26	7	4	15	46	66	25
Fochabers	26	5	6	15	30	69	21
Kinloss	26	3	2	21	26	93	11

NORTH SECTION

'GREAT NORTHERN TROPHIES' NORTH REGIONAL CUP

Third Round

Culter	v	Turriff United	4-1	Fraserburgh Utd	v	Lads Club	2-1
Stonehaven	v	Cruden Bay	1-1, 3-4	Sunnybank	v	Hermes	2-2, 0-3

Semi-finals

Cruden Bay	v	Fraserburgh United	5-2	Hermes	v	Culter	2-1

FINAL HERMES v CRUDEN BAY 2-1

MATTHEW CUP

Second Round

Buckie Rovers	v	Portgordon	1-2	Islavale	v	Deveronside	1-2
New Elgin	v	Lossiemouth United	0-1	RAF Lossiem'th	v	Nairn St Ninian	0-3

Semi-finals

Lossiemouth United	v	Deveronside	1-2	Portgordon Utd	v	Nairn St Ninian	0-10

FINAL DEVERONSIDE v NAIRN ST NINIAN 1-2

NICHOLSON CUP

Second Round

Islavale	v	Deveronside	0-3	Kinloss	v	Bishopmill United	1-5
RAF Lossiemouth	v	Fochabers	4-0	Strathspey Th.	v	Nairn St Ninian	1-3

Semi-finals

Bishopmill United	v	Nairn St Ninian	0-2	Deveronside	v	RAF Lossiemouth	4-0

FINAL NAIRN ST NINIAN v DEVERONSIDE 4-3

STEWART MEMORIAL TROPHY

First Round

Bishopmill United	v	Nairn St Ninian	1-1, 3p1	Busghead Thistle	v	Lossiemouth United	0-3

FINAL LOSSIEMOUTH v STRATHSPEY TH. 1-0

GORDON WILLIAMSON CUP

Second Round							
Kinloss	v	Deveronside	1-2	Lossiemouth Utd	v	New Elgin	4-2
Nairn St Ninian	v	Bishopmill United	2-1	Stra\thspey Th.	v	Buckie Rovers	2-1
Semi-finals							
Deveronside	v	Nairn St Ninian	1-1, 4p2	Lossiemouth Utd	v	Strathspey Thistle	5-2
FINAL	DEVERONSIDE		v	LOSSIEMOUTH UTD	5-2		

ROBERTSON CUP

Semi-finals							
Buckie Rovers	v	Deveronside	1-3	Islavale	v	New Elgin	2-0
FINAL	DEVERONSIDE		v	ISLAVALE	1-0		

TOM GORDON TROPHY

Semi-finals							
Portgordon	v	Kinloss	7-6 aet	RAF Lossiemouth	v	Fochabers	0-1
FINAL	PORTGORDON		v	FOCHABERS	2-1		

CONNON CUP

Second Round							
Buckie Rovers	v	Bishopmill Utd	2-2, 3p4	Burghead Thistle	v	Nairn St Ninian	0-5
Forres Thistle	v	Strathspey Thistle	3-4	Lossiemouth Utd	v	Kinloss	6-2
Semi-finals							
Nairn St Ninian	v	Lossiemouth United	3-1	Stra\thspey Thistle	v	Bishopmill United	2-1
FINAL	STRATHSPEY THISTLE		v	NAIRN ST NINIAN	2-1		

OTHER COMPETITIONS

'FAMOUS GROUSE' SCOTTISH AMATEUR CUP

Eighth Round							
Dalziel HS FP	v	St Pats FP	3-1	Norton House	v	Heathside	1-2
Strathclyde Police	v	Bannockburn	1-3	West Kilbride	v	Riverside Athletic	3-0
Semi-finals							
Heathside	v	Dalziel HS FP	3-6	West Kilbride	v	Bannockburn	2-0
FINAL	DALZIEL HS FP		v	WEST KILBRIDE	2-1		(aet). Att: 2,370.

HIGHLAND AMATEUR CUP

Quarter-finals							
Avoch	v	Ness	2-3	Chieftain	v	Fluke HOE	2-0
Contin	v	Point	5-1	Pentland United	v	Kirkwall Rovers	0-3
Semi-final							
Contin	v	Chieftain	4-0	Kirkwall Rovers	v	Ness	1-0
FINAL	Kirkwall Rovers		v	Contin	4-2		

WESTERN ISLES CUP

Semi-finals							
Harris	v	Tong	5-2	Ness	v	Lochs	6-2
FINAL	NESS		v	HARRIS	5-0		

MILNE CUP

SHETLAND v ORKNEY 5-0

'FAMOUS GROUSE' SCOTTISH SUNDAY AMATEUR CUP

FINAL CATHKIN (Burnside League) v PARKHOUSE (Glasgow League) 4-2

SCOTTISH WOMEN'S CUP

FINAL CUMBERNAULD v GIULLIANOS 3-1

AMATEUR FOOTBALL ALLIANCE

Secretary: W.P. Goss
55 Islington Park Street, London N1 1QB
Tel: 0171 359 3493 Fax: 0171 359 5027

A F A SENIOR CUP

1st Round Proper

Old Minchendenians	2 - 1	Old Parkonians
Alleyn Old Boys	2 - 4	Nat Westminster Bank
Polytechnic	4* - 2*	Old Meadonians
Old Grammarians	1 - 3	Barclays Bank
Carshalton	6 - 0	Old Wokingians
Cardinal Mann. OB	4*:0 - 4*:4	Civil Service
Old Kingsburians	3 - 5	Old Finchleians
Old Woodhouseians	2 - 3	Nottsborough
Latymer Old Boys	4 - 3	Old Southallians
Old Danes	0 - 3	Old Salesians
Old Bealonians	1*:0 - 1*:5	Wake Green
Shene Old Gramm's	2*:2 - 2*:6	Old Tenisonians
Old Latymerians	4* - 3*	Old Salvatorians
Witan	0 - 1	Alexandra Park
Old Bromleians	6 - 4	Old Esthameians
Old Vaughanianss	6 - 0	Mill Hill Village
City of London	w/o - w/d	Old Haberdashers
Cuaco	2 - 6	Crouch End Vampires
West Wickham	3 - 1	Ulysses
Lensbury	1 - 0	Glyn Old Boys
Merton	0 - 5	Norsemen
Brent	1*:0 - 1*:7	Southgate County
Old Parmiterians	w/d a w/o	Old Tiffinian
Old Reptonian	2 - 3	East Barnet OG's
Old Foresters	0 - 2	Old Ignatians
Old Isleworthians	2*:2 - 2*:4	Old Cholmeleians
Brentham	0 - 5	Old Owens
Old Chigwellians	0 - 4	Midland Bank
Old Stationers	11 - 2	Old Camdenians
Old Buckwellians	4 - 5	Enfield Old Gramm's
Old Aloysians	1 - 0	Lloyds Bank
Old Wilsonians	3 - 0	Old Salopians

(a - awarded after abandonment) (* - after extra time)

2nd Round Proper

Old Minchendenians	2 - 5	Nat Westminster Bank
Polytechnic	3 - 2	Barclays Bank
Carshalton	2 - 1	Civil Service
Old Finchleians	5 - 3	Nottsborough
Latymer Old Boys	2 - 4	Old Salesians
Wake Green	0 - 1	Old Tenisonians
Old Latymerians	3*:4* - 3*:6*	Alexandra Park
Old Bromleians	3 - 2	Old Vaughanians
City of London	1 - 2	Crouch End Vampires
West Wickham	1 - 0	Lensbury
Norsemen	3 - 1	Southgate County
Old Tiffinian	2 - 0	East Barnet OG
Old Ignatians	4 - 0	Old Cholmeleians
Old Owens	3 - 1	Midland Bank
Old Stationers	3 - 2	Enfield O Gramm's
Old Aloysians	3 - 2	Old Wilsonians

3rd Round Proper

Nat Westminster Bank	5 - 2	Polytechnic
Carshalton	1*:0 - 1*:4	Old Finchleians
Old Salesians	2 - 1	Old Tenisonians
Alexandra Park	1 - 3	Old Bromleians
Crouch End Vampires	2 - 5	West Wickham
Norsemen	3 - 1	Old Tiffinian
Old Ignatians	6* - 1*	Old Owens
Old Stationers	3 - 4	Old Aloysians

4th Round Proper

Nat Westminster Bank	0 - 4	Old Finchleians
Old Salesians	4 - 2	Old Bromleians
West Wickham	3* - 2*	Norsemen
Old Ignatians	2 - 5	Old Aloysians

Semi-Finals

Old Finchleians	4 - 0	Old Salesians
West Wickham	1* - 2*	Old Aloysians

OTHER A F A CUP RESULTS

INTERMEDIATE
O. Actonians Ass'n Rs 3 - 2 Lloyds Bank Res

JUNIOR
Polytechnic 3rd 2 - 0 Old Tenisonians 3rd

MINOR
Midland Bank 4th 1*:1* - 1*:0* Silhill 4th

SENIOR NOVETS
Old Meadonians 5th 1 - 5 Old Finchleians 5th

INTERMEDIATE NOVETS
Midland Bank 6th 2 - 1 City of London 6th

JUNIOR NOVETS
Norsemen 8th 3 - 0 Old Parmiterians 10th

VETERANS
City of London 1 - 0 Old Grammarians

OPEN VETERANS
Port of London Auth'ty 3 - 0 Snaresbrook

YOUTH
Old Salesians 3 - 1 Norsemen

ESSEX SENIOR
Old Bealonians 6* -8* Old Buckwellians

MIDDLESEX SENIOR
Old Aloysians 4 - 0 Old Ignatians

SURREY SENIOR
Old Salesians 0*:0 - 0*:1 Nat West Bank

ESSEX INTERMEDIATE
Old Bealonians Res. 0 - 1 Hale End Athletic Res.

KENT INTERMEDIATE
Midland Bank Res 2 - 0 Chase Manhattan Bank

MIDDLESEX INTERMEDIATE
Winchmore Hill Res 2 - 1 O. Actonians Ass'n Res

SURREY INTERMEDIATE
Carshalton Res 1 - 0 Kew Association Res

GREENLAND MEMORIAL
Old Parmiterians 4 - 1 Old Foresters

ARTHUR DUNN CUP

Old Foresters 3 - 1 Old Brentwoods

ARTHURIAN LEAGUE

PREMIER DIVISION	P	W	D	L	F	A	Pts
Old Foresters	16	13	2	1	63	22	*25
Old Brentwoods	16	113	2		39	17	25
Lancing Old Boys	16	9	3	4	50	30	21
Old Etonians	16	7	2	7	29	30	16
Old Chigwellians	16	6	2	8	36	31	14
Old Carthusians	16	6	2	8	34	39	14
Old Salopians	16	5	2	9	25	44	12
Old Cholmeleians	16	3	3	10	25	38	9
Old Haberdashers	16	2	1	13	18	68	5

DIVISION ONE	P	W	D	L	F	A	Pts
Old Reptonians	16	11	3	2	56	16	25
Old Bradfieldians	16	10	1	5	31	22	21
Old Wellingburians	16	8	2	6	45	25	18
Old Harrovians	16	8	2	6	51	46	18
Old Aldenhamians	16	7	4	5	27	30	18
Old Witleians	16	5	4	7	28	36	14
Old Malvernians	16	2	7	7	22	41	11
Old Haileyburians	16	3	4	9	29	40	10
Old Wykehamists	16	3	3	10	30	63	9

DIVISION TWO	P	W	D	L	F	A	Pts
Old Etonians Res.	14	12	0	2	33	10	24
Old Brentwoods Res.	14	9	1	4	34	20	19
Old Etonians 3rd.	14	6	4	4	28	25	16
Old Chigwellians Res.	14	6	3	5	31	32	15
Old Cholmeleians 3rd.	14	6	1	7	23	33	13
Old Cholmeleians Res.	14	4	3	7	22	23	11
Old Foresters Res.	14	4	1	9	29	39	*6
Old Carthusians Res.	14	2	1	11	20	38	5

DIVISION THREE	P	W	D	L	F	A	Pts
Old Millhillians	16	12	2	2	46	17	26
Lancing Old Boys Res.	16	9	4	3	40	25	*21
Old Brentwoods 3rd.	16	7	2	7	37	32	*15
Old Westminsters	16	6	3	7	28	40	15
Old Harrovians Res.	16	7	0	9	31	40	14
Old Cholmeleians 4th.	16	5	4	7	22	31	14
Old Salopians Res.	16	7	3	6	30	28	*13
Old Eastbournians	16	3	3	10	25	33	9
Old Aldenhamians Res.	16	4	3	9	37	50	*9

DIVISION FOUR	P	W	D	L	F	A	Pts
Old Reptonians Res.	14	7	5	2	35	19	19
Old Foresters 3rd.	14	10	2	2	35	20	1*9
Old Haileyburians Res.	14	6	3	5	27	25	15
Old Malvernians Res.	14	5	5	4	29	29	15
Old Haberdashers Res.	14	5	2	7	33	33	12
Old Foresters 4th.	14	5	4	5	25	24	*11
Old Ardinians	14	4	2	8	37	41	10
Old Carthusians 3rd.	14	1	3	10	23	53	5

DIVISION FIVE	P	W	D	L	F	A	Pts
Old Bradfieldians Res.	12	9	3	0	48	8	21
Old Chigwellians 4th.	12	6	2	4	28	27	14
Old Cholmeleians 5th.	12	4	4	4	29	26	12
Old Brentwoods 5th.	12	3	4	5	20	27	10
Old Brentwoods 4th.	12	2	5	5	23	28	9
Old Salopians 3rd.	12	4	3	5	25	35	*9
Old Chigwellians 5th.	12	3	1	8	16	38	7

(* Points deducted - breach of rule)

JUNIOR LEAGUE CUP:
Lancing Old Boys Res. 3 Old Brentwood Res. 2

DERRIK MOORE VETERANS CUP:
O. Chigwellians Vets 4 Old Cholmeleians Vets. 1

JIM DIXSON VI-A-SIDE: Won by Old Bradfieldians

LONDON FINANCIAL F.A.

DIVISION ONE	P	W	D	L	F	A	Pts
Kleinwort Benson	16	11	3	2	38	25	36
Churchill Insurance	16	11	2	3	34	18	35
Royal Sun Alliance	16	9	1	6	40	30	28
Bank America	16	7	2	7	30	21	23
Coutts & Co.	16	7	1	8	35	34	22
Morgan Guaranty	16	4	6	6	33	39	18
Allied Irish Bank	16	5	2	9	18	33	17
Royal Bank of Scotland	16	4	2	10	42	48	14
J & H Marsh & McLennan	16	4	1	11	22	44	*12

DIVISION TWO	P	W	D	L	F	A	Pts
C.F.I. Vantage	18	15	2	1	64	23	47
Union Bank of Switzl'd	18	13	3	2	55	25	42
Granby	18	12	2	4	59	34	38
Citibank	18		93	6	63	36	30
Chase Manhattan Bank	18	8	6	4	40	26	30
Eagle Star	18	5	4	9	39	38	19
Temple Bar	18	6	1	11	52	56	19
Salomon Brothers	18	5	0	13	25	62	15
Century Life	18	4	2	12	26	51	14
R Bank of Scotland Res	18	1	1	16	27	99	4

DIVISION THREE	P	W	D	L	F	A	Pts
Standard Chartered	18	14	2	2	66	20	44
J&H Marsh & McLennan R	18	13	3	2	63	34	42
Foreign & Commonw'th	18	11	3	4	72	35	36
Credit Suisse Finan'l Pr's	18	9	3	6	48	37	*29
Lincoln	18	8	3	7	41	34	27
Bank America Res.	18	8	2	8	37	41	26
ANZ Banking Group	18	5	5	8	35	42	20
Noble Lowndes	18	6	0	12	27	58	18
Royal Sun Alliance Res.	18	2	2	14	24	56	8
Coutts & Co. Res.	18	2	1	15	13	69	7

DIVISION FOUR	P	W	D	L	F	A	Pts
C Hoare & Co.	20	17	1	2	73	25	52
Abbey National	20	14	4	2	88	36	46
Royal Sun Alliance 3rd	20	14	2	4	48	27	44
Eagle Star Res.	20	12	3	5	60	31	39
Citibank Res.	20	9	3	8	43	40	30
British Gas	20	6	5	9	42	46	23
Churchill Insurance Res	20	6	4	10	40	56	22
Granby Res.	20	5	3	12	38	56	18
Bank of Ireland	20	4	3	13	27	76	15
Noble Lowndes Res.	20	4	1	15	28	72	13
Royal Bank of Scot. 3rd	20	2	5	13	40	62	11

DIVISION FIVE	P	W	D	L	F	A	Pts
J & H Marsh & McL'n 3rd	18	16	1	1	68	20	49
Temple Bar Res.	18	10	4	4	63	29	34
Standard Chartered Res.	18	9	1	8	60	54	28
Royal Bank of Scot. 4th	18	7	5	6	28	28	26
Gaflac	18	8	1	9	45	48	25
Lensbury 6th.	18	2	3	13	24	56	9
Eagle Star 3rd.	18	2	3	13	30	85	9

* Points deducted - breach of Rule

REPRESENTATIVE MATCHES

v Southern Olympian League	Drawn 1 - 1
v Royal Marines	Lost 2 - 6
v Southern Amateur League "B"	Lost 0 - 3
v Old Boys' League	Drawn 2 - 2
v Bristol Insurance Institute	Lost 1 - 6
v Stock Exchange F A	Cancelled

LONDON LEGAL LEAGUE

DIVISION ONE	P	W	D	L	F	A	Pts
Gray's Inn	18	14	2	2	53	22	30
Slaughter & May	18	13	3	2	57	23	29
Cameron McKenna	18	8	1	9	46	35	17
Lovell White Durrant	18	6	5	7	25	31	17
Pegasus (Inner Temple)	18	8	1	9	39	45	17
Herbert Smith	18	6	4	8	39	49	16
Wilde Sapte	18	6	3	9	32	49	15
Linklaters & Paines	18	4	6	8	24	26	14
Nabarro Nathanson	18	6	2	10	25	38	14
Taylor Joynson Garrett	18	3	5	10	26	48	11

DIVISION TWO	P	W	D	L	F	A	Pts
Rosling King	18	15	1	2	53	22	31
Clifford Chance	18	15	0	3	81	26	30
Stephenson Harwood	18	10	3	5	39	25	23
Allen & Overy	18	10	1	7	43	32	21
Kennedy's	18	7	3	8	40	35	17
Norton Rose	18	7	3	8	30	39	17
Freshfields	18	7	0	11	33	55	14
D.J. Freeman	18	4	2	12	19	55	10
Macfarlanes	18	4	1	13	22	47	9
S.J. Berwin	18	3	2	13	29	53	8

DIVISION THREE	P	W	D	L	F	A	Pts
K.P.M.G.	18	14	3	1	61	11	31
Denton Hall	18	11	4	3	46	24	26
Simmons & Simmons	18	11	3	4	42	31	25
Nicholson Graham & Jones	18	9	1	8	31	29	19
Titmus Sainer Dechert	18	7	4	7	24	32	18
Barlow Lyde & Gilbert	18	6	3	9	32	29	15
Watson Farley & Wlliams	18	5	3	10	23	43	13
Hammond Suddards	18	6	1	11	32	58	13
Richards Butler	18	5	1	12	39	44	11
Baker Mackenzie	18	3	3	12	19	48	9

LEAGUE CHALLENGE CUP :
Gray's Inn 0* Lovell White Durrant 1*

WEAVERS ARMS CUP :
Wilde Sapte 3* K.P.M.G. 2*

INVITATION CUP:
Rosling King 4 D.J. Freeman 0
(* after extra time)

LONDON OLD BOYS' CUP

Senior
Old Meadonians 4 - 2 Enfield Old Gramm's

Intermediate
Old Salvatorians Res. 2 - 0 Latymer Old Boys Res.

Junior
Old Meadonians 3rd. 1 * 0 Old Alpertonians Res.

Minor
Old Alpertonians 3rd. 3 - 0 City of London 4th.

Novets
Old Actonians Ass'n 5th. 3 - 1 Old Suttonians 5th.

Drummond
Albanian 6th. 4 - 2 Old Addeyans 6th.

Nemean
Old Manorians 7th. 2 - 1 Old Parmiterians 10th.

Veterans
Old Salvatorians Vets. 3 - 2 Old Meadonians Vets.
(* after exta time)

OLD BOYS' INVITATION CUPS

Senior
Old Wilsonians 2 - 0 Old Stationers

Junior
Old Tenisonians Res. 0 - 1 Old Woodhouseians Rs.

Minor
Old Finchleians 3rd. 2 - 1 Old Colfeians 3rd.

4th XI
Glyn Old Boys 4th. 3 - 4 Old Finchleians 4th.

5th XI
Old Stationers 5th. 6 - 3 Old Suttonians 5th.

6th XI
Glyn Old Boys 6th. 5 - 0 Old Stationers 6th.

7th XI
Old Stationers 7th. 1 - 0 East Barnet O G 7th.

Veterans
Old Bromleians Vets. 5 - 1 Old Stationers Vets.

OLD BOYS' LEAGUE

PREMIER DIVISION	P	W	D	L	F	A	Pts
Old Tenisonians	20	13	5	2	48	18	31
Old Aloysians	20	14	2	4	55	24	30
Old Hamptonians	20	12	2	6	41	25	26
Old Ignatians	20	11	1	8	34	36	23
Old Vaughanians	20	7	5	8	27	33	19
Old Meadonians	20	7	4	9	29	38	18
Enfield Old Grammarians	20	7	3	10	26	39	17
Glyn Old Boys	20	5	6	9	34	40	16
Cardinal Manning O.B.	20	6	3	11	21	31	15
Latymer Old Boys	20	4	6	10	19	32	14
Old Suttonians	20	2	7	11	23	41	11

SENIOR DIVISION ONE	P	W	D	L	F	A	Pts
Old Buckwellians	20	13	2	5	66	33	28
Old Salvatorians	20	11	4	5	37	27	26
Phoenix Old Boys	20	9	6	5	52	29	24
Old Wilsonians	20	9	4	7	48	37	22
Old Kingsburians	20	6	8	6	37	40	20
Old Tiffinians	20	9	3	8	33	33*	19
Old Reigatians	20	7	5	8	30	30	19
Old Isleworthians	20	6	5	9	35	34	17
Old Manorians	20	7	3	10	32	45	17
Clapham Old Xaverians	20	6	2	12	29	56	14
Chertsey Old Salesians	20	5	2	13	23	58	12

SENIOR DIVISION TWO	P	W	D	L	F	A	Pts
Old Dorkinians	20	14	1	5	38	20	29
Shene Old Grammarians	20	11	5	4	55	32	27
Old Tollingtonians	20	9	6	5	48	33	24
Old Camdenians	20	9	3	8	46	46	21
Old Tenisonians Res.	20	9	3	8	40	44	21
Old Danes	20	7	6	7	41	36	20
Old Sinjuns	20	7	6	7	59	44*	18
Old Meadonians Res.	20	7	2	11	44	47	16
Old Minchendenians	20	6	4	10	33	49	16
Latymer Old Boys Res.	20	5	3	12	31	53	13
Mill Hill County O.B	20	5	3	12	25	56	13

SENIOR DIVISION THREE	P	W	D	L	F	A	Pts
John Fisher Old Boys	20	14	1	5	50	26	29
Old Vaughanians Res.	20	12	4	4	37	24	28
Old Wokingians	20	10	4	6	46	26	24
Old Uffingtonians	20	11	2	7	45	33	24
Old Addeyans	20	9	3	8	39	31	21
Old Aloysians Res.	20	7	7	6	36	35	21
Phoenix Old Boys Res.	20	8	4	8	40	34	20
Old Hamptonians Res.	20	7	2	11	41	59	16
Old St. Marys	20	7	1	12	36	55	15
Old Southallians	20	5	1	14	35	51	11
Enfield O. Grammarians Rs	20	4	3	13	26	57	11

* points deducted for breach of rule

(OLD BOYS' LEAGUE - cont)

Intermediate Division North
12 Teams - Won by - Queen Mary College Old Boys

Intermediate Division South
12 Teams - Won by - Old Dorkinians Res.

Division One North
9 Teams - Won by - Old Edmontonians

Division One South
11 Teams - Won by - Old Wilsonians Res.

Division One West
9 Teams - Won by - Old Isleworthians Res.

Division Two North
10 Teams - Won by - Wood Green Old Boys Res.

Division Two South
11 Teams - Won by - Old Paulines

Division Two West
9 Teams - Won by - Old Salvatorians 4th.

Division Three North
10 Teams - Won by - Wood Green Old Boys 3rd.

Division Three South
12 Teams - Won by - Fitzwilliam Old Boys

Division Three West
10 Teams - Won by - Old Danes 3rd.

Division Four North
9 Teams - Won by - Old Salvatorians 5th.

Division Four South
12 Teams - Won by - John Fisher Old Boys 3rd.

Division Four West
10 Teams - Won by - Old Salvatorians 6th.

Division Five North
10 Teams - Won by - Enfield O.Grammarians 6th.

Division Five South
11 Teams - Won by - Old Meadonians 7th.

Division Five West
9 Teams - Won by - Old Challoners 3rd.

Division Six North
8 Teams - Won by - Leyton County Old BOys 5th.

Division Six South
12 Teams - Won by - Fitzwilliam Old Boys Res.

Division Six West
8 Teams - Won by - Old Manorians 6th.

Division Seven North
8 Teams - Won by - Davenant Wanderers 3rd.

Division Seven South:
10 Teams - Won by - Old Sinjuns 4th.

Division Seven West
7 Teams - Won by - Holland Park Old Boys 5th.

Division Eight South
9 Teams - Won by - Old Paulines Res.

Division Eight West
8 Teams - Won by - Old Manorians 7th.

Division Nine South
10 Teams - Won by - Old Thorntonians 5th.

MIDLAND AMATEUR ALLIANCE

PREMIER DIVISION	*P*	*W*	*D*	*L*	*F*	*A*	*Pts*
Beeston Old Boys Assn.	22	19	0	3	75	31	57
Old Elizabethans	22	16	1	5	71	23	49
Kirton B.W.	22	15	2	5	71	31	47
Derbyshire Amateurs	22	15	1	6	70	31	46
Beeston Town "A"	22	12	6	4	75	46	42
Lady Bay	22	11	1	10	73	61	34
P K F Steelers	22	9	2	11	62	52	29
Bassingfield	22	9	2	11	53	54	29
Caribbean Cavaliers	22	7	3	12	50	66	24
Racing Toton	22	4	2	16	34	77	14
Magdala Amateurs "A"	22	3	4	15	34	72	13
County Nalgo	22	0	0	22	16	140	0

DIVISION ONE	*P*	*W*	*D*	*L*	*F*	*A*	*Pts*
Tibshelf Old Boys	22	18	0	4	73	32	54
Parkhead Academicals	22	16	4	2	58	22	52
Dynamo Baptist	22	12	4	6	59	35	40
Nottinghamshire	22	10	4	8	57	38	34
Woodborough United	22	9	6	7	50	53	33
Edwinstowe J G	22	9	4	9	51	50	31
Bassingfield Res.	22	8	5	9	39	52	29
Old Elizabethans Res.	22	8	4	10	45	53	28
Radcliffe Olympic Res.	22	7	4	11	43	54	25
Ilkeston Rangers	22	6	3	13	49	62	21
Cadland Chilwell	22	3	5	14	24	54	14
Lady Bay Res.	22	3	3	16	21	64	12

DIVISION TWO	*P*	*W*	*D*	*L*	*F*	*A*	*Pts*
A S C Dayncourt	24	24	0	0	136	15	72
Hucknall Sports Y C	24	18	1	5	93	61	55
Derbyshire Amateurs Res	24	13	6	5	54	41	45
Arnold & Carlton College	24	11	6	7	70	55	39
Old Elizabethans 3rd.	24	10	4	10	53	57	34
Southwell Amateurs	24	10	3	11	52	52	33
Gresham United	24	10	2	12	59	70	32
Magdala Amateurs Res	24	9	4	11	58	85	31
Beeston Old Boys Res.	24	7	3	14	48	70	24
Brunts Old Boys	24	7	2	15	45	65	23
Nottinghamshire Res	24	5	8	11	52	74	23
Ilkeston Rangers Res.	24	4	5	15	42	85	17
Racing Toton Res	24	4	4	16	38	70	16

DIVISION THREE	*P*	*W*	*D*	*L*	*F*	*A*	*Pts*
Nottingham I.C.	22	20	1	11	32	11	61
A S C Dayncourt Res	22	17	1	4	82	34	52
Hucknall Sports Y C Res	22	14	2	6	69	46	44
Derbyshire Amateurs 3rd	22	13	3	6	86	56	42
Sherwood	22	13	1	8	81	68	40
E M T E C	22	7	6	9	57	70	27
Old Elizabethans 4th.	22	8	3	11	49	80	27
Dynamo Baptist Res.	22	8	2	12	58	63	26
Nottinghamshire 3rd	22	7	3	12	45	61	24
Old Bemrosians	22	5	3	14	39	61	18
Tibshelf Old Boys Res.	22	2	4	16	33	96	10
West-Clif	22	2	3	17	32	11	79

LEAGUE CUPS WINNERS:

Senior:	Derbyshire Amateurs
Intermediate:	Old Elizabethans Res.
Minor:	A S C Dayncourt
H.B. Poole Trophy:	Lady Bay

SOUTHERN AMATEUR LEAGUE 1997-98

SENIOR SECTION:

FIRST DIVISION	P	W	D	L	F	A	Pts
Norsemen	22	12	6	4	55	39	30
Lensbury	22	11	6	5	52	39	28
E.Barnet O. Grammarians	22	10	7	5	44	30	27
Crouch End Vampires	22	10	5	7	56	33	25
O.Actonians Association	22	10	3	9	35	34	23
Lloyds Bank	22	9	4	9	37	36	22
Old Parmiterians	22	9	4	9	42	43	22
Polytechnic	22	6	9	7	31	33	21
Carshalton	22	7	7	8	37	46	21
West Wickham	22	9	2	11	32	38	20
Civil Service	22	7	5	10	39	42	19
South Bank Polytechnic	22	3	0	19	26	79	6

SECOND DIVISION	P	W	D	L	F	A	Pts
National Westmin'r Bank	22	11	8	3	60	34	30
Barclays Bank	22	13	4	5	52	32	30
Midland Bank	22	11	7	4	49	21	29
Old Esthameians	22	9	7	6	43	26	25
Old Owens	22	11	3	8	45	41	25
Old Parkonians	22	8	8	6	33	28	24
Old Salesians	22	9	4	9	41	39	22
Winchmore Hill	22	8	6	8	28	41	22
Alexandra Park	22	6	9	7	31	38	21
Old Lyonians	22	3	10	9	17	40	16
Cuaco	22	1	9	12	20	48	11
Old Latymerians	22	2	5	15	25	56	9

THIRD DIVISION	P	W	D	L	F	A	Pts
Old Stationers	20	13	3	4	65	38	29
Old Bromleians	20	13	2	5	66	39	28
Brentham	20	11	6	3	38	21	28
Bank of England	20	11	4	5	43	22	26
Broomfield	20	11	4	5	47	33	26
Kew Association	20	11	2	7	42	30	24
Alleyn Old Boys	20	8	3	9	48	48	19
Ibis	20	6	4	10	34	45	16
Southgate Olympic	20	3	3	14	25	54	9
Merton	20	2	4	14	27	60	8
O. Westminster Citizens	20	1	5	14	23	69	7

RESERVE TEAMS SECTION:

First Division 12 Teams - Won by - Old Act's Ass'n Rs.
Second Division 12 Teams - Won by - Carshalton Res.
Third Division 11 Teams - Won by - Midland Bank Res.

3RD. TEAMS SECTION:

First Division 12 Teams - Won by - Barclays Bank 3rd.
Second Division 12 Teams - Won by - S'gate Olymp. 3rd
Third Division 11 Teams - Won by - Old Owens 3rd.

4TH. TEAMS SECTION:

First Division 12 Teams - Won by - Old Act's Ass'n 4th.
Second Division 12 Teams - Won by - S'gate Olymp. 4th
Third Division 11 Teams - Won by - Broomfield 4th.

5TH. TEAMS SECTION:

First Division 10 Teams - Won by - Midland Bank 5th.
Second Division 11 Teams - Won by - O Estham'ns 5th
Third Division 11 Teams - Won by - West Wickham 5th.

6TH. TEAMS SECTION:

First Division 10 Teams - Won by - Old Act's Ass'n 6th.
Second Division 9 Teams - Won by - Midland Bank 6th.
Third Division 5 Teams - Won by - Lloyds Bank 6th.

MINOR SECTION:

First Division 10 Teams - Won by - Polytechnic 7th.
Second Division 10 Teams - Won by - O. Act's Ass'n 9th
Third Division 10 Teams - Won by - Norsemen 8th.
Fourth Division 10 Teams - Won by - Nat West B. 10th.

SOUTHERN OLYMPIAN LEAGUE 1998-98

SENIOR SECTION:

Division One	P	W	D	L	F	A	Pts
Old Finchleians	18	11	4	3	54	31	26
Hon. Artillery Company	18	9	4	5	35	20	22
Nottsborough	18	8	4	6	38	36	20
Witan	18	7	5	6	34	34	19
Hale End Athletic	18	7	5	6	28	32	19
Parkfield	18	6	6	6	32	33	18
City of London	18	6	4	8	36	37	16
Southgate County	18	6	4	8	34	39	16
Ulysses	18	6	3	9	25	38	15
St. Mary's College	18	4	1	13	22	38	9

Division Two	P	W	D	L	F	A	Pts
Old Grammarians	18	10	7	1	38	16	27
Old Woodhouseians	18	11	3	4	39	28	25
Albanian	18	10	3	5	41	31	23
Fulham Compton Old Boys	18	9	1	8	53	44	19
Hampstead Heathens	18	6	6	6	38	35	18
UCL Academicals	18	8	2	8	30	33	18
Mill Hill Village	18	7	1	10	44	49	15
Wandsworth Borough	18	5	3	10	42	47	13
Ealing Association	18	5	2	11	39	53	12
Westerns	18	5	0	13	36	64	10

Division Three	P	W	D	L	F	A	Pts
Old Bealonians	18	15	2	1	80	27	32
Pegasus (Inner Temple)	18	11	4	3	50	30	26
B.B.C.	18	6	8	4	46	38	20
Hadley	18	8	4	6	38	32	20
Duncombe Sports	18	9	2	7	51	46	20
Inland Revenue	18	8	1	9	36	47	17
New Scotland Yard Comets	18	6	3	9	26	45	15
Old Colfeians	18	5	4	9	32	38	14
London Welsh	18	4	1	13	32	63	9
Mayfield Athletic	18	2	3	13	28	53	7

Division Four	P	W	D	L	F	A	Pts
Brent	16	11	5	0	38	6	27
Cardinal Pole Old Boys	16	13	0	3	47	19	26
Tesco Country Club	16	8	2	6	32	26	18
London Airways	16	8	2	6	36	33	18
Centymca	16	6	3	7	30	29	15
Birkbeck College	16	5	2	9	23	32	12
Old Fairlopians	16	5	2	9	23	32	12
Economicals	16	5	1	10	32	45	11
Tansley	16	2	1	13	24	63	5

INTERMEDIATE SECTION:

Division One 10 Teams - Won by - Old Finchleians Res.
Division Two 10 Teams - Won by - Old Bealonians Res.
Division Three 10 Teams - Won by - O Finchleians 3rd.

JUNIOR SECTION:

Division One 11 Teams - Won by - The Cheshunt Club
Division Two N 10 Teams - Won by - Parkfield 4th.
Division Two S&W 11 Teams - Won by - B B C 3rd
Division Three N 10 Teams - Won by - Hamp. Hths 4th.
Division 3 S&W 12 Teams - Won by - Ful. Comp. OB 4th
Division Four N 10 Teams - Won by - Parkfield 6th.
Division 4 S&W 11 Teams - Won by - City of London 6th
Division Five N 9 Teams - Won by - Parkfield 7th.

Senior Challenge Bowl Won by - City of London
Senior Challenge Shield Won by - Old Finchleians
Intermediate Challenge Cup Won by - Hale End Ath Res
Intermediate Challenge Shield Won by - Parkfield Res
Junior Challenge Cup Won by - Old Finchleians 3rd
Junior Challenge Shield Won by - Old Bealonians 3rd
Mander Cup Won by - Albanian 4th
Mander Shield Won by - UCL Acad's 4th
Burntwood Trophy Won by - Southgate Co 5th
Burntwood Shield Won by - B B C 5th
Thomas Parmiter Cup Won by - City of London 6th
Thomas Parmiter Shield Won by - Parkfield 6th
Veterans' Challenge Cup Won by - Old Fairlopians Vets
Veterans' Challenge Shield Won by - O Finchleians Vets

UNIVERSITY OF LONDON INTER-COLLEGIATE MENS' LEAGUE

PREMIER DIVISION:	P	W	D	L	F	A	Pts
Q. Mary Westfield College	14	11	1	2	44	17	34
London School of Economics	14	8	2	4	33	25	26
University College	14	8	1	5	38	28	25
Imperial College	14	6	3	5	41	33	21
King's College	14	5	3	6	27	35	18
Goldsmiths' College	14	4	2	8	24	30	14
Royal Holloway College	13	2	5	6	28	32	11
U.M.D.S.	13	2	1	10	11	46	7

DIVISION ONE	P	W	D	L	F	A	Pts
University College Res.	18	13	3	2	51	15	42
R. Holloway College Res.	17	13	2	2	48	16	41
Goldsmiths' College Res.	18	13	0	5	46	27	39
Q.Mary Westfield Coll. Res.	18	10	1	7	38	42	31
London School Econ's R.	18	6	4	8	41	41	22
Royal School of Mines (IC)	17	6	2	9	28	36	20
Ch. Cross & W'min. H. MS	18	6	2	10	35	49	20
UCL & Middx Hosp M.S.	18	6	1	11	42	55	19
Royal Holloway College 3rd	18	4	2	12	29	41	14
King's College Hosp. M.S.	18	3	1	14	30	66	10

DIVISION TWO	P	W	D	L	F	A	Pts
R.Lon'n & St.Bart's M. S.	18	14	2	2	56	19	44
St Mary's Hospital MS	18	11	6	1	84	19	39
Royal Veterinary College	18	8	5	5	41	33	29
Imperial College Res.	18	8	3	7	36	35	27
Royal Free Hosp. Sch. Med.	18	6	5	7	27	46	23
University College 3rd	18	6	4	8	33	42	22
London Sch. Economics 3rd.	18	6	3	9	30	59	21
King's College Res.	18	5	4	9	35	52	19
St George's Hospital MS	18	4	2	12	24	38	14
Q.Mary Westfield Coll. 3rd.	18	4	2	12	23	46	14

DIVISION THREE	P	W	D	L	F	A	Pts
Imperial College 3rd.	18	13	2	3	54	15	41
S.Slav. & E.Europ'n Studies	18	12	2	4	62	31	38
London Sch. Economics 4th.	18	10	4	4	48	38	34
U C & Middx. Hosp. MS R.	18	9	2	7	54	36	29
Imperial College 4th.	18	8	1	9	39	35	25
Royal Holloway College 4th	18	6	5	7	39	49	23
Wye College	18	5	4	9	36	42	19
University College 4th	18	5	2	11	32	59	17
King's College 3rd.	16	3	3	10	30	52	12
St George's Hosp. MS Res.	16	3	3	10	21	58	12

DIVISION FOUR	P	W	D	L	F	A	Pts
King's College 4th.	18	14	2	2	77	22	44
University College 5th.	18	12	1	5	57	38	37
Royal Holloway College 5th.	18	9	4	5	50	31	31
London Sch. Economics 5th.	18	9	1	8	48	35	28
Q. Mary Westf'd College 4th.	18	7	2	9	34	34	23
Q. Mary Westf'd College 5th.	18	7	2	9	50	53	23
Birkbeck Students	18	6	4	8	38	60	22
Goldsmiths' College 3rd.	16	6	2	8	45	48	20
Ch.Cross & W'min.HMS R.	16	6	0	10	42	53	18
School of Pharmacy	14	1	0	13	11	78	3

DIVISION FIVE	P	W	D	L	F	A	Pts
King's College 5th	18	18	0	0	84	14	54
R. Free Hos. Sch. Med. R	18	12	2	4	54	31	38
University College 6th	18	9	3	6	48	32	30
R.Lon. & St.Barts HMC R	18	8	2	8	44	43	26
Q. Mary Westf'd College 6th	18	7	2	9	40	56	23
Imperial College 5th	18	5	5	8	26	30	20
Royal Holloway College 6th	18	6	2	10	33	50	20
U.M.D.S. Res	18	5	3	10	28	50	18
Ch.Cross & W'min. HMS 3rd	17	4	3	10	35	51	15
Royal School of Mines Res	17	2	4	11	23	58	10

DIVISION SIX	P	W	D	L	F	A	Pts
St. Mary's Hospital MS Rs	19	18	1	0	101	14	55
London Sch. Economics 6th	19	13	1	5	79	32	40
Goldsmiths' College 4th	20	13	1	6	83	45	40
King's College Hos MS Res	20	9	2	9	57	56	29
University College 7th	20	9	0	11	37	64	27
Royal Academy of Music	15	8	1	6	61	43	25
Imperial College 6th	20	7	2	11	46	57	23
King's College 6th	16	6	1	9	42	54	19
R.Lon. & St.Barts HMC 3rd	17	6	11	0	35	62	19
U.M.D.S. Res	15	3	0	12	22	67	9
St George's Hos. MS 3rd	17	2	0	15	19	88	6

* includes allocated or deducted points

Challenge Cup
Imperial College 0 London School of Economics 4

Upper Reserves Cup
St. Mary's Hosp M Sch. 3 University College H. MS 2

Lower Reserves Cup
R. Academy of Music 7 London Sch.Economics 6th 3

LONDON UNIVERSITY MEN'S XI REPRESENTATIVE MATCH RESULTS

Old Boys' League	Lost 0-2
Ulysses	Won 3-2
Southern Amateur League	Won 2-1
Arthurian League	Won 3-1
SE Region BUSA	Lost 0-4
Metropolitan Police	Lost 1-3
Army Crusaders	Won 5-4
Southern Olympian League	Won 4-2
Oxford University	Drawn 0-0
Amateur Football Alliance	Lost 2-3

West London Institute, Chelsea XI (twice), Lloyds of London, Cambridge University London Legal League all lost to bad weather

UNIVERSITY OF LONDON INTER-COLLEGIATE WOMENS' LEAGUE

PREMIER DIVISION	P	W	D	L	F	A	Pts
R.Lon'n H. & Q. Mary West.	14	13	1	0	75	6	40
University College	14	11	1	2	56	22	34
Royal Holloway College	14	10	1	3	79	15	31
London School of Econ.	12	4	2	6	31	22	14
Imperial College	14	4	1	9	21	61	13
King's College	13	4	0	9	19	57	12
St. George's Hospital MS	13	2	1	10	19	69	7
R.Free Hos. Sch. Med. Res	12	1	1	10	2	50	4

FIRST DIVISION	P	W	D	L	F	A	Pts
Wye College	12	10	0	2	60	13	30
U.M.D.S.	12	9	1	2	42	6	28
Royal Free Hospital Res	12	7	1	4	26	26	22
University College Hospital	12	6	1	5	27	22	19
University College Res	12	4	0	8	25	42	12
Royal Holloway College Res	12	2	1	9	13	44	7
Goldsmiths' College	12	2	0	10	11	51	6

Womens' Challenge Cup
University College 3 King's College 1

In Support Of Youth Development

This is an often talked about subject, but what do we really mean. Is it just time spent with youngsters letting them play their matches and shouting from the sidelines or does it involve more than this?

True youth development is to provide a learning and truly supportive environment where personal aptitude, diet, fitness and health awareness, technical skills, teamwork, and knowledge of the game and its rules can be nurtured and perfected.

The objective is to ensure each player is taken carefully, caringly and, above all, safely along the path to reach his or her full potential in a competitive environment for the benefit of country, club and player.

The responsibility therefore placed upon coaches and their assistants is considerable. They must draw upon experience and a deep knowledge of the game together with reviewing and assimilating new understanding and ways of coaching on an ongoing basis. Even this is not enough, they must be able to communicate their skills effectively with their players and report on progress to directors, managers and not least parents.

This reporting on all aspects of individual and team progress is essential to justify the levels of financial support that will need to be made as a joint contribution towards success.

As coaching becomes more and more professional within a structured national framework then the amount of information both generated and required will be significant. The sometimes challenging transition of changing from a long established, time consuming, manual systems to newly introduced computer based systems will have to be made to allow for detailed registration, performance monitoring, medical and injury management, effective reporting, accurate recording and to reduce administration time and cost.

Price Patrick & Associates are fully supportive of current initiatives in the development of youth in football.

Surrey Youth v Lancashire Youth

FA County Youth Cup - Semi Final

Photograph: D Nicholson

The appointment of Howard Wilkinson as Technical Director of the Football Association in January 1996 and his recent introduction of a "Quality Charter" are seen as a very positive and long awaited approach. These FA initiatives deserve to be fully endorsed.

We shall continue to develop and produce management systems that meet the stated requirements of the F.A. and other governing bodies, in this country and world-wide.

EuroFocus FC series have been designed to cover all areas of football from boys clubs and amateur clubs right up to the top professional teams. This is achieved by using carefully constructed modules that cater for an identified and specific area of football club management.
Each module is extremely functional and powerful in its own right.

Sponsorship By Local Business & Other Organisations

Price Patrick realise that the cost of management systems and supporting computer equipment may be difficult for a club to finance.

We provide a unique opportunity for companies and organisations to sponsor the management systems.

Business has for a very long time recognised the promotional potential from success in football.

The time is now exactly right for business to be associated with the movement for a structured approach to youth development in clubs.

Price Patrick will be pleased to provide an information pack to interested clubs and or business organisations on this sponsorship option.

Girls and Women's Football

Women's World Cup in the USA 1999

Women's football is developing at a fast pace. The draw for the 1997/1999 European Qualifying Competition for the 3rd FIFA Women's World Cup took place, in Geneva on 19th February 1997.
A total of 34 countries entered the

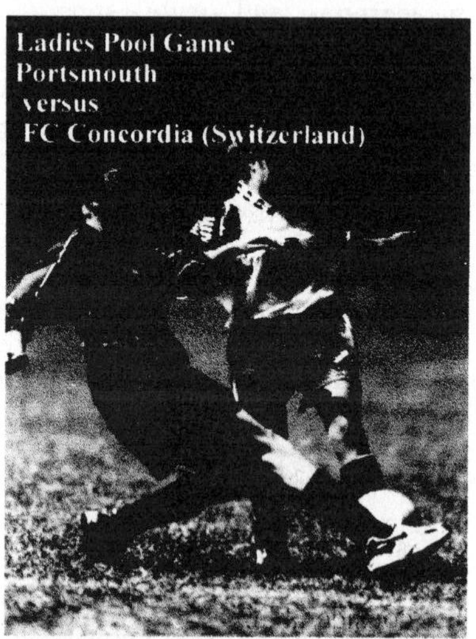

Ladies Pool Game
Portsmouth
versus
FC Concordia (Switzerland)

qualifying competition. Qualifying matches will be played against each group member in home and away matches. These qualifying matches are due to begin in September 1997.
England are in Group 3 along with Norway, Germany, Netherlands.
For the record: Group 1 Sweden, Spain, Iceland, Ukraine.
Group 2 Italy, Finland, France, Switzerland.
Group 4 Russia, Denmark, Portugal, Belgium.

THE ENGLISH SCHOOLS' FOOTBALL ASSOCIATION

Chief Executive: Malcolm Berry, 1/2 Eastgate Street, Stafford ST16 2NQ
Tel: 01785 251142 Fax: 01785 255485

Publicity: M Simmonds
19 The Spinney, Bulcote, Burton Joyce, Nottingham NG14 5GX
Tel: 0115 931 3299 Fax: 0115 931 2758

THE INTERNATIONAL SEASON

THE UNDER 15 SQUAD

Nearly a century of tradition came to an end on a high note as the last ever England Schools' Under 15 side defeated old rivals West Germany 1-0 in the Olympic Stadium in Berlin on May 27th in front of a 67,000 crowd. From next season, as part of the new Football Association 'Charter for Quality', the team will be under the control of F.A. personnel, a decision which the E.S.F.A. challenged vigorously but was ultimately unable to prevent.

The professional way in which the year's programme was conducted, as indeed has been the case since the first ever schools' international match in 1907, has set a very high standard for the F.A. to follow. Apart from the highlight in Berlin, the squad distinguished itself by finishing in third place in the annual Montaigu tournament in France which attracted 32 international teams although a dip in form in mid-season cost them the Victory Shield which they had won for the past four seasons.

RESULTS

v Belgium	won 4-2 (Boothroyd 2, Dodd, Parnaby)	at Brussels
v Wales	won 1-0 (Davis - Victory Shield)	at Bury
v N Ireland	won 3-0 (Clarke, Dodd, Boothroyd - Victory Shield)	at Barnsley
v Brazil	drew 0-0	at Wembley
v Brazil	lost 1-2	at Middlesbrough
v Scotland	lost 1-3 (Boothroyd - Victory Shield)	at Raith
v Hungary	won 1-0 (Parnaby)	at Old Trafford
v Germany	won 1-0 (Davis)	at Berlin

MONTAIGU TOURNAMENT

	v Tunisia	drew 0-0
	v Colombia	won 3-2
	v Romania	won 5-0
Quarter Final	v Republic of Ireland	won 1-0
Semi Final	v France	lost 0-1
3rd Place Play Off	v Italy (England won on penalties)	drew 0-0

APPEARANCES & GOALSCORERS IN FULL INTERNATIONALS

J Bewers	Willingborough & Rushden	8	
J Boothroyd	Islington & Camden	5 + 3 sub	(4 goals)
B Clark	Derwentside	9	
P Clarke	Sefton	9	(1 goal)
P Crookes	Liverpool	4 + 2 sub	
J Davis	Redditch	8 + 1 sub	(2 goals)
J Defoe	Newham	5 + 2 sub	
A Dodd	Stafford	7 + 1 sub	(2 goals)
R Evans	Swindon	6 + 1 sub	
M Hamshaw	Rotherham	6 + 2 sub	
R Logan	West Suffolk	6 + 3 sub	
D Nardiello	Halesowen & Stourbridge	2 + 4 sub	(1 goal)
C O'Brien	Liverpool	9 (captain)	
S Parnaby	Bishop Auckland	7 + 1 sub	(2 goals)
M Rose	Salford	1 + 1 sub	
P Senior	Liverpool	0 + 1 sub	
M Szmid	Nuneaton	6 + 3 sub	
A Tapp	Croydon	6	
P Thornton	Spelthorne	1	

England Under 15 Squad 1997-98

Back Row (L-R): Jay Bothroyd, Ben Clark, Rhys Evans, Matthew Hamshaw, Philip Senior, Richard Logan, Daniel Nardiello
Middle: Dr Arthur Tabor, Stuart Parnaby, Ashley Dodd, Marek Szmid, Peter Clarke, Alexander Tapp, Jonathon Brewers, James Davis

Front: Ian Shead (Goalkeeping Coach), Mark Eales (Physiotherapist), Jermain Defoe, Alan Heads (Chairman), Chris O'Brien, Dave Parnaby (Manager), Vic Bragg (Assistant Manager)

Photo: Action Images

THE UNDER 18 INTERNATIONAL SQUAD

The Under 18 Schools' international squad, chosen only from those in full time education had a disappointing season mainly due to injuries which struck even before the first match when Matthew Strode, who was to captain the side, fractured his leg playing for the Chelsea Youth team.

Against Belgium, Sam Parking gave England an early lead after good work by Neil Dix but agin the injury jinx hit the squad when Steven Young broke his nose. This upset England's rhythm and the professionals of Belgium equalised just before the interval. Good work by keeper Tim Mulloch and central defender Lee Bromby restricted Belgium to only two chances and England could take great credit from their draw against more experienced players. The big surprise of the season came at Glentoran when in the Heinz Centenary Shield, England failed to take their chances when they dominated the first half and although Mark Preston put them ahead, it was the Irish who took control and scored a late winner to bring them a 2-1 victory.

England reserved their worst performance for the game in Austria and never recovered from going two behind in the first five minutes. Only a good display by keeper Martin Hutt kept the final score to four. Strode returned for the final match, the third place play-off in the Centenary Shield, making the defence much more solid. Ryan Baker opened the scoring from twenty yards just after half-time and Sam Parkin scored a second three minutes later. Although Wales fought back well, they could not breach the home defence who held on for their only victory of the season.

RESULTS

v Belgium	at Yeovil	drew 1-1	(Parkin)
v N Ireland	at Belfast	lost 1-2	(Preston)
v Austria	at Purgstall	lost 0-4	
v Wales	at Scunthorpe	won 2-1	(Parkin, Baker)

SQUAD AND APPEARANCES

C Anderson	Northumberland	3	
R Baker	Cheshire	3 + 1 sub	(1 goal)
L Bromley	West Yorkshire	4	
K Campello	Wiltshire	2	
N Dix	Wiltshire	3 + 1 sub	
J Fattorusso	Bedfordshire	1 + 3 sub	
S Futcher	Wiltshire	4 (captain)	
M Hutt	Berkshire	2	
N McFarlane	Warwickshire	2	
R McPartlin	Cambridgeshire	4	
T Mullock	Cheshire	2 + 1 sub	
D O'Brien	Durham	2	
S Parkin	Surrey	4	(2 goals)
M Preston	Hampshire	2	(1 goal)
M Strode	Devon	1 (captain v Wales)	
P Tisdale	Somerset	0	
A Young	Inner London	3 + 1 sub	
S Young	Northumberland	2 + 1 sub	

Team Manager	David Cook
Assistant Team Manager	Malcolm Hird
Goalkeeper Coach	Mark Wallington
Physio	A Gallafant
Doctor	D Baron

England Under 18 International Squad 1997-98, at the final Coaching Weekend at Lilleshall National Sports Centre
Back Row (L-R): Mark Preston, Adam Young, Christopher Anderson, Ryan Baker
Middle: Mr David Cook (Team Manager), Steven Young, Neil Dix, Timothy Mullock, Martin Hutt, Nicholas McFarlane, Sam Parkin, Mr Malcolm Hird (Assistant Team Manager)
Front: Daniel O'Brien, Jay Fattorusso, Leigh Bromby, Mr Alan Heads (ESFA Chairman), Matthew Strode (Captain), Simon Futcher, Richard McPartlin

THE ENGLISH SCHOOLS' FA FUJI FILMS TROPHY 1997-98

FINAL					
1st Leg	Bristol & S Gloucester	v	Barnsley	0-1	(at Ashton Gate, Bristol)
2nd Leg	Barnsley	v	Bristol & S Gloucester	0-1	(at Oakwell, Barnsley)
Aggregate:	Bristol & S Gloucester	1	Barnsley	1	(Trophy shared)

For the first time in many years a side from the West Country reached the final of the premier competition in the E.S.F.A. calendar but Bristol's hopes of a first victory in the competition since 1979 seemed thin after they lost the first leg at home to a 20th minute effort from Barnsley's Adam Marsh. The visitors held on to this single goal advantage quite comfortably despite an incredible 11 minutes of injury time and went into the home leg in confident mood. Bristol, who had lacked ideas and invention in the first game, turned the tables at Oakwell and well deserved their share of the Trophy.

ROUTES TO THE FINAL

Bristol & South Gloucester SFA

Round 1	Brigend & District	A	won 14-0
Round 2	Ebbw Vale	H	won 4-0
Round 3	East Berkshire	H	won 4-2
Round 4	Swindon	H	won 5-0
Round 5	South East Sussex	H	won 6-2
Qtr-final	Reading	A	won 3-1
Semi-final	Blackheath	A	won 2-0

Barnsley

Round 1	Spen Valley	A	won 3-2
Round 2	Hambleton & R'mond	H	won 4-0
Round 3	Manchester	H	won 2-1
Round 4	Blackpool	A	won 2-0*
Round 5	East Riding	H	won 4-2*
Round 6	Lincoln	A	drew 0-0*
Replay		H	won 2-1
Semi-final	Bradford	A	drew 0-0*
Replay		H	won 3-0

THE VICTORIOUS SQUADS

Bristol & South Gloucestershire

Blue and White Shirts/Blue Shorts

1	Daniel Hooper	Hengrove, Bristol
2	Mike Newell	John Cabot, S Glos
3	Peter Ball	St Mary Redcliffe, Bristol
4	David Horseman	Henbury, Bristol
5	Adam Misiatto	Patchway, S Glos
6	Oliver Price	Hartcliffe, Bristol
7	Ryan Nicholls	Hengrove, Bristol
8	Lewis Hogg	Patchway, S Glos
9	Gary Cripps	St Mary Redcliffe, Bristol
10	Simon Bryan (capt)	Hanham, S Glos
11	Marvin Brown	St Thomas More, Bristol
12	Dan Cleverley	Hanham, S Glos
14	Rob Scott	Brimsham Grn, S Glos
15	Peter Shepherd	Bedminster Down, Bristol
16	David Garrett	Kingsfield, S Glos
GK	James Aylott	Chipping Sodbury, S Gls

Team Managers: Mr T Shears and Mr K Warrant

Barnsley

Red Shirts, White Shorts

1	Craig Parry	Foulstone
2	Neil Fox	Priory
3	Craig Sedgewick	Willowgarth
4	Liam Wharton	Wombwell
5	Neil Austin	Holgate
6	Matthew Clamp	Holgate
7	Gary Reece	Royston
8	Peter Kitchen	Dearne
9	Adam Marsh	Darton
10	Antony Kay	Foulstone
11	Andrew West	Dearne
GK	Andrew Taylor	Royston
12	Adam Smith	Darton
14	John Dowle	Holgate
15	Steven Asquith	Priory
16	Karl Rose	Priory
	William Keena	St Michaels
	Shane Kelsey	Kingstone

Barnsley Schools' Under 15 Squad - Joint winners of the E.S.F.A. Fuji Films Trophy 1997-98

THE E.S.F.A. PREMIER LEAGUE UNDER 16 COUNTY CHAMPIONSHIP

QUARTER-FINAL

West Midlands	v	Lancashire	2-2, 4p5	Durham	v	Staffordshire	0-0, 0-1
Bedfordshire	v	Berkshire	1-2	Devon	v	Middlesex	1-0

SEMI-FINAL

Lancashire	v	Staffordshire	3-0	Berkshire	v	Devon	2-1

FINAL

LANCASHIRE	v	BERKSHIRE	2-1

Lancashire, having made impressive progress to the final, fell behind early in the game and still trailed at the interval despite heavy pressure. The second half started in similar vein but a substitution changed the game with Peter Wright striking home a splended volley to equalise. Lancashire continued to dominate the game but an impressive Berkshire kept them at bay until a minute from time. Then a header from Wright hit the bar and in the ensuing melee, a Berkshire defender sliced into his own goal to bring Lancashire the Trophy for the first time.

THE E.S.F.A. PREMIER LEAGUE UNDER 19 COUNTY CHAMPIONSHIP

QUARTER-FINAL

Humberside	v	Merseyside	1-0	Northumberland	v	West Midlands	2-1
Hampshire	v	Bedfordshire	3-1	Essex	v	Dorset	7-0

SEMI-FINAL

Humberside	v	Northumberland	0-1	Hampshire	v	Essex	0-2

FINAL

ESSEX	v	NORTHUMBERLAND	2-1	after extra time, played at Roots Hall, Sunderland

THE E.S.F.A. ADIDAS PREMIER UNDER 11 7-A-SIDE CHAMPIONSHIP

Played at Wembley Stadium

SEMI-FINAL

Newham	v	Stoke-on-Trent	0-0	Newham won on corners
Peterlee	v	Bristol	1-1	Bristol won on corners

FINAL

NEWHAM	v	BRISTOL	0-0	Trophy shared

THE INDIVIDUAL SCHOOLS' COMPETITIONS

THE E.S.F.A. GOODYEAR UNDER 16 CHAMPIONSHIP (In Association with Channel 4)

FINAL

BLUECOAT SCHOOL (MERSEYSIDE)	v	DOUAY MARTYRS SCHOOL (MIDDLESEX)	6-2

A crowd of over 1500 at Molineux Stadium, Wolverhampton saw the impressive Bluecoat School romp to one of the biggest victories in an E.S.F.A. final in recent seasons with a five goal first half blitz to which Douay had no answer. Kevin Nolan scored after seven minutes and then came three goals in nine minutes which effectively settled the game. David Eaton scored off teh post after 24 minutes, then Nolan headed his second a minute later before Peter Lamb made it four. Eaton made it 5-0 with his second of the game on the stroke of half-time. Douay, to their great credit, made a game of it after the break with Kevin O'Connor scoring after four minutes and Marcus Gonzales in teh last minute. Paul Lin, however, had added Bluecoat's sixth of the game in the meantime to ensure that his school were champions of England.

ROAD TO MOLINEUX

	Blue Coats				Martyrs		
Round 1	Ellesmere Port (Cheshire)	(H)	5-0	Round 1	Woodside (Essex)	(H)	3-1
Round 2	Dronfield (Sheffield)	(H)	5-0	Round 2	Alice Owens (Herts)	(H)	1-0
Round 3	St Wilfreds (Blackburn)	(A)	7-1	Round 3	Eastfields (Surrey)	(A)	3-0
Round 4	Gained by a bye			Round 4	Barking Abbey (Essex)	(H)	3-0
Semi-final	Rawlings (Leicester)	(H)	2-1	Semi-final	Forest Boys' (Berks)	(H)	3-0

Both teams also played 5 Rounds in their County competitions to reach the national stages.

THE E.S.F.A. WAGONWHEELS 5-A-SIDE CHAMPIONSHIP

BOYS' FINAL

Nicholas Chamberlaine School (Nuneaton)	v	King's Hill School (Chester)	2-1

GIRLS' FINAL

Mountain Ash School (Cynon Valley)	v	Cockshut Hill School (Birmingham)	1-0

THE E.S.F.A. PREDATOR 6-A-SIDE TROPHY

SEMI-FINAL

St Vincent's R C (Newcastle)	v	St Philip Neri's R C (Mansfield)	0-1
Botwell House R C (Hayes)	v	Courthouse Junior (Maidenhead)	1-1

Hayes won on corners

THIRD PLACE

St Vincent's R C (Newcastle)	v	Courthouse School (Maidenhead)	4-0

FINAL

St Philip Neri's R C (Mansfield)	v	Botwell House R C (Hayes)	0-3

Played at Old Trafford on 9th May

THE E.S.F.A. SMALL PRIMARY SCHOOLS 6-A-SIDE COMPETITION

FINAL

Newstead School (Notts)	v	Crick School (Northants)	0-1

Played at Leicester City FC on 20th April

THE PANINI UNDER 11 6-A-SIDE COMPETITION

ESFA/PFA Community Scheme activity

FINAL

Fernwood School	v	Headlington Middle School	1-0

Played at Wembley Stadium on 19th April

NATIONWIDE SCHOOLS CHALLENGE

DIVISION ONE PLAY-OFF
FINAL

Hylton Red House School (Sunderland FC)	v	Bexley & Erith Tech High (Charlton Ath FC)	1-2

DIVISION TWO PLAY-OFF
FINAL

Waltham Toll Bar School (Grimsby Town FC)	v	The Ferrers School (Northampton Town FC)	4-0

DIVISION THREE PLAY-OFF
FINAL

The Gilberd School (Colchester United FC)	v	Westlands School (Torquay United FC)	1-1

THE E.S.F.A. VIMTO TROPHY

Valley School won the most exciting of all the national finals when they recovered from a 2-0 half-time deficit to become the third team from Nottinghamshire to win the competition in the four years of its existence.

Valley made a slow start and found themselves trailing to a superb goal from Darrick Wood striker, Jessica Smith. The same player soon hit the post and then scored her second to give the Kent side a 2-0 interval lead. Valley were a different side after the break and took heart from Michelle Davies' 18 yard shot three minutes into the second half. Her sister Suzanne then made it 2-2 and she then touched home another from close range to put Valley ahead for the first time. Darrick Wood were not finished, however, and when Smith again created havoc she set up Samantha Sydney who shot through the legs of Amy Tomlinson in Valley's. The latter atoned with two good saves and Valley's winner came three minutes from time when Suzanne Davies completed her hat-trick to give Valley their 4-3 win.

THE ROUTES TO THE FINAL

Darrick Wood

Five matches to win the Kent Championship

Round 1	St Philomena (Surrey)	3-2
Round 2	Hatch End High (Middlesex)	2-0
Round 3	Haverhill (Suffolk)	3-0
Round 4	Nicholas Chamberlaine (Warwicks)	3-2
Semi-final	Willingdon (Sussex)	4-1

Valley

Four matches to win the Nottinghamshire Championship

Round 1	Meadowhead School (Sth Yorkshire)	8-3
Round 2	High Storrs (Sth Yorkshire)	3-1
Round 3	King's Norton School (West Midlands)	4-2
Round 4	Netherthorpe School (Derbyshire)	3-2
Semi-final	Montgomery High School (Lancashire)	3-1

Valley School - Winners of the Vimto Trophy

CHANNEL ISLAND FOOTBALL ROUND-UP 1997-98

Within the Channel Islands the success or failure of the Guernsey and Jersey football teams is all-too-often measured on the result of the annual Muratti match against the other island. In this respect, 1997-98 was Jersey's season - they captured all but one of the major Representative matches between the two islands - the Guernsey Ladies having restored some green-and-white pride with a 2-0 victory in Jersey in only the second Ladies Muratti. Having won 3-0 on home soil twelve months previous, the Guernsey Ladies have yet to concede a goal to the old enemy - a record of which they are justly proud, and one of which they are all too keen to remind their male counterparts!

The Senior Muratti match, the first to be played at the new Springfield Stadium in Jersey, was watched by a crowd nudging 4,000 who witnessed a comfortable 2-0 victory for the home side. In the Under 21 match, Jersey triumphed by 4-1 in Guernsey - but strange as it may seem, this was a much closer match, and one which was in the balance until the closing stages. The Under 18 match saw Jersey triumph 1-0 on Guernsey soil; and the Jersey Under 15's completed the male clean sweep by scoring a 3-1 home victory.

It was left to Sylvans - Guernsey champions for the fifth successive season - to restore inter island pride. In the annual match for the Upton Park Cup (the Channel Islands Championship) they became the first Guernsey club since the mid sixties to secure the trophy for three successive seasons, with a resounding 4-0 home victory over Jersey Scottish, the Jersey champions. Sylvans three victories have all been over Jersey Scottish (1-0; 1-0; and 4-0) and all six of their goals over the three seasons have been scored by one player - Paul Nobes. After a season during which he had spent most of his time injured on the sidelines, "Nobby" returned to score four in his clubs's most important match of the year.

The Guernsey champions secured six first team trophies in all - only missing out on Guernsey's Jeremie Cup - also retaining Jersey's premier knockout trophy, the Wheway Cup, for the third successive season.

Together with Northerners, Sylvans carried the Guernsey flag into English competitions, entering the Hampshire Senior Cup. Whilst the Northerners' Dorset Cup challenge came to a swift end in the First Round with a 6-0 away defeat at the hands of Hamworthy United, the Guernsey champions came up with their best ever performance in the competition. Drawn away to Fareham Town in the Second Round (they had previously eliminated Aerostructures of Hamble for the second successive season), they pushed the Dr Martens League club all the way - finally bowing out 3-6 after extra time. Having led 3-2 during the normal period, they had been within sight of victory before the superior fitness of the semi professionals finally told.

November saw the Jersey Football Association reject - at least for the time being - the formation of a Channel Islands Football League. The Guernsey Football Association had previously given its unanimous support to the plan, which would have seen two divisions of ten Channel Islands' clubs competing within a league structure for the first time.The Associations have undertaken to meet again during the 1998-99 season to see whether Jersey opinion has altered.

The GFA did not let the grass grow under their feet, however, and immediately took steps to ensure that they were able to offer their better players at least , the opportunity of playing regular competitive football against superior opposition.

An application for the Guernsey Senior side to participate in the South West Counties Football Championship, was accepted by the SWCFC Annual General Meeting on May 15th 1998 - and Guernsey will thus compete in Group "B" of the Championship during the coming season. The green and whites will play against Somerset (home); Cornwall (home); Devon (away); Gloucestershire (away); and Wiltshire (home) - with the added incentive of staging the Final if they finish top of their Group. This is perhaps hoping too much - but the island's entry into the competition has certainly sent a "buzz" through the whole of island football. October 31st - when Somerset visit Guernsey for the first Guernsey match - promises to be a momentous day in the history of Guernsey football.

GUERNSEY FOOTBALL ASSOCIATION

BARCLAYS PRIAULX LEAGUE

	P	W	D	L	F	A	Pts
Sylvans	21	17	1	3	93	23	52
Belgrave's	21	14	3	4	76	39	45
Vale Recreation	21	13	2	6	60	39	41
Northerners	21	9	3	9	60	46	30
St Martins	21	8	3	10	46	44	27
Rovers	21	7	3	11	51	62	24
Rangers	21	6	3	12	38	50	21
Port City	21	1	0	21	19	140	3

BARCLAYS RAILWAY LEAGUE

	P	W	D	L	F	A	Pts
Sylvans	18	15	2	1	70	14	47
Vale Recreation	18	14	2	2	56	24	44
Belgrave's	18	11	1	6	61	32	34
St Martin's	18	8	2	8	54	49	26
Rovers	18	8	2	8	37	35	26
Alderney Nomads	18	7	2	9	39	51	23
Northerners	18	4	6	8	29	38	18
Police	18	5	3	10	33	61	18
Rangers	18	5	2	11	29	55	17
Port City	18	1	2	15	25	74	5

BARCLAYS JACKSON LEAGUE

	P	W	D	L	F	A	Pts
Belgrave's	21	17	2	2	101	24	53
Sylvans	21	15	3	3	76	29	48
Vale Recreation	21	12	2	7	56	35	38
Northerners	21	10	5	6	60	42	35
Rovers	21	9	2	10	51	52	29
St Martin's	21	5	3	13	39	67	18
Rangers	21	5	1	15	46	67	16
Port City	21	1	2	18	21	134	5

BARCLAYS YOUTH DIVISION ONE

	P	W	D	L	F	A	Pts
Vale Recreation	18	16	0	2	81	20	48
Northerners	18	12	4	2	53	16	40
Rangers	18	7	6	5	50	37	27
St Martin's	18	7	4	7	48	44	25
Sylvans	18	5	3	10	25	63	18
Belgrave's	18	3	4	11	26	63	13
Rovers	18	2	1	15	14	54	7

BARCLAYS YOUTH DIVISION TWO

	P	W	D	L	F	A	Pts
St Martin's	18	16	0	2	79	15	48
Sylvans	18	15	1	2	71	22	46
Northerners	18	8	4	6	41	32	28
Belgrave's	18	7	3	8	39	47	24
Rovers	18	4	3	11	29	59	15
Vale Recreation	18	3	4	11	29	55	13
Rangers	18	1	3	14	25	83	5

JERSEY EUROPEAN FOOTBALL COMBINATION 1997-98

DIVISION ONE

	P	W	D	L	F	A	Pts
Scottish	20	14	5	1	67	13	47
St Peter	20	13	3	4	54	31	42
Rozel Rovers	20	13	2	5	55	32	41
Wanderers	20	10	4	6	66	32	34
First Tower	20	9	4	7	44	27	31
Magpies	20	8	3	9	35	43	27
St Paul's	20	7	5	8	30	27	26
St Martin	20	8	2	10	45	45	26
Portuguese	20	7	3	10	37	42	24
Sporting Acs	20	1	5	14	17	69	8
Beeches OB	20	0	4	16	23	90	4

MURATTI VASE

Jersey retained the Muratti Vase after a 2-0 home victory at Springfield. Jersey had defeated Alderney in the semi-final by the same margin.

ISLE OF MAN FOOTBALL REVIEW 1997-98

St Mary's from Douglas have dominated Manx Football this season winning all the senior trophies they could, that being four in all, the League Championship, Railway Cup, Hospital Cup and FA Cup.

In the league the only people to catch them out were the disciplinary committee of the Isle of Man FA who deducted six points early on for two separate technical infringements.

The first trophy to go into their cabinet was the Railway Cup which came as a result of a win over Douglas High School Old Boys. The final scoreline was 3-0 and the Man of the Match was the Saints Martin Reilly.

The second triumph cam in the FA Cup with the same defeated opponents, but this time it took a replay and Chris Higgins won the top player award. The league was just a matter of time as the Saints just kept on winning.

Peter Langridge won the Golden Boot Award for the season and his tally helped seal trophy number three with Old Boys, who represented the Island in the FA Vase only to lose out to Glasshoughton Welfare, the runners up yet again.

The final triumph was over Douglas Royal, a side who were in the final for the first time in their history. The winning margin this time was 4-1 with Reilly again the Man of the Match.

The relegation battle was decided on the last match when Braddan beat Laxey to send the Miners down to Division Two. Colby only managed to stay up for one year and go back to climb the mountain again.

At the start of the season there were high hopes of Peel following up their great season but an early season internal dispute, later settled, took away their opportunity to gain more silverware with only the Junior Cup ending in the Westerners hands.

Marown took the Second Division title and also the Woods Cup. The goals of Juan Killip were a major factor and he ended up joint top scorer for Division Two along with Martin Costain from Foxdale.

St John's United had a great revival to take the runners up spot along with the Paul Henry Trophy, the first award for the club in 14 years. Nick Hurt, their influential midfield man represented the Island for the first time, one of just two second division representatives with Nigel Shimmin from Marown being the other.

Ramsey were the team that might have been getting to two finals but due to the bad weather had the misfortune to play them both in a five day period and to lose out on each occasion.

The Isle of Man National side played three games in the season starting with two in the Guiness Cup competition. In the semi finals they defeated Northern Ireland on penalties after a 1-1 draw in normal time.

Nick Hurt scored the only goal in that game but there were no goals for the Manx team in the final of this amateur/semi professional tournament when they lost 2-0 to second half scores from the Republic of Ireland. Scotland had lost 2-1 to the Republic in the semi final.

The third match was a home fixture against Runcorn which, having given a good account of themselves, the Manx team lost 4-2 with the goals for the Island coming from debutant Daniel Lace and from Peter Langridge.

The future for Manx Football was made to look rosy, however, by the first appearance for a number of years of an Island Under 18 team. They opened in style with a 7-2 success over the same age group from the Runcorn Club. They are now looking for further fixtures.

The next season will see players trying for a place in the Isle of Man team to play in the Island Games which will be held in Gotland in the Baltic in the summer of 1999.

Dave Phillips

TAYLOR WOODROW DIVISION ONE

	P	W	D	L	F	A	Pts
St Mary's	24	24	0	0	93	13	66
DHSOB	24	16	3	5	63	28	51
Rushen Utd	24	15	3	6	73	35	48
Castletown	24	13	4	7	54	36	43
Gymnasium	24	12	5	7	58	41	41
Douglas Royal	24	30	5	9	43	40	35
Peel	24	10	4	10	64	36	34
St George's	24	10	3	11	62	56	33
Police	24	8	4	12	63	75	28
Ayre United	24	8	2	14	39	74	26
Bradbar	24	4	3	17	34	97	15
Laxey	24	4	2	18	35	89	14
Colby	24	2	2	20	26	87	8

St Mary's have had 6 points deducted

Total goals scored	707
Average goals per game	4.53
Highest score	St Mary's 9 Braddan 0
Goalless draws	Gynmns v Rushen
	Castletown v Rushen
	Castletown v D. Royal
Top Scorer	Peter Langridge (St Mary's)
Most goals in a game	Nick Cray (Police) 4
	David Kinrade (St George's) 4
	Jimmy Williams (OB) 4
Total hat-tricks	32
Most hat-tricks	Peter Langridge (St Mary's) 4

DIVISION ONE GOLDEN BOOT

Peter Langridge	St Mary's	33
Nick Cray	Police	22
Ian Kelly	Rushen	19
Tony Duncan	Gymns	17
Brian Gartland	Old Boys	15
Jimmy Williams	Old Boys	15

MARSH McLENNAN DIVISION TWO

	P	W	D	L	F	A	Pts
Marown	26	22	1	3	113	33	67
St John's United	26	21	2	3	104	31	65
Corinthians	26	18	4	4	107	47	58
Foxdale	26	17	2	7	117	55	53
Pulrose United	26	15	6	5	82	40	51
Ramsey	26	14	3	9	70	43	45
Union Mills	26	12	5	9	73	46	41
Michael United	26	11	5	10	83	62	38
Onchan	26	10	3	13	66	68	33
Jurby	26	6	3	17	48	102	21
Ronaldsway	26	5	3	18	49	106	18
Malew	26	4	3	19	49	109	15
Barclays	26	3	1	22	31	130	10
RYCOB	26	3	1	22	29	149	10

Total goals scored	1021
Average goals per game	5.61
Highest score	Foxdale 16 Jurby 1
Goalless draws	None
Top Scorer	Martin Costain (Foxdale) 37
	Juan Killip (Marown) 37
Most goals in a game	Mark Watterson (Fox) 8
	David Kinrade (St George's) 4
	Jimmy Williams (OB) 4
Total hat-tricks	49
Most hat-tricks	Martin Costain (Foxdale) 7
	including double hat-trick

DIVISION TWO SILVER BOOT

Sponsored by the Manx Independent

Martin Costain	Foxdale	37
Juan Killip	Marown	37
Ricky Lovett	Marown	31
Chris Bass	St John's	28
Nigel Moodie	Corinthians	27
Mark Watterson	Foxdale	21

St Mary's FC 1997-98

WOMEN'S FOOTBALL

Compiled by Cathy Gibb

The 1997-98 women's football season produced some enthralling encounters and some possibly unpredictable outcomes when eventually four teams found themselves well placed in the hunt for the Premier League championship crown.

Once again there was the never ending revolving roundabout of moves. Arsenal, last year's league champions, looked to have strengthened their squad somewhat with the signing of a key England defender, Wembley's Carol Harwood, and former England goalkeeper Lesley Higgs who had returned to her old club after a spell with Wembley. Tina Mapes left Croydon for Arsenal, and the young talented 17 year old Nina Downham, who made it into the Under 18 England squad, left Millwall Lionesses for the Gunners.

These signings have made up for the loss of such talent as England's forward Kelly Smith who had taken up a scholarship in America, but she is still managing to play her role in England's pursuit of World Cup qualification in the USA for 1999. And then the England pair Joanne Broadhurst and Sam Britton, and later in the season Sharon Barber and Lisa Spry, were all to leave Arsenal to join their former team mate, now player/manager, Debbie Bampton at Croydon.

While Croydon picked up two players from Wembley, Sue Smith and Ayala Liran, Brian Broadhurst, Joanne's father, decided to take up the position as Assistant Manager having spent a spell managing the successful Doncaster Belles. One time England defender Julie Fletcher was soon to be prized away from Millwall Lionesses.

England's outstanding player Karen Burke and her tenacious international team mate Becky Easton both left Liverpool for arch rivals Everton. Burke is no stranger to Everton having joined them before, only this time she said the move felt right. It was Karen Burke who scored the only goal to give Everton a 1-0 win to take the prestigious pre-season Reebok tournament by seeing off finalists Doncaster Belles 1-0.

The top game opening the new season on September 7th 1997 saw the defending league champions Arsenal take on challengers Everton. This resulted in an enthralling 2-2 draw, but after just two games it was Doncaster Belles who became the only club to have a 100 percent record intact, having narrowly defeated Millwall Lionesses 1-0 at home, and then Tranmere Rovers 2-0 away.

Come October 12th, it was all change at the top with Arsenal enjoying a slightly better goal difference from Everton despite both teams on thirteen points from five games as Doncaster Belles, having played one game more, had slipped to third spot after the losses to Croydon 1-0 at home and Everton 2-1 away.

Everton were soon to find themselves top of the Premier league with sixteen points from six matches after they saw off visitors Tranmere Rovers 3-2 on October 21st. Arsenal went down to hosts Doncaster Belles 2-1, while Everton enjoyed a resounding 8-0 triumph over visitors Wembley with four goals from Kerry Halfpenny.

Then they grabbed a 3-1 victory over defending league champions Arsenal at Marine FC on November 16th which saw Doncaster Belles take a tumble losing 2-1 away to Liverpool FC Ladies. Everton with a point (22) enjoyed two games (eight played) in hand, over second placed Doncaster Belles.

Doncaster were soon to go back at the top when they themselves caused an upset as they sunk hosts Croydon 3-1 at Croydon's The Arena ground. But only two days later Everton leapfrogged back to first spot.

On Tuesday 9th December, the Anfield stadium became the venue for top local derby game between Liverpool FC Ladies and Everton. Anfield has never been a good omen for the Liverpool women's side having played their twice before when they lost 2-0 in 1996 and 6-0 last year both times against Arsenal. They didn't get much change out of Everton either. But according to Sylvia Gore, their Secretary and Youth Team Manager, "I wasn't impressed with Everton at all. We totally dominated the first half but just failed to capitalise on our goal chances after hitting the bar twice. Our problem at Liverpool has always been that we lack prolific goalscorers".

It turned out to be a crucial goal from their former Liverpool player and England star Karen Burke who put Everton ahead in the eighteenth minute. And Tina Mason killed off a spirited Liverpool side with a second and winning goal in the 70th minute.

But with Everton soon pre-occupied with a Third round League Cup action seeing off visitors Tranmere Rovers 2-1 with two headed goals from Kerry Halfpenny and England's Mo Marley, meant that Doncaster could possibly go back to the top if they could secure a win over hosts Millwall Lionesses. On November 14th, it was Doncaster's turn to return to the top finally killing off Millwall Lionesses who had taken the lead through Joanne Sharp only for Gail Borman and Karen Walker to score late goals. Everton though still had three games in hand and were still the only side unbeaten in the Premier League so far.

The defending league champions Arsenal had found themselves in third spot by leapfrogging over Croydon (who too were involved in league cup action) after a convincing 9-1 victory over Wembley with a hat trick for England's Rachel Yankey and two from her England team mate Natasha Daly and former international Marieanne Spacey, and one a piece from ex-England stars Sian Williams and Kirsty Pealling.

But Everton went into the short Christmas break having regained pole position after convincingly defeating their Merseyside rivals Liverpool FC Ladies 4-1. This win was to cost them dearly after they lost two key players. Andy McGrady sustained fractured ribs and her replacement Kerry Halfpenny was taken to hospital with suspected ligament damage. Both players had collided with Liverpool's young England goalkeeper, Rachel Brown who came out of it unscathed.

England's central defender Mo Marley gave Everton a dream fifth minute lead with a powerful header. Everton capitalised on their superiority with further goals from ex Liverpool and Doncaster Belles player Louise Ryde (twentieth minute), Becky Easton (35th minute) and Karen Burke netting the fourth killer goal in the 90th minute to extend their impressive unbeaten run to eleven league games.

Interruption by wintery conditions caused postponements of cup fixtures in the early part of January 1998. Doncaster Belles, despite being held 1-1 at home by Tranmere rovers on January 25th, soon capitalised on Everton's involvement in the Women's FA Cup when they claimed top spot after beating Berkhamsted Town 4-0 at Armthorpe Miners Welfare ground with two goals from England's Vicky Exley.

A slim 1-0 triumph over Millwall Lionesses but an impressive 5-0 home victory over Berkhamsted Town was enough to see Everton claim back the number one spot with two games in hand over Doncaster Belles who now trailed Everton by three points.

Come March 15th Everton were to suffer their first league defeat in fourteen league games at the hands of Doncaster Belles going down 2-1 which meant that Doncaster Belles were to go top on the slightly better goal difference, yet Everton were still to have those precious two games in hand. The Merseysiders travelled back North on top of the tree after condemning Wembley to relegation with a 7-0 triumph. Karen Burke hit a hat-trick with two apiece for Welsh star Louise Thomas and Louise Ryde.

A goalless draw with Croydon and Everton were soon celebrating afterwards knowing that mathematically they couldn't be caught unless a catastrophe struck. The challengers and the defending league champions Arsenal needed to win their three remaining matches if they were to pip Everton on better goal difference.

But Arsenal were the only side that could spoil it for Everton, because they had two games in hand but looked to have thrown away any chance of title hopes when they were involved in a thrilling game with Croydon, who at one stage had every chance themselves of taking the title. And don't forget neither side wanted to play such a league game just four days before they were to meet one another again in the FA Women's Cup Final at Millwall's The New Den ground on Monday May 4th which was televised by Sky.

Arsenal made a remarkable recovery in a game in one of Croydon's best matches of the season contrary to Arsenal's feelings that they were the side that dominated the first half hitting the cross bar twice and the post.

Three times Croydon were ahead and three times Arsenal came back through Carol Harwood, super sub England's Rachel Yankey and Kelly Few clinching a point with Few's life saving header in the dying seconds on resigning the North London club to runners-up spot with their battle now on with Doncaster Belles.

Twice Highbury stadium was booked for Arsenal's two final league matches, Bradford City on Friday May 8th resulted in a 4-2 victory for the home side. Despite a spirited Bradford side who took the lead through Claire Popplewell in the fourth minute, the visitors were unfortunate not to find themselves 3-0 up with further misses from England's Melanie Garside and Sonia Moore. Marieanne Spacey came to Arsenal's rescue with a superb looping equaliser.

Kim Jerray-Silver and Faye White made it 3-1 for the Gunners after the break only for the Arsenal substitute Tammy Scrivens to gift Bradford their second goal with a well executed headed goal from a perfectly flighted cross from Garside in the 83rd minute. Spacey was to have the final say with her second goal and Arsenal's fourth and final goal superbly scored in the 88th minute.

It was now nicely set up to see who would finish runners-up as Doncaster Belles, who had monopolised second spot for the majority of the season were to be Arsenal's final opponents at Highbury on Sunday May 10th.

Again Arsenal were indebted to Marieanne Spacey whose deflected goal scored in the 22nd minute was to be the final winner to secure them the runners-up spot and leave Doncaster Belles surprisingly empty handed and dumped into third place. But the future looks bright for the Yorkshire side who now boast some excellent up and coming youngsters (including their Under 16 player of the year, Sarah Abrahams), who are now making it through to the senior squad.

As you have guessed by now, Everton did go on to clinch their first ever league championship title even though they were to be denied the chance of winning it the first time around on Easter Sunday because the Millwall Lionesses pitch at Fisher Athletic's ground was waterlogged and the game was postponed. They had in fact won the league without even kicking a ball when their nearest rivals Arsenal were held in that enthralling 3-3 draw by Croydon on Thursday evening.

It was an action packed 1-1 draw at the Nat West ground, temporary home of Millwall Lionesses, that saw Everton eventually toast their achievement. Maureen Marley had put Everton ahead in the 27th minute only for England's Danielle Murphy to equalise for Millwall with a superbly lobbed 30 yard goal over the head of substitute goalie Jo Fletcher in the 49th minute to share the points. But the league celebrations had to be put on hold for one player, goalkeeper Annie Wright, who had to be taken to hospital after tragically sustaining a broken leg in the 23r minute.

"I just can't believe we've won the title. I must admit it hasn't been by pure good footballing performances that has won us this piece of coveted silverware, but dogged determination cemented with excellent team spirit and consistency has seen us crowned Premier League champions for the first time ever. And it's a great feeling. I'm just proud of all of my players", said Manager Billy Jackson. They went out to collect their league trophy at a packed Goodison Park in front of an appreciative full house before the men's final game against Coventry City.

Wembley and Berkhamsted Town (newcomers to the Premier League) were relegated from the Premier Division. Wembley who lost a good majority of senior players pre-season including moving to Hanwell Town from Wembley's Vale Farm and despite playing out of their skin for the majority of their games, they never managed to win a point, while Berkhamsted, who have since lost Manager Steve Emmanuel, who resigned after threatening to do so last year, were only a point behind (eleven) the other Premier League newcomers Bradford City who eventually had to fight all the way to remain in the eh Premier League next season.

Berkhamsted had sneaked a 1-0 away victory over Bradford on February 15th with a solitary Jo Clearly goal in the 89th minute when they both played out a thrilling 3-3 draw on September 21st 1997.

Little did Berkhamsted know that they were the ones who were to be relegated along with Wembley after having had a great start and were at one stage second behind early leaders Doncaster Belles and it was Bradford City who had occupied the second bottom slot.

The Northern Division was handsomely won by Ilkeston Town who will now play Premier League football next season. Collecting 51 points from eighteen games scoring 59 goals but conceding only six, the best defence record in the entire national league, but like champions Everton they too only suffered one loss. They were crowned the League Champions as early as March 22nd when they celebrated their promotion with a resounding 7-1 defeat of visitors Coventry City.

Midfielder Deb White knows that Ilkeston will not be taking anything for granted next season, after their defection two seasons ago when they were relegated following a 3-0 drubbing by Liverpool FC Ladies. "I'm confident we'll do well. We do have a good mix of young with experienced players which is the right recipe needed to take the Premier League by storm."

Garswood Saints was the only team to take three points off Ilkeston Town, winning 2-1 on March 29th at Ilkeston Town FC. Garswood Saints were to finish up as runners-up despite trailing Ilkeston by a massive twelve points.

Bloxwich Town, formerly known as Stourport Swifts, were the side to be relegated from the Northern Division having only drawn two matches (1-1 with Arnold Town away and 0-0 with Coventry at home) hence two points collected from eighteen matches.

The Southern Division was less cut and dried, as there were quite a few teams in contention for the crown. Brighton & Hove Albion were soon to give Southampton Saints (relegated from the Premier Division last season) a run for their money when they emerged as the early leaders in October 1997 with fifteen points from six matches despite having already lost a game (losing 1-0 to newcomers Barry Town away on September 14th).

Playing rivals and hosts Three Bridges on October 12th, their former player Tammy Waine fired in two goals for Brighton, but it was a superb seventh minute 25 yarder from Nicky Rose that initially unnerved the Three Bridges side who just couldn't recover from Brighton's fire power.

Southampton themselves were held to a 1-1 draw at hosts Ipswich Town despite Rachel McArthur giving the Saints the lead only for Debbie Morley to net the equaliser and salvage a point for Ipswich.

Southampton took over at the top on December 7th 1997 after their rugby score of 9-0 away to Rushden & Diamonds (the team who like Wembley failed to collect a point and were to end up relegated from the Southern Division).

Then The Saints were held at 1-1 home by Whitehawk and their nearest rivals Wimbledon defeated Three Bridges 4-1 at home which allowed The Dons to take pole position with two points, the chasing pair being Langford and Southampton.

From January 18th to April 12th, the top position changed no less than six times between Brighton & Hove Albion, Wimbledon, and Southampton Saints who were eventually to take the title after seeing off visitors Langford 4-1 with two goals from substitute Lorraine Haycock.

But there was a late surge by Brighton who came from fourth spot to pip Langford and one of the league favourites Wimbledon for runners-up spot. It was a solitary late second half goal by Kerry Dawkins that sunk visitors Barry Town 1-0 ensuring that they finished second behind champions Southampton Saints.

As for the team that was relegated there was only one side in it, Rushden & Diamonds. They, like Wembley didn't even win a point losing all their eighteen matches, but they did pick up a piece of silverware winning the Northants, Cambridgeshire, Huntingdon County Cup final.

The two national league cup competitions ended up being monopolised by Arsenal. The league cup saw the eventual winners Arsenal demolish Huddersfield Town 6-2 in the first round; narrowly defeat London rivals Millwall Lionesses 2-1 in the second round; claim an impressive 4-0 victory over Berkhamsted Town in the quarter finals; overcome a spirited Bradford City on penalties in the semi-finals.

Arsenal's cup final opponents enjoyed a slim 3-2 triumph over hosts Three Bridges in the first round; and saw off Second Round hosts Ilkeston Town by the same score 3-2; beat Liverpool FC Ladies at home 2-1, but denied Everton any chance of a double by putting them out in the semi-final stage winning 2-0.

The final itself was an action packed affair down at Barnet's sloping Underhill stadium on March 22nd with neither side able to make their goal chances count as they played out a goalless draw only to go into penalties. It was Arsenal's Number 2 England goalkeeper Sarah Reed who stole the show and won The Gunners the cup for a fifth time after saving from ex Arsenal's Gill Wylie and ex England star Kerry Davis. And Arsenal won it by 4-3 on penalties.

"It was tremendous to still keep our record going of never having lost in a final", said a joyous Arsenal General Manager Vic Akers afterwards, who had more reason to reiterate these words because his side were to go on to achieve the double by winning another final and beating Croydon again, this time in the FA Women's Cup Final on

May 10th at the New Den stadium. The final, attended by 2,205 fans, saw Croydon's Joanne Broadhurst break the deadlock converting from the penalty spot in the tenth minute only to be cancelled out by a freakish equaliser courtesy of Marieanne Spacey in the eighteenth minute.

Just seven minutes into the second half and the talented striker Rachel Yankey had superbly run round Croydon's outstanding goalkeeper Louise Cooper to put Arsenal 2-1 in front in the 52nd minute. Hope Powell, playing her last game for Croydon before taking up her post as England Coach in July 1998, had a significant say in this final by snatching another important equaliser in the 55th minute. But, with the Cup Final looking destined for extra time, up popped the trusty Arsenal defender Kelly Few to steal the trophy from under the noses of Croydon with a cruel late winner to give the Gunners their third taste of glory in this prestigious competition. They first won it in 1993 when they sunk Doncaster Belles 3-0 and then were crowned the 1995 cup winners after beating finalists Liverpool FC Ladies 3-2.

One team that still felt hard done by, especially if you don't read your rule book, is Liverpool FC Ladies who were all set to play their semi-final match against Arsenal. It was all because they played an ineligible player, Jody Handley, in the quarter final replay that they won 3-1 over holders Millwall Lionesses after the first game resulted in a 2-2 draw (aet) at Fisher Athletic ground on March 1st.

They were contravening Competition Rule 17(viii) which states that 'A player must have been a registered member of her Club at least seven days previous to the time fixed for playing the round. In the case of postponed, drawn or replayed matches only those players shall be allowed to play who were eligible at the time fixed for playing the round.' Liverpool were removed from the competition and the holders Millwall Lionesses were reinstated to face Arsenal.

Liverpool, don't forget, had knocked out one to the cup favourites Everton 1-0 (a Lianne Duffy goal) away from home in the he Fourth Round when all Premier Leagues entered into the competition, and then they defeated Ilkeston Town 2-0 at home in the Fifth Round. A team like Liverpool Ladies FC needed the boost to keep their season alive having experienced yet another disappointing season.

Former England player and ex Welsh Manager Sylvia Gore decided to resign from Liverpool after five years loyal service. She blamed herself for Liverpool being dumped out of the FA Women's Cup competition. But the Sports Division of the Knowsley District Sports Council Leisure Community honoured Sylvia in February with a special award for her 44 years loyal service to women's football and ten years voluntary service to women's football in the Knowsley area. And in May, she received from the English Sports Council, "The Barclay's VIP" award for recognition of all the work she has done in women's football, the development side, and to crown it all Arsenal approached Sylvia Gore in the close season asking her to become their commercial manager next season, which Sylvia felt she couldn't refuse.

There was even more stunning news in the world of women's football when in April 1998 it was announced out of the blue that former Millwall Lionesses and Friends of Fulham and now ex Croydon and England player Hope Powell with 65 caps and 25 goals had been appointed England National Coach after the apparent resignation of Manager Ted Copeland. And finally women's football had at last been recognised when it was announced that the Croydon's player/manager Debbie Bampton, a former England player, had been honoured in the Queen's birthday honours list in June as the first woman footballer to receive an MBE for her services to women's football.

Heightening the profile of women's football, The Express newspaper temporarily ran a regular Tuesday slot written by Jean Simpson which started in the New Year but came to an abrupt halt at the end of the season after a sudden change of editor.

The Express in conjunction with sponsors Nike and a selective panel including myself, Sylvia Gore and Hope Powell chose the following top three players from the three national leagues for the players of the year awards etc. All winners received expensive football boots and the latest designer tracksuits. And this was the result:

Premier Division

Player of the Season	1st	Faye White (Arsenal)
	2nd	Karen Burke (Everton)
	3rd	Maureen Marley (Everton)
Young Player of the Season	1st	Katie Chapman (Millwall Lionesses)
	2nd	Rachel Yankey (Arsenal)
	3rd	Rachel Brown (Liverpool FC Ladies)
Most Improved Player of the Season	1st	Sarah Reed (Arsenal)
	2nd	Angela Ralph (Liverpool FC Ladies)
	3rd	Gemma Hunt (Millwall Lionesses)

Northern Division

Player of the Season	1st	Deb White (Ilkeston Town)
	2nd	Lisa Scattergood (Garswood Saints)
	3rd	Julie Whittle (Aston Villa FC Ladies)
Young Player of the Season	1st	Aaron Embleton (Blyth Spartans Kestrels)
	2nd	Annette Wale (Ilkeston Town)
	3rd	Lara Hartley (Coventry City)
Most Improved Player of the Season	1st	Chris Ashworth (Aston Villa FC Ladies)
	2nd	Sarah Green (Arnold Town)
	3rd	Anisha Bateman (Garswood Saints)

Southern Division

Player of the Season	1st	Kim Lofthouse (Wimbledon)
	2nd	Lynn Armstrong (Southampton Saints)
	3rd	Sarah Howard (Ipswich Town)
Young Player of the Season	1st	Gemma Cough (Wimbledon)
	2nd	Rae McRickus (Wimbledon)
	3rd	Jo Vermeer (Whitehawk)
Most Improved Player of the Season	1st	Lisa Langrish (Southampton Saints)
	2nd	Kerry Dawkins (Brighton & Hove Albion)
	3rd	Layla Richards (Leyton Orient)

There was success at last for Millwall Lionesses over their London arch rivals Arsenal in this year's London County Cup final. Arsenal, always the winners, came a cropper this time against Millwall who celebrated a 2-1 victory to lift up the trophy against their London rivals.

The two teams that have won national league status for next season through play off matches were Leeds United in the Northern Division and Reading Royals in the Southern Division.

The Yorkshire and Humberside Premier League champions Leeds United finally saw off the North West Division One League champions Preston North End WFC on penalties in the preliminary round; sunk East Midlands Premier Division League champions Mansfield Town 5-0 in the semi-final; while the other semi-final match resulted in the Northern Division One League champions Middlesbrough defeating the West Midlands Premier League champions Newcastle Town 4-1 at the Riverside Stadium. And then the final on May 17th resulted in Middlesbrough losing 0-2 to Leeds United.

In the Southern Division play offs, the Southern Premier League champions Reading Royals killed off Hampton from the Greater London Regional league 2-0 (aet) in the preliminary round; enjoyed a 4-1 triumph over the South East Counties Premier League champions and the Kent County Cup winners Charlton in the semi final; and then defeated the South West Premier League champions Cardiff County at home 2-0 for a place in the Southern Division next season.

On the international front there was success for Scotland but not England, Wales or the Republic of Ireland as they attempted to qualify for the 1999 World Cup competition in the USA. (Northern Ireland didn't enter for financial reasons.)

England failed miserably to qualify in what was a very difficult Group Three losing on a home and away basis to the four times European champions Germany 3-0 in Dessau on 25th September 1997; but they narrowly lost 1-0 on 8th March 1998 at Millwall's new Den ground.

England defeated Holland 1-0 courtesy of a Sue Smith goal at West Ham on October 30th 1997, only to lose to the Dutch on the away leg 2-1 on the 23rd of May 1998 in Waalwijk.

And although the England caretaker Manager Dick Bate had at last seen sense and brought back (not before time too) one of the best strikers in England, Doncaster Belles' Karen Walker, after an absence of two years, who unfortunately looked to have been instrumental in netting an own goal after challenging with Norway's Monica Knudsen for a header from a corner, they went down in a 2-1 thriller at Oldham Athletic's ground on 14th May 1998. Arsenal's Faye White equalised but a late Margunn Haugenes goal was a killer blow to England's chances of qualifying. The 1987, 1993 and current European champions and the present World champions Norway will need to defeat England on home soil on the 15th of August 1998 which would see them and not Germany as the Group Three winners and would mean automatic qualification through to the World Cup, leaving Germany, who had led the Group from the beginning, having to be involved in a play off.

There were also a few friendlies thrown in for good measure. Doncaster Belles' Gillian Coultard collected her 100th cap during their friendly international with Scotland at Almondvale Stadium, Livingston on Saturday August 23rd 1997. On that occasion England won it 4-0 as Croydon's Kerry Davis netted two goals; her Croydon team mate Sam Britton and Arsenal's Rachel Yankey were England's other goalscorers.

But then against France in Alencon on the 15th of February 1998 with 18 year old Melanie Garside from Bradford City making her debut, England were involved in an enthralling but disappointing 3-2 defeat, Karen Burke and Kerry Davis being the goalscorers; and then they met Italy in a friendly international at West Bromwich Albion on 21st April 1998 and lost that encounter 2-1 despite Arsenal's Faye White scoring her first goal for England to give them the lead with a well taken header in the fourth minute.

Better news for England though is the appointment of Hope Powell as the England coach, which should see fresh ideas and a new breed of personnel, and, with the Under 18 England well underway involving themselves again in European competitions, it can only be food for the continued growth of the game on an international level.

Four wins plus two draws like the Czech Republic saw Scotland win their Group Five 1997/1999 UEFA Qualifying competition for the FIFA World Championship because of better goal difference after a resounding 17-0 onslaught to see off Lithuania in their last Group match on Sunday May 31st at Scotstoun Leisure Centre, Glasgow.

Scotland, like Wales and the Republic, were placed in a group deemed by UEFA to be the 'second category' of women's teams in Europe. The carrot of the group winner being a play-off, home and away, against the fourth placed team in Group One of the 'first category' teams - i.e. those who are already playing matches to go to the World Cup in America next year.

That implies matches against the lowest placed country out of Sweden, Iceland, Ukraine and Spain scheduled for September 12/13 (first leg) and October 10/11 (second leg).

Scotland's previous qualifying home game was against temporary leaders the Czech Republic on Saturday May 23rd 1998 at Caledonian Stadium, Inverness, when Scotland salvaged a precious point with Julie Fleeting scoring the all important equaliser in the 72nd minute.

Both Wales and the Republic of Ireland had been drawn in the same qualifying Group Six and twice the Republic achieved convincing victories over Wales, winning 3-0 in Bangor City on 7th December 1997 and then 4-0 at home (Bray) on 8th March 1998.

But it was the heavy defeat 5-1 at home (Barry Town) on 1st May 1998 by Group winners Poland that sealed Wales' fate of non qualification even though they did in fact hold Poland to a 2-2 away from home (Zomosc) on 8th October 1997.

The Republic, finishing up second behind Group Six winners Poland, fared slightly better and were at one stage in with a shout of qualifying.

But with the addition of Millwall's captain and full back Abbie Walsh it was their second last game with Poland that became a deciding factor. They found the humidity, the early kick off of 11am and the wearisome travelling a destructive factor before being overpowered by Poland 3-0 in Lukow on 6th June 1998, and with nothing to play for in their remaining game with Belarus, which ended in a goalless draw in Drogheda on the 27th of June 1998, brought the Republic's qualification to a swift end, but they, like Wales, gained great experience and will be geared up for the next competitive encounter.

Remember you can hear what's happening in the women's game both on the domestic and international front by calling Cathy Gibb's one and only Women's Football Phoneline. The number is 0930 555871. Where else would you get up to the minute news on the women's game?

Cathy Gibb

FINAL LEAGUE TABLES 1997-98

NATIONAL DIVISION

	P	*W*	*D*	*L*	*F*	*A*	*Pts*
Everton LFC	18	13	4	1	54	14	43
Arsenal LFC	18	12	4	2	55	22	40
Doncaster Belles	18	12	2	4	54	18	38
Croydon WFC	18	10	5	3	46	14	35
Millwall Lionesses	18	8	5	5	37	15	29
Liverpool FC Ladies	18	8	3	7	33	25	27
Tranmere Rovers	18	5	4	9	33	43	19
Bradford City WFC	18	3	3	12	39	52	12
Berkhamsted Town	18	3	2	13	22	64	11
Wembley LFC	18	0	0	18	3	109	0

NORTHERN DIVISION

	P	*W*	*D*	*L*	*F*	*A*	*Pts*
Ilkeston Town	18	17	0	1	68	6	51
Garswood Saints	18	12	3	3	43	23	39
Aston Villa Ladies	18	10	2	6	38	23	32
Wolverhampton W	18	8	5	5	33	20	29
Blyth Sp. Kestrels	18	8	4	5	40	23	28
Sheffield Wed.	18	8	3	7	39	40	27
Huddersfield Town	18	7	3	8	32	31	24
Coventry City	18	2	6	10	22	62	12
Arnold Town	18	2	4	12	11	36	10
Bloxwich Town	18	0	2	16	12	74	2

SOUTHERN DIVISION

	P	*W*	*D*	*L*	*F*	*A*	*Pts*
Southampton Saints	18	12	6	0	50	14	42
Brighton & Hove A	18	12	2	4	64	21	38
Wimbledon	18	11	3	4	64	31	36
Langford	18	10	4	4	52	33	34
Whitehawk	18	9	4	5	69	30	31
Three Bridges	18	7	1	10	47	37	22
Ipswich Town	17	5	3	9	33	31	18
Barry Town	15	3	5	7	23	29	14
Leyton Orient	18	3	2	13	24	62	11
Rushden & Dia.	18	0	0	16	10	148	0

CSI F.A. WOMEN'S CUP 1997-98

THIRD ROUND

Huddersfield Town	v	Leeds City Vixens	4-2 aet	Liverpool Feds	v	Sheffield Wed.	1-5
Blyth Spartans K	v	Garswood Saints	1-3 aet	Oldham Athletic	v	Preston North End	0-2
Warrington Grange	v	Newcastle Town	3-5	Stockport	v	Blackburn Rovers	4-2
Bloxwich Town	v	Highfield Rangers	6-1	Canary Racers	v	Arnold Town	6-0
Coventry City	v	Birmingham C	4-4 aet, 5-0	Aston Villa	v	Wolverhampton W	1-0
Ilkeston Town	v	Derby County	6-0	Wembley Mill Hill	v	Whitehawk	1-4
Brighton & Hove A	v	Langford	3-3 aet, 3-2	Three Bridges	v	Watford & Evergreen	0-6
Queens Pk Rangers	v	Wimbledon	3-4	Leyton Orient	v	Reading R.	2-2 aet, 0-1
Fulham	v	Tottenham Hotspur	4-7 aet	West Ham Utd	v	Charlton	0-7
Hendon	v	St Georges (Eltham)	0-6	Truro City	v	Barry Town	0-4
Binfield	v	Southampton Saints	0-6	Cardiff County	v	Portsmouth	3-0

FOURTH ROUND

Huddersfield Town	v	Wimbledon	3-2	Bradford City	v	Aston Villa	5-1
Tranmere Rovers	v	Berkhamsted Town	4-2	Bloxwich Town	v	Ilkeston Town	0-2
Whitehawk	v	Coventry City	5-0	Cardiff County	v	Millwall Lionesses	0-6
Tottenham Hotspur	v	Brighton & Hove Alb	2-1	Wembley	v	Croydon	0-10
Doncaster Belles	v	St Georges (Eltham)	10-0	Southampton Snts	v	Newcastle Town	2-1
Garswood Saints	v	Preston North End	4-1	Sheffield Wed.	v	Watford & E'green	3-2
Everton	v	Liverpool	0-1	Canary Racers	v	Arsenal	0-12
Charlton	v	Stockport	1-2	Reading Royals	v	Barry Town	0-2

FIFTH ROUND

Tranmere Rovers	v	Garswood Saints	1-2	Doncaster Belles	v	Huddersfield Town	6-0
Liverpool	v	Ilkeston Town	2-0	Croydon	v	Tottenham Hotspur	4-1
Millwall Lionesses	v	Whitehawk	2-0	Bradford City	v	Sheffield Wednesday	4-1
Barry Town	v	Stockport	2-1	Southampton S	v	Arsensal	0-1

SIXTH ROUND

Croydon	v	Bradford City	3-2	Garswood Saints	v	Barry Town	1-2 aet
Doncaster Belles	v	Arsenal	1-2 aet	Millwall Lionesses	v	Liverpool	2-2 aet, 3-1*

* Awarded to Millwall Lionesses as Liverpool played an ineligible player

SEMI-FINALS

Barry Town	v	Croydon	0-1	at Forest Green Rovers FC
Arsenal	v	Millwall Lionesses	1-0	at Kingstonian FC

FINAL

Arsenal	v	Croydon	3-2	at Millwall FC

F.A.WOMEN'S CUP - PREVIOUS WINNERS & RUNNERS-UP

1971	Southampton	v	Stewarton & Thistle	4-1	1985	Friends of Fulham	v	Doncaster Belles	2-0
1972	Southampton	v	Lee's Ladies	3-2	1986	Norwich	v	Doncaster Belles	4-3
1973	Southampton	v	Westhorn United	2-0	1987	Doncaster Belles	v	St Helens	2-0
1974	Foxdens	v	Southampton	2-1	1988	Doncaster Belles	v	Leasowe Pacific	3-1
1975	Southampton	v	Warminster	4-2	1989	Leasowe Pacific	v	Friends of Fulham	3-2
1976	Southampton	v	Queens Pk Rangers	2-1	1990	Doncaster Belles	v	Friends of Fulham	1-0
1977	Queens Pk Rgrs	v	Southampton	1-0	1991	Millwall Lionesses	v	Doncaster Belles	1-0
1978	Southampton	v	Queens Pk Rangers	8-2	1992	Doncaster Belles	v	Red Star S'hampton	4-0
1979	Southampton	v	Lowestoft	1-0	1993	Arsenal	v	Doncaster Belles	3-0
1980	St Helens	v	Preston North End	1-0	1994	Doncaster Belles	v	Knowsley United	1-0
1981	Southampton	v	St Helens	4-2	1995	Arsenal	v	Liverpool	3-2
1982	Lowestoft	v	Cleveland Spartans	2-0	1996	Croydon	v	Liverpool	1-1
1983	Doncaster Belles	v	St Helens	3-2		Croydon won on penalty kicks			
1984	Howbury Grange	v	Doncaster Belles	4-2	1997	Millwall Lionesses	v	Wembley	1-0

FINAL LEAGUE RESULTS 1997-98

EAST MIDLANDS LEAGUE

Premier Division

	Pld	Pts
Mansfield Town	22	58
Derby County	20	42
Kilnhurst	22	42
Chesterfield	21	41
Calverton MW	22	40
Leicester Vixens	22	36
Highfield Rangers	18	35
Leicester City	22	26
Tamworth	22	22
Nottingham Forest	22	9
Nettisham United	22	6
Sheffield Wed Res	21	6

EASTERN LEAGUE

Premier Division

	Pld	Pts
Canary Racers	20	55
Bedford Bells	20	45
Norwich United	20	37
Colchester Ladies	20	35
Colchester United	20	29
Statham Seahawks	20	28
Gorleston	20	26
Walkern	20	25
U G Sports	20	17
Harlow Town	20	10
Pye	20	10

GREATER LONDON LEAGUE

Premier Division

	Pld	Pts
Wembley Mill Hill	22	56
Hampton	22	55
Chelsea	22	48
Enfield	22	45
Collier Row	22	43
Tesco Country Club	22	30
Chelmsford City	22	27
Queens Park Rangers	22	24
Barnet	22	20
Romford	22	10
Newham	22	9
Dulwich Hamlet	22	5

NORTH WEST LEAGUE

Division One

	Pld	Pts
Preston North End WFC	16	40
Bangor City	15	39
Stockport LFC	18	39
Manchester United	18	29
Oldham Athletic	15	28
Blackburn Rovers	17	21
Blackpool Wren Rovers	17	20
Liverpool Feds	18	17
Droylsden	17	7
Newsham PH	18	3

NORTHERN LEAGUE

Division One

	Pld	Pts
Middlesbrough	18	51
Sunderland	18	40
Chester le Street	18	38
Newcastle	18	38
Blyth Spartans K Res	18	26
Boldon	18	22
Darlington	18	18
Cleveland	18	16
Hedlington Terriers	18	10
Carlisle	18	1

SOUTH EAST COUNTIES LEAGUE

Premier Division

	Pld	Pts
Charlton	16	41
Clapton	16	41
Hassocks	16	29
Crowborough Athletic	16	24
Malling	16	23
Redhill	16	16
Gillingham	16	10
Sittingbourne	16	8
Farnborough	16	7

SOUTH WEST LEAGUE

Premier Division

	Pld	Pts
Cardiff County	22	56
Bath City	22	50
Cable Tel (Newport)	22	50
Saltash Pilgrims	22	34
Truro City	22	34
Elmore Eagles	21	33
Frome Sportshouse	22	25
Sherborne	22	24
Bristol City	22	23
Newton Abbot	21	23
Cam Bulldogs	22	16
Freeway	22	0

SOUTHERN LEAGUE

Premier Division

	Pld	Pts
Reading Royals	19	51
Swindon Town	20	44
Cheltenham YMCA	20	39
Swindon Spitfires	19	30
Southampton WFC	18	29
Portsmouth	19	27
Oxford United	20	24
Southampton Saints Res	20	23
Launton	20	21
Binfield	20	14
Horndean	20	4

WEST MIDLANDS LEAGUE

Premier Division

	Pld	Pts
Newcastle Town	18	46
Villa Aztecs	18	41
Birmingham City	18	40
Stratford	18	28
Tipton Town	18	24
Shrewsbury Town	18	21
Rea Valley Rovers	18	20
Worcester City	18	19
Telford	18	13
Coventry City Res	18	0

YORKSHIRE & HUMBERSIDE LEAGUE

Premier Division

	Pld	Pts
Leeds United	18	52
Doncaster Rovers	18	46
Doncaster Belles Res	18	30
Scunthorpe Lionesses	18	30
York City	18	23
Hull City	18	21
Barnsley	18	20
AFC Preston	18	19
Huddersfield Town Res	18	11
Sheffield Hallam Utd	18	1

DORSET COUNTY LEAGUE

	Pld	Pts
Corfe Hills United	18	48
Dorchester	18	45
Okeford United	18	43
Bournemouth Poppies	18	31
Queen Bees	18	26
Salisbury Girls	18	19
Swanage	18	18
Southmoor Girls	18	18
Allendale	18	11
Poole Town Youth	18	10

WESTWARD DEVELOPMENTS DEVON FA COUNTY LEAGUE

Premier Division

	Pld	Pts
Activate	12	36
North Prospect Brunos	12	25
Exeter Rangers	12	24
Marjons	12	16
Torbay Girls	12	9
Axmouth United	12	7
University of Exeter	12	6

ESSEX COUNTY LEAGUE

	Pld	Pts
White Notley	8	21
Chelmsford City 3rds	8	15
Colchester United Res	8	0

SOCCEROOTS WALES LEAGUE

	Pld	Pts
Newcastle Emlyn	20	56
BP Llandarey	20	50
Gowerton Sports	20	44
UWIC	20	35
Merthyr Tydfil	20	33
Newport Civil Service	20	33
Cogan Coronation	20	24
Cwm. Allstars	20	23
Abergavenny Thursdays	20	19
Dafen Welfare	20	9
Thornhill Athletic	20	0

TEXACO PEMBROKESHIRE LEAGUE

Division One

	Pld	Pts
Milford Haven	14	42
Goodwick	14	34
Haverfordwest	14	31
Carmarthen	14	18
Monkton Swifts	14	16
Templeton	14	13
Neyland	14	11
Tenby	14	0

WIRRAL PROGRAMME CLUB

The non-profit making Club formed in March 1967

Secretary: I.R.W. Runham

3 Tansley Close, Newton, West Kirby, Wirral. L48 9XH Tel: 0151 625 9554

23rd NON-LEAGUE FOOTBALL PROGRAMME OF THE YEAR SURVEY 1997-98

Entries were received from 1131 clubs, 105 more than last year. Everything was running to schedule until the postal dispute on Merseyside. Results sheets were lost/delayed causing the results being issued later than intended. With reserve and youth programmes there were 1202 places, up 117 on last season.

Again there were many superb programmes with numerous clubs showing improvement on last season. It is again pleasing to see clubs issuing for the first time plus some after a gap of many years. ALL clubs that issue a programme are to be congratulated, a single sheet is better than nothing. There would be no programmes without the hard work that the editors and any helpers they can find put in, I'm sure most supporters and many committee member s do not realise the time and effort needed to produce a programme so our special thanks go to all these people. I must also thank all those who sent in programmes for the survey and helped to spread the word, the clubs themselves, their supporters, our members, other collectors, the Football Association, all the League Secretaries, the Non League Club Directory, Team Talk, Non League Traveller, Welsh Football and all those who lent us some programmes. Sincere apologies to anyone inadvertently omitted.

Some clubs only issue for a Saturday game, some for special games, some change their style, content, price, editor, etc, during the season, some have special connections with printers, etc., often we are not aware of these circumstances. Obviously we can only survey the programmes we receive. Some are from early in the season, others from just before the closing date, most from in between. the results always create a lot of interest with varying points being expressed, some of these we hear second or third hand but most miss our ears, if you have any comments on the survey please let us know. I am sure the day will never come when there is complete agreement over the results, however the more discussion there is over the survey the better, it will keep programmes to the forefront and hopefully encourage clubs to at least maintain or even improve the standards, better still it may encourage more clubs to issue next season.

The club with the overall winning programme will receive a framed certificate, the winners of each league will also receive a certificate. Please note the programmes have been surveyed, not as many assume voted upon. Marks were awarded to each programme s follows (the maximum marks available in each section are given):
Cover 15 (design 10, match details 5), **Page size** 10, **Team layout and position** within the programme 10,
Results 10, **League tables** 10, **Price** 15, **Pictures** 15, **Printing and paper quality** 20, **Frequency of issue** 20,
Value for money 20 (this takes into account the ratio of adverts to content, the club's league etc),
Contents 105 (other than those listed) taking into account their relevance to the club, its league, environs etc, the size of the print used, the spacing between the lines, the size of the margins, and if the contents are original or reproduced (from League Bulletins, newspapers, magazines etc).
To gain full marks in the Frequency of issue section we needed to receive programmes from 10 different current season matches for each team entered (allowances were made if 10 home games were not played by the closing date and we were informed of this), the minimum entry was one programme.
As many programmes varied from issue to issue all the programmes received were surveyed, the marks in each section totalled and divided by the number of issues to get the final mark for each section, the marks from each section were then totalled to get the final score.
A new standard of marks is set each season so this season's totals should not be compared with those of earlier seasons as the comparison will almost certainly be inaccurate, a programmed identical to last season's will almost certainly have gained different marks.

We have already received many entries for the Specials section of the survey (for one-offs, big cup ties, friendlies, testimonials, charity matches, etc), the closing date for receiving these is 30th June 1998. To receive the results, expected by the end of July, we should appreciate it if you could send a stamped sae. Thank you.

The results of this season's survey are as follows:

Best Non-League Programme Nationally 1997-98	**1st**	Langney Sports	210 points
	2nd	Denaby United	197 points
	3rd	Northwood	191 points

NATIONAL TOP 30: 1 Langney Sports 201; **2** Denaby United 197; **3** Northwood 191; **4** Hoddesdon Town 187;
5 Aldeshot Town 181; **6=** Hucknall Town, Raunds Town 179; **8** Peppard 168; **9** Pelsall Villa 167;
10 Witney Town 166; **11** Yateley Green 165; **12** Willenhall Town 163; **13** Gorleston 162;
14 St Leonards Stamcroft 161; **15** Newtown 160; **16** Poole Town 159;
17= Dagenham & Redbridge, Swindon Supermarine, Uxbridge 157; **20** Mercedes Benz 156;
21= Enfield, Folkestone Invicta 155; **23=** Baldock Town, Knypersley Victoria 154; **25** Sutton United 153;
26= Anglians, Chelmsford City, Denbigh Town, Rushden & Diamonds, Rylands, Woking 152

INDIVIDUAL LEAGUE RESULTS The first number after the club's name is the number of programmes received - 10 shows ten or more different programmes were received, or every programme if less than ten matches were played, the second number is the total points gained. The leagues are in no particular order.

LEAGUE + No of entries			**FIRST**		**SECOND**		**THIRD**	
Vauxhall Conference		21	Rushden & Dia	1-152			Hayes	10-146
			Woking =	1-152				
Dr Martens	Overall	63	Raund Town	10-179	Witney Town	10-166	St Leonards Stam	10-161
	Prem Div	22	St Leonards Stam	10-161	Cambridge City	10-141	Nuneaton Boro =	1-147
							Tamworth =	1-147
	Mid Div	20	Raunds Town	10-179	Stourbridge	10-141	Ilkeston Town	10-140
	Sth Div	21	Witney Town	10-166	Baldock Town	10-154	Chelmsford City	10-152
Rymans	Overall	74	Northwood	10-191	Aldershot Town	10-181	Dag & Redbridge=	10-157
							Uxbridge =	10-157
	Prem Div	22	Dag & Redbridge	10-157	Enfield	3-156	Sutton United	10-153
	Div One	22	Aldershot Town	10-181	Uxbridge	10-157	Barton Rovers	10-134
	Div Two	19	Northwood	10-191	Wealdstone	10-150	Chalfont St Peter	2-142
	Div Three	11	Lewes	10-136	Croydon Athletic	1-133	Epsom & Ewell	4-131
Unibond	Overall	42	Barrow	10-149	Bradford Park Ave	10-142	Blyth Spartans	10-141
	Prem Div	22	Barrow	10-149	Blyth Spartans	10-141	Altrincham =	10-130
							Colwyn Bay =	1-130
	Div One	20	Bradford Park Ave	10-142	Witton Albion	10-136	Workington	10-135
Minerva	Overall	52	Hoddesdon Town	10-187	Mercedes Benz	10-156	Arlesey Town	10-151
Spartan	Prem Nth	15	Hoddesdon Town	10-187	Arlesey Town	10-151	Potters Bar Town	10-148
South	Prem Sth	13	Cockfosters	1-131	Beaconsfield SY	10-129	Brimsdown Rovers	1-118
Midlands	Sen Div	14	Mercedes Benz	10-156	Holmer Green	1-128	Tring Athletic	10-120
	Div One Nth	10	Old Bradwell Utd	10-128	Bridger Packaging	1-117	Walden Rangers	1-98
Courage Combined Co		15	Walton Casuals	10-137	Ash United	10-125	Sandhurst Town	10-121
Winstonlead Kent		18	Folkestone Invicta	10-155	Cray Wanderers	10-128	Canterbury City	10-125
Essex Senior		4	Stansted	10-135	Brentwood	1-105	Ilford	1-83
Unijet	Overall	35	Langney Sports	10-201	Ifield	10-142	Broadbridge Hth =	10-132
Sussex							Ringmer =	10-132
County	Div One	13	Langney Sports	10-201	Ringmer	10-132	Mile Oak	1-122
	Div Two	10	Broadbridge Hth	10-132	Lancing	1-121	Southwick	1-103
	Div Three	12	Ifield	10-142	Bosham	10-102	Buxted	10-101
Jewson	Overall	32	Gorleston	10-162	Diss Town	10-141	Sudbury Town	10-139
Eastern	Prem Div	21	Gorleston	10-162	Diss Town	10-141	Sudbury Town	10-139
Counties	Div One	11	Mildenhall Town	10-123	Cambridge City R	8-115	Malden Town	1-109
Jewson Wessex		13	Cowes Sports	1-112	Christchurch	1-110	Wimborne Town	10-106
Complete	Overall	23	Swindon Super.	10-157	Carterton Town	10-112	Purton	10-110
Music	Prem Div	14	Swindon Super.	10-157	Carterton Town	10-112	Banbury United	1-102
Hellenic	Div One	9	Purton	10-110	Yarnton	1-107	Ross Town	1-101
Uhlsport	Overall	24	St Neots Town	1-143	Yaxley	10-138	Eynesbury Rvrs =	10-130
United							Northampton S =	10-130
Counties	Prem Div	18	St Neots Town	1-143	Yaxley	10-138	Eynesbury Rvrs =	10-130
							Northampton S =	10-130
	Div One	6	Newport Pagnell T	1-105	Higham Town	1-93	St Ives Town	1-92
Screwfix	Overall	27	Torrington	10-151	Mangotsfield Utd	10-140	Paulton Rovers	10-135
Direct	Prem Div	18	Torrington	10-151	Mangotsfield Utd	10-140	Paulton Rovers	10-135
Western	Div One	9	Crediton United	10-104	Warminster Town	1-89	Exmouth Town	1-86
Interlink Midland Alliance		19	Pelsall Villa	10-167	Willenhall Town	10-163	Knypersley Vic	10-154
North	Overall	36	St Helens Town	10-142	Newcastle Town	10-137	Clitheroe	10-135
West	Div One	20	St Helens Town	10-142	Newcastle Town	10-137	Clitheroe	10-135
Counties	Div Two	16	Skelmersdale	10-133	Garswood United	8-122	Woodley Sports	5-114
Northern	Overall	30	Denaby United	10-197	Hucknall Town	10-179	Arnold Town	10-142
Counties	Prem Div	18	Denaby United	10-197	Hucknall Town	10-179	Arnold Town	10-142
East	Div One	12	Brodsworth MW	10-128	Winterton Rngrs	1-107	Hall Road Rngrs	1-93
Arnott	Overall	27	Durham City	10-150	Guisborough Town	1-145	Chester le Street T	10-134
Insurance	Div One	18	Durham City	10-150	Guisborough Town	1-145	Crook Town	10-130
Northern	Div Two	9	Chester le St T	10-134	Ashington	1-81	Marske United	1-78
Middlesex County		6	Beaconsfield S Rs	10-108	Deportivo Galicia	1-99	Ealing Shamrock	1-83
Keyline Dorset Comb.		8	Blandford United	1-139	Sturminster Marshall	1-91	Hamworthy United	7-84
Gloucestershire County		5	Frampton Athletic	1-102	Brockworth	10-97	Viney St Swithins	1-72
Clubsaver	Overall	21	Yateley Green	10-165	Poole Town	10-159	Colden Common	10-148
Hampshire	Div One	8	Poole Town	10-159	Colden Common	10-148	Mayflower	1-134
	Div Two	5	Yateley Green	10-165	Co-op Sports	7-97	Tadley	1-94
	Div Three	8	Covies	10-124	Queens Keep	10-101	Four Marks	10-95
Westward Dev. Devon		11	Newton Abbot Sp	10-151	Stoke Gabriel	10-111	Budleigh Salterton	10-103
Cherry Red	Overall	18	Peppard	10-168	Quarry Nomads	10-143	Penn & Tylers Grn	10-139
Records	Prem Div	12	Peppard	10-168	Quarry Nomads	10-143	Penn & Tylers Grn	10-139
Chiltonian	Divs 1, 2	6	Penn & Tylers G R	3-129	Quarry Nomads R	10-120	Finchampstead Rs	10-107
Herts Senior Co		4	Met Police Bushey	10-127	Hatfield Town	1-93	Sun Postal Sports	1-85
Longwell Blake Ang Comb		8	Beccles Town	10-114	Attleborough Town	1-110	Holt United	7-98
PJ McGinty	Overall	9	Orwell Athletic =	1-104			Orwell Athletic Res	1-99
& Sons			Walsham le Will =	1-104				
Suffolk &	Sen Div	5	Walsham le Willows	1-104	Stonham Aspal	9-95	Westerfield United	1-89
Ipswich	Other Divs	4	Orwell Athletic	1-104	Orwell Athletic Res	1-99	Claydon	1-63
Jewson Sth Western		8	Truro City	1-118	Bodmin Town	1-98	Newquay	1-74
Essex Intermediate		7	Laindon Athletic =	10-116			Great Baddow Rs	10-106
			Laindon Ath Res =	10-116				
Skurrys Wiltshire		8	Minety	1-128	Purton Res	10-94	Marshfield	1-87
Springbank Vend. Mid		7	Eccleshall	10-120	Goldenhill Wndrs	10-101	Stone Dominoes	8-93
Redfern Int	Overall	33	Mickleover Sports	1-141	Hucknall Rolls	10-137	Rossington	1-132
Removers	Sup Div	16	Mickleover Sports	1-141	Rossington	1-132	Thorne Colliery	1-130
Cent. Mids	Prem Div	17	Hucknall Rolls	10-137	Goole	10-125	Selston	4-110

Endsleigh	Overall	37	Meir KA	10-135	Hams Hall	10-116	Monica Star	10-112
Insurance	Prem Div	20	Meir KA	10-135	Knowle	10-109	Bolehall Swifts	10-108
Midland	Div One	9	Hams Hall	10-116	Monica Star	10-112	Northfield Town	1-81
Comb.	Divs 2, 3	8	Alvis	1-106	Burntwood	10-85	Earlswood Town	1-79
Banks's	Overall	15	Stourport Swifts	1-105	Darlaston =	1-92		
Brewery					Westfields =	10-92		
	Prem Div	8	Stourport Swifts	1-105	Darlaston =	1-92		
					Westfields =	1-92		
	Div 1 Nth	4	Heath Hayes	1-89	Lucas Flight Control	1-68	Brereton Town	1-56
	Div 1 Sth	3	Birmingham C Food	1-91	Leominster	1-61	Wellington	1-56
KB Essex/Suffolk Border		4	St Osyth	1-123	Long Melford	1-83	Stowmarket Tn Res	2-77
Lincolnshire		3	Sleaford	10-120	BRSA Retford	10-96	Grimsby/Immingham	1-75
Everards	Overall	9	Coalville	2-126	Loughborough Dyn	1-120	Anstey Nomads	1-85
Brewery	Prem Div	5	Coalville	2-126	Anstey Nomads	1-85	Oadby Town	1-74
Leic'shire	Div One	4	Loughborough Dyn	1-120	Saffron Dynamo	1-78	Huncote Sports & S	1-74
Powerleague Notts All		6	Rainworth MW	10-128	Wollaton	1-103	Wollaton Res	1-90
JPL Wade Northern All		7	West Allotment C	10-110	Carlisle City	1-82	N Shields St Colum.	1-79
Vaux Wearside		8	N Sheilds Athletic	10-131	Birtley Town	9-92	Wolviston	1-72
SGL Seat	Overall	9	Lytham St Annes	8-88	Charnock Richard	1-85	Barnoldswick Utd	1-78
Cars West	Div One	5	Charnock Richard	1-85	Padiham	1-71	Springfields	1-63
Lancashire	Div Two	4	Lytham St Annes	8-88	Barnoldswick Utd	1-78	Bootle	1-77
East Lancashire		4	Trawden Celtic	1-101	Oswaldtwistle	1-76	Stackheads St Jos.	1-74
Carlsberg West Cheshire		4	New Brighton	10-122	Poulton Victoria	1-96	Blacon Youth Club	10-75
Green Con Ser Mid Chesh		4	Rylands	9-152	Rylands Res	1-128	Whitchurch Alport	1-87
Horton Print	Overall	7	Brighouse Town	10-124	Wibsey	10-118	Wibsey Res	8-113
Group West	Prem Div	4	Brighouse Town	10-124	Wibsey	10-118	Hemsworth MW	1-71
Riding Co A	Divs 1, 2	3	Wibsey Res	8-113	Morley Town	1-71	Heckmondwike Tn	1-48
West Yorkshire		7	York RI	10-133	Knaresborough Tn	10-125	Nostell MW	1-110
East Riding		4	Easington United	8-127	Easington Utd Rs	7-123	Bridlington Town	4-120
Manchester		6	Prestwich Heys	1-103	G Manchester Police	9-90	Springhead	1-79
Other English Leagues		39	Ifield Reserves	1-145	Portishead	10-141	Thornbury Town	10-132
Reserves		37	Colden Comm. Rs	10-150	Ifield Reserves	1-145	Penn & Ty. Grn Rs	3-129
Youth Clubs/Schools		13	St Andrews U13	10-136	St Andrews U15	10-135	St Andrews U11	8-125
Club Youth XI's		6	Hendon	10-120	East Harling	1-86	Beaconsfield SYCOB	3-80
FA Youth Cups		25	Gresford Athletic	2-118	Curzon Ashton	1-100	Southwick	1-83
Wales	Overall	89	Newtown	10-160	Denbigh Town	10-152	Cwmtillery	10-150
League of Wales		20	Newtown	10-160	Caernarfon Town =	10-144		
					Caersws =	10-144		
E Evans Cars Cymru All		15	Denbigh Town	10-152	Cefn Druids	10-129	Llandudno	10-98
CC Sports	Overall	23	Llanelli	10-135	Port Talbot Ath	10-108	Newport YMCA	10-101
Welsh	Div One	13	Llanelli	10-130	Port Tablbot Ath	10-108	Cardiff Civil Service	10-99
	Div Two	4	Risca United	1-96	Gwynfi United	1-91	Pontypridd Town	1-63
	Div Three	6	Newport YMCA	10-101	Tonyrefail Welfare	1-70	Fields Pk Pontllanfr.	1-69
Fitlock Welsh Alliance		7	Prestatyn Town	1-114	Nantlle Vale	1-90	Colwyn Bay YMCA	1-74
Welsh National Wrexham		3	Gresford Athletic	10-130	Castell Alun Colts	1-68	Corwen	1-69
Hyfforddiant Gwynedd		6	Penrhyndeudraeth	10-113	Llanrwst United	1-80	Y Felinheli	1-79
Spar Mid Wales		4	Presteign St And	1-80	Guilsford	1-74	Montgomery	1-59
Gwent County		4	Cwmtillery	10-150	Lucas Cwmbran	1-102	Cwm Welfare	1-86
Highadmit Profects Am		3	Cwmaman	10-140	Llantwit Major	1-80	Kenfig Hill	1-67
Other Welsh Leagues		4	Llangeinor Res	1-115	Rhyl Delta	10-113	Caerswys	1-96
Scotland	Overall	64	Kirkintilloch RR	10-145	Ardeer Thistle	10-133	Tayport	10-125
Highland		11	Elgin City	1-99	Lossiemouth	10-93	Buckie Thistle	1-90
East Scotland		4	Gala Fairydean	1-74	Tollcross United	1-68	Peebles Rovers	1-62
Central	Overall	20	Kirkintilloch RR	10-145	Pollok	1-94	Rutherglen Glencairn	1-87
Region	Prem Div	8	Pollok	1-94	Lesmahagow	1-80	Arthurlie	1-81
	Divs 1, 2	12	Kirkintilloch RR	10-145	Rutherglen Glencairn	1-87	Cumbernauld Utd	1-85
Ayrshire	Overall	10	Ardeer Thistle	10-133	Largs Thistle	10-120	Auchinleck Talbot	1-92
Region	Div One	5	Largs Thistle	10-120	Auchinleck Talbot	1-92	Irvine Meadow	3-76
	Div Two	5	Ardeer Thistle	10-133	Lugar Boswell Thistle	1-61	Irvine Victoria	1-60
Eastern	Overall	9	Blackburn Utd	3-117	Haddington Athletic	3-101	Dunbar United	1-84
Region	Div One	5	Camelon =	1-79			Newtongrange Star	1-78
			Tranent =	1-79				
	Div Two	4	Blackburn United	3-117	Haddington Athletic	3-101	Dunbar United	1-84
Fife Region		4	Newburgh	10-99	Kelty Hearts	9-73	Thornton Hibs	1-62
Tayside Region		3	Tayport	10-125	Downfield	1-82	Carnoustie Panmure	1-78
Other Scottish Leagues		3	Inverurie Loco W	1-72	Strathspey Thistle	1-49	Maxwelltown HSFP	1-48
Ladies	Overall	42	Langford =	8-150			Wembley	7-128
			Stockport Celtic	10-150				
Premier	Overall	22	Langford	8-150	Wembley	7-128	Blyth Spartans Kestrels	10-119
League	Nat Div	5	Wembley	7-128	Berkhamsted Town =	10-105		
					Millwall Lionesses =	10-105		
	Nth Div	10	Blyth Spartans Kestrels	10-119	Huddersfield Town	2-113	Wolverhampton	1-110
	Sth Div	7	Langford	8-150	Ipswich Town	1-98	Three Bridges	1-88
Greater London		8	Chelsea	1-119	Chelmsford	10-117	Wembley Mill Hill	10-107
North West		3	Stockport Celtic	10-150	Warrington Grange	10-120	Winsford United	10-113
South West		3	Sth Bristol Wand	3-112	Cinderford Town	10-92	Cardiff County	1-89
Other Ladies Leagues		6	Colchester	10-119	Chelmsford Res	10-111	Leeds United	1-110
FA Womens Cup		43	Langford =	1-141			Huddersfield Town	1-114
			Stockport Celtic	1-141				
Sunday Leagues		14	Anglians	10-152	Penn Old Boys	8-143	Worfield	10-113
FA Sunday Cup		29	BRSC Aidan	1-85	St Margarets	1-77	Mailcoach =	1-75
							Park Inn =	1-75

VARSITY MATCH

OXFORD UNIVERSITY 4

CAMBRIDGE UNIVERSITY 0

If in 1997 one was forced to comment on a scoreless draw that both teams were lucky to get nil, the reverse was the case in the 1998 match between the old blues rivals. Cambridge made a brave contribution to a much better contest and it can truthfully be said that they were extremely unlucky to finish with a blank sheet, as they hit the woodwork twice after half time.

In fact, a scoreline of a single goal lead to the Dark Blues with a superb Joe Parker shot just before referee David Elleray signalled tea-time tells a story of missed chances by both sides thanks especially to some marvellous goalkeeping by Oxford skipper John Park. Instead of trailing at the break the Light Blues could have been well on the way to their first win in this fixture since it was moved from Wembley for the 1988 match at Highbury.

After the interval, two early counters from Jim Probert virtually settled the match in Oxford's favour and in injury time substitute Peter Richards added a fourth.

So, the Cambridge hoodoo continues, but pride in playing in such an important blues encounter was restored by both teams. Let us hope for more of the same next year.

Oxford: J Park (captain), M Loebinger, A Buckley, A Lea, A O'Brien, W Spencer, J Parker, J Probert, C Cairnes, M Goff, M Kintish.

Substitutes: W Wardle for Loebinger 20 minutes, J Calver for Kintish 72 minutes, P Richards for Goff 75 minutes.

Scorers: Parker 45 minutes, Probert 48, 50 minutes, Richards 90 minutes

Cambridge: J Gort, S Ball (captain), W House, C Dobson, M Pett, I Mowart, A Fearnley, D Eales, M Walsh, T Fearnley, S Arhmed.

Substitutes: S Ghaemmaghami for House 70 minutes, D Elliot for Arhmed 70 minutes, J Miller for Dobson 78 minutes.

Referee: D R Elleray, Middlesex

BRITISH UNIVERSITY XI

British University XI squad v FA XI at Durham City

HALIFAX TOWN F.C.

CONFERENCE CHAMPIONS 1997-98

Above:
Geoff Horsforth
- Leading Conference Goalscorer.
Photo: Paul Redding Photography

Top Left:
George Mulhall - the man in charge.
Photo: Peter Barnes

Left:
Jamie Patterson
- Conference Player of the Year
Photo: Neil Thaler

HALIFAX TOWN - Match Facts 1997-98

Match No	Date	Venue H / A	Comp	Opponents	Result & Score		Att	Goalscorers	League Position
1	16.08	A	VC	Hayes	W	2-1	*907*	Horsfield 30, Lyons 67.	4
2	23.08	A	VC	Slough Town	D	1-1	*790*	Paterson 74 (pen).	8
3	25.08	A	VC	Southport	D	0-0	*1,889*		11
4	30.09	H	VC	Welling United	W	1-0	1,011	Paterson 31.	7
5	02.09	A	VC	Telford United	W	3-0	*805*	Brook 14, Horsfield 34, 47.	2
6	06.09	H	VC	Yeovil Town	W	3-1	1,500	**Horsfield 3** (42, 55, 75).	1
7	16.09	H	VC	Telford United	**W**	**6-1**	1,119	**Horsfield 3** (2, 9, 59), O'Regan 46, Stoneman 48, Hulme 70.	1
8	20.09	A	VC	Farnborough Town	W	2-1	*919*	Horsfield 45, Brook 62.	1
9	30.09	H	VC	Leek Town	W	2-1	1,329	Paterson 27, Bradshaw 67.	1
10	04.10	H	VC	Kettering Town	W	3-0	1,836	Hulme 28, Bradshaw 43, Thackeray 63.	1
11	18.10	H	VC	Stevenage Borough	W	4-0	2,138	Horsfield 29, 65, Hulme 46, Bradshaw 52 (pen).	1
12	28.10	A	VC	Morecambe	D	1-1	*3,914*	Horsfield 19.	1
13	01.11	A	VC	Cheltenham Town	L	0-4	*2,508*		2
14	08.11	H	VC	Kidderminster Harriers	W	2-1	1,799	Paterson 52, Kilcline 77.	2
15	15.11	A	VC	Stalybridge Celtic	W	1-0	*1,421*	Stoneman 43.	1
16	22.11	H	VC	Hereford United	W	3-0	2,214	**Horsfield 3** (64, 78, 88).	1
17	29.11	A	VC	Woking	D	2-2	*3,319*	Horsfield 62, Paterson 72 (pen).	1
18	05.12	H	VC	Stalybridge Celtic	W	3-1	2,453	Lyons 34, Horsfield 45, 57.	1
19	09.12	H	VC	Northwich Victoria	W	4-2	2,165	Lyons 59, Bradshaw 70, Paterson 81, 87.	1
20	13.12	A	VC	Leek Town	L	0-2	*1,282*		1
21	20.12	H	VC	Hednesford Town	D	1-1	3,338	Horsfield 56	1
22	26.12	A	VC	Gateshead	D	2-2	*1,239*	Paterson 5, Horsfield 7	1
23	29.12	A	VC	Kettering Town	D	1-1	*2,276*	Philliskirk 49	1
24	01.01	H	VC	Gateshead	W	2-0	3,194	Horsfield 64,77	1
25	17.01	A	VC	Stevenage Borough	W	2-1	*2,946*	Hulme 59, Philliskirk 89.	1
26	24.01	H	VC	Slough Town	W	1-0	2,098	Horsfield 24.	1
27	07.02	A	VC	Rushden & Diamonds	L	0-4	*3,675*		1
28	14.02	A	VC	Dover Athletic	W	1-0	*1,316*	Hulme 2.	1
29	21.02	A	VC	Yeovil Town	W	1-0	*2,584*	Paterson 45 (pen).	1
30	28.02	H	VC	Farnborough Town	W	1-0	2,352	Horsfield 36.	1
31	07.03	H	VC	Dover Athletic	D	1-1	1,949	Hulme 45.	1
32	14.03	A	VC	Hednesford Town	D	0-0	*1,856*		1
33	17.03	H	VC	Morecambe	W	5-1	2,507	Bradshaw 34, Thackeray 38, Paterson 46, Kilcline 51, Horsfield 58.	1
34	21.03	H	VC	Rushden & Diamonds	W	2-0	3,951	OG (Wooding) 72, Paterson 85..	1
35	28.03	H	VC	Hayes	D	1-1	2,506	Horsfield 13.	1
36	04.04	H	VC	Woking	W	1-0	2,826	Hulme 22.	1
37	11.04	A	VC	Hereford United	D	0-0	*3,304*		1
38	13.04	H	VC	Southport	W	4-3	4,701	Paterson 42, Hulme 50, Hanson 82, 84.	1
39	18.04	A	VC	Kidderminster Harriers	W	2-0	*3,151*	Horsfield 43, Paterson 80.	1
40	20.04	A	VC	Northwich Victoria	L	0-2	*2,106*		1
41	25.04	H	VC	Cheltenham Town	D	1-1	6,357	Horsfield 41.	1
42	02.05	A	VC	Welling United	**L**	**2-6**	*1,344*	Horsfield 20, Brook 78.	1

CUP COMPETITIONS SCC Spalding Challenge Cup

Date	Venue	Comp	Opponents	Result	Score	Att	Goalscorers
13.09	H	**FAC** 1Q	Droylsden	W	4-1	799	Brooks 37, 51, Paterson 54, Horsfield 90.
27.09	H	2Q	Leigh RMI	W	4-0	1,103	Paterson 32 (pen), 64, Brook 51, Horsfield 90.
11.10	H	3Q	Ossett Town	W	5-0	1,060	Horsfield 15, Hulme 20, 45, Brook 39, 52.
25.10	A	4Q	Gainsborough Trinity	L	1-2	1,730	Horsfield 33.
10.01	H	**FAT** 1	Blyth Spartans	W	2-1	1,712	Brook 11, Lyons 90.
31.01	H	2	Slough Town	D	1-1	1,633	Peterson 51.
03.02	A	2 R	Slough Town	L	0-2	876	
07.10	A	**SCC** 1	Stalybridge Celtic	L	1-3	489	Boardman 85.

THE FOOTBALL ASSOCIATION

FIXTURE LIST 1998-99

SEPTEMBER 1998

5 Sat*	Sweden v England (EC)
	FA Cup P
	FA Youth Cup 1Q+
12 Sat	FA Vase 1Q
15 Tue	UEFA Cup 1 (1)
16 Wed	Champions League 1 (1)
17 Thu	ECWC 1 (1)
19 Sat	FA Cup 1Q
26 Sat	FA Youth Cup 2Q+
27 Sun	FA Women's Cup 1
29 Tue	UEFA Cup 1 (2)
30 Wed	Champions League 1 (2)

OCTOBER 1998

1 Thu	ECWC 1 (2)
3 Sat	FA Cup 2Q
10 Sat*	England v Bulgaria (EC)
	FA Vase 2Q
	FA County Youth Cup 1+
14 Wed	Luxembourg v England (EC)
17 Sat	FA Cup 3Q
	FA Youth Cup 3Q+
20 Tue	UEFA Cup 2 (1)
21 Wed	Champions League 2 (1)
22 Thu	ECWC 2 (1)
24 Sat	FA Trophy 1
25 Sun	FA Sunday Cup 1
31 Sat	FA Cup 4Q

NOVEMBER 1998

1 Sun	FA Women's Cup 2
3 Tue	UEFA Cup 2 (2)
4 Wed	Champions League 2 (2)
5 Thu	ECWC 2 (2)
7 Sat	FA Vase 1P
	FA Youth Cup 1P+
10 Tue	FA XI v Northern Premier League
14 Sat	International (F)
	FA Cup 1P
	FA Youth Cup 1P+
18 Wed	International (F)
21 Sat	FA Trophy 2
22 Sun	FA Sunday Cup 2
24 Tue	UEFA Cup 3 (1)
25 Wed	Champions League 3 (1)
28 Sat	FA Vase 2P
	FA Youth Cup 2P+

DECEMBER 1998

5 Sat	FA Cup 2P
6 Sun	FA Women's Cup 3
8 Tue	FA XI v Southern League
	UEFA Cup 3 (2)
9 Wed	Champions League 3 (2)
	FA XI v Isthmian League
12 Sat	FA Vase 3P
13 Sun	FA Sunday Cup 3
19 Sat	FA County Youth Cup 3+

JANUARY 1999

2 Sat	FA Cup 3P
5 Tue	FA XI v Combined Services
9 Sat	International (not UEFA date)
	FA Vase 4P
	FA Youth Cup 3P+
10 Sun	FA Women's Cup 4
13 Wed	International (not UEFA date)
	FA Cup 3P replay
16 Sat	FA Trophy 3
17 Sun	FA Sunday Cup 4
23 Sat	FA Cup 4P
30 Sat	FA Vase 5P
	FA Youth Cup 4P+
	FA County Youth Cup 4+

FEBRUARY 1999

2 Tue	FA XI v British Students
3 Wed	FA Cup 4P Replay
6 Sat	International (not UEFA date)
	FA Trophy 4
7 Sun	FA Women's Cup 5
10 Wed	International (F)
13 Sat	FA Cup 5P
14 Sun	FA Sunday Cup 5
20 Sat	FA Vase 6P
	FA Youth Cup 5P+
24 Wed	FA Cup 5P Replay
27 Sat	FA Trophy 5

MARCH 1999

2 Tue	Semi-Pro International
	UEFA Cup QF (1)
3 Wed	Champions League QF (1)
4 Thu	ECWC QF (1)
6 Sat	FA Cup 6P
7 Sun	FA Women's Cup 6
10 Wed	FA Cup 6P Replay (prov)
13 Sat	FA Vase SF (1)
	FA Youth Cup 6P+
	FA County Youth Cup SF+
16 Tue	UEFA Cup QF (2)
17 Wed	Champions League QF (2)
	FA Cup 6P Replay (prov)
18 Thu	ECWC QF (2)
20 Sat	FA Vase SF (2)
27 Sat	England v Poland (EC)
	FA Trophy 6
28 Sun	FA Sunday Cup SF
30 Tue	Semi-Pro International
31 Wed	International (EC)

APRIL 1999

4 Sun	FA Women's Cup SF
6 Tue	UEFA Cup SF (1)
7 Wed	Champions League SF (1)
8 Thu	ECWC SF (1)
10 Sat	FA Trophy SF (1)
	FA Youth Cup SF+
11 Sun	FA Cup SF
14 Wed	FA Cup SF Replay
17 Sat	FA Trophy SF (2)
20 Tue	UEFA Cup SF (2)
21 Wed	Champions League SF (2)
22 Thu	ECWC SF (2)
24 Sat	FA County Youth Cup Final (fixed date)
25 Sun	FA Sunday Cup Final
28 Wed	International (F)

MAY 1999

3 Mon	FA Women's Cup Final
8 Sat	End of Football League season
12 Wed	UEFA Cup Final
15 Sat	FA Trophy Final - Wembley Stadium 3.00
	FA Youth Cup Final+
16 Sun	FA Vase Final - Wembley Stadium 3.00
	End of FA Premier League Season
	FL Play-Offs SF (1)
19 Wed	European Cup Winners Cup Final
	FL Play-Offs SF (2)
22 Sat	FA Cup Final - Wembley Stadium 3.00
26 Wed	European Champions League Final
27 Thu	FA Cup Final Replay
29 Sat	FL Play-Offs Final Div 3
30 Sun	FL Play-Offs Final Div 2
31 Mon	FL Play-Offs Final Div 1

to be dated - FA XI v Highland League

JUNE 1999

5 Sat	England v Sweden (EC)
9 Wed	Bulgaria v England (EC)

+ closing date of round
* no FA Premier League games
EC = UEFA European Championship

ENGLAND

SEMI-PRO CAPS 1979-98 (Max 52)

KEY to COUNTRY CODES

E - Eire
I - Italy
F - Finland
G - Gibralter
H - Holland
N - Norway)
S - Scotland
W - Wales

Players capped for the first time during the 1997-98 season are boxed

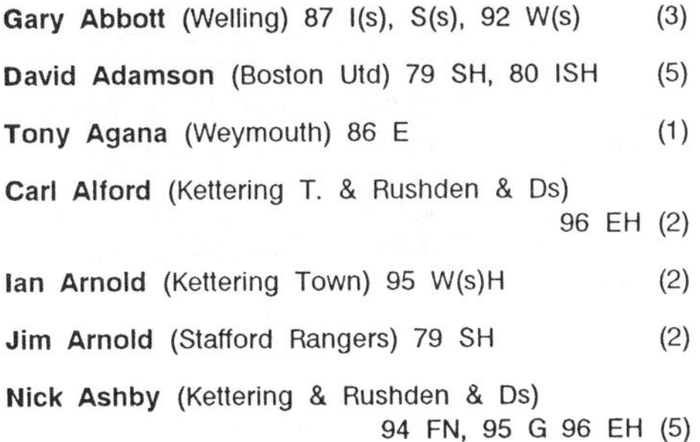

Gary Abbott (Welling) 87 I(s), S(s), 92 W(s) (3)

David Adamson (Boston Utd) 79 SH, 80 ISH (5)

Tony Agana (Weymouth) 86 E (1)

Carl Alford (Kettering T. & Rushden & Ds) 96 EH (2)

Ian Arnold (Kettering Town) 95 W(s)H (2)

Jim Arnold (Stafford Rangers) 79 SH (2)

Nick Ashby (Kettering & Rushden & Ds) 94 FN, 95 G 96 EH (5)

Noel Ashford (Enfield & Redbridge For.) 82 GHS, 83 IHS, 84 WHSI, 85 WI(s), 86 EE, 87 W(s), IHS, 90 WE, 91 I(s) (21)

John Askey (Macclesfield) 90 W (1)

Paul Bancroft (Kidderminster H.) 89 IW, 90 IWE, 91 W (6)

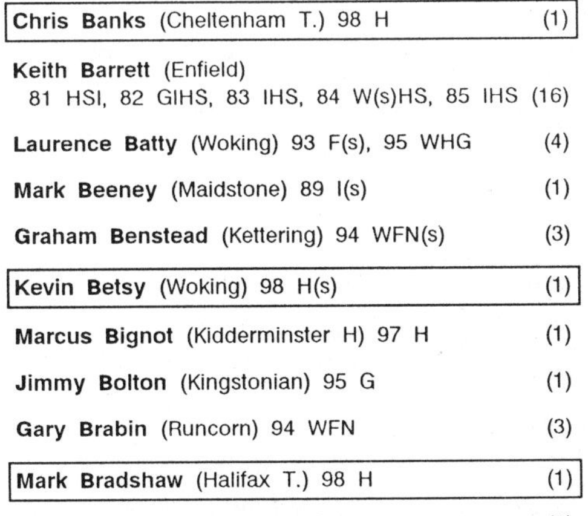

Chris Banks (Cheltenham T.) 98 H (1)

Keith Barrett (Enfield) 81 HSI, 82 GIHS, 83 IHS, 84 W(s)HS, 85 IHS (16)

Laurence Batty (Woking) 93 F(s), 95 WHG (4)

Mark Beeney (Maidstone) 89 I(s) (1)

Graham Benstead (Kettering) 94 WFN(s) (3)

Kevin Betsy (Woking) 98 H(s) (1)

Marcus Bignot (Kidderminster H) 97 H (1)

Jimmy Bolton (Kingstonian) 95 G (1)

Gary Brabin (Runcorn) 94 WFN (3)

Mark Bradshaw (Halifax T.) 98 H (1)

Colin Brazier (Kidderminster) 87 W (1)

DEAN HOOPER (Kingstonian & England)
The only player from outside the Conference to gain a cap this year.
Photo: Andrew Chitty

Stewart Brighton (Bromsgrove) 94 W (1)

Steve Brooks (Cheltenham) 88 W(s), 90 WE (3)

Derek Brown (Woking) 94 F(s)N (2)

Kevan Brown (Woking) 95 WHG 96 H 97 E (5)

Corey Browne (Dover) 94 F(s)N(s), 95 H(s) (3)

David Buchanan (Blyth) 86 E(s)E (2)

Brian Butler (Northwich) 93 F (1)

Gary Butterworth (Rushden & Diamonds) 97 EH 98 H (3)

Steve Butler (Maidstone) 88 W, 89 IW (3)

Chris Byrne (Macclesfield T.) 97 H (1)

Mark Carter (Runcorn & Barnet)
87 WIHS, 88 W, 89 IW, 90 IE, 91 IW(s) (11)

Kim Casey (Kidderminster) 86 WEE(s), 87 WI (5)

Paul Cavell (Redbridge) 92 W, 93 F (2)

Kevin Charlton (Telford) 85 WI (2)

Andrew Clarke (Barnet) 90 EE (2)

David Clarke (Blyth Spartans)
80 IS(s)H, 81 HSI, 82 IHS, 83 HS, 84 HSI (14)

Gary Clayton (Burton) 86 E (1)

Robert Codner (Barnet) 88 W (1)

John Coleman (Morecambe) 93 F(s) (1)

Darren Collins (Enfield) 93 F(s), 94 WFN (4)

Andy Comyn (Hednesford T.) 98 H(s) (1)

Steve Conner (Dartford, Redbridge & Dagenham & R)
90 I, 91 IW, 92 W, 93 F (5)

David Constantine (Altrincham) 85 IHS, 86 W (4)

Robbie Cooke (Kettering) 89 W(s), 90 I (2)

Scott Cooksey (Hednesford T.) 97 E 98 H(s) (2)

Alan Cordice (Wealdstone)
83 IHS, 84 WS(s), I(s), 85 IHS (9)

Ken Cramman (Gateshead & Rushden & Diamonds)
96 E 97 EH (3)

Paul Cuddy (Altrincham) 87 IHS (3)

Paul Culpin (Nuneaton B) 84 W, 85 W(s) IHS (5)

Paul Davies (Kidderminster H.)
86 W, 87 WIS, 88 W, 89 W (6)

John Davison (Altrincham)
79 SH, 80 IS, 81 HSI, 82 GIHS, 83 IHS,
84 WHIS, 85 IHS, 86 WEE (24)

John Denham (Northwich Victoria) 80 H (1)

Peter Densmore (Runcorn) 88 W, 89 I (2)

Phil Derbyshire (Mossley) 83 H(s)S(s) (2)

Mick Doherty (Weymouth) 86 W(s) (1)

Neil Doherty (Kidderminster H.) 97 E (1)

Lee Endersby (Harrow Bor.) 96 H (1)

Mick Farrelly (Altrincham) 87 IHS (3)

Steve Farrelly (Macclesfield) 95 H(s)G(s) (2)

Trevor Finnegan (Weymouth) 81 HS (2)

Richard Forsyth (Kidderminster) 95 WHG (3)

Paul Furlong (Enfield) 90 IEE, 91 IW (5)

Mark Gardiner (Macclesfield T.) 97 E (1)

BRIAN HEALY (Morecambe & England)
Photo: Andrew Chitty

Jerry Gill (Yeovil T.) 97 E (1)

John Glover (Maidstone Utd) 85 WIHS (4)

Mark Golley (Sutton Utd.)
87 H(s)S, 88 W, 89 IW, 92 W (6)

Paul Gothard (Dagenham & Redb.) 97 E(s) (1)

Neil Grayson (Cheltenham T.) 98 H (1)

Phil Gridelet (Hendon & Barnet) 89 IW, 90 WEE (5)

Steve Guppy (Wycombe W.) 93 W (1)

Steve Hancock (Macclesfield) 90 W (1)

David Harlow (Farnborough T.) 97 E(s)H (2)

Barry Hayles (Stevenage Bor.) 96 EH (2)

Brian Healy (Morecambe) 98 H (1)

Tony Hemmings (Northwich) 93 F (1)

Andy Hessenthaler (Dartford) 90 I (1)

Kenny Hill (Maidstone Utd) 80 ISH (3)

Mark Hine (Gateshead) 95 W(s)H (2)

Simeon Hodson (Kidderminster) 94 WFN (3)

Colin Hogarth (Guiseley) 95 WH (2)

Steven Holden (Kettering) 94 WFN(s), 95 HG (5)

Mark Hone (Welling) 90 I, 93 F, 94 W(s)F(s)N (5)

Gary Hooley (Frickley) 85 W (1)

Dean Hooper (Kingstonian) 98 H (1)

Keith Houghton (Blyth Spartans) 79 S (1)

Barry Howard (Altrincham) 81 HSI, 82 GIHS (7)

Neil Howarth (Macclesfield) 95 H(s) 97 E (2)

David Howell (Enfield)
85 H(s)S(s), 86 WE, 87 WIHS, 88 W,
89 IW, 90 IEE (14)

Lee Howells (Cheltenham T.) 98 H (1)

Lee Hughes (Kidderminster) 96 EH 97 EH (4)

Delwyn Humphreys (Kidderminster H.)
91 W(s), 92 W, 94 WFN, 95 WH (7)

Steve Humphries (Barnet) 87 H(s) (1)

Nicky Ironton (Enfield) 83 H(s), 84 W (2)

Tony Jennings (Enfield)
79 SH, 80 ISH, 81 HSI, 82 GIHS (12)

Jeff Johnson (Altrincham)
81 SI, 82 GIHS, 83 IHS, 84 HSI,
84 IHS, 86 W(s)EE (18)

Tom Jones (Weymouth) 87 W (1)

Anton Joseph (Telford Utd. & Kidderminster H.)
84 S(s), 85 WIHS, 86 W(s), 87 WI(s)H,
88 W, 89 IW, 90 IEE (14)

Andy Kerr (Wycombe) 93 W (1)

Ged Kimmins (Hyde Utd.) 96 E(s)H(s) 97 E(s) (3)

Mike Lake (Macclesfield) 89 I (1)

Andy Lee (Telford U. & Witton A.) 89 I(s), 91 IW (3)

David Leworthy (Farnborough & Rushden & Diamonds)
93 W, 94 W 97 EH (4)

Kenny Lowe (Barnet) 91 IW (2)

Martin McDonald (Macclesfield) 95 G(s) (1)

John McKenna (Boston Utd)
88 W(s), 90 IEE, 91 IW, 92 W (7)

Leroy May (Stafford R.) 95 G(s) (1)

Bobby Mayes (Redbridge) 92 W (1)

Paul Mayman (Northwich Vic) 80 IS (2)

Stewart Mell (Burton) 85 W (1)

Neil Merrick (Weymouth) 80 I(s)S (2)

Russell Milton (Dover) 94 FN (2)

Trevor Morley (Nuneaton) 84 WHSI, 85 WS(s) (6)

Les Mutrie (Blyth Spartans) 79 SH, 80 ISH (5)

Mark Newson (Maidstone U) 84 WHSI, 85 W (5)

MARK SMITH (Stevenage Borough & England)
Photo: Andrew Chitty

Doug Newton (Burton) 85 WHS (3)

Paul Nicol (Kettering T) 91 IW, 92 W (3)

Steve Norris (Telford) 88 W(s) (1)

Joe O'Connor (Hednesford T.) 97 EH(s) (2)

Eamon O'Keefe (Mossley) 79 SH (2)

Frank Ovard (Maidstone) 81 H(s)S(s)I(s) (3)

Andy Pape (Harrow Bor. & Enfield)
85 W(s)HS, 86 W(s)E 87 WIHS,
88 W, 89 IW, 90 IWE (15)

Brian Parker (Yeovil Town) 80 S (1)

Steve Payne (Macclesfield T.) 97 H (1)

Trevor Peake (Nuneaton Bor) 79 SH (2)

David Pearce (Harrow Bor) 84 I(s) (1)

Brendan Phillips (Nuneaton Bor. & Kettering T.)
79 SH, 80 S(s)H (4)

Gary Philips (Barnet) 82 G (1)

Owen Pickard (Yeovil T.) 98 H(s) (1)

Phil Power (Macclesfield T.) 96 E(s)H(s) (2)

Ryan Price (Stafford R. & Macclesfield)
92 W(s) 93 WF 96 EH 97 H (6)

Steve Prindiville 98 H(s) (1)

Simon Read (Farnborough) 92 W(s) (1)

Andy Reid (Altrincham) 95 W (1)

Carl Richards (Enfield) 86 E (1)

Derek Richardson (Maidstone U) 83 I, 84 W, 86 E (4)

Ian Richardson (Dagenham & Red) 95 G (1)

Kevin Richardson (Bromsgrove) 94 WFN (3)

Paul Richardson (Redbridge) 92 W, 93 WF (3)

Terry Robbins (Welling) 92 W, 93 WF, 94 WFN (6)

Peter Robinson (Blyth S) 83 IHS, 84 WI, 85 W (6)

John Rogers (Altrincham) 81 HSI, 82 I(s)S (5)

Paul Rogers (Sutton) 89 W, 90 IE(2), 91 IW (6)

Colin Rose (Witton Alb.) 96 E(s)H (2)

Kevin Rose (Kidderminster) 94 F(s)N (2)

Brian Ross (Marine) 93 W(s)F(s), 94 W(s) 95 WH (5)

Tim Ryan (Southport) 98 H (1)

Neil Sellars (Scarboro) 81 HSI, 82 GH(s)S, 83 IHS (9)

Mark Shail (Yeovil T.) 93 W (1)

Peter Shearer (Cheltenham) 89 I(s) (1)

Paul Shirtliff (Frickley A. & Boston U.)
86 EE, 87 WIH, 88 W, 89 IW,
90 IWEE, 92 W, 93 WF (15)

Paul Showler (Altrincham) 91 I(s)W (2)

Gordon Simmonite (Boston Utd.)
79 S(s)H(s), 80 ISH (5)

Gary Simpson (Stafford R.)
86 EE, 87 IHS, 90 IWEE (9)

Wayne Simpson (Stafford) 94 FN(s) (2)

Glenn Skivington (Barrow) 90 IWE, 91 IW (5)

Alan Smith (Alvechurch) 82 GIS (3)

Ian Smith (Mossley) 80 ISH(s) (3)

Mark Smith (Stevenage Bor.) 96 EH 98 H (3)

Ossie Smith (Runcorn) 84 W (1)

Tim Smithers (Nuneaton), 85 W(s)I, 86 W (3)

Simon Stapleton (Wycombe) 93 W (1)

Mickey Stephens (Sutton), 82 GS(s), 86 WEE(s) (5)

Billy Stewart (Southport) 98 H (1)

Bob Stockley (Nuneaton Bor) 80 H (1)

Steve Stott (Kettering T. & Rushden & Ds)
95 WH(s)G 96 EH (5)

Peter Taylor (Maidstone) 84 HSI (3)

Steve Taylor (Bromsgrove R.) 95 G (1)

Shaun Teale (Weymouth) 88 W (1)

Stuart Terry (Altrincham) W (1)

Brian Thompson (Yeovil & Maidstone)
79 SH, 81 HSI, 82 IHS, 83 IHS, 84 WHSI (15)

Steve Thompson (Wycombe) 93 W (1)

Kevin Todd (Berwick Rangers) 91 W (1)

Mark Tucker (Woking) 96 E (1)

Tony Turner (Telford) 85 W (1)

David Venables (Stevenage Bor.)
94 W(s), 95 HG 96 EH(s) (5)

Jamie Victory (Cheltenham T.) 98 H(s) (1)

David Waite (Enfield) 82 G (1)

Paul Walker (Blyth) 86 WEE(s), 87 S(s) (4)

Steve Walters (Northwich Victoria) 97 H (1)

Mark Ward (Northwich Victoria) 83 S(s) (1)

Dale Watkins (Cheltenham T.) 98 H (1)

John Watson (Wealdstone, Scarborough &
Maidstone) 79 S(s)H, 80 ISH, 81 HSI,
82 IHS, 83 IHS, 84 W(s)HSI (18)

Liam Watson (Marine) 95 WH(s) (2)

Paul Watts (Redbridge Forest)
89 W, 90 IEE, 91 I, 92 W, 93 WF (8)

Paul Webb (Bromsgrove R & Kidderminster H)
93 F, 94 WFN(s) 95 WHG 96 EH 97 EH (11)

Mark West (Wycombe W) 91 W (1)

Barry Whitbread (Runcorn & Altrincham)
79 SH, 80 ISH, 81 I (6)

Russ Wilcox (Frickley) 86 WE (2)

Colin Williams (Scarborough & Telford Utd.)
81 HS, 82 IHS (5)

Roger Willis (Barnet) 91 I(s) (1)

Paul Wilson (Frickley) 86 W (1)

THE PHOTO THAT SAYS IT ALL - Here we see striker Dave Hallam in the back of the net after heading the winning goal for Rainworth Miners' Welfare in the F.A. Vase semi-final second leg against Barton Rovers in 1982. Leaping for joy is team-mate Brian Knowles. Photo: Deryk Wills.

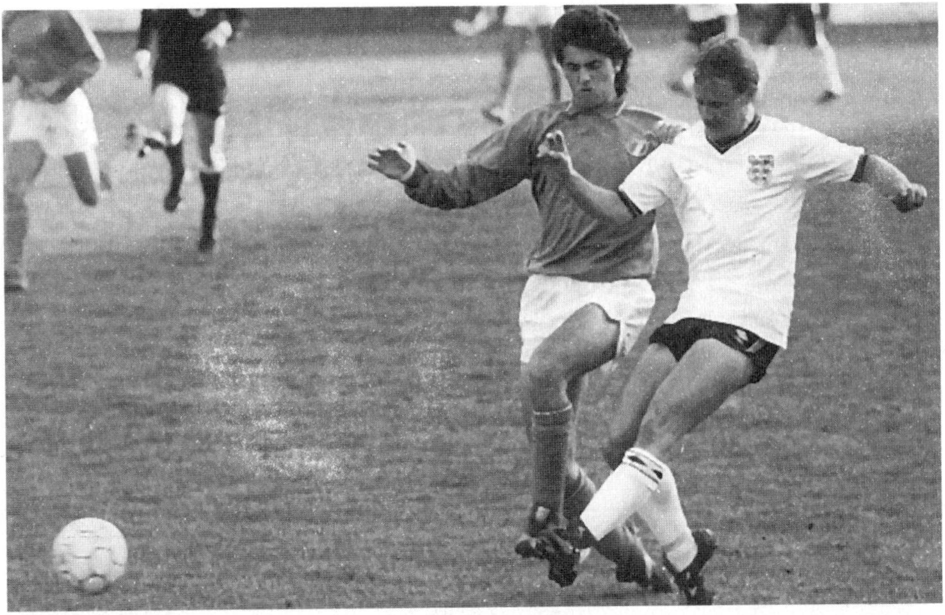

MARK CARTER (Bangor City, Runcorn, Barnet, Bury, Rochdale, Ashton United).
England Semi-Professional's Top International Goalscorer with 12 in 10 + 1 sub appearance.
Photo: Tom Scott

PAUL DAVIES of Kidderminster Harriers, seen here in England colours, was the leading Football Conference goalscorer with 183 at the beginning of the currect season.
Photo: Tom Scott

ALAN SMITH was the first England Semi-Professional international to win a full England international cap.

Right - JOHN DAVISON (standing on the left) is England's most capped player with 24 appearances, is seen here with three Altrincham club colleagues also in the England squad - Barry Howard (standing), Jeff Johnson (front left) and John Rogers.

The England squad which won all three of their International matches in the 1983 Four Nations Tournament at Scarborough was arguably the best that has represented the country at this level.

The England team that faced Italy: (L-R), Derek Richardson, Dave Clarke, Nick Ironton, Mark Ward, Mick Joyce, Phil Derbyshire, Neil Sellers, Noel Ashford, Alan Cordice, Keith Barrett, Colin Williams, Brian Thompson, John Davison, Jeff Johnson, Peter Robinson, John Watson. Photo: Mike Joss

Back Row (L-R): David Clarke (Blyth Spartans), Mickey Stephens (Sutton Utd), John Davison (Altringham), Keith Barrett (Enfield), Brian Thompson, John Watson, Derek Richardson (all Maidstone Utd), Jeff Johnson (Altringham), Peter Robinson (Blyth Spartan); Front Row: Colin Williams (Telford), Alan Cordice (Wealdstone), Noel Ashford (Enfield), Mark Ward (Northwich Victoria), Nicky Ironton (Enfield) Photo: Tony Bartholomew

TOP
Telford United twice beat three League clubs in one F.A. Cup season and reached the Third Round for three successive seasons. Here we see the end of their 1984-85 run at Goodison Park.
Photo: Eric Marsh.

MIDDLE
Matthew Hanlan, one of Sutton United's goalscoring heroes in action against First Division Coventry City when Sutton won 2-1 in 1988-89.

BOTTOM
Yeovil Town have knocked out seventeen League clubs from the F.A. Cup but on this occasion Q.P.R. won at the old 'Huish'. Yeovil skipper Steve Rutter takes on Gary Bannister.
Photo: Fred Lander.

TOP
Graham Heathcote (now Altrincham's secretary) scored from the spot at Anfield in 1981 - quite a feeling! Photo: John Rooney.

MIDDLE
This was the season (1993-94) when Kidderminster Harriers didn't reach the Football League. The game with West Ham United prevented work to the ground being completed on time but they enjoyed the glamour of victories over Birmingham City and Preston North End.
Photo: Dennis Nicholson.

BOTTOM
That's the way to celebrate! The Aylesbury Ducks have won in the F.A. Cup at Kingstonian in 1994.
Photo: Mark Sandom.

BARNET - Conference Runners-up 86-87, 87-88 & 89-90, Champions 90-91. L-R, Back Row: Andy McDade (physio), Al James Hannigan, Jonathon Hunt, Paul Wilson, Kevin Durham, Gary Phillips, Mark Flashman, Richard Nugent, David Howell, Gary Poole, Gordon Hendricks, Gordon Ogbourne (Kit man.). Front: Derek Payne, Gary Bull, Hakan Hayrettin, Edwin Stein, Barry Fry (manager), Andy Clarke, Tony Lynch, Phil Stacey, Frank Murphy.

KIDDERMINSTER HARRIERS - Conference Champions 93-94. FA Trophy: Winners 87, Runners-up 91 & 95. L-R, Back Row: C Brazier, C Jones, C Boxall, J Maulders, J Arnold, M Hazelwood, M Weir, M Tuohy, P Davies. Middle: J Conway, C Burton, A Canning, J Dimmock, R Jones, J Barton, M Woodhall, A Nicholls, B Kenning. Front: M Brown, A O'Dowd, M Hatton, G Mackenzie, G Allner, K Collins, K Casey, J Pearson, J Price. Photo: Marshall's Sports Service.

WYCOMBE WANDERERS - Conference Champions 92-93, Runners-up 91-92. F.A. Trophy Winners 91, 93. Their efforts in 1993 made them only the third Conference and Trophy double winners. L-R, Back Row: Jason Cousins, Dave Carroll, Paul Hyde, Keith Scott, Trevor Roffey, Simon Stapleton. Middle: Dave Jones (Physio), Geoff Cooper, Keith Ryan, Matt Crossley, Andy Kerr, Simon Hutchinson, Steve Thompson, Steve Guppy, Paul Franklin (coach). Front: John Reardon (asst. man.), Kim Casey, Mark West, Gary Smith, Glyn Creaser, Martin O'Neill (manager), Dennis Greene, Ty Gooden, Gavin Covington, John Deakin.

LEAGUE INDEX

Leagues are listed alphabetically below with their relevant page numbers. Where a league entry runs to more than one page, the number indicated is that of the first page of the section. As in previous years, sponsors names have been omitted to ease reference. League sponsors, however, get their deserved recognition in the appropriate sections.

Each club is shown with its league & division on brackets. The league Abbreviations used are as follows:

C.Co - Combined Counties
DM - Dr Martens
EAST - Eastern Counties
ESX - Essex Senior
GMVC - Conference
HELL - Hellenic
ICIS - Rymans League
KENT - Kent League
M.All - Midland Alliance
M.COMB - Midland Combination
NCE - Northern Counties East
NTH - Northern League
NWC - North West Counties
SSM - Spartan South Midlands
SSX - Sussex
UCL - United Counties
UNIB - Unibond League
WALES - League of Wales
WEST - Western League
W.MID - West Midlands
WSX - Wessex